HANDBOOK OF FLUID DYNAMICS

OTHER McGRAW-HILL HANDBOOKS OF INTEREST

AMERICAN INSTITUTE OF PHYSICS · American Institute of Physics Handbook
AMERICAN SOCIETY OF MECHANICAL ENGINEERS · ASME Handbooks:
    Engineering Tables   Metals Engineering—Processes
    Metals Engineering—Design   Metals Properties
ARCHITECTURAL RECORD · Time-Saver Standards
BAUMEISTER AND MARKS · Standard Handbook of Mechanical Engineers
BERRY, BOLLAY, AND BEERS · Handbook of Meteorology
BLATZ · Radiation Hygiene Handbook
BRADY · Materials Handbook
BURINGTON · Handbook of Mathematical Tables and Formulas
BURINGTON AND MAY · Handbook of Probability and Statistics with Tables
CHOW · Handbook of Applied Hydrology
CONDON AND ODISHAW · Handbook of Physics
CONSIDINE · Process Instruments and Controls Handbook
CONSIDINE AND ROSS · Handbook of Applied Instrumentation
COOKE AND MARKUS · Electronics and Nucleonics Dictionary
ETHERINGTON · Nuclear Engineering Handbook
FLÜGGE · Handbook of Engineering Mechanics
GRANT · Hackh's Chemical Dictionary
GRUENBERG · Handbook of Telemetry and Remote Control
HAMSHER · Communication System Engineering Handbook
HARRIS AND CREDE · Shock and Vibration Handbook
HENNEY · Radio Engineering Handbook
HUNTER · Handbook of Semiconductor Electronics
HUSKEY AND KORN · Computer Handbook
IRESON · Reliability Handbook
JURAN · Quality Control Handbook
KALLEN · Handbook of Instrumentation and Controls
KING AND BRATER · Handbook of Hydraulics
KLERER AND KORN · Digital Computer User's Handbook
KNOWLTON · Standard Handbook for Electrical Engineers
KOELLE · Handbook of Astronautical Engineering
KORN AND KORN · Mathematical Handbook for Scientists and Engineers
LANDEE, DAVIS, AND ALBRECHT · Electronic Designer's Handbook
LANGE · Handbook of Chemistry
MACHOL · System Engineering Handbook
MANTELL · Engineering Materials Handbook
MEITES · Handbook of Analytical Chemistry
PERRY · Engineering Manual
RICHEY · Agricultural Engineers' Handbook
ROTHBART · Mechanical Design and Systems Handbook
TERMAN · Radio Engineers' Handbook
TOULOUKIAN · Retrieval Guide to Thermophysical Properties Research Literature
TRUXAL · Control Engineers' Handbook
URQUHART · Civil Engineering Handbook
WOLMAN · Handbook of Clinical Psychology

HANDBOOK OF
FLUID DYNAMICS

VICTOR L. STREETER, Editor-in-Chief

Professor of Hydraulics
University of Michigan

FIRST EDITION

McGRAW-HILL BOOK COMPANY, INC.

NEW YORK   TORONTO   LONDON

1961

HANDBOOK OF FLUID DYNAMICS

CONTRIBUTORS

ALVIN G. ANDERSON, *University of Minnesota, Minneapolis, Minnesota.* (Section 18, *Sedimentation*)

THEODORE BAUMEISTER, *Columbia University in the City of New York, New York.* (Section 19, *Turbomachinery*)

D. BERSHADER, *Stanford University, Stanford, California.* (Section 27, *Magnetohydrodynamics*)

R. C. BINDER, *University of Southern California, Los Angeles, California.* (Section 14, *Flow Measurement*)

R. BYRON BIRD, *The University of Wisconsin, Madison, Wisconsin.* (Section 6, *Transport Phenomena in Multicomponent Systems*)

ALI BULENT CAMBEL, *Northwestern University, Evanston, Illinois.* (Section 8, *Compressible Flow*)

VEN TE CHOW, *University of Illinois, Urbana, Illinois.* (Section 24, *Open-channel Flow*)

R. L. DAUGHERTY, *California Institute of Technology, Pasadena, California.* (Section 1, *Fluid Properties*)

ROBERT C. DEAN, JR., *Thermal Dynamics Corporation, Lebanon, New Hampshire, and Dartmouth College, Hanover, New Hampshire.* (Section 11, *Separation and Stall*)

PHILLIP EISENBERG, *Hydronautics, Inc., Rockville, Maryland.* (Section 12, *Cavitation*)

A. G. FREDRICKSON, *University of Minnesota, Minneapolis, Minnesota.* (Section 6, *Transport Phenomena in Multicomponent Systems*)

DUDLEY D. FULLER, *Columbia University in the City of New York, New York.* (Section 22, *Lubrication Mechanics*)

BERNARD A. GALLER, *University of Michigan, Ann Arbor, Michigan.* (Section 25, *The Digital Computer for Fluid-flow Calculations*)

DONALD R. F. HARLEMAN, *Massachusetts Institute of Technology, Cambridge, Massachusetts.* (Section 26, *Stratified Flow*)

MAURICE HOLT, *University of California, Berkeley, California.* (Section 15, *Dimensional Analysis*)

ROLF LANDSHOFF, *Lockheed Missiles and Space Division, Palo Alto, California.* (Section 27, *Magnetohydrodynamics*)

v

LOUIS LANDWEBER, *State University of Iowa, Iowa City, Iowa.* (Section 13, *Motion of Immersed and Floating Bodies*)

A. B. METZNER, *University of Delaware, Newark, Delaware.* (Section 7, *Flow of Non-Newtonian Fluids*)

S. I. PAI, *Institute for Fluid Dynamics and Applied Mathematics, University of Maryland, College Park, Maryland.* (Section 5, *Laminar Flow*)

HENRY M. PAYNTER, *Massachusetts Institute of Technology, Cambridge, Massachusetts.* (Section 20, *Fluid Transients in Engineering Systems*)

JOSEPH G. RICHARDSON, *Humble Oil & Refining Company, Houston, Texas.* (Section 16, *Flow through Porous Media*)

H. SCHLICHTING, *Aerodynamische Versuchsanstalt, Göttingen, and Technical University, Braunschweig, West Germany.* (Section 9, *Boundary-layer Theory*)

ASCHER H. SHAPIRO, *Massachusetts Institute of Technology, Cambridge, Massachusetts.* (Section 2, *Basic Equations of Fluid Flow*)

J. L. SHEARER, *Massachusetts Institute of Technology, Cambridge, Massachusetts.* (Section 21, *Conversion, Transmission, and Control of Fluid Power*)

M. R. TEK, *University of Michigan, Ann Arbor, Michigan.* (Section 17, *Two-phase Flow*)

A. A. TOWNSEND, *Emmanuel College, University of Cambridge, Cambridge, England.* (Section 10, *Turbulence*)

MARSHALL P. TULIN, *Hydronautics, Inc., Rockville, Maryland.* (Section 12, *Cavitation*)

JOHN K. VENNARD, *Stanford University, Stanford, California.* (Section 3, *One-dimensional Flow*)

FRANK H. WESTERVELT, *University of Michigan, Ann Arbor, Michigan.* (Section 25, *The Digital Computer for Fluid-flow Calculations*)

CHIA-SHUN YIH, *University of Michigan, Ann Arbor, Michigan.* (Section 4, *Ideal-fluid Flow*)

M. J. ZUCROW, *Purdue University, Lafayette, Indiana.* (Section 23, *Thermal-jet and Rocket-jet Propulsion*)

PREFACE

New methods for attacking fluid dynamics problems are being developed in all phases of the subject. A panel of outstanding authorities, who are actively contributing to advances in the field of fluid dynamics, have joined their efforts to produce this handbook. The present status, latest theory, and the most promising methods of analysis are presented for fields of application covering most of the engineering profession.

This handbook is directed to the engineer or scientist with some background in fluid mechanics and mathematics. Each section is written for the nonspecialist in this phase of fluid flow. No attempt has been made to develop any of the mathematics used in the handbook, since mathematical references are generally available.

The first half of the handbook deals with fundamental concepts and principles, while the second half is devoted to applied fields. Because of size restrictions of the handbook, careful selection of applied topics was necessary. An endeavor was made to obtain a balanced treatment indicating the diverse methods of solving flow problems. In general, the sections are comprehensive and stand by themselves with a minimum of detailed dependence on earlier sections. Derivations are not carried out, but careful attention is given to underlying assumptions and to interpretations of the theory. The references at the end of each section are selected to enable the reader to pursue the subject in as much detail as he desires.

No common notation is feasible for the whole handbook. Each author has used a notation common to the literature in his field, a procedure which aids in reference work. A few specific items, particularly the dimensionless parameters, were given the same notation and treatment throughout.

One section has been devoted to a discussion of the use of compiler methods in applying the digital computer to fluid-flow problems. The ease with which a complex problem may be programmed makes the digital computer an efficient and speedy aid in design work.

Appreciation is expressed to all those who aided in an advisory capacity in the planning and reviewing of manuscripts and to Pauline Bentley, James Wiggert, and Evelyn Streeter for their aid in manuscript preparation and proofreading.

Victor L. Streeter

CONTENTS

HANDBOOK OF FLUID DYNAMICS

Section 1

FLUID PROPERTIES

By

R. L. DAUGHERTY, *California Institute of Technology, Pasadena, California*

FLUID PROPERTIES

1.1. Introduction and Definitions

In fluid dynamics the properties of density and viscosity occur most frequently. In addition, surface tension and vapor pressure are necessary properties to take into account in a limited number of applications. Occasionally thermal conductivity is important, but usually it is treated under the broad heading of heat transfer. This section concentrates on the properties of density and viscosity, with a brief discussion of the other fluid properties. Section 7 is concerned with the properties of non-Newtonian fluids.

A *fluid* is a substance that, no matter how viscous, will yield in time to the slightest stress; whereas a *solid*, no matter how plastic, requires a certain magnitude of stress before it will flow. With a fluid, tangential stresses between adjacent particles are proportional to the velocity of deformation and disappear when motion ceases; whereas with a solid, the tangential stresses remain and tend to restore the body to its original figure.

A fluid may be either a *liquid* or a *gas*. A liquid can have a free surface, that is, a surface from which all pressure is removed except that of its own vapor. A liquid is relatively incompressible. A gas is very compressible, and when all external pressure is removed, it tends to expand indefinitely. A gas is therefore in equilibrium only when it is completely enclosed.

A *vapor* is a gas whose temperature and pressure are such that it is very near the liquid phase. Conversely, a gas is a highly superheated vapor; that is, its state is far removed from the liquid phase. The farther a gas is removed from the liquid phase, the more nearly do its characteristics approach those of the imaginary *perfect* gas.

The same substance may exist in any one of the three phases, solid, liquid, or gas. An example is ice, water, and steam. Fluid dynamics is concerned with liquid and gas phases. The volume of a gas or a vapor is greatly affected by changes in either pressure or temperature. Since temperature involves heat phenomena, the mechanics of gases and vapors is called thermodynamics. Thus fluid dynamics and thermodynamics are interrelated.

1.2. Notation

For consistency, the foot-pound(force)-second system of units will be adhered to unless an exception is clearly indicated. The following notation is employed:

c specific heat, Btu/(lb)(°F)
c_p specific heat at constant pressure
c_v specific heat at constant volume
E_v volume modulus of elasticity
g acceleration of gravity in ft/sec² = 32.174 (standard)
m molecular weight
p'' fluid pressure, psi
p fluid pressure, psf
p_v vapor pressure
s specific gravity relative to water for liquids and relative to air or hydrogen for gases
v specific volume, ft³/lb $= 1/\gamma$
γ specific weight, lb/ft³ $= 1/v = g\rho$
ρ density, slugs/ft³ $= \gamma/g$

μ absolute viscosity, $(lb)(sec)/ft^2$
ν kinematic viscosity, $ft^2/sec = \mu/\rho$

1.3. Density, Specific Weight, Specific Volume, and Specific Gravity

Density is *mass* per unit volume, while specific weight is *weight* per unit volume. In the English engineers', or gravitational, system density is in $(lb)(sec^2)/ft^4$, while specific weight is in lb/ft^3. Specific volume is in ft^3/lb.

Specific gravity of a liquid is the ratio of its density to that of pure water at a standard temperature. Physicists use 4°C or 39.2°F as the standard, while engineers use 60°F. The specific gravity of a gas is the ratio of its density to that of either hydrogen or air, but there is no agreement on these standards, and so they must be stated in a given case. As the density of a fluid varies with temperature, specific gravities must be indicated at particular temperatures.

1.4. Baumé and API Gravities

The specific gravity of liquids is usually measured by some form of hydrometer, the most common scales for which are the Baumé and the API. For liquids lighter than water

$$s_{60/60} = \frac{140}{130 + °Bé} \tag{1.1}$$

and for liquids heavier than water

$$s_{60/60} = \frac{145}{145 - °Bé} \tag{1.2}$$

if $s_{60/60}$ is the specific gravity of the liquid at 60°F relative to water at 60°F.

The American Petroleum Institute has adopted a slightly different hydrometer for oils lighter than water for which the scale is

$$s_{60/60} = \frac{141.5}{131.5 + °API} \tag{1.3}$$

The specific gravity of an oil at any other temperature t may be determined by

$$s_t = \frac{s_{60}}{1 + \beta(t - 60)} \tag{1.4}$$

in which $\beta = e^{0.0106 \times °API - 8.05}$, and $e = 2.7183$. Values of β calculated from Eq. (1.4) are shown in Table 1.1.

1.5. Compressibility

The compressibility of any fluid is inversely proportional to its volume modulus of elasticity defined as $E_v = -v\,dp/dv = -(v/dv)\,dp$, from which a finite change of spe-

Table 1.1. Values of β in Eq. (1.4)

°API at 60°F	Sp gr at 60°F	β	°API at 60°F	Sp gr at 60°F	β
10	1.00	0.000355	. . .	0.75	0.000585
. .	0.95	0.000384	60	. . . .	0.000603
20	. . . .	0.000395	70	. . . .	0.000670
. .	0.90	0.000419	. . .	0.70	0.000675
30	. . . .	0.000439	80	. . . .	0.000745
. .	0.85	0.000462	. . .	0.65	0.000794
40	. . . .	0.000488	90	. . . .	0.000828
. .	0.80	0.000515	100	. . . .	0.000921
50	. . . .	0.000542	. . .	0.60	0.000962

Table 1.2 Specific Gravity at 60°F for Liquids Lighter than Water Corresponding to Degrees Baumé at 60°F

°Bé	s	°Bé	s	°Bé	s	°Bé	s	°Bé	s
10	1.0000	28	0.8861	46	0.7955	64	0.7216	82	0.6604
12	0.9859	30	0.8750	48	0.7865	66	0.7143	84	0.6542
14	0.9722	32	0.8642	50	0.7778	68	0.7071	86	0.6482
16	0.9589	34	0.8537	52	0.7692	70	0.7000	88	0.6422
18	0.9459	36	0.8434	54	0.7609	72	0.6931	90	0.6364
20	0.9333	38	0.8333	56	0.7527	74	0.6863	92	0.6306
22	0.9211	40	0.8235	58	0.7447	76	0.6796	94	0.6250
24	0.9091	42	0.8140	60	0.7368	78	0.6731	96	0.6195
26	0.8974	44	0.8046	62	0.7292	80	0.6667	98	0.6140

Table 1.3 Specific Gravity at 60°F for Liquids Heavier than Water Corresponding to Degrees Baumé at 60°F

°Bé	s	°Bé	s	°Bé	s	°Bé	s	°Bé	s
0	1.0000	14	1.1069	28	1.2393	42	1.4078	56	1.6292
2	1.0140	16	1.1240	30	1.2609	44	1.4356	58	1.6667
4	1.0284	18	1.1417	32	1.2832	46	1.4646	60	1.7059
6	1.0432	20	1.1600	34	1.3063	48	1.4948	62	1.7470
8	1.0584	22	1.1789	36	1.3303	50	1.5263	64	1.7901
10	1.0741	24	1.1983	38	1.3551	52	1.5591	66	1.8354
12	1.0902	26	1.2185	40	1.3810	54	1.5934	68	1.8831

Table 1.4. Specific Gravity at 60°F Corresponding to Degrees API at 60°F

°API	s	°API	s	°API	s	°API	s	°API	s
10	1.0000	28	0.8871	46	0.7972	64	0.7238	82	0.6628
12	0.9861	30	0.8762	48	0.7883	66	0.7165	84	0.6566
14	0.9725	32	0.8654	50	0.7796	68	0.7093	86	0.6506
16	0.9593	34	0.8550	52	0.7711	70	0.7022	88	0.6446
18	0.9465	36	0.8448	54	0.7628	72	0.6953	90	0.6388
20	0.9340	38	0.8348	56	0.7547	74	0.6886	92	0.6331
22	0.9218	40	0.8251	58	0.7467	76	0.6819	94	0.6275
24	0.9100	42	0.8155	60	0.7389	78	0.6754	96	0.6220
26	0.8984	44	0.8063	62	0.7313	80	0.6690	98	0.6166

cific volume is $\Delta v = -v \, \Delta p / E_{v\,\text{av}}$. In Table 1.5 are shown values of the modulus for water. It is seen that water has a minimum compressibility at about 120°F.

For most practical purposes water may be considered as incompressible, but actually it is about 100 times as compressible as steel and, in some cases such as water hammer, it is necessary to take compressibility into account. Oils are somewhat more compressible than water, the volume modulus ranging from 270,000 to 185,000. On the other hand, mercury is less compressible, its modulus being about 4,000,000 psi.

For a gas in an isothermal process, $E_v = p$, its pressure, while for an adiabatic process, $E_v = kp$, where k is the ratio of c_p/c_v. For air at normal temperature $k = 1.4$.

Table 1.5. Modulus of Elasticity of Water, in Psi

Pressure, psi	Temperature, °F				
	32	68	120	200	300
15	292,000	320,000	332,000	308,000	. . . . . .
1,500	300,000	330,000	342,000	319,000	248,000
4,500	317,000	348,000	362,000	338,000	271,000
15,000	380,000	410,000	426,000	405,000	350,000

Table 1.6. Some Properties of Gases

Gas	m	R	c_p	c_v	$k = c_p/c_v$
Helium................	4.0	386.3	1.25	0.754	1.66
Argon.................	40.0	38.7	0.124	0.0743	1.67
Air...................	29.0	53.3	0.241	0.1725	1 40
Oxygen...............	32.0	48.3	0.217	0.1549	1 40
Nitrogen..............	28.0	55.16	0.247	0.1761	1.40
Hydrogen.............	2.0	766.8	3.42	2.435	1.40
Carbon monoxide........	28.0	55.19	0.243	0.1721	1.41
Carbon dioxide..........	44.0	35.13	0.205	0.1599	1 28
Water vapor in air........	18.0	85.6	0.46	0.36	1 28
Ammonia..............	17.0	90.77	0.523	0.4064	1·29
Methane...............	16.0	96.37	0.593	0.4692	1.26

1.6. Perfect Gas

There is no such thing as a perfect gas, but air and other real gases that are far removed from the liquid phase may usually be so considered. For a perfect gas the equation of state is

$$pv = RT \tag{1.5}$$

where

        p = absolute pressure
        v = specific volume
        T = absolute temperature (°F + 459.69°)
        R = a gas constant, the value of which depends upon the particular gas

For a perfect gas $mR = 1545$ in the foot-pound-second system of units, but for real gases the value of mR ranges between 1512 and 1546, in which m is molecular weight. It is thus possible to obtain an approximate value for R for any gas whose molecular weight is known (Table 1.6). Thus water vapor in the air, because of its low partial pressure, may be treated as a perfect gas, with $R = 1540/18 = 85.6$. (For higher steam pressures this is not applicable and it is necessary to use steam tables.)

Knowing the value of R, the specific volume for a gas may be found by the preceding equation or its specific weight may be found by $\gamma = p/RT$.

Values of specific heat in Table 1.6 are for temperatures near normal atmosphere. Values of specific heat increase with temperature. The above are "instantaneous" values. For a large change in temperature, it is necessary to use the *mean* specific heat for that range. Values of instantaneous specific heats through a temperature range and also values of mean specific heats may be found in texts on thermodynamics.

1.7. Nonideal Gases

With higher pressures and lower temperatures all gases approach the liquid phase and can no longer be treated as perfect or ideal gases. The equations of state become complicated and are empirical in nature. Specific weight and other properties are then obtained from vapor tables such as exist for steam, ammonia, sulfur dioxide, Freon, and other vapors in common use.

When tables are lacking and the perfect-gas equation is inapplicable, resort must be had to empirical equations such as those of van der Waals or Beattie-Bridgeman. These equations contain constants whose values must be determined for each gas for which they are employed. The latter equation gives fairly reliable values at pressures below the critical when the constants are known for the particular gas.†

A simpler and more general procedure is to introduce a dimensionless compressibility factor or correction factor Z into the perfect-gas equation such that

† Values for the constants in the Beattie-Bridgeman equation for a number of gases may be found in *Proc. Am. Acad. Arts Sci.*, **63**: 229–308 (1928); *J. Am. Chem. Soc.*, **59**: 1587–1596 (1937), **61**: 26–27 (1939); J. H. Keenan, "Thermodynamics," p. 356, Wiley, New York, 1941; H. C. Weber, "Thermodynamics for Chemical Engineers," p. 74, Wiley, New York, 1939.

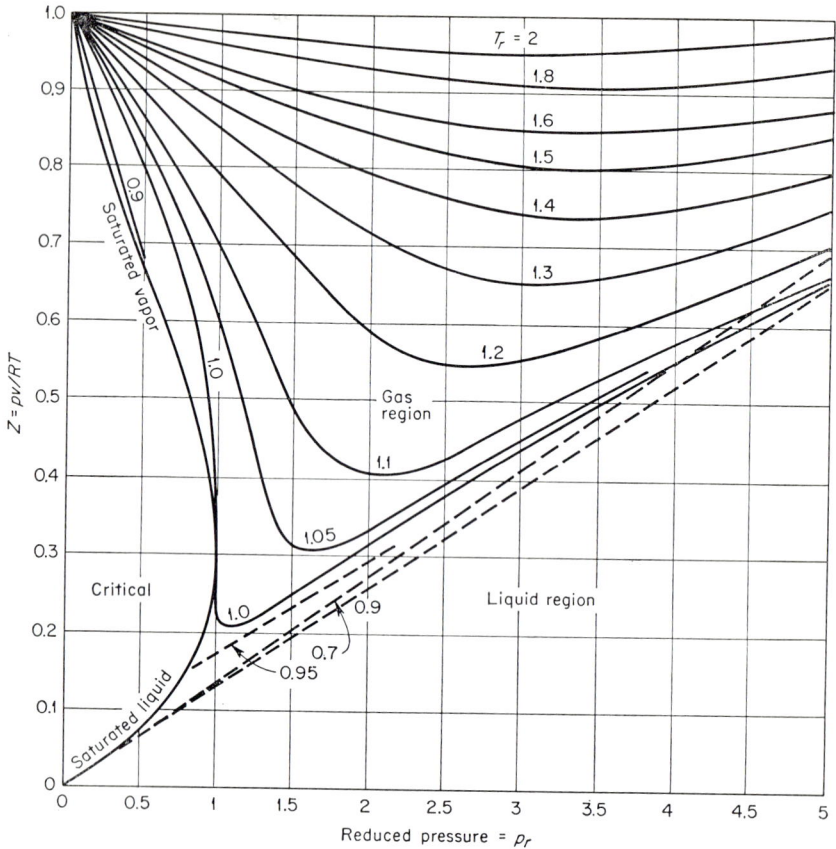

FIG. 1.1. Compressibility factors for gases and vapors. (*By permission of H. C. Weber,* "*Thermodynamics for Chemical Engineers,*" pp. 108, 109, 1939, *Wiley.*)

$$pv = ZRT \tag{1.6}$$

Values of Z may be obtained from Figs. 1.1 and 1.2 for any gas whose critical values are known. Critical values are to be found in Table 1.7. The charts are plotted with *reduced* values of pressure and temperature, that is, $p_r = p_{\text{act}}/p_{\text{cr}}$ and $T_r = T_{\text{act}}/T_{\text{cr}}$. Values of Z are then found for p_r and T_r. Values of specific volume obtained may not be as precise as those obtained from vapor tables or by use of an empirical equation of state devised for the particular gas or vapor, but are more nearly correct than if the perfect-gas law alone were used.

For at least three gases better values of Z are obtained by using not the true critical, but instead the pseudo-critical, values of pressure and temperature given in Table 1.8.

1.8. Absolute, or Dynamic, Viscosity

The viscosity of a fluid is a measure of its resistance to shear or angular deformation. Consider two parallel plates as in Fig. 1.3, sufficiently large so that edge conditions may be neglected, placed a small distance Y apart, the space between being filled with the fluid. Assume that the upper one is moved relative to the lower one with a velocity U by the application of a force F corresponding to some area A of the upper plate. Such a

Table 1.7. Critical Pressures and Temperatures

Gas	Formula	m	p''_c, psi	T_c, abs
Acetylene	C_2H_2	26.02	912	556
Ammonia	NH_3	17.03	1640	730
Benzene	C_6H_6	78.05	702	1011
Butane	C_4H_{10}	58.08	550	765
Carbon dioxide	CO_2	44	1070	548
Carbon monoxide	CO	28	508	239
Carbon tetrachloride	CCl_4	153.83	663	1001
Chlorine	Cl_2	70.91	1120	751
Decane	$C_{10}H_{22}$	142.17	313	1115
Ethane	C_2H_6	30.05	708	550
Ethanol	C_2H_5OH	46.05	928	929
Ethylene	C_2H_4	28.03	748	509
Heptane	C_7H_{16}	100.12	396	972
Hexane	C_6H_{14}	86.11	536	914
Hydrogen cyanide	HCN	27.02	735	822
Methane	CH_4	16.03	673	343
Nitric oxide	NO	30.01	955	323
Octane	C_8H_{18}	114.14	352	1025
Oxygen	O_2	32.00	740	278
Pentane	C_5H_{12}	72.09	485	847
Propane	C_3H_8	44.06	619	666
Sulfur dioxide	SO_2	64.06	1140	775
Sulfur trioxide	SO_3	80.06	1229	885
Toluene	C_7H_8	92.06	612	1069
Water	H_2O	18.02	3206	705

Table 1.8

Gas	Formula	m	p'_c	T'_c
Helium	He	4.00	151.5	8.3
Hydrogen	H_2	2.02	306	41.3
Neon	Ne	20.18	498	52.5

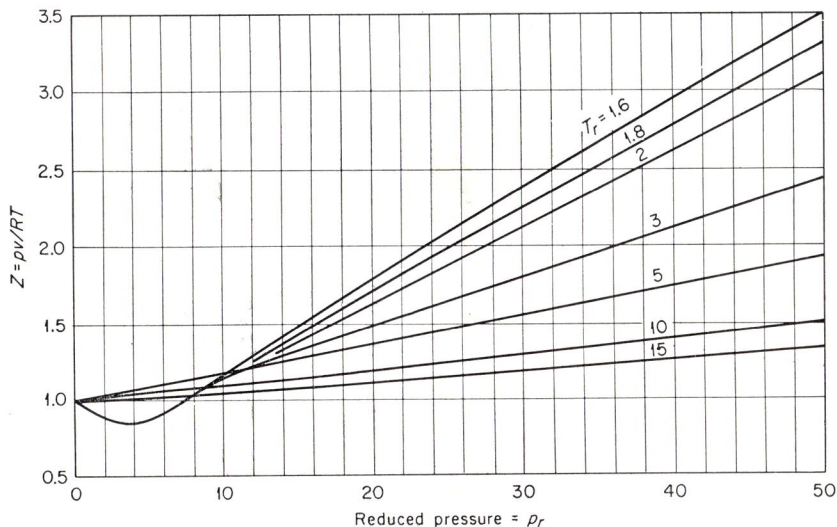

Fig. 1.2. Compressibility factors for higher ranges. (*By permission of H. C. Weber, "Thermodynamics for Chemical Engineers,"* pp. 108, 109, 1939, *Wiley.*)

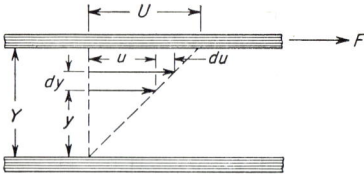

FIG. 1.3

condition is approximated in the clearance space of a flooded journal bearing. Particles of fluid in contact with each plate will adhere to the surfaces, and if the distance Y is not too great or the velocity U too high, the velocity gradient will be a straight line. The action is much as if the fluid were made up of a series of thin sheets, each of which would slip a little relative to the next. Experiment has shown that for a large class of fluids $F \sim AU/Y$. It may be seen from similar triangles that U/Y can be replaced by the velocity gradient du/dy. If a constant of proportionality μ is introduced, the shearing stress between any two thin sheets of fluid is $\tau = F/A = \mu U/Y = \mu\, du/dy$, which is called Newton's equation of viscosity. By transformation, $\mu = \tau/(du/dy)$, which is called the coefficient of viscosity, the absolute viscosity, or the dynamic viscosity.

A distinction among various kinds of fluids and solids is shown by Fig. 1.4. In the case of a solid, the shear stress is proportional to the *magnitude* of the deformation, while in a fluid the shear stress is proportional to the *time rate* of (angular) deformation.

A fluid for which the constant of proportionality (i.e., the viscosity) does not change with the rate of deformation is said to be a "Newtonian fluid" and is represented by the straight line in Fig. 1.4. The slope of this line is determined by the viscosity. The ideal fluid, for which the viscosity is zero, is represented by the horizontal axis, while a true elastic solid is represented by the vertical axis. A plastic, which sustains a certain amount of stress before suffering a plastic flow, is shown by a straight line intersecting the vertical axis at the yield point.

There are certain non-Newtonian fluids in which the viscosity varies with the rate of deformation. For information on such see Sec. 7 of this handbook. In the present section the treatment will be confined to Newtonian fluids.

1.9. Viscosity Dimensions and Units

In the English gravitational or engineers' system [foot-pound(force)-second] absolute viscosity is expressed in terms of pounds per second per square foot or slugs per foot per second. There is no name for the unit. [In the English absolute, or physicists', system [foot-pound(mass)-second] absolute viscosity would be in poundal seconds per square foot or pounds per foot-second. This system is rarely used.]

In the metric absolute, or physicists', system the dimensions of absolute viscosity are dyne-seconds per square centimeter or grams per centimeter-second. The unit of one dyne-second per square centimeter is called the *poise*. (The metric gravitational system is rarely used.)

As most fluids have low viscosities, the *centipoise* ($= 0.01$ poise) is frequently a more convenient unit. It has the further advantage that since the viscosity of water at 68.4° F is 1 centipoise, the value of viscosity in centipoises is an indication of the viscosity of any fluid relative to that of water. Therefore the value in centipoises is numerically equal to the *specific viscosity* (a dimensionless ratio) of the fluid relative to that of water at 68.4°F.

Values of viscosity found in practically all tables are given in the metric system, and that custom will be followed here. The viscosities of some common fluids are shown in Fig. 1.5 as a function of temperature, and other values are found in Tables 1.9 and 1.10.

It is seen that as the temperature in-

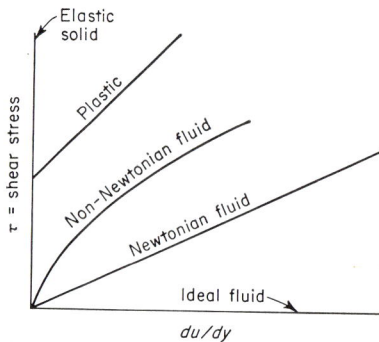

FIG. 1.4

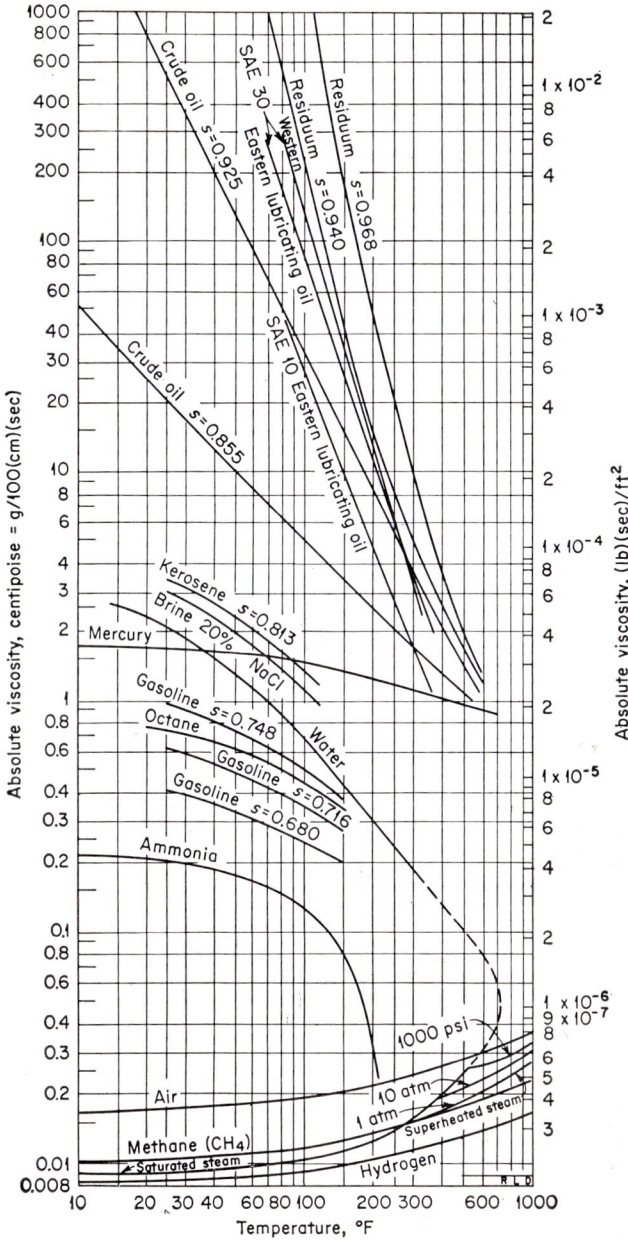

FIG. 1.5. Values of absolute viscosity.

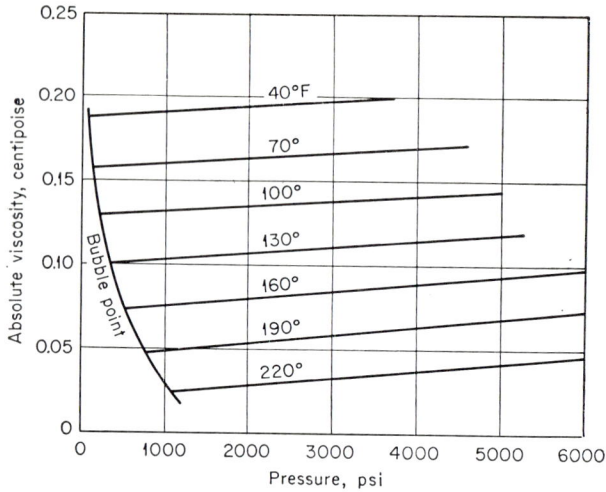

Fig. 1.6. Viscosity of liquid ammonia at high pressures. [*By permission of L. T. Carmichael and B. H. Sage, Ind. Eng. Chem.*, **44**:2728 (November, 1952).]

creases, the viscosities of all liquids decrease while those of all gases or vapors increase. Viscosity is due to the cohesion between particles and also to the interchange of molecules between the layers of different velocities. The force of cohesion, which diminishes with temperature, predominates with liquids, while with gases the interchange of molecules predominates. It is seen that the viscosities for water and saturated steam merge at the critical temperature, and this is true for the liquid and saturated vapor phase of all fluids.

The absolute viscosity of either a liquid or a gas is practically independent of pressure for the range that is ordinarily encountered in engineering work. But at very high pressures the values are increased, as is shown by a few specific cases in Figs. 1.6 to 1.9.

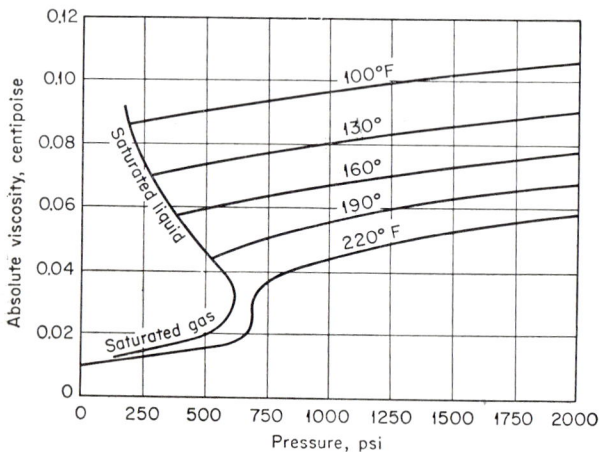

Fig. 1.7. Effect of Pressure on the absolute viscosity of liquid propane. [*By permission of B. H. Sage and W. N. Lacey, Ind. Eng. Chem.*, **30**:829 (1938).]

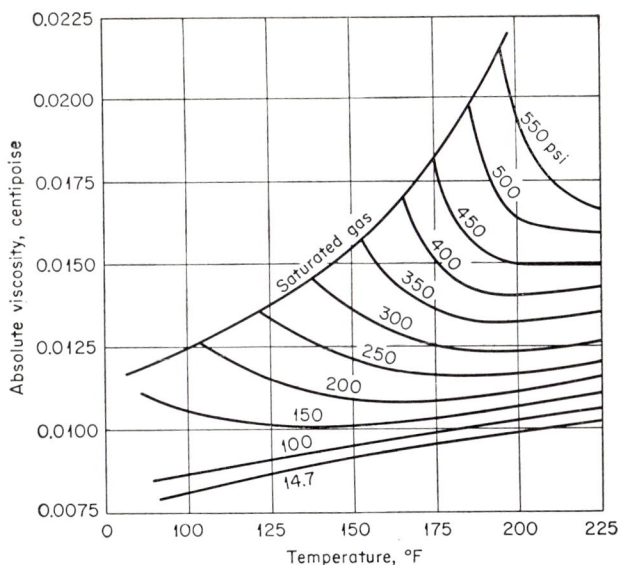

Fig. 1.8. Viscosity of gaseous propane. [*By permission of B. H. Sage and W. N. Lacey, Ind. Eng. Chem.,* **30**:829 (1938).]

1.10. Kinematic Viscosity

In many problems involving viscosity, there frequently appears the value of viscosity divided by density. This quotient is called *kinematic* viscosity, because no force is involved, the only dimensions being length and time. Viscosity in pound(force)-seconds

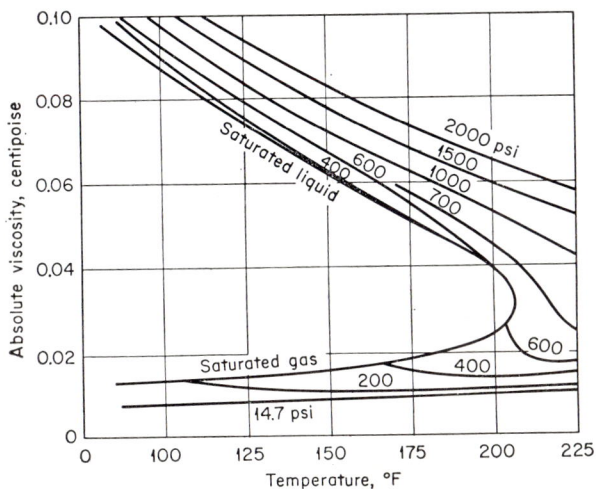

Fig. 1.9. Viscosity-temperature diagram for propane in liquid, gaseous, and critical regions. [*By permission of B. H. Sage and W. N. Lacey, Ind. Eng. Chem.,* **30**:829 (1938).]

Table 1.9. Viscosity of Liquids, in Centipoises

Fluid	°F	Viscosity	Fluid	°F	Viscosity
Ammonia.........	10	0.213	Ethyl alcohol.......	−25.6	3.84
	20	0.205		+0.4	2.68
	60	0.165		32	1.77
	100	0.131		50	1.47
	140	0.095		68	1.20
	180	0.060		86	1.00
	200	0.035		104	0.834
	220	0.025		122	0.702
Castor oil..........	50	2,420		140	0.592
	68	986		158	0.504
	86	451	Mercury..........	−4	1.855
	104	231		+14	1.764
	212	17		32	1.685
Glycerin...........	32	12,110		50	1.615
	43	6,260		68	1.554
	59	2,330		86	1.499
	68	1,490		104	1.450
	77	954		122	1.407
	86	629		140	1.367
	150	70		158	1.331
Methyl alcohol......	−8	1.22		176	1.298
	32	0.82		194	1.268
	59	0.62		212	1.240
	68	0.60		302	1.130
	77	0.55		392	1.052
	86	0.51		482	0.995
	104	0.46		572	0.950
	122	0.40		644	0.921

Table 1.10. Viscosity of Gases or Vapors, in Centipoises

Fluid	°F	Viscosity	Fluid	°F	Viscosity
Air...........	−25	0.0154	Ammonia............	32	0.00918
	+10	0.0162		68	0.00982
	20	0.0167		122	0.0109
	30	0.0171		212	0.0128
	40	0.0176		302	0.0146
	60	0.0180		392	0.0165
	80	0.0185		482	0.0181
	100	0.0190		572	0.0199
	120	0.0194	Carbon dioxide........	32	0.0140
	130	0.0196		59	0.0146
	150	0.0201		68	0.0148
	165	0.0210		86	0.0153
	200	0.0215		104	0.0157
	300	0.0239		220	0.0189
	400	0.0251		455	0.0241
	500	0.0282		576	0.0268
	600	0.0300		1930	0.0478
	700	0.0316	Ethyl alcohol.........	212	0.0108
	800	0.0340	CH_3CH_2OH	268	0.0117
	900	0.0359	$m = 46.07$	339	0.0129
	1000	0.0374		377	0.0135
	1150	0.0392		414	0.0140
	1180	0.0401		485	0.0152
	1380	0.0426		587	0.0167
	1490	0.0442	Methyl alcohol.......	152	0.0135
	1690	0.0464	CH_3OH	232	0.0126
	1895	0.0491	$m = 44.09$	422	0.0162
	2075	0.0521		592	0.0192

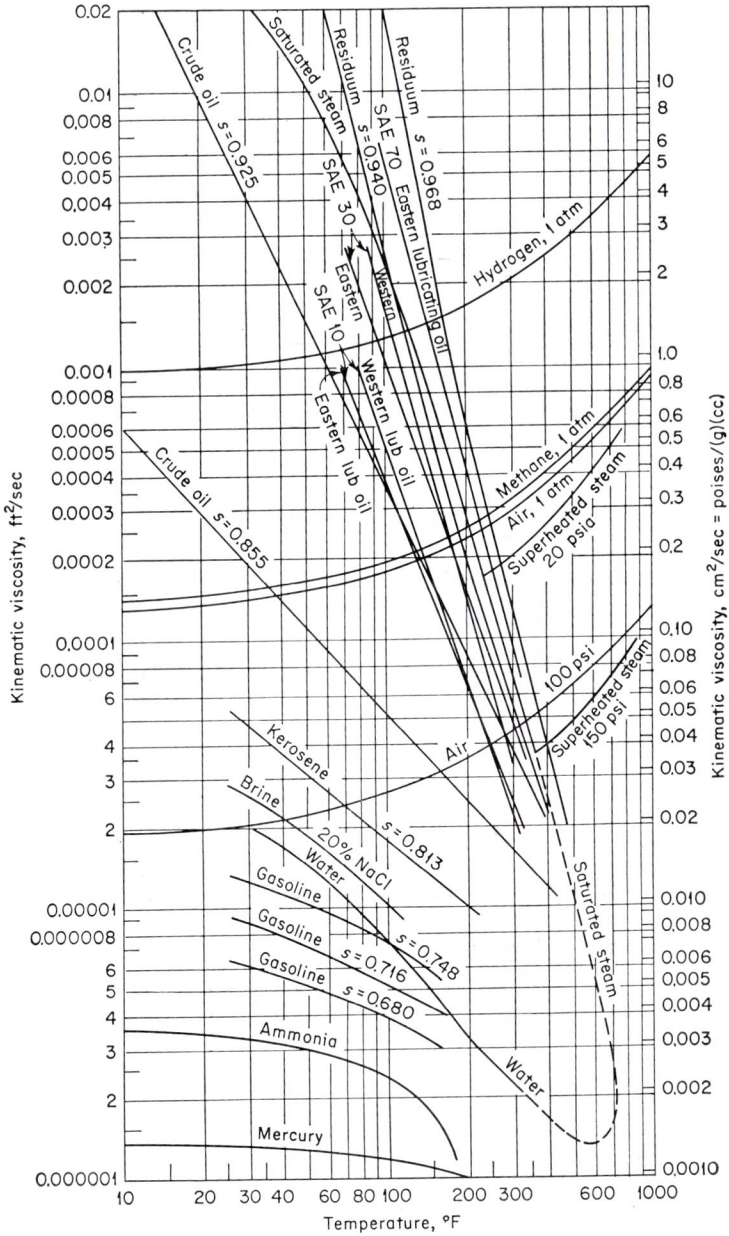

Fig. 1.10. Values of kinematic viscosity.

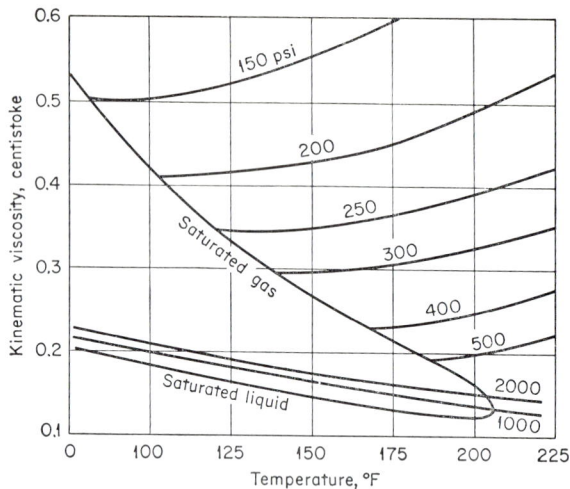

FIG. 1.11. Kinematic viscosity of propane. [*By permission of B. H. Sage and W. N. Lacey, Ind. Eng. Chem.*, **30**:829 (1938).]

per square foot divided by density in slugs per cubic foot is kinematic viscosity in square feet per second. (The same result would be obtained by dividing viscosity in poundal-seconds per square foot by specific weight in pound per cubic foot.) There is no name for this unit.

In the metric system viscosity in poises divided by density in grams per cubic centimeter gives kinematic viscosity in square centimeters per second. The unit of one square centimeter per second is called a *stoke*. The *centistoke* (= 0.01 stoke) is often a more convenient unit and is obtained by dividing centipoises by grams per cubic centimeter.

At 68.4°F the kinematic viscosity of water is 1 centistoke. Hence the value of the kinematic viscosity of any fluid expressed in centistokes is also its kinematic viscosity relative to that of water at 68.4°F.

Kinematic viscosities of some common fluids are shown in Fig. 1.10 as a function of temperature. For gases or vapors the values are also functions of pressure.

1.11. Measurement of Viscosity

There are various laboratory instruments for the measurement of absolute viscosity, but the more commonly used instruments measure kinematic viscosity, usually by noting the time required for a certain volume of liquid to flow under a definite head through a short tube of small diameter. Thus kinematic viscosity is reported as a certain number of seconds. The most commonly used viscosimeter, or viscometer, used in the United States is the Saybolt (Art. 14.21), of which there are two types, the Universal, used for lower viscosities, and the Furol (a word contracted from fuel and road oil), used for more viscous liquids. The latter has a tube of larger bore, and the time of flow for the same viscosity is approximately one-tenth as long as with the former. Other viscometers less commonly used in the United States are the Redwood (England) and the Engler (Germany).

For strict accuracy an individual viscometer should be calibrated, but the following equations may be used in the absence of such calibration. The equations give the kinematic viscosity in stokes for any time t in seconds for the flow of 60 ml of the liquid. These equations are applicable with very slight error for any temperature of the fluid in the test. Thus for the same kinematic viscosity the time of efflux from the Saybolt is about 0.7 per cent longer at 210°F than at 100°F.

Viscometer	Stokes	Equation no.
Saybolt Universal:		
$t = 32\text{-}100$ sec	$0.00226t - 1.95/t$	(1.7)
$t > 100$ sec	$0.00220t - 1.35/t$	(1.8)
Saybolt Furol:		
$t = 25\text{-}40$ sec	$0.0224t - 1.84/t$	(1.9)
$t > 40$ sec	$0.0216t - 0.60/t$	(1.10)
Redwood No. 1:		
$t = 34\text{-}100$ sec	$0.00260t - 1.79/t$	(1.11)
$t > 100$ sec	$0.00247t - 0.50/t$	(1.12)
Redwood Admiralty	$0.027t - 20/t$	(1.13)
Engler	$0.00147t - 3.74/t$	(1.14)

Kinematic viscosity in centistokes may be found from Table 1.11 for Saybolt seconds computed from the preceding formulas multiplied by 100.   For times longer than are given in the table, the last term in Eqs. (1.8) and (1.10) becomes negligible within the limits of experimental error, and then the kinematic viscosity is practically proportional to the number of Saybolt seconds.

Since viscosity varies so much with temperature, its numerical value has no meaning unless the corresponding temperature is specified.   There is no one standard temperature employed, but those commonly used for the Saybolt Universal viscometer are 70, 100, 130, and 210°F.   For the Saybolt Furol, the standard temperatures are 77, 100, 122, and 210°F.

The Saybolt Universal is used for flow times not less than 32 sec nor more than 1000 sec.   The minimum time for the Furol is 25 sec.

1.12. Viscosity Conversion Factors

Viscosity is usually given in poises or centipoises in tables, and it is necessary to convert to other units if the foot-pound-second system is employed.

1 poise = 100 centipoises = 1 dyne-second per square centimeter
  = 1,000 millipoises
  = 1,000,000 micropoises
  = 0.00209 pound(force)-second per square foot
  = 0.0672 poundal second per square foot
  = 0.0672 pound(mass)per foot-second
1 pound(force)-second per square foot = 478.7 poises
1 poundal-second per square foot = 14.88 poises
1 stoke = 100 centistokes = 1 square centimeter per second
  = 0.001076 square foot per second

$$1 \text{ square foot per second} = \frac{0.000672 \times \text{centipoises}}{\text{pound per cubic foot}}$$

Table 1.11. Kinematic-viscosity Conversion from Saybolt Seconds to Centistokes

Saybolt seconds Universal	Centi-stokes	Saybolt seconds Universal	Centi-stokes	Saybolt seconds Furol	Centi-stokes	Saybolt seconds Furol	Centi-stokes
32	1.13	54	8.59	25	48.64	42	89.30
34	1.95	56	9.16	26	51.16	44	93.68
36	2.81	58	9.74	27	53.66	46	98.06
38	3.45	60	10.31	28	56.15	48	102.43
40	4.16	64	11.40	29	58.62	50	106.80
42	4.84	70	13.03	30	61.07	52	111.17
44	5.50	80	15.64	32	65.93	54	115.53
46	6.16	100	20.65	34	70.76	56	119.89
48	6.78	120	25.28	36	75.53	58	125.25
50	7.40	140	29.84	38	80.28	60	128.60
52	7.72	160	34.36	40	85.00	65	139.48
		200	43.32			75	161.12

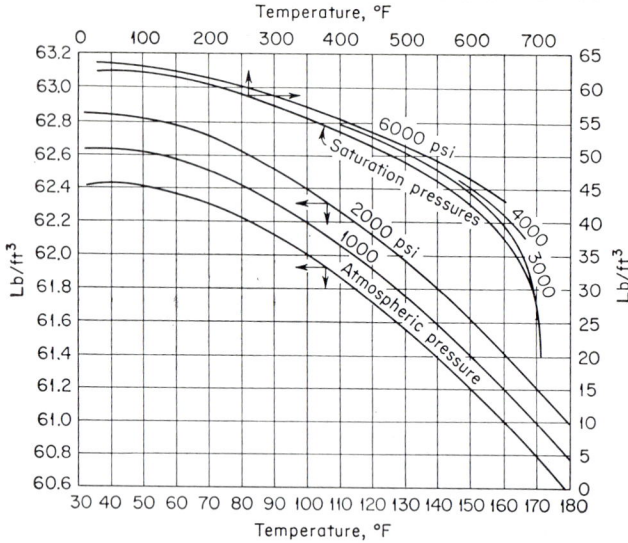

Fig. 1.12. Specific weight of pure water.

1.13. Some Properties of Liquid Water

The effect of pressure upon the specific weight of water is shown by Fig. 1.12. For other and even higher pressures values can be calculated by use of Table 1.5. (See also Table 1.13.)

Values of specific weight and viscosity of water at saturation pressures are given in Table 1.12. The decrease in the specific volume of water below its value at the saturation condition is shown in Table 1.13.

For any liquid the saturation pressure is the pressure at a given temperature at which the liquid will begin to boil if there is any reduction below that pressure or if there is any transfer of heat into the liquid at that pressure. This is known as the vapor pressure and also as the bubble point.

1.14. Specific Weights of Some Gases and Liquids

The specific weight of any gas that closely follows the perfect-gas law, $pv = RT$, may be found for any temperature and pressure, in which R can be obtained as in Table 1.6. For other gases and vapors approximate values may be found by the use of Eq. (1.6) in conjunction with Figs. 1.1 and 1.2. Values for some gases and vapors are shown for one temperature and pressure in Table 1.15 and for some liquids in Table 1.16.

1.15. Specific Weight of Moist Air

From Dalton's law of partial pressures, the total atmospheric pressure as given by the barometer equals the sum of the partial pressure of the (dry) air and the partial pressure of the water vapor in the air. Thus $p_{bar} = p_{air} + p_{vapor}$. The partial pressure of the water vapor equals the relative humidity times the saturation pressure as given in steam tables or in Table 1.17.

For example, assume a barometer reading of 28 in. Hg, a temperature of 80°F, and a relative humidity of 70 per cent. The total pressure = $28 \times 0.491 \times 144 = 13.75 \times 144 = 1980$ psfa. At 80°F the saturation temperature of water vapor is 0.5069 psia, and at 70 per cent relative humidity the vapor pressure equals $0.70 \times 0.5069 \times 144 =$

Table 1.12. Some Properties of Water at Saturation Pressures

Temperature		Specific weight, lb/ft³	Absolute viscosity, centipoises	Kinematic viscosity	
°C	°F			Centistokes	$\nu \times 10^5$ ft²/sec
0	32	62.418	1.792	1.793	1.929
	35	62.422	1.692	1.693	1.819
4	39.2	62.427	1.567	1.567	1.684
	40	62.426	1.546	1.546	1.662
5		62.425	1.519	1.519	1.633
	45	62.420	1.419	1.419	1.525
10	50	62.40	1.308	1.309	1.407
	55	62.38	1.210	1.211	1.302
15		62.37	1.140	1.141	1.227
	60	62.35	1.124	1.130	1.216
	65	62.34	1.047	1.050	1.127
20		62.30	1.005	1.010	1.083
20.2	68.4	62.30	1.000	1.000	1.076
	70	62.29	0.9785	0.9985	1.054
	75	62.25	0.9166	0.9182	0.988
25		62.24	0.8937	0.8959	0.964
	80	62.20	0.8609	0.8638	0.929
	85	62.16	0.8062	0.8085	0.870
30		62.15	0.8007	0.8018	0.864
	90	62.11	0.7644	0.7677	0.826
35	95	62.05	0.7225	0.7267	0.782
	100	62.00	0.6843	0.6886	0.741
40		61.94	0.6560	0.6608	0.711
	105	61.92	0.6439	0.6487	0.698
	110	61.84	0.6160	0.6208	0.668
45		61.82	0.5988	0.6041	0.650
	115	61.80	0.5871	0.5920	0.637
	120	61.73	0.5599	0.5660	0.609
50		61.68	0.5494	0.5558	0.598
	125	61.65	0.5345	0.5409	0.582
	130	61.54	0.5155	0.5223	0.562
55		61.53	0.5064	0.5130	0.552
	135	61.46	0.4890	0.4963	0.534
60	140	61.38	0.4688	0.4768	0.513
	145	61.27	0.4498	0.458	0.493
65		61.22	0.4355	0.444	0.478
	150	61.20	0.4300	0.438	0.472
	155	61.09	0.4155	0.435	0.457
70		61.04	0.4061	0.415	0.447
	160	61.01	0.4000	0.409	0.440
	165	60.90	0.3855	0.396	0.426
75		60.86	0.3799	0.390	0.420
	170	60.79	0.3713	0.382	0.411
	175	60.68	0.3590	0.368	0.397
80		60.66	0.3565-	0.366	0.394
	180	60.57	0.3469	0.357	0.384
85	185	60.46	0.3355	0.346	0.372
	190	60.35	0.3247	0.337	0.362
90		60.31	0.3165	0.328	0.353
	195	60.24	0.3146	0.326	0.351
	200	60.13	0.3049	0.317	0.341
	205	60.00	0.2955	0.308	0.331
100	212	59.83	0.2838	0.296	0.318
105	221	59.77	0.270	0.282	0.304
110	230	59.38	0.250	0.263	0.283
120	248	58.86	0.232	0.246	0.264
130	266	58.34	0.212	0.227	0.244
140	284	57.80	0.196	0.216	0.232
150	302	57.24	0.184	0.201	0.216
160	320	56.66	0.174	0.191	0.205

Table 1.13. Decrease in Specific Volume of Water from
the Saturation Volume $= (v_f - v) \times 10^5$ †

Pressure, psia	Temperature, °F								
	32	100	200	300	400	500	600	700	705.4
1000	5.7	5.1	5.4	6.9	8.7	6.4			
1500	8.4	7.5	8.1	10.4	14.1	17.3			
2000	11.0	9.9	10.8	13.8	19.5	27.8	32.6		
2500	13.7	12.3	13.4	17.2	24.8	37.7	61.9		354
3000	16.3	14.7	16.0	20.7	30.0	47.1	87.9		
3206.2	17.5	15.7	17.1	22.2	32.1	51.0	98.0	354	
4000	21.5	19.2	21.0	27.5	40.0	64.5	132.2	821	2079
5000	26.7	23.6	26.0	34.0	49.6	80.5	169.3	1017	2309
6000	31.7	27.8	30.8	40.5	58.7	96.1	202.9		

† L. S. Marks, "Mechanical Engineers' Handbook," 6th ed., p. 4-7, McGraw-Hill, New York, 1958
(abstracted from J. H. Keenan and F. G. Keyes, "Thermodynamic Properties of Steam," Wiley, New
York, 1948).

Table 1.14. Saturation Pressure and Saturation Volume for Water †

°F	Pressure, psia	Ft³/lb, v_f	°F	Pressure, psia	Ft³/lb, v_f
32	0.08854	0.01602	180	7.510	0.01651
40	0.12170	0.01602	190	9.339	0.01657
50	0.17811	0.01603	200	11.526	0.01663
60	0.2563	0.01604	210	14.123	0.01670
70	0.3631	0.01606	212	14.696	0.01672
80	0.5069	0.01608	220	17.186	0.01677
90	0.6982	0.01610	230	20.780	0.01684
100	0.9492	0.01613	250	29.825	0.01700
110	1.2478	0.01617	300	67.013	0.01745
120	1.6924	0.01620	350	134.63	0.01799
130	2.2225	0.01625	400	247.31	0.01864
140	2.8886	0.01629	450	422.6	0.0194
150	3.718	0.01634	500	680.8	0.0204
160	4.741	0.01639	600	1542.9	0.0236
170	5.335	0.01645	705.4	3206.2	0.0503

† J. H. Keenan and F. G. Keyes, "Thermodynamic Properties of Steam," Wiley, New York, 1948.

Table 1.15. Specific Weight of Some Gases and Superheated
Vapors at 32°F and 14.7 Psia, Lb/Ft³

Gas or vapor	Symbol	Specific weight, lb/ft³	Gas or vapor	Symbol	Specific weight, lb/ft³
Acetylene	C_2H_2	0.07323	Helium	He	0.01114
Air		0.08071	Hydrogen	H_2	0.005611
Ammonia	NH_3	0.04813	Hydrogen sulfide	H_2S	0.09608
n-Butane	C_4H_{10}	0.1683	Methane	CH_4	0.04475
Isobutane	C_4H_{10}	0.1669	Nitric oxide	NO	0.08367
Carbon dioxide	CO_2	0.1234	Nitrogen	N_2	0.07807
Carbon monoxide	CO	0.07086	Nitrous oxide	NO_2	0.1235
Chlorine	Cl_2	0.2006	Oxygen	O_2	0.08921
Ethane	C_2H_6	0.08469	Ozone	O_3	0.1338
Ethylene	C_2H_4	0.07868	Propane	C_3H_8	0.1261
Fluorine	F_2	0.1059	Sulfur dioxide	SO_2	0.1827

$0.35483 \times 144 = 51.096$ psfa. The partial pressure of the (dry) air is $1980 - 51.1 =$
1928.9 psfa. Hence the weight of the air is $\gamma = p/RT = 1928.9/53.3 \times 540 =$
0.06702 lb/ft³. The weight of the water vapor $= 51.096/85.6 \times 540 = 0.0011054$ lb/ft³.
(By use of the steam tables a more precise value is $0.70/633.1 = 0.0011057$ lb/ft³.)

Table 1.16. Specific Weight of Some Liquids, Lb/Ft³

Liquid	°F	Specific weight, lb/ft³	Liquid	°F	Specific weight, lb/ft³
Alcohol..........	68.4	50	Mercury.......	32	848.7
Ammonia........	−100	45.52		39.2	848.1
	−50	43.49		50	847.2
	0	41.34		60	846.3
	+50	39.00		68.4	845.7
	100	36.40		80	844.7
	150	33.39		90	843.8
	200	29.63		100	843.0
	250	23.7		140	839.6
Fuel oil..........	60	56–64		212	833.6
Gasoline.........	60	41–48		300	804.2
Glycerin..........	32	78.6	Sea water......	60	64.0
Lubricating oil....	60	55–59			

The total weight of the moist air = 0.06702 + 0.001106 = 0.068126 lb/ft³. (For the same barometer pressure and temperature and zero humidity, the weight of air = 0.068793 lb/ft³.) Table 1.17 defines the standard atmosphere in aeronautics.

1.16. Vapor Pressure of Liquids

All liquids tend to evaporate or vaporize, which they do by projecting molecules into the space above their free surfaces. If this is a confined space, the partial pressure exerted by the molecules increases until the rate at which molecules reenter the liquid is equal to the rate at which they leave. For this equilibrium condition the vapor pressure is known as the *saturation* pressure.

Molecular activity increases with increasing temperature, and hence the saturation pressure increases with temperature. At any one temperature the pressure on the liquid surface may be higher than this value, but it cannot be any lower, as any slight reduction induces a rapid rate of evaporation known as "boiling."

The wide variation in the saturation vapor pressure of a few liquids all at 70°F is given in Table 1.18. This table shows the great value of mercury in the barometer, where there is almost, but not quite, a perfect vacuum at the top of the column. It also shows that a much greater pressure must be maintained on a fluid such as gasoline to prevent its boiling or evaporating than is necessary for a liquid such as water. Hence it is not possible to lift gasoline by suction to as great a height as water. Values of the saturation vapor pressures for a few liquids are also given in Table 1.18.

1.17. Surface Tension and Capillarity

Liquids have properties such as cohesion and adhesion, both of which are forms of molecular attraction. *Cohesion* enables a liquid to resist tensile stress, while *adhesion*

Table 1.17. Standard Atmosphere in Aeronautics

Altitude above sea level, ft	Temperature, °F	Pressure, psfa	Density, slugs/ft³	Kinematic viscosity, 1 × 10⁻⁴ ft²/sec
0	59	2116.2	0.002378	1.564
1,000	55.44	2040.9	0.002310	1.602
2,000	51.87	1967.7	0.002242	1.641
3,000	48.31	1896.7	0.002177	1.681
4,000	44.74	1827.7	0.002112	1.723
5,000	41.18	1760.8	0.002049	1.766
10,000	23.36	1455.4	0.001756	2.002
15,000	5.54	1194.3	0.001497	2.280
20,000	−12.28	972.6	0.001267	2.608
25,000	−30.10	785.3	0.001066	2.999

Table 1.18. Saturation Vapor Pressure, in Psia

Liquid	°F	Saturation pressure	Liquid	°F	Saturation pressure
Mercury........	70	0.000,025	Ammonia........	−100	1.24
Water..........	70	0.363		−50	7.67
Kerosene.......	70	0.492		0	30.42
Methyl alcohol...	70	1.965		+50	89.19
Gasoline........	70	4.42		100	211.9
Water..........	32	0.089		150	433.2
	40	0.122		200	794.7
	50	0.178		250	1347
	60	0.256	Sulfur dioxide....	32	22.5
	80	0.507		68	47.5
	90	0.698		140	150.7
	100	0.949		212	407
	120	1.692		230	500
	140	2.887	Carbon dioxide...	32	505
	160	4.739		68	831
	180	7.510	Mercury........	32	0.000,00358
	200	11.525		50	0.000,00948
	212	14.696		68	0.000,0232
	250	29.825		140	0.000,0488
	300	67.013		212	0.00528
	400	247.3		230	0.00885
	500	680.8		320	0.08102

enables it to adhere to another body. *Surface tension* (Table 1.19) is due to cohesion between particles at the surface of a liquid. *Capillarity* is due to both cohesion and adhesion. When the former is of less effect than the latter, the liquid will wet a solid surface with which it is in contact and rise at the point of contact. If cohesion predominates, the liquid surface will be depressed at the point of contact. Thus capillarity causes water to rise in a glass tube while mercury is depressed below the true level, as is shown by the insert in Fig. 1.13, which is drawn to scale and reproduced actual size.

The capillary rise or depression is determined by the equation

$$2\,s = (\gamma_1 - \gamma_2)bh \tag{1.15}$$

in which s = surface tension in units of force per unit length, such as lb/ft
       γ_1 = specific weight of liquid below as herein meniscus
       γ_2 = specific weight of fluid above meniscus (a gas or another liquid)
       b = radius of curvature at bottom or top of meniscus
       h = capillary rise or depression

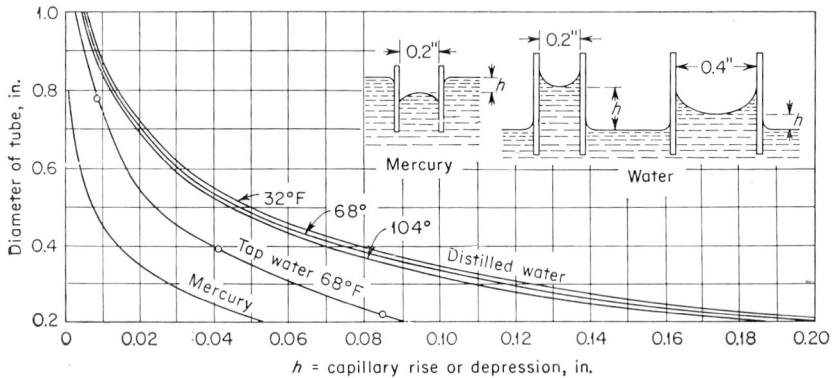

FIG. 1.13. Capillarity in circular glass tubes.

Table **1.19.** Values of Surface Tension of Water and Mercury in Contact with Air

Liquid	Temp., °F	Lb/ft	Liquid	Temp., °F	Lb/ft
Water.........	32	0.00518	Water.........	120	0.00467
	40	0.00514		140	0.00454
	50	0.00509		160	0.00440
	60	0.00504		180	0.00427
	70	0.00498		200	0.00413
	80	0.00492		212	0.00404
	90	0.00486	Mercury.......	59	0.0333
	100	0.00480		68	0.0324

Table **1.20.** Thermal Conductivities, $\text{Btu}/(\text{Hr})(\text{Ft}^2)(\text{Ft of Thickness})(°F)$ †

Substance	°F	k	Substance	°F	k
Liquid:			Gas:		
Ammonia............	45	0.29	Hydrogen...........	32	0.0917
Ethyl alcohol........	68	0.105		212	0.115
Glycerin............	68	0.165	Methane............	32	0.0175
Kerosene............	68	0.086	Nitrogen............	32	0.0140
Methyl alcohol.......	68	0.124	Oxygen.............	32	0.0142
Water..............	32	0.335	Sulfur dioxide........	32	0.005
	140	0.377	Air................	32	0.0140
Gas:				200	0.0179
Ammonia............	32	0.0128		400	0.0224
	212	0.0175		600	0.0269
Carbon dioxide.......	32	0.0085		800	0.0314
	212	0.0133		1000	0.0359
Helium.............	32	0.0802			

† From L. S. Marks, "Mechanical Engineers' Handbook," 6th ed., p. 4-95, McGraw-Hill, New York, 1958·

The practical difficulty in applying this equation is that it is impossible to measure the radius of curvature of the liquid surface, and therefore certain assumptions are necessary. Thus, if the diameter of the tube is less than 0.1 in., the meniscus may be assumed to be spherical with a radius $b = r/\cos\theta$, in which r is the radius of the tube and θ is the contact angle between liquid and tube. If the surface is clean, this angle is 0° for water and about 140° for mercury. For larger diameters no such simple solution is possible. With increasing diameter of tube the radius of curvature of the meniscus increases, so that the rise or depression becomes much less. For tube diameters of 0.5 in. or more, the capillary action is negligible for water and mercury.‡

Surface tension decreases with increasing temperature, but the effect upon capillary height is rather small, as seen in Fig. 1.13. The capillary effect is less for mercury than for water, but when the mercury reading is multiplied by the specific gravity of mercury to obtain a pressure measured in height of a water column, the error will be greater than for a water column in the same-size tube. The curves in Fig. 1.13 are for water and mercury in contact with air. If the mercury is in contact with water, the surface-tension effect is less than when it is in contact with air, but in this case the change in the value of $\gamma_1 - \gamma_2$ is practically in the same proportion as the change in the surface tension, so the values of the capillary depression for mercury and air are almost identical with those for mercury and water.

1.18. Thermal Conductivity of Gases and Liquids

The thermal conductivity of any substance may be defined as the quantity of heat in Btu that flows in a unit of time, as one hour, through a unit area of one square foot per

‡ The curve for tap water in Fig. 1.13 was determined experimentally at the California Institute of Technology by Dr. R. G. Folsom. He found dirty water to give even lower values· The curves for pure water and for mercury were computed by the author.

foot of thickness per one degree Fahrenheit difference in temperature. Thus the total heat flow per hour is

$$\text{Btu} = kA\,\frac{t_1 - t_2}{L} \tag{1.16}$$

where
A = cross-section area at right angles to heat flow
L = thickness in direction of flow
$t_1 - t_2$ = difference in temperature of two faces
k = coefficient of thermal conductivity

Table 1.20 gives the values of k for various liquids and gases.

Section **2**

BASIC EQUATIONS OF FLUID FLOW

By

ASCHER H. SHAPIRO, *Massachusetts Institute of Technology, Cambridge, Massachusetts*

BASIC EQUATIONS OF FLUID FLOW

2.1. Introduction

The purpose of this section is to set out the fundamental concepts, definitions, and laws of fluid dynamics, as background material for the remaining sections of this handbook.

It is assumed in this section that one is dealing with a fluid Newtonian in character. Other rheological formulations are treated in Sec. 7. It is also assumed that the dimensions of the problem are large enough compared with molecular distances so that the fluid may be treated as a continuous medium without loss of essential detail.

This section begins with a statement of basic concepts and definitions. Then, since fluid dynamics treats essentially of the relationships between the fluid motion and the forces acting in the fluid, the subjects discussed are the kinematics of fluid motion, the origins of forces in fluids, and ultimately the dynamical equations of motion. In addition to the latter, the principle of mass conservation and the two laws of thermodynamics are introduced as governing relationships which the fluid must also obey. Some general theorems consequent upon the four governing relationships (Newton's dynamical law, mass conservation, and two thermodynamical laws) are presented.

Two types of mathematical formulation are used concurrently: vectorial coordinates, for conciseness and clarity, and three-dimensional coordinates (usually both cartesian and cylindrical), for convenience of reference.

2.2. Notation

A, $\mathbf{A}$	area
a_x, a_y, a_z	cartesian acceleration components
$\mathbf{a}$	vector acceleration
B	total value of b for finite mass
b	generalized property per unit mass
F, $\mathbf{F}$	force
h	enthalpy per unit mass
h_0	stagnation enthalpy per unit mass
$\mathbf{i}$, $\mathbf{j}$, $\mathbf{k}$	unit vectors along x, y, z
m	mass
p	pressure
$\mathbf{r}$	vector radius from origin
r, θ, z	cylindrical coordinates
s	entropy per unit mass
$\mathbf{S}$	acceleration of origin of moving reference frame
T	absolute temperature
t	time
u	internal energy per unit mass, exclusive of motion, capillarity, and force fields
u, v, w	components of V in cartesian coordinates
V, $\mathbf{V}$	velocity
v_r, v_θ, v_z	components of V in cylindrical coordinates
$\mho$	volume
W, $\mathbf{W}$	velocity referred to moving reference frame

X, Y, Z	components of body force per unit volume
x, y, z	cartesian coordinates
Γ	circulation
γ	rate of shear deformation
ϵ	rate of lineal strain
λ	surface tension
μ	ordinary coefficient of viscosity
μ'	dilational coefficient of viscosity
ν	kinematic viscosity μ/ρ
ξ, η, ζ	cartesian components of ω
ρ	mass density
σ	normal stress
τ	shear stress
ϕ	velocity-potential function
Φ	dissipation function
ψ	potential energy in conservative body-force field
ω	vorticity, $\nabla \times \mathbf{V}$
Ω	angular velocity of rotating reference frame

2.3. Basic Concepts and Definitions

What Is a Fluid? A *fluid* is here treated as an isotropic substance the individual pieces of which (treated on the macroscopic scale) continue to deform as the result of applied surface stresses. These deformations imply changes in shape, whether lineal or shear strains. Conversely, applied surface stresses will produce continuously increasing strains.

An important corollary is that there are no shear stresses in a fluid not undergoing deformation.

Fluids comprise both liquids and gases.

Continuum Model of a Fluid. Fluid matter, whether liquid or gaseous, is discrete on the microscopic, i.e., the molecular, level. When one is dealing with problems in which the dimensions are very large compared with molecular distances, however, it is convenient to think of lumps of fluid containing many molecules and to work with the average statistical properties of such large numbers of molecules. The detailed molecular structure is thus washed out completely and is replaced by a continuous model of matter having appropriate *continuum properties* so defined as to ensure that on the macroscopic scale the behavior of the model duplicates the behavior of the real fluid.

When the characteristic dimensions of a problem are not large compared with molecular distances, the continuum model is invalid.

Fluid Particle. The smallest lump of material having sufficient molecules to allow statistically of a continuum interpretation is here called a *fluid particle*. When the molecular dimensions are very small compared with the characteristic dimensions of the problem, the average properties of the fluid particle are in the limit assigned to a point, thus making possible a field representation of the continuum properties.

Continuum Properties. For incompressible fluids, the continuum properties necessary to describe the kinematical and dynamical behavior are the density, the velocity, the internal stresses, and the viscosity.

DENSITY. As an illustration of the limiting process by which the local continuum properties are defined, imagine a small volume $\delta\mathcal{V}$ surrounding a point P and let δm be instantaneously the total mass of material in $\delta\mathcal{V}$. Now the ratio $\delta m/\delta\mathcal{V}$ will, except as noted below, asymptote toward some limit as $\delta\mathcal{V}$ is made smaller. When $\delta\mathcal{V}$ reaches some value $\delta\mathcal{V}^*$, which may be thought of as the volume of a *fluid particle*, significant random fluctuations begin to appear because the number of molecules in $\delta\mathcal{V}$ is too small, and the notion of the ratio $\delta m/\delta\mathcal{V}$ then loses practical utility. Thus the mass density at the point P is defined as

$$\rho \equiv \lim_{\delta\mathcal{V}\to\delta\mathcal{V}^*} \frac{\delta m}{\delta\mathcal{V}} \qquad (2.1)$$

in which the limiting process is carried only to $\delta \mathcal{U}^*$, with the understanding, however, that ρ is associated with the point P itself.

VELOCITY. This is defined as the ratio of the total momentum carried by the molecules of the fluid particle $\delta \mathcal{U}^*$ to the total mass δm^* of those molecules. The velocity vector $\mathbf{V}$ thus defined is the appropriate mean quantity in the dynamical sense required by Newton's laws of motion.

STATE OF STRESS. Consider an area δA^* lying in some plane through the point P and including point P, where the dimensions of δA^* correspond to the dimensions of the fluid particle $\delta \mathcal{U}^*$. The fluid materials which contact each other on the two sides of the surface δA^* appear, on the macroscopic scale, to be exerting equal and opposite forces, δF^*, on each other. The limiting ratio $\delta F/\delta A$ as δA approaches δA^* is called the *surface stress* at the point P.

The surface stress at P may be resolved into a normal component and a tangential (or shear) component. Moreover, there will be a different vectorial surface stress at P for each orientation of the plane δA. Accordingly, the state of stress at a point is characterized by nine cartesian components. Furthermore, these nine quantities obey the transformation laws of a tensor. The stress tensor is represented by

$$\begin{bmatrix} \sigma_x & \tau_{xy} & \tau_{xz} \\ \tau_{yx} & \sigma_y & \tau_{yz} \\ \tau_{zx} & \tau_{zy} & \sigma_z \end{bmatrix} \tag{2.2a}$$

in which σ_x is the normal stress (positive when tensile) acting on a face normal to x; τ_{xy} is a shear stress acting in the y direction on a face normal to x, positive when the material at greater x exerts a shear in the positive y direction on the material at lesser y; and so on.

It may be shown from considerations of angular momentum that the stress tensor is symmetrical, that is, $\tau_{xy} = \tau_{yx}$, etc. Thus six, rather than nine, quantities suffice to determine the state of stress at a point.

In a fluid at rest, or in the absence of deformation of fluid particles, all the τ's vanish. It may then be shown from equilibrium considerations that the normal stress at a point is the same in all directions. The state of stress is then described as *hydrostatic* and is given by

$$\begin{bmatrix} -p & 0 & 0 \\ 0 & -p & 0 \\ 0 & 0 & -p \end{bmatrix} \tag{2.2b}$$

in which p is the uniform *hydrostatic pressure*.

The stress tensor, Eq. (2.2a), has three invariants, I_1, I_2, and I_3; and moreover, there is one set of orthogonal axes—the *principal axes*—for which the shear stresses vanish and on which there remain only the *principal normal stresses* σ_1, σ_2, σ_3. The three invariants are as follows:

$$\left. \begin{aligned} I_1 &\equiv \sigma_x + \sigma_y + \sigma_z = \sigma_1 + \sigma_2 + \sigma_3 \\ I_2 &\equiv \sigma_x\sigma_y + \sigma_y\sigma_z + \sigma_z\sigma_x - \tau_{xy}{}^2 - \tau_{yz}{}^2 - \tau_{zx}{}^2 = \sigma_1\sigma_2 + \sigma_2\sigma_3 + \sigma_3\sigma_1 \\ I_3 &\equiv \begin{vmatrix} \sigma_x & \tau_{xy} & \tau_{xz} \\ \tau_{yx} & \sigma_y & \tau_{yz} \\ \tau_{zx} & \tau_{zy} & \sigma_z \end{vmatrix} = \sigma_1\sigma_2\sigma_3 \end{aligned} \right\} \tag{2.2c}$$

For the principal axes, the stress tensor is simply

$$\begin{bmatrix} \sigma_1 & 0 & 0 \\ 0 & \sigma_2 & 0 \\ 0 & 0 & \sigma_3 \end{bmatrix}$$

VISCOSITY. The stress tensor is connected with the rate-of-strain tensor through the coefficients of viscosity (Art. 2.8).

OTHER CONTINUUM PROPERTIES. In a compressible fluid, the density depends on such properties as the pressure and temperature. In a viscous fluid, moreover, the viscosity may change strongly with temperature. In either of these circumstances one must augment purely mechanical laws by thermodynamical laws, for the temperature of the fluid is largely governed by thermodynamical effects. This makes it necessary to deal with such additional continuum properties as *temperature, compressibility, internal energy, entropy,* and *heat conductivity.*

When dealing with electrically conducting fluids (liquid metals and ionized gases) carrying currents or in the presence of magnetic fields, the properties of *electrical conductivity, dielectric constant,* and *magnetic permeability* also enter.

Field Representation of the Continuum Model. Let b represent any of the continuum properties heretofore mentioned. Then the essential mathematical simplification of the continuum model is that the average properties in the volume $\delta\mathcal{U}^*$ surrounding point P are assigned in the limit to the point P itself. Thus one arrives at an equivalent but fictitious continuous material, locally homogeneous and unstructured, having a value of b at every point of space at each instant of time. One thinks of the "field of b" as being described implicitly by an equation of the form

$$b = b(\mathbf{r},t) \qquad \text{or} \qquad b = b(x,y,z,t) \tag{2.3a}$$

In fluid dynamics one deals with scalar fields (e.g., density), with vector fields (e.g., velocity), and with tensor fields (e.g., the stress tensor).

2.4. Kinematics

Streamlines, Path Lines, and Streak Lines.† At any instant of time there is at every point of the fluid a velocity vector with a definite direction. The instantaneous curves which are everywhere tangent to this direction field are called the *streamlines* of the flow.

Since an element of arc length $d\mathbf{r}$ along a streamline is tangent to the local velocity vector $\mathbf{V}$, the equation of the streamline is

$$\mathbf{V} \times d\mathbf{r} = 0 \qquad \text{or} \qquad dx:dy:dz = u:v:w \tag{2.4}$$

Consider all the streamlines passing through some closed curve which is cut once by each streamline. These streamlines generate a tube which is called a *streamtube.* The latter has the property that it is apparently impervious to the fluid, since there is no component of the velocity vector normal to the surface of the tube.

A streamtube of infinitesimally small cross section, such that all its cross-section area is concentrated upon its axis (which is also a streamline), is called a *stream filament.*

A *path line* is the trajectory of a fluid particle of fixed identity.

A *streak line* is the current location of fluid particles all of which passed through a fixed point in space at some previous time.

Imagine an open flume carrying water past some immersed obstacle. On the water surface are solid particles so small that they follow exactly the motion of the fluid particles whose places they occupy. A stationary camera looks at the particles on the flowing surface.

Suppose that the entire surface is sprinkled with particles and that a brief time exposure is made. The photograph then shows many short streaks defining the instantaneous direction field. Faired curves through these streaks constitute the instantaneous *streamlines.*

Suppose next that only a few particles are on the surface and that they are photographed with the shutter open as they move from the upstream end to the downstream end. The photograph now shows the trajectories of the particles, that is, the *path lines.*

Finally, suppose that at the upstream end a series of particles is dropped in rapid succession on to the surface at a fixed point and that at some later time the shutter is opened so briefly as to stop the motion. The photograph now shows the *streak line* through the given point. The usual methods of flow visualization, involving the injection of smoke or of dye, thus give pictures of the streak lines.

† See Art. 4.1 for additional discussion of kinematics.

Steady vs. Unsteady Flow.   In general, the fluid properties at a given position in space vary with time.   The flow is then described as *unsteady*.

Sometimes, however, the fluid properties at a fixed position in space do not change with time as successive fluid particles come to occupy the point.   The flow is then described as *steady*.   The description of the field, Eq. (2.3*a*), then takes the simpler form

$$b = b(\mathbf{r}) \quad \text{or} \quad b = b(x,y,z) \tag{2.3b}$$

In an unsteady flow, the path lines, streak lines, and streamlines do not generally coincide.   In a steady flow, however, they do coincide, and this is why the pattern of streak lines made visible by dye or smoke injection also then gives the picture of the streamlines.

Galilean Transformation.   The acceleration of a particle relative to one reference frame is exactly the same as the acceleration relative to a second reference frame only if the latter moves in uniform, linear motion with respect to the first reference frame.   Thus the dynamical laws are identical in form for two reference frames so related.   A change between two such reference frames is called a *Galilean transformation*.

When a body moves with uniform velocity through an otherwise stationary sea of infinite fluid, the flow appears unsteady to an observer in the reference frame of the fluid.   But by a Galilean transformation to a reference frame attached to the moving body, the motion becomes steady with respect to the second reference frame.   This eliminates one variable, namely, time, from the problem and produces great mathematical simplifications.

By reason of the dynamical invariance inherent in the Galilean transformation, the motion of an airplane flying through a stationary atmosphere, for instance, may be modeled in a wind tunnel with a uniform airstream flowing past a stationary airplane.

Lagrangian Description.   In the so-called Lagrangian description of the motion (actually due to Euler), one describes the trajectories of individual particles of fixed identity.   The identity of each particle is characterized by its position $\mathbf{r}_o$ (or by x_o,y_o,z_o) at some reference time t_o.   Thus the description of the motion begins with a statement of the positions of all particles at all times:

$$\mathbf{r} = \mathbf{r}(t,\mathbf{r}_o) \tag{2.5}$$

The instantaneous velocities of the fluid particles are then of the form

$$\mathbf{V} = \left(\frac{\partial \mathbf{r}}{\partial t}\right)_{\mathbf{r}_0 = \text{const}} = \mathbf{V}(t,\mathbf{r}_o) \tag{2.6}$$

while the instantaneous accelerations are of the form

$$\mathbf{a} = \left(\frac{\partial^2 \mathbf{r}}{\partial t^2}\right)_{\mathbf{r}_0 = \text{const}} = \mathbf{a}(t,\mathbf{r}_o) \tag{2.7}$$

Eulerian Description.   Usually the Lagrangian description is less convenient for subsequent mathematical manipulation than the so-called Eulerian description of the motion.   In the latter, one does not follow individual particles, but rather describes what happens at every fixed point in space as a function of time.   Equation (2.3*a*) represents implicitly the Eulerian form of description.

The Substantial Derivative.   Let *b* represent the value of some fluid property (e.g., pressure, density, velocity, entropy) for a *particle of fixed identity*.   Employing the Eulerian formulation, it is desired to calculate the time rate of change of the value of *b* associated with this *particular* particle of *unchanging identity*.   Note that the task is to represent a concept essentially Lagrangian in nature in the Eulerian language.

Using cartesians, Eq. (2.3*a*) implies that for *arbitrary* and *independent* increments dx, dy, dz, dt, the increment db is

$$db = \frac{\partial b}{\partial x}\,dx + \frac{\partial b}{\partial y}\,dy + \frac{\partial b}{\partial z}\,dz + \frac{\partial b}{\partial t}\,dt$$

Passing now from arbitrary increments to the increments perceived while following in time a particle of fixed identity, the increments dx, dy, and dz are no longer independent but are rather related to dt by

$$dx = u\,dt \qquad dy = v\,dt \qquad dz = w\,dt$$

Accordingly, the special value of db/dt associated with the following of a material particle of fixed identity, to which is assigned the special symbol Db/Dt, is given by

$$\frac{Db}{Dt} = u\frac{\partial b}{\partial x} + v\frac{\partial b}{\partial y} + w\frac{\partial b}{\partial z} + \frac{\partial b}{\partial t} \tag{2.8a}$$

or, in vectors,

$$\frac{Db}{Dt} = (\mathbf{V}\cdot\boldsymbol{\nabla})b + \frac{\partial b}{\partial t} \tag{2.8b}$$

The various names given to Db/Dt include *substantial derivative*, *material derivative*, and *particle derivative*, all to connote the tracking of material substance of fixed identity.

The sum of the first three terms of Eq. (2.8a), or the first term of Eq. (2.8b), is called the *convective derivative*, inasmuch as it represents the change in b caused by convection of the particle from one location to a second location having a different value of b. The term $\partial b/\partial t$, associated with unsteady time variations at a fixed position, is called the *local derivative*.

Acceleration at a Point. One of the most important substantial derivatives is that of the velocity vector, for this gives the acceleration of a fluid particle of fixed identity in the sense required by Newton's laws. Thus

$$\frac{D\mathbf{V}}{Dt} = \mathbf{a} = (\mathbf{V}\cdot\boldsymbol{\nabla})\mathbf{V} + \frac{\partial \mathbf{V}}{\partial t} \tag{2.9a}$$

which, by means of vector identities, may also be expressed as

$$\frac{D\mathbf{V}}{Dt} = \boldsymbol{\nabla}\frac{V^2}{2} - \mathbf{V}\times(\boldsymbol{\nabla}\times\mathbf{V}) + \frac{\partial \mathbf{V}}{\partial t} \tag{2.9b}$$

In cartesian coordinates, the acceleration components are

$$a_x = \frac{Du}{Dt} = u\frac{\partial u}{\partial x} + v\frac{\partial u}{\partial y} + w\frac{\partial u}{\partial z} + \frac{\partial u}{\partial t}$$

$$a_y = \frac{Dv}{Dt} = u\frac{\partial v}{\partial x} + v\frac{\partial v}{\partial y} + w\frac{\partial v}{\partial z} + \frac{\partial v}{\partial t} \tag{2.10}$$

$$a_z = \frac{Dw}{Dt} = u\frac{\partial w}{\partial x} + v\frac{\partial w}{\partial y} + w\frac{\partial w}{\partial z} + \frac{\partial w}{\partial t}$$

In cylindrical coordinates r, θ, z with velocity components v_r, v_θ, v_z, the components of acceleration are

$$a_r = v_r\frac{\partial v_r}{\partial r} + \frac{v_\theta}{r}\frac{\partial v_r}{\partial \theta} + v_z\frac{\partial v_r}{\partial z} - \frac{v_\theta^2}{r} + \frac{\partial v_r}{\partial t}$$

$$a_\theta = v_r\frac{\partial v_\theta}{\partial r} + \frac{v_\theta}{r}\frac{\partial v_\theta}{\partial \theta} + v_z\frac{\partial v_\theta}{\partial z} + \frac{v_r v_\theta}{r} + \frac{\partial v_\theta}{\partial t} \tag{2.11}$$

$$a_z = v_r\frac{\partial v_z}{\partial r} + \frac{v_\theta}{r}\frac{\partial v_z}{\partial \theta} + v_z\frac{\partial v_z}{\partial z} + \frac{\partial v_z}{\partial t}$$

Transport and Deformation of the Fluid. Let the velocity at some point have the instantaneous components u, v, w and consider the velocity at closely neighboring points at the same instant. For convenience, place the origin at the first point and let the neighboring point be removed by the distance x, y, z. Then a Taylor-series expansion yields, for the velocity at the neighboring point,

$$u + \delta u = u + \frac{\partial u}{\partial x}\delta x + \frac{\partial u}{\partial y}\delta y + \frac{\partial u}{\partial z}\delta z + \cdots$$

$$v + \delta v = v + \frac{\partial v}{\partial x}\delta x + \frac{\partial v}{\partial y}\delta y + \frac{\partial v}{\partial z}\delta z + \cdots$$

$$w + \delta w = w + \frac{\partial w}{\partial x}\delta x + \frac{\partial w}{\partial y}\delta y + \frac{\partial w}{\partial z}\delta z + \cdots$$

Now a purely algebraic rearrangement allows these to be rewritten as

$$
\begin{aligned}
\delta u &= \epsilon_x\,\delta x + \gamma_{xy}\,\delta y + \gamma_{xz}\,\delta z + \eta\,\delta z - \zeta\,\delta y \\
\delta v &= \gamma_{xy}\,\delta x + \epsilon_y\,\delta y + \gamma_{yz}\,\delta z + \zeta\,\delta x - \xi\,\delta z \\
\delta w &= \gamma_{xz}\,\delta x + \gamma_{yz}\,\delta y + \epsilon_z\,\delta z + \xi\,\delta y - \eta\,\delta x
\end{aligned}
\qquad (2.12)
$$

in which, by definition,

$$\epsilon_x \equiv \frac{\partial u}{\partial x} \qquad \epsilon_y \equiv \frac{\partial v}{\partial y} \qquad \epsilon_z \equiv \frac{\partial w}{\partial z} \qquad (2.13a)$$

$$\gamma_{xy} \equiv \frac{1}{2}\left(\frac{\partial v}{\partial x} + \frac{\partial u}{\partial y}\right) \qquad \gamma_{yz} \equiv \frac{1}{2}\left(\frac{\partial w}{\partial y} + \frac{\partial v}{\partial z}\right) \qquad \gamma_{zx} \equiv \frac{1}{2}\left(\frac{\partial u}{\partial z} + \frac{\partial w}{\partial x}\right) \qquad (2.13b)$$

$$\xi \equiv \frac{1}{2}\left(\frac{\partial w}{\partial y} - \frac{\partial v}{\partial z}\right) \qquad \eta \equiv \frac{1}{2}\left(\frac{\partial u}{\partial z} - \frac{\partial w}{\partial x}\right) \qquad \zeta \equiv \frac{1}{2}\left(\frac{\partial v}{\partial x} - \frac{\partial u}{\partial y}\right) \qquad (2.13c)$$

Imagine a rectangular fluid particle of fixed identity, having originally the sides δx, δy, δz, with one corner placed at the origin. Consider the relative motions of the two ends of each line, determined by the nine derivatives of u, v, w with respect to x, y, z. Then the total motion of the particle may, according to Eqs. (2.12) and (2.13), be decomposed into the sum of four parts:

1. A pure *translation*, with the velocity components u, v, w
2. An average angular *rotation*, with the components ξ, η, ζ
3. A dilatation, formed by the three *lineal strain* rates ϵ_x, ϵ_y, ϵ_z
4. Three *rates of shear deformation*, γ_{xy}, γ_{yz}, γ_{zx}

The translation and rotation occur without change of shape and affect only displacement of the fluid element. All the deformation of the fluid particle is embodied in the ϵ's and the γ's.

The six quantities involved in the deformation depend on the orientation of the reference axes x, y, z, but in a change to new axes they follow the transformation laws of tensors. The *rate-of-strain* tensor, which is symmetrical, is as follows:

$$
\begin{bmatrix}
\epsilon_x & \gamma_{xy} & \gamma_{xz} \\
\gamma_{yx} & \epsilon_y & \gamma_{yz} \\
\gamma_{zx} & \gamma_{zy} & \epsilon_z
\end{bmatrix}
\qquad (2.14)
$$

As with the stress tensor, there are principal axes of strain for which the γ's vanish and for which there remain only pure lineal strains, the so-called *principal rates of strain*, ϵ_1, ϵ_2, ϵ_3. The invariants of the rate-of-strain tensor are formally identical with the invariants of the stress tensor, Eqs. (2.2c).

Vorticity. Each of the quantities ξ, η, and ζ in Eq. (2.13c) defines the *mean* angular velocity of two mutually perpendicular fluid lines; they represent for a deformable medium the generalization of the concept of angular velocity of a rigid body. It may be shown that ξ, η, and ζ are proportional, respectively, to the integrated components of angular momentum, referred to the center of gravity, for the entire fluid particle. Moreover, the value of ζ, say, for a fixed orientation of the z axis, is invariant to the particular orientations chosen for the x and y axes.

ξ, η, and ζ are the cartesian components of the *vorticity* vector, or *fluid rotation* vector, ω:

$$\omega \equiv \nabla \times V = 2(\mathbf{i}\xi + \mathbf{j}\eta + \mathbf{k}\zeta) \qquad (2.15)$$

Circulation. The instantaneous line integral of the velocity around any closed contour C is called the circulation Γ, taken positive when C is traversed so that the bounded area is to the left:

$$\Gamma \equiv \oint_C \mathbf{V} \cdot d\mathbf{r} = \oint_C (u\,dx + v\,dy + w\,dz) \qquad (2.16a)$$

It may be shown that the line integral around any curve C bounding an area A (singly or multiply connected) is the sum of the line integrals around all the lesser areas into which A might arbitrarily be divided.

Stokes' Theorem. The fluid vorticity and the circulation are connected by Stokes' theorem:

$$\Gamma = \oint_C \mathbf{V} \cdot d\mathbf{r} = \iint_A \boldsymbol{\omega} \cdot d\mathbf{A} \qquad (2.16b)$$

in which $d\mathbf{A}$ is a vectorial element of any area bounded by C. Thus the circulation around C is equal to the "flux of vorticity" through the bounded area A.

Accelerating Reference Frames. Imagine a reference frame whose origin accelerates at the rate $\mathbf{S}$ with respect to inertial space and which also rotates with the angular velocity $\boldsymbol{\Omega}$ relative to inertial space. Let $\mathbf{V}$, as before, represent the velocity in an inertial reference frame, while $\mathbf{W}$ refers to the velocity in the accelerating reference frame. Then the acceleration relative to inertial space is

$$\mathbf{a} = \frac{D\mathbf{W}}{Dt} + \mathbf{S} + 2\boldsymbol{\Omega} \times \mathbf{W} + \boldsymbol{\Omega} \times (\boldsymbol{\Omega} \times \mathbf{r}) + \frac{d\boldsymbol{\Omega}}{dt} \times \mathbf{r} \qquad (2.17)$$

in which $D\mathbf{W}/Dt$ is the acceleration perceived by an observer in the accelerating reference frame. The remaining terms are contributions due to the acceleration of the reference frame.

CORIOLIS ACCELERATION. The term $2\boldsymbol{\Omega} \times \mathbf{W}$ is the so-called Coriolis acceleration. If the z axis is made to coincide with the axis of $\boldsymbol{\Omega}$, then the resultant Coriolis acceleration is $2\Omega W_{xy}$, in which W_{xy} is the projection of $\mathbf{W}$ on the xy plane, and it lies in the xy plane pointing in a direction normal to W_{xy}. With this same alignment of the axes, the x and y components are, respectively, $-2\Omega W_y$ and $2\Omega W_x$; while the cylindrical components are $-2\Omega W_\theta$ along r, $2\Omega W_r$ along θ, and zero along z.

CENTRIFUGAL ACCELERATION. The term $\boldsymbol{\Omega} \times (\boldsymbol{\Omega} \times \mathbf{r})$ is the so-called centrifugal acceleration. If the z axis is once again made identical with the axis of $\boldsymbol{\Omega}$, then the resultant centrifugal acceleration is $\Omega^2 r_{xy}$, in which r_{xy} is the perpendicular distance from the point in question to the z axis, and it lies in the xy plane pointing toward the z axis. The x and y components are then $-\Omega^2 x$ and $-\Omega^2 y$, respectively, while the cylindrical components are $-\Omega^2 r$ along r and zero in the θ and z directions.

2.5. Origins of Forces in Fluid Dynamics

The various forces which may act on the fluid are conveniently placed in the categories of surface forces, body forces, and line forces. Of particular concern now is a preliminary discussion of the form and origin of these forces as they relate to each and every fluid particle. The fluid particle is thought of as having the instantaneous dimensions δx, δy, and δz, which in the limit pass to zero. The force $\delta \mathbf{F}$ acting on this particle, when divided by the product $\delta x\,\delta y\,\delta z$, yields the *force per unit volume of fluid* acting at the point.

Surface Forces. These arise from the differences in tractions exerted by all the surrounding fluid on the faces of the element $\delta x\,\delta y\,\delta z$. The net surface force per unit volume is given by the derivatives of the stresses:

$$\frac{\delta \mathbf{F}}{\delta x\,\delta y\,\delta z} = \mathbf{i}\left(\frac{\partial \sigma_x}{\partial x} + \frac{\partial \tau_{yx}}{\partial y} + \frac{\partial \tau_{zx}}{\partial z}\right) + \mathbf{j}\left(\frac{\partial \tau_{xy}}{\partial x} + \frac{\partial \sigma_y}{\partial y} + \frac{\partial \tau_{zy}}{\partial z}\right)$$
$$+ \mathbf{k}\left(\frac{\partial \tau_{xz}}{\partial x} + \frac{\partial \tau_{yz}}{\partial y} + \frac{\partial \sigma_z}{\partial z}\right) \qquad (2.18a)$$

When a state of hydrostatic stress prevails, the force per unit volume becomes simply the negative gradient of the pressure:

$$\frac{\delta \mathbf{F}}{\delta x \, \delta y \, \delta z} = -\boldsymbol{\nabla} p \tag{2.18b}$$

Body Forces. These arise either from action at a distance (e.g., gravity or electromagnetic forces), or they appear as "effective" d'Alembert forces by reason of the choice of an accelerating reference frame. In either case they are proportional either to the mass or to the volume of the fluid.

The *gravity* force per unit volume is $\rho \mathbf{G}$, in which $\mathbf{G}$ is the local acceleration of gravity.

The *electromagnetic* force per unit volume is $\mathbf{J} \times \mathbf{B}$, with $\mathbf{J}$ the current-flux density and $\mathbf{B}$ the magnetic induction.

A reference frame whose origin accelerates at the rate $\mathbf{S}$ with respect to inertial space produces inertial forces of magnitude $(-\rho \mathbf{S})$ per unit volume.

A reference frame rotating with the angular velocity $\boldsymbol{\Omega}$ relative to inertial space produces an inertial force per unit volume of magnitude:

$$-\rho \left[2\boldsymbol{\Omega} \times \mathbf{W} + \boldsymbol{\Omega} \times (\boldsymbol{\Omega} \times \mathbf{r}) + \frac{d\boldsymbol{\Omega}}{dt} \times \mathbf{r} \right] \tag{2.19}$$

in which the first term is the Coriolis force, the second is the centrifugal force, and the third is due to the angular acceleration of the reference frame.

Capillary Forces. Surface-tension forces do not appear directly in the equations of motion, but enter only in the boundary conditions. At any point of the interface between two phases, there is a pressure jump across the interface given by

$$\Delta p = \lambda \left(\frac{1}{R_1} + \frac{1}{R_2} \right) \tag{2.20}$$

in which R_1 and R_2 are the principal radii of curvature of the surface, and the pressure is higher on the concave face of the surface.

2.6. Governing Laws of Fluid Dynamics

Omitting relativistic and quantum effects, the universal governing laws—universal in the sense of being the same for all fluids—are (1) the law of conservation of mass, (2) Newton's dynamical law of motion, (3) the first law of thermodynamics, (4) the second law of thermodynamics, and (5) Maxwell's electrodynamic equations. For very massive bodies, Newton's universal law of gravitation would also play a role.

The System of Fixed Identity. All the universal laws cited above refer in the first instance to a *system*, that is, to a collection of material of fixed identity. For a system in an inertial reference frame, the first four laws are as follows:

Conservation of Mass

$$\frac{D}{Dt} \int dm = 0 \tag{2.21}$$

Newton's Law for Momentum

$$\Sigma \mathbf{F} = \frac{D}{Dt} \int \mathbf{V} \, dm \tag{2.22}$$

in which $\Sigma \mathbf{F}$ includes all forces, body and surface forces, exerted by the outside world on the system.

Newton's Law for Moment of Momentum

$$\Sigma(\mathbf{F} \times \mathbf{r}) = \frac{D}{Dt} \int (\mathbf{V} \times \mathbf{r}) \, dm \tag{2.23}$$

First Law of Thermodynamics

$$\frac{D}{Dt} \int \left(u + \frac{V^2}{2} + \psi \right) dm = \frac{dQ}{dt} - \frac{dW}{dt} \tag{2.24}$$

in which u is a *property*, such that $\oint du = 0$, and the terms on the right-hand side represent, respectively, the rate of heat transfer *to* the system and the rate of work delivery *from* the system.

Second Law of Thermodynamics

$$\frac{D}{Dt} \int s \, dm \geq \Sigma \frac{1}{T} \frac{dQ}{dt} \tag{2.25}$$

in which the equal sign applies in all reversible processes, the unequal sign applies in all irreversible processes, and the entropy s is a property defined through a reversible change in state.

In all these formulas the integrals on which the substantial derivative D/Dt operates are summed up over all the elements of mass of the system.

The Control Volume Fixed in Space.   For many problems in fluid mechanics, it is convenient to think in terms of a *control volume*, that is, a *volume fixed in space*, through which the fluid flows.   Note that Eqs. (2.21) to (2.25) represent a Lagrangian point of view, while the control volume implies the Eulerian viewpoint.

In each of the foregoing equations there appears a substantial time derivative of the total amount of some quantity integrated over all the submasses of the system.   Let B represent this total quantity (e.g., mass, momentum, etc.), and let b represent its magnitude per unit mass, such that $b \equiv B/m$.   Then one may show generally that the value of DB/Dt reckoned for the material system instantaneously occupying but passing through the control volume is given by

$$\frac{DB}{Dt} = \iiint_{\mathcal{V}} \frac{\partial}{\partial t} (\rho b) \, d\mathcal{V} + \oiint_{A} b \rho \mathbf{V} \cdot d\mathbf{A} \tag{2.26}$$

in which the first integral is taken through the control volume $\mathcal{V}$, and the second integral is taken over the surface A bounding $\mathcal{V}$.   The first integral represents the time rate of accumulation of B within the control space and vanishes for a steady flow.   The second integral is the algebraic excess of the "outflux of B" through the control surface over the "influx of B."

Using the transformation law [Eq. (2.26)] between the system and the control volume, the governing laws for the control volume may now be written as follows:

Conservation of Mass

$$\iiint \frac{\partial \rho}{\partial t} \, d\mathcal{V} = - \oiint \rho \mathbf{V} \cdot d\mathbf{A} \tag{2.27}$$

Newton's Law for Momentum

$$\Sigma \mathbf{F} = \iiint \frac{\partial (\rho \mathbf{V})}{\partial t} \, d\mathcal{V} + \oiint \mathbf{V} (\rho \mathbf{V} \cdot d\mathbf{A}) \tag{2.28}$$

in which $\Sigma \mathbf{F}$ is the total force exerted by the outside world on the material instantaneously occupying the control volume.

Newton's Law for Moment of Momentum

$$\Sigma (\mathbf{F} \times \mathbf{r}) = \iiint \frac{\partial (\rho \mathbf{V} \times \mathbf{r})}{\partial t} \, d\mathcal{V} + \oiint (\mathbf{V} \times \mathbf{r}) (\rho \mathbf{V} \cdot d\mathbf{A}) \tag{2.29}$$

First Law of Thermodynamics

$$\frac{dQ}{dt} - \frac{dW_{\text{shear}}}{dt} - \frac{dW_{\text{elec}}}{dt} = \iiint \frac{\partial}{\partial t}\left[\rho\left(u + \frac{V^2}{2} + \psi\right)\right] d\mathcal{V}$$

$$+ \oiint \rho\left(h + \frac{V^2}{2} + \psi\right)(\mathbf{V}\cdot d\mathbf{A}) \quad (2.30)$$

in which dQ/dt is the rate of heat transfer to the material instantaneously in $\mathcal{V}$; dW_{shear}/dt is the instantaneous rate of work delivery, due to shear forces, by this material; and dW_{elec}/dt is the instantaneous rate of electrical work delivery.

Second Law of Thermodynamics

$$\iiint \frac{\partial(\rho s)}{\partial t} d\mathcal{V} + \oiint \rho s \mathbf{V}\cdot d\mathbf{A} \geq \oiint \frac{1}{T}\frac{dQ}{dt} \quad (2.31)$$

2.7. Mass Conservation

Using Green's theorem, the mass-flow integral on the right-hand side of Eq. (2.27) may be expressed as

$$\oiint_A \rho\mathbf{V}\cdot d\mathbf{A} = \iiint_{\mathcal{V}} (\boldsymbol{\nabla}\cdot\rho\mathbf{V}) \, d\mathcal{V}$$

Then, since this as well as Eq. (2.27) must apply to each and every infinitesimal control volume, the principle of mass conservation may be expressed by the differential equation

$$\frac{\partial\rho}{\partial t} + \boldsymbol{\nabla}\cdot(\rho\mathbf{V}) = 0 \quad (2.32a)$$

which is usually called the *equation of continuity*. Expansion of Eq. (2.32a) yields

$$\frac{\partial\rho}{\partial t} + \rho(\boldsymbol{\nabla}\cdot\mathbf{V}) + (\boldsymbol{\nabla}\rho)\cdot\mathbf{V} = 0 \quad (2.32b)$$

For *steady* flow, the term $\partial\rho/\partial t$ disappears, so that the divergence of the $\rho\mathbf{V}$ vector must everywhere vanish.

In an *incompressible* flow, the density ρ varies neither with time nor position. Hence the condition that the volume of each fluid mass is unalterable takes the form

$$\boldsymbol{\nabla}\cdot\mathbf{V} = 0 \quad (2.33)$$

In cartesian coordinates, Eq. (2.32a) has the form

$$\frac{\partial\rho}{\partial t} + \frac{\partial}{\partial x}(\rho u) + \frac{\partial}{\partial y}(\rho v) + \frac{\partial}{\partial z}(\rho w) = 0 \quad (2.34)$$

while in cylindrical coordinates, it appears as

$$\frac{\partial\rho}{\partial t} + \frac{1}{r}\frac{\partial}{\partial r}(\rho r v_r) + \frac{1}{r}\frac{\partial}{\partial\theta}(\rho v_\theta) + \frac{\partial}{\partial z}(\rho v_z) = 0 \quad (2.35)$$

2.8. The Stress-Strain Law of a Newton-Stokes Fluid

Newton hypothesized that the "viscous" force resisting the shearing strain of a fluid is linearly proportional to the rate of shear. It is known now that only some fluids have this characteristic, and then perhaps only if the deformation rates are not too large. Nevertheless all gases and most liquids of reasonably simple chemical structure seem to fit the hypothesis.

The present generalization of Newton's rather crude formulation is due to Stokes. Four premises underlie the Stokesian formulation:

1. The fluid is *isotropic;* i.e., it has no preferred directions. Hence the principal axes of stress and strain must coincide.

2. Mere translation and rotation do not induce resisting stresses, but any deformation is resisted by "viscous" stresses. Each of the six components of viscous stress is assumed to be linearly proportional to a linear sum of the six deformation rates (three ϵ's and three γ's).

3. The linear stress-strain law must have the same form for any orientation of the coordinate system.

4. In the absence of deformation, the stress tensor must reduce to the hydrostatic pressure.

The linear hypothesis of premise 2 gives rise to 36 viscous proportionality "constants." Introduction of the isotropicity hypothesis, premise 1, reduces these to nine in number. Premise 3 invokes symmetry conditions which finally allow of only two viscosity coefficients. The most general stress-strain law satisfying premises 1 to 4 may then be written as follows:

$$\sigma_x = -p - \tfrac{2}{3}(\mu - \mu')\left(\frac{\partial u}{\partial x} + \frac{\partial v}{\partial y} + \frac{\partial w}{\partial z}\right) + 2\mu \frac{\partial u}{\partial x}$$

$$\sigma_y = -p - \tfrac{2}{3}(\mu - \mu')\left(\frac{\partial u}{\partial x} + \frac{\partial v}{\partial y} + \frac{\partial w}{\partial z}\right) + 2\mu \frac{\partial v}{\partial y} \qquad (2.36)$$

$$\sigma_z = -p - \tfrac{2}{3}(\mu - \mu')\left(\frac{\partial u}{\partial x} + \frac{\partial v}{\partial y} + \frac{\partial w}{\partial z}\right) + 2\mu \frac{\partial w}{\partial z}$$

$$\tau_{xy} = \mu \left(\frac{\partial v}{\partial x} + \frac{\partial u}{\partial y}\right)$$

$$\tau_{yz} = \mu \left(\frac{\partial w}{\partial y} + \frac{\partial v}{\partial z}\right) \qquad (2.37)$$

$$\tau_{zx} = \mu \left(\frac{\partial u}{\partial z} + \frac{\partial w}{\partial x}\right)$$

in which μ is the ordinary, or Newtonian, coefficient of viscosity, and μ' is the second, or bulk, coefficient of viscosity, which induces viscous stresses only by reason of changes in volume of the fluid element.

In incompressible flows, the terms in μ' vanish. In compressible flows, however, both viscosity coefficients enter, but it is difficult to perform experiments to measure μ'. For monatomic gases, kinetic theory shows that $\mu' = 0$. It seems generally to be small, if not zero. Sometimes it is argued, speciously, that the mean of the three normal stresses (which is an invariant) must reduce to the pressure p in Eqs. (2.36), and this leads to the result that $\mu' = 0$. For substances in which μ' is so small as to be negligible, Eqs. (2.36) reduce to

$$\sigma_x = -p - \tfrac{2}{3}\mu(\boldsymbol{\nabla} \cdot \mathbf{V}) + 2\mu \frac{\partial u}{\partial x}$$

$$\sigma_y = -p - \tfrac{2}{3}\mu(\boldsymbol{\nabla} \cdot \mathbf{V}) + 2\mu \frac{\partial v}{\partial y} \qquad (2.38)$$

$$\sigma_z = -p - \tfrac{2}{3}\mu(\boldsymbol{\nabla} \cdot \mathbf{V}) + 2\mu \frac{\partial w}{\partial z}$$

This formulation is used hereafter.

2.9. The Navier-Stokes Equations

General Form. The surface forces, Eq. (2.18a), may now be expressed in terms of the velocity field through Eqs. (2.37) and (2.38). The dynamical equations of motion for a Newton-Stokes fluid are then obtained by equating the total force acting on an elementary system instantaneously of dimensions δx, δy, δz to the product of the mass, $\rho \, \delta x \delta y \delta z$, with the acceleration as given by Eq. (2.9). In vector form, the result is

$$\rho \frac{D\mathbf{V}}{Dt} = \rho \left[\frac{\partial \mathbf{V}}{\partial t} + \nabla \frac{V^2}{2} - \mathbf{V} \times (\nabla \times \mathbf{V}) \right] = \rho \mathbf{F}_{\text{body}} - \nabla p$$

$$+ \tfrac{4}{3} \nabla (\mu \nabla \cdot \mathbf{V}) + \nabla (\mathbf{V} \cdot \nabla \mu) - \mathbf{V} \nabla^2 \mu$$

$$+ \nabla \mu \times (\nabla \times \mathbf{V}) - (\nabla \cdot \mathbf{V}) \nabla \mu - \nabla \times (\nabla \times \mu \mathbf{V}) \qquad (2.39)$$

in which $\mathbf{F}_{\text{body}}$ is the sum of all the body forces per unit volume as set out in Art. 2.5.

In cartesian coordinates, the Navier-Stokes equations are

$$\rho \frac{Du}{Dt} = \rho \left(\frac{\partial u}{\partial t} + u \frac{\partial u}{\partial x} + v \frac{\partial u}{\partial y} + w \frac{\partial u}{\partial z} \right)$$

$$= \rho X - \frac{\partial p}{\partial x} + \frac{\mu}{3} \frac{\partial}{\partial x} (\nabla \cdot \mathbf{V}) + \mu \nabla^2 u + 2 \frac{\partial u}{\partial x} \frac{\partial \mu}{\partial x} - \tfrac{2}{3} (\nabla \cdot \mathbf{V}) \frac{\partial \mu}{\partial x}$$

$$+ \left(\frac{\partial v}{\partial x} + \frac{\partial u}{\partial y} \right) \frac{\partial \mu}{\partial y} + \left(\frac{\partial u}{\partial z} + \frac{\partial w}{\partial x} \right) \frac{\partial \mu}{\partial z} \qquad (2.40a)$$

$$\rho \frac{Dv}{Dt} = \rho \left(\frac{\partial v}{\partial t} + u \frac{\partial v}{\partial x} + v \frac{\partial v}{\partial y} + w \frac{\partial v}{\partial z} \right)$$

$$= \rho Y - \frac{\partial p}{\partial y} + \frac{\mu}{3} \frac{\partial}{\partial y} (\nabla \cdot \mathbf{V}) + \mu \nabla^2 v + 2 \frac{\partial v}{\partial y} \frac{\partial \mu}{\partial y} - \tfrac{2}{3} (\nabla \cdot \mathbf{V}) \frac{\partial \mu}{\partial y}$$

$$+ \left(\frac{\partial w}{\partial y} + \frac{\partial v}{\partial z} \right) \frac{\partial \mu}{\partial z} + \left(\frac{\partial v}{\partial x} + \frac{\partial u}{\partial y} \right) \frac{\partial \mu}{\partial x} \qquad (2.40b)$$

$$\rho \frac{Dw}{Dt} = \rho \left(\frac{\partial w}{\partial t} + u \frac{\partial w}{\partial x} + v \frac{\partial w}{\partial y} + w \frac{\partial w}{\partial z} \right)$$

$$= \rho Z - \frac{\partial p}{\partial z} + \frac{\mu}{3} \frac{\partial}{\partial z} (\nabla \cdot \mathbf{V}) + \mu \nabla^2 w + 2 \frac{\partial w}{\partial z} \frac{\partial \mu}{\partial z} - \tfrac{2}{3} (\nabla \cdot \mathbf{V}) \frac{\partial \mu}{\partial z}$$

$$+ \left(\frac{\partial u}{\partial z} + \frac{\partial w}{\partial x} \right) \frac{\partial \mu}{\partial x} + \left(\frac{\partial w}{\partial y} + \frac{\partial v}{\partial z} \right) \frac{\partial \mu}{\partial y} \qquad (2.40c)$$

Fluid with Constant Viscosity. When the variation in viscosity is negligible, Eq. (2.39) reduces to

$$\frac{D\mathbf{V}}{Dt} = \frac{\partial \mathbf{V}}{\partial t} + \nabla \frac{V^2}{2} - \mathbf{V} \times (\nabla \times \mathbf{V}) = \mathbf{F}_{\text{body}} - \frac{1}{\rho} \nabla p + \frac{\nu}{3} \nabla (\nabla \cdot \mathbf{V}) + \nu \nabla^2 \mathbf{V} \qquad (2.41)$$

the x component of which, for example, is

$$\frac{Du}{Dt} = \frac{\partial u}{\partial t} + u \frac{\partial u}{\partial x} + v \frac{\partial u}{\partial y} + w \frac{\partial u}{\partial z}$$

$$= X - \frac{1}{\rho} \frac{\partial p}{\partial x} + \frac{\nu}{3} \frac{\partial}{\partial x} \left(\frac{\partial u}{\partial x} + \frac{\partial v}{\partial y} + \frac{\partial w}{\partial z} \right) + \nu \left(\frac{\partial^2 u}{\partial x^2} + \frac{\partial^2 u}{\partial y^2} + \frac{\partial^2 u}{\partial z^2} \right) \qquad (2.42a)$$

and so on for the y and z directions.

Incompressible Fluid with Constant Viscosity. For *incompressible* flows with *constant viscosity*, the dynamical equation has the relatively simple form

$$\frac{D\mathbf{V}}{Dt} = \mathbf{F}_{\text{body}} - \frac{1}{\rho}\nabla p + \nu\nabla^2\mathbf{V} \tag{2.43}$$

of which the x component, for example, is

$$\frac{Du}{Dt} = X - \frac{1}{\rho}\frac{\partial p}{\partial x} + \nu\left(\frac{\partial^2 u}{\partial x^2} + \frac{\partial^2 u}{\partial y^2} + \frac{\partial^2 u}{\partial z^2}\right) \tag{2.44}$$

and so on for the y and z directions.

The cylindrical components of Eq. (2.43) are as follows:

$$\frac{\partial v_r}{\partial t} + v_r\frac{\partial v_r}{\partial r} + \frac{v_\theta}{r}\frac{\partial v_r}{\partial \theta} + v_z\frac{\partial v_r}{\partial z} - \frac{v_\theta^2}{r} = F_r - \frac{1}{\rho}\frac{\partial p}{\partial r} + \nu\left(\nabla^2 v_r - \frac{2}{r^2}\frac{\partial v_\theta}{\partial \theta} - \frac{v_r}{r^2}\right) \tag{2.45a}$$

$$\frac{\partial v_\theta}{\partial t} + v_r\frac{\partial v_\theta}{\partial r} + \frac{v_\theta}{r}\frac{\partial v_\theta}{\partial \theta} + v_z\frac{\partial v_\theta}{\partial z} + \frac{v_r v_\theta}{r} = F_\theta - \frac{1}{\rho r}\frac{\partial p}{\partial \theta} + \nu\left(\nabla^2 v_\theta + \frac{2}{r^2}\frac{\partial v_r}{\partial \theta} - \frac{v_\theta}{r^2}\right) \tag{2.45b}$$

$$\frac{\partial v_z}{\partial t} + v_r\frac{\partial v_z}{\partial r} + \frac{v_\theta}{r}\frac{\partial v_z}{\partial \theta} + v_z\frac{\partial v_z}{\partial z} = F_z - \frac{1}{\rho}\frac{\partial p}{\partial z} + \nu\nabla^2 v_z \tag{2.45c}$$

Eulerian Equations of Motion for Nonviscous Flow. In a nonviscous flow, Eq. (2.43) reduces to the so-called Eulerian equations of motion

$$\frac{D\mathbf{V}}{Dt} = \frac{\partial\mathbf{V}}{\partial t} + \nabla\frac{V^2}{2} - \mathbf{V}\times(\nabla\times\mathbf{V}) = \mathbf{F}_{\text{body}} - \frac{1}{\rho}\nabla p \tag{2.46}$$

or

$$\frac{Du}{Dt} = \frac{\partial u}{\partial t} + u\frac{\partial u}{\partial x} + v\frac{\partial u}{\partial y} + w\frac{\partial u}{\partial z} = X - \frac{1}{\rho}\frac{\partial p}{\partial x} \tag{2.47}$$

and so on for the y and z directions.

There are two situations in which the Eulerian equations of motion have special integrals:

1. If one integrates along a streamline and if the body force is conservative (i.e., if it is irrotational, or has a potential), one obtains

$$\frac{\partial}{\partial t}\int\mathbf{V}\cdot d\mathbf{r} + \frac{V^2}{2} + \int\frac{dp}{\rho} + \psi = \text{const along each streamline} \tag{2.48a}$$

in which ψ is the body force potential such that $\mathbf{F}_{\text{body}} = -\nabla\psi$. When the flow is, in addition, steady and incompressible, Eq. (2.48a) reduces to Bernoulli's equation,

$$\frac{V^2}{2} + \frac{p}{\rho} + \psi = \text{const along each streamline} \tag{2.48b}$$

2. When the motion is irrotational, i.e., when $\nabla\times\mathbf{V} = 0$ and when the body force is conservative, integration of Eq. (2.46) with respect to space (not necessarily along a streamline) yields

$$\int\frac{\partial\mathbf{V}}{\partial t}\cdot d\mathbf{r} + \frac{V^2}{2} + \int\frac{dp}{\rho} + \psi = \text{const everywhere} \tag{2.49a}$$

But if $\nabla\times\mathbf{V} = 0$, the velocity field is expressible as the gradient of a scalar potential function, for example, $\mathbf{V} = -\nabla\phi$. Then one obtains

$$-\frac{\partial\phi}{\partial t} + \frac{V^2}{2} + \int\frac{dp}{\rho} + \psi = \text{const everywhere} \tag{2.49b}$$

With an incompressible flow, this reduces to

$$-\frac{\partial \phi}{\partial t} + \frac{V^2}{2} + \frac{p}{\rho} + \psi = \text{const everywhere} \tag{2.49c}$$

2.10. The Energy Equations

Consider an infinitesimal fluid *system* instantaneously having the dimensions δx, δy, δz and occupying the volume $\delta \mathbb{U} = \delta x \delta y \delta z$. The first law of thermodynamics may be written

$$\rho \delta \mathbb{U} \frac{D}{Dt}\left(u + \frac{V^2}{2} + \psi\right) = \delta \mathbb{U}\frac{Dq}{Dt} - \delta \mathbb{U}\frac{Dw}{Dt}$$

in which Dq/Dt is the net rate at which heat is received by the system per unit volume through conduction or radiation, and Dw/Dt is the rate of net work per unit volume performed at the boundaries of the system by all the surface stresses. The value of Dw/Dt is found by multiplying each of the three stresses acting on each of the six faces of the cube [as given by Eqs. (2.37) and (2.38)] by the appropriate velocity component. Introduction of the Navier-Stokes equations eliminates the "conservative" work terms, i.e., those leading to an increase in kinetic or potential energy, and there is left, finally,

$$\rho \frac{Du}{Dt} + \rho p \frac{D}{Dt}\left(\frac{1}{\rho}\right) = \frac{Dq}{Dt} + \Phi \tag{2.50a}$$

or

$$\rho \frac{Dh}{Dt} - \frac{Dp}{Dt} = \frac{Dq}{Dt} + \Phi \tag{2.50b}$$

in which, by definition, the term Φ, which is called the *dissipation function*, is given by

$$\Phi \equiv \tfrac{2}{3}\mu\left[\left(\frac{\partial u}{\partial x} - \frac{\partial v}{\partial y}\right)^2 + \left(\frac{\partial v}{\partial y} - \frac{\partial w}{\partial z}\right)^2 + \left(\frac{\partial w}{\partial z} - \frac{\partial u}{\partial x}\right)^2\right]$$
$$+ \mu\left[\left(\frac{\partial u}{\partial y} + \frac{\partial v}{\partial x}\right)^2 + \left(\frac{\partial v}{\partial z} + \frac{\partial w}{\partial y}\right)^2 + \left(\frac{\partial w}{\partial x} + \frac{\partial u}{\partial z}\right)^2\right] \tag{2.51}$$

In the details of the calculation it is found that Φ is that part of the work done by the stress tensor which accounts for the deformation of the fluid; Φ does not include, however, the part of the work done by the surface stresses associated with nondissipative changes in kinetic or potential energy.

Note that Φ has the same role in the energy equation as an actual heat transfer. Therefore it is often called the "frictional heating." It is always positive (as though heat were received, or "generated"); it is directly proportional to the coefficient of viscosity; and it is proportional to the square of the speed, which causes frictional heating to become especially prominent at high speeds.

2.11. The Second Law of Thermodynamics

The second law may be expressed by defining the *irreversibility per unit volume* $\mathcal{I}$ through the equation

$$\frac{D\mathcal{I}}{Dt} = T\frac{Ds}{Dt} - \frac{Dq}{Dt} \tag{2.52}$$

and then noting from Eq. (2.25) that $\mathcal{I}$ can only increase; that is,

$$\frac{D\mathcal{I}}{Dt} \geq 0 \tag{2.53}$$

Introduction of the thermodynamic equation

$$T\frac{Ds}{Dt} = \frac{Du}{Dt} + p\frac{D}{Dt}\left(\frac{1}{\rho}\right) \tag{2.54}$$

and comparison with Eq. (2.50a) then reveals the identity

$$\frac{D\mathcal{I}}{Dt} = \Phi \tag{2.55}$$

In other words, the function Φ is a measure of dissipation in the sense that it is essentially identical with the thermodynamic loss of availability. It is also clear from Eqs. (2.53), (2.55), and (2.51) that the viscosity coefficient μ must always be a positive number.

2.12. The Circulation Theorem

The notation $D\Gamma/Dt$ signifies the time rate of change of circulation for a *fluid curve*, i.e., a closed circuit always composed of the *same* fluid particles. In what follows, the viscosity μ will be assumed constant.

Introducing the definition of Γ, one gets

$$\frac{D\Gamma}{Dt} = \frac{D}{Dt} \oint \mathbf{V} \cdot d\mathbf{r} = \oint \frac{D\mathbf{V}}{Dt} \cdot d\mathbf{r} + \oint \mathbf{V} \cdot \frac{D}{Dt}(d\mathbf{r})$$

But since $D(d\mathbf{r})/Dt = d\mathbf{V}$, the second integral vanishes. Substitution of Eq. (2.41) for $D\mathbf{V}/Dt$ then leads to

$$\frac{D\Gamma}{Dt} = \oint \mathbf{F}_{\text{body}} \cdot d\mathbf{r} - \oint \frac{dp}{\rho} + \nu \oint \nabla^2 \mathbf{V} \cdot d\mathbf{r} + \frac{\nu}{3} \oint d(\nabla \cdot \mathbf{V}) \tag{2.56}$$

The four cyclic integrals on the right-hand side indicate the circumstances which can generate a chronological change in Γ for a closed fluid curve:

1. If the body force is conservative (e.g., any central force such as gravity), the first integral vanishes. But electromagnetic or Coriolis forces, for instance, can change Γ.

2. The term $\oint dp/\rho$ vanishes only when the density variation is *barotropic*, i.e., when ρ depends only on p. In practice, this situation arises either for an incompressible fluid ($\rho = \text{const}$) or when the entropy is everywhere the same. Nonuniform density distributions in general produce a change in circulation, except for the special homentropic case.

3. The last two terms, of which the second is due purely to dilatation, are viscous contributions and vanish only when the viscous shear work is negligible.

Kelvin's theorem, which is a special case of Eq. (2.56), states that the circulation around a closed fluid curve is conserved in time if the body forces are irrotational, if the fluid is nonviscous, and if the density variation is barotropic.

When the body force is conservative and the fluid is incompressible, but viscosity is present, Eq. (2.56) reduces to

$$\frac{D\Gamma}{Dt} = \nu \oint (\nabla^2 \mathbf{V}) \cdot d\mathbf{r}$$

which, through use of vector differentiation formulas and Stokes' theorem, may also be written as

$$\frac{D\Gamma}{Dt} = \nu \iint (\nabla^2 \boldsymbol{\omega}) \cdot d\mathbf{A} \tag{2.57}$$

This formula shows that the effect of viscosity in producing changes in circulation is associated with the diffusion of the vorticity $\boldsymbol{\omega}$.

2.13. The Vorticity Equation and Helmholtz's Vortex Laws

By eliminating the pressure from the equations of motion, the latter may be expressed in terms of the vorticity vector. It is assumed here (1) that the viscosity μ is constant, (2) that the body-force field is conservative, and (3) that the density variation is barotropic. Taking the curl of Eq. (2.41) (which eliminates p) and performing some algebraic rearrangements, one arrives at the generalization of a formula found originally by Helmholtz for the special case of incompressible, nonviscous flow:

$$\frac{D}{Dt}\left(\frac{\omega}{\rho}\right) = \left(\frac{\omega}{\rho}\cdot\boldsymbol{\nabla}\right)\mathbf{V} + \frac{\mu}{\rho^2}\nabla^2\omega \qquad (2.58)$$

When the viscosity is zero, the last term disappears. Then, from either Eq. (2.58) or from the equivalent result of Eq. (2.56), namely, $D\Gamma/Dt = 0$, one may deduce the following geometrical consequences known as Helmholtz's vortex theorems:

1. A fluid line which once coincides with a vortex line† forever after coincides with a vortex line. Thus the vortex lines may be said to be "frozen" in the fluid.

2. Along each element of length dl of a fluid line which is also a vortex line, the ratio $\omega/\rho\ dl$ remains forever constant, where ω is the magnitude of the vorticity vector. Stretching of a fluid-vortex line, for instance, increases the vorticity of the fluid.

3. The product ωA, representing the flux of vorticity through a vortex tube generated by vortex lines, is the same at all cross sections of the tube.‡ Moreover, it does not change with time.

From these results, it follows that a nonviscous, barotropic motion with conservative body forces, if once irrotational, will forever remain irrotational.

The last term in Eq. (2.58) shows that the effect of viscosity is to "unlock" the vortex lines from the fluid lines. This term represents the diffusion of vorticity through the fluid by means of viscosity, and its physical consequence is that the vortex lines may slip across the fluid lines.

2.14. Crocco's Theorem

Consider a *nonviscous* fluid, in the *absense of body forces*. Then the equation of motion [Eq. (2.46)] is

$$\frac{\partial\mathbf{V}}{\partial t} - \mathbf{V}\times(\boldsymbol{\nabla}\times\mathbf{V}) = -\frac{1}{\rho}\boldsymbol{\nabla}p - \boldsymbol{\nabla}\frac{V^2}{2}$$

But, from thermodynamics,

$$T\boldsymbol{\nabla}s = \boldsymbol{\nabla}h - \frac{1}{\rho}\boldsymbol{\nabla}p$$

Also, by definition, the stagnation enthalpy is

$$h_0 \equiv h + \frac{V^2}{2}$$

Thus the dynamical equation may be written in the form

$$\frac{\partial\mathbf{V}}{\partial t} - \mathbf{V}\times\omega = T\boldsymbol{\nabla}s - \boldsymbol{\nabla}h_0 \qquad (2.59a)$$

while, for incompressible flow, it has the special form

$$\frac{\partial\mathbf{V}}{\partial t} - \mathbf{V}\times\omega = -\frac{1}{\rho}\boldsymbol{\nabla}p_0 \qquad (2.59b)$$

in which p_0 is the total pressure, $p_0 \equiv p + \rho V^2/2$.

Several consequences follow from Eqs. (2.59):

1. If the flow has everywhere the same entropy and stagnation enthalpy (or same stagnation pressure if incompressible), then the vorticity must be everywhere zero unless the flow is unsteady.

---

† A vortex line is a curve everywhere tangent to the vector $\omega \equiv \boldsymbol{\nabla}\times\mathbf{V}$.

‡ This result follows purely from the fact that since ω is the curl of a vector, its divergence vanishes ($\boldsymbol{\nabla}\cdot\omega = 0$), thus ensuring continuity in the flux of ω through the vortex tubes.

2. Vorticity may be produced in a steady flow only through phenomena (e.g., combustion, curved shocks, boundary-layer formation, etc.) which generate gradients of entropy or stagnation enthalpy.

3. In a homentropic, irrotational flow, the stagnation enthalpy (or stagnation pressure) can vary from point to point only if the flow is unsteady.

REFERENCES

1. Lamb, H.: "Hydrodynamics," 6th ed., Dover, New York, 1945.
2. Milne-Thomson, L. M.: "Theoretical Hydrodynamics," 2d ed., St. Martin's, New York, 1949.
3. Sommerfeld, A.: "Mechanics of Deformable Bodies," Academic Press, New York, 1950.
4. Prandtl, L., and O. G. Tietjens: "Fundamentals of Hydro- and Aeromechanics," McGraw-Hill, New York, 1934.
5. Prandtl, L.: "Essentials of Fluid Dynamics," Hafner, New York, 1952.
6. Howarth, L. (ed.): "Modern Developments in Fluid Dynamics: High Speed Flow," vol. I, Oxford, New York, 1953.
7. Tsien, H. S.: The Equations of Gas Dynamics, in H. W. Emmons (ed.), "Fundamentals of Gas Dynamics," Princeton University Press, Princeton, N. J., 1958.
8. Rouse, H. (ed.): "Advanced Mechanics of Fluids," Wiley, New York, 1959.

Section 3

ONE-DIMENSIONAL FLOW

By

JOHN K. VENNARD, *Stanford University, Stanford, California*

ONE-DIMENSIONAL FLOW

3.1. Introduction

The purpose of this treatment of one-dimensional flow is to provide the engineer with a condensed review of this useful but most elementary phase of fluid dynamics. Emphasis at the beginning is on the basic assumptions and justification of the one-dimensional method, after which the emphasis changes to specific situations, mostly in confined flow (pipes), but some examples of open flow are also cited. Although treatment has been restricted to the *incompressible* fluid (see Sec. 8 of this handbook for treatment of compressible flow), application of the material to the flow of slightly compressible fluids (such as liquids or gases, the latter with small density change) is warranted for engineering use. Many of the concepts of fluid flow have been reviewed in Sec. 2, and so they have not been redeveloped here. One-dimensional unsteady flows and flows with chemical reaction have been omitted, since these are treated in Secs. 20 and 6, respectively. The reader will also find extensions of many topics (such as laminar flow, open-channel flow, boundary layers, turbulence, cavitation, and separation) mentioned only briefly, in later sections of this handbook. With problems of one-dimensional fluid flow so widely scattered throughout engineering practice, most engineers meet them at some time; this section is written for those who encounter them infrequently and desire some brief review of fundamentals, limitations, and methods for handling such problems.

3.2. Notation

A area, ft^2
C Chezy coefficient, ft$^{1/2}$/sec
C_c coefficient of contraction
C_{hw} Hazen and Williams coefficient
d pipe diameter or depth of open flow, ft
E energy, ft-lb/lb
e size of roughness, ft
F force, lb
f Darcy-Weisbach friction factor
g acceleration due to gravity, ft/sec^2
h_L head loss, ft
I internal energy, ft-lb/lb
K loss coefficient
k coefficient in equation $h_L = kQ^n$, as required
L, l length, ft
M momentum flux, lb
n (1) Manning's roughness coefficient, ft$^{1/6}$
      (2) exponent in equation $h_L = kQ^n$
P wetted perimeter, ft
p static pressure, psf
Q flow rate, ft^3/sec
q flow rate per unit width, ft^2/sec
R hydraulic radius, ft
$\mathbf{R}$ Reynolds number, Vd/ν
S_0 slope of open channel

V	mean velocity, fps
v	local velocity, fps
v_*	friction velocity, fps
W	weight, lb
z	height above datum, ft
α	kinetic-energy correction factor
β	momentum correction factor
γ	specific weight, lb/ft³
κ	von Kármán's turbulence constant
μ	viscosity, lb sec/ft²
ν	kinematic viscosity, ft²/sec
ρ	density, lb sec²/ft⁴
τ	shearing stress, psf

3.3. Equations and Limitations for One-dimensional Flow

The motion of fluid along a single streamline or through a streamtube of differential cross section (Fig. 3.1) is a pure example of one-dimensional flow. For an incompressible fluid the following basic equations apply (assuming no addition or subtraction of mechanical energy):

Continuity: $$dQ = v_1\, dA_1 = v_2\, dA_2 \tag{3.1}$$

Bernoulli: $$\left(\frac{p}{\gamma} + z + \frac{v^2}{2g}\right)_1 = \left(\frac{p}{\gamma} + z + \frac{v^2}{2g}\right)_2 + h_{L12} \tag{3.2}$$

Energy: $$\left(I + \frac{p}{\gamma} + z + \frac{v^2}{2g}\right)_1 = \left(I + \frac{p}{\gamma} + z + \frac{v^2}{2g}\right)_2 + E_H \tag{3.3}$$

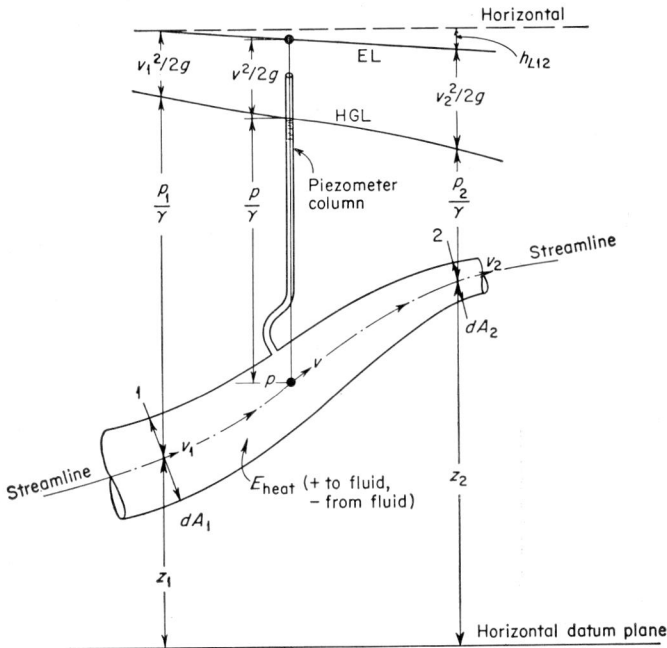

FIG. 3.1. Flow through a streamtube of differential cross section

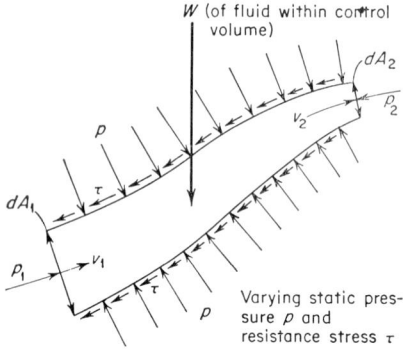

FIG. 3.2. Section of a streamtube as a control volume.

Impulse momentum:

$$\Sigma F = dQ\rho(v_2 - v_1) \qquad (3.4)$$

Regarding these equations the following observations may be made:

1. Because of the differential size of the streamtube, p, z, v, and I are constant over any cross section dA.

2. All the terms of the Bernoulli and energy equations may be considered to be "specific energies," i.e., energy per unit weight of fluid (ft-lb/lb). Because of this they may also be taken to be vertical linear distances and the Bernoulli equation visualized as indicated in Fig. 3.1.

3. Comparison of the Bernoulli and energy equations shows that the "head loss" h_{L12} represents not an energy loss, but a combination of heat and internal energies defined by

$$h_{L12} = I_2 - I_1 \pm E_H$$

Thus the use of head loss in the Bernoulli equation makes the latter equivalent to the energy equation without requiring specific knowledge of heat or internal energies.

4. The fall of the energy line (EL) over a length of streamtube depicts (Fig. 3.1) the head loss occurring therein, whereas the hydraulic grade line (HGL) shows by its vertical distance from the streamtube the local static pressure in the flowing fluid. These lines are widely used in the analysis of engineering problems; they are also known as the total head line and piezometric head line, respectively.

5. The impulse-momentum equation is a vector equation in which ΣF represents the summation of all external forces (pressure, gravity, resistance, etc.) acting on the section of streamtube treated as a "control volume" (Fig. 3.2).

To deal with streamtubes of finite cross-sectional area (such as pipes or open channels) the engineer frequently assumes the flow to be *essentially* one-dimensional and applies the foregoing equations with little or no correction to obtain practical results. However, this assumption is an approximation having many pitfalls and limitations, the nature of which must now be examined. Difficulties arise from flow curvature and/or fluid resistance, which alter the assumed constancy of p, v, and z over the cross section of the streamtube; the only situation in which such difficulties may be overcome easily in real flow problems is that of flow in finite streamtubes wherein the streamlines are all essentially straight and parallel.

Consider the flow in a cylindrical pipe in which all streamlines are precisely parallel to the pipe's axis (Fig. 3.3). Let the static pressure at the intersection of centerline and flow cross section be designated by p and the pressure at any other point in the flow cross section by p'. Let the corresponding values of height above

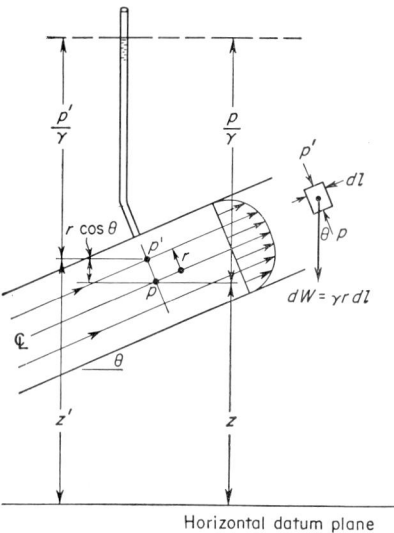

FIG. 3.3. Constancy of $(p/\gamma) + z$ in one-dimensional confined flow.

datum for these points be z and z', respectively. An impulse-momentum analysis applied (in the r direction) to the control volume $r\,dl$ yields

$$(p - p')dl - \gamma r\,dl\cos\theta = 0$$

resulting in

$$\frac{p}{\gamma} - \frac{p'}{\gamma} = r\cos\theta = z' - z$$

or

$$\frac{p}{\gamma} + z = \frac{p'}{\gamma} + z'$$

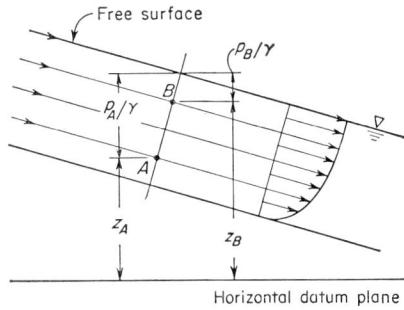

Fig. 3.4.   Constancy of $(p/\gamma) + z$ in one-dimensional open flow.

From this it is seen that although the quantities p and z may vary considerably over the flow cross section, the quantity $p/\gamma + z$ remains constant. Thus over any flow cross section of a streamtube of finite size, a single value of this quantity is applicable to the whole flow or to any of the individual streamlines or streamtubes which compose it; accordingly, it may be concluded that no correction to the quantity $p/\gamma + z$ of Eq. (3.2) is required as the streamtube is expanded from infinitesimal to finite, *assuming the streamlines are precisely straight and parallel.* In practice such streamline configurations are seldom so well defined and the engineer may use the assumption (as an approximation) where streamlines are *essentially* straight and parallel, i.e., *slightly* convergent, divergent, or curved; if they are sharply convergent, divergent, or curved, $p/\gamma + z$ cannot possibly be constant over the flow cross section and the flow picture cannot be considered one-dimensional.

A similar analysis applied to uniform open-channel flow (Fig. 3.4) (if the streamlines are precisely straight and parallel) yields

$$\left(\frac{p}{\gamma} + z\right)_A = \left(\frac{p}{\gamma} + z\right)_B$$

Although streamlines in open-channel flow are even less likely to be precisely straight and parallel than those in pipes, this assumption is widely used in open-channel practice, both for regular canals and natural streams. It is usually tenable because of low velocities and gradual curvatures, divergence, or convergence of the streamlines, but is obviously inapplicable in, over, or near hydraulic structures such as weirs, drops, overfalls, etc.

Having noted the limitations for constancy of $p/\gamma + z$ in streamtubes of finite cross section, the kinetic aspects of the flow must now be examined. Again assuming streamlines precisely straight and parallel (Fig. 3.5), it is to be expected that boundary resistance will produce a "velocity profile" featuring higher velocity at the center of the passage than near the walls. Although the whole flow is a bundle of small parallel streamtubes to each of which Eqs. (3.1) to (3.4) will apply, actual application of these equations to each tiny streamtube would be far too inconvenient for use in engineering problems. To circumvent this difficulty, the engineer alters the basic equations so that they appear in terms of *mean velocity* and apply to the whole flow rather than to individual small streamtubes. Clearly, the total flow rate Q is the sum of all the flow rates dQ in the small streamtubes. Therefore

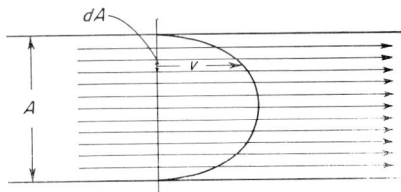

Fig. 3.5. Flow with nonuniform velocity distribution.

$$Q = \int dQ = \int_A v \, dA \tag{3.5}$$

The momentum per unit time of the whole flow is also the sum of the separate momenta of the flows in the streamtubes.   Thus

$$M = \int \rho v \, dQ = \int \rho v^2 \, dA = \rho \int_A v^2 \, dA$$

The total power represented by the kinetic energy of the whole flow is similarly the sum of those in the small streamtubes:

$$(\text{Power})_{\text{KE}} = \int dQ \, \gamma \frac{v^2}{2g} = \frac{\gamma}{2g} \int_A v^3 \, dA$$

The mean velocity V is now conveniently defined by

$$V = \frac{Q}{A} = \frac{1}{A} \int_A v \, dA$$

the momentum per unit time, M, is expressed by

$$M = \beta Q \rho V$$

and the kinetic power is expressed by

$$(\text{Power})_{\text{KE}} = \alpha Q \gamma \frac{V^2}{2g}$$

By equating the above expressions for (power)$_{\text{KE}}$ and M, respectively, and after substituting AV for Q,

$$\beta = \frac{\int_A v^2 \, dA}{AV^2} \quad \text{and} \quad \alpha = \frac{\int_A v^3 \, dA}{AV^3} \tag{3.6}$$

from which the engineer can calculate α and β if the velocity profile is known or can estimate their approximate values to judge the effect of their inclusion in the Bernoulli and impulse-momentum equations.   These equations now become for a streamtube of finite cross section, through which the streamlines are essentially straight and parallel,

$$Q = A_1 V_1 = A_2 V_2$$

$$\left(\frac{p}{\gamma} + z + \alpha \frac{V^2}{2g} \right)_1 = \left(\frac{p}{\gamma} + z + \alpha \frac{V^2}{2g} \right)_2 + h_{L12}$$

$$\Sigma F = \beta_2 Q \rho V_2 - \beta_1 Q \rho V_1$$

It will be noted from Eqs. (3.6) defining α and β that both of these coefficients will be unity when the velocities in all the small streamtubes are the same (uniform velocity distribution) and greater than unity if these velocities differ and that α will always be larger than β for the latter case.   Typical velocity profiles of laminar and turbulent flows are shown (to scale) on Fig. 3.6 with calculated values of α and β.   For the turbulent flows, with their characteristically "flat" velocity profiles, α and β are seen to be only a few per cent above unity and thus likely to be negligible in many engineering problems.   For the laminar flows with their relatively high values of α and β it appears that these coefficients should always be considered in technical applications; however, in such problems it frequently develops that their *effects* are negligible because of the relatively small velocities, momenta, and kinetic energies characteristic of many laminar flows.

The refinement of the Bernoulli equation by introduction of the coefficients α_1 and α_2 defines the exact head loss h_{L12} as

$$(\text{Exact})h_{L12} = \left(\frac{p}{\gamma} + z + \alpha\,\frac{V^2}{2g}\right)_1 - \left(\frac{p}{\gamma} + z + \alpha\,\frac{V^2}{2g}\right)_2$$

However, in view of the small effect of the α coefficients on the equation, it has been standard engineering practice (for over a century) to define the (conventional) head loss by

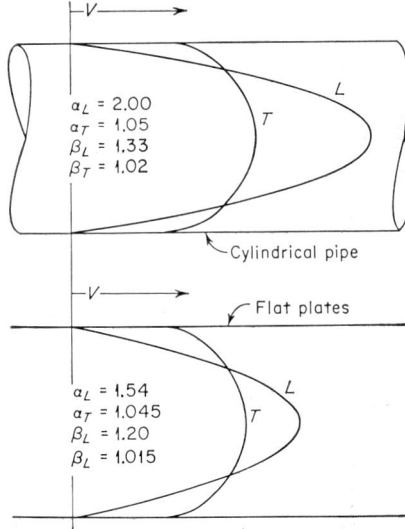

$a_L = 2.00$
$a_T = 1.05$
$\beta_L = 1.33$
$\beta_T = 1.02$

Cylindrical pipe

Flat plates

$a_L = 1.54$
$a_T = 1.045$
$\beta_L = 1.20$
$\beta_L = 1.015$

FIG. 3.6. Comparison of laminar- and turbulent-velocity profiles (to scale) for same mean velocity.

$$(\text{Conventional})h_{L12} = \left(\frac{p}{\gamma} + z + \frac{V^2}{2g}\right)_1 - \left(\frac{p}{\gamma} + z + \frac{V^2}{2g}\right)_2$$

This practice is equivalent to absorbing the effects of changes of velocity profile into the head loss; seldom does this result in any significant error, and it is an obvious boon to rapid calculations.

Finally, the three basic equations of one-dimensional flow may be written for practical use:

Continuity:
$$Q = A_1V_1 = A_2V_2 \tag{3.7}$$

Bernoulli:
$$\left(\frac{p}{\gamma} + z + \frac{V^2}{2g}\right)_1 = \left(\frac{p}{\gamma} + z + \frac{V^2}{2g}\right)_2 + h_{L12} \tag{3.8}$$

Impulse momentum:
$$\Sigma F = (\beta Q\rho V)_2 - (\beta Q\rho V)_1 \tag{3.9}$$

Example 1. Water discharges from the 6-in. pipe through the 3-in. nozzle into the atmosphere. The gauge pressure on the centerline at section 1 is 70 psi. Calculate the flow rate and the horizontal component of force exerted on the bolts. Assume that the (conventional) head loss between sections 1 and 2 may be calculated (Art. 3.5) from $0.05V_2^2/2g$, $\beta_1 = 1.03$, and $\beta_2 = 1.00$.

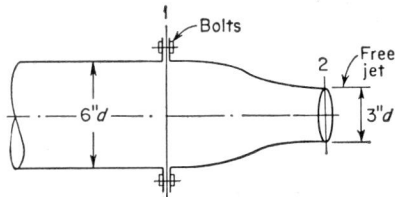

Bolts

2 Free jet

$6''d$

$3''d$

Example 1

SOLUTION

$$\pi(0.25)^2 V_1 = \pi(0.125)^2 V_2 = Q \tag{3.7}$$

$$\frac{70 \times 144}{62.4} + \frac{V_1^2}{2g} = 0 + \frac{V_2^2}{2g} + 0.05\frac{V_2^2}{2g} \tag{3.8}$$

By solving Eqs. (3.7) and (3.8) simultaneously,

$$V_1 = 25.7 \text{ fps} \qquad V_2 = 102.8 \text{ fps} \qquad Q = 5.05 \text{ cfs}$$

Now by taking the volume between sections 1 and 2 as the control volume and by assuming forces and velocities positive to the right, the external horizontal forces acting on the control volume are $p_1 A_1$ at section 1 and zero at section 2 (because the static pressure in the issuing jet is zero) and the horizontal component of force *by nozzle on water*. These compose ΣF_x of Eq. (3.9).

$$70\pi(3)^2 - F_x = 5.05 \times 1.935(102.8 - 1.03 \times 25.7) \tag{3.9}$$
$$F_x = +1233 \text{ lb} \qquad \text{(to the left by nozzle on}$$
$$\text{water or to the right by water on nozzle)}$$

Example 2. After neglecting frictional effects, predict the flow rate through this venturimeter carrying gasoline of specific gravity 0.80.

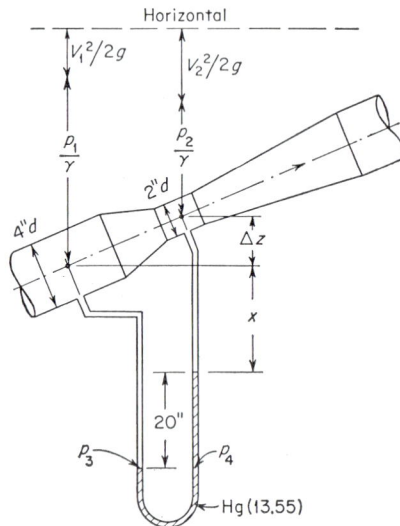

Example 2

SOLUTION. Visualize the terms of the Bernoulli equation as depicted on Fig. 3.1. From the accompanying sketch

$$\frac{V_2^2}{2g} - \frac{V_1^2}{2g} = \frac{p_1}{\gamma} - \frac{p_2}{\gamma} - \Delta z$$

$$V_2 = \left(\frac{A_1}{A_2}\right) V_1 = 4V_1 \tag{3.7}$$

The quantity $p_1/\gamma - p_2/\gamma - \Delta z$ may be determined from the manometer reading by noting that $p_3 = p_4$ and equating separate expressions for p_3 and p_4 as follows:

$$p_1 + (x + {}^{20}\!/_{12})62.4 \times 0.80 = p_2 + (\Delta z + x)62.4 \times 0.80 + {}^{20}\!/_{12}(13.55 \times 62.4)$$

whence

$$\frac{p_1}{\gamma} - \frac{p_2}{\gamma} - \Delta z = \frac{20}{12}\left(\frac{13.55 - 0.80}{0.80}\right) = 26.55 \text{ ft of gasoline}$$

With this value inserted in the first equation the Bernoulli and continuity equations (above) may be solved simultaneously to yield

$$V_1 = 10.7 \text{ fps} \qquad V_2 = 42.8 \text{ fps} \qquad Q = 0.937 \text{ cfs}$$

Example 3. By disregarding frictional effects, calculate the propulsive force developed by this "ducted propeller unit" (when attached to a fixed test stand) if the flow rate through it is 5000 cfs of air of specific weight 0.075 lb/ft³.

SOLUTION. Since all change of momentum of the moving air is caused by the unit, the propulsive force must be exactly equal to this change of momentum per unit time.

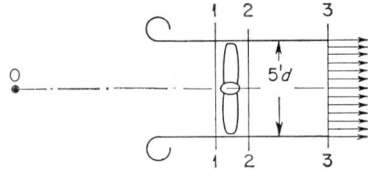

Example 3

Applying Eq. (3.9), noting that the original velocity of the air is zero,

$$\Sigma F = Q\rho V_2 = \frac{Q^2 \rho}{A_2} = \frac{(5000)^2 \times 0.075}{32.2\pi(2.5)^2}$$

$$\Sigma F = \text{propulsive force} = 2960 \text{ lb}$$

It is also of interest to calculate the separate contributions of the propeller and duct to this propulsive force. First apply Eq. (3.7) to determine the mean velocities at sections 1, 2, and 3; these velocities are 255 fps. Equation (3.8) may now be used to obtain the centerline pressure at section 1; writing this equation between point 0 (which is far to the left of the unit where the pressure is p_0 and velocity zero) and the center of section 1,

$$\frac{p_0}{0.075} + 0 = \frac{p_1}{0.075} + \frac{(255)^2}{2g}$$

$$p_1(\text{psf}) = p_0 - 75.8$$

The centerline pressure at section 2 may now be determined by the following reasoning. The mean pressure just outside the duct around section 3 is essentially p_0 to the extent the fluid is at rest there; thus, with streamlines straight and parallel, $p_3 = p_0$. However, there is no change of V or z [Eq. (3.8)] between sections 2 and 3; therefore $p_2 = p_3 = p_0$. Accordingly, the rise of pressure across the propeller disc (between sections 1 and 2) is

$$p_2 - p_1 = p_0 - (p_0 - 75.8) = 75.8 \text{ psf}$$

and the force exerted by the propeller on the air must therefore be

$$75.8\pi(2.5)^2 = 1485 \text{ lb}$$

which is observed to be exactly one half of the total propulsive force produced by the unit. From this it may be deduced that the other half of the total propulsive force is produced by the duct and results from reduced pressures acting on the duct entrance.

The power supplied to the unit may be calculated by considering the work done by the propeller on the air per unit of time; this is

$$\text{Horsepower} = 1485 \times {}^{255}\!/_{550} = 688$$

3.4. Head Losses Caused by Boundary Resistance

Experimental Results. Resistance to open or closed flow may be visualized as shown in Fig. 3.7, the shear (or frictional) stress τ_0 being the basic item to consider. Treating the element of length dl as a control volume, an impulse-momentum analysis (there being no change of momentum) yields

$$d\left(\frac{p}{\gamma} + z\right) = \left(\frac{\tau_0 P}{\gamma A}\right) dl$$

in which P, the *wetted perimeter*, is the line of contact between flowing fluid and solid boundary in the plane A. The ratio A/P is a constant of the cross-section geometry termed the *hydraulic radius* R. By inserting this and by integrating from 1 to 2 a fundamental relation between τ_0 and h_L results.

$$\tau_0 = \frac{\gamma R}{l} h_{L12}$$

Experimental observations on the flow of water in cylindrical pipes led Darcy and Weisbach (over a century ago) to express the head loss by

$$h_{L12} = f \frac{l}{d} \frac{V^2}{2g} \tag{3.10}$$

Since $R = d/4$ for a cylindrical passage, the expression for frictional stress at the boundary becomes

$$\tau_0 = f\rho \frac{V^2}{8} \tag{3.11}$$

In both of the preceding equations the *friction factor f* appears, and it is obvious that accurate numerical values for this factor will be needed for the solution of engineering problems which require information on boundary shear or head loss. It is to be noted that f is an experimental coefficient, usually determined by direct measurement of h_L,

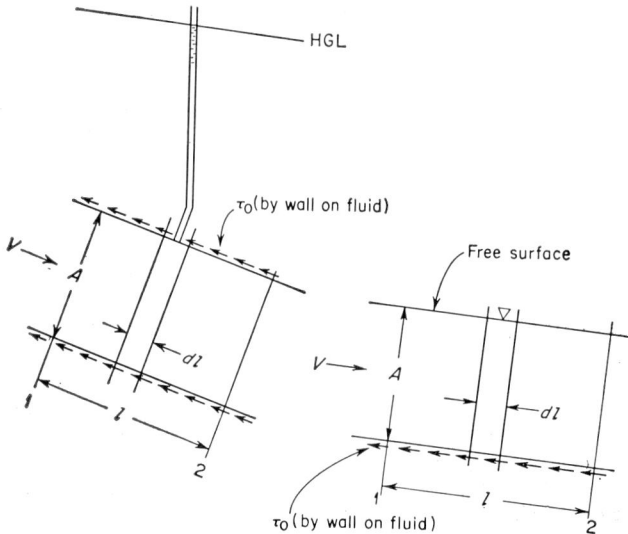

FIG. 3.7. Wall shear in confined and open flow.

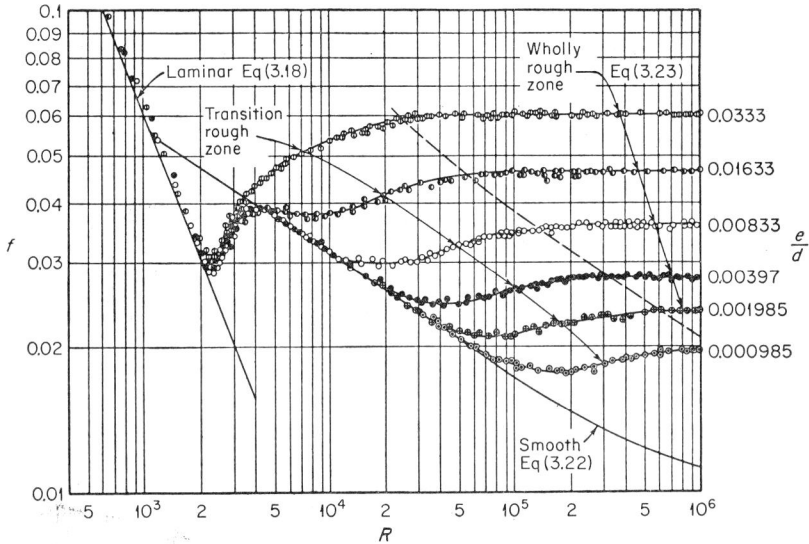

FIG. 3.8. Nikuradse's experimental results for pipes of uniform sand grain roughness.

l, d, and V in Eq. (3.10); it is not obtainable by analytical methods without the introduction of other experimentally confirmed relationships.

Although the early hydraulicians considered the friction factor to depend wholly on boundary roughness, Stanton[1] showed it to be a function of Reynolds number and through this relationship extended its application to the flow of all fluids.

Probably the largest increment in understanding of the friction factor since Stanton's time was produced by the accurate and systematic tests of Nikuradse,[2] who used *measurable roughness* produced by uniform sand grains of diameter e. Through the use of such artificial roughness Nikuradse was able to show that the friction factor depended upon Reynolds number and the *relative roughness* e/d. A summary of Nikuradse's work is shown on the "Stanton diagram" of Fig. 3.8. From this diagram many useful facts may be observed:

1. For Reynolds numbers below approximately 2000 (the regime of laminar flow), a single line passes through all the experimental points, whether these were obtained from pipes of large or small roughness. From this it may be concluded that boundary roughness has no effect on wall shear or head loss in laminar flow and thus that such shear or head loss must derive from the physical properties of the fluid only.

2. In turbulent flow (Reynolds number greater than 2000) the friction factor depends very much upon the surface roughness, unless such surface roughness is very small. For this case, all experimental points fall again on a single line, giving a minimum friction factor for any Reynolds number. Boundary surfaces yielding such minimum friction factors are defined as surfaces of *ultimate smoothness*, whatever the magnitude of their roughness projections. Important conclusions to be drawn from this are: (1) smoothness is defined not only by small magnitude of roughness but also by fluid behavior; and (2) for such smooth surfaces, wall shear and head loss result (as in laminar flow) only from the physical properties of the fluid.

3. At high Reynolds number and high relative roughness the friction factor becomes wholly a function of the relative roughness and independent of the Reynolds number. When a surface exhibits this behavior it is defined as being *wholly rough* since its friction factor depends wholly on the size of its roughness and is independent of the physical properties of the flowing fluid.

4. Between the *smooth* and *wholly rough* zones lies an area of transition roughness.

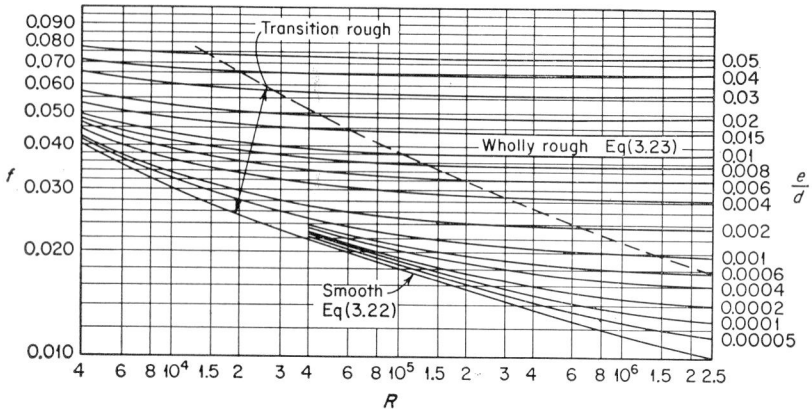

FIG. 3.9. Moody diagram for pipes of commercial roughness.

The unique behavior of the friction factor in this zone (where it is obviously dependent upon both Reynolds number and relative roughness) results from the uniformity and regularity of Nikuradse's sand grain roughness. For the more random and irregular roughnesses of pipe and channel surfaces encountered in engineering practice a very different dependency of friction factor upon Reynolds number and relative roughness is to be expected (Fig. 3.9).

Application of Nikuradse's basic work to practical engineering roughnesses was accomplished by Colebrook and White,[3] who used the fact that any rough pipe when tested to high enough Reynolds number produced a friction factor no longer dependent upon Reynolds number. Through comparison of the Nikuradse friction factors with those of commercial pipes at high Reynolds number, an *equivalent sand grain roughness* could be deduced for the latter, allowing the engineer to estimate with reasonable accuracy the friction factor to be expected with any size of roughness. Colebrook and White were also able to correlate the results of many laboratory tests on commercial pipes over a wide range of Reynolds number and roughness and showed that these could be characterized by the equation

$$\frac{1}{\sqrt{f}} - 2 \log_{10} \frac{d}{e} = 1.14 - 2 \log_{10} \left[1 + \frac{9.28}{R(e/d)\sqrt{f}} \right] \tag{3.12}$$

Moody[4] plotted Eq. (3.12) for practical use on the Stanton diagram of Fig. 3.9 (now termed the "Moody diagram") and extended the work of Colebrook and White to other materials and roughnesses; his values of equivalent sand grain roughness are given in Table 3.1.

Because of the wide range of e for any material shown in the table, the reader may at first be skeptical of the value of this contribution. However, it is to be noted that very wide variation in the roughness causes considerably smaller changes of friction factor f. This approach therefore allows the engineer to make fairly accurate predictions of f

Table 3.1. Size of Various Roughnesses

Material	Equivalent sand grain roughness e, ft
Commercial steel or wrought iron	0.00015
Asphalted cast iron	0.0004
Galvanized iron	0.0005
Cast iron	0.00085
Wood stave	0.0006–0.003
Concrete	0.001–0.01
Riveted steel	0.003–0.03

from estimates of roughness size and thus provides a scientific approach to replace the older "art" of selecting friction factors from wordy descriptions of surface texture.

Analytical Treatment of Laminar Flow. By starting with the Newtonian hypothesis that in laminar flow the shearing stress between adjacent fluid layers may be expressed by

$$\tau = \mu \frac{dv}{dy} \qquad (3.13)$$

and by applying an impulse-momentum analysis, enlightening and useful results may be worked out for one-dimensional laminar flows.

Consider first the established laminar flow of fluid in a cylindrical pipe (Fig. 3.10). Application of Eq. (3.9) to the cylindrical control volume of radius r and length l will yield

$$\tau = \frac{\gamma h_{L12}}{2l} r \qquad (3.14)$$

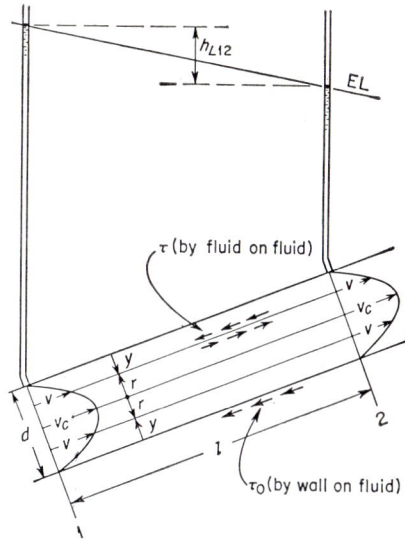

FIG. 3.10. Definition sketch for laminar flow.

showing that shearing stress within the flowing fluid may be calculated from the head loss and that this shearing stress varies linearly with distance from the centerline of the passage.

By equating these expressions for shearing stress,

$$\mu \frac{dv}{dy} = \frac{\gamma h_{L12}}{2l} r$$

Integration of this equation is accomplished by noting that y increases from the wall into the fluid (i.e., toward the centerline of the pipe) whereas r increases from centerline toward the wall. Accordingly, an increment of y is a decrement of r, allowing dy to be replaced by $-dr$; thus

$$-\mu \frac{dv}{dr} = \frac{\gamma h_{L12}}{2l} r$$

After separating variables and after integrating,

$$-\mu v = \frac{\gamma h_{L12}}{2l} \frac{r^2}{2} + C \qquad (3.15)$$

By noting that where $r = 0$, $v = v_c$, the constant of integration is evaluated as $-\mu v_c$. Substituting this in Eq. (3.15),

$$v_c - v = \frac{\gamma h_{L12}}{4\mu l} r^2$$

showing that the velocity profile is parabolic, with maximum velocity at the pipe centerline and a velocity of zero at the pipe wall.

The flow rate Q may now be calculated by use of Eq. (3.5).

$$Q = \int_A v \, dA = \int_0^{d/2} \left(v_c - \frac{\gamma h_{L12}}{4\mu l} r^2 \right) 2\pi r \, dr$$

yielding (after $\gamma h_{L12} d^2 / 16\mu l$ is substituted for v_c)

$$Q = \frac{\pi}{128} \frac{\gamma h_{L12}}{\mu l} d^4$$

By equating this expression for Q to V $(\pi d^2/4)$,

$$V = \frac{\gamma h_{L12}}{32\mu l} d^2 \qquad (3.16)$$

Comparison of this with the above expression for v_c shows that for laminar flow in a cylindrical passage the mean velocity V is exactly one-half the maximum velocity v_c, which is usually expressed

$$\frac{V}{v_c} = 0.5 \qquad (3.17)$$

Rearrangement of Eq. (3.16) yields a useful expression for head loss in laminar flow in cylindrical pipes

$$h_L = \frac{32\mu l V}{\gamma d^2}$$

demonstrating the characteristic linear relationship between velocity and head loss. When this expression is set equal to Eq. (3.10), the Darcy friction factor for laminar flow in cylindrical pipes is found to be

$$f = \frac{64}{\mathbf{R}} \qquad (3.18)$$

The fact that this relationship agrees accurately with experimental results (Fig. 3.8) validates the Newtonian hypothesis, Eq. (3.13), for shearing stress in laminar flow.

Reinterpretation of Fig. 3.10 as laminar flow between parallel planes of infinite extent allows analogous formulas to be derived by the same methods·

$$\tau = \frac{\gamma h_L}{l} r$$

For velocity profile: $\qquad\qquad v_c - v = \frac{\gamma h_L}{2\mu l} r^2$

For flow rate: $\qquad\qquad\qquad q = \frac{\gamma h_L d^3}{12\mu l}$

in which the flow rate q is that through a flow cross section of unit (1-ft) width normal to the plane of the paper. The analogous equation for mean velocity is

$$V = \frac{\gamma h_L d^2}{12\mu l}$$

and that for velocity ratio

$$\frac{V}{v_c} = 0.667$$

For head loss

$$h_L = \frac{12\mu l V}{\gamma d^2}$$

Another example of laminar flow is that of open flow, which usually occurs in thin sheets (Fig. 3.11) in industrial or drainage practice. Many of the foregoing formulas may be applied directly without further analysis once Fig. 3.11 is reinterpreted as the lower half of Fig. 3.10. Here $h_L/l = \sin\theta$, so the equation for velocity profile becomes

$$v_c - v = \frac{\gamma \sin\theta}{2\mu l} r^2$$

The flow rate,

$$q = \frac{1}{2}\left[\frac{1}{12}\frac{\gamma(2d)^3 \sin\theta}{\mu}\right] = \frac{1}{3}\frac{\gamma d^3 \sin\theta}{\mu}$$

The mean velocity,

$$V = \frac{1}{3}\frac{d^2 \sin\theta}{\mu}$$

and velocity ratio $V/v_s = 0.667$ as before.
Of these three equations, the second is the
most used since it relates depth of flow,

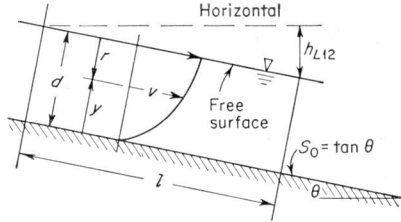

FIG. 3.11. Laminar sheet flow.

channel slope, and fluid properties to flow rate. Since channel slopes are usually small,
the approximation $\sin\theta = \tan\theta = S_0$ is allowable; also ρg may be substituted for γ,
and ν for μ/ρ. Thus the equation is frequently written

$$q = \frac{1}{3}\frac{gd^3 S_0}{\nu}$$

for use in many practical problems where the Reynolds number Vd/ν is less than the
critical value of about 500.

Semianalytical Treatment of Turbulent Flow. As an extension of the "mixing length"
hypothesis of Prandtl and from the experimental results of Nikuradse, von Kármán[5]
proposed an expression for shear stress in turbulent flow analogous to that of Newton
for laminar flow. This expression is

$$\tau = \rho\kappa^2 \frac{(dv/dy)^4}{(d^2v/dy^2)^2} \tag{3.19}$$

Two features of this expression are noteworthy: (1) the density of the fluid is the only
physical property included—which is consistent with the idea of turbulent exchange of
momentum being the cause of shearing stresses in turbulent flow; since viscosity does
not appear, this expression for turbulent shear cannot be expected to apply in the close
vicinity of smooth surfaces, where turbulence is not completely developed and where
viscous action is strong. (2) The "constant" κ (having a value of about 0.4) is not
precisely constant, disclosing some small imperfections in the theory and necessitating
the adjustment of other "constants" in
equations derived from the expression for
turbulent shearing stress. In spite of
these slight difficulties the Prandtl-Kár-
mán expression for turbulent shearing
stress is a major stride in the development
of a theoretical framework for the equations of turbulent flow which are in engineering use.

Application of this equation to established turbulent flow in cylindrical pipes
(Fig. 3.12) proceeds analogously to that
used in laminar flow (Art. 3.4, p. 3-13).
Equation (3.14) is rearranged to read

$$\tau = \tau_0 \frac{r}{r_0} = \tau_0 \left(1 - \frac{y}{r_0}\right)$$

and equated to Eq. (3.19),

$$\tau_0\left(1 - \frac{y}{r_0}\right) = \rho\kappa^2 \frac{(dv/dy)^4}{(d^2v/dy^2)^2}$$

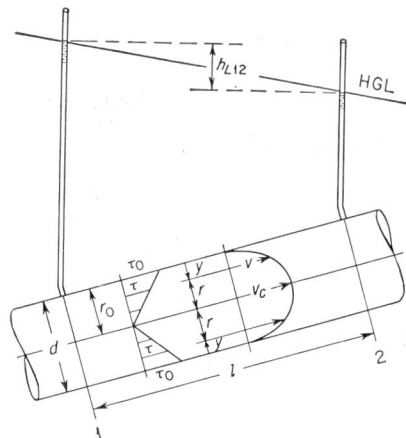

FIG. 3.12. Definition sketch for turbulent
flow.

After two integrations[6] and some simplifications of the resulting equations, a general expression for velocity profile results:

$$\frac{v_c - v}{\sqrt{\tau_0/\rho}} = \frac{1}{\kappa} \log_e \frac{r_0}{y}$$

which is applicable to smooth and rough cylindrical pipes above Reynolds numbers of about 5000 and accurate enough for engineering predictions of velocity profiles except in the vicinity of the pipe walls. Dimensional considerations show $\sqrt{\tau_0/\rho}$ to have dimensions of a velocity and [from Eq. (3.11)] equal to $V\sqrt{f/8}$, containing the friction factor. For these reasons this term is called the *friction velocity* and is usually written as v_*. For engineering use the logarithmic base is usually changed to 10 and a value of 0.40 used for κ, allowing a universal equation for velocity profile to be written[6]

$$\frac{v_c - v}{v_*} = 5.75 \log_{10} \frac{r_0}{y} \tag{3.20}$$

A relation between mean velocity and centerline velocity may be obtained [analogously to Eq. (3.17)] by

$$Q' = (v_c - V)\pi r_0{}^2 = \int_A (v_c - v)dA$$

in which Q' is the flow rate represented by the difference between centerline and mean velocities. The result is[6]

$$\frac{V}{v_c} = \frac{1}{1 + (3/2\kappa)\sqrt{f/8}}$$

Here a value of κ of 0.37 is needed for this equation to agree with experimental results; hence it is generally used as[6]

$$\frac{V}{v_c} = \frac{1}{1 + 4.07\sqrt{f/8}} \tag{3.21}$$

The use of Eqs. (3.20) and (3.21) provides a means for the accurate prediction of velocity profiles in pipes from data on flow rate, Reynolds number, and roughness.

After allowing for the differences in the nature of resistance offered by smooth and rough surfaces, Eqs. (3.20) and (3.21) may be combined to yield[6] (with some adjustment of coefficients) expressions for friction factor for pipes which are *ultimately smooth* or *wholly rough*. For ultimately smooth pipes,

$$\sqrt{\frac{1}{f}} = -0.80 + 2 \log_{10} \mathbf{R}\sqrt{f} \tag{3.22}$$

For wholly rough pipes,

$$\sqrt{\frac{1}{f}} = 1.14 + 2 \log_{10} \frac{d}{e} \tag{3.23}$$

The former may be used directly in the selection of minimum friction factors; its line is plotted on both Figs. 3.8 and 3.9. The latter is of vast engineering importance in showing the systematic variation of friction factor with roughness and in the Colebrook-White approach to the establishment of numerical values of roughness size for engineering surfaces.

Although Eq. (3.23) has been established for pipe flow it may also be applied fruitfully to uniform open-channel flow to explore the nature of certain empirical resistance coefficients now in wide use. In such flows water is usually the flowing fluid, Reynolds numbers are high, and channel walls are not of ultimate smoothness.

By applying the impulse-momentum principle (Art. 24.7) to the control volume contained between sections 1 and 2 of Fig. 3.13 (there being no change of momentum),

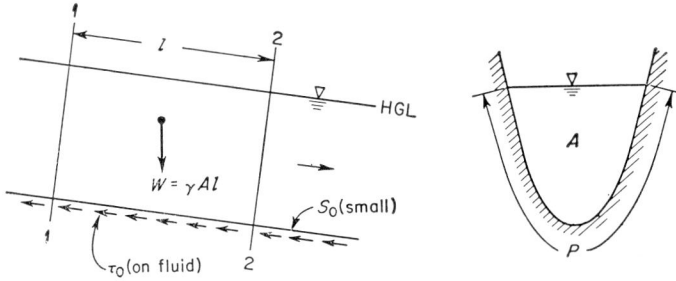

Fig. 3.13. Uniform flow in an open channel.

$$\gamma A l \sin \theta - \tau_0 P l = 0 \qquad (3.24)$$

For small S_0, $\sin \theta = \tan \theta = S_0$ and A/P is recognized as the hydraulic radius R. Accordingly, Eq. (3.24) may be written

$$\tau_0 = \gamma R S_0$$

Setting the expression for τ_0 equal to that of Eq. (3.11) and solving for V,

$$V = \sqrt{\frac{8g}{f}} \sqrt{R S_0}$$

The form of this equation was established by Chezy in 1775 and written by him

$$V = C\sqrt{R S_0}$$

in which C has become known as the "Chezy coefficient." It is evident from this comparison of equations that since C is directly related to f, it can (like f) be expected to depend on both Reynolds number and relative roughness.

In American open-channel practice an empirical expression proposed by Manning[7] is widely used for the determination of C; his formula is

$$C = \frac{1.49}{n} R^{1/6}$$

from which (through the preceding relations) may be derived

$$\sqrt{\frac{1}{f}} = \frac{1.49}{\sqrt{8g}} \frac{R^{1/6}}{n} \qquad (3.25)$$

By equating Eq. (3.23) to Eq. (3.25) there results ($4R$ having been substituted for d)

$$\frac{1.49}{\sqrt{8g}} \frac{R^{1/6}}{n} = 1.14 + 2 \log_{10} \frac{4R}{e} \qquad (3.26)$$

which allows some useful conclusions to be drawn concerning the relation between n and e:

1. Equating the expressions implies that the Chezy-Manning expression on the left-hand side applies only to the *wholly rough* situation where roughness and Reynolds number are both relatively high. However, this is justifiable in view of the nature of most open-channel flows and Manning's intention that n be a number obtainable from a descriptive statement of the channel roughness.

2. If the foregoing premise is accepted, values of n may be derived from roughness size e and descriptive statements tend to become unnecessary.

3. The form of the equation shows that n is a relatively insensitive measure of e, large variations in e causing relatively small variations in n.

4. Experience with the equation also shows it to be essentially a relationship between e and n, the effect of R approximately canceling out. Thus it may be concluded that n is (like e) a measure of the size of roughness projections (not of the relative roughness).

5. The reader must not expect from the foregoing conclusions that Eq. (3.26) can be used for precise prediction of n from the values of e given in Table 3.1; however, he can expect that satisfactory estimates may be made for many engineering problems.

3.5. Head Losses Other than Those of Boundary Resistance

Head losses in one-dimensional flow may result from features of flow other than boundary resistance; such features are abrupt changes in flow cross section, separation of flow from boundary walls, large accelerations (or decelerations), boundary-layer growth, secondary flows, and combinations of these. Such effects, usually resulting from changes in the form of flow cross section, are highly localized and for these reasons are termed *local phenomena* and their head losses *form losses* or *minor losses*—*minor* because in many engineering problems they are very small compared with the *major* losses produced by boundary friction. Only in rare cases can such local losses be predicted analytically, and these only for the simplest of boundary geometries. However, the subject may be handled adequately for many engineering purposes by the use of certain basic analytical and empirical tools.

The complexities of flow phenomena for even a simple boundary geometry may be seen in Fig. 3.14, and the head loss produced by the conical contraction suitably defined. It is to be noted that the presence of the contraction disturbs the flow a very short distance upstream and a considerable distance downstream, flow disturbances dying out in this extended region, accompanied by boundary-layer growth which restores established flow at and beyond section 2. The present "state of the art" does not permit productive analysis of these physical phenomena, so the following empiricism is resorted to, both to define the local loss h_{Lc} and to allow it to be obtained by simple measurements: the established flow energy lines are extended downstream to the beginning of the contraction and upstream to the end of the contraction, and the vertical distance by which they do not meet is defined as the head loss h_{Lc}. This means that h_{L12} between two zones of one-dimensional established flow is simply the sum of assumed established flow losses and local losses in spite of the complex and unknown interaction between these. Stated in another way, the local loss is defined as the excess loss "over and above" that produced by assumed established one-dimensional flows in the appropriate passages analogous to those of Fig. 3.14. Defining the minor losses in this manner provides an easy solution to many technical problems. For example, the total

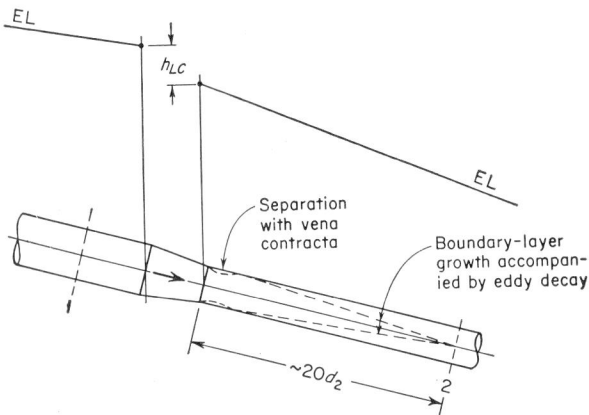

Fig. 3.14. Definition of form losses.

losses in a pipeline containing contractions, enlargements, or other "pipe fittings" becomes a simple numerical sum of the local losses (defined in the manner above) and the losses of established pipe flow discussed in the preceding articles.

An additional complication seems to appear in the application of the foregoing methods to pipelines where fittings are in close proximity and disturbances do not die out before others begin. Although there have been few experiments on this effect, experience has shown that the total loss produced by fittings in close proximity is somewhat less than their sum when calculated individually; thus the sum of the individual losses gives the engineer a conservative (larger-than-actual) estimate of losses to be expected.

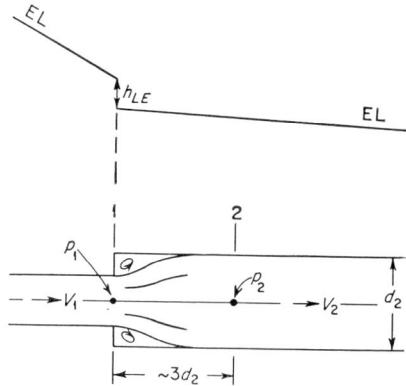

Fig. 3.15. Abrupt enlargement.

Form losses are usually calculated by the use of suitable experimentally determined *loss coefficients* K in the equation

$$h_L = K \frac{V^2}{2g}$$

(3.27)

which originated from the observation by early hydraulicians that in (turbulent) flow such head losses varied closely with the square of some appropriate mean velocity V, "appropriateness" of such velocity to be decided on the basis of approximate analytical solutions, convenience in use, standard practice, etc. Examples which illustrate this are provided below. More recent experiments have revealed K to be a function of Reynolds number and boundary roughness as well as over-all boundary geometry; for precise calculations these factors must be considered, but in many practical cases they may be safely ignored. This approximation is generally allowable in turbulent flows because of the essential constancy of K over a wide range of Reynolds number and the small extent of the area of roughness; in laminar flows, although the coefficients may be large, the low velocities result in losses which are usually negligible unless great precision is desired.

The only form-loss coefficient which can be calculated by simple analytical methods is that for the axisymmetric abrupt enlargement (Fig. 3.15). This problem was first treated by Borda and Carnot and is widely known as the "Borda-Carnot loss." A review of this may serve to outline the possibilities, assumptions, limitations, complexities, etc., of analytical approaches to such problems. Isolate the zone between sections 1 and 2 as a control volume and apply the impulse-momentum equation in the horizontal direction, assuming $\beta = 1$ and wall friction negligible.

$$p_1 A_2 - p_2 A_2 = Q\rho(V_2 - V_1)$$

By writing the Bernoulli equation between sections 1 and 2, assuming that the local head loss is consummated in this zone and that there are no other losses,

$$\frac{p_1}{\gamma} - \frac{p_2}{\gamma} = \frac{V_2^2}{2g} - \frac{V_1^2}{2g} + h_{LE}$$

By substituting $A_2 V_2$ for Q in the first equation and by solving the two equations simultaneously with the elimination of $(p_1 - p_2)$,

$$h_{LE} = \frac{(V_1 - V_2)^2}{2g} = K_E \frac{(V_1 - V_2)^2}{2g}$$

(3.28)

in which $K_E = 1$ from this simple analysis. Although the reader may be uneasy about

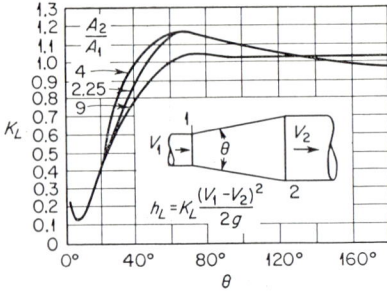

Fig. 3.16. Gibson's loss coefficients for conical diffusers.

some of the assumptions of the Borda-Carnot approach, laboratory experiments confirm the value of K_E within a few per cent, a fact which tends to validate these assumptions. From this some useful generalizations may be deduced: (1) that the losses may be considered for practical purposes to occur in a much more localized flow region than is implied by Fig. 3.14; and (2) the steady-flow picture of Fig. 3.15 is a useful approximation to a truer but much more complicated unsteady-flow picture obtained in laboratory experiments where the expanding stream can be seen sloshing from side to side, eddies forming, reforming, and swept downstream to decay in a large section downstream of section 2 (Fig. 3.15).

The limiting case of $A_2 \to \infty$, $V_2 \to 0$ is of practical interest since it represents the discharge of a small fluid stream into a relatively larger and static body of the same fluid. Here the result is

$$h_{LE} \cong \frac{V_1{}^2}{2g} \qquad (3.29)$$

meaning that substantially all the kinetic energy of the stream is dissipated in the process.

Although there is only one possible boundary geometry for an axisymmetric abrupt enlargement, there are an infinite number of possibilities for gradual enlargements. Such enlargements are usually called "diffusers" and are employed to minimize head losses under conditions where reduction of velocity is required, such as downstream from the throat of a venturi meter or at the outlets of pumps or turbines. Diffusers may also be used to maximize pressure recovery during velocity reduction, and a variety of designs have been suggested for this purpose, some containing internal vanes.

The experiments of Gibson[8] on diffusers of conical form may be quoted to demonstrate trends and reasonable values of the loss coefficients. Here the shape may be completely defined as a function of cone angle and area ratio. If the loss coefficient is defined by Eq. (3.28), the results appear as in Fig. 3.16; from this it may be concluded that a conical diffuser of central angle near 7° will be close to optimum if it follows a long reach of pipe containing established flow. For a given area ratio, diffusers of very small cone angle yield very high losses because of excessive wall area in contact with the flowing fluid. Before reaching a value near unity at a cone angle of 180°, the loss

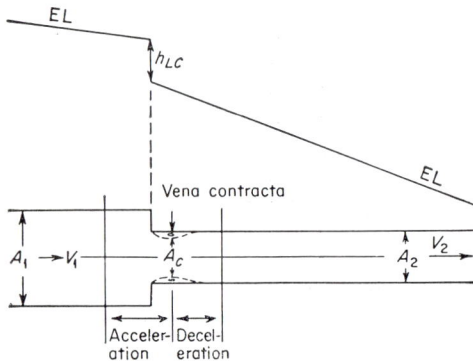

Fig. 3.17. Abrupt contraction.

Table 3.2. Properties of Contractions

$\dfrac{A_2}{A_1}$	0	0.1	0.2	0.3	0.4	0.5	0.6	0.7	0.8	0.9	1.0
C_c		0.617	0.624	0.632	0.643	0.659	0.681	0.712	0.755	0.813	0.892	1.00
$\left(\dfrac{1}{C_c}-1\right)^2$		0.38	0.36	0.34	0.31	0.27	0.22	0.16	0.10	0.05	0.02	0
K_c		0.50	0.46	0.41	0.36	0.30	0.24	0.18	0.12	0.06	0.02	0
$K_c-\left(\dfrac{1}{C_c}-1\right)^2$		0.12	0.10	0.07	0.05	0.03	0.02	0.02	0.02	0.01	0	0
$C_c{}^2\left[K_c-\left(\dfrac{1}{C_c}-1\right)^2\right]$	0.045	0.04	0.03	0.02	0.015	0.01	0.01	0.01	0.005	0	0

coefficient becomes large and the diffuser inefficient; obviously this describes a geometry to be avoided by the designer.

The opposite of the abrupt enlargement is the abrupt contraction, depicted on Fig. 3.17. Here the main flow features are an acceleration zone leading to the development of a vena contracta, followed by a deceleration zone similar to that analyzed by Borda and Carnot. Using Weisbach's[9] observed values (Table 3.2) for the coefficient of contraction $C_c = A_c/A_2$ (which he showed to be a function of A_2/A_1), a fair estimate of the loss coefficient of the abrupt contraction may be made. Calculating the head loss in the deceleration zone, using the Borda-Carnot result,

$$h_{L_{decel}} = 1.0\,\frac{(V_c - V_2)^2}{2g} = \frac{(V_2/C_c - V_2)^2}{2g} = \left(\frac{1}{C_c}-1\right)^2\frac{V_2{}^2}{2g}$$

Defining the total head loss (including both acceleration and deceleration zones) by

$$h_{Lc} = K_c\,\frac{V_2{}^2}{2g} \tag{3.30}$$

it is observed that $(1/C_c - 1)^2$ is a large portion of K_c, the remainder being attributable to the acceleration zone. By comparing these (Table 3.2, lines 3 and 4), it is seen that the head lost in the deceleration zone is the major part of the total head loss caused by the contraction. The head loss in the acceleration zone may now be computed from

$$h_{L_{accel}} = \left[K_c - \left(\frac{1}{C_c}-1\right)^2\right]\frac{V_2{}^2}{2g}$$

from which a useful loss coefficient for the acceleration zone may be deduced; this is defined by

$$h_{L_{accel}} = K_a\,\frac{V_c{}^2}{2g}$$

By equating these two expressions and after substituting V_2/C_c for V_c,

$$K_a = C_c{}^2\left[K_c - \left(\frac{1}{C_c}-1\right)^2\right]$$

approximate values of which are shown in the last line of Table 3.2. Experiments indicate that such values of K_a may be used for good estimates (not precise calculations) of head losses in similar short

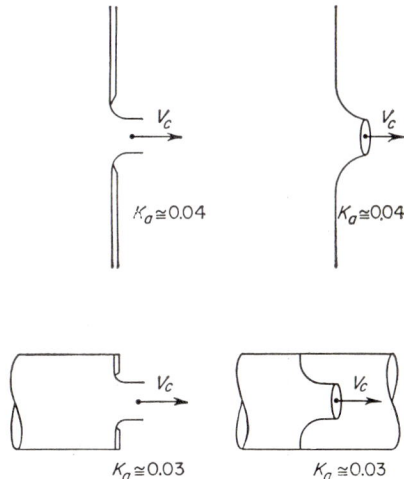

Fig. 3.18. Short acceleration zones.

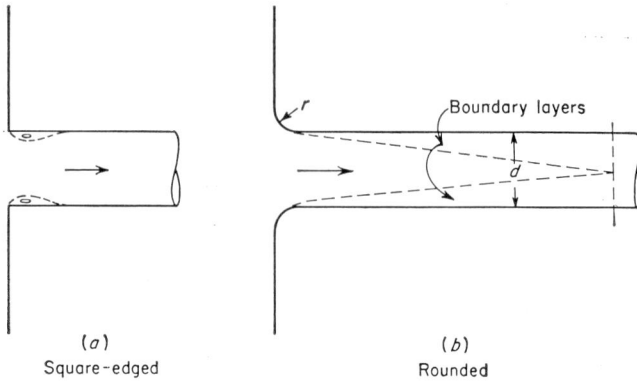

FIG. 3.19. Entrances.

acceleration zones such as those of Fig. 3.18. They cannot of course be used for long gradual contractions where wall friction will play a large role, giving K_a's considerably larger than those of the table; such values must be determined either by experiment or by boundary-layer analysis.

The limiting case of the abrupt contraction is the square-edged pipe entrance of Fig. 3.19. Here $A_1 \to \infty$, $A_2/A_1 \to 0$, and K_c is generally taken as 0.50 as given in Table 3.2. Great improvement of such an entrance can be obtained by rounding corners (streamlining), thereby eliminating separation, vena contracta, and deceleration zone. Hamilton[10] has shown that the radius of rounding needs to be greater than only $0.12d$ to accomplish this, whereupon the loss coefficient falls from 0.5 to about 0.1 for turbulent flow.

With a well-rounded entrance the loss coefficients may be calculated successfully using boundary-layer theory. Schiller[11] and Langhaar[12] have worked on the problem where laminar boundary layers grow up into established laminar flow. The widely accepted (laminar-flow) loss coefficient for the cylindrical pipe is 1.20 and for the two-dimensional passage 0.62. The first of these values is of great importance for the accurate determination of fluid viscosity when using tube-type viscometers. For turbulent boundary layers growing into established turbulent flow in smooth cylindrical pipes, it can be shown that the loss coefficient for the entrance depends on the Reynolds number of the established flow and ranges between 0.1 and 0.2. If a long laminar boundary layer can be maintained upstream from the turbulent one, the resulting loss coefficients may become as little as one-tenth of the above values.

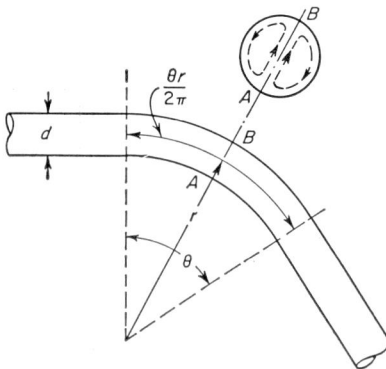

FIG. 3.20. Circular pipe bend.

Bends of large radius of curvature in closed passages (Fig. 3.20) illustrate the production of another type of localized head loss. Here such losses are due primarily to the twin-eddy "secondary flow" and its decay downstream from the bend. Such problems are too complex for analytical treatment, but good (although somewhat inconsistent and conflicting) experimental results are available. A typical result is that of Beij[13], illustrated in Fig. 3.21, giving bend loss coefficients for a 90° circular bend for Reynolds number range between 20,000 and 400,000. Hofmann[14] has also investigated this problem, giving experimental determinations of K_B for wide ranges

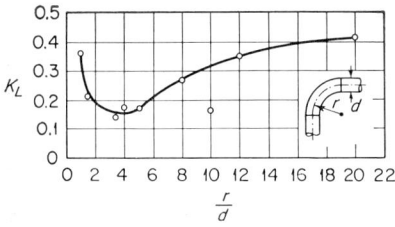

Fig. 3.21. Beij's loss coefficients for 90° smooth bends.

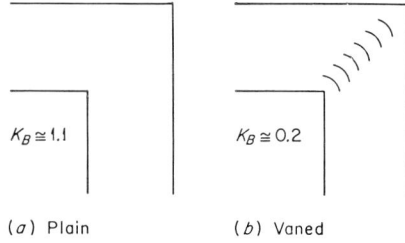

(a) Plain   (b) Vaned

Fig. 3.22. Elbows.

of bend shape, roughness, and Reynolds number. It is to be noted that the loss coefficient K_B to be used in the equation

$$h_{LB} = K_B \frac{V^2}{2g}$$

yields not the total head loss caused by the bend, but rather the excess head loss over and above that which would have occurred in established flow through a passage of length equal to the axis of the bend; thus the total head loss caused by the bend would be calculated from

$$h_L = \left(K_B + f \frac{\theta r}{d} \right) \frac{V^2}{2g}$$

in which θ, the angle of the bend, must be expressed in radians.

The limiting case of the circular bend is the *miter bend*, or *elbow* (Fig. 3.22), in which $r = 0$. In such elbows separation of flow from boundaries is superposed on the twin-eddy secondary flow mentioned above. The loss coefficient K_B for the basic 90° miter bend is generally taken to be close to 1.1, considerably larger than those for the larger radius bends. Nevertheless, the miter bend is attractive to engineering designers because of its small space and low cost; its loss coefficient can be reduced to that of the best smooth bend by the introduction of a carefully designed set of guide vanes, resulting in the *vaned elbow* of Fig. 3.22.

There are hundreds (possibly thousands) of pipe fittings such as valves, tees, reducers, elbows, etc., of different designs produced by many manufacturers. All such fittings produce local losses by disrupting established pipe flows in a variety of ways. Primary considerations in the design of such fittings are low cost, ease of handling, etc.; only in the case of fittings for very special designs is the minimizing of head loss given much consideration. It would be inappropriate (if not impossible) to include an exhaustive

Table 3.3. Loss Coefficients for a Few Standard (Threaded) Pipe Fittings

Globe valve, wide open	10.0
Angle valve, wide open	5.0
Gate valve, wide open	0.2
Gate valve, half open	5.6
Return bend	2.2
Tee	1.8
90° elbow	0.9
45° elbow	0.4

summary of such losses here; however, approximate loss coefficients for certain well-known fittings can be studied profitably to acquire some feeling for the relation of superficial appearance and internal-passage geometry to size of loss coefficient. Such values will be found in Table 3.3; these are intended for use in Eq. (3.27), in which the velocity is the mean velocity in the pipes connected to such fittings.

3.6. Flow through Single-pipe Systems

Problems of incompressible steady flow through single-pipe systems may be solved by use of the Bernoulli and continuity equations and with information on the expected frictional and local losses. Frequently in engineering problems the local losses may be so small compared with the frictional losses that the former may be neglected entirely without significant error; this possibility can usually be decided in advance by comparison of the K_L's for the local losses and the fl/d's for the friction losses, such comparison being valid only if these factors are adjusted for multiplication into the same velocity head.

Solution of such problems by algebraic manipulations alone is not usually safe because of the danger of missing critical points of low pressure in the line. Figure 3.23 illustrates this point. The Bernoulli equation written from reservoir to reservoir is (the local and frictional losses being written in order down the line)

$$H_1 = H_2 + K_E \frac{V_A^2}{2g} + \left(f\frac{l}{d}\right)_A \frac{V_A^2}{2g} + \frac{(V_A - V_B)^2}{2g} + \left(f\frac{l}{d}\right)_B \frac{V_B^2}{2g} + \frac{V_B^2}{2g} \quad (3.31)$$

The continuity equation is

$$Q = V_A A_A = V_B A_B \quad (3.32)$$

By knowing reservoir elevations, pipe dimensions, friction factors, and loss coefficients, V_A and V_B may be obtained and the flow rate predicted. However, the predicted flow rate may not be obtained because of the possibility of excessive negative pressures in the system which are overlooked in such an algebraic solution. The possibility of this is seen immediately if energy lines and hydraulic grade lines are sketched on the pipe diagram of Fig. 3.23, since such lines must slope more steeply over pipe A than over pipe B.

Negative pressures in pipelines (indicated where the hydraulic grade line runs below the pipe) are a major source of performance and operational troubles in pipeline practice. If such negative pressures are considerably less than $p_{\text{barom}} - p_{\text{vapor}}$, no special problems occur if the pipe and joints are vacuum-tight. With negative pressures approaching $p_{\text{barom}} - p_{\text{vapor}}$, cavitation is to be expected, with possible destruction of boundary walls and vibration problems. When pipeline solutions show negative pressures larger than $p_{\text{barom}} - p_{\text{vapor}}$, flow-rate predictions will be invalid, with actual flow rates less than predicted; this is a situation to be avoided at all costs since such flows are usually not accurately predictable and tend to be unsteady as well, leading to undesirable and unpredictable vibration problems. To avoid such problems in pipeline designs, negative pressures should be held less than about two-thirds of $p_{\text{barom}} - p_{\text{vapor}}$, but even with this conservative limit some release of dissolved gases can be expected, possibly requiring special gas-removal appurtenances if velocities are not large enough to carry such bubbles of gas along with the flowing liquid.

Single pipeline problems may be divided into three general classes: (1) prediction of pressures, head losses, etc., from known end conditions, pipe dimensions, and flow rates; (2) prediction of flow rate from end conditions and pipe characteristics; and (3) determination of suitable pipe size to pass a desired flow rate for known end conditions. The first of these is solved routinely and directly by use of the methods and data presented in this and in the foregoing articles. For the second and third, trial-and-error solutions must be used for precise calculations. This results from Reynolds numbers being uncalculable without knowledge of flow rate and pipe size. In practice, however, such trial-and-error solutions are frequently avoided (at the sacrifice of some accuracy) by capitaliz-

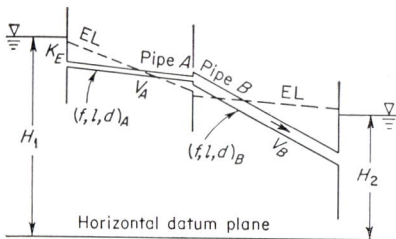

Fig. 3.23. Single pipeline.

ing on the fact that loss coefficients and friction factors vary relatively little with large changes of Reynolds number; thus they may be assumed constant to yield direct solutions. In calculating pipe sizes the designer is further aided by a knowledge of available standard diameters; starting with these, he can quickly "oversatisfy" the basic equations by providing a standard size slightly larger than that which satisfies the equations.

Example 4. Determine the minimum pressure in the pipeline of Fig. 3.23 if water is flowing. Assume $H_1 = 500$ ft, $H_2 = 400$ ft, $K_E = 0.50$, $f_A = 0.020$, $l_A = 1,000$ ft, $d_A = 8$ in., $f_B = 0.025$, $l_B = 1000$ ft, $d_B = 12$ in. The height of the pipe junction above datum is 430.0 ft.

SOLUTION. Insert the foregoing quantities in Eqs. (3.31) and (3.32) and solve for the velocities. These are $V_A = 13.4$ fps and $V_B = 5.95$ fps, yielding a flow rate of 4.68 cfs. The fall of the energy line from reservoir 1 to the pipe junction is

$$K_E + \left(f\frac{l}{d}\right)_A \frac{V_A^2}{2g} = 84.5 \text{ ft}$$

The elevation of the energy line at the junction is therefore $500 - 84.5 = 415.5$ ft above datum. The elevation of the hydraulic grade line at the junction is $415.5 - (13.4)^2/2g = 412.7$ ft above datum, and $430.0 - 412.7 = 17.3$ ft below the pipe. Thus the pressure head in the pipe at the junction is -17.3 ft of water, -7.5 psi, or 15.25 in. of mercury vacuum.

Example 5. Three cubic feet per second of water is to be pumped from reservoir 1 to reservoir 2. How many horsepower must the pump deliver to the fluid to accomplish this?

SOLUTION. After sketching the energy lines, it is evident that the pump must supply sufficient head to offset the 100-ft difference of elevation and the sum of the head losses in the pipes, entrance, and exit. By use of Eqs. (3.10), (3.30), and (3.29), these head losses are 17.2 ft (8-in pipe), 123.0 ft (6-in. pipe), 0.6 ft and 3.6 ft, respectively. Therefore $H_p = 17.2 + 123.0 + 0.6 + 3.6 + 100.0 = 244.4$ ft. This means that the pump must supply 244.4 ft-lb of energy to each pound of water passing through the system. The flow rate (lb/sec) may be calculated from $Q\gamma = 3 \times 62.4 = 187.2$ lb/sec. The total energy per second (power) supplied by the pump is therefore $187.2 \times 244.4 = 45,800$ ft-lb/sec, or 83.3 hp.

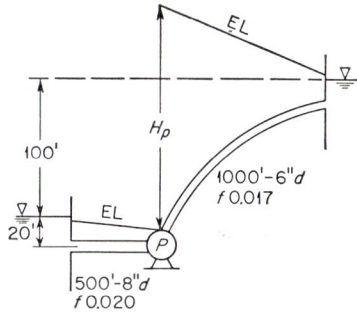

Example 5

3.7. Multiple-pipe Systems

The classic three-reservoir problem of Fig. 3.24, in which magnitude and direction of the flow rates in the pipes are to be predicted, serves as a useful starting point in the analysis of multiple-pipe systems. The unique feature of this problem is the meeting of all pipes at a common junction. Since the energy lines for all pipes must also meet at a common point on a vertical line through the junction, the position of this point becomes critical in the solution of the problem.

Such problems may frequently be solved satisfactorily by disregarding the variation of friction factor with Reynolds number, the Darcy equation being written in terms of flow rate and all pipe dimensions and properties (l, d, f) absorbed in one constant, k_d, as follows:

$$h_L = f\frac{l}{d}\frac{V^2}{2g} = f\frac{l}{d}\frac{1}{2g}\frac{Q^2}{(\pi d^2/4)^2} = k_d Q^2 \tag{3.33}$$

More accurate solutions may be obtained by the use of empirical formulas which to

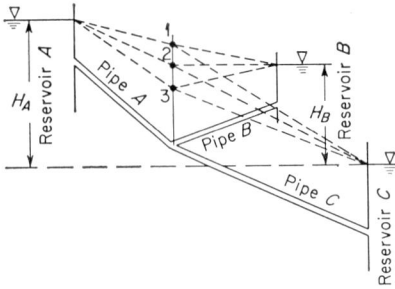

FIG. 3.24. Three-reservoir problem.

some extent allow for the variation of friction factor with Reynolds number. Widely used for this purpose in American practice is the formula of Hazen and Williams[15]:

$$Q = 1.318 C_{hw} \left(\frac{d}{4}\right)^{0.63} \left(\frac{h_L}{l}\right)^{0.54} \frac{\pi d^2}{4}$$

which may be revised to read

$$h_L = \left(\frac{4.7}{C_{hw}^{1.85}} \frac{l}{d^{4.86}}\right) Q^{1.85} = k_{hw} Q^{1.85} \quad (3.34)$$

To generalize the Darcy and Hazen-Williams approaches through the remainder of this section, Eqs. (3.33) and (3.34) will be written as

$$h_L = kQ^n$$

Returning now to the three-reservoir problem (Fig. 3.24) and considering energy-line positions, three possibilities (1, 2, 3) are evident. From the sketch two Bernoulli equations and one continuity equation may be written for each of the three possibilities cited. Writing these for situation 1, it being noted that the slopes of the energy lines imply flow out of reservoir A and into reservoirs B and C,

$$H_A - k_A Q^n_A = H_B + k_B Q^n_B$$
$$H_B + k_B Q^n_B = k_C Q^n_C$$
$$Q_A = Q_B + Q_C$$

For situation 3,

$$H_A - k_A Q^n_A = H_B - k_B Q^n_B$$
$$H_B - k_B Q^n_B = k_C Q^n_C$$
$$Q_A + Q_B = Q_C$$

For situation 2, $Q_B = 0$ and the above sets of equations become identical. In view of the physical flow picture, only one of these sets of equations can be expected to be satisfied; this set may be discovered by a preliminary calculation using situation 2: from the reservoir elevations Q_A and Q_C may be easily computed. If $Q_A > Q_C$, it can be seen from the continuity equation that the first set of equations should be used; if $Q_A < Q_C$, the second set will yield a solution. Having identified the set of equations valid for the problem, these are then solved by trial to yield flow rates Q_A, Q_B, and Q_C.

Multiple-pipe systems reach their maximum complexity in "pipe networks" such as those of a city water-distribution system. Such networks may contain components which are also multiple pipes, and some investigation of this is appropriate and useful in approaching the network problem.

Pipes in Series and Parallel. Pipes laid "in series" are shown in Fig. 3.25. Total head loss in the whole line may be calculated (neglecting minor losses) from pipe sizes, friction factors, and flow rate in the usual way. It is sometimes useful, however, to reduce the pipeline to an equivalent single pipe, which *for the same over-all length and total head loss will pass the same flow rate.* The properties of this equivalent pipe, defined in the above manner, are

$$Q = Q_A = Q_B = \cdots$$
$$h_L = kQ^n = (kQ^n)_A + (kQ^n)_B + \cdots = \Sigma(kQ^n)$$
$$L = l_A + l_B + \cdots = \Sigma(l)$$

From the first two equations

$$k = k_A + k_B + \cdots = \Sigma(k)$$

whence (with the use of the third equation) the diameter of the equivalent pipe may be calculated from any friction factor or empirical resistance coefficient.

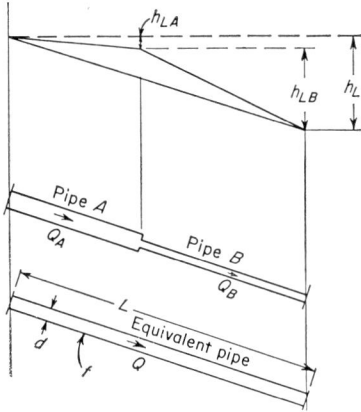

FIG. 3.25. Single-pipe equivalent to pipes in series.

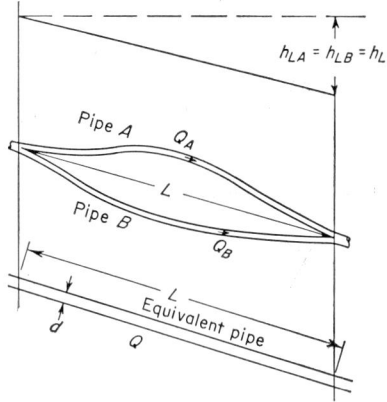

FIG. 3.26. Single-pipe equivalent to pipes in parallel.

Pipes laid "in parallel" (Fig. 3.26) may be reduced to an equivalent pipe which *will pass the total flow rate from junction to junction with the same head loss.* Equations analogous to the foregoing are

$$Q = Q_A + Q_B + \cdots = \Sigma(Q)$$
$$h_L = kQ^n = (kQ^n)_A = (kQ^n)_B = \cdots$$

from which

$$\left(\frac{1}{k}\right)^{1/n} = \left(\frac{1}{k_A}\right)^{1/n} + \left(\frac{1}{k_B}\right)^{1/n} + \cdots = \Sigma\left(\frac{1}{k}\right)^{1/n}$$

whence the diameter of the equivalent pipe may be computed (from k) for any assumed resistance coefficient, L usually being taken as the straight-line distance between the junctions.

Pipe Networks. A pipe network (Fig. 3.27) is a complex combination of branching, series, and parallel pipes to which many of the foregoing equations and techniques may be applied. Here the single objective will be the prediction of the flow rates in all the pipes from the knowledge of inflow to and outflow from the network. The solution must satisfy the continuity and Bernoulli principles throughout the network: the continuity principle states that the total flow rates toward and away from any junction must be exactly equal; the Bernoulli principle requires that at any junction there be only one position of the energy line, which means that the net head loss around any single *loop* (Fig. 3.28) of the network must be zero; in addition, the direction of flow must always be in the direction of falling energy line. By utilizing these principles, the following equations may be written for the single loop of Fig. 3.28:

$$Q_B = Q_{BC} + Q_{AB}$$
$$Q_{BC} + Q_C = Q_{CD}$$
$$Q_{CD} + Q_{AD} = Q_D$$
$$Q_A + Q_{AB} = Q_{AD}$$
$$(kQ^n)_{BC} + (kQ^n)_{CD} = (kQ^n)_{AB} + (kQ^n)_{AD}$$

If Q_A, Q_B, Q_C, and Q_D and pipeline properties are known, solution of the equations (by trial) will yield the flow rates Q_{AD}, Q_{CD}, Q_{BC}, and Q_{AB}. Although this is a basic and relatively simple procedure for a single loop, trial-and-

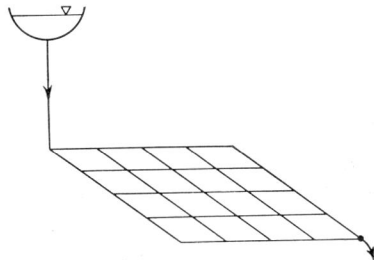

FIG. 3.27. Pipeline network.

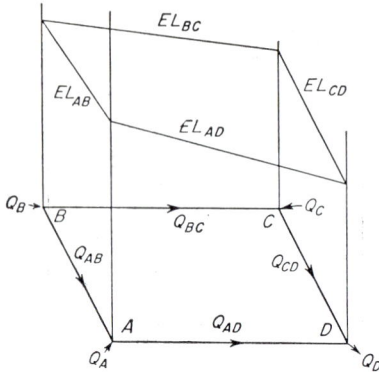

FIG. 3.28. Single loop of a pipeline network.

error solution becomes practically hopeless of application to a network composed of many (sometimes hundreds of) loops whose effects are all interrelated. To overcome this difficulty and make the problem reasonably tractable, Cross[16] developed a controlled trial-and-error technique which yields satisfactorily accurate solutions from but a few trials. The theory behind this technique may be easily grasped by its application to the single loop of Fig. 3.28 as a basic component of a large network. Assume magnitude and directions of flow rates Q_0 in all pipes of the network so that the continuity equation is satisfied at all junctions. Define Δ as the difference between the real flow rate Q and the assumed flow rate Q_0, that is,

$$Q = Q_0 + \Delta \tag{3.35}$$

When the head-loss equation is satisfied,

$$(kQ^n)_{BC} + (kQ^n)_{CD} - (kQ^n)_{AB} - (kQ^n)_{AD} = 0 \tag{3.36}$$

After substituting $Q_0 + \Delta$ for each Q,

$$k_{BC}(Q_0 + \Delta)^n_{BC} + k_{CD}(Q_0 + \Delta)^n_{CD} - k_{AB}(Q_0 + \Delta)^n_{AB} - k_{AD}(Q_0 + \Delta)^n_{AD}$$
$$= \Sigma[k((Q_0 + \Delta)^n] = 0$$

After expanding this by the binomial theorem and retaining only the first two terms, on the assumption that Δ is small,

$$\Sigma(kQ_0^n + kn\,\Delta Q_0^{n-1}) = 0$$

and solving for Δ,

$$\Delta = -\frac{\Sigma(kQ_0^n)}{\Sigma(knQ_0^{n-1})} \tag{3.37}$$

which may be used in Eq. (3.35) to obtain Q from the assumed Q_0. The flow rates Q (in each pipe) will be found to be closer to the flow rates which will simultaneously satisfy the continuity and head-loss equations. These flow rates are then taken as the Q_0's of a second trial, and the process repeated until the values of Δ become negligibly small for the accuracy desired in the solution.

Because flow direction is also the direction of falling energy line it is customary to set up the following sign convention in numerical problems: (1) Proceed around each loop in a clockwise direction, considering the terms of Eq. (3.36) positive if flow direction is clockwise, negative if counterclockwise. (2) Note that satisfaction of the continuity equations at the junctions will require that for the pipes in which the head-loss terms are negative, the values of Δ will also be negative. This procedure leads to the conclusion that the denominator of Eq. (3.37) will always be positive and the sign of the calculated Δ thus determined by the sign of the numerator alone. Since Δ is the same value for all the pipes composing a separate and isolated loop, it is apparent that in a network of many loops all the "internal" pipes of the network will form the boundaries of two contiguous loops; this means that when Q is computed from Eq. (3.35) for such pipes, two values of Δ (one from each of the contiguous loops) must be used for the pipe which is common to the two loops. This involves no new principle, but is merely a swift calculation technique to satisfy the continuity equation at all junctions for the Q_0's to be used in the next trial. The following numerical problem will serve to illustrate application of the foregoing principles.

Example 6. Calculate the magnitudes and directions of the flow rates in the five pipes of this simple network. All pipes are 2000 ft long and have Hazen-Williams coefficients of 100.

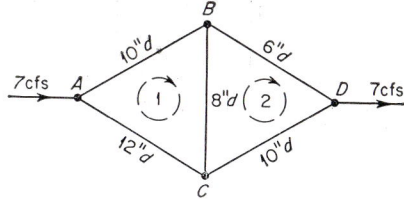

Example 6

SOLUTION. Calculating from Eq. (3.34), the k's are found to be 54.8, 13.5, 4.57, and 1.88 for the 6-in., 8-in., 10-in., and 12-in. pipes, respectively. Assume magnitude and direction of each flow rate in all the pipes, satisfying the continuity condition at all junctions: as a first assumption, 3 cfs from A to B, 4 cfs from A to C, 1 cfs from B to C, 2 cfs from B to D, and 5 cfs from C to D. Using the Cross technique and solving Eq. (3.37) in the accompanying tabular calculation, the flow rates are found to be 2.39 cfs from A to B, 4.61 cfs from A to C, 0.88 cfs from B to C, 1.51 cfs from B to D, and 5.49 cfs from C to D.

Circuit	Pipe	Q_0	$kQ_0^{1.85}$	$1.85kQ_0^{0.85}$	Δ
1	AB	3	+34.8	21.4	First trial:
	AC	4	−24.4	11.4	
	BC	1	+13.5	25.0	$\Delta_1 = -\dfrac{+23.9}{57.8} = -0.41$
	Σ		+23.9	57.8	
2	BC	1	−13.5	25.0	
	BD	2	+197.0	182.1	$\Delta_2 = -\dfrac{+94.0}{240.2} = -0.39$
	CD	5	−89.5	33.1	
	Σ		+94.0	240.2	
1	AB	2.59	+26.6	19.0	Second trial:
	AC	4.41	−29.2	12.3	
	BC	0.98	+13.0	24.6	$\Delta_1 = -\dfrac{+10.4}{55.9} = -0.18$
	Σ		+10.4	55.9	
2	BC	0.98	−13.0	24.6	
	BD	1.61	+132.0	151.7	$\Delta_2 = -\dfrac{+16.2}{211.7} = -0.07$
	CD	5.39	−102.8	35.4	
	Σ		+16.2	211.7	
1	AB	2.41	+22.3	17.8	Third trial:
	AC	4.59	−31.5	12.7	
	BC	0.87	+10.4	22.2	$\Delta_1 = -\dfrac{+1.2}{52.7} = -0.02$
	Σ		+1.2	52.7	
2	BC	0.87	−10.4	22.2	
	BD	1.54	+121.7	146.3	$\Delta_2 = -\dfrac{+5.6}{204.2} = -0.03$
	CD	5.46	−105.7	35.7	
	Σ		+5.6	204.2	

Although the Cross technique permits numerical solution of problems hopeless of solution by ordinary trial-and-error methods, it still involves a vast amount of time and effort for networks containing large numbers of loops. Because such extensive networks are common in water- and gas-distribution systems, analogue- and digital-computer solutions have recently been developed.

The invention by McIlroy[17] of an electric resistance across which the voltage drop varies with the 1.85 power of the current allows simulation of a pipe network by an electrical one, the voltage drop and current becoming analogous to head loss and flow rate, respectively, the latter quantities being related by the Hazen-Williams formula, Eq. (3.34), in which head loss varies with the 1.85 power of flow rate. From such an analogous electrical network, information on head loss, flow distribution, etc., may be obtained without trial-and-error calculations; an analogue of this type also has the obvious advantage of predicting rapidly the effects of changes of pipe dimensions, which in general requires a numerical recomputation for the whole network.

The utility of a digital computer for pipe-network calculations has been demonstrated by Hoag and Weinberg,[18] thus giving the engineer two possible methods of avoiding laborious calculations. However, the Cross method remains a basic analytical tool for on-the-spot solutions of network problems when economically justifiable.

REFERENCES

1. Stanton, T. E., and J. R. Pannell: Similarity of Motion in Relation to the Surface Friction of Fluids, *Phil. Trans. Roy. Soc. London*, ser. A, vol. 214, 1914.
2. Nikuradse, J.: Strömungsgesetze in rauhen Rohren, *VDI-Forschungsheft*, no. 361, 1933. Translation available in *NACA Tech. Mem.* 1292.
3. Colebrook, C. F.: Turbulent Flow in Pipes, with Particular Reference to the Transition Region between the Smooth and Rough Pipe Laws, *J. Inst. Civil Engrs. (London)*, February, 1939.
4. Moody, L. F.: Friction Factors for Pipe Flow, *Trans. ASME*, vol. 66, 1944.
5. von Kármán, T.: Turbulence and Skin Friction, *J. Aeronaut. Sci.*, vol. 1, no. 1, 1936.
6. Bakhmeteff, B. A.: "The Mechanics of Turbulent Flow," Princeton University Press, Princeton, N.J., 1936.
7. Manning, R.: Flow of Water in Open Channels and Pipes, *Trans. Inst. Civil Engrs. (Ireland)*, vol. 20, 1890.
8. Gibson, A. H.: "Hydraulics and Its Applications," 5th ed., Constable, London, 1952.
9. Weisbach, J.: "Die Experimentalhydraulik," J. S. Engelhardt, Freiburg, 1855.
10. Hamilton, J. B.: The Suppression of Intake Losses by Various Degrees of Rounding, *Univ. Wash. Expt. Sta. Bull.* 51, 1929.
11. Schiller, L.: Untersuchungen über laminare und turbulente Strömung, *VDI-Forschungsheft*, no. 248, 1922.
12. Langhaar, H. L.: Steady Flow in the Transition Length of a Straight Tube, *J. Appl. Mechanics*, vol. 9, 1942.
13. Beij, K. H.: Pressure Losses for Fluid Flow in 90° Pipe Bends, *J. Research Nat. Bur. Standards*, vol. 21, 1938.
14. Hofmann, A.: Loss in 90-degree Pipe Bends of Constant Circular Cross-section, *Trans. Hydrol. Inst. Munich Tech. Univ. Bull.* 3, *ASME*, 1935.
15. Hazen, A., and G. S. Williams: "Hydraulic Tables," 3d ed. Wiley, New York, 1920.
16. Cross, H.: Analysis of Flow in Networks of Conduits or Conductors, *Univ. Illinois Eng. Expt. Sta. Bull.* 286, 1936.
17. McIlroy, M. S.: Direct Reading Electric Analyzer for Pipeline Networks, *J. AWWA*, vol. 42, April, 1950.
18. Hoag, L. N., and G. Weinberg: Analysis of Pipeline Networks by Electronic Digital Computers, *J. AWWA*, vol. 49, 1957.

Section 4

IDEAL-FLUID FLOW

By

CHIA-SHUN YIH, *University of Michigan, Ann Arbor, Michigan*

IDEAL-FLUID FLOW

4.1. Introduction

In this section the mechanics of an incompressible and inviscid fluid (the ideal fluid) is discussed. The first part deals with the continuity equation and its consequences (the stream functions) and the basic kinematic quantities. In the second part Euler's equations of motion are presented and the persistence of irrotationality established, as a prelude to the study of irrotational flows. The third part deals with the integration of the Euler equations. The result of this integration is, of course, the Bernoulli equation. It is remarkable that the Euler equations, which are nonlinear, can be avoided in the study of the kinematics of irrotational flows of an ideal fluid, which are governed by the Laplace equation. After the velocity field is determined, the pressure can be found from the Bernoulli equation, in which, and in which alone, the nonlinearity of the Euler equations is manifested. Thus the way is paved for the study of the Laplace equation, with which the following two parts are concerned. In the fourth part general three-dimensional flows (whether axisymmetric or not) are discussed. In the fifth part the technique of conformal mapping is used throughout to discuss two-dimensional flows. Finally, in the last part, rotational flow of an ideal fluid is discussed briefly.

Wave motion is not discussed here. The Lagrangian description of hydrodynamics (see Art. 2.4) has been omitted because it is not used for presenting any of the material contained in this section.

In discussing harmonic functions in various coordinate systems, the author has relied heavily upon the celebrated work of Lamb.[3] In presenting the sphere and circle theorems, Milne-Thomson's work[2] has been found helpful. The author's burden has been greatly lightened by the permission of the McGraw-Hill Book Company to use the figures in Professor Streeter's book.[9] Mr. Chintu Lai, a Ph.D. candidate at the University of Michigan, has rendered invaluable assistance in the final preparation of the manuscript for the printer. The author is grateful for the help he has received from all these and other sources.

4.2. Notation

a	magnitude of acceleration or semimajor axis of an ellipse
b	semiminor axis of an ellipse
c	$\sqrt{a^2-b^2}$, half the distance between the foci of an ellipse
a, b, c	semiaxes of an ellipsoid
f, g	functions, especially stream functions
g	gravitational acceleration
h_1, h_2, h_3	metric for general orthogonal coordinates
h, k	h_1 and h_2 for a surface
l, m, n or n_1, n_2, n_3	direction cosines of $\mathbf{n}$
m	strength (or discharge) of a source or sink
n	distance along $\mathbf{n}$
(n_4, n_5, n_6)	$\mathbf{r} \times \mathbf{n}$
$\mathbf{n}$	normal to S
p	pressure
q	speed
$\mathbf{r}$	radius vector
s	distance along an arc

t	time or a complex variable
$u_\alpha\,(\alpha = 1, 2, \ldots, 6)$	velocity and angular-velocity components of a solid body
u, v, w	velocity components
w	complex potential
x, y, z	cartesian coordinates
R, θ, φ	spherical coordinates
r, φ, z	cylindrical coordinates
z	the complex variable $x + iy$
$\bar{z}$	complex conjugate of z
$A_{\alpha\beta}$	added-mass tensor
$B_{\alpha\beta}$	mass or inertia tensor
C	circuit
C_D	coefficient of drag
D	drag or domain
M	mass of a solid body
M'	added mass A_{11}
M_i	moment components
P, Q	points
S	surface
T	kinetic energy
U, V, W	functions (in Green's theorem) or velocity components of a solid body (same as u_1, u_2, u_3)
X, Y, M	forces and moment on two-dimensional body
X, Y, Z	body-force components per unit mass
α, β, γ	general coordinates
β	angle of attack
γ	specific weight
ζ, μ, ω	coordinates for ellipsoids of revolution
θ	argument of a complex quantity or one of the spherical coordinates
κ	circulation
λ	scale factor
λ, μ, ν	general elliptic coordinates
μ	$\cos\theta$, θ being a spherical coordinate, or strength of a doublet
ξ, η, ζ	vorticity components
ξ, η	two-dimensional elliptic coordinates, $\zeta = \xi + i\eta$
ρ	density
σ	cavitation number
τ	time
ψ	Lagrange's or Stokes' stream function
$\omega_1, \omega_2, \omega_3$	angular-velocity components of a solid body, same as u_4, u_5, u_6
ω_n	vorticity component in the direction of $\mathbf{n}$
ϕ	velocity potential
ϕ_α	velocity potential corresponding to u_α
Γ	circulation
Ω	body-force potential or solid angle or $-\ln(-dw/dz)$
D/Dt	$\partial/\partial t + u(\partial/\partial x) + v(\partial/\partial y) + w(\partial/\partial z)$
∇^2	Laplacian operator
$\times$	vector multiplication

When coordinates are used as subscripts, partial differentiation is indicated. Other subscripts do not indicate partial differentiation. Symbols not defined here either are defined in the text or have meanings obvious from the context.

FUNDAMENTALS

4.3. Streamlines, Path Lines, and Streak Lines

The concept of streamlines, path lines, and streak lines (Art. 2.4) is very important for the understanding of fluid flows and for the interpretations of visual observations made on these flows. A streamline is a line which is tangent to the velocity vectors at all its points, a path line is the locus of a particular fluid particle, and a streak line is the line consisting of the fluid particles that have passed through a fixed point in space, where they may be marked by injection of dye.

For steady flows, i.e., for flows whose *local* properties (velocity, pressure, density, etc.) are independent of time, streamlines, path lines, and streak lines coincide. For unsteady flows, they are in general distinct. In cartesian coordinates x, y, z, with u, v, w denoting the corresponding velocity components, the equations for the streamlines at time t_0 are

$$\frac{dx}{u} = \frac{dy}{v} = \frac{dz}{w} \tag{4.1}$$

in which u, v, and w are evaluated at time t_0 and are hence functions of the space coordinates only. For path lines, the parametric equations are

$$dt = \frac{dx}{u} = \frac{dy}{v} = \frac{dz}{w} \tag{4.2}$$

in which the velocity components are now functions of x, y, z, and time t, with the space coordinates considered as functions of time. If the parametric equation for the path line of a fluid particle that passed through a fixed point P at time τ is given by

$$x = x(t, \tau) \qquad y = y(t, \tau) \qquad z = z(t, \tau) \tag{4.3}$$

the streak line at any fixed time t_0 is given by

$$x = x(t_0, \tau) \qquad y = y(t_0, \tau) \qquad z = z(t_0, \tau) \tag{4.4}$$

with τ as the parameter which varies from zero (origin of time, or the time at which dye begins to be injected) to t_0.

4.4. Continuity

From Fig. 4.1 the net rate of mass outflow through the two planes perpendicular to the x axis is, with ρ denoting the density,

$$\frac{\partial(\rho u)}{\partial x} \, dx \, dy \, dz$$

Similarly, the net rates of mass outflow in the directions of y and z are, respectively,

$$\frac{\partial(\rho v)}{\partial y} \, dx \, dy \, dz \qquad \text{and} \qquad \frac{\partial(\rho w)}{\partial z} \, dx \, dy \, dz$$

Thus the net rate of mass outflow from the parallelepiped is

$$\left[\frac{\partial(\rho u)}{\partial x} + \frac{\partial(\rho v)}{\partial y} + \frac{\partial(\rho w)}{\partial z} \right] dx \, dy \, dz$$

On the other hand, the rate of decrease of mass in the volume $dx \, dy \, dz$ is

$$-\frac{\partial \rho}{\partial t} \, dx \, dy \, dz$$

When this rate is equated to the net rate of mass outflow, the equation of continuity is obtained:

$$\frac{\partial \rho}{\partial t} + \frac{\partial(\rho u)}{\partial x} + \frac{\partial(\rho v)}{\partial y} + \frac{\partial(\rho w)}{\partial z} = 0 \tag{4.5}$$

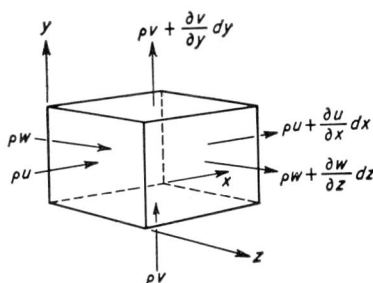

FIG. 4.1. Mass flow rate per unit area through faces of a parallelepiped.

For a fluid of constant density, Eq. (4.5) reduces to

$$\frac{\partial u}{\partial x} + \frac{\partial v}{\partial y} + \frac{\partial w}{\partial z} = 0 \qquad (4.6)$$

whether the flow is steady or not, i.e., whether the flow is locally dependent on time or not. Actually, Eq. (4.6) applies not merely to a fluid of constant density, but also to a fluid of variable density, provided the fluid is incompressible and nondiffusive.† For such a fluid the density of a fluid particle does not change as it moves about. In other words, the substantial derivative of the density of such a fluid is zero.

$$\frac{D\rho}{Dt} \equiv \left(\frac{\partial}{\partial t} + u\frac{\partial}{\partial x} + v\frac{\partial}{\partial y} + w\frac{\partial}{\partial z} \right)\rho = 0 \qquad (4.7)$$

Subtraction of Eq. (4.7) from Eq. (4.5) produces Eq. (4.6), valid without the restriction of constant density. Again, the validity of Eq. (4.6) is independent of the steadiness of flow.

4.5. Stream Functions

The solutions of the equations for the streamlines, Eqs. (4.1), can be written in the form

$$f(x,y,z) = a \qquad (4.8)$$

$$g(x,y,z) = b \qquad (4.9)$$

which represent two families of surfaces whose intersections are the streamlines. Since the streamlines are imbedded in these surfaces, the latter can be called stream surfaces and the functions f and g stream functions.

The normals to the surfaces represented by Eqs. (4.8) and (4.9) have direction numbers (f_x, f_y, f_z) and (g_x, g_y, g_z), respectively, with the subscripts denoting partial differentiation. Since (u,v,w) are the direction numbers of the streamlines at any point, it follows that

$$uf_x + vf_y + wf_z = 0 \qquad (4.10)$$

$$ug_x + vg_y + wg_z = 0 \qquad (4.11)$$

and

$$u = \lambda(f_y g_z - f_z g_y) \qquad v = \lambda(f_z g_x - f_x g_z) \qquad w = \lambda(f_x g_y - f_y g_x) \qquad (4.12)$$

in which λ is a scale factor, which up to now can be any function of x, y, and z.

For incompressible fluids, Eq. (4.6) must be satisfied, and the satisfaction of Eq. (4.6) by the expressions for u, v, and w given in Eqs. (4.12) demands that λ be a function of f and g only. It can be shown that there is no loss of generality if λ is taken to be unity. Thus, for incompressible fluids, the velocity components can be expressed in terms of the stream functions by the formula

$$(u,v,w) = \text{grad } f \times \text{grad } g \qquad (4.13)$$

For steady flows of a compressible fluid, the appropriate formula is‡

$$(u,v,w) = \frac{1}{\rho} \text{grad } f \times \text{grad } g \qquad (4.14)$$

For two-dimensional flows which are independent of z, g can be taken to be $-z$, since

---

† For simplicity, such a fluid will henceforth be referred to as an incompressible fluid.
‡ Essentially, this formula originated with Euler and was used by Clebsch for expressing vorticity instead of velocity components. It was rediscovered by Maeder and Wood and, independently, by Yih.[1]

the surfaces z = constant are stream surfaces. With f rewritten as ψ (Lagrange's stream function), Eq. (4.13) becomes

$$u = -\psi_y \qquad v = \psi_x \tag{4.15}$$

in which the subscript indicates partial differentiation with respect to itself.

For axisymmetric flows, whether cylindrical coordinates r, φ, z or spherical coordinates R, θ, φ are used, g can be taken to be $-\varphi$ and f the Stokes stream function ψ, and Eq. (4.13) yields, for cylindrical coordinates,

$$u = \frac{1}{r}\psi_z \qquad w = -\frac{1}{r}\psi_r \tag{4.16}$$

in which u and w are, respectively, the velocity components in the directions of r and z. For spherical coordinates the velocity components u and v in the directions of R and θ are given by

$$u = -\frac{1}{R^2 \sin \theta}\psi_\theta \qquad v = \frac{1}{R \sin \theta}\psi_R \tag{4.17}$$

4.6. Relationship between Discharges and Stream Functions

In a surface intersecting the streamlines a set of orthogonal coordinates (α, β) can be introduced. The square of an infinitesimal distance ds is then given by

$$ds^2 = h^2\, d\alpha^2 + k^2\, d\beta^2$$

in which h and k constitute the metric for the surface and are in general functions of α and β. The velocity component normal to the surface is given by Eq. (4.13):

$$v_n = \frac{f_\alpha g_\beta - f_\beta g_\alpha}{hk}$$

The area of an element of the surface is

$$ds = hk\, d\alpha\, d\beta$$

Consequently, the discharge through a portion s of the surface bounded by the traces of

$$f(x,y,z) = f_1 \qquad f(x,y,z) = f_2$$

$$g(x,y,z) = g_1 \qquad \text{and} \qquad g(x,y,z) = g_2$$

is

$$Q = \iint_S v_n\, ds = \iint_S (f_\alpha g_\beta - f_\beta g_\alpha)d\alpha\, d\beta$$

$$= \int_{g_1}^{g_2}\int_{f_1}^{f_2} df\, dg = (f_2 - f_1)(g_2 - g_1) \tag{4.18}$$

In employing Eq. (4.18), it must be remembered that if the directions of increasing α, β, and n form a right-handed system, those of increasing f, g, and n must also form a right-handed system.

In two-dimensional flows, the discharge per unit length in z across an arc AB (Fig. 4.2) is $\psi_B - \psi_A$, with ψ the Lagrange stream function. In axisymmetric flows, the discharge across the surface generated by a revolving arc AB about the axis of symmetry is $2\pi(\psi_B - \psi_A)$, in which ψ is now the Stokes stream function.

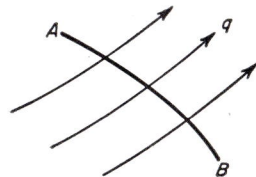

Fig. 4.2. Discharge per unit length across an arc.

The discussion of the discharge of an incompressible fluid is also true for the *mass* discharge of a compressible fluid, if its flow is steady.

4.7. Vorticity and Rates of Deformation

The nine quantities describing the rates of relative displacement in cartesian coordinates (per unit time per unit length) form the tensor (Art. 2.4)

$$T = \begin{bmatrix} u_x & u_y & u_z \\ v_x & v_y & v_z \\ w_x & w_y & w_z \end{bmatrix}$$

This tensor can be resolved into two parts

$$T = V + \tfrac{1}{2}D$$

$$\text{in which} \quad V = \begin{bmatrix} 0 & -\zeta & \eta \\ \zeta & 0 & -\xi \\ -\eta & \xi & 0 \end{bmatrix} \tag{4.19}$$

is the vorticity tensor, and

$$D = \begin{bmatrix} a & h & g \\ h & b & f \\ g & f & c \end{bmatrix} \tag{4.20}$$

is the rate-of-deformation tensor. In Eqs. (4.19) and (4.20),

$$\xi = \tfrac{1}{2}(w_y - v_z) \qquad \eta = \tfrac{1}{2}(u_z - w_x) \qquad \zeta = \tfrac{1}{2}(v_x - u_y) \tag{4.21}$$

are the vorticity components, and

$$\begin{aligned} a &= 2u_x & b &= 2v_y & c &= 2w_z \\ f &= w_y + v_z & g &= u_z + w_x & h &= v_x + u_y \end{aligned} \tag{4.22}$$

are the rates of deformation. The tensor V is antisymmetric, and its three distinct elements transform like the components of a vector in cartesian coordinates. That is why vorticity components can be treated as a vector. The tensor D is symmetric, and its symmetry guarantees the existence of the principal directions, for which the shear rates of deformation vanish.

A vortex line is a line which is tangent to the vorticity vectors at all points. The equations for vortex lines are

$$\frac{dx}{\xi} = \frac{dy}{\eta} = \frac{dz}{\zeta} \tag{4.23}$$

A tube bounded by a surface containing vortex lines is called a vortex tube.

4.8. Circulation

The circulation Γ of a fluid along a curve C is defined to be the line integral along C of the inner product (or dot product) of the velocity vector and the displacement vector ds along the curve (Art 2.4). In cartesian coordinates,

$$\Gamma = \int_C (u\,dx + v\,dy + w\,dz) \tag{4.24}$$

For a *closed* curve C, the Stokes theorem gives

$$\int_C (u\,dx + v\,dy + w\,dz) = \iint [(v_x - u_y)dx\,dy + (w_y - v_z)dy\,dz + (u_z - w_x)dz\,dx]$$

$$= 2 \iint_S (\xi l + \eta m + \zeta n)dS = 2 \iint_S \omega_n\,dS \tag{4.25}$$

in which S = any surface with C as the boundary
   l, m, n = direction cosines of the normal to S
         ω_n = vorticity component in the direction of this normal

Thus the circulation along a closed curve C is twice the vorticity discharge through any surface bounded by C. The similarity between Eqs. (4.23) and Eqs. (4.1) and between Eq. (4.6) and the (identically satisfied) equation

$$\xi_x + \eta_y + \zeta_z = 0 \qquad (4.26)$$

permits the use of vorticity functions analogous to the stream functions f and g. The circulation along any curve lying in the vorticity surfaces

$$f = f_1 \qquad f = f_2 \qquad g = g_1 \qquad g = g_2$$

is then

$$\Gamma = 2(f_2 - f_1)(g_2 - g_1)$$

One consequence of this is that the circulation around any vortex tube at any instant is constant at all sections of the tube.

4.9. Acceleration

To find the acceleration of a fluid particle (Art. 2.4), one must find the rate of change of its velocity by following the particle. Thus, although the space coordinates x, y, z and time t are independent variables, the displacement of the particle (dx, dy, dz) is a function of time, and indeed in such a way that

$$u = \frac{dx}{dt} \qquad v = \frac{dy}{dt} \qquad w = \frac{dz}{dt} \qquad (4.27)$$

Now, as the particle is displaced in time dt, the component u of its velocity is changed by the amount

$$u_t\, dt + u_x\, dx + u_y\, dy + u_z\, dz$$

Thus, in virtue of Eqs. (4.27), the rate of change of u, or the acceleration in the x direction, is

$$a = u_t + uu_x + vu_y + wu_z$$

The operator

$$\frac{D}{Dt} = \frac{\partial}{\partial t} + u\frac{\partial}{\partial x} + v\frac{\partial}{\partial y} + w\frac{\partial}{\partial z} \qquad (4.28)$$

is very useful in fluid mechanics, as has already been demonstrated by Eq. (4.7), which defines an incompressible fluid. The operation that D/Dt stands for is called the substantial differentiation. Thus a is the substantial derivative of u. If b and c are the acceleration components in the directions of increasing y and z,

$$(a, b, c) = \frac{D}{Dt}\,(u,v,w) \qquad (4.29)$$

THE EQUATIONS OF MOTION

4.10. Euler Equations

Since the net force per unit volume due to pressure change is

$$-\operatorname{grad} p = -(p_x,\, p_y,\, p_z)$$

the equations of motion of an inviscid fluid, namely, a fluid with the stress tensor

$$\begin{bmatrix} -p & 0 & 0 \\ 0 & -p & 0 \\ 0 & 0 & -p \end{bmatrix}$$

are

$$\rho \frac{Du}{Dt} = -p_x + \rho X$$

$$\rho \frac{Dv}{Dt} = -p_y + \rho Y \tag{4.30}$$

$$\rho \frac{Dw}{Dt} = -p_z + \rho Z$$

in which X, Y, and Z are the components of the body force per unit mass in the directions of x, y, and z, respectively.

If the body force is a conservative force,

$$X, Y, Z = -(\Omega_x, \Omega_y, \Omega_z)$$

in which Ω is the body-force potential, and Eqs. (4.30) become

$$\rho \frac{Du}{Dt} = -(p_x + \rho \Omega_x)$$

$$\rho \frac{Dv}{Dt} = -(p_y + \rho \Omega_y) \tag{4.31}$$

$$\rho \frac{Dw}{Dt} = -(p_z + \rho \Omega_z)$$

4.11. Vorticity Equations and the Persistence of Irrotationality

For a fluid of constant density, cross differentiation of Eqs. (4.31) produces, with the utilization of Eq. (4.6), the equations governing the variation of vorticity with time:

$$\frac{D}{Dt} (\xi, \eta, \zeta) = \left(\xi \frac{\partial}{\partial x} + \eta \frac{\partial}{\partial y} + \zeta \frac{\partial}{\partial z} \right) (u, v, w) \tag{4.32}$$

The right-hand side of Eqs. (4.32) represents the effect of turning or stretching (or shortening) of a vortex line on the rate of change of vorticity with respect to time at any point on the vortex line. For a compressible fluid, if the pressure is only a function of the density all over the field of flow (homentropic flow), equations similar to Eqs. (4.32) can be obtained:

$$\rho \frac{D}{Dt} \left(\frac{\xi, \eta, \zeta}{\rho \;\; \rho \;\; \rho} \right) = \left(\xi \frac{\partial}{\partial x} + \eta \frac{\partial}{\partial y} + \zeta \frac{\partial}{\partial z} \right) (u, v, w) \tag{4.33}$$

One very important consequence of Eqs. (4.32) and (4.33) is that if the vorticity is zero at some initial time or at a section upstream, it will remain zero at subsequent times or at all downstream positions. Thus irrotationality will persist in the flow of an inviscid fluid of constant density, or in homentropic flows of a compressible fluid.

For two-dimensional motions Eqs. (4.32) and (4.33) reduce to

$$\frac{D\zeta}{Dt} = 0 \tag{4.34}$$

and

$$\frac{D}{Dt} \left(\frac{\zeta}{\rho} \right) = 0 \tag{4.35}$$

respectively. Thus, in the case of constant density, vorticity (not merely irrotationality) will persist along a path line, and in the case of homentropic flows, the ratio of vorticity to density will persist along a path line.

4.12. Persistence of Circulation

The persistence of irrotationality of an inviscid fluid is a special case of the persistence of circulation around a circuit consisting of the same fluid particles, as they move about.

Let dx, dy, dz be the three components of a line element ds along a material circuit. Then

$$\frac{D}{Dt}(dx,dy,dz) = (du,dv,dw)$$

if du, dv, and dw are the increments of the velocity components for the line element ds, and

$$\frac{D}{Dt}(u\,dx + v\,dy + w\,dz) = dx\frac{Du}{Dt} + dy\frac{Dv}{Dt} + dz\frac{Dw}{Dt} + u\,du + v\,dv + w\,dw$$

Thus, by virtue of the Euler equations,

$$\frac{D}{Dt}(u\,dx + v\,dy + w\,dz) = -\left(\frac{1}{\rho}dp + d\Omega\right) + \tfrac{1}{2}d(u^2 + v^2 + w^2)$$

If ρ is constant or a function of p alone (homentropic flows), then with C indicating the (closed) circuit,

$$\frac{D}{Dt}\Gamma = \frac{D}{Dt}\oint_C (u\,dx + v\,dy + w\,dz)$$

$$= -\oint_C\left[d\left(\int \frac{dp}{\rho} + \Omega\right) + \tfrac{1}{2}d(u^2 + v^2 + w^2)\right] = 0 \quad (4.36)$$

since ρ, Ω, u, v, and w are single-valued. Equation (4.36) states that the circulation along any material circuit of an inviscid fluid does not change with time if ρ is constant or a function of p alone. Since D/Dt signifies the substantial differentiation (or differentiation with respect to time as the material points move about) and since the integration is over the material circuit at an instant, the operator D/Dt can be exchanged with the integration operation.

If an inviscid fluid to whose motion Eq. (4.36) applies is initially at rest, or if the circulation around *any* circuit in an upstream plane cutting all the streamlines is zero, it follows from Eqs. (4.25) and (4.36) that the subsequent motion will be irrotational.

4.13. Irrotational Flows

The persistence of irrotationality of an inviscid fluid of constant ρ or with ρ dependent only on p makes the study of irrotational flows important. For irrotational flows

$$w_y - v_z = 0 \qquad u_z - w_x = 0 \qquad v_x - u_y = 0 \qquad\qquad (4.37)$$

and a velocity potential ϕ exists in terms of which the velocity components can be expressed in the following way:

$$u = -\phi_x \qquad v = -\phi_y \qquad w = -\phi_z \qquad\qquad (4.38)$$

or, more generally,

$$(u,v,w) = -\operatorname{grad}\phi \qquad\qquad (4.38a)$$

for general coordinates. That Eqs. (4.37) are necessary for the validity of Eqs. (4.38) is obvious. One needs only to note that Eqs. (4.37) are identically satisfied by Eqs. (4.38) and that if Eqs. (4.37) were not true, Eqs. (4.38) would be invalid. That Eqs. (4.37) are sufficient for Eqs. (4.38) to be valid can be proved by Stokes' theorem. According to this theorem,

$$\oint_C (u\,dx + v\,dy + w\,dz) = \iint_S [(v_x - u_y)\,dx\,dy + (w_y - v_z)\,dy\,dz + (u_z - w_x)\,dz\,dx]$$

(4.25)

in which C is a closed circuit, and S is a surface bounded by C. If the flow is irrotational,

$$\oint_C (u\,dx + v\,dy + w\,dz) = 0$$

no matter what the circuit is (so long as it does not enclose a concentrated vortex line). This means that

$$u\,dx + v\,dy + w\,dz$$

is an exact differential. If this exact differential is denoted by $-d\phi$, it follows that

$$u\,dx + v\,dy + w\,dz = -d\phi = -\phi_x\,dx - \phi_y\,dy - \phi_z\,dz$$

and Eqs. (4.38) follow.

For an incompressible fluid moving irrotationally, Eqs. (4.6) and (4.38) yield

$$\nabla^2 \phi = 0$$

(4.39)

in which ∇^2 is the Laplace operator

$$\frac{\partial^2}{\partial x^2} + \frac{\partial^2}{\partial y^2} + \frac{\partial^2}{\partial z^2}$$

The principal (although not the sole) concern of this section is the solution of Eq. (4.39).

If the flow is axisymmetric and irrotational, Eqs. (4.16) and the equation of irrotationality (for cylindrical coordinates)

$$\frac{\partial w}{\partial r} - \frac{\partial u}{\partial z} = 0$$

yield

$$\frac{\partial^2 \psi}{\partial r^2} - \frac{1}{r}\frac{\partial \psi}{\partial r} + \frac{\partial^2 \psi}{\partial z^2} = 0$$

(4.40)

in cylindrical coordinates.

INTEGRATION OF THE EULER EQUATIONS

4.14. Bernoulli Equation along a Streamline

For steady flows of an inviscid fluid with constant density, the Euler equation can be written in the following form:

$$q\frac{\partial q}{\partial s} = -\frac{1}{\rho}\frac{\partial p}{\partial s} - \frac{\partial \Omega}{\partial s}$$

(4.41)

in which q is the speed and s is the distance along a streamline. Integration of this equation with respect to s yields

$$\frac{q^2}{2} + \frac{p}{\rho} + \Omega = C$$

(4.42)

in which C is a constant that varies from streamline to streamline if the flow is not irrotational.

If the fluid is compressible but the change of state along a streamline is isentropic, p is a function of ρ alone along a streamline, and integration of Eq. (4.41) produces

$$\frac{q^2}{2} + \int \frac{dp}{\rho} + \Omega = C$$

(4.42a)

in which C is again a constant only along a streamline if the flow is not irrotational.

4.15. Bernoulli Equation for the Whole Field of Flow

For irrotational flows of an inviscid fluid with constant density or with a density that depends only on the pressure (homentropic flows), the Euler equations can be integrated over the whole field of flow. In these cases the Euler equations are

$$\frac{D}{Dt}(u,v,w) = -\text{grad}\left(\int \frac{dp}{\rho} + \Omega\right)$$

and because of the irrotationality, Eqs. (4.38) can be substituted into them to produce

$$\frac{\partial}{\partial x}\left(-\frac{\partial \phi}{\partial t} + \frac{u^2 + v^2 + w^2}{2} + \int \frac{dp}{\rho} + \Omega\right) = 0$$

$$\frac{\partial}{\partial y}\left(-\frac{\partial \phi}{\partial t} + \frac{u^2 + v^2 + w^2}{2} + \int \frac{dp}{\rho} + \Omega\right) = 0$$

$$\frac{\partial}{\partial z}\left(-\frac{\partial \phi}{\partial t} + \frac{u^2 + v^2 + w^2}{2} + \int \frac{dp}{\rho} + \Omega\right) = 0$$

Integration of these equations yields the Bernoulli equation

$$-\frac{\partial \phi}{\partial t} + \frac{u^2 + v^2 + w^2}{2} + \int \frac{dp}{\rho} + \Omega = F(t)$$

But since ϕ can be changed by any arbitrary function of time without in any way affecting the flow, the term $F(t)$ can be absorbed in $-\partial\phi/\partial t$, and the Bernoulli equation can be written

$$-\frac{\partial \phi}{\partial t} + \frac{u^2 + v^2 + w^2}{2} + \int \frac{dp}{\rho} + \Omega = C \qquad (4.43)$$

in which C can be taken to be zero if one prefers, but it is more convenient to retain C as a constant (for the entire flow) that can be chosen as one pleases.

The Bernoulli equation merely relates the pressure to the velocity, the velocity potential, and the body-force potential (the potential energy per unit mass) Ω. The velocity field is to be determined from Eq. (4.39) if the fluid is incompressible and from a somewhat more complicated equation for homentropic flows of a compressible fluid. For such flows, the term $\int dp/\rho$ in Eq. (4.43) can be evaluated once the relationship between p and ρ is known.

For a frame of reference which is itself in motion, the Bernoulli equation takes on a different form. If U, V, and W are the velocity components of the origin of a moving coordinate system and ω_1, ω_2, and ω_3 its angular velocity components in the directions of x, y, and z, all referred to fixed axes which at that instant coincide with the coordinate axes, the Bernoulli equation for irrotational flows of a fluid with constant density ρ is

$$\frac{p}{\rho} = \frac{\partial \phi}{\partial t} - \Omega - \frac{1}{2}[(u - U)^2 + (v - V)^2 + (w - W)^2]$$

$$- \omega_1\left(y\frac{\partial \phi}{\partial z} - z\frac{\partial \phi}{\partial y}\right) - \omega_2\left(z\frac{\partial \phi}{\partial x} - x\frac{\partial \phi}{\partial z}\right) - \omega_3\left(x\frac{\partial \phi}{\partial y} - y\frac{\partial \phi}{\partial x}\right) \qquad (4.44)$$

in which u, v, w are the velocity components which, together with ϕ, are referred to fixed axes coinciding instantaneously with the moving axes. Again, if p is a function of ρ alone, p/ρ is to be replaced by $\int \frac{dp}{\rho}$. It should be noted that for a body translating with constant velocity U in the x direction, $\partial\phi/\partial t$ vanishes, and Eq. (4.44) reduces to

$$\frac{p}{\rho} = -\Omega - \tfrac{1}{2}[(u - U)^2 + v^2 + w^2]$$

which is the Bernoulli equation for steady flows.

GENERAL THREE-DIMENSIONAL IRROTATIONAL FLOWS

4.16. Uniqueness of the Solution of the Laplace Equation

Equation (4.39), the Laplace equation for the velocity potential ϕ, governs irrotational flows of an incompressible fluid. Whether or not the solution of Eq. (4.39) is unique depends on the type of boundary conditions to be imposed.

If Eq. (4.39) is satisfied by ϕ in a domain D at the boundary (S) of which ϕ is specified, so that

$$\phi = f(x,y,z) \qquad \text{on } S \tag{4.45}$$

the problem is called a Dirichlet problem. If, instead of ϕ, it is the normal derivative $\partial\phi/\partial n$ that is specified on S, so that

$$\frac{\partial\phi}{\partial n} = g(x,y,z) \qquad \text{on } S \tag{4.46}$$

the problem is called a Neumann problem. More generally, ϕ may be specified on a part of S, and $\partial\phi/\partial n$ specified on the rest of S. For convenience the corresponding problem may be called a Dirichlet-Neumann problem.

The solution of a Dirichlet-Neumann problem is unique. To prove this statement, Green's theorem can be used. For any three arbitrary functions U, V, and W which are single-valued and differentiable on S, Green's theorem states that

$$-\iint_S (lU + mV + nW)dS = \iiint_D \left(\frac{\partial U}{\partial x} + \frac{\partial V}{\partial y} + \frac{\partial W}{\partial z}\right) dx\, dy\, dz \tag{4.47}$$

in which l, m, and n are the direction cosines of the normal n (to S) drawn into the domain D (Fig. 4.3). If a Dirichlet-Neumann problem is specified by Eq. (4.39) and the boundary conditions

$$\phi = f(x,y,z) \qquad \text{on } S_1$$

$$\frac{\partial\phi}{\partial n} = g(x,y,z) \qquad \text{on } S_2$$

in which S_1 and S_2 collectively constitute S, and if there are two solutions ϕ_1 and ϕ_2, one can define ϕ to be the difference of these two solutions:

$$\phi = \phi_1 - \phi_2$$

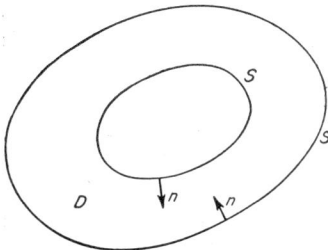

Then ϕ satisfied Eq. (4.39) and the boundary conditions

$$\phi = 0 \qquad \text{on } S_1$$

$$\frac{\partial\phi}{\partial n} = 0 \qquad \text{on } S_2 \tag{4.48}$$

If $\qquad (U, V, W) = \left(\phi\,\dfrac{\partial\phi}{\partial x}, \phi\,\dfrac{\partial\phi}{\partial y}, \phi\,\dfrac{\partial\phi}{\partial z}\right)$

Fig. 4.3. Direction for positive normal in fluid domain D.

Eq. (4.47) gives (with subscripts again denoting partial differentiation)

$$- \iint\limits_{S} \phi \frac{\partial \phi}{\partial n} ds = \iiint\limits_{D} (\phi_x{}^2 + \phi_y{}^2 + \phi_z{}^2) dx\, dy\, dz$$

$$+ \iiint\limits_{D} \phi \nabla^2 \phi \, dx\, dy\, dz = \iiint\limits_{D} (\phi_x{}^2 + \phi_y{}^2 + \phi_z{}^2) dx\, dy\, dz \quad (4.49)$$

since $\nabla^2 \phi$ is zero, with both ϕ_1 and ϕ_2 satisfying Eq. (4.39). In virtue of Eq. (4.48), Eq. (4.49) becomes

$$\iiint\limits_{D} (\phi_x{}^2 + \phi_y{}^2 + \phi_z{}^2) dx\, dy\, dz = 0$$

which states that

$$\phi_x = \phi_y = \phi_z = 0$$

in D, or ϕ is a constant or a function of time only in D. Hence ϕ_1 and ϕ_2 can differ by a constant or a function of t only, and the flow represented by ϕ_1 is identical with that represented by ϕ_2, since the velocity components are given by the spatial derivatives of the velocity potential.

In the proof just presented, ϕ has been assumed single-valued. If ϕ is not single-valued, the solution of a Dirichlet-Neumann problem is in general not unique. An example of the lack of uniqueness due to multivaluedness of ϕ will be provided in Art. 4.34, in which flows with circulation will be discussed.

If the boundary condition is neither of the Dirichlet nor the Neumann type but involves both ϕ and $\partial \phi / \partial n$ at the *same* portion of S, the solution of $\nabla^2 \phi = 0$ is in general not unique.

4.17. The Maximum or Minimum of Harmonic Functions

A function that satisfies the Laplace equation is called a harmonic function. One interesting and important property of a harmonic function is that in a singularity-free region its maximum or minimum can occur only on the boundary of that region.

If ϕ is a harmonic function, it can be identified with a velocity potential for an irrotational flow of an incompressible fluid. Consider a sphere of radius r and center at 0, situated entirely in the region under consideration. Since the radial velocity at the surface of the sphere is $-\partial \phi / \partial r$ and since the region is free from singularities, so that the net inflow across the surface of the sphere must be zero, one has

$$\iint \frac{\partial \phi}{\partial r} r^2 \, d\Omega = 0$$

in which $d\Omega$ is the solid angle subtending an area element on the surface of the sphere. Since r is constant on the spherical surface,

$$\iint \frac{\partial \phi}{\partial r} d\Omega = 0$$

or

$$\frac{\partial}{\partial r} \iint \phi \, d\Omega = 0 \qquad (4.50)$$

But

$$\frac{1}{4\pi} \iint \phi \, d\Omega = \frac{1}{4\pi r^2} \iint \phi r^2 \, d\Omega$$

is the mean value of ϕ over the spherical surface. Thus Eq. (4.50) states that the mean value of ϕ over the surface of a sphere of radius r is independent of r. Since there is no singularity in the region considered, ϕ is continuous, and for a sphere with vanishing radius the mean value of ϕ over its surface approaches ϕ_0 in the limit, if ϕ_0 denotes the value of ϕ at the center of the sphere. Since the mean value of ϕ over a spherical surface with the center 0 is independent of the radius r, it follows that this mean value is precisely ϕ_0. Thus, ϕ_0 cannot be a maximum or minimum of ϕ in the region under consideration. Since 0 is any interior point, it follows that the maximum or minimum value of ϕ must occur on the boundary of that region, unless ϕ is a constant, in which case it has no maximum or minimum.

One important corollary of the result just obtained is that in a singularity-free region the maximum speed of an incompressible fluid in irrotational flow must occur on the boundary of that region. The proof is simple. Since the velocity potential ϕ satisfies the Laplace equation, its derivatives with respect to cartesian coordinates x, y, and z must also satisfy the Laplace equation. At any interior point 0, let the direction of the velocity be taken as the x direction. Then the speed at 0 is

$$u_0 = -\phi_x|_0$$

But since $-\phi_x$ is a harmonic function, over a spherical surface with 0 as the center there must be a point at which $-\phi_x$ is greater than u_0, in virtue of the result obtained in the last paragraph. At this point the speed is

$$(\phi_x{}^2 + \phi_y{}^2 + \phi_z{}^2)^{\frac{1}{2}}$$

which is a fortiori greater than u_0, the speed at 0. Thus, since 0 is any interior point, the maximum speed cannot occur in the interior of a singularity-free region, and hence must occur on the boundary of that region. In virtue of the Bernoulli equation, the minimum pressure in such a region must therefore occur on the boundary of that region, if the flow is irrotational and steady and the fluid incompressible. Corresponding results for maximum speed and minimum pressure have been obtained for homentropic irrotational flows of a compressible fluid, provided the flow is subsonic.†

There is a theorem concerning the maximum acceleration in two-dimensional potential flows of an incompressible fluid. This will be presented in Art. 4.32. Unfortunately, the result cannot be generalized to apply to three-dimensional flows.

4.18. Added Masses

If ϕ denotes the velocity potential, Eq. (4.49) can be multiplied by $\rho/2$ to produce

$$-\frac{\rho}{2} \iint\limits_{S} \phi \frac{\partial \phi}{\partial n}\, ds = \frac{\rho}{2} \iiint\limits_{D} \left[\left(\frac{\partial \phi}{\partial x} \right)^2 + \left(\frac{\partial \phi}{\partial y} \right)^2 + \left(\frac{\partial \phi}{\partial z} \right)^2 \right] dx\, dy\, dz \quad (4.49a)$$

But the right-hand side is the total kinetic energy T of the fluid in D. Thus Eq. (4.49a) allows this kinetic energy to be evaluated on the surface S of D.

Let u_1, u_2, and u_3 denote the three components of the velocity of a solid body immersed in an infinite fluid, and u_4, u_5, and u_6 denote the three components of its angular velocity ω. Furthermore, let ϕ_α (α = any number from 1 to 6) be the velocity potential for the fluid when the body is moving with u_α equal to unity. Since the boundary condition for ϕ_α (for any value of α from 1 to 6) is that the velocity component normal to the surface of the solid body must be the same for fluid and solid and since the Laplace equation is linear, the velocity potential for the fluid set in motion by a combined translation and rotation of the solid can be obtained by superposition:

$$\phi = u_\alpha \phi_\alpha \tag{4.51}$$

in which repeated indices indicate summation over α from 1 to 6. Substitution of Eq. (4.51) into Eq. (4.49a) produces, after multiplication by 2,

$$2T = -\rho \iint\limits_{S} \phi \frac{\partial \phi}{\partial n}\, ds = A_{\alpha\beta} u_\alpha u_\beta \tag{4.52}$$

† See *Quart. Appl. Math.*, **16**: 178–180 (1958).

in which
$$A_{\alpha\beta} = -\rho \iint_S \phi_\alpha \frac{\partial\phi_\beta}{\partial n} \, ds \qquad (4.53)$$

The coefficients $A_{\alpha\beta}$ are called added masses. The 36 added masses constitute a tensor, which can be called the added-mass tensor. It can be shown by the use of Green's theorem that

$$A_{\alpha\beta} = A_{\beta\alpha} \qquad (4.54)$$

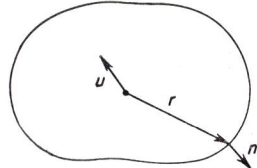

FIG. 4.4. Notation for solid body immersed in a fluid.

The term $\partial\phi_\beta/\partial n$ in the expression for $A_{\alpha\beta}$ can be simplified. With **u** denoting the velocity vector (Fig. 4.4) and **r** the position vector (x,y,z) or (x_1,x_2,x_3), and with **n** denoting the unit normal vector (n_1,n_2,n_3), it is clear that the boundary condition requiring equality of normal fluid velocity and normal solid-body velocity at the surface is

$$-\frac{\partial\phi}{\partial n} = (\mathbf{u} + \boldsymbol{\omega} \times \mathbf{r}) \cdot \mathbf{n} = u_\alpha n_\alpha \qquad (\alpha = 1 \text{ to } 6)$$

The quantities n_4, n_5, and n_6 are defined to be

$$(n_4, n_5, n_6) = \mathbf{r} \times \mathbf{n} \qquad (4.55)$$

Thus
$$-u_\alpha \frac{\partial\phi_\alpha}{\partial n} = u_\alpha n_\alpha$$

for all values of u_α, and hence

$$-\frac{\partial\phi_\alpha}{\partial n} = n_\alpha \qquad \text{or} \qquad -\frac{\partial\phi_\beta}{\partial n} = n_\beta \qquad (4.56)$$

Equation (4.53) can then be written in the simple form

$$A_{\alpha\beta} = \rho \iint_S \phi_\alpha n_\beta \, ds \qquad (4.57)$$

Of the 36 added masses, there are only 21 $(= 6 + \frac{30}{2})$ distinct components, because of the symmetry of $A_{\alpha\beta}$ $(A_{\alpha\beta} = A_{\beta\alpha})$. The first three diagonal ones A_{11}, A_{22}, and A_{33} are for pure translations in the directions of the coordinate axes. The other three diagonal ones $(A_{44}, A_{55}, \text{ and } A_{66})$ are for pure rotations about the coordinate axes. The elements A_{12}, A_{13}, and A_{23} indicate the interactions of translations in more than one coordinate direction. The elements A_{45}, A_{46}, and A_{56} indicate the interactions of rotations about more than one coordinate axis. Finally, the elements A_{14}, A_{15}, A_{16}, etc., indicate the interactions between translation and rotation.

Evaluation of the added masses from the singularities generating the flow will be dealt with later. The physical significance of the added masses can be illustrated by the case of a solid body in accelerated motion in an inviscid and incompressible fluid. Let the mass of the body be M and its velocity $U(t)$ be in the x direction. The force F that must be applied to the body in order to produce the acceleration $U'(t)$ can be computed from the principle that the rate of work performed by F must be equal to the rate of kinetic-energy increase of the body and of the fluid, if the x axis is horizontal. Thus

$$FU = MUU' + A_{11}UU'$$
or
$$F = (M + A_{11})U'$$

Consequently, when the solid is being accelerated, the required force is not equal to, but greater than, the product of its mass and the acceleration, as if its mass had been increased. The *apparent* increase of its mass is exactly A_{11}, which is therefore called the added mass. The sum $M + A_{11}$ can be called the virtual mass. In the literature, the term virtual mass is sometimes used to indicate what is called an added mass here.

4.19. Three-dimensional Sources, Sinks, and Doublets

If the spherical coordinates (R, θ, φ) are used, so that

$$R^2 = x^2 + y^2 + z^2$$

it can be verified readily that $1/R$ is a harmonic function. The velocity potential

$$\phi = \frac{m}{4\pi R} \qquad (4.58)$$

represents a flow issuing from a point source situated at the origin. The velocity is entirely radial and is given by

$$u = -\frac{\partial \phi}{\partial R} = \frac{m}{4\pi R^2} \qquad v = w = 0 \qquad (4.59)$$

so that the discharge through a spherical surface of radius R is precisely m.

To find Stokes' stream function for source flow, Eqs. (4.17) can be used with Eq. (4.59):

$$-\frac{1}{R^2 \sin \theta} \psi_\theta = \frac{m}{4\pi R^2} \qquad \psi_R = 0$$

Integration of these equations produces

$$\psi = \frac{m \cos \theta}{4\pi} \qquad (4.60)$$

with the constant of integration suppressed for brevity. The flow due to a point sink is described by Eqs. (4.58) to (4.60), with m negative, and the pattern is shown in Fig. 4.5.

If $1/R$ is differentiated with respect to x, the resulting expression is $-x/R^3$, which again satisfies the Laplace equation. What flow does the potential

$$\phi = \frac{\mu x}{R^3} \qquad (4.61)$$

represent? With the x axis as the polar axis, this potential can be written as

$$\phi = \frac{\mu \cos \theta}{R^2} \qquad (4.62)$$

and Eqs. (4.17) and (4.38a) can be combined to produce

$$-\frac{1}{R^2 \sin \theta} \psi_\theta = -\phi_R = \frac{2\mu \cos \theta}{R^3}$$

$$\frac{1}{R \sin \theta} \psi_R = -\frac{1}{R} \phi_\theta = \frac{\mu \sin \theta}{R^3}$$

Integration of these equations readily yields

$$\psi = \frac{\mu \cos 2\theta}{2R} + F(R) = \frac{\mu(1 - 2 \sin^2 \theta)}{2R} + F(R)$$

and $\psi = -\frac{\mu \sin^2 \theta}{R} + G(\theta)$

Thus $F(R) = -\frac{\mu}{2R} \qquad G(\theta) = 0$

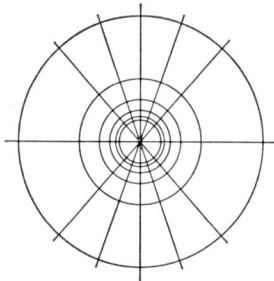

Fig. 4.5. Streamlines and equipotential lines for a source. (Ref. 9.)

and $\psi = -\frac{\mu \sin^2 \theta}{R} \qquad (4.63)$

Equation (4.63) can be plotted for constant values of ψ to show the pattern of stream-lines (Fig. 4.6). But the question can still be raised: Since $-x/R^3$ is obtained by differentiation of $1/R$, which represents the potential function for source flow (aside from a constant), should not the potential given in Eq. (4.61) be connected in some physical way to source flow? The answer is in the affirmative.

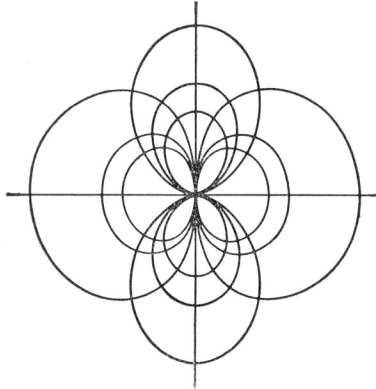

FIG. 4.6. Streamlines and equipotential lines for a three-dimensional doublet. (*Ref.* 9.)

Consider a source of strength m and a sink of the same strength situated $2a$ apart on the x axis (Fig. 4.7). The coordinates are

$$\text{Source:}\quad (x,y,z) = (a,0,0)$$
$$\text{Sink:}\quad (x,y,z) = (-a,0,0)$$

The combined potential can be obtained by superposition (since the Laplace equation is linear):

$$\phi = \frac{m}{4\pi R_1} - \frac{m}{4\pi R_2} = \frac{m}{4\pi}\left(\frac{1}{\sqrt{(x-a)^2 + y^2 + z^2}} - \frac{1}{\sqrt{(x+a)^2 + y^2 + z^2}}\right)$$

As a approaches zero, the quantity in the parentheses can be represented by the differential

$$\left(\frac{\partial}{\partial x}\frac{1}{R}\right)(-2a) = \frac{2ax}{R^3}$$

by first principles of the differential calculus. Thus if a is made very small but m is made to increase in such a way that $ma/2\pi$ is equal to μ, in the limit

$$\phi = \frac{\mu x}{R^3}$$

which is precisely Eq. (4.61). The flow represented by Eq. (4.61) is therefore that due to a doublet of strength μ. If μ is positive, the axis of the doublet points in the same direction as the x axis. If μ is negative, it points in the opposite direction.

Similarly,

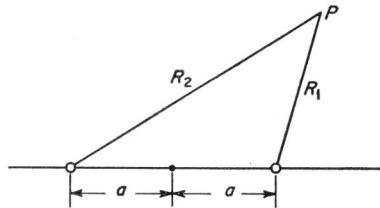

FIG. 4.7. Notation for source and sink.

$$\phi = \frac{\mu y}{R^3} \qquad \text{and} \qquad \phi = \frac{\mu z}{R^3}$$

represent doublets of strength μ with axes pointing in the positive directions of y and z, respectively. A doublet of strength μ pointing in any arbitrary direction is represented by

$$\phi = \frac{\mu x'}{R^3}$$

if the axis of the doublet is taken to be the x' axis. If the direction cosines of this axis is (l,m,n),

$$x' = lx + my + nz$$

and the potential is given by

$$\phi = \frac{\mu}{R^3}\,(lx + my + nz) \tag{4.64}$$

which is a superposition of the potentials of three doublets with axes coinciding with the coordinate axis.

In the foregoing discussion the sources and doublets have been assumed to be situated at the origin (except in the discussion of the genesis of a doublet). If they are situated elsewhere, the potentials and stream functions can be obtained by a simple transformation of coordinates. The flow patterns are merely shifted through a distance from the origin.

The potential of a doublet can be successively differentiated to yield potentials of singularities of higher orders. Each differentiation corresponds to a physical limiting process, as has been demonstrated for the case of doublets. Although sources, sinks, doublets, and higher singularities seem to be mere artifices to create potential flows, they are nevertheless very useful, because the flow caused by a moving body can be represented by the flow created by singularities *inside* the body, which need not be realized in the fluid.

4.20. Combination of Uniform Flow with Flows Generated by Singularities

The function (U = constant or a function of time)

$$\phi = -Ux \tag{4.65}$$

obviously satisfies the Laplace equation. Since

$$u = -\frac{\partial \phi}{\partial x} = U \qquad v = w = 0$$

the function $-Ux$ represents the velocity potential for uniform flow with velocity U in the x direction. Combination of this potential with the potentials for singularities can produce flows past solid bodies outside of which no singularities are present.

The flow resulting from the combination of a uniform flow with the flow due to a source can best be studied by the use of Stokes' stream function in spherical coordinates. For uniform flow, the stream function is, in cylindrical and spherical coordinates, respectively,

$$\psi = \frac{-U}{2}\,r^2 \qquad \psi = -\frac{1}{2}\,UR^2 \sin^2\theta \tag{4.66}$$

It can be verified from Eqs. (4.16) and the first of Eqs. (4.66) that the velocity is in the z direction (the x direction in cartesian coordinates) and is U. For a source situated at the origin with strength m, Eq. (4.60) gives, in spherical coordinates,

$$\psi = \frac{m \cos \theta}{4\pi} \tag{4.67}$$

Combination of Eqs. (4.66) and (4.67) produces the new stream function

$$\psi = -\frac{U}{2} R^2 \sin^2 \theta + \frac{m \cos \theta}{4\pi}$$

The streamline $\psi = -m/4\pi$ has two branches:

$$\theta = \pi \qquad R^2 = \frac{m}{2\pi U} \frac{1 + \cos \theta}{\sin^2 \theta} = \frac{m}{4\pi U} \csc^2 \frac{\theta}{2}$$

or

$$\theta = \pi \qquad R = \sqrt{\frac{m}{4\pi U}} \csc \frac{\theta}{2} \qquad (4.68)$$

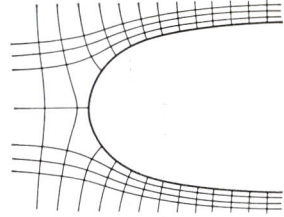

Fig. 4.8. Streamlines and equipotential lines for a half body. (*Ref. 9.*)

The flow pattern is shown in Fig. 4.8. The streamline described by the second of Eqs. (4.68), shown in the figure as the boundary streamline, can be replaced by a solid boundary. The solid is called a half body. Since the velocity at infinity is U and the discharge from the source is m, the asymptotic radius of the half body is

$$a = \sqrt{\frac{m}{\pi U}}$$

and is twice the distance from the source to the stagnation point, which is located at [from Eqs. (4.68)]

$$\theta = \pi \qquad R = \sqrt{\frac{m}{4\pi U}}$$

It can be shown that the integral of the forces (from normal pressure) on the surface in the x direction is zero. This fact has not been as widely recognized as it should be.

Another example is furnished by superposing a uniform flow to the flow due to a source and a sink on the uniform flow in the same direction as the line joining the source and the sink. With reference to Fig. 4.9, the stream function for the source at $(-a,0)$ and the sink at $(a,0)$ is

$$\psi = \frac{m}{4\pi} (\cos \theta_2 - \cos \theta_1)$$

and the stream function for the combined flow is, in spherical coordinates,

$$\psi = -\frac{1}{2} U R^2 \sin^2 \theta + \frac{m}{4\pi} (\cos \theta_2 - \cos \theta_1) \qquad (4.69)$$

The corresponding velocity potential can most conveniently be expressed in terms of cylindrical coordinates:

$$\phi = -Uz + \frac{m}{4\pi} \left(\frac{1}{\sqrt{(z - a)^2 + r^2}} \right.$$

$$\left. - \frac{1}{\sqrt{(z + a)^2 + r^2}} \right) \qquad (4.70)$$

The flow pattern described by Eqs. (4.69) and (4.70) is shown in Fig. 4.10. The radius h of the largest cross section can be readily shown to be the positive root of the equation

$$h^2 = \frac{m}{\pi U} \frac{a}{\sqrt{h^2 + a^2}}$$

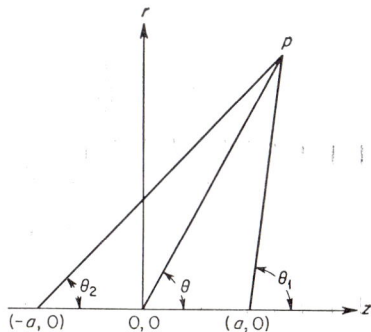

Fig. 4.9. Auxiliary coordinate systems used for Rankine body.

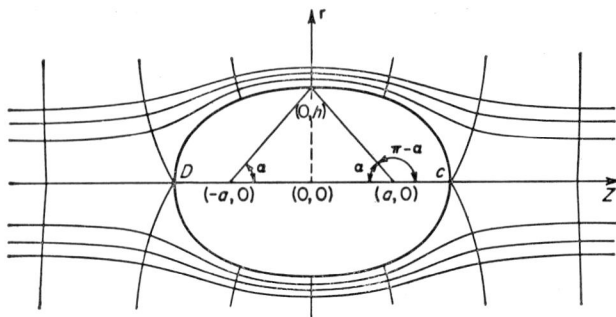

FIG. 4.10. Rankine body.   (*Ref.* 9.)

The important case of flow past a sphere can be obtained by superposing a doublet of strength μ and axis pointing in the *negative z* direction on a uniform flow of velocity U in the z direction.   The stream function is, from Eqs. (4.63) and (4.66),

$$\psi = -\tfrac{1}{2}UR^2 \sin^2\theta + \frac{\mu \sin^2\theta}{R} = \left(-\frac{UR^2}{2} + \frac{\mu}{R}\right)\sin^2\theta$$

The corresponding velocity potential is, by virtue of Eqs. (4.62) and (4.65),

$$\phi = -UR\cos\theta - \frac{\mu\cos\theta}{R^2}$$

For μ equal to $Ua^3/2$, $\psi = 0$ on the sphere $R = a$.   At infinity the effect of the doublet vanishes and the velocity is U.   Therefore

$$\psi = -\frac{Ua^2}{2}\left[\left(\frac{R}{a}\right)^2 - \frac{a}{R}\right]\sin^2\theta \qquad \text{and} \qquad \phi = -Ua\left(\frac{R}{a} + \frac{a^2}{2R^2}\right)\cos\theta \tag{4.71}$$

describe the flow with uniform velocity U at infinity past a sphere of radius a.   The pattern is shown in Fig. 4.11.

The added mass of the sphere can be calculated with the potential given by Eq. (4.71) with the part corresponding to uniform flow removed:

$$\phi = -\frac{Ua^3}{2R^2}\cos\theta \tag{4.72}$$

which corresponds to the flow due to a sphere of radius a moving with velocity U in the negative z direction.   The added mass is given by Eqs. (4.53), with α and β equal to 1 and ϕ_1 equal to $-a^3\cos\theta/2R^2$

$$M' = A_{11} = -\rho \iint_S \phi\frac{\partial\phi}{\partial R}\,ds = \frac{\rho a^6}{2a^5}\int_0^\pi 2\pi a^2\cos^2\theta\sin\theta\,d\theta = \tfrac{2}{3}\pi a^3\rho \tag{4.73}$$

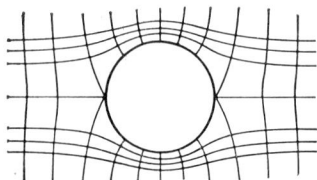

FIG. 4.11. Streamlines and equi-potential lines for uniform flow about a sphere at rest.   (*Ref.* 9.)

Thus the added mass is just one-half the mass of the fluid displaced by the sphere.

4.21. Method of Images

Problems of potential flows involving straight, circular, or spherical boundaries can often be solved by the method of images.   In this section, examples will be given to illustrate the application of this method to axisymmetric or truly three-dimensional flows. The application to two-dimensional flows will be presented later.

Flow Due to a Source in the Presence of an Infinite Plane. For the flow due to a source of strength m situated at the point with cartesian coordinates $(-a,0,0)$, in the presence of the wall $x = 0$, the wall must be a stream surface (Fig. 4.12). In order to ensure that this condition be satisfied, the flow due to the mirror image of the source is superposed on that due to the source itself. Since the Laplace equation is linear, the combined potential function again satisfies the Laplace equation. The boundary condition at the wall is now automatically satisfied. The resulting potential function is

$$\phi = \frac{m}{4\pi}\left(\frac{1}{\sqrt{(x+a)^2+y^2+z^2}} + \frac{1}{\sqrt{(x-a)^2+y^2+z^2}}\right)$$

Axisymmetric Flow into a Sink Midway between Two Parallel Infinite Planes. In this case there are two planes present, and it is necessary to use infinitely many images, as shown in Fig. 4.13. The potential function is

$$\phi = -\frac{m}{4\pi}\left[\frac{1}{\sqrt{x^2+y^2+z^2}} + \frac{1}{\sqrt{(x-a)^2+y^2+z^2}} + \frac{1}{\sqrt{(x+a)^2+y^2+z^2}} \right.$$
$$\left. + \frac{1}{\sqrt{(x-2a)^2+y^2+z^2}} + \frac{1}{\sqrt{(x+2a)^2+y^2+z^2}} + \cdots\right]$$

Flow Due to a Source in the Presence of Three Orthogonal Planes. If a source of strength m is situated at the point (a,b,c) in the first octant, in the presence of three orthogonal planes coinciding with the three coordinate planes, seven images must be used. The resulting potential function is

$$\phi = \frac{m}{4\pi}(\phi_1 + \phi_2 + \cdots + \phi_8)$$

in which

$$\phi_1 = \frac{1}{\sqrt{(x-a)^2+(y-b)^2+(z-c)^2}} \qquad \phi_2 = \frac{1}{\sqrt{(x-a)^2+(y-b)^2+(z+c)^2}}$$

. . . .

$$\phi_7 = \frac{1}{\sqrt{(x+a)^2+(y+b)^2+(z-c)^2}} \qquad \phi_8 = \frac{1}{\sqrt{(x+a)^2+(y+b)^2+(z+c)^2}}$$

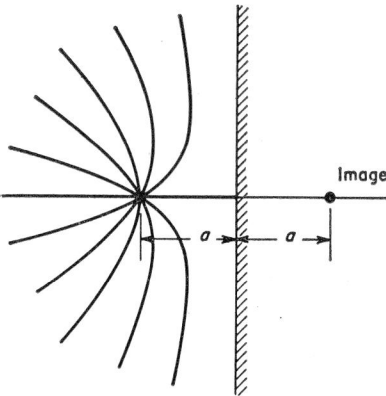

FIG. 4.12. Source near a wall.

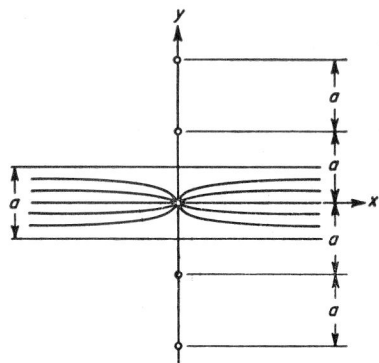

FIG. 4.13. Point source midway between two parallel planes.

The images are at the points

$$(a,b,-c), \ (-a,b,c), \ (-a,b,-c), \ (a,-b,c), \ (a,-b,-c), \ (-a,-b,c), \ (-a,-b,-c)$$

The resulting flow is truly three-dimensional (without axisymmetry).

Butler's Sphere Theorem. Flows about a sphere can often be obtained by using images inside the sphere. The image of an isolated singularity inside the sphere is a singularity the flow due to which can be added to that due to the original singularity to produce one with the sphere as a stream surface. There is a theorem, due to S. F. J. Butler, which can be used not only to find the images (inside the sphere) of outside singularities, but also to find the image of the outside flow, which may not contain any singularity or may contain only distributed singularities. However, Butler's theorem applies only to axisymmetric flows. The statement of this theorem is as follows: For an axisymmetric irrotational flow of an incompressible fluid, with no rigid boundaries, characterized by the stream function

$$\psi_0 = \psi_0(R,\theta)$$

with $\psi_0(0,\theta) = 0$ and with no singularities at a radial distance less than a, the stream function for the flow, after a sphere with center at the origin and radius a is introduced, is

$$\psi = \psi_0 - \psi^*_0 = \psi_0(R,\theta) - \frac{R}{a} \psi_0 \left(\frac{a^2}{R}, \theta \right) \tag{4.74}$$

That the stream function ψ^*_0 corresponds to an irrotational flow follows from the fact that the corresponding vorticity is

$$R^2 \frac{\partial^2 \psi^*_0}{\partial R^2} + \sin\theta \frac{\partial}{\partial \theta} \left(\frac{1}{\sin\theta} \frac{\partial \psi^*_0}{\partial \theta} \right)$$

which can be shown to be zero if the vorticity corresponding to ψ_0 is zero. Thus if ψ_0 corresponds to an irrotational flow, ψ^*_0 corresponds to another. Hence ψ corresponds to an irrotational flow. That ψ is constant at $R = a$ is self-evident. Furthermore, since ψ_0 has no singularities inside the sphere, ψ^*_0 has none outside. Finally, since ψ_0 is of the order of r^2 near the origin, ψ^*_0 varies as $1/r$ at infinity and certainly does not alter the condition there. Thus ψ is the stream function sought.

Butler's theorem is a special case of Weiss's sphere theorem,[2] stated as follows. If $\phi(x,y,z)$ characterizes an irrotational flow of an incompressible fluid, with no singularities at a radial distance less than a, the potential function for the flow, after the sphere with center at the origin and with radius a is introduced, is

$$\phi(x,y,z) + \frac{a}{R} \phi \left(\frac{a^2 x}{R^2}, \frac{a^2 y}{R^2}, \frac{a^2 z}{R^2} \right) - \frac{2}{aR} \int_0^a \lambda \phi \left(\frac{\lambda x}{R^2}, \frac{\lambda y}{R^2}, \frac{\lambda z}{R^2} \right) d\lambda \tag{4.75}$$

Weiss' theorem applies to general three-dimensional flow (not merely axisymmetric flow) and is based on Kelvin's inversion theorem[2] that if $\phi(x,y,z)$ is harmonic, so is

$$\frac{1}{R} \phi \left(\frac{x}{R^2}, \frac{y}{R^2}, \frac{z}{R^2} \right)$$

In the following paragraphs of this article, a few examples will be given to illustrate the application of Butler's sphere theorem.

Uniform (at Infinity) Flow Past a Sphere. Here the function ψ_0 is

$$-\frac{U}{2} R^2 \sin^2\theta$$

so that
$$\psi = -\frac{U}{2} R^2 \sin^2\theta - \frac{R}{a} \left(-\frac{U}{2} \frac{a^4}{R^2} \sin^2\theta \right)$$

$$= -\frac{U}{2} R^2 \sin^2\theta + \frac{Ua^3}{2R} \sin^2\theta$$

which agrees with Eq. (4.71).

Image of a Doublet in a Sphere. The flow due to a doublet near a sphere can be obtained by finding the image of the doublet in the sphere by the use of the Butler theorem. Thus, for a doublet situated as shown in Fig. 4.14, with strength μ and axis in the negative x direction, the function ψ_0 is

$$-\frac{\mu \sin^2 \theta_1}{R_1} = -\frac{\mu R^2 \sin^2 \theta}{(R^2 + b^2 - 2Rb \cos \theta)^{3/2}}$$

so that

$$-\psi^*_0 = \frac{\mu a^3 R^2 \sin^2 \theta}{(a^4 + b^2 R^2 - 2a^2 Rb \cos \theta)^{3/2}}$$

which corresponds to a doublet of strength

$$\frac{\mu a^3}{b^3}$$

situated at the inverse point Q, with axis in the positive x direction.

When two spheres approach each other along the line of centers, the flow due to the motion of either sphere can be created by placing a doublet at the center of the sphere, if the presence of the other sphere is ignored. To take care of the interaction of the spheres, successive images must be used inside each sphere. The resulting stream function or potential function converges rather rapidly, particularly when the spheres are not too near, since the images decrease in strength each time of reflection by a factor equal to the third power of a number less than 1.

The method of taking the image of a doublet can be applied to the flow due to the translation of a sphere within a fixed concentric (momentarily) spherical shell, or to the flow about a fixed sphere due to the translation of a concentric spherical shell. In either case the space between the sphere and the shell is filled with fluid. Successive images must be taken, but these images are all located at the center of the sphere and hence can be added together in an infinite series. The results can be obtained otherwise—by superposing a potential of the type $AR \cos \theta$ on one of the type $BR^{-2} \cos \theta$. With a and b denoting the radius of the sphere and that of the shell, respectively, the results for the first case are

$$\phi_1 = \frac{a^3 U}{b^3 - a^3}\left(R + \frac{b^3}{2R^2}\right)\cos\theta \qquad \psi_1 = \frac{a^3 U}{2(b^3 - a^3)}\left(r^2 - \frac{b^3}{r}\right)\sin^2\theta$$

in which U is the velocity of translation of the sphere. For the second case the results are

$$\phi_2 = \phi_1 + UR \cos \theta \qquad \psi_2 = \psi_1 + \frac{UR^2}{2}\sin^2\theta$$

with U now denoting the velocity of translation of the shell. It is, of course, obvious that ϕ_1 and ϕ_2 should differ by the potential corresponding to a uniform flow with velocity U and that ψ_1 and ψ_2 should differ by the stream function for this uniform flow.

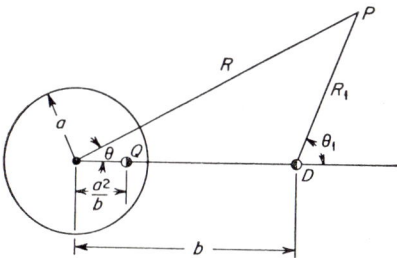

FIG. 4.14. Notation for doublet near a sphere.

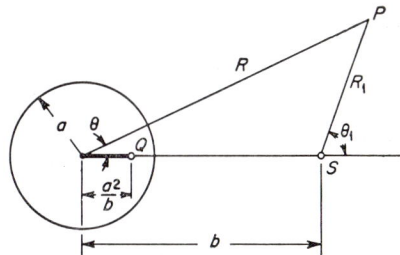

FIG. 4.15. Notation for source near a sphere.

Flow Due to a Source near a Sphere (Fig. 4.15). Let the source be situated at $R = b \ (>a)$, $\theta = 0$.

Then
$$\psi_0 = \frac{m}{4\pi} \cos \theta_1$$

But
$$\cos \theta_1 = \frac{R \cos \theta - b}{\sqrt{R^2 + b^2 - 2Rb \cos \theta}}$$

therefore
$$-\psi^*_0 = \frac{-mR}{4\pi a} \frac{a^2 \cos \theta - Rb}{\sqrt{a^4 + b^2 R^2 - 2a^2 Rb \cos \theta}}$$

which corresponds to a source of strength ma/b at Q, a sink of total strength ma/b, uniformly distributed over OQ, and a circulatory motion about the polar axis, because the inside sources have the stream function

$$\frac{ma}{4\pi b} \frac{R \cos \theta - a^2/b}{\sqrt{R^2 - (2a^2/b)R \cos \theta + a^4/b^2}} - \frac{m}{4\pi a} \int_0^{a^2/b} \frac{R \cos \theta - \xi}{\sqrt{R^2 + \xi^2 - 2R\xi \cos \theta}} \, d\xi$$

$$= \frac{ma}{4\pi b} \frac{Rb \cos \theta - a^2}{\sqrt{a^4 + b^2 R^2 - 2a^2 Rb \cos \theta}} + \frac{m}{4\pi a} \sqrt{R^2 + \xi^2 - 2R\xi \cos \theta} \Big|_0^{a^2/b}$$

$$= -\frac{mR}{4\pi a} \frac{a^2 \cos \theta - Rb}{\sqrt{a^4 + b^2 R^2 - 2a^2 Rb \cos \theta}} - \frac{mR}{4\pi a}$$

and the term $-mR/4\pi a$ corresponds to a circulatory motion about the axis. The circulatory motion is characterized by

$$v = \frac{1}{R \sin \theta} \frac{\partial}{\partial R} \left(-\frac{mR}{4\pi a} \right) = -\frac{m}{4\pi a R \sin \theta}$$

$$u = 0$$

This circulatory motion can be removed without violating any requirements on the outside flow.

4.22. Harmonic Functions

In general orthogonal coordinates (α, β, γ), the square of an infinitesimal length is (Fig. 4.16)
$$ds^2 = (h_1 \, d\alpha)^2 + (h_2 \, d\beta)^2 + (h_3 \, d\gamma)^2$$

It can be shown that the Laplacian operator is, in general coordinates,

$$\nabla^2 = \frac{1}{h_1 h_2 h_3} \left[\frac{\partial}{\partial \alpha} \left(\frac{h_1}{h_2 h_3} \frac{\partial}{\partial \alpha} \right) + \frac{\partial}{\partial \beta} \left(\frac{h_2}{h_3 h_1} \frac{\partial}{\partial \beta} \right) + \frac{\partial}{\partial \gamma} \left(\frac{h_3}{h_1 h_2} \frac{\partial}{\partial \gamma} \right) \right] \qquad (4.76)$$

The Laplace equation is therefore

$$\frac{\partial}{\partial \alpha} \left(\frac{h_1}{h_2 h_3} \frac{\partial \phi}{\partial \alpha} \right) + \frac{\partial}{\partial \beta} \left(\frac{h_2}{h_3 h_1} \frac{\partial \phi}{\partial \beta} \right) + \frac{\partial}{\partial \gamma} \left(\frac{h_3}{h_1 h_2} \frac{\partial \phi}{\partial \gamma} \right) = 0 \qquad (4.77)$$

For cartesian coordinates,
$$h_1 = h_2 = h_3 = 1$$

and the Laplace equation assumes the form given before. For other coordinate systems, the forms of the Laplace equation are less simple. But so long as only orthogonal coordinates are used, the method of separation of variables can always be used to solve the Laplace equations. The solutions are called harmonic functions, or for brevity, harmonics. Depending on the coordinate system involved, they are called cartesian harmonics, spherical harmonics, cylindrical harmonics, or ellipsoidal harmonics. These will now be examined in some detail.

Cartesian Harmonics. The Laplace equation in cartesian coordinates

$$\frac{\partial^2 \phi}{\partial x^2} + \frac{\partial^2 \phi}{\partial y^2} + \frac{\partial^2 \phi}{\partial z^2} = 0$$

is satisfied by functions of the type

$$\cos lx \cos my \cosh nz$$

if

$$n = \sqrt{l^2 + m^2}$$

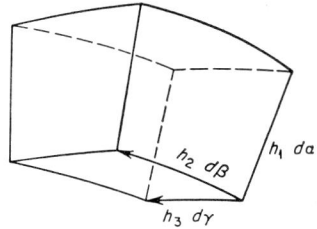

Fig. 4.16. Volume element in general orthogonal coordinates.

Either (or both) of the cosines can be replaced by a sine, and the hyperbolic cosine can be replaced by a hyperbolic sine or an exponential function. With sine u for l/n and cos u for m/n, the function

$$e^{n(z + ix \cos u + iy \sin u)}$$

has both its real and imaginary parts of the type described above and is hence a (complex) harmonic function. More generally, one can write

$$\phi = \int_{-\pi}^{\pi} f(z + ix \cos u + iy \sin u, u) \, du \tag{4.78}$$

It can be shown by direct differentiation that the ϕ given by this formula is harmonic.

Spherical Harmonics. In spherical coordinates (R, θ, φ),

$$h_1 = 1 \qquad h_2 = R \qquad h_3 = R \sin \theta$$

so that the Laplace equation is, after multiplying by R^2,

$$\frac{\partial}{\partial R}\left(R^2 \frac{\partial \phi}{\partial R}\right) + \frac{1}{\sin \theta}\frac{\partial}{\partial \theta}\left(\sin \theta \frac{\partial \phi}{\partial \theta}\right) + \frac{1}{\sin^2 \theta}\frac{\partial^2 \phi}{\partial \varphi^2} = 0 \tag{4.79}$$

With

$$\mu = \cos \theta \qquad \phi = R^n S_n(\mu)\binom{\sin s\varphi}{\cos s\varphi} \qquad (s = \text{integer}) \tag{4.80}$$

the equation satisfied by $S_n(\mu)$ is, after simplification,

$$\frac{d}{\partial \mu}\left[(1 - \mu^2)\frac{dS_n}{d\mu}\right] + \left[n(n+1) - \frac{s^2}{1 - \mu^2}\right]S_n = 0 \tag{4.81}$$

There are two independent solutions of this equation. It can be shown that, as a consequence of the fact that s is an integer, one of these solutions terminates. The solution that terminates is called the associated Legendre function and has the form

$$P_n{}^s(\mu) \equiv \frac{(2n)!}{2^n(n-s)!n!}(1 - \mu^2)^{s/2}\left[\mu^{n-s} - \frac{(n-s)(n-s-1)}{2 \cdot (2n-1)}\mu^{n-s-2}\right.$$

$$\left. + \frac{(n-s)(n-s-1)(n-s-2)(n-s-3)}{2 \cdot 4 \cdot (2n-1)(2n-3)}\mu^{n-s-4} + \cdots\right] \tag{4.82}$$

in which the first (fractional) mul'iplier has been chosen for convenience.

For $s = 0$, the Legendre function $P_n{}^s(\mu)$ becomes

$$P_n(\mu) = \frac{1 \cdot 3 \cdot 5 \cdots (2n-1)}{n!}\left[\mu^n - \frac{n(n-1)}{2(2n-1)}\mu^{n-2}\right.$$

$$\left. + \frac{n(n-1)(n-2)(n-3)}{2 \cdot 4 \cdot (2n-1)(2n-3)}\mu^{n-4} + \cdots\right] \tag{4.83}$$

The functions $P_n(\mu)$ are called Legendre polynomials and can be expressed simply as

$$P_n(\mu) = \frac{1}{2^n n!} \frac{d^n}{d\mu^n} (\mu^2 - 1)^n \tag{4.84}$$

which is proportional to

$$R^{n+1} \frac{\partial^n}{\partial x^n} \frac{1}{R}$$

The first four Legendre polynomials are

$$P_0(\mu) = 1 \qquad P_1(\mu) = \mu \qquad P_2(\mu) = \tfrac{1}{2}(3\mu^2 - 1) \qquad P_3(\mu) = \tfrac{1}{2}(5\mu^3 - 3\mu)$$

In terms of the Legendre polynomials, the associated Legendre functions can be expressed simply as

$$P_n{}^s(\mu) = (1 - \mu^2)^{s/2} \frac{d^s P_n(\mu)}{d\mu^s} \tag{4.85}$$

The solution of Eq. (4.81) that does not terminate (as a power series in μ) is denoted by $Q_n{}^s(\mu)$ and is called the associated Legendre function of the second kind. If, for $s = 0$, $Q_n{}^s(\mu)$ is denoted by $Q_n(\mu)$, then

$$Q_n{}^s(\mu) = (1 - \mu^2)^{s/2} \frac{d^s Q_n(\mu)}{d\mu^s} \tag{4.86}$$

in which $Q_n(\mu)$ is given by

$$Q_n(\mu) = \tfrac{1}{2} P_n(\mu) \ln \frac{1+\mu}{1-\mu} - \frac{2n-1}{1 \cdot n} P_{n-1}(\mu) - \frac{2n-5}{3(n-1)} P_{n-3}(\mu)$$

$$- \frac{2n-9}{5(n-2)} P_{n-5}(\mu) - \cdots \tag{4.87}$$

up to the term for which the subscript of the Legendre polynomial becomes negative. For instance,

$$Q_0(\mu) = \tfrac{1}{2}\ln \frac{1+\mu}{1-\mu} \qquad Q_1(\mu) = \frac{\mu}{2} \ln \frac{1+\mu}{1-\mu} - 1$$

$$Q_2(\mu) = \tfrac{1}{4}(3\mu^2 - 1)\ln \frac{1+\mu}{1-\mu} - \frac{3\mu}{2}$$

$$Q_3(\mu) = \tfrac{1}{4}(5\mu^2 - 1)\ln \frac{1+\mu}{1-\mu} - \frac{5\mu^2}{2} + \tfrac{2}{3}$$

Since the number $n(n + 1)$ remains unchanged when n is replaced by $-(n + 1)$, the functions

$$R^{-(n+1)} P_n{}^s(\mu) \begin{pmatrix} \cos \varphi \\ \sin \varphi \end{pmatrix}$$

are also spherical harmonics. For $s = 0$, the spherical harmonics are

$$\begin{pmatrix} R^n \\ R^{-(n+1)} \end{pmatrix} P_n(\mu) \tag{4.88}$$

For $n = 0$, the spherical harmonic $1/R$ corresponds to the velocity potential for a source or sink. For $n = 1$, one harmonic is of the form $R\mu$ or $R \cos \theta$ and corresponds to the velocity potential for uniform flow. The other harmonic for $n = 1$, $\cos \theta/R^2$, corresponds to the velocity potential for a doublet. As has been seen already, the combination

$$AR \cos \theta + \frac{B}{R^2} \cos \theta$$

corresponds to ambiently uniform flow past a sphere.

The Legendre functions satisfy the orthogonal conditions

$$\int_{-1}^{1} P_m{}^s(\mu) P_n{}^s(\mu) d\mu = 0 \qquad \text{for } m \neq n$$

$$\int_{-1}^{1} [P_n{}^s(\mu)]^2 d\mu = \frac{(n+s)!}{(n-s)!} \frac{2}{2n+1}$$

(4.89)

These conditions make it possible to expand any finite, piecewise smooth function in the interval $-1 \le \mu \le 1$, in terms of associated Legendre functions. By taking s equal to zero, the orthogonal conditions for Legendre polynomials are obtained.

Cylindrical Harmonics. For cylindrical coordinates (r,θ,z),

$$h_1 = 1 \qquad h_2 = r \qquad h_3 = 1$$

and the Laplace equation is of the form

$$\frac{\partial^2 \phi}{\partial r^2} + \frac{1}{r} \frac{\partial \phi}{\partial r} + \frac{1}{r^2} \frac{\partial^2 \phi}{\partial \varphi^2} + \frac{\partial^2 \phi}{\partial z^2} = 0$$

If ϕ is expressed in the form

$$\phi = f(r) e^{\lambda z} \begin{pmatrix} \sin n\varphi \\ \cos n\varphi \end{pmatrix} \qquad (n = \text{integer})$$

(4.90)

the function $f(r)$ satisfies the equation

$$\frac{d^2 f}{dr^2} + \frac{1}{r} \frac{df}{dr} + \left(\lambda^2 - \frac{n^2}{r^2} \right) f = 0$$

This is Bessel's equation, having, for $n =$ an integer, two solutions $J_n(\lambda r)$ and $Y_n(\lambda r)$, called the Bessel function of the first and the second kind, respectively. For n equal to a positive integer, $J_n(\lambda r)$ and its derivatives are analytic for all finite values of r, whereas $Y_n(\lambda r)$ has a singularity at the origin.

For λ equal to an imaginary number, both $J_n(\lambda r)$ and $Y_n(\lambda r)$ approach infinity as r approaches infinity. But a suitable combination of the two (called the Hankel function) can be found, which is regular at infinite r.

Ellipsoidal Harmonics. Solutions of the Laplace equation for boundary conditions related to ellipsoids can best be expressed in ellipsoidal coordinates and, when so expressed, are called ellipsoidal harmonics. A discussion of ellipsoidal coordinates for prolate and oblate ellipsoids of revolution and for general ellipsoids follows essentially the treatment given in Lamb.[3]

1. For a prolate ellipsoid of revolution, i.e., for an ellipsoid with the axis of revolution (x axis, say) along its longest axis, the coordinates to be used are ζ, μ, ω defined by

$$x = k \cos \theta \cosh \eta = k\mu\zeta \qquad y = r \cos \omega \qquad z = r \sin \omega$$

(4.91)

in which

$$r = k \sin \theta \sinh \eta = k(1 - \mu^2)^{\frac{1}{2}}(\zeta^2 - 1)^{\frac{1}{2}}$$

(4.92)

In these coordinates,

$$h_\zeta = k \left(\frac{\zeta^2 - \mu^2}{\zeta^2 - 1} \right)^{\frac{1}{2}} \qquad h_\mu = k \left(\frac{\zeta^2 - \mu^2}{1 - \mu^2} \right)^{\frac{1}{2}} \qquad h_\omega = k(1 - \mu^2)^{\frac{1}{2}}(\zeta^2 - 1)^{\frac{1}{2}}$$

(4.93)

and the Laplace equation becomes

$$\frac{\partial}{\partial \zeta}\left[(\zeta^2 - 1)\frac{\partial \phi}{\partial \zeta} \right] + \frac{\partial}{\partial \mu}\left[(1 - \mu^2)\frac{\partial \phi}{\partial \mu} \right] + \frac{\zeta^2 - \mu^2}{(1 - \mu^2)(\zeta^2 - 1)}\frac{\partial^2 \phi}{\partial \omega^2} = 0$$

or
$$\frac{\partial}{\partial \zeta}\left[(\zeta^2 - 1)\frac{\partial \phi}{\partial \zeta} \right] + \frac{1}{1 - \zeta^2}\frac{\partial^2 \phi}{\partial \omega^2} = \frac{\partial}{\partial \mu}\left[(1 - \mu^2)\frac{\partial \phi}{\partial \mu} \right] + \frac{1}{1 - \mu^2}\frac{\partial^2 \phi}{\partial \omega^2} \qquad (4.94)$$

If ϕ is independent of ω, the solutions of Eq. (4.94) are, when the dependence of ϕ on μ is in the form of $P_n(\mu)$,

$$\phi = P_n(\mu)P_n(\zeta) \qquad (4.95)$$
and
$$\phi = P_n(\mu)Q_n(\zeta) \qquad (4.96)$$

in which $Q_n(\mu)$ is given in Eq. (4.87) and $Q_n(\zeta)$ has the slightly different form

$$Q_n(\zeta) = \tfrac{1}{2}P_n(\zeta)\ln\frac{\zeta + 1}{\zeta - 1} - \frac{2n - 1}{1 \cdot n}P_{n-1}(\zeta) - \frac{2n - 5}{3(n - 1)}P_{n-3}(\zeta) - \cdots \qquad (4.97)$$

Thus
$$Q_0(\zeta) = \tfrac{1}{2}\ln\frac{\zeta + 1}{\zeta - 1} \qquad Q_1(\zeta) = \frac{\zeta}{2}\ln\frac{\zeta + 1}{\zeta - 1} - 1 \qquad \text{etc.}$$

In terms of Stokes' stream function, the velocity components in the directions of increasing ζ and μ for axisymmetric flows are

$$V_\zeta = \frac{1}{rh_\mu}\frac{\partial \psi}{\partial \mu} \qquad V_\mu = -\frac{1}{rh_\zeta}\frac{\partial \psi}{\partial \zeta} \qquad (4.98)$$

as can be derived either from Eq. (4.14) or from Eq. (4.16). On the other hand, if ϕ is the velocity potential for an irrotational flow,

$$V_\zeta = -\frac{1}{h_\zeta}\frac{\partial \phi}{\partial \zeta} \qquad V_\mu = -\frac{1}{h_\mu}\frac{\partial \phi}{\partial \mu} \qquad (4.99)$$

Thus, from Eqs. (4.92), (4.93), (4.98), and (4.99),

$$\frac{\partial \psi}{\partial \mu} = -k(\zeta^2 - 1)\frac{\partial \phi}{\partial \zeta} \qquad \frac{\partial \psi}{\partial \zeta} = k(1 - \mu^2)\frac{\partial \phi}{\partial \mu} \qquad (4.100)$$

From these equations it can be deduced that, if ϕ is given by Eq. (4.95),

$$\psi = -\frac{k}{n(n + 1)}(1 - \mu^2)\frac{dP_n(\mu)}{d\mu} \cdot (\zeta^2 - 1)\frac{dP_n(\zeta)}{d\zeta} \qquad (4.101)$$

and, if ϕ is given by Eq. (4.96),

$$\psi = \frac{k}{n(n + 1)}(1 - \mu^2)\frac{dP_n(\mu)}{d\mu} \cdot (\zeta^2 - 1)\frac{dQ_n(\zeta)}{d\zeta} \qquad (4.102)$$

Equation (4.102) can be applied to the case of axisymmetric motion of an infinite fluid due to the translation of a prolate ellipsoid along its axis. If a and c are the polar and equilateral semiaxes and

$$e = \sqrt{1 - \frac{c^2}{a^2}}$$

is the eccentricity, and if, on the ellipsoid $\zeta = \zeta_0$, one has, from Eqs. (4.91) and (4.92),

$$k = ae \qquad \zeta_0 = \frac{1}{e}$$

$$k(\zeta_0^2 - 1)^{1/2} = c$$

The surface condition is, for $\zeta = \zeta_0$,

$$\psi = -\tfrac{1}{2}Ur^2 + C = -\tfrac{1}{2}Uk^2(1 - \mu^2)(\zeta^2 - 1) + C$$

if U is the velocity in the x direction.   Putting $n = 1$ in Eq. (4.102), one obtains

$$\psi = \tfrac{1}{2}Ak(1 - \mu^2)(\zeta^2 - 1)\left(\tfrac{1}{2}\ln\frac{\zeta + 1}{\zeta - 1} - \frac{\zeta}{\zeta^2 - 1}\right) \tag{4.103}$$

in which A is a constant which can be determined from the boundary condition at $\zeta = \zeta_0$ and is

$$A = Ua\left(\frac{1}{1 - e^2} - \frac{1}{2e}\ln\frac{1 + e}{1 - e}\right)^{-1} \tag{4.104}$$

The velocity potential corresponding to the ψ given in Eq. (4.103) is

$$\phi = A\mu\left(\tfrac{1}{2}\zeta\ln\frac{\zeta + 1}{\zeta - 1} - 1\right) \tag{4.105}$$

For flows without axisymmetry, s is different from zero, and the general solutions are

$$\phi = P_n{}^s(\mu) \cdot P_n{}^s(\zeta)\begin{pmatrix}\cos s\omega\\ \sin s\omega\end{pmatrix} \tag{4.106}$$

$$\phi = P_n{}^s(\mu) \cdot Q_n{}^s(\zeta)\begin{pmatrix}\cos s\omega\\ \sin s\omega\end{pmatrix} \tag{4.107}$$

in which $P_n{}^s(\mu)$ is given by Eq. (4.85), and

$$P_n{}^s(\zeta) = (\zeta^2 - 1)^{1/2}\frac{d^sP_n(\zeta)}{d\zeta^s} \tag{4.108}$$

$$Q_n{}^s(\zeta) = (\zeta^2 - 1)^{1/2}\frac{d^sQ_n(\zeta)}{d\zeta^s} \tag{4.109}$$

the change from $1 - \zeta^2$ [according to Eq. (4.85)] to $\zeta^2 - 1$ having been made to avoid imaginary numbers.   The expressions for ϕ given by Eqs. (4.106) and (4.107) are called tesseral, or sectional, harmonics when s is not equal to zero.   For $s = 0$, these expressions coincide with those given for ϕ in Eqs. (4.95) and (4.96) and are called zonal harmonics. Of course, the same terms apply in the same way to spherical harmonics, too.

One important application of sectional ellipsoidal harmonics is to the potential flow of an infinite fluid due to the translation of a prolate ellipsoid parallel to an equatorial axis, say, the y axis.   The boundary condition is (V = velocity of translation)

$$\frac{\partial\phi}{\partial\zeta} = -V\frac{\partial y}{\partial\zeta} \tag{4.110}$$

on the ellipsoid, on which $\zeta = \zeta_0$.   The solution is

$$\phi = A(1 - \mu^2)^{1/2}(\zeta^2 - 1)^{1/2}\left(\tfrac{1}{2}\ln\frac{\zeta + 1}{\zeta - 1} - \frac{\zeta}{\zeta^2 - 1}\right)\cos\omega \tag{4.111}$$

in which $\qquad\qquad A = -kV\left(\tfrac{1}{2}\ln\frac{\zeta_0 + 1}{\zeta_0 - 1} - \frac{\zeta_0}{\zeta_0{}^2 - 1}\right)^{-1}$

with k equal to ae and e equal to $1/\zeta_0$, as before.   This solution is of the type of Eq. (4.107), with n and s both equal to 1.

Another example is furnished by the potential flow of an infinite fluid due to the rotation of a prolate ellipsoid about an equatorial axis, say, the y axis.   The boundary condition is, for $\zeta = \zeta_0$,

$$\frac{\partial\phi}{\partial\zeta} = -\Omega_y\left(z\frac{\partial x}{\partial\zeta} - x\frac{\partial z}{\partial\zeta}\right) \tag{4.112}$$

The solution can be obtained by putting $n = 2$ and $s = 1$ in Eq. (4.107) and is

$$\phi = A\mu(1 - \mu^2)^{\frac{1}{2}}(\zeta^2 - 1)^{\frac{1}{2}} \left(\tfrac{3}{2}\zeta\ln \frac{\zeta + 1}{\zeta - 1} - 3 - \frac{1}{\zeta^2 - 1} \right) \sin \omega \qquad (4.113)$$

in which A can be determined to satisfy the boundary condition Eq. (4.112), in a straight-forward manner.

2. For an oblate ellipsoid of revolution, i.e., for an ellipsoid with the shortest axis as the axis of revolution, the coordinates ζ, μ, ω are now related to x, y, z in the following manner:

$$x = k \cos \theta \sinh \eta = k\mu\zeta \qquad y = r \cos \omega \qquad z = r \sin \omega \qquad (4.114)$$

in which

$$r = k \sin \theta \cosh \eta = k(1 - \mu^2)^{\frac{1}{2}}(\zeta^2 + 1)^{\frac{1}{2}} \qquad (4.115)$$

In the coordinates ζ, μ, ω, the Laplace equation becomes

$$\frac{\partial}{\partial \mu}\left[(1 - \mu^2)\frac{\partial \phi}{\partial \mu}\right] + \frac{1}{1 - \mu^2}\frac{\partial^2 \phi}{\partial \omega^2} = -\frac{\partial}{\partial \zeta}\left[(\zeta^2 + 1)\frac{\partial \phi}{\partial \zeta}\right] + \frac{1}{\zeta^2 + 1}\frac{\partial^2 \phi}{\partial \omega^2} \qquad (4.116)$$

the solutions of which are, for axisymmetric motion (independent of ω),

$$\phi = P_n(\mu) \cdot p_n(\zeta) \qquad (4.117)$$
$$\phi = P_n(\mu) \cdot q_n(\zeta) \qquad (4.118)$$

with

$$p_n(\zeta) = \frac{1 \cdot 3 \cdot 5 \cdots (2n - 1)}{n!}\left[\zeta^n + \frac{n(n - 1)}{2(2n - 1)}\zeta^{n-2}\right.$$

$$\left. + \frac{n(n - 1)(n - 2)(n - 3)}{2 \cdot 4(2n - 1)(2n - 3)}\zeta^{n-4} + \cdots \right] \qquad (4.119)$$

and

$$q_n(\zeta) = (-1)^n\left[p_n(\zeta)\cot^{-1}\zeta - \frac{2n - 1}{1 \cdot n}p_{n-1}(\zeta) + \frac{2n - 5}{3(n - 1)}p_{n-3}(\zeta) + \cdots \right]$$

$$(4.120)$$

The series for $p_n(\zeta)$ obviously terminates, and the series for $q_n(\zeta)$ in the form of Eq. (4.120) terminates at the term the next to which would have a negative subscript for p. The stream functions corresponding to the velocity potentials given by Eqs. (4.117) and (4.118) are

$$\psi = \frac{k}{n(n + 1)}(1 - \mu^2)\frac{dP_n(\mu)}{d\mu} \cdot (\zeta^2 + 1)\frac{dp_n(\zeta)}{d\zeta} \qquad (4.121)$$

$$\psi = \frac{k}{n(n + 1)}(1 - \mu^2)\frac{dP_n(\mu)}{d\mu} \cdot (\zeta^2 + 1)\frac{dq_n(\zeta)}{d\zeta} \qquad (4.122)$$

The solution [ψ derived directly from ϕ, without using Eq. (4.122)]

$$\phi = A\cot^{-1}\zeta \qquad \psi = Ak\mu \qquad (4.123)$$

corresponds to the irrotational flow of a fluid through a circular aperture in an infinite plane wall, without separation after passage through the aperture.

The motion due to the translation (with velocity U parallel to its axis of symmetry) of an oblate ellipsoid ($\zeta = \zeta_0$) is given by

$$\phi = A\mu(1 - \zeta\cot^{-1}\zeta) \qquad \psi = \tfrac{1}{2}Ak(1 - \mu^2)(\zeta^2 + 1)\left(\frac{\zeta}{\zeta^2 + 1} - \cot^{-1}\zeta\right)$$

in which

$$A = -kU\left(\frac{\zeta_0}{\zeta_0{}^2 + 1} - \cot^{-1}\zeta_0\right)^{-1}$$

In terms of the polar radius a, equatorial radius c, and eccentricity

$$e = \sqrt{1 - \frac{a^2}{c^2}}$$

the constant A is given by

$$A = -Uc \left[(1 - e^2)^{\frac{1}{2}} - \frac{1}{e} \sin^{-1} e \right]$$

because $\quad\quad a = k\zeta_0 \quad\quad c = k(\zeta_0^2 + 1)^{\frac{1}{2}} \quad\quad e = (\zeta_0^2 + 1)^{-\frac{1}{2}}$

The solutions of Eqs. (4.116) without axisymmetry are

$$\phi = P_n{}^s(\mu) p_n{}^s(\zeta) \cdot \binom{\cos s\omega}{\sin s\omega} \tag{4.124}$$

$$\phi = P_n{}^s(\mu) q_n{}^s(\zeta) \cdot \binom{\cos s\omega}{\sin s\omega} \tag{4.125}$$

in which

$$p_n{}^s(\zeta) = (\zeta^2 + 1)^{s/2} \frac{d^s p_n(\zeta)}{d\zeta^s}$$

$$q_n{}^s(\zeta) = (\zeta^2 + 1)^{s/2} \frac{d^s q_n(\zeta)}{d\zeta^s}$$

The motion due to the translation of an oblate ellipsoid ($\zeta = \zeta_0$) with velocity V parallel to an equatorial axis (say, the y axis) is given by Eq. (4.125) with $n = 1$, $s = 1$:

$$\phi = A(1 - \mu^2)^{\frac{1}{2}}(\zeta^2 + 1)^{\frac{1}{2}} \left(\frac{\zeta}{\zeta^2 + 1} - \cot^{-1} \zeta \right) \cos \omega$$

in which the constant A is determined from the boundary condition at $\zeta = \zeta_0$:

$$\frac{\partial \phi}{\partial \zeta} = -V \frac{\partial y}{\partial \zeta}$$

or

$$A \left(\frac{\zeta_0^2 + 2}{\zeta_0(\zeta_0^2 + 1)} - \cot^{-1} \zeta_0 \right) = -kV$$

For the motion due to rotation of the ellipsoid $\zeta = \zeta_0$ about the y axis, the solution is given by Eqs. (4.125) with $n = 2$, $s = 1$:

$$\phi = A\mu(1 - \mu^2)^{\frac{1}{2}} (\zeta^2 + 1)^{\frac{1}{2}} \left(3\zeta \cot^{-1} \zeta - 3 + \frac{1}{\zeta^2 + 1} \right) \sin \omega$$

The constant A is to be determined from the boundary condition at $\zeta = \zeta_0$:

$$\frac{\partial \phi}{\partial \zeta} = -\Omega_y \left(z \frac{\partial x}{\partial \zeta} - x \frac{\partial z}{\partial \zeta} \right) = -\frac{k^2 \Omega_y}{(\zeta_0^2 + 1)^{\frac{1}{2}}} \mu(1 - \mu^2)^{\frac{1}{2}} \sin \omega$$

3. For ellipsoids with three unequal axes, general ellipsoidal coordinates must be used. If λ, μ, and ν are the three roots (for θ) of the equation (in which $a > b > c > 0$),

$$\frac{x^2}{a^2 + \theta} + \frac{y^2}{b^2 + \theta} + \frac{z^2}{c^2 + \theta} - 1 = 0$$

for any point (x,y,z), then

$$\frac{x^2}{a^2 + \theta} + \frac{y^2}{b^2 + \theta} + \frac{z^2}{c^2 + \theta} - 1 = \frac{(\lambda - \theta)(\mu - \theta)(\nu - \theta)}{(a^2 + \theta)(b^2 + \theta)(c^2 + \theta)} \tag{4.126}$$

identically for all θ. One of the roots (say, λ) lies between ∞ and $-c^2$, another (say, μ) between $-b^2$ and $-c^2$, and still another (ν) between $-a^2$ and $-b^2$. A surface for which

λ is a constant is an ellipsoid; a surface for which μ is a constant is a hyperboloid of one sheet; and a surface for which ν is a constant is a hyperboloid of two sheets.   The three families of surfaces are orthogonal to each other.

From Eq. (4.126) one easily obtains, by the method usually used for finding the numerators of partial fractions, that

$$x^2 = \frac{(a^2 + \lambda)(a^2 + \mu)(a^2 + \nu)}{(a^2 - b^2)(a^2 - c^2)}$$

$$y^2 = \frac{(b^2 + \lambda)(b^2 + \mu)(b^2 + \nu)}{(b^2 - c^2)(b^2 - a^2)} \tag{4.127}$$

$$z^2 = \frac{(c^2 + \lambda)(c^2 + \mu)(c^2 + \nu)}{(c^2 - a^2)(c^2 - b^2)}$$

from which $\dfrac{\partial x}{\partial \lambda} = \dfrac{1}{2}\dfrac{x}{a^2 + \lambda} \qquad \dfrac{\partial y}{\partial \lambda} = \dfrac{1}{2}\dfrac{y}{b^2 + \lambda} \qquad \dfrac{\partial z}{\partial \lambda} = \dfrac{1}{2}\dfrac{z}{c^2 + \lambda}$

Thus for a displacement perpendicular to a λ surface,

$$h_1^2(d\lambda)^2 = ds^2 = dx^2 + dy^2 + dz^2 = \frac{1}{4}\left[\frac{x^2}{(a^2 + \lambda)^2} + \frac{y^2}{(b^2 + \lambda)^2} + \frac{z^2}{(c^2 + \lambda)^2}\right](d\lambda)^2$$

and $$\frac{1}{h_1^2} = \frac{1}{4}\left[\frac{x^2}{(a^2 + \lambda)^2} + \frac{y^2}{(b^2 + \lambda)^2} + \frac{z^2}{(c^2 + \lambda)^2}\right]$$

or, from Eq. (4.126) by differentiation with respect to θ and setting $\theta = \lambda$,

$$h_1^2 = 4\frac{(a^2 + \lambda)(b^2 + \lambda)(c^2 + \lambda)}{(\lambda - \mu)(\lambda - \nu)}$$

Similarly, $$h_2^2 = 4\frac{(a^2 + \mu)(b^2 + \mu)(c^2 + \mu)}{(\mu - \nu)(\mu - \lambda)} \tag{4.128}$$

$$h_3^2 = 4\frac{(a^2 + \nu)(b^2 + \nu)(c^2 + \nu)}{(\nu - \lambda)(\nu - \mu)}$$

The Laplace equation is then given by Eq. (4.76):

$$\nabla^2\phi = -\frac{4}{(\mu - \nu)(\nu - \lambda)(\lambda - \mu)}\left\{(\mu - \nu)\left[(a^2 + \lambda)^{\frac{1}{2}}(b^2 + \lambda)^{\frac{1}{2}}(c^2 + \lambda)^{\frac{1}{2}}\frac{\partial}{\partial\lambda}\right]^2\right.$$

$$+ (\nu - \lambda)\left[(a^2 + \mu)^{\frac{1}{2}}(b^2 + \mu)^{\frac{1}{2}}(c^2 + \mu)^{\frac{1}{2}}\frac{\partial}{\partial\mu}\right]^2$$

$$\left. + (\lambda - \mu)\left[(a^2 + \nu)^{\frac{1}{2}}(b^2 + v)^{\frac{1}{2}}(c^2 + \nu)^{\frac{1}{2}}\frac{\partial}{\partial\nu}\right]^2\right\}\phi \tag{4.129}$$

The boundary condition for the motion of an infinite body of fluid caused by the translation of an ellipsoid ($\lambda = 0$)

$$\frac{x^2}{a^2} + \frac{y^2}{b^2} + \frac{z^2}{c^2} = 1 \tag{4.130}$$

in the x direction with velocity U is

$$\frac{\partial\phi}{\partial x} = -U\frac{\partial x}{\partial\lambda} \qquad \text{for } \lambda = 0$$

If a solution of the form

$$\phi = x\chi(\lambda)$$

is sought, it can be shown in a straightforward manner that

$$\phi = Cx \int_\lambda^\infty \frac{d\lambda}{(a^2 + \lambda)\Delta}$$ (4.131)

in which $\Delta = [(a^2 + \lambda)(b^2 + \lambda)(c^2 + \lambda)]^{1/2}$

$$C = \frac{abc}{2 - \alpha_0} U \qquad \text{(from the boundary condition)}$$

$$\alpha_0 = abc \int_0^\infty \frac{d\lambda}{(a^2 + \lambda)\Delta}$$

The solution for fluid motion caused by translation of the same ellipsoid in the y or z direction can be obtained similarly, and by superposition the solution for fluid motion due to any arbitrary translatory motion of the ellipsoid can be obtained. The motion of a fluid contained in an ellipsoidal shell in translation can be shown to be a solid-body translation.

For the (irrotational) motion of an infinite fluid caused by the rotation of the ellipsoid [Eq. (4.130)] about the x axis with angular velocity Ω_x, the solution is in the form

$$\phi = \frac{(b^2 - c^2)^2}{2(b^2 - c^2) + (b^2 + c^2)(\beta_0 - \gamma_0)} abc\Omega_x yz \int_\lambda^\infty \frac{d\lambda}{(b^2 + \lambda)(c^2 + \lambda)\Delta}$$ (4.132)

This result is for the fluid outside of the ellipsoid. If the fluid is contained in an ellipsoidal shell, the corresponding result is

$$\phi = -\frac{b^2 - c^2}{b^2 + c^2} \Omega_x yz$$

The following remark applies to all the special harmonic functions discussed in this section. If the boundary conditions are to be applied on a surface which is a coordinate surface for any orthogonal coordinates, the solution can be written in a series of the pertinent harmonics and a Fourier analysis applied to satisfy the boundary conditions on the surface in question. For the particular case of flow due to a moving sphere, the harmonic chosen must vanish at infinity and the Fourier analysis produces just one term for the velocity potential, which is of the form $-\mu \cos \theta / R^2$.

4.23. Distributed Sources and Applications

For a line source of strength $m(\xi)$ extending from $\xi = 0$ to $\xi = a$, the stream function can be found by superposition:

$$\psi = \frac{1}{4\pi} \int_0^a m(\xi) \cos \alpha \, d\xi$$ (4.133)

in which α is defined in Fig. 4.17, from which one has, in cylindrical coordinates,

$$z - \xi = r \cot \alpha \qquad d\xi = r \csc^2 \alpha \, d\alpha$$

If $m(\xi)$ is constant, Eq. (4.133) can be integrated:

$$\psi = \frac{mr}{4\pi} \int_{\alpha_1}^{\alpha_2} \frac{\cos \alpha}{\sin^2 \alpha} d\alpha = \frac{mr}{4\pi} \left(\frac{1}{\sin \alpha_1} - \frac{1}{\sin \alpha_2} \right) = \frac{m}{4\pi} (\overline{PO} - \overline{PA})$$

Thus the streamlines are confocal hyperbolas with foci at O and A. The potential "lines" are confocal ellipses with the same foci (Fig. 4.18).

Equation (4.133) can be written in the form

$$\psi = \frac{1}{4\pi} \int_0^a m(\xi) \frac{z - \xi}{\sqrt{(z - \xi)^2 + r^2}} d\xi$$ (4.134)

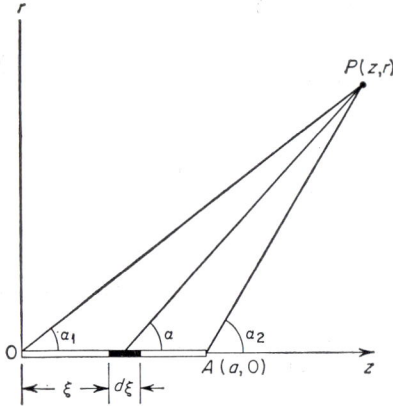

Fig. 4.17. Notation for line source.

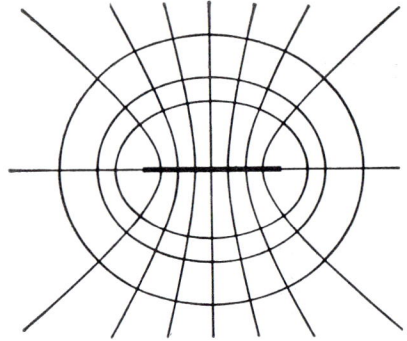

Fig. 4.18. Streamlines and equipotential lines for finite-line source. (*Ref. 9.*)

The corresponding potential is

$$\phi = \frac{1}{4\pi} \int_0^a \frac{m(\xi)}{\sqrt{(z-\xi)^2 + r^2}}\, d\xi$$

For a line doublet of varying strength $\mu(\xi)$, the potential function is, with x changed to $z - \xi$ in Eq. (4.61),

$$\phi = \int_0^a \mu(\xi)\, \frac{z-\xi}{[(z-\xi)^2 + r^2]^{3/2}}\, d\xi$$

$$= \frac{2\mu(a)}{\sqrt{(z-a)^2 + r^2}} - \frac{2\mu(0)}{\sqrt{z^2 + r^2}} - \int_0^a \frac{2}{\sqrt{(z-\xi)^2 + r^2}}\, \frac{d\mu(\xi)}{d\xi}\, d\xi$$

Thus the doublet distribution $\mu(\xi)$ is equivalent to a source of strength $8\pi\mu(a)$ at $(a,0)$, a sink of the same strength at the origin and a distributed source of strength

$$-8\pi \frac{d\mu(\xi)}{d\xi}$$

over the interval $(0,a)$. By similar arguments distributed singularities of higher orders can be reduced to isolated singularities plus a line source of varying strength, provided the strength of these singularities (as a function of ξ) can be differentiated a sufficient number of times.

4.24. Linearized Theory for Axisymmetric Flow Past Slender Bodies

The axisymmetric potential flow past a slender body the shape of which is described by

$$r = F(z)$$

can be approximated by superposing the potential of a line source of varying strength on that of a uniform flow. The combined potential is

$$\phi = -Uz + \frac{1}{4\pi} \int_0^a \frac{m(\xi)}{\sqrt{(z-\xi)^2 + r^2}}\, d\xi \qquad (4.135)$$

in which U is the uniform velocity at infinity, in the z direction. The slender body extends from $z = 0$ to $z = a$.   From Eq. (4.135) the velocity components can be obtained by differentiation:

$$w = -\frac{\partial \phi}{\partial z} = U + \frac{1}{4\pi} \int_0^a \frac{m(\xi)(z - \xi)}{[(z - \xi)^2 + r^2]^{3/2}} \, d\xi \qquad (4.136)$$

$$u = -\frac{\partial \phi}{\partial r} = \frac{1}{4\pi} \int_0^a \frac{m(\xi)r}{[(z - \xi)^2 + r^2]^{3/2}} \, d\xi \qquad (4.137)$$

Equation (4.137) can be written in the form

$$u = \frac{1}{4\pi r} \int_{-z/r}^{(a-z)/r} \frac{m(\xi)}{\left[\left(\frac{\xi - z}{r}\right)^2 + 1\right]^{3/2}} \, d\frac{\xi - z}{r}$$

Since r is very small for a slender body, the term $[(\xi - z)/r]^2$ is very large except for values of ξ near z.   Hence $m(\xi)$ can be replaced by $m(z)$ and the limits by $-\infty$ and ∞, so that the last equation can be written as

$$u = \frac{1}{4\pi r} m(z) \int_{-\infty}^{\infty} \frac{d\eta}{(\eta^2 + 1)^{3/2}} = \frac{1}{2\pi r} m(z)$$

On the other hand, the velocity in the z direction is approximately U, so that to the first order of approximation

$$u = U \frac{dF(z)}{dz} \qquad (4.138)$$

Thus, for the boundary, at which $r = F(z)$,

$$m(z) = 2\pi U F(z) \frac{dF(z)}{dz} \qquad (4.139)$$

The velocity component w is then evaluated from Eq. (4.136), by expanding $m(\xi)$ in powers of $\xi = z$:

$$m(\xi) = m(z) + m'(z)(\xi - z) + \tfrac{1}{2}m''(z)(\xi - z)^2 + \cdots \qquad (4.140)$$

in which $m'(z) = \dfrac{dm(z)}{dz}$ $m''(z) = \dfrac{d^2m(z)}{dz^2}$ etc.

and $z = a$

Near $z = 0$ and $z = a$, w is near zero, and the difference of w from U is large, so that the linearization process is invalid.   However, the solution by linearization is valid elsewhere.   The method of solution can be modified to deal with subsonic flows of a compressible fluid past slender bodies.

4.25. Taylor Theorem

There is a theorem, due to Taylor[4] and improved by Birkhoff[5] and Landweber,[6] which connects the added masses (except those for pure rotations) with the singularities within the body that generate the irrotational motion in the infinite fluid outside.   For translations, Eqs. (4.57) become

$$A_{\alpha j} = \rho \iint_S \phi_\alpha n_j \, dS$$

in which the English letter j ranges only over 1, 2, and 3, since only translations are considered.

Equation (4.49) can be applied by taking U, V, W to be, in two separate applications,

$$\phi\,\frac{\partial\psi}{\partial x} \qquad \phi\,\frac{\partial\psi}{\partial y} \qquad \phi\,\frac{\partial\psi}{\partial z}$$

and

$$\psi\,\frac{\partial\phi}{\partial x} \qquad \psi\,\frac{\partial\phi}{\partial y} \qquad \psi\,\frac{\partial\phi}{\partial z}$$

The difference of the results is, with the normal now drawn *outward* from the region between S and S',

$$\iint_S \left(\phi\,\frac{\partial\psi}{\partial n} - \psi\,\frac{\partial\phi}{\partial n}\right) dS = \iiint_V (\phi\nabla^2\psi - \psi\nabla^2\phi)d\tau - \iint_{S'} \left(\phi\,\frac{\partial\psi}{\partial n} - \psi\,\frac{\partial\phi}{\partial n}\right) dS'$$

$$(4.141)$$

in which S can be identified with the surface of an immersed body of volume V, S' the collection of spherical surfaces enclosing the isolated singularities, ϕ is the velocity potential, and ψ is for the moment unspecified.

Since

$$n_j = \frac{\partial x_j}{\partial n}$$

Eq. (4.140) can be written

$$A_{\alpha j} = \rho \iint_S \phi_\alpha\,\frac{\partial x_j}{\partial n}\,dS$$

The potential function ϕ_α satisfies the Poisson equation

$$\nabla^2\phi_\alpha = -\sigma_\alpha \qquad (4.142)$$

in which σ_α is the strength of distributed sources or sinks for the αth motion. Identifying x_j with ψ and ϕ_α with ϕ in Eq. (4.141), one has

$$A_{j\alpha} = A_{\alpha j} = \rho \iint_S \phi_\alpha\,\frac{\partial x_j}{\partial n}\,dS = \rho \iint_S x_j\,\frac{\partial\phi_\alpha}{\partial n}\,dS + \iiint_V x_j\sigma_\alpha\,d\tau$$

$$+ \rho \iint_{S'} \left(x_j\,\frac{\partial\phi_\alpha}{\partial n} - \phi_\alpha n_i\right) dS' \quad (4.143)$$

But

$$\rho \iint_S x_j\,\frac{\partial\phi_\alpha}{\partial n}\,dS = -\rho \iint_S x_j n_\alpha\,dS = -B_{\alpha j} \qquad (4.144)$$

The quantities $B_{\alpha j}$ are defined by

$$2T_B = B_{\alpha\beta}U_\alpha U_\beta \qquad (4.145)$$

in which T_B is the kinetic energy of the displaced fluid, considered as a solid body with the velocity components u_1, u_2, u_3 and the angular velocity u_4, u_5, u_6. Thus

$$B_{11} = B_{22} = B_{33} = \rho V \qquad B_{12} = B_{23} = B_{31} = 0 \qquad \text{etc.}$$

if V is the volume of the solid body. Furthermore,

$$\iint_S x_j\,\frac{\partial\phi_\alpha}{\partial n}\,dS' = \sum_S m_\alpha x_{js} \qquad (4.146)$$

in which m_α is the strength of the source located at x_{js} and can be denoted by $m_{\alpha s}$ if the additional subscript adds to clarity. For an isolated doublet of strength μ_α situated at x_{jd},

$$x_{jd}\frac{\partial\phi_\alpha}{\partial n} = x_{jd}\frac{\partial\phi'_\alpha}{\partial n} - \frac{2x_{jd}\mu_{\alpha i}n_i}{r_d{}^3} + \frac{2\mu_{\alpha i}n_i n_j}{r_d{}^3} \tag{4.147}$$

in which ϕ'_α is the difference between ϕ_α and the potential of the doublet in question, r_d is the radius of the sphere surrounding the doublet.　The integral

$$\iint\limits_{S'} x_j\frac{\partial\phi'_\alpha}{\partial n}\,dS'$$

vanishes as r_d approaches zero.　The integral

$$2x_{jd}\mu_{\alpha i}\iint\limits_{S'}\frac{n_i}{r_d{}^3}\,dS'$$

is zero because of antisymmetry.　Finally, again because of antisymmetry,

$$\iint\limits_{S'}\frac{2\mu_{\alpha i}n_i n_j}{r_d{}^2}\,dS' = 2\mu_{\alpha i}\iint\limits_{S'}\frac{n_j n_i}{r_d{}^2}\,dS' = \frac{8\pi}{3}\,\mu_{\alpha j} \tag{4.148}$$

in which j is unsummed.　The last integral in Eq. (4.143) to be accounted for is

$$-\iint\limits_{S'}\phi_\alpha n_i\,dS'$$

This is equal to

$$-\iint\limits_{S'}\left(\phi'_\alpha - \frac{\mu_{\alpha i}n_i}{r_d{}^2}\right)dS' = \mu_{\alpha j}\iint\limits_{S'}\frac{n_j n_i}{r_d{}^2}\,dS' = \frac{4\pi}{3}\,\mu_{\alpha j} \tag{4.149}$$

in which j is again not summed.　By substituting Eqs. (4.144) to (4.149) in Eq. (4.143), one has

$$A_{\alpha j} + B_{\alpha j} = \rho\left[\iiint\limits_{V}\sigma_\alpha x_j\,d\tau + \Sigma(m_\alpha x_{js} + 4\pi\mu_{\alpha j})\right] \tag{4.150}$$

which is the Taylor theorem.[7]

4.26. Forces and Moments

Since hydrostatic forces can be accounted for separately and straightforwardly, only the forces and moments due to dynamic pressures will be discussed.　With p standing for dynamic pressure and with

$$(v_1,v_2,v_3) = (u,v,w) \qquad (u_1,u_2,u_3) = (U,V,W)$$

Eq. (4.44) can be written

$$\frac{p}{\rho} = \frac{\partial\phi}{\partial t} - W \qquad W = \tfrac{1}{2}(u_j u_j + v_j v_j) - v_i(u_j + \epsilon_{jkl}\omega_k x_l) \tag{4.151}$$

in which ϵ_{jkl} is zero if any two of its subscripts are alike; 1 if jkl is permuted cyclically like 123; -1 if it is permuted cyclically like 213.

The force acting on an immersed body with surface S is then, apart from buoyancy,

$$F_i = -\iint\limits_{S}pn_i\,dS = -\rho\iint\limits_{S}\left(\frac{\partial\phi}{\partial t} - W\right)n_i\,dS$$

$$= -\rho\frac{d}{dt'}\iint\limits_{S}\phi n_i\,dS + \rho\iint\limits_{S}Wn_i\,dS \tag{4.152}$$

in which the prime in t' denotes that the variation with time is (like ϕ) relative to the coordinate system rotating with the body. The boundary condition on S is

$$v_i n_i = (u_i + \epsilon_{ijk}\omega_j x_k) n_i$$

or

$$V_i n_i = 0 \tag{4.153}$$

with

$$V_i = -v_i + u_i + \epsilon_{ijk}\omega_j x_k$$

Since ϕ satisfies $\nabla^2\phi = -4\pi\sigma$ and $v_i = -\partial\phi/\partial x_i$,

$$\frac{\partial W}{\partial x_i} = \frac{\partial}{\partial x_j}(-v_i V_j + \epsilon_{ijk}\phi\omega_k) - \sigma v_i \tag{4.154}$$

With V and S' defined as in Art. 4.25,

$$\iint_S W n_i \, dS = \iiint_V \frac{\partial W}{\partial x_i} \, d\tau - \iint_{S'} W n_i \, dS'$$

$$= \iiint_V \frac{\partial}{\partial x_j}(-v_i V_i + \epsilon_{ijk}\phi\omega_k) \, d\tau - \iiint_V \sigma v_i \, d\tau - \iint_{S'} W n_i \, dS'$$

But application of Green's theorem [Eq. (4.47)] and Eq. (4.153) to the first integral yields

$$\iiint_V \frac{\partial}{\partial x_j}(-v_i V_j + \epsilon_{ijk}\phi\omega_k) d\tau = \epsilon_{ijk}\omega_k \iint_S \phi n_i \, dS + \iint_{S'} (-v_i V_j + \epsilon_{ijk}\phi\omega_k) n_j \, dS'$$

So

$$F_i = -\rho \frac{d}{dt'} \iint_S \phi n_i \, dS + \rho\epsilon_{ijk}\omega_k \iint_S \phi n_j \, dS - \rho \iiint_V \sigma v_i \, d\tau$$

$$+ \rho \iint_{S'} [(-v_i V_j + \epsilon_{ijk}\phi\omega_k) n_j - W n_j] dS'$$

The first two integrals combine to form the absolute time derivative of $-\rho \iint_S \phi n_i \, dS$;

the last integral is, by the same method as employed in Art. 4.25 (with mutual actions between internal singularities canceling themselves),

$$\Sigma\left(m v'_i + 4\pi\mu_j \frac{\partial v'_i}{\partial x_j}\right)$$

in which the primes in v'_i denote that in evaluating the velocity at the location of the isolated singularities, the contribution of the singularity under consideration to the (local) velocity is to be discounted. Thus

$$F_i = -\rho \frac{d}{dt} \iint_S \phi n_i \, dS - \rho \left[\iiint_V \sigma v_i \, d\tau + \Sigma\left(m v'_i + 4\pi\mu_j \frac{\partial v'_i}{\partial x_j}\right)\right] \tag{4.155}$$

The task remains to express the first integral on the right-hand side in terms of internal singularities. It is convenient to write

$$\phi = \phi_0 + u_\alpha \phi_\alpha$$

in which ϕ_0 is the potential due to external boundaries or singularities. With Eq. (4.57) and the method employed in Art. 4.25,

$$\rho \iint\limits_{S} \phi n_i \, dS = u_\alpha A_{\alpha i} + \rho \iint\limits_{S} \phi_0 n_i \, dS$$

$$= u_\alpha A_{\alpha i} + \rho \left[\iiint\limits_{V} \sigma_0 x_i \, d\tau + \Sigma(m_0 x_i + 4\pi\mu_0) \right] \qquad (4.156)$$

in which σ_0, m_0, and μ_0 represented internal singularities corresponding to ϕ_0. By sub-stituting Eq. (4.156) into Eq. (4.155), one has

$$F_i = -\frac{d}{dt}(u_\alpha A_{\alpha i}) - \rho\frac{d}{dt}\left[\iiint\limits_{V} \sigma_0 x_i \, d\tau + \Sigma(m_0 x_i + 4\pi\mu_0) \right]$$

$$- \rho\left[\iiint\limits_{V} \sigma v_i \, d\tau + \Sigma\left(mv'_i + 4\pi\mu_j \frac{\partial v'_i}{\partial x_j} \right) \right] \qquad (4.157)$$

Now, as proved in books on dynamics,

$$u_\alpha B_{\alpha i} = u_j B_{ji} + \omega_j B_{3+j,i} = B(u_i + \epsilon_{ijk}\omega_j\bar{x}_k) = B\bar{u}_i \qquad (4.158)$$

in which $\bar{u}_i$ is the ith velocity component of the centroid of the solid body. With Eqs. (4.150) and (4.158), Eq. (4.157) can finally be written

$$F_i = B\frac{d\bar{u}_i}{dt} - \rho\frac{d}{dt}\left[\iiint\limits_{V} \sigma x_i \, d\tau + \Sigma(mx_i + 4\pi\mu_i) \right]$$

$$- \rho\left[\iiint\limits_{V} \sigma v_i \, d\tau + \Sigma\left(mv'_i + 4\pi\mu_i \frac{\partial v'_i}{\partial x_j} \right) \right] \qquad (4.159)$$

Now *all* the internal singularities are involved in either of the brackets. The last bracket, with its cofactor, represents the force acting on the body (which may be moving or at rest) due to the presence of outside boundaries and singularities (Lagally theorem), because for a closed body the interactions of internal singularities cancel each other, as can be proved. This force is called the Lagally force.

By a similar procedure, one can prove that the moment from dynamic pressure has the components

$$M_i = -\rho\epsilon_{ijk}\left[\frac{d}{dt}\iint\limits_{S} \phi x_j n_k \, dS + u_j \iint\limits_{S} \phi n_k \, dS \right] + M_{iL}(v)$$

in which $M_{iL}(v)$ is the Lagally moment[7]

$$-\rho\epsilon_{ijk}\left[\iiint\limits_{V} \sigma x_j v_k \, d\tau + \Sigma\left(mx_j v'_k + 4\pi\mu_j v'_k + 4\pi x_j \mu_l \frac{\partial v'_k}{\partial x_l} \right) \right] \qquad (4.160)$$

4.27. Integral Equations

Integral equations associated with potential-flow problems are discussed in books on potential theory.[8] Here only the forms of these equations will be presented.

If it is desired to solve the Dirichlet problem by a doublet distribution on the surface S of a moving body immersed in fluid, one can write

$$\phi = \frac{1}{2\pi}\iint\limits_{S} \mu \frac{\partial}{\partial n}\left(\frac{1}{r} \right) dS$$

in which μ is proportional to the strength of the doublet on S with axis perpendicular to S and n is the normal to S. If one approaches S from outside, in the limit

$$\phi_+(p) = \mu(p) + \frac{1}{2\pi} \iint_S \mu(q) \frac{\partial}{\partial n} \left(\frac{1}{r}\right) dS \tag{4.161}$$

This is an integral equation of the Fredholm type, in which $\phi_+(p)$ is specified and $\mu(p)$ is the unknown, with p denoting a point on S and q a variable point on S over which the integral is performed.

For the Neumann problem a potential function of the form (σ proportional to the strength of the source or sink distribution on S)

$$\phi = \frac{1}{2\pi} \iint_S \sigma \frac{1}{r} dS$$

is sought. This leads to the integral equation

$$\frac{\partial \phi(p)}{\partial n_+} = -\sigma(p) + \frac{1}{2\pi} \iint_S \sigma(q) \frac{\partial}{\partial n} \left(\frac{1}{r}\right) dS \tag{4.162}$$

in which the left-hand side is specified, and $\sigma(p)$ is the unknown.

The kernel $\dfrac{\partial}{\partial n} \left(\dfrac{1}{r}\right)$ in Eq. (4.161) stands for

$$\frac{\partial}{\partial n} \frac{1}{\sqrt{(x_p - x)^2 + (y_p - y)^2 + (z_p - z)^2}}$$

with the point $Q(x,y,z)$ then replaced by $q(x_q,y_q,z_q)$. The same symbol in Eq. (4.162), however, stands for

$$\frac{\partial}{\partial n} \frac{1}{\sqrt{(x - x_q)^2 + (y - y_q)^2 + (z - z_q)^2}}$$

with the point $P(x,y,z)$ then replaced by $p(x_p,y_p,z_p)$. Thus, if $\dfrac{\partial}{\partial n} \left(\dfrac{1}{r}\right)$ in Eq. (4.161) is denoted by $K(p,q)$, that in Eq. (4.162) is $K(q,p)$. Hence Eqs. (4.161) and (4.162) can be written

$$\phi_+(p) = \mu(p) + \frac{1}{2\pi} \iint_S \mu(q) K(p,q) dS \tag{4.163}$$

$$\frac{\partial \phi(p)}{\partial n_+} = -\sigma(p) + \frac{1}{2\pi} \iint_S \sigma(q) K(q,p) dS \tag{4.164}$$

TWO-DIMENSIONAL IRROTATIONAL FLOWS

4.28. Cauchy-Riemann Equations, Laplace Equation

From Eqs. (4.15) and (4.38), it follows that

$$\phi_x = \psi_y \qquad \phi_y = -\psi_x \tag{4.165}$$

with subscripts again indicating partial differentiations. These equations are called Cauchy-Riemann equations. By cross differentiations, one obtains

$$\nabla^2 \phi = \phi_{xx} + \phi_{yy} = 0 \tag{4.166}$$
$$\nabla^2 \psi = \psi_{xx} + \psi_{yy} = 0 \tag{4.167}$$

Thus both the velocity potential ϕ and Lagrange's stream function ψ satisfy the Laplace equation. The chief concern of any study of two-dimensional irrotational flows of an incompressible fluid is to find solutions of Eqs. (4.166) and (4.167) that satisfy specific boundary conditions.

4.29. Orthogonality of Potential Lines and Streamlines, Flow Nets

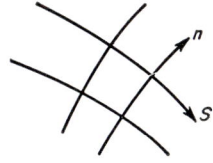

Fig. 4.19. Flow-net element.

The lines along which ϕ is constant are called potential lines. The lines along which ψ is constant have been shown in Art. 4.5 to be streamlines. It will now be shown that the potential lines and the streamlines are orthogonal.

The slope of a potential line is

$$\frac{dy}{dx}\bigg|_\phi = -\frac{\phi_x}{\phi_y}$$

whereas that of a streamline is

$$\frac{dy}{dx}\bigg|_\psi = -\frac{\psi_x}{\psi_y}$$

From the Cauchy-Riemann equations, it follows, then,

$$\frac{dy}{dx}\bigg|_\phi \cdot \frac{dy}{dx}\bigg|_\psi = -1$$

i.e., the potential lines and the streamlines are orthogonal.

If the distance along the streamlines is denoted by s (Fig. 4.19) and that along the potential lines by n, then Eqs. (4.165) produce

$$\frac{\partial \phi}{\partial s} = \frac{\partial \psi}{\partial n}$$

or, *approximately,*

$$\frac{\Delta \phi}{\Delta s} = \frac{\Delta \psi}{\Delta n}$$

for finite Δs and Δn. If now one chooses

$$\Delta \phi = \Delta \psi$$

it follows that, approximately,

$$\Delta s = \Delta n$$

This means that if one chooses the increment of ϕ and that of ψ to be equal, the orthogonal net formed by the potential lines and the streamlines then consists of squares. Such a net is called a flow net for irrotational flows. It provides a graphic means of solving the Laplace Eqs. (4.166) and (4.167). All one has to do is to let the fixed boundaries be streamlines, assign appropriate values for ψ at the sections where the flow is uniform (constant velocity), and try again and again (making ample use of erasers) until an orthogonal net of squares is achieved. Then the speed q, which is approximately $\Delta\phi/\Delta s$ or $\Delta\psi/\Delta n$, is simply inversely proportional to the linear size of the squares and the direction of flow given by the streamlines.

4.30. Analyticity of a Complex Function with Respect to the Complex Variable z

The combination $x + iy$ is called a complex variable and is usually denoted by z, which can also be written as $re^{i\theta}$, in which r is called the modulus and θ the argument (or phase) of the complex variable z. Consider the complex function

$$w = \phi(x,y) + i\psi(x,y)$$

in which ϕ and ψ are for the moment not identified with the potential function and the stream function. If, at every point (x,y), w is single-valued (or can be made to be so) and possesses a unique derivative with respect to z irrespective of the manner in which the point is approached in the limiting process of differentiation, the function w is called regular or analytic. What are the necessary and sufficient conditions for w to be analytic? These conditions are that ϕ and ψ be single-valued (or can be made to be so) and that they satisfy the Cauchy-Riemann equations and therefore differentiable at least once. It can be shown that if the Cauchy-Riemann equations are satisfied, w can be differentiated infinitely many times. But at the moment it is desired to prove that the conditions stated are indeed necessary and sufficient for the analyticity of w.

One notes immediately that the single-valuedness of ϕ and ψ is certainly necessary, for otherwise w would not be single-valued. To prove that the satisfaction of the Cauchy-Riemann equations is necessary, one needs only to differentiate w with respect to x and iy and demand equality of the results:

$$\phi_x + i\psi_x = \frac{1}{i}\left(\phi_y + i\psi_y\right)$$

This leads to the Cauchy-Riemann equations, which are therefore necessary for the analyticity of w.

To prove the sufficiency of the conditions, let

$$\Delta z = \Delta x + i\,\Delta y$$

in which Δx and Δy are unrelated to each other. The corresponding change in w is

$$\Delta w = \phi(x + \Delta x, y + \Delta y) - \phi(x,y) + i\,[\psi(x + \Delta x, y + \Delta y) - \psi(x,y)]$$

$$= \frac{\partial \phi}{\partial x}\Delta x + \frac{\partial \phi}{\partial y}\Delta y + i\left(\frac{\partial \psi}{\partial x}\Delta x + \frac{\partial \psi}{\partial y}\Delta y\right) + \text{terms of higher orders in } \Delta x \text{ and } \Delta y$$

Thus, in virtue of the Cauchy-Riemann equations,

$$\Delta w = \left(\frac{\partial \phi}{\partial x} + i\frac{\partial \psi}{\partial x}\right)\Delta z + \text{higher-order terms}$$

and

$$\frac{dw}{dz} = \lim_{\Delta z \to 0}\frac{\Delta w}{\Delta z} = \frac{\partial \phi}{\partial x} + i\frac{\partial \psi}{\partial x} = \frac{\partial w}{\partial x} \tag{4.168}$$

irrespective of the manner in which Δz approaches zero. Since the single-valuedness of ϕ and ψ ensures that of w, its possession of a unique derivative, as demonstrated above, indicates that w is analytic.

If w is a function of z alone and can be differentiated with respect to z except at the singular points, its real and imaginary parts satisfy the Cauchy-Riemann equations (and hence the Laplace equation) and therefore can be identified with the potential function and the stream function. Conversely, since the potential function ϕ and the stream function ψ satisfy the Cauchy-Riemann equations, $w = \phi + i\psi$ must be an analytical function of z.

4.31. Conformal Mapping

If $w(z)$ is an analytic function of z, for each point in the z plane there corresponds a point in the w plane, with ϕ and ψ as coordinates. With reference to Fig. 4.20, the small triangle PQR in the z plane is transformed to the small triangle $P'Q'R'$ in the w plane. It will be shown that the two triangles are similar. Let the directed lines PQ and PR be represented by Δz_1 and Δz_2 and the directed lines $P'Q'$ and $P'R'$ by Δw_1 and Δw_2. Since w possesses a unique derivative at P,

$$\frac{\Delta w_2}{\Delta z_2} \doteq \frac{\Delta w_1}{\Delta z_1} \doteq \frac{dw}{dz} = re^{i\beta} \qquad \text{(say)}$$

Thus, approximately,

$$\frac{\overline{P'R'}}{\overline{PR}} = \frac{\overline{P'Q'}}{\overline{PQ}}$$

and since the arguments (or phases) of Δw_2 and Δw_1 are greater than those, respectively, of Δz_2 and Δz_1 by the same amount β,

$$\alpha = \alpha'$$

Thus, approximately, PQR and $P'Q'R'$ are similar, the degree of similarity increasing with the smallness of the triangles. For the limiting case of infinitesimal triangles, the similarity is complete. For this reason, the transformation from the z plane to the w plane represented by the function $w(z)$ is called a conformal transformation, or conformal mapping. The potential lines and streamlines, which are orthogonal but in general curvilinear in the z plane, are mapped into orthogonal straight lines parallel to the two coordinate axes. The function $w(z)$ is called the complex potential.

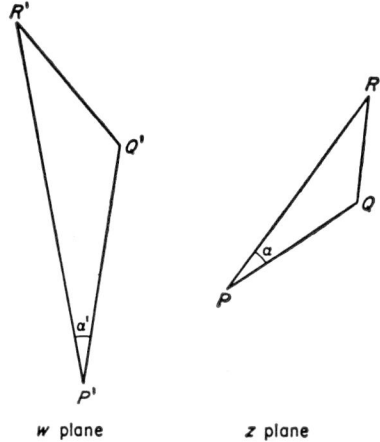

w plane   **z plane**

FIG. 4.20. Transformation of elemental triangle from the z plane to the w plane.

4.32. Velocity and Magnitude of the Acceleration in Terms of the Complex Potential

From Eqs. (4.168) and (4.165) it follows that

$$\frac{dw}{dz} = \phi_x + i\psi_x = -u + iv = -qe^{-i\theta} \qquad (4.169)$$

if w is the complex potential. Thus the speed q at any point is simply $\left|\dfrac{dw}{dz}\right|$, and the angle of inclination θ of the velocity is just the negative of the argument of dw/dz. The plane with $-u$ and v (or u and $-v$) as coordinates is called the hodograph plane, and a curve in this plane a hodograph.

For *steady* flows, the acceleration components are

$$b = uu_x + vu_y \qquad c = uv_x + vv_y$$

By virtue of the equation of continuity

$$u_x + v_y = 0$$

and the equation of irrotationality

$$u_y - v_x = 0$$

the square of the magnitude of acceleration in steady two-dimensional irrotational flow is

$$a^2 = b^2 + c^2 = (u^2 + v^2)(u_x{}^2 + u_y{}^2) = q^2(u_x{}^2 + u_y{}^2)$$

But
$$q^2 = |w'|^2$$

and
$$u_x{}^2 + u_y{}^2 = u_x{}^2 + v_x{}^2 = |w''|^2$$

So
$$a^2 = |w'w''|^2$$

which states that a^2 is the square of the speed of a new potential flow with the new complex potential $w'^2/2$. In view of the theorem that in a singularity-free region of an irrotational flow the maximum speed must occur on the boundary of the region, it can be concluded that the maximum acceleration in such a region must also occur on the boundary, provided the flow is steady and two-dimensional.[8]

4.33. Examples of Analytic Functions Representing Irrotational Flows

Each conformal mapping by the function $w(z)$ between the z plane and the w plane represents an irrotational flow in the z plane. The simplest example is

$$w = -Uz = -Ux - iUy \tag{4.170}$$

Since
$$\frac{dw}{dz} = -u + iv = \phi_x + i\psi_x = -U$$

the complex potential $-Uz$ corresponds to uniform flow with velocity U in the x direction.

Another example is

$$w = Az^n = Ar^n e^{in\theta} = Ar^n(\cos n\theta + i \sin n\theta)$$

The streamline $\psi = 0$ has the branches

$$\theta = \frac{m\pi}{n} \qquad m = 0, 1, \ldots, 2n - 1$$

For $n = 2$, the flow pattern is given in Fig. 4.21.

The complex potential

$$w = -\frac{m}{2\pi} \ln z = -\frac{m}{2\pi}(\ln r + i\theta) \tag{4.171}$$

represents a two-dimensional source (or line source) of discharge (per unit length in the direction perpendicular to the xy plane) m, because

$$\phi = -\frac{m}{2\pi} \ln r$$

and the radial velocity is

$$-\phi_r = \frac{m}{2\pi r}$$

so that the discharge per unit length is $2\pi r(-\phi_r) = m$. The streamlines are radial, and the potential lines concentric circles with the common center at the origin. The complex potential for a source at the point $z = a$ is simply

$$w = -\frac{m}{2\pi} \ln(z - a) \tag{4.172}$$

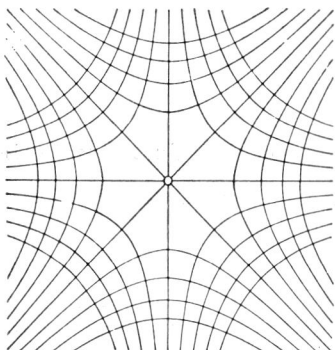

Fig. 4.21. Flow net for $w = Az^2$. (*Ref.* 9.)

The complex potentials for a sink are given by Eqs. (4.171) and (4.172), with the negative signs removed and m positive.

It is obvious that by multiplying w by an imaginary number, one has

$$w_1 = iw = -\psi + i\phi$$

so that the potential lines for w become the streamlines for w_1 and the streamlines for w become the potential lines for w_1. Thus

$$w = \frac{im}{2\pi} \ln z = \frac{m}{2\pi}(-\theta + i \ln r)$$

represents a flow whose streamlines are concentric circles with the origin as the center. The velocity is in the direction of increasing θ. This flow is called a vortex flow, with the concentrated vortex at the origin. The flow due to a concentrated vortex at $z = a$ is represented by

$$w = \frac{im}{2\pi} \ln(z - a) \tag{4.173}$$

As in the case of three-dimensional flows, the potential for a doublet is obtained by differentiation of the potential for a source or a sink. Thus the complex potential for a doublet at $z = a$ is

$$w = \mu \frac{d}{dz} \ln(z - a) = \frac{\mu}{z - a}$$

$$= \frac{\mu[(x - a) - iy]}{(x - a)^2 + y^2} \tag{4.174}$$

with the velocity on the x axis always in the positive x direction, i.e., with the axis of the doublet in the positive x direction, if μ is real. The axis of the doublet can be made to take any direction whatever by assigning suitable complex values for μ.

4.34. Application of the Superposition Principle

As in the case of three-dimensional flow, the superposition of a uniform flow and a flow from a two-dimensional source produces a flow past a half body. The complex potential for this combined flow is

$$w = -\frac{m}{2\pi} \ln(z - a) - Uz \tag{4.175}$$

Far downstream (large x), the flow is again uniform and the height of the half body is

$$h = \frac{m}{U}$$

It can be shown that the total force acting on the surface of the half body is merely the buoyancy; the dynamic pressure has no net contribution whatever.

A flow past a closed body can be obtained by superposing a uniform flow on the flow due to a source and a sink, with the axis joining the source to the sink in the same direction as the velocity of the uniform flow. The complex potential is, with a real,

$$w = -Uz - \frac{m}{2\pi} \ln(z + a) + \frac{m}{2\pi} \ln(z - a) \tag{4.176}$$

The streamline $\psi = 0$ consists of two straight-line segments and a closed curve. The closed curve can be taken to be the boundary of a solid body, past which the fluid flows. This body is called a Rankine body. The usage of the term Rankine body has now been broadened to include all bodies generated by an external flow and internal singularities. Since *all* closed bodies can be generated this way, any closed body is a Rankine body, and the usage of the term indicates not a special class of bodies but the emphasis placed on the generation of closed bodies by internal singularities.

The flow (uniform at infinity) past a circular cylinder can be obtained by superposing a uniform flow on the flow due to a doublet and is a limiting case of the flow past the *simple* Rankine body described in the preceding paragraph. The complex potential is

$$w = -U \left(z + \frac{a^2}{z} \right) \tag{4.177}$$

in which a is the radius of the cylinder. Obviously, on the cylinder $z = ae^{i\theta}$, and the imaginary part of w is zero. Therefore $\psi = 0$ on the surface of the cylinder, which is therefore a stream surface, or a streamline with the understanding that one is speaking of the trace of the surface (on a plane perpendicular to the axis of the cylinder) rather than the surface itself. The flow pattern is shown in Fig. 4.22.

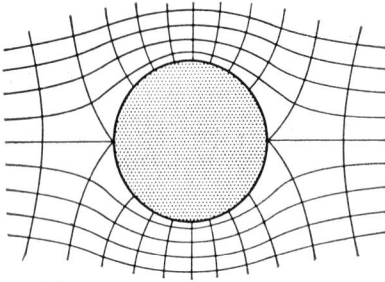

FIG. 4.22. Flow around a circular cylinder without circulation. (*Ref.* 9.)

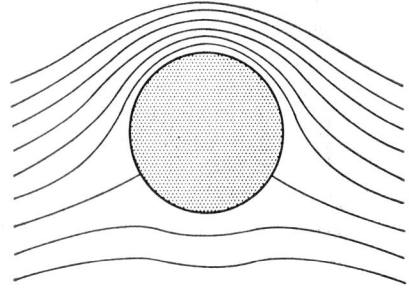

FIG. 4.23. Flow around a circular cylinder with circulation. (*Ref.* 9.)

The complex potential for a vortex can obviously be superposed on that given by Eq. (4.177) without affecting either the uniform flow at infinity or the satisfaction of the boundary condition at the surface of the cylinder. The result is

$$w = -U\left(z + \frac{a^2}{z}\right) + \frac{i\kappa}{2\pi}\ln z \qquad (4.178)$$

in which κ is the circulation around the cylinder. For a negative value of κ and a positive U, the flow pattern is shown in Fig. 4.23. Since the boundary conditions at infinity and on the circle are the same, whether there is circulation or not, this example effectively demonstrates the lack of uniqueness of the solution of the Dirichlet-Neumann problem when the velocity potential is multivalued. It can be shown by direct integration, and will be shown by the use of the Blasius theorem, that the lift on the cylinder is equal to $-\rho U\kappa$.

The principle of superposition can be readily utilized to solve the Laplace equation if the boundary conditions are specified on a circle. If the domain involved is the inside of the circle, one can assume

$$w = A_0 + A_1 z + A_2 z_2 + \cdots \qquad (4.179)$$

in which the A's are complex constants. This function is analytic everywhere within the circle, provided the series converges therein. For convenience, the circle can be taken to be a unit circle, without loss of generality. The stream function on the unit circle is then

$$\psi = C_0 + C_1 \cos\theta + B_1 \sin\theta + C_2 \cos 2\theta + B_2 \sin 2\theta + \cdots$$

in which

$$A_n = B_n + iC_n$$

The boundary condition on the circle is of the type

$$\psi = f(\theta)$$

where the function $f(\theta)$ is specified. Thus, by the use of the Fourier analysis, one can determine the B's and C's, and hence the A's, and the solution is provided by Eq. (4.179).

If the domain involved is the outside of the circle, the appropriate series to use is, for *quiescent* condition or uniform flow at infinity,

$$w = A_0 + A_1 z + \frac{A_{-1}}{z} + \frac{A_{-2}}{z^2} + \cdots$$

The Fourier analysis can again be applied.

4.35. Method of Images

When straight or circular boundaries are present in a flow, the method of images can often be employed to find the complex potential. The method of images consists of the finding of the images of singularities (or an external flow) across the boundary or boundaries and the superposition of the flow due to these images on the original flow.

The flow into a sink placed midway between two parallel walls spaced at distance a apart can be found with the method of images. Let the sink, of strength m, be situated at the origin. Its complex potential, in the absence of the walls, would be

$$\frac{m}{2\pi} \ln z$$

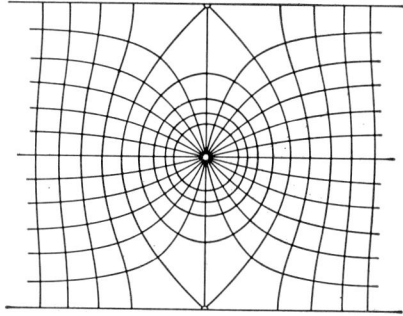

FIG. 4.24. Flow net for one of a series of equal and equidistant sources. (*Ref. 9.*)

This complex potential, however, does not make the walls $(y = \pm a/2)$ streamlines. To make the upper wall $(y = a/2)$ a streamline, the complex potential

$$\frac{m}{2\pi} \ln(z - ai) \tag{4.180}$$

is added. Similarly, to make the lower wall a streamline, the complex potential

$$\frac{m}{2\pi} \ln(z + ai) \tag{4.180a}$$

must be added. But this new addition makes the upper wall not a streamline in exactly the same way that the first addition makes the lower wall not a streamline. Further images must be taken, ad infinitum. Aside from a constant, which can be dropped without affecting the flow, the complex potentials (4.180) and (4.180a) can be combined to form

$$\frac{m}{2\pi} \ln \left(1 + \frac{z^2}{a^2} \right)$$

Successive images produce, by superposition, the final complex potential

$$w = \frac{m}{2\pi} \left[\ln z + \ln \left(1 + \frac{z^2}{a^2} \right) + \ln \left(1 + \frac{z^2}{4a^2} \right) + \cdots \right]$$

$$= \frac{m}{2\pi} \ln z \prod_{n=1}^{\infty} \left(1 + \frac{z^2}{4a^2} \right) = \frac{m}{2\pi} \ln \sinh \frac{\pi z}{a} \tag{4.181}$$

The flow pattern for the space between the two walls is shown in Fig. 4.24.

An example involving nonparallel walls is furnished by the flow due to a source of strength m situated at $b + ic$, with the coordinate axes as fixed boundaries. The complex potential is the sum of potentials of four sources, each situated in a different quadrant but with the same strength m:

$$w = \frac{m}{2\pi} \{ \ln [z - (b + ic)] + \ln [z - (b - ic)]$$

$$+ \ln [z + (b + ic)] + \ln [z + (b - ic)] \}$$

$$= \frac{m}{2\pi} \{ \ln [(z - b)^2 + c^2] + \ln [(z + b)^2 + c^2] \}$$

The images in a circle can best be found by the use of the *circle theorem*. This theorem states that if the complex potential with no rigid boundaries present is $f(z)$, with no singularities within a distance a from the origin, the complex potential after a circle of radius a is introduced at the origin is

$$w = f(z) + \bar{f}\left(\frac{a^2}{z}\right) \tag{4.182}$$

in which $\bar{f}$ is the complex conjugate of f, for the *same* variable (or argument). The proof is simple. Since the singularities of $f(z)$ are all outside of the circle, those of $\bar{f}(a^2/z)$ are all inside of the circle, as desired. (Otherwise the nature of the external flow would be unnecessarily modified.) Furthermore, on the circle $z = ae^{i\theta}$, and Eq. (4.182) shows clearly that $\psi = 0$, as desired.

If
$$f(z) = -Uz$$

$$w = -U\left(z + \frac{a^2}{z}\right)$$

which is identical with Eq. (4.177). Another example is furnished by

$$f(z) = -\frac{m}{2\pi}\ln(z - b) \qquad (b > a)$$

for which
$$w = -\frac{m}{2\pi}\left[\ln(z - b) + \ln\left(\frac{a^2}{z} - b\right)\right]$$

or, after addition of a constant,

$$w = -\frac{m}{2\pi}\left[\ln(z - b) + \ln\left(z - \frac{a^2}{b}\right) - \ln z\right] \tag{4.183}$$

This corresponds to a source at the original place, a source at the inverse point, and a sink at the origin, all of the same strength.

If
$$f(z) = \frac{\mu e^{i\alpha}}{z - b} \qquad (b > a)$$

in which μ is the strength of a doublet and α the inclination of its axis, then

$$w = \frac{\mu e^{i\alpha}}{z - b} + \frac{\mu e^{-i\alpha}}{(a^2/z) - b}$$

or, apart from a constant,

$$w = \frac{\mu e^{i\alpha}}{z - b} - \frac{\mu a^2}{b^2}\frac{e^{-i\alpha}}{z - a^2/b} \tag{4.184}$$

The image is therefore situated at the inverse point a^2/b, with strength $\mu a^2/b^2$, and axis inclined at an angle $-\alpha$.

There are many other applications of the circle theorem. But since the applications are straightforward, no more examples will be given.

4.36. Elliptic Coordinates

If $\zeta = \xi + i\eta$ is a new complex variable and

$$z = c \cosh \zeta \tag{4.185}$$

then
$$x = c \cosh \xi \cos \eta$$
$$y = c \sinh \xi \sin \eta \tag{4.186}$$

If η is eliminated from Eqs. (4.186),

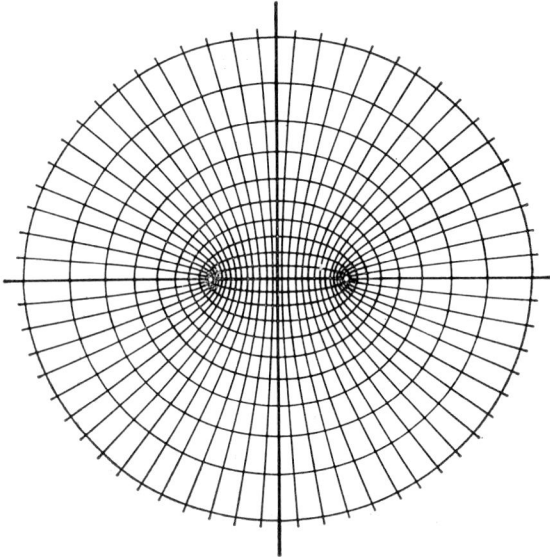

FIG. 4.25. Elliptic coordinates. (*Ref.* 9.)

$$\frac{x^2}{c^2 \cosh^2 \xi} + \frac{y^2}{c^2 \sinh^2 \xi} = 1 \tag{4.187}$$

so that $\xi = \xi_0$ corresponds to an ellipse in the z plane, with semimajor axis $c \cosh \xi_0$ and semiminor axis $c \sinh \xi_0$. The distance between the foci is $2c$. If ξ is eliminated from Eqs. (4.186), the result is

$$\frac{x^2}{c^2 \cos^2 \eta} - \frac{y^2}{c^2 \sin^2 \eta} = 1 \tag{4.188}$$

so that $\eta = \eta_0$ corresponds to hyperbolas with the foci at $x = \pm c$. The curves $\xi = $ constant and $\eta = $ constant are therefore confocal ellipses and hyperbolas in the z plane, as shown in Fig. 4.25.

Seepage underneath a Dam. One immediate application of the transformation Eq. (4.185) is to the problem of seepage underneath an impermeable dam. If h is the piezometric head, the velocity of seepage is given by (Darcy's law)

$$u = -\mu \frac{\partial \phi}{\partial x} \qquad v = -\mu \frac{\partial \phi}{\partial y}$$

in which ϕ is γh, γ being the specific weight, and μ is the permeability. Since the equation of continuity for incompressible fluids is still

$$\frac{\partial u}{\partial x} + \frac{\partial v}{\partial y} = 0$$

ϕ again satisfies the Laplace equation. For the dam shown in Fig. 4.26, the solution is exactly

$$z = c \cosh \frac{i\pi w}{\gamma H} \tag{4.189}$$

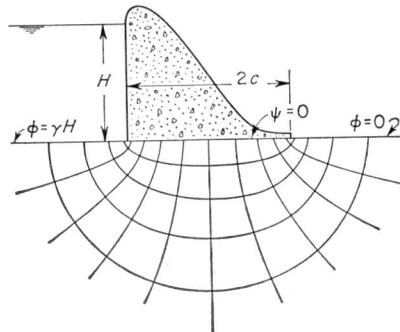

FIG. 4.26. Seepage under a dam.

and the flow pattern is shown in the lower half of Fig. 4.25.

Translation of an Elliptic Cylinder. For the flow due to the translation of an elliptic cylinder ($\xi = \xi_0$) with velocity U in the x direction, the boundary condition is, with s measured along the ellipse,

$$-\frac{\partial \psi}{\partial s} = U \frac{\partial y}{\partial s} \qquad \text{for } \xi = \xi_0$$

or

$$\psi = -Uy \qquad \text{for } \xi = \xi_0$$

In elliptic coordinates, this becomes

$$\psi = -Uc \sinh \xi_0 \sin \eta \tag{4.190}$$

on the ellipse. Now for the complex potential

$$w = Ce^{-\zeta} \tag{4.191}$$

the stream function is

$$\psi = -Ce^{-\xi} \sin \eta$$

Thus if

$$C = Uc \sinh \xi_0 e^{\xi_0}$$

the boundary condition Eq. (4.190) is satisfied. If a and b are the semiaxes of the ellipse,

$$a = c \cosh \xi_0 \qquad b = c \sinh \xi_0 \qquad c = \sqrt{a^2 - b^2}$$

and

$$e^{\xi_0} = \sqrt{\frac{a + b}{a - b}}$$

Thus

$$C = Ub \sqrt{\frac{a + b}{a - b}} \tag{4.192}$$

which, together with Eq. (4.191), gives the desired complex potential.

Similarly, if the same elliptic cylinder is traveling in the direction of y with velocity V, the complex potential is

$$w = iVa \sqrt{\frac{a + b}{a - b}} e^{-\zeta} \tag{4.193}$$

For the flow due to the translation of the elliptic cylinder in any arbitrary direction, the complex potential can be obtained by superposing the complex potentials given in Eqs. (4.191) and (4.193). The flow (uniform at infinity) past an elliptic cylinder can be obtained by superposing a uniform flow on the flow due to the translation of the cylinder, the velocity of the uniform flow being equal and opposite to the translational velocity of the cylinder.

Fluid Flow Within a Rotating Elliptic Cylinder. For any solid cylinder rotating in a fluid with angular velocity ω, the boundary condition is

$$\frac{\partial \psi}{\partial s} = \omega r \frac{\partial r}{\partial s}$$

in which r is the radial distance from the center of rotation (taken to be the origin) to the boundary. This boundary condition can be integrated to yield

$$\psi = \tfrac{1}{2}\omega r^2 + \text{const} \tag{4.194}$$

Since ψ satisfies the Laplace equation, the problem is analogous to the problem of prismatic torsion, with ψ corresponding to the harmonic function conjugate to the torsion function or the stress function plus $r^2/2$. It is also analogous to the problem of laminar flow in a pipe of arbitrary cross section. Here ψ corresponds to the longitudinal velocity plus $Kr^2/2$, with K equal to the longitudinal pressure gradient divided by the dynamic viscosity.

The complex potential for the flow within a rotating elliptic cylinder is

$$w = iAz^2 \tag{4.195}$$

Since
$$\psi = A(x^2 - y^2)$$

the boundary condition [Eq. (4.194)] is satisfied if

$$A(x^2 - y^2) = \tfrac{1}{2}\omega(x^2 + y^2) - C$$

on the ellipse. But this is precisely the equation for the ellipse

$$\frac{x^2}{a^2} + \frac{y^2}{b^2} = 1$$

if
$$a^2 = \frac{C}{\tfrac{1}{2}\omega - A} \qquad b^2 = \frac{C}{\tfrac{1}{2}\omega + A}$$

or if
$$A = \tfrac{1}{2}\omega \frac{a^2 - b^2}{a^2 + b^2} \tag{4.196}$$

Equations (4.195) and (4.196) then constitute the solution.

Flow outside of a rotating Elliptic Cylinder. The complex potential for this case is

$$w = iCe^{-2\zeta} \tag{4.197}$$

in which the constant C is determined by the boundary condition to be

$$C = \tfrac{1}{2}\omega(a + b)^2$$

4.37. Successive Transformations

The technique of successive transformations is an important one, not only because it provides solutions to many problems of potential flow, but also because much insight into the properties of potential flow is gained through the use of this technique.

One of the simplest examples of successive transformations is furnished by the solution of uniform (at infinity) flow past an elliptic cylinder, with or without circulation. It is known that the complex potential for flow past a circular cylinder of radius a is given by Eq. (4.178), in which the circulation κ may be zero or nonzero. If the physical plane is transformed into a new one through the formula (Fig. 4.27),

$$z' = z + \frac{b^2}{z} \qquad (b < a) \tag{4.198}$$

the circle $|z| = b$ or $z = be^{i\theta}$ is transformed into the straight line of length $4b$:

$$z' = 2b \cos \theta$$

The circle $z = ae^{i\theta}$ is transformed into

$$z' = ae^{i\theta} + \frac{b^2}{a} e^{-i\theta}$$

or $x' = \left(a + \dfrac{b^2}{a}\right) \cos \theta \qquad y' = \left(a - \dfrac{b^2}{a}\right) \sin \theta$

which obviously represents an ellipse of semiaxes

$$a + \frac{b^2}{a} \qquad \text{and} \qquad a - \frac{b^2}{a}$$

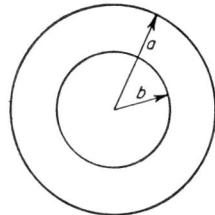

Now the transformation Eq. (4.198) does not at all affect the situation that the boundary—a circle in the z plane but an ellipse in the z' plane—is a streamline or that the flow has the uniform velocity U at infinity. Consequently, Eqs. (4.178) and (4.198) jointly furnish the solution for flow past an ellip-

Fig. 4.27. Notation for transformation of a circle.

tic cylinder in the z' plane. From the axes of the cylinder, a and b can be obtained, as explained in the preceding paragraph.

The question may be raised: If the small circle (of radius b) in the z plane goes into a straight line in the z' plane, what has happened to the interior of the small circle? The answer is that it has been transformed to the entire z' plane once again. It can be seen from Eq. (4.198) that for each value of z there is only one corresponding value of z', but for each value of z', two values of z. In fact, it can be easily verified that the circle

$$z = \frac{b^2}{a} e^{i\theta}$$

is transformed into the same ellipse as the circle

$$z = a e^{i\theta}$$

Usually, the letter z is reserved for the actual physical plane, so that the roles of z and z' in the foregoing discussion should be interchanged to conform to convention.

Another example is furnished by the flow around a circular arc. One starts from an

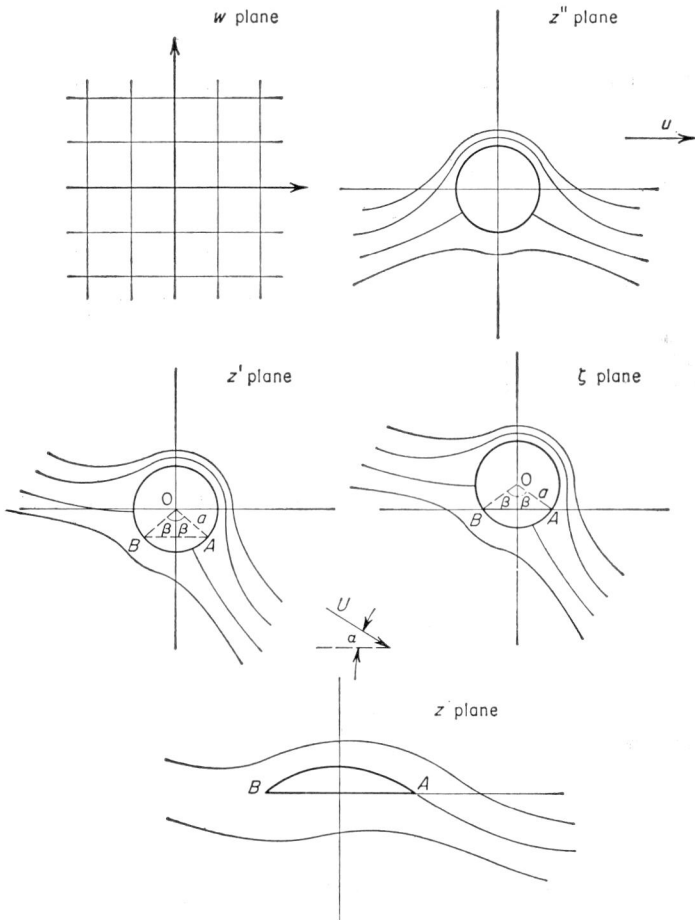

Fig. 4.28. Transformation for flow around a circular arc. (*Ref.* 9.)

intermediate plane, the z'' plane, in which the flow is one past a circular cylinder of radius a, with circulation $-\kappa$ (κ positive). Thus

$$w = -U\left(z'' + \frac{a^2}{z''}\right) - \frac{i\kappa}{2\pi}\ln z'' \quad (4.179a)$$

FIG. 4.29. Joukowski airfoil section.

the velocity at infinity being U, in the positive x direction. The transformation

$$z'' = z'e^{i\alpha} \tag{4.199}$$

tilts the flow pattern through an angle $-\alpha$. The transformation

$$z' = \zeta - me^{i\delta} \tag{4.200}$$

shifts the origin in the second intermediate plane (the z' plane) through a displacement $-me^{i\delta}$. Finally, the transformation

$$z = \zeta + \frac{b^2}{\zeta} \tag{4.201}$$

in which $\rho = a\sin\beta$ (Fig. 4.28) transforms the circle into a circular arc if $\delta = \pi/2$.

In general, the velocities at A and B in the physical plane are infinite. However, the circulation can be adjusted so that either the velocity at A or that at B is finite. For finite velocity at A,

$$\kappa = 4\pi aU \cos(\alpha + \beta) \tag{4.202}$$

and for finite velocity at B,

$$\kappa = 4\pi aU \cos(\alpha - \beta) \tag{4.203}$$

The flow pattern in the physical plane with finite velocity at B is shown in Fig. 4.28, along with the flow patterns in the intermediate planes.

If δ is not $\pi/2$, the body in the physical plane is in general in the form of an airfoil, called the Joukowski airfoil, after its originator. For $\delta = \pi/3$ and $m/a = 0.2$, the airfoil is shown in Fig. 4.29. The geometrical construction of the airfoil, which corresponds to the transformations Eqs. (4.199) to (4.201), is explained in most textbooks.[9] The circulation needed to make the velocity finite at the trailing edge is still given by Eq. (4.203), in which β is the angle $BO'O$ in Fig. 4.30, the circles being tangent at B.

If a closed contour (on which the boundary condition is imposed) can be transformed into a unit circle, the Fourier analysis described at the end of Art. 4.34 can again be employed. After the solution is obtained in the intermediate plane (in which the boundary appears in the form of a unit circle), that for the physical plane can be obtained by the inverse transformation that transforms the intermediate plane into the physical plane.

4.38. Free-streamline Problems, Application of the Schwarz-Christoffel Transformation

The Schwarz-Christoffel transformation is one that transforms the interior of a polygon into the entire upper (or lower) half plane of another variable, say, t. This transformation is very useful for solving free-

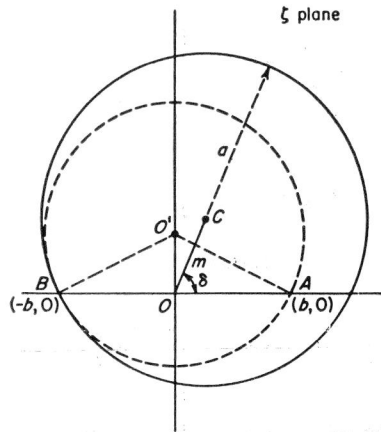

FIG. 4.30. Notation for Joukowski transformation.

streamline problems in hydrodynamics, because, for straight fixed boundaries, the logarithmic hodograph for such problems is a polygon. The polygon $A'B'C'D'E'A'$ (Fig. 4.31) in the Ω plane (say) can be transformed into the upper half t plane by the Schwarz-Christoffel transformation

$$\Omega = M \int_0^t \frac{dt}{(t-a)^{\alpha/\pi}(t-b)^{\beta/\pi}(t-c)^{\gamma/\pi}(t-d)^{\delta/\pi}(t-e)^{\epsilon/\pi}} + N \qquad (4.204)$$

It can be seen from Eq. (4.204) that every time t crosses any of the values a, b, c, d, and e, the argument of $d\Omega/dt$ will change by the appropriate value (α, β, γ, δ, or ϵ), but will remain constant (as will $d\Omega$) otherwise, as the value of t is changed along the real axis. Of the seven constants (a, b, c, d, e, M, and N), three can be chosen arbitrarily and the remaining four determined from the positions of A', B', C', and D'—or any four of the five vertices. So long as the polygon is a closed one, so that

$$\alpha + \beta + \gamma + \delta + \epsilon = 2\pi$$

there is no need to impose the condition that E' is where it is, for if A', B', C', and D' are where they should be and the lines $E'A'$ and $D'E'$ have the correct inclinations, E' can only be at the place where it should be. The same argument applies to a polygon of n sides. Three (usually not M or N) of the $n+2$ constants can always be chosen arbitrarily.

One point has to be kept in mind. If any of the constants associated with the vertices in the t plane should be infinite, the corresponding factor should be dropped. For instance, if e is infinite, the factor

$$(t-e)^{\epsilon/\pi}$$

should simply be dropped[9] from Eq. (4.204).

Two examples of free-streamline flow will be presented to illustrate the use of the Schwarz-Christoffel transformation. The first concerns a jet issuing from a slot in an infinite flat plate (Fig. 4.32). For convenience, the asymptotic width of the jet will be taken to be π and the speed on the free streamlines unity. The quantity Ω is defined to be

$$\Omega = -\ln\left(-\frac{dw}{dz}\right) = -\ln(qe^{-i\theta}) = \ln\frac{1}{q} + i\theta$$

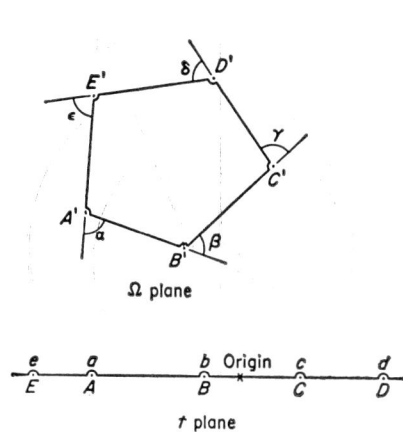

Fig. 4.31. Transformation of interior of polygon into upper half plane.

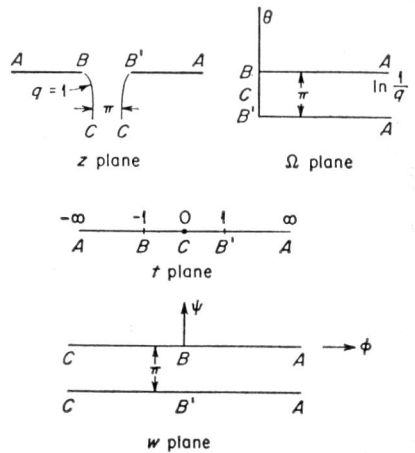

Fig. 4.32. Jet issuing from a slot.

The boundary $ABCCB'A$ in the physical plane then appears in the Ω plane (the logarithmic hodograph plane) as a polygon† $ABCB'A$. In the t plane, the abscissas associated with B, C, and B' are chosen arbitrarily to be $-1, 0$, and 1. By symmetry the point A is mapped into the point at infinity in the t plane, so that the factor associated with the vertex A in the Ω plane is simply ignored in the Schwarz-Christoffel transformation:

$$\Omega = M \int \frac{dt}{\sqrt{t^2 - 1}} + N = M \cosh^{-1} t + N$$

But
$$\Omega_B = 0 = M \cosh^{-1} - 1 + N = iM\pi + N$$
$$\Omega_{B'} = -\pi i = M \cosh^{-1} 1 + N = N$$
so that
$$N = -\pi i \qquad M = 1$$
and
$$\Omega = \cosh^{-1} t - i\pi$$

In the w plane the streamlines are at a distance π apart, because in the physical plane the asymptotic speed of the jet is unity and the asymptotic width π. The polygon in the w plane can be mapped into the upper half of the t plane by the transformation

$$w = M' \int \frac{dt}{t} + N' = M' \ln t + N'$$

Since $w_{B'} = -\pi i$ and $w_B = 0$, one has

$$M' \ln 1 + N' = N' = -\pi i$$
$$M' \ln (-1) + N' = iM'\pi - \pi i = 0$$
from which
$$M' = 1 \qquad N' = -\pi i$$
and
$$w = \ln t - \pi i$$

Actually, since the point C is the origin of the t plane and represents a sink of strength‡ 2π in the t plane, the term $-\pi i$ is just an additive constant resulting from the arbitrary choice of the origin in the w plane.

Now on the free streamline BC, $w = \phi$, since ψ is zero. If s is measured along BC from B,

$$\phi = -s$$

since $q = 1$ on BC. Thus

$$ds = -d\phi = -dw = -\frac{dt}{t}$$

But, on BC,

$$\Omega = i\theta \qquad t = \cosh i(\pi + \theta) = \cos (\pi + \theta) = -\cos \theta$$

so that

$$ds = \frac{-\sin \theta}{\cos \theta} d\theta = -\tan \theta \, d\theta$$

The parametric differential equations for the curve BC are then

$$dx = \cos \theta \, ds = -\sin \theta \, d\theta$$

$$dy = \sin \theta \, ds = -\frac{\sin^2 \theta}{\cos \theta} d\theta$$

which can be integrated to be

$$x = 1 + \cos \theta$$

$$y = \sin \theta - \ln \tan \left(\frac{\theta}{2} + \frac{\pi}{4} \right)$$

---

† The free streamlines are streamlines of constant pressure. Since gravity effects are neglected, they are also streamlines of constant speed.

‡ The actual discharge in the jet is π. But for the entire t plane the strength of the sink at C must be 2π in order that the discharge from the upper half plane be π.

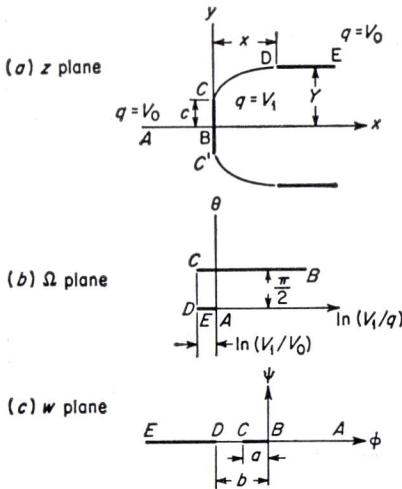

(a) z plane

(b) Ω plane

(c) w plane

Fig. 4.33. Transition curves of constant pressure.

the constants of integration being determined by taking B as the origin of the physical plane. These equations are the parametric equations for the free streamline BC. As C is approached, θ approaches $-\pi/2$ and x approaches 1. Taking into consideration the symmetry of the jet, the total width of the slot is $\pi + 2$, and the coefficient of contraction is then

$$ C_c = \frac{\pi}{\pi + 2} = 0.611 $$

This is an early (1869) result of Kirchhoff.[10]

A second example is furnished by the work of Gerber and McNown[11] on transition curves of constant pressure. The vertical plate (Fig. 4.33) $C'BC$ is joined by two transition curves of constant pressure to two horizontal plates. In the example just presented (Kirchhoff's result), the jet width and the speed on the free streamlines are arbitrarily fixed, for the sake of convenience, to be π and unity,

respectively. If the width is b and the speed V_1, all one needs to do is to multiply all linear dimensions by b/π and all speeds and velocities by V_1. In the present example, no linear dimension or speed will be arbitrarily fixed, in order to demonstrate how the results can be made completely explicit and to exhibit dimensional homogeneity.

The several planes are shown in Fig. 4.33. Since the flow above the streamline $ABCDE$ occupies the entire *lower* half w plane, the w plane can serve as the t plane and the introduction of a new variable t is unnecessary. The only difference is that the polygon is mapped into the lower, instead of the upper, half of the w plane. This, however, introduces no difficulty whatever. A review of the Schwarz-Christoffel transformation will reveal the fact that whether the lower half or the upper half of the t plane (in this case w plane) is used is immaterial. All one has to do is to make the indentations below, instead of above, the real axis of the t plane, if its lower half is to be used. The Schwarz-Christoffel transformation provides the following relationship between Ω and w:

$$ \Omega = \frac{i}{2} \cos^{-1} \frac{m(w + K)}{w} - \tfrac{1}{2} \cosh^{-1} m \tag{4.205} $$

in which, with reference to Fig. 4.33,

$$ b = \frac{Km}{m - 1} \qquad a = \frac{Km}{m + 1} \tag{4.206} $$

and

$$ m = \frac{1}{2}\left[\left(\frac{V_1}{V_0}\right)^2 + \left(\frac{V_0}{V_1}\right)^2 \right] \qquad (> 1) \tag{4.207} $$

The scale factor K (having the dimension of the velocity potential) is related to the speeds V_0 and V_1 and to the width $(2c)$ of the vertical plate. Since (with v as the vertical velocity along BC)

$$ c = \int_0^c dy = -\int_0^a \frac{d\phi}{v} $$

and, from Eq. (4.205),

$$ v = V_1 \exp\left[-\tfrac{1}{2} \cosh^{-1} \frac{m(\phi + K)}{\phi} \right] $$

one integration produces

$$c = \frac{K}{V_1}\frac{V_1^4 + V_0^4}{V_1^4 - V_0^4}\left[\frac{V_1^2 - V_0^2}{V_1^2 + V_0^2} + \frac{V_1}{V_0}\tan^{-1}\frac{V_1}{V_0} - \frac{V_0}{V_1}\tan^{-1}\frac{V_0}{V_1}\right] \qquad (4.208)$$

As to the form of the transition curves, the approach is the same as that used in the last example. The results are

$$x = \frac{mK}{2V_1}\left[\frac{\cos\theta}{(m+1)/2 - \cos^2\theta} - \sqrt{\frac{2}{m+1}}\tanh^{-1}\left(\sqrt{\frac{2}{m+1}}\cos\theta\right)\right]$$

$$y = c + \frac{mK}{2V_1}\left\{\frac{\sin\theta}{(m-1)/2 + \sin^2\theta} - \frac{2}{m-1} + \sqrt{\frac{2}{m-1}}\right.$$

$$\left.\left[\tan^{-1}\sqrt{\frac{2}{m-1}} - \tan^{-1}\left(\sqrt{\frac{2}{m-1}}\sin\theta\right)\right]\right\}$$

For point B,

$$x = \frac{mK}{2V_1}\left(\frac{2}{m-1} - \sqrt{\frac{2}{m+1}}\tanh^{-1}\sqrt{\frac{2}{m+1}}\right) \qquad (4.209)$$

$$y = c + \frac{mK}{2V_1}\left(\sqrt{\frac{2}{m-1}}\tan^{-1}\sqrt{\frac{2}{m-1}} - \frac{2}{m-1}\right) \qquad (4.210)$$

The value m, defined by Eq. (4.207), is related to

$$\sigma = \frac{p_0 - p_1}{\rho V_0^2/2} \qquad (4.211)$$

by

$$m = \frac{1}{2}\left(1 + \sigma + \frac{1}{1 + \sigma}\right) \qquad (4.212)$$

Thus, if σ is known and V_0 is known, m and V_1 are known. From a known c the value of K can be computed from Eq. (4.208), and the transition curves are completely determined. It may be noted that comparison with experimental results for axisymmetric cavity flows shows a fortuitous agreement with the analytical results just presented for two-dimensional flows.

For free-streamline flow past a flat plate broadside on (Fig. 4.34), the Schwarz-Christoffel transformation produces the result (with c as the origin of the physical plane)

$$x = \frac{2l}{\pi + 4}\left(\sin\theta + \frac{\pi}{4}\right)$$

$$y = \frac{l}{\pi + 4}\left[\sec\theta\tan\theta - \ln\tan\left(\frac{\pi}{4} + \frac{\theta}{2}\right)\right]$$

in which l is the width of the plate. The pressure in the cavity is the same as that at infinity, and the drag coefficient is

$$C_D = \frac{D}{\rho U^2 l/2} = \frac{2\pi}{\pi + 4} = 0.88 \qquad (4.213)$$

in which D = drag
ρ = density of fluid
U = speed of flow at infinity

For well-defined cavities (with liquid-gas inter-

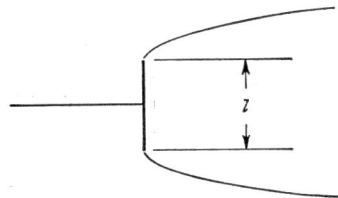

FIG. 4.34. Flow around a flat plate normal to approach velocity.

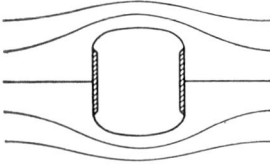

FIG. 4.35. Flow around finite cavity.

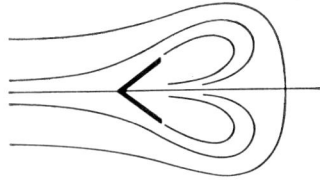

FIG. 4.36. Reentrant jet.

face), the drag formula is supported by experiments. The results for this flow were obtained by Kirchhoff.[10] The corresponding problem for a class of unsteady flows has been solved by von Kármán.†

The cavity in the Kirchhoff flow just discussed is infinite. Riabouchinsky[12] later constructed a symmetric flow model with a finite cavity (Fig. 4.35). The Schwarz-Christoffel transformation again provides the key for the solution. The cavity pressure is now lower than the pressure at infinity. If the cavity number σ is defined by

$$\sigma = \frac{p_\infty - p_c}{\rho U^2/2} \tag{4.214}$$

in which U = flow velocity at infinity
p_∞ = pressure at infinity
p_c = cavity pressure

for small σ, Riabouchinsky's analysis gives the result

$$C_D(\sigma) = (1 + \sigma)C_D(0) \tag{4.215}$$

with

$$C_D(0) = \frac{2\pi}{\pi + 4}$$

For larger values of σ, Riabouchinsky's analysis also provides the exact value of $C_D(\sigma)$.

Another model is the model with the reentrant jet (Fig. 4.36). This model was initiated in the same year (1946) by authors in the United States (Gilbarg and Rock), the United Kingdom (Kreisel), and the Soviet Union (Efros) and further developed by other authors (see Ref. 13, p. 56).

Finally, Shiffman's reflection principle[14] should be mentioned. This principle enables one to extend the flow analytically across the free streamline and to find the boundaries and singularities beyond the free streamline. (For details see Ref. 14 or 2, p. 313.)

4.39. Inverse Methods for Free-streamline Flows

An inverse method for constructing free-surface flows was given by Richardson.[15] His formula is

$$-\frac{dz}{dw} = [3gG(w)]^{-1/3}\{[1 - G'^2(w)]^{1/2} + iG'(w)\} \tag{4.216}$$

in which g is the gravitational acceleration, w is the complex potential which is real on the free streamline ($\psi = 0$), and G, G', and $G^{1/3}$ are real for real w. It can be shown that the Bernoulli equation, with the gravity term included, is exactly satisfied on the free streamline. Also, once $G(w)$ is given, parametric equations for the free streamline are furnished by Eq. (4.216). If one sets

$$H(w) = \left[\frac{3G(w)}{2}\right]^{2/3} \tag{4.217}$$

† T. von Kármán, Accelerated Flow of an Incompressible Fluid with Wake Formation, *Annali di Mat. pura ed appl.*, ser. IV, **29** : 247–249 (1949).

Eq. (4.216) becomes

$$-\frac{dz}{dw} = (2g)^{-\frac{1}{3}} \left\{ \left[\frac{1}{H(w)} - H'^2(w) \right]^{\frac{1}{2}} + iH'(w) \right\} \tag{4.218}$$

If the free streamline does not represent a surface of constant pressure but an interface between a stagnant fluid of density ρ_1 and a moving layer of density ρ_2 ($> \rho_1$), Eqs. (4.216) and (4.218) can still be used if g is changed to g', which is defined to be

$$g' = g \frac{\rho_2 - \rho_1}{\rho_1} \tag{4.219}$$

If both layers are moving, two complex potentials, one for each fluid, must be used. The appropriate formulas, given by Yih,[16] are

$$-\frac{dz}{dw_1} = (2g')^{-\frac{1}{3}} [(kF_1^{-1} - G'_1{}^2)^{\frac{1}{2}} + iG'_1] \tag{4.220}$$

$$-\frac{dz}{dw_2} = (2g')^{\frac{1}{3}} \{[(F_1 + G_1)^{-1} - K'_2{}^2]^{\frac{1}{2}} + iK'_2\} \tag{4.221}$$

in which w_1 is for the upper layer and w_2 for the lower layer, F_1 and G_1 are functions of w_1 and K_2 a function of w_2, and k is the density ratio ρ_1/ρ_2. Furthermore,

$$G_1(w_1) = K_2(w_2) \tag{4.222}$$

as required by the location of the interface.

So far the inverse methods described are all for steady flows. The extension to unsteady flows with a free surface of constant pressure has been achieved by John.[17] (See also Ref. 23.)

4.40. Added Masses

Since the Taylor theorem, as improved by Birkhoff and Landweber, enables one to compute the added masses (except those for pure rotation) for three-dimensional bodies from the internal singularities, the corresponding theorem for two-dimensional flows can be obtained by integration. It is, however, much simpler to derive the two-dimensional counterpart of Taylor's theorem directly. Using α to denote the subscripts 1, 2, and 6, in the rotation of Art. 4.18, one can, with s denoting the distance along the boundary of the body and $z = x_1 + ix_2$, write Eq. (4.57) in the form

$$A_{\alpha1} + iA_{\alpha2} = \rho \oint \phi_\alpha n_1 \, ds + i\rho \oint \phi_\alpha n_2 \, ds = i\rho \oint \phi_\alpha \, dz$$

$$= -i\rho \left[\oint w_\alpha \, dz - i \int \psi_\alpha \, ds \right] = -i\rho \oint w_\alpha \, dz - \rho \oint z n_\alpha \, ds$$

But

$$\rho \oint z n_\alpha \, ds = B_{\alpha1} + iB_{\alpha2}$$

in which

$$B_{\alpha1} = \rho \oint x_1 n_\alpha \, ds \qquad B_{\alpha2} = \rho \oint x_2 n_\alpha \, ds \tag{4.223}$$

and in particular

$$B_{ij} = B\delta_{ij} \qquad (i, j = 1, 2)$$

$$\tag{4.224}$$

$$B_{61} = -B\bar{x}_2 \qquad B_{62} = B\bar{x}_1$$

with B as the displaced mass per unit length, and $\bar{x}_1$ and $\bar{x}_2$ denoting the coordinates of the mass center of the cross section of the two-dimensional body. Thus

$$A_{\alpha 1} + B_{\alpha 1} + i(A_{\alpha 2} + B_{\alpha 2}) = -i\rho \oint w_\alpha \, dz$$

By using theorems in the theory of functions of a complex variable, Yih[7] has shown that the preceding equation can be written

$$A_{\alpha 1} + B_{\alpha 1} + i(A_{\alpha 2} + B_{\alpha 2}) = \rho \left[\int \sigma_{\alpha z} \, dA + \Sigma(m_\alpha z_s + 2\pi\mu_\alpha) \right] \qquad (4.225)$$

in which σ_α = strength of distributed sources
m_α = strength of isolated sources
μ_α = strength of isolated doublets

per unit length of the cylinder and for the αth motion.

For the case of translation of a circular cylinder, $\alpha = 1$, and the only singularity is a doublet with strength μ equal to a^2 since (for unit velocity in the x direction)

$$\mu = \mu_1 = a^2$$

Thus $A_{11} + B_{11} = A_{11} + B = A_{11} + \rho\pi a^2 = 2\pi\rho a^2$

and the added mass is

$$A_{11} = \rho\pi a^2 = B$$

This result, of course, can be obtained by a direct calculation, without the use of Eq. (4.225).

4.41. Forces and Moment, Blasius Theorems

The forces and moment acting on a two-dimensional body can be obtained by integration from the generalized Lagally theorem presented in Art. 4.26. However, for steady two-dimensional flows, the forces and moment can be obtained most simply by a direct calculation. The results constitute what is known as the Blasius theorems.

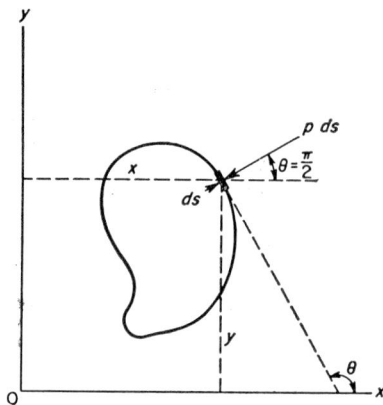

FIG. 4.37. Fluid force on element of a cylinder. (*Ref. 9.*)

With reference to Fig. 4.37, the components of the force acting on the infinitesimal distance ds are

$$dX = -p \, ds \cos\left(\theta - \frac{\pi}{2}\right)$$

$$dY = -p \, ds \sin\left(\theta - \frac{\pi}{2}\right)$$

in which p is the pressure. Thus

$$dF = dX + i\,dY = ip\,ds\,e^{i\theta}$$

and, since $dz = ds\,e^{i\theta}$,

$$d\overline{F} = dX - i\,dY = -ip\,ds\,e^{-i\theta} = ip\,dz\,e^{-i2\theta} \qquad (4.226)$$

The moment about the origin of the force acting on ds is

$$dM = -y\,dX + x\,dY = p\,ds\left[\,y\cos\left(\theta - \frac{\pi}{2}\right) - x\sin\left(\theta - \frac{\pi}{2}\right)\right]$$

$$= p\,ds(y\sin\theta + x\cos\theta)$$

which is the real part of

$$pz\,dz\,e^{-i2\theta} = iz\,d\overline{F}$$

Hence

$$dM + i\,dN = iz\,d\overline{F} = pz\,dz\,e^{-i2\theta} \qquad (4.227)$$

in which $i\,dN$ is merely the imaginary part of $iz\,d\overline{F}$.

Now, since the contribution of the hydrostatic pressure to forces and moment can be separately and easily computed, p will be used to denote only the dynamic pressure. Hence, for steady irrotational flows,

$$p = c - \frac{\rho}{2}q^2$$

in which q is the speed, and c is a constant. The contribution of the constant part c of the pressure to forces and moment is of course zero. Thus one can take

$$p = -\frac{\rho}{2}q^2$$

Since

$$\frac{dw}{dz} = -qe^{-i\theta}$$

the (dynamic) pressure is

$$p = -\frac{\rho}{2}\left(\frac{dw}{dz}\right)^2 e^{i2\theta} \qquad (4.228)$$

By substituting Eq. (4.228) into Eqs. (4.226) and (4.227) and after integrating, one has

$$X - iY = \frac{i}{2}\rho\oint\left(\frac{dw}{dz}\right)^2 dz \qquad (4.229)$$

$$M + iN = -\frac{\rho}{2}\oint z\left(\frac{dw}{dz}\right)^2 dz \qquad (4.230)$$

These are the Blasius theorems.

4.42. Application of the Blasius Theorems

To facilitate the application of the Blasius theorems, several important theorems in the theory of functions of a complex variable will be recorded here, some of them without proof.

The Cauchy Integral Theorem. If a function $f(z)$ is analytic and single-valued inside and on a simple closed contour C, then

$$\int_C f(z)\,dz = 0 \qquad (4.231)$$

PROOF. Let $f(z) = \xi + i\eta$. Then, under the conditions stated and in virtue of the Stokes theorem [Eq. (4.25)],

$$\int_C f(z)\, dz = \int_C (\xi\, dx - \eta\, dy) + i \int_C (\eta\, dx + \xi\, dy)$$

$$= -\iint_D \left(\frac{\partial \eta}{\partial x} + \frac{\partial \xi}{\partial y} \right) dx\, dy + i \iint_D \left(\frac{\partial \xi}{\partial x} - \frac{\partial \eta}{\partial y} \right) dx\, dy$$

in which D is the domain enclosed by C. The Cauchy-Riemann equations are

$$\frac{\partial \xi}{\partial x} = \frac{\partial \eta}{\partial y} \qquad \frac{\partial \xi}{\partial y} = -\frac{\partial \eta}{\partial x}$$

Hence the theorem.

It may seem redundant, in view of the definition of analyticity, to state that $f(z)$ is single-valued. The purpose of that statement is to emphasize the requirement that C be taken on one sheet of a Riemann surface if the function is not single-valued but can be made to be so by the introduction of a multisheeted Riemann surface.

The converse of Cauchy's integral theorem is also true and is known as Morera's theorem. The proof is omitted.

Cauchy's Integral. Under the same conditions as stated for the Cauchy integral theorem, with z inside C,

$$f(z) = \frac{1}{2\pi i} \int_C \frac{f(t)}{t - z}\, dt \tag{4.232}$$

This result can be generalized to

$$f^{(n)}(z) = \frac{n!}{2\pi i} \int_C \frac{f(t)}{(t - z)^{n+1}}\, dt \tag{4.233}$$

in which $f^{(n)}(z)$ is the nth derivative of $f(z)$. Although the proofs of these results are omitted, a simple and direct proof for the special case $f(z) = $ constant can be given. Let

$$t - z = re^{i\theta}$$

then on the unit circle surrounding z, $dt = ire^{i\theta}\, d\theta$, and

$$\int_C \frac{dt}{t - z} = i \int_C d\theta = 2\pi i \tag{4.234}$$

$$\int_C \frac{dt}{(t - z)^n} = \frac{i}{r^{n-1}} \int_C e^{i(1-n)\theta}\, d\theta = 0 \qquad (n \neq 1) \tag{4.235}$$

Equations (4.234) and (4.235) correspond, respectively, to Eqs. (4.232) and (4.233).

Taylor Series. If $f(z)$ is analytic on and inside a simple closed contour C, and if a is a point inside C, then

$$f(z) = f(a) + (z - a)f'(a) + \cdots + \frac{(z - a)^n}{n!} f^n(a) + \cdots$$

convergent inside C.

Laurent Series. If $f(z)$ is analytic on and between two concentric circles C and C' with center a, then $f(z)$ can be expanded in positive and negative powers of $z - a$, convergent at all points of the ring-shaped region.

It may be mentioned that if $f(z)$ can be expanded in the form

$$f(z) = \sum_{n=-\infty}^{\infty} A_n (z - a)^n$$

the integral

$$\int_C f(z)\, dz$$

will, in virtue of Eqs. (4.231), (4.234), and (4.235), be equal to $A_{-1}2\pi i$. [The value can be different from zero because $f(z)$ is not necessarily analytic inside the smaller circle C.] The coefficient A_{-1} is called the residue of $f(z)$ at a.

An example of the application of the Blasius theorem can now be given. For flow past a circular cylinder with circulation, the complex potential is given by Eq. (4.178), and

$$\left(\frac{dw}{dz}\right)^2 = \left[-U\left(1 - \frac{a^2}{z^2}\right) + \frac{i\kappa}{2\pi z}\right]^2$$

$$z\left(\frac{dw}{dz}\right)^2 = z\left[-U\left(1 - \frac{a^2}{z^2}\right) + \frac{i\kappa}{2\pi z}\right]^2$$

Thus the residue of $(dw/dz)^2$ is $-i\kappa U/\pi$, and so Eq. (4.229) gives

$$X - iY = \frac{i\rho}{2}\left(\frac{-i\kappa U}{\pi}\right)2\pi i = \rho\kappa U i$$

or
$$X = 0 \qquad Y = -\rho\kappa U \qquad (4.236)$$

which, as mentioned before, can also be obtained by a direct integration of the forces on the cylinder. The residue of $z(dw/dz)^2$ is real, so that the integral in Eq. (4.230), being $2\pi i$ times the residue, is purely imaginary. Thus Eq. (4.230) gives

$$M = 0$$

The second of Eqs. (4.236) is called the Kutta-Joukowski theorem and applies in general to any uniform flow (with velocity U at infinity) past a finite body, with circulation κ. A rough proof is as follows. Since the body is finite, the algebraic sum of the strengths of sources and sinks (isolated or distributed) is zero and contributes nothing to the residue. Doublets produce terms of the type A/z^2 in dw/dz, and since the flow is uniform at infinity, the term of the highest order in z in dw/dz is $-U$. Thus doublets, too, contribute nothing to the residue of $(dw/dz)^2$. If κ is the *total* circulation around the body, it is then obvious that the residue of $(dw/dz)^2$ is $-i\kappa U/\pi$, and the theorem follows. Of course, singularities of higher (negative) orders contribute nothing to the residue, in virtue of Eq. (4.235).

4.43. Source-sink Method for Symmetric Flow Past a Slender Body

Consider a symmetric slender two-dimensional body moving along its axis of symmetry (x axis) with velocity U in otherwise quiescent fluid. The profile of the body is given by

$$y = F(x)$$

with $a \leq x \leq b$. Assuming a continuous distribution of sources and sinks of strength $m(\xi)$ between a and b along the x axis, one has, with $f(\xi) = -m(\xi)$,

$$\phi = \frac{1}{2\pi}\int_a^b f(\xi)\ln\sqrt{(x-\xi)^2 + y^2}\,d\xi \qquad (4.237)$$

in which $f(\xi)$ is the strength of the sink (or source) at $x = \xi$. This ϕ satisfies the Laplace equation and can be identified with the velocity potential. The boundary condition on the surface of the body is, with higher-order terms neglected,

$$v = \pm U\frac{dy}{dx} = \pm U\frac{dF}{dx} \qquad (4.238)$$

with the positive sign for the upper half and the negative sign for the lower half of the body. The problem is to find the proper $f(\xi)$ so that the boundary conditions (4.238) are satisfied.

Differentiation of Eq. (4.237) with respect to x and y produces

$$u = -\frac{1}{2\pi} \int_a^b \frac{f(\xi)(x - \xi)\, d\xi}{(x - \xi)^2 + y^2} \qquad v = -\frac{y}{2\pi} \int_a^b \frac{f(\xi)\, d\xi}{(x - \xi)^2 + y^2} \qquad (4.239)$$

The second of Eqs. (4.239) can be written as

$$v = -\frac{1}{2\pi} \int_{\eta_a}^{\eta_b} \frac{f(\xi)\, d\eta}{1 + \eta^2} \qquad (4.240)$$

in which

$$\eta = \frac{\xi - x}{y}$$

For small positive y, Eq. (4.240) can be approximated by

$$v = -\frac{1}{2\pi} f(x) \int_{-\infty}^{\infty} \frac{d\eta}{1 + \eta^2} = \frac{-f(x)}{2\pi} \tan^{-1} \eta \Big|_{-\infty}^{\infty} = \frac{-f(x)}{2} \qquad (4.241)$$

For small negative y, the corresponding result is

$$v = \frac{f(x)}{2} \qquad (4.242)$$

From Eq. (4.238) it then follows that

$$f(x) = -2U \frac{dF(x)}{dx} \qquad (4.243)$$

The component u can then be evaluated by the first of Eqs. (4.239). For small y, u is the principal value of

$$-\frac{1}{2\pi} \int_a^b \frac{f(\xi)\, d\xi}{x - \xi}$$

or

$$u = -\frac{1}{2\pi} \lim_{\epsilon \to 0} \left[\int_a^{x-\epsilon} \frac{f(\xi)\, d\xi}{x - \xi} - \int_{x+\epsilon}^b \frac{f(\xi)\, d\xi}{\xi - x} \right] \qquad (4.244)$$

4.44. Munk's Vortex-sheet Theory

A sheet on which vorticity is concentrated, i.e., across which there is a discontinuity of the velocity component tangential to the line, is called a vortex sheet. There is in general a circulation around the sheet, and this will give rise to a lift in the presence of a uniform stream.

If the upper surface of an (infinite) airfoil is given by $y = y_1(x)$ and the lower one by $y = y_2(x)$, then the middle line of the foil is given by

$$y = \frac{y_1(x) + y_2(x)}{2}$$

For very thin airfoils at small angles of attack, this middle line can be assumed to coincide with the x axis. Consider a potential of the form (with the uniform flow excluded)

$$\phi = \frac{1}{2\pi} \int_0^a f(\xi) \tan^{-1} \frac{y}{x - \xi}\, d\xi \qquad (4.245)$$

The tangential velocity on the airfoil is, approximately,

$$u = -\frac{\partial \phi}{\partial x} = -\frac{y}{2\pi} \int_0^a f(\xi) \frac{1}{(x - \xi)^2 + y^2}\, d\xi \qquad (4.246)$$

This is similar to Eq. (4.239), and results similar to Eqs. (4.241) and (4.242) follow. For small y,

$$u_+ = -\frac{f(x)}{2} \qquad u_- = \frac{f(x)}{2} \qquad (4.247)$$

and the discontinuity in u is

$$[u] = -f(x) \qquad (4.248)$$

The discontinuity in ϕ is therefore

$$[\phi] = \int_0^x f(\xi)\,d\xi \qquad (4.249)$$

with the potential higher on the upper surface if $f(\xi)$ is positive, or counterclockwise, and lower on the upper surface in the opposite case.

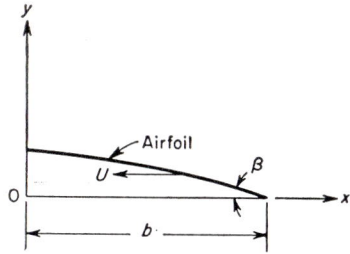

FIG. 4.38. Notation for thin airfoil.

To find $f(\xi)$, the component v on the thin foil must be considered. With β as the (small) angle of attack (Fig. 4.38), the normal velocity component is, approximately,

$$v = U\left(\frac{dy}{dx} - \beta\right) \qquad (4.250)$$

in which U is the speed of flight as shown in Fig. 4.38. Thus, from Eq. (4.245), for small y

$$v = -\frac{\partial\phi}{\partial y} = -\frac{1}{2\pi}\int_0^a \frac{f(\xi)}{x-\xi}\,d\xi \qquad (4.251)$$

with v given in Eq. (4.250). This integral equation is to be solved with the additional condition that

$$f(a) = 0 \qquad (4.252)$$

which ensures that there is no infinite velocity at the trailing edge. The solution of Eqs. (4.251) and (4.252) was given by Keldish and Sedov.[18]

$$f(x) = -\frac{2}{\pi}\sqrt{\frac{a-x}{x}}\int_0^a \sqrt{\frac{\xi}{a-\xi}}\,\frac{v(\xi)\,d\xi}{\xi-x} \qquad (4.253)$$

A similar approach was applied by Tulin[19] to the study of supercavitated hydrofoils, with proper adaptations to suit the new features presented by the cavitation phenomenon.

4.45. The Relaxation Method

Problems of potential flow of an incompressible fluid can always be solved numerically, by the so-called relaxation method developed by Southwell.[20]

The method consists of (1) the construction of a square (or rectangular, triangular, hexagonal) net at every joint of which roughly suitable initial values of the stream function (or the velocity potential) are assigned, and (2) the successive refinement of these values according to finite-difference formulas representing the Laplace equation.

Consider the star as shown in Fig. 4.39. By the Taylor expansion, one has, up to terms of the second degree in a,

$$\psi_1 = \psi_0 - \psi_x\lambda_1 a + \psi_{xx}\frac{\lambda_1^2 a^2}{2}$$

$$\psi_2 = \psi_0 + \psi_x\lambda_2 a + \psi_{xx}\frac{\lambda_2^2 a^2}{2}$$

$$\psi_3 = \psi_0 - \psi_y\lambda_3 a + \psi_{yy}\frac{\lambda_3^2 a^2}{2}$$

$$\psi_4 = \psi_0 + \psi_y\lambda_4 a + \psi_{yy}\frac{\lambda_4^2 a^2}{2}$$

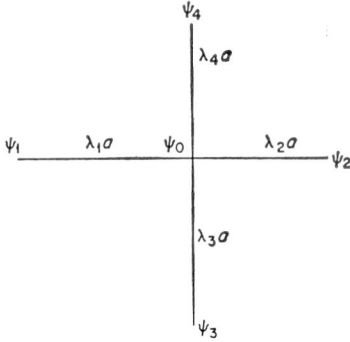

FIG. 4.39. Relaxation star.

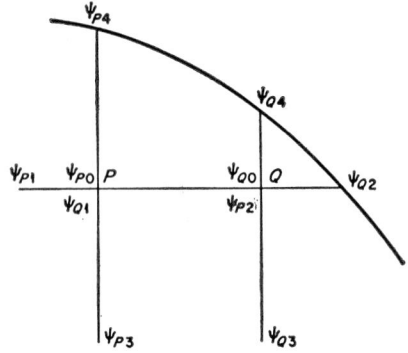

FIG. 4.40. Irregular relaxation star.

in which the subscripts x and y indicate partial differentiation. Eliminating ψ_x from the first two formulas,

$$\lambda_2\psi_1 + \lambda_1\psi_2 - (\lambda_1 + \lambda_2)\psi_0 = \frac{a^2}{2}\lambda_1\lambda_2(\lambda_1 + \lambda_2)\psi_{xx}$$

Similarly,

$$\lambda_4\psi_3 + \lambda_3\psi_4 - (\lambda_3 + \lambda_4)\psi_0 = \frac{a^2}{2}\lambda_3\lambda_4(\lambda_3 + \lambda_4)\psi_{yy}$$

Thus the Laplace equation $\psi_{xx} + \psi_{yy} = 0$ becomes

$$\frac{\psi_1}{\lambda_1(\lambda_1 + \lambda_2)} + \frac{\psi_2}{\lambda_2(\lambda_1 + \lambda_2)} + \frac{\psi_3}{\lambda_3(\lambda_3 + \lambda_4)} + \frac{\psi_4}{\lambda_4(\lambda_3 + \lambda_4)} - \left(\frac{1}{\lambda_1\lambda_2} + \frac{1}{\lambda_3\lambda_4}\right)\psi_0 = 0$$

$$(4.254)$$

For a regular star, $\lambda_1 = \lambda_2 = \lambda_3 = \lambda_4$, and Eq. (4.254) becomes, after multiplication by 2,

$$\psi_1 + \psi_2 + \psi_3 + \psi_4 - 4\psi_0 = 0 \qquad (4.255)$$

which states that the value of ψ at the center of a regular star is the mean of the ψ values at the surrounding points.

The process of relaxation will be discussed for the general case of irregular stars. For the purpose of discussion Eq. (4.254) can be written, for joint P (Fig. 4.40), in the form (R = residue)

$$R_P = A_P\psi_{P1} + B_P\psi_{P2} + C_P\psi_{P3} + D_P\psi_{P4} - E_P\psi_{P0} = 0$$

and, for joint Q, in the form

$$R_Q = A_Q\psi_{Q1} + B_Q\psi_{Q2} + C_Q\psi_{Q3} + D_Q\psi_{Q4} - E_Q\psi_{Q0} = 0$$

If R_P is not zero, it can be made to be equal to zero by increasing ψ_{P0} by R_P/E_P. But ψ_{P0} is ψ_{Q1}, and increasing ψ_{Q1} by R_P/E_P means increasing R_Q by $A_Q R_P/E_P$, and this increase (or decrease) has to be added to (or subtracted from) R_Q. The process goes on until all joints are balanced, i.e., all residues are eliminated.

As to boundary conditions, on a stationary boundary the stream function ψ is constant. Thus in Fig. 4.40, $\psi_{P4} = \psi_{Q4} = \psi_{Q2}$ = whatever value is assigned to the boundary streamline. These values of ψ therefore are not changed throughout the relaxation process. If the velocity potential ϕ is used as the unknown, the condition at a stationary boundary is $\partial\phi/\partial n = 0$, in which n is the distance normal to the boundary. This condition can be translated into one involving ϕ values at the joints of the net. Other boundary conditions may be somewhat more complicated, but can always be imposed in terms of the ψ or ϕ values at the joints of the net.

VORTEX FLOW

4.46. Velocity and Velocity Potential Due to a Vortex Element

For an incompressible fluid the velocity components u, v, w can be expressed as the curl of a fictitious vector, with F, G, and H as the components:

$$u = \frac{\partial H}{\partial y} - \frac{\partial G}{\partial z}$$

$$v = \frac{\partial F}{\partial z} - \frac{\partial H}{\partial x} \qquad (4.256)$$

$$w = \frac{\partial G}{\partial x} - \frac{\partial F}{\partial y}$$

which automatically satisfy the equation of continuity.   The vorticity components ξ, η, ζ are then given by

$$2\xi = \frac{\partial}{\partial x} J - \nabla^2 F \qquad 2\eta = \frac{\partial}{\partial y} J - \nabla^2 G \qquad 2\zeta = \frac{\partial}{\partial z} J - \nabla^2 H \qquad (4.257)$$

in which
$$J = \frac{\partial F}{\partial x} + \frac{\partial G}{\partial y} + \frac{\partial H}{\partial z} \qquad (4.258)$$

The velocity field corresponding to a given vorticity field is, of course, not unique, since two velocity fields differing by an irrotational velocity field correspond to the same vorticity field.   A particular solution of Eqs. (4.257) can be obtained by resolving them into two sets of equations:

$$J = 0 \qquad (4.259)$$

and
$$\nabla^2 F = -2\xi \qquad \nabla^2 G = -2\eta \qquad \nabla^2 H = -2\zeta \qquad (4.260)$$

The solutions of the Poisson equations are, by the use of Green's function in infinite space,

$$F = \frac{1}{2\pi} \iiint \frac{\xi'}{r} dx' \, dy' \, dz'$$

$$G = \frac{1}{2\pi} \iiint \frac{\eta'}{r} dx' \, dy' \, dz' \qquad (4.261)$$

$$H = \frac{1}{2\pi} \iiint \frac{\zeta'}{r} dx' \, dy' \, dz'$$

with
$$r^2 = (x - x')^2 + (y - y')^2 + (z - z')^2$$

Equations (4.261) can be shown to satisfy Eq. (4.259), hence Eq. (4.257).   If the vorticity components are everywhere zero, F, G, and H are everywhere zero, and hence the velocity components are everywhere zero.   Therefore the velocity components obtained from Eqs. (4.261) and (4.256) are due to the vorticity components alone.

For a volume element δV situated at (x', y', z'), the induced velocity components are

$$\delta u = \frac{1}{2\pi} \left[\zeta' \frac{\partial}{\partial y} \left(\frac{1}{r} \right) - \eta' \frac{\partial}{\partial z} \left(\frac{1}{r} \right) \right] \delta V = -\frac{1}{2\pi} \left[(y - y')\zeta' - (z - z')\eta' \right] \frac{\delta V}{r^3}$$

$$\delta v = \frac{1}{2\pi} \left[\xi' \frac{\partial}{\partial z} \left(\frac{1}{r} \right) - \zeta' \frac{\partial}{\partial x} \left(\frac{1}{r} \right) \right] \delta V = -\frac{1}{2\pi} \left[(z - z')\xi' - (x - x')\zeta' \right] \frac{\delta V}{r^3}$$

$$\delta w = \frac{1}{2\pi} \left[\eta' \frac{\partial}{\partial x} \left(\frac{1}{r} \right) - \xi' \frac{\partial}{\partial y} \left(\frac{1}{r} \right) \right] \delta V = -\frac{1}{2\pi} \left[(x - x')\eta' - (y - y')\xi' \right] \frac{\delta V}{r^3}$$

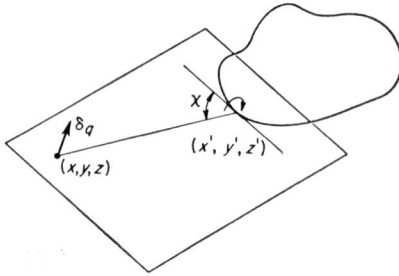

FIG. 4.41. Velocity element due to segment of a vortex.

From these equations it can be easily shown that

$$(x - x')\delta u + (y - y')\delta v + (z - z')\delta w = 0$$

and $$\xi'\,\delta u + \eta'\,\delta v + \zeta'\,\delta w = 0$$

Thus the induced velocity is perpendicular to both the line that joins the point (x',y',z'), where the vorticity is, to the point (x,y,z), where the induced velocity is being calculated, and the vorticity line through (x',y',z'). That is, it is normal to the plane containing the vorticity line and the line of length r (Fig. 4.41). The magnitude of the velocity is

$$\delta q = \sqrt{\delta u^2 + \delta v^2 + \delta w^2} = \frac{\delta V}{2\pi r^2}\,\omega' \sin \chi \tag{4.262}$$

with $$\omega'^2 = \xi'^2 + \eta'^2 + \zeta'^2$$

and χ defined in Fig. 4.41. With σ and $\delta s'$ as the cross-section area and length, respectively, of δV, and $\delta s'$ along the vorticity line,

$$\kappa ds' = 2\omega'\sigma\,ds' = 2\omega'\,\delta V$$

in which κ is the circulation. Thus

$$\delta q = \frac{\kappa\,ds'}{4\pi}\,\frac{\sin \chi}{r^2} \tag{4.263}$$

If the direction of the vortex line at (x',y',z') is taken to be the polar direction and φ is the angle for longitudes, the velocity potential $\delta\phi$ can be obtained from Eq. (4.263) to be

$$\delta\phi = -\frac{\kappa\,\delta s'}{4\pi}\,\frac{\sin^2 \chi}{r}\,\varphi \tag{4.264}$$

4.47. Vortex Streets

Two-dimensional motions due to regular arrays of rectilinear vortices have been studied extensively. For double rows of vortices symmetrically placed, the arrangement is unstable. For unsymmetric, evenly staggered arrangements (Fig. 4.42), the motion is stable only if the ratio b/a is 0.281, as shown by von Kármán.[21] The unsymmetric arrays are known as the Kármán vortex street.

4.48. Flow with Constant Vorticity

The flow with constant vorticity ω is governed by the Poisson equation (ψ = Lagrange's stream function)

$$\frac{\partial^2\psi}{\partial x^2} + \frac{\partial^2\psi}{\partial y^2} = -2\omega \tag{4.265}$$

Problems involving such flows are analogous to problems involving laminar flow of a viscous fluid through a pipe, problems involving irrotational motion of a fluid contained in a rotating cylinder (of other than circular cross section), and problems involving elastic torsion of a prismatic bar.

An equation similar to the Bernoulli equation for irrotational flows exists for steady

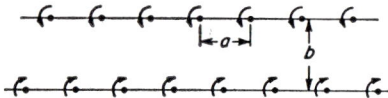

FIG. 4.42. Kármán vortex street.

flows with constant vorticity. The Euler equations are, for steady flows under the action of conservative body forces,

$$u\,\frac{\partial u}{\partial x} + v\,\frac{\partial u}{\partial y} = -\frac{1}{\rho}\frac{\partial p}{\partial x} - \frac{\partial \Omega}{\partial x}$$

$$u\,\frac{\partial v}{\partial x} + v\,\frac{\partial v}{\partial y} = -\frac{1}{\rho}\frac{\partial p}{\partial y} - \frac{\partial \Omega}{\partial y}$$

in which Ω is the body-force potential per unit mass. If ρ is constant or a function of p alone, these equations can be written as

$$v\left(\frac{\partial u}{\partial y} - \frac{\partial v}{\partial x}\right) = -2\omega\,\frac{\partial \psi}{\partial x} = -\frac{\partial}{\partial x}\left(\int \frac{dp}{\rho} + \Omega + \frac{u^2 + v^2}{2}\right) \qquad (4.266)$$

$$u\left(\frac{\partial v}{\partial x} - \frac{\partial u}{\partial y}\right) = -2\omega\,\frac{\partial \psi}{\partial y} = -\frac{\partial}{\partial y}\left(\int \frac{dp}{\rho} + \Omega + \frac{u^2 + v^2}{2}\right) \qquad (4.267)$$

Integration of these equations produces

$$\int \frac{dp}{\rho} + \Omega + \frac{u^2 + v^2}{2} - 2\omega\psi = \text{const} \qquad (4.268)$$

Equation (4.268) is valid for constant vorticity even for fluids with constant (nonzero) viscosity, exactly as the Bernoulli equation is valid for irrotational flows of a viscous fluid. That irrotational flows and flows with constant vorticity do not satisfy the condition of nonslip for a viscous fluid at a solid boundary is quite another question.

4.49. An Example of Flow with Nonconstant Distributed Vorticity

For steady flows of a fluid of constant density, Eq. (4.34) can be written in the form

$$\frac{\partial^2 \psi}{\partial x^2} + \frac{\partial^2 \psi}{\partial y^2} = f(\psi) \qquad (4.269)$$

For a rotational flow into a line sink (Fig. 4.43), with the upstream velocity

$$U = U_{\max} \cos \frac{\pi}{2}\,y$$

or dimensionless velocity

$$u = \frac{U}{U_{\max}} = \cos \frac{\pi}{2}\,y$$

the dimensionless stream function (with the negative sign suppressed in this case, for convenience) is, far upstream,

$$\psi = \int_0^y \cos \frac{\pi}{2}\,y\,dy = \frac{2}{\pi} \sin \frac{\pi}{2}\,y \quad (4.270)$$

The vorticity far upstream is

$$-\nabla^2 \psi = \frac{\pi}{2} \sin \frac{\pi}{2}\,y = \frac{1}{4}\,\pi^2 \psi \quad (4.271)$$

Thus the function $f(\psi)$ in Eq. (4.269) is $-(\pi^2/4)\psi$, not only far upstream, but at every point where the flow has originated upstream (i.e., it is not going in closed circuits). Hence the governing equation becomes

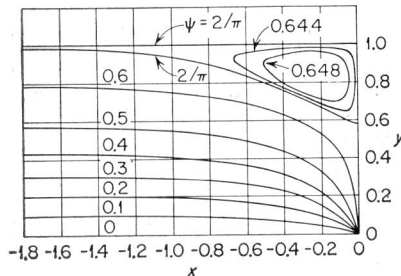

FIG. 4.43. Streamlines for two-dimensional flow into a sink. (*Ref.* 22.)

$$\nabla^2 \psi = -\frac{\pi^2}{4} \psi \tag{4.272}$$

With reference to Fig. 4.43, the boundary conditions are

(1)
$$\psi \rightarrow \frac{2}{\pi} \sin \frac{\pi y}{2} \quad \text{as} \quad x \rightarrow -\infty$$

(2)
$$\psi = \pm \frac{2}{\pi} \quad \text{for} \quad y = \pm 1$$

(3)
$$\psi = \mp \frac{2}{\pi} \quad \text{for} \quad y \begin{array}{l} < 0 \\ > 0 \end{array} \quad \text{and} \quad x = 0$$

The solution of Eq. (4.272) satisfying these boundary conditions is given[22] by

$$\psi = \frac{2}{\pi} \sin \frac{\pi}{2} y + \sum_{n=1}^{\infty} \frac{4}{n\pi^2}\left(1 + \frac{\cos n\pi}{4n^2 - 1}\right) \sin n\pi y \exp\left[(n^2 - \tfrac{1}{4})^{1/2}\pi x\right] \tag{4.273}$$

The velocity components are given by

$$u = \frac{\partial \psi}{\partial y} \qquad v = -\frac{\partial \psi}{\partial x}$$

The flow pattern is shown in Fig. 4.43, in which one of the two corner eddies is evident. Strictly speaking, there is no a priori reason why Eq. (4.272) should apply to the eddy regions, since the flow in those regions does not originate far upstream. The solution obtained is based on the arbitrary assumption that Eq. (4.272) applies to the whole field of flow. For laminar flows of real fluids with small viscosity, the upstream-velocity distribution is parabolic, not far from the cosine distribution on which the solution Eq. (4.273) is based. Thus for such flows the flow pattern outside of the eddies, shown in Fig. 4.43, can be expected to approximate the actual flow.

The corresponding problem of rotational axisymmetric flow into a point sink, with parabolic velocity distribution far upstream, has also been solved.[22] According to the solution, a ring-shaped eddy region is present at the corner where the pipe meets the wall perpendicularly.

REFERENCES

1. Yih, C.-S.: Stream Functions in Three-dimensional Flows, *La Houille blanche*, **1957**: 439–450.
2. Milne-Thomson, L. M.: "Theoretical Hydrodynamics," 3d ed., Macmillan, New York, 1955.
3. Lamb, H.: "Hydrodynamics," Dover, New York, 1955.
4. Taylor, G. I.: The Energy of a Body Moving in an Infinite Fluid, with an application to airships, *Proc. Roy. Soc. (London)*, **A 120:** 13 (1928).
5. Birkhoff, G.: "Hydrodynamics," Princeton University Press, Princeton, N. J., 1953.
6. Landweber, L.: On a Generalization of Taylor's Virtual Mass Relation for Rankine Bodies, *Quart. Appl. Math.*, **14:** 51 (1956).
7. Landweber, L., and C. -S. Yih: Forces, Moments, and Added Masses for Rankine Bodies, *J. Fluid Mech.*, **1:** 319 (1956).
8. Yih, C.-S.: Maximum Acceleration in Two-dimensional Steady Flows of an Ideal Fluid, *Quart. Appl. Math.*, **13:** 202–203 (1955).
9. Streeter, V. L.: "Fluid Dynamics," McGraw-Hill, New York, 1948.
10. Kirchhoff, G.: Zur Theorie freier Flüssigkeitsstrahlen, *Crelle*, **70:** 289–298 (1869).
11. Gerber, R., and J. S. McNown: Transition Curves of Constant Pressure, I. Streamlined Struts, *State Univ. Iowa, Studies in Eng. Bull.* 35, pp. 15–20, 1953.
12. Riabouchinsky, D.: On Steady Fluid Motions with Free Surfaces, *Proc. Math. Soc. London*, ser. 2, **19:** 206–215 (1919).
13. Birkhoff, G., and E. H. Zarantonello: "Jets, Wakes, and Cavities," Academic Press, New York, 1957.

14. Shiffman, M.: On Free Boundaries of an Ideal Fluid, I, *Comm. Pure and Appl. Math.*, **1**: 89–99 (1948), II, **2**: 1–11 (1949).
15. Richardson, A. R.: Stationary Waves in Water, *Phil. Mag.*, ser. 6, **40**:97–110 (1920).
16. Yih, C.-S.: Stratified Flows in a Gravitational Field, *Tellus*, **9**: 220–228 (1957).
17. John, F.: Two-dimensional Potential Flows with a Free Boundary, *Comm. Pure and Appl. Math.*, **6**: 497–503 (1953).
18. Sedov, L. I.: "Two-dimensional Motion of an Ideal Fluid," Oborongiz, Moscow, 1939.
19. Tulin, M.: Steady Two-dimensional Cavity Flows about Slender Bodies, *David Taylor Model Basin Rept.* 834, 1953.
20. Southwell, R. V.: "Relaxation Methods in Theoretical Physics," Oxford, New York, 1946.
21. von Kármán, T.: Flüssigkeits- und Luftwiderstand, *Phys. Z.*, **13**: 49 (1911).
22. Yih, C.-S.: Two Solutions of Inviscid Rotational Flow with Corner Eddies, *J. Fluid Mech.*, **5**: 36–40 (1959).
23. Yih, C.-S.: Finite Two-dimensional Cavities, *Proc. Roy, Soc. (London)*, **A 258**: 90–100 (1960).

Section 5

LAMINAR FLOW

By

S. I. PAI, *Institute for Fluid Dynamics and Applied Mathematics, University of Maryland, College Park, Maryland*

LAMINAR FLOW†

5.1. Introduction

In the flow of an ideal fluid, which has been discussed in Sec. 4, there is no tangential force between adjoining layers of fluid but only the normal force, that is, the pressure. The theory of an ideal fluid gives satisfactory explanations for some phenomena of the flow such as wave motion, the lift and the induced drag of an airfoil, and so forth. However, this theory fails to explain other phenomena such as skin friction, form drag of a body, no slippage on the surface of a solid body, and the like. In order to explain these phenomena, one must investigate the flow of actual fluids.

Actual fluids are, in general, viscous and compressible. Viscosity represents that property of an actual fluid which exhibits a certain resistance to alteration of form. Although this resistance is comparatively small for many practically important fluids, such as water or gases, it is not negligible. For other fluids, such as oil, glycerin, etc., this resistance is quite large. In a viscous fluid, both tangential and normal forces exist. Some of the kinetic energy of flow will be dissipated as heat through the viscous forces.

In this section, only the so-called Newtonian fluids are considered. Let such a fluid be between two parallel plates separated by a distance y_0 from each other (Fig. 5.1). Let the lower plate be fixed, while the upper plate is moving uniformly with a velocity U and in a direction parallel to the lower one. A resistance D is experienced which is given by the formula

$$D = A_0 \mu \frac{U}{y_0} \tag{5.1}$$

in which A_0 is the area of the upper plate, and μ is a constant of proportionality called the coefficient of viscosity.

It is an experimental fact that for an ordinary fluid the relative velocity at the solid surface is zero; i.e., there is no slip at the wall. The fluid in Fig. 5.1 is displaced in such a manner that the various layers of the fluid slide uniformly over one another; the velocity u of a layer of the fluid at a distance y from the lower plate is then

$$u = \frac{Uy}{y_0} \tag{5.2}$$

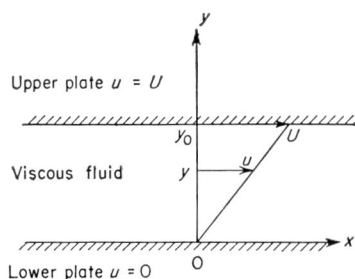

Upper plate $u = U$

Viscous fluid

Lower plate $u = 0$

FIG. 5.1. Plane Couette flow of a viscous incompressible fluid.

Experimental results show that the tangential force per unit area, or the shearing stress τ, is proportional to the slope of the velocity profile; i.e.,

$$\tau = \mu \frac{\partial u}{\partial y} \tag{5.3}$$

The shearing stress of Eq. (5.3) is only one component of the stress tensor in the more general case, as discussed in Sec. 2.

For gases at ordinary temperature, the coef-

† Many materials in this section have been taken from the author's book.[11] Permission of the publisher to use these materials is gratefully acknowledged.

ficient of viscosity is a function of temperature and independent of the pressure. In practice,

$$\frac{\mu}{\mu_0} = \left(\frac{T}{T_0}\right)^n \tag{5.4}$$

in which n is a factor between $\frac{1}{2}$ and 1. For air at ordinary temperature n is usually taken as 0.76. As the temperature increases, n decreases toward $\frac{1}{2}$.

The mechanism of heat conduction in a fluid is analogous to that producing viscous stress; hence the heat conduction and viscous stresses should be treated together in the flow problems of actual fluids. The heat Q transferred by conduction is given by the following formula:

$$Q = -\kappa \frac{\partial T}{\partial y} \tag{5.5}$$

in which κ is the coefficient of thermal conductivity. The relative importance of viscosity and heat conduction may be indicated by the Prandtl number $\mathbf{P}$, which is defined as follows:

$$\mathbf{P} = \frac{\mu/\rho}{\kappa/C_p\rho} = \frac{\text{kinematic viscosity}}{\text{thermal diffusivity}} = \frac{\text{momentum diffusivity}}{\text{thermal diffusivity}} \tag{5.6}$$

For gases, the Prandtl number is of the order of unity, while for some liquids the Prandtl number may be very large.

In this section, the essential characteristics of flow problems are discussed, including the effects of viscosity and heat conduction.

5.2. Notation

The following is a list of the important notation used in this section:

A_0	area
C_D	drag coefficient
C_f	coefficient of skin friction
C_p	specific heat at constant pressure
C_v	specific heat at constant volume
D	drag
g	gravitational acceleration
H	$C_p T$ = enthalpy
L	typical length
$\mathbf{M}$	Mach number
p	pressure
$\mathbf{P}$	$\mu C_p/\kappa$ = Prandtl number
Q	heat transferred
$q_r,\ q_\theta,\ q_z$	rth, θth, and zth velocity components, respectively
R_t	$t_0 U/L$ = time parameter
R	gas constant
$r,\ \theta,\ z$	cylindrical coordinates: radial, tangential, and axial, respectively
$\mathbf{R}$	UL/ν = Reynolds number
T	temperature
t	time
U	typical velocity
$u,\ v,\ w$	xth, yth, and zth velocity components, respectively
$u_i,\ u_j,\ u_k$	ith, jth, and kth velocity components, respectively
$x,\ y,\ z$	cartesian coordinates
α	wave number
γ	C_p/C_v = ratio of specific heats
δ	boundary-layer thickness
κ	coefficient of thermal conductivity

μ coefficient of viscosity
ν μ/ρ = coefficient of kinematic viscosity
ρ density of the fluid
τ shearing stress
ϕ velocity potential
ψ stream function
Ψ nondimensional stream function
ω_j jth component of vorticity
Δ $\nabla \cdot \nabla$ = Laplacian operator

Subscript 0 refers to some typical reference value of the quantity. Subscript i, j, or k refers to 1, 2, or 3 of a vector. Asterisk * refers to nondimensional value of the quantity.

5.3. Potential Flow and Navier-Stokes Equations

In discussing flow problems including viscosity and heat conduction, one should study the fundamental equations of a viscous compressible fluid, which are very complicated. In order to bring out the essential characteristics, the case of a viscous incompressible fluid is considered first. The velocity components of the fluid u_i and the pressure are given by the Navier-Stokes equations

$$\frac{\partial u_i}{\partial t} + u_k \frac{\partial u_i}{\partial x_k} = -\frac{1}{\rho}\frac{\partial p}{\partial x_i} + \nu \frac{\partial^2 u_i}{\partial x_k^2} \qquad (5.7)$$

$$\frac{\partial u_k}{\partial x_k} = 0 \qquad (5.8)$$

in which the summation convention† is used and i, k = 1, 2, or 3.
The energy equation is

$$\rho C_v \left(\frac{\partial T}{\partial t} + u_k \frac{\partial T}{\partial x_k}\right) = \kappa \frac{\partial^2 T}{\partial x_k^2} + \mu \left(\frac{\partial u_i}{\partial x_k} + \frac{\partial u_k}{\partial x_i}\right)\frac{\partial u_i}{\partial x_k} \qquad (5.9)$$

Equations (5.7) and (5.8) form a system of equations for four unknowns u_i and p, which are independent of the temperature T. One may solve this system of equations for u_i and p. After u_i are known, Eq. (5.9) gives the temperature distribution of the problem. Since Eq. (5.9) is linear in T, the discussion of its general properties is much simpler than the nonlinear Navier-Stokes equations. Equation (5.9) is discussed briefly in Arts. 5.5 and 5.9. The main purpose of this section is the investigation of laminar-flow problems based on Navier-Stokes equations, Eqs. (5.7) and (5.8).

The first question is: What is the relation between the flow field given by Navier-Stokes equations and the corresponding flow field of a potential flow of an ideal fluid discussed in Sec. 4? For ideal fluid, Kelvin's theorem holds true: it states that the rate of change of circulation with respect to time is zero. Thus, for a flow started from rest, the total circulation of the flow field must be zero. As a result, one of the assumptions usually made in the analysis of flow problems of an ideal fluid is that the flow is irrotational and that there exists a velocity potential ϕ such that

$$u_i = -\frac{\partial \phi}{\partial x_i} \qquad (5.10)$$

By substituting Eq. (5.10) into Eq. (5.8),

† The summation convention:

$$\frac{\partial u_k}{\partial x_k} = \frac{\partial u_1}{\partial x_1} + \frac{\partial u_2}{\partial x_2} + \frac{\partial u_3}{\partial x_3}$$

$$u_k \frac{\partial u_i}{\partial x_k} = u_1 \frac{\partial u_i}{\partial x_1} + u_2 \frac{\partial u_i}{\partial x_2} + u_3 \frac{\partial u_i}{\partial x_3}$$

$$\frac{\partial^2 \phi}{\partial x_k^2} = 0 \tag{5.11}$$

But
$$\frac{\partial^2 u_i}{\partial x_k^2} = -\frac{\partial^2}{\partial x_k^2}\left(\frac{\partial \phi}{\partial x_i}\right) = -\frac{\partial}{\partial x_i}\left(\frac{\partial^2 \phi}{\partial x_k^2}\right) = 0 \tag{5.12}$$

For the flow with velocity potential ϕ, the viscous terms in Eq. (5.7) are identically zero. This means that the solution of the irrotational flow of an inviscid, incompressible fluid satisfies the Navier-Stokes equations. The viscous forces that are individually present in an actual fluid are collectively in equilibrium. This fact explains the results of many solutions of viscous flow approaching the corresponding value for the potential-flow problem at a large distance from the solid wall.

Even though the solution of the potential flow satisfies the differential equations of motion of a viscous fluid, it cannot satisfy all the boundary conditions of a viscous fluid. Because in the potential-flow problem one simply lets the coefficient of viscosity be zero, the order of the differential equations, Eqs. (5.7), is lowered by one. The arbitrary constants in the solution will also be reduced by one. As a result, it is necessary to relax one of the boundary conditions of the original problem. In the flow of an actual fluid, ordinarily both the tangential and normal velocity components on the surface of a solid wall are zero, owing to no-slip conditions. But in the potential-flow problem, the motion is completely determined by the condition of zero normal velocity component on the solid surface; and there is no possibility of making the tangential velocity component vanish simultaneously with the normal component. Hence the solutions of the Navier-Stokes equations represent flow fields in general and are different from those of potential flow. However, when the coefficient of viscosity is very small, or more exactly when the Reynolds number (Art. 5.4) is very large, one would expect that a major portion of the flow field given by the Navier-Stokes equations differs only slightly from that of the corresponding potential flow field. This point is discussed further in Art. 5.6. In general, the flow field of viscous fluids is rotational.

5.4. Some General Properties of Navier-Stokes Equations

The fundamental equation of potential flow is the Laplace Eq. (5.11), which is linear. However, the most important property of the Navier-Stokes Eqs. (5.7) is their nonlinearity. Hence, if $u_i(x_i,t)$ and $p(x_i,t)$ are solutions of the Navier-Stokes equations, $ku_i(x_i,t)$ and $kp(x_i,t)$ are, in general, not solutions of these equations, in which k is an arbitrary constant. Furthermore, if $u'_i(x_i,t)$ and $p'(x_i,t)$ and $u''_i(x_i,t)$ and $p''(x_i,t)$ are a pair of solutions of the Navier-Stokes equations, $u'_i(x_i,t) + u''_i(x_i,t)$, and $p'(x_i,t) + p''(x_i,t)$ are, in general, not solutions of these equations. On the other hand, from the elementary transformation that preserves the solution of the Navier-Stokes equations, one has:

1. If $u_i(x_i,t)$ and $p(x_i,t)$ are solutions of the Navier-Stokes equations, $u_i(x_i + h_i, t + c)$ and $p(x_i + h_i, t + c)$ are also solutions of these equations for any value of h_i and c; that is, the solutions are preserved by any translation in the four-dimensional space. This property is due to the fact that neither the space coordinates x_i nor the time t occurs explicitly in the Navier-Stokes equations.

2. If $u_i(x_i,t)$ and $p(x_i,t)$ are solutions of the Navier-Stokes equations, $ku_i(kx_i,k^2t)$ and $k^2p(kx_i,k^2t)$ are solutions of these equations for any value of the real parameter k. The factor multiplying the time is always positive, because of the fact that the flow in a viscous fluid is an irreversible process in which the energy of the system is continuously dissipated.

The main difficulty in the Navier-Stokes equations is in the nonlinear terms. However, in some special cases, the Navier-Stokes equations can be simplified so that the nonlinear terms drop out. One of these cases is the parallel flow, in which

$$u_1 = u_1(x_2,x_3,t) \qquad u_2 = u_3 = 0 \tag{5.13}$$

Under the conditions of Eqs. (5.13), the Navier-Stokes equations, Eqs. (5.7), give the following simple results:

$$\frac{\partial u_1}{\partial t} - \nu \left(\frac{\partial^2 u_1}{\partial x_2{}^2} + \frac{\partial^2 u_1}{\partial x_3{}^2} \right) = -\frac{1}{\rho} \frac{\partial p}{\partial x_1} = \text{const} \qquad (5.14)$$

and

$$p = k_1 x_1 + k_2 \qquad (5.15)$$

in which k_1 and k_2 are constants. Equation (5.14) for u_1 is a linear equation; hence the principle of superposition is applicable to the solutions of this equation. If u' and u'' are two solutions of the equation, $au' + bu''$ is another solution of the equation, in which a and b are arbitrary constants.

Many interesting flow problems may be obtained from the solutions of Eq. (5.14). It gives the unsteady flow in a pipe. The simplest case is the steady flow between parallel plates, in which u_1 is a function of x_2 only; i.e.,

$$u_1 = \tfrac{1}{2} k_1 x_2{}^2 + A x_2 + B \qquad (5.16)$$

in which A and B are arbitrary constants to be determined by the boundary conditions, which depend on whether the plates are at rest or in uniform motion. This is the plane Poiseuille flow or plane Couette flow.

In order to show the effect of nonlinear terms, the steady flow between nonparallel plates is discussed in Art. 5.9, under convergent and divergent channels. The flow differs greatly from that between parallel plates given by Eq. (5.16). The most interesting point is that the direction of the flow has a great influence on the flow field. In other words, the flow in a divergent channel differs greatly from that in a convergent channel.

In order to bring out the essential parameters of laminar flow, the fundamental equations, Eqs. (5.7) to (5.9), are rewritten in nondimensional forms. The following nondimensional quantities are introduced:

$$t^* = \frac{t}{t_0} \qquad x^*_i = \frac{x_i}{L} \qquad u^*_i = \frac{u_i}{U} \qquad p^* = \frac{p}{\rho U^2}$$

$$T^* = \frac{T}{T_0} \qquad R_t = \frac{t_0 U}{L} \qquad \mathbf{R} = \frac{UL}{\nu} \qquad \gamma = \frac{C_p}{C_v} \qquad (5.17)$$

$$\mathbf{P} = \frac{C_p \mu}{\kappa} \qquad \mathbf{M} = \frac{U}{\sqrt{\gamma(\gamma - 1)C_v T_0}} = \frac{U}{a_0}$$

After substituting the nondimensional quantities of Eqs. (5.17) into Eqs. (5.7) to (5.9), the following nondimensional equations are obtained:

$$R_t \frac{\partial u^*_i}{\partial t^*} + u^*_k \frac{\partial u^*_i}{\partial x^*_k} = -\frac{\partial p^*}{\partial x^*_i} + \frac{1}{\mathbf{R}} \frac{\partial^2 u^*_i}{\partial x^{*2}_k} \qquad (5.18)$$

$$\frac{\partial u^*_k}{\partial x^*_k} = 0 \qquad (5.19)$$

$$R_t \frac{\partial T^*}{\partial t^*} + u^*_k \frac{\partial T^*}{\partial x^*_k} = \frac{\gamma}{\mathbf{PR}} \frac{\partial^2 T^*}{\partial x^{*2}_k} + \frac{\gamma(\gamma - 1)\mathbf{M}^2}{\mathbf{R}} \left(\frac{\partial u^*_i}{\partial x^*_k} + \frac{\partial u^*_k}{\partial x^*_i} \right) \frac{\partial u^*_i}{\partial x^*_k} \qquad (5.20)$$

From Eqs. (5.18) to (5.20), there are five nondimensional parameters, R_t, γ, $\mathbf{R}$, $\mathbf{P}$, and $\mathbf{M}$, that characterize the laminar-flow problems. The significance of these parameters is as follows:

1. The time parameter R_t is a measure of the unsteadiness of the flow.
2. The ratio of the specific heats γ is a measure of the relative internal complexity of the molecules of a gas.
3. The Reynolds number $\mathbf{R}$ is the most important parameter for laminar flow, which is a measure of the ratio of the inertial force to the viscous force; i.e.,

$$\frac{\text{Inertial force}}{\text{Viscous force}} = \frac{\rho U^2 L^2}{\mu U L} = \frac{\rho U L}{\mu} = \frac{U L}{\nu} = \mathbf{R} \tag{5.21}$$

When the Reynolds number of a system is small, the viscous force is predominant and the effect of viscosity is important in the whole flow field (Art. 5.6). When the Reynolds number is large, the inertial force is predominant and the effect of viscosity is important only in the narrow boundary-layer region near the solid boundary or in any other region of large variation in velocity (Art. 5.7). Most of the flow problems are investigated under the limiting cases of very large Reynolds number or very small Reynolds number. These limiting cases are discussed in Arts. 5.6 and 5.7.

4. The Mach number $\mathbf{M}$ is a measure of the compressibility of the fluid. The quantity a_0 is the speed of sound corresponding to the temperature T_0. The compressibility effect may be due to the variation of velocity or to the temperature variation in the flow field. In most of the flow problems of an incompressible fluid, the Mach number $\mathbf{M}$ is very small. As a result, the viscous-dissipation terms in Eq. (5.20) may be neglected in the calculation of the temperature distribution.

5. The Prandtl number $\mathbf{P}$ is a measure of the relative importance of viscosity and heat conduction. The Prandtl number may be written as follows:

$$\mathbf{P} = \frac{\nu}{\kappa/C_p\rho} = \frac{\text{kinematic viscosity}}{\text{thermal diffusivity}} \tag{5.22}$$

The value of ν shows the effect of viscosity of a fluid. If other things are the same, the smaller the value of ν, the narrower will be the region affected by viscosity. The thermal diffusivity shows the effect of heat conduction of a fluid. If other things are the same, the smaller the value of thermal diffusivity, the narrower will be the region affected by heat conduction. Thus the Prandtl number shows the relative importance of viscosity and heat conduction in the flow field.

In the velocity distribution of the laminar flow of an incompressible fluid, from Eqs. (5.18) and (5.19) it is evident that the most important parameter is the Reynolds number $\mathbf{R}$, because the parameter R_t is usually of the order of unity. Two of the classes of laminar-flow problems that have been successfully treated are the limiting cases of very small Reynolds number and of very large Reynolds number. These two cases are discussed in Arts. 5.6 and 5.7, respectively.

For compressible flow and for the temperature distributions, one should consider the other parameters such as Mach number, Prandtl number, etc., simultaneously with the Reynolds number.

5.5. Vorticity Transport Equation and Stream Function

Since the flow of a viscous fluid is rotational and the rotationality of the flow is represented by the distribution of vorticity in the flow field, it will be shown how the vorticity of the flow is distributed in the viscous fluid.

The vorticity of the flow is defined as follows:

$$\omega_j = \frac{\partial u_i}{\partial x_k} - \frac{\partial u_k}{\partial x_i} \tag{5.23}$$

in which i, j, k = 1, 2, 3. One-half of the vorticity gives the angular rotation of an element of the fluid. For potential flow it is easy to show that $\omega_j = 0$ because of Eq. (5.10).

If the pressure terms are eliminated in Eqs. (5.7), one obtains the vorticity equation, as follows:

$$\frac{D\omega_j}{Dt} - \omega_k \frac{\partial u_j}{\partial x_k} = \frac{\partial \omega_j}{\partial t} + u_k \frac{\partial \omega_j}{\partial x_k} - \omega_k \frac{\partial u_j}{\partial x_k} = \nu \frac{\partial^2 \omega_j}{\partial x_k^2} \tag{5.24}$$

The first term on the left-hand side of Eq. (5.24) represents the total variation of vorticity with time, which includes the variation due to time alone and the variation along the streamlines. The second term on the left-hand side of Eq. (5.24) represents the deformation of a vortex tube. The extension of vortex lines will increase the vorticity. It is a very important process in turbulent flow. The term on the right-hand side of Eq. (5.24) represents the diffusion of vorticity due to viscosity.

For two-dimensional flow, the terms for the deformation of the vortex tube vanish and the vorticity equation consists of only the transport terms and the diffusion terms; hence Eq. (5.24) becomes

$$\frac{\partial \omega}{\partial t} + u_k \frac{\partial \omega}{\partial x_k} = \nu \frac{\partial^2 \omega}{\partial x_k{}^2} \tag{5.25}$$

in which $k = 1$ or 2 only

and $\omega = \dfrac{\partial u_2}{\partial x_1} - \dfrac{\partial u_1}{\partial x_2}$

For the two-dimensional flow, one may introduce a stream function ψ such that

$$\frac{\partial \psi}{\partial x_2} = u_1 \qquad \frac{\partial \psi}{\partial x_1} = -u_2 \tag{5.26}$$

After substituting Eqs. (5.26) into the equation for vorticity (5.23),

$$\omega = -\left(\frac{\partial^2 \psi}{\partial x_1{}^2} + \frac{\partial^2 \psi}{\partial x_2{}^2} \right) = -\Delta \psi \tag{5.27}$$

Equation (5.25) with the help of Eqs. (5.26) and (5.27) becomes

$$\frac{\partial \Delta \psi}{\partial t} + \frac{\partial \psi}{\partial x_2} \frac{\partial \Delta \psi}{\partial x_1} - \frac{\partial \psi}{\partial x_1} \frac{\partial \Delta \psi}{\partial x_2} = \nu \, \Delta \Delta \psi \tag{5.28}$$

The vorticity transport equation [Eq. (5.28)] contains only one unknown ψ.

It is interesting to notice that Eqs. (5.25) are exactly of the same form as the two-dimensional equation for the temperature distribution, Eq. (5.9), if the dissipation terms are negligible. From Eqs. (5.20), if the Mach number **M** is very small, one may neglect the viscous-dissipation terms. By writing $\omega^* = \omega(L/U)$, the nondimensional form of Eq. (5.25) is

$$\mathbf{R}_t \frac{\partial \omega^*}{\partial t^*} + u^*_k \frac{\partial \omega^*}{\partial x^*_k} = \frac{1}{\mathbf{R}} \frac{\partial^2 \omega^*}{\partial x^{*2}_k} \tag{5.29}$$

The corresponding nondimensional equation for temperature distribution without dissipation is identical with Eq. (5.29) except that the parameter **R** is replaced by **PR**, which is known as *Peclet* number.

In order to see qualitatively the distribution of vorticity in the flow of viscous fluids for different Reynolds numbers, the case of the temperature distribution of a two-dimensional flow of a cold fluid passing over a hot body is considered. From the experience of heat conduction, if the flow is very slow, that is, a small Peclet number, it is noted that the temperature will be able to spread in all directions; but if the flow is fast, that is, a large Peclet number, only a relatively thin layer of fluid near the body will be warmed by this hot body. Hence, in a similar manner, one would expect that for a small Reynolds number the vorticity will be found everywhere in the flow field, whereas for large Reynolds numbers the vorticity is concentrated in the immediate neighborhood of the surface of the solid body. This fact shows that for small Reynolds number the viscous effect is important in the whole flow field while for large Reynolds number the viscous effect will be important only in the boundary-layer region, as shown in the results of Arts. 5.6 and 5.7.

5.6. Limiting Cases for Small Reynolds Number—Stokes and Oseen Methods

For very small Reynolds numbers, that is, very small velocities and dimensions of the body or very great viscosity of the fluid, the inertial forces are much smaller than the frictional force. For a first approximation, the higher-order terms of inertial forces in the Navier-Stokes equations may be neglected, and the Stokes equations are as follows:

$$\rho\frac{\partial u_i}{\partial t} = -\frac{\partial p}{\partial x_i} + \mu\frac{\partial^2 u_i}{\partial x_k{}^2} \tag{5.30}$$

$$\frac{\partial u_k}{\partial x_k} = 0 \tag{5.31}$$

Equations (5.30) and (5.31) are the fundamental equations for very slow motion of a viscous fluid. The boundary conditions are that both the tangential v_t and the normal v_n velocity components relative to the surface of the solid body are equal to zero.

After taking the divergence of Eqs. (5.30),

$$\frac{\partial^2 p}{\partial x_k{}^2} = 0 \tag{5.32}$$

The pressure $p(x_i)$ is a harmonic function for very slow motion.

In two-dimensional steady flow, Eqs. (5.30) become

$$\left(\frac{\partial^2}{\partial x_k{}^2}\right)^2 \psi = 0 \tag{5.33}$$

in which the stream function ψ is defined by Eqs. (5.26). For very slow motion, of two-dimensional steady flow, the stream function ψ is a biharmonic function.

The pressure function that corresponds to the very slow motion of a sphere of radius r_0 moving with a uniform speed U is

$$p = -\frac{3}{2}\frac{\mu U r_0{}^2 x_1}{r^3} \tag{5.34}$$

in which $r^2 = x_1{}^2 + x_2{}^2 + x_3{}^2$, and x_1 is the coordinate in the direction of U.

From Eq. (5.34), it can be shown that the drag coefficient of the sphere at small Reynolds numbers is

$$C_D = \frac{\text{drag}}{(\rho/2)U^2\pi r_0{}^2} = \frac{24}{2r_0 U/\nu} = \frac{24}{\mathbf{R}} \tag{5.35}$$

Even though Eq. (5.35) checks experimental values very well at small Reynolds numbers, the velocity distribution given by Stokes' Eqs. (5.30) and (5.31) for the sphere at large distance from the sphere is not correct. The Stokes solution gives a velocity distribution symmetrical with respect to $x_1 = 0$. The actual velocity distribution is not symmetrical with respect to $x_1 = 0$ because there is a wake behind the sphere. In fact, the ratio of the nonlinear inertial term $\rho u_k(\partial u_i/\partial x_k) = 0(\rho U^2/r)$ to the viscous force $\mu(\partial^2 u_i/\partial x_k{}^2) = 0(\mu U/r^2)$ is of the order of $\rho U r/\mu$. Hence, at large distance from the sphere, the value of r is large, and then the nonlinear inertial terms cannot be neglected entirely.

In order to improve Stokes' analysis, Oseen considered the case in which the resultant flow deviates slightly from a known flow. The simplest type of the known flow is a uniform flow of velocity U. In this case,

$$u_1 = U + u'_1 \qquad u_2 = u'_2 \qquad u_3 = u'_3 \tag{5.36}$$

in which u'_i is assumed to be much smaller than U. After substituting into the Navier-Stokes equations and neglecting the products and squares of u'_i, Oseen's equations are as follows:

$$\frac{\partial u'_i}{\partial t} + U\frac{\partial u'_i}{\partial x_1} = -\frac{1}{\rho}\frac{\partial p}{\partial x_i} + \nu\frac{\partial^2 u'_i}{\partial x^2{}_k}$$

$$\frac{\partial u'_k}{\partial x_k} = 0 \tag{5.37}$$

The additional terms $U(\partial u'_i/\partial x_1)$ improve the conditions at large r for the very-slow-motion problems.

For steady flow, Eqs. (5.37) may be solved by writing

$$u'_i = u_{1i} + u_{2i} \qquad (5.38)$$

in which u_{1i} is derived from a velocity potential ϕ such that

$$u_{1i} = -\frac{\partial \phi}{\partial x_i} \qquad (5.39)$$

By making

$$\frac{\partial^2 \phi}{\partial x_k{}^2} = 0 \qquad (5.40)$$

and

$$p = \rho U \frac{\partial \phi}{\partial x_1} \qquad (5.41)$$

Eqs. (5.37) are satisfied by u_{1i}, which serves to balance the pressure-gradient term.

The portion u_{2i} serves to balance the frictional force with the inertial force. By writing

$$u_{2i} = \frac{\partial W}{\partial x_i} - \delta_i \frac{U}{\nu} W \qquad (5.42)$$

in which $\delta_1 = 1$ and $\delta_2 = \delta_3 = 0$, the function W satisfies the differential equation

$$\frac{\partial W}{\partial x_1} = \frac{\nu}{U} \frac{\partial^2 W}{\partial x_k{}^2} \qquad (5.43)$$

Oseen's analysis is to find the proper solutions of Eqs. (5.40) and (5.43) for any given problem. It has been solved for the problem of a sphere moving at a uniform speed U, and the corresponding drag coefficient is

$$C_D = \frac{24}{\mathbf{R}} \left(1 + \frac{3\mathbf{R}}{16} \right) \qquad (5.44)$$

When $\mathbf{R}$ is very small, Eq. (5.44) reduces to the Stokes Eq. (5.35), but it gives better results than Stokes' equation for $\mathbf{R} \geqq 1$.

Oseen's analysis is good only for small Reynolds numbers. In order to extend the region of validity for larger Reynolds number, one may express the solution of Navier-Stokes equations in power series of $\mathbf{R}$. Oseen's solution corresponds to the term of the first power of $\mathbf{R}$. However, it has been found[4] that the convergence of this series is rather poor and that the solution is not good for $\mathbf{R} \geqq 2$.

Another method that has been used to calculate the flow at small Reynolds number is to divide the whole flow field into two parts: one part near the solid body, which may be called the inner region, and the other part extending to infinity, which may be called the outer region. The flow in the inner region may be treated by the Stokes approximation, while the flow in the outer region may be calculated by the Oseen approximation or by the inviscid-flow approximation. These two regions should be joined smoothly to each other in order to get a satisfactory flow pattern as a whole. Imai[4] found that this method gives a better drag formula than the result of Oseen's analysis.

5.7. Limiting Cases for Large Reynolds Number

Boundary-layer Flow and Discontinuous Potential Flow. All the important practical problems in aerodynamics and hydrodynamics are cases involving very large Reynolds numbers. In dealing with these problems two different approximate methods may be used. The most obvious one is to drop the viscous terms that are small in comparison with the inertial terms. The Navier-Stokes equations are then reduced to the Euler equations of inviscid fluid. As discussed in Art. 5.3, the order of the equations is lowered by one and one of the boundary conditions cannot be satisfied. Even though the solutions of inviscid fluid (Sec. 4) give good approximate results at places far away from the solid wall, it is no longer a good approximation for the region near the solid wall. Thus many important phenomena cannot be explained by the solution of inviscid fluids such as skin friction and heat transfer. In order to explain these important phenomena, other approximations should be used so that a better solution for the flow near the solid wall is obtained.

It was Prandtl[12] who in 1904 first introduced the concept of the boundary layer when he stated that the viscous effects are confined in a very thin layer near the boundary when the Reynolds number is very large. The theory of the boundary layer (Sec. 9) opened a new era for the fluid dynamics of viscous fluid.

For simplicity, the two-dimensional steady flow of an incompressible fluid only is considered. In nondimensional form, our fundamental equation for this problem, Eq. (5.28), becomes

$$\frac{\partial \psi^*}{\partial x^*_2} \frac{\partial \Delta^* \psi^*}{\partial x^*_1} - \frac{\partial \psi^*}{\partial x^*_1} \frac{\partial \Delta^* \psi^*}{\partial x^*_2} = \frac{1}{\mathbf{R}} \Delta^* \Delta^* \psi^* \tag{5.45}$$

in which $x_i = x^* L$
$$\Delta^* = L^2 \Delta$$
$$\psi = U \psi^*$$
$$\mathbf{R} = UL/\nu$$

Consider the flow past a semi-infinite flat plate, parallel to a stream, lying on $x^*_2 = 0$ and $x^*_1 \geqq 0$. According to the boundary-layer theory, the viscous effects are confined in a narrow region near the plate. Let δ be a measure of the thickness of this boundary layer and L be the characteristic length of the plate. Then $\delta/L = 0(1/\sqrt{\mathbf{R}})$. In order to investigate the boundary-layer region, one must amplify the x^*_2 distance in the boundary layer by the following transformation:

$$x = x^*_1 \qquad y = \sqrt{\mathbf{R}}\, x^*_2 \qquad \Psi = \sqrt{\mathbf{R}}\, \psi^* \tag{5.46}$$

After substituting Eqs. (5.46) into Eq. (5.45),

$$\frac{\partial}{\partial y}\left(\frac{\partial^3 \Psi}{\partial y^3} + \frac{\partial \Psi}{\partial x}\frac{\partial^2 \Psi}{\partial y^2} - \frac{\partial \Psi}{\partial y}\frac{\partial^2 \Psi}{\partial x\, \partial y}\right) + \frac{1}{\mathbf{R}}\left(2\frac{\partial^4 \Psi}{\partial x^2\, \partial y^2} + \frac{\partial \Psi}{\partial x}\frac{\partial^3 \Psi}{\partial x^2\, \partial y} - \frac{\partial \Psi}{\partial y}\frac{\partial^3 \Psi}{\partial x^3}\right)$$

$$+ \frac{1}{\mathbf{R}^2}\frac{\partial^4 \Psi}{\partial x^4} = 0 \tag{5.47}$$

By assuming that $\mathbf{R}$ tends to infinity, the derivatives in Eq. (5.47) remain finite and Eq. (5.47) becomes the boundary-layer equation when $\mathbf{R}$ tends to infinity; i.e., the boundary-layer equation is obtained from Eq. (5.47) by putting $1/\mathbf{R} = 0$. The boundary-layer equation is

$$\frac{\partial^3 \Psi}{\partial y^3} + \frac{\partial \Psi}{\partial x}\frac{\partial^2 \Psi}{\partial y^2} - \frac{\partial \Psi}{\partial y}\frac{\partial^2 \Psi}{\partial x\, \partial y} = P(x) \tag{5.48}$$

in which the function $P(x)$, obtained from the integration with respect to y, is simply the pressure gradient in the main stream outside the boundary layer. In treating the boundary-layer problems, it is assumed that the pressure gradient $P(x)$ is known, which corresponds to the inviscid solution outside the boundary layer. It can be shown that the variation of the pressure across the boundary layer, i.e., in the direction of y, is zero in the boundary-layer approximation.

For the so-called streamline body, e.g., a flat plate in the direction of a stream, at high Reynolds number, the boundary-layer theory has been well established in the calculation of skin friction (or drag) and heat-transfer problems. In this theory, the flow field around the given body, and especially the pressure distribution on the surface of the body, is first determined. Then, using the pressure distribution obtained, the boundary-layer equations are solved to get the flow field in the boundary layer on the surface of the body. From the velocity distribution in the boundary layer, one may calculate the skin friction and temperature distribution along the surface of the body. There are two distinct regions, an inviscid main flow field that is practically independent of the boundary layer and a boundary-layer flow.

The exact division of the flow field into these two distinct regions is not always possible. The most obvious case in which such sharp division of the flow field into these two distinct regions is not possible is the flow field around a bluff body, e.g., a flat plate perpendicular to an incoming stream. In this case, even though the flow field may still be divided into two parts—one is the wake region I in which the fluid is in violent agitation, and the other is the region outside the wake II in which the flow is steady and irrotational—these two regions I and II are closely correlated with each other so that the determination of one of them is only possible with the knowledge of the other.

The flow field of region II can be determined by the well-known Kirchhoff's theory of discontinuous flow or free streamline flow (Sec. 4). Imai[3] has shown that if the continuous potential flow around a given obstacle has such a pressure distribution that the boundary-layer separation does not occur, the potential flow is the possible asymptotic-flow pattern for vanishing viscosity. On the other hand, the asymptotic flow is given by the free-streamline flow of the Kirchhoff type, where the separation points of the free streamlines are coincident with those predicted by the boundary-layer theory from the pressure distribution given by the same discontinuous flow. In this case, there are two possibilities: one is that the free streamlines have a finite curvature equal to that of the obstacle at the separation point, and the other is that the separation occurs at a corner (if it exists) of the obstacle such as the case of a flat plate perpendicular to the oncoming stream. Imai also gave a formula for the drag coefficient for any arbitrary two-dimensional bluff body, as follows:[4]

$$C_D = \frac{\text{drag}}{\frac{1}{2}\rho U^2 L} = (C_{D\infty}^{\frac{1}{2}} + k\mathbf{R}^{\frac{1}{2}})^2 \qquad (5.49)$$

in which $C_{D\infty}$ is the drag coefficient determined by Kirchhoff's theory of inviscid fluid, and k is a constant, depending on the shape of the body. For a flat plate perpendicular to an oncoming stream, $C_{D\infty} = 0.880$ and $k = 2.89$.

It is of great theoretical interest to study asymptotic-flow pattern when the viscosity tends to zero. For the case of a semi-infinite flat plate in the direction of a stream, as ν tends to zero, the boundary-layer thickness tends to zero. The asymptotic-flow pattern may be considered as the classical flow with vortex sheets at the surface of the plate so that its velocity drops from the free-stream velocity to zero on the surface. But if the plate is finite, there is a wake behind the plate. Then the classical potential flow with vortex sheets at the solid surface does not give the correct limit as the viscosity tends to zero.

Even though the boundary-layer Eq. (5.48) gives a fairly good description of the viscous flow over a streamline body in general, the boundary-layer solution is not valid near the front stagnation point of any semi-infinite cylinder or the leading edge of the flat plate because the boundary-layer approximations do not hold there.

Other cases in which the interaction of the boundary-layer flow and the inviscid main flow is not negligible are the hypersonic viscous flow and the incidence of shock wave on the boundary layer. For hypersonic flow, the shock waves and Mach lines are so close to the surface of the body that the shape of the shock depends on the flow field in the boundary layer. Hence the inviscid-flow field and the boundary layer should be solved simultaneously. For the problem of the incidence of a shock wave on the boundary, in the region near the point of incidence, the boundary-layer approximations do not hold.

From Eq. (5.48), it is observed that the boundary-layer solution is the asymptotic solution near the wall when $\mathbf{R}$ tends to infinity. In order to improve the boundary-layer solution for large but finite $\mathbf{R}$, one may expand the solution of the stream function Ψ in a power series of a small parameter $\epsilon = \mathbf{R}^{-\frac{1}{2}}$ as follows:

$$\Psi = \Psi^{(0)} + \epsilon\Psi^{(1)} + \epsilon^2\Psi^{(2)} + \cdots \qquad (5.50)$$

After substituting Eq. (5.50) into Eq. (5.47) and collecting terms of the same power of ϵ, one obtains the differential equations for various $\Psi^{(n)}$. The zeroth-order equation is the ordinary boundary-layer Eq. (5.48). All these equations for $\Psi^{(n)}$ are linear when $n > 0$. The equation for $\Psi^{(n)}$ contains the functions $\Psi^{(m)}$ only where $m = 0, 1, \ldots,$ $n - 1$. Hence these $\Psi^{(n)}$ may be solved successively. The main difficulty of this method of successive approximation lies in the fact that the solution of the zeroth-order equations, the ordinary boundary-layer equations, is singular in the whole line $x = 0$. According to Lighthill's theory,[6] these singularities will be passed on, in an accentuated form, to the rest of the successive approximations. Lighthill proposed a transformation of coordinates so that the singularities in the zeroth-order equation can be frozen during the course of the successive approximation. For higher-order approximations, the flow in the inviscid region depends on the flow field in the boundary-layer region. Kuo[5] has worked out the Lighthill theory for viscous flow over a finite flat plate. He gave the drag formula for the second approximation over a finite plate of length L as follows:

$$C_f = \frac{\text{skin friction}}{\frac{1}{2}\rho U^2 2L} = \frac{1.328}{\mathbf{R}^{\frac{1}{2}}} + \frac{4.12}{\mathbf{R}} \tag{5.51}$$

in which $\mathbf{R} = UL/\nu$. Kuo's formula [Eq. (5.51)] is believed to be valid for $15 \leq \mathbf{R} \leq \infty$.

5.8. Linearized Theory of a Viscous Compressible Fluid

Sound Waves in a Viscous Compressible Fluid. The main difficulty of Navier-Stokes equations is due to the nonlinearity of the equations. If these equations are linearized, the properties of the resultant equations can be easily discussed and some essential features of the original equations may be revealed. One way to linearize the Navier-Stokes equations is to write them in the following form:

$$\nu \frac{\partial^2 u_i}{\partial x^2_k} - \frac{1}{\rho}\frac{\partial p}{\partial x_i} - \frac{\partial u_i}{\partial t} = X_i$$

$$\frac{\partial u_i}{\partial x_i} = 0 \tag{5.52}$$

in which $X_i = u_k(\partial u_i/\partial x_k)$ is considered as a given function of x_i and t. This method was first used by Oseen,[10] who was able to express u_i and p in terms of integrals of X_i.

The other method is to consider the small deviation of a uniform flow U. This method is applied to discuss the flow of a compressible, viscous, and heat-conducting fluid. First

$$\begin{array}{cccc} u_1 = U + u'_1 & u_2 = u'_2 & u_3 = u'_3 & \\ p = p_0 + p' & \rho = \rho_0 + \rho' & T = T_0 + T' \end{array} \tag{5.53}$$

in which p_0, ρ_0, T_0 are, respectively, the pressure, density, and temperature of the fluid corresponding to the uniform flow of velocity U. The perturbed quantities u'_i, p', ρ', and T' are assumed to be small quantities so that the second- and higher-order terms of these quantities are negligible. After substituting Eqs. (5.53) into the fundamental equations of a viscous, heat-conducting, and compressible fluid and neglecting the higher-order terms, six linear equations for the perturbed quantities u'_i, p', ρ', and T' are obtained, as follows (Sec. 2):

The equation of state: $\qquad\qquad \dfrac{p'}{p_0} = \dfrac{\rho'}{\rho_0} + \dfrac{T'}{T_0} \tag{5.54}$

The equation of continuity: $\qquad \dfrac{\partial \rho'}{\partial t} + U\dfrac{\partial \rho'}{\partial x_1} + \rho_0\dfrac{\partial u'_i}{\partial x_i} = 0 \tag{5.55}$

The equations of motion:

$$\frac{\partial u'_i}{\partial t} + U\frac{\partial u'_i}{\partial x_1} = \frac{F_i}{\rho_0} - \frac{1}{\rho_0}\frac{\partial p'}{\partial x_i} + \frac{\nu_0}{3}\frac{\partial}{\partial x_i}\left(\frac{\partial u_k}{\partial x_k}\right) + \nu_0\frac{\partial^2 u_i}{\partial x_k^2} \tag{5.56}$$

The energy equation:

$$\left(\frac{\partial}{\partial t} + U \frac{\partial}{\partial x_1}\right)\left(\frac{p'}{p_0} - \gamma \frac{\rho'}{\rho_0}\right) = \frac{\gamma - 1}{p_0} \kappa_0 \frac{\partial^2 T'}{\partial x_k{}^2} \tag{5.57}$$

It is interesting to notice that if the fluid is non-heat-conducting, i.e., $\kappa_0 = 0$, Eq. (5.57) gives

$$\frac{p'}{p_0} - \gamma \frac{\rho'}{\rho_0} = f(x_1 - Ut) = 0 \tag{5.58}$$

if the disturbances are initially zero. Hence, for this case, the flow is isentropic.

Equations (5.54) to (5.57) are studied for two special cases:

1. Linearized theory of a jet mixing. A two-dimensional jet in a uniform stream U issuing from a nozzle is considered. At the exit of the nozzle the jet stream has the velocity components $u_1 = U + u_0$ and $u_2 = 0$. The location of the exit of the nozzle is at $x_1 = 0$ and x_2 from $+1$ to -1. The flow is steady. Furthermore, the boundary-layer approximations are applicable here. As a result, the equation of motion for u'_1 becomes

$$\frac{\partial u'_1}{\partial x_1} = b^2 \frac{\partial^2 u'_1}{\partial x_2{}^2} \tag{5.59}$$

in which $b^2 = \nu_0/U$.

The initial conditions at the exit of the nozzle are, at $x_1 = 0$,

$$\begin{aligned} u'_1 &= u_0 = \text{const} \quad &&\text{for} \quad -1 < x_2 < +1 \\ u'_1 &= 0 \quad &&\text{for} \quad -1 > x_2 \quad \text{and} \quad x_2 > 1 \end{aligned} \tag{5.60}$$

The solution of Eq. (5.59) with the initial conditions (5.60) is

$$u'_1 = \frac{u_0}{2}\left[\text{erf}\left(\frac{1 - x_2}{2b\sqrt{x_1}}\right) + \text{erf}\left(\frac{1 + x_2}{2b\sqrt{x_1}}\right)\right] \tag{5.61}$$

in which

$$\text{erf}(y) = \frac{2}{\sqrt{\pi}} \int_0^y e^{-x^2}\, dx$$

is the error function. The divergence of the jet is proportional to b. The velocity distribution of Eq. (5.61) is qualitatively the same as the results of nonlinear theory. It is well known from the experimental results of jet mixing that the velocity distribution in the jet-mixing region may be approximated by a certain error function.

2. Sound speed in a viscous and heat-conducting fluid. Sound waves are waves of infinitesimal amplitude propagated in a compressible fluid. For simplicity, consider the wave propagation in the x_1 direction only. Hence all the perturbed quantities in Eqs. (5.54) to (5.57) are functions of $x = x_1$ and t only. Under this condition, the six perturbed quantities are divided into two groups:

a. The velocity components u'_2 and u'_3 are independent of all the other perturbed quantities. Each of them is determined by its corresponding equation of motion alone. Since they are in the directions perpendicular to the direction of propagation of the wave, these waves are called transverse waves.

b. The perturbed quantities u'_1, p', ρ', and T' are interrelated. They belong to the longitudinal wave, which is the ordinary sound wave.

Since Eqs. (5.54) to (5.57) are linear, the method of superposition is applicable. Hence it is sufficient to look for periodic solutions in which all the perturbed quantities are proportional to

$$\exp(i\omega t - i\lambda x) \tag{5.62}$$

in which ω is a given real quantity, and $i = \sqrt{-1}$. Substituting these variables into Eqs. (5.54) to (5.57), a determinantal equation is obtained for each group of these variables. The eigenvalues λ of these determinantal equations give the different modes of wave propagation in the medium.

For the transverse wave,

$$\frac{\partial u'_2}{\partial t} = \nu_0 \frac{\partial^2 u'_2}{\partial x^2} \tag{5.63}$$

with an identical equation for u'_3. The determinantal equation for Eq. (5.63) is

$$\nu_0 \lambda^2 + i\omega = 0 \tag{5.64}$$

Equation (5.64) shows a damped wave in a viscous medium, as shown in Art. 5.9 for the unsteady-flow problem. This wave is independent of the compressibility effect of the medium.

The determinantal equation for the longitudinal wave is as follows:

$$(\nu_0 \lambda^2 + i\omega) \left\{ \kappa_0 \left(\frac{1}{\rho_0} + \frac{i4\omega\nu_0}{3p_0} \right) \lambda^4 - \left[\frac{\omega^2 \kappa_0}{p_0} + \frac{4\nu_0\omega^2}{3T_0(\gamma-1)} - i\omega C_p \right] \lambda^2 - \frac{i\omega^3}{T_0(\gamma-1)} \right\} = 0 \tag{5.65}$$

The first quantity, in parentheses, is the viscous wave, which is the same as in the transverse wave and which is one of the basic modes of wave propagation in a viscous medium. The quantity in braces represents a sound wave in a viscous and heat-conducting fluid. In general, there are two speeds of propagation of sound in a viscous and heat-conducting fluid, because the equation is a quadratic equation in λ^2. For inviscid ($\nu_0 = 0$) and non-heat-conducting ($\kappa_0 = 0$) fluid, the expression in braces becomes

$$\lambda^2 = \frac{\omega^2}{T_0(\gamma-1)C_p} = \frac{\omega^2}{RT_0\gamma} = \frac{\omega^2}{a_0^2} \tag{5.66}$$

in which a_0 is the ordinary sound speed of an inviscid fluid, which is a function of temperature T_0 only. The velocity of wave propagation is $\omega/\lambda = a_0$.

For a viscous ($\nu_0 \neq 0$) but non-heat-conducting fluid ($\kappa_0 = 0$), the expression in braces becomes

$$\lambda^2 = \frac{\omega^2}{a_0^2[1 - i(4\nu_0\omega/3a_0^2)]} \tag{5.67}$$

Since λ is now a complex number, the real part represents the speed of propagation while the imaginary part represents the damping of the wave. If the viscosity is very small, for first approximation Eq. (5.67) gives

$$V_\omega = \frac{\omega}{\lambda} = a_0 - i\frac{2\nu_0\omega}{3a_0} \tag{5.68}$$

Hence the wave is propagated with a speed a_0 and the damping of the wave is directly proportional to ν_0 and ω and inversely proportional to a_0.

If the viscosity is very large, Eq. (5.67) becomes

$$\lambda^2 = i\frac{\omega^2}{\frac{4}{3}\nu_0\omega} \tag{5.69}$$

This is just a longitudinal viscous wave. It is similar in form to the viscous wave of Eq. (5.64), except for the factor of $\frac{4}{3}$, which is due to the compressibility effect.

For a viscous ($\nu_0 \neq 0$) and heat-conducting ($\kappa_0 \neq 0$) fluid, the equation for the eigenvalue of the sound-wave propagation is

$$\kappa_0 \left(\frac{1}{\rho_0} + \frac{i4\nu_0\omega}{3p_0} \right) \lambda^4 - \left[\frac{\omega^2 \kappa_0}{p_0} + \frac{4\nu_0\omega^2}{3T_0(\gamma-1)} - i\omega C_p \right] \lambda^2 - \frac{i\omega^3}{T_0(\gamma-1)} = 0 \tag{5.70}$$

In general equation (5.70) gives two roots of λ^2 which represent two different modes of sound-wave propagation in this medium. These two roots are

$$\lambda_{1,2}^2 = \frac{\left[\dfrac{\omega^2\kappa_0}{p_0} + \dfrac{4\nu_0\omega^2}{3T_0(\gamma - 1)} - i\omega C_p\right] \pm B}{2\kappa_0(1/p_0 + i4\nu_0\omega/3p_0)} \tag{5.71}$$

in which $B = \sqrt{\left[\dfrac{\omega^2\kappa_0}{p_0} + \dfrac{4\nu_0\omega^2}{3T_0(\gamma - 1)} - i\omega C_p\right]^2 + 4\dfrac{i\omega^3\kappa_0}{T_0(\gamma - 1)}\left(\dfrac{1}{p_0} + \dfrac{4i\nu_0\omega}{3p_0}\right)}$

If both the coefficient of heat conductivity ($\kappa_0 \to 0$) and the viscosity ($\nu_0 \to 0$) are very small, for first approximation, the two roots of Eq. (5.70), i.e., (5.71), may be expressed in the following forms:

$$V_1 = \frac{\omega}{\lambda_1} = a_0 - i\frac{\kappa_0\omega}{2\rho_0 C_p a_0} \tag{5.72}$$

and

$$V_2 = \frac{\omega}{\lambda_2} = \sqrt{\frac{\omega\kappa_0}{2C_p\rho_0}}\,(1 + i) \tag{5.73}$$

The first sound wave is a modification of the ordinary sound wave with a damping term depending on the coefficient of heat conductivity. The second sound wave is a heat wave that tends to zero as κ_0 tends to zero.

If only κ_0 is small and ν_0 is finite, it is easy to show that the first sound wave V_1 will tend to the viscous sound wave, Eq. (5.67), as κ_0 tends to zero, while the second sound wave tends to zero as κ_0 tends to zero, which is now a viscous heat wave under the influence of compressibility.

For the general case, one of the sound waves is closely associated with the ordinary sound wave while the other is a viscous heat wave. Both of these waves are influenced by the compressibility of the medium.

5.9. Some Exact Solutions of the Navier-Stokes Equations

In Arts. 5.6 to 5.8, viscous flows are discussed which are approximately true either for the case of limited range of viscosity or for the case of negligible nonlinear effect. It would be interesting if one could discuss the laminar-flow problems that are valid for all the values of viscosity and that include the nonlinear effects. One way to obtain such results is to find the exact solutions of the nonlinear Navier-Stokes equations. In this article some exact solutions are discussed for incompressible fluid, and in Art. 5.10 some exact solutions are discussed for compressible fluid.

Hamel Spiral Motion.[1]   First consider two-dimensional steady flow of an incompressible fluid whose fundamental equation is [(5.28)]:

$$\frac{\partial\psi}{\partial x_2}\frac{\partial\Delta\psi}{\partial x_1} - \frac{\partial\psi}{\partial x_1}\frac{\partial\Delta\psi}{\partial x_2} = \nu\,\Delta\Delta\psi \tag{5.74}$$

The potential flow $\psi = \phi$ and $\Delta\phi = 0$ is a solution of Eq. (5.74). However, the boundary conditions cannot all be satisfied by this potential flow as discussed in Art. 5.3. Hamel found solutions of Eq. (5.74) that satisfy all the boundary conditions on the solid wall and whose streamlines are the same as those for a potential flow. He found the solution of Eq. (5.74) such that

$$\psi = f(\phi) \tag{5.75}$$

with $\Delta\phi = 0$ but $\Delta\psi \neq 0$. In other words, the second derivative of the function f with respect to ϕ, that is, $f''(\phi)$, is different from zero.

The stream function ψ is a function of x_1 and x_2. One may introduce an analytic function $W(z) = W(x_1 + ix_2)$ such that

$$W(z) = \phi + iH \tag{5.76}$$

It is possible to express the stream function in terms of the curvilinear coordinates ϕ

and H. Then $\psi = \psi(\phi,H)$. Hamel found that if the analytic function W satisfies the following condition,

$$2 \frac{d^2 W/dz^2}{(dW/dz)^2} = a + ib = \text{const} \tag{5.77}$$

the stream function ψ will be a function of ϕ only, that is, $\psi = f(\phi)$ and the function $f(\phi)$ satisfies the following equation:

$$f''f'b = \nu[f^{iv} + f''(a^2 + b^2) + 2f'''a] \tag{5.78}$$

in which prime refers to differentiation with respect to ϕ.

The integration of Eq. (5.77) gives

$$\phi = -\frac{2}{a^2 + b^2}(a \log r + b\theta) + \phi_0 \tag{5.79}$$

in which ϕ_0 is a constant of integration and the polar coordinates r and θ are defined by the relation

$$z - z_0 = re^{i\theta} \tag{5.80}$$

with z_0 a constant. The streamline $\phi = \text{constant}$ is a logarithmic spiral; i.e.,

$$a \log r + b\theta = \text{const}$$

When $a = 0$, the streamlines are radial lines $\theta = \text{constant}$; when $b = 0$, the streamlines are concentric circles $r = \text{constant}$.

The radial component of velocity is

$$q_r = \frac{1}{r}\frac{\partial \psi}{\partial \theta} = f'\frac{1}{r}\frac{\partial \phi}{\partial \theta} = -\frac{2b}{a^2 + b^2}\frac{f'}{r} \tag{5.81}$$

$$q_\theta = -\frac{\partial \psi}{\partial r} = -f'\frac{\partial \phi}{\partial r} = \frac{2a}{a^2 + b^2}\frac{f'}{r} \tag{5.82}$$

Hence the resultant velocity is

$$|q| = \frac{2}{\sqrt{a^2 + b^2}}\frac{f'}{r} \tag{5.83}$$

Hence, on a solid wall, $f' = 0$.

Without loss of generality, consider a left-hand spiral so that r increases with θ. Thus a and b have different signs. We shall choose

$$a \geqq 0 \qquad b \leqq 0 \tag{5.84}$$

As a result, $f' > 0$ means outflow with positive velocity components and $f' < 0$ means inflow with negative velocity components. Because of the nonlinear effects, the flow field for outflow differs greatly from that for the inflow, as can be seen in the flow of convergent and divergent channels.

Hamel showed that a free motion in logarithmic spiral is always a potential motion. However, there exist other flows on logarithmic spirals between solid walls.

The two limiting cases of logarithmic spiral, that is, $b = 0$ and $a = 0$, are discussed further.

Couette Flow. If $b = 0$, the streamlines are concentric circles. Equation (5.78) gives

$$f' = C + r^2(A + B \log r) \tag{5.85}$$

in which A, B, and C are constants of integration. The velocity components are

$$q_r = 0 \qquad q_\theta = \frac{2}{a}\left(\frac{C}{r} + Ar + Br \log r\right) \tag{5.86}$$

A special case of Eq. (5.86) is the flow between two concentric rotating cylinders. In this case, because the pressures at $\theta = \theta$ and $\theta = \theta + 2\pi$ are the same, the constant B must be zero. The other constants a, A, and C are determined by the boundary conditions on the two rotating cylinders. Let r_1 and r_2 be the radii of the inner and outer cylinders, respectively; let ω_1 and ω_2 be their angular velocities, respectively. The tangential velocity component is then

$$q_\theta = \frac{1}{r_2{}^2 - r_1{}^2}\left[r(\omega_2 r_2{}^2 - \omega_1 r_1{}^2) - \frac{r_1{}^2 r_2{}^2}{r}(\omega_2 - \omega_1) \right] \qquad (5.87)$$

and the pressure p is

$$p = p_1 + \frac{\rho}{(r_2{}^2 - r_1{}^2)^2}\left[(\omega_2 r_2{}^2 - \omega_1 r_1{}^2)^2 \frac{r^2 - r_1{}^2}{2} \right.$$
$$- 2r_1{}^2 r_2{}^2(\omega_2 - \omega_1)(\omega_2 r_2{}^2 - \omega_1 r_1{}^2)\log\frac{r}{r_1}$$
$$\left. + r_1{}^4 r_2{}^4(\omega_2 - \omega_1)^2\left(\frac{1}{r^2} - \frac{1}{r_1{}^2}\right)\right] \qquad (5.88)$$

After the velocity distribution is known, the temperature distribution may be calculated from the energy equation. In the present problem, the energy equation is

$$\frac{1}{r}\frac{\partial}{\partial r}\left(r\frac{\partial T}{\partial r}\right) = -\frac{\mu}{\kappa}\left(\frac{\partial q_\theta}{\partial r} - \frac{q_\theta}{r}\right)^2 \qquad (5.89)$$

By considering the case of two cylinders at some constant temperature, i.e.,

$$r = r_1 \qquad T = T_1 \qquad \text{and} \qquad r = r_2 \qquad T = T_2 \qquad (5.90)$$

the solution of Eq. (5.89) with the boundary conditions (5.90) and the velocity distribution (5.87) is

$$T = T_1 + \frac{\mu}{\kappa}\frac{r_1{}^4 r_2{}^4(\omega_1 - \omega_2)^2}{(r_1{}^2 - r_2{}^2)^2}\left(\frac{1}{r_1{}^2} - \frac{1}{r^2}\right)$$
$$- \frac{\left[T_1 - T_2 + \dfrac{\mu}{\kappa}\dfrac{r_1{}^4 r_2{}^4(\omega_1 - \omega_2)^2[(1/r_1{}^2 - 1/r_2^2)]}{(r_1{}^2 - r_2{}^2)^2}\right]}{\log(r_2/r_1)}\log\frac{r}{r_1} \qquad (5.91)$$

Convergent and Divergent Channels. If $a = 0$, the streamlines are radial lines which correspond to the flow in a convergent channel if $f' < 0$ or to the flow in a divergent channel if $f' > 0$. For convenience, take $b = -2$ and $\phi_0 = 0$ so that Eq. (5.79) gives $\phi = \theta$ and Eq. (5.78) after integration with respect to θ gives

$$F^2 + (4F + F'') + K = 0 \qquad (5.92)$$

in which $F = f'$, and prime refers to differentiation with respect to θ. The radial component of velocity is then

$$q_r = \frac{F}{r} \qquad (5.93)$$

By taking $\theta = 0$ to be one of the walls, $F(0) = 0$. The constant of integration K is then

$$K = -\nu F''(0) = -\frac{1}{\rho}\left(\frac{\partial p}{\partial r}\right)_{\theta=0}\cdot r^3 \qquad (5.94)$$

Thus the value of the constant K is directly associated with the radial pressure gradient. By multiplying Eq. (5.92) by $6F'$ and after integrating the resultant equation,

$$2F^3 + 12F^2 + 3F'^2 + 6FK = \text{const} = 2K_1 \tag{5.95}$$

in which $2K_1$ is the constant of integration.

Equation (5.95) may be written in the following form:

$$\sqrt{\frac{2}{3\nu}}\,\theta = \int_0^F \frac{ds}{\sqrt{(e_1 - s)(s - e_2)(s - e_3)}} \tag{5.96}$$

in which the constants e_1, e_2, and e_3 are connected by the relations

$$e_1 + e_2 + e_3 = -6\nu \qquad e_1 e_2 + e_2 e_3 + e_3 e_1 = 3K \qquad e_1 e_2 e_3 = K_1 \tag{5.97}$$

Equation (5.96) may be expressed in terms of Jacobian elliptic functions. The different possible cases of this type of flow have been discussed in detail by Hamel[1] and also by Millsaps and Pohlhausen.[8] For flows directed toward the center, that is, accelerated flows in a convergent channel, reasonable solutions can always be obtained. These motions are such that for small viscosity the flow in the interior of the channel coincides with that for the simple flow toward a sink except in the neighborhood of a wall where q_r is zero. However, for outward flow, that is, retarded flows in a divergent channel, solutions capable of a practical interpretation can be given only for relatively narrow wedge-shaped channels with an angle of wedge of the order of magnitude $\sqrt{\nu/F_{\max}}$. For large divergent angles of the channel, the flow in the center portion of the channel is outward while that near the wall may be inward. For large Reynolds number, the velocity distribution across the divergent channel may be oscillating in nature; that is, there are a number of jet and back flow regions occurring in the channel.

It is interesting to notice that because of the transcendental nature of the Jacobian elliptical functions, theoretically it is possible to construct an infinite number of possible velocity distributions with both symmetrical and asymmetrical configurations in a divergent channel as well as in a convergent channel. This possibility of infinite velocity distributions was first noted by Rosenhead.[13] The discussion of the flows in the last paragraph is based on the fundamental mode of the solution of the elliptical function.

After the velocity distribution is determined, the temperature distribution across a convergent or a divergent channel may be determined from the following energy equation:

$$C_V\left(q_r \frac{\partial T}{\partial r} + \frac{q_\theta}{r}\frac{\partial T}{\partial \theta}\right) = \frac{\kappa}{\rho}\left(\frac{\partial^2 T}{\partial r^2} + \frac{1}{r}\frac{\partial T}{\partial r} + \frac{1}{r^2}\frac{\partial^2 T}{\partial \theta^2}\right) + \nu\,(2e_{rr}^2 + 2e_{\theta\theta}^2 + e_{r\theta}^2) \tag{5.98}$$

in which

$$e_{rr} = \frac{\partial q_r}{\partial r} \qquad e_{\theta\theta} = \frac{1}{r}\frac{\partial q_\theta}{\partial \theta} + \frac{q_r}{r} \qquad e_{r\theta} = \frac{1}{r}\frac{\partial q_r}{\partial \theta} + \frac{\partial q_\theta}{\partial r} - \frac{q_\theta}{r} \tag{5.99}$$

Consider the case that the temperature T of the walls of the channel is constant; then by use of the transformation,

$$T = \frac{g(\theta)}{r^2} + T_W \tag{5.100}$$

so that Eq. (5.98) becomes an ordinary differential equation of $g(\theta)$; i.e.,

$$-2C_V F g = -(4g + g'') + \nu(4F^2 + F'^2) \tag{5.101}$$

Millsaps and Pohlhausen[8] calculated various temperature distributions for convergent and divergent channels.

For convergent channels, there are definite thermal boundary layers near the walls, and the temperature of the fluid increases rapidly from the wall to a maximum and then decreases toward the center of the channel with a minimum at the channel axis. For large Reynolds numbers, a considerable portion of the fluid near the center of the channel has almost constant temperature.

For divergent channels, the temperature distributions contain oscillations with maxima and minima above the wall temperature and with their number depending on the Prandtl number of the fluid and the number of the fundamental flow regions in the velocity distributions.

Laminar Flow from a Rotating Disc. In the last three cases, only the two-dimensional cases were discussed. Exact solutions of the Navier-Stokes equations for three-dimensional steady flow have also been found. One case is the laminar flow due to an infinite rotating plane disc of constant angular velocity which was first solved exactly by von Kármán[18] and the associate heat-transfer problem by Millsaps and Pohlhausen.[9]

It is convenient to use cylindrical coordinates r, θ, z in the present problem. The Navier-Stokes equations of an incompressible fluid in cylindrical coordinates are

$$\frac{1}{r}\frac{\partial q_r r}{\partial r} + \frac{1}{r}\frac{\partial q_\theta}{\partial \theta} + \frac{\partial q_z}{\partial z} = 0 \tag{5.102}$$

$$\frac{Dq_r}{Dt} - \frac{q_\theta^2}{r} = -\frac{1}{\rho}\frac{\partial p}{\partial r} + \nu\left(\Delta q_r - \frac{q_r}{r^2} - \frac{2}{r^2}\frac{\partial q_\theta}{\partial \theta}\right) \tag{5.103}$$

$$\frac{Dq_\theta}{Dt} + \frac{q_r q_\theta}{r} = -\frac{1}{\rho r}\frac{\partial p}{\partial \theta} + \nu\left(\Delta q_\theta + \frac{2}{r^2}\frac{\partial q_r}{\partial \theta} - \frac{q_\theta}{r^2}\right) \tag{5.104}$$

$$\frac{Dq_z}{Dt} = -\frac{1}{\rho}\frac{\partial p}{\partial z} + \Delta q_z \tag{5.105}$$

in which

$$\frac{D}{Dt} = \frac{\partial}{\partial t} + q_r\frac{\partial}{\partial r} + \frac{q_\theta}{r}\frac{\partial}{\partial \theta} + q_z\frac{\partial}{\partial z}$$

and

$$\Delta = \frac{\partial^2}{\partial r^2} + \frac{1}{r}\frac{\partial}{\partial r} + \frac{1}{r^2}\frac{\partial^2}{\partial \theta^2} + \frac{\partial^2}{\partial z^2}$$

By assuming that the angular velocity of the disc is ω, the boundary conditions of the present problem are

$$q_r(r,\theta,0) = 0 \qquad q_\theta(r,\theta,0) = r\omega \qquad q_z(r,\theta,0) = 0$$
$$q_r(r,\theta,\infty) = 0 \qquad q_\theta(r,\theta,\infty) = 0 \tag{5.106}$$

where the disc is situated at $z = 0$.

In the present problem, all the variables are independent of the angular coordinate θ. In order to satisfy the boundary conditions, Eqs. (5.106), the velocity components and the pressure are placed in the following forms:

$$q_r = rf(z) \qquad q_\theta = rg(z) \qquad q_z = h(z) \qquad p = p(z) \tag{5.107}$$

After substituting Eqs. (5.107) into Eqs. (5.102) to (5.105), a system of ordinary differential equations for f, g, h, and p are obtained, as follows:

$$2f + h' = 0$$
$$f^2 - g^2 + hf' = \nu f''$$
$$2fg + hg' = \nu g'' \tag{5.108}$$

$$hh' = -\frac{p'}{\rho} + \nu h''$$

Equations (5.108) and the corresponding boundary conditions may be transformed into nondimensional form by writing

$$f = \omega F \qquad g = \omega G \qquad h = \sqrt{\nu\omega}H \qquad p = \rho\nu\omega P$$
$$r = \left(\frac{\nu}{\omega}\right)^{1/2}R \qquad z = \left(\frac{\nu}{\omega}\right)^{1/2}Z \tag{5.109}$$

In terms of the nondimensional parameters of Eqs. (5.109), Eqs. (5.108) become

$$H' + 2F = 0$$
$$F'' - HF' - F^2 = -G^2$$
$$G'' - HG' + 2FG = 0 \qquad (5.110)$$
$$P' - H'' + HH' = 0$$

in which the primes now mean differentiation with respect to Z.

The boundary conditions for F, H, G, and P are

$$\begin{array}{ll} F(0) = 0 & F(\infty) = 0 \\ G(0) = 1 & G(\infty) = 0 \qquad (5.111) \\ H(0) = 0 & P(0) = P_0 \end{array}$$

Equations (5.110) may be solved by series-expansion method or by numerical integration. The functions of F, G, and H are given in Fig. 5.2.

If P_0 is the value of P at the disc,

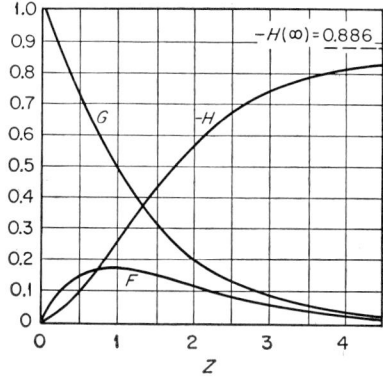

FIG. 5.2. Numerical values of F, G, and H calculated by Cochran. (*Millsaps and Pohlhausen, Ref. 9, fig. 2, reproduced by permission of IAS.*)

$$P - P_0 = \tfrac{1}{2}H^2 - H' = \tfrac{1}{2}H^2 + 2F \qquad (5.112)$$

Strictly speaking, the above results apply only to an infinite disc; by neglecting the edge effect one may find the frictional moment on a rotating disc of radius r_0 by the above results. The shearing stress at the disc is

$$\tau_{z\theta} = \rho\nu \frac{\partial q_\theta}{\partial z} = \rho(\nu\omega^3)^{\frac{1}{2}} rG'(0) \qquad (5.113)$$

so that the moment is

$$M_0 = -2 \int_0^r 2\pi r^2 \tau_{z\theta}\, dr = -\pi r_0^4 \rho(\nu\omega^3)^{\frac{1}{2}} G'(0) = -\frac{\rho\omega^2 r_0^5 \pi G'(0)}{R^{\frac{1}{2}}} \qquad (5.114)$$

in which the Reynolds number $R = r_0^2\omega/\nu$. The moment coefficient is

$$C_M = \frac{M_0}{\tfrac{1}{2}r_0^3\omega^2\pi r_0^2} = -\frac{2G'(0)}{R^{\frac{1}{2}}} = \frac{1.232}{R^{\frac{1}{2}}} \qquad (5.115)$$

After the velocity distribution is obtained, the temperature distribution may be obtained from the energy equation. By considering that the disc has a constant temperature T_w and the fluid at infinity has a constant temperature T_∞, the temperature expression may be written in the following form:

$$T = \left(\frac{\nu\omega}{C_V}\right) T_1 = \frac{\nu\omega}{C_V} [R^2 S(Z) + Q(Z) + T_{1\infty}] \qquad (5.116)$$

The equations for the functions S and Q are then

$$\begin{array}{c} S'' - P_1 H S' + P_1 H' S = -P_1(F'^2 + G'^2) \\ Q'' - P_1 H Q' = -(4S + 12P_1 F^2) \end{array} \qquad (5.117)$$

in which $P_1 = C_V\mu/\kappa$. The boundary conditions are

$$\begin{array}{ll} S(0) = 0 & S(\infty) = 0 \\ Q(0) = T_{1w} - T_{1\infty} & Q(\infty) = 0 \end{array} \qquad (5.118)$$

The function S may be obtained from Eqs. (5.117) by numerical integration, and the function Q can be easily calculated after S is obtained because the second of Eqs. (5.117) is a first-order linear total differential equation of Q'. The function Q may be written as

$$Q = Q_1(T_{1w} - T_1) + Q_2 \tag{5.119}$$

The total amount of heat flow per unit time from one side of a disc of radius r_0 is

$$e = E\rho\nu^{5/2}\omega^{1/2} \tag{5.120}$$

in which

$$E = -\frac{\pi R_0^2}{P_1}\left[\frac{R_0^2}{2}S'(0) + (T_{1w} - T_1)Q'_1(0) + Q'_2(0)\right] \tag{5.121}$$

The values of $S'(0)$, $Q'_1(0)$, and $Q'_2(0)$ for various modified Prandtl numbers are given in Fig. 5.3.

Exact Solutions of Unsteady Flow. Only the exact solutions of steady flow have been discussed. There are exact solutions for unsteady flows. Two typical cases for the unsteady flow are given, as follows:

UNSTEADY MOTION OF A FLAT PLATE. Consider the unsteady motion of a flat plate in its own plane. The only component of velocity different from zero is that parallel to the plate. If the plate is infinitely long, both the velocity and the pressure of the fluid will be functions of the time and the distance perpendicular to the plate only. Take the x axis to be that of the plate and its direction of motion, and take the y axis perpendicular to the plate. The equations of motion for the present problem of an incompressible fluid are

$$\frac{\partial u}{\partial t} = \nu \frac{\partial^2 u}{\partial y^2} \tag{5.122}$$

and

$$p = \text{const}$$

Equation (5.122) is the well-known heat-conduction equation, whose general solution may be easily written down. The well-known Rayleigh problem will be considered in which the plate moves suddenly in its own plane with a constant velocity U. The boundary conditions are:

$$
\begin{array}{lll}
t = 0: & u = 0 & \text{for all } y \\
t > 0: & u = U & \text{for } y = 0 \\
 & u = 0 & \text{for } y = \infty
\end{array}
\tag{5.123}
$$

The solution of Eq. (5.122) satisfying the boundary conditions, Eqs. (5.123), is

$$u = U\left(1 - \frac{2}{\sqrt{\pi}}\int_0^z e^{-z^2}\,dz\right) = U(1 - \operatorname{erf} z) \tag{5.124}$$

in which $z = y/2\sqrt{\nu t}$. The thickness of the layer of the fluid set in motion is of the order of $2\sqrt{\nu t}$. This result verifies the result of boundary-layer flow discussed in Art. 5.7.

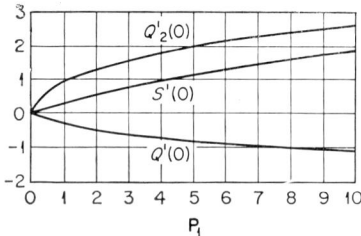

FIG. 5.3. Initial slopes of S, Q_1, and Q_2 as functions of the Prandtl number P_1. (*Millsaps and Pohlhausen, Ref. 9, fig. 9, reproduced by permission of IAS.*)

If the plate oscillates with a constant amplitude and frequency, the boundary condition is

$$y = 0 \qquad u = U\cos\omega t \tag{5.125}$$

in which U is the maximum velocity of the plate and ω is the frequency of oscillation of the plate. The solution is then

$$u = Ue^{-\lambda y}\cos(\omega t - \lambda y) \tag{5.126}$$

in which $\lambda = \sqrt{\omega/2\nu}$.

The velocity of propagation of the wave generated by the plate is

$$V = \sqrt{2\nu\omega} \tag{5.127}$$

This result checks with the discussion of wave motion in Art. 5.8, i.e., Eq. (5.64).

DISSOLUTION OF A VORTEX FILAMENT. In an ideal fluid, the vortex filament moves with the fluid without dissolution. However, in a viscous fluid, the vortex filament will decay because of the viscous stresses. Consider a simple vortex filament with its axis as the z axis in cylindrical coordinates. The vorticity is then

$$\zeta = \frac{\partial q_\theta}{\partial r} + \frac{q_\theta}{r} \tag{5.128}$$

In an incompressible fluid, the differential equation for ζ is

$$\frac{\partial \zeta}{\partial t} = \nu \left(\frac{\partial^2 \zeta}{\partial r^2} + \frac{1}{r} \frac{\partial \zeta}{\partial r} \right) \tag{5.129}$$

The fundamental solution of Eq. (5.129) is

$$\zeta = \frac{A}{t} e^{-r^2/4\nu t} \tag{5.130}$$

in which A is a positive constant. The vorticity is everywhere finite and positive for time greater than zero.

The circulation Γ around a circle of radius r is equal to twice the surface integral of vorticity inside the circle; i.e.,

$$\Gamma = 4\pi \int_0^r \zeta r \, dr = 8\pi \nu A (1 - e^{-r^2/4\nu t})$$
$$= \Gamma_1 (1 - e^{-r^2/4\nu t}) \tag{5.131}$$

in which $\Gamma_1 = 8\pi \nu A =$ the circulation of the vortex filament around an infinitely large circle, which corresponds to the value in a potential flow at $t = 0$.

$$q_\theta = \frac{\Gamma}{2\pi r} = \frac{\Gamma_1}{2\pi r} (1 - e^{-r^2/4\nu t}) \tag{5.132}$$

Equation (5.132) shows that at $t = 0$, the velocity distribution is the same as that of a vortex filament in an ideal fluid. As the time t increases, the velocity at $r = 0$ is zero, and at the neighborhood of $r = 0$, there is a vortex core in which the velocity is less than that of the value of the corresponding potential flow. This core diffuses outward as the time increases.

5.10. Some Exact Solutions of the Navier-Stokes Equations of a Compressible Fluid

It is much more difficult to find the exact solutions of the Navier-Stokes equations of a compressible fluid than in the case of an incompressible fluid because one must solve the equations of motion simultaneously with the energy equation, equation of state, and the continuity equation. The only possible exact solution for the flow of a viscous compressible fluid is steady flow with one spatial coordinate, which includes the problem of the structure of a normal shock and the Couette flow of a viscous compressible fluid.

Shock-wave Structure. Consider one-dimensional steady flow in which only the x velocity component u is different from zero and all the variables u and state variables p, T, and ρ are functions of x only. The Navier-Stokes equations of a viscous compressible fluid become

$$p = \rho R T \tag{5.133a}$$

$$\frac{d(\rho u)}{dx} = 0 \tag{5.133b}$$

$$\rho u \frac{du}{dx} + \frac{dp}{dx} - \frac{4}{3} \frac{d}{dx} \left(\mu \frac{du}{dx} \right) = 0 \tag{5.133c}$$

$$\rho u \frac{dh_0}{dx} - \frac{4}{3}\frac{d}{dx}\left(\mu u \frac{du}{dx}\right) - \frac{d}{dx}\left(\kappa \frac{dT}{dx}\right) = 0 \tag{5.133d}$$

in which $h_0 = C_p T + u^2/2 = $ stagnation enthalpy.

Integration of Eqs. (5.133) with respect to x gives

$$\rho u = \text{const} = m \tag{5.134a}$$

$$mu + p - \tfrac{4}{3}\mu \frac{du}{dx} = \text{const} = mC_1 \tag{5.134b}$$

$$mh_0 - \tfrac{4}{3}\mu u \frac{du}{dx} - \kappa \frac{dT}{dx} = \text{const} = mC_2 \tag{5.134c}$$

Equation (5.134c) may be written in the form

$$\frac{\kappa}{mR}\frac{d(RT)}{dx} = C_v T - \frac{u^2}{2} + C_1 u - C_2 \tag{5.135}$$

Now by introducing the nondimensional variables,

$$\frac{u}{u_1} = \xi \qquad \frac{RT}{u_1^2} = \tau \qquad P = \frac{p_1}{\rho_1 u_1^2} = \frac{1}{\gamma \mathbf{M}_1^2} \tag{5.136}$$

in which $\mathbf{M}$ is the Mach number and the subscript 1 refers to the value of a uniform state with

$$\frac{du}{dx} = \frac{dT}{dx} = 0 \tag{5.137}$$

Equations (5.134b) and (5.135) in terms of the nondimensional variables, Eqs. (5.136), become

$$\frac{4}{3}\frac{\mu}{m}\xi\frac{d\xi}{dx} = \tau + \xi^2 - (1+P)\xi \tag{5.138}$$

$$\frac{\kappa}{mR}\frac{d\tau}{dx} = \frac{\tau}{\gamma-1} - \frac{\xi^2}{2} + (1+P)\xi - \tfrac{1}{2} - \frac{\gamma P}{\gamma-1} \tag{5.139}$$

Equations (5.138) and (5.139) give the following relation for the uniform states (5.137):

$$(\xi-1)\left(\xi - \frac{\gamma-1}{\gamma+1} - \frac{2\gamma P}{\gamma+1}\right) = (\xi-1)(\xi-\xi_2) = 0 \tag{5.140}$$

There are two solutions for Eq. (5.140), in which $\xi = 1$ represents the original flow and $\xi = \xi_2$ gives the uniform flow behind a normal shock. Hence Eqs. (5.138) and (5.139) may be used to describe the transition region connecting $\xi = 1$ to $\xi = \xi_2$, and it gives the structure of a normal shock wave.

After eliminating x from Eqs. (5.138) and (5.139), a first-order differential equation for τ in terms of ξ is obtained, as follows:

$$\frac{d\tau}{d(\xi^2/2)} = \frac{4}{3}\frac{\mathbf{P}}{\gamma}\frac{\tau - \tau_0}{\tau - \tau_\infty} \tag{5.141}$$

in which $\mathbf{P} = C_p\mu/\kappa = $ Prandtl number.

$$\tau_0 = P - (\gamma-1)\left[\frac{\xi^2}{2} + (1+P)\xi - \tfrac{1}{2} - P\right] \tag{5.142}$$

$$\tau_\infty = -\xi^2 + (1+P)\xi \tag{5.143}$$

If $\mathbf{P} = \tfrac{3}{4}$, a simple analytic solution of Eq. (5.141) may be found. In general, Eq. (5.141) may be integrated numerically in order to obtain the function $\tau = \tau(\xi)$. The two solutions of Eq. (5.140) give two singular points of Eq. (5.141). For the structure of a shock wave, the integral curve $\tau = \tau(\xi)$ connecting these two singular points is desired. After $\tau = \tau(\xi)$ is obtained, the x coordinate may be obtained by simple quadrature; i.e.,

$$\frac{\rho_1 u_1}{\mu_1} x = \frac{4}{3} \int \frac{\mu/\mu_1}{\tau - \tau_\infty} \, d\left(\frac{\xi^2}{2}\right) \tag{5.144}$$

The transition region has a large change in velocity in a very short distance. Thus the thickness of the shock wave is very small and of the order of a few mean free paths. This is the reason that, to a first approximation, the shock wave may be considered as a surface of discontinuity in the analysis of inviscid fluid.

Similar analysis may be applied to discuss the flame-front structure in which chemical reaction takes place.

Couette Flow of a Compressible Fluid. Exact solutions for both plane and circulating Couette flows of a compressible fluid have been found by Illingworth:[2]

PLANE COUETTE FLOW. Consider that all the flow variables are functions of one space coordinate y only. The flow between two infinite parallel plates is a special case of this problem. The plates may be assumed at $y = \pm 1$. The equation of continuity is then

$$\frac{d(\rho v)}{dy} = 0 \tag{5.145}$$

or

$$\rho v = \text{const} = 0 \qquad \text{or} \qquad v = 0$$

because at the plate $v = 0$. The equations of motion are

$$\frac{d}{dy}\left(\mu \frac{du}{dy}\right) = 0 \tag{5.146}$$

$$\frac{dp}{dy} = 0 \tag{5.147}$$

$$\frac{d}{dy}\left(\mu \frac{dw}{dy}\right) = 0 \tag{5.148}$$

Equation (5.147) shows that $p = $ constant, and Eq. (5.148) shows that $w = 0$ because $w = 0$ at $y = \pm 1$. Equation (5.146) gives

$$\frac{du}{dy} = \text{const} = b_1 \tag{5.149}$$

or

$$\int_0^\mu \mu \, du = b_1(y + 1) \tag{5.149a}$$

If μ is independent of the temperature and then of the velocity, the velocity distribution is linear. However, μ is in general a function of temperature, and thus a function of velocity u, and the velocity distribution of plane Couette flow is no longer linear. The relation between the temperature T and the velocity u may be obtained from the energy equation, which is

$$\mu\left(\frac{du}{dy}\right)^2 + \frac{1}{P}\frac{d}{dy}\left(\mu \frac{dH}{dy}\right) = 0 \tag{5.150}$$

in which $H = C_p T = $ enthalpy, and it is assumed that the Prandtl number is constant. Integration of Eq. (5.150) with the help of Eq. (5.149) gives

$$\mu \frac{dH}{dy} + P b_1 u = \text{const} = b_2 \tag{5.151}$$

Further integration of Eq. (5.151) with respect to u yields

$$H + \mathbf{P}\frac{u^2}{2} - \frac{b_2}{b_1} u = \text{const} = H_0 \tag{5.152}$$

in which H_0 is the stagnation enthalpy. Equation (5.152) gives the relation between the temperature and the velocity, even if the specific heat at constant pressure C_p is not a constant such as the case of dissociated gas.

After the function $T(u)$ is obtained, then $\mu(T) = \mu(u)$. Then Eq. (5.149a) gives the velocity distribution $u(y)$. Also, $T(u) = T(y)$. Finally, the density distribution is

$$\rho(y) = \frac{p}{RT(y)} = \frac{\text{const}}{T(y)} \tag{5.153}$$

COUETTE FLOW BETWEEN ROTATING CYLINDERS. In this case, assume that all the variables are functions of r only. It can be easily shown that the only velocity component different from zero is q_θ. The fundamental equations for p, ρ, T, and q_θ are then

$$\frac{dp}{dr} - \rho \frac{q_\theta^2}{r} = 0 \tag{5.154}$$

$$\frac{d}{dr}\left[r^2 \mu \left(\frac{dq_\theta}{dr} - \frac{q_\theta}{r} \right) \right] = 0 \tag{5.155}$$

$$\frac{1}{\mathbf{P}r} \frac{d}{dr}\left(r\mu \frac{dH}{dr} \right) + \mu \left(\frac{dq_\theta}{dr} - \frac{q_\theta}{r} \right)^2 = 0 \tag{5.156}$$

The angular velocity $\omega(r)$ defined by $q_\theta = \omega r$ may be introduced. Equations (5.155) and (5.156) become

$$\mu r^3 \frac{d\omega}{dr} = \text{const} = b \tag{5.157}$$

$$r\mu \frac{dH}{dr} + \mathbf{P}b\omega = \text{const} \tag{5.158}$$

Since μ is a function of H, it is necessary to solve Eqs. (5.157) and (5.158) simultaneously. A numerical-integration method may be used for any given $\mu(H)$.

After $T(r)$ is obtained, the pressure and the density may be obtained by solving Eq. (5.154) with the equation of state

$$p = \rho RT \tag{5.159}$$

5.11. Stability of a Laminar Flow

One of the most interesting problems in fluid dynamics is the problem of the stability of a laminar flow and its transition to turbulence. There are two schools of thought in regard to the cause of transition from steady laminar flow to turbulent conditions. One school contends that transition is due to a definite instability of the flow, i.e., to a condition in which infinitesimal disturbances grow exponentially. The second school regards the motion in most cases as definitely stable for infinitesimal disturbances but liable to be made turbulent by suitable disturbances of finite magnitude or by sufficiently large pressure gradients. The present knowledge of transition indicates that both causes exist. Laminar flow is basically unstable for large Reynolds numbers. But if the outside disturbance is large enough, it may cause transition at a much lower Reynolds number than at that due to the basic instability of the flow.

The stability problem may be attacked by either the theory of finite disturbances or of small disturbances. Mathematical investigations of finite disturbances are mainly based on the considerations of the energy or of the square of the vorticity of the disturbances, because the solution of the nonlinear equations satisfied by these disturbances is extremely difficult to obtain. For small disturbances, the energy and the vorticity methods may also be used. But the energy and the vorticity methods can only give sufficient conditions for stability. These methods usually give too low a limit of stability as indicated by experiments.

To get more concrete results, it is necessary to solve the linearized equations satisfied by the disturbances. The most successful case appeared to be Taylor's treatment of Couette flow between concentric cylinders.[17] The most extensive discussion of hydrodynamic stability seems to be the treatment of parallel flows by solving the eigenvalue problem associated with the linearized equations governing the disturbances.[7] Both cases have been verified experimentally. These two cases are discussed in the following paragraphs.

Stability of a Parallel Flow of a Viscous Incompressible Fluid. Consider the basic flow as a two-dimensional steady parallel flow with the following velocity components and pressure:

$$u = U(y) \qquad v = w = 0 \qquad p = Ax + B \qquad (5.160)$$

in which A and B are constant and $U(y)$ is a function of y only. The basic flow is perturbed by a small disturbance. In the resultant disturbed motion

$$u = U(y) + u_x \qquad v = u_y \qquad w = u_z \qquad p = Ax + B + p' \qquad (5.161)$$

in which u_x, u_y, u_z, and p' are the perturbed quantities that are assumed to be small. After substituting the quantities of Eqs. (5.161) into the Navier-Stokes equations [Eqs. (5.7) and (5.8)] and by neglecting the quadratic terms of the perturbed quantities, the equations for the disturbances are as follows:

$$\frac{\partial u_x}{\partial t} + U \frac{\partial u_x}{\partial x} + u_y \frac{\partial U}{\partial y} = -\frac{1}{\rho}\frac{\partial p'}{\partial x} + \nu \nabla^2 u_x$$

$$\frac{\partial u_y}{\partial t} + U \frac{\partial u_y}{\partial x} = -\frac{1}{\rho}\frac{\partial p'}{\partial y} + \nu \nabla^2 u_y$$

$$\frac{\partial u_z}{\partial t} + U \frac{\partial u_z}{\partial x} = -\frac{1}{\rho}\frac{\partial p'}{\partial z} + \nu \nabla^2 u_z \qquad (5.162)$$

$$\frac{\partial u_x}{\partial x} + \frac{\partial u_y}{\partial y} + \frac{\partial u_z}{\partial z} = 0$$

Now assume that the disturbances may be analyzed into an infinite number of principal disturbances, each of which involves the time only through a single exponential factor. The disturbance is also supposed to be analyzed into constituents that are simple harmonic functions both in x and z. Then, the equations being linear, one need consider only a single constituent. Thus the perturbed quantities take the following forms:

$$\begin{aligned}
u_x &= u_1(y) \exp i(\alpha x + \alpha_1 z - \beta t)\\
u_y &= v_1(y) \exp i(\alpha x + \alpha_1 z - \beta t)\\
u_z &= w_1(y) \exp i(\alpha x + \alpha_1 z - \beta t)\\
p' &= p_1(y) \exp i(\alpha x + \alpha_1 z - \beta t)
\end{aligned} \qquad (5.163)$$

in which either the real or the imaginary part may be taken at the end to give u_x, u_y, etc., real values. Here α and α_1 are positive real numbers that are the wave numbers of the disturbances; β is the phase velocity of the disturbance which may be complex, that is, $\beta = \beta_r + i\beta_i$. The value of β is to be found to satisfy all the conditions of any particular problem. If the imaginary part of β is positive, the motion is unstable, while if the imaginary part of β is negative, the motion is stable.

By substituting Eqs. (5.163) into (5.162),

$$u''_1 + \left(i\frac{\beta}{\nu} - \alpha^2 - \alpha_1{}^2\right)u_1 = i\frac{\alpha}{\rho\nu}p_1 + \frac{v_1}{\nu}U' + i\frac{\alpha}{\nu}Uu_1$$

$$v''_1 + \left(i\frac{\beta}{\nu} - \alpha^2 - \alpha_1{}^2\right)v_1 = \frac{1}{\rho\nu}p'_1 + i\frac{\alpha}{\nu}Uv_1 \qquad (5.164)$$

$$w''_1 + \left(i\frac{\beta}{\nu} - \alpha^2 - \alpha_1{}^2\right)w_1 = i\frac{\alpha_1}{\rho\nu}p_1 + i\frac{\alpha}{\nu}Uw_1$$

$$i\alpha u_1 + v'_1 + i\alpha_1 w_1 = 0$$

By eliminating u_1, w_1, and p_1 from Eqs. (5.164), a single equation for v_1 follows:

$$\left(\frac{d^2}{dy^2} - \alpha^2 - \alpha_1{}^2\right)\left(\frac{d^2}{dy^2}2 + i\frac{\beta}{\nu} - \alpha^2 - \alpha_1{}^2\right)v_1$$

$$- i\frac{\alpha}{\nu}U\left(\frac{d^2}{dy^2} - \alpha^2 - \alpha_1{}^2\right)v_1 + i\frac{\alpha}{\nu}v_1 U'' = 0 \quad (5.165)$$

in which prime refers to differentiation with respect to y. Equation (5.165) is the stability equation of laminar parallel flow with three-dimensional disturbances. In stability analysis, one usually considers only the two-dimensional disturbances in which $w = 0$ and $\alpha_1 = 0$. Equation (5.165) reduces to

$$(U - c)(v''_1 - \alpha^2 v_1) - v_1 U'' = -i\frac{\nu}{\alpha}(v_1^{iv} - 2\alpha^2 v''_1 + \alpha^4 v_1) \qquad (5.166)$$

in which $c = \beta/\lambda$. Equation (5.166) is the well-known Orr-Sommerfeld equation of hydrodynamic stability.

In terms of nondimensional quantities

$$U^* = \frac{U}{U_0} \qquad c^* = \frac{c}{U_0} \qquad v^* = \frac{v_1}{U_0} \qquad y^* = \frac{y}{L} \qquad \alpha^* = \alpha L \qquad \mathbf{R} = \frac{U_0 L}{\nu}$$

Eq. (5.166) becomes

$$(U^* - c^*)(v^{*''} - \alpha^{*2}v^*) - v^* U^{*''} = -\frac{i}{\alpha^* \mathbf{R}}(v^{*iv} - 2\alpha^{*2}v^{*''} + \alpha^{*4}v^*) \qquad (5.167)$$

It should be noted that Eq. (5.165) may be reduced to exactly the same form as Eq. (5.167) by making

$$\alpha_2 = (\alpha^2 + \alpha_1{}^2)^{1/2} \qquad \alpha U_3 = \alpha_2 U_2 \qquad (5.168)$$

in which α_2 is the corresponding two-dimensional wave number, U_3 is the characteristic velocity in the case of a three-dimensional disturbance, and U_2, that of a two-dimensional disturbance. Hence the solution of Eq. (5.167) may be used to derive the corresponding solution of Eq. (5.165). Particularly it can be shown that the minimum Reynolds number for instability for the three-dimensional disturbance is larger than the corresponding value of the two-dimensional disturbance. This transformation is known as the Squire[16] theorem of hydrodynamic stability.

Now the solution of the Orr-Sommerfeld equation, Eq. (5.167), is discussed briefly. The Orr-Sommerfeld equation has a fundamental system of four solutions that are analytic functions of y [wherever $U^*(y)$ is analytic] and are entire functions of α^*, c^*, and $\mathbf{R}$. These solutions were first given by Heisenberg and carried out in greater detail by Lin[7] and others.

Two of the solutions, called *inviscid solutions*, can be obtained by development of the solution in powers of $(\alpha^* \mathbf{R})^{-1}$. The function $v^*(y)$ may be written as

$$v^*(y) = \phi^{(0)}(y) + (\alpha^* \mathbf{R})^{-1}\phi^{(1)}(y) + (\alpha^* \mathbf{R})^{-2}\phi^{(2)}(y) + \cdots \qquad (5.169)$$

The function $\phi^{(0)}$ can be solved by development in powers of α^{*2}:

$$\phi_1^{(0)} = (U^* - c^*)[h_0(y) + \alpha^{*2}h_2(y) + \alpha^{*4}h_4(y) + \cdots] \tag{5.170}$$

in which $h_0(y) = 1$.

$$h_{2n+2} = \int_{y_1}^{y} dy \, (U^* - c^*)^{-2} \int_{y_1}^{y} dy \, (U^* - c^*)^2 h_{2n}(y) \qquad n \geqq 0 \tag{5.171}$$

in which y_1 is a certain convenient fixed point.

$$\phi_2^{(0)} = (U^* - c^*)[k_1(y) + \alpha^{*2}k_3(y) + \alpha^{*4}k_5(y) + \cdots] \tag{5.172}$$

in which $k_1(y) = \int_{y_1}^{y} dy \, (U^* - c^*)^{-2}$.

$$k_{2n+3}(y) = \int_{y_1}^{y} dy \, (U^* - c^*)^{-2} \int_{y_1}^{y} dy \, (U^* - c^*)^2 k_{2n+1}(y) \qquad n \geqq 0 \tag{5.173}$$

Similarly, the functions $\phi^{(1)}$ may be expressed also in power series of α^* in the same manner as in Eqs. (5.170) and (5.172).

In the analysis of the stability of the flow with at least one solid boundary, only $\phi^{(0)}$ will be used. For flows without a solid boundary such as the flow of jets and wakes, both $\phi^{(0)}$ and $\phi^{(1)}$ will be used.

The other two solutions are known as viscous solutions, which in asymptotic form are

$$\phi_3 = (U^* - c^*)^{-5/4} \exp\left[-\int_{y_0}^{y} \sqrt{i\alpha^* R(U^* - c^*)} \, dy \right]$$
$$\phi_4 = (U^* - c^*)^{-5/4} \exp\left[+\int_{y_0}^{y} \sqrt{i\alpha^* R(U^* - c^*)} \, dy \right] \tag{5.174}$$

with $U^* = c^*$ at $y = y_0$.

The solution of the stability equation is then

$$v^* = C_1\phi_1 + C_2\phi_2 + C_3\phi_3 + C_4\phi_4 \tag{5.175}$$

in which C_1, C_2, C_3, and C_4 are constants to be determined by the boundary conditions. For flow between two parallel plates situated at $y = \pm 1$,

$$v^* = v^{*\prime} = 0 \qquad \text{at } y^* = \pm 1 \tag{5.176}$$

After substituting Eqs. (5.175) into conditions (5.176), four homogeneous equations in the C's result. The determinantal equation must vanish, and

$$F(\alpha^*, R, c^*) = 0 \tag{5.177}$$

For each pair of real values of α^* and R, there is a characteristic value of c^*. Since the value of the imaginary part of c^* determines the stability of the flow, boundary of the stability region is usually desired that is given by the curve $c^*_i = 0$ in the α^*R plane. A typical curve for plane Poiseuille flow, calculated by Shen,[15] is shown in Fig. 5.4. There is a minimum critical Reynolds number of 6800 below which the flow is stable.

Within the boundary-layer approximations, the Orr-Sommerfeld equation, Eq. (5.167), can be used to study the stability of boundary-layer flows. For the bound-

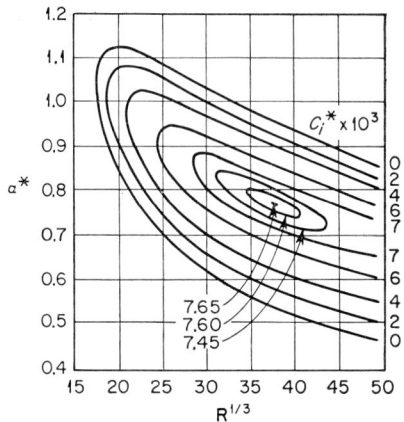

Fig. 5.4. Stability curves of a plane Poiseuille flow. Shen, (Ref. 15, fig. 1, reproduced by permission of IAS.)

ary-layer flow over a flat plate, the neutral curve has a form similar to that of Fig. 5.4. Schubauer and Skramstad[14] were the first ones to verify experimentally the occurrence of the oscillations, so-called Tollmien-Schlichting oscillations, predicted by the Orr-Sommerfeld equations in boundary-layer flow over a flat plate.

Stability of Laminar Flow between Rotating Cylinders. The most successful investigation of a stability problem is probably Taylor's treatment of the Couette flow between concentric cylinders for an incompressible fluid in which the centrifugal force plays a dominant part. In the present problem it is convenient to write the fundamental equations in cylindrical coordinates r, θ, z as follows:

$$\frac{Dq_r}{Dt} - \frac{q_\theta^2}{r} = -\frac{1}{\rho}\frac{\partial p}{\partial r} + \nu\left(\nabla^2 q_r - \frac{2}{r^2}\frac{\partial q_\theta}{\partial \theta} - \frac{q_r}{r^2}\right)$$

$$\frac{Dq_\theta}{Dt} + \frac{q_\theta q_r}{r} = -\frac{1}{\rho r}\frac{\partial p}{\partial \theta} + \nu\left(\nabla^2 q_\theta + \frac{2}{r^2}\frac{\partial q_r}{\partial \theta} - \frac{q_\theta}{r^2}\right)$$

$$\frac{Dq_z}{Dt} = -\frac{1}{\rho}\frac{\partial p}{\partial z} + \nu\nabla^2 q_z \tag{5.178}$$

$$\frac{\partial q_r}{\partial r} + \frac{q_r}{r} + \frac{1}{r}\frac{\partial q_\theta}{\partial \theta} + \frac{\partial q_z}{\partial z} = 0$$

in which

$$\frac{D}{Dt} = \frac{\partial}{\partial t} + q_r\frac{\partial}{\partial r} + \frac{q_\theta}{r}\frac{\partial}{\partial \theta} + q_z\frac{\partial}{\partial z}$$

and

$$\nabla^2 = \frac{\partial^2}{\partial r^2} + \frac{1}{r}\frac{\partial}{\partial r} + \frac{1}{r^2}\frac{\partial^2}{\partial \theta^2} + \frac{\partial^2}{\partial z^2}$$

The basic steady flow between rotating cylinders, Eqs. (5.87) and (5.88), may be written as follows:

$$q_r = q_z = 0 \qquad q_\theta = V(r) = Ar + \frac{B}{r} \qquad \frac{\partial p}{\partial r} = \frac{\rho V^2}{r} \tag{5.179}$$

in which the constants A and B depend on the radii and the angular velocities of the two cylinders as given in Eq. (5.87).

In the disturbance motion, one has

$$q_r, \; V(r) + q_\theta, \; q_z, \text{ and } \frac{\partial p}{\partial r} = \frac{\rho V^2}{r} + p' \tag{5.180}$$

where q_r, q_θ, q_z, and p' are small quantities. Assume that the perturbed velocity components are of the following form:

$$\begin{aligned} q_r &= e^{\omega t}u(r)\cos\lambda z \\ q_\theta &= e^{\omega t}v(r)\cos\lambda z \\ q_z &= e^{\omega t}w(r)\cos\lambda z \end{aligned} \tag{5.181}$$

After substituting Eqs. (5.180) and (5.181) into Eqs. (5.178) and by neglecting the high-order terms, the linearized equations for the disturbances are obtained. In these equations, it is possible to eliminate the variables w and p' and finally have the following system of stability equations:

$$\frac{\nu}{\lambda^2}\left(DD_1 - \lambda^2 - \frac{\omega}{\nu}\right)v - 2Au = 0$$

$$\frac{\nu}{\lambda^2}\left(DD_1 - \lambda^2 - \frac{\omega}{\nu}\right)(DD_1 - \lambda^2)u = 2\left(A + \frac{B}{r^2}\right)v \tag{5.182}$$

in which $D = d/dr$ and $D_1 = D + 1/r$.

The boundary conditions are

$$u = v = D_1 u = 0 \quad \text{at} \quad r = r_1 \quad \text{and} \quad r = r_2 \qquad (5.183)$$

Hence the stability problem leads again to an eigenvalue problem with a determinantal equation such as

$$F\left(\omega, \lambda, \frac{r_2}{r_1}, \frac{\omega_2}{\omega_1}, \mathbf{R}\right) = 0 \qquad (5.184)$$

in which the Reynolds number $\mathbf{R} = \omega_1 r_1^2 / \nu$.

The general solution of Eqs. (5.182) is very difficult. One may obtain an approximate solution by assuming the following:

1. The gap between the cylinders is small compared with the mean radius of the two cylinders; i.e.,

$$d = (r_2 - r_1) \ll \tfrac{1}{2}(r_2 + r_1) = r_0 \qquad (5.185)$$

Under this condition, no distinction is made between D and D_1.

2. The two cylinders are rotating in the same direction. The following approximations can be made·

$$A + \frac{B}{r} \cong A + \frac{B}{r_0} = \omega_0$$

$$\frac{B}{r^2} \cong \frac{B}{r_0^2} \qquad (5.186)$$

Under these conditions, it was found that instability depends on a characteristic number known as Taylor's number $\mathbf{T}$ as follows:

$$\mathbf{T} = -4 \frac{\omega_0 A}{\nu^2} d^4 \qquad (5.187)$$

A typical stability curve is shown in Fig. 5.5. The interesting result is that these types of disturbances form cellular vortices with axial symmetry that persist even at very large Reynolds numbers. Taylor himself verified his theoretical prediction experimentally.

Stability of a Layer of Fluid Heated from Below. This problem is particularly interesting in many astrophysical and geophysical problems. It was first investigated by Rayleigh, Jeffreys, and others.[7] The main results are (1) that the fluid becomes unstable when the Rayleigh number [Eq. (5.206)] exceeds a certain value and (2) that the motion must have a cellular pattern when instability occurs. This has been verified experimentally.

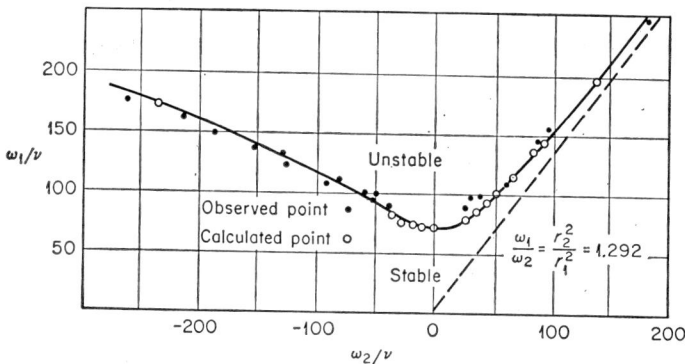

Fig. 5.5. Stability curve of flow between rotating cylinders. (Taylor, *Ref.* 17, *fig.* 18, *reproduced by permission of the Royal Society.*)

Another interesting point is that the present problem and that of rotating cylinders are closely related from the mathematical point of view. Taylor's criterion [Eq. (5.187)] for the onset of rotational instability can be deduced from Rayleigh's criterion for thermal instability by replacing $\kappa\nu$ by ν^2.

In the present problem, the gravitational force $\mathbf{F}_g$ should be added to the equations of motion, Eqs. (5.7); i.e.,

$$\mathbf{F}_g = -\rho g \lambda \tag{5.188}$$

in which λ is a unit vector in the vertical direction.

The density Eq. (5.188) may be written as

$$\rho = \rho_0(1 - \alpha \, \Delta T) \tag{5.189}$$

with ρ_0 the average density, which corresponds to a temperature T_0. In the acceleration terms Du/Dt, one may still put $\rho = \rho_0$. Here α is the coefficient of volume expansion. The local temperature deviation is

$$\Delta T = T - T_0 \tag{5.190}$$

The local temperature T may be written as

$$T = T_0 + \beta \lambda_i x_i + \theta \tag{5.191}$$

in which a constant mean temperature gradient $\beta = \pm|\beta|$ is assumed to be maintained by an external agency.

$$\beta = \frac{\partial T}{\partial x_i} \lambda_i \tag{5.192}$$

θ is the deviation of temperature from the local mean value $T_0 + \beta \lambda_i x_i$.

The equation of motion for the problem is then

$$\frac{\partial u_i}{\partial t} + \frac{\partial(u_i u_j)}{\partial x_j} = \nu \nabla^2 u_i + \Gamma \theta \lambda_i - \frac{\partial p_t}{\partial x_i} \tag{5.193}$$

with

$$\Gamma = \alpha g \tag{5.194}$$

$$p_t = \frac{p}{\rho_0} + g\lambda_j x_j - \frac{1}{2}\beta\Gamma\lambda_i\lambda_j x_i x_j \tag{5.195}$$

The energy equation that governs θ is

$$\frac{\partial \theta}{\partial t} + \beta\lambda_j u_j + u_j \frac{\partial \theta}{\partial x_j} = \kappa_1 \nabla^2 \theta \tag{5.196}$$

in which $\kappa_1 = \kappa\rho_0/C_v$. Both κ and C_v are assumed to be constant here.

It is convenient to introduce a new variable

$$w = u_i \lambda_i \tag{5.197}$$

The linearized equation for the variables θ and w are

$$\frac{\partial \theta}{\partial t} = -\beta w + \kappa_1 \nabla^2 \theta \tag{5.198a}$$

$$\frac{\partial w}{\partial t} = \Gamma \theta + \nu \nabla^2 w - \lambda_i \frac{\partial p_t}{\partial x_i} \tag{5.198b}$$

One may assume $w = u(x,y,z)e^{\omega t}$ and $\theta = \theta(x,y,z)e^{\omega t}$.

By considering a horizontal layer of fluid of depth d, confined between two parallel planes at $z = 0$ and $z = d$, the boundary conditions are

$$\theta = w = 0 \qquad \text{at } z = 0 \qquad \text{and} \qquad z = d$$

$$\frac{\partial^2 w}{\partial z^2} = 0 \qquad \text{on a free surface} \tag{5.199}$$

$$\frac{\partial w}{\partial z} = 0 \qquad \text{on a rigid surface}$$

The condition in marginal stability is the real part of $\omega = \omega_R = 0$. If the imaginary part of $\omega = \omega_i$ is also equal to zero, this case is called the principle of exchange of stability, which is the case that was assumed to be true. Then for marginal stability with $\lambda = (0, 0, 1)$, the stability equation is

$$\nabla^6 w = \frac{|\beta|\Gamma}{\kappa\nu}\left(\frac{\partial^2 w}{\partial x^2} - \frac{\partial^2 w}{\partial y^2}\right) \tag{5.200}$$

The equation for θ is of exactly the same form as w.

The method of separation of variables may be used to solve Eq. (5.200). By writing

$$w = f(x,y)W(z) \tag{5.201}$$

with
$$d^2\left(\frac{\partial^2 f}{\partial x^2} + \frac{\partial^2 f}{\partial y^2}\right) = -a^2 f \tag{5.202}$$

a^2 is a certain "characteristic number" determined by the conditions on the cell walls. The solution for f, when the boundary of the cell is a rectangle with sides L_1 and L_2, is

$$f = A_{mn}\cos\frac{mx}{L_1}\cos\frac{ny}{L_2} \tag{5.203}$$

in which m and n are arbitrary even integers, A_{mn} is a constant, and

$$a^2 = d^2\pi^2\left(\frac{m^2}{L_1} + \frac{n^2}{L_2}\right) \tag{5.204}$$

For other shapes of cell, different solutions may be obtained.

The equation for $W(z) = W(\zeta/d)$ is

$$(D^2 - a^2)^3 W = -a^2\mathbf{R}_a W \tag{5.205}$$

where $D = d/d\zeta$ and

$$\mathbf{R}_a = \frac{|\beta|\Gamma}{\kappa\nu}d^4 \qquad \text{Rayleigh number} \tag{5.206}$$

It is interesting to notice the similarity of the Rayleigh number, Eq. (5.206), and the Taylor number, Eq. (5.187).

The boundary conditions for W are, at $\zeta = 0$ and $\zeta = 1$,

$$\begin{aligned}
W = (D^2 - a^2)^2 W &= 0 \\
DW = 0 \qquad &\text{on a rigid surface} \\
D^2 W = 0 \qquad &\text{on a free surface}
\end{aligned} \tag{5.207}$$

If the Rayleigh number exceeds a certain critical value, the flow will be unstable.

Stability of a Laminar Flow of a Compressible Fluid. Even though the variation of density due to the variation of temperature was considered (p. 5-32), the variation of density was assumed to be small, and the fluid may be still considered as an incompressible fluid. For high-speed flow and for flow with large variation of temperature, the compressibility effect should be taken into account. The analysis for a parallel flow (pp. 5-27 to 5-30) has been extended for the compressible fluid. The analysis is, of course, much more complicated than that for an incompressible fluid. One interesting result is that Squire's theorem does not hold for a three-dimensional disturbance in a compressible fluid.   Another interesting result is that the two-dimensional disturbances can be completely stabilized by sufficient cooling of the solid boundary.

REFERENCES

1. Hamel, G.: Spiralfoermige Bewegungen zaeher Fluessigkeiten, *Jahresber. deut. math. Vereinigung*, **25**: 34 (1916); also *NACA Tech. Mem.* 1342.
2. Illingworth, C. R.: Some Solutions of the Equations of Flow of a Viscous Compressible Fluid, *Proc. Cambridge Phil. Soc.*, **46**: 469–478 (1950).
3. Imai, I.: Discontinuous Potential Flow as the Limiting Form of the Viscous Flow for Vanishing Viscosity, *J. Physiol. Soc. Japan*, **8**: 399–402 (1953).
4. Imai, I.: Theory of Bluff Bodies, *Univ. Maryland, Inst. Fluid Dynamics and Appl. Math., Univ. Tech. Note BN-104*, 1957.
5. Kuo, Y. H.: On the Flow of an Incompressible Viscous Fluid Past a Flat Plate at Moderate Reynolds Number, *J. Math. and Phys.*, **32** (2–3): 83–101 (1953).
6. Lighthill, M. J.: A Technique for Rendering Approximate Solutions to Physical Problems Uniformly Valid, *Phil. Mag.*, **40**: 1179–1201 (1949).
7. Lin, C. C.: "Hydrodynamic Stability," Cambridge, New York, 1955.
8. Millsaps, K., and K. Pohlhausen: Thermal Distribution in Jeffery-Hamel Flows between Non-parallel Plane Walls, *J. Aeronaut. Sci.*, **20** (3): 187–196 (March, 1953).
9. Millsaps, K., and K. Pohlhausen: Heat Transfer by Laminar Flow from a Rotating Plate, *J. Aeronaut. Sci.*, **19** (2): 120–126 (1952).
10. Oseen, C. W.: "Hydrodynamik," Akademie-Verlag G.m.b.H., Leipzig, 1927.
11. Pai, S. I.: "Viscous Flow Theory.   I. Laminar Flow," Van Nostrand, Princeton, N.J., 1956.
12. Prandtl, L.: Ueber Fluessigkeitsbewegung bei sehr kleiner Reibung, *Verhandel. III. Dritt. Intern. Math. Kong.*, Heidelberg, 1904.
13. Rosenhead, L.: The Steady Two-dimensional Radial Flow of Viscous Fluid between Two Inclined Walls, *Proc. Roy. Soc. (London)*, **175**: 436 (1940).
14. Schubauer, G. B., and H. K. Skramstad: Laminar Boundary Layer Oscillations and Transition on a Flat Plate, *NACA W-8ACR.*, April, 1943; also *NACA Tech. Rept.* 909, 1948.
15. Shen, S. F.: Calculated Amplified Oscillations in Plane Poiseuille and Blasius Flows, *J. Aeronaut. Sci.*, **21** (1): 62–64 (1954).
16. Squire, H. B.: On the Stability of the Three-dimensional Disturbances of Viscous Flow between Parallel Walls, *Proc. Roy. Soc. (London)*, **A142**: 621–628 (1933).
17. Taylor, G. I.: Stability of a Viscous Liquid Contained between Two Rotating Cylinders, *Phil. Trans.*, **A223**: 289–343 (1923).
18. Von Kármán, T.: Laminare und turbulente Reibung, *ZAMM*, **1**: 235 (1921); also *NACA Tech. Mem.* 1092, September, 1946.

Section 6

TRANSPORT PHENOMENA IN MULTICOMPONENT SYSTEMS

By

A. G. FREDRICKSON, *University of Minnesota, Minneapolis, Minn.*
R. BYRON BIRD, *The University of Wisconsin, Madison, Wisconsin*

TRANSPORT PHENOMENA IN MULTICOMPONENT SYSTEMS

6.1. Introduction

In Secs. 1 to 5 of this handbook the equations describing the flow of a pure fluid have been discussed. In this section the previous sections are enlarged upon by considering the equations which describe the flow of chemically reacting multicomponent mixtures in which heat and mass transport may be occurring. In addition, the equations are formulated in such a way that non-Newtonian materials are described.

The subject material in this section may also be designated by the all-encompassing term "transport phenomena," in view of the fact that the transport of mass (diffusion), momentum (viscous flow), and energy (heat conduction) are dealt with. In discussing this subject, two complementary viewpoints may be taken: (1) the *molecular viewpoint*, in which the laws of conservation of mass, momentum, and energy in molecular systems lead to the kinetic theory of the transport phenomena, or (2) the *continuum viewpoint*, in which the same three conservation laws applied to a fluid, without reference to the molecular nature of matter, lead to the "equations of change" for concentration, velocity, and temperature profiles.

In this review the molecular approach is ignored, and the reader is referred to treatises in which the subject is discussed.[1-3] For the continuum approach to the field as a whole an undergraduate textbook has recently been prepared, from which much of the material for this section has been taken.[4] In addition, there are several treatises on special subdivisions of the field, such as the books of Jakob,[5] McAdams,[6] Grigull,[7] and Eckert and Drake[8] on heat transfer; the books of Sherwood and Pigford[9] and Treybal[10] on mass transfer; the monographs of Hougen and Watson[11] and Jungers et al.[12] on chemical kinetics; and the treatise edited by Eirich[13] on rheology. In presenting the continuum approach in Art. 6.3, the expressions are presented for the rates of mass, momentum, and energy transport within a fluid mixture; these expressions are for the most part linear relations between a flux and a driving force. In Art. 6.4, a brief outline of the subject of chemical reaction rates is given, which are in general not linear. Then in Art. 6.5, the equations of change, or conservation equations, for mass, momentum, and energy are presented. In Art. 6.6, some examples of analytical solutions to the equations of change are given, in order to indicate in somewhat more detail the meanings of the individual terms. In Art. 6.7, the general integrals of the equations of change are given; these "macroscopic balances," or "over-all balances," which are useful design relations, are better understood in the light of their relations to the equations of change. These balances contain interphase transport contributions; in Art. 6.8, a brief survey of the types of semiempirical methods which are available for estimating interphase transfer rates are presented.

A number of topics in transport phenomena have been omitted from this survey. The most glaring omissions are turbulent-transport processes, boundary-layer flows with transport phenomena and chemical reactions, and energy transport by radiation. For an introduction to these topics and further literature references, the reader is referred to the textbook of Bird, Stewart, and Lightfoot.[4]

6.2. Notation

For the most part the notation used here is the same as that used by Bird, Stewart, and Lightfoot.[4] For the reader's convenience a short summary of vector and tensor operations is given in Appendix B at the end of this section.

a_α	activity of species α
$b_{\alpha j}$	stoichiometric numbers
$\hat{C}_p$	heat capacity at constant pressure (per unit mass)
c	total molar concentration
c_α	molar concentration of species α
D	diameter of a sphere or of a tube
$D_{\alpha\beta}$	multicomponent diffusivity
$D_A{}^T$	thermal-diffusion coefficient
$\mathfrak{D}_{AB}$	binary diffusivity of the system AB
E_{tot}	total energy (internal + potential + kinetic) in a flow system
E_v	rate at which mechanical energy is irreversibly degraded into thermal energy
e_v	friction loss factor
$\mathbf{e}$	energy flux with respect to stationary coordinates
f	friction factor
$\mathbf{F}$	force of the fluid on a solid in a flow system
$\mathbf{F}^{(m)}$	rate of addition of momentum across a mass-transfer surface
$\hat{\mathbf{F}}_\alpha$	force per unit mass acting on species α
G	Gibbs free energy (or free enthalpy)
$\mathbf{g}$	acceleration associated with gravity
H	enthalpy
h	heat-transfer coefficient
I_j	jth invariant of the rate of deformation tensor
$\mathbf{J}_\alpha$	molar flux relative to a moving reference frame
$\mathbf{j}_\alpha$	mass flux relative to a moving reference frame
k	chemical-reaction rate constant
k_T	thermal-diffusion ratio
k_x	mass-transfer coefficient defined for a mole-fraction driving force
L	length of a tube
M_α	molecular weight of species α
$m_{\alpha,tot}$	total mass of α in a flow system
m,n	parameters in the Ostwald-de Waele model
$\mathbf{N}_\alpha$	molar flux relative to a fixed reference frame
$\mathbf{n}$	unit normal vector, outwardly directed
$\mathbf{n}_\alpha$	mass flux relative to a fixed reference frame
p	static pressure
$\mathbf{P}_{tot}$	total momentum contained within a flow system
Q	energy added to a system through the walls
$Q^{(m)}$	energy added to a system across a mass-transfer interface
$\mathbf{q}$	energy-flux vector with respect to coordinate frame moving with the mass-average velocity v
R	(1) radius of a tube or of a sphere
	(2) gas constant
R_α	rate of production of species α per unit volume in moles
r_α	rate of production of species α per unit volume in mass units
T	temperature (absolute)
t	time
U	internal energy
V	volume
$\mathbf{v}$	mass-average velocity
$\mathbf{v}^\star$	molar-average velocity
$\mathbf{v}^\blacksquare$	volume-average velocity
$w_\alpha{}^{(m)}$	rate of mass transfer across a mass-transfer interface in mass units
$\mathcal{W}_\alpha{}^{(m)}$	rate of mass transfer across a mass-transfer interface in molar units
x_α	mole fraction of species α
x,y,z	coordinates
α	thermal diffusivity
β	coefficient of volume expansion with temperature
$\boldsymbol{\delta}$	unit tensor

ε	rate of deformation tensor
ζ	coefficient of volume expansion with concentration
η	non-Newtonian viscosity
η_c	non-Newtonian cross viscosity
κ	bulk viscosity
λ	thermal conductivity
μ	viscosity
π	3.14159 . . .
$\boldsymbol{\pi}$	pressure tensor, or momentum-flux tensor with respect to the mass-average velocity
ρ	mass density
ρ_α	mass concentration of species α
$\boldsymbol{\tau}$	viscous part of the momentum-flux tensor
$\boldsymbol{\phi}$	momentum-flux tensor with respect to fixed coordinates
Φ	potential energy
ω_α	mass fraction of species α
Gr	Grashof number for heat transfer
Gr$_{AB}$	Grashof number for mass transfer in the binary system AB
Nu	Nusselt number for heat transfer
Nu$_{AB}$	Nusselt number for mass transfer in the binary system AB (also called the Sherwood number and given the symbol Sh)
Pr	Prandtl number
Re	Reynolds number
Sc$_{AB}$	Schmidt number for the system AB

—	(above symbol)	partial molal quantity
^	(above symbol)	quantity per unit mass
~	(above symbol)	quantity per mole
$\langle\ \rangle$	(around symbol)	average over a cross section of the flow channel
(m)	(superscript)	associated with a mass-transfer surface
(c)	(superscript)	associated with a catalyst surface
tot	(subscript)	total amount of entity in a flow system
1	(subscript)	quantity evaluated at the entrance to a flow system
2	(subscript)	quantity evaluated at the exit to a flow system

6.3. Physical Rate Processes in Multicomponent Systems

In this article the rates of transport of mass, momentum, and energy are discussed. In order to give expressions for these rates it is necessary to give the notation for concentrations and velocities in the flow system.

Four kinds of *local concentrations* are used in the ensuing treatment:

c_α = moles of species α per unit volume
ρ_α = mass of species α per unit volume
x_α = mole fraction of species α
ω_α = mass fraction of species α

Relations among these quantities are given in Table 6.1 for a fluid composed of ν chemical species, with molecular weights M_α.

Let the *local velocity of species* α be designated by the vector $\mathbf{v}_\alpha$. This is the velocity with respect to fixed coordinates. It is *not* the velocity of the individual molecules of species α, but rather the average velocity (Ref. 1, p. 453) with which the molecules of species α in a small region are moving. Another way of defining $\mathbf{v}_\alpha$ is in terms of the amount of species α that crosses a small element of surface dS (small with respect to the dimensions of the flow system, but large with respect to the molecular mean free path). If the orientation of the surface dS is specified by the normal unit vector $\mathbf{n}$, then $\rho_\alpha(\mathbf{v}_\alpha \bullet \mathbf{n})\, dS$ gives the mass of species α crossing dS per unit time.

Table 6.1. Relations among Concentrations in a ν-component Mixture

$$\sum_{\alpha=1}^{\nu} c_\alpha = c \quad (1) \qquad\qquad \sum_{\alpha=1}^{\nu} x_\alpha = 1 \quad (2)$$

$$\sum_{\alpha=1}^{\nu} \rho_\alpha = \rho \quad (3) \qquad\qquad \sum_{\alpha=1}^{\nu} \omega_\alpha = 1 \quad (4)$$

$$x_\alpha = \frac{c_\alpha}{c} \quad (5) \qquad\qquad \omega_\alpha = \frac{\rho_\alpha}{\rho} \quad (6)$$

$$c_\alpha = \frac{\rho_\alpha}{M_\alpha} \quad (7) \qquad\qquad \rho_\alpha = c_\alpha M_\alpha \quad (8)$$

$$x_\alpha = \frac{\omega_\alpha / M_\alpha}{\displaystyle\sum_{\beta=1}^{\nu} \frac{\omega_\beta}{M_\beta}} \quad (9) \qquad\qquad \omega_\alpha = \frac{x_\alpha M_\alpha}{\displaystyle\sum_{\beta=1}^{\nu} x_\beta M_\beta} \quad (10)$$

$$\frac{\rho}{c} = \sum_{\alpha=1}^{\nu} x_\alpha M_\alpha \quad (11) \qquad\qquad \frac{c}{\rho} = \sum_{\alpha=1}^{\nu} \frac{\omega_\alpha}{M_\alpha} \quad (12)$$

It is convenient to define several kinds of *local average velocities*:

$$\mathbf{v} = \sum_{\alpha=1}^{\nu} \omega_\alpha \mathbf{v}_\alpha = \text{mass-average velocity} \qquad \mathbf{v}^\star = \sum_{\alpha=1}^{\nu} x_\alpha \mathbf{v}_\alpha = \text{molar-average velocity}$$

$$\mathbf{v}^\blacksquare = \sum_{\alpha=1}^{\nu} c_\alpha \overline{V}_\alpha \mathbf{v}_\alpha = \text{volume-average velocity}$$

In the latter relation $\overline{V}_\alpha$ is the partial molal volume† of species α. All three kinds of average velocities have found use in the technical literature. The mass-average velocity $\mathbf{v}$ is that which would be measured by a pitot tube; in future discussions "the velocity" of the fluid will mean $\mathbf{v}$. The molar-average velocity $\mathbf{v}^\star$ is often used by chemists and chemical engineers in dealing with diffusion problems in dilute gases. The volume-average velocity $\mathbf{v}^\blacksquare$ is used in systems with local volume changes due to mixing. The three average velocities must not be confused; in general, they have neither the same magnitude nor the same direction.

In the ensuing discussion the Greek miniscule subscripts α, β, γ, etc., are used to designate the components in a multicomponent system. Some formulas are valid only in binary systems; in such relations the Roman majuscules A and B will be used to specify the two species.

This section is devoted primarily to a summary of the *fluxes of mass, momentum, and energy* in flow systems. For simple one-dimensional transport the empirical relations between the fluxes with respect to the mass-average velocity and the driving forces may be written in the parallel form

† For a discussion of partial molal quantities see, for example, Hougen et al.[14] Note that $\Sigma_\alpha c_\alpha \overline{V}_\alpha = 1$.

$$\left(\begin{matrix}\text{Flux of mass of } A \\ \text{in the } y \text{ direction}\end{matrix}\right) = j_{Ay} = -\rho \mathfrak{D}_{AB} \frac{d\omega_A}{dy} \qquad (6.1)$$

$$\left(\begin{matrix}\text{Flux of } x \text{ momentum} \\ \text{in the } y \text{ direction}\end{matrix}\right) = \tau_{xy} = -\mu \frac{dv_x}{dy} \qquad (6.2)$$

$$\left(\begin{matrix}\text{Flux of energy} \\ \text{in the } y \text{ direction}\end{matrix}\right) = q_y = -\lambda \frac{dT}{dy} \qquad (6.3)$$

These three linear relations between a flux and a driving force are called, respectively, Fick's law, Newton's law, and Fourier's law. In subsequent paragraphs it is shown that the above relations are really just special cases of more general relations. The coefficients of proportionality in these linear laws are the *transport properties*: the diffusivity $\mathfrak{D}_{AB}$, the viscosity μ, and the thermal conductivity λ. They are physical properties of the fluids, which indicate the rate at which mass, momentum, and energy are transported, under given driving forces, by molecular processes within a given fluid. The prediction of the dependence of the transport properties on the temperature, pressure, and concentration by molecular theory is one of the objects of the kinetic theory, or the nonequilibrium statistical mechanics.†

The dimensions and units of the fluxes and the transport properties are as given in the accompanying table (with M = mass, L = length, t = time, T = temperature). Two

Quantity	Dimensions	Units, cgs system
j_{Ay}	$ML^{-2}t^{-1}$	g/(cm²)(sec)
τ_{xy}	$ML^{-1}t^{-2}$	dyne/cm²
q_y	Mt^{-3}	cal/(cm²)(sec)
$\mathfrak{D}_{AB}$	L^2t^{-1}	cm²/sec
μ	$ML^{-1}t^{-1}$	g/(cm)(sec)
λ	$MLt^{-3}T^{-1}$	cal/(cm)(sec)(°K)

additional defined material properties frequently used are the *kinematic viscosity* $\nu = \mu/\rho$ and the *thermal diffusivity* $\alpha = \lambda/\rho\hat{C}_p$. Both of these quantities have dimensions of L^2t^{-1}, the same as $\mathfrak{D}_{AB}$.

Rate of Mass Transport. Mass transport occurs predominantly as a result of concentration gradients (*ordinary diffusion*). Hence the relations for ordinary diffusion are first summarized for binary systems and then for multicomponent systems.

Mass transport may also occur as a result of temperature gradients (*thermal diffusion*), pressure gradients (*pressure diffusion*), and unequal external forces (*forced diffusion*). Thermal diffusion and pressure diffusion are generally exceedingly small; forced-diffusion effects, which are observed primarily in ionic systems, may be quite large. These topics, which are somewhat more complicated, are treated last.

In describing the local rates of mass transport several kinds of fluxes are used. All of them are products of a concentration and a velocity. The most common fluxes are defined as follows:

$$
\begin{aligned}
\mathbf{n}_\alpha &= \rho_\alpha \mathbf{v}_\alpha & &= \text{mass flux with respect to fixed axes} \\
\mathbf{j}_\alpha &= \rho_\alpha(\mathbf{v}_\alpha - \mathbf{v}) & &= \text{mass flux with respect to the mass-average velocity} \\
\mathbf{j}^\star_\alpha &= \rho_\alpha(\mathbf{v}_\alpha - \mathbf{v}^\star) & &= \text{mass flux with respect to the molar-average velocity} \\
\mathbf{j}^\blacksquare_\alpha &= \rho_\alpha(\mathbf{v}_\alpha - \mathbf{v}^\blacksquare) & &= \text{mass flux with respect to the volume-average velocity}
\end{aligned}
$$

$$
\begin{aligned}
\mathbf{N}_\alpha &= c_\alpha \mathbf{v}_\alpha & &= \text{molar flux with respect to fixed axes} \\
\mathbf{J}_\alpha &= c_\alpha(\mathbf{v}_\alpha - \mathbf{v}) & &= \text{molar flux with respect to the mass-average velocity} \\
\mathbf{J}^\star_\alpha &= c_\alpha(\mathbf{v}_\alpha - \mathbf{v}^\star) & &= \text{molar flux with respect to the molar-average velocity} \\
\mathbf{J}^\blacksquare_\alpha &= c_\alpha(\mathbf{v}_\alpha - \mathbf{v}^\blacksquare) & &= \text{molar flux with respect to the volume-average velocity}
\end{aligned}
$$

† Hirschfelder et al.,[1] chap. 8 (dilute gases), chap. 9 (dense gases and liquids), and chap. 10 (quantum effects).

Table **6.2.** Relations among **Mass and Molar Fluxes** for **Binary Systems**

$$j^\star_A = \left(\frac{\rho}{cM_B}\right) j_A \tag{1}$$

$$j^\blacksquare_A = \left(\frac{\rho \overline{V}_B}{M_B}\right) j_A \tag{2}$$

$$n_A = \omega_A(n_A + n_B) + j_A = \rho_A v + j_A \tag{3}$$

$$N_A = x_A(N_A + N_B) + J^\star_A = c_A v^\star + J^\star_A \tag{4}$$

Lower-case letters are used for the mass fluxes (mass of α per unit area per unit time), and capital letters for the molar fluxes (moles of α per unit area per unit time). The fluxes n_α and N_α are with respect to laboratory-fixed axes, whereas the various j's and J's are fluxes measured with respect to various average velocities. Some of the relations between the fluxes for binary systems are given in Table 6.2; relations for multicomponent systems are given in Table 6.3.

CAUTION: In reading the published literature on diffusion and mass transport, one must be particularly careful to understand the definition of the mass and molar fluxes used, particularly as regards the reference frame used.

To illustrate graphically the meaning of n_α and j_α, refer to Fig. 6.1. In part a is shown a small element of area dA fixed in space. The mass (in grams) of species α which crosses dA in time dt is $n_{\alpha x}\, dA\, dt$. In part b the element of area dA is moving with the local mass-average velocity v_x. The mass (in grams) of species α which crosses dA in time dt is $j_{\alpha x}\, dA\, dt$.

ORDINARY DIFFUSION IN BINARY SYSTEMS. The relation between the mass or molar flux and the gradient in the composition is given by Fick's first law of diffusion, Eq. (6.1). This law may be generalized for three-dimensional transport and assumes a variety of forms, depending on the choice of flux and composition gradient. For the fluxes with respect to coordinate systems moving with the various average velocities

Table **6.3.** Relations among **Mass** and **Molar Fluxes** for **Multicomponent Systems**

Relations between mass and molar fluxes:

$$n_\alpha = M_\alpha N_\alpha \tag{1}$$
$$j_\alpha = M_\alpha J_\alpha \tag{2}$$
$$j^\star_\alpha = M_\alpha J^\star_\alpha \tag{3}$$
$$j^\blacksquare_\alpha = M_\alpha J^\blacksquare_\alpha \tag{4}$$

Summation relations:

$$\sum_{\alpha=1}^{\nu} n_\alpha = \rho v \tag{5}$$

$$\sum_{\alpha=1}^{\nu} N_\alpha = c v^\star \tag{6}$$

$$\sum_{\alpha=1}^{\nu} j_\alpha = 0 \tag{7}$$

$$\sum_{\alpha=1}^{\nu} J_\alpha = c(v^\star - v) \tag{8}$$

$$\sum_{\alpha=1}^{\nu} j^\star_\alpha = \rho(v - v^\star) \tag{9}$$

$$\sum_{\alpha=1}^{\nu} J^\star_\alpha = 0 \tag{10}$$

$$\sum_{\alpha=1}^{\nu} j^\blacksquare_\alpha = \rho(v - v^\blacksquare) \tag{11}$$

$$\sum_{\alpha=1}^{\nu} J^\blacksquare_\alpha = c(v^\star - v^\blacksquare) \tag{12}$$

Relations between fluxes and velocities (flux with respect to fixed axes = diffusive flux + convective flux):

$$n_\alpha = j_\alpha + \rho_\alpha v \tag{13}$$
$$n_\alpha = j^\star_\alpha + \rho_\alpha v^\star \tag{15}$$
$$n_\alpha = j^\blacksquare_\alpha + \rho_\alpha v^\blacksquare \tag{17}$$

$$N_\alpha = J_\alpha + c_\alpha v \tag{14}$$
$$N_\alpha = J^\star_\alpha + c_\alpha v^\star \tag{16}$$
$$N_\alpha = J^\blacksquare_\alpha + c_\alpha v^\blacksquare \tag{18}$$

$$\mathbf{j}_A = -\rho \mathfrak{D}_{AB} \nabla \omega_A = -\frac{c^2}{\rho} M_A M_B \mathfrak{D}_{AB} \nabla x_A \tag{6.4}$$

$$\mathbf{J^\star}_A = -c\mathfrak{D}_{AB} \nabla x_A = -\frac{\rho^2}{cM_AM_B} \mathfrak{D}_{AB} \nabla \omega_A \tag{6.5}$$

$$\mathbf{j}^\blacksquare_A = -\mathfrak{D}_{AB} \nabla \rho_A = -M_A \mathfrak{D}_{AB} \nabla c_A \tag{6.6}$$

$$\mathbf{J}^\blacksquare_A = -\mathfrak{D}_{AB} \nabla c_A = -\frac{1}{M_A} \mathfrak{D}_{AB} \nabla \rho_A \tag{6.7}$$

For the fluxes with respect to laboratory-fixed coordinates

$$\mathbf{n}_A = \omega_A(\mathbf{n}_A + \mathbf{n}_B) - \rho \mathfrak{D}_{AB} \nabla \omega_A \tag{6.8}$$

$$\mathbf{N}_A = x_A(\mathbf{N}_A + \mathbf{N}_B) - c\mathfrak{D}_{AB} \nabla x_A \tag{6.9}$$

All these relations are mathematically equivalent; many more such equations can be obtained by using the information in Tables 6.1 to 6.3. All these relations are valid for position-dependent ρ and c. The binary diffusivity $\mathfrak{D}_{AB}$ in all these forms of Fick's law is exactly the same. The pronounced difference in the proportionality factors emphasizes the great importance in specifying clearly the reference frame for the flux and the definition of the composition variable.

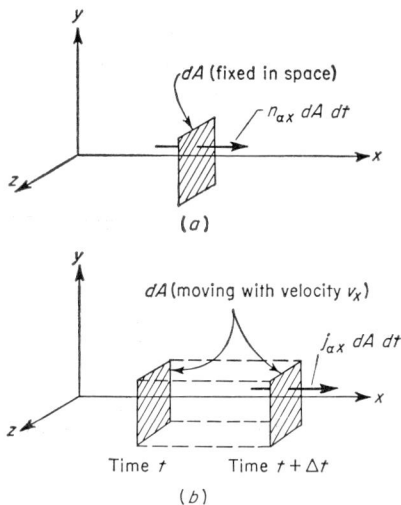

FIG. 6.1. Pictorial representation of fluxes in fixed and moving coordinate system.

The above relations may also be written for species B by interchanging the subscripts A and B everywhere. Hence, according to Eq. (6.4),

$$\mathbf{j}_A = -\frac{c^2}{\rho} M_A M_B \mathfrak{D}_{AB} \nabla x_A \tag{6.10}$$

$$\mathbf{j}_B = -\frac{c^2}{\rho} M_B M_A \mathfrak{D}_{BA} \nabla x_B \tag{6.11}$$

When these are added together and use is made of the fact that $\mathbf{j}_A + \mathbf{j}_B = 0$ (Table 6.3) and the fact that $\nabla x_A = -\nabla x_B$ (Table 6.1), it may be seen that $\mathfrak{D}_{AB} = \mathfrak{D}_{BA}$. Hence the binary diffusivity $\mathfrak{D}_{AB}$ is a physical property characteristic of the *pair* of species A and B.

High values of $\mathfrak{D}_{AB}$ mean that the mutual diffusion process is rapid; low values mean that the rate of intermingling of the two species is slow, for the same composition gradient.

The definition of the binary diffusivity $\mathfrak{D}_{AB}$ given in Eqs. (6.4) to (6.9) is that generally used in the chemistry, physics, and engineering literature. The experimental values reported are generally consistent with this definition. This quantity is a function of temperature, pressure, and composition. A binary diffusivity which is presumably less composition-dependent than $\mathfrak{D}_{AB}$ is the quantity D_{AB}, which is defined by

$$\mathfrak{D}_{AB} = D_{AB} \left(\frac{\partial \ln a_A}{\partial \ln x_A} \right)_{p,T} \tag{6.11a}$$

The diffusivity D_{AB} is less often used because it requires auxiliary experimental data on the composition dependence of the activity[15] a_A. For dilute gas mixtures and "ideal" liquid mixtures D_{AB} and $\mathfrak{D}_{AB}$ are identical.

To indicate the order of magnitude of the diffusivity $\mathfrak{D}_{AB}$, some sample values are given in Table 6.4. The diffusivity of dilute gases is virtually independent of the concentration, whereas that of liquids may be highly concentration-dependent. Summaries of experimental values may be found in the literature.[16-18] Particular attention should be called to the excellent summary of estimation methods given by Reid and Sherwood.

ORDINARY DIFFUSION IN MULTICOMPONENT SYSTEMS. For multicomponent mixtures of *gases or liquids* the mass flux $\mathbf{j}_\alpha$ is given by

$$\mathbf{j}_\alpha = \frac{c^2}{\rho RT} \sum_{\beta=1}^{\nu} M_\alpha M_\beta D_{\alpha\beta} \left[x_\beta \sum_{\substack{\gamma=1 \\ \gamma \neq \beta}}^{\nu} \left(\frac{\partial \overline{G}_\beta}{\partial x_\gamma} \right)_{T,p,x_\delta} \nabla x_\gamma \right] \qquad \alpha = 1, 2, \ldots, \nu \tag{6.12}$$

in which $\overline{G}_\beta$ is the partial molal *Gibbs free energy*, or *free enthalpy* ($\overline{G}_\beta = \overline{H}_\beta - T\overline{S}_\beta$), and

Table 6.4. Experimental Values of Diffusivities in Binary Systems

A	B	T, °C	x_A	$\mathfrak{D}_{AB}$, cm²/sec
		Gases (1 atm)[19]		
CO_2	N_2O	0	0 — 1.0	0.096
CO_2	CO	0	0 — 1.0	0.139
CO_2	N_2	0	0 — 1.0	0.144
		15		0.158
		25		0.165
H_2	SF_6	25	0 — 1.0	0.420
H_2	CH_4	25	0 — 1.0	0.726
		Liquids[17]		
C_6H_5Cl	C_6H_5Br	39.97	0.0332	1.584×10^{-5}
			0.2642	1.691×10^{-5}
			0.5122	1.806×10^{-5}
			0.7617	1.902×10^{-5}
			0.9652	1.996×10^{-5}
C_2H_5OH	H_2O	25	0.05	1.13×10^{-5}
			0.50	0.90×10^{-5}
			0.95	2.20×10^{-5}
		Solids (Ref. 1, pp. 141, 222, 275)		
H_2	Ni	85	~0	1.16×10^{-8}
		165	~0	10.5×10^{-8}
Hg	Pb	20	~0	2.5×10^{-15}
Al	Cu	20	~0	1.3×10^{-30}
Sb	Ag	20	~0	3.5×10^{-21}
Cd	Cu	20	~0	2.7×10^{-15}

$D_{\alpha\beta}$ are the Curtiss-Hirschfelder multicomponent diffusivities,[20] which have the following properties:

$$D_{\alpha\alpha} = 0 \tag{6.13}$$

$$D_{\alpha\beta} \neq D_{\beta\alpha} \tag{6.14}$$

$$\sum_{\alpha=1}^{\nu} (M_\alpha M_\beta D_{\alpha\beta} - M_\alpha M_\alpha D_{\alpha\gamma}) = 0 \tag{6.15}$$

$$D_{\alpha\beta} \to D_{AB} \qquad \text{of Eq. (6.11a) for two-component systems} \tag{6.16}$$

According to Eq. (6.12) the mass flux of any one component depends in a very complicated way on the c oncentration gradients of all species present.

For *dilute gas mixtures* Eq. (6.12) becomes

$$\mathbf{j}_\alpha = \frac{c^2}{\rho} \sum_{\beta=1}^{\nu} M_\alpha M_\beta D_{\alpha\beta} \nabla x_\beta \qquad \alpha = 1, 2, \ldots, \nu \tag{6.17}$$

Curtiss and Hirschfelder (Ref. 1, chap. 7) have succeeded in showing by kinetic-theory arguments that this set of ν equations may be inverted to obtain to a very good approximation

$$\nabla x_\alpha = \sum_{\beta=1}^{\nu} \frac{x_\alpha \mathbf{N}_\beta - x_\beta \mathbf{N}_\alpha}{c \mathfrak{D}_{\alpha\beta}} \qquad \alpha = 1, 2, \ldots, \nu \tag{6.18}$$

which had earlier been known as the Stefan-Maxwell equations. Note that these equations contain the ordinary binary diffusivities $\mathfrak{D}_{\alpha\beta}$, rather than the multicomponent $D_{\alpha\beta}$. Inasmuch as the $\mathfrak{D}_{\alpha\beta}$ are virtually concentration-independent, the Stefan-Maxwell equations are rather useful.

THERMAL, PRESSURE, AND FORCED DIFFUSION IN BINARY SYSTEMS. For a two-component system of A and B the complete expression for $\mathbf{j}_A$ is

$$\mathbf{j}_A = -\frac{c^2}{\rho RT} M_A{}^2 M_B D_{AB} x_A \left[\nabla \left(\frac{\bar{G}_A}{M_A} \right) + \frac{\rho_B}{\rho} (\hat{\mathbf{F}}_A - \hat{\mathbf{F}}_B) - \left(\frac{\bar{V}_A}{M_A} - \frac{1}{\rho} \right) \nabla p \right] - D_A{}^T \nabla \ln T \tag{6.19}$$

in which $D_A{}^T$ is the thermal-diffusion coefficient. There are thus four contributions to $\mathbf{j}_A$: the *ordinary diffusion*, dependent upon the gradient in the Gibbs free energy; the *forced diffusion*, dependent upon the difference in the external forces in A and B; the *pressure diffusion*, dependent upon the gradient in the pressure; and the *thermal diffusion*, dependent upon the thermal gradient.

Equation (6.19) may be rewritten by using the thermodynamics identity $\nabla \bar{G}_A = RT \nabla \ln a_A$ and defining the "thermal-diffusion ratio," $k_T = (\rho/c^2 M_A M_B)(D_A{}^T/D_{AB})$:

$$\mathbf{j}_A = -\frac{c^2}{\rho} M_A M_B D_{AB} \left[\left(\frac{\partial \ln a_A}{\partial \ln x_A} \right)_{T,p} \nabla x_A - \frac{M_A \rho_B x_A}{\rho RT} (\hat{\mathbf{F}}_A - \hat{\mathbf{F}}_B) \right.$$
$$\left. + \frac{M_A x_A}{RT} \left(\frac{\bar{V}_A}{M_A} - \frac{1}{\rho} \right) \nabla p + k_T \nabla \ln T \right] \tag{6.20}$$

This equation is the starting point for studying the thermal-, pressure-, and forced-diffusion effects. Note that if $k_T > 0$, A moves toward the cold region, whereas if $k_T < 0$, A moves toward the hot region.

Other defined quantities related to k_T are

$$\text{Thermal-diffusion factor} = \alpha = \frac{k_T}{x_A x_B}$$

$$\text{Soret coefficient} = \sigma = \frac{k_T}{x_A x_B T}$$

Values of k_T may be found in the monograph of Grew and Ibbs.[21]

THERMAL, PRESSURE, AND FORCED DIFFUSION IN MULTICOMPONENT SYSTEMS. Equation (6.19) has been generalized to multicomponent systems. The expressions are quite lengthy and have up to the present been very little used. The interested reader will find the general expressions given in several references (e.g., Ref. 4, chap. 18).

Rate of Momentum Transport. In the discussion on mass transport at the beginning of Art. 6.3, four reference frames commonly used for mass fluxes are given. For momentum transport there are only two reference frames which deserve attention. Hence two second-order tensors‡ are defined:

$\boldsymbol{\pi}$ = momentum flux with respect to the mass average velocity (also called the "pressure tensor")

$\boldsymbol{\phi}$ = momentum flux with respect to fixed axes

It is standard practice to split $\boldsymbol{\pi}$ into two parts: $p\boldsymbol{\delta}$, the contribution of the pressure, and $\boldsymbol{\tau}$ the contribution of the viscous forces. The pressure p is specified at any point in the fluid by the equation of state $p = p(\rho_1, \rho_2, \rho_3, \ldots, \rho_\nu; T)$. Hence the relations needed are

$$\boldsymbol{\pi} = p\boldsymbol{\delta} + \boldsymbol{\tau} \tag{6.21}$$

$$\boldsymbol{\phi} = \boldsymbol{\pi} + \rho\mathbf{vv} \tag{6.22}$$

if $\boldsymbol{\delta}$ is the unit tensor and $\mathbf{vv}$ is a dyadic product. Clearly $\boldsymbol{\phi}$ is made up of two contributions: the transport of momentum by virtue of the bulk motion of the fluid $\rho\mathbf{vv}$, and the transport of momentum, by virtue of molecular transport $\boldsymbol{\pi}$. The tensors $\boldsymbol{\pi}$, $\boldsymbol{\phi}$, and $\boldsymbol{\tau}$ are all symmetric (that is, $\pi_{ij} = \pi_{ji}$, etc.).

CAUTION: In the preceding, p is the thermodynamic pressure. This definition is unique for fluids which are compressible, and actually all fluids are compressible. For fluids which are only slightly compressible, it is customary and convenient to set ρ equal to a constant and thereby define a (hypothetical) *incompressible fluid*. For this model, p can no longer be defined as the thermodynamic pressure. For the incompressible model, $p = \frac{1}{3} \text{tr } \boldsymbol{\pi}$ for Newtonian fluids and for non-Newtonian models of the form $\boldsymbol{\tau} = -\eta\boldsymbol{\epsilon}$ [Eq. (6.28)]. For more general non-Newtonian fluids the definition of p is more complicated.[22]

MOMENTUM TRANSPORT IN NEWTONIAN FLUIDS. For gases and simple liquids (that is, fluids other than suspensions, polymer solutions, and molten polymers) the generalization of Eq. (6.2) to flow in three dimensions is, for *pure fluids and multicomponent mixtures*,

$$\boldsymbol{\tau} = -\mu\boldsymbol{\epsilon} - \frac{1}{2}(\kappa - \frac{2}{3}\mu)\boldsymbol{\delta} \text{ tr } \boldsymbol{\epsilon} \tag{6.23}$$

in which $\boldsymbol{\epsilon}$ is rate of deformation tensor $\boldsymbol{\epsilon} = \nabla\mathbf{v} + (\nabla\mathbf{v})^\dagger$, where $(\nabla\mathbf{v})^\dagger$ is the transpose of the dyadic $\nabla\mathbf{v}$; that is, in cartesian coordinates the components ϵ_{ij} are $(\partial v_i/\partial x_j + \partial v_j/\partial x_i)$; the components of $\boldsymbol{\epsilon}$ in the three most commonly used coordinate systems are given in Appendix B at the end of this section.

Two phenomenological coefficients appear in Eq. (6.23): the *shear viscosity* μ (generally

‡ The rate of flow of momentum across an element of area dA with unit normal vector $\mathbf{n}$ is

$$[\boldsymbol{\phi} \cdot \mathbf{n}]dA = [\boldsymbol{\pi} \cdot \mathbf{n}]dA + [\rho\mathbf{vv} \cdot \mathbf{n}]dA$$

if the element is fixed in space, or

$$[\boldsymbol{\pi} \cdot \mathbf{n}]dA = p\mathbf{n} + [\boldsymbol{\tau} \cdot \mathbf{n}]$$

if the element moves with the local mass-average velocity (Sec. 2).

called the *viscosity*) [23-25] and the *bulk viscosity†* κ. The physical properties μ and κ depend on the thermodynamic state of the fluid at a point—temperature, density, and composition—but *not* on the dynamical state of the system (i.e., not on ϵ). In Sec. 1 of this handbook one can find a more extensive discussion of shear viscosity, together with references to experimental values.

MOMENTUM TRANSPORT IN NON-NEWTONIAN FLUIDS. As has been seen, the relation between τ and ϵ is linear for Newtonian fluids. However, there exist fluids for which the linear relation is inadequate; such fluids are said to be *non-Newtonian*. This nonlinear behavior is almost always associated with slurries, melts, and solutions of polymers, suspensions, pastes, etc. In Sec. 7 the reader will find a discussion of the technology of non-Newtonian materials, together with references to some of the data which have been gathered.

It has been shown by Reiner[26] and by Rivlin[33] that the most general relation between the two isotropic tensors τ and ϵ, not involving time or space derivatives of τ and ϵ, for an *inelastic incompressible* fluid may be written thus:

$$\tau = -\eta\epsilon - \tfrac{1}{2}\eta_c\{\tau \cdot \epsilon\} \tag{6.24}$$

in which η and η_c are the *viscosity* and *cross viscosity* (or *normal stress coefficient*), respectively. Both η and η_c are scalars, but are in general functions of ϵ. If this is to be the case, then η and η_c must be functions of the three invariants of ϵ, which are

$$I_1 = \text{tr } \epsilon \tag{6.25}$$

$$I_2 = (\epsilon : \epsilon) \tag{6.26}$$

$$I_3 = \det \epsilon \tag{6.27}$$

For the incompressible fluid $\text{tr } \epsilon = 2(\nabla \cdot \mathbf{v}) = 0$, and hence $\eta = \eta(I_2, I_3)$ and $\eta_c = \eta_c(I_2, I_3)$.

Very little is known about the quantity η_c. It can, however, be shown that if η_c is zero, then η must be independent of I_3. Consequently, if it is desired to exclude η_c from Eq. (6.24),

$$\tau = -\eta\epsilon \tag{6.28}$$

in which $\eta = \eta(I_2)$. To date most of the analytical solutions of the equations of motion for inelastic non-Newtonian liquids have been for empirical rheological relations of the form of Eq. (6.28).

For example, for some polymers and polymer solutions the *Ostwald–de Waele* (power-function) model is satisfactory over rather wide ranges of rate of deformation:

$$\tau = -m[\tfrac{1}{2}(\epsilon : \epsilon)]^{(n-1)/2}\epsilon \tag{6.29}$$

if m and n are the rheological parameters to be determined from experimental data. For pseudoplastic fluids ($n < 1$), the viscosity decreases with increasing shear rate; for dilatant fluids ($n > 1$), the viscosity increases with increasing shear rate. This empirical model simplifies to the Newtonian fluid when $n = 1$ and $m = \mu$. The merits and drawbacks of the power model have been discussed at length by Reiner[27]. Flow measurements in tubes have tended to indicate that the power-function model is rather generally useful; recent measurements on flow in annuli[28] and flow around spheres[29] have shown that caution must be used in applying this empirical relation to other geometries.

It should be noted that for $n < 1$ (pseudoplastic fluids) the viscosity becomes infinite for vanishing velocity gradients. In tube flow this defect is not too serious in view of the fact that the region of nearly zero velocity gradient is only a tiny circular portion of the tube cross section near the axis. In annular flow, on the other hand, the region of nearly zero velocity gradient is a ring-shaped portion of the annular cross

---

† For dilute monatomic gases, κ is identically zero. For dilute polyatomic gases and all dense gases and liquids, κ is not zero. However, when incompressibility is assumed, $\text{tr } \epsilon = 0$ and the term containing κ drops out. Hence it has been common practice to neglect κ in hydrodynamic problems. There are experimental situations, however, where κ cannot be neglected, e.g., propagation of acoustical vibrations in liquids and shock-wave phenomena.

section—proportionately a larger region than in the tube. It is for this reason that the Ostwald–de Waele model is inadequate for annuli, particularly at low rates of flow.

Another well-known example of an empirical rheological model is the *Bingham* fluid, which seems to describe some slurries and suspensions rather well:[30]

$$\tau = -\left\{\mu_0 - \frac{\tau_0}{\sqrt{\frac{1}{2}(\epsilon : \epsilon)}}\right\} \epsilon \quad \text{for } \frac{1}{2}(\tau : \tau) > \tau_0^2 \tag{6.30}$$

$$\epsilon = 0 \qquad\qquad \text{for } \frac{1}{2}(\tau : \tau) < \tau_0^2 \tag{6.31}$$

Here the two rheological parameters to be experimentally determined are μ_0 and τ_0. The Bingham fluid does not flow unless the local shear stress exceeds a limiting value of τ_0.

The advantage of writing the empirical models in terms of the invariant $I_2 = (\epsilon : \epsilon)$ is that non-Newtonian flow problems in curvilinear coordinates may be set up directly by looking up the expressions for ϵ and $(\epsilon : \epsilon)$ in the desired coordinate system (see Appendix B at end of this section).

Equation (6.24) is really quite simple when compared with some of the equations which have been proposed for *viscoelastic fluids*. A viscoelastic fluid cannot be described by the hypothesis that τ is a function of ϵ alone; one must also assume that τ, and perhaps its time derivatives, are functions of ϵ and its time derivatives. The proper manner of formulating the time derivatives of τ and ϵ is a matter of some difficulty and complexity, and the reader is referred to a paper by Oldroyd[31] on the subject. Generalizations of Eq. (6.24) for viscoelastic fluids have been published by Rivlin and Ericksen,[32] Rivlin,[33] and Oldroyd.[31] The generalization of Rivlin has been used by Fredrickson[34] to solve the problem of the helical flow of a viscoelastic fluid in an annulus, and Oldroyd, Strawbridge, and Toms[35] have used a solution obtained by Oldroyd[36] to calculate relaxation times for viscoelastic fluids from their experimental data.

Rate of Energy Transport. Just as for mass and momentum transport, so also for energy transport it is important at the outset to specify carefully the reference frames for the fluxes. For energy transport only two reference frames need be mentioned. The energy flux vectors are

q = energy flux with respect to the mass-average velocity
e = energy flux with respect to fixed axes

The relation between **e** and **q** is

$$e = \rho(\tfrac{1}{2}v^2 + \hat{U})v + [\pi \cdot v] + q \tag{6.32}$$

That is, the energy flux with respect to fixed coordinates is the sum of three contributions: the transport by bulk flow of kinetic energy $\frac{1}{2}\rho v^2$ and internal energy $\rho\hat{U}$; the work done by pressure and viscous forces by the moving fluid $[\pi \cdot v]$; and finally, the energy transport by molecular processes **q**.

HEAT CONDUCTION IN PURE FLUIDS AND SOLIDS. The relation between the energy flux and the gradient in the temperature is given by *Fourier's law of heat conduction*

$$q = -\lambda \nabla T \tag{6.33}$$

in which **q** is the energy flux with respect to a coordinate system moving with the fluid velocity **v**. The thermal conductivity λ is a function of temperature and pressure. Some representative values for pure gases, liquids, and solids may be found in Sec. 1 of this handbook. The similarity of Fourier's law to Fick's first law of diffusion provides the basis for a number of analogies between heat conduction and diffusion, both in solids and in flowing fluids.

HEAT TRANSPORT BY CONDUCTION AND DIFFUSION IN MULTICOMPONENT FLUID MIXTURES. In multicomponent fluid mixtures the energy flux is given by

$$q = -\lambda \nabla T + \sum_{\alpha=1}^{\nu} J_\alpha \overline{H}_\alpha \tag{6.34}$$

in which J_α is the molar flux of species α with respect to the mass-average velocity, and $\bar{H}_\alpha$ is the corresponding partial molal enthalpy. Hence, in mixtures, energy transport by molecular processes consists primarily of two contributions: the transport by *conduction*, characterized by the thermal conductivity, which is a function of temperature, pressure, and composition; and the transport by the *diffusion* of the species, characterized by the diffusivities of the various species, which are also functions of temperature, pressure, and composition. There is also a third contribution to the molecular flux, namely, that associated with the "Dufour effect," or "diffusion-thermo effect"; it is generally of negligible importance.

6.4. Chemical Rate Processes in Multicomponent Systems

The developments of the previous article have dealt with what may be called *physical rate processes*: mass, momentum, and energy transport. It was shown that the rates of these physical transport processes, as measured by the fluxes, could be expressed as linear functions of the various driving forces. The driving forces, in turn, were found to be the *gradients* of various intensity, or concentration factors.

When one considers *chemical rate processes*, however, the situation is entirely different. By a chemical rate process, one means a process whereby matter as one set of chemical species is transformed into matter as a different set of chemical species.

A chemical rate process is not necessarily to be associated with a change in composition of some part of a flow system, for clearly such a change may be brought about by the physical process of mass transport (diffusion). Instead, a chemical rate process is to be associated only with the creation and simultaneous destruction of chemical species within the system or on its boundaries. As such, chemical rate processes, or *chemical reactions*, act as sources and sinks of chemical species.[37]

Chemical reactions may be either *homogeneous* or *heterogeneous*. A chemical reaction is said to be homogeneous if it occurs within a single phase and, further, if the presence of a second phase is not a prerequisite for the occurrence of that reaction. A chemical reaction is said to be heterogeneous if it occurs at the *surface* of the phase in question.

An example of a homogeneous reaction is the esterification of acetic acid by ethanol in the presence of sulfuric acid:

$$CH_3COOH + C_2H_5OH \rightleftharpoons CH_3COOC_2H_5 + H_2O$$

The reaction as written represents the *net* change appearing in the system; it is not necessarily indicative of the course, or *mechanism*, of the reaction. As a matter of fact, it is obvious that the reaction as written cannot describe the mechanism, for sulfuric acid, a prerequisite component for the occurrence of the reaction at an appreciable rate, does not appear in the equation. Hence a reaction equation such as that above which represents only the net change is called a *stoichiometric equation*.

As examples of heterogeneous reactions, one may cite the numerous reactions which are promoted by contact catalysis. The substance to be reacted (usually, but not necessarily, a gas) is contacted with a catalytic surface (solid). Reaction occurs on the surface, and the products of the reaction may either be retained on the surface or be transferred back to the reactant phase. A specific example is the manufacture of a sulfuric acid by the contact process: gaseous sulfur dioxide (SO_2) and oxygen are contacted on a platinum-gauze catalyst to form sulfur trioxide (SO_3):

$$2SO_2 + O_2 \rightleftharpoons 2SO_3$$

Once again, the equation as written represents only the stoichiometry of the reaction.

It is evident from the examples cited that the study of chemical rate processes involves not only the reactions per se, but also the physical rate processes, or transport phenomena. For example, the actual rate of conversion depends upon the rate at which matter can be brought into or away from a zone of reaction. Further, almost all reactions either liberate heat (*exothermic*) or absorb heat (*endothermic*), or they may proceed only at relatively high temperature. Hence considerations of energy transport are often of importance. Finally, the reacting fluid is usually set in motion by some system of applied forces, so that momentum transport must also be considered.

Chemical Reaction Rates for Homogeneous and Heterogeneous Reactions. Consider a single fluid phase, consisting of ν chemical species, wherein one or more chemical reactions may be occurring. For each reaction there is a stoichiometric equation describing the net change in the system due to that reaction. Thus, if the system contains species $A_1, A_2, \ldots, A_\nu$, the stoichiometric equations for the K chemical reactions occurring may be written as

$$\sum_{\alpha=1}^{\nu} b_{\alpha j} A_\alpha = 0 \qquad j = 1, 2, \ldots, K \qquad (6.35)$$

The numbers $b_{\alpha j}$ are called the *stoichiometric numbers* for the jth chemical reaction. Thus, if A_α is a *product* of the jth reaction, $b_{\alpha j} < 0$; if A_α is a *reactant* in the jth reaction, $b_{\alpha j} > 0$; if A_α takes no part in the jth reaction, $b_{\alpha j} = 0$. Thus, suppose the jth reaction under consideration is

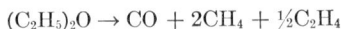

$$(C_2H_5)_2O \rightarrow CO + 2CH_4 + \frac{1}{2}C_2H_4$$

If one defines

$$
\begin{aligned}
A_1 &= (C_2H_5)_2O && \text{(ethyl ether)} \\
A_2 &= CO && \text{(carbon monoxide)} \\
A_3 &= CH_4 && \text{(methane)} \\
A_4 &= C_2H_4 && \text{(ethylene)}
\end{aligned}
$$

then $b_{1j} = 1$, $b_{2j} = -1$, $b_{3j} = -2$, and $b_{4j} = -\frac{1}{2}$. The convention which has been established above will simplify the notation in subsequent developments.

HOMOGENEOUS REACTIONS. For a homogeneous reaction, the *chemical reaction rate* for the αth chemical species is defined to be the rate at which species A_α is created by chemical reactions per unit volume of the system. (Clearly, if A_α is destroyed by chemical reactions, then it has a negative chemical reaction rate.) As such, the chemical reaction rate is a function of position and time; that is, its value at any point depends on the conditions of temperature, composition, and pressure at any given point. If the reaction rate is given in terms of moles, the reaction rate for the αth chemical species will be denoted by the symbol R_α; if the reaction rate is given in mass units (grams, pounds, etc.), the symbol r_α will be used. Hence it is seen that

$$r_\alpha = M_\alpha R_\alpha \qquad (6.36)$$

if M_α is the molecular weight of species α.

The reaction rates R_α and r_α contain contributions from all chemical reactions in which species A_α is a reactant or product. Thus, if $R_{\alpha j}$ is the production rate for species A_α from the jth reaction, then the total rate of production of α is

$$R_\alpha = \sum_{j=1}^{K} R_{\alpha j} \qquad (6.37)$$

if K is the number of reactions which are occurring in the system. Thus, in the esterification reaction cited previously, two reactions occur simultaneously:

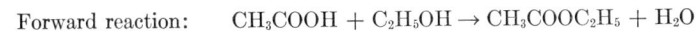

Forward reaction: $\quad CH_3COOH + C_2H_5OH \rightarrow CH_3COOC_2H_5 + H_2O$

Backward reaction: $\quad CH_3COOC_2H_5 + H_2O \rightarrow CH_3COOH + C_2H_5OH$

Let the forward reaction be reaction 1 and the backward reaction be reaction 2; then the production rate for the ester (call this species A_3) is

$$R_3 = R_{31} + R_{32} \qquad (6.38)$$

R_{31} is the (positive) rate of the forward reaction, and R_{32} is the (negative) rate of the back reaction.

Since mass is neither created nor destroyed in a chemical reaction, it follows that

$$\sum_{\alpha=1}^{\nu} r_{\alpha j} = 0 \qquad j = 1, 2, \ldots, K \tag{6.39}$$

However, the sum of the $R_{\alpha j}$ for a given reaction is *not* necessarily zero. Since for all j reactions and for all species A_α and A_β,

$$\frac{1}{b_{\alpha j}} R_{\alpha j} = \frac{1}{b_{\beta j}} R_{\beta j} \tag{6.40}$$

so that it is easy to see that

$$\sum_{\alpha=1}^{\nu} R_{\alpha j} = \frac{R_{\beta j}}{b_{\beta j}} \sum_{\alpha=1}^{\nu} b_{\alpha j} \tag{6.41}$$

Hence, $\Sigma R_{\alpha j}$ will be zero only if there is no change in the number of moles present in the system.

In many books on chemical kinetics, the reader will find the rate of reaction per unit volume to be defined as dc_α/dt. In so far as one speaks of a *batch* system which is held at *constant volume*, this is a satisfactory definition. However, if one considers a chemical reaction in a steady-state flow system, the time derivative $\partial c_\alpha/\partial t$ vanishes at every point in the system. Further, in batch systems wherein the volume is changing, the definition above leads to erroneous conclusions concerning the time course of the reaction. Hence, in setting up kinetic problems, it is better to use the general definitions of reaction rates given herein, together with the equations of continuity (i.e., mass balances) which will be developed in Art. 6.5.

HETEROGENEOUS REACTIONS. For heterogeneous reactions, it is possible to define reaction rates based on a unit volume or on a unit area. Since heterogeneous reactions occur on a surface, it is more consistent to define the reaction rates on the basis of a unit area of catalytic surface (c). Hence, $R_{\alpha j}^{(c)}$ is the chemical reaction rate of species A_α by the jth heterogeneous reaction. The units of $R_{\alpha j}^{(c)}$ are moles of species A_α produced per unit time per unit surface area. Similarly, one defines $r_{\alpha j}^{(c)}$ as the heterogeneous reaction rate in mass units. Both $R_{\alpha j}^{(c)}$ and $r_{\alpha j}^{(c)}$ follow the corresponding equations [Eqs. (6.39) to (6.40)] for $R_{\alpha j}$ and $r_{\alpha j}$. Further, $R_{\alpha j}^{(c)}$ and $r_{\alpha j}^{(c)}$ are point functions of temperature, pressure, fluid composition, position on the surface, and the nature of the surface. In cases where "poisoning," or inhibition of the surface, occurs, the heterogeneous reaction rates also depend on the past history of the surface.[38]

In the book of Hougen and Watson (Ref. 38, p. 910), reaction rates for heterogeneous reactions are based on a unit mass of the solid upon whose surface the reaction occurs. One can convert reaction rates on this basis to reaction rates used in this section if the porosity (fractional void space) of the solid ϵ, the specific surface area (area per unit volume) of the solid A_c, and the density of the solid ρ_s are known:

$$\text{Reaction rate per unit mass of solid} = \frac{A_c}{\epsilon \rho_s} R_{\alpha j}^{(c)} \tag{6.42}$$

As Hougen and Watson point out, the value of $A_c/\epsilon \rho_s$ for the porous materials most often used in promoting reactions is rarely known, so that for *practical* purposes, it is better to work with reaction rates based on a unit mass of solid.

Mechanism of Chemical Reactions—Reaction Order. By experiment, it is found that the rate of many simple chemical reactions of the form Eq. (6.35) can be described by expressions of the form

$$R_{\alpha j} = k_j \prod_{\beta=1}^{L_j} c_\beta^{b_{\beta j}} \qquad \begin{array}{l} j = 1, 2, \ldots, K \\ \alpha = 1, 2, \ldots, L_j \end{array} \tag{6.43}$$

if L_j is the number of reactants in the jth reaction.   The parameter k_j is called the *rate constant* for the jth reaction.   The terminology is rather unfortunate, since k_j is not a constant, but exhibits a strong dependence on temperature and perhaps also on composition.[39]   In many cases, the rate constant is given to a good approximation by the *Arrhenius equation* (Ref. 39, pp. 1ff.).

$$k_j = F_j \exp \frac{-E_{Aj}}{RT} \tag{6.44}$$

in which F_j is the *frequency factor* and E_{Aj} is the *activation energy* of the jth chemical reaction.

A reaction described by Eq. (6.43) is said to be of *order* b_{1j} with respect to species A_1, or order b_{2j} with respect to species A_2, and of order $b_{1j} + b_{2j} + \cdots + $ over-all.

Reactions which are described by the same stoichiometric relation do not always obey the same rate equation.   To emphasize this point, compare two apparently bimolecular gas-phase reactions:

1. Hydrogen-iodine reaction, $H_2 + I_2 \rightarrow 2HI$: For this reaction the rate of disappearance of hydrogen (and iodine) is given by[40]

$$-R_{H_2} = -R_{I_2} = +kc_{H_2}c_{I_2} \tag{6.45}$$

if $k = 2(10^{11}) \exp(-40{,}000/RT)$ liters/(mole) (sec).   From simple kinetic theory the number of collisions between the reactants is proportional to the product $c_{H_2}c_{I_2}$.   Hence one can deduce that the mechanism of this second-order reaction is bimolecular.

2. Hydrogen-bromine reaction, $H_2 + Br_2 \rightarrow 2HBr$: For this reaction the rate of disappearance of hydrogen (and bromine) is given by

$$-R_{H_2} = -R_{Br_2} = \frac{kc_{H_2}\sqrt{c_{Br_2}}}{1 + c_{HBr}/kc_{Br_2}} \tag{6.46}$$

Hence it is apparent that this reaction proceeds by a different mechanism than the hydrogen-iodine reaction.   Indeed, it has been proposed that the reaction between hydrogen and bromine occurs through a chain of reactions (Ref. 40, pp. 204-208):

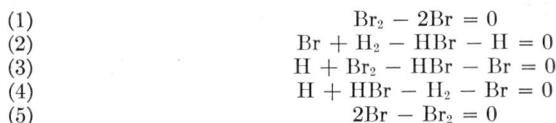

(1)	$Br_2 - 2Br = 0$
(2)	$Br + H_2 - HBr - H = 0$
(3)	$H + Br_2 - HBr - Br = 0$
(4)	$H + HBr - H_2 - Br = 0$
(5)	$2Br - Br_2 = 0$

It has further been shown how this mechanism can lead to the observed rate law [Eq. (6.46)].   The over-all reaction between hydrogen and bromine is thus of first order with respect to hydrogen and of *complex order* with respect to bromine and hydrogen bromide.

Experimental data on a vast number of reactions have been compiled by the National Bureau of Standards.[41]   Further references to experimental data may be found in Hougen and Watson,[11] Smith,[42] Jungers et al.,[12] and Frost and Pearson.[43]

6.5. The Equations of Intraphase Transport

The equations of intraphase transport (the equations of change) are the statement of the principles of conservation of mass, momentum, and energy† as applied to a flow system.   The resultant three equations are, respectively:

1. The *equations of continuity* (one for each chemical species), which contain the mass fluxes $\mathbf{n}_\alpha$ or $\mathbf{j}_\alpha$
2. The *equation of motion*, which contains the momentum flux $\boldsymbol{\phi}$ or $\boldsymbol{\pi}$
3. The *equation of energy*, which contains the energy flux $\mathbf{e}$ or $\mathbf{q}$

---

† There is also an equation expressing the principle of conservation of angular momentum, which has not as yet received much study (see, for example, Curtiss[44] and Livingston and Curtiss[45]).

First the equations of change are given in terms of the fluxes. Then various expressions for the fluxes are inserted to give the equations of change in terms of the transport coefficients. It is usually in this latter form that the equations are used.

In the derivation of each equation the conservation statement is written for an arbitrary volume V with surface S through which the fluid is flowing. The volume V is fixed with respect to the laboratory system of coordinates. The orientation of any surface element dS of the volume V is given by an outwardly directed unit normal vector $\mathbf{n}$.

The Equation of Continuity. When the principle of conservation of mass of species α is applied to the region within volume V, there results the statement

$$\begin{pmatrix} \text{Rate of } increase \\ \text{of mass of } \alpha \\ \text{within } V \end{pmatrix} = \begin{pmatrix} \text{rate at which mass of} \\ \text{species } \alpha \text{ crosses} \\ into \ V \text{ over} \\ \text{surface } S \end{pmatrix} + \begin{pmatrix} \text{rate at which mass} \\ \text{of } \alpha \text{ is } produced \\ \text{within } V \text{ by} \\ \text{chemical reaction} \end{pmatrix}$$

In mathematical terms this statement becomes

$$\frac{d}{dt} \int_V \rho_\alpha \, dV = - \int_S (\mathbf{n}_\alpha \bullet \mathbf{n}) \, dS + \int_V r_\alpha \, dV \tag{6.47}$$

Because V is fixed, d/dt may be moved inside the integral sign on the left side. The surface integral may be transformed into a volume integral by means of the divergence theorem. Hence the equation may be rewritten

$$\int_V \frac{\partial \rho_\alpha}{\partial t} \, dV = - \int_V (\boldsymbol{\nabla} \bullet \mathbf{n}_\alpha) \, dV + \int_V r_\alpha \, dV \tag{6.48}$$

Now all integrals are over the same volume V. This volume is, however, arbitrary, and therefore the integral signs may be removed to give

$$\frac{\partial \rho_\alpha}{\partial t} = -(\boldsymbol{\nabla} \bullet \mathbf{n}_\alpha) + r_\alpha \qquad \alpha = 1, 2, \ldots, \nu \tag{6.49}$$

or in molar units

$$\frac{\partial c_\alpha}{\partial t} = -(\boldsymbol{\nabla} \bullet \mathbf{N}_\alpha) + R_\alpha \qquad \alpha = 1, 2, \ldots, \nu \tag{6.50}$$

Either of these equations is the *equation of continuity for species* α. When all ν equations are added together, one obtains either

$$\frac{\partial \rho}{\partial t} = -(\boldsymbol{\nabla} \bullet \rho\mathbf{v}) \tag{6.51}$$

or

$$\frac{\partial c}{\partial t} = -(\boldsymbol{\nabla} \bullet c\mathbf{v}^\star) + \Sigma_\alpha R_\alpha \tag{6.52}$$

These are the *equations of continuity for the mixture*. The equation in terms of ρ is simpler because use could be made of the fact that $\Sigma_\alpha r_\alpha$ is always zero, whereas $\Sigma_\alpha R_\alpha$ is zero only if the number of moles happens to be conserved. Note further the following special cases:

Mixture of constant ρ (frequently approximately true for liquids):

$$(\boldsymbol{\nabla} \bullet \mathbf{v}) = 0 \tag{6.53}$$

Mixture of constant c (frequently approximately true for gases):

$$(\boldsymbol{\nabla} \bullet \mathbf{v}^\star) = c^{-1}\Sigma_\alpha R_\alpha \tag{6.54}$$

ALTERNATE FORMS OF THE EQUATIONS OF CONTINUITY IN TERMS OF THE FLUXES. In deriving the equation of continuity above, fluxes with respect to fixed coordinates were used. In terms of fluxes with respect to moving coordinate frames,

$$\frac{\partial \rho_\alpha}{\partial t} = -(\nabla \bullet \rho_\alpha \mathbf{v}) - (\nabla \bullet \mathbf{j}_\alpha) + r_\alpha \qquad \alpha = 1, 2, \ldots, \nu \tag{6.55}$$

$$\frac{\partial c_A}{\partial t} = -(\nabla \bullet c_\alpha \mathbf{v}^\star) - (\nabla \bullet \mathbf{J}_\alpha^\star) + R_\alpha \qquad \alpha = 1, 2, \ldots, \nu \tag{6.56}$$

The first of these may be written in terms of the substantial derivative by adding $(\mathbf{v} \bullet \nabla \rho_\alpha)$ to both sides.

$$\frac{D\rho_\alpha}{Dt} = -\rho_\alpha(\nabla \bullet \mathbf{v}) - (\nabla \bullet \mathbf{j}_\alpha) + r_\alpha \qquad \alpha = 1, 2, \ldots, \nu \tag{6.57}$$

This describes the change in concentration of α following the motion of the fluid.

SPECIAL FORMS OF THE EQUATION OF CONTINUITY IN TERMS OF THE DIFFUSIVITY. For binary systems in which only ordinary diffusion is occurring, substitution of Fick's law into Eqs. (6.55) and (6.56) gives, respectively,

$$\frac{\partial \rho_A}{\partial t} = -(\nabla \bullet \rho_A \mathbf{v}) + (\nabla \bullet \rho \mathcal{D}_{AB} \nabla \omega_A) + r_A \tag{6.58}$$

$$\frac{\partial c_A}{\partial t} = -(\nabla \bullet c_A \mathbf{v}^\star) + (\nabla \bullet c \mathcal{D}_{AB} \nabla x_A) + R_A \tag{6.59}$$

with similar relations for component B. There are two special cases of the above equations which deserve mention:

Constant ρ and $\mathcal{D}_{AB}$:

$$\frac{\partial \rho_A}{\partial t} + (\mathbf{v} \bullet \nabla \rho_A) = \mathcal{D}_{AB} \nabla^2 \rho_A + r_A \tag{6.60}$$

Constant c and $\mathcal{D}_{AB}$:

$$\frac{\partial c_A}{\partial t} + (\mathbf{v}^\star \bullet \nabla c_A) = \mathcal{D}_{AB} \nabla^2 c_A + R_A - \frac{c_A}{c}(R_A + R_B) \tag{6.61}$$

Note also that the following equation holds for the total density ρ.

Constant c and $\mathcal{D}_{AB}$; no reactions:

$$\frac{\partial \ln \rho}{\partial t} + (\mathbf{v} \bullet \nabla \ln \rho) = \mathcal{D}_{AB} \nabla^2 \ln \rho \tag{6.62}$$

Finally, for systems with no reactions and constant $\mathcal{D}_{AB}$, one obtains for (1) systems with constant ρ, and $\mathbf{v} = 0$, or (2) systems with constant c, and $\mathbf{v}^\star = 0$,

$$\frac{\partial c_A}{\partial t} = \mathcal{D}_{AB} \nabla^2 c_A \tag{6.63}$$

which is sometimes called *Fick's second law of diffusion*, or simply *the diffusion equation*.

The Equation of Motion. When the principle of conservation of momentum is applied to the multicomponent fluid within the arbitrary volume V, there results the statement:

$$\begin{pmatrix} \text{Rate of } increase \\ \text{of momentum} \\ \text{within } V \end{pmatrix} = \begin{pmatrix} \text{rate at which} \\ \text{momentum crosses } into \\ V \text{ over surface } S \end{pmatrix} + \begin{pmatrix} \text{sum of external} \\ \text{forces acting on} \\ \text{fluid within } V \end{pmatrix}$$

In mathematical terms this statement becomes

$$\frac{d}{dt} \int_V \rho \mathbf{v} \, dV = -\int_S [\boldsymbol{\phi} \bullet \mathbf{n}] \, dS + \int_V \sum_{\alpha=1}^{\nu} \rho_\alpha \hat{\mathbf{F}}_\alpha \, dV \tag{6.64}$$

Here $\hat{\mathbf{F}}_\alpha$ is the external force (per unit mass) acting on species α. This may be rewritten by moving d/dt inside the integral and by converting the surface integral into a volume integral by the use of the tensor analogue of the divergence theorem.

$$\int_V \frac{\partial}{\partial t} \rho \mathbf{v} \, dV = - \int_V [\boldsymbol{\nabla} \bullet \boldsymbol{\phi}] \, dV + \int_V \sum_{\alpha=1}^{\nu} \rho_\alpha \hat{\mathbf{F}}_\alpha \, dV \qquad (6.65)$$

Because all integrals are now written over the same *arbitrary* volume V the integral signs may be removed to give

$$\frac{\partial}{\partial t} \rho \mathbf{v} = -[\boldsymbol{\nabla} \bullet \boldsymbol{\phi}] + \sum_{\alpha=1}^{\nu} \rho_\alpha \hat{\mathbf{F}}_\alpha \qquad (6.66)$$

This is the equation of motion for a multicomponent mixture.

ALTERNATIVE FORMS OF THE EQUATION OF MOTION IN TERMS OF THE FLUXES. It is more usual to express the equation of motion, not in terms of $\boldsymbol{\phi}$, the momentum flux with respect to fixed coordinates, but rather in terms of $\boldsymbol{\pi} = p\boldsymbol{\delta} + \boldsymbol{\tau}$, the flux with respect to the mass average velocity $\mathbf{v}$. The alternative form is

$$\frac{\partial}{\partial t} \rho \mathbf{v} = -[\boldsymbol{\nabla} \bullet \rho \mathbf{v}\mathbf{v}] - \boldsymbol{\nabla} p - [\boldsymbol{\nabla} \bullet \boldsymbol{\tau}] + \sum_{\alpha=1}^{\nu} \rho_\alpha \hat{\mathbf{F}}_\alpha \qquad (6.67)$$

This may also be rewritten in terms of the substantial derivative, thus:

$$\rho \frac{D\mathbf{v}}{Dt} = -\boldsymbol{\nabla} p - [\boldsymbol{\nabla} \bullet \boldsymbol{\tau}] + \sum_{\alpha=1}^{\nu} \rho_\alpha \hat{\mathbf{F}}_\alpha \qquad (6.68)$$

This equation may be interpreted as the statement of Newton's second law of motion as applied to a small region of fluid moving with velocity $\mathbf{v}$. The reader will note that in this form the equation of motion is *mass* $\times$ *acceleration* $=$ *pressure forces* $+$ *viscous forces* $+$ *external forces*.

In the absence of viscous forces Eq. (6.68) becomes

$$\rho \frac{D\mathbf{v}}{Dt} = -\boldsymbol{\nabla} p + \sum_{\alpha=1}^{\nu} \rho_\alpha \hat{\mathbf{F}}_\alpha \qquad (6.69)$$

which is known as *Euler's equation of motion*.

SPECIAL FORMS OF THE EQUATION OF MOTION IN TERMS OF THE VISCOSITY. Substitution of the expression for $\boldsymbol{\tau}$ given in Eq. (6.23) gives the equation of motion for a Newtonian fluid.

$$\rho \frac{D\mathbf{v}}{Dt} = -\boldsymbol{\nabla} p + [\boldsymbol{\nabla} \bullet \{\mu \boldsymbol{\epsilon}\}] - [\boldsymbol{\nabla} \bullet \{(\tfrac{2}{3} \mu - \kappa)(\boldsymbol{\nabla} \bullet \mathbf{v})\boldsymbol{\delta}\}] + \sum_{\alpha=1}^{\nu} \rho_\alpha \hat{\mathbf{F}}_\alpha \qquad (6.70)$$

in which μ and κ are functions of temperature, pressure, and composition. There are several special simplified forms of this equation which are generally used as the starting point for fluid mechanics:

Constant μ and κ:

$$\rho \frac{D\mathbf{v}}{Dt} = -\boldsymbol{\nabla} p + \mu \boldsymbol{\nabla}^2 \mathbf{v} + (\tfrac{1}{3} \mu + \kappa)\boldsymbol{\nabla}(\boldsymbol{\nabla} \bullet \mathbf{v}) + \sum_{\alpha=1}^{\nu} \rho_\alpha \hat{\mathbf{F}}_\alpha \qquad (6.71)$$

Constant μ and κ:

$$\rho \frac{D\mathbf{v}}{Dt} = -\nabla p - \mu[\nabla \times [\nabla \times \mathbf{v}]] + (\tfrac{4}{3}\mu + \kappa)\nabla(\nabla \cdot \mathbf{v}) + \sum_{\alpha=1}^{\nu} \rho_\alpha \hat{\mathbf{F}}_\alpha \qquad (6.72)$$

Constant μ and ρ:

$$\rho \frac{D\mathbf{v}}{Dt} = -\nabla p + \mu\nabla^2\mathbf{v} + \sum_{\alpha=1}^{\nu} \rho_\alpha \hat{\mathbf{F}}_\alpha \qquad (6.73)$$

Constant μ and ρ:

$$\rho \left[\frac{\partial \mathbf{v}}{\partial t} + \nabla \tfrac{1}{2} v^2 - [\mathbf{v} \times [\nabla \times \mathbf{v}]] \right] = -\nabla p + \mu\nabla^2\mathbf{v} + \sum_{\alpha=1}^{\nu} \rho_\alpha \hat{\mathbf{F}}_\alpha \qquad (6.74)$$

Clearly, if the forces acting on the individual species are the same, say, $\hat{\mathbf{F}}$, then the last term simplifies to $\rho\hat{\mathbf{F}}$.

For steady flow with constant ρ and μ and a force $\hat{\mathbf{F}}$ derivable from a potential (that is, $\hat{\mathbf{F}} = -\nabla\hat{\Phi}$), the equation of motion simplifies to the following when, in addition, the inertial terms are identically zero or negligible:

Constant μ and ρ; ($\hat{\mathbf{F}} = -\nabla\hat{\Phi}$, $\partial\mathbf{v}/\partial t = 0$, $[\mathbf{v} \cdot \nabla\mathbf{v}] = 0$):

$$0 = -\nabla(p + \rho\hat{\Phi}) + \mu\nabla^2\mathbf{v} \qquad (6.75)$$

This equation can be shown to be the Euler-Lagrange equation corresponding to the variational problem (Helmholtz theorem) (see Ref. 46, p. 617).

$$\delta E_v \equiv -\delta \int_R (\boldsymbol{\tau} : \nabla\mathbf{v})\, dV = \tfrac{1}{2}\mu\delta \int_R (\boldsymbol{\epsilon} : \boldsymbol{\epsilon})\, dV = 0 \qquad (6.76)$$

if $\boldsymbol{\tau} = -\mu\boldsymbol{\epsilon}$, and R is the region, fixed in space, in which the velocity distribution is to be found. That is, problems corresponding to Eq. (6.75) can be formulated in terms of a *variational principle*, which states essentially that the *total entropy production is a minimum*. That is, for this type of viscous-flow problem, one can assume reasonable-looking velocity profiles $\mathbf{v}(\mathbf{r}; \alpha_1, \alpha_2, \alpha_3, \ldots)$ in which $\alpha_1, \alpha_2, \alpha_3, \ldots$ are arbitrary parameters selected so that $\partial E_v/\partial \alpha_j$ will be zero. The variational principle given above is valid when the velocity distribution is specified over the entire containing surface. A similar principle exists for problems in which the velocity is specified on part of the surface and the momentum flux is specified on the remainder of the surface (Ref. 46, p. 619).

THE EQUATIONS OF MOTION FOR VARIOUS SPECIAL NON-NEWTONIAN FLUIDS. To date most analytical solutions to non-Newtonian flow problems have been for rheological models of the form $\boldsymbol{\tau} = -\eta\boldsymbol{\epsilon}$ where η is a function of $I_2 = (\boldsymbol{\epsilon} : \boldsymbol{\epsilon})$ [Eq. (6.28)]. Hence, for *incompressible* fluids of this type, the equation of motion is, for an external force $\hat{\mathbf{F}}$,

$$\rho \frac{D\mathbf{v}}{Dt} = -\nabla p + [\nabla \cdot \eta\boldsymbol{\epsilon}] + \rho\hat{\mathbf{F}} \qquad (6.77)$$

The term $[\nabla \cdot \eta\boldsymbol{\epsilon}]$ may be evaluated in cartesian, cylindrical, and spherical coordinates by using the tabulation in Appendix B at the end of this section.

For problems corresponding to Eq. (6.75) for Newtonian fluids, one has, for rheological models of the form $\boldsymbol{\tau} = -\eta\boldsymbol{\epsilon}$ [Eq. (6.28)], the problem of solving

Constant m, n, ρ ($\hat{\mathbf{F}} = -\nabla\hat{\Phi}$ $\partial\mathbf{v}/\partial t = 0$, $[\mathbf{v} \cdot \nabla\mathbf{v}] = 0$):

$$0 = -\nabla(p + \rho\hat{\Phi}) + [\nabla \cdot \eta\boldsymbol{\epsilon}] \qquad (6.78)$$

This equation can be shown to be the Euler-Lagrange equation corresponding to the following variational problem:†

$$\delta B \equiv \delta \int_{R} \left(\tfrac{1}{2} \int_{0}^{I_2} \eta \, dI_2 \right) dV = 0 \tag{6.79}$$

wherein $\eta = \eta(I_2)$, and R is a region fixed in space. Note that this *variational principle* does not in general state that the total entropy production is a minimum. For the exceptional case of the Ostwald–de Waele fluid, however, Eq. (6.79) does predict that the flow corresponds to minimal total entropy production.[47] The variational principle given above is valid only when the velocity distribution is specified over the entire containing surface. Variational principles for more general boundary conditions and for more general non-Newtonian fluids have been formulated by M. W. Johnson.‡

RELATION BETWEEN THE EQUATION OF MOTION AND THE MECHANICAL-ENERGY EQUATION. When the local mass-average velocity $\mathbf{v}$ is dotted into the equation of motion in the form given in Eq. (6.67), the following equation results:

$$\frac{\partial}{\partial t}(\tfrac{1}{2}\rho v^2) \quad = \quad -(\boldsymbol{\nabla} \cdot \tfrac{1}{2}\rho v^2 \mathbf{v}) \quad + \quad \sum_{\alpha=1}^{\nu}(\mathbf{v} \cdot \rho_\alpha \hat{\mathbf{F}}_\alpha)$$

$$\begin{bmatrix}\text{Rate of increase in kinetic}\\\text{energy per unit volume}\end{bmatrix} \qquad \begin{bmatrix}\text{Net rate of input of kinetic}\\\text{energy by bulk flow}\end{bmatrix} \qquad \begin{bmatrix}\text{Rate of work done by ex-}\\\text{ternal body forces}\end{bmatrix}$$

$$-(\boldsymbol{\nabla} \cdot p\mathbf{v}) \qquad\qquad -(\boldsymbol{\nabla} \cdot [\boldsymbol{\tau} \cdot \mathbf{v}])$$

$$\begin{bmatrix}\text{Rate of } work \text{ done by pres-}\\\text{sure}\end{bmatrix} \qquad\qquad \begin{bmatrix}\text{Rate of } work \text{ done by vis-}\\\text{cous forces}\end{bmatrix}$$

$$- p(-\boldsymbol{\nabla} \cdot \mathbf{v}) \qquad\qquad -(-\boldsymbol{\tau} : \boldsymbol{\nabla}\mathbf{v})$$

$$\begin{bmatrix}\text{Rate of } reversible \text{ conversion}\\\text{to internal energy}\end{bmatrix} \qquad \begin{bmatrix}\text{Rate of } irreversible \text{ conver-}\\\text{sion to internal energy}\end{bmatrix}$$

$$\tag{6.80}$$

This equation indicates how the mechanical energy may be used to do mechanical work or work against external forces or be converted into internal energy reversibly or irreversibly. The quantity $(-\boldsymbol{\tau} : \boldsymbol{\nabla}\mathbf{v})$, representing the rate of conversion from mechanical to thermal energy, plays a key role in the Helmholtz variational principle (p. 6-21) and also in the dimensional analysis of the friction losses in turbulent flow systems (Art. 6.8). Note that for Newtonian fluids

$$(-\boldsymbol{\tau} : \boldsymbol{\nabla}\mathbf{v}) = +\tfrac{1}{2}\,\mu(\{\boldsymbol{\epsilon} - \tfrac{2}{3}(\boldsymbol{\nabla} \cdot \mathbf{v})\boldsymbol{\delta}\} : \{\boldsymbol{\epsilon} - \tfrac{2}{3}(\boldsymbol{\nabla} \cdot \mathbf{v})\boldsymbol{\delta}\}) + \kappa(\boldsymbol{\nabla} \cdot \mathbf{v})^2 \tag{6.81}$$

This expression is made up of sums of squares of functions of velocity gradients and is hence inherently positive. This is why this term has been labeled as "irreversible" in the previous equation.

For the incompressible non-Newtonian models of the form $\boldsymbol{\tau} = -\eta\boldsymbol{\epsilon}$,

$$(-\boldsymbol{\tau} : \boldsymbol{\nabla}\mathbf{v}) = +\tfrac{1}{2}\,\eta(\boldsymbol{\epsilon} : \boldsymbol{\epsilon}) = \tfrac{1}{2}\,\eta\Sigma_i\Sigma_j\epsilon_{ij}\epsilon_{ji} \tag{6.82}$$

is clearly automatically positive inasmuch as η depends only on $I_2 = (\boldsymbol{\epsilon} : \boldsymbol{\epsilon})$. For the more general functional relationship in Eq. (6.24), $\boldsymbol{\tau} = -\eta\boldsymbol{\epsilon} - \tfrac{1}{2}\,\eta_c\{\boldsymbol{\epsilon} \cdot \boldsymbol{\epsilon}\}$, there is no insurance that $-(\boldsymbol{\tau} : \boldsymbol{\nabla}\mathbf{v})$ will always be positive. This point has been discussed by Truesdell (Ref. 22, pp. 125–300).

The Equation of Energy. The application of the principle of conservation of energy to a multicomponent fluid within the arbitrary volume V gives

$$\begin{pmatrix}\text{Rate of } increase \text{ of}\\\text{internal and kinetic}\\\text{energy within } V\end{pmatrix} = \begin{pmatrix}\text{rate at which}\\\text{energy crosses}\\into\ V\text{ over}\\\text{the surface } S\end{pmatrix} + \begin{pmatrix}\text{work done on the}\\\text{various species}\\\text{by external forces}\end{pmatrix}$$

† R. B. Bird, *Phys. Fluids,* **3**:539–541 (1960).

‡ M. W. Johnson, *Physics of Fluids,* in press.

This statement may be formulated mathematically thus:

$$\frac{d}{dt} \int_V \rho(\hat{U} + \tfrac{1}{2} v^2) \, dV = -\int_S (\mathbf{e} \bullet \mathbf{n}) \, dS + \int_V \sum_{\alpha=1}^{\nu} \rho_\alpha(\mathbf{v}_\alpha \bullet \hat{\mathbf{F}}_\alpha) \, dV \qquad (6.83)$$

This may be rewritten thus:

$$\int_V \frac{\partial}{\partial t} \rho(\hat{U} + \tfrac{1}{2} v^2) = -\int_V (\boldsymbol{\nabla} \bullet \mathbf{e}) \, dS + \int_V \sum_{\alpha=1}^{\nu} \rho_\alpha(\mathbf{v}_\alpha \bullet \hat{\mathbf{F}}_\alpha) \, dV \qquad (6.84)$$

Because the volume V is arbitrary, the integral signs may be removed to give

$$\frac{\partial}{\partial t} \rho(\hat{U} + \tfrac{1}{2} v^2) = -(\boldsymbol{\nabla} \bullet \mathbf{e}) + \sum_{\alpha=1}^{\nu} \rho_\alpha(\mathbf{v}_\alpha \bullet \hat{\mathbf{F}}_\alpha) \qquad (6.85)$$

which is one of the many forms that the *energy equation* can assume.

ALTERNATIVE FORMS OF THE ENERGY EQUATION IN TERMS OF THE FLUXES.   It is more usual to express the energy equation in terms of $\mathbf{q}$ rather that $\mathbf{e}$.   Hence Eq. (6.85) becomes

$$\frac{\partial}{\partial t} \rho(\hat{U} + \tfrac{1}{2} v^2) = -(\boldsymbol{\nabla} \bullet \rho(\hat{U} + \tfrac{1}{2} v^2)\mathbf{v}) - (\boldsymbol{\nabla} \bullet \mathbf{q}) - (\boldsymbol{\nabla} \bullet p\mathbf{v})$$

$$- (\boldsymbol{\nabla} \bullet [\boldsymbol{\tau} \bullet \mathbf{v}]) + \sum_{\alpha=1}^{\nu} (\mathbf{n}_\alpha \bullet \hat{\mathbf{F}}_\alpha) \quad (6.86)$$

When Eq. (6.80) (the mechanical-energy equation) is subtracted from Eq. (6.86), there results an equation for $\hat{U}$:

$$\frac{\partial}{\partial t} \rho\hat{U} = -(\boldsymbol{\nabla} \bullet \rho\hat{U}\mathbf{v}) - (\boldsymbol{\nabla} \bullet \mathbf{q}) - p(\boldsymbol{\nabla} \bullet \mathbf{v}) - (\boldsymbol{\tau} : \boldsymbol{\nabla}\mathbf{v}) + \sum_{\alpha=1}^{\nu} (\mathbf{j}_\alpha \bullet \hat{\mathbf{F}}_\alpha) \quad (6.87)$$

Note that the terms $p(\boldsymbol{\nabla} \bullet \mathbf{v})$ and $(\boldsymbol{\tau} : \boldsymbol{\nabla}\mathbf{v})$ appear in Eqs. (6.80) and (6.87) with opposite signs.

Equation (6.87) may also be written in terms of the substantial derivative:

$$\rho\frac{D\hat{U}}{DT} = -(\boldsymbol{\nabla} \bullet \mathbf{q}) - p(\boldsymbol{\nabla} \bullet \mathbf{v}) - (\boldsymbol{\tau} : \boldsymbol{\nabla}\mathbf{v}) + \sum_{\alpha=1}^{\nu} (\mathbf{j}_\alpha \bullet \hat{\mathbf{F}}_\alpha) \qquad (6.88)$$

By use of standard thermodynamic transformations this equation may be rewritten (with no assumptions) in terms of the temperature by introducing the "caloric equation of state," $\hat{U} = \hat{U}(T; \rho_1, \rho_2, \ldots, \rho)$

$$\rho\hat{C}_p\frac{DT}{Dt} = -(\boldsymbol{\nabla} \bullet \mathbf{q}) - (\boldsymbol{\tau} : \boldsymbol{\nabla}\mathbf{v}) + \sum_{\alpha=1}^{\nu} (\mathbf{j}_\alpha \bullet \hat{\mathbf{F}}_\alpha)$$

$$\quad(a)\qquad\qquad(b)\qquad\qquad(c)\qquad\qquad(d)$$

$$+ \left(\frac{\partial \ln \hat{V}}{\partial \ln T}\right)_{p,x_\beta}\frac{Dp}{Dt} + \sum_{\alpha=1}^{\nu} \bar{H}_\alpha(\boldsymbol{\nabla} \bullet \mathbf{J}_\alpha) - \sum_{\alpha=1}^{\nu} \bar{H}_\alpha R_\alpha \quad (6.89)$$

$$\qquad\qquad(e)\qquad\qquad\qquad(f)\qquad\qquad\qquad(g)$$

Under certain conditions some of these terms may be simplified:

1. Term c is generally quite small except in high-speed flows where viscous heating becomes appreciable.

2. Term f is identically zero if the force acting on all species is the same; if gravity is the only external force, then this term vanishes.

3. Term e is zero for incompressible flow and is Dp/Dt for ideal gases; term e is also zero in isopiestic systems.

4. Term f is zero in pure fluids or in nondiffusing gas mixtures.

5. Term g, which is the heat of reaction, is zero in nonreacting gas mixtures.

Note that Eq. (6.89) contains two terms which may be regarded as _thermal-energy sources_: the viscous-heat effect $S_v = -(\boldsymbol{\tau} : \boldsymbol{\nabla}\mathbf{v})$, which is always positive, and the heat of chemical reaction $S_r = -\Sigma_\alpha \overline{H}_\alpha R_\alpha$, which is positive for _exothermic_ reactions and negative for _endothermic_ reactions. If a more complete energy equation had been used, accounting for electric and magnetic energy, an additional thermal-energy source, namely, the electrical _ohmic heating_ S_e, would appear.[48] A similar remark holds for heat production by the nuclear fission process S_n.

SPECIAL FORMS OF THE EQUATION OF ENERGY IN TERMS OF THE THERMAL CONDUCTIVITY. In order to use Eq. (6.89) to calculate temperature profiles, it is necessary to insert into it the expression for $\mathbf{q}$ in Eq. (6.33) (for pure fluids) or that in Eq. (6.34) (for fluid mixtures). One must also insert an expression for $\boldsymbol{\tau}$ in terms of the velocity gradients (that is, in terms of $\boldsymbol{\epsilon}$). Then

$$\rho \hat{C}_p \frac{DT}{Dt} = (\boldsymbol{\nabla} \cdot \lambda \boldsymbol{\nabla} T) + \sum_{\alpha=1}^{\nu} (\mathbf{j}_\alpha \cdot \hat{\mathbf{F}}_\alpha) + \left(\frac{\partial \ln \hat{V}}{\partial \ln T}\right)_{p,x_\beta} \frac{Dp}{Dt} + \Sigma_i S_i - \sum_{\alpha=1}^{\nu} (\mathbf{J}_\alpha \cdot \boldsymbol{\nabla} \overline{H}_\alpha)$$

$$(6.90)$$

if $\Sigma_i S_i$ is the sum of the thermal-source terms mentioned previously. Several special cases of Eq. (6.90) are of importance:

Pure, incompressible fluids with constant λ:

$$\frac{DT}{Dt} = \alpha \boldsymbol{\nabla}^2 T + \frac{S_v}{\rho \hat{C}_p}$$

$$(6.91)$$

Pure solids with $\mathbf{v} = 0$ and $\lambda = \text{const}$:

$$\frac{\partial T}{\partial t} = \alpha \boldsymbol{\nabla}^2 T$$

$$(6.92)$$

Equation (6.92), the heat-conduction equation of Fourier, has exactly the same form as the diffusion equation of Fick.

THE ENERGY EQUATION FOR NON-NEWTONIAN FLUIDS. Equation (6.89) may also be used for non-Newtonian flow problems. The non-Newtonian nature of the fluid enters in two ways: (1) in the calculation of $\mathbf{v}$ in the substantial derivative DT/Dt, and (2) in the calculation of the viscous-dissipation heating $(-\boldsymbol{\tau} : \boldsymbol{\nabla}\mathbf{v})$. The calculation of the latter for non-Newtonian fluids of the form $\boldsymbol{\tau} = -\eta\boldsymbol{\epsilon}$ has been discussed in connection with the mechanical-energy equation (6.80).

6.6. Analytical Solutions of the Equations of Change

In this article we give a few analytical solutions of the partial differential equations of intraphase transport. The purpose of the solutions is to clarify the meaning of some of the terms in the equations rather than to provide a glossary of analytical solutions. In each case the problem is set up by discarding unnecessary terms in the equations of change. Many more illustrations may be found in the textbook of Bird, Stewart, and Lightfoot.[4]

Momentum Transport. Many problems in Newtonian flow are to be found in standard treatises[46,49,50] as well as in the current journals in engineering and physics. Here the illustrations chosen are examples of non-Newtonian flow, just to show how such problems may be handled.

STEADY FLOW IN A CIRCULAR TUBE. Let it be desired to find the relation between volume rate of flow and pressure drop in tube flow for an inelastic, non-Newtonian fluid described by Eq. (6.24):

$$\tau = -\eta\epsilon - \tfrac{1}{2}\,\eta_c\{\epsilon \bullet \epsilon\} \tag{6.24}$$

If end effects are neglected, then the only nonvanishing velocity component is v_z, which is a function of r alone. For this case, the only nonvanishing component of ϵ is $\epsilon_{rz} = dv_z/dr$, and the three invariants of ϵ are

$$I_1 = I_3 = 0 \qquad I_2 = 2\left(\frac{dv_z}{dr}\right)^2$$

so that the viscosity η and the cross viscosity η_c are functions of I_2, and hence of r alone. From Eq. (6.24), one finds the nonvanishing components of τ to be

$$\tau_{rr} = \tau_{zz} = -\tfrac{1}{2}\,\eta_c\left(\frac{dv_z}{dr}\right)^2 \tag{6.93}$$

$$\tau_{rz} = -\eta\,\frac{dv_z}{dr} \tag{6.94}$$

Equation (6.93) shows that a motion of simple shear generates normal stresses in the fluid. This is a characteristic of non-Newtonian fluids and is called the Weissenberg effect (Ref. 26, pp. 52-53).

The r equation of motion for laminar axial flow in a tube is

$$0 = -\frac{dp}{dz} - \frac{1}{r}\frac{d}{dr}\,(r\tau_{rz}) + \rho g_z \tag{6.95}$$

If there is a pressure drop Δp over a length L, then this equation becomes

$$\frac{1}{r}\frac{d}{dr}\,(r\tau_{rz}) = \frac{\Delta p}{L} + \rho g_z \equiv P \tag{6.96}$$

This equation may be integrated to give

$$\tau_{rz} = \frac{Pr}{2} \tag{6.97}$$

wherein the constant of integration has been set equal to zero, inasmuch as the momentum flux may not be infinite at $r = 0$.

This expression is then substituted into Eq. (6.94), and the resulting equation integrated with the boundary condition that $v_z = 0$ at the tube wall $r = R$. The velocity profile thus found is

$$v_z = \frac{P}{2}\int_r^R \frac{dr}{r\eta} \tag{6.98}$$

Integration of the velocity over the tube cross section gives the following expression for the volume rate of flow Q:

$$Q = \frac{\pi P}{2}\int_0^R \frac{r^3\,dr}{\eta} \tag{6.99}$$

When $\eta = \mu = $ const, this simplifies to the Hagen-Poiseuille formula for Newtonian fluids. Substitution of one of the models for non-Newtonian fluids (for instance, the Ostwald–de Waele model) and integration will give an expression in closed form for the volume rate of flow of a non-Newtonian fluid.

UNSTEADY FLOW OF A VISCOELASTIC FLUID IN A CIRCULAR TUBE.[31] Let it once again be desired to find the relation between Q and P for a *Maxwell fluid*, which is a model formed by a superposition of the Newton liquid and Hooke solid. For sufficiently small velocities, the relation between $\boldsymbol{\tau}$ and $\boldsymbol{\epsilon}$ is[51]

$$\boldsymbol{\tau} + t_0 \frac{\partial}{\partial t}\boldsymbol{\tau} = -\mu_0\boldsymbol{\epsilon} \tag{6.100}$$

in which μ_0 is a viscosity and t_0 is a relaxation time.

It is possible to obtain a solution of the equation of motion for the Maxwell model if one assumes very slow, incompressible, periodic, linearized flow. Hence the $[\mathbf{v} \bullet \boldsymbol{\nabla}\mathbf{v}]$ term in the equation of motion may be neglected, and further, Eq. (6.100) will be valid. The assumption of periodicity means that the τ_{ij} are taken to be $\tau_0 \exp i\omega t$, so that $\dot{\tau}_{ij} = i\omega\tau_{ij}$. Hence to this approximation the Maxwell model may be restated for the tube flow with $v_z = v_z(r,t)$ as

$$\tau_{rz}(1 + i\omega t_0) = -\mu_0\frac{\partial v_z}{\partial r} \tag{6.101}$$

that is, the fluid behaves as a viscous fluid with a complex viscosity $\mu_0/(1 + i\omega t_0)$.

The corresponding linearized equation of motion is

$$\rho\frac{\partial v_z}{\partial t} = -\frac{\partial p}{\partial z} - \frac{1}{r}\frac{\partial}{\partial r}(r\tau_{rz}) \tag{6.102}$$

Then the Maxwell model expression for τ_{rz} is inserted into the equation of motion. Because the motion is periodic one may set

$$-\frac{\partial p}{\partial z} = p_0 e^{i\omega t} \quad = \text{pressure gradient} \tag{6.103}$$

$$v_z(r,t) = v_0(r)e^{i\omega t} = \text{local velocity} \tag{6.104}$$

$$Q(t) = Q_0 e^{i\omega t} \quad = \text{volume rate of flow} \tag{6.105}$$

Then the equation of motion becomes

$$\frac{1}{r}\frac{d}{dr}\left(r\frac{dv_0}{dr}\right) + k^2 v_0 = \frac{1 + i\omega t_0}{\mu_0}p_0 \tag{6.106}$$

in which $k^2 = -i\omega(1 + i\omega t_0)\rho/\mu_0$. The solution to this equation with v_0 finite at $r = 0$ and $v_0 = 0$ at the tube wall $r = R$ is

$$v_0(r) = \frac{p_0}{i\omega\rho}\left[1 - \frac{J_0(kr)}{J_0(kR)}\right] \tag{6.107}$$

in which J_0 is the zero-order Bessel function. Integration over the tube cross section then gives the volume rate of flow:

$$Q_0 = \frac{\pi R^2 p_0}{i\omega\rho}\left[1 - \frac{2J_1(kR)}{kRJ_0(kR)}\right] \tag{6.108}$$

if the Bessel functions are expanded in a power series; then for $\omega t_0 \ll 1$ the following relation between Q and P is obtained:

$$Q = \frac{\pi p_0 R^4}{8\mu_0}\left[\cos\omega t - \omega t_0\left(1 - \frac{\rho R^2}{6\mu_0 t_0}\right)\sin\omega t\right] \tag{6.109}$$

Note that the out-of-phase components are $\omega t_0 \sin\omega t$ (the elastic term) and $(\omega\rho R^2/6\mu_0)\sin\omega t$ (the inertial term). The dimensionless group $(\rho R^2/\mu_0 t_0)$ which appears represents the ratio of inertial to elastic forces.[51]

UNSTEADY FLOW OF A PSEUDOPLASTIC NEAR A MOVING WALL. Consider a semi-infinite mass of fluid extending from $y = 0$ to $y = \infty$. The fluid is bounded at $y = 0$ by a flat surface which for time $t > 0$ is caused to move in the x direction with a uniform velocity V. For $t \leq 0$, the fluid is at rest. It is desired to find the velocity distribution for an Ostwald–de Waele fluid [Eq. (6.29)].

When the rheological model

$$\tau_{xy} = -m \left| \frac{\partial v_x}{\partial y} \right|^{n-1} \frac{dv_x}{dy} \tag{6.110}$$

is substituted into the equation of motion

$$\rho \frac{\partial v_x}{\partial t} = -\frac{\partial \tau_{xy}}{\partial y} \tag{6.111}$$

one obtains

$$\rho \frac{\partial v_x}{\partial t} = +mn \left(-\frac{\partial v_x}{\partial y} \right)^{n-1} \frac{\partial^2 v_x}{\partial y^2} \tag{6.112}$$

This is to be solved with the boundary and initial conditions at $t = 0$, $v_x = 0$; at $y = 0$, $v_x = V$; and at $y = \infty$, $v_x = 0$.

This may be solved approximately by a boundary-layer method. Assume similar profiles $v_x/V = \phi(\eta)$ where $\eta = y/\delta(t)$; here δ is a time-dependent boundary-layer thickness beyond which v_x is taken to be identically zero. Substitution of these similar profiles into the partial differential equation, Eq. (6.112), gives

$$-\eta \phi' \left(\frac{\dot{\delta}}{\delta} \right) = \frac{mnV^{n-1}}{\rho} \left(-\frac{\phi'}{\delta} \right)^{n-1} \frac{\phi''}{\delta^2} \tag{6.113}$$

in which primes and dots indicate derivatives with respect to η and t, respectively. When this equation is multiplied by δ^{n+1} and integrated over η from $\eta = 0$ to $\eta = 1$,

$$B\delta^n \dot{\delta} = \nu_n A \tag{6.114}$$

whence

$$\delta = \left(\frac{A}{B} \right)^{1/(n+1)} [(1 + n)\nu_n t]^{1/(n+1)} \tag{6.115}$$

in which

$$\nu_n = \frac{mnV^{n-1}}{\rho}$$

Here A and B are the integrals:

$$A = \int_0^1 (-\phi')^{n-1} \phi'' d\eta \tag{6.116}$$

$$B = -\int_0^1 \eta \phi' d\eta \tag{6.117}$$

The procedure to get the velocity $v_x(y,t)$ is then as follows:
1. Select a function $\phi(\eta)$ which has a reasonable shape, e.g.,

$$\phi(\eta) = 1 - \tfrac{3}{2} \eta + \tfrac{1}{2} \eta^3 \tag{6.118}$$

2. Evaluate A and B; for $n = \tfrac{1}{2}$ one obtains for the above $\phi(\eta)$

$$A = \sqrt{6} \qquad B = \tfrac{3}{8} \tag{6.119}$$

3. Calculate δ from Eq. (6.115)

$$\delta = (\tfrac{8}{3}\sqrt{6})^{\tfrac{2}{3}}(\tfrac{3}{2}\nu_n t)^{\tfrac{2}{3}} \tag{6.120}$$

4. Then obtain the velocity profiles

$$\frac{v_x}{V} = 1 - \frac{3}{2} \left[\frac{y}{(\tfrac{8}{3}\sqrt{6})^{\tfrac{2}{3}}(\tfrac{3}{2}\nu_n t)} \right] + \frac{1}{2} \left[\frac{y}{(\tfrac{8}{3}\sqrt{6})^{\tfrac{2}{3}}(\tfrac{3}{2}\nu_n t)^{\tfrac{2}{3}}} \right]^3 \tag{6.121}$$

This result is in moderately good agreement with the exact analytical solution.[52]   Time-dependent boundary-layer approaches such as the above are frequently useful for order-of-magnitude calculations.

Energy Transport.   In solids energy is transported through the medium by *conduction* alone.   The resulting temperature profiles are obtained by analytical or numerical solution of the heat-conduction equation $\partial T/\partial t = \alpha \nabla^2 T$.   Thousands of solutions to this equation have been found, corresponding to different boundary and initial conditions.   The reader is referred to the monumental treatise of Carslaw and Jaeger on this subject.[53]

In fluids energy is transported by both *conduction* (i.e., molecular transport) and *convection* (i.e., transport resulting from the motion of the fluid).   If the fluid motion is brought about by some mechanical device (pump, fan) then it is *forced convection*.   If the fluid motion is a result of the inequalities in density (these being in turn caused by temperature gradients), then it is *free convection*.   Convective heat-transfer problems involve the simultaneous solution of the equations of continuity, motion, and energy.   Many analytical solutions may be found in standard textbooks[4,5,59] as well as in the current periodicals.

In this article several examples of forced convection and one example of free convection are given.   These examples should indicate how the equations of change are used to set up problems involving the flow of nonisothermal pure fluids.   In all these examples the viscosity and thermal conductivity are assumed to be constant.   Actually, the viscosity of many fluids changes considerably with the temperature, and hence it would be desirable to have more analytical or numerical solutions available for systems with variable properties.

THE GRAETZ-NUSSELT PROBLEM FOR A PSEUDOPLASTIC FLUID.   An incompressible fluid at a uniform temperature T_0 is flowing in a cylindrical tube of radius R with a fully developed laminar-velocity profile.   At some plane designated as $z = 0$ the wall of the tube is raised to temperature T_w and maintained at that temperature for all $z > 0$.   It is desired to find the temperature profiles and the heat flux at the tube wall.   The classical Graetz-Nusselt problem was for Newtonian fluids[54]; here the extension to non-Newtonian fluids described by the Ostwald–de Waele model is considered, which for tube flow is written thus:

$$\tau_{rz} = -m \left| \frac{dv_z}{dr} \right|^{n-1} \frac{dv_z}{dr} = +m \left(-\frac{dv_z}{dr} \right)^n \tag{6.122}$$

if m and n are the constants describing the fluid.

By postulating that $v_z = v_z(r)$ and $v_\theta = v_r = 0$, the equation of continuity is automatically satisfied.   The equations of motion and energy in terms of the fluxes are

$$0 = -\frac{dp}{dz} - \frac{1}{r}\frac{d}{dr}(r\tau_{rz}) + \rho g_z \tag{6.123}$$

$$\rho \hat{C}_p v_z \frac{\partial T}{\partial z} = -\frac{1}{r}\frac{\partial}{\partial r}(r q_r) \tag{6.124}$$

Into these equations must be substituted the expression for τ_{rz} above and the expression for the radial transport of energy by conduction, namely, $q_r = -\lambda(\partial T/\partial r)$.

When the equation of motion is integrated,

$$v_z = v_{\max} \left[1 - \left(\frac{r}{R} \right)^{s+1} \right] \tag{6.125}$$

in which $s = 1/n$, and $v_{\max} = (PR/2m)^s R/(s+1)$.   When this velocity distribution is inserted into the energy equation,

$$(1 - \xi^{s+1}) \frac{\partial \Theta}{\partial \zeta} = \frac{1}{\xi}\frac{\partial}{\partial \xi}\left(\xi \frac{\partial \Theta}{\partial \xi} \right) \tag{6.126}$$

in which $\xi = r/R$
$\Theta = (T - T_1)/(T_0 - T_1)$
$\zeta = (\lambda/\rho \hat{C}_p v_{\max} R^2)z$

This is to be solved with the boundary conditions:

$$\Theta = 1 \text{ at } \zeta = 0; \Theta = 0 \text{ at } \xi = 1; \text{ and } \partial\Theta/\partial\xi = 0 \text{ at } \xi = 0.$$

A formal solution is easily obtained by the method of separation of variables, and the radial portion of the problem is of the Sturm-Liouville type. Hence the temperature profiles have the form

$$\Theta(\rho,\zeta) = \sum_{k=1}^{\infty} (-1)^{k+1} B_k \phi_k(\xi) e^{-b_k \zeta} \tag{6.127}$$

The $\phi_k(\rho)$ are orthogonal on the range $\xi = 0$ to $\xi = 1$ with respect to the weight function $\xi(1 - \xi^{s+1})$; they are obtained from a power-series solution of

$$\frac{1}{\xi}\frac{d}{d\xi}\left(\xi\frac{d\phi_k}{d\xi}\right) + b_k^2(1 - \xi^{s+1})\phi_k = 0 \tag{6.128}$$

The b_i are eigenvalues which are obtained when the function $\phi_k(\xi)$ is required to be zero at $\xi = 1$. The coefficients B_k are

$$B_k = \frac{\int_0^1 \phi_k(1 - \xi^{s+1})\xi \, d\xi}{\int_0^1 \phi_k^2(1 - \xi^{s+1})\xi \, d\xi} \tag{6.129}$$

Some values of b_k, B_k, and ϕ_k are given elsewhere.[54] The solution given in Eq. (6.127) converges rapidly for large ζ, but is not of much value at small ζ.

One of the major difficulties in problems of the above type is the computation of the eigenvalues b_k, for k greater than about 4. It is useful to have a scheme for computing the higher eigenvalues. Such a scheme is provided by the WKB (Wentzel-Kramers-Brillouin) method, which was developed for calculating high-energy states in quantum mechanics.† For the Ostwald–de Waele fluid under consideration the WKB method yields the asymptotic expression for high k values.[56]

$$b_k = \frac{(\tfrac{2}{3} + k)\pi}{\int_0^1 \sqrt{1 - \xi^{s+1}} \, d\xi} \tag{6.130}$$

The WKB method also yields information about the slope of the eigenfunctions $\phi_k(\xi)$ at the wall. The latter can be used to calculate the heat flux at the wall.†

For small values of ζ, that is, in the neighborhood of the wall-temperature discontinuity, the solution by separation of variables given above is of little value. An alter-
native solution for small ζ may easily be obtained by noting that the penetration of heat into the flowing stream is only very slight. Hence it is convenient to introduce $\Psi = 1 - \Theta$ and a new variable $\sigma = 1 - \xi$ and rewrite the original partial-differential equation [Eq. (6.126)] thus:

$$[1 - (1 - \sigma)^{s+1}]\frac{\partial\Psi}{\partial\zeta} = \frac{1}{1 - \sigma}\frac{\partial}{\partial\sigma}\left[(1 - \sigma)\frac{\partial\Psi}{\partial\sigma}\right] \tag{6.131}$$

If now use is made of the fact that the bulk of the heat conduction occurs where $\sigma \ll 1$, then this equation may be simplified to give

$$(s + 1)\sigma\frac{\partial\Psi}{\partial\zeta} = \frac{\partial^2\Psi}{\partial\sigma^2} \tag{6.132}$$

which is to be solved with boundary conditions: $\Psi = 0$ at $\zeta = 0$, $\Psi = 1$ at $\sigma = 0$, and $\Psi = 1$ at $\sigma = \infty$. The last boundary condition is permissible because the penetration

---

† The solution to the Graetz-Nusselt problem for Newtonian flow was obtained by the WKB method by Sellars, Tribus, and Klein.[55]

depth is so small.   The above equation is easily solved by the method of combination of variables to give

$$\Psi = \frac{1}{\Gamma(\tfrac{4}{3})} \int_{\eta}^{\infty} \exp\,(-\eta^3)\, d\eta \tag{6.133}$$

if

$$\eta = [(s+1)\sigma^3/9\zeta]^{\frac{1}{3}}$$

Similar procedures may be used for the problem of heat transfer to a fluid with constant wall-heat flux.[57]

VISCOUS HEAT EFFECTS IN A NON-NEWTONIAN LUBRICANT.   Heating may occur in a medium because of chemical reactions, nuclear fission, electrical dissipation (ohmic heating), or because of viscous dissipation [the $(-\boldsymbol{\tau} : \boldsymbol{\nabla}\mathbf{v})$ term in the energy equation].   It is the latter type of heat source that is considered here.

Consider the flow of a lubricant in the annular space between two cylinders.   If the annular space is small compared with the diameter of the cylinders, then the system may be treated as though it were a plane slit; that is, curvature effects may be neglected. Let the thickness of the slit be b; let the lower plane be located at $z = 0$ and the upper plane at $z = b$, the upper plane moving in the $+x$ direction with a uniform speed V. The plate at $z = 0$ is maintained at temperature T_0, and that at b is kept at T_b.   It is desired to find the steady-state temperature distribution.

For this system in steady motion the equations of motion and energy for an incompressible fluid are:

Motion:
$$0 = -\frac{d\tau_{xz}}{dz} \tag{6.134}$$

Energy:
$$0 = -\frac{dq_z}{dz} - \tau_{xz}\frac{dv_x}{dz} \tag{6.135}$$

the last term in the energy equation representing the heat produced by the degradation of mechanical energy.

Into the above equations the expressions for the fluxes are substituted.   Let it here be assumed that the lubricant is approximately described by the Ostwald–de Waele model; then

Motion:
$$0 = -\frac{d}{dz}\left(-m\left|\frac{dv_x}{dz}\right|^{n-1}\frac{dv_x}{dz}\right) \tag{6.136}$$

Energy:
$$0 = \lambda\frac{d^2T}{dz^2} + m\left|\frac{dv_x}{dz}\right|^{n-1}\left(\frac{dv_x}{dz}\right)^2 \tag{6.137}$$

The equation of motion may be integrated with the boundary conditions that $v_x = 0$ at $z = 0$ and $v_x = V$ at $z = b$, to give $v_x/V = z/b$ for the velocity profile.   Then the energy equation becomes

$$0 = \lambda\frac{d^2T}{dz^2} + m\left(\frac{V}{b}\right)^{n+1} \tag{6.138}$$

This may be integrated with respect to z to give

$$(T - T_0) = (T_b - T_0)\frac{z}{b} + \frac{1}{2}\left(\frac{mV^{n+1}}{\lambda b^{n-1}}\right)\left[\frac{z}{b} - \left(\frac{z}{b}\right)^2\right] \tag{6.139}$$

This result may be used to estimate the temperature rise in the lubricant.   Note that m and λ have both been assumed to be constant.

Viscous heating may be a disturbing factor in precise viscometric measurements; calculations similar to the above have been made for the rotating-cylinder viscometer[58] and for the capillary viscometer.[59]

TRANSPIRATION COOLING.   Consider the radial flow of a gas between two porous spherical shells of radii κR and R, when $\kappa < 1$.   The inner shell at $r = \kappa R$ is maintained at temperature T_κ, and the outer shell at $r = R$ is kept at T_1.   It is desired to get the temperature distribution in this system at steady state.

For this flow system the equations of continuity, motion, and energy are written in spherical coordinates, by postulating that $v_\theta = v_\phi = 0$ and that $v_r = v_r(r)$, $T = T(r)$, and $p = p(r)$; it is further assumed that ρ, μ, and λ are all constant.

Continuity:
$$\frac{1}{r^2}\frac{d}{dr}(r^2 v_r) = 0 \tag{6.140}$$

Motion:
$$\rho v_r \frac{dv_r}{dr} = -\frac{dp}{dr} + \mu\left[\frac{1}{r^2}\frac{d}{dr}\left(r^2\frac{dv_r}{dr}\right) - \frac{2}{r^2}v_r\right] \tag{6.141}$$

Energy:
$$\rho \hat{C}_p v_r \frac{dT}{dr} = \lambda \frac{1}{r^2}\frac{d}{dr}\left(r^2\frac{dT}{dr}\right) \tag{6.142}$$

From the equation of continuity,

$$v_r = \frac{w_r}{4\pi r^2 \rho} \tag{6.143}$$

in which w_r is the radial mass rate of flow, a constant. Insertion of this into the equation of motion and integration with respect to r gives the pressure difference between the two shells

$$p_1 - p_\kappa = \frac{w_r^2(1 - \kappa^4)}{32\pi^2 \rho \kappa^4 R^4} \tag{6 144}$$

Similarly, substitution of the velocity into the energy equation and integration gives

$$\frac{T - T_1}{T_\kappa - T_1} = \frac{e^{-R_0/r} - e^{-R_0/R}}{e^{-R_0/\kappa R} - e^{-R_0/R}} \tag{6.145}$$

in which $R_0 = w_r \hat{C}_p/4\pi\lambda$. This result may be used to compare the rate of heat removal at the inner sphere with gas flow with that without gas flow, that is, to calculate the effect of transpiration on heat transfer.

FREE CONVECTION IN A THIN ANNULAR SLIT. A Newtonian fluid is contained in the very thin annular space between two long cylinders of almost the same diameter. One cylinder is maintained at a high temperature, and the other at a low temperature. The fluid near the heated cylinder ascends, and that near the cooled surface descends; mechanical devices at the ends of the columns adjust the flow so that the volume rate of flow upward is the same as that downward. Such a situation exists in a Clusius-Dickel column for thermal diffusion of liquids.

If the annular space is sufficiently thin, then the problem may be treated as though it were flow in a plane slit. Hence, consider two parallel planes at a distance $2b$ apart. The plane at $y = -b$ is maintained at a uniform temperature T_2; the plate at $y = +b$ is maintained at a uniform temperature T_1 (with $T_2 > T_1$). It is desired to find the velocity profiles $v_z(y)$ resulting from the temperature profile $T(y)$.

If the variation of thermal conductivity λ may be neglected, the energy equation becomes

$$\frac{d^2 T}{dy^2} = 0 \tag{6.146}$$

This may be integrated to give

$$T = T_m - \tfrac{1}{2}\Delta T \frac{y}{b} \tag{6.147}$$

in which $\Delta T = T_2 - T_1$, and $T_m = \tfrac{1}{2}(T_1 + T_2)$.

The equation of motion for constant μ and almost constant ρ becomes for slit flow

$$0 = -\frac{dp}{dz} + \mu\frac{d^2 v_z}{dy^2} - \rho g \tag{6.148}$$

in which, by the sign on the ρg term, it is implied that the $+z$ direction is oriented oppositely to gravity. The equation of motion in this form is not appropriate to problems in free convection. It can be modified by expanding the density in a power series in temperature about some temperature $\overline{T}$ (as yet unspecified).

$$\rho = \rho\Big|_{T=\overline{T}} + \frac{\partial\rho}{\partial T}\Big|_{T=\overline{T}}(T - \overline{T}) + \cdots \approx \bar\rho - \bar\rho\bar\beta(T - \overline{T}) \qquad (6.149)$$

wherein $\bar\rho$ and $\bar\beta$ are the properties ρ and β evaluated at $\overline{T}$. The quantity β is the coefficient of volumetric expansion $-\rho^{-1}(\partial\rho/\partial T)_p$. If the pressure gradient in the system is due solely to the weight of the fluid in the slit, then

$$-\frac{dp}{dz} \approx \bar\rho g \qquad (6.150)$$

When these approximate expressions for ρ and $-dp/dz$ are substituted into the equation of motion above,

$$\mu\frac{d^2 v_z}{dy^2} = -\bar\rho\bar\beta g(T - \overline{T}) \qquad (6.151)$$

Insertion of the temperature profile into this equation then gives

$$\mu\frac{d^2 v_z}{dy^2} = -\bar\rho\bar\beta g\left[(T_m - \overline{T}) - \tfrac{1}{2}\,\Delta T\,\frac{y}{b}\right] \qquad (6.152)$$

When this is integrated with the condition that $v_z = 0$ at $y = \pm b$,

$$v_z = \frac{\bar\rho\bar\beta g b^2\,\Delta T}{12\mu}\,(\eta^3 - A\eta^2 - \eta + A) \qquad (6.153)$$

in which $A = 6(T_m - \overline{T})/\Delta T$ and $\eta = y/b$. The condition that the *net* volume flow in the z direction be zero requires that

$$\int_{-1}^{+1} v_z\,d\eta = 0 \qquad (6.154)$$

from which it is found that $A = 0$ or $\overline{T} = T_m$. Hence the final velocity distribution is

$$v_z = \frac{\bar\rho\bar\beta g b^2\,\Delta T}{12\mu}\,(\eta^3 - \eta) \qquad (6.155)$$

This result may be rewritten by defining a dimensionless velocity $\phi = b v_z \bar\rho/\mu$

$$\phi = \tfrac{1}{12}\,\mathbf{Gr}(\eta^3 - \eta) \qquad (6.156)$$

if **Gr** is the Grashof number.

$$\mathbf{Gr} = \frac{\bar\rho^2\bar\beta g b^3\,\Delta T}{\mu^2} \qquad (6.157)$$

The Grashof number generally arises in analytical or empirical consideration of free-convection heat transfer.

Mass Transport. Mass is transported by *molecular processes* (ordinary, thermal, pressure, or forced diffusion) and also by *free and forced convection*. If mass is transported by ordinary diffusion alone and if the concentration of the diffusing species is very low, then the concentration profiles may be obtained from the solution of Fick's second law $\partial c_A/\partial t = \mathfrak{D}_{AB}\nabla^2 c_A$. Because this is the same as the heat-conduction equation, many problems in ordinary diffusion in solids or stationary liquids may be solved by using the heat-conduction treatise of Carslaw and Jaeger.[53] In addition, the monograph of Crank[60] supplies solutions to many additional problems, including those involving chemical reactions. A survey article[61] by one of the present authors provides some solutions for flow systems, and still other solutions are given in standard textbooks.[4,9]

Although many ordinary diffusion problems can be solved by analogy with heat-conduction problems, there are some which cannot. Of particular mention is gas-phase diffusion from evaporating surfaces with the concentration of the diffusing species large. This situation is discussed in the following illustration. Other examples to be discussed are diffusion with homogeneous reactions, diffusion with heterogeneous reactions, and simultaneous heat and mass transfer.

UNSTEADY-STATE DIFFUSIONAL EVAPORATION.[62]   It is desired to derive an equation for the rate of evaporation of liquid into vapor B in a tube of infinite length. The liquid-vapor interface is taken to be at $z = 0$, and the gas phase occupies the region for which $z > 0$. It is assumed that B is insoluble in A and that the vapors A and B form an ideal gas mixture. The entire system is maintained at constant temperature so that the molar density c is a constant throughout the entire gas phase.

According to the equations of continuity for a binary mixture given in Art. 6.3,

$$\frac{\partial c_A}{\partial t} = -\frac{\partial N_A}{\partial z} \tag{6.158}$$

$$\frac{\partial c_B}{\partial t} = -\frac{\partial N_B}{\partial z} \tag{6.159}$$

When these are added and use is made of the fact that c is constant, one concludes that $N_A + N_B$ is independent of z. Since at $z = 0$, $N_B = 0$, the sum $N_A + N_B$ must just equal the evaporation rate of material A at the gas-liquid interface.

$$N_A + N_B = -\frac{c\mathcal{D}_{AB}}{1 - x_{A0}} \frac{\partial x_A}{\partial z}\bigg|_{z=0} \tag{6.160}$$

if x_{A0} is the mole fraction of A at the interface. Hence the flux of A at any plane in the gas is

$$N_A = -c\mathcal{D}_{AB}\frac{\partial x_A}{\partial z} - x_A\left(\frac{c\mathcal{D}_{AB}}{1 - x_{A0}}\right)\frac{\partial x_A}{\partial z}\bigg|_{z=0} \tag{6.161}$$

Substitution of this expression for N_A into the continuity equation for A above leads to the partial differential equation

$$\frac{\partial x_A}{\partial t} = \mathcal{D}_{AB}\frac{\partial^2 x_A}{\partial z^2} + \frac{\mathcal{D}_{AB}}{1 - x_{A0}}\frac{\partial x_A}{\partial z}\bigg|_{z=0}\frac{\partial x_A}{\partial z} \tag{6.162}$$

This equation is to be solved with the initial and boundary conditions: at $t = 0$, $x_A = 0$; at $z = 0$, $x_A = x_{A0}$; at $z = \infty$, $x_A = 0$.

The above equation has been solved by Arnold[62] to give

$$\frac{x_A}{x_{A0}} = \frac{1 - \mathrm{erf}\,[(z/\sqrt{4\mathcal{D}_{AB}t}) - \phi]}{1 + \mathrm{erf}\,\phi} \tag{6.163}$$

if ϕ is a function of x_{A0} defined by

$$x_{A0} = \frac{1}{1 + [\sqrt{\pi}(1 + \mathrm{erf}\,\phi)\phi\exp\phi^2]^{-1}} \tag{6.164}$$

The function $\phi(x_{A0})$ has been tabulated by Arnold.

From the above concentration profiles one may calculate the volume of vapor A produced from an interface of area S up to a time t after evaporation has commenced.

$$V_A = Sx_{A0}\sqrt{\frac{4\mathcal{D}_{AB}t}{\pi}}\,\psi \tag{6.165}$$

in which $\psi(x_{A0}) = \phi\sqrt{\pi}/x_{A0}$. If Fick's law, $\partial x_A/\partial t = \mathcal{D}_{AB}\partial^2 x_A/\partial z^2$, had been used instead of Eq. (6.162), then ψ would be 1. Hence the quantity ψ gives a measure of deviations from Fick's second law (i.e., the "heat-conduction equation"). Some sample values of ψ are as shown in the table that follows.

x_{A0}	ψ
0	1.000
¼	1.108
½	1.268
¾	1.564
1	∞

These figures give some quantitative notion as to the importance of the corrective transport term in Eq. (6.162) in evaporating systems. Only very little has been done on the subject of unsteady-state diffusion in multicomponent systems.[63,64]

DIFFUSION AND HOMOGENEOUS CHEMICAL REACTION IN A FALLING LIQUID FILM. A film of liquid B is flowing in laminar motion along a plane which makes an angle β with the vertical. The flow rate is such that the film thickness is δ. A gas of pure species A is flowing countercurrently to the liquid. It is assumed that B is nonvolatile; species A is absorbed by B and undergoes a first-order reaction with A to form a product AB. It is presumed that the rate of reaction is so slow that only a negligible amount AB is present; then the system may be regarded as binary. The liquid-phase concentration of A at $z = 0$ is called c_{A0}.

Take the z axis to be pointing in the direction of flow and the x axis to be pointing into the liquid film; that is, the liquid-vapor interface is the plane $x = 0$ and the liquid-solid interface is at $x = \delta$. The equation of continuity of species A and the equation of motion are:

Continuity of A:
$$v_z \frac{\partial c_A}{\partial z} = \mathfrak{D}_{AB} \frac{\partial^2 c_A}{\partial x^2} - k_1 c_A \tag{6.166a}$$

Motion:
$$0 = \mu \frac{d^2 v_z}{dx^2} + \rho g \cos \beta \tag{6.166b}$$

From the equation of motion the velocity distribution is

$$v_z = v_{\max} \left[1 - \left(\frac{x}{\delta} \right)^2 \right] \tag{6.167}$$

if $v_{\max} = (\rho g \delta^2 / 2\mu) \cos \beta$. When this velocity distribution is inserted into Eq. (6.166a),

$$v_{\max} \left[1 - \left(\frac{x}{\delta} \right)^2 \right] \frac{\partial c_A}{\partial z} = \mathfrak{D}_{AB} \frac{\partial^2 c_A}{\partial x^2} - k_1 c_A \tag{6.168}$$

If now restricted to "short contact times" (that is, z is sufficiently small so that A does not have time to penetrate very far into the fluid B), then the deviation of v_z from $v_{\max}$ will not be significant and Eq. (6.168) may be simplified to

$$v_{\max} \frac{\partial c_A}{\partial z} = \mathfrak{D}_{AB} \frac{\partial^2 c_A}{\partial x^2} - k_1 c_A \tag{6.169}$$

if k_1 is the first-order-reaction rate constant.

We now introduce dimensionless quantities $\Gamma = c_A/c_{A0}$, $\zeta = z/L$, $\xi = x/\sqrt{\mathfrak{D}_{AB}L/v_{\max}}$, and $N = k_1 L/v_{\max}$, in which L is the length of the film. Then Eq. (6.169) becomes

$$\frac{\partial \Gamma}{\partial \zeta} = \frac{\partial^2 \Gamma}{\partial \xi^2} - N\Gamma \tag{6.170}$$

which is to be solved with the boundary conditions: at $\zeta = 0$, $\Gamma = 0$; at $\xi = 0$, $\Gamma = 1$; at $\xi = \infty$, $\Gamma = 0$ (the latter boundary condition being consistent with the assumption of "short contact times").

The p-multiplied transform of the above-stated problem is

$$p\bar{\Gamma} = \frac{d^2 \bar{\Gamma}}{d\xi^2} - N\bar{\Gamma} \tag{6.171}$$

with $\bar{\Gamma} = 1$ at $\xi = 0$ and $\bar{\Gamma} = 0$ at $\xi = \infty$. The solution to Eq. (6.171) is

$$\bar{\Gamma} = \exp\left(-\sqrt{N + p}\, \xi \right) \tag{6.172}$$

of which the inverse transform is

$$\Gamma = \tfrac{1}{2} \exp\left(-\xi\sqrt{N}\right) \text{erfc}\left(\xi/\sqrt{4\zeta} - \sqrt{N\zeta}\right)$$
$$+ \tfrac{1}{2} \exp\left(\xi\sqrt{N}\right) \text{erfc}\left(\xi/\sqrt{4\zeta} + \sqrt{N\zeta}\right) \tag{6.173}$$

The flux at the interface is

$$N_A\Big|_{x=0} = -C_{A0} \sqrt{\frac{v_{\max}\mathfrak{D}_{AB}}{L}} \frac{\partial\Gamma}{\partial\xi}\Big|_{\xi=0}$$

$$= C_{A0} \sqrt{\frac{v_{\max}\mathfrak{D}_{AB}}{L}} \left(\sqrt{N}\,\text{erf}\,\sqrt{N\zeta} + \frac{1}{\sqrt{\pi\zeta}}\, e^{-N\zeta}\right) \tag{6.174}$$

Hence, the total rate of absorption in a film of width W is

$$\mathfrak{W}_A = W \int_0^L N_A\Big|_{x=0} dz = WL \int_0^1 N_A\Big|_{x=0} d\zeta$$

$$= C_{A0}WL \sqrt{\frac{v_{\max}\mathfrak{D}_{AB}}{L}} \int_0^1 \left(\sqrt{N}\,\text{erf}\,\sqrt{N\zeta} + \frac{1}{\sqrt{\pi\zeta}}\, e^{-N\zeta}\right) d\zeta$$

$$= C_{A0}Wv_{\max} \sqrt{\frac{\mathfrak{D}_{AB}}{k_1}} \left[(\tfrac{1}{2} + N)\,\text{erf}\,\sqrt{N} + \sqrt{\frac{N}{\pi}}\, e^{-N} \right] \tag{6.175}$$

In the limit of no chemical reaction $(N \to 0)$ we get

$$\mathfrak{W}_A = c_{A0}WL \sqrt{\frac{4\mathfrak{D}_{AB}v_{\max}}{\pi L}} \tag{6.176}$$

for the rate of absorption of A in g moles/sec.

DIFFUSION AND HETEROGENEOUS CHEMICAL REACTION IN A STAGNANT-GAS FILM.[63] Suppose a gas A diffuses through a film of stagnant gas B, bounded by the planes $z = 0$ and $z = \delta$, to a catalytic surface at $z = \delta$. At the surface the irreversible polymerization reaction

$$nA \to A_n \tag{6.177}$$

occurs. At the catalyst surface $(z = \delta)$ A is removed at a rate which may be expressed as

$$N_A = k_h x_A{}^h \qquad z = \delta \tag{6.178}$$

Here k_h is the reaction-rate constant and h is the order of the surface reaction. It is desired to develop an expression for the over-all rate of the diffusion-reaction process, given the gas-phase composition at the outer edge of the film. Constant temperature and pressure are assumed, and the gases are presumed to be ideal.

If no homogeneous reactions occur in the gas film, then in steady state the equations of continuity require that N_A, N_{A_n}, and N_B be constants; N_B is zero inasmuch as it is stagnant. The stoichiometry requires that

$$N_A = -nN_{A_n} \tag{6.179}$$

If the following dimensionless quantities are introduced,

$$\nu = \frac{N_A\delta}{c\mathfrak{D}_{AB}} \qquad r = \frac{\mathfrak{D}_{A_nB}}{\mathfrak{D}_{AB}} \qquad s = \frac{\mathfrak{D}_{A_nB}}{\mathfrak{D}_{AA_n}} \qquad \zeta = \frac{z}{\delta} \tag{6.180}$$

then the Stefan-Maxwell equations for multicomponent ordinary diffusion become

$$\frac{1}{\nu}\frac{dx_A}{d\zeta} = s\left(1 - \frac{1}{n}\right)x_A + (s - r)x_B - s \tag{6.181}$$

$$\frac{1}{\nu}\frac{dx_B}{d\zeta} = \left(r - \frac{1}{n}\right)x_B \tag{6.182}$$

The third equation (for x_{A_n}) is not needed inasmuch as $x_A + x_{A_n} + x_B = 1$. Equations (6.181) and (6.182) are to be solved with the boundary conditions that $x_A = x_{A0}$ and $x_B = x_{B0}$ at $\zeta = 0$ (that is, at the outer edge of the film).

The equation for x_B may easily be integrated to give

$$x_B = x_{B0} \exp R\nu\zeta \tag{6.183}$$

if $R = r - (1/n)$. Then the equation for x_A may be integrated to yield

$$x_A = (x_{A0} - N^{-1} + M^{-1}x_{B0}) \exp (Ns\nu\zeta) + N^{-1} - M^{-1}x_{B0} \exp R\nu\zeta \tag{6.184}$$

Here $N = 1 - n^{-1}$, and $M = (1 - n^{-1})[(1 - s)/(r - s)]$.

From the concentration profile of A in Eq. (6.184) and the expression for the kinetics at the wall [Eq. (6.178)],

$$\sqrt[h]{\nu/K} = (x_{A0} - N^{-1} + M^{-1}x_{B0}) \exp Ns\nu + N^{-1} - M^{-1} \exp R\nu \tag{6.185}$$

in which $K = k_h\delta/c\mathfrak{D}_{A_nB}$. This is a transcendental equation for ν (the dimensionless rate of diffusion plus chemical reaction) in terms of K, n, r, s, x_{A0}, and x_{B0}. Other more complex problems in diffusion-controlled catalysis can be set up and solved by similar procedures.

SIMULTANEOUS HEAT AND MASS TRANSFER. Many problems in condensation, absorption, and psychrometry involve the simultaneous transport of material and energy. Consider the situation in Fig. 6.2. A hot, condensable vapor A diffuses from the main stream through a stagnant film of noncondensable gas B. The vapor A condenses at the cold surface and runs down the surface as a thin film. Suppose that the concentration of A and the temperature are both known at the plane $z = 0$ (the liquid-vapor boundary) and at the plane $z = \delta$ (the vaguely defined boundary between the main gas stream and the stagnant-gas film). It is desired to find the concentration and temperature profiles.

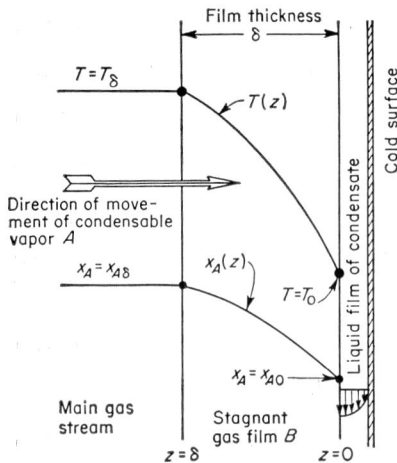

FIG. 6.2. Simultaneous heat and mass transfer.

The starting point is the equation of continuity of A and the energy equation, which at steady state assume the following one-dimensional form [Eqs. (6.50) and (6.85)]:

$$\frac{dN_{Az}}{dz} = 0 \tag{6.186}$$

$$\frac{de_z}{dz} = 0 \tag{6.187}$$

These equations state that N_{Az} and e_z are constant through the film.

The *concentration profiles* are obtained by inserting the expression for N_{Az} for diffusion of A through stagnant B

$$N_{Az} = -\frac{c\mathfrak{D}_{AB}}{1 - x_A}\frac{dx_A}{dz} \tag{6.188}$$

into Eq. (6.186) and by integrating to obtain

$$\frac{1 - x_A}{1 - x_{A0}} = \left(\frac{1 - x_{A\delta}}{1 - x_{A0}}\right)^{z/\delta} \tag{6.189}$$

for the concentration profiles. The constant molar flux is then

$$N_{Az} = \frac{c\mathfrak{D}_{AB}}{\delta} \ln \frac{1 - x_{A\delta}}{1 - x_{A0}} \tag{6.190}$$

Combination of these two results leads to

$$\frac{x_{A0} - x_{Az}}{x_{A0} - x_{A\delta}} = \frac{1 - \exp\left[-(N_{Az}/c\mathfrak{D}_{AB})z\right]}{1 - \exp\left[-(N_{Az}/c\mathfrak{D}_{AB})\delta\right]} \tag{6.191}$$

The *temperature profiles* are obtained by inserting into Eq. (6.187) the expression for e_z. Now $\mathbf{e}$ is given by Eq. (6.32); the latter may be simplified by neglecting the contributions $[\boldsymbol{\tau} \bullet \mathbf{v}]$ and $(\tfrac{1}{2} \rho v^2)\, \mathbf{v}$, so that

$$\mathbf{e} = -\lambda \nabla T + \sum_{\alpha=1}^{\nu} \overline{H}_\alpha \mathbf{J}_\alpha + \rho \mathbf{v} + \rho \hat{U} \mathbf{v}$$

$$= -\lambda \nabla T + \sum_{\alpha=1}^{\nu} \overline{H}_\alpha \mathbf{J}_\alpha + \rho \hat{H} \mathbf{v}$$

$$= -\lambda \nabla T + \sum_{\alpha=1}^{\nu} \overline{H}_\alpha \mathbf{J}_\alpha + \sum_{\alpha=1}^{\nu} c_\alpha \overline{H}_\alpha \mathbf{v} \tag{6.192}$$

From the expressions for mass fluxes in Table 6.3,

$$\mathbf{e} = -\lambda \nabla T + \sum_{\alpha=1}^{\nu} \mathbf{N}_\alpha \overline{H}_\alpha \tag{6.193}$$

By assuming an ideal gas mixture,

$$e_z = -\lambda \frac{dT}{dz} + N_{Az}\tilde{C}_{pA}(T - T_0) \tag{6.194}$$

if $T = T_0$ has been selected as the datum plane for the enthalpy; $\tilde{C}_{pA}$ is the heat capacity of A per mole. Insertion of this expression for e_z into Eq. (6.187) and integration between the limits $T = T_0$ at $z = 0$ and $T = T_\delta$ at $z = \delta$ gives

$$\frac{T - T_0}{T_\delta - T_0} = \frac{1 - \exp\left[-\left(\dfrac{N_{Az}\tilde{C}_{pA}}{\lambda}\right)z\right]}{1 - \exp\left[-\left(\dfrac{N_{Az}\tilde{C}_{pA}}{\lambda}\right)\delta\right]} \tag{6.195}$$

Hence the temperature profile is not in general linear and is directly linked to the mass-transfer rate. For further discussions of simultaneous heat, mass, and momentum transfer from both the film-theory viewpoint and the boundary-layer-theory viewpoint, see Ref. 4, chap. 21.

6.7. The Macroscopic Balances

In many engineering applications it is convenient to make use of the macroscopic balances, or over-all balances, which are integrated forms of the equations of change. These balances give relations between the flow state at the input and output to a flow system, such as that shown in Fig. 6.3.

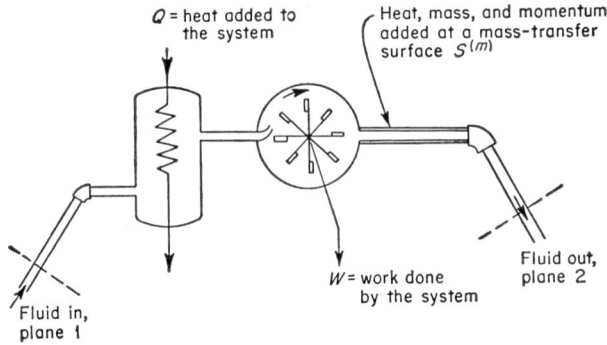

FIG. 6.3. A sample macroscopic flow system.

When the equations of continuity, motion, and energy are integrated over the volume of an arbitrary flow system, one obtains, respectively, the macroscopic mass, momentum, and energy balances. A fourth balance may be obtained by integrating the mechanical-energy equation (Art. 6.4) over the flow system to obtain the macroscopic mechanical-energy balance, or Bernoulli equation. For details of the integrations (which take into account the moving parts in the system) the reader is referred to the original work.[4.65]

In the following paragraphs $\Delta f = f_2 - f_1$ means "f evaluated at plane 2 minus f evaluated at plane 1." Quantities labeled with a superscript (m) are contributions to the input of mass, momentum, and energy associated with regions of the boundary surface across which mass transfer occurs (either by injection through porous walls or by interphase mass transport).

The Macroscopic Mass, Momentum, and Energy Balances. Integration of the equations of continuity of species α, motion, and energy over the volume of the arbitrary flow system in Fig. 6.3 gives

$$\frac{d}{dt} m_{\alpha \text{ tot}} = -\Delta w_\alpha + w_\alpha{}^{(m)} + r_{\alpha \text{ tot}} \qquad \alpha = 1, 2, \ldots, \nu \tag{6.196}$$

$$\frac{d}{dt} \mathbf{P}_{\text{tot}} = -\Delta \left(\frac{\langle v^2 \rangle}{\langle v \rangle} \mathbf{w} + p\mathbf{S} \right) + \mathbf{F}^{(m)} - \mathbf{F} + m_{\text{tot}}\mathbf{g} \tag{6.197}$$

$$\frac{d}{dt} E_{\text{tot}} = -\Delta \left(\hat{U} + p\hat{V} + \frac{1}{2} \frac{\langle v^3 \rangle}{\langle v \rangle} + \hat{\Phi} \right) w + Q^{(m)} + Q - W \tag{6.198}$$

The first of these three relations expresses the law of conservation of mass of species α: the rate of increase of mass of α in the system depends upon the net influx of α across surfaces 1, 2, and m and upon the total rate of production within the system by homogeneous and heterogeneous reaction. The second relation indicates that the total momentum within the system depends on the rate of momentum input and output at 1 and 2, the pressures at the two ends of the system, the addition of momentum across the mass-transfer surface m, the reaction force $\mathbf{F}$, and the external gravity force $m_{\text{tot}}\mathbf{g}$. The quantity $\mathbf{S}_1$ is a vector whose magnitude is the cross-section area at plane 1 and whose direction is in the direction of fluid flow; similarly, $\mathbf{w} = \rho\langle v \rangle \mathbf{S}$, if $\langle v \rangle$ is the velocity averaged over the cross section. The third relation above is a statement of the first law of thermodynamics as applied to the flow system: the change in the total (internal + kinetic + potential) energy results from flow of these entities across surfaces 1, 2, and m, from heat addition *to* the system through the walls Q, from pressure-volume work $\Delta(p\hat{V}w)$, and from work W done *by* the system *on* the surroundings by mechanical means. Clearly, all ν equations of continuity may be added together to give

$$\frac{d}{dt} m_{\text{tot}} = -\Delta w + w^{(m)} \tag{6.199}$$

which is the mass balance for the totality of ν species. In getting this relation use was made of the fact that $\Sigma_\alpha r_{\alpha \text{ tot}} = 0$ by the law of conservation of mass.

In applying the balances above to problems in turbulent flow, one may to a very good approximation usually replace $\langle v^2 \rangle / \langle v \rangle$ by $\langle v \rangle$ and $\langle v^3 \rangle / \langle v \rangle$ by $\langle v \rangle^2$.

In order to define in somewhat greater detail some of the quantities given in the balance, it is noted that

$$m_{\alpha \text{ tot}} = \int_V \rho_\alpha \, dV \qquad (6.200) \qquad w_\alpha^{(m)} = -\int_{S^{(m)}} (\mathbf{n} \bullet \rho_\alpha \mathbf{v}_\alpha) \, dS \qquad (6.203)$$

$$\mathbf{P}_{\text{tot}} = \int_V \rho v \, dV \qquad (6.201) \qquad \mathbf{F}^{(m)} = -\int_{S^{(m)}} (\mathbf{n} \bullet \rho \mathbf{v}\mathbf{v}) \, dS \qquad (6.204)$$

$$E_{\text{tot}} = \int_{\rho V} (\hat{U} + \tfrac{1}{2} v^2 + \hat{\Phi}) \, dV \quad (6.202) \qquad Q^{(m)} \approx -\int_{S^{(m)}} (\mathbf{n} \bullet \Sigma_\alpha c_\alpha \mathbf{v}_\alpha \overline{H}_\alpha) \, dS \quad (6.205)$$

in which V is the volume of the flow system, and $\mathbf{n}$ is the normal unit vector. Equation (6.205) is approximate in that the contributions of viscous work, kinetic energy, and potential energy are usually of no significance [Eq. (6.193)]. Note also that for a circular tube

$$\langle v^n \rangle = \frac{\int_0^{2\pi} \int_0^R v^n r \, dr \, d\theta}{\int_0^{2\pi} \int_0^R r \, dr \, d\theta} \qquad (6.206)$$

with similar definitions for conduits of other cross sections.

For non-Newtonian fluids of the Ostwald–de Waele type $\langle v^2 \rangle / \langle v \rangle^2 = (3n + 1)/(2n + 1)$ and $\langle v^3 \rangle / \langle v \rangle^3 = 3(3n + 1)^2/(2n + 1)(5n + 3)$ for laminar flow in tubes. The values for Newtonian fluids are $4/3$ and 2, respectively.

The Macroscopic Mechanical-energy Balance (Bernoulli Equation). Integration of the mechanical-energy equation [Eq. (6.80)] over the volume of the flow system V gives a macroscopic balance containing only terms relating to the interchange of various forms of mechanical energy or its degradation into thermal energy. (For pure inviscid fluids the result is known as Bernoulli's equation, although many engineering texts have used this name to describe the analogous equations for a viscous fluid.)

When the fluid is a multicomponent mixture with chemical reactions occurring and with mass-transfer surfaces, the mechanical-energy balance cannot be written in any simple form. Hence this treatment is limited to several special cases involving no chemical reactions and no mass-transfer surfaces.

Isothermal flow:

$$\frac{d}{dt} (K_{\text{tot}} + \Phi_{\text{tot}} + A_{\text{tot}}) = -\Delta \left(\frac{1}{2} \frac{\langle v^3 \rangle}{\langle v \rangle} + \hat{\Phi} + \hat{G} \right) w - W - E_v \qquad (6.207a)$$

Isentropic flow:

$$\frac{d}{dt} (K_{\text{tot}} + \Phi_{\text{tot}} + U_{\text{tot}}) = -\Delta \left(\frac{1}{2} \frac{\langle v^3 \rangle}{\langle v \rangle} + \hat{\Phi} + \hat{H} \right) w - W - E_v \qquad (6.207b)$$

in which A_{tot} is the total (Helmholtz) free energy $(A = U - TS)$ in the system, $\hat{G}$ is the (Gibbs) free energy (or free enthalpy) per unit mass, W is the rate at which the flow system does work on the surroundings, and E_v is the rate at which mechanical energy is being dissipated into heat. For *incompressible* fluids both of the above equations reduce to†

$$\frac{d}{dt} (K_{\text{tot}} + \Phi_{\text{tot}}) = -\Delta \left(\frac{1}{2} \frac{\langle v^3 \rangle}{\langle v \rangle} + \hat{\Phi} + \frac{p}{\rho} \right) w - W - E_v \qquad (6.208)$$

† For the derivation of this equation see Ref. 4, example 7.3-1 and problem 7.R.

and for *steady-state flow* of compressible fluids both Eqs. (6.207a and b) become

$$\Delta \frac{1}{2}\frac{\langle v^3 \rangle}{\langle v \rangle} + \Delta \hat{\Phi} + \int_{p_1}^{p_2} \frac{dp}{\rho} + \hat{W} + \hat{E}_v = 0 \qquad (6.209)$$

in which $\hat{W}$ and $\hat{E}_v$ are evaluated on a per-unit-mass basis. The integral over p in Eq. (6.207) is $(RT/M)\ln p_2/p_1$ for ideal gases and $\Delta p/\rho$ for incompressible fluids. In turbulent flow $\langle v^3 \rangle / \langle v \rangle$ is generally replaceable by $\langle v \rangle^2$. And for most problems $\Delta \hat{\Phi}$ just becomes $g\,\Delta z$, if z is the height above some datum plane.

In order to define some of the quantities in the Bernoulli balance in somewhat greater detail, it is noted that

$$K_{\text{tot}} = \int_V \frac{1}{2}\rho v^2 \, dV \qquad (6.210)$$

$$\Phi_{\text{tot}} = \int_V \rho \hat{\Phi} \, dV \qquad (6.211)$$

$$A_{\text{tot}} = \int_V \rho \hat{A} \, dV \qquad (6.212)$$

and

$$E_v = -\int (\boldsymbol{\tau} : \boldsymbol{\nabla} \mathbf{v}) \, dV \qquad (6.213)$$

This latter quantity, the total rate of dissipation, is the quantity which must be minimized in the Helmholtz variational principle for Newtonian flow, Eq. (6.81).

Applications of the Macroscopic Balances. In analyzing flow systems by the macroscopic-balance method one should make use of the information provided by all four balances. One simply discards the terms which are not needed in any given problem, and thereby a set of ordinary differential equations is obtained for unsteady-state problems or a set of algebraic equations for steady-state problems. From these equations one gets information about power requirements, heat requirements, outlet conditions, or friction losses.

The macroscopic balances may be used in two ways: they may be applied as written directly to a flow system between planes 1 and 2, or they may be applied to a differential volume[66] $S dl$ of a flow system, if dl is a differential distance in the direction of flow at a plane of cross-section area S. This latter approach is used when the rates of heat and mass transfer through the walls are a function of position. In such problems one has to integrate over l to get the relations between the flow properties at planes 1 and 2.

ISOTHERMAL FLOW OF INCOMPRESSIBLE FLUIDS IN CONDUITS WITH SUDDEN EXPANSION; DISCHARGE INTO MANIFOLDS. An incompressible fluid flows out of several circular tubes into a larger circular tube with a net increase in cross section, as shown in Fig. 6.4. Such systems are of importance in heat exchangers of certain types, for which the expansion and contraction losses account for an appreciable fraction of the over-all pressure drop. In some cases the flow in the small tubes may be laminar and that in the large tubes may be turbulent; in the solution which follows no restrictions are made regarding the nature of the flow regime.

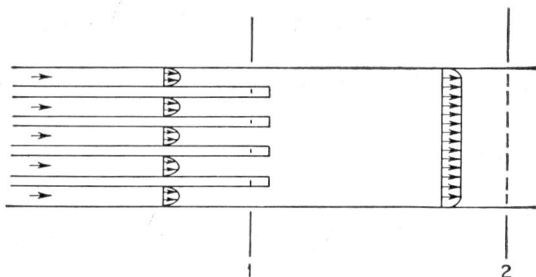

FIG. 6.4. Multiple discharge into a common conduit.

As plane 1, the collection of cross sections of all the small tubes leading into the big tube is selected; plane 2 is taken to be a plane far enough down the tube so that a distinct velocity profile has been established. Over the system enclosed between these two planes three balances are made; the fourth balance, namely, the over-all energy balance, is not needed inasmuch as the flow is isothermal.

MASS BALANCE. At steady state $w_1 = w_2$, or for an incompressible fluid,

$$\langle v_1 \rangle S_1 = \langle v_2 \rangle S_2 \qquad (6.214)$$

whence

$$\beta \equiv \frac{S_1}{S_2} = \frac{\langle v_2 \rangle}{\langle v_1 \rangle} \qquad (6.215)$$

which defines a quantity β.

MOMENTUM BALANCE. When the $d\mathbf{P}/dt$ and $m_{\text{tot}}g$ terms are neglected,

$$\rho \langle v_1^2 \rangle S_1 - \rho \langle v_2^2 \rangle S_2 + p_1 S_1 - p_2 S_2 - F = 0 \qquad (6.216)$$

The force F of the fluid on the solid will consist of the viscous forces acting tangentially at the walls (which is neglected) and the normal force $p_1(S_2 - S_1)$ acting in the direction *opposite* to the direction of flow. Hence

$$\rho \langle v_1^2 \rangle S_1 - \rho \langle v_2^2 \rangle S_2 + p_1 S_1 - p_2 S_2 + p_1(S_2 - S_1) = 0 \qquad (6.217)$$

This result may be rewritten by using the mass balance and the definition of a set of quantities $K_i^{(j)}$ defined as

$$K_i^{(j)} = \frac{\langle v_i^j \rangle}{\langle v_i \rangle^j} \qquad (6.218)$$

These are just dimensionless numbers which can be calculated when the velocity profiles are known. In terms of these quantities and β the momentum balance finally becomes

$$\frac{p_2 - p_1}{\rho \langle v_1 \rangle^2} = \beta K_1^{(2)} - \beta^2 K_2^{(2)} \qquad (6.219)$$

Several special cases of this dimensionless-pressure *rise* are of interest:

1. If the flow is highly turbulent in the small tubes and the large tube so that the velocity profiles are almost flat, then the $K_i^{(j)}$ are unity and $p_2 - p_1 = \rho v_2(v_1 - v_2)$.

2. For turbulent flow in the large tube, $K_2^{(2)}$ varies from about 1.07 at Re = 2000 to 1.04 at Re = 20,000. Hence setting $K_2^{(2)} = 1$ is valid for many engineering calculations.

3. For laminar flow in the small tubes $K_1^{(2)} = 4/3$. This is easily verified by inserting the parabolic profiles into the definition of the $K_i^{(2)}$.

4. If the total cross section of the small tubes is the same as that for the large tube, then $\beta = 1$ and

$$\frac{p_2 - p_1}{\rho \langle v_1 \rangle^2} = K_1^{(2)} - 1 \qquad (6.220)$$

if turbulent flow prevails in the large tube.

MECHANICAL-ENERGY BALANCE. When this balance is solved for $\hat{E}_v$,

$$\hat{E}_v = \frac{p_1 - p_2}{\rho} + \frac{1}{2}\left(\frac{\langle v_1^3 \rangle}{\langle v_1 \rangle} - \frac{\langle v_2^3 \rangle}{\langle v_2 \rangle} \right) \qquad (6.221)$$

Now insert the expression above for $p_1 - p_2$ (obtained from the momentum balance) and make use of the mass balance to introduce β. In this way the following expression for a dimensionless mechanical-energy "loss" is obtained.

$$K_e \equiv \frac{\hat{E}_v}{\frac{1}{2}K_1^{(3)}\langle v_1 \rangle^2} = 1 - 2\beta \frac{K_1^{(2)}}{K_1^{(3)}} + \beta^2 \left(2\frac{K_2^{(2)}}{K_1^{(3)}} - \frac{K_2^{(3)}}{K_1^{(3)}} \right) \qquad (6.222)$$

Several special cases of interest are:

1. For $\beta = 0$ (i.e., for discharge into a large tank) the kinetic energy of the entering stream is completely dissipated, regardless of the flow regime in the small tube.

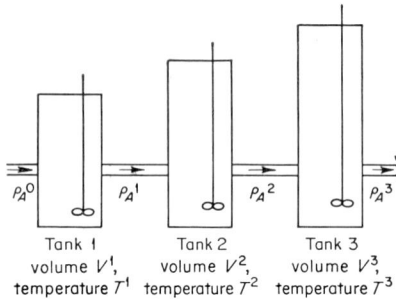

Tank 1
volume V^1,
temperature T^1

Tank 2
volume V^2,
temperature T^2

Tank 3
volume V^3,
temperature T^3

FIG. 6.5. Series of continuous, stirred-tank reactors.

2. For flat velocity profiles and no change of cross section $\hat{E}_v = 0$.

3. If the velocity profiles in the small tubes are less "flat" than the profile in the big tube (this is nearly always the case), then $\hat{E}_v$ has a finite value even if there is no change in cross section.

4. For laminar flow in small tubes and highly turbulent flow in the large tube and with $\beta \approx 1$, $K_1^{(3)} = 2$ and $K_2^{(3)} \doteq 1$, so that $K_e \doteq 1 - \frac{4}{3} + \frac{1}{2} = \frac{1}{6}$.

SERIES OF CONTINUOUS, STIRRED-TANK REACTORS. Suppose a liquid stream is fed to a series of stirred tanks as shown in Fig. 6.5 with a volumetric flow rate Q. The feed to the first tank contains species A at a concentration ρ_{A0}. In the tanks, A disappears by a first-order chemical reaction. It is desired to know the concentration of A in each tank when a steady state is reached.

Let $\rho_A{}^i$ and $\rho_A{}^{i+1}$ be the concentration of species A in the streams leaving the ith and $(i + 1)$st tank, respectively. Then the mass balance written around the $(i + 1)$st tank gives

$$w_A{}^i - w_A{}^{i+1} + r_{A \text{ tot}}^{i+1} = 0 \tag{6.223}$$

in the steady state. By neglecting density changes one may write the mass flows w_A as $w_A{}^i = Q\rho_A{}^i$. For a first-order reaction

$$r_{A \text{ tot}}^i = + \int_{V_i} r_A{}^i dV = - \int_{V_i} k^i \rho_A{}^i dV \tag{6.224}$$

in which V_i is the volume of the ith tank, and k^i is the reaction rate constant in the ith tank. The k^i are not in general all the same, since the temperature may be different in the various tanks.

In practice, it is reasonable to assume that agitation in each tank is sufficient to give a uniform temperature and composition in each tank. Hence Eq. (6.224) reads simply

$$Q(\rho_A{}^i - \rho_A{}^{i+1}) - k^{i+1}\rho_A{}^{i+1}V^{i+1} = 0 \tag{6.225}$$

Let the nominal holding time in the ith tank V_i/Q be called $t_h{}^i$. Then Eq. (6.225) shows that

$$\rho_A{}^{N-1} = \rho_A{}^N(1 + k^N t_h{}^N)$$

$$\rho_A{}^{N-2} = \rho_A{}^{N-1}(1 + k^{N-1} t_h{}^{N-1})$$

$$= \rho_A{}^N(1 + k^N t_h{}^N)(1 + k^{N-1} t_h{}^{N-1}) \tag{6.226}$$

$$\rho_A{}^{N-m} = \rho^N \prod_{i=0}^{m-1} (1 - k^{N-i} t_h{}^{N-i})$$

if N is the total number of tanks connected in series. The mass density of species A in the effluent from the last tank is then

$$\rho_A{}^N = \frac{\rho_A{}^0}{\displaystyle\prod_{i=0}^{N-1} (1 - k^{N-i} t_n{}^{N-i})} \tag{6.227}$$

Hence, the degree of conversion at the exit of the series of tanks is

$$\frac{\rho_A{}^0 - \rho_A{}^N}{\rho_A{}^0} = \prod_{i=0}^{N-1} (1 - k^{N-i} t_h{}^{N-i})^{-1} - 1 \tag{6.228}$$

For transient systems of this type see a review article by Acrivos and Amundson.[67]

END CORRECTIONS IN CAPILLARY-TUBE VISCOMETERS.[28] In calculating fluid viscosities from capillary-tube flow data, it is necessary to correct the data for entrance and exit effects and for changes in kinetic energy. A rigorous method of correcting capillary-tube flow data is as follows.

With a capillary tube of length L_A fitted to the viscometer reservoir (Fig. 6.6) a (gauge) pressure p_A is applied to the reservoir and the rate of efflux w and the head of liquid in the reservoir l_A are noted. Next, a new tube, of identical radius but of length $L_B(L_B > L_A)$, is fitted to the reservoir. The pressure in the reservoir is adjusted until the rate of efflux is the *same* as prevailed with the tube of length L_A and the pressure p_A in the reservoir. Let the required pressure with the tube of length L_B be p_B.

Application of the steady-state† mechanical-energy balance for incompressible fluids then gives for the two expressions

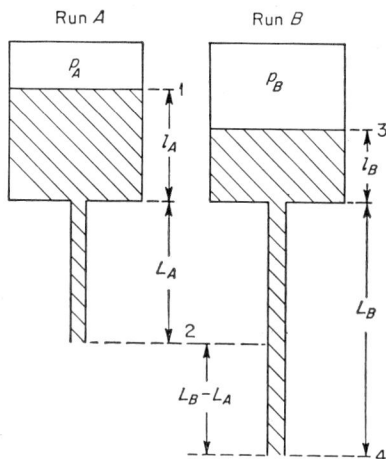

FIG. 6.6. Two tube-viscometer runs with the *same* volume rate of flow. Pressures p_A and p_B are maintained by an inert gas.

$$\frac{1}{2}\frac{\langle v_2^3\rangle}{\langle v_2\rangle} - \frac{1}{2}\frac{\langle v_1^3\rangle}{\langle v_1\rangle} + (\hat{\Phi}_2 - \hat{\Phi}_1) - \frac{1}{\rho}p_A = (-\hat{E}_v)_A \qquad (6.229)$$

$$\frac{1}{2}\frac{\langle v_4^3\rangle}{\langle v_4\rangle} - \frac{1}{2}\frac{\langle v_3^3\rangle}{\langle v_3\rangle} + (\hat{\Phi}_4 - \hat{\Phi}_3) - \frac{1}{\rho}p_B = (-\hat{E}_v)_B \qquad (6.230)$$

in which the subscripts A and B on the terms on the right-hand sides of the equations refer to viscous dissipation with the two different tubes at the same flow rate w. By subtraction

$$\frac{1}{\rho}(p_B - p_A) + (\hat{\Phi}_2 - \hat{\Phi}_1 - \hat{\Phi}_4 + \hat{\Phi}_3) = -[(-\hat{E}_v)_B - (-\hat{E}_v)_A] \qquad (6.231)$$

as the kinetic-energy terms have exactly canceled each other, since the flow rates in both cases are adjusted to be exactly the same.

The right-hand side of Eq. (6.229) represents the viscous dissipation of mechanical energy per unit of mass in a tube of length $L_B - L_A$. If now *both* tubes are long enough so that fully developed flow is attained at least in part of each tube, then it is possible to calculate exactly the right-hand side of Eq. (6.229). By the definition of $\hat{E}_v$, one has

$$-[(-\hat{E}_v)_B - (-\hat{E}_v)_A] = -\frac{1}{w}\int_{V_B-V_A}(\boldsymbol{\tau}:\boldsymbol{\nabla}\mathbf{v})\,dV$$

$$= \frac{1}{w}\int_{V_B-V_A}(\mathbf{v}\cdot[\boldsymbol{\nabla}\cdot\boldsymbol{\tau}])\,dV - \int_{S_B-S_A}([\boldsymbol{\tau}\cdot\mathbf{v}]\cdot\mathbf{n})\,dS \qquad (6.232)$$

In which S_B and S_A are solid surfaces plus control surfaces in contact with the liquid in the two cases. In the second line, the relation $(\boldsymbol{\tau}:\boldsymbol{\nabla}\mathbf{v}) = -(\mathbf{v}\cdot[\boldsymbol{\nabla}\cdot\boldsymbol{\tau}]) + (\boldsymbol{\nabla}\cdot[\boldsymbol{\tau}\cdot\mathbf{v}])$ has been used; then the volume integral of $(\boldsymbol{\nabla}\cdot[\boldsymbol{\tau}\cdot\mathbf{v}])$ changed to the surface integral over $S_B - S_A$ by means of the divergence theorem. Clearly, the surface integral must vanish, since $\mathbf{v}$ vanishes at the solid surfaces and the contributions at the control surfaces just cancel each other.

---

† This is an approximation, since efflux causes changing levels in the reservoirs. Hence l_A and l_B represent averages.

In the region $V_B - V_A$, flow is fully established (and laminar) so that from the equation of motion, one finds

$$(\mathbf{v} \bullet [\boldsymbol{\nabla} \bullet \boldsymbol{\tau}]) = v_z P \qquad (6.233)$$

as $P \equiv -\partial p/\partial z + \rho g$ and v_z is the axial velocity in the tube. Then by integration

$$\frac{1}{w} \int_{V_B - V_A} (\mathbf{v} \bullet [\boldsymbol{\nabla} \bullet \boldsymbol{\tau}]) \, dV = \frac{2\pi(L_B - L_A)P}{w} \int_0^R v_z r \, dr = (L_B - L_A)\frac{P}{\rho} \qquad (6.234)$$

in which R is the radius of the tube. If the potential energy at control surface 4 is set equal to zero, one finally obtains for the effective pressure gradient P

$$P = \frac{p_B - p_A}{L_B - L_A} + \rho g \left(1 + \frac{l_B - l_A}{L_B - L_A}\right) \qquad (6.235)$$

Since flow is laminar, for Newtonian fluids the law of Hagen-Poiseuille applies in the fully developed region, and the viscosity is obtained from experimental measurements by

$$\mu = \frac{\pi R^4 \rho}{8w} \left[\frac{p_B - p_A}{L_B - L_A} + \rho g \left(1 + \frac{l_B - l_A}{L_B - L_A}\right)\right] \qquad (6.236)$$

The result in Eq. (6.235) may also be used for non-Newtonian fluids.

ADIABATIC, FRICTIONLESS EXPANSION OF REACTING GASES THROUGH A NOZZLE. An equimolar mixture of gases A and B is injected into a reaction chamber equipped with a converging-diverging nozzle as shown in Fig. 6.7. The figure is an idealized representation of a liquid-fuel rocket. In the chamber the reversible chemical reaction occurs: $A + B \rightleftharpoons R + S$. Given that the rates of both forward and reverse reactions are very fast, the velocity of flow at the nozzle throat is computed.

At any point in the system, the net rate of reaction, say, for species A_A, is

$$R_A = k_2 c_R c_S - k_1 c_A c_B \qquad (6.237)$$

if k_1 and k_2 are the reaction rate constants for the forward and reverse reactions, respectively. Since the rates are very fast, they tend to balance each other, and the net rate of production of any species at a point will be essentially zero. In other words, the system is very nearly in *chemical equilibrium* at every point.[4] Hence one has

$$\frac{c_R c_S}{c_A c_B} = \frac{x_R x_S}{x_A x_B} = \frac{k_1}{k_2} \equiv K \qquad (6.238)$$

if K is the equilibrium constant. From the Arrhenius equation [Eq. (6.44)], it is seen that K depends on T alone; hence the composition at any point in the system depends only on T. If, however, the reactions had resulted in a net change in the number of moles present in the system, composition would also depend on pressure.

Since reactants are introduced in stoichiometric amounts, $x_A = x_B$ and $x_R = x_S$, and

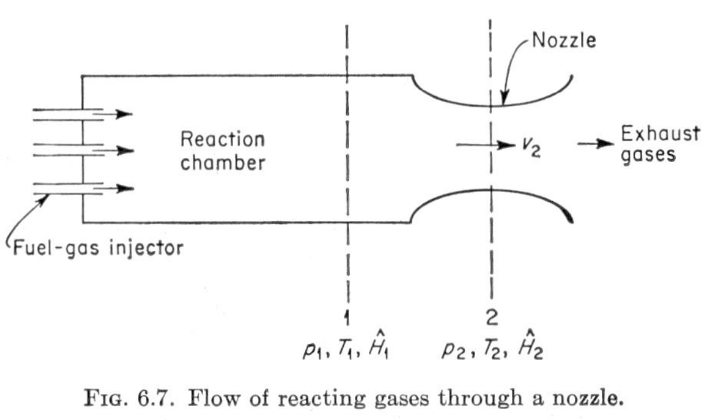

FIG. 6.7. Flow of reacting gases through a nozzle.

further, since the sum of the mole fractions must be unity, $x_A = \frac{1}{2} - x_R$. Substitution of these expressions into Eq. (6.238) then gives the quadratic equation

$$(K - 1)x_R^2 - Kx_R + \tfrac{1}{4}K = 0 \tag{6.239}$$

which relates composition to temperature at any point.

Assuming that the velocity in the chamber may be neglected, that the velocity profile in the throat is flat, that the process is adiabatic, and that changes in potential energy are small, the steady-state energy balance [Eq. (6.185)] between control surfaces 1 and 2 may be written

$$\tfrac{1}{2}\langle v \rangle^2 = \hat{H}_1 - \hat{H}_2 \tag{6.240}$$

in which subscripts 1 and 2 refer to conditions in the tank and at the nozzle throat, respectively. The enthalpy change may be evaluated from the relation

$$d\hat{H} = \frac{1}{\rho}\, dp \tag{6.241}$$

which is obtained by eliminating $d\frac{1}{2}v^2$ from the macroscopic energy balance and the macroscopic mechanical-energy balance, both written in differential form. For ideal gases

$$p = \frac{\rho RT}{\displaystyle\sum_{\alpha=1}^{\nu} x_\alpha M_\alpha} \tag{6.242}$$

and

$$\hat{H} = \frac{\overline{H}}{\displaystyle\sum_{\alpha=1}^{\nu} x_\alpha M_\alpha}$$

$$= \frac{\displaystyle\sum_{\alpha=1}^{\nu} x_\alpha[\overline{H}_\alpha{}^0 + \overline{C}_{p\alpha}(T - T_0)]}{\displaystyle\sum_{\alpha=1}^{\nu} x_\alpha M_\alpha} \tag{6.243}$$

wherein $\overline{H}_\alpha{}^0 =$ molal enthalpy of species A_α at the reference temperature T_0, and $\overline{C}_{p\alpha} =$ molal heat capacity at constant pressure† of species A_α. Combination of the last three equations and integration then leads to

$$R \ln \frac{p_2}{p_1} \approx \int_{T_1}^{T_2} \frac{d\overline{H}}{dT}\, dT \tag{6.244}$$

in which

$$\frac{d\overline{H}}{dT} = \sum_{\alpha=1}^{\nu} \overline{C}_{p\alpha} x_\alpha + \sum_{\alpha=1}^{\nu} [\overline{H}_\alpha{}^0 + \overline{C}_{p\alpha}(T - T_0)] \frac{dx_\alpha}{dT} \tag{6.245}$$

Approximate equality is indicated in Eq. (6.244), since in differentiating $\hat{H}$, it was assumed that terms of the form $\overline{H}\, d \ln (\Sigma_\alpha x_\alpha M_\alpha)/d \ln T$ could be neglected (if all molecular weights M_α were the same, then no approximation would be involved).

Equation (6.210) determines the temperature, and hence the enthalpy at the nozzle throat. In order to evaluate the integral, a numerical integration must be used, since

† Equation (6.241) bears the implicit assumption that molar-heat capacities are independent of temperature.

the x_α and the dx_α/dT are complex functions of T which can be obtained from Eq. (6.237) and the temperature dependence of K.   Once the enthalpy at the throat has been found, the velocity in the throat can be calculated immediately from Eq. (6.238).

6.8. The Interphase-transfer Coefficients and the Friction-loss Factors

In the macroscopic mass, momentum, and energy balances, a term appears which represents interphase transfer: $W_\alpha{}^{(m)}$ represents the molar rate of transfer of species α across a mass-transfer interface; Q represents the rate of heat transfer across a solid-fluid interface; and F represents the rate at which the fluid imparts momentum to the solid bounding surfaces.   There are standard correlation methods available for estimating interphase transfer, and an introduction to this topic is given in this article.

In the mechanical-energy balance a term E_v appears which accounts for the friction loss.   There are also correlation methods available for this quantity.

The Definition of the Transfer Coefficients.   In each case the general definitions of the transfer coefficients are first given.   Then the definitions are considered further for two specific systems.

Momentum Transport: Friction Factors.   Consider a fluid flowing in a system in such a way that the force F exerted by the fluid on the solid is in the same direction as the average fluid motion.   Then by defining a dimensionless friction factor f,

$$F = fAK \tag{6.246}$$

in which A is a characteristic area, and K is a characteristic quantity with units of kinetic energy per unit volume.

For flow around a sphere of diameter D, with the fluid approaching with a velocity v_∞, it is customary to write

$$F = f \cdot \frac{\pi D^2}{4} \cdot \tfrac{1}{2}\,\rho v_\infty{}^2 \tag{6.247}$$

if ρ is the fluid density.

For flow in a smooth, cylindrical pipe of diameter D and length L, with the average velocity given by $\langle v \rangle$, it is customary to define f by

$$F = f \cdot \pi DL \cdot \tfrac{1}{2}\,\rho \langle v \rangle^2 \tag{6.248}$$

Note that for any given geometry, the definition of f depends on how A and K are chosen.   Generally, for conduits, A is taken to be the wetted area, whereas for submerged objects, A is taken to be the area "seen" by the approaching fluid

Energy Transport: Heat-transfer Coefficients.   The rate at which heat is exchanged between a wall and fluid is written

$$Q = hA\Delta T \tag{6.249}$$

in which Q = heat flow, Btu/hr
           A = area of heat-transfer surface
          ΔT = some characteristic temperature difference

For flow around a sphere of diameter D, with the surface temperature at T_0 and the temperature of the approaching fluid T_∞ (with $T_0 > T_\infty$), the rate of heat loss from the sphere is

$$Qh \cdot \tfrac{1}{6}\,\pi D^3 \cdot (T_0 - T_\infty) \tag{6.250}$$

For flow through a circular tube of diameter D and length L the situation is more complex because ΔT may be defined in several ways.   Let the surface temperature of the inside of the tube be T_0, the fluid inlet temperature be uniform at T_1, the bulk† fluid

---

† By bulk temperature T_b is meant the "cup-mixing" temperature, which, for example, for circular tubes is

$$T_b = \frac{\langle v_z T \rangle}{\langle v_z \rangle} = \frac{\displaystyle\int_0^{2\pi}\!\!\int_0^R v_z T r\, dr\, d\theta}{\displaystyle\int_0^{2\pi}\!\!\int_0^R v_z r\, dr\, d\theta}$$

exit temperature be T_2. Then three different h's may be defined in terms of the rate at which heat is transferred to the fluid.

$$Q = h_1 \cdot \pi DL \cdot (T_0 - T_1) \qquad (6.251)$$

$$Q = h_a \cdot \pi DL \cdot \frac{(T_0 - T_1) + (T_0 - T_2)}{2} \qquad (6.252)$$

$$Q = h_{\ln} \cdot \pi DL \cdot \frac{(T_0 - T_1) - (T_0 - T_2)}{\ln\left[(T_0 - T_1)/(T_0 - T_2)\right]} \qquad (6.253)$$

This illustration should certainly emphasize the importance of specifying the driving force ΔT in the definition of h for flow in conduits. Note that h is *not* dimensionless; however, the combination hD/λ, when λ is the fluid thermal conductivity, is dimensionless. It is called the *Nusselt number for heat transfer* and is given the symbol **Nu**.

MASS TRANSPORT: MASS-TRANSFER COEFFICIENTS. The rate at which mass of A is exchanged between a solid surface of A and B and a fluid stream of A and B is written

$$\mathcal{W}_A - x_{A0}(\mathcal{W}_A + \mathcal{W}_B) = k_x A \Delta x_A \qquad (6.254)$$

in which x_{A0} is the concentration of A at the interface, and $\mathcal{W}_A$ and $\mathcal{W}_B$ are the molar rates of transfer. The index on k indicates that a mole-fraction driving force Δx_A is being used.

For flow of a mixture of A and B around a sphere made of A and B one would write

$$\mathcal{W}_A - x_{A0}(\mathcal{W}_A + \mathcal{W}_B) = k_x \cdot \tfrac{1}{6}\,\pi D^3 \cdot (x_{A0} - x_{A\infty}) \qquad (6.255)$$

if $x_{A\infty}$ is the mole fraction of A in the approaching stream.

For flow in circular tubes one has the option of defining k_{x1}, k_{ra}, and $k_x \ln$ analogously to h_1, h_a, and $h_{\ln}$. Note that the k_x's are *not* dimensionless. However, the group $k_x D/c\mathfrak{D}_{AB}$ is dimensionless. This group is called the *Nusselt number for mass transfer* in the system AB and is given the symbol **Nu**$_{AB}$ (it is also called the *Sherwood number* and given the symbol **Sh**).

It should be emphasized that Eqs. (6.246, 6.249, 6.254) are *definitions* for f, h, and k_x and are *not* physical laws [although Eq. (6.249) is often given the misleading name "Newton's law of cooling"].

For multicomponent systems, for systems with simultaneous heat, mass, and momentum transfer, and for transfer between two fluid phases, the definitions of the transfer coefficients become more difficult.

> CAUTION: The above definitions are for the simplest situations only. The reader should consult more complete treatises for information about multicomponent mass-transfer coefficients,[4] mass transfer between two fluid phases,[4,9] and simultaneous heat, mass, and momentum transfer.[4]

The Correlations for the Transfer Coefficients. The dimensionless quantities f, **Nu**, and **Nu**$_{AB}$ may be represented as functions of a handful of dimensionless numbers which occur in the literature on applied transport phenomena. The general form of the correlations may be deduced from dimensional analysis of the equations of change.[4,50] The numerical values appearing in the correlations are generally obtained from experimental data; for some simple systems the numerical constants may be obtainable from solutions of the equations of change for laminar or turbulent flow.

Several examples of correlations for flow around spheres and flow in tubes are cited here. The reader will find an extensive literature on the subject of transfer-coefficient correlations.[6,9,50]

> CAUTION: In using the transfer-coefficient correlations in the literature one must take careful note of (1) the driving force used in the definition of the transfer coefficient, (2) the conditions under which the physical properties are to be evaluated, (3) the nature of the flow—laminar or turbulent, (4) the range of dimensionless groups for which the correlation has been substantiated by experiment, and (5) the theoretical basis for the correlation if such exists.

FRICTION FACTORS. For isothermal flow around solid spheres the friction factor is given as a function of the Reynolds number $\mathbf{Re} = Dv_\infty\rho/\mu$; the function $f(\mathbf{Re})$ has been given graphically in many references.[68]　This curve is given approximately by

$$f = \frac{24}{\mathbf{Re}} \qquad \begin{array}{c} \mathbf{Re} < 0.1 \\ \text{(Stokes-law region)} \end{array} \qquad (6.256)$$

$$f \doteq \frac{18.5}{\mathbf{Re}^{3/5}} \qquad \begin{array}{c} 2 < \mathbf{Re} < 5 \times 10^2 \\ \text{(Intermediate-law region)} \end{array} \qquad (6.257)$$

$$f \doteq 0.44 \qquad \begin{array}{c} 5 \times 10^2 < \mathbf{Re} < 2 \times 10^5 \\ \text{(Newton's-law region)} \end{array} \qquad (6.258)$$

Many deviations from the standard $f(\mathbf{Re})$ correlation have been studied, such as internal circulation of droplets, hindered settling, nonspherical particles, etc.[69]

For isothermal flow in very long smooth circular tubes with diameter D with an average velocity $\langle v \rangle$, the friction factor is given as a function of a Reynolds number $\mathbf{Re} = D\langle v \rangle\rho/\mu$. This relation is

$$f = \frac{16}{\mathbf{Re}} \qquad \begin{array}{c} \mathbf{Re} < 2.1 \times 10^3 \\ \text{(Laminar)} \end{array} \qquad (6.259)$$

$$f \doteq \frac{0.0791}{\mathbf{Re}^{1/4}} \qquad \begin{array}{c} 2.1 \times 10^3 < \mathbf{Re} < 10^5 \\ \text{(Turbulent)} \end{array} \qquad (6.260)$$

Roughness effects have been extensively studied for this system.[50]　For *turbulent flow in noncircular conduits* Eq. (6.260) may be used by replacing D by $4R_h$ if R_h is the mean hydraulic radius, defined as the ratio of the cross section S to the wetted perimeter Z.

HEAT-TRANSFER COEFFICIENTS.　For heat losses from spheres in *forced* convection (placed in a stream of velocity v_∞) the h in Eq. (6.250) is given by a correlation of $\mathbf{Nu} = hD/\lambda$ as a function of the Reynolds number $\mathbf{Re} = Dv_\infty\rho/\mu$ and the Prandtl number $\mathbf{Pr} = \hat{C}_p\mu/\lambda$.

$$\mathbf{Nu} = 2.0 + 0.60\mathbf{Re}^{1/2}\mathbf{Pr}^{2/3} \qquad (6.261)$$

Here all physical properties are to be calculated at a "film temperature" defined as the arithmetic average of the surface temperature T_0 and the approaching fluid temperature T_∞; that is, $T_f = \frac{1}{2}(T_0 + T_\infty)$.

For the heat loss from spheres in *free* convection (i.e., in a quiescent fluid), the h in Eq. (6.250) is given as a correlation of $\mathbf{Nu} = hD/\lambda$ as a function of $\mathbf{Pr} = C_p\mu/\lambda$ and the Grashof number $\mathbf{Gr} = D^3\rho^2 g\beta(T_0 - T_\infty)\mu^2$:

$$\mathbf{Nu} = 2.0 + 0.60\mathbf{Gr}^{1/4}\mathbf{Pr}^{1/3} \qquad \mathbf{Gr}^{1/4}\mathbf{Pr}^{1/3} < 200 \qquad (6.262)$$

Here all fluid properties are to be evaluated at $T_f = \frac{1}{2}(T_0 + T_\infty)$.

For heat exchange between a fluid and a long tube $(L/D > 10)$, the experimental data are fairly well summarized by two relations for the heat-transfer coefficient in Eq. (6.253).

$$\mathbf{Nu}_{\ln} = 1.86 \left(\frac{\mathbf{Re}\mathbf{Pr}D}{L}\right)^{1/3} \left(\frac{\mu}{\mu_0}\right)^{0.14} \qquad \text{(laminar flow, } \mathbf{Re}\mathbf{Pr}D/L > 10\text{)} \qquad (6.263)$$

$$\mathbf{Nu}_{\ln} = 0.026\mathbf{Re}^{0.8}\mathbf{Pr}^{1/3} \left(\frac{\mu}{\mu_0}\right)^{0.14} \qquad \text{(highly turbulent flow,} \qquad (6.264)$$

$$\mathbf{Re} > 20{,}000,\ 0.6 < \mathbf{Pr} < 100$$

Here μ_0 is the viscosity calculated at the wall temperature T_0. All other physical properties are calculated at the mean bulk temperature $\frac{1}{2}(T_1 + T_2)$.

MASS-TRANSFER COEFFICIENTS.　For getting the mass-transfer coefficients at *low mass transfer* rates, the analogy between heat and mass transfer may be used, as shown in the accompanying tabulation.

	Heat transfer	Mass transfer
Dimensionless transfer coefficient..........	$\mathbf{Nu} = hD/\lambda$	$\mathbf{Nu}_{AB} = k_x D/c\mathcal{D}_{AB}$
Physical-property group..................	$\mathbf{Pr} = \hat{C}_p\mu/\lambda$	$\mathbf{Sc}_{AB} = \mu/\rho\mathcal{D}_{AB}$
Forced-convection group.................	$\mathbf{Re} = Dv_\infty\rho/\mu$	$\mathbf{Re} = Dv_\infty\rho/\mu$
Free-convection group..................	$\mathbf{Gr} = D^3\rho^2\beta\,\Delta T/\mu^2$	$\mathbf{Gr}_{AB} = D^3\rho^2\zeta\,\Delta x_A/\mu^2$

Hence any heat-transfer formula may be translated into a mass-transfer formula by appropriate change in the notation. For example, for forced-convection mass transfer from spherical particles, by analogy with Eq. (6.259),

$$\mathbf{Nu}_{AB} = 2.0 + 0.60\mathbf{Re}^{1/2}\mathbf{Sc}_{AB}^{1/3} \tag{6.265}$$

in which the physical properties are to be evaluated at a film concentration $x_{Af} = \frac{1}{2}(x_{A0} + x_{A\infty})$.

For *high mass-transfer* rates correction factors have been worked out by several theories which are too lengthy to present here (Ref. 4, chap. 21).

The Friction-loss Factor. The energy dissipation (per unit mass) E_v may be written for flow in closed channels as

$$\hat{E}_v = \frac{1}{2}\langle v\rangle^2 e_v \tag{6.266}$$

which defines the *friction-loss factor* e_v.

For the special case of steady flow of a fluid of constant ρ in straight conduits of arbitrary but constant cross section S and length L, then from the macroscopic momentum and energy balances, one gets

$$\hat{E}_v = \frac{F}{\rho S} \tag{6.267}$$

If the fluid is in turbulent flow, then

$$\hat{E}_v = \frac{1}{2}\langle v\rangle^2 \frac{L}{R_h} f \tag{6.268}$$

if f is the friction factor. Comparison of Eq. (6.268) with Eq. (6.266) shows that, for this case, $e_v = (L/R_h)_f$. This explains why friction factors, defined basically in terms of the momentum balance, can be used in the mechanical-energy balance.

For straight lengths of pipe in a pipe network Eq. (6.268) gives the contribution to $\hat{E}_v$. If in the flow system there are various obstacles such as fittings, valves, or meters, additional contributions must be included. Rough values of e_v are known (Table 6.5) for many of these obstacles, with the convention that $\langle v\rangle$ in Eq. (6.266) is the average velocity *downstream* from the disturbance; these values are for turbulent flow.

Table 6.5. Friction-loss Factors for Turbulent Flow [for use with Eq. (6.269)] †

Obstacles	e_v
Sudden contraction...........	$0.45(1 - \beta)$
Sudden expansion.............	$\left(\frac{1}{\beta} - 1\right)^2$
Sharp-edged orifice............	$2.7(1 - \beta)(1 - \beta^2)\frac{1}{\beta^2}$
90° bend (rounded)...........	0.4–0.9
Globe valve (open)............	6–10
Gate valve (open).............	0.2

† $\beta = \dfrac{\text{smaller cross-section area}}{\text{larger cross-section area}}$.

On the basis of the foregoing discussion, the steady-state mechanical-energy balance may be rewritten

$$\Delta \frac{1}{2} \langle v \rangle^2 + g\, \Delta z + \int_{p_1}^{p_2} \frac{1}{\rho}\, dp + W + \Sigma \left(\frac{1}{2} \langle v \rangle^2 \frac{L}{R_h} f \right)_i + \Sigma \left(\frac{1}{2} \langle v \rangle^2 e_v \right)_i = 0$$

$$\underbrace{}_{\substack{\text{Sum on all straight} \\ \text{sections of pipe}}} \quad \underbrace{}_{\substack{\text{Sum on all fit-} \\ \text{tings, valves,} \\ \text{meters, etc.}}}$$

(6.269)

This expression is valid for *turbulent flow* only.

APPENDIX A. VECTOR AND TENSOR IDENTITIES AND DEFINITIONS

Scalars are indicated by lightface symbols.
Vectors are indicated by **boldface** Roman symbols.
Tensors are indicated by **boldface** Greek symbols.
Dot-product operations which result in scalars are enclosed in parentheses.
Dot- and cross-product operations resulting in vectors are enclosed in brackets.
Dot-product operations which yield tensors are enclosed in braces.

$\mathbf{v}$	vector with three cartesian components v_x, v_y, v_z
$\boldsymbol{\tau}$	tensor with nine cartesian components τ_{zz}, τ_{zy}, τ_{zz}, τ_{yz}, etc.
$\mathbf{vw}$	dyadic product of v and w with nine components v_xw_x, v_xw_y, v_xw_z, etc.
v^2	$(\mathbf{v} \cdot \mathbf{v}) = v_x{}^2 + v_y{}^2 + v_z{}^2$
$(\mathbf{v} \cdot \mathbf{w})$	$v_xw_x + v_yw_y + v_zw_z$ = scalar (dot) product of $\mathbf{v}$ and $\mathbf{w}$
$[\mathbf{v} \times \mathbf{w}]_x$	$v_yw_z - v_zw_y$ = x component of vector (cross) product
$[\boldsymbol{\tau} \cdot \mathbf{v}]_x$	$\tau_{xx}v_x + \tau_{xy}v_y + \tau_{xz}v_z$
$[\mathbf{v} \cdot \boldsymbol{\tau}]_x$	$v_x\tau_{xx} + v_y\tau_{yx} + v_z\tau_{zx}$
$(\boldsymbol{\sigma} : \boldsymbol{\tau})$	$\Sigma_i\Sigma_j\sigma_{ij}\tau_{ji}$
$\{\boldsymbol{\sigma} \cdot \boldsymbol{\tau}\}_{xy}$	$\sigma_{xx}\tau_{xy} + \sigma_{xy}\tau_{yy} + \sigma_{xz}\tau_{zy}$
$\boldsymbol{\delta}$	second-order unit tensor with three components $\delta_{ii} = 1$ and six components $\delta_{ij} = 0$ $(i \neq j)$

APPENDIX B. Vector and Tensor Operations in Curvilinear or Coordinates

B.1. Summary of Differential Operations Involving the ∇ Operator in Rectangular Coordinates† x, y, z

$$(\nabla \cdot \mathbf{v}) = \frac{\partial v_x}{\partial x} + \frac{\partial v_y}{\partial y} + \frac{\partial v_z}{\partial z} \tag{A}$$

$$(\nabla^2 s) = \frac{\partial^2 s}{\partial x^2} + \frac{\partial^2 s}{\partial y^2} + \frac{\partial^2 s}{\partial z^2} \tag{B}$$

$$(\boldsymbol{\tau} : \nabla \mathbf{v}) = \tau_{xx}\left(\frac{\partial v_x}{\partial x}\right) + \tau_{xy}\left(\frac{\partial v_y}{\partial y}\right) + \tau_{zz}\left(\frac{\partial v_z}{\partial z}\right) + \tau_{xy}\left(\frac{\partial v_x}{\partial y} + \frac{\partial v_y}{\partial x}\right)$$
$$+ \tau_{yz}\left(\frac{\partial v_y}{\partial z} + \frac{\partial v_z}{\partial y}\right) + \tau_{zx}\left(\frac{\partial v_z}{\partial x} + \frac{\partial v_x}{\partial z}\right) \tag{C}$$

$$[\nabla s]_x = \frac{\partial s}{\partial x} \tag{D}$$

$$[\nabla s]_y = \frac{\partial s}{\partial y} \tag{E}$$

$$[\nabla s]_z = \frac{\partial s}{\partial z} \tag{F}$$

$$[\nabla \times \mathbf{v}]_x = \frac{\partial v_z}{\partial y} - \frac{\partial v_y}{\partial z} \tag{G}$$

$$[\nabla \times \mathbf{v}]_y = \frac{\partial v_x}{\partial z} - \frac{\partial v_z}{\partial x} \tag{H}$$

$$[\nabla \times \mathbf{v}]_z = \frac{\partial v_y}{\partial x} - \frac{\partial v_x}{\partial y} \tag{I}$$

$$[\nabla \cdot \boldsymbol{\tau}]_x = \frac{\partial \tau_{xx}}{\partial x} + \frac{\partial \tau_{xy}}{\partial y} + \frac{\partial \tau_{xz}}{\partial z} \tag{J}$$

$$[\nabla \cdot \boldsymbol{\tau}]_y = \frac{\partial \tau_{xy}}{\partial x} + \frac{\partial \tau_{yy}}{\partial y} + \frac{\partial \tau_{yz}}{\partial z} \tag{K}$$

$$[\nabla \cdot \boldsymbol{\tau}]_z = \frac{\partial \tau_{xz}}{\partial x} + \frac{\partial \tau_{yz}}{\partial y} + \frac{\partial \tau_{zz}}{\partial z} \tag{L}$$

$$[\nabla^2 \mathbf{v}]_x = \frac{\partial^2 v_x}{\partial x^2} + \frac{\partial^2 v_x}{\partial y^2} + \frac{\partial^2 v_x}{\partial z^2} \tag{M}$$

$$[\nabla^2 \mathbf{v}]_y = \frac{\partial^2 v_y}{\partial x^2} + \frac{\partial^2 v_y}{\partial y^2} + \frac{\partial^2 v_y}{\partial z^2} \tag{N}$$

$$[\nabla^2 \mathbf{v}]_z = \frac{\partial^2 v_z}{\partial x^2} + \frac{\partial^2 v_z}{\partial y^2} + \frac{\partial^2 v_z}{\partial z^2} \tag{O}$$

$$[\mathbf{v} \cdot \nabla \mathbf{v}]_x = v_x\frac{\partial v_x}{\partial x} + v_y\frac{\partial v_x}{\partial y} + v_z\frac{\partial v_x}{\partial z} \tag{P}$$

$$[\mathbf{v} \cdot \nabla \mathbf{v}]_y = v_x\frac{\partial v_y}{\partial x} + v_y\frac{\partial v_y}{\partial y} + v_z\frac{\partial v_y}{\partial z} \tag{Q}$$

$$[\mathbf{v} \cdot \nabla \mathbf{v}]_z = v_x\frac{\partial v_z}{\partial x} + v_y\frac{\partial v_z}{\partial y} + v_z\frac{\partial v_z}{\partial z} \tag{R}$$

$$\epsilon_{xx} = 2\frac{\partial v_x}{\partial x} \tag{S}$$

$$\epsilon_{yy} = 2\frac{\partial v_y}{\partial y} \tag{T}$$

$$\epsilon_{zz} = 2\frac{\partial v_z}{\partial z} \tag{U}$$

$$\epsilon_{xy} = \epsilon_{yx} = \frac{\partial v_x}{\partial y} + \frac{\partial v_y}{\partial x} \tag{V}$$

$$\epsilon_{yz} = \epsilon_{zy} = \frac{\partial v_y}{\partial z} + \frac{\partial v_z}{\partial y} \tag{W}$$

$$\epsilon_{zx} = \epsilon_{xz} = \frac{\partial v_x}{\partial z} + \frac{\partial v_z}{\partial x} \tag{X}$$

† Operations involving the tensor $\boldsymbol{\tau}$ are given for *symmetrical* $\boldsymbol{\tau}$ only.

B.2. Summary of Differential Operations Involving the ∇ Operator in Cylindrical Coordinates† r, θ, z

$$(\nabla \cdot \mathbf{v}) = \frac{1}{r}\frac{\partial}{\partial r}(rv_r) + \frac{1}{r}\frac{\partial v_\theta}{\partial \theta} + \frac{\partial v_z}{\partial z} \tag{A}$$

$$(\nabla^2 s) = \frac{1}{r}\frac{\partial}{\partial r}\left(r\frac{\partial s}{\partial r}\right) + \frac{1}{r^2}\frac{\partial^2 s}{\partial \theta^2} + \frac{\partial^2 s}{\partial z^2} \tag{B}$$

$$(\tau : \nabla\mathbf{v}) = \tau_{rr}\left(\frac{\partial v_r}{\partial r}\right) + \tau_{\theta\theta}\left(\frac{1}{r}\frac{\partial v_\theta}{\partial \theta} + \frac{v_r}{r}\right) + \tau_{zz}\left(\frac{\partial v_z}{\partial z}\right) + \tau_{r\theta}\left(r\frac{\partial}{\partial r}\left(\frac{v_\theta}{r}\right) + \frac{1}{r}\frac{\partial v_r}{\partial \theta}\right)$$

$$+ \tau_{\theta z}\left(\frac{1}{r}\frac{\partial v_z}{\partial \theta} + \frac{\partial v_\theta}{\partial z}\right) + \tau_{rz}\left(\frac{\partial v_z}{\partial r} + \frac{\partial v_r}{\partial z}\right) \tag{C}$$

$$[\nabla s]_r = \frac{\partial s}{\partial r} \tag{D}$$

$$[\nabla s]_\theta = \frac{1}{r}\frac{\partial s}{\partial \theta} \tag{E}$$

$$[\nabla s]_z = \frac{\partial s}{\partial z} \tag{F}$$

$$[\nabla \times \mathbf{v}]_r = \frac{1}{r}\frac{\partial v_z}{\partial \theta} - \frac{\partial v_\theta}{\partial z} \tag{G}$$

$$[\nabla \times \mathbf{v}]_\theta = \frac{\partial v_r}{\partial z} - \frac{\partial v_z}{\partial r} \tag{H}$$

$$[\nabla \times \mathbf{v}]_z = \frac{1}{r}\frac{\partial}{\partial r}(rv_\theta) - \frac{1}{r}\frac{\partial v_r}{\partial \theta} \tag{I}$$

$$[\nabla \cdot \tau]_r = \frac{1}{r}\frac{\partial}{\partial r}(r\tau_{rr}) + \frac{1}{r}\frac{\partial}{\partial \theta}\tau_{r\theta} - \frac{1}{r}\tau_{\theta\theta} + \frac{\partial \tau_{rz}}{\partial z} \tag{J}$$

$$[\nabla \cdot \tau]_\theta = \frac{1}{r}\frac{\partial \tau_{\theta\theta}}{\partial \theta} + \frac{\partial \tau_{r\theta}}{\partial r} + \frac{2}{r}\tau_{r\theta} + \frac{\partial \tau_{\theta z}}{\partial z} \tag{K}$$

$$[\nabla \cdot \tau]_z = \frac{1}{r}\frac{\partial}{\partial r}(r\tau_{rz}) + \frac{1}{r}\frac{\partial \tau_{\theta z}}{\partial \theta} + \frac{\partial \tau_{zz}}{\partial z} \tag{L}$$

$$[\nabla^2\mathbf{v}]_r = \frac{\partial}{\partial r}\left[\frac{1}{r}\frac{\partial}{\partial r}(rv_r)\right] + \frac{1}{r^2}\frac{\partial^2 v_r}{\partial \theta^2} - \frac{2}{r^2}\frac{\partial v_\theta}{\partial \theta} + \frac{\partial^2 v_r}{\partial z^2} \tag{M}$$

$$[\nabla^2\mathbf{v}]_\theta = \frac{\partial}{\partial r}\left[\frac{1}{r}\frac{\partial}{\partial r}(rv_\theta)\right] + \frac{1}{r^2}\frac{\partial^2 v_\theta}{\partial \theta^2} + \frac{2}{r^2}\frac{\partial v_r}{\partial \theta} + \frac{\partial^2 v_\theta}{\partial z^2} \tag{N}$$

$$[\nabla^2\mathbf{v}]_z = \frac{1}{r}\frac{\partial}{\partial r}\left(r\frac{\partial v_z}{\partial r}\right) + \frac{1}{r^2}\frac{\partial^2 v_z}{\partial \theta^2} + \frac{\partial^2 v_z}{\partial z^2} \tag{O}$$

$$[\mathbf{v}\cdot\nabla\mathbf{v}]_r = v_r\frac{\partial v_r}{\partial r} + \frac{v_\theta}{r}\frac{\partial v_r}{\partial \theta} - \frac{v_\theta^2}{r} + v_z\frac{\partial v_r}{\partial z} \tag{P}$$

$$[\mathbf{v}\cdot\nabla\mathbf{v}]_\theta = v_r\frac{\partial v_\theta}{\partial r} + \frac{v_\theta}{r}\frac{\partial v_\theta}{\partial \theta} + \frac{v_r v_\theta}{r} + v_z\frac{\partial v_\theta}{\partial z} \tag{Q}$$

$$[\mathbf{v}\cdot\nabla\mathbf{v}]_z = v_r\frac{\partial v_z}{\partial r} + \frac{v_\theta}{r}\frac{\partial v_z}{\partial \theta} + v_z\frac{\partial v_z}{\partial z} \tag{R}$$

$$\epsilon_{rr} = 2\frac{\partial v_r}{\partial r} \tag{S}$$

$$\epsilon_{\theta\theta} = 2\left(\frac{1}{r}\frac{\partial v_\theta}{\partial \theta} + \frac{v_r}{r}\right) \tag{T}$$

$$\epsilon_{zz} = 2\frac{\partial v_z}{\partial z} \tag{U}$$

$$\epsilon_{r\theta} = \epsilon_{\theta r} = r\frac{\partial}{\partial r}\left(\frac{v_\theta}{r}\right) + \frac{1}{r}\frac{\partial v_r}{\partial \theta} \tag{V}$$

$$\epsilon_{\theta z} = \epsilon_{z\theta} = \frac{\partial v_\theta}{\partial z} + \frac{1}{r}\frac{\partial v_z}{\partial \theta} \tag{W}$$

$$\epsilon_{zr} = \epsilon_{rz} = \frac{\partial v_z}{\partial r} + \frac{\partial v_r}{\partial z} \tag{X}$$

† Operations involving the tensor τ are given for *symmetrical* τ only.

B.3. Summary of Differential Operations Involving the ∇ Operator in Spherical Coordinates† r, θ, ϕ

$$(\nabla \cdot \mathbf{v}) = \frac{1}{r^2}\frac{\partial}{\partial r}(r^2 v_r) + \frac{1}{r\sin\theta}\frac{\partial}{\partial\theta}(v_\theta\sin\theta) + \frac{1}{r\sin\theta}\frac{\partial v_\phi}{\partial\phi} \tag{A}$$

$$(\nabla^2 s) = \frac{1}{r^2}\frac{\partial}{\partial r}\left(r^2\frac{\partial s}{\partial r}\right) + \frac{1}{r^2\sin\theta}\frac{\partial}{\partial\theta}\left(\sin\theta\frac{\partial s}{\partial\theta}\right) + \frac{1}{r^2\sin^2\theta}\frac{\partial^2 s}{\partial\phi^2} \tag{B}$$

$$(\tau : \nabla\mathbf{v}) = \tau_{rr}\left(\frac{\partial v_r}{\partial r}\right) + \tau_{\theta\theta}\left(\frac{1}{r}\frac{\partial v_\theta}{\partial\theta} + \frac{v_r}{r}\right) + \tau_{\phi\phi}\left(\frac{1}{r\sin\theta}\frac{\partial v_\phi}{\partial\phi} + \frac{v_r}{r} + \frac{v_\theta\cot\theta}{r}\right) + \tau_{r\theta}\left(\frac{\partial v_\theta}{\partial r} + \frac{1}{r}\frac{\partial v_r}{\partial\theta} - \frac{v_\theta}{r}\right)$$

$$+ \tau_{r\phi}\left(\frac{\partial v_\phi}{\partial r} + \frac{1}{r\sin\theta}\frac{\partial v_r}{\partial\phi} - \frac{v_\phi}{r}\right) + \tau_{\theta\phi}\left(\frac{1}{r}\frac{\partial v_\phi}{\partial\theta} + \frac{1}{r\sin\theta}\frac{\partial v_\theta}{\partial\phi} - \frac{\cot\theta}{r}v_\phi\right) \tag{C}$$

$$[\nabla s]_r = \frac{\partial s}{\partial r} \tag{D}$$

$$[\nabla s]_\theta = \frac{1}{r}\frac{\partial s}{\partial\theta} \tag{E}$$

$$[\nabla s]_\phi = \frac{1}{r\sin\theta}\frac{\partial s}{\partial\phi} \tag{F}$$

$$[\nabla \times \mathbf{v}]_r = \frac{1}{r\sin\theta}\frac{\partial}{\partial\theta}(v_\phi\sin\theta) - \frac{1}{r\sin\theta}\frac{\partial v_\theta}{\partial\phi} \tag{G}$$

$$[\nabla \times \mathbf{v}]_\theta = \frac{1}{r\sin\theta}\frac{\partial v_r}{\partial\phi} - \frac{1}{r}\frac{\partial}{\partial r}(rv_\phi) \tag{H}$$

$$[\nabla \times \mathbf{v}]_\phi = \frac{1}{r}\frac{\partial}{\partial r}(rv_\theta) - \frac{1}{r}\frac{\partial v_r}{\partial\theta} \tag{I}$$

$$[\nabla \cdot \tau]_r = \frac{1}{r^2}\frac{\partial}{\partial r}(r^2\tau_{rr}) + \frac{1}{r\sin\theta}\frac{\partial}{\partial\theta}(\tau_{r\theta}\sin\theta) + \frac{1}{r\sin\theta}\frac{\partial\tau_{r\phi}}{\partial\phi} - \frac{\tau_{\theta\theta} + \tau_{\phi\phi}}{r} \tag{J}$$

$$[\nabla \cdot \tau]_\theta = \frac{1}{r^2}\frac{\partial}{\partial r}(r^2\tau_{r\theta}) + \frac{1}{r\sin\theta}\frac{\partial}{\partial\theta}(\tau_{\theta\theta}\sin\theta) + \frac{1}{r\sin\theta}\frac{\partial\tau_{\theta\phi}}{\partial\phi} + \frac{\tau_{r\theta}}{r} - \frac{\cot\theta}{r}\tau_{\phi\phi} \tag{K}$$

$$[\nabla \cdot \tau]_\phi = \frac{1}{r^2}\frac{\partial}{\partial r}(r^2\tau_{r\phi}) + \frac{1}{r}\frac{\partial\tau_{\theta\phi}}{\partial\theta} + \frac{1}{r\sin\theta}\frac{\partial\tau_{\phi\phi}}{\partial\phi} + \frac{\tau_{r\phi}}{r} + \frac{2\cot\theta}{r}\tau_{\theta\phi} \tag{L}$$

$$[\nabla^2\mathbf{v}]_r = \nabla^2 v_r - \frac{2v_r}{r^2} - \frac{2}{r^2}\frac{\partial v_\theta}{\partial\theta} - \frac{2v_\theta\cot\theta}{r^2} - \frac{2}{r^2\sin\theta}\frac{\partial v_\phi}{\partial\phi} \tag{M}$$

$$[\nabla^2\mathbf{v}]_\theta = \nabla^2 v_\theta + \frac{2}{r^2}\frac{\partial v_r}{\partial\theta} - \frac{v_\theta}{r^2\sin^2\theta} - \frac{2\cos\theta}{r^2\sin^2\theta}\frac{\partial v_\phi}{\partial\phi} \tag{N}$$

$$[\nabla^2\mathbf{v}]_\phi = \nabla^2 v_\phi - \frac{v_\phi}{r^2\sin^2\theta} + \frac{2}{r^2\sin\theta}\frac{\partial v_r}{\partial\phi} + \frac{2\cos\theta}{r^2\sin^2\theta}\frac{\partial v_\theta}{\partial\phi} \tag{O}$$

$$[\mathbf{v} \cdot \nabla\mathbf{v}]_r = v_r\frac{\partial v_r}{\partial r} + \frac{v_\theta}{r}\frac{\partial v_r}{\partial\theta} + \frac{v_\phi}{r\sin\theta}\frac{\partial v_r}{\partial\phi} - \frac{v_\theta^2 + v_\phi^2}{r} \tag{P}$$

$$[\mathbf{v} \cdot \nabla\mathbf{v}]_\theta = v_r\frac{\partial v_\theta}{\partial r} + \frac{v_\theta}{r}\frac{\partial v_\theta}{\partial\theta} + \frac{v_\phi}{r\sin\theta}\frac{\partial v_\theta}{\partial\phi} + \frac{v_r v_\theta}{r} - \frac{v_\phi^2\cot\theta}{r} \tag{Q}$$

$$[\mathbf{v} \cdot \nabla\mathbf{v}]_\phi = v_r\frac{\partial v_\phi}{\partial r} + \frac{v_\theta}{r}\frac{\partial v_\phi}{\partial\theta} + \frac{v_\phi}{r\sin\theta}\frac{\partial v_\phi}{\partial\phi} + \frac{v_\phi v_r}{r} + \frac{v_\theta v_\phi\cot\theta}{r} \tag{R}$$

$$\epsilon_{rr} = 2\frac{\partial v_r}{\partial r} \tag{S}$$

$$\epsilon_{\theta\theta} = 2\left(\frac{1}{r}\frac{\partial v_\theta}{\partial\theta} + \frac{v_r}{r}\right) \tag{T}$$

$$\epsilon_{\phi\phi} = 2\left(\frac{1}{r\sin\theta}\frac{\partial v_\phi}{\partial\phi} + \frac{v_r}{r} + \frac{v_\theta\cot\theta}{r}\right) \tag{U}$$

$$\epsilon_{r\theta} = \epsilon_{\theta r} = r\frac{\partial}{\partial r}\left(\frac{v_\theta}{r}\right) + \frac{1}{r}\frac{\partial v_r}{\partial\theta} \tag{V}$$

$$\epsilon_{\theta\phi} = \epsilon_{\phi\theta} = \frac{\sin\theta}{r}\frac{\partial}{\partial\theta}\left(\frac{v_\phi}{\sin\theta}\right) + \frac{1}{r\sin\theta}\frac{\partial v_\theta}{\partial\phi} \tag{W}$$

$$\epsilon_{r\phi} = \epsilon_{\phi r} = \frac{1}{r\sin\theta}\frac{\partial v_r}{\partial\phi} + r\frac{\partial}{\partial r}\left(\frac{v_\phi}{r}\right) \tag{X}$$

† Operations involving the tensor τ are given for *symmetrical* τ only.

REFERENCES

1. Hirshfelder, J. O., C. F. Curtiss, and R. B. Bird: "Molecular Theory of Gases and Liquids," Wiley, New York, 1954.
2. Curtiss, C. F.: *Ann. Rev. Phys. Chem.*, **9**: 379–394 (1958).
3. Chapman, S., and T. G. Cowling: "Mathematical Theory of Non-uniform Gases," 2d ed., Cambridge, New York, 1952.
4. Bird, R. B., W. E. Stewart, and E. N. Lightfoot: "Transport Phenomena," Wiley, New York, 1960.
5. Jakob, M.: "Heat Transfer," Wiley, New York, vol. 1, 1949, vol. 2, 1957.
6. McAdams, W. H.: "Heat Transmission," 3d ed., McGraw-Hill, New York, 1954.
7. Grigull, U.: "Wärmeübertragung," Springer, Berlin, 1955.
8. Eckert, E. R. G., and R. M. Drake, Jr.: "Heat and Mass Transfer," McGraw-Hill, New York, 1959.
9. Sherwood, T. K., and R. L. Pigford: "Absorption and Extraction," 2d ed., McGraw-Hill, New York, 1952.
10. Treybal, R. E.: "Mass-transfer Operations," McGraw-Hill, New York, 1955.
11. Hougen, O. A., and K. M. Watson: "Kinetics and Catalysis," Wiley, New York, 1947.
12. Jungers, J. C., et al.: "Cinétique chimique appliquée," Institut. Français de Pétrole, Paris, 1958.
13. Eirich, F. R. (ed.): "Rheology," Academic Press, New York, vol. 1, 1956, vol. 2, 1958, vol. 3, 1960.
14. Hougen, O. A., K. M. Watson, and R. A. Ragatz: "Chemical Process Principles," vol. I, pp. 330–334, Wiley, New York, 1954.
15. Klotz, I. M.: "Chemical Thermodynamics," pp. 286–299, Prentice-Hall, Englewood Cliffs, N.J., 1950.
16. Reid, R. C., and T. K. Sherwood: "Properties of Gases and Liquids," McGraw-Hill, New York, 1958.
17. Johnson, P. A., and A. L. Babb: *Chem. Rev.*, **56**: 387–453 (1956).
18. Gosting, L. J.: *Advances in Protein Chem.*, vol. 11, 1956.
19. Barrer, R. M.: "Diffusion in and through Solids," pp. 141, 275, Macmillan, New York, 1941.
20. Bird, R. B., C. F. Curtiss, and J. O. Hirshfelder: *Chem. Eng. Progr. Symp. Ser.*, **51**(16): 69–85, 1955.
21. Grew, K. E., and T. L. Ibbs: "Thermal Diffusion in Gases," Cambridge, New York, 1952.
22. Truesdell, C.: *J. Rational Mech. and Analysis*, **1**: 125–300, 164–165, 227–228 (1952).
23. Litovitz, T. A., and T. Lyon: *J. Acoust. Soc. Am.*, **30**: 856 (1958).
24. Lyon, T., and T. A. Litovitz: *J. Appl. Phys.*, **27**: 179 (1956).
25. Tisza, L.: *Phys. Rev.*, **61**: 531 (1942).
26. Reiner, M.: Reference 13, vol. 1, chap. 1.
27. Reiner, M.: "Deformation and Flow," chap. 5, Lewis, London, 1949.
28. Fredrickson, A. G.: Ph.D. thesis, University of Wisconsin, Madison, Wis., 1959.
29. Slattery, J. C.: Ph.D. thesis, University of Wisconsin, Madison, Wis., 1959.
30. Oldroyd, J. G.: Reference 13, vol. 1, chap. 16.
31. Oldroyd, J. G.: *Proc. Roy. Soc. (London)*, **A200**:523 (1950).
32. Rivlin, R. S., and J. L. Ericksen: *J. Rational Mech. and Analysis*, **4**:323 (1955).
33. Rivlin, R. S.: *J. Rational Mech. and Analysis*, **4**:181 (1955).
34. Fredrickson, A. G.: *Chem. Eng. Sci.*, **11**:252 (1960).
35. Oldroyd, J. G., P. J. Strawbridge, and B. A. Toms, *Proc. Phys. Soc. (London)*, **B64**:44 (1951).
36. Oldroyd, J. G.: *Quart. J. Mech. and Appl. Math.*, **4**:271 (1951).
37. Prager, S.: *CEP Symp. Ser.*, vol. **55**. no. 25, 1959.
38. Hougen, O. A., and K. M. Watson: "Chemical Process Principles," vol. 3, pp. 930–932, Wiley, New York, 1947.
39. Glasstone, S., K. J. Laidler, and H. Eyring: "The Theory of Rate Processes," p. 402, McGraw-Hill, New York, 1941.
40. K. J. Laidler: "Chemical Kinetics," pp. 57–59, McGraw-Hill, New York, 1950.
41. "Tables of Chemical Kinetics," *Natl. Bur. Standards (U.S.) Cir.* 510, 1951; Supplement 1, 1956.
42. Smith, J. M.: "Chemical Engineering Kinetics," McGraw-Hill, New York, 1956.
43. Frost, A. A., and R. G. Pearson: "Kinetics and Mechanism," Wiley, New York, 1953.
44. Curtiss, C. F.: *J. Chem. Phys.*, **24**:225 (1956).
45. Livingston, P. M., and C. F. Curtiss: *J. Chem. Phys.*, **31**:1643 (1959).
46. Lamb, H.: "Hydrodynamics," 6th ed., Dover, New York, 1945.

47. Tomita, Y.: *Bull. Japan. Soc. Mech. Engrs.*, **2**:469–474 (1959).
48. Chu, B-T.: *Phys. Fluids*, **2**:473–484 (1959).
49. Milne-Thomson, L. M.: "Theoretical Hydrodynamics," 3d ed., Macmillan, New York, 1955.
50. Schlichting, H.: "Boundary Layer Theory," 2d ed., McGraw-Hill, New York, 1960.
51. Broer, L. J. F.: *Appl. Sci. Research*, **A,6**:226–236 (1957).
52. Bird, R. B.: *AIChE J.*, **5**:565 (1959).
53. Carslaw, H. S., and J. C. Jaeger: "Heat Conduction in Solids," 2d ed., Oxford, New York, 1959.
54. Lyche, B. C., and R. B. Bird: *Chem. Eng. Sci.*, **6**:35–41 (1956).
55. Sellars, J. R., M. Tribus, and J. S. Klein: *Trans. ASME*, **78**:441–448 (1956).
56. Whiteman, I. R., and W. B. Drake: *Trans. ASME*, **80**:728–732 (1958).
57. Bird, R. B.: *Chem. Ing.-Tech.*, **31**:569–572 (1959).
58. Weltman, R. N., and P. W. Kuhns: *J. Colloid Sci.*, **7**:218–226 (1952).
59. Bird, R. B.: *SPE Journal*, **11**:35–40 (1955).
60. Crank, J.: "The Mathematics of Diffusion," Oxford, New York, 1956.
61. Bird, R. B.: *Advances in Chem. Eng.*, **1**:155–240 (1956); errata, **2**:325 (1958).
62. Arnold, J. H.: *Trans. AIChE*, **40**:361–378 (1944).
63. Hsu, H. W., and R. B. Bird: *AIChE Journal*, vol. 6, 1960.
64. Hellund, E. J.: *Phys. Rev.*, **57**:737–744 (1940).
65. Bird, R. B.: *Chem. Eng. Sci.*, **6**:123–131 (1957).
66. Hougen, O. A., K. M. Watson, and R. A. Ragatz: "Chemical Process Principles," vol. 2, chap. 16, Wiley, New York, 1959.
67. Acrivos, A., and N. R. Amundson: *Ind. Eng. Chem.*, **47**:1533–41 (1955).
68. Perry, J. H.: "Chemical Engineers' Handbook," p. 1018, McGraw-Hill, New York, 1950.
69. Schiller, L.: in "Handbuch der Experimentalphysik," vol. 4, chap. 2, pp. 339–391, 1932.

Section 7

FLOW OF NON-NEWTONIAN FLUIDS

By

A. B. METZNER, *University of Delaware, Newark, Delaware*

FLOW OF NON-NEWTONIAN FLUIDS

INTRODUCTION AND PERSPECTIVE

7.1. Notation

a	Constant in Eq. (7.75), dimensionless.
a_n	Numerator of approximate equation for turbulent friction factors, dimensionless
A	Grouping of constants in Oldroyd's phenomenological equations for stress distribution, defined by Eqs. (7.15) and (7.42).
A_{EP}	Constant in Eq. (7.6), (length)^2/(force).
A_{1n}	Function of flow-behavior index defined by Eqs. (7.66) and (7.67), dimensionless
b_n	Reynolds-number exponent in turbulent-friction-factor approximation, dimensionless.
B	(1) Grouping of constants in Oldroyd's phenomenological equations, defined by Eqs. (7.15) and (7.42).
	(2) Constant in Eyring-Powell Eq. (7.6), (time)$^{-1}$.
	(3) Wall-to-centerline spacing of parallel flat plates (i.e., separation $= 2B$), length.
C	Pressure-drop factor for flow downstream from an abrupt contraction, defined by Eq. (7.58), dimensionless.
C'_n	Function of flow-behavior index in Eqs. (7.66) and (7.68), dimensionless.
C_R	Factor defined by Eq. (7.36) and given in Table 7.2, dimensionless.
D	Diameter, length. D_i and D_0 refer to the bob-and-cup diameters of a rotational viscometer, respectively.
D_h	The hydraulic diameter equal to four times the area-to-perimeter ratio, length.
f	Fanning friction factor, $2g_c\tau_w/\rho V^2$, dimensionless.
g_c	Dimensional conversion factor, (mass)(length)/(force)(time)^2.
H	Point value of stress exerted vertically perpendicular to the direction of shear in a cone-and-plate viscometer, (force)/(length)^2.
k_1, k_2	Dimensionless instrument constants appearing in Eq. (7.34):

$$k_1 = \frac{s^2 - 1}{2s^2}\,(1 + \tfrac{2}{3}\ln s)$$

$$k_2 = \frac{s^2 - 1}{6s^2}\,\ln s$$

K, K'	Consistency indexes defined by Eqs. (7.4), (7.5), (7.61), and (7.62), (force)(time)^n/(length)^2 and (force)(time)$^{n'}$/(length)^2, respectively.
l	Length or bob length.
L	Length or tube length.
n	Flow-behavior index defined by Eq. (7.4), dimensionless.
n'	Flow-behavior index defined by Eqs. (7.5) and (7.26), dimensionless.
n''	$d(\log t)/d(\log N)$, dimensionless.
N	Rotational speed, (revolutions)/(time).
N'_{Re}	Generalized Reynolds number defined by Eq. (7.64), dimensionless.

$N_{\mathrm{Re}\,x}$	Length Reynolds number for power-law fluids (dimensionless). $N_{\mathrm{Re}\,x} = x^n U_\infty^{2-n}/K g_c$.
p	Pressure, (force)/(length)^2.
p_0	Point value of p at entrance to the tube.
q'	Volumetric flow rate per foot of channel width, for flow between parallel flat plates, (length)^2/(time).
Q	Volumetric flow rate, (length)^3/(time).
r	Radial or lineal distance, length.
R	Tube or cone radius, length. R_j refers to the radius of a fluid jet, and R_i and R_o designate the inner and outer radii of an annular space, respectively.
s	$s = D_0/D_i$, dimensionless.
t	Torque, (force)(length).
u	Point velocity, (length)/(time)
u'	Shear rate, (time)$^{-1}$. u'_w and u'_i refer to the shear rates at a wall and at the bob of a rotational viscometer, respectively.
U_∞	Uniform velocity at a large distance from the surface, (length)/(time).
v_s	Velocity of fluid "slipping" past a surface, (length)/(time).
V	Mean or volumetric mean velocity, (length)/(time). V_j refers to the uniform velocity of a fluid jet.
W	Constant defined by Eq. (7.38), dimensionless.
x	Distance from entrance to a tube or from leading edge of a flat plate, length.
X	Constant defined by Eq. (7.37), dimensionless.
y	Distance measured perpendicular to a flat plate, length.
Y	Dimensionless function of R_i/R_o and n, for flow in annuli, given by Fig. 7.13.
α	In Eq. (7.30): angle between the cone and the plate in a cone-and-plate viscometer, radians.
α	Kinetic-energy factor in Eq. (7.57), dimensionless.
β	Slip coefficient defined by Eq. (7.28), (length)^3/(force)(time).
γ	(1) Denominator of the generalized Reynolds number, defined by Eq. (7.65), (mass)(time)$^{n'-2}$/(length).
	(2) In Table 7.1 denotes strain, dimensionless.
Δ	Denotes a difference of the quantity following.
η_0	(Newtonian) fluid viscosity at low shear rates, appearing in Eqs. (7.15) to (7.21), (force)(time)/(length)^2.
θ	Time.
λ	Radial position function, dimensionless.
Λ	Dimensionless grouping of terms equal to $(y/x)(N_{\mathrm{Re}\,x})^{1/(1+n)}$.
μ	Viscosity, (mass)/(time)(length). The apparent viscosity μ_a is a function of shear rate.
μ_0, μ_1, μ_2	Constants in Eqs. (7.15) to (7.21), time.
ν_1, ν_2	Constants in Eqs. (7.15) to (7.21), time.
π	3.14 . . . , dimensionless.
ρ	Density, (mass)/(length)^3.
τ	Normal or shearing stress, (force)/(length)^2. τ_w and τ_i denote the shearing stresses at a wall and at the inner of two concentric cylindrical surfaces, respectively.
ϕ, ϕ_1, ϕ_2	Terms denoting an unspecified functional relationship.

7.2. General Position of Non-Newtonian Materials within the Spectrum of Known Types of Fluid Behavior

Table 7.1 lists the various types of real-fluid behavior as they appear to be known at the present time. While problems of magnetohydrodynamics (category V) and of molecular flow (category VI) will not be discussed in this section, it is interesting to note that with the exception of these two areas and the special case of Newtonian behavior (category Ia) all real-fluid systems are non-Newtonian in behavior.

Rheologists (see, for example, Reiner[75]) have argued that probably most fluids fall into categories III or IV and, at least under special conditions, will display all the

Table 7.1. Types of Fluid Behavior

Category I: Purely Viscous Fluids. Fluids for which shear rate depends only on the imposed shearing stress:

(a) Newtonian:

$$u' = \left(\frac{g_c}{\mu}\right)\tau$$

or

$$\tau = \left(\frac{\mu}{g_c}\right)u'$$

(b) Non-Newtonian: One example is that of fluids which approximate the so-called "power-law" behavior:

$$\tau = K(u')^n$$

Category II: Time-dependent Fluids. Non-Newtonian fluids for which shear rate depends on imposed stress and, in addition, on the duration of the stress:

$$u' = \phi_1(\tau, \theta)$$

Category III: Viscoelastic Systems. Materials for which shear rate depends on the imposed stress and the extent of deformation (strain):

$$u' = \phi_2(\tau, \gamma)$$

Category IV: Complex Rheological Bodies. Systems exhibiting the complexities of categories I, II, and III materials combined.

Category V: Fluids for which shear rate depends on shear stress and intensity of an imposed magnetic field.

Category VI: Fluids which must be considered as being made up of discrete particles rather than as continuous media.

possible properties of such complex systems. For example, an extensive and as yet unresolved argument has been waged[14,32,37,76,96] over the question of whether or not air, normally considered Newtonian, exhibits viscoelastic properties at high shear rates. If this is so, i.e., if the categories of Table 7.1 represent oversimplifications, a material which is conventionally considered purely viscous (category I), for example, may under special circumstances have to be treated as a category II, III, or IV system. This possible disadvantage of the system of classifications given in Table 7.1 is entirely offset by the fact that many systems at least approximate only one simple type of behavior, such as purely viscous properties; hence the classification method used is very useful from an engineering viewpoint. Following it one may first analyze the simplest type of behavior (and this analysis will apply to many real fluids as an excellent approximation) and then proceed progressively to more complex systems. This is the procedure followed in the present section.

7.3. Specific Types of Fluid Behavior

Category I: Purely Viscous Systems. Purely viscous fluid systems are defined herein as those which may be fully characterized by their shear-stress–shear-rate relationship under conditions of simple shear in steady, laminar flow. In view of the wide range of these variables over which measurements usually need to be made, it is convenient to plot the flow curve (as the shear-stress–shear-rate relationship is termed) on logarithmic coordinates as shown in Fig. 7.1. The types of behavior depicted in Fig. 7.1 may be summarized as follows. More complete descriptions are available elsewhere.[47,51,53]

1. A single constant (the viscosity μ) in the equation

$$\tau = \frac{\mu}{g_c}(u') \tag{7.1}$$

serves to define the flow behavior of incompressible *Newtonian fluids* completely at a given temperature. Gases and low-molecular-weight (i.e., nonpolymeric) liquids are almost always Newtonian under conventional rates of shear (say, 1 to 10^5 sec^{-1}).

Obviously, more than a single constant or parameter is required to characterize the flow curves of the other systems depicted in Fig. 7.1.

2. While *Bingham plastic* behavior is of importance historically,[75] no convincing evidence[53] is available to support the suggestion that any real fluids obey the equation

$$\tau = \tau_y + \frac{\mu_{BP}}{g_c}(u') \qquad (7.2)$$

or the *Saint-Venant* special case, $\mu_{BP} = 0$.

3. The terms *pseudoplastic* and *dilatant* are applied to slopes of the logarithmic flow curves of less than unity and greater than unity, respectively. The "apparent" viscosity

$$\mu_a = \tau \frac{g_c}{(u')} \qquad (7.3)$$

decreases with increasing shear rate in pseudoplastic fluids and increases in dilatant systems.

Figures 7.2 and 7.3 show that pseudoplastic and dilatant behavior may in practice be associated only with limited ranges of shear rate, particularly in the case of dilatancy. The results shown are quite general. At the extremes of very low- and very high-shear-rate polymer solutions, polymer melts and most slurries of limited concentration are found to be Newtonian

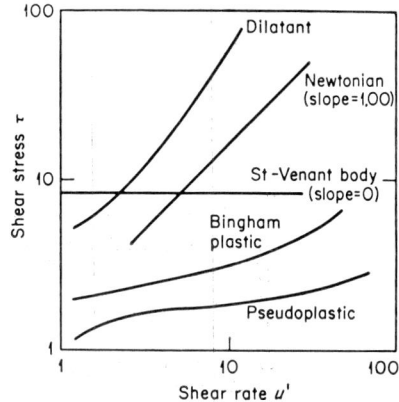

Fig. 7.1. Logarithmic flow curves depicting the various types of purely viscous fluid behavior. (*Reproduced from Metzner*[47] *with permission.*)

in shear and pseudoplasticity is restricted to an intermediate range of shear rates. While this "intermediate range" may sometimes be broad, the fact that it is only finite emphasizes the importance of restricting any extrapolations of the fluid properties to modest levels, unless the extrapolating equation is sufficiently complex to portray these changes accurately. The microscopic phenomena leading to pseudoplastic[47,51] and dilatant behavior[52] are understood qualitatively, and many examples are known.[47] Most polymeric solutions and melts fall into category III (viscoelastic), and most dilute slurries into category II (thixotropic), but under conditions of steady and simple shear these complications may often be neglected (see pp. 7-6 to 7-9 and Art. 7.9).

Dilatancy is common to extremely concentrated suspensions. As Fig. 7.3 shows, these may change from pseudoplastic to dilatant over a very small range of shear rates. The literature on dilatancy, including a tabulation of fluid systems displaying these properties, has been compactly summarized by Metzner and Whitlock.[52]

A nearly endless variety of equations has been proposed for portrayal of purely viscous non-Newtonian-flow behavior, particularly for pseudoplastic fluids. Only two are of sufficient interest to warrant discussion.

1. The "power-law" equation

$$\tau = K(u')^n \qquad (7.4)$$

has been found to be remarkably versatile and useful[7,16,21,29,47,53] because it portrays fluid behavior correctly over a range of shear rates adequate for many applications and, possessing only two constants, is the simplest type of equation possible. While it is obviously applicable only over the ranges of shear rate for which the curves of Figs. 7.1 to 7.3 may be approximated by straight lines, this is frequently a 100- to 1000-fold range in pseudoplastic systems.

An even more useful equation applica-

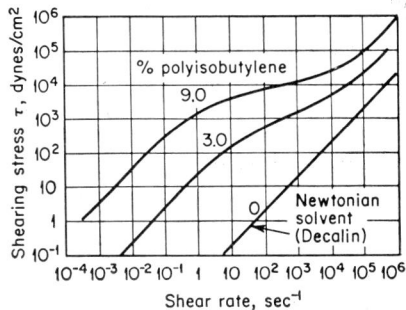

Fig. 7.2. Typical flow curves of fluids exhibiting psuedoplasticity in steady shear. (*Compiled from Brodnyan, Gaskins, and Philippoff*[9] *with permission.*)

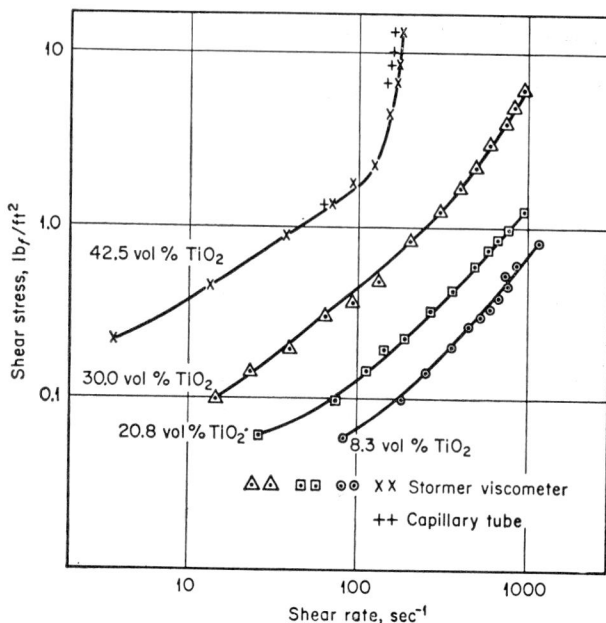

FIG. 7.3. Typical flow curves of concentrated suspensions exhibiting dilatancy at the higher shear rates and concentrations. (*Reproduced from Metzner and Whitlock[52] with permission.*)

ble to the important problem of laminar flow through round tubes is of a similar form:

$$\tau_w = \frac{D\,\Delta P}{4L} = K' \left(\frac{8V}{D}\right)^{n'} \tag{7.5}$$

but directly relates the pressure drop ΔP to the mean fluid velocity V. As a result, integration of shear-stress–shear-rate equations such as Eq. (7.4) (to obtain pressure-drop–flow-rate relations) and any attendant assumptions such as constancy of K and n may be completely avoided: if K' and n' vary with stress or with the term $8V/D$, it is simply necessary to evaluate them at the appropriate point. The only assumptions in the development of Eq. (7.5) are that purely viscous behavior prevails and that no "slip" occurs at the tube wall.[47,50,51,56,71]

2. The three-parameter Eyring-Powell[30,70,73] equation

$$\tau = \mu(u') + \frac{1}{B}\sinh^{-1}\frac{(u')}{A_{EP}} \tag{7.6}$$

correctly predicts the Newtonian regions at low and high shear rates in otherwise pseudoplastic systems and has also been applied to dilatant systems with some success.[74] The fact that its theoretical basis has been challenged[2,55] is not so limiting as is its complexity: it cannot be solved explicitly for shear rate. As its ability to fit data over modest shear-rate ranges is only a slight improvement over Eq. (7.4), very few engineering applications of this equation are available.[12] In those problems where its greater accuracy over broad shear-rate ranges is of importance its use may prove to be profitable.

Category II: Time-dependent Systems. Fluids that show a decrease in viscosity or shear stress with time, under isothermal conditions and steady shear, are termed *thixotropic*. Those that show increases, on the other hand, are termed *rheopectic*, or sometimes *antithixotropic*.[51] The latter behavior is relatively uncommon.

Thixotropic systems are of great commercial importance, especially in the paint and food industries. However, processing equipment must usually be designed to accommodate extremes of physical properties, which in this case are encountered after very short times of shear. Under these conditions the time dependency is of no importance since the design becomes the same as for purely viscous (category I) systems. Other design problems in which thixotropy must be considered have not yet been analyzed.[49] Only one recommended theoretical study of thixotropic systems[30] in which the Eyring-Powell

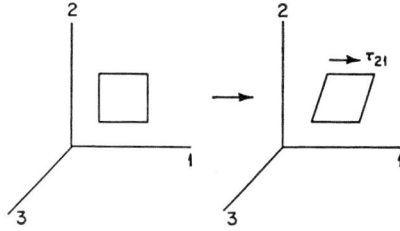

FIG. 7.4. Coordinate directions used in description of simple shear.

equation was applied to elucidate the flow mechanisms is available.

Category III: Viscoelastic Systems. This category will herein be considered to describe all fluid systems exhibiting normal stress effects. It may be shown (see Oldroyd,[59,60] Reiner,[75] and later parts of this article) that normal stress effects do not necessarily depend solely on fluid elasticity, but this is generally the case,[47] and the usual as well as the most outstanding and important examples of systems exhibiting normal stress effects are clearly elastic in nature.

The pioneering studies of Weissenberg†[101,102] demonstrated the "climbing" of elastic fluids onto a shaft rotating within the fluid, in opposition to centrifugal forces. This *Weissenberg effect* is also manifested by an axial tension in such a fluid: if it is sufficiently viscous to be "cut" (as in the case of a molten polymer), the liquid that has climbed up the shaft may be observed to contract longitudinally.

Three approaches have been used to study this type of fluid behavior:

1. Fundamental (tensor) equations, which assume only that the stress components at a point are determined by the first, second, . . . , nth gradients of velocity at that point[80,81,83] or by the strains, the strain rates, and the total time derivatives of the elements of the stress tensor,[59-62] have been solved for the forces required to produce a variety of assumed physical deformations of an element of incompressible fluid which was isotropic at rest. These phenomenological theories have been extensively discussed by Markovitz,[42] Philippoff,[67] and Jobling and Roberts.[38] Generally, no attempt has been made to relate the observed fluid behavior to molecular characteristics. In fact, Pao[63] has pointed out that this approach in reality assumes the form of the end result and then works back to what are really the true fluid properties.

2. An approach similar to the theory of rubberlike elasticity in solids has been applied to polymeric melts and solutions, particularly by Lodge,[41] Pao,[63] Rouse,[87] and Takemura.[94] While these approaches in principle lead to a more direct understanding of the important molecular characteristics, this possible advantage has not yet been exploited since these theories have been far less completely developed than those of Rivlin[80] and Oldroyd.[59]

3. Experimentation to test the above theoretical predictions or to develop new theoretical concepts has been very limited and largely qualitative in nature. In fact, it has been suggested[79] that the major remaining progress will be due to such experimental studies.

Consider the incompressible fluid element shown undergoing steady, simple shear in Fig. 7.4. The shear rate is equal to u'. The nine possible stresses τ_{jk} required‡ to maintain this state of shear are:

τ_{11} Tensile stress acting in the direction of flow upon surface 1.

τ_{21} Shearing stress on surface 2. This stress is the only one of interest in purely viscous fluids [i.e., it is the τ in Eqs. (7.1) to (7.6)].

τ_{31} Shearing stress on surface 3.

† Weissenberg may not have been the first to make experimental investigations of normal stresses, but the brilliance and clarity of his studies are exceptional. The historical development of this area is reviewed elsewhere.[38,47]

‡ Using the standard notation, the first subscript refers to the surface on which the stress acts and the second to the direction in which it acts. The j surface is defined as that surface normal to the j axis.

τ_{21}, τ_{22}, τ_{23}, τ_{31}, τ_{32}, τ_{33} may be similarly defined. Under conditions of simple shear, by definition, the shearing stresses τ_{13}, τ_{23}, τ_{32}, τ_{31} are zero. To avoid rotation of the element, τ_{12} must equal τ_{21}. For the normal stresses and this single shear stress Rivlin[80] predicts

$$\tau_{11} = -p + \alpha_3(u')^2 \tag{7.7}$$
$$\tau_{12} = u'[\alpha_1 + 2\alpha_5(u')^2 + 4\alpha_7(u')^4] \tag{7.8}$$
$$\tau_{22} = -p + (u')^2[(2\alpha_2 + \alpha_3) + 4(\alpha_4 + \alpha_6)(u')^2 + 8\alpha_8(u')^4] \tag{7.9}$$
$$\tau_{33} = -p \tag{7.10}$$

in which p is an arbitrary, indeterminate hydrostatic pressure which may be a polynomial in $(u')^2$, $(u')^4$, and $(u')^6$. The sign convention is such that a positive normal stress denotes a tension. The α's are also polynomials in $(u')^2$, $(u')^4$, and $(u')^6$. While Eqs. (7.7) to (7.10) are entirely acceptable on the basis of available experimental measurements of the stresses involved,[38,42] they are too general to be of direct practical value at the present time, since they simply state that the normal stresses are some (unknown) function of $(u')^2$, $(u')^4$, and $(u')^6$ and the functional dependency would have to be determined experimentally. Accordingly, a less general approach will be sought.

Even with drastic simplifications of Oldroyd's[59,62] more general theories, it is possible to predict either negative (his fluid A) or positive (fluid B) Weissenberg effects, as well as an inelastic fluid (i.e., one which possesses no recovery from a deformation)—Oldroyd's fluid C—but which gives rise to a Weissenberg effect through what has been variously termed a *coefficient of cross viscosity*,[75] or a *normal stress coefficient*.[82] For his fluid B,

$$\tau_{11} = -p + 2\eta_0(\mu_1 - \mu_2)(u')^2 \tag{7.11}$$
$$\tau_{12} = \eta_0(u') \tag{7.12}$$
$$\tau_{22} = -p \tag{7.13}$$
$$\tau_{33} = -p \tag{7.14}$$

in which η_0 = viscosity

μ_1, μ_2 = arbitrary scalar, physical constants ($\mu_1 > \mu_2$) having the dimensions of time

p = an arbitrary isotropic pressure

Since Eqs. (7.12) and (7.1) are identical except for nomenclature, the velocity profile of Oldroyd's fluid B (flowing through a long round tube, for example) is the Newtonian parabola. It would also behave as a Newtonian fluid in the sense that doubling the applied stress or pressure gradient would double the flow rate. However, at the exit of the tube the axial tension described by Eq. (7.11) would be relieved. Provided the term $2\eta_0(\mu_1 - \mu_2)(u')^2$ is sufficiently great, the jet would expand, rather than contract, in the region downstream from the tube.†

Appreciable axial tensions have apparently been reported only for fluids which are non-Newtonian in shear. To bring out this effect, one must assume nonzero values for at least two of the additional arbitrary constants (with dimensions of time) in the general theory. More generally, Oldroyd[59] recommends the six-constant equation which leads to the following results:

$$\tau_{11} = [(2\mu_1 - \nu_1)F(u') - (2\mu_2 - \nu_2)\eta_0](u')^2 - p \tag{7.15}$$
$$\tau_{12} = \tau_{21} = (u')F(u') \tag{7.16}$$
$$\tau_{22} = \tau_{33} = -[\nu_1 F(u') - \nu_2 \eta_0](u')^2 - p \tag{7.17}$$
$$\tau_{13} = \tau_{31} = \tau_{23} = \tau_{32} = 0$$

in which

$$F(u') = \frac{\tau_{12}}{u'} \quad \text{(the ``apparent'' viscosity in steady shear)} \tag{7.18}$$

$$F(u') = \frac{\eta_0[1 + \sigma_2(u')^2]}{1 + \sigma_1(u')^2} \tag{7.19}$$

† In any event the fluid would not contract by as much as the 13 per cent decrease in radius which occurs in Newtonian fluids.[48]

and
$$\sigma_2 = \mu_1\mu_2 + \mu_0(\mu_2 - \tfrac{3}{2}\nu_2) - \mu_1(\mu_2 - \nu_2) \tag{7.20}$$
$$\sigma_1 = \mu_1{}^2 + \mu_0(\mu_1 - \tfrac{3}{2}\nu_1) - \mu_1(\mu_1 - \nu_1) \tag{7.21}$$

In order to predict pseudoplasticity in steady shear, σ_1 must be greater than σ_2 and both must be positive. Equation (7.19) then predicts the required Newtonian behavior in shear at the extremes of very low and very high shear rates, the viscosities being η_0 and $\eta_0\sigma_2/\sigma_1$, respectively. Furthermore, Oldroyd has shown that the observed fluid behavior also requires that the following inequalities be satisfied:

$$\mu_0\mu_1 + (\mu_1 - \tfrac{3}{2}\mu_0)\nu_1 > \mu_0\mu_2 + (\mu_1 - \tfrac{3}{2}\mu_0)\nu_2 \geq \tfrac{1}{9}\left[\mu_0\mu_1 + (\mu_1 - \tfrac{3}{2}\mu_0)\nu_1\right] > 0 \tag{7.22}$$
and
$$(\mu_1 - \tfrac{3}{2}\mu_0)(\mu_1\nu_2 - \mu_2\nu_1) \geq 0 \tag{7.23}$$

In view of the number of constants in Eqs. (7.19) to (7.21), the fact that good approximations over appreciable shear-rate ranges are obtainable by use of Eq. (7.4) is surprising but reassuring. In the special case for which

$$\mu_0 = \mu_1 = \mu_2 = \nu_1 = \nu_2 = 0 \tag{7.24}$$

Oldroyd's equations reduce to Eq. (7.1) for a Newtonian fluid.

Category IV: Complex Rheological Bodies. No quantitative study has yet been made of fluid systems which may have viscoelastic, time-dependent, and viscous properties all superimposed. Jobling and Roberts[38] describe several fascinating qualitative observations, however, to which the reader is referred.

7.4. Effects of Temperature and Pressure on Flow Properties

Viscous (Shear) Properties. Metzner[47] and Westover[108] discuss in some detail the changes in n and K, Eq. (7.4), with temperature for molten polymers, as well as the scanty information available on pressure effects in these systems. A brief discussion of temperature and concentration effects in slurries and solutions is given by Metzner.[51] They are not reproduced here because of the comparative availability of these references and the restricted nature of the available results.

Elastic Properties. The constants of Eqs. (7.15) to (7.21) have not yet been determined for any real fluids, to the author's knowledge.

Summary

It is seen that most of the kinds of fluid behavior known are of a non-Newtonian variety. Newtonian fluids form one subgroup of a more general category of non-Newtonian behavior (purely viscous materials). Most engineering design problems are likely to be concerned with either category I (purely viscous) or with category III (viscoelastic) systems.

It is suggested that Eq. (7.4) (the power law) is probably the most generally useful relation for application to purely viscous fluid systems. The general equations of Oldroyd, Eqs. (7.15) to (7.23), are recommended for viscoelastic fluids in simple (and steady) shear. The reasons leading to these choices are discussed.

MEASUREMENT OF FLOW PROPERTIES

7.5. Viscometry

Since viscometry is concerned with measurement of the relationships between shearing stress and rate of shear, it is only possible to characterize category I (purely viscous) and category II (time-dependent) systems completely by means of viscometric measurements alone. The characterization of viscoelastic systems will be discussed under rheogoniometry.

Two general problems may occur in all types of viscometric measurements. In the first place, movement of suspended solids or polymeric molecules away from the walls of the containing vessel may take place under the influence of the velocity gradient, leaving a thin film of low-viscosity fluid next to the wall. If this occurs, much of the velocity change may take place in this low-viscosity region and the rheological data obtained will obviously be in error. If the film is thin enough, the problem posed is similar to what would occur if the fluid were homogeneous but "slipped" at the wall. Such "slip" is readily observable in open channels carrying coarse suspensions, such as paper pulp, and, of course, in toothpastes. The magnitude of the effect has been both calculated and measured in polymer solutions.[90] Finke and Heinz[23] have used roughened surfaces in a rotational viscometer to avoid slip of chocolates and toothpastes, and the problem may in principle be eliminated by the same technique in capillary tubes. However, in view of the close tolerances and small clearances required for temperature control, such uniform roughening may be difficult to achieve in practice in most instruments.

The inverse of this problem has also been observed,[23,36,93,99] especially in blood vessels[17]: solid or polymeric material may be adsorbed onto the walls of the system. If this occurs, the dimensions of the system may be appreciably altered (the attendant dilution of the solution is usually negligible).

Whenever possible the scale of the apparatus should be changed to prove the absence of both the positive or negative adsorptive processes. In addition, Mooney's[56] detailed treatment of corrections for slip, reviewed herein, may be employed.

Purely Viscous Fluid Systems. Of the various kinds of useful viscometric equipment developed,[47] only three types are of general interest. In addition, an enormous variety of empirical instruments exist. These usually are claimed to be of some control value but are of no use whatever as a source of scientific or engineering data.

CAPILLARY-TUBE VISCOMETERS. In these instruments the fluid is forced through a long, smooth, cylindrical tube under conditions of laminar flow. Providing there is no slip at the wall, it has been shown[56,71] (see also Metzner[47,51,53]) that for *all Category I fluids* the shear rate at the wall under conditions of well-developed flow is

$$(u')_w = \frac{3n' + 1}{4n'} \frac{8V}{D} \tag{7.25}$$

in which

$$n' = \frac{d(\ln \tau_w)}{d\ln (8V/D)} \tag{7.26}$$

The shear stress τ_{12} at the wall for any well-developed flow through a round tube is abbreviated τ_w and is given by a simple force balance as

$$\tau_w = \frac{D \, \Delta P}{4L} \tag{7.27}$$

Therefore, by measuring ΔP as a function of V (or Q), the true shear-stress–shear-rate relationships as well as the $\tau_w - 8V/D$ relations useful in pipeline design may be derived. Some confusion still exists in the literature concerning the shear rate at the wall (it is *not* equal to $8V/D$ except in the special case of $n' = 1.00$) and over the fact that the shear stress $[(r \, \Delta P)/2L]$ is variable with radius. This last fact is clearly irrelevant to both Eqs. (7.25) and (7.27), the only important point being that the stress and shear rate are both calculated at the same point in the fluid. Literature statements to the effect that true shear-stress–shear-rate data are difficult to obtain with capillary-tube units because of the radial variation of the shear stress are obviously completely incorrect.

An important advantage of the capillary tube over the other types of viscometric equipment lies in the fact that the fluid resides in the tube only for very short times. The continuous fluid replenishment reduces the accumulation of heat due to viscous-energy dissipation in the fluid. In the other types of viscometric equipment all the energy must be conducted out of the fluid sample to avoid errors due to nonisothermal flow conditions. Toor's[97] calculations indicate the following: for a fluid having a viscosity of 1000 cp at a shear rate of 10^4 per second flowing through a 0.025-in.-diameter tube with an L/D of 500, the maximum temperature rise anywhere in the fluid would be less than 1°F. These flow conditions, requiring a pressure drop of about 3000 psi per foot of tube length, are obviously extreme, so that the temperature rise may usually be neglected in solutions and slurries. In molten polymers the viscosities may be in the millions, however, and the same is not true. In this case additional complications arise because of energy consumed by volumetric expansion of the fluid as the pressure on it decreases (during flow through the tube) and to the change in flow properties with pressure. The several publications in this field have been reviewed recently,[47,97] but no entirely definitive study is as yet available. Fortunately, these systems are frequently studied and processed at lower shear rates, where these effects become smaller.

The assumption that laminar flow prevails [used in deriving Eq. (7.25)] may be checked by calculation of the appropriate non-Newtonian Reynolds number [Eq. (7.64)]. The assumption of steady flow (no end effects) will frequently be met only in the case of inconveniently long tubes; hence end corrections are necessary to the ΔP term in Eq. (7.27). For Newtonian fluids, the total correction is 2.25 velocity heads $(2.25\rho V^2/2g_c)$; for non-Newtonian fluids appreciably smaller values have been predicted,[8] but the only carefully measured values in purely viscous fluids are identical with the Newtonian correction.[8,106] Accordingly, its use is recommended for all purely viscous fluids.†

In viscoelastic systems, the end effects[4,11,46,66] may be very much larger than $2.25\rho V^2/g_c$, but the precise factor has not yet been defined. Accordingly, any end effect must be determined experimentally by obtaining ΔP as a function of L/D and extrapolating the linear portion to a zero L/D. The same is true of the very concentrated suspensions exhibiting dilatancy if solids deposit at the entrance to the tube, as is frequently the case.[78] The ΔP term in Eq. (7.27) must, of course, include any gravitational forces due to the head of fluid in the tube and reservoir.

Oldroyd[60] has reviewed the several treatments of slip at the walls of the capillary tube. The most direct method of detecting and correcting for slip is due to Mooney[56]: data are obtained in several tubes of different radii; values of $Q/\pi R^3$ are plotted against $1/R$ at various constant values of the wall shear stress τ_w. The slope of the curve will be equal to $\tau_w\beta$, in which β is the slip coefficient at the particular value of τ_w employed, as defined by the equation

$$\beta\tau_w = v_s \tag{7.28}$$

By knowing v_s, the value of the total efflux Q may be corrected to give the true efflux at the shear stress of interest which would be obtained in the absence of slip:

$$Q_{\text{true}} = Q_{\text{measured}} - v_s(\pi R^2) \tag{7.29}$$

Two additional points concerning capillary-tube viscometers must be emphasized. In the first place, the basic instrument is very versatile; simply by interchanging tubes and varying the applied pressures, 10^8-fold ranges of shear rate and 10^6-fold ranges in viscosity may be studied.[25] Ranges of 10^4 and 10^3, respectively, are, moreover, very easy to obtain. No other single instrument is so versatile. Second, an important practical disadvantage must be pointed out: the time required to measure any given part of the flow curve is an order of magnitude greater than with rotational units, largely because of cleaning and assembly problems.

ROTATIONAL CONE-AND-PLATE VISCOMETERS. In this type of instrument the fluid is sheared in a small gap between a flat plate and a cone.[45,68] The fluid is held in the gap, against the action of centrifugal forces, purely by the viscous traction.‡ If the cone angle is small (fractions of a degree are used in the commercial units), the temperature control is quite good because the layer of fluid being sheared is very thin. If in addition the unit is designed so that the apex of the cone just touches the surface of the plate, the shear rate is uniform throughout the entire fluid sample and is given by[45]

$$u' = \frac{2\pi N}{\alpha} \tag{7.30}$$

† Article 7.7 discusses end corrections in further detail.
‡ In viscoelastic systems the normal elastic stresses also force the fluid toward the apex of the cone.

The corresponding shearing stress is obtained from the measured torque by the equation

$$\tau = \frac{3t}{2\pi R^3} \tag{7.31}$$

Difficulties are experienced with systems of low viscosity, especially at higher shear rates. This is probably due to the material being partially thrown out of the viscometer, although secondary flow due to centrifugal forces may also be a problem.[47] If slip occurs at either surface in this type of viscometer, it is impossible to obtain useful data with it.[60]

ROTATIONAL BOB-AND-CUP INSTRUMENTS. The fluid sample is sheared in the annular gap between a cylindrical bob and a somewhat larger cup. If the ratio of the diameters of the cup to the bob is very large (so that no appreciable fluid motion occurs at the cup), the shear rate at the bob is rigorously given by the relation

$$u'_i = \frac{4\pi N}{n''} \tag{7.32}$$

for all purely viscous fluids.[3,40,51] It should be noted that the value of n'' will not be a constant for non-power-law fluids, hence must be evaluated at the particular value of N at which u'_i is to be evaluated.

The corresponding shearing stress at the bob is given[51] by

$$\tau_i = \frac{2t}{\pi D_i^2 l} \tag{7.33}$$

provided there are no end effects. In this type of instrument end effects are difficult to eliminate but good results (as determined by agreement with the flow curves for *non-Newtonian* systems obtained on another type of viscometer) have been obtained[47,53] by simply calibrating the instrument with a Newtonian oil, thereby computing an "effective" bob length l, which is somewhat greater than its geometric length alone.

These instruments are handy, but the ranges of variables that can be covered, particularly with respect to shear rate, are very modest.

Alternatively, one may be interested in a bob-and-cup instrument in which the cup fits closely to the bob. In this case much higher shear rates may be obtained (comparable to those of cone-and-plate instruments), though not as high as in a capillary-tube unit. The shear stress is still given by Eq. (7.33). End effects are again corrected for by the above procedure unless the bob and cup have the conical Mooney-Ewart[58] end design.

The shear rate at the bob is given rigorously, for all purely viscous fluids, by the Krieger-Maron or Pawlowski[40,65] equation

$$u'_i = \frac{4\pi N}{1 - 1/s^2} \left\{ 1 + k_1 \left(\frac{1}{n''} - 1 \right) + k_2 \left[\left(\frac{1}{n''} - 1 \right)^2 + \frac{d(1/n'' - 1)}{d(\log t)} \right] \right\} \tag{7.34}$$

provided the cup-to-bob diameter ratio is less than 1.2. Should this not be the case, additional terms of the infinite series inside the braces are required.

As discussed earlier, the power law, Eq. (7.4), almost always is valid over small ranges of shear rate. In this case Eq. (7.34) may be simplified by deletion of the $d(1/n'' - 1)$ terms. Using this assumption, Calderbank and Moo-Young[10] have calculated enough terms in the infinite series expansion to obtain a 1 per cent accuracy when the diameter ratio s is as great as 1.75. Equation (7.34) was rewritten as

$$u'_i = \frac{4\pi N}{1 - 1/s^2} C_R \tag{7.35}$$

in which

$$C_R = 1 + \frac{s^2 - 1}{2s^2} \times \left(1 + \frac{2}{3} \ln s + \tfrac{1}{3}W - \tfrac{1}{45}W^3 + \frac{2W^5}{945} - \frac{W^7}{4725} + \ldots \right) \tag{7.36}$$

and
$$X = \frac{1}{n''} - 1 = \frac{1}{n} - 1 \qquad (7.37)$$

$$W = X \ln s \qquad (7.38)$$

Their computed values of C_R are given in Table 7.2.

As the cup-to-bob diameter ratio approaches unity, the instrument approaches the ideal of a fluid being sheared between a moving flat plate and a stationary parallel one. Equation (7.32) reduces to

$$u' = \frac{2\pi RN}{\Delta R} \qquad (7.39)$$

for this case.

The reader is referred directly to the literature[15,44,45,107] for a discussion of heat generation in rotational viscometers.

Determination of slip in rotational units requires experiments in which the ratio of diameters s is varied.[56] If three combinations of radii $(R_a, R_b;\ R_b, R_c;\ R_a, R_c)$ are used and the rotational speeds required for a given torque t are measured, the coefficient of slip β_b (i.e., at the stress at surface R_b) is obtained from

$$2\pi(N_{ab} + N_{bc} - N_{ac}) = \frac{t\beta_b}{\pi R_b{}^2} \qquad (7.40)$$

By repeating this experiment at various values of t the variation of the coefficient β with stress may be determined. After obtaining this information, the viscometric curve (t versus N) may now be corrected for slip as follows:

From Eq. (7.33) the stress τ_i at a given value of t may be determined. The velocity of the slipping fluid at the bob is obtained by subtracting $\beta\tau_i$ [Eq. (7.28)] from the measured rotational speed. A similar correction is applied at the surface of the cup, and the shear rate is calculated by multiplying Eq. (7.39) or Eq. (7.34) by the ratio of the true velocity change (from bob to cup) to the velocity change calculated in the absence of slip.

Table 7.2. Calderbank, Moo-Young Tabulation of Shear-rate Factors C_R

$n =$ \ $s =$	1.07	1.15	1.166	1.25	1.40	1.746
0.05	2.72	5.00	5.44			
0.10	1.71	2.62	2.80	3.74	5.18	
0.20	1.29	1.62	1.69	2.03	2.59	3.62
0.30	1.16	1.34	1.38	1.55	1.84	2.38
0.40	1.10	1.21	1.23	1.34	1.51	1.83
0.50	1.07	1.14	1.15	1.22	1.33	1.52
0.60	1.05	1.09	1.10	1.14	1.21	1.34
0.70	1.03	1.06	1.06	1.09	1.13	1.21
0.80	1.02	1.03	1.04	1.05	1.08	1.12
0.90	1.01	1.02	1.02	1.02	1.03	1.05
1.00	1.00	1.00	1.00	1.00	1.00	1.00
1.25	....	....	0.97	....	0.94	0.91
1.50	....	....	0.95	....	0.90	0.85
1.75	....	....	0.94	....	0.88	0.81
2.00	....	....	0.93	....	0.86	0.79
2.25	....	....	0.92	....	0.84	0.76
2.50	....	....	0.92	....	0.83	0.75
2.75	....	....	0.91	....	0.82	0.73
3.00	....	....	0.91	....	0.81	0.72
3.25	....	....	0.90	....	0.81	0.71
3.50	....	....	0.90	....	0.80	0.70
3.75	....	....	0.90	....	0.80	0.70
4.00	....	....	0.89	....	0.79	0.69

Taylor vortices[95] which occur at higher rotational speeds set up secondary-flow patterns that invalidate the above relations. Vortices may be minimized by rotating the cup instead of the bob and by use of small clearances. The reader is referred to the literature[39,69,95] for a discussion of these complications.

Time-dependent Systems. Thixotropy (and rheopexy) may be characterized by either the change in shear stress with time (at constant shear rate) or by the area of the *hysteresis loop* between flow curves obtained with progressively increasing, then decreasing, shear rates.[30,31,104,105] As no peculiar difficulties are encountered, the reader is referred directly to the literature.

Since change of properties with time is involved, rotational viscometers with small clearances between the moving surfaces (hence a very nearly constant rate of shear in all parts of the fluid sample) must be used. Capillary tubes of various lengths or diameters may be used only to determine qualitatively the presence or absence of time-dependent effects.[3,51]

7.6. Rheogoniometry †

The complete description of a viscoelastic fluid [as by Eqs. (7.15) to (7.23)] requires measurement of normal stresses as well as of the shear component τ_{12} [which may be obtained by any of the methods described for purely viscous fluids (Arts. 7.5 and 7.9)].

A rheogoniometer (which essentially consists of a cone-and-plate viscometer fitted for measurement of normal as well as shearing stresses) has been designed which enables the direct determination[9,38,42,59,67,84] of the difference $\tau_{11} - \tau_{22}$ by means of the relationship

$$\tau_{11} - \tau_{22} = \frac{d(H)}{d(\ln R)} \tag{7.41}$$

or by measurement of the force H integrated over the entire plate, depending on the instrument used. These data have been extended to higher shear rates by means of a birefringence technique.[9] However, the few direct determinations of τ_{22} and τ_{33} discussed by Jobling and Roberts[38] appear to be the only available measurements of separate normal stresses rather than of the above difference.

Simple rheogoniometric measurements alone, on a cone-and-plate instrument, therefore do not enable determination of all the constants in Eqs. (7.15) to (7.21). Markovitz[42] and Oldroyd[59] have discussed use of goniometric measurements employing coaxial cylinders, but no experimental data on a given fluid appear to have been obtained on two different instruments, so that at present the experimental verification of the Oldroyd equations is incomplete.

The swelling of a jet of fluid emerging from a tube has been suggested[26] as a means of determining viscoelasticity parameters. This method would appear to be particularly appropriate since it may readily be employed over a wide range of shear rates and, together with data from a conventional rheogoniometer, would enable determination of all six constants in Eqs. (7.15) to (7.21). The development of the appropriate equations follows.

Just upstream from the outlet of the tube, the hydrostatic pressure is negligibly small and Eq. (7.15) may be written as

$$\tau_{11} = \left(\frac{A\tau_{12}}{u'} - B \right) (u')^2 \tag{7.42}$$

in which A and B are constants. Using $\tau_{12} = (r\,\Delta P)/2L$, $(\Delta P/L$ is the measured pressure gradient within the tube) and Eq. (7.4), the power law, to approximate the $\tau_{12} - u'$ relationship, ‡ Eq. (7.42) becomes

† Jobling and Roberts[38] define rheogoniometry as the measurement of the distribution of stresses and strains within the flowing material in all directions of space.

‡ Noting that the normal stresses as given by Eq. (7.42) decrease rapidly as one moves away from the wall, one may conclude that the power law will be an excellent approximation.

$$\tau_{11} = \frac{A}{K^{1/n}}\left(\frac{r\,\Delta P}{2L}\right)^{(n+1)/n} - \frac{B(r\,\Delta P/2L)^{2/n}}{K^{2/n}} \tag{7.43}$$

A force balance between the exit of the tube and a downstream position in the jet at which the elastic stresses τ_{11} have been relaxed and the velocity has also become uniform (neglecting gravitational and surface forces) gives

$$\int_0^R 2\pi r(u^2\rho - \tau_{11})dr = \rho V_j{}^2\pi R_j{}^2 \tag{7.44}$$

Similarly, a mass balance gives

$$\int_0^R 2\,\rho u^2\pi r\,dr = \rho V_j\pi R_j{}^2 \tag{7.45}$$

On substitution of Eq. (7.43) for τ_{11} into Eq. (7.44), carrying out the integration and simplifying by use of Eq. (7.45), one obtains

$$\left(\frac{2n\tau_w{}^{(n+1)/n}}{(3n+1)K^{1/n}}\right)A - \left(\frac{n\tau_w{}^{2/n}}{(n+1)K^{2/n}}\right)B = \rho V^2\left[\frac{3n+1}{2n+1} - \left(\frac{R}{R_j}\right)^2\right] \tag{7.46}$$

For the special case of Newtonian behavior in shear, this simplifies to

$$\mu A - B = \frac{\rho R^2}{8}\left[\frac{4}{3} - \left(\frac{R}{R_j}\right)^2\right] \tag{7.47}$$

This is Oldroyd's fluid B [Eq. (7.11)] for which

$$\mu A - B = 2\eta_0(\mu_1 - \mu_2) \tag{7.48}$$

Hence a constant ratio R/R_j is predicted which is independent of the flow rate used for any given fluid.

By making measurements at several velocities (knowing K and n, hence τ_w, from viscometric measurements) one may determine A and B in Eq. (7.46). This defines the quantities $(2\mu_1 - \nu_1)$ and $(2\mu_2 - \nu_2)\eta_0$. The rheogoniometric measurements serve to determine μ_1, μ_2, and η_0. Thus of the six constants, only μ_0 remains to be calculated. Application of Eq. (7.20) to the viscometric data determines this directly. Equation (7.21) may be used to obtain an independent check for consistency on the three constants μ_1, μ_0, and ν_1.

It is obvious that similar manipulations of other phenomenological equations, e.g., Eqs. (7.7) to (7.10), are possible.

Summary

This subsection has discussed the principles of viscometry and rheogoniometry required to evaluate fluid properties. The equations used to interpret experimental data, together with the corrections required, have been discussed in detail.

It is seen that for measuring the steady-flow properties of fluids that are either purely viscous or viscoelastic, the capillary-tube viscometer is the most versatile instrument available. If time-dependent viscometric properties are required, however, a rotational viscometer with close clearances must be used.

Rheogoniometric measurements and birefringence determinations have both been used to determine normal stresses. Additionally, equations are presented for calculation of the primary tensile elastic stress τ_{11} from the observed swelling of a fluid jet as it emerges from a capillary tube.

LAMINAR FLOW THROUGH ROUND TUBES

7.7. Purely Viscous Fluids

Pressure-loss–Flow-rate Relationships. In view of the fact that the τ_w to $8V/D$ relationship must be independent of tube diameter in the absence of slip for all purely viscous fluids (Art. 7.5), if capillary tubes or pipeline measurements of the flow properties are available, they may be used directly in design of larger pipes.[3,50,54,56] It is important to note that this is not an approximation but an entirely rigorous design procedure. Furthermore, when slip is present, as in some suspensions, it is simply necessary to correct for it by the methods outlined in Art. 7.5. That considerable confusion still exists over these facts is evidenced in a number of recent publications.[18,91] A practical application of slip—that of transporting very viscous oils by addition of water which coats a portion of the pipe and permits flow at appreciably reduced pressure gradients—has recently been discussed in detail.[88]

While the above procedure represents the best possible approach, frequently data will not be available in the form of τ_w to $8V/D$ information but in terms of the shear-stress–shear-rate equation

$$u' = -\frac{du}{dr} = \phi(\tau) \tag{7.49}$$

$$= \phi\left(\frac{r\,\Delta P}{2L}\right) \tag{7.50}$$

By integrating once,

$$\int_0^{u'} du = u = -\int_{r=R}^{r} \phi\left(\frac{r\,\Delta P}{2L}\right) dr \tag{7.51}$$

the velocity profile is obtained. Usually one is interested in the bulk-velocity–pressure-drop relationship, which may be obtained by a second integration:

$$V\pi R^2 = \int_{r=0}^{r=R} 2\pi r u \, dr \tag{7.52}$$

If the power law [Eq. (7.4)] is used as the above u' to τ relation, one obtains

$$\frac{D\,\Delta P}{4L} = K\left(\frac{3n+1}{n}\frac{2V}{D}\right)^n \tag{7.53}$$

or

$$\frac{D\,\Delta P}{4L} = K\left(\frac{3n+1}{n}\frac{8Q}{\pi D^3}\right)^n \tag{7.54}$$

More complete integrations of Eqs. (7.51) and (7.52) have been considered elsewhere.[47]

In so far as Eq. (7.4) is an approximation, so will Eqs. (7.53) and (7.54) be only approximations. However, if the power-law parameters K and n are chosen to represent the true-fluid behavior accurately at the tube wall (i.e., at $\tau_{12} = \tau_w = D\,\Delta P/4L$), the approximation will be a very good one: in all but very exceptional cases this power law will be an excellent approximation over at least a threefold range of shear stresses. This means that the equation fits correctly over 89 per cent of the cross-section area of the tube (from R to $R/3$), and even gross deviations from the assumed equation over the central portion of the tube will contribute but little to the over-all error.

Velocity Profiles. Combination of Eqs. (7.51) and (7.52) gives, for power-law fluids,[51]

$$\frac{u}{V} = \frac{1+3n}{1+n}\left[1 - \left(\frac{r}{R}\right)^{(n+1)/n}\right] \tag{7.55}$$

In the special case of Newtonian behavior, the flow-behavior index (n) is equal to unity and the familiar parabola is reproduced. Figure 7.5 shows several typical profiles; as n approaches zero, the profiles flatten (approaching plug flow); as n approaches infinity, the profiles steepen toward the triangular.

While Eq. (7.55) is also only an approximation, since it rests upon the power law, the degree of approximation is again quite good if the flow-behavior index n and the consistency index K are evaluated at or close to the shearing stress at the wall. In spite of the fact that Eq. (7.55) is a more sensitive test of an equation than is the integrated flow-rate–pressure-drop relationship, in one instance tested the power law described the

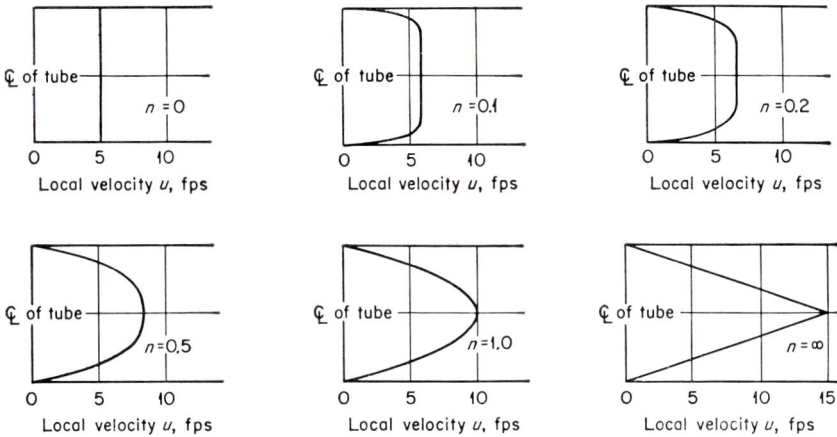

FIG. 7.5. Velocity profiles of power-law fluids in laminar flow inside a round tube. Average velocity is 5 fps in all cases. (*Reproduced from Metzner*[51] *with permission.*)

data as well as the Eyring-Powell equation,[30,92] while the Bingham plastic relation (7.2), which is frequently applied to greases and slurries on the basis of limited data, failed markedly.

Fluid Kinetic Energy. The kinetic energy of a power-law fluid is given[51]

$$\text{Kinetic energy, ft-lb}_f/\text{lb}_m = \frac{V^2}{\alpha g_c} \tag{7.56}$$

in which

$$\alpha = \frac{(4n + 2)(5n + 3)}{3(3n + 1)^2} \tag{7.57}$$

The factor α ranges from a value of 2.0 when $n = 0$ (plug flow) through 1.00 at $n = 1.00$ (Newtonian flow) to 0.741 at $n = \infty$ (infinitely dilatant fluid). A graphical solution of Eq. (7.57) is given in Fig. 7.6.

End Effects. Bogue[8] has used the von Kármán integral method (see, for example, Schlichting[89]) together with the assumption of power-law behavior in the conventional boundary-layer equations to calculate both the length of the entrance region (in which the velocity profile is developing) and the excess pressure drop in this region, for purely viscous fluids entering a tube from a large upstream reservoir. The results are shown in Figs. 7.7 to 7.9.

The length of the entrance region, x/R, was defined as the distance required for the boundary layers, developing from the tube walls, to merge at the centerline. This definition gives an entrance length about half as long as that required for 99 per cent development of the centerline velocity, but most of the interesting effects (including most of the pressure losses, Fig. 7.8) take place in a much shorter tube length. The Reynolds number used is the power-law special case of that defined by Eq. (7.64).

The pressure-drop correction factor C of Fig. 7.9 is defined as the difference between the total pressure drop in the entrance

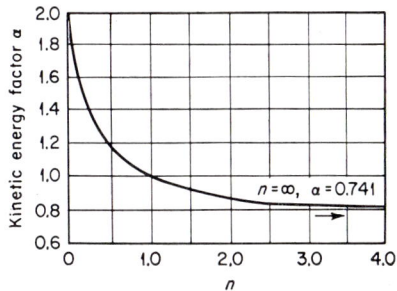

FIG. 7.6. Dependence of the kinetic-energy factor of Eq. (7.56) upon the flow-behavior index. (*Reproduced from Metzner.*[51])

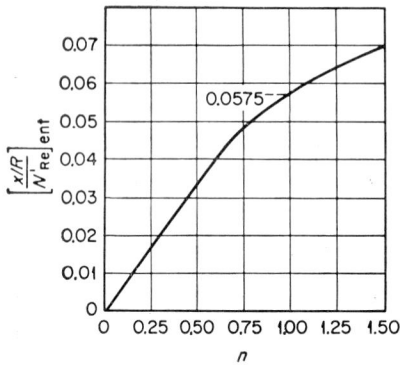

FIG. 7.7. Dependence of the entrance length x upon flow-behavior index of purely viscous fluids. (*Reproduced with permission from Bogue.*[8])

region and that due to well-developed flow in a round tube of the same length, Eq. (7.53), expressed in velocity heads. To this excess pressure loss downstream from the contraction,

$$\Delta P_{\text{excess downstream}} = \frac{C \rho V^2}{2g_c} \qquad (7.58)$$

must be added the pressure drop upstream from the contraction, if the total excess pressure drop due to flow into and through the inlet region is to be computed. This excess upstream pressure drop will be due to the momentum change of the accelerating fluid and any frictional drag in this region. The former may be shown to be equal to one velocity head; therefore, by neglecting the latter as in the corresponding Newtonian case, one obtains

$$\Delta P_{\text{entrance}} = (C + 1) \frac{\rho V^2}{2g_c} \qquad (7.59)$$

in which $\Delta P_{\text{entrance}}$ denotes the *total* excess pressure drop due to the entrance. For Newtonian fluids ($n = 1.00$), $C + 1$ is equal to 2.16, which compares well with the observed value[8],[77] of 2.25 (Art. 7.5). For slurries having a flow-behavior index of 0.4, $C + 1$ is predicted to be only 1.6, but the only experimental data available give 2.2, or a value identical with the Newtonian one. Obviously, further work is needed to resolve the disagreement, which is possibly due to appreciable upstream frictional losses. Until this is done, the conservative procedure of using the Newtonian end correction along with Fig. 7.7 to estimate the length of the inlet region is recommended. No direct experimental confirmation of Fig. 7.7 is available.

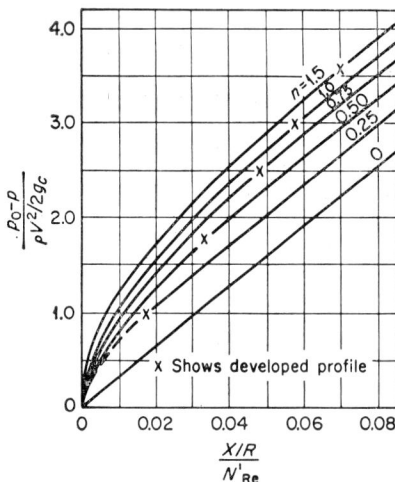

The above approach does not apply to extremely concentrated and dilatant suspensions. In this case, separation of solids from the slurry may occur and the entrance may be partially blocked. For example, Riggs[78] measured entrance-pressure losses of as high as 325 diameters of equivalent tube length at modest flow rates for which the losses calculated by means of Eq. (7.59) would have been less than 1 per cent of this value.

FIG. 7.8. Predicted pressure gradient (of purely viscous fluids) under laminar-flow conditions in the entrance region of a round tube. (*Reproduced from Bogue*[8] *with permission.*)

7.8. Category II (Time-dependent) Fluids

No quantitative observations or calculations of any kind concerning the behavior of thixotropic and rheopectic systems inside tubes appear to be available.

7.9. Viscoelastic Systems

Pressure-loss–Flow-rate Relationships and Velocity Profiles. In steady, well-de-

veloped laminar flow through a cylindrical conduit the longitudinal elastic
stresses cancel out of any force balance
and the shear stress at radius r is equal to
$r \, \Delta P/2L$, just as in the case of purely
viscous behavior. Furthermore, in simple
shear the shearing rate is still uniquely
defined by the shearing stress as in Eqs.
(7.16) and (7.18), for example. Therefore all the methods and equations of
Art. 7.7 are applicable here as well and
no new complications are introduced.

Normal Stresses. While the calculation of pressure drop or velocity profiles
poses no new problems, the radial (outward) pressure on the tube wall [as given
by Eq. (7.17), for example] now differs
from the applied hydrostatic pressure, and
due allowance for these differences must
be made in design calculations.

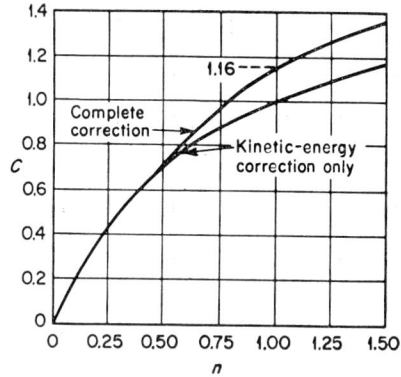

FIG. 7.9. Dependence of the downstream
pressure-drop correction factor C upon
flow-behavior index. (*Reproduced from
Bogue*[8] *with permission.*)

Entrance Effects. Flow into the en-
trance of a tube differs from the purely viscous fluid case in that an additional pressure
loss must now be experienced in order to develop the elastic stresses as well as the
velocity profile. Furthermore, the boundary layers will probably develop differently
than in the absence of elastic stresses; hence the entrance lengths and the viscous-
energy-dissipation terms will probably differ from those for purely viscous fluids.
While the data of several investigators[4,6,11,46,64] are available to show that the entrance
pressure losses are much larger than in the corresponding purely viscous case, no
analysis or correlation of these effects has yet been made. The only design recommen-
dation which it is possible to make at this time is to refer to the literature for data on
specific systems.

Exit Phenomena. The increase in diameter of a viscoelastic stream emerging from a
tube has been treated in Art. 7.6. The violent irregularities appearing at high shear
stresses have still not been characterized completely, and the reader is referred to the
several recent reviews and publications on this subject.[4,11,13,47,48,64,98]

Summary

Steady flow-rate–pressure-loss relationships may be scaled up most readily by making
use of the rigorous uniqueness of the τ_w and $8V/D$ relationship, in both viscoelastic
and purely viscous fluid systems. Alternatively, the double integration of shear-
stress–shear-rate data in the form of the power law usually gives good approximations.
In the viscoelastic-fluid case additional calculation of the normal stresses is required if
the total radial pressure or hoop tension is to be calculated.

Velocity profiles and kinetic energies calculated by use of the power law are also
presented. While these cannot be rigorous for any real fluid, the error may frequently
be too small to be measurable. These results also apply to both the viscoelastic and
the purely viscous fluid systems.

Entrance effects have been calculated for power-law purely viscous fluids. While
the agreement with experimental data in the special case of Newtonian behavior is
excellent, the one set of non-Newtonian data available shows major disagreement with
the calculations. As a result the conservative procedure of using the excess pressure
loss as calculated for Newtonian fluids is recommended for pseudoplastics. Entrance
pressure losses may be unusually high in dilatant systems and must be experimentally
determined. The same is true of viscoelastic fluids at the present time, although
experimental data are available for many specific systems in this case.

None of these problems has as yet been treated for time-dependent fluid systems.

TURBULENCE IN NON-NEWTONIAN FLUIDS

7.10. Purely Viscous Fluids

Pressure-loss Relationships and Velocity Profiles. Of the several major publications in this area[8,21,54,91,103] in the recent literature, one[91] is believed to be influenced by viscoelastic effects[21] and is discussed in Art. 7.12. A large number of earlier references†‌ to "premature turbulence" or to "structural turbulence" in non-Newtonian systems may be entirely discredited[20,48] and will not be discussed here.

In view of the rigorous and unique relationship between τ_w and $8V/D$ developed by Rabinowitsch and Mooney (Art. 7.5), one may define[54] an index of non-Newtonian behavior by the derivative given in Eq. (7.26):

$$n' = \frac{d(\log \tau_w)}{d[\log (8V/D)]} \tag{7.26}$$

The index n', like the power-law exponent n, may vary from zero to infinity and has a value of unity in the special case of Newtonian behavior. In view of Eq. (7.26) one may also write

$$\tau_w = K' \left(\frac{8V}{D}\right)^{n'} \tag{7.60}$$

For the special case in which n' is independent of $8V/D$ or τ_w, Eq. (7.60) will depict the physical relationship between τ_w and $8V/D$. If n' is not a constant, Eq. (7.60) simply represents the equation of the tangent to the curve at the particular value of τ_w or $8V/D$ chosen.[51]

It may be shown[47] that the constant K' may be related to the analogous power-law constant K [Eq. (7.4)] as follows:

$$K' = K \left(\frac{3n' + 1}{4n'}\right)^n \left(\frac{8V}{D}\right)^{n-n'} \tag{7.61}$$

If the fluid obeys the power law, $n = n'$ and

$$K' = K \left(\frac{3n + 1}{4n}\right)^n \tag{7.62}$$

Since Eq. (7.60) rigorously portrays the laminar-flow behavior of the fluid (provided n' and K' are evaluated at the correct shear stress), one may use it to define a Reynolds number which is rigorously applicable to all purely viscous fluids under laminar-flow conditions. This dimensionless group, by analogy to the simpler Newtonian case, may also be of value under turbulent conditions and for predicting the transition to turbulent flow. It may be derived simply by letting

$$f = \frac{16}{N'_{\mathrm{Re}}} \tag{7.63}$$

and is given by[54]

$$N'_{\mathrm{Re}} = \frac{D^{n'} V^{2-n'} \rho}{\gamma} \tag{7.64}$$

in which

$$\gamma = g_c K' 8^{n'-1} \tag{7.65}$$

The applicability of this Reynolds number to various specific kinds of behavior (Bingham plastics, power-law fluids, etc.) has been considered in detail.[50] For the special case of power-law behavior it reduces to the less general Reynolds number used by Shaver and Merrill[91] and by Bogue.[8]

The form of the friction-factor–Reynolds-number relationship under fully turbulent conditions has been developed theoretically by von Kármán[100] for the special case of

† As well as the recent paper of Rogachev.[86]

Newtonian behavior. Extension of this approach to power-law non-Newtonians gives[20,21]

$$\sqrt{\frac{1}{f}} = A_{1n} \log \left[N'_{Re}(f)^{1-0.5n'} \right] + C'_n \tag{7.66}$$

in which A_{1n} and C'_n are parameters dependent on the flow-behavior index n. While the choice of the power-law equation in the derivation requires that the Reynolds number used in Eq. (7.66) be the power-law special case of Eq. (7.64), it has been shown[21] that any errors due to this approximation are less important under turbulent-flow conditions than in the laminar region. For example, if the power law broke down completely at stresses below $0.80\tau_w$ (i.e., if it described the fluid properties correctly only over the 25 per cent range from $0.8\tau_w$ to τ_w), the error incurred would be less than 7 per cent. This assumes an enormously greater change in flow properties than has ever been found in any real fluids at high shear rates. Therefore the exact definition of the Reynolds number [i.e., whether one uses Eq. (7.64) or the analogous special case for power-law fluids] is unimportant under turbulent-flow conditions. Since Eq. (7.64) defines the best possible choice in the laminar region, its use under both laminar- and turbulent-flow conditions is recommended.

The utility of Eq. (7.66) and of the Reynolds number outside the laminar region is shown in Fig. 7.10. The agreement of the experimental data with the curves shown is excellent: the 146 non-Newtonian points had a mean deviation[21] of only 1.9 per cent. Furthermore, the deviations from the smooth curves of Fig. 7.10 were no greater for those fluids which did not obey the power law than for those which did.

The parameters A_{1n} and C'_n of Eq. (7.66) must be evaluated empirically, just as in the simpler case of Newtonian behavior. The data upon which Fig. 7.10 is based gave

$$A_{1n} = \frac{4.0}{(n')^{0.75}} \tag{7.67}$$

$$C'_n = \frac{-0.40}{(n')^{1.2}} \tag{7.68}$$

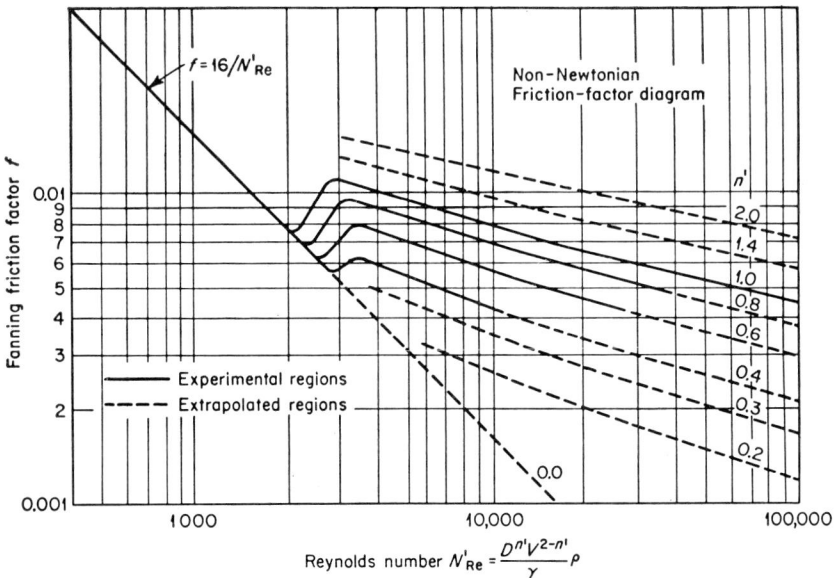

Fig. 7.10. Friction-factor–Reynolds-number design chart for purely viscous fluids. (*Reproduced from Dodge and Metzner*[21] *with permission.*)

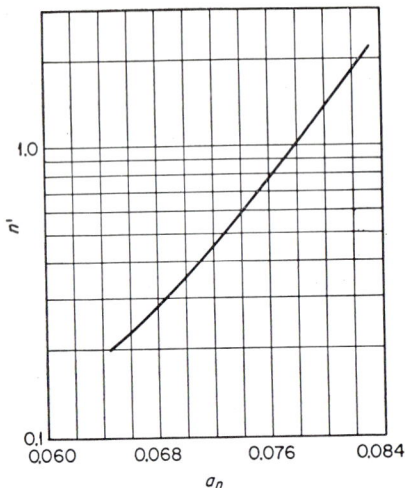

FIG. 7.11. Dependence of a_n [Eq. (7.69)] upon the flow-behavior index. (*Reprinted from Dodge and Metzner*[21] *with permission.*)

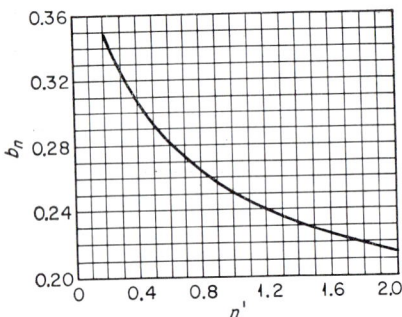

FIG. 7.12. Dependence of b_n [Eq. (7.69)] upon the flow-behavior index. (*Reprinted from Dodge and Metzner*[21] *with permission.*)

It is seen that the critical Reynolds number at which the transition from laminar to turbulent flow begins (Fig. 7.10) increases slowly as the flow-behavior index n or n' decreases.[†] Earlier correlations,[54,103] based on inadequate literature data, did not predict these effects precisely. Dye-filament studies of the flow[72] showed that even under conditions of well-developed turbulence, the rates of turbulent mixing were much lower in a pseudoplastic fluid ($n' = 0.62$) than in a Newtonian fluid and the scale of the turbulence appeared to be much larger.[‡] These effects are, of course, reflected in the lower friction factors in Fig. 7.10.

The curves of Fig. 7.10 may also be characterized by a Blasius type of approximation between Reynolds numbers of 5000 and 10^5, which may be of value when an equation explicit in the friction factor is required:

$$f = \frac{a_n}{(N'_{\mathrm{Re}})^{b_n}} \qquad (7.69)$$

Figures 7.11 and 7.12 give the dependence of a_n and b_n upon n'.

The theoretical analysis used to develop Eq. (7.66) also yielded equations for the fully turbulent velocity profiles. As the assumptions required were somewhat more stringent than in the analogous Newtonian case and as no experimental verification of these equations is available as yet, the results are not reproduced here.

It has been implicitly assumed that the data of Fig. 7.10 are entirely free from viscoelastic complications. The agreement of the slurry data with data obtained on polymeric solutions constitutes strong evidence in this direction, as no measurable or observable elasticity was present in any of the slurries used. However, in view of the controversy caused by the data discussed in Art. 7.12, further verification of the data summarized by Fig. 7.10 would be desirable.[§]

End Effects. Only a single measurement[106] of the entrance loss under turbulent-flow conditions appears to be available on non-Newtonian fluids. The value of 1.3 velocity heads (for a magnesium slurry, flow rates not specified) agrees with the corresponding Newtonian value. The length of the entrance region in which the pressure gradient is

[†] In the limiting case of $n' = 0$, turbulence cannot occur at all[21] and the friction-factor–Reynolds-number relation is given by Eq. (7.63) at all Reynolds numbers.

[‡] These data were similar qualitatively to data published more recently for flow of carboxymethylcellulose dispersions.[91]

[§] NOTE ADDED IN PROOF: Such data have become available since this section was written; additionally, the absence of an elasticity in the slurries used has been demonstrated under the high shear-rate conditions of interest.

higher than under well-developed flow conditions was qualitatively observed[21] to be less than 15 diam, again in approximate agreement with Newtonian fluids, and appeared to be insensitive to changes in velocity and Reynolds number.

Both of these observations were on fluid systems having flow-behavior indices of less than unity; this restriction is not serious since dilatant systems are normally too viscous to develop turbulence.

Flow through Rough Tubes. Generalizations of the usual Newtonian formulas for pressure drop which should be applicable to all purely viscous systems [analogous to Eq. (7.66) for the smooth-tube case] exist for fully developed turbulent flow inside rough tubes.[20] As no careful experimental determination of the constants in the equation has as yet been carried out, the equation is not reproduced here. However, the usual Newtonian friction factors for rough tubes may be used as a conservative estimate since preliminary data indicate that the actual friction factors for pseudoplastic fluids may be slightly smaller, as suggested by comparison with Fig. 7.10 for flow through smooth tubes.

7.11. Time-dependent Fluids

No literature exists on the turbulent flow of thixotropic or rheopectic systems.

7.12. Viscoelastic Systems

Preliminary data on the flow of appreciably viscoelastic carboxymethylcellulose solutions through round tubes show the following interesting behavior.[20,21] In the laminar region, the usual $f = 16/N'_{Re}$ line was followed, as it must be since elastic effects do not influence the steady shear behavior in any anomalous manner (Art. 7.9). However, between generalized Reynolds numbers of 3000 and 90,000, the data followed an extension of the laminar line much more closely than the turbulent curves of Fig. 7.10. Since fluid elasticity would qualitatively be expected to dampen any turbulent-velocity fluctuations, this behavior is not unexpected, but no general correlation of these effects has as yet been made.

The results of Shaver and Merrill[91] yielded friction factors appreciably lower than those depicted by Fig. 7.10. It has been suggested that this was due to viscoelasticity. While undoubtedly several of their systems were viscoelastic (one of their fluids, a polyisobutylene solution, is a classic example of viscoelastic behavior), it is not known whether this is the only reason for the difference between their results and those of Dodge and Metzner.[21] In any case, both the friction factors and velocity profiles reported by Shaver and Merrill await verification and, if viscoelasticity is present, cannot be generally useful in view of the fact that none of the parameters required to define the degree of viscoelasticity were measured. Therefore the currently recommended design procedure is to use Fig. 7.10 even for viscoelastic fluids, since it will be conservative in those cases in which it is incorrect. The same may not be true of the curves of Shaver and Merrill.

No data are available on entrance effects, flow through rough tubes, etc., for turbulent viscoelastic systems.

Summary

Development of the "generalized" Reynolds number, applicable to all purely viscous fluids, and its relation to Reynolds numbers based upon specific shear-stress–shear-rate relationships have been considered in some detail. It is shown that the onset of turbulence occurs at slightly increasing Reynolds numbers as the flow-behavior index decreases. Within the turbulent region, use of Fig. 7.10 [based upon Eqs. (7.66) to (7.68)] is recommended for all purely viscous fluid systems flowing through round tubes. Equation (7.69) gives an approximate equation which is explicit in the friction factor. While the mean deviation of the data used to develop Fig. 7.10 was less than 2 per cent, additional data on other fluid systems would be desirable to confirm its generality.

Table **7.3.** Numerical Values of the Fredrickson-Bird Y Function
(in Condensed Form)

$R_i/R_o =$ $n =$	0.01	0.1	0.2	0.4	0.6	0.8	0.9
1.00	0.6051	0.5908	0.6237	0.7094	0.8034	0.9008	0.9502
0.50	0.6929	0.6270	0.6445	0.7179	0.8064	0.9015	0.9504
0.33	0.7468	0.6547	0.6612	0.7246	0.8081	0.9022	0.9506
0.20	0.8064	0.6924	0.6838	0.7342	0.8128	0.9032	0.9510
0.10	0.8673	0.7367	0.7130	0.7462	0.8124	0.9054	0.9519

The few available data on entrance effects suggest the use of the usual Newtonian equations, at least as an approximation, in pressure-drop calculations for purely viscous fluids.

No quantitative data are as yet available on turbulent flow through rough tubes. Use of the Newtonian friction factors is suggested as a conservative design procedure.

Conclusive data on the turbulent flow of viscoelastic systems are also not available. Qualitative results suggest the conservative procedure of using Fig. 7.10 for flow through smooth, round tubes. No information is available on the behavior of viscoelastic systems under any other non-laminar-flow conditions.

MISCELLANEOUS FLOW PROBLEMS

7.13. Flow through Annuli

For the important case of power-law fluids flowing longitudinally through concentric annuli, Fredrickson and Bird[24] have shown that

$$\frac{R_o \, \Delta P}{2L} = K \left[\frac{(2n + 1)Q}{n\pi R_o^3 Y (1 - R_i/R_o)^{(2n+1)/n}} \right]^n \tag{7.70}$$

The factor Y is given in Table 7.3 and in Fig. 7.13 as a function of the radius ratio R_i/R_o.

The corresponding shear stresses at the outer and inner tube walls are

$$\tau_o = \frac{R_o \, \Delta P}{2L} (1 - \lambda^2) \tag{7.71}$$

$$\tau_i = \frac{R_o \, \Delta P}{2L} \left(\frac{R_i}{R_o} \right) \left(1 - \frac{\lambda^2 R_o^2}{R_i^2} \right) \tag{7.72}$$

The radial position at which the velocity is a maximum is equal to λR_o; values of λ are given in Table 7.4 and in Fig. 7.14.

In this flow situation the shearing stress (taken positive at the outer radius) decreases to a negative value at radius R_i, passing through zero at λR_o. The breakdown of the power law at shearing stresses near zero (Art. 7.3) was observed not to be a serious

Table **7.4.** Radial Position of the Fluid Element of Maximum Velocity
(Condensed from Frederickson and Bird[24])

$R_i/R_o =$ $n =$	0.01	0.1	0.2	0.4	0.6	0.8	0.9
1.00	0.3295	0.4637	0.5461	0.6770	0.7915	0.8981	0.9495
0.50	0.2318	0.4192	0.5189	0.6655	0.7872	0.8972	0.9493
0.33	0.1817	0.3932	0.5030	0.6587	0.7847	0.8967	0.9492
0.20	0.1503	0.3712	0.4856	0.6509	0.7818	0.8960	0.9491
0.10	0.1237	0.3442	0.4687	0.6429	0.7784	0.8953	0.9489

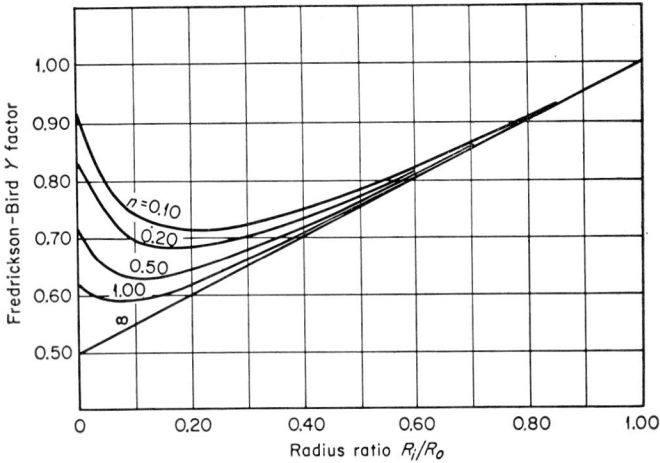

FIG. 7.13. Fredrickson-Bird Y factor of Eq. (7.70). (*Compiled from Fredrickson and Bird*[24] *with permission.*)

limitation in flow through round tubes since the region near the centerline in which this would occur contributed but little to the over-all flow. In this case the breakdown occurs near the radial position λR_o; since this region contributes materially to the over-all flow unless R_i/R_o approaches zero, it is evident that the use of Eq. (7.70) may not

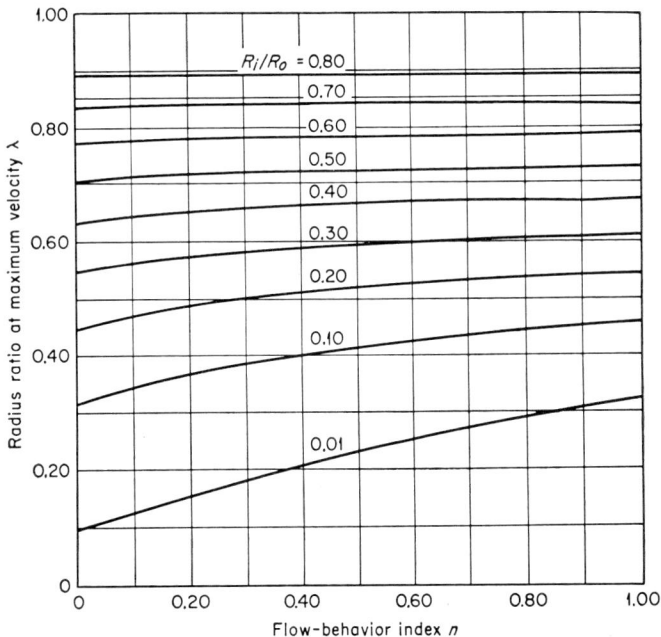

FIG. 7.14. Dependence of position of maximum velocity in annular flow upon the flow-behavior index. (*Compiled from Fredrickson and Bird*[24] *with permission.*)

be a good approximation to the behavior of real fluids.† However, it is still recommended in preference to work based on the Bingham-plastic model, for example. It is obviously important to determine the parameters K and n at stresses close to τ_o, to ensure their best possible application to the problem.[47]

The flow of fluids through annular spaces when one of the cylinders is rotating has been considered by Rivlin.[80] Until his phenomenological equations of fluid behavior (Art. 7.3) have been applied to any real materials, this work remains of academic interest.

7.14. Flow through Fittings

Hasegawa's several publications on flow through orifices[34] are of no value since the slurries used were Newtonian under the stresses encountered in the fittings themselves. The same error was carried into a later study on nozzles.[33] Dombrowski et al.[22] obtained precise data on pressure drop through nozzles, but the rheological data required to interpret these measurements are incomplete.

Head[34a] pointed out that because the pressure drop on flow through tubes is quite insensitive to flow rate in highly pseudoplastic systems [Eqs. (7.53) and (7.60)], one cannot simply meter by measuring the pressure drop over a length of tube under laminar-flow conditions. His work indicates pressure losses for non-Newtonian fluids flowing through fittings to be generally similar to those of Newtonian fluids, under laminar-flow conditions. The same general type of conclusion may be reached from other data,[22,35,106] although there is no agreement on exact values.

The design of control valves for use with pseudoplastic fluids in laminar flow has been considered by De Haven,[19] who essentially assumed that the flow could be treated as that between parallel flat plates. For the several designs described, this may be an appropriate assumption. The neglect of end effects implies not only that the passages are reasonably long but that viscoelasticity is absent.

7.15. Flow between Parallel Flat Plates

Integration of equations analogous to Eqs. (7.51) and (7.52) for the case of power-law fluids flowing between parallel flat plates gives,[47,57] neglecting edge and end effects,

$$\frac{B\,\Delta P}{L} = K\left(\frac{2n+1}{2n}\frac{q'}{B^2}\right)^n \tag{7.73}$$

The term $(B\,\Delta P)/L$ is equal to the shearing stress at the wall, and the term inside the parentheses gives the corresponding shear rate. Equation (7.73) represents one limiting case of Eqs. (7.70) to (7.72) for flow through annuli.

7.16. Flow over Flat Plates (Boundary-layer Development)

Acrivos, Shah, and Peterson[1] integrated the usual boundary-layer equations[89] for flow of purely viscous power-law fluids over a flat plate. Figures 7.15 and 7.16 show the development of the velocity profiles along a flat plate immersed in an infinite fluid having a velocity U_∞. The local shearing stress at the wall is given by

$$\frac{\tau_w}{\rho U_\infty{}^2} = c(n)(N_{\mathrm{Re}\,x})^{-1/(1+n)} \tag{7.74}$$

The function $c(n)$ is given in Table 7.5. No experimental check on either the calculated profiles or the shearing stress exists.

---

† It has been pointed out[47] that the approximation improves as the stress τ_o increases since the power law then may be valid over a greater fraction of the annular cross section. Unless measurements are confined to such higher stresses, it is obvious that the suggestion that these equations may be used to derive rheological properties from experimental measurements[24] may be subject to appreciable error.

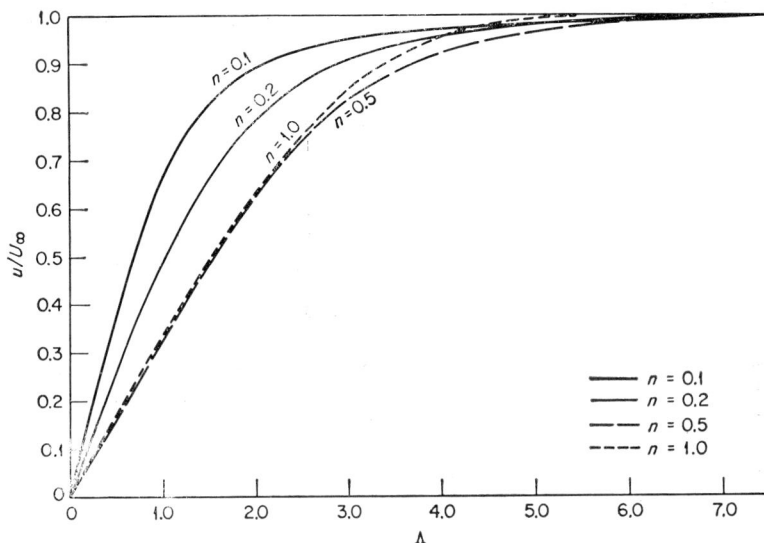

FIG. 7.15. Development of velocity profiles: pseudoplastic power-law fluids flowing over a flat plate. (*Reproduced from Acrivos, Shah, and Peterson*[1] *with permission.*)

7.17. Extrusion and Molding

Many studies on these and related operations used in the processing of polymeric materials have recently been reported and compiled.[5,7,16] Almost all these have presupposed purely viscous behavior, yet in view of the secondary flows and end effects in the processing equipment, any viscoelasticity would be of major importance. As a

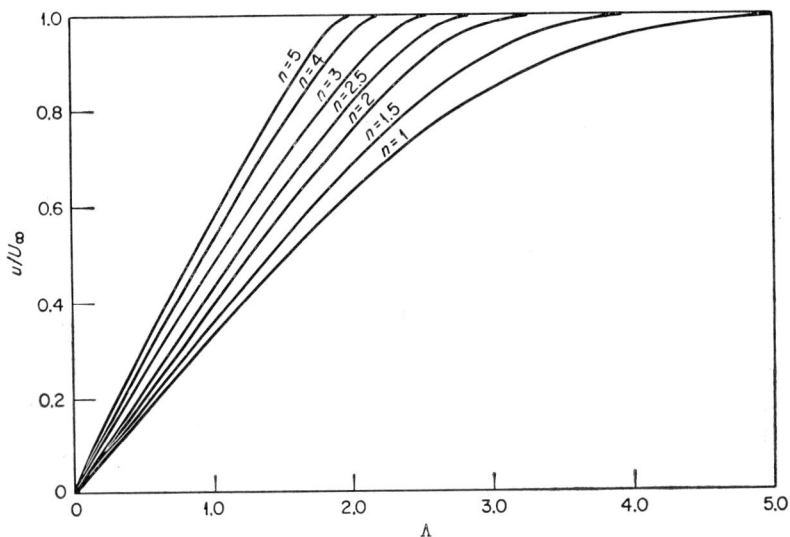

FIG. 7.16. Development of velocity profiles: dilatant power-law fluids flowing over a flat plate. (*Reproduced from Acrivos, Shah, and Peterson*[1] *with permission.*)

Table 7.5. Values of Coefficient $c(n)$ in Eq. (7.74) for the Local Shear Stress
on a Flat Plate

(From Acrivos, Shah, and Peterson[1])

n	$c(n)$
0.1	0.973
0.2	0.861
0.3	0.751
0.5	0.58
1.0	0.332
1.5	0.211
2.0	0.161
2.5	0.120
3.0	0.0915
4.0	0.062
5.0	0.046

result, the work to date is primarily of value as a qualitative guide except in extrusion of inelastic pastes. Matsumoto and coworkers[43] have made a start on the determination of the actual flow patterns in screw extruders.

7.18. Elliptical and Rectangular Ducts

Oldroyd[59,60] and Green and Rivlin[27] have considered flow through ducts of several geometries, including an elliptical cross section, with a view toward determining whether the flow can be rectilinear or whether secondary flows are necessary to satisfy the equations of motion in viscoelastic fluids.

Robinson[85] has considered the laminar flow of purely viscous non-Newtonians through rectangular tubes and recommends the equation

$$\frac{D_h \, \Delta P}{4L} = K(a + 2)^n \left(\frac{V}{2B}\right)^n \tag{7.75}$$

The term $a + 2$ is shown as a function of aspect ratio in Fig. 7.17. Equation (7.75) and Fig. 7.17 are rigorous in the special case of Newtonian behavior and were found to

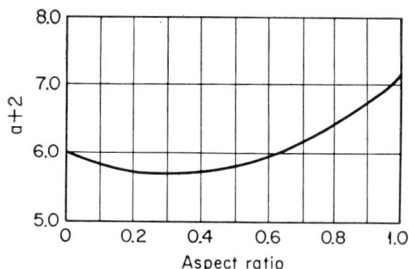

Fig. 7.17. Flow through rectangular ducts: dependence of the geometric term $a + 2$ [Eq. (7.75)] upon aspect ratio.

give a fairly good correlation of the non-Newtonian data over a range of flow-behavior indices from 0.3 to 3.6 in ducts having aspect ratios between 0.5 and 1.0. However, it does not yield Eq. (7.73) for flow between parallel plates as the aspect ratio approaches zero unless the fluid is Newtonian.

ACKNOWLEDGMENT

The author wishes to acknowledge the aid received during stimulating discussions with a number of scientists, particularly J. G. Oldroyd, Yoh-Han Pao, and W. Philippoff.

Much of the author's background in this area has been developed during studies sponsored by the Office of Ordnance Research, U.S. Army.

REFERENCES

1. Acrivos, A., M. J. Shah, and E. E. Peterson: *AIChE Journal,* **6:** 312 (1960).
2. Alfrey, T., Jr.: "Mechanical Behavior of High Polymers," Interscience, New York, 1948.
3. Alves, G. E., D. F. Boucher, and R. L. Pigford: *Chem. Eng. Progr.,* **48:**385 (1952).
4. Bagley, E. B.: *J. Appl. Phys.,* **28:**624 (1957); **30:**597 (1959).
5. Ballman, R. L., T. Shusman, and H. L. Toor: *Ind. Eng. Chem.,* **51:**847 (1959).
6. Bauer, W. H., N. Weber, and S. E. Wiberley: *J. Phys. Chem.,* **62:**1245 (1958).
7. Bernhardt, E. C.: "Processing of Thermoplastic Materials," Reinhold, New York, 1959.
8. Bogue, D. C.: *Ind. Eng. Chem.,* **51:**874 (1959).
9. Brodnyan, J. G., F. H. Gaskins, and W. Philippoff: *Trans. Soc. Rheol.,* **1:**109 (1957).
10. Calderbank, P. H., and M. B. Moo-Young: *Trans. Inst. Chem. Engrs. (London),* **37:**26 (1959).
11. Carley, E. L.: B.Ch.E. thesis, University of Delaware, Newark, Del., 1959.
12. Christiansen, E. B., N. W. Ryan, and W. E. Stevens: *AIChE Journal,* **1:**544 (1955).
13. Clegg, P. L.: in P. Mason and N. Wookey (eds.), "The Rheology of Elastomers," Pergamon Press, New York, 1958.
14. Cohen, H.: *Bull. Research Council Israel,* **2:**425 (1953).
15. Colwell, R. E.: *SPE Journal,* **11**(7):24 (1955).
16. Colwell, R. E., and K. R. Nickolls: *Ind. Eng. Chem.,* **51:**841 (1959).
17. Copley, A. L., and G. W. Scott Blair: *Rheologica Acta,* **1:**170 (1958).
18. Daily, J. W., and G. Bugliarello: *Ind. Eng. Chem.,* **51:**887 (1959).
19. De Haven, E. S.: *Ind. Eng. Chem.,* **51**(7):63A (1959).
20. Dodge, D. W.: Ph.D. thesis in chemical engineering, University of Delaware, Newark, Del., 1957.
21. Dodge, D. W., and A. B. Metzner: *AIChE Journal,* **5:**189 (1959).
22. Dombrowski, N., P. Eisenklam, and R. P. Fraser: *J. Inst. Fuel,* **30:**198, 399 (1957).
23. Finke, A., and W. Heinz: *Kolloid Z.,* **152:**148 (1957).
24. Fredrickson, A. G., and R. B. Bird: *Ind. Eng. Chem.,* **50:**347 (1958).
25. Gaskins, F. H., and W. Philippoff: *Ind. Eng. Chem.,* **51:**871 (1959).
26. Gaskins, F. H., and W. Philippoff: *Trans. Soc. Rheol.,* **3:**181 (1959).
27. Green, A. E., and R. S. Rivlin: *Quart. Appl. Math.,* **14:**299 (1956).
28. Gundiah, S., and S. L. Kapur: *J. Polymer Sci.,* **31:**202 (1958).
29. Gunnerson, H. L., and J. P. Gallagher: *Ind. Eng. Chem.,* **51:**854 (1959).
30. Hahn, S. J., T. Ree, and H. Eyring: *Ind. Eng. Chem.,* **51:**856 (1959).
31. Hahn, S. J., T. Ree, and H. Eyring: *NLGI Spokesman,* **21**(3):12 (1957); **23**(3): (1959).
32. Hanin, M.: *Bull. Research Council Israel,* **C6:**87 (1951).
33. Hasegawa, T.: *Chem. Eng. (Japan),* **23:**18 (1959).
34. Hasegawa, T.: *Chem. Eng. (Japan),* **20:**50 (1956); **19:**58 (1955).
34a. Head, V. P.: *TAPPI,* **35:**260 (1952).
35. Houghton, G. L., and G. P. K. Ching: B.Ch.E. thesis, University of Delaware, Newark, Del., 1955.
36. Huque, M. M., M. Fishman, and D. A. I. Goring: *J. Phys. Chem.,* **63:**766 (1959).
37. Jabotinsky, E.: *Bull. Research Council Israel,* **A6:**65 (1956).
38. Jobling, A., and J. E. Roberts: in F. R. Eirich (ed.), "Rheology," vol. 2, Academic Press, New York, 1958.
39. Kaye, J., and E. C. Elgar: *Trans. ASME,* **80:**753 (1958).
40. Krieger, I. M., and S. H. Maron: *J. Appl. Phys.,* **25:**72 (1954).
41. Lodge, A. S.: *Trans. Faraday Soc.,* **52:**120 (1956).
42. Markovitz, H.: *Trans. Soc. Rheol.,* **1:**37 (1957).
43. Matsumoto, K., S. Yoshikawa, and E. Akatsuka: *Chem. Eng. (Japan),* **22:**208 (1958).
44. McKelvey, J. M., J. Gavis, and T. G. Smith: *SPE Journal,* **13**(9):29 (1957).
45. McKennell, R.: *Kolloid-Z.,* **145:**114 (1956), and *Anal. Chem.,* **28:**1710 (1956).
46. McMillen, E. L.: *Chem. Eng. Progr.,* **44:**537 (1948).
47. Metzner, A. B.: in E. C. Bernhardt (ed.), "Processing of Thermoplastic Materials," Reinhold, New York, 1959.
48. Metzner, A. B.: *Ind. Eng. Chem.,* **50:**1577 (1958); **51:**225 (1959).
49. Metzner, A. B.: *Rheologica Acta,* **1:**205 (1958).
50. Metzner, A. B.: *Ind. Eng. Chem.,* **49:**1429 (1957).
51. Metzner, A. B.: in T. B. Drew and J. W. Hoopes, Jr. (eds.), "Advances in Chem. Eng.," vol. 1, Academic Press, New York, 1956.

52. Metzner, A. B. and M. Whitlock.: *Trans. Soc. Rheol.*, **2**:239 (1958).
53. Metzner, A. B., and R. E. Otto: *AIChE Journal*, **3**:3 (1957).
54. Metzner, A. B., and J. C. Reed: *AIChE Journal*, **1**:434 (1955).
55. Mooney, M.: *Trans. Soc. Rheol.*, **1**:63 (1957).
56. Mooney, M.: *J. Rheol.*, **2**:210 (1931).
57. Mooney, M., and S. A. Black: *J. Colloid Sci.*, **7**:204 (1952).
58. Mooney, M., and R. H. Ewart: *Physics* (now *J. Appl. Phys.*), **5**:350 (1934).
59. Oldroyd, J. G.: *Proc. Roy. Soc. (London)*, **A245**:278 (1958).
60. Oldroyd, J. G.: in F. R. Eirich (ed.), "Rheology," vol. 1, Academic Press, New York, 1956.
61. Oldroyd, J. G.: *Quart. J. Mech. Appl. Math.*, **4**:271 (1951).
62. Oldroyd, J. G.: *Proc. Roy. Soc. (London)*, **A200**:523 (1950).
63. Pao, Yoh-Han: *J. Appl. Phys.*, **28**:591 (1957).
64. Park, I. K.: B.Ch.E. thesis, University of Delaware, Newark, Del., 1959.
65. Pawlowski, J.: *Kolloid-Z.*, **130**:129 (1953).
66. Philippoff, W.: *Ind. Eng. Chem.*, **51**:883 (1959).
67. Philippoff, W.: *Trans. Soc. Rheol.*, **1**:95 (1957).
68. Piper, G. H., and J. R. Scott: *J. Sci. Instr.*, **22**:206 (1945).
69. Popov, M.: *Rheologica Acta*, **1**:70 (1958).
70. Powell, R. E., and H. Eyring: *Nature*, **154**:427 (1944).
71. Rabinowitsch, B. Z.: *Physik. Chem.*, **A145**:1 (1929).
72. Rau, D., and H. Anderson: B.Ch.E. thesis, University of Delaware, Newark, Del., 1956.
73. Ree, T., and H. Eyring: in F. R. Eirich (ed.), "Rheology," vol. 2, Academic Press, New York, 1958.
74. Ree, T., and H. Eyring: in Report of Symposium VII on Incendiary Gels (unclassified), U.S. Army Chemical Corps, Army Chemical Center, Maryland, 1955.
75. Reiner, M.: Phenomenological Macrorheology in F. R. Eirich (ed.), "Rheology," vol. 1, Academic Press, New York, 1956.
76. Reiner, M.: 1956 *Technion Research Rep.* and *Bull. Research Council Israel*, **2**:65 (1952), **3**:372 (1954); and *Proc. Roy. Soc. (London)*, **A240**:173 (1957).
77. Rieman, W.: *J. ACS*, **50**:46 (1928).
78. Riggs, L. C.: B.Ch.E. thesis, University of Delaware, Newark, Del., 1956.
79. Rivlin, R. S.: *Phys. Today*, **12**:32 (May, 1959).
80. Rivlin, R. S.: *J. Rational Mech. and Analysis*, **5**:179 (1956).
81. Rivlin, R. S.: *J. Rational Mech. and Analysis*, **4**:681 (1955).
82. Rivlin, R. S.: *Proc. Roy. Soc. (London)*, **A193**:260 (1948).
83. Rivlin, R. S., and J. L. Eriksen.: *J. Rational Mech. and Analysis*, **4**:323 (1955).
84. Roberts, J. E.: *Proc. Second Intern. Congr. on Rheol.*, 1954, and unpublished Ministry of Supply report.
85. Robinson, W. D.: B.Ch.E. thesis, University of Delaware, Newark, Del., 1958.
86. Rogachev, I. I.: *Kolloid Zhur.* (English transl.), **16**:441 (1954).
87. Rouse, P. E., Jr.: *J. Chem. Phys.*, **21**:1272 (1953).
88. Russell, T. W. F., and M. E. Charles: *Can. J. Chem. Eng.*, **37**:18 (1959).
89. Schlichting, H.: "Boundary Layer Theory," McGraw-Hill, New York, 1960.
90. Schultz-Grunow, F.: *Rheologica Acta*, **1**:289 (1958).
91. Shaver, R. G., and E. W. Merrill: *AIChE Journal*, **5**:181 (1959).
92. Sisko, A. W.: *Ind. Eng. Chem.*, **50**:1789 (1958).
93. Takeda, M., and R. Endo: *J. Phys. Chem.*, **60**:1202 (1956).
94. Takemura, T.: *J. Polymer Sci.*, **27**:549 (1958).
95. Taylor, G. I.: *Phil. Trans Roy. Soc. (London)*, **A223**:289 (1923).
96. Taylor, G. I., and P. G. Saffman: *J. Aeronaut. Sci.*, **24**:553 (1957).
97. Toor, H. L.: *AIChE Journal*, **4**:319 (1958), and *Trans. Soc. Rheol.*, **1**:177 (1957).
98. Tordella, J. P.: *Rheologica Acta*, **1**:216 (1958).
99. Tuijnman, C.A.F., and J. J. Hermans: *J. Polymer Sci.*, **25**:385 (1957).
100. von Kármán, T.: *Nachr. Ges. Wiss. Göttingen, Math.-physik. Kl.*, vol. 58 (1930), and *Natl. Advisory Comm. Aeronaut. Tech. Mem.* 611, 1931.
101. Weissenberg, K.: *Proc. First Intern. Rheol. Congr.*, p. 29, 1948.
102. Weissenberg, K.: *Conf. Brit. Rheologists' Club*, London, 1946, and *Nature*, **159**:310 (1947).
103. Weltmann, R. N.: *Ind. Eng. Chem.*, **48**:386 (1956).
104. Weltmann, R. N.: *J. Appl. Phys.*, **14**:343 (1943).
105. Weltmann, R. N.: *Ind. Eng. Chem. (Anal. Ed.)*, **15**:424 (1943).
106. Weltmann, R. N., and T. A. Keller: *Natl. Advisory Comm. Aeronaut. Tech. Mem.* 3889, 1957.
107. Weltmann, R. N., and P. W. Kuhns: *J. Colloid Sci.*, **7**:218 (1952).
108. Westover, R. F.: in E. C. Bernhard (ed.), "Processing of Thermoplastics," Reinhold, New York, 1959.

Section 8

COMPRESSIBLE FLOW

By

ALI BULENT CAMBEL, *Northwestern University, Evanston, Illinois*

COMPRESSIBLE FLOW

GENERAL CONSIDERATIONS

8.1. Introduction and Definitions. Notation

The science of *gas dynamics* describes the dynamic motion of gases experiencing thermal effects. It is also the science that combines fluid mechanics and thermodynamics. Gas dynamics differs from gas statics in that there is motion, and it also differs from gas kinematics because the forces exerted on or by the gas must be taken into consideration.

Several other names have been used to define the subject. For example, aerothermodynamics, aerothermochemistry, compressible flow, supersonic aerodynamics, and hypersonics. The term aerothermodynamics has the shortcoming of limiting itself to air (aero), although it specifically mentions that thermodynamics is to be considered. Aerothermochemistry, too, specifies air as the fluid and states that chemical effects are to be studied. Compressible fluid flow implies that the fluid is compressible, while supersonic aerodynamics deals with phenomena taking place in air at velocities faster than the speed of sound. Finally, by definition, hypersonics deals with air-flow velocities at least five times the speed of sound. In this section the names of gas dynamics and compressible flow will be used interchangeably.

In the classical sense gas dynamics excludes factors such as magnetism and electricity. However, in some reentry and propulsion applications, these effects must be considered. One then deals with magnetogas dynamics, which is discussed in Sec. 27.

Regardless of the name used, the important implication in compressible-flow studies is that the gas acts as a compressible medium. Although one commonly assumes that gases are compressible, there are flow processes in which the gas may be treated as an incompressible medium. Examples of this are most air-conditioning problems or the flight of lighter-than-air dirigibles. In this section compressibility phenomena in both the subsonic and supersonic regimes are considered.

In the following list of symbols any consistent set of units may be employed.

Notation

A	area
F	Gibbs free energy
$\mathbf{F}$	force
J	(1) Jacobian
	(2) mechanical equivalent of heat
K	equilibrium constant
$\mathbf{K}$	Knudsen number
L	characteristic length
M	mass
M_i	molecular weight of species i
$\mathbf{M}$	Mach number
Q	heat
R	gas constant $R = R_0/M_i$
R_0	universal gas constant
$\mathbf{R}$	Reynolds number
T	temperature

T_c	critical temperature
T_r	reduced temperature $T_r = T/T_c$
V_A	Alfvén wave-propagation velocity
V_i	diffusion velocity $\mathbf{V}_i = \mathbf{v}_i - \mathbf{V}$
V_n	normal velocity component
V_t	tangential velocity component
V_x, V_y, V_z	x, y, and z components of velocity

$$V_x{}^2 + V_y{}^2 + V_z{}^2 = V^2$$

W	work
Z	departure coefficient of compressibility factor
a	acoustic velocity
c_p	specific heat at constant pressure
c_v	specific heat at constant volume
g	coefficient of gravity acceleration
h	enthalpy
h	heat-transfer coefficient
h	Planck's constant $h = 4.135 \times 10^{-15}$ ev sec
k	(1) thermal conductivity
	(2) Boltzmann's constant $k = 86.1 \times 10^{-6}$ ev °K
l	mean free path
n	number of moles
p	pressure
p_c	critical pressure
p_r	reduced pressure $p_r = p/p_c$
t	time
u	internal energy
$\vec{v_i}$	average velocity of species i
$\dot{w_i}$	rate of production of species i
x, y, z	space coordinates or variables
x	percentage dissociation
α	number fraction of ionization
α_m	thermal coefficient of expansion
ζ, η, ξ	space coordinates or variables
η_n	nozzle efficiency
θ	characteristic temperature $= h\nu/k$
μ	dynamic viscosity
ν	frequency
ρ	density
o	subscript reservoir or other reference condition
$*$	superscript corresponds to $\mathbf{M} = 1$

8.2. Compressibility

The density of a gas is defined as its mass per unit volume. If in a flow system the density of the fluid remains constant, not only with regard to time but also with regard to coordinates, then the fluid is said to be incompressible. If, on the other hand, the density varies, then the fluid is said to be a compressible one.

The density of a gas may vary in different ways. Thus the system may undergo drastic temperature changes or it may undergo appreciable pressure changes, or both the temperature and the pressure acting upon it may vary. If the temperature of a gas is changed while its pressure remains constant, its density will be a function of the temperature only, and this is expressed as

$$\rho = f(T)_p \tag{8.1}$$

More specifically, one may write the equation for the variation of density with temperatures as follows:

$$\rho = \rho_0[1 - \alpha_m(T - T_0)]_p \tag{8.2}$$

In Eq. (8.2) ρ_0 is the standard density corresponding to the temperature T_0, and α_m is the mean *coefficient of thermal expansion*. The density ρ corresponds to the temperature T. The subscript p indicates that the relationship holds for constant-pressure processes. In general, the instantaneous coefficient of expansion α is defined as follows:

$$\alpha = -\frac{1}{\rho_0}\left(\frac{\partial \rho}{\partial T}\right)_p \tag{8.3}$$

If the velocity is high (say, about 400 fps or more for air), the pressure change associated with the generation of this velocity would be large enough to affect the density, and thus the flow becomes compressible. In such cases, not only temperature, but also pressure, influences the gas density. Accordingly, Eq. (8.2) is no longer sufficient, and the equation of state for the gas must be used. The appropriate equation of state depends on several considerations, and these are discussed in Art. 8.10. However, the equation of state has the following form:

$$\phi(p,\rho,T,\beta_i) = 0 \tag{8.4}$$

in which p = pressure
$\quad\quad\rho$ = density
$\quad\quad T$ = temperature
$\quad\quad\beta_i$ = concentration and accounts for chemistry in mixtures

As is obvious from the foregoing discussion, the density of air is different at different altitudes.

8.3. Regimes of Gas Dynamics

The definition of density has meaning only if the fluid volume under consideration contains a large number of gas molecules or if a state of continuum exists (Art. 2.3). Thus the stipulations concerning density must be revised if highly rarefied gases are under consideration. To ascertain that continuum considerations are valid one defines the Knudsen number **K** as follows:

$$\mathbf{K} = \frac{l}{L} \tag{8.5}$$

in which l is the mean free path of the gas, and L is the characteristic length of the body in the stream.

The mean free path is defined as the mean distance that the particles of the gas may traverse between collisions. At high pressures or at low altitudes the particles are closely packed, and hence the mean free path is very small. For example, for air at 1 atm pressure and at 32°F the mean free path is found to be of the order of 2.4×10^{-6} in. On the other hand, at high altitudes the pressure decreases in accordance with the fluid-static equation, and the molecules of nitrogen and oxygen as well as of the other gases making up the air are not as closely packed. For example, at an altitude of 75 miles the mean free path is of the order of 1 ft. It follows that for the same device, the Knudsen number will increase with increasing altitude or with lower pressure or density. The flow regimes are then defined in accordance with Table 8.1 and are sketched in Fig. 8.1. Thus, one can use classical gas dynamics only for small Knudsen numbers.

Table 8.1. Flow Regimes Classified by Knudsen Number

Knudsen number	Regime
$\frac{l}{L} \leq 0.01$	Continuum gas dynamics
$\frac{l}{L} \cong 1$	Slip flow
$\frac{l}{L} \geq 10$	Free molecule flow

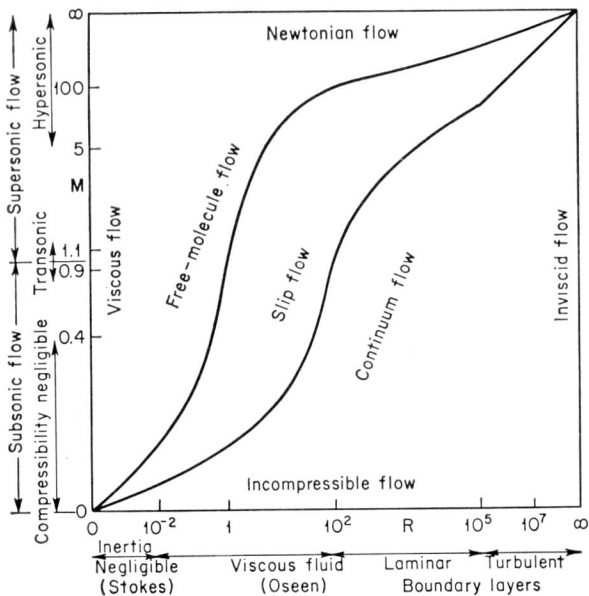

FIG. 8.1. Flow regimes.

When the Knudsen number is high, kinetic theory or statistical concepts must be applied. Flow, occurring at high Knudsen numbers, has been called *superaerodynamics* by Tsien.[1]

Figure 8.1 shows the various flow regimes without consideration of the real-gas effects such as condensation, dissociation, or ionization.

It may be shown[2] that the Knudsen number is related to the Mach number and the Reynolds number.

$$K \cong \frac{M}{R} \tag{8.6}$$

The Mach number M is defined as the ratio of the local flow velocity to the acoustic velocity, namely,

$$M = \frac{V}{a} \tag{8.7}$$

As usual, the Reynolds number is defined as $R = VL\rho/\mu$ and specifies the ratio of the inertia effects to the viscous effects.

The Mach number is the basis of many gas-dynamics criteria. For example, flow regimes may be classified by specifying the appropriate Mach number. In doing this the terminology in Table 8.2 is used.

Table 8.2. Flow Regimes Classified by Mach Number

Mach number	Regime
$M < 1$	Subsonic flow
$M = 1$	Sonic flow
$0.9 < M < 1.1$	Transonic flow
$M > 1$	Supersonic flow
$M \geq 5$	Hypersonic flow

Table **8.3.** Table of Units and Dimensions

Dimension	Symbol	Unit
Mass............	M	Slug
Length..........	L	Foot
Time............	t	Second
Temperature......	T	°Rankine

8.4. Units and Dimensions

As in any other science, the choice of units and dimensions in gas dynamics is a matter of taste. However, there are certain dimensions that must be included in setting up a practical system of units. Thus, because compressible flow deals with thermal effects, it is necessary that temperature be included. As extensions of gas dynamics to plasmas and magnetohydrodynamics (Sec. 27) are considered, it becomes necessary to incorporate a unit for electrical charge.

In this section dimensional homogeneity will not be considered in the derivations to simplify the mathematical manipulations. Because electromagnetic effects will not be considered in this section, the engineering units are chosen and these are listed in Table 8.3.

Frequently engineering data are given in pounds mass (lb_m) rather than in slugs. By definition, one slug is that mass that experiences an acceleration of one foot per second per second when acted upon by a force of one pound. It follows that

$$1 \text{ slug} = 32.1739 \text{ lb}_m$$

or, more approximately,

$$1 \text{ slug} \cong 32.2 \text{ lb}_m$$

In compressible-flow equations temperature ratios are frequently calculated. When this is done one must use the absolute temperature scales. The temperature in degrees Rankine is calculated from the Fahrenheit scale as follows:

$$°R \cong °F + 460$$

in which °R and °F denote, respectively, degrees Rankine and degrees Fahrenheit.

8.5. Standard Conditions

Every field has its specific standard conditions, and these are usually chosen as a matter of convenience. In aerodynamics *standard air* at sea level is specified to be at a temperature of 59°F and at a pressure of one standard atmosphere. The standard conditions for air are summarized in Table 8.4 from the data of NACA Report 1235.

Table 8.4. Standard Conditions for Dry Air

Elevation at sea level = 0 ft
Acceleration due to gravity = g_0 = 32.17405 ft/sec² $\cong$ 32.2 ft/sec²
Temperature = 59°F or 518.688°R $\cong$ 519°R $\cong$ 520°R
Pressure = 29.92126 in. Hg at 32°F or 2116.2 lb_f/ft²
Density = 0.0023769 slug/ft³ or 0.076475 lb_m/ft³
Specific weight = 0.076475 lb_f/ft³
Apparent molecular weight = 28.966 $\cong$ 29
Gas constant R = 53.342 $\cong$ 53.3 ft-lb_f/(lb_m)(°R) $\cong$ 1716 ft-lb_f/(slug)(°R) $\cong$ 1716 ft²/(sec²)(°R)
Heat capacity at constant pressure c_p = 6012.4 ft-lb_f/(slug)(°R)
Dynamic viscosity μ = 0.00001205 lb_m/ft-sec = 0.000000374 slug/ft-sec
Kinematic viscosity = 0.0001574 ft²/sec
Specific-heat ratio $c_p/c_t = \gamma$ = 1.40

8.6. Control Volume

In solving problems in statics it is customary to sketch a *free-body diagram* in formulating the interaction of the forces. Similarly, in thermodynamic analyses one defines a *system* and then specifies the mass and the energy transport across the system boundaries. In gas dynamics it is customary to use the concept of the *control volume*. This is an arbitrarily defined volume which fluid may enter or leave. The fundamental laws of fluid mechanics and thermodynamics when applied to the control volume form the basis of gas dynamics. The configuration of the control volume may be chosen to make the analysis most convenient. Furthermore, the control volume may be either infinitesimally small or it may be finite in size. Both mass and energy may cross the control surface circumscribing the control volume.

8.7. Dimensionless Parameters

As will be seen shortly, arriving at solutions of gas-dynamics equations is not always possible. Furthermore, experimental work in compressible fluid flow yields tremendous amounts of data that need to be correlated and interpreted. Finally, the design and construction of airplanes and missiles is most complex and hence must rely on model studies. For the above reasons, similitude and dimensional analysis are used very extensively in compressible-flow studies. Already in this section, the Knudsen number, the Mach number, and the Reynolds number have been mentioned. There are many other dimensionless parameters which are powerful aids, and these are discussed in detail in Sec. 15. However, for the convenience of the reader, Table 8.5 lists the more important dimensionless parameters used in gas dynamics.

THERMODYNAMICS

8.8. Definitions and Scope

Gas dynamics was characterized previously as the science bridging the gap between thermodynamics and fluid dynamics. Because the principles of fluid dynamics are capably treated in other sections of this volume, they will not be repeated here. However, some aspects of thermodynamics of interest to the gas dynamicist will be reviewed here.

Generally, thermodynamics is defined as the science dealing with nonrelativistic conversions of energy from one form into another. Thermodynamics deals with a global system as a whole and does not consider the individual particles such as atoms, molecules, or ions which make up the fluid under consideration. Finally, it is necessary to stipulate

Table 8.5. List of Dimensionless Parameters

Name	Symbol	Defining terms	Application
Cauchy number	C	$F/L\rho^2 V^2$	Elastic effect
Damkohler's first ratio	Dam-1	t_{trans}/t_{relax}	Real-gas effects
Froude number	F	V^2/Lg	Gravitational effect
Grashof number	G	$\beta(\Delta T)gL^3\rho^2/\mu^2$	Gravitational effect in free convection
Hartmann number	H	$BL\sigma^{1/2}/\mu^{1/2}$	Magnetohydrodynamic effect
Kármán number	Ka	V/V_A	Magnetohydrodynamic disturbance
Knudsen number	K	l/L	Continuum criteria
Mach number	M	V/a	Compressibility effect
Magnetic Mach number	M_m	$V/(a + V_A)$	Magnetic compressibility
Magnetic Reynolds number	R_m	VL/m	Magnetic dissipation
Nusselt number	Nu	hL/k	Heat flow
Peclet number	Pe	$c\rho VL/k$	Temperature field
Prandtl number	Pr	$c\mu/k$	Temperature distribution
Pressure coefficient	Np	$p/V^2\rho$	Pressure drop
Reynolds number	R	$\rho VL/\mu$	Viscosity effect
Schmidt number	Sc	$\mu\rho/\mathfrak{D}$	Diffusion effect
Specific-heat ratio	γ	c_p/c_v	Thermodynamics
Weber number	W	$\rho V^2L/\sigma$	Capillary action

that thermodynamics deals with reversible processes taking place between equilibrium states.

No practical device will operate reversibly. Furthermore, it has been suggested that the classical thermodynamics be named thermostatics, because under equilibrium conditions the system can be only in a static state. Although most engineering problems are irreversible in nature, fortunately it is possible, at least as a first approximation, to apply thermodynamic analyses to many gas-dynamic phenomena. The thermodynamics of irreversible processes has been developed, and the interested reader is referred to Prigogine.[3]

8.9. Fundamental Laws of Thermodynamics

As in other well-established sciences, there are certain basic laws that must be satisfied if a problem is to be solved thermodynamically. There are four fundamental laws in thermodynamics, namely, the zeroth law (because it was formulated after the first law had been enunciated), the first law, the second law, and the third law. These are now stated briefly.

The Zeroth Law. This law states: If two systems are in thermal equilibrium with a third, they are in equilibrium with one another. The zeroth law is the basis of thermometry and makes possible the development of thermometric scales.

The First Law. The first law is the thermodynamic statement of the principle of conservation of energy. The first law states that when a system undergoes a cyclic process, the relationship between the heat Q and the work W is

$$\oint dQ = \oint dW \qquad (8.8a)$$

More often heat is given in British thermal units (Btu) and work in foot-pounds. Using the mechanical equivalent of heat J (778 ft-lb $\cong$ 1 Btu) one may write

$$\oint dQ = \frac{1}{J} \oint dW \qquad (8.8b)$$

If a cycle is not completed, there will be a change in the internal energy u of the system, so that for any process one may write

$$dQ = du + dW \qquad (8.8c)$$

In Eqs. (8.8a, b, and c) heat and work are path functions and depend both on the end points and the path followed. Thus, although they may be expressed as line integrals, their differentials are not exact. On the other hand, the internal energy is a property of the system and its differential is exact. It follows that

$$\oint du = 0 \qquad (8.9)$$

It will be noted in subsequent parts of this section that in many problems the internal energy occurs together with the so-called flow work p/ρ. It is therefore found convenient to define the enthalpy h as follows:

$$h = u + \frac{p}{\rho} \qquad (8.10)$$

The first law of thermodynamics states that energy in any form is equivalent to energy in any other form, but it does not state how much mechanical energy may actually be obtained from any quantity of thermal energy supplied to a device. It is a quantitative law which, for the solving of many engineering problems, is insufficient in itself. The maximum amount of energy that may be converted in any engineering application is defined by the second law of thermodynamics, which is qualitative in nature.

The Second Law. The second law is based on the concept of reversibility enunciated by Sadi Carnot. There are many ways of stating the second law. The statement by Clausius is reviewed here, namely: It is impossible to raise energy from a lower to a higher potential without the aid of an external agent.

The internal energy follows as a consequence of the first law and, mathematically speaking, is an integrating factor. Similarly, the entropy s follows as a consequence of the second law. It is defined as follows:

$$ds = \left(\frac{dQ}{T}\right)_{\text{reversible}} \tag{8.11}$$

The entropy is a property of the system, and its differential ds is exact. Thus

$$\oint ds = 0 \tag{8.12}$$

For an isolated system (one which may exchange neither mass nor energy with its surroundings) the entropy will either increase or remain constant, but it may never decrease. Thus

$$ds \geq 0 \tag{8.13}$$

The equality holds when the process is reversible, and the inequality when the process is irreversible.

It is often convenient to write the combined first and second laws. Thus, combining Eqs. (8.8c) and (8.11), one obtains

$$T \, ds = du + dW \tag{8.14}$$

The Third Law. Also called Nernst's[4] law, it is questionable that the third law is truly thermodynamic. Actually, it can be more conclusively discussed if statistical techniques are applied. Thus, whereas the first and second laws are valid regardless of the properties of the system matter, the third law depends on the properties.

Eastman's[5] statement of the third law is: "Any phase cooled to the neighborhood of the absolute zero under conditions such that unconstrained thermodynamic equilibrium is attained at all stages of the process approaches a state of zero entropy." Thus

$$\lim_{T \to 0} s = 0 \tag{8.15}$$

Consider a process taking place between two state points 1 and 2. The entropies at these state points are, respectively,

$$s_1 = f_1(T,p) + s_{10}$$
and
$$s_2 = f_2(T,p) + s_{20}$$

in which s_{10} and s_{20} are constants of integration, as yet undetermined. In some applications the engineer deals with single components only, for which $s_{10} = s_{20}$, and thus it is not necessary to know the values of the constants of integration. However, in other problems, such as those encountered in combustion processes or in chemically reacting boundary layers,

$$s_{10} \neq s_{20}$$
and
$$f_1(T,p) \neq f_2(T,p)$$

For the solution of such problems, the third law is very valuable because it specifies the absolute value of entropy.

8.10. Thermal Equations of State

Any n-dimensional function, interrelating n independent thermodynamic properties of a system, defines the system and is called its thermal equation of state. The simplest thermal equation of state relates the pressure, density, and temperature. Thus for a single component gas,

$$\phi(p,\rho,T) = 0 \tag{8.16}$$

It can be surmised that such an equation is represented by a three-dimensional surface. The form of the function can be obtained either analytically or experimentally. If determined analytically, the function depends upon a considerable number of assumptions. Thus for a *perfect gas* one assumes that there are no interparticle forces of repulsion or attraction and that although the particles have mass they occupy no space. The appropriate equation of state is then

$$p = \rho R T \tag{8.17}$$

in which p = absolute pressure, lb/ft²
            ρ = density, slugs/ft³
            R = specific gas constant, ft-lb$_f$/(lb$_m$)(°R)
            T = absolute temperature, °R

For any gas, the specific gas constant is

$$R = \frac{R_0}{m}$$

when R_0 is the universal gas constant, which is 1545, and m is the molecular weight of the gas. For example, the molecular weight of air is 28.97 (Table 8.4), and thus the gas constant for air is approximately equal to 53.3.

At low temperatures and pressures, one may assume that air behaves as a perfect gas. Combining the various constants, the equation of state for air is written as follows:

$$\frac{p}{\rho} = 1716T \tag{8.18}$$

8.11. Real-gas Thermodynamics

Gases behave in accordance with the perfect-gas equation of state only under idealized conditions. When a gas deviates from a perfect gas, Eq. (8.17) can be corrected by incorporating a departure coefficient or compressibility factor Z as follows:

$$p = Z\rho R T \tag{8.19}$$

Obviously, for a perfect gas $Z = 1$. In general

$$Z = f(p_r, T_r) \tag{8.20}$$

if p_r and T_r are the reduced pressure and temperature, respectively. Thus

$$p_r = \frac{p}{p_{cr}} \quad \text{and} \quad T_r = \frac{T}{T_{cr}} \tag{8.21}$$

in which p and T are the pressure and temperature of the gas at the specified condition, while p_{cr} and T_{cr} are the critical pressure and temperature, respectively. Departure coefficients for high pressure and for high temperature must be recognized.[38] In high-speed gas dynamics, such as hypersonic flow, it is primarily the latter that is important.

At normal temperature and pressure, a diatomic gas has generally five degrees of freedom. Three of these are translational (Fig. 8.2) and are in the x, y, and z directions. In turn, two are rotational degrees of freedom as shown in Fig. 8.3a. It can be shown by kinetic theory[6] that the specific heat ratio γ is given by

$$\frac{c_p}{c_v} = \gamma = 1 + \frac{2}{f} \tag{8.22}$$

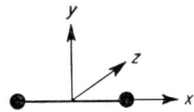

Fig. 8.2. Translational degrees of freedom.

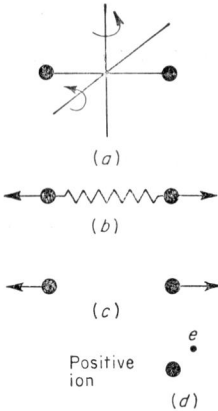

(a)

(b)

(c)

Positive
ion
(d)

FIG. 8.3. (a) Rotational
degrees of freedom. (b)
Vibrational degrees of
freedom. (c) Dissocia-
tion to neutral atoms.
(d) Ionization.

if f is the number of degrees of freedom. For nitrogen,
oxygen, or air $f = 5$, and hence $\gamma = 1.40$ at normal temperatures. It can be recognized in Eq. (8.22) that as $f \to \infty$,
$\gamma \to 1$. However, as the gas temperature increases, the
diatomic molecule shown in Fig. 8.3b no longer acts as a
rigid dumbbell or rotator, but starts vibrating as a result of
the intermolecular collisions. Because vibration increases f
in Eq. (8.22), it follows that the specific-heat ratio will decrease as the temperature increases. Actually, as the temperature is further increased, the diatomic molecules break
up into their neutral atoms (Fig. 8.3c) and the gas is said to
be *dissociated*. At still higher temperatures, electrons may
be knocked off from outer shells of neutral atoms and the
gas is said to be *ionized* (Fig. 8.3d) and is called a *plasma*.
A neutral plasma consists of positive ions and negative electrons in equal amounts. The electrical charges render the
gas electrically conducting, and thus susceptible to magnetic effects. Because of the electrical charges, plasmas have
been called the fourth state of matter. The behavior of
gases at the higher temperature where the additional
degrees of freedom occur and where electronic excitation
and subsequently ionization set in is generally termed
real-gas phenomena. Real-gas phenomena occur extensively
in high-velocity flow. For example, at hypersonic speeds
the gas behind the bow shock ahead of a blunt missile may be
dissociated or ionized. Figure 8.4 shows dissociation and ionization for oxygen and
nitrogen. Similar phenomena occur in the flow of mixtures in chemical rocket motors
or ramjet engines.

For a dissociated gas, the equation of state may be written

$$p = \rho R T (1 + x) \tag{8.23}$$

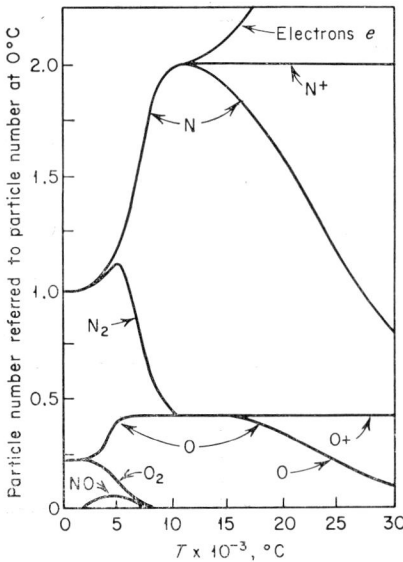

FIG. 8.4. Air composition.

if x is the percentage dissociation which is
a function of both temperature and pressure. The dissociation may be evaluated
from the equilibrium constant K for the
dissociation reaction under consideration.
It can be shown[7] that the equilibrium
coefficient is a function of temperature.
Furthermore, the percentage dissociation
x and the equilibrium coefficient K are
related [38] as follows:

$$\frac{4x^2}{1 - x^2} = \frac{K}{p} \tag{8.24}$$

For a plasma the perfect-gas equation
of state becomes [38]

$$p = \rho R T (1 + \alpha) \tag{8.25}$$

in which α is the number fraction of ionization.

The fraction of ionization is related to
the ionization equilibrium coefficient by
the following equation:

$$\alpha = \frac{K}{p + K} \tag{8.26}$$

Except at exceedingly high temperatures as may be encountered in fusion reactors, a real gas is actually a complex of unexcited and excited molecules, neutral atoms, positive ions, and electrons. For a mixture of dissociated gas and plasma the equation of state is

$$p = \rho R T (1 + x + 2\alpha) \qquad (8.27)$$

For any singly ionized plasma in equilibrium Saha's equation gives the relationship among the ionization, the temperature, and the pressure.

$$\frac{\alpha^2}{1 - \alpha^2} p^2 = 3.16 \times 10^{-7} \times T^{5/2} e^{-(eV_i/kT)} \qquad (8.28)$$

In the Saha equation the following notation and units are used:

α fraction of ionization
p pressure, atm
T temperature, °K
V_i ionization potential of gas
eV_i ionization energy, ergs
k Boltzmann's constant

It should be noted that a real gas in compressible flow and a real fluid in fluid dynamics are not synonymous. Thus a real gas is a thermodynamic concept and implies that the gas does not behave in accordance with the perfect-gas equation of state. Or it may mean that the gas is excited beyond its rotational degree of freedom. A real fluid, on the other hand, is a fluid mechanical concept. By it is meant that the fluid is viscous. Of course, it is quite possible that one may be studying the phenomena associated with a viscous gas which is also excited.

In studying real-gas phenomena one determines for convenience whether the flow is in "equilibrium" or is "frozen." This is done by evaluating Damköhler's first ratio, which is defined

$$\mathbf{Dam} = \frac{t_{trans}}{t_{relax}}$$

in which t_{trans} is the time the gas is in transit, and t_{relax} is the time required for a gas to return to its equilibrium state. If $\mathbf{Dam} < 1$, frozen flow applies, whereas if $\mathbf{Dam} > 1$, equilibrium flow applies.

8.12. Caloric Equations of State

Relations which define the thermal properties are called *caloric equations of state*. For example, the internal energy may be defined as a function of the temperature T, and the specific volume $v = 1/\rho$. Thus

$$u = u(T,v) \qquad (8.29)$$

Differentiation of Eq. (8.29) yields

$$du = \left(\frac{\partial u}{\partial T} \right)_v dT + \left(\frac{\partial u}{\partial v} \right)_T dv \qquad (8.30)$$

Table 8.6. Critical Properties and First Ionization Potentials

Element	t_c, °C	p_c, atm	Ionization potential, ev
Argon...........	−122.44	48.00	15.755
Helium..........	−267.95	2.26	24.58
Nitrogen........	−146.9	33.54	14.54
Oxygen..........	−118.38	50.14	13.614

Table 8.7. Types of Internal Energy

Name	Symbol	Atomic gas	Polyatomic gas
Kinetic energy of translation	u_t	✓	✓
Kinetic energy of rotation	u_r		✓
Kinetic energy of vibration	u_v		✓
Energy of dissociation	u_d		✓
Energy of electronic excitation	u_e	✓	✓
Energy of ionization	u_i	✓	✓

in which the partial differentials represent thermal coefficients. Thus $(\partial u/\partial T)_v$ is the specific heat at constant volume, namely,

$$c_v = \left(\frac{\partial u}{\partial T}\right)_v \tag{8.31}$$

Because for a perfect gas the internal energy is a function of temperature only,[8] one may write

$$c_v = \left(\frac{\partial u}{\partial T}\right)_v = \frac{du}{dT} \tag{8.32}$$

One must differentiate among the types of internal energy that may occur in a monatomic gas as opposed to a polyatomic gas. These are summarized in Table 8.7.

The total internal energy is then the summation of the various internal energies which may occur in a certain gas at a given temperature:

$$u = \sum_k u_k$$

$$= u_t + u_r + u_v + u_d + u_e + u_i \tag{8.33}$$

The various energies are related to their respective specific heats. Thus the vibrational constant-volume specific heat per mode of vibration is defined as follows:

$$c_v \text{ vib} = \frac{\partial}{\partial t}(u_{\text{vib}})_v \tag{8.34}$$

In Eq. (8.34) u_{vib} is the harmonic oscillator energy for each mode of vibration and is defined as

$$u_{\text{vib}} = RT \frac{\theta/T}{e^{\theta/T} - 1} \tag{8.35}$$

if θ is the characteristic temperature defined as $\theta = h\nu/k$. In this definition of the characteristic temperature,

h Planck's constant $(h = 4.135 \times 10^{-15} \text{ ev/sec})$
ν frequency
k Boltzmann's constant $(k = 86.1 \times 10^{-6} \text{ ev/°K})$

The vibrational constant-volume specific heat becomes

$$c_v \text{ vib} = R \sum^{\substack{3n-5 \\ \text{or} \\ 3n-6}} e^{\theta/T} \left(\frac{\theta/T}{e^{\theta/T} - 1}\right)^2 \tag{8.36}$$

in which the summation is taken over the degrees of freedom and must also consider whether the molecule is linear or not. Thus, for a straight molecule, the summation is over $3n - 5$, while for a nonlinear molecule it is $3n - 6$, n being the degrees of freedom.

Similarly, constant-volume specific heats may be calculated for dissociation, and this can be shown to be

$$\frac{c_{v_d}}{R} = \left(\frac{q_d}{RT}\right)^2 \frac{x(1-x)}{2-x} \tag{8.37}$$

if q_d is energy of dissociation, and $q_d/R = \theta_d$, the characteristic temperature of dissociation.

The reader has now been introduced to the evaluation of the real-gas thermodynamic properties. Unfortunately, the limited scope of this section does not permit further detailed treatment. For more rigorous discussions, Refs. 9, 10, and 38 may be consulted. It should be remembered, however, that in evaluating the total internal energy of a gas or its specific heat, all the various contributions must be considered.

The specific heat at constant pressure is obtained from the caloric equation of the enthalpy. Thus one writes the enthalpy as a function of temperature and pressure:

$$h = h(T,p) \tag{8.38}$$

By differentiating, one obtains

$$dh = \left(\frac{\partial h}{\partial T}\right)_p dT + \left(\frac{\partial h}{\partial p}\right)_T dp \tag{8.39}$$

in which

$$c_p = \left(\frac{\partial h}{\partial T}\right)_p \tag{8.40}$$

Again, by definition, the enthalpy of a perfect gas is a function of temperature alone. Thus

$$c_p = \left(\frac{\partial h}{\partial T}\right)_p = \frac{dh}{dT} \tag{8.41}$$

The specific-heat ratio $\gamma = c_p/c_v$ is used extensively in gas-dynamic equations. In the strictest sense, this ratio should be written only for perfect gases. It can be shown by elementary thermodynamics that

$$c_p = \frac{\gamma R}{\gamma - 1} \tag{8.42}$$

and

$$c_v = \frac{R}{\gamma - 1} \tag{8.43}$$

When real-gas effects need to be taken into consideration it is advisable[31] to define an effective specific-heat ratio γ_e. This may be defined and evaluated in different ways, depending on the availability of the needed information. Thus if acoustic velocity data are available, γ_e may be evaluated from the following equation:

$$\gamma_e = \frac{a^2 \rho}{p} \tag{8.44a}$$

If, on the other hand, it is more convenient to calculate theoretically the constant-volume specific heats, the effective specific-heat ratio is calculated from

$$\gamma_e = \frac{c'_v}{c'_v - 1} \tag{8.44b}$$

if c'_v is the real-gas, constant-volume specific heat.

8.13. Thermodynamic Equations and Functions

In gas-dynamic analyses the associated thermodynamic equations often become rather involved. The situation can become particularly aggravated when real-gas effects such as dissociation or when multiple-phase flow are considered. Bridgman[11] has compiled the important relations, and the reader may conveniently find the desirable equations without having to derive them himself.

A convenient technique of deriving many thermodynamic equations and relationships which may not be found conveniently has been developed by Norman Shaw.[12]

This method is based on one fundamental relation of Jacobians. It can be shown that an equation of state $\phi(x,y,z) = 0$ will exist if the Jacobian $J(x,y,z/\xi,\eta,\zeta)$ vanishes. The Jacobian is defined

$$J\left(\frac{x,y,z}{\xi,\eta,\zeta}\right) \equiv \frac{\partial(x,y,z)}{\partial(\xi,\eta,\zeta)} \equiv \begin{vmatrix} \dfrac{\partial x}{\partial \xi} & \dfrac{\partial x}{\partial \eta} & \dfrac{\partial x}{\partial \zeta} \\[2mm] \dfrac{\partial y}{\partial \xi} & \dfrac{\partial y}{\partial \eta} & \dfrac{\partial y}{\partial \zeta} \\[2mm] \dfrac{\partial z}{\partial \xi} & \dfrac{\partial z}{\partial \eta} & \dfrac{\partial z}{\partial \zeta} \end{vmatrix} \tag{8.45}$$

in which $w = w(\xi,\eta,\zeta)$, $x = x(\xi,\eta,\zeta)$, $y = y(\xi,\eta,\zeta)$, $z = z(\xi,\eta,\zeta)$.

One can then write

$$\overline{J(x,y)}^2 + J(y,z)J(x,w) + J(z,x)J(y,w) = 0 \tag{8.46}$$

Further, one defines the following references Jacobian:

$$J(x,y) = b \qquad J(x,z) = l$$
$$J(y,z) = a \qquad J(y,w) = n$$
$$J(x,w) = c$$

in which $x = p$
$$y = v = 1/\rho$$
$$z = T$$
$$w = s$$

In terms of the reference Jacobian, the basic equation for Norman Shaw's technique becomes

$$b^2 + ac - ln = 0 \tag{8.47}$$

By using this relation, Norman Shaw constructed Table 8.8, which is used to establish the desired thermodynamic relationship.

Example 1. Find a relation between the thermal coefficients, represented by the following partials:

$$\alpha = \frac{l}{v}\left(\frac{\partial v}{\partial T}\right)_p \qquad \gamma = \frac{l}{p}\left(\frac{\partial p}{\partial T}\right)_v \qquad c_p = \left(\frac{\partial Q}{\partial T}\right)_p \qquad c_v = \left(\frac{\partial Q}{\partial T}\right)_v$$

SOLUTION.   From Table 8.8, it is seen that

$$\frac{l}{v}\left(\frac{\partial v}{\partial T}\right)_p = \frac{l}{v}\frac{b}{l} \qquad \frac{l}{p}\left(\frac{\partial p}{\partial T}\right)_v = -\frac{b}{pa}$$

$$\left(\frac{\partial Q}{\partial T}\right)_p = \frac{Tc}{l} \qquad \left(\frac{\partial Q}{\partial T}\right)_v = \frac{Tn}{a}$$

After solving for the reference Jacobians and by satisfying Eq. (8.47), one finds the following relationship:

$$\alpha v - \frac{c_p}{pT\gamma} + \frac{c_v}{pT\gamma} = 0$$

This method of Jacobians applies to simple systems. For real gases Arave[43] has extended this technique and has developed additional tables of Jacobian functions.

Table 8.8. Table of Values of J (x,y)

$$b^2 + ac = ln = 0$$

x \ y	p	v	T	s	E	I	F	G	Q	W
p	0	b	l	c	$Tc - pb$	Tc	$-sl - pb$	$-sl$	Tc	pb
v	$-b$	0	a	n	Tn	$Tn - vb$	$-sa$	$-sa - vb$	Tn	0
T	$-l$	$-a$	0	b	$Tb + pa$	$Tb - vl$	pa	$-vl$	Tb	$-pa$
s	$-c$	$-n$	$-b$	0	$-pn$	vc	$-sb - pn$	$-sb + vc$	0	pn
E	$Tc - pb$	Tn	$Tb + pa$	pn	0	$\dfrac{Tvc}{} + p(Tn - vb)$	$-T(sb + pn) - psa$	$-T(sb - vc) - p(sa + vb)$	pTn	Tpn
I	Tc	$Tn - vb$	$Tb - vl$	$-vc$	$-Tvc - p(Tn - vb)$	0	$-T(sb + pn) + v(sl + pb)$	$-T(sb - vc) + vsl$	$-vTc$	$Tpn - vpb$
F	$sl + pb$	sa	$-pa$	$-sb - pn$	$T(sb + pn) + psa$	$\begin{array}{l}T(sb + pn)\\ -v(sl + pb)\end{array}$	0	$\begin{array}{l}svl\\ +p(sa + vb)\end{array}$	$-sTb - pTn$	$-spa$
G	sl	$sa + vb$	vl	$-sb + vc$	$T(sb - vc) + p(sa + vb)$	$T(sb - vc) - vsl$	0	0	$sTb - vTc$	$-spa - vpb$
Q	$-Tc$	$-Tn$	$-Tb$	0	$-pTn$	vTc	$-sTb - pTn$	$-sTb + vTc$	0	Tpn
W	$-pb$	0	pa	pn	Tpn	$Tpn - vpb$	$-spa$	$spa + vpb$	$-Tpn$	0

Table 8.9. Perfect-gas Formulas

Process →	Constant volume, $v = C$	Constant pressure, $p = C$	Isothermal, $T = C$	Isentropic, $s = C$	Polytropic, $pv^n = C$
p, v, T relations	$\dfrac{T_2}{T_1} = \dfrac{p_2}{p_1}$	$\dfrac{T_2}{T_1} = \dfrac{v_2}{v_1}$	$p_1 v_1 = p_2 v_2$	$\begin{cases} p_1 v_1{}^\gamma = p_2 v_2{}^\gamma \\ \dfrac{T_2}{T_1} = \left(\dfrac{v_1}{v_2}\right)^{\gamma-1} \\ \quad = \left(\dfrac{p_2}{p_1}\right)^{(\gamma-1)/\gamma} \end{cases}$	$p_1 v_1{}^n = p_2 v_2{}^n$ $\dfrac{T_2}{T_1} = \left(\dfrac{v_1}{v_2}\right)^{n-1}$ $\quad = \left(\dfrac{p_2}{p_1}\right)^{(n-1)/n}$
$\displaystyle\int_1^2 p\,dv$	0	$p(v_2 - v_1)$	$p_1 v_1 \ln \dfrac{v_2}{v_1}$	$\dfrac{p_2 v_2 - p_1 v_1}{1 - \gamma}$	$\dfrac{p_2 v_2 - p_1 v_1}{1 - n}$
$u_2 - u_1$	$c_v(T_2 - T_1)$	$c_v(T_2 - T_1)$	0	$c_v(T_2 - T_1)$	$c_v(T_2 - T_1)$
Q	$c_v(T_2 - T_1)$	$c_p(T_2 - T_1)$	$p_1 v_1 \ln \dfrac{v_2}{v_1}$	0	$c_n(T_2 - T_1)$
n	∞	0	1	γ	$-\infty$ to $+\infty$
Specific heat	c_v	c_p	∞	0	$c_n = c_v \dfrac{\gamma - n}{1 - n}$
$h_2 - h_1$	$c_p(T_2 - T_1)$	$c_p(T_2 - T_1)$	0	$c_p(T_2 - T_1)$	$c_p(T_2 - T_1)$
$s_2 - s_1$	$c_v \ln \dfrac{T_2}{T_1}$	$c_p \ln \dfrac{T_2}{T_1}$	$R \ln \dfrac{v_2}{v_1}$	0	$c_n \ln \dfrac{T_2}{T_1}$

Because in gas dynamics one frequently considers a perfect gas, the thermodynamic relationships are summarized in Table 8.9.

8.14. Transport Phenomena

Rate, or transport, processes cannot be expressed by equilibrium equations. Regardless of the variety of transport phenomena, rate processes can be expressed as follows:

$$\overrightarrow{\text{Rate}} = \vec{k}\, \frac{\overrightarrow{\text{potential}}}{\overleftrightarrow{\text{resistance}}} \tag{8.48}$$

if k is a velocity coefficient. For example, the Fourier heat-conduction equation is a specific way of writing Eq. (8.48). Thus

$$\dot{q} = -kA \frac{\Delta T}{\Delta x} \tag{8.49}$$

The heat conduction per unit time $\dot{q}$ is the rate of energy transport, the thermal conductivity k is a velocity coefficient, the temperature difference ΔT constitutes the driving potential, while the slab thickness Δx is a resistance.

The other transport equations of interest in compressible flow are:

Fick's law for diffusion:

$$\frac{\partial c}{\partial t} = \mathcal{D} \frac{\partial^2 c}{\partial x^2} \tag{8.50}$$

Newton's law for momentum transfer:

$$\tau = \mu \frac{dV}{dz} \tag{8.51}$$

Ohm's law for the transport of electrical energy:

$$I = \frac{E}{R} \tag{8.52}$$

Now consider a reversible chemical reaction in which a moles of A and b moles of B react to yield c moles of C and d moles of D. Thus

$$aA + bB \rightleftharpoons cC + dD$$

At the start the reaction may progress rapidly from left to right under the influence of the law of mass action. However, as soon as products form, a reaction in the opposite direction also develops. Eventually the corresponding rates of both reactions become equal, and the reaction process is said to be in equilibrium. At equilibrium, the rate of formation of products and of decomposition is the same.

$$\underset{\longrightarrow}{\text{rate}} = \underset{\longleftarrow}{\text{rate}}$$

$$\frac{\underset{\longrightarrow}{(k)} (\text{potential}) A \text{ and } B}{\underset{\longrightarrow}{\text{resistance}}} = \frac{\underset{\longleftarrow}{(k)} (\text{potential}) B \text{ and } C}{\underset{\longleftarrow}{\text{resistance}}}$$

Then

$$\frac{\underset{\longrightarrow}{k} \underset{\longleftarrow}{\text{resistance}}}{\underset{\longleftarrow}{k} \underset{\longrightarrow}{\text{resistance}}} = \frac{(\text{potential}) B \text{ and } C}{(\text{potential}) A \text{ and } B} = K$$

if K is the equilibrium constant. It can be shown[7] that

$$\Delta F^{\circ} = -RT \ln K \qquad (8.53)$$

if ΔF is the change in Gibbs free energy F, which is defined as $F = h - Ts$. If in a reaction $\Delta F < 0$, the reaction is possible; if $\Delta F = 0$, the reaction is reversible; and if $\Delta F > 0$, the reaction is impossible.

Typical examples of transport phenomena of interest to the gas dynamicist are diffusion (mass or chemical) or mass transport, viscosity or momentum transport, conductivity (thermal and/or electrical) or energy transport. Although these are different phenomena, they may be treated in basically the same manner. Assume that a portion of gas is bounded by two horizontal planes AA' and BB' and divided by another horizontal plane CC' as shown in Fig. 8.5. One may assume then that the *transport* occurs across the plane CC', and further one notes that the transport is not necessarily steady but can vary with time. Assume further that along the plane CC' one can select an appropriate generalized functional magnitude. If the process proceeds from plane CC' to plane AA' in linear manner, it is easily possible to find the gradient of the generalized function. Of course, the transported magnitude will be different in each transport phenomenon. For example, in thermal phenomena the transported magnitude is kinetic energy of the molecules. Consider that the gas between AA' and CC' is at a higher temperature than that between CC' and BB'. In kinetic theory the temperature of a gas is defined by the kinetic energy of its constituent particles. It follows that the particles coming from AA' and crossing CC' will possess higher kinetic energy than those coming from BB' and crossing CC'. Eventually, the gas between AA' and BB' will

tend to equalize in temperature, but this will happen only when sufficient kinetic energy has been transported across CC'. Thus one concludes that in the case of thermal conductivity in gases, the transported magnitude is kinetic energy. One may reason in a similar manner about the viscosity. It may be assumed that the layer BB' is stationary while layer AA' is in motion. Thus the momenta of the particles above layer CC' are greater than the momenta of the particles below it. Since faster molecules lose momentum

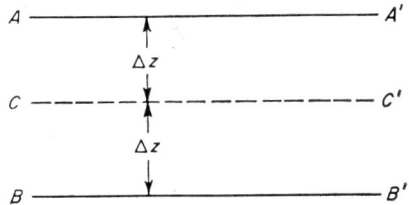

FIG. 8.5. Generalized system for transport phenomena.

and slower ones gain momentum, it follows that viscosity can be considered as momentum transport.

For a simplified case, it may be shown by kinetic theory that the thermal conductivity k, the viscosity μ, and the diffusivity $\mathfrak{D}$ are defined, respectively, by the following equations:

$$k = \tfrac{1}{3}\rho Vl \qquad (8.54)$$
$$\mu = \tfrac{1}{3}\rho Vlc_v \qquad (8.55)$$
$$\mathfrak{D} = \tfrac{1}{3}Vl \qquad (8.56)$$

if V is the particle velocity and l is the mean free path.

Quite frequently one deals with *coupled transport phemomena* where occurrence of one transport phenomenon gives rise to another, and the reverse also applies. For example, in a thermocouple an electric current in a circuit incorporating dissimilar metallic conductors will cause evolution of heat at respective junctions. Conversely, when the junctions are kept at different temperatures, an electromotive force will appear in the circuit.

In order to generalize transport phenomena, it can be considered that there is a *flux* denoted by J and a *driving potential*, or *force X*, causing the flux. The force and the flux are related through a *phenomenological coefficient L*, and in a simple transport process

$$J = LX \qquad (8.57)$$

It should be mentioned that techniques are available to treat nonlinear cases also, but a study of these is outside the scope of this text.

If coupled-transport phenomena exist, one must consider several forces, fluxes, and coefficients. Consider a coupled transport of two phenomena. There are, then, two fluxes J_1 and J_2, two forces X_1 and X_2, and four coefficients L_{11}, L_{12}, L_{21}, and L_{22}. The coefficients L_{11} and L_{22} are for a specific transport, while L_{12} and L_{21} are the coefficients concerned with the cross effects. One writes a set of simultaneous equations, namely,

$$J_1 = L_{11}X_1 + L_{12}X_2 \qquad (8.58)$$
and
$$J_2 = L_{21}X_1 + L_{22}X_2 \qquad (8.59)$$

By using symbolic notation, these become

$$J_i = \sum_{k=1}^{n} L_{ik}X_k \qquad \begin{matrix} i = 1, 2, \ldots, n \\ k = 1, 2, \ldots, n \end{matrix} \qquad (8.60)$$

By the application of the concept of *microscopic reversibility,* Onsager arrived at the *reciprocal relations*, namely,

$$L_{ik} = L_{ki} \qquad (8.61)$$

More detailed discussion of *irreversible thermodynamics* and transport phenomena is beyond the appropriate scope of this section. However, these methods constitute most powerful tools to solve real-gas problems and to better understand high-temperature phenomena. Those who wish to study further in these areas are referred to the literature.[3,7,9,13]

Thermodynamic tables and thermophysical properties are developed constantly. Because of the rapid developments, property tables are not reproduced in this section, but the gas tables by Keenan and Kaye[14] are recommended for convenient use. The reader would do well to use the most recent tables available at the time. Permanent sources where such information may be obtained are the Thermophysical Properties Research Center of Purdue University and the U.S. National Bureau of Standards.

FUNDAMENTAL EQUATIONS OF COMPRESSIBLE FLOW

8.15. Introduction

In this article the basic equations underlying compressible-flow phenomena are reviewed with the intent of applying them in subsequent portions of this section (see Sec. 2).

In order to solve a compressible-flow problem, one must satisfy and specify the following set of equations and definitions:

1. Equations of change
   a. Continuity equation
   b. Momentum equation
   c. Energy equation
   d. Entropy equation
2. Thermal equation of state
3. Caloric equations of state
4. Thermophysical and transport properties
5. Dimensionless parameters

In this article, the equations of change are developed briefly. The thermal and the caloric equations of state were discussed in Arts. 8.10 and 8.12. The fluid properties are also treated in greater detail in Sec. 1. Finally, the dimensionless parameters of interest to the gas dynamicist are listed in Art. 8.7.

The equations of change will be written in their general form. However, later, when they are applied, the analysis will be for one-dimensional steady flow. Using a one-dimensional approach is indeed an approximation, because in the true sense it is valid only for flow through stream tubes of infinitesimal size. Obviously, engineering problems are not represented by such a naive model. However, the one-dimensional analysis will give acceptable results whenever changes in the flow properties are greater in the direction of flow than in the other two directions. Fortunately, this is true of many engineering applications.

8.16. The Continuity Equation

The continuity equation states that when relativistic considerations are nonexistent, mass can neither be created nor destroyed. The continuity equation may be written either on a global basis or for the various species. The former is used in cases where the concentration and the variety of the individual species making up the gas do not change.

The Global Continuity Equation. The global continuity equation applies to a mass of fluid and is commonly written as follows:

$$\operatorname{div}(\rho \mathbf{V}) + \frac{\partial \rho}{\partial t} = 0 \qquad (8.62)$$

The first term defines the changes with respect to the space coordinates while the second indicates changes with respect to time and specifies the acceleration or deceleration. For steady flow the continuity equation becomes

$$\operatorname{div}(\rho \mathbf{V}) = 0 \qquad (8.63)$$

while for steady, incompressible flow it is

$$\operatorname{div} \mathbf{V} = 0 \qquad (8.64)$$

For one-dimensional flow in the x direction, the continuity equation is written

$$\frac{\partial}{\partial x}(\rho V_x A) + \frac{\partial}{\partial t}(\rho A) = 0 \qquad (8.65)$$

in which V_x is the velocity component in the x direction, and A is the cross-section area.   Because for steady flow there are no changes with respect to time, the one-dimensional continuity equation becomes

$$d(\rho V_x A) = 0 \tag{8.66}$$

Frequently it is convenient to express this as a logarithmic differential. Thus, one writes

$$\frac{d\rho}{\rho} + \frac{dV}{V} + \frac{dA}{A} = 0 \tag{8.67}$$

The Species Continuity Equation.   If the gas undergoes chemical changes, the conservation of the species must be accounted for.   This is the case when a mixture of fuel and oxidizer is burnt in a combustion chamber, or if the air behind the bow shock of a hypersonic missile dissociates or ionizes.

In developing the microscopic equation of continuity one defines the following:

$\dot{w}_i$ rate of production (or annihilation) of species i
n_i number of moles of species i per unit volume
$\mathbf{v}_i$ average velocity of particles of species i
M_i molecular weight of species i
$\mathbf{V}$ average macroscopic flow velocity $\mathbf{V} = (1/\rho)\Sigma n_i M_i \mathbf{v}_i$
$\mathbf{V}_i$ diffusion velocity $\mathbf{V}_i = \mathbf{v}_i - \mathbf{V}$

Conservation of the species i can be represented by the following equation:

$$\text{div }(n_i \mathbf{v}_i) + \frac{\partial n_i}{\partial t} = w_i \tag{8.68}$$

If Eq. (8.68) is multiplied by M_i, if a substitution is made for $\mathbf{v}_i$ and the summation is performed, one obtains

$$\sum_i M_i \frac{\partial n_i}{\partial t} + \sum_i \nabla \cdot (n_i M_i \mathbf{V}) + \sum_i \nabla \cdot n_i M_i \mathbf{V}_i = \sum_i M_i \dot{w}_i \tag{8.69}$$

Equation (8.69) describes the continuity of all species i.   In aerothermochemical problems a continuity equation and an equation of state must be written for each species.

By the principle of conservation of mass,

$$\sum_i M_i \dot{w}_i = 0 \tag{8.70}$$

Furthermore,

$$\rho = \sum_i n_i M_i \quad \text{and} \quad \sum_i n_i M_i \mathbf{V}_i = 0$$

It follows then that the species continuity equation [Eq. (8.69)] reverts to the global continuity equation [Eq. (8.62)].

8.17. The Momentum Equation

The momentum equation expresses the conservation of momentum.   It may take into consideration terms accounting for friction as well as external body forces such as gravity and magnetism.   Other names for the momentum equation are the *equation of motion*, the *Navier-Stokes equation*, and *Euler's equation*.

The momentum equation is generally written for the gross flow.   The general form is given by

$$\frac{D\mathbf{V}}{Dt} = -\frac{1}{\rho}\,\text{grad } p + \nu\,\nabla^2 V + \frac{\nu}{3}\,\text{grad }(\nabla \cdot \mathbf{V}) + \mathbf{F}_g + \mathbf{F}_e + \mathbf{F}_m \tag{8.71}$$

In this equation the term D/Dt represents the mobile operator, or the convective derivative, which is defined as

$$\frac{D}{Dt} = \frac{\partial}{\partial t} + \mathbf{V} \cdot \text{grad}$$

The first term on the right-hand side of Eq. (8.71) represents the forces on the fluid-control-volume boundaries. The second and third terms on the right-hand side define the viscous effects. Finally, $\mathbf{F}_g$, $\mathbf{F}_e$, and $\mathbf{F}_m$ represent, respectively, the gravity forces, the electric forces, and the magnetic forces. It is evident that Eq. (8.71) is all-embracing and may be used in classical gas dynamics, in aerothermochemistry as well as in magnetohydrodynamics. Written in vectorial form, Eq. (8.71) actually represents the various directions. Thus, in three-dimensional cartesian coordinates, the equation will have to be written for the x, y, and z directions. It may, of course, not be necessary to consider all terms. For example, if electromagnetic effects do not enter the case under study, then one simply neglects the terms $\mathbf{F}_e$ and $\mathbf{F}_m$. Again, if inviscid flow is being considered, then the second and third terms on the right-hand side are neglected. Finally, if the flow under study is steady, then the term $\partial/\partial t$ in the mobile operator is zero.

The momentum equation, when written with the viscous effects in mind, is called the *Navier-Stokes equation*. No general solution exists for the Navier-Stokes equations, and thus each case must be solved individually. The name of the momentum equation, when it is written for an inviscid fluid and when external forces such as magnetism and gravity are neglected, is *Euler's equation*. Thus

$$\frac{\partial \mathbf{V}}{\partial t} + \text{curl } \mathbf{V} \times \mathbf{V} + \text{grad } \frac{V^2}{2} = -\frac{1}{\rho} \text{grad } p \qquad (8.72)$$

In its one-dimensional form, Euler's equation for steady flow is

$$\frac{dp}{\rho} + V\, dV = 0 \qquad (8.73)$$

Euler's equation applies to reversible flow only. When Euler's equation is integrated one obtains Bernoulli's equation, which, because it is derived from Euler's equation, is valid for reversible processes. The incompressible Bernoulli's equation is

$$\frac{p}{\rho} + \frac{V^2}{2} = \text{const} \qquad (8.74)$$

while the compressible Bernoulli equation (also called Saint-Venant's equation) is

$$\frac{\gamma}{\gamma - 1} \frac{p}{\rho} + \frac{V^2}{2} = \text{const} \qquad (8.75)$$

In compressible-flow analyses, the momentum equation is frequently written in the following convenient form:

$$p_1 A_1 + \rho_1 A_1 V_1^2 = p_2 A_2 + \rho_2 A_2 V_2^2 \qquad (8.76)$$

From this one defines the thrust function F as follows:

$$F = pA + \rho A V^2 \qquad (8.77)$$

The thrust function is very advantageous in computing the thrust of air-breathing engines because the difference of the exit and inlet thrust functions is the thrust of the engine. Tables of thrust functions have been calculated by Shapiro.[14]

8.18. The Energy Equation

The energy equation expresses the conservation of energy. In thermodynamics it is called the first fundamental law of thermodynamics (Art. 8.9). In its most general form, the energy equation is written as follows:

$$\frac{dQ}{dt} = \frac{du}{dt} + \frac{d}{dt}\left(\frac{p}{\rho}\right) + \frac{d}{dt}\left(\frac{V^2}{2}\right) + Q_J + \frac{dQ_R}{dx} + \phi \tag{8.78}$$

In Eq. (8.78) the left-hand term defines the heat transferred across the control-volume surfaces by conduction, namely, the Fourier conduction. In turn, the terms on the right-hand side denote, respectively, the internal energy, the flow energy, the kinetic energy, the magnetic energy, the rate of energy flow by radiation, and the dissipation function, which accounts for the work necessary in overcoming the losses.

As with the momentum equation, not all terms need to be considered in Eq. (8.78) if the physical problem does not include them. For example, if the flow is adiabatic, the term dQ/dt would be zero. If electromagnetic effects are negligible, the Joule heat term Q_J will disappear and at low temperatures the radiation term will drop out. Finally, if no irreversibilities accompany the flow, then the dissipation term is zero. Otherwise the dissipation function ϕ is defined by the following equation [Eq. (2.51)]:

$$\phi = -\tfrac{2}{3}\mu\left(\frac{\partial V_x}{\partial x} + \frac{\partial V_y}{\partial y} + \frac{\partial V_z}{\partial z}\right)^2 + \mu\left\{2\left[\left(\frac{\partial V_x}{\partial x}\right)^2 + \left(\frac{\partial V_y}{\partial y}\right)^2 + \left(\frac{\partial V_z}{\partial z}\right)^2\right]\right.$$
$$\left. + \left(\frac{\partial V_z}{\partial y} + \frac{\partial V_y}{\partial z}\right)^2 + \left(\frac{\partial V_x}{\partial z} + \frac{\partial V_z}{\partial x}\right)^2 + \left(\frac{\partial V_y}{\partial x} + \frac{\partial V_x}{\partial y}\right)^2\right\} \tag{8.79}$$

The steady-flow energy equation is frequently written in simplified form as follows:

$$Q = (u_2 - u_1) + \left(\frac{p_2}{\rho_2} - \frac{p_1}{\rho_1}\right) + \frac{V_2{}^2 - V_1{}^2}{2} + z_2 - z_1 + W_s \tag{8.80}$$

By applying the definition of enthalpy, one can write

$$Q = (h_2 - h_1) + \frac{V_2{}^2 - V_1{}^2}{2} + (z_2 - z_1) + W_s \tag{8.81}$$

For a perfect gas, $dh = c_p\, dT = \gamma R/(\gamma - 1)$. Furthermore, when variations in altitude can be neglected and when the external work is zero, the energy equation in differential form becomes

$$dQ = \frac{\gamma R}{\gamma - 1}\, dT + V\, dV \tag{8.82}$$

Equation (8.82) will be used extensively in the following articles.

8.19. The Entropy Equation

In solving compressible-flow problems one must solve a set of equations. Frequently one finds that the number of unknowns exceeds the number of equations available. In such situations the entropy equation may be written, although it usually introduces at least one additional unknown, and thus its presence may not improve the situation. The entropy equation is written for an adiabatic case.

$$\frac{\partial s}{\partial t} + \operatorname{div}(s\mathbf{V}) = 0 \tag{8.83}$$

In writing the entropy equation, one must recall that a control volume may receive and discharge mass, momentum, energy, and entropy. Thus the entropy, being increased because of internal irreversibilities, must be differentiated from the entropy crossing the boundaries. The former is denoted by ds_i and is called the internal entropy change, whereas the latter is denoted by ds_e and is called the external entropy change. It follows that

$$ds_i \geq 0 \tag{8.84}$$

whereas

$$ds_e \gtrless 0 \tag{8.85}$$

Finally $$ds = ds_i + ds_e \tag{8.86}$$

For the details of the entropy equation the reader should consult Refs. 3 and 9.

The background of compressible flow has now been laid. In the next parts these fundamentals are applied to multifarious-flow phenomena.

ISENTROPIC FLOW

8.20. Introduction

Ideal flow conditions are said to exist when it is specified that the flow is isentropic. By definition, isentropic means that the process under consideration is both adiabatic and reversible. It follows that there are no viscosity or friction effects, no heat losses, no turbulence, and no rotationality. Indeed, isentropic flow specifies an ideal flow which cannot be experienced in reality but which nevertheless is representative of compressible-flow phenomena from a theoretical viewpoint.

8.21. Acoustic Velocity and Mach Number

Previously the Mach number was defined and its usefulness in gas dynamics was mentioned. Here some additional details associated with the Mach number are considered.

By definition the acoustic velocity a is the velocity with which a small disturbance or pressure wave is propagated into a medium at equilibrium. The acoustic velocity in a gas is given by

$$a = \left(\frac{\partial p}{\partial \rho} \right)_{s=c} \tag{8.87}$$

in which the partial differential of pressure with respect to density at constant entropy s indicates that the disturbances must be very small. By substituting the equation $p/\rho^\gamma = c$, the acoustic velocity in a perfect gas can be calculated from the equation

$$a = \sqrt{\gamma R T} \tag{8.88}$$

Consider a point source traveling with a velocity $V < a$ as shown in Fig. 8.6. At the reference time $t = 0$, the point disturbance is assumed to be at point A. At one unit time t later, the point source will have moved through a distance Vt to B. At two time units later, namely, $2t$, the source will have moved through a distance $2Vt$ to point C. Meanwhile, the spherical-pressure wavefront which started out from A will have grown after time $2t$ to a radius $2at$, and the wavefront from B, which could not start until the source reached B, will have grown to a radius at. At time $2t$ the source will have just reached point C. This step-by-step analysis of a point source moving at subsonic velocity indicates that each succeeding wavefront will be contained always within the initial or preceding wavefront sphere.

If the point source moves at a speed V such that $V > a$, the wavefront circles will no longer contain the source. The condition is shown in Fig. 8.7. The envelope to this family of circles is a straight line, known as the *Mach line*. It is easy to recognize that $\sin \alpha = a/V$, and hence $\alpha = \arcsin 1/\mathbf{M}$. The angle between the Mach line and the direction of flow is known as the *Mach angle*.

The Mach line constitutes a demarcation. It is easy to see that in Fig. 8.7 the fluid outside the Mach line will not receive any signal from the source because the disturbances travel with a speed equal to that of sound. Von Kármán has appropriately called this

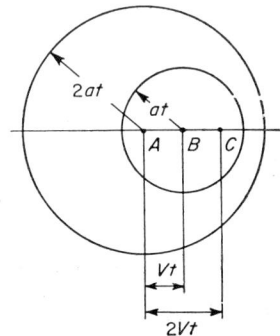

FIG. 8.6. Wavefronts produced by a point source moving at subsonic velocity.

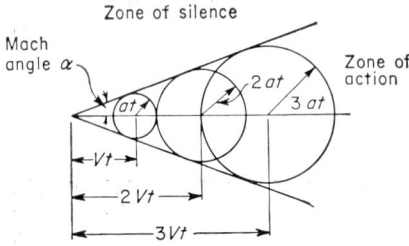

Fig. 8.7. Rule of forbidden signals from a
point source moving at supersonic velocity.

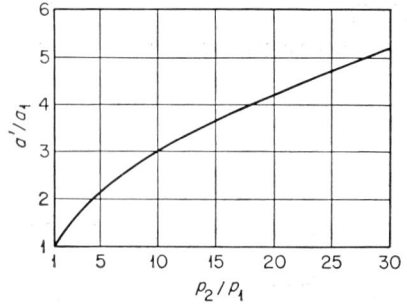

Fig. 8.8. Disturbance velocity ratio for air.

phenomenon "the rule of forbidden signals." Further, von Kármán called the region ahead of the Mach lines "the zone of silence" and the region inside the Mach lines "the zone of action."

Although small disturbances move with the speed of sound, strong disturbances move at higher velocities. Thus, let the pressure ratio across any disturbance be p_2/p_1. Furthermore, denote the velocity of a small isentropic disturbance by a_1 where the subscript 1 corresponds to the undisturbed regime. If the velocity of any disturbance (weak or strong) is denoted by a', it can be shown[7] that

$$\frac{a'}{a_1} = \sqrt{\frac{1}{2\gamma}\left[\gamma - 1 + (\gamma + 1)\frac{p_2}{p_1}\right]} \qquad (8.89)$$

and $a' \to a_1$ as $p_2 \to p_1$. Thus, a pressure wave propagates at acoustic velocity if the pressure change across it is infinitesimal. Equation (8.89) is shown graphically in Fig. 8.8.

For air at normal pressures and temperatures (when the air constituents are not excited, dissociated, or ionized), the acoustic velocity may be computed conveniently by the relation

$$a = 49.1\sqrt{T} \qquad (8.90)$$

if a is given in feet per second and T in degrees Rankine.

Regardless of the gross stream velocity of a gas-dynamics system, the molecules making up the gas are constantly in random motion. Because different molecules have different velocities at varying times, any gas on a molecular basis is considered to satisfy the concepts of statistical probability. Kinetic theory and Maxwell-Boltzmann distributions are used extensively in such studies, and the mean-square velocity is defined by

$$\overline{V}^2 = \frac{\Sigma V_i^2}{n} \qquad (8.91)$$

in which n is the number of molecules in a control volume, and V_i is the velocity of specific molecules. It may be shown further by kinetic theory that the root-mean-square velocity V is

$$\overline{V} = 388\sqrt{\frac{T}{M}} \qquad (8.92)$$

in which M = molecular weight, T = temperature in degrees Rankine, and the velocity is given in feet per second.

It follows that for any perfect gas, the root-mean-square velocity and the acoustic velocity are related by the ratio

$$\frac{\overline{V}}{a} = \sqrt{\frac{3}{k}} \qquad (8.93)$$

provided that they are both considered to be at the same temperature. This is an interesting relationship because it gives a semimicroscopic insight into gas motion. Furthermore, in rarefied-gas dynamics (at very low densities) it has been suggested that a modified Mach number be defined as $M_M = V/\overline{V}$.

Example 2. Compute the root-mean-square velocity and the acoustic velocity for nitrogen at 68°F.

SOLUTION. By Eq. (8.92),

$$\overline{V} = 388 \sqrt{\frac{528}{28}}$$

$$= 1690 \text{ fps}$$

By Eq. (8.88),

$$a = \sqrt{1.4 \times 32.2 \times \frac{1545}{28} \times 528}$$

$$= 1150 \text{ fps}$$

This example shows that the root-mean-square velocity is greater than the velocity with which a disturbance travels in a system. This seems logical, because the position of the fluid particles determines the position of the disturbance wave.

8.22. The Flow System

Essentially, all problems of gas dynamics may be considered to take place in a flow system, which may be considered as represented in Fig. 8.9. This consists of an infinite reservoir and a flow section. The conditions in the reservoir are denoted by the subscript 0. The flow section may be of any shape. It may be a convergent section, a straight section, or a convergent-divergent section. If it is convergent or convergent-divergent, the narrowest section is termed the *throat*.

To define a flow, the properties of the system must be known. It should be remembered that the flow properties of a system which define the state of the system are the static properties and not the dynamic properties. In other words, the properties which define a state are those which are determined by measuring devices which have a velocity of zero relative to the flow stream.

The enthalpy $(h = u + p/\rho)$ of a perfect gas above an appropriate datum can be written as

$$h - h_0 = c_p(T - T_0) = \frac{\gamma R}{\gamma - 1}(T - T_0) \tag{8.94}$$

For adiabatic (either reversible or irreversible) flow in the absence of shaft work and when no changes in elevation occur, the energy equation when combined with Eq. (8.94) becomes

$$\frac{\gamma R}{\gamma - 1} dT + V \, dV = 0 \tag{8.95}$$

Equation (8.95) is basic to most derivations involving adiabatic flow. From it many equations may be obtained, as, for example, the variation of the velocity with temperature.

After dividing Eq. (8.95) by kRT, there results

$$\frac{1}{\gamma - 1} \frac{dT}{T} + \frac{V}{\gamma} \frac{dV}{RT} = 0$$

After multiplying and after dividing the second term by V and rearranging, it can be shown that

$$\frac{dT}{T} = (1 - \gamma)M^2 \frac{dV}{V} \tag{8.96}$$

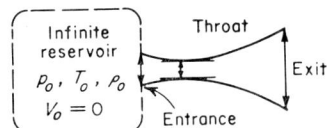

FIG. 8.9. Flow system.

8.23. Flow Parameters

The integration of Eq. (8.95) between conditions in the reservoir and any point in the flow section gives

$$\frac{\gamma R}{\gamma - 1} \int_{T_0}^{T} dT + \int_{V_0 = 0}^{V} V \, dV = 0$$

$$\frac{\gamma R}{\gamma - 1} T + \frac{V^2}{2} = \frac{\gamma R}{\gamma - 1} T_0 \tag{8.97}$$

By introducing the definition of the acoustic velocity into Eq. (8.97)

$$\frac{a^2}{\gamma - 1} + \frac{V^2}{2} = \frac{a_0{}^2}{\gamma - 1} \tag{8.98}$$

if a_0 is the sound velocity corresponding to the reservoir condition. Equation (8.98) implies that in an adiabatic-expansion process, the acoustic velocity based on the reservoir conditions is greater than the local acoustic velocity at any point of the flow section. This can be understood easily if it is remembered that a gas is cooled when it is expanded reversibly and adiabatically.

As a hypothetical experiment let the temperature at some point in the expansion section be reduced to absolute zero. The local velocity V should reach a maximum but finite value which is determined by the existing reservoir conditions. After denoting the local velocity corresponding to the absolute vacuum by V_{max}, one gets

$$V^2_{max} = \frac{2}{k - 1} a_0{}^2 \tag{8.99}$$

By evaluating Eq. (8.99) for air, it is found that

$$V_{max} = 2.24 a_0 \tag{8.100}$$

It follows that the maximum velocity for any particular gas is determined by the temperature existing in the reservoir. For air V_{max} in feet per second is defined as follows:

$$V_{max} = 109.7 \sqrt{T_0} \tag{8.101}$$

In practical applications, V_{max} is not reached. Nevertheless Eq. (8.101) shows why the air entering supersonic wind tunnels may have to be heated if extremely high velocities are desired in the test section. It follows that for any particular reservoir the maximum possible velocity is limited. However, it should not be inferred from this that the speed of aircraft is limited by these same considerations. Theoretically, there is no limit on the maximum speed that airplanes may reach. To study such high-velocity vehicles in the laboratory, aerodynamicists use shock tubes,[15,16] hot-shot tunnels,[17] or plasma generators.[18]

As a second hypothetical experiment consider subsonic flow and imagine a gradual increase of the local velocity V until the acoustic velocity is approached at a particular location. The expansion and the accompanying increase in velocity results in a lowering of the local temperature, and this lowers the local acoustic velocity. Thus, while the local velocity increases, the local acoustic velocity decreases. With further expansion, the stream velocity could become equal to the acoustic velocity $V = a$. At this condition, the acoustic speed is said to have reached its critical condition and this point is conventionally denoted by a^*. It follows from Eq. (8.98) that

$$a^{*2} = \frac{2}{k + 1} a_0{}^2 \tag{8.102}$$

For air, the critical acoustic velocity and the acoustic velocity in the reservoir are related by

$$a^* = 0.913a_0 \tag{8.103}$$

Example 3. Find the highest possible velocity that could result from the expansion of air at standard temperature 59°F.

SOLUTION. The highest velocity will be obtained when all the thermal energy is converted into kinetic energy, and this would happen at zero absolute temperature. The limiting velocity V_{max} is related to the reservoir acoustic speed. Thus

$$V_{max} = 2.24a_0$$
$$a_0 = 49.1\sqrt{519} = 1120 \text{ fps}$$

Therefore $V_{max} = 2.24 \times 1120 = 2508$ fps.

In certain problems the critical acoustic velocity serves a very useful purpose, and thus the critical Mach number is defined as follows:

$$\mathbf{M}^* = \frac{V}{V^*} = \frac{V}{a^*} \tag{8.104}$$

in which V is the velocity at any point, and $V^* = a^*$. Although this is in the form of a Mach number, it pertains to no particular local conditions but constitutes a reference ratio. There are at least two advantages to defining $\mathbf{M}^*$. First, it is a parameter which for any particular section is a function of the velocity only. Second, at extremely high speeds the acoustic velocity decreases (because of the decrease in temperature due to the rapid expansion) while the velocity itself increases. Hence the Mach number tends toward infinity, complicating its use in equations. Defining the Mach number $\mathbf{M}$ based on a^* obviates this difficulty.

8.24. Stagnation Temperature

If a thermometer is introduced into a nozzle through which flows a gas at high velocity, the thermometer reading will not be the true gas (free-stream or static) temperature but will be the *stagnation temperature*. This is so because the gas immediately surrounding the thermometer sensing element is brought to rest. Thus the kinetic energy of the gas is converted into thermal energy, which results in the higher temperature reading. To explain this phenomenon, consider that a gas is ejected from a reservoir at temperature T_0 as shown in Fig. 8.10. The energy equation is integrated as follows:

$$\frac{\gamma R}{\gamma - 1} \int_{T=T_0}^{T=T_t} dT + \int_{V=V_0=0}^{V=V_t=0} dV = 0 \tag{8.105}$$

Therefore $T_t = T_0$.

Because for a perfect gas the enthalpy is $dh = c_p \, dT$, it follows that theoretically the enthalpy of the gas brought to rest at the thermometer equals the enthalpy in the reservoir, and therefore this is called the *stagnation enthalpy*. Furthermore, the temperature read by the stationary thermometer is equal theoretically to the temperature read in the reservoir. Irrespective of the location of the thermometer, the stagnation conditions are set by the reservoir conditions. For a thermometer to read the gas temperature it is necessary that it travel at the same velocity as the gas. This is, of course, impractical, and hence the temperature of the gas is generally calculated from indirect measurements.

It should be noted that only a small portion of the gas passing by the thermometer is brought to rest. The rest travels at high velocity, and the energy equation is then written as

$$c_p T + \frac{V^2}{2} = c_p T_0 \tag{8.106}$$

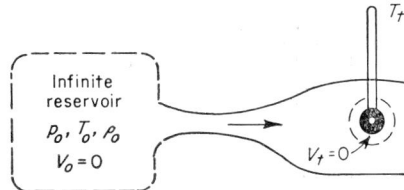

FIG. 8.10. Isentropic stagnation.

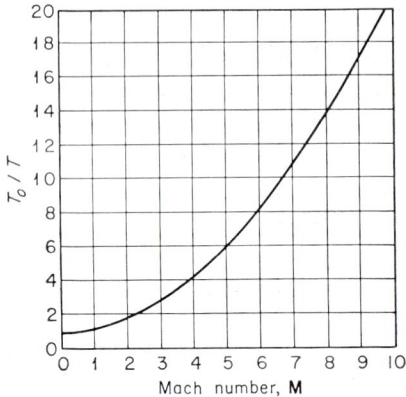

FIG. 8.11. Stagnation temperature-rise ratio at high Mach number (for ideal gas).

Therefore the stagnation temperature is given by

$$T_0 = T + \frac{V^2}{2c_p} \qquad (8.107)$$

Because it is practical to determine the Mach number experimentally, the stagnation temperature may be written as a function of the Mach number. Thus, dividing Eq. (8.107) by the acoustic velocity throughout and rearranging, one obtains the following important equation:

$$\frac{T_0}{T} = 1 + \frac{\gamma - 1}{2} M^2 \qquad (8.108)$$

This equation is shown graphically in Fig. 8.11 for a perfect gas having $\gamma = 1.40$. It should be noted that unless specifically designed for the purpose, a stagnation thermometer will read a slightly different temperature from the theoretical stagnation temperature because of boundary-layer effects and heat losses. Thus, to each thermometer is ascribed a *recovery factor* which corrects for this deviation. Finally, at high Mach numbers it is necessary to use a specific-heat ratio γ other than the perfect-gas value in order to take care of the real-gas effects.

8.25. Stagnation Pressure

A relation between the stagnation pressure (or total pressure) and the *static pressure* may be had by using certain of the perfect-gas relationships. For a perfect gas undergoing isentropic flow, the relationship between pressure and temperature is given in Table 8.9. Then from Eq. (8.108) and Table 8.6 one may write

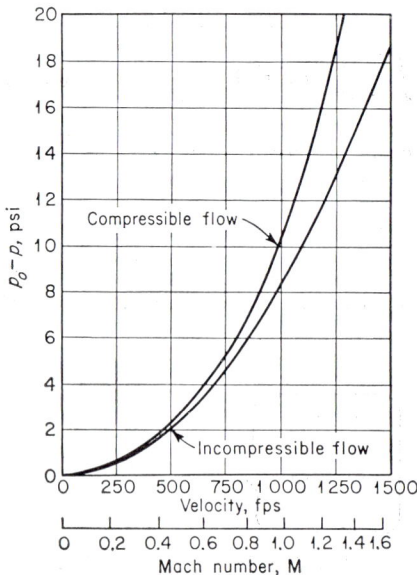

FIG. 8.12. Stagnation pressure rise.

$$\frac{p_0}{p} = \left(1 + \frac{\gamma - 1}{2}\,\mathbf{M}^2\right)^{\gamma/(\gamma-1)} \tag{8.109}$$

The *dynamic pressure* q is usually defined as

$$q = \tfrac{1}{2}\,\rho V^2 = \tfrac{1}{2}\,\gamma p\mathbf{M}^2 \tag{8.110}$$

Introducing the dynamic pressure into Eq. (8.109) and expanding in series form, one obtains

$$p_0 = p + \tfrac{1}{2}\,\rho V^2\left(1 + \frac{\mathbf{M}^2}{4} + \frac{2-\gamma}{24}\,\mathbf{M}^4 \ldots\right) \tag{8.111}$$

In contrast, for incompressible flow, the Bernoulli equation for the stagnation condition is

$$p_0 = p + \tfrac{1}{2}\,\rho V^2$$

These two equations are compared graphically in Fig. 8.12 for a perfect diatomic gas.

WAVE PHENOMENA

8.26. Introduction

It has already been stated that the acoustic velocity is the speed with which rarefactions or compressions of infinitely small amplitude propagate. When the compressions in the flow are of finite amplitude, there usually occurs a discontinuous rise of pressure, and a shock wave exists. In addition to discontinuities in the pressure, there occur discontinuous increases in temperature, density, entropy, and other fluid properties. If initially the air is still and the wave is moving, then, after the passing of the wave, the air will move in the direction of the wave. Gas compressions that have a finite amplitude travel faster than the speed of sound, as is the case in big explosions. Although variations in flow density are generally observed by optical methods such as the Toepler-schlieren technique (Sec. 14), jet-aircraft pilots are reported to have seen, by eye alone, shock waves springing out from the wings of their aircraft. Observers of atomic explosions are also known to have seen shock waves. The gray phenomena mentioned by the survivors of the Pompeian holocaust may also be attributed to the shock wave developed by the eruption of the volcano.

Across a shock wave the fundamental flow equations, namely, the equation of continuity, the energy equation, and momentum equation, apply. However, across a shock wave there is an increase in entropy. Therefore, the flow takes place adiabatically, although of course not reversibly.

Shock waves are one type of wave phenomenon, but it should be clearly recognized that all wave phenomena are not shock occurrences. To clarify this point it appears desirable to classify the various wave phenomena which are encountered. If wave phenomena are arbitrarily and qualitatively classified, one would meet both *weak waves* and *shock waves*. A Mach wave, for example, is a very weak wave. There are weak compression waves as well as weak expansion waves. The former would occur at a wall having a concave corner as shown in Fig. 8.13. In contrast, a weak expansion wave would occur at a convex wall corner as shown in Fig. 8.14. With very weak waves, it may be assumed that there are no drastic discontinuities because the deflec-

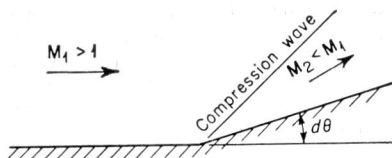

FIG. 8.13. Compression wave at concave corner.

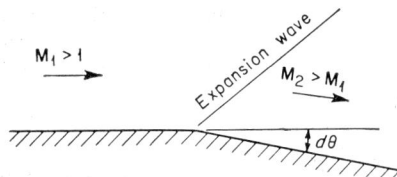

FIG. 8.14. Expansion wave at convex corner.

tion angle $d\theta$ is infinitesimally small and isentropic-flow analysis is applicable across such a wave. Across a compression wave, the flow is decelerated and the gas density is increased, and across an expansion wave the flow is accelerated. A shock wave, on the other hand, can only be of the compression type, and there is no rarefaction shock because this would require that the entropy decrease in an adiabatic process—clearly a violation of the second law of thermodynamics. In this section waves exhibiting entropy increases are called *shock waves*, whereas waves across which the entropy is substantially constant are referred to simply as *waves*.

Another manner of classifying waves is according to their relative velocity. Thus one may speak of *stationary shock waves*. A shock wave may be rendered stationary by making the mass of gas in which it propagates travel at a speed equal to that of the shock but opposite in direction. Such occurrences may be observed in nozzles, for example. Stationary shock waves may be either *attached* to an object or they may be *detached*, depending on the shape of the object and the Mach number. Nonstationary shock waves can readily be developed in shock tubes.[15,16]

Finally, shock waves may be situated at right angles to the flow, in which case they are called *normal shocks*, or they may be located at an angle, in which case they are called *oblique shocks*. Normal shocks may be treated by a one-dimensional-flow analysis, but oblique wave phenomena (whether shock waves or weak waves) require two-dimensional-flow analysis. The discussion of wave phenomena can be quite complex, and for more sophisticated details, the reader is referred to Refs. 19 and 20.

One characteristic common to wave phenomena is that the stagnation temperature on each side of the wave is the same. This follows from the application of the energy equation to perfect gases undergoing an adiabatic process. Thus, if the upstream conditions for a wave are denoted by the subscript 1 and the conditions downstream by 2,

$$T_{01} = T_{02}$$

There appears to be an erroneous tendency to think that wave phenomena are always undesirable. Actually, shock fronts may be made to operate to good advantage in stabilizing certain flows or may furnish the basis of studying numerous real-gas phenomena.

8.27. Piston Analogy of Shock Formation

The formation of a shock wave may be described conveniently by imagining the acceleration of a piston confined in a cylinder. The processes may be understood more conveniently by a model in which one considers a series of impulses given to the piston rather than a continually increasing velocity.

Consider a long slender tube open at one end and having a piston at the other end as shown in Fig. 8.15a. Assume that originally both the gas confined in the tube and the piston are at rest and in equilibrium. Now impart to the piston a small velocity, thus compressing the gas. This will produce a compression wave which will travel into the tube with the speed of sound. As this disturbance passes through the gas, consecutive portions of it are accelerated. The portions of the gas closest to the piston are set into motion sooner than those farther away. Thus a portion of the gas is at a slightly higher pressure than existed previously, and so is the density. This is represented in Fig. 8.15b. Now impart to the piston an additional pulse and thereby produce another compression wave. Again the gas is compressed adiabatically and its pressure, density, and temperature are raised locally as shown in Fig. 8.15c. By successive repetitions of this process a series of wave terraces are formed. Each upper terrace has a higher velocity than the lower ones because the fluid in the upper terraces is at respectively higher temperatures and thus each has, respectively, a higher acoustic velocity. In each case the message produced will travel at acoustic speed relative to the fluid between two successive pulses. As the process is continued, the steps become steeper (Fig. 8.15d) and eventually merge, completely forming a normal shock as in Fig. 8.15e.

Once the shock wave has been formed, it will travel ahead of the column of gas being pushed by the piston and its velocity will be greater than that of the piston. If the piston were stopped abruptly, a rarefaction wave would develop and would follow the shock wave.

In further analyzing shock phenomena, assume that an observer moves with the wave as in Fig. 8.16. The gas previously unaffected will appear to this observer as entering the shock with a velocity V_1 and leaving it adiabatically compressed at a smaller velocity V_2. For inviscid adiabatic flow, one may write the continuity, momentum, and energy equations. Upon eliminating the velocities V_1 and V_2 one obtains the equation for the internal-energy difference across the wave.

$$u_2 - u_1 = \frac{(p_1 + p_2)(\rho_2 - \rho_1)}{2\rho_1\rho_2} \quad (8.112)$$

This is the well-known *Hugoniot equation*, which can be used for determining the temperature rise across a normal shock if the

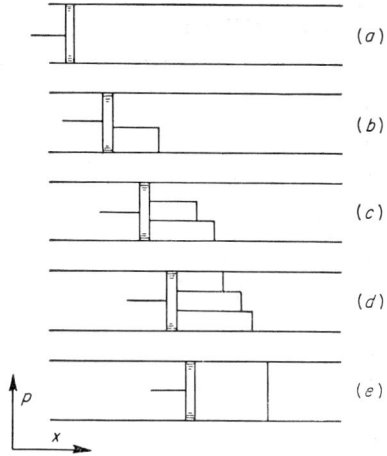

Fig. 8.15. Wave fronts in piston-cylinder model.

functional relationship between internal energy and temperature is known.

Instead of a piston inside a tube, one may imagine a body which is given a series of impulses. As before, each impulse will generate a sound wave emanating from the body. The initial amplitude will differ at the various points of the body because it depends on the component of the acceleration perpendicular to the surface element. The pulse changes the flow characteristics of every point it passes. This pressure and velocity persist until a new pulse arrives and changes the flow properties. The pulses will radiate in all directions from the body, provided the velocity is subsonic relative to the body everywhere. The flow pattern would extend to an infinite distance from the body.

Assume now that the body itself is brought to supersonic speed. In this case the flow pattern, which formerly may have extended a great distance in front of the body, will be overtaken by the body itself. Thus let a body be accelerated from just less than the sonic value to just greater than the sonic value. The pressure pulses will merge into a single wave, the speed of which is slightly greater than the acoustic velocity a. This wave may be seen in Fig. 8.17. The wave will be halted at some distance from the body. It will be normal to the velocity vector of the fluid at the axis of the body. Away from the axis the magnitude of the wave will diminish, so that at infinity the limiting position of the wave will form the Mach angle. If the velocity of the body is gradually increased, it will be found to approach the pressure wave. Under certain conditions the body may actually make contact with the pressure wave, in which case there exists a condition of attached shock. This happens with pointed bodies. If the nose of the body is very blunt, then the shock at even high Mach numbers may be detached.

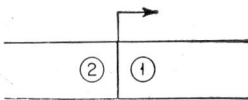

Fig. 8.16. Observer moving with normal wave.

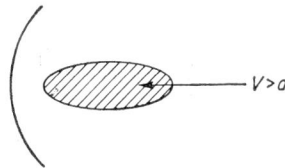

Fig. 8.17. Detached shock.

8.28. Weak Waves

Wave phenomena take place so rapidly that they may be considered to be adiabatic processes. Although some wave phenomena may also be reversible, and thus subject to isentropic criteria, not all wave phenomena may be treated by isentropic considerations.

A Mach line is an example of a type of wave phenomenon which occurs isentropically. It was shown in Art. 8.21 that a Mach wave is formed when a slight disturbance exists. It may also occur when a wedge having a very small angle is introduced into a supersonic flow. Thus consider, for example, the arrangement depicted in Fig. 8.18, in which the wedge angle $d\theta$ is infinitesimally† small. Such a flow obviously cannot be treated completely by one-dimensional analysis. One therefore assigns two components to the flow velocity, namely, the velocity component V_n which is normal to the wave and the component V_t which is tangent to it. It is of interest to determine the magnitude of the velocity normal to the Mach wave. By the equation of continuity one may write across the wave

$$d(\rho V_n) = 0 \qquad (8.113)$$

The velocity component normal to the wave is considered because the tangential component will obviously not contribute to mass transfer across the wave.

Writing Euler's equation (Eq. 8.73) across the wave, it is seen that

$$\frac{dp}{\rho} + V_n \, dV_n = 0 \qquad (8.114)$$

By combining Eqs. (8.113) and (8.114) and after solving for V_n, one finds

$$V_n = \sqrt{\frac{dp}{d\rho}} \qquad (8.115)$$

As this conforms to the definition of acoustic velocity, V_n is equal to the speed of sound upstream of the wave. Downstream from the wave the normal component of the velocity will be less than acoustic if the position of the wedge is as shown in Fig. 8.18.

Expansion Wave. When supersonic flow occurs over a convex corner, an expansion wave is created, as shown in Fig. 8.19. Such a wave may be encountered in a diverging passage.

As before, the divergence in the wall surface will be felt by the fluid and, because of this disturbance, a Mach wave springs out at 0. Because of the expansion, the pressure downstream from the Mach line will be less than the pressure on the upstream side. Thus there is a pressure gradient across the wave which acts at right angles to it. This pressure gradient will further accelerate the air so that the Mach number is increased. Obviously, the direction of flow will tend to be parallel to the wall surface.

For an expansion wave (but equally true for compression and Mach waves), the following observations are pertinent:

1. All the turning of the flow will occur at the Mach line.
2. The angle which the Mach line makes with the original flow direction depends on the original Mach number only and is

† In practice, a wedge angle of less than about 3° may be considered to result in a weak wave.

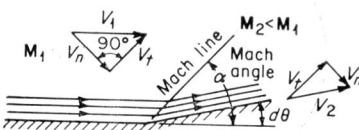

FIG. 8.18. Compression wave.

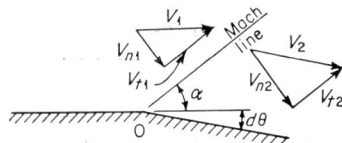

FIG. 8.19. Expansion wave.

$$\alpha = \arcsin \frac{1}{M} \qquad (8.116)$$

3. The turning is identical all along the Mach wave, and hence the change in flow properties is the same at all points on the Mach wave. This follows from the assumption that the flow is two-dimensional. The wall is presumed to extend infinitely in the direction normal to the plane of the paper.

4. Because there is no pressure differential along the wave, the tangential velocity component V_t on each side of the wave will be the same.

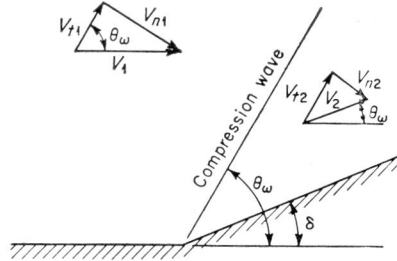

FIG. 8.20. Compression wave, finite deflection.

5. The normal velocity component V_n will change across the wave.

6. The change in the flow parameters is infinitesimal.

7. A supersonic flow may negotiate relatively large-angle sharp expansions without experiencing losses.

8.29. Oblique Shock Waves

Consider a stationary wedge in a flow system as shown in Fig. 8.20, so that the fluid must undergo a concave change of direction, and assume that the wedge angle is relatively large. Because of the wedge, a shock will appear, and this will make an angle θ_w with the original flow direction. This angle is called the *wave angle* and will be larger than the Mach angle.

Consider that upstream from the shock wave, the velocity V_1, the density ρ_1, and the pressure p_1 are known and further that the wave angle θ_w can be determined. Starting from these data it is desired to find the velocity V_2, pressure p_2, and density ρ_2 after the shock wave. As before, each velocity has a tangential component V_t and a normal component V_n. The fundamental equations must apply to the flow.

From Fig. 8.20 it can be seen that the shock wave results in a change of flow direction. The wave angle θ_w and the deflection angle δ are then related as follows:

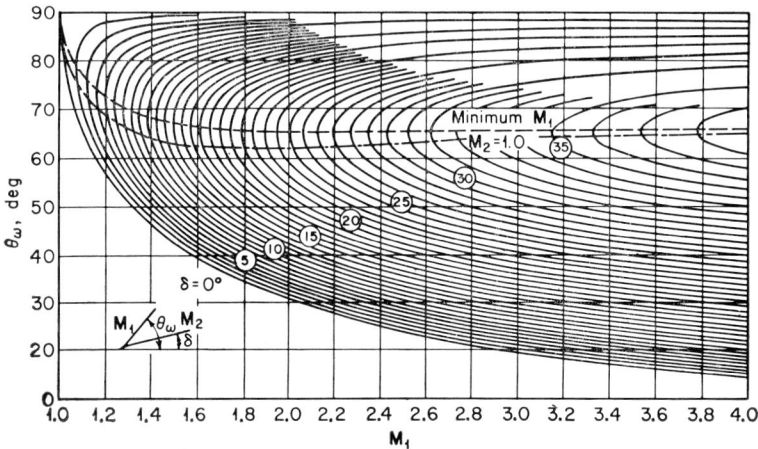

FIG. 8.21. Plane shock angles.

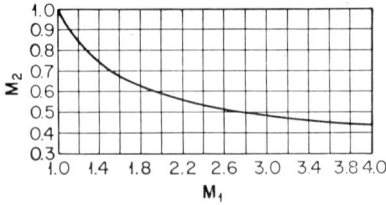

FIG. 8.22. Mach number across a normal shock.

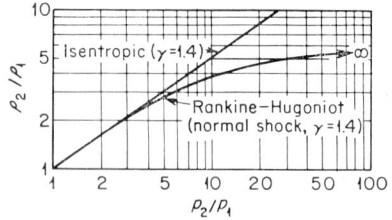

FIG. 8.23. Comparison of isentropic and Rankine-Hugoniot flows.

$$\frac{\tan \theta_w}{\tan (\theta_w - \delta)} = \frac{V_{n1}}{V_{n2}} \tag{8.117}$$

The significant conclusions which may be drawn from the shock equations are shown in Fig. 8.21, for various deflection angles and for a diatomic gas having a constant specific-heat ratio $\gamma = 1.4$. From this figure it is apparent that for a given Mach number and a particular deflection angle, two waves, both attached, are possible. One of these will turn the flow more than the other. Experience indicates that the wave which commonly occurs is the weaker wave, namely, the one which turns the flow to a lesser extent. It may be observed further from Fig. 8.21 that for any given Mach number there is a maximum deflection angle beyond which the wave will become detached from the wedge and the shock equations derived in this section will be no longer applicable.

If, instead of a wedge, a cone with its axis parallel to the stream is considered, the shock wave will take the form of a cone.

8.30. Normal Shock Waves

A shock wave is said to be normal if the flow direction upstream and downstream from it is the same. Equations for normal shock can be derived simply from the fundamental flow equations or from the oblique shock relationships. For example, for normal shock $V_t = 0$ and $V_n = V$. Thus

$$V_1 V_2 = a^{*2} \tag{8.118}$$

Equation (8.118) is the Rankine-Hugoniot equation for normal shock. It states that the velocity downstream of a normal shock is always subsonic. Figure 8.22 shows the Mach number across a normal shock, with $\mathbf{M}_1$ being the Mach number upstream of the shock and $\mathbf{M}_2$ the Mach number downstream of the shock. In contrast for oblique shock, the downstream Mach number is always less than the upstream Mach number, but it is not necessarily subsonic.

In comparing shock phenomena with isentropic conditions, one may evaluate the Rankine-Hugoniot equations. The graphical comparison is shown in Fig. 8.23.

When a pitot tube is introduced into a supersonic flow, a bow shock will occur as shown in Fig. 8.24. The measurement of pressure should then be undertaken in accordance with the Rayleigh-Pitot equation

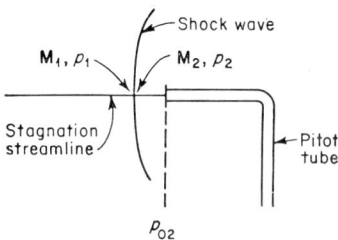

FIG. 8.24. Supersonic total-head tube.

$$\frac{p_{02}}{p_1} = \left\{ \frac{[\mathbf{M}_1{}^2(\gamma + 1)/2]^\gamma}{2\gamma \mathbf{M}_1{}^2/(\gamma + 1) - (\gamma - 1)/(\gamma + 1)} \right\}^{1/(\gamma-1)} \tag{8.119}$$

For the convenience of the reader this equation is shown graphically in Fig. 8.25.

8.31. Chapman-Jouguet Hypothesis

Of considerable importance to the engineer are the phenomena associated with the propagation of a flame front or explosion wave. Applications may be found in combustion-chamber design or in the prevention of explosions. For a simple analysis assume that a combustible mixture is contained in a tube and is subsequently ignited so that a flame front propagates downstream, as depicted in Fig. 8.26. Further, make the following assumptions: (1) The flow takes place in a constant-area duct. (2) The flow is steady. (3) The gases on each side of the wave front are uniform and inviscid and obey the perfect-gas equation of state. No changes in molecular weight occur, and the gases are thermally nonconducting. These are admittedly strict requirements, but they permit, nevertheless, the interpretation of the phenomena by the Chapman-Jouguet hypothesis. This is depicted in Fig. 8.27 and shows the allowable and the forbidden circumstances. For example, according to classical Chapman-Jouguet analysis, a weak detonation and a strong deflagration are excluded. In Fig. 8.27 there are two curves, namely, one for $Q = 0$ and the other for $Q > 0$. The first is a wave phenomenon represented by the Rankine-Hugoniot equation

$$u_2 - u_1 = \frac{(p_1 + p_2)(\rho_1 - \rho_2)}{2\rho_1\rho_2} \tag{8.112}$$

whereas the second one is represented by the Hugoniot equation

$$u_b - u_u - Q = \frac{(p_u + p_b)(\rho_b - \rho_u)}{2\rho_u\rho_b} \tag{8.120}$$

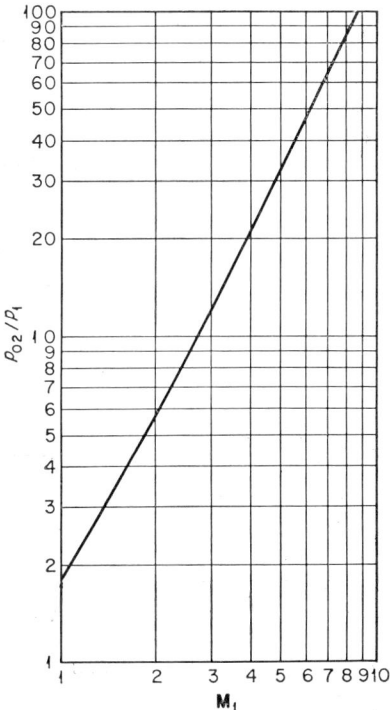

FIG. 8.25. Rayleigh-Pitot equation.

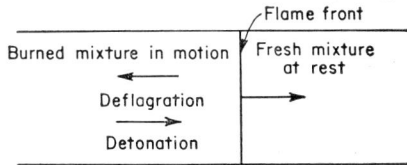

FIG. 8.26. Model for detonation and deflagration.

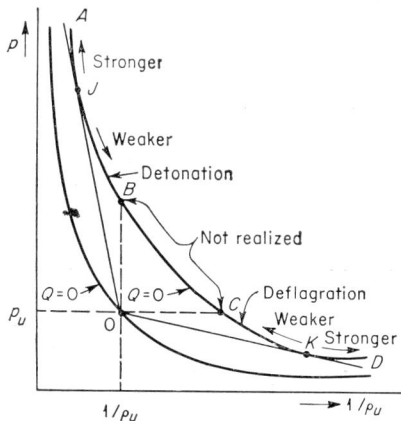

FIG. 8.27. Chapman-Jouguet condition.

Table 8.10. Detonation and Deflagration Criteria

	M_u	M_b	p_b/p_u	V_b/V_u	v_b/v_u	T_b/T_u
Detonation.......	>1	≷1	>1	<1	>1	>1
Deflagration......	<1	<1	<1	>1	<1	>1

Whether detonation or deflagration will occur depends on the various conditions, and these are summarized in Table 8.10 where the subscripts u and b refer, respectively, to the unburned and burned mixtures.

Wave phenomena offer opportunities for much experimental and analytical study, but unfortunately the underlying details are beyond the scope of this brief description. For more rigorous treatises the reader should consult Refs. 19 to 21.

FLOW IN NOZZLES AND DIFFUSERS

8.32. Introduction

In many engineering devices, the flow of gas is either accelerated or decelerated. In gas turbines and rocket motors nozzles are used to convert the thermal energy into kinetic energy. In wind tunnels, both nozzles and diffusers are used to accelerate and decelerate the flow for experimental studies.

If in any configuration the flow is accelerated, one has a nozzle, whereas if the flow is decelerated, one has a diffuser. It will be shown shortly that the contour of the flow section by itself does not determine the particular trend of the velocity change.

8.33. Velocity Variation in Isentropic Flow

For a perfect gas, one can easily obtain the velocity at any section of a contour by applying the steady-flow energy equation for isentropic circumstances. Thus

$$\frac{\gamma R}{\gamma - 1} dT + V\, dV = 0$$

By integrating, by combining with the continuity equation, and after solving for the velocity at any downstream section of the nozzle, one obtains

$$V_s = \frac{1}{\sqrt{1 - (A/A_1)^2(p_2/p_1)^{2/\gamma}}} \sqrt{\frac{2\gamma p_1}{(\gamma - 1)\rho_1}\left[1 - \left(\frac{p_2}{p_1}\right)^{(\gamma-1)/\gamma}\right]} \qquad (8.121)$$

In Eq. (8.121) the subscript 1 denotes the entrance of the nozzle. The velocity V_s is due to an isentropic expansion. The first radical on the right side of Eq. (8.121) is an area correction factor. In many applications it may be assumed that the entrance is an infinitely large reservoir and thus the approach velocity is neglected. One may then write the velocity at any section along the nozzle as follows:

$$V_s = \sqrt{\frac{2\gamma R}{\gamma - 1} T_0\left[1 - \left(\frac{p}{p_0}\right)^{(\gamma-1)/\gamma}\right]} \qquad (8.122)$$

In Eq. (8.122) p is the only variable and governs the magnitude of the velocity.

The mass velocity G of the flow may be computed from Eq. (8.122) upon combination with the continuity equation. Thus

$$G = \rho\sqrt{\frac{2\gamma R}{\gamma - 1} T_0\left[1 - \left(\frac{p}{p_0}\right)^{(\gamma-1)/\gamma}\right]} \qquad (8.123)$$

Using the isentropic-gas relationship, Eq. (8.123) may be written as follows:

$$G = \rho_0\sqrt{\frac{2\gamma R T_0}{\gamma - 1}\left[\left(\frac{p}{p_0}\right)^{2/\gamma} - \left(\frac{p}{p_0}\right)^{(\gamma+1)/\gamma}\right]} \qquad (8.124)$$

Because for steady flow the flow rate is constant although in a nozzle the cross-section area varies, the mass velocity G must have a maximum at some point in the nozzle. This condition is obtained by differentiating Eq. (8.124) with respect to p/p_0, setting the differential equal to zero and then solving for p/p_0, arriving at the so-called critical-pressure ratio p_c/p_0. Thus

$$\frac{p_c}{p_0} = \left(\frac{2}{\gamma + 1}\right)^{\gamma/(\gamma-1)} \tag{8.125}$$

Equation (8.125) shows that the specific-heat ratio is the influencing factor of the critical pressure for any entrance pressure. For air at low temperatures where $\gamma = 1.4$, the *critical pressure ratio* p_c/p_0 equals 0.528.

Because for a convergent-divergent nozzle the mass velocity G is necessarily a maximum at the throat, it follows that the critical pressure p_c exists at the throat. By introducing Eq. (8.125) into Eq. (8.122) and after solving for the velocity at the throat, it is seen that

$$V_t = \sqrt{\frac{2\gamma}{\gamma + 1} RT_0} \tag{8.126}$$

It is at once recognized from Eq. (8.126) that for the throat condition

$$V_t = a^* = a_0 \sqrt{\frac{2}{\gamma + 1}} = \sqrt{kRT_t} \tag{8.127}$$

Isentropic flow in a nozzle predicates that the flow takes place reversibly and that there are no losses experienced in the conversion of thermal energy to kinetic energy. Because of the losses inherent in practical devices, the actual exit velocity V_2 is less than the isentropic exit velocity V_{2s}. The difference is given by the nozzle efficiency η_n, which is defined as follows:

$$\eta_n = \frac{V_2{}^2}{V_{2s}{}^2} \tag{8.128}$$

8.34. Area Variation in Isentropic Flow

In developing a relationship between the velocity and the area one combines the equation of continuity with the definition of the Mach number, obtaining the following equation:

$$\frac{dA}{A} = \frac{dV}{V}(\mathbf{M}^2 - 1) \tag{8.129}$$

It follows that:
1. For a convergent section and $\mathbf{M}^2 > 1$, the velocity decreases.
2. For a divergent section and $\mathbf{M}^2 > 1$, the velocity increases.
3. For a convergent section and $\mathbf{M}^2 < 1$, the velocity increases.
4. For a divergent section and $\mathbf{M}^2 < 1$, the velocity decreases.
5. The condition $dA = 0$ occurs at $\mathbf{M} = 1$.

For example, if one is dealing with a supersonic flow and wishes to accelerate it further, this requires a divergent contour, whereas if it is desired to decelerate the gas, the flow section should be convergent in shape.

8.35. Effect of Pressure Ratio

When the flow completely fills the nozzle, exit pressures below the critical cannot exist in a convergent nozzle. However, in convergent-divergent nozzles the pressure along the nozzle may be less than the critical at any point past the throat.

Consider a convergent-divergent nozzle inserted between two reservoirs as in Fig. 8.28. There will be no flow if the ratio of exit pressure to reservoir pressure $p_e/p_0 = 1$, case *a* in Fig. 8.29. If p_e is reduced so that it is slightly less than the entrance pressure, the

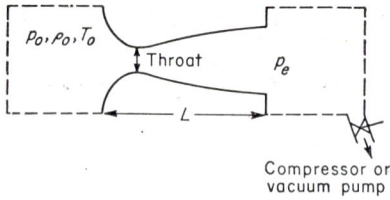

FIG. 8.28. Convergent-divergent nozzle.

convergent-divergent nozzle will act like a conventional venturi tube as represented by curve b in Fig. 8.29. For this case, the flow is always subsonic and resembles incompressible flow. When the exit pressure is reduced further, the critical pressure can be reached at the throat, as curve g shows. In this case, the velocity is sonic at the throat, but is never supersonic within the nozzle, even though the pressure at the throat corresponds to the critical. The minimum pressure which can exist in the nozzle is depicted by point d. For this case also, the pressure at the throat will be the critical and the velocity in the converging section is subsonic. In the diverging section it is supersonic, and at the throat it is sonic. For the range of exit pressures from curve d up to curve g, the rate of flow curve is the same and is plotted in Fig. 8.30. The flow rate reaches a maximum value and remains at this value over this wide range of exit pressures.

The convergent-divergent nozzle in the absence of friction can give truly isentropic performance for the range of exhaust pressures from curve a to curve g in Fig. 8.29, and for only one other pressure, namely, that at curve d. The pressures p_g and p_d are the significant exit design pressures for a given nozzle. For the exhaust pressure range between p_d and p_g, shock occurs in the nozzle followed by diffusion or pressure rise from and after the shock point.

The exit pressure of a nozzle which corresponds to the isentropic pressure (p_d in Fig. 8.29) is the *design pressure*. If the reservoir into which the nozzle is exhausting is at a pressure other than the nozzle design pressure, there occur standing waves outside the nozzle. As the reservoir pressure is raised, the shock travels upstream into the nozzle, as may be seen in Fig. 8.31.

8.36. Diabatic Nozzle Flow

In the discussions so far it was assumed that the flow in nozzles and diffusers is adiabatic. This is not necessarily so. For example, in the nozzles of rocket motors there occur dissociation and recombination. The energy of recombination which must be accommodated is quite high (Art. 8.11). Thus it is understandable that it might make up the temperature drop due to expansion, tending to make the flow isothermal. It can be shown[7] that for isothermal flow the velocity V corresponding to the pressure p in a nozzle is given by

$$V = \sqrt{2\left(RT \ln \frac{p_1}{p} + \frac{V_1^2}{2}\right)} \qquad (8.130)$$

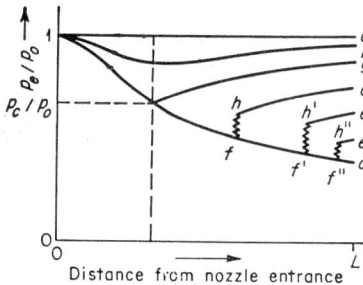

FIG. 8.29. Pressure distribution in convergent-divergent nozzle.

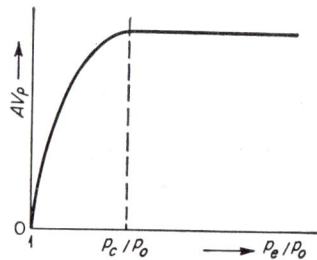

FIG. 8.30. Flow rate.

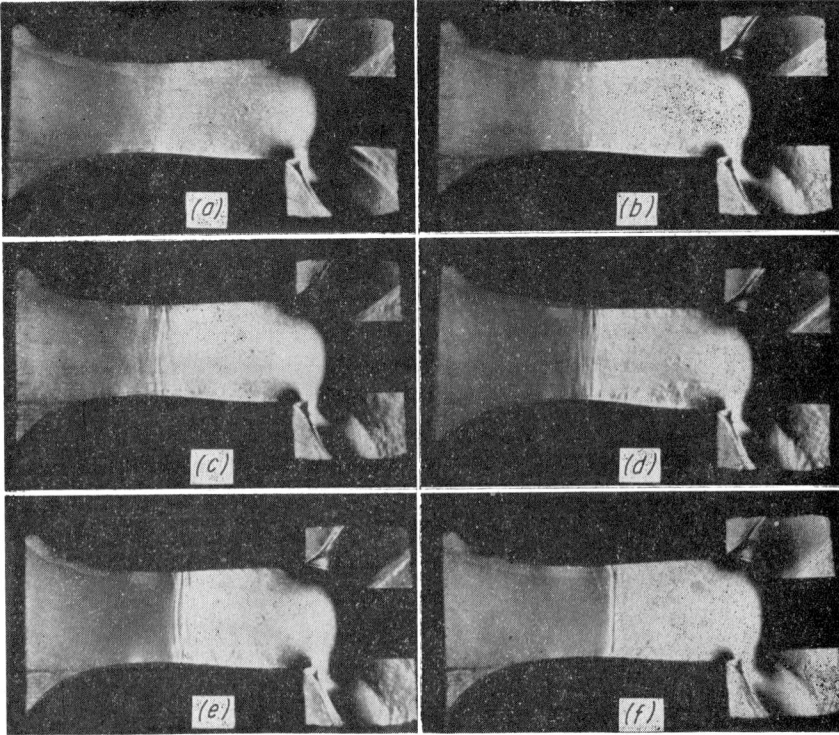

FIG. 8.31. Schlieren photographs of flow through a two-dimensional nozzle showing the development of a shock. The flow is from left to right. The obstacle at the atmospheric end of the nozzle is moved slightly backward in each picture, raising the throat Mach number. (*NACA photo.*)

For isothermal flow, the critical pressure ratio is

$$\frac{p_c}{p_0} = 0.607 \tag{8.131}$$

In Fig. 8.32 are compared the variations in velocity, density, and Mach number in a hypothetical nozzle for isothermal and isentropic flow. It is obvious that the thermodynamics of the process must be taken into consideration in designing nozzles. The situation is particularly serious in the design of nozzles discharging real gases or chemically reacting mixtures.

8.37. Nozzle Design

In the design of supersonic nozzles, care must be taken to prevent shock formation within the nozzle. This may be done by the so-called *method of characteristics*,[2,22] which is applicable to the divergent portion of convergent-divergent nozzles. In order that the method be applied, it is necessary that the flow be approximated by the following: (1) the flow is steady; (2) the flow is isentropic and thus irrotational; (3) the flow is two-dimensional and supersonic; (4) external forces such as gravity and magnetism can be neglected; (5) the gas is perfect. The method of characteristics is a numerical

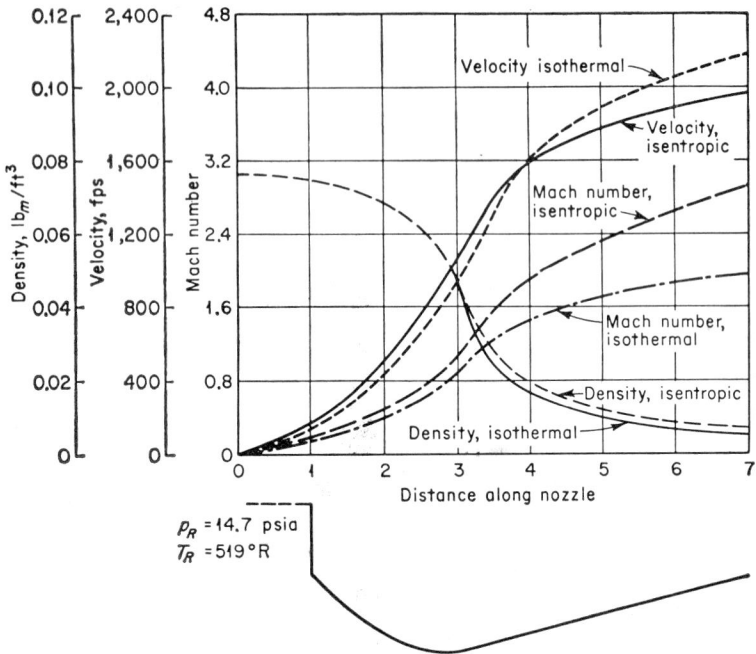

Fig. 8.32. Comparison of velocity, density, and Mach number in a hypothetical nozzle in reversible isothermal flow ($\gamma = 1.4$, perfect gas, $T_R = 519°R$, $P_R = 1$ atm).

approximation which reduces the number of waves to one by replacing a curved boundary by a number of straight-line segments.

In Art. 8.28 it was explained that when a supersonic stream passes over a sudden expansion having an angle $d\theta$, a standing wave will occur and the flow will be deflected through an angle $d\theta$.

It can be shown[2,22] that

$$\theta = \frac{\gamma + 1}{\gamma - 1} \arctan\left(\frac{\gamma - 1}{\gamma + 1} \sqrt{M^2 - 1}\right) - \arctan \sqrt{M^2 - 1} \qquad (8.132)$$

For each Mach number, then, there exists a maximum deflection angle θ_{max} beyond which flow without compression waves cannot be obtained. Tables of characteristic functions are then available[2,22] which may be used in the graphical design of nozzle contours.

FLOW WITH HEAT EXCHANGE

8.38. Introduction

In the foregoing articles of this section, it was frequently conjectured that the flow is adiabatic or that no thermal energy crosses the control volume. However, in many engineering applications the assumption of adiabaticity is not valid. Heat exchangers are a typical example of this. Again in some applications, such as in combustion chambers, the thermal energy of the medium is raised by the liberation of chemical energy although no heating is done across the chamber walls.

8.39. Rayleigh Flow

Flow which is not adiabatic (reversibly or irreversibly) is called diabatic flow. Since the integration of the differential equations representing diabatic flow is complex, it is customary to make some simplifying assumptions. Although these assumptions are not truly realistic, they nevertheless permit the evaluation of problems as a first approximation. The simplifications which are then made are the following: (1) the flow takes place in a duct with a constant-area cross section; (2)

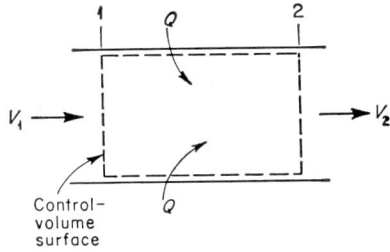

FIG. 8.33. Heat-exchanger model.

there is no friction; (3) the gas is perfect and has constant specific heats; (4) the composition of the gas does not change; (5) there are no devices in the system that deliver or receive mechanical work; (6) the flow is steady.

Equations which conform to the aforementioned requirements are called Rayleigh equations, and the associated flow is designated as Rayleigh flow. Figures 8.33 and 8.34 show models of Rayleigh flow.

For the Rayleigh-flow assumptions, the energy equation is

$$Q_{1-2} = c_p(T_2 - T_1) + \frac{V_2{}^2 - V_1{}^2}{2} = h_2 - h_1 + \frac{V_2{}^2 - V_1{}^2}{2} \qquad (8.133)$$

If the stagnation enthalpy is introduced,

$$Q_{1 \to 2} = h_{02} - h_{01} \qquad (8.134)$$

This in turn can be expressed for a perfect gas in terms of stagnation temperatures:

$$Q_{1 \to 2} = c_p(T_{02} - T_{01}) \qquad (8.135)$$

Since for diabatic flow $Q_{1 \to 2} \neq 0$ and as $c_p > 0$ always, it follows that

$$T_{02} \neq T_{01} \qquad (8.136)$$

This inequality states that in diabatic flow the stagnation temperature is not solely determined by the *reservoir conditions*, as is the case with adiabatic flow. Heating raises the stagnation temperature, and cooling lowers it.

The locus of points for constant G during a constant-area frictionless flow with heat exchange is called the *Rayleigh line*. By substituting the definition of the mass velocity into the momentum equation one obtains

$$p + \frac{G^2}{\rho} = \text{const} \qquad (8.137)$$

8.40. Pressure Ratio in Rayleigh Flow

By definition, Rayleigh equations are derived by combining the continuity and the momentum equation in accordance with the restrictions cited in Art. 8.39. To determine the change in pressure for Rayleigh flow one proceeds as follows. The momentum equation is

$$p_1 + \rho_1 V_1{}^2 = p_2 + \rho_2 V_2{}^2$$

Furthermore, for a perfect gas, $V^2\rho = \gamma p \mathbf{M}^2$. Combining these equations and solving for p_2/p_1, one obtains

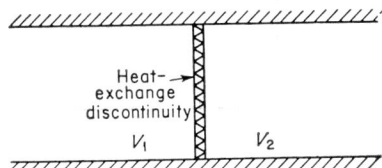

FIG. 8.34. Heat addition.

Table 8.11. Frictionless, Constant-area Flow with Change in Stagnation Temperature†

Perfect gas, $\gamma = 1.4$ exactly

M	T_0/T^*_0	T/T^*	p/p^*	p_0/p^*_0	$\dfrac{\rho/\rho^*}{V/V^*}$	M	T_0/T^*_0	T/T^*	p/p^*	p_0/p^*_0	$\dfrac{\rho^*/\rho}{V/V^*}$
0	0	0	2.400,0	1.2679	0	0.65	0.8683,3	0.960,81	1.5080	1.0582,0	0.6371,3
0.01	$0.0_4 4.80$	$0.0_4 5.76$	2.399,7	1.2678	$0.0_3 2.40$	0.66	0.8770,9	0.968,16	1.4098	1.0550,2	0.6494,1
0.02	0.001,92	0.002,30	2.398,7	1.2675	$0.0_3 9.59$	0.67	0.8854,8	0.975,03	1.4738	1.0519,2	0.6615,9
0.03	0.004,31	0.005,16	2.397,0	1.2671	0.002,16	0.68	0.8935,0	0.981,44	1.4569	1.0489,0	0.6736,7
0.04	0.007,65	0.009,17	2.394,6	1.2665	0.003,83	0.69	0.9011,7	0.987,39	1.4401	1.0459,6	0.6856,4
0.05	0.011,92	0.014,30	2.391,6	1.2657	0.005,98	0.70	0.9085,0	0.992,89	1.4235	1.0431,0	0.6975,1
0.06	0.017,12	0.020,53	2.388,0	1.2647	0.008,60	0.71	0.9154,8	0.997,96	1.4070	1.0403,3	0.7092,7
0.07	0.023,22	0.027,84	2.383,7	1.2636	0.011,68	0.72	0.9221,2	1.002,60	1.3907	1.0376,4	0.7209,3
0.08	0.030,21	0.036,21	2.378,7	1.2623	0.015,22	0.73	0.9284,3	1.0068,2	1.3745	1.0350,4	0.7324,8
0.09	0.038,07	0.045,62	2.373,1	1.2608	0.019,22	0.74	0.9344,2	1.0106,2	1.3585	1.0325,3	0.7439,2
0.10	0.046,78	0.056,02	2.366,9	1.2591	0.023,67	0.75	0.9400,9	1.0140,3	1.3427	1.0301,0	0.7552,5
0.11	0.056,30	0.067,39	2.360,0	1.2573	0.028,56	0.76	0.9454,6	1.0170,6	1.3270	1.0277,6	0.7664,6
0.12	0.066,61	0.079,70	2.352,6	1.2554	0.033,88	0.77	0.9505,2	1.0197,1	1.3115	1.0255,2	0.7775,5
0.13	0.077,68	0.092,90	2.344,5	1.2533	0.039,62	0.78	0.9552,8	1.0219,8	1.2961	1.0233,7	0.7885,2
0.14	0.089,47	0.106,95	2.335,9	1.2510	0.0457,8	0.79	0.9597,5	1.0239,0	1.2809	1.0213,1	0.7993,8
0.15	0.101,96	0.121,81	2.326,7	1.2486	0.0523,5	0.80	0.9639,4	1.0254,8	1.2658	1.0193,4	0.8101,2
0.16	0.115,11	0.137,43	2.317,0	1.2461	0.0593,1	0.81	0.9678,6	1.0267,2	1.2509	1.0174,6	0.8207,5
0.17	0.128,88	0.153,77	2.306,7	1.2434	0.0666,6	0.82	0.9715,2	1.0276,3	1.2362	1.0156,9	0.8312,6
0.18	0.143,24	0.170,78	2.295,9	1.2406	0.0743,8	0.83	0.9749,2	1.0282,3	1.2217	1.0139,9	0.8416,4
0.19	0.158,14	0.188,41	2.284,5	1.2377	0.0824,7	0.84	0.9780,7	1.0285,3	1.2073	1.0124,0	0.8519,0
0.20	0.173,55	0.206,61	2.2727	1.2346	0.0909,1	0.85	0.9809,7	1.0285,4	1.1931	1.0109,1	0.8620,4
0.21	0.189,4,3	0.225,33	2.2604	1.2314	0.0996,9	0.86	0.9836,3	1.0282,6	1.1791	1.00951	0.8720,6
0.22	0.2057,4	0.2445,2	2.2477	1.2281	0.1087,9	0.87	0.9860,7	1.0277,1	1.1652	1.00819	0.8819,6
0.23	0.2224,4	0.2641,3	2.2345	1.2248	0.1182,0	0.88	0.9882,8	1.0269,0	1.1515	1.00698	0.8917,5
0.24	0.2394,8	0.2841,1	2.2209	1.2213	0.1279,2	0.89	0.9902,8	1.0258,3	1.1380	1.00587	0.9014,2
0.25	0.2568,4	0.3044,0	2.2069	1.2177	0.1379,3	0.90	0.9920,7	1.0245,1	1.1246	1.0048,5	0.9109,7
0.26	0.2744,6	0.3249,6	2.1925	1.2140	0.1482,1	0.91	0.9936,6	1.0229,7	1.1114	1.0039,3	0.9203,9
0.27	0.2923,1	0.3457,3	2.1777	1.2102	0.1587,6	0.92	0.9950,6	1.0212,0	1.0984,2	1.0031,0	0.9297,0
0.28	0.3103,5	0.3666,7	2.1626	1.2064	0.1695,5	0.93	0.9962,7	1.0192,1	1.0855,5	1.0023,7	0.9388,9
0.29	0.3285,5	0.3877,3	2.1472	1.2025	0.1805,8	0.94	0.9972,9	1.0170,2	1.0728,5	1.0017,4	0.9479,6

M						M					
0.30	0.3468,6	0.4088,7	2.1314	1.1985	0.1918,3	0.95	0.9981,4	1.0146,3	1.0603,0	1.0012,1	0.9569,2
0.31	0.3652,5	0.4300,4	2.1154	1.1945	0.2032,9	0.96	0.9988,3	1.0120,5	1.0479,2	1.0007,7	0.9657,6
0.32	0.3836,9	0.4511,9	2.0991	1.1904	0.2149,4	0.97	0.9993,5	1.0092,9	1.0357,0	1.0004,3	0.9744,9
0.33	0.4021,4	0.4722,8	2.0825	1.1863	0.2267,8	0.98	0.9997,2	1.0063,6	1.0236,4	1.0001,9	0.9831,1
0.34	0.4205,7	0.4932,7	2.0657	1.1821	0.2387,9	0.99	0.9999,3	1.0032,6	1.0117,4	1.0000,4	0.9916,1
0.35	0.4389,4	0.5141,3	2.0487	1.1779	0.2509,6	1.00	1.0000,0	1.0000,0	1.0000,0	1.0000,0	1.0000,0
0.36	0.4572,3	0.5348,2	2.0314	1.1737	0.2632,7	1.01	0.9999,3	0.9965,9	0.9884,1	1.0000,4	1.0082,8
0.37	0.4754,1	0.5553,0	2.0140	1.1695	0.2757,2	1.02	0.9997,3	0.9930,4	0.9769,7	1.0001,9	1.0164,4
0.38	0.4934,6	0.5755,3	1.9964	1.1652	0.2882,8	1.03	0.9994,0	0.9893,6	0.9656,9	1.0004,3	1.0245,0
0.39	0.5113,4	0.5954,9	1.9787	1.1609	0.3009,5	1.04	0.9989,5	0.9855,5	0.9545,6	1.0007,7	1.0324,6
0.40	0.5290,3	0.6151,5	1.9608	1.1566	0.3137,2	1.05	0.9983,8	0.9816,1	0.9435,8	1.0012,1	1.0403,0
0.41	0.5465,1	0.6344,8	1.9428	1.1523	0.3265,8	1.06	0.9976,9	0.9775,5	0.9327,5	1.0017,5	1.0480,4
0.42	0.5637,6	0.6534,5	1.9247	1.1480	0.3395,1	1.07	0.9969,0	0.9733,9	0.9220,6	1.0023,8	1.0556,7
0.43	0.5807,5	0.6720,5	1.9065	1.1437	0.3525,1	1.08	0.9960,0	0.9691,3	0.9115,2	1.0031,1	1.0632,0
0.44	0.5974,8	0.690,25	1.8882	1.1394	0.36556	1.09	0.9950,1	0.9647,7	0.9011,2	1.0039,4	1.0706,2
0.45	0.6139,3	0.708,03	1.8699	1.1351	0.37865	1.10	0.9939,2	0.9603,1	0.8908,6	1.0048,6	1.0779,5
0.46	0.6300,7	0.725,38	1.8515	1.1308	0.39178	1.11	0.9927,4	0.9557,7	0.8807,5	1.0058,8	1.0851,8
0.47	0.6458,9	0.742,28	1.8331	1.1266	0.40493	1.12	0.9914,8	0.9511,5	0.8707,8	1.0069,9	1.0923,0
0.48	0.6613,9	0.758,71	1.8147	1.1224	0.41810	1.13	0.9901,3	0.9464,6	0.8609,4	1.0082,0	1.0993,3
0.49	0.6765,5	0.774,66	1.7962	1.1182	0.43127	1.14	0.9887,1	0.9416,9	0.8512,3	1.0095,1	1.1062,6
0.50	0.6913,6	0.790,12	1.7778	1.1140	0.44445	1.15	0.9872,1	0.9368,5	0.8416,6	1.0109,2	1.1131
0.51	0.7058,1	0.805,09	1.7594	1.1099	0.45761	1.16	0.9856,4	0.9319,5	0.8322,2	1.0124,3	1.1198
0.52	0.7199,0	0.819,55	1.7410	1.1059	0.47075	1.17	0.9840,0	0.9270,0	0.8229,2	1.0140,3	1.1264
0.53	0.7336,1	0.833,51	1.7226	1.1019	0.48387	1.18	0.9823,0	0.9220,0	0.8137,4	1.0157,2	1.1330
0.54	0.7469,5	0.846,95	1.7043	1.0979	0.49696	1.19	0.9805,4	0.9169,5	0.8046,8	1.0175,2	1.1395
0.55	0.7599,1	0.859,87	1.6860	1.09397	0.5100,1	1.20	0.9787,2	0.91185	0.7957,6	1.0194,1	1.1459
0.56	0.7724,8	0.872,27	1.6678	1.09010	0.5230,2	1.21	0.9768,5	0.90671	0.7869,5	1.0214,0	1.1522
0.57	0.7846,7	0.884,15	1.6496	1.08630	0.5359,7	1.22	0.9749,2	0.90153	0.7782,7	1.0234,8	1.1584
0.58	0.7964,7	0.895,52	1.6316	1.08255	0.5488,7	1.23	0.97294	0.89632	0.7697,1	1.0256,6	1.1645
0.59	0.8078,9	0.906,37	1.6136	1.07887	0.5617,0	1.24	0.97092	0.89108	0.7612,7	1.0279,4	1.1705
0.60	0.8189,2	0.916,70	1.5957	1.0752,5	0.5744,7	1.25	0.96886	0.88581	0.7529,4	1.0303,2	1.1764
0.61	0.8295,6	0.926,53	1.5780	1.0717,0	0.5871,6	1.26	0.96675	0.88052	0.7447,3	1.0328,0	1.1823
0.62	0.8398,2	0.935,85	1.5603	1.068,21	0.5997,8	1.27	0.96461	0.87521	0.7366,3	1.0353,6	1.1881
0.63	0.8497,0	0.944,66	1.5427	1.0648,0	0.6123,2	1.28	0.96243	0.86988	0.7286,5	1.0380,3	1.1938
0.64	0.8592,0	0.952,98	1.5253	1.0614,6	0.6247,7	1.29	0.96022	0.86453	0.7207,8	1.0408,0	1.1994

† From Shapiro, Hawthorne, and Edelman.[24]

NOTES: (1) For values of M from 0 to 3.00, all digits to the left of the comma are valid for linear interpolation. Where no comma is indicated in this region, all digits are valid for linear interpolation. (2) The notation 5370 signifies 5,370,000. The notation 0.0429 signifies 0.000429.

Table 8.11. Frictionless, Constant-area Flow with Change in Stagnation Temperature† (Continued)

Perfect gas, $\gamma = 1.4$ exactly

M	T_0/T^*_0	T/T^*	p/p^*	p_0/p^*_0	ρ^*/ρ V/V^*	M	T_0/T^*_0	T/T^*	p/p^*	p_0/p^*_0	ρ^*/ρ V/V^*
1.30	0.95798	0.85917	0.71301	1.04365	1.2050	1.95	0.80359	0.54774	0.37954	1.4516	1.4432
1.31	0.95571	0.85380	0.70535	1.04661	1.2105	1.96	0.80152	0.54391	0.37628	1.4616	1.4455
1.32	0.95341	0.84843	0.69780	1.04967	1.2159	1.97	0.79946	0.54012	0.37306	1.4718	1.4478
1.33						1.98	0.79742	0.53636	0.36988	1.4821	1.4501
1.34	0.94873	0.83766	0.68301	1.05608	1.2264	1.99	0.79540	0.53263	0.36674	1.4925	1.4523
1.35	0.94636	0.83227	0.67577	1.05943	1.2316	2.00	0.79339	0.52893	0.36364	1.5031	1.4545
1.36	0.94397	0.82689	0.66863	1.06288	1.2367	2.01	0.79139	0.52526	0.36057	1.5138	1.4567
1.37	0.94157	0.82151	0.66159	1.06642	1.2417	2.02	0.78941	0.52161	0.35754	1.5246	1.4589
1.38	0.93915	0.81613	0.65464	1.07006	1.2467	2.03	0.78744	0.51800	0.35454	1.5356	1.4610
1.39	0.93671	0.81076	0.64778	1.07380	1.2516	2.04	0.78549	0.51442	0.35158	1.5467	1.4631
1.40	0.93425	0.80540	0.64102	1.07765	1.2564	2.05	0.78355	0.51087	0.34866	1.5579	1.4652
1.41	0.93178	0.80004	0.63436	1.08159	1.2612	2.06	0.78162	0.50735	0.34577	1.5693	1.4673
1.42	0.92931	0.79469	0.62779	1.08563	1.2659	2.07	0.77971	0.50386	0.34291	1.5808	1.4694
1.43	0.92683	0.78936	0.62131	1.08977	1.2705	2.08	0.77781	0.50040	0.34009	1.5924	1.4714
1.44	0.92434	0.78405	0.61491	1.09400	1.2751	2.09	0.77593	0.49697	0.33730	1.6042	1.4734
1.45	0.92184	0.77875	0.60860	1.0983	1.2796	2.10	0.77406	0.49356	0.33454	1.6161	1.4753
1.46	0.91933	0.77346	0.60237	1.1028	1.2840	2.11	0.77221	0.49018	0.33181	1.6282	1.4773
1.47	0.91682	0.76819	0.59623	1.1073	1.2884	2.12	0.77037	0.48683	0.32912	1.6404	1.4792
1.48	0.91431	0.76294	0.59018	1.1120	1.2927	2.13	0.76854	0.48351	0.32646	1.6528	1.4811
1.49	0.91179	0.75771	0.58421	1.1167	1.2970	2.14	0.76673	0.48022	0.32383	1.6653	1.4830
1.50	0.90928	0.75250	0.57831	1.1215	1.3012	2.15	0.76493	0.47696	0.32122	1.6780	1.4849
1.51	0.90676	0.74731	0.57250	1.1264	1.3054	2.16	0.76314	0.47373	0.31864	1.6908	1.4867
1.52	0.90424	0.74215	0.56677	1.1315	1.3095	2.17	0.76137	0.47052	0.31610	1.7037	1.4885
1.53	0.90172	0.73701	0.56111	1.1367	1.3135	2.18	0.75961	0.46734	0.31359	1.7168	1.4903
1.54	0.89920	0.73189	0.55553	1.1420	1.3175	2.19	0.75787	0.46419	0.31110	1.7300	1.4921
1.55	0.89669	0.72680	0.55002	1.1473	1.3214	2.20	0.75614	0.46106	0.30864	1.7434	1.4939
1.56	0.89418	0.72173	0.54458	1.1527	1.3253	2.21	0.75442	0.45796	0.30621	1.7570	1.4956
1.57	0.89167	0.71669	0.53922	1.1582	1.3291	2.22	0.75271	0.45489	0.30381	1.7707	1.4973
1.58	0.88917	0.71168	0.53393	1.1639	1.3329	2.23	0.75102	0.45184	0.30143	1.7846	1.4990
1.59	0.88668	0.70669	0.52871	1.1697	1.3366	2.24	0.74934	0.44882	0.29908	1.7986	1.5007

					M						M
1.5024	1.8128	0.29675	0.44582	0.74767	2.25	1.3403	1.1756	0.5235,6	0.70173	0.88419	1.60
1.5040	1.8271	0.29445	0.44285	0.74602	2.26	1.3439	1.1816	0.5184,8	0.69680	0.88170	1.61
1.5056	1.8416	0.29218	0.43990	0.74438	2.27	1.3475	1.1877	0.5134,6	0.69190	0.87922	1.62
1.5072	1.8562	0.28993	0.43698	0.74275	2.28	1.3511	1.1939	0.5085,1	0.68703	0.87675	1.63
1.5088	1.8710	0.28771	0.43409	0.74114	2.29	1.3546	1.2002	0.5036,3	0.68219	0.87429	1.64
1.5104	1.8860	0.28551	0.43122	0.73954	2.30	1.3580	1.2066	0.4988,1	0.67738	0.87184	1.65
1.5119	1.9012	0.28333	0.42837	0.73795	2.31	1.3614	1.2131	0.4940,5	0.67259	0.86940	1.66
1.5134	1.9165	0.28118	0.42555	0.73638	2.32	1.3648	1.2197	0.4893,5	0.66784	0.86696	1.67
1.5150	1.9320	0.27905	0.42276	0.73482	2.33	1.3681	1.2264	0.4847,1	0.66312	0.86453	1.68
1.5165	1.9476	0.27695	0.41999	0.73327	2.34	1.3713	1.2332	0.4801,4	0.65843	0.86211	1.69
1.5180	1.9634	0.27487	0.41724	0.73173	2.35	1.3745	1.2402	0.4756,3	0.65377	0.85970	1.70
1.5195	1.9794	0.27281	0.41451	0.73020	2.36	1.3777	1.2473	0.4711,7	0.64914	0.85731	1.71
1.5209	1.9955	0.27077	0.41181	0.72868	2.37	1.3809	1.2545	0.4667,7	0.64455	0.85493	1.72
1.5223	2.0118	0.26875	0.40913	0.72718	2.38	1.3840	1.2618	0.4624,2	0.63999	0.85256	1.73
1.5237	2.0283	0.26675	0.40647	0.72569	2.39	1.3871	1.2692	0.4581,3	0.63546	0.85020	1.74
1.5252	2.0450	0.26478	0.40383	0.72421	2.40	1.3901	1.2767	0.4539,0	0.63096	0.84785	1.75
1.5266	2.0619	0.26283	0.40122	0.72274	2.41	1.3931	1.2843	0.4497,2	0.62649	0.84551	1.76
1.5279	2.0789	0.26090	0.39863	0.72129	2.42	1.3960	1.2920	0.4455,9	0.62205	0.84318	1.77
1.5293	2.0961	0.25899	0.39606	0.71985	2.43	1.3989	1.2998	0.4415,2	0.61765	0.84087	1.78
1.5306	2.1135	0.25710	0.39352	0.71842	2.44	1.4018	1.3078	0.4375,0	0.61328	0.83857	1.79
1.5320	2.1311	0.25523	0.39100	0.71700	2.45	1.4046	1.3159	0.4335,3	0.60894	0.83628	1.80
1.5333	2.1489	0.25337	0.38850	0.71559	2.46	1.4074	1.3241	0.4296,0	0.60463	0.83400	1.81
1.5346	2.1669	0.25153	0.38602	0.71419	2.47	1.4102	1.3324	0.4257,3	0.60036	0.83174	1.82
1.5359	2.1850	0.24972	0.38356	0.71280	2.48	1.4129	1.3408	0.4219,1	0.59612	0.82949	1.83
1.5372	2.2033	0.24793	0.38112	0.71142	2.49	1.4156	1.3494	0.4181,3	0.59191	0.82726	1.84
1.5385	2.2218	0.24616	0.37870	0.71005	2.50	1.4183	1.3581	0.4144,0	0.58773	0.82504	1.85
1.5398	2.2405	0.24440	0.37630	0.70870	2.51	1.4209	1.3669	0.41072	0.58359	0.82283	1.86
1.5410	2.2594	0.24266	0.37392	0.70736	2.52	1.4235	1.3758	0.40708	0.57948	0.82064	1.87
1.5422	2.2785	0.24094	0.37157	0.70603	2.53	1.4261	1.3848	0.40349	0.57540	0.81846	1.88
1.5434	2.2978	0.23923	0.36923	0.70471	2.54	1.4286	1.3940	0.39994	0.57135	0.81629	1.89
1.5446	2.3173	0.23754	0.36691	0.70340	2.55	1.4311	1.4033	0.39643	0.56734	0.81414	1.90
1.5458	2.3370	0.23587	0.36461	0.70210	2.56	1.4336	1.4127	0.39297	0.56336	0.81200	1.91
1.5470	2.3569	0.23422	0.36233	0.70081	2.57	1.4360	1.4222	0.38955	0.55941	0.80987	1.92
1.5482	2.3770	0.23258	0.36007	0.69953	2.58	1.4384	1.4319	0.38617	0.55549	0.80776	1.93
1.5494	2.3972	0.23096	0.35783	0.69825	2.59	1.4408	1.4417	0.38283	0.55160	0.80567	1.94

† From Shapiro, Hawthorne, and Edelman.[24]

NOTES: (1) For values of **M** from 0 to 3.00, all digits to the left of the comma are valid for linear interpolation. Where no comma is indicated in this region, all digits are valid for linear interpolation. (2) The notation 0.0429 signifies 0.000429. The notation 5370 signifies 5,370,000.

Table 8.11. **Frictionless, Constant-area Flow with Change in Stagnation Temperature**† *(Continued)*

Perfect gas, γ = 1.4 exactly

M	T_0/T^*_0	T/T^*	p/p^*	p_0/p^*_0	$\dfrac{\rho^*/\rho}{V/V^*}$	M	T_0/T^*_0	T/T^*	p/p^*	p_0/p^*_0	$\dfrac{\rho^*/\rho}{V/V^*}$
2.60	0.69699	0.35561	0.22936	2.4177	1.5505	2.85	0.66955	0.30568	0.19399	3.0013	1.5757
2.61	0.69574	0.35341	0.22777	2.4384	1.5516	2.86	0.66752	0.30389	0.19274	3.0277	1.5766
2.62	0.69450	0.35123	0.22620	2.4593	1.5527	2.87	0.66650	0.30211	0.19151	3.0544	1.5775
2.63	0.69327	0.34906	0.22464	2.4804	1.5538	2.88	0.66549	0.30035	0.19029	3.0813	1.5784
2.64	0.69205	0.34691	0.22310	2.5017	1.5549	2.89	0.66449	0.29860	0.18908	3.1084	1.5792
2.65	0.69084	0.34478	0.22158	2.5233	1.5560	2.90	0.66350	0.29687	0.18788	3.1358	1.5801
2.66	0.68964	0.34267	0.22007	2.5451	1.5571	2.91	0.66252	0.29515	0.18669	3.1635	1.5809
2.67	0.68845	0.34057	0.21857	2.5671	1.5582	2.92	0.66154	0.29344	0.18551	3.1914	1.5818
2.68	0.68727	0.33849	0.21709	2.5892	1.5593	2.93	0.66057	0.29175	0.18435	3.2196	1.5826
2.69	0.68610	0.33643	0.21562	2.6116	1.5603	2.94	0.65961	0.29007	0.18320	3.2481	1.5834
2.70	0.68494	0.33439	0.21417	2.6342	1.5613	2.95	0.65865	0.28841	0.18205	3.2768	1.5843
2.71	0.68378	0.33236	0.21273	2.6571	1.5623	2.96	0.65770	0.28676	0.18091	3.3058	1.5851
2.72	0.68263	0.33035	0.21131	2.6802	1.5633	2.97	0.65676	0.28512	0.17978	3.3351	1.5859
2.73	0.68150	0.32836	0.20990	2.7035	1.5644	2.98	0.65583	0.28349	0.17867	3.3646	1.5867
2.74	0.68038	0.32638	0.20850	2.7270	1.5654	2.99	0.65490	0.28188	0.17757	3.3944	1.5875
2.75	0.67926	0.32442	0.20712	2.7508	1.5663	3.00	0.65398	0.28028	0.17647	3.4244	1.5882
2.76	0.67815	0.32248	0.20575	2.7748	1.5673	3.50	0.61580	0.21419	0.13223	5.3280	1.6198
2.77	0.67704	0.32055	0.20439	2.7990	1.5683	4.00	0.58909	0.16831	0.10256	8.2268	1.6410
2.78	0.67595	0.31864	0.20305	2.8235	1.5692	4.50	0.56983	0.13540	0.08177	12.502	1.6559
2.79	0.67487	0.31674	0.20172	2.8482	1.5702	5.00	0.55555	0.11111	0.06667	18.634	1.6667
2.80	0.67380	0.31486	0.20040	2.8731	1.5711	6.00	0.53633	0.07849	0.04669	38.946	1.6809
2.81	0.67273	0.31299	0.19909	2.8982	1.5721	7.00	0.52437	0.05826	0.03448	75.414	1.6896
2.82	0.67167	0.31114	0.19780	2.9236	1.5730	8.00	0.51646	0.04491	0.02649	136.62	1.6954
2.83	0.67062	0.30931	0.19652	2.9493	1.5739	9.00	0.51098	0.03565	0.02098	233.88	1.6993
2.84	0.66958	0.30749	0.19525	2.9752	1.5748	10.00	0.50702	0.02897	0.01702	381.62	1.7021
						∞	0.48980	0	0	∞	1.7143

† From Shapiro, Hawthorne, and Edelman.[24]

Notes: (1) For values of M from 0 to 3.00, all digits to the left of the comma are valid for linear interpolation. Where no comma is indicated in this region, all digits are valid for linear interpolation. (2) The notation 0.0₄29 signifies 0.000429. The notation 5370₄ signifies 5,370,000.

$$\frac{p_2}{p_1} = \frac{1 + \gamma \mathbf{M}_1^2}{1 + \gamma \mathbf{M}_2^2} \qquad (8.138)$$

It was shown already that in diabatic flow the stations before and after the heat addition have different corresponding reservoir conditions because the stagnation temperature changes. Therefore a new type of reference condition must be used, and it is convenient to define this at the conditions where the Mach number is unity. Arbitrarily selecting this condition at station 1 and denoting the reference by the asterisk so that $\mathbf{M}_1 = \mathbf{M}^* = 1$, one obtains

$$\frac{p}{p^*} = \frac{1 + \gamma}{1 + \gamma \mathbf{M}^2} \qquad (8.139)$$

Using the relationships in Table 8.6, the stagnation pressure ratio becomes

$$\frac{p_{02}}{p_{01}} = \frac{1 + \gamma \mathbf{M}_1^2}{1 + \gamma \mathbf{M}_2^2} \left\{ \frac{1 + [(\gamma - 1)/2]\mathbf{M}_2^2}{1 + [(\gamma - 1)/2]\mathbf{M}_1^2} \right\}^{\gamma/(\gamma - 1)} \qquad (8.140)$$

By letting $\mathbf{M}_1 = 1$ as before and denoting this station by the asterisk, one can obtain a relation for the stagnation pressure ratio p_0/p^*_0.

8.41. Temperature Changes in Rayleigh Flow

It was already shown that during Rayleigh flow, the stagnation temperature does not remain constant as in adiabatic flow. It follows that for each and every section in the flow system, there corresponds a certain stagnation temperature. By considering Fig. 8.33 as a model and writing Eq. (8.108) for stations 1 and 2, respectively, and then by solving for the ratio T_{02}/T_{01} one obtains an equation relating temperatures and Mach numbers. Thus

$$\frac{T_{02}}{T_{01}} = \frac{T_2}{T_1} \frac{1 + [(\gamma - 1)/2]\mathbf{M}_2^2}{1 + [(\gamma - 1)/2]\mathbf{M}_1^2} \qquad (8.141)$$

By introducing the definitions of a perfect gas, and the Mach number, as well as the continuity equation into Eq. (8.141), one can obtain the following relationships:

$$\frac{T_2}{T_1} = \left(\frac{\mathbf{M}_2}{\mathbf{M}_1} \frac{1 + \gamma \mathbf{M}_1^2}{1 + \gamma \mathbf{M}_2^2} \right)^2 \qquad (8.142)$$

$$\frac{T_{02}}{T_{01}} = \frac{\mathbf{M}_2^2 (1 + \gamma \mathbf{M}_1^2)^2 \{1 + [(\gamma - 1)/2]\mathbf{M}_2^2\}}{\mathbf{M}_1^2 (1 + \gamma \mathbf{M}_2^2)^2 \{1 + [(\gamma - 1)/2]\mathbf{M}_1^2\}} \qquad (8.143)$$

Again letting $\mathbf{M}_1 = \mathbf{M}^* = 1$, one can write

$$\frac{T}{T^*} = \frac{\mathbf{M}^2 (1 + \gamma)^2}{(1 + \gamma \mathbf{M}^2)^2} \qquad (8.144)$$

and

$$\frac{T_0}{T_0^*} = \frac{2\mathbf{M}^2(\gamma + 1)\{1 + [(\gamma - 1)/2]\mathbf{M}^2\}}{(1 + \gamma \mathbf{M}^2)^2} \qquad (8.145)$$

Tabulated values of T_0/T_0^*, T/T^*, p/p^*, p_0/p_0^*, ρ^*/ρ, and V/V^* as a function of Mach number will be found in the appropriate tables in the literature[24] and in abbreviated form in this volume (Table 8.11). It should be noted that for each value of γ a different table must be constructed; however, in this volume tables for $\gamma = 1.4$ are included only.

Example 4. Dry air at standard temperature and pressure and having a Mach number of 1.8 is heated in a 2-in.-ID pipe in a frictionless manner so that it is decelerated to a Mach number of unity. Find the change in temperature.

SOLUTION. The change in temperature will be the difference between the final

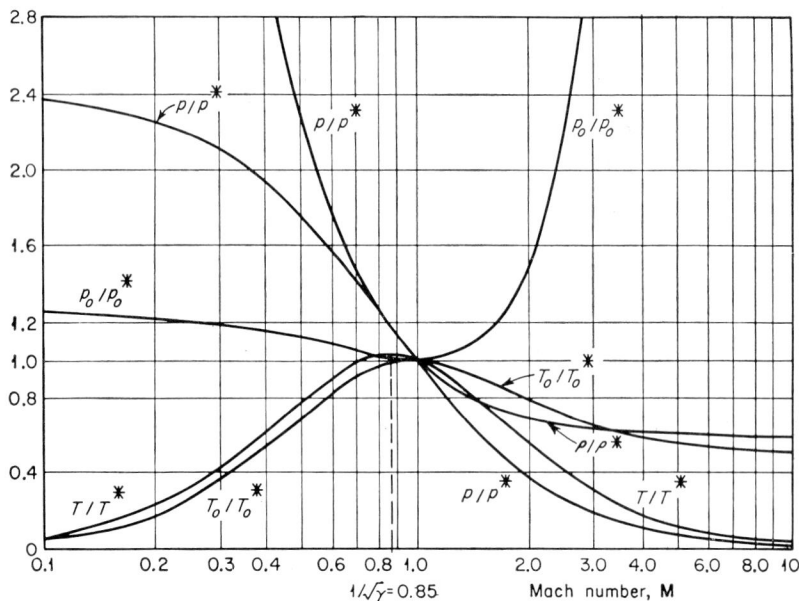

FIG. 8.35. Diabatic-flow parameters.

and the initial temperatures. From Table 8.11 one finds $(T/T^*)_1 = 0.60894$. Because the final Mach number is unity, it follows that $T_2 = T^*$. Therefore

$$T_2 = \frac{519}{0.60894} = 853°\text{R}$$

Hence the change in temperature is

$$853 - 519 = 334°\text{R}$$

The loci of the various parameters associated with Rayleigh are plotted in Fig. 8.35 for $\gamma = 1.4$.

The fact that the curve for T_0/T^*_0 in Fig. 8.35 reaches a maximum at a Mach number of unity indicates that it is impossible to pass from one flow domain into the other by the same heat-transfer process. Thus, if heat is added to a subsonic flow, the flow can be accelerated until its Mach number becomes unity. Further addition of heat will not cause any accelerations, but will result in *choking* of the flow. As a consequence of this, the flow must readjust itself, which it will do by lowering its initial Mach number. Addition of heat along the subsonic portion of the Rayleigh curve will tend to

Table 8.12. Variation of Flow Properties for Rayleigh Flow

Property	Heating		Cooling	
	$M > 1$	$M < 1$	$M > 1$	$M < 1$
T_0	Increases	Increases	Decreases	Decreases
p	Increases	Decreases	Decreases	Increases
p_0	Decreases	Decreases	Increases	Increases
V	Decreases always	Increases when $M < 1/\sqrt{\gamma}$; decreases when $M > 1/\sqrt{\gamma}$	Decreases always	Decreases when $M < 1/\sqrt{\gamma}$; increases when $M > 1/\sqrt{\gamma}$

lower the Mach number. This is shown in Fig. 8.36. Table 8.12 summarizes qualitatively the Rayleigh phenomena.

8.42. Maximum Heat Addition

Previously in this section it was shown that there are limitations to the amount of heat that may be added in Rayleigh flow. Two criteria which are helpful in evaluating the amount of permissible heat exchange are the entropy change and Damköhler's second ratio. These are discussed individually.

The familiar expression for the entropy differential is

$$ds = \frac{\gamma R}{\gamma - 1} \frac{dT}{T} - R \frac{dp}{p}$$

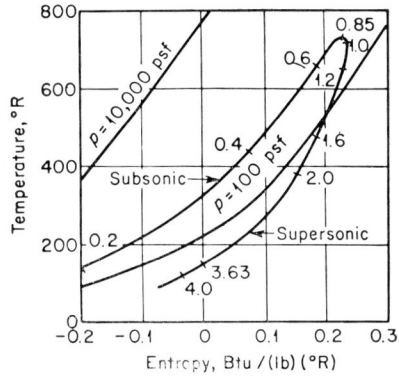

FIG. 8.36. Rayleigh flow.

When this is integrated between stations 1 and 2 and if it is assumed that $p_1 = 0$, $T_1 = 0$, for $s_1 = 0$ and $\mathbf{M}_1 = \mathbf{M}^* = 1$, one obtains

$$s - s^* = \frac{\gamma R}{\gamma - 1} \ln \left[\mathbf{M}^2 \left(\frac{\gamma + 1}{1 + \gamma \mathbf{M}^2} \right)^{(\gamma+1)/\gamma} \right] \tag{8.146}$$

By using Eq. (8.146) one may conveniently plot the Rayleigh line on the Ts plane of coordinates. The next example demonstrates how this is done.

Example 5. Construct a Ts diagram for air under Rayleigh flow conditions, considering the air flowing from a standard reservoir. Draw lines for the constant pressures 100 and 10,000 psfa. Apply to a flow of $G = \rho V = 0.2$ slug/(ft²)(sec).

SOLUTION. In solving the problem, Fig. 8.37 is used as a model. First find the initial Mach number at station 1. This is necessary because the conditions in an imaginary reservoir have been given. To do this, consider a hypothetical nozzle to lead from the stipulated reservoir to the entrance of the Rayleigh flow in Fig. 8.37.

By combining the definitions of the Mach number with Eq. (8.108) which defines the stagnation temperature, one obtains upon substitution in the continuity equation the following equation:

$$\rho_0 \left\{ \frac{1}{1 + [(\gamma - 1)/2]\mathbf{M}_1{}^2} \right\}^{1/(\gamma-1)} \mathbf{M}_1 \sqrt{\frac{\gamma R T_0}{1 + [(\gamma - 1)/2]\mathbf{M}_1{}^2}} = G$$

One now substitutes the values of ρ_0, γ, R, T_0, and G in this equation in order to solve for $\mathbf{M}_1$ by trial and error. The resulting computational equation is

$$\mathbf{M}_1 \left(\frac{1}{5 + \mathbf{M}_1{}^2} \right)^3 = 0.000603$$

Solution by trial and error gives two values for $\mathbf{M}_1$, namely,

$$\mathbf{M}_1 = 0.0753 \quad \text{and} \quad \mathbf{M}_1 = 3.63$$

Theoretically, the Rayleigh flow can start with either one. It is now necessary to find the corresponding temperatures and pressures. Thus

$$T_1 = \frac{519}{1 + \mathbf{M}_1{}^2/5}$$

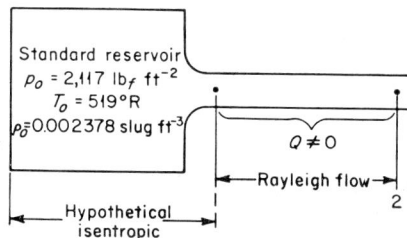

FIG. 8.37. Rayleigh flow system for representative flow condition.

and
$$p_1 = 2117 \left(\frac{T_1}{T_0}\right)^{\gamma/(\gamma-1)}$$

One finds, for $\mathbf{M}_1 = 0.0753$,

$$p_1 = 2.115 \text{ psf} \qquad T_1 = 518°\text{R}$$

and for $\mathbf{M}_1 = 3.63$,

$$p_1 = 23.2 \text{ psf} \qquad T_1 = 142.8°\text{R}$$

The Rayleigh line satisfying $\mathbf{M}_1 = 3.63$ can now be drawn. To do this, it is necessary to set up a table for $\mathbf{M}_2$, T_2, and s_2, defining the temperature and entropy as follows:

$$T_2 = T_1 \left[\frac{\mathbf{M}_2(1 + \gamma\mathbf{M}_1{}^2)}{\mathbf{M}_1(1 + \gamma\mathbf{M}_2{}^2)}\right]^2$$

$$s_2 - s_1 = \frac{\gamma R}{\gamma - 1} \log\left[\frac{\mathbf{M}_2{}^2}{\mathbf{M}_1{}^2}\left(\frac{1 + \gamma\mathbf{M}_1{}^2}{1 + \gamma\mathbf{M}_2{}^2}\right)^{(\gamma+1)/\gamma}\right]$$

After substituting the data for the initial station in these two equations, it is possible to solve for T_2 and s_2 at various assumed values of $\mathbf{M}_2$. The data compiled following this procedure appear in Fig. 8.36.

The curve plotted in Fig. 8.36 is the Rayleigh-line curve. It can be seen that the maximum entropy occurs when the Mach number is unity. Because, by the second law, the entropy change in a nonadiabatic process must bear the same sign as the conventional sign appropriate to the heat transfer, it follows that heating will tend to make the Mach number approach unity and cooling will tend to make the Mach number recede from unity. Since the trend is the same both in subsonic and in supersonic flow, it is impossible to pass from one domain into the other by continuing the transfer of heat in the same direction. Otherwise, the entropy change would have to assume a sign opposite to the direction of heat transfer, a clear violation of the second law.

It was stated already that the amount of heat that may be added to a gas-dynamical system is given by Eq. (8.135). By dividing by $c_p T_1 T_{01}$ and after rearranging, one obtains *Damköhler's second ratio*

$$\frac{Q}{c_p T_1} = \frac{T_{01}}{T_1}\left(\frac{T_{02}}{T_{01}} - 1\right) \tag{8.147}$$

This equation gives the ratio of heat added to a system when T_1, T_{01}, and T_{02} are known.

In order to find the maximum amount of heat that may be added at any Mach number, it is necessary to express Eq. (8.147) in terms of the Mach number. This is accomplished by substituting for T_{01}/T_1 its equivalent $1 + [(\gamma - 1)/2]\mathbf{M}_1{}^2$. Also, letting $\mathbf{M}_2 = 1$ for maximum Q, one obtains

$$\frac{Q}{c_p T_1} = \frac{(\mathbf{M}^2 - 1)^2}{2\mathbf{M}^2(\gamma + 1)} \tag{8.148}$$

It is evident that in order to accelerate a very slow flow, exceedingly large amounts of heat must be added. Thus, if the Mach number is zero, $Q/c_p T_1 \to \infty$.

Previously the flow parameters a_0, a^*, and $V_{\max}$ were defined for isentropic flow. These parameters exist for diabatic flow, but as one must account for the heat transfer, they are somewhat different. Thus the reservoir acoustic velocity a_0 is defined as follows:

$$\frac{a_0{}^2}{\gamma - 1} = \frac{a^2}{\gamma - 1} + \frac{V^2}{2} - Q \tag{8.149}$$

The critical acoustic velocity a^* is

$$\frac{a^{*2}(1 + \gamma)}{2(\gamma - 1)} = \frac{a_0{}^2}{\gamma - 1} + Q \tag{8.150}$$

The maximum velocity $V_{\max}$ is given by the following relation:

$$\frac{V_{\max}^2}{2} = \frac{a_0^2}{\gamma - 1} + Q \tag{8.151}$$

Equation (8.151) shows clearly that the maximum velocity can be increased by increasing the reservoir temperature and by adding heat to the gas.

8.43. Isothermal Flow Functions

When a compressible flow expands reversibly while receiving heat energy, the gas temperature may remain constant. Flow functions for reversible isothermal flow have been derived.[7] Their variation with Mach number is shown in Fig. 8.38.

FLOW WITH FRICTION

The flow in practical devices is accompanied by friction, and hence is not reversible. Already one application of this was mentioned in connection with the nozzle efficiency associated with irreversible flow in nozzles.

8.44. Fanno Flow

As with the flow incorporating thermal-energy exchange, frictional-flow problems are difficult to solve analytically, and hence it is customary to make certain simplifying assumptions. These are the following: (1) the cross-section area of the duct confining the gas is constant throughout; (2) the flow is adiabatic; (3) the gas is perfect and has constant specific heats; (4) the flow must be steady; and (5) there are no devices in the system which deliver or receive mechanical work. A hypothetical flow conforming to these requirements is called Fanno flow. Numerous Fanno equations may be derived by combining the continuity and the energy equations.

To determine the pressure drop dp, experienced by frictional flow through a length dx, either the Darcy-Weisbach or the Fanning equation may be written. The Darcy-Weisbach equation is the following:

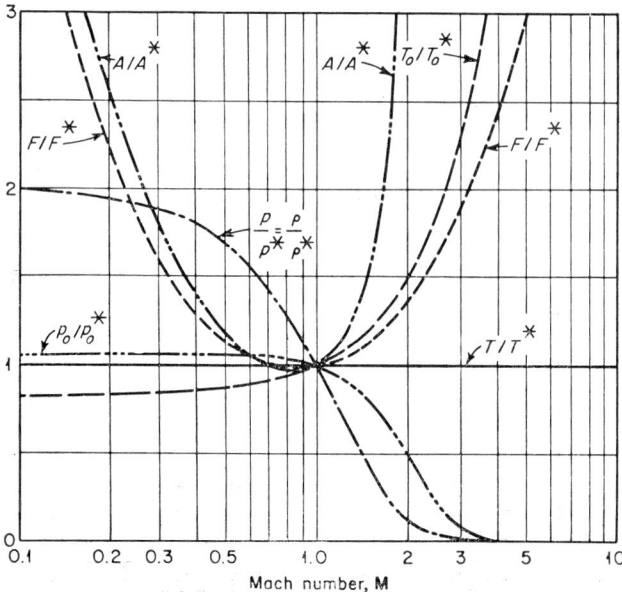

Fig. 8.38. Reversible isothermal condition for a perfect gas ($\gamma = 1.4$).

Table 8.13. Frictional, Adiabatic, Constant-area Flow†

Perfect gas, $\gamma = 1.4$ exactly

M	T/T^*	p/p^*	p_0/p_0^*	$V/V^*=\rho^*/\rho$	F/F^*	$4fL_{max}/D$	M	T/T^*	p/p^*	p_0/p_0^*	$V/V^*=\rho^*/\rho$	F/F^*	$4fL_{max}/D$
0	1.2000	∞	∞	0	∞	∞	0.65	1.10650	1.618,3	1.135,6	0.68374	1.0731,4	0.324,60
0.01	1.2000	10.9,544	5.7,874	0.01095	4.5,650	7.134,40	0.66	1.10383	1.591,9	1.126,5	0.69342	1.0677,7	0.297,85
0.02	1.1999	5.4,770	2.8,942	0.02191	22.834	1.778,45	0.67	1.10114	1.566,2	1.117,9	0.70306	1.0627,1	0.272,95
0.03	1.1998	3.6,511	1.9,300	0.03286	15.232	7.87,08	0.68	1.09842	1.541,3	1.109,7	0.71267	1.0579,2	0.249,78
0.04	1.1996	27.382	14.,482	0.04381	11.435	4.40.35	0.69	1.09567	1.517,0	1.101,8	0.72225	1.0534,0	0.228,21
0.05	1.1994	21.903	11.,5914	0.05476	9.1584	2.80.02	0.70	1.09290	1.493,4	1.0943,6	0.73179	1.0491,5	0.208,14
0.06	1.1991	18.251	9.6,659	0.06570	7.6,428	19.3,03	0.71	1.09010	1.470,5	1.0872,9	0.74129	1.0451,4	0.189,49
0.07	1.1988	15.6,42	8.2,915	0.07664	6.5,620	14.0,66	0.72	1.08727	1.448,2	1.0805,7	0.75076	1.0413,7	0.172,15
0.08	1.1985	13.6,84	7.2,616	0.08758	5.7,529	10.6,72	0.73	1.08442	1.426,5	1.0741,9	0.76019	1.0378,3	0.156,06
0.09	1.1981	12.1,62	6.4,614	0.09851	5.1,249	8.3,496	0.74	1.08155	1.405,4	1.0681,5	0.76958	1.0345,0	0.141,13
0.10	1.1976	10.9,435	5.8,218	0.10943	4.6,236	66.922	0.75	1.07856	1.384,8	1.0624,2	0.77893	1.0313,7	0.127,28
0.11	1.1971	9.9,465	5.2,992	0.12035	4.2,146	54.,688	0.76	1.07573	1.364,7	1.0570,0	0.78825	1.0284,4	0.114,46
0.12	1.1966	9.1,156	4.8,643	0.13126	3.8,747	45.,408	0.77	1.07279	1.345,1	1.0518,8	0.79753	1.0257,0	0.102,62
0.13	1.1960	8.4,123	4.4,968	0.14216	3.58,80	38.,207	0.78	1.06982	1.326,0	1.0470,5	0.80677	1.0231,4	0.091,67
0.14	1.1953	7.8,093	4.1,824	0.15306	3.34,32	32.,511	0.79	1.06684	1.3074	1.0425,0	0.81598	1.0207,5	0.081,59
0.15	1.1946	7.2,866	3.91,03	0.16395	3.13,17	27.,932	0.80	1.06383	1.2892	1.0382,3	0.82514	1.0185,3	0.072,29
0.16	1.1939	6.82,91	3.67,27	0.17482	2.94,74	24.,198	0.81	1.06080	1.2715	1.0342,2	0.83426	1.0164,6	0.063,75
0.17	1.1931	6.42,52	3.46,35	0.18568	2.78,55	21.,115	0.82	1.05775	1.2542	1.0304,7	0.84334	1.0145,5	0.055,93
0.18	1.1923	6.06,62	3.27,79	0.19654	2.64,22	18.5,43	0.83	1.05468	1.2373	1.0269,6	0.85239	1.0127,8	0.048,78
0.19	1.1914	5.74,48	3.11,23	0.20739	2.51,46	16.3,75	0.84	1.05160	1.2208	1.0237,0	0.86140	1.0111,5	0.042,26
0.20	1.1905	5.45,55	2.96,35	0.21822	2.40,04	14.5,33	0.85	1.04849	1.2047	1.0206,7	0.87037	1.0096,6	0.036,32
0.21	1.1895	5.19,36	2.82,93	0.22904	2.29,76	12.9,56	0.86	1.04537	1.1889	1.0178,7	0.87929	1.0082,9	0.030,97
0.22	1.1885	4.95,54	2.70,76	0.23984	2.20,46	11.5,96	0.87	1.04223	1.1735	1.0152,9	0.88818	1.0070,4	0.026,13
0.23	1.1874	4.73,78	2.59,68	0.25063	2.12,03	10.4,16	0.88	1.03907	1.1584	1.0129,4	0.89703	1.0059,1	0.021,80
0.24	1.1863	4.53,83	2.49,56	0.26141	2.04,34	9.3,865	0.89	1.03589	1.1436	1.0108,0	0.90583	1.0049,0	0.017,93
0.25	1.1852	4.35,46	2.40,27	0.27217	1.97,32	8.4,834	0.90	1.03270	1.1291,3	1.0088,7	0.91459	1.0039,9	0.0145,13
0.26	1.1840	4.18,50	2.31,73	0.28291	1.90,88	7.6,876	0.91	1.02950	1.1150,0	1.0071,4	0.92332	1.0031,8	0.0115,19
0.27	1.1828	4.02,80	2.23,85	0.29364	1.84,96	6.9,832	0.92	1.02627	1.1011,4	1.0056,0	0.93201	1.0024,8	0.0089,16
0.28	1.1815	3.88,20	2.16,56	0.30435	1.795,0	6.3,572	0.93	1.02304	1.0875,8	1.0042,6	0.94065	1.0018,8	0.0066,94
0.29	1.1802	3.74,60	2.09,79	0.31504	1.744,6	5.7,989	0.94	1.01978	1.0743,0	1.0031,1	0.94925	1.0013,6	0.0048,15

						M							M
0.0032,80	1.0009,3	0.95782	1.0021,5	1.0612,9	1.01652	0.95	5.2,992	1.697,9	0.32572	2.035,1	3.61,90	1.1788	0.30
0.0020,56	1.0005,9	0.96634	1.0013,7	1.0485,4	1.01324	0.96	4.8,507	1.654,6	0.33637	1.976,5	3.50,02	1.1774	0.31
0.0011,35	1.0003,3	0.97481	1.0007,6	1.0360,5	1.00995	0.97	4.4,468	1.614,4	0.34700	1.921,9	3.38,88	1.1759	0.32
0.0004,93	1.0001,4	0.98324	1.0003,3	1.0237,9	1.00664	0.98	4.08,21	1.576,9	0.35762	1.870,8	3.28,40	1.1744	0.33
0.0001,20	1.0000,3	0.99164	1.0000,8	1.0117,8	1.00333	0.99	3.75,20	1.542,0	0.36822	1.822,9	3.18,53	1.1729	0.34
0	1.0000,0	1.00000	1.0000,0	1.0000,0	1.00000	1.00	3.45,25	1.509,4	0.37880	1.778,0	3.09,22	1.1713	0.35
0.0001,14	1.0000,3	1.00831	1.0000,8	0.9884,4	0.99666	1.01	3.18,01	1.478,9	0.38935	1.735,8	3.004,2	1.1697	0.36
0.0004,58	1.0001,3	1.01658	1.0003,3	0.9771,1	0.99331	1.02	2.93,30	1.450,3	0.39988	1.696,1	2.920,9	1.1680	0.37
0.0010,13	1.0003,0	1.02481	1.0007,3	0.9659,8	0.98995	1.03	2.70,55	1.423,6	0.41039	1.658,7	2.842,0	1.1663	0.38
0.0017,71	1.0005,3	1.03300	1.0013,0	0.9550,6	0.98658	1.04	2.49,83	1.398,5	0.42087	1.623,4	2.767,1	1.1646	0.39
0.0027,12	1.0008,2	1.04115	1.0020,3	0.9443,5	0.98320	1.05	2.30,85	1.374,9	0.43133	1.590,1	2.695,8	1.1628	0.40
0.0038,37	1.0011,6	1.04925	1.0029,1	0.9338,3	0.97982	1.06	2.13,44	1.352,7	0.44177	1.558,7	2.628,0	1.1610	0.41
0.0051,29	1.0015,5	1.05731	1.0039,4	0.9235,0	0.97642	1.07	1.97,44	1.331,8	0.45218	1.528,9	2.563,4	1.1591	0.42
0.0065,82	1.0020,0	1.06533	1.0051,2	0.9133,5	0.97302	1.08	1.82,72	1.312,2	0.46257	1.500,7	2.501,7	1.1572	0.43
0.0081,85	1.0025,0	1.07331	1.0064,5	0.9033,8	0.96960	1.09	1.69,15	1.293,7	0.47293	1.473,9	2.442,8	1.1553	0.44
0.0099,33	1.00305	1.08124	1.0079,3	0.8935,9	0.96618	1.10	1.56,64	1.276,3	0.48326	1.448,6	2.386,5	1.1533	0.45
0.0118,13	1.00365	1.08913	1.0095,5	0.8839,7	0.96276	1.11	1.45,09	1.259,8	0.49357	1.424,6	2.332,6	1.1513	0.46
0.0138,24	1.00429	1.09698	1.0113,1	0.8745,1	0.95933	1.12	1.34,42	1.244,3	0.50385	1.401,8	2.280,9	1.1492	0.47
0.0159,49	1.00497	1.10479	1.0132,2	0.8652,2	0.95589	1.13	1.24,53	1.229,6	0.51410	1.380,1	2.231,4	1.1471	0.48
0.0181,87	1.00569	1.11256	1.0152,7	0.8560,8	0.95244	1.14	1.15,39	1.215,8	0.52433	1.359,5	2.183,8	1.1450	0.49
0.0205,3	1.00646	1.1203	1.0174,6	0.8471,0	0.94899	1.15	1.06,908	1.202,7	0.53453	1.339,9	2.138,1	1.1429	0.50
0.0229,8	1.00726	1.1280	1.0197,8	0.8382,7	0.94554	1.16	0.99,042	1.190,3	0.54469	1.321,2	2.094,2	1.1407	0.51
0.0255,2	1.00810	1.1356	1.0222,4	0.8295,8	0.94208	1.17	0.91,741	1.178,6	0.55482	1.303,4	2.051,9	1.1384	0.52
0.0281,4	1.00897	1.1432	1.0248,4	0.8210,4	0.93862	1.18	0.84,963	1.167,5	0.56493	1.286,4	2.011,2	1.1362	0.53
0.0308,5	1.00988	1.1508	1.0275,7	0.8126,3	0.93515	1.19	0.786,62	1.157,1	0.57501	1.270,2	1.971,9	1.1339	0.54
0.0336,4	1.01082	1.1583	1.0304,4	0.8043,4	0.93168	1.20	0.728,05	1.147,2	0.58506	1.254,9	1.934,1	1.1315	0.55
0.0365,0	1.01178	1.1658	1.0334,4	0.7962,3	0.92820	1.21	0.673,57	1.137,8	0.59507	1.240,3	1.897,6	1.1292	0.56
0.0394,2	1.01278	1.1732	1.0365,7	0.7882,2	0.92473	1.22	0.622,86	1.128,9	0.60505	1.226,3	1.862,3	1.1268	0.57
0.0424,1	1.01381	1.1806	1.0398,3	0.7803,4	0.92125	1.23	0.575,68	1.120,5	0.61500	1.213,0	1.828,2	1.1244	0.58
0.0454,7	1.01486	1.1879	1.0432,3	0.7725,8	0.91777	1.24	0.513,74	1.112,6	0.62492	1.200,3	1.795,2	1.1219	0.59
0.04858	1.01594	1.1952	1.0467,6	0.7649,5	0.91429	1.25	0.490,81	1.1050,4	0.63481	1.188,2	1.763,4	1.1194	0.60
0.05174	1.01705	1.2025	1.0504,1	0.7574,3	0.91080	1.26	0.452,70	1.0979,3	0.64467	1.176,6	1.732,5	1.1169	0.61
0.05494	1.01818	1.2097	1.0541,9	0.7500,3	0.90732	1.27	0.417,20	1.0912,0	0.65449	1.165,6	1.702,6	1.1144	0.62
0.05820	1.01933	1.2169	1.0580,9	0.7427,4	0.90383	1.28	0.384,11	1.0848,5	0.66427	1.155,1	1.673,7	1.1118	0.63
0.06150	1.02050	1.2240	1.0621,3	0.7355,6	0.90035	1.29	0.353,30	1.0788,3	0.67402	1.145,1	1.645,6	1.1091	0.64

† From Shapiro, Hawthorne, and Edelman.[24]

NOTES: (1) For values of M from 0 to 3.00, all digits to the left of the comma are valid for linear interpolation. Where no comma is indicated in this region, all digits are valid for linear interpolation. (2) The notation 0.0429 signifies 0.000429. The notation 5370,4 signifies 5,370,000.

M	T/T^*	p/p^*	p_0/p^*_0	V/V^* ρ^*/ρ	F/F^*	$4fL_{max}/D$
1.30	0.89686	0.72848	1.06630	1.2311	1.02169	0.06483
1.31	0.89338	0.72152	1.07060	1.2382	1.02291	0.06820
1.32	0.88989	0.71465	1.07502	1.2452	1.02415	0.07161
1.33	0.88641	0.70789	1.07957	1.2522	1.02540	0.07504
1.34	0.88292	0.70123	1.08424	1.2591	1.02666	0.07850
1.35	0.87944	0.69466	1.08904	1.2660	1.02794	0.08199
1.36	0.87596	0.68818	1.09397	1.2729	1.02924	0.08550
1.37	0.87249	0.68180	1.09902	1.2797	1.03056	0.08904
1.38	0.86901	0.67551	1.10419	1.2864	1.03189	0.09259
1.39	0.86554	0.66931	1.10948	1.2932	1.03323	0.09616
1.40	0.86207	0.66320	1.1149	1.2999	1.03458	0.09974
1.41	0.85860	0.65717	1.1205	1.3065	1.03595	0.10333
1.42	0.85514	0.65122	1.1262	1.3131	1.03733	0.10694
1.43	0.85168	0.64536	1.1320	1.3197	1.03872	0.11056
1.44	0.84822	0.63958	1.1379	1.3262	1.04012	0.11419
1.45	0.84477	0.63387	1.1440	1.3327	1.04153	0.11782
1.46	0.84133	0.62824	1.1502	1.3392	1.04295	0.12146
1.47	0.83788	0.62269	1.1565	1.3456	1.04438	0.12510
1.48	0.83445	0.61722	1.1629	1.3520	1.04581	0.12875
1.49	0.83101	0.61181	1.1695	1.3583	1.04725	0.13240
1.50	0.82759	0.60648	1.1762	1.3646	1.04870	0.13605
1.51	0.82416	0.60122	1.1830	1.3708	1.05016	0.13970
1.52	0.82075	0.59602	1.1899	1.3770	1.05162	0.14335
1.53	0.81734	0.59089	1.1970	1.3832	1.05309	0.14699
1.54	0.81394	0.58583	1.2043	1.3894	1.05456	0.15063
1.55	0.81054	0.58084	1.2116	1.3955	1.05604	0.15427
1.56	0.80715	0.57591	1.2190	1.4015	1.05752	0.15790
1.57	0.80376	0.57104	1.2266	1.4075	1.05900	0.16152
1.58	0.80038	0.56623	1.2343	1.4135	1.06049	0.16514
1.59	0.79701	0.56148	1.2422	1.4195	1.06198	0.16876

M	T/T^*	p/p^*	p_0/p^*_0	V/V^* ρ^*/ρ	F/F^*	$4fL_{max}/D$
1.95	0.68162	0.42339	1.6193	1.6099	1.1155	0.28989
1.96	0.67861	0.42030	1.6326	1.6146	1.1170	0.29295
1.97	0.67561	0.41724	1.6461	1.6193	1.1184	0.29599
1.98	0.67262	0.41421	1.6597	1.6239	1.1198	0.29901
1.99	0.66964	0.41121	1.6735	1.6284	1.1213	0.30201
2.00	0.66667	0.40825	1.6875	1.6330	1.1227	0.30499
2.01	0.66371	0.40532	1.7017	1.6375	1.1241	0.30796
2.02	0.66076	0.40241	1.7160	1.6420	1.1255	0.31091
2.03	0.65783	0.39951	1.7305	1.6465	1.1269	0.31384
2.04	0.65491	0.39670	1.7452	1.6509	1.1283	0.31675
2.05	0.65200	0.39389	1.7600	1.6553	1.1297	0.31965
2.06	0.64910	0.39110	1.7750	1.6597	1.1311	0.32253
2.07	0.64621	0.38834	1.7902	1.6640	1.1325	0.32538
2.08	0.64333	0.38562	1.8056	1.6683	1.1339	0.32822
2.09	0.64047	0.38292	1.8212	1.6726	1.1352	0.33104
2.10	0.63762	0.38024	1.8369	1.6769	1.1366	0.33385
2.11	0.63478	0.37760	1.8528	1.6811	1.1380	0.33664
2.12	0.63195	0.37498	1.8690	1.6853	1.1393	0.33940
2.13	0.62914	0.37239	1.8853	1.6895	1.1407	0.34215
2.14	0.62633	0.36982	1.9018	1.6936	1.1420	0.34488
2.15	0.62354	0.36728	1.9185	1.6977	1.1434	0.34760
2.16	0.62076	0.36476	1.9354	1.7018	1.1447	0.35030
2.17	0.61799	0.36227	1.9525	1.7059	1.1460	0.35298
2.18	0.61523	0.35980	1.9698	1.7099	1.1474	0.35564
2.19	0.61249	0.35736	1.9873	1.7139	1.1487	0.35828
2.20	0.60976	0.35494	2.0050	1.7179	1.1500	0.36091
2.21	0.60704	0.35254	2.0228	1.7219	1.1513	0.36352
2.22	0.60433	0.35017	2.0409	1.7258	1.1526	0.36611
2.23	0.60163	0.34782	2.0592	1.7297	1.1539	0.36868
2.24	0.59895	0.34550	2.0777	1.7336	1.1552	0.37124

Fanno flow functions (M = 1.60 to 1.94)[†]

M						
1.60	0.17236	1.06348	1.4254	1.2502	0.5567,9	0.79365
1.61	0.17595	1.06498	1.4313	1.2583	0.5521,6	0.79030
1.62	0.17953	1.06648	1.4371	1.2666	0.5475,9	0.78695
1.63	0.18311	1.06798	1.4429	1.2750	0.5430,8	0.78361
1.64	0.18667	1.06948	1.4487	1.2835	0.5386,2	0.78028
1.65	0.19022	1.07098	1.4544	1.2922	0.5342,1	0.77695
1.66	0.19376	1.07249	1.4601	1.3010	0.5298,6	0.77363
1.67	0.19729	1.07399	1.4657	1.3099	0.5255,6	0.77033
1.68	0.20081	1.07550	1.4713	1.3190	0.5213,1	0.76703
1.69	0.20431	1.07701	1.4769	1.3282	0.5171,1	0.76374
1.70	0.20780	1.07851	1.4825	1.3376	0.5129,7	0.76046
1.71	0.21128	1.08002	1.4880	1.3471	0.5088,7	0.75718
1.72	0.21474	1.08152	1.4935	1.3567	0.5048,2	0.75392
1.73	0.21819	1.08302	1.4989	1.3665	0.5008,2	0.75067
1.74	0.22162	1.08453	1.5043	1.3764	0.4968,6	0.74742
1.75	0.22504	1.08603	1.5097	1.3865	0.4929,5	0.74419
1.76	0.22844	1.08753	1.5150	1.3967	0.4890,9	0.74096
1.77	0.23183	1.08903	1.5203	1.4070	0.4852,7	0.73774
1.78	0.23520	1.09053	1.5256	1.4175	0.4814,9	0.73453
1.79	0.23855	1.09202	1.5308	1.4282	0.4777,6	0.73134
1.80	0.24189	1.09352	1.5360	1.4390	0.47407	0.72816
1.81	0.24521	1.09500	1.5412	1.4499	0.47042	0.72498
1.82	0.24851	1.09649	1.5463	1.4610	0.46681	0.72181
1.83	0.25180	1.09798	1.5514	1.4723	0.46324	0.71865
1.84	0.25507	1.09946	1.5564	1.4837	0.45972	0.71551
1.85	0.25832	1.1009	1.5614	1.4952	0.45623	0.71238
1.86	0.26156	1.1024	1.5664	1.5069	0.45278	0.70925
1.87	0.26478	1.1039	1.5714	1.5188	0.44937	0.70614
1.88	0.26798	1.1054	1.5763	1.5308	0.44600	0.70304
1.89	0.27116	1.1068	1.5812	1.5429	0.44266	0.69995
1.90	0.27433	1.1083	1.5861	1.5552	0.43936	0.69686
1.91	0.27748	1.1097	1.5909	1.5677	0.43610	0.69379
1.92	0.28061	1.1112	1.5957	1.5804	0.43287	0.69074
1.93	0.28372	1.1126	1.6005	1.5932	0.42967	0.68769
1.94	0.28681	1.1141	1.6052	1.6062	0.42651	0.68465

Fanno flow functions (M = 2.25 to 2.59)[†]

M						
2.25	0.37378	1.1565	1.7374	2.0964	0.34319	0.59627
2.26	0.37630	1.1578	1.7412	2.1154	0.34091	0.59361
2.27	0.37881	1.1590	1.7450	2.1345	0.33865	0.59096
2.28	0.38130	1.1603	1.7488	2.1538	0.33641	0.58833
2.29	0.38377	1.1616	1.7526	2.1733	0.33420	0.58570
2.30	0.38623	1.1629	1.7563	2.1931	0.33200	0.58309
2.31	0.38867	1.1641	1.7600	2.2131	0.32983	0.58049
2.32	0.39109	1.1653	1.7637	2.2333	0.32767	0.57790
2.33	0.39350	1.1666	1.7673	2.2537	0.32554	0.57532
2.34	0.39589	1.1678	1.7709	2.2744	0.32342	0.57276
2.35	0.39826	1.1690	1.7745	2.2953	0.32133	0.57021
2.36	0.40062	1.1703	1.7781	2.3164	0.31925	0.56767
2.37	0.40296	1.1715	1.7817	2.3377	0.31720	0.56514
2.38	0.40528	1.1727	1.7852	2.3593	0.31516	0.56262
2.39	0.40760	1.1739	1.7887	2.3811	0.31314	0.56011
2.40	0.40989	1.1751	1.7922	2.4031	0.31114	0.55762
2.41	0.41216	1.1763	1.7956	2.4254	0.30916	0.55514
2.42	0.41442	1.1775	1.7991	2.4479	0.30720	0.55267
2.43	0.41667	1.1786	1.8025	2.4706	0.30525	0.55021
2.44	0.41891	1.1798	1.8059	2.4936	0.30332	0.54776
2.45	0.42113	1.1810	1.8092	2.5168	0.30141	0.54533
2.46	0.42333	1.1821	1.8126	2.5403	0.29952	0.54291
2.47	0.42551	1.1833	1.8159	2.5640	0.29765	0.54050
2.48	0.42768	1.1844	1.8192	2.5880	0.29579	0.53810
2.49	0.42983	1.1856	1.8225	2.6122	0.29395	0.53571
2.50	0.43197	1.1867	1.8257	2.6367	0.29212	0.53333
2.51	0.43410	1.1879	1.8290	2.6615	0.29031	0.53097
2.52	0.43621	1.1890	1.8322	2.6865	0.28852	0.52862
2.53	0.43831	1.1901	1.8354	2.7117	0.28674	0.52627
2.54	0.44040	1.1912	1.8386	2.7372	0.28498	0.52394
2.55	0.44247	1.1923	1.8417	2.7630	0.28323	0.52163
2.56	0.44452	1.1934	1.8448	2.7891	0.28150	0.51932
2.57	0.44655	1.1945	1.8479	2.8154	0.27978	0.51702
2.58	0.44857	1.1956	1.8510	2.8420	0.27808	0.51474
2.59	0.45059	1.1967	1.8541	2.8689	0.27640	0.51247

[†] From Shapiro, Hawthorne, and Edelman.[24]

NOTES: (1) For values of M from 0 to 3.00, all digits to the left of the comma are valid for linear interpolation. Where no comma is indicated in this region, all digits are valid for linear interpolation. (2) The notation 0.0_4429 signifies 0.000429. The notation 5370_4 signifies 5,370,000.

Table 8.13. Frictional, Adiabatic, Constant-area Flow † (Continued)

Perfect gas, $\gamma = 1.4$ exactly

M	T/T^*	p/p^*	p_0/p_0^*	V/V^* ρ^*/ρ	F/F^*	$4fL_{max}/D$
2.60	0.51020	0.27473	2.8960	1.8571	1.1978	0.45259
2.61	0.50795	0.27307	2.9234	1.8602	1.1989	0.45457
2.62	0.50571	0.27143	2.9511	1.8632	1.2000	0.45654
2.63	0.50349	0.26980	2.9791	1.8662	1.2011	0.45840
2.64	0.50127	0.26818	3.0074	1.8691	1.2021	0.46044
2.65	0.49906	0.26658	3.0359	1.8721	1.2031	0.46237
2.66	0.49687	0.26499	3.0647	1.8750	1.2042	0.46429
2.67	0.49469	0.26342	3.0938	1.8779	1.2052	0.46619
2.68	0.49251	0.26186	3.1234	1.8808	1.2062	0.46807
2.69	0.49035	0.26032	3.1530	1.8837	1.2073	0.46996
2.70	0.48820	0.25878	3.1830	1.8865	1.2083	0.47182
2.71	0.48606	0.25726	3.2133	1.8894	1.2093	0.47367
2.72	0.48393	0.25575	3.2440	1.8922	1.2103	0.47551
2.73	0.48182	0.25426	3.2749	1.8950	1.2113	0.47734
2.74	0.47971	0.25278	3.3061	1.8978	1.2123	0.47915
2.75	0.47761	0.25131	3.3376	1.9005	1.2133	0.48095
2.76	0.47553	0.24985	3.3695	1.9032	1.2143	0.48274
2.77	0.47346	0.24840	3.4017	1.9060	1.2153	0.48452
2.78	0.47139	0.24697	3.4342	1.9087	1.2163	0.48628
2.79	0.46933	0.24555	3.4670	1.9114	1.2173	0.48803
2.80	0.46729	0.24414	3.5001	1.9140	1.2182	0.48976
2.81	0.46526	0.24274	3.5336	1.9167	1.2192	0.49148
2.82	0.46324	0.24135	3.5674	1.9193	1.2202	0.49321
2.83	0.46122	0.23997	3.6015	1.9220	1.2211	0.49491
2.84	0.45922	0.23861	3.6359	1.9246	1.2221	0.49660
2.85	0.45723	0.23726	3.6707	1.9271	1.2230	0.49828
2.86	0.45525	0.23592	3.7058	1.9297	1.2240	0.49995
2.87	0.45328	0.23458	3.7413	1.9322	1.2249	0.50161
2.88	0.45132	0.23326	3.7771	1.9348	1.2258	0.50326
2.89	0.44937	0.23196	3.8133	1.9373	1.2268	0.50189
2.90	0.44743	0.23066	3.8498	1.9398	1.2277	0.50651
2.91	0.44550	0.22937	3.8866	1.9423	1.2286	0.50812
2.92	0.44358	0.22809	3.9238	1.9448	1.2295	0.50973
2.93	0.44167	0.22682	3.9614	1.9472	1.2304	0.51133
2.94	0.43977	0.22556	3.9993	1.9497	1.2313	0.51291
2.95	0.43788	0.22431	4.0376	1.9521	1.2322	0.51447
2.96	0.43600	0.22307	4.0763	1.9545	1.2331	0.51603
2.97	0.43413	0.22185	4.1153	1.9569	1.2340	0.51758
2.98	0.43226	0.22063	4.1547	1.9592	1.2348	0.51912
2.99	0.43041	0.21942	4.1944	1.9616	1.2357	0.52064
3.00	0.42857	0.21822	4.2346	1.9640	1.2366	0.52216
3.50	0.34783	0.16850	6.7896	2.0642	1.2743	0.58643
4.00	0.28571	0.13363	10.719	2.1381	1.3029	0.63306
4.50	0.23762	0.10833	16.562	2.1936	1.3247	0.66764
5.00	0.20000	0.08944	25.000	2.2361	1.3416	0.69381
6.00	0.14634	0.06376	53.180	2.2953	1.3655	0.72987
7.00	0.11111	0.04762	104.14	2.3333	1.3810	0.75281
8.00	0.08696	0.03686	190.11	2.3591	1.3915	0.76820
9.00	0.06977	0.02935	327.19	2.3772	1.3989	0.77898
10.00	0.05714	0.02390	535.94	2.3905	1.4044	0.78683
∞	0	0	∞	2.4495	1.4289	0.82153

† From Shapiro, Hawthorne, and Edelman.[24]

NOTES: (1) For values of M from 0 to 3.00, all digits to the left of the comma are valid for linear interpolation. Where no comma is indicated in this region, all digits are valid for linear interpolation. (2) The notation $0.0_4 29$ signifies 0.000129. The notation 5370_4 signifies 5,370,000.

$$dp = -f_{\text{D-W}} \frac{\rho V^2}{2D} dx \qquad (8.152)$$

The Fanning equation is

$$dp = -f_F \frac{\rho V^2}{2r_h} dx \qquad (8.153)$$

in which dp = pressure drop due to friction, psf.
         ρ = density, slugs/ft³.
         V = velocity, fps.
         dx = passage length, ft.
         D = diameter, ft.
         r_h = hydraulic radius, ft.   The hydraulic radius is defined as the ratio of the cross-section area to the wetted perimeter.   For a circular duct $r_h = D/4$.
   $f_{\text{D-W}}$ = Darcy-Weisbach friction factor.
     f_F = Fanning friction factor.

It follows that for a circular duct, $f_{\text{D-W}} = 4f_F$. Although in fluid dynamics one generally uses the Darcy-Weisbach equation, the Fanning equation will be used in this section because most compressible flow data are given for the latter. Furthermore, in some aerodynamic problems (such as in aircraft intake scoops) ducts are not circular and hence the use of the Fanning equation is convenient. In the absence of gravity forces, the total pressure drop over a distance dx is given by the following equation:

$$dp = -4f \frac{V^2}{2D} dx - \rho V \, dV \qquad (8.154)$$

By dividing Eq. (8.154) by p, applying the perfect-gas equation of state and the continuity equation, one obtains upon rearranging

$$4f \frac{dx}{D} = \frac{2(1 - \mathbf{M}^2) \, d\mathbf{M}}{\gamma \mathbf{M}^3 \{[(\gamma - 1)/2]\mathbf{M}^2 + 1\}} \qquad (8.155)$$

This equation relates the drop in pressure in relation to the Mach number in a constant-area duct when the flow is accompanied by friction. Equation (8.155) is integrated using a Mach number of unity as the reference. Thus

$$\int_{x=0}^{x=L_{\max}} 4f \frac{dx}{D} = 4f \frac{L_{\max}}{D} = \int_{\mathbf{M}}^{1} \frac{2(1 - \mathbf{M}^2)}{\mathbf{M}^3 \{[(\gamma - 1)/2]\mathbf{M}^2 + 1\}\gamma} \, d\mathbf{M} \qquad (8.156)$$

The term $4fL_{\max}/D$ is called the *friction parameter*, and Table 8.13 lists values of it for $\gamma = 1.4$.

Example 6.   Air is decelerated from $\mathbf{M} = 3$ to sonic speed in a 2-in.-ID pipe having a friction factor of 0.002.   Find the length of the pipe.

Solution.   The length of the pipe can be found by the use of Table 8.13.   At $\mathbf{M} = 3$,

$$4f \frac{L_{\max}}{D} = 0.52216$$

and obviously, for $\mathbf{M} = 1$,

$$4f \frac{L_{\max}}{D} = 0$$

Then $\Delta L = L_2 - L_1 = \dfrac{2 \times 0.52216}{12 \times 4 \times 0.002}$

$$L = 10.88 \text{ ft pipe length}$$

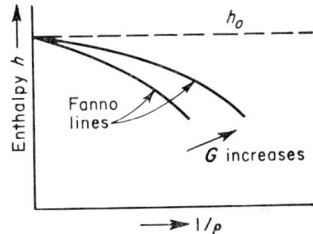

FIG. 8.39. Fanno-line trends.

By definition, equations resulting from the combination of the continuity equation and the energy equation in accordance with the Fanno requirements are called Fanno equations. Thus, for example, one may write

$$h_0 = h + \frac{G'^2}{2\rho^2} \qquad (8.157)$$

This equation is represented in Fig. 8.39.

Again one may combine, for a perfect gas, the energy equation, the entropy expression, and Eq. (8.156), obtaining

$$\frac{ds}{d\mathbf{M}} = \frac{R(1 - \mathbf{M}^2)}{\mathbf{M}\{[(\gamma - 1)/2]\mathbf{M}^2 + 1\}} \qquad (8.158)$$

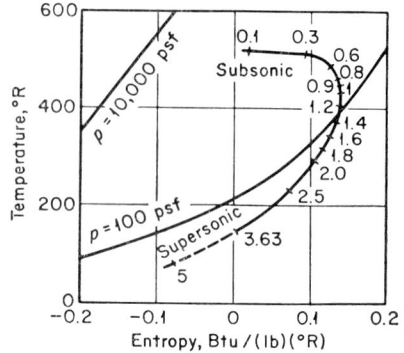

Fig. 8.40. Fanno flow line.

According to Eq. (8.158) the maximum for the entropy occurs when $\mathbf{M} = 1$. As in the case of Rayleigh flow, in Fanno flow it is impossible by virtue of the second law of thermodynamics to pass from one flow regime to the other (subsonic into supersonic, or vice versa) unless the mass velocity is readjusted.

Example 7. Construct a Ts diagram for air undergoing Fanno flow, having a mass velocity $G = \rho V = 0.2$ slug/(sec)(ft²). Assume a standard reservoir.

SOLUTION. The solution of this problem is very similar to that employed previously in plotting the Rayleigh line. The conditions just before the application of the friction must be found, but these are the same as for the Rayleigh problem, because the same reservoir conditions apply. Thus

$$p_1 = 23.2 \text{ psfa} \qquad T_1 = 142.9°R \qquad \mathbf{M}_1 = 3.63$$

From the Fanno Table 8.13, one obtains

$$\frac{T_1}{T^*} = 0.3317 \qquad T^* = 431°R$$

$$\frac{p_1}{p^*} = 0.15942 \qquad p^* = 145.5$$

When the computed values along the Fanno line are plotted, one obtains Fig. 8.40.

Upon increasing the length of the pipe in Fanno flow when the initial flow is subsonic, the Mach number tends to increase, the maximum permissible length being that corresponding to $\mathbf{M} = 1$. Along the supersonic portion of the Fanno line an increase in duct length tends to reduce the Mach number toward unity. However, here shock phenomena precede choking conditions.

The flow functions for Fanno flow are shown graphically in Fig. 8.41. Table 8.14 describes the trends of the flow functions qualitatively.

Table 8.14. Fanno-flow Phenomena

Property	Initial flow is subsonic	Initial flow is supersonic
$\mathbf{M}$	Increases	Decreases
V	Increases	Decreases
p	Decreases	Increases
T	Decreases	Increases
ρ	Decreases	Increases

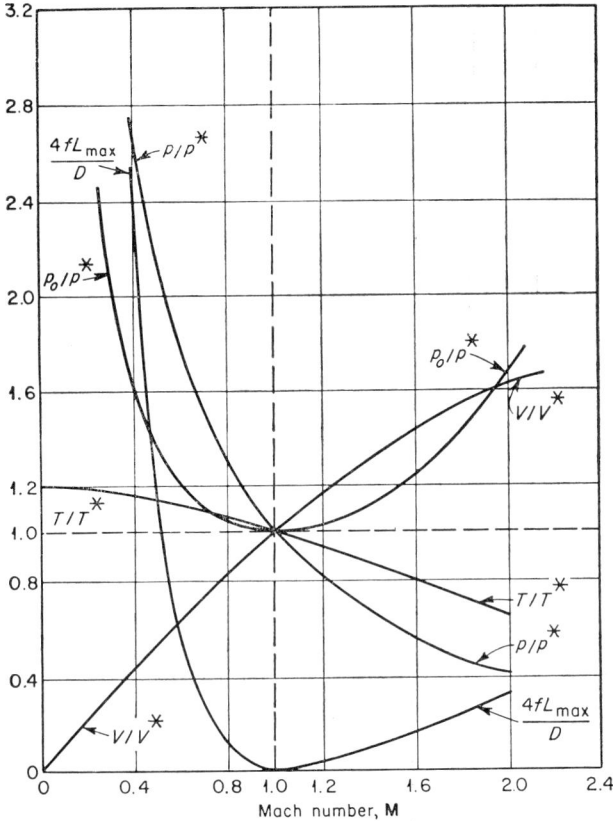

FIG. 8.41. Functions for constant-area flow with friction ($\gamma = 1.4$).

From the fundamental flow equations, the pressure ratio for Fanno flow is found to be

$$\frac{p_2}{p_1} = \frac{\mathbf{M}_1 \sqrt{1 + [(\gamma - 1)/2]\mathbf{M}_1{}^2}}{\mathbf{M}_2 \sqrt{1 + [(\gamma - 1)/2]\mathbf{M}_2{}^2}} \qquad (8.159)$$

When for the same constant mass velocity the Fanno and the Rayleigh lines are plotted, the curves will look as in Fig. 8.42. In Fig. 8.42 one notices that the Rayleigh and Fanno lines have two points of intersection which are denoted by a and b. A normal shock wave connects these two points. Because a shock wave constitutes an irreversibility, there will be associated with it an increase in entropy. Thus point b will always lie to the right of point a.

8.45. Generalized One-dimensional Flow

In the gas-dynamic analyses discussed heretofore the flow was simplified to make the mathematical solutions tractable. Actually, most engineering applications combine multifarious factors. For example, one may encounter in a rocket-motor nozzle not only area change, but also friction and heat addition, with change in chemical composition. To analyze such multiple-process flows, Shapiro and Hawthorne[25] have developed

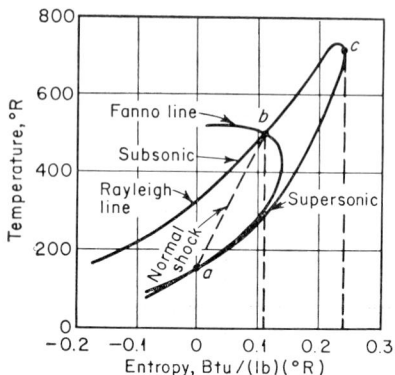

FIG. 8.42. Rayleigh and Fanno lines.

a generalized method. By this method it is possible to account for area change, wall friction, drag of internal bodies, external-heat exchange, chemical reactions, phase changes, mixing of streams, and changes in specific heat and in molecular weight.

To employ the generalized flow technique, one must assume the following: (1) the flow is one-dimensional; (2) the flow is steady; (3) changes in stream properties are continuous; (4) the gas properties vary with temperature only. Shapiro and Hawthorne have set up a table of influence coefficients which is reproduced here in Table 8.15. By using this table one can conveniently solve for the dependent variables. Table 8.15 may be used for perfect as well as real gases because it allows for changes in the specific heat and the molecular weight. For cases when these properties do not vary, Shapiro and Hawthorne have developed tables based on the logarithmic differential of the stagnation temperature, and these are reproduced here in Table 8.16. The numerical integration associated with these solutions may be undertaken by using the tables of Edelman and Shapiro.[26]

Table 8.15. Table of Influence Coefficients;†

	$\dfrac{dA}{A}$	$\dfrac{dQ - dW_x + dH}{c_p T}$	$4f\dfrac{dx}{D} + \dfrac{dX}{\frac{1}{2}\,\gamma p A \mathbf{M}^2} - 2y\dfrac{dw}{w}$
$\dfrac{d\mathbf{M}^2}{\mathbf{M}^2}$	$-\dfrac{2\left(1 + \dfrac{\gamma-1}{2}\mathbf{M}^2\right)}{1 - \mathbf{M}^2}$	$\dfrac{1 + \gamma\mathbf{M}^2}{1 - \mathbf{M}^2}$	$\dfrac{\gamma\mathbf{M}^2\left(1 + \dfrac{\gamma-1}{2}\mathbf{M}^2\right)}{1 - \mathbf{M}^2}$
$\dfrac{dV}{V}$	$-\dfrac{1}{1 - \mathbf{M}^2}$	$\dfrac{1}{1 - \mathbf{M}^2}$	$\dfrac{\gamma\mathbf{M}^2}{2(1 - \mathbf{M}^2)}$
$\dfrac{dc}{c}$	$\dfrac{\dfrac{\gamma-1}{2}\mathbf{M}^2}{1 - \mathbf{M}^2}$	$\dfrac{1 - \gamma\mathbf{M}^2}{2(1 - \mathbf{M}^2)}$	$-\dfrac{\gamma(\gamma-1)\mathbf{M}^4}{4(1 - \mathbf{M}^2)}$
$\dfrac{dT}{T}$	$\dfrac{(\gamma-1)\mathbf{M}^2}{1 - \mathbf{M}^2}$	$\dfrac{1 - \gamma\mathbf{M}^2}{1 - \mathbf{M}^2}$	$-\dfrac{\gamma(\gamma-1)\mathbf{M}^4}{2(1 - \mathbf{M}^2)}$
$\dfrac{d\rho}{\rho}$	$\dfrac{\mathbf{M}^2}{1 - \mathbf{M}^2}$	$-\dfrac{1}{1 - \mathbf{M}^2}$	$-\dfrac{\gamma\mathbf{M}^2}{2(1 - \mathbf{M}^2)}$
$\dfrac{dp}{p}$	$\dfrac{\gamma\mathbf{M}^2}{1 - \mathbf{M}^2}$	$-\dfrac{\gamma\mathbf{M}^2}{1 - \mathbf{M}^2}$	$-\dfrac{\gamma\mathbf{M}^2[1 + (\gamma-1)\mathbf{M}^2]}{2(1 - \mathbf{M}^2)}$
$\dfrac{dF}{F}$	$\dfrac{1}{1 + \gamma\mathbf{M}^2}$	0	$-\dfrac{\gamma\mathbf{M}^2}{2(1 + \gamma\mathbf{M}^2)}$
ds/c_p ‡	0	1	$\dfrac{(\gamma-1)\mathbf{M}^2}{2}$

† Each influence coefficient represents the partial derivative of the variable in the left-hand column with respect to the variable in the top row; for example,

$$\frac{d\mathbf{M}^2}{\mathbf{M}^2} = -\frac{2\left(1 + \dfrac{\gamma-1}{2}\mathbf{M}^2\right)}{1 - \mathbf{M}^2}\frac{dA}{A} + \frac{1 + \gamma\mathbf{M}^2}{1 - \mathbf{M}^2}\frac{dQ - dW_x + dH}{c_p T} + \cdots - \frac{d\gamma}{\gamma}$$

THE DYNAMICS OF REAL GASES

8.46. Introduction

In Art. 8.11, the thermodynamics of real gases was outlined briefly. Otherwise, the gas-dynamic analyses in this section were based on the concepts of a perfect gas. This was done because explaining a subject as vast in scope as gas dynamics for a real gas from the onset would have resulted in considerable confusion. In this section an attempt will be made to review briefly real-gas dynamics.

Real-gas dynamics may occur either within engines such as rocket motors or around bodies traveling at hypersonic speeds. In these applications the gas may deviate from a perfect gas either on account of excessively high pressures or extremely high temperatures. In aerodynamic applications it is most likely that the real-gas characteristics will occur because of thermal effects. If real-gas effects are brought about because of high pressures, then in Eq. (8.19), the departure coefficient Z is defined by Eq. (8.20). If, however, high temperatures are the cause of real-gas effects, the departure coefficient Z should be defined by Eq. (8.23), (8.25), or (8.27), depending upon whether the gas is dissociated, ionized, or a mixture.

8.47. Real-gas Data

There exists a variety of compilations of the thermodynamic properties of real gases, and the user should be cautious in employing the correct values. Thus data calculated

Variable Specific Heat and Molecular Weight

	$\dfrac{dw}{w}$	$\dfrac{dW}{W}$	$\dfrac{d\gamma}{\gamma}$
$\dfrac{dM^2}{M^2}$	$\dfrac{2(1+\gamma M^2)\left(1+\dfrac{\gamma-1}{2}M^2\right)}{1-M^2}$	$-\dfrac{1+\gamma M^2}{1-M^2}$	-1
$\dfrac{dV}{V}$	$\dfrac{1+\gamma M^2}{1-M^2}$	$-\dfrac{1}{1-M^2}$	0
$\dfrac{dc}{c}$	$-\dfrac{\dfrac{\gamma-1}{2}M^2(1+\gamma M^2)}{1-M^2}$	$\dfrac{\gamma M^2-1}{2(1-M^2)}$	$\tfrac{1}{2}$
$\dfrac{dT}{T}$	$-\dfrac{(\gamma-1)M^2(1+\gamma M^2)}{1-M^2}$	$\dfrac{(\gamma-1)M^2}{1-M^2}$	0
$\dfrac{d\rho}{\rho}$	$-\dfrac{(\gamma+1)M^2}{1-M^2}$	$\dfrac{1}{1-M^2}$	0
$\dfrac{dp}{p}$	$-\dfrac{2\gamma M^2\left(1+\dfrac{\gamma-1}{2}M^2\right)}{1-M^2}$	$\dfrac{\gamma M^2}{1-M^2}$	0
$\dfrac{dF}{F}$	0	0	0
ds/c_p‡	$(\gamma-1)M^2$	0	0

Source: Tables of numerical values of the influence coefficients appear in Edelman and Shapiro.[26]
‡ For unaltered chemical composition only and referring to entropy change of main stream.

Table 8.16. Table of Influence Coefficients;†

	$\dfrac{dA}{A}$	$\dfrac{dT_0}{T_0}$
$\dfrac{d\mathbf{M}^2}{\mathbf{M}^2}$	$-\dfrac{2\left(1+\dfrac{\gamma-1}{2}\mathbf{M}^2\right)}{1-\mathbf{M}^2}$	$\dfrac{(1+\gamma\mathbf{M}^2)\left(1+\dfrac{\gamma-1}{2}\mathbf{M}^2\right)}{1-\mathbf{M}^2}$
$\dfrac{dV}{V}$	$-\dfrac{1}{1-\mathbf{M}^2}$	$\dfrac{1+\dfrac{\gamma-1}{2}\mathbf{M}^2}{1-\mathbf{M}^2}$
$\dfrac{dc}{c}$	$\dfrac{\dfrac{\gamma-1}{2}\mathbf{M}^2}{1-\mathbf{M}^2}$	$\dfrac{\dfrac{1-\gamma\mathbf{M}^2}{2}\left(1+\dfrac{\gamma-1}{2}\mathbf{M}^2\right)}{1-\mathbf{M}^2}$
$\dfrac{dT}{T}$	$\dfrac{(\gamma-1)\mathbf{M}^2}{1-\mathbf{M}^2}$	$\dfrac{(1-\gamma\mathbf{M}^2)\left(1+\dfrac{\gamma-1}{2}\mathbf{M}^2\right)}{1-\mathbf{M}^2}$
$\dfrac{d\rho}{\rho}$	$\dfrac{\mathbf{M}^2}{1-\mathbf{M}^2}$	$-\dfrac{1+\dfrac{\gamma-1}{2}\mathbf{M}^2}{1-\mathbf{M}^2}$
$\dfrac{dp}{p}$	$\dfrac{\gamma\mathbf{M}^2}{1-\mathbf{M}^2}$	$-\dfrac{\gamma\mathbf{M}^2\left(1+\dfrac{\gamma-1}{2}\mathbf{M}^2\right)}{1-\mathbf{M}^2}$
$\dfrac{dp_0}{p_0}$	0	$-\dfrac{\gamma\mathbf{M}^2}{2}$
$\dfrac{dF}{F}$	$\dfrac{1}{1+\gamma\mathbf{M}^2}$	0
$\dfrac{ds}{c_p}$	0	$1+\dfrac{\gamma-1}{2}\mathbf{M}^2$

† Each influence coefficient represents the partial derivative of the variable in the left-hand column with respect to the variable in the top row; for example,

$$\frac{d\mathbf{M}^2}{\mathbf{M}^2} = -\frac{2\left(1+\dfrac{\gamma-1}{2}\mathbf{M}^2\right)}{1-\mathbf{M}^2}\frac{dA}{A} + \frac{(1+\gamma\mathbf{M}^2)\left(1+\dfrac{\gamma-1}{2}\mathbf{M}^2\right)}{1-\mathbf{M}^2}\frac{dT_0}{T_0}$$

$$+\frac{\gamma\mathbf{M}^2\left(1+\dfrac{\gamma-1}{2}\mathbf{M}^2\right)}{1-\mathbf{M}^2}\left(4f\frac{dx}{D}+\frac{dX}{\frac12\gamma p A\mathbf{M}^2}-2y\frac{dw}{w}\right)+\frac{2(1+\gamma\mathbf{M}^2)\left(1+\dfrac{\gamma-1}{2}\mathbf{M}^2\right)}{1-\mathbf{M}^2}\frac{dw}{w}$$

prior to 1955 are based on what is believed to be a low dissociation energy for nitrogen, namely, $q_0 = 7.37$ ev/molecule. It should rather be $q_d = 9.76$ ev/molecule. Furthermore, some compilations do not consider the formation of NO or disregard some of the components of air. The present state of the art suggests[38] that one can employ the data of Gilmore,[27] Logan et al.,[28] or Hilsenrath and Beckett.[29] Because these tables are being extended in some cases, the reader would do well to attempt securing the latest information.

The transport properties of real gases must be chosen with great care, both for analytical as well as experimental reasons. For dissociated gases and for plasmas that are slightly ionized, the short-range forces need be considered only, and hence the properties may be calculated from kinetic theory and Boltzmann statistics.[13] When a plasma is completely ionized, the long-range forces must be taken into consideration, and this requires development of new theoretical considerations.[30] With plasmas the

Constant Specific Heat and Molecular Weight

	$4f \dfrac{dx}{D} + \dfrac{dX}{\frac{1}{2}\gamma pA\mathbf{M}^2} - 2y\dfrac{dw}{w}$	$\dfrac{dw}{w}$
$\dfrac{d\mathbf{M}^2}{\mathbf{M}^2}$	$\dfrac{\gamma \mathbf{M}^2 \left(1 + \dfrac{\gamma-1}{2}\mathbf{M}^2\right)}{1 - \mathbf{M}^2}$	$\dfrac{2(1 + \gamma \mathbf{M}^2)\left(1 + \dfrac{\gamma-1}{2}\mathbf{M}^2\right)}{1 - \mathbf{M}^2}$
$\dfrac{dV}{V}$	$\dfrac{\gamma \mathbf{M}^2}{2(1 - \mathbf{M}^2)}$	$\dfrac{1 + \gamma \mathbf{M}^2}{1 - \mathbf{M}^2}$
$\dfrac{dc}{c}$	$-\dfrac{\gamma(\gamma-1)\mathbf{M}^4}{4(1 - \mathbf{M}^2)}$	$-\dfrac{\dfrac{\gamma-1}{2}\mathbf{M}^2(1 + \gamma\mathbf{M}^2)}{1 - \mathbf{M}^2}$
$\dfrac{dT}{T}$	$-\dfrac{\gamma(\gamma-1)\mathbf{M}^4}{2(1 - \mathbf{M}^2)}$	$-\dfrac{(\gamma-1)\mathbf{M}^2(1 + \gamma\mathbf{M}^2)}{1 - \mathbf{M}^2}$
$\dfrac{d\rho}{\rho}$	$-\dfrac{\gamma\mathbf{M}^2}{2(1 - \mathbf{M}^2)}$	$-\dfrac{(\gamma+1)\mathbf{M}^2}{1 - \mathbf{M}^2}$
$\dfrac{dp}{p}$	$-\dfrac{\gamma\mathbf{M}^2[1 + (\gamma-1)\mathbf{M}^2]}{2(1 - \mathbf{M}^2)}$	$-\dfrac{2\gamma\mathbf{M}^2\left(1 + \dfrac{\gamma-1}{2}\mathbf{M}^2\right)}{1 - \mathbf{M}^2}$
$\dfrac{dr_0}{r_0}$	$-\dfrac{\gamma\mathbf{M}^2}{2}$	$-\gamma\mathbf{M}^2$
$\dfrac{dF}{F}$	$-\dfrac{\gamma\mathbf{M}^2}{2(1 + \gamma\mathbf{M}^2)}$	0
$\dfrac{ds}{c_p}$	$\dfrac{(\gamma-1)\mathbf{M}^2}{2}$	$(\gamma-1)\mathbf{M}^2$

SOURCE: Tables of numerical values of the influence coefficients appear in Edelman and Shapiro.[26]

determination of the transport properties is further complicated if magnetic fields are applied because the transport properties otherwise scalar become tensor quantities.

8.48. Thermodynamic Effects

There are several thermodynamic effects germane to real gases which the aerodynamicist must recognize. Thus, as the temperature is increased, the molecular weight decreases as the real-gas characteristics become more prominent. Another important factor is the drastic increase of the specific heats. Thus, for air at 7000°K, the specific heat at constant pressure is about twelve times as large as at normal temperature.

The speed of sound of a real gas must be defined with utmost care. The speed of sound in a gas or a liquid is defined as follows:

$$a = \sqrt{\dfrac{G}{\rho}} \tag{8.160}$$

if G is the adiabatic compression factor. For a perfect gas this equation leads to the well-known speed of sound relation (8.88), namely,

$$a = \sqrt{\gamma R T} = \sqrt{\gamma \frac{p}{\rho}} \qquad (8.88)$$

Equation (8.88) predicates that the gas is perfect, namely, that the specific-heat ratio $\gamma = c_p/c_v$ is a ratio of two constants and that there is no change in the chemical composition. These two assumptions are not valid for a real gas, and hence due deliberation must be exercised in redefining or reinterpreting Eq. (8.88). The derivations may occur because of dissipative-transport processes as well as chemical changes. Hirschfelder, Curtiss, and Bird[9] have shown that the dissipative effects may be neglected but that the chemical changes must be considered. One may still define the acoustic velocity as by Eq. (8.88), provided γ is written[31] as an effective specific-heat ratio γ_{eff}. Thus

$$\gamma_{\text{eff}} = \frac{a^2 \rho}{p} \qquad (8.161)$$

The effective specific-heat ratio γ_{eff} may either be determined by laboratory experiments or may be calculated from kinetic theory because

$$\gamma_{\text{eff}} = 1 + \frac{R_{\text{eff}}}{c_{v\ \text{eff}}} \qquad (8.162)$$

In observing chemical reactions for a gas which is also electrically conducting and subject to a magnetic field, the acoustic velocity may be written

$$a_{eq} = a_{fr} + a_{ch} + V_A \qquad (8.163)$$

in which a_{eq} = equilibrium acoustic velocity
a_{fr} = frozen acoustic velocity
a_{ch} = contribution due to chemical change
V_A = Alfvén velocity

Because magnetohydrodynamics is outside the scope of this section the Alfvén velocity V_A need not be considered. One then writes, for Eq. (8.163),

$$a_{eq} = \left(\frac{\partial p}{\partial \rho}\right)_{\substack{s \\ c_i}} + \sum_{i=1}^{n} \left(\frac{\partial p}{\partial c_i}\right)_{\substack{s \\ c_i}} \left(\frac{\partial c_i}{\partial \rho}\right)_{\substack{s \\ F}} \qquad (8.164)$$

in which the first term on the right side is the expression for the frozen speed of sound used in classical compressible-flow calculations, and the summation term accounts for the chemical changes. Furthermore, s is the entropy, c_i the concentration of the ith

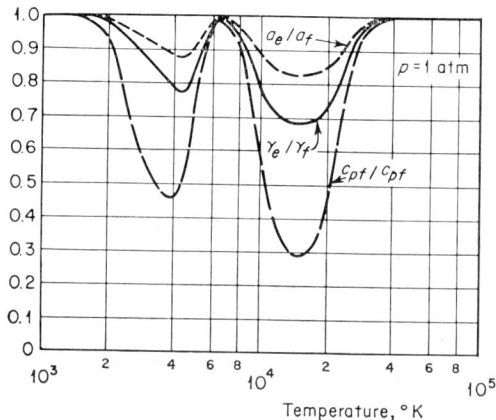

FIG. 8.43. Effect of dissociation and ionization of hydrogen.

species, and F the Gibbs free-energy function. Gross and Eisen[17] have evaluated the various real-gas effects, and Fig. 8.43 shows the variation of the frozen and equilibrium properties for hydrogen which they calculated.

FLUID-DYNAMICAL EFFECTS

The thermodynamic characteristics of real gases discussed just previously influence the dynamics of the flow. Consider, for example, a blunt body traveling at hypersonic speeds. Behind the bow shock there will be an important entropy increase. The gas between the shock wave and the body may be dissociated and/or ionized. Later as it expands over the missile it may recombine or it may be neutralized. The recombination and deionization energies are very appreciable and must be properly controlled if the missile is to operate properly. Real-gas aerodynamics is most complex and is rapidly being developed. The reader should consult Refs. 10, 17, 31 to 36, and 38 for details. However, the principal observations are summarized here.

8.49. Isentropic Flow

For isentropic flow, when the initial conditions and the final pressure remain unaltered, a real gas in comparison with a perfect gas will have (1) a higher final static temperature and acoustic velocity; (2) a lower density; (3) a higher velocity but a lower Mach number; and (4) a greater area ratio.

8.50. Prandtl-Meyer Expansion

For the same initial conditions and area ratio, a real gas in Prandtl-Meyer flow will have (1) a greater final pressure; (2) a higher final temperature; (3) a higher velocity; and (4) a smaller Mach number.

8.51. Shock Waves

In normal shock phenomena, for a fixed shock velocity and the same free-stream conditions, a real gas will exhibit (1) a greater density ratio ρ_2/ρ_1 across the shock, (2) a greater pressure ratio p_2/p_1, but (3) a smaller temperature ratio T_2/T_1.

With an oblique shock wave, in real gases the limiting wedge angle before the shock becomes detached is greater than is the case in ideal gases.

8.52. Boundary-layer Phenomena

In considering the modifications in the boundary layer due to real-gas effects, it is found that (1) the temperature in the boundary is less than for a perfect gas; (2) the skin friction is less except at very high angles of attack; and (3) the heat transfer is not substantially modified if the gas is real but is not undergoing chemical reactions. However, the heat transfer is drastically altered if chemical reactions take place.

Hydraulic Analogy

People who have watched the flow of water in open channels have noticed the qualitative resemblance between supersonic gas flow and the supercritical flow of water (see Sec. 24). That this resemblance might be used for analogic technique was proposed by Jouguet.[39] Since then the method has been used quite extensively in gas dynamics, both in the presence of combustion[40] and in the absence of combustion.[41]

In the absence of combustion, the analogy between a gas-dynamic system and a hydraulic system is due to the similarity among the equations of two-dimensional isentropic gas flow and the equations of two-dimensional open-channel flow of incompressible fluids. In order for the equations to be analogic, it is necessary that the gas be treated as perfect and that it have a specific heat ratio $\gamma = 2.0$.

A small disturbance in a gas-dynamic system is propagated with the speed of sound. On the other hand, Lamb[42] has shown that long gravity-surface waves in a shallow, horizontal, open channel propagate with a velocity $V_w = \sqrt{gz}$, provided the amplitude of the wave is considerably smaller than the depth of the water at that point. In an open channel the depth of the stream will vary with changes in mass flow, and thus the hydraulic-stream depth corresponds to density in the gas-dynamic stream.

In Table 8.17 the equations of gas dynamics and hydraulics are compared.

Table 8.17

	Hydraulic system	Gas-dynamic system
Continuity equation........	$\dfrac{\partial z}{\partial t} + \dfrac{\partial(z V_x)}{\partial x} + \dfrac{\partial(z V_y)}{\partial y} = 0$	$\dfrac{\partial \rho}{\partial t} + \dfrac{\partial(\rho V_x)}{\partial x} + \dfrac{\partial(\rho V_y)}{\partial y} = 0$
Energy equation..........	$z + \dfrac{V^2}{2g} = z_0 + \dfrac{V_0^2}{2g}$	$\dfrac{\gamma R T}{\gamma - 1} + \dfrac{V^2}{2} = \dfrac{\gamma R T_0}{\gamma - 1} + \dfrac{V_0^2}{2}$
Gravity effect............	Froude number $\mathbf{F} = \dfrac{V^2}{gz} = \dfrac{V}{V_w}$	
Compressibility effect......	....	Mach number $\mathbf{M} = \dfrac{V}{a}$

z = height of water surface
x, y = coordinates (horizontal)
V_x = velocity component in x direction
V_y = velocity component in y direction
V_w = water-wave velocity

Because V_0 is negligibly small, the energy equation for the hydraulic system becomes

$$z + \frac{V^2}{2g} = z_0 \tag{8.165}$$

Substituting the Froude number in this and solving for the ratio z_0/z, one obtains

$$\frac{z_0}{z} = 1 + \tfrac{1}{2}\mathbf{F}^2 \tag{8.166}$$

The stagnation temperature is defined by Eq. (8.108):

$$\frac{T_0}{T} = 1 + \frac{\gamma - 1}{2}\mathbf{M}^2 \tag{8.108}$$

The stagnation pressure is defined

$$\frac{p_0}{p} = \left(1 + \frac{\gamma - 1}{2}\mathbf{M}^2\right)^{\gamma/(\gamma - 1)} \tag{8.109}$$

For isentropic processes the density and the temperature are related as follows (Table 8.9):

$$\frac{\rho_0}{\rho} = \left(\frac{T_0}{T}\right)^{1/(\gamma - 1)}$$

It follows that the stagnation density is defined as follows:

$$\frac{\rho_0}{\rho} = \left(1 + \frac{\gamma - 1}{2}\mathbf{M}^2\right)^{1/(\gamma - 1)} \tag{8.167}$$

Equation (8.166) is similar to Eq. (8.108) if $\gamma = 2.0$. Thus for a perfect gas having such a specific-heat ratio, Eqs. (8.108), (8.109), and (8.167) become, respectively,

$$\frac{T_0}{T} = 1 + \tfrac{1}{2}\mathbf{M}^2 \tag{8.168}$$

$$\frac{p_0}{p} = (1 + \tfrac{1}{2}\mathbf{M}^2)^2 \tag{8.169}$$

$$\frac{\rho_0}{\rho} = 1 + \tfrac{1}{2}\mathbf{M}^2 \tag{8.170}$$

It follows at once that the following analogous quantities exist:

Gas-dynamic system	Hydraulic analogue
$\mathbf{M} = \dfrac{V}{a}$	$\mathbf{F} = \dfrac{V}{V_w}$
$\dfrac{T}{T_0}$	$\dfrac{z}{z_0}$
$\dfrac{p}{p_0}$	$\left(\dfrac{z}{z_0}\right)^2$
$\dfrac{\rho}{\rho_0}$	$\dfrac{z}{z_0}$

It is evident that one may study and design a gas-dynamic system such as a nozzle, rocket motor, venturi, etc., by setting up a hydraulic analogue and measuring the height of the free-water surface.

There are several factors which will influence the validity of the hydraulic analogue. The first that comes to mind is the value of the specific-heat ratio. In the analogue it is assumed that $\gamma = 2$, but for most gases γ is more nearly in the range 1.2 to 1.5. Fortunately, this error is not too serious in both the subsonic and in the supersonic regimes. Other errors that may be introduced are the boundary layer developed on the bottom of the water stream, the viscosity, the thermal conductivity, and the surface tension. In the case of shock phenomena the analogy will fail if the experimenter does not replace the gas-dynamic equations by shock equations and the steady-flow hydraulic equations by hydraulic-jump equations.

REFERENCES

1. Tsien, H. S.: Superaerodynamics: Mechanics of Rarefied Gases, *J. Aeronaut Sci.*, **13**(2):653 (1946).
2. Shapiro, A. H.: "The Dynamics and Thermodynamics of Compressible Fluid Flow," vols. 1 and 2, Ronald, New York, 1958.
3. Prigogine, I.: "Introduction to the Thermodynamics of Irreversible Processes," Charles C Thomas, Springfield, Ill., 1955.
4. Nernst, W.: Über die Berechnung chemischer Gleichgewichte aus thermischen Messungen, *Nachr. Ges. Wiss. Göttingen Math-physik Kl.*, **1**:1 (1906).
5. Eastman, E. D.: The Third Law of Thermodynamics, *Chem. Revs.*, **18**:257 (1936).
6. Kennard, E. H.: "Kinetic Theory of Gases," McGraw-Hill, New York, 1938.
7. Cambel, A. B., and B. H. Jennings: "Gas Dynamics," McGraw-Hill, New York, 1958.
8. Lee, J. F., and F. W. Sears: "Thermodynamics," Addison-Wesley, Reading, Mass., 1955.
9. Hirshfelder, J. O., C. F. Curtis, and R. B. Bird: "The Molecular Theory of Gases and Liquids," Wiley, New York, 1954.
10. Herzfeld, K. F.: Relaxation Phenomena in Gases, part H, p. 646, in F. D. Rossini (ed.), "Thermodynamics and Physics of Matter," Princeton University Press, Princeton, N. J., 1955.
11. Bridgman, P. W.: "A Condensed Collection of Thermodynamic Formulas," Harvard University Press, Cambridge, Mass., 1925.
12. Shaw, A. N.: The Derivation of Thermodynamical Relations for a Simple System, *Phil. Trans.*, **A234**:299 (1935).
13. Cambel, A. B., and J. B. Fenn (eds.): "Transport Properties in Gases," Northwestern University Press, Evanston, Ill., 1958.
14. Keenan, J. H., and J. Kaye: "Gas Tables," Wiley, New York, 1946.

15. Glass, I. I.: Shock Tubes, *UTIA Rev.*, no. 12, pt. 1, May, 1958.
16. Hall, J. G.: Shock Tubes, *UTIA Rev.*, no. 12, pt. 2, May, 1958.
17. Cambel, A. B., and J. B. Fenn (eds.): "The Dynamics of Conducting Gases," Northwestern University Press, Evanston, Ill., 1960.
18. Giannini, G. M.: The Plasma Jet and Its Applications, *AFOSR* TN-57-520, *ASTIA* AD-136505.
19. Courant, R., and D. Friedrichs: "Supersonic Flow and Shock Waves," Interscience, New York, 1948.
20. Rudinger, G.: "Wave Diagrams for Nonsteady Flow in Ducts," Van Nostrand, Princeton, N. J., 1955.
21. Oppenheim, A. K.: Gas Dynamics Analysis of the Development of Gaseous Detonation and Its Hydraulic Analogy, *Fourth Symp. on Combustion*, p. 471, 1953.
22. Puckett, A. E., Jr.: Supersonic Nozzle Design, *J. Appl. Mechanics*, **68**:A265 (1946).
23. Streeter, V. L.: "Fluid Dynamics," McGraw-Hill, New York, 1948.
24. Shapiro, A. H., W. R. Hawthorne, and G. M. Edelman: The Mechanics and Thermodynamics of Steady One-dimensional Gas Flow with Tables for Numerical Solutions, *Bur. Ordnance Meteor. Rept.* 14, Contract NOrd 9661, Dec. 1, 1947.
25. Shapiro, A. H., and W. R. Hawthorne: The Mechanics and Thermodynamics of Steady, One-dimensional Gas Flow, *J. Appl. Mechanics*, **14**(4):A317 (1947).
26. Edelman, G. M., and A. H. Shapiro: Numerical Solution of Problems in the Mechanics and Thermodynamics of Steady One-dimensional Gas Flow without Discontinuities, *J. Appl. Mechanics*, vol. **14**, no. 4 (December, 1947)
27. Gilmore, F. R.: Equilibrium Composition and Thermodynamic Properties of Air to 24,000°K, *Rand Corp. Rept.* RM-1543, Aug. 24, 1955.
28. Logan, J. G., Jr.: The Calculation of the Thermodynamic Properties of Air at High Temperatures, *Cornell Aeronaut. Lab. Rept.* AD-1052-A-1, May, 1956.
29. Tables of Thermodynamic Properties of Argon Free Air to 15,000°K, *AEDC* TN-56-12, September, 1956.
30. Prigogine, I.: "Introduction to Statistical Mechanics of Irreversible Processes," Interscience, New York, 1960.
31. Hayes, W. D., and R. F. Probstein: "Hypersonic Flow Theory," Academic Press, New York, 1959.
32. Truitt, R. W.: "Hypersonic Aerodynamics," Ronald, New York, 1959.
33. Lighthill, M. J.: Dynamics of a Dissociating Gas. *J. Fluid Mech.*, pt. I, **1**(2):1ff. (January, 1957).
34. Lees, L.: Convective Heat Transfer with Mass Addition and Chemical Reactions, Combustion and Propulsion, *Third AGARD Colloq.*, 1958.
35. Fay, J. A., and F. R. Riddell: Theory of Stagnation Point Heat Transfer in Dissociated Air, *J. Aeronaut. Sci.*, vol. 25, no. 2, February, 1958.
36. Oswatitsch, K.: "Gas Dynamics," Academic Press, New York, 1956.
37. Liepmann, H. W., and A. Roshko: "Elements of Gas Dynamics," Wiley, New York, 1956.
38. Cambel, A. B., et al.: The Kinetics of Gases, *AEDC* TN-60-130, July 1960.
39. Jouguet, E. J.: Quelques problèmes de hydrodynamique générale, *J. Math. pure et appl.*, vol. 8, 1920.
40. Oppenheim, A. K.: Water-channel Analog to High-velocity Combustion, *J. Appl. Mechanics*, March, 1953, p. 115.
41. Shapiro, A. H.: An Appraisal of the Hydraulic Analogue to Gas Dynamics, *MIT Meteor. Rept.* 34, 1949.
42. Lamb, H.: "Hydrodynamics," p. 245, Dover, New York, 1945.
43. Arave, R. J.: Concise, Systematic Jacobian Thermodynamics for High Temperature Real Gases, *J. Aero/Space Sci.*, **26** (4): 250 (April 1959).

Section 9

BOUNDARY-LAYER THEORY

By

H. SCHLICHTING, *Aerodynamische Versuchsanstalt, Göttingen, and Technical University, Braunschweig, West Germany*

BOUNDARY-LAYER THEORY†

9.1. Introduction

The laws of motion of frictionless fluids have been treated in Secs. 2 and 4, and the laws of motion of real fluids have been treated in Secs. 3 and 5. This section deals with the flow of real fluids, where the viscous effects may be considered as confined to a narrow region adjacent to the fluid boundaries. The essential physical difference between the flow of frictionless fluids and viscous fluids is exhibited in the fact that in the former two contacting layers experience only normal forces (pressures), while in the latter tangential forces (shearing stresses) are apparent. These tangential, or friction, forces cause an adhesion of the fluid to a wall wetted by it; that is, both the normal and the tangential velocity components are uniformly zero at a boundary (condition of no slip). This situation is depicted in Fig. 9.1, in which the upper half shows the slip of a frictionless

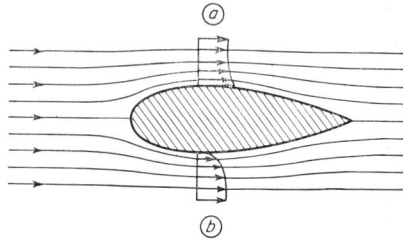

FIG. 9.1. Boundary conditions for the velocity at the wall for flow past a body. (a) Frictionless flow, slipping: $v_n = 0$, $v_t \neq 0$. (b) Viscous fluid, no slip: $v_n = 0$, $v_t = 0$.

fluid while the lower half shows the adhesion of a viscous fluid. From the theoretical viewpoint, the inclusion of frictional forces causes great difficulty; hence ideal-fluid theory has been developed to greater perfection than that of viscous fluids. In real-fluid flow one must rely on experimental results to a greater extent than for ideal-fluid flow.

For simplification, an incompressible viscous fluid is first considered. The more difficult case of a compressible viscous fluid is treated in Arts. 9.19 to 9.23.

9.2. Notation

a	(1) semimajor axis of elliptic cylinder, ft
	(2) speed of sound, fps
a_1	thermal diffusivity, ft²/sec
A	(1) constant
	(2) area element, ft²
b	width of plate, height of body, semiminor axis of elliptic cylinder, ft
c_D	drag coefficient, dimensionless
c_f	skin-friction coefficient, dimensionless
c'_f	local skin-friction coefficient, dimensionless
c_L	lift coefficient, dimensionless
c_Q	suction-volume coefficient, dimensionless
c_p	specific heat at constant pressure, Btu/(lb)(°F)
c_v	specific heat at constant volume, Btu/(lb)(°F)

† Translated by Victor J. Streeter.

D	(1) diameter of sphere, ft
	(2) constant
	(3) drag force, lb
D_f	component of drag due to skin-friction forces, lb
D_p	component of drag due to pressure forces, lb
f	function
F	function
$g(x)$	transverse scale factor, dimensionless
G	function
h	spacing between plates, ft
H	shape factor of boundary-layer velocity profile, dimensionless
k	(1) isentropic exponent $= c_p/c_v$, dimensionless
	(2) height of roughness element, ft
k_s	diameter of sand grain roughness, ft
l	mixing length, characteristic length, plate length, ft
l'	half circumference of cylinder
L	plate length, ft
m	exponent, dimensionless
$\mathbf{M}$	Mach number, dimensionless
n	exponent
p	pressure, psf
P	pressure of basic flow, psf
$\mathbf{P}$	Prandtl number, dimensionless
q	(1) dynamic head, psf
	(2) heat flow, Btu/(ft^2)(sec)
R	(1) gas constant, ft/$^\circ$F
	(2) pipe radius, ft
$\mathbf{R}$	Reynolds number, dimensionless
T	(1) absolute temperature, $^\circ$R
	(2) degree of turbulence, dimensionless
u	velocity, x component of velocity in the boundary layer, fps
u'	velocity fluctuations, x direction, fps
U, U_∞	velocity outside of boundary layer, free streamline velocity, fps
v'	velocity fluctuation, y direction, fps
v	velocity, y component of velocity, fps
v_*	friction velocity $= \sqrt{\tau_0/\rho}$, fps
V	velocity, fps
w	z component of velocity, fps
w_n	normal component of velocity, fps
w_t	tangential component of velocity, fps
x	cartesian coordinate, ft
x_t	length along plate to transition point, ft
X	x component of force per unit volume, lb/ft^3
y	cartesian coordinate, ft
Y	y component of force per unit volume, lb/ft^3
z	cartesian coordinate, ft
α	(1) coefficient, dimensionless
	(2) $= 2\pi/\lambda$, 1/ft
β	(1) complex amplitude coefficient, 1/sec
	(2) coefficient, dimensionless
	(3) angle
δ	boundary-layer thickness, ft
δ^*	displacement thickness of boundary layer, ft
η	(1) shape factor of boundary-layer velocity profile, dimensionless
	(2) transverse coordinate, dimensionless
θ	angle, dimensionless
Θ	momentum thickness of boundary layer, dimensionless
κ	universal constant, dimensionless

λ   (1) friction factor, dimensionless
        (2) heat conductivity, Btu/(ft)(sec)(°F)
        (3) wavelength, ft
Λ   shape factor of boundary-layer velocity profile, dimensionless
μ   viscosity, (lb)(sec)/ft²
ν   kinematic viscosity, ft²/sec
ξ   distance along plate, dimensionless
ρ   mass density, slugs/ft³
τ   shear stress, psf
φ   (1) function
        (2) angle, dimensionless
ψ   stream function, ft²/sec
ω   viscosity exponent, dimensionless

GENERAL CONSIDERATIONS OF THE BOUNDARY LAYER

9.3. Newton's Law of Viscosity; Reynolds' Principle of Similarity

The nature of viscous forces is most easily visualized in the flow between two parallel plates, one at rest and the other moving in its own plane at constant velocity (Fig. 9.2). For this simple case (Couette flow) the velocity distribution between the plates is linear because of the condition of no slip and can be represented as $u(y) = Uy/h$, if U is the velocity of the upper plate and h is the distance between plates. On every surface element parallel to the walls, either in the fluid itself or at one of the walls, a frictional force per unit area (shearing stress) is acting with magnitude

$$\tau = \mu \frac{du}{dy} \tag{9.1}$$

Here, $du/dy = U/h$ is the constant velocity gradient between the plates and μ is the dynamic viscosity of the fluid. Values of μ for air and water are given in Table 9.1. Equation (9.1) represents *Newton's law of viscosity*; it is a purely empirical law that, by experience, has been well confirmed for air and water.

Reynolds' Principle of Similarity. The flow of a viscous incompressible fluid is governed by *Reynolds' principle of similarity*. This principle states that with flow of different fluids about geometrically similar bodies, the streamline patterns are similar if the dimensionless Reynolds number has the same value for each flow.

$$\mathbf{R} = \frac{\rho Vl}{\mu} = \frac{Vl}{\nu} = \text{const} \tag{9.2}$$

in which l = a characteristic length of body in the flow
               V = a characteristic velocity (e.g., undisturbed velocity)
               $\nu = \mu/\rho$ = kinematic viscosity

Values of the density ρ and the kinematic viscosity ν of air and water are given in Table 9.1. (See Sec. 1 for values for other fluids.) Reynolds number may be interpreted physically as the ratio of inertial forces to viscous forces in the flow. Small Reynolds numbers signify flows with a preponderance of friction forces, whereas large Reynolds numbers signify flows with a preponderance of inertial forces. The first case ($\mathbf{R}$ very small) occurs for a body of small size, combined with a very small approach velocity and a large kinematic viscosity, as in the case of the settling of a fog particle (creeping motion). However, in most technical applications the opposite case of a very large Reynolds

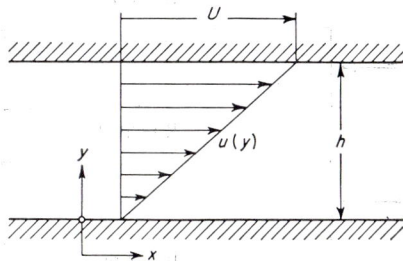

Fig. 9.2. Velocity distribution of a viscous fluid between two parallel-plane walls (from Newton's law of viscosity).

Table 9.1. Density, Viscosity, and Kinematic Viscosity of Water and Air
in Terms of Temperature

Temperature		Water			Air at a pressure of 760 mm Hg, 14.696 psi		
°C	°F	Density ρ, (lb)(sec²)/ft⁴	Viscosity, $\mu \times 10^6$, (lb)(sec)/ft²	Kinematic viscosity, $\nu \times 10^6$, ft²/sec	Density ρ, (lb)(sec²)/ft⁴	Viscosity, $\mu \times 10^6$, (lb)(sec)/ft²	Kinematic viscosity, $\nu \times 10^6$, ft²/sec
−20	−4	.....	.....	.....	0.00270	0.326	122
−10	14	.....	.....	.....	0.00261	0.338	130
0	32	1.939	37.5	19.4	0.00251	0.350	140
10	50	1.939	27.2	14.0	0.00242	0.362	150
20	68	1.935	21.1	10.9	0.00234	0.375	160
40	104	1.924	13.68	7.11	0.00217	0.399	183
60	140	1.907	9.89	5.19	0.00205	0.424	207
80	176	1.886	7.45	3.96	0.00192	0.449	234
100	212	1.861	5.92	3.19	0.00183	0.477	264

number occurs, since for the technically most important fluids, air and water, the kinematic viscosities are very small while the sizes and velocities are usually large.† In this latter case, as shall be examined more closely later, the effect of viscosity is confined to a thin layer near the body and a small wake behind the body (boundary layer or friction layer) while the rest of the fluid flow is essentially frictionless. The effect of Reynolds number on the flow around a body is in many cases very great. To exemplify this, Fig. 9.3 shows the flow around a circular cylinder for various Reynolds numbers. For small Reynolds numbers the flow in the wake proceeds in well-ordered parallel layers. This flow is called *laminar*. For large Reynolds numbers regular formations of vortices develop, which are designated as a Kármán vortex street. For increasing Reynolds numbers irregular transverse movements are formed more strongly in the wake, causing an intermixture of the neighboring layers. This flow is called *turbulent*. The tendency of the flow past a circular cylinder to change with increasing Reynolds numbers from a well-ordered parallel (laminar) flow to a more disordered flow with vortices, as seen in

† The Reynolds number for a circular cylinder of diameter $l = 1$ ft with an approach velocity of 100 fps in air ($\nu = 1.6 \times 10^{-4}$ ft²/sec) is $\mathbf{R} = Vl/\nu = 6.25 \times 10^5$.

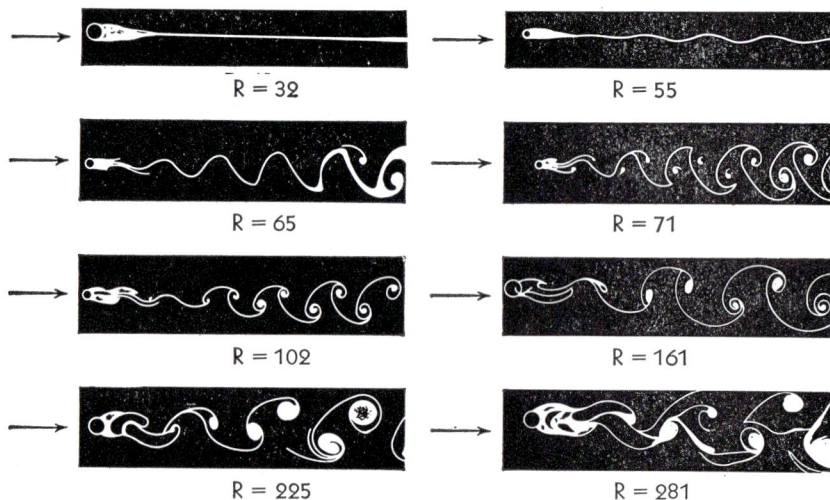

FIG. 9.3. The effect of Reynolds number on the flow past a body. (*From Homann.*[73])

Fig. 9.3, is generally valid and is discussed further in the concluding subsection.   Newton's law of viscosity, given by Eq. (9.1), is valid only for laminar flow.   For turbulent
flow another law is applicable, which is discussed in Arts. 9.15 to 9.18.

9.4. Resistance of Bodies Moving through a Fluid

If a body of arbitrary shape is moved with constant velocity along a linear path
through a fluid at rest, or what amounts to the same, if a fluid flows by a body at rest,
the body experiences a force from the flow, which in general has a component in the direction of flow as well as one perpendicular to the direction of flow.   The component of this
force in the direction of flow is called the *drag*, and the component perpendicular to the
direction of flow is called the *lift*.   For a symmetrical body facing the flow symmetrically,
there is no lift, and the force from the flow is equal to the drag on the body.   Only the
drag is examined closely in this section.

Since Reynolds number is very large for many technical applications of flow problems
(refer to the footnote on page 9-6), one would expect a useful agreement between theory
and experiment, if for the first approximation the viscosity were neglected (assuming a
frictionless fluid).   This proves correct for certain body shapes, e.g., streamlined bodies,
and for certain problems, viz., the determination of the pressure distribution and the lift.
For other body shapes, however, especially those of blunt form, the frictionless flow deviates very strongly from the experimental results for very large Reynolds numbers.   In
the resistance problem, ideal-fluid theory and experimental determinations vary greatly
for all body shapes with high Reynolds numbers.   An inviscid flow furnishes no force in
the direction of motion of an arbitrary body moving uniformly through an infinitely
extended fluid; therefore the resistance is zero (d'Alembert's paradox).   This is in sharp
contradiction to the observation that every body has a resistance, which, to be sure, can
be very small in the case of a slender body placed with its length parallel to the flow.

A theoretical calculation of drag is possible when viscosity is taken into account.   As
an elucidation of the drag problem, several particulars have been given on flow around a
sphere.   In Fig. 9.4 the actual pressure distribution along a meridian section is given
for two large Reynolds numbers as well as for the flow of an ideal fluid (potential flow).
The measured pressure distribution varies considerably with Reynolds number.   At the
front of the sphere the measured pressure distribution agrees fairly well with potential
theory.   The deviations at the rear of the sphere, however, are very large.   The measurement for the larger Reynolds numbers ($R = 4.4 \times 10^5$) lies closer to the pressure
distribution of potential theory than that for the smaller Reynolds numbers ($R = 1.6 \times 10^5$).   The deviations of the measured pressure distributions of potential theory

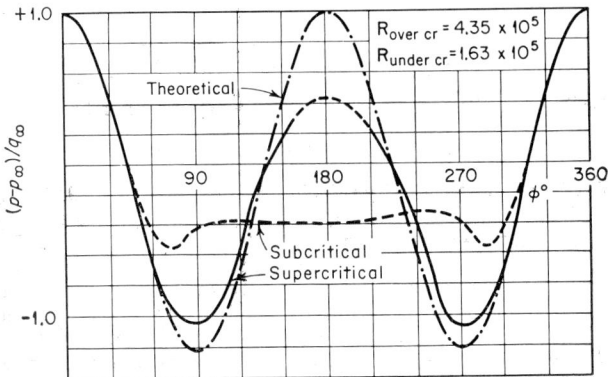

Fig. 9.4. The pressure distribution around a sphere in the subcritical and supercritical region
of Reynolds number from measurements by Flachsbart.[74]

are related to drag on the sphere. In the previous case the drag is smaller for the larger Reynolds numbers than for the smaller. The cause of this is discussed next.

Form Drag and Skin-friction Drag. In general, the drag of an immersed body is dependent not only on the pressure differences (normal stresses) on the surface of the body, but also on the tangential stresses (shearing stresses), which emanate from the viscosity. These two parts of the drag may be computed separately by integrating the pressure and the shear stress over the surface of the body. If p denotes the pressure on a surface element dA of the body surface, and ϕ is the angle between the direction of flow and the normal to the surface element, integration of the pressure yields the form drag D_p; thus

$$D_p = \oint p \cos \phi \, dA \tag{9.3}$$

in which the integration is carried out over the entire surface. Likewise, the skin-friction drag is obtained through integration of the shearing stress τ_0 at the wall, by

$$D_f = \oint \tau_0 \sin \phi \, dA \tag{9.4}$$

The total drag D is the sum of the form drag and the skin-friction drag.

$$D = D_p + D_f \tag{9.5}$$

For blunt body shapes, such as circular cylinders and spheres, the contribution of form drag is substantially larger than that of skin-friction drag, while for a flat plate at zero incidence, the total drag consists only of the skin-friction drag.

If the drag on a body is due primarily to pressure differences on its surface, that is, if the form drag is preponderant, then for large Reynolds numbers the drag is proportional to the square of the undisturbed velocity V since the pressure differences on the body surface are proportional to ρV^2. A dimensionless coefficient c_D is introduced for drag by the equation

$$D = c_D A (\rho/_2) V^2 = c_D A q \tag{9.6}$$

in which $q = \rho V^2/2$ is the dynamic head, and A is a suitably chosen area for the immersed body, for example, its frontal area normal to the direction of flow. The drag expression in Eq. (9.6) is called *Newton's resistance law*.

Law of Resistance. One may expect, from the laws of mechanical similarity of flows, that the drag coefficient c_D will have the same value for geometrically similar bodies immersed in different fluids if the physically standard dimensionless constants, such as Reynolds number and Mach number, are equal. For geometrically similar bodies oriented similarly to the direction of flow, the dimensionless drag coefficient can depend only on Reynolds number and Mach number

$$c_D = f(\mathbf{R},\mathbf{M}) \qquad \text{(compressible)} \tag{9.7}$$

For incompressible flow the dependence is only on Reynolds number

$$c_D = f(\mathbf{R}) \qquad \text{(incompressible)} \tag{9.8}$$

As an example of Reynolds' similarity principle for drag [as in Eq. (9.8)], Fig. 9.5 shows the drag coefficient of spheres for a very large range of Reynolds numbers. Experimental results provide excellent confirmation of the Reynolds' similarity principle in this case. The drag coefficients of spheres with greatly varying diameters fit very well on a single curve. The measurements in Fig. 9.5 show that the quadratic resistance law, Eq. (9.6), with constant c_D (independent of $\mathbf{R}$) is fulfilled to some extent only for Reynolds numbers between 10^3 and 10^5. For very small Reynolds numbers ($\mathbf{R} < 10^2$, creeping motion) the quadratic resistance law is not valid. For very large Reynolds numbers between $\mathbf{R} = 2 \times 10^5$ and $\mathbf{R} = 4 \times 10^5$ there is a sudden, strong decrease of the drag coefficient, which is connected with the large difference between the two pressure distributions in Fig. 9.4. This change of the flow past the sphere, caused by increasing

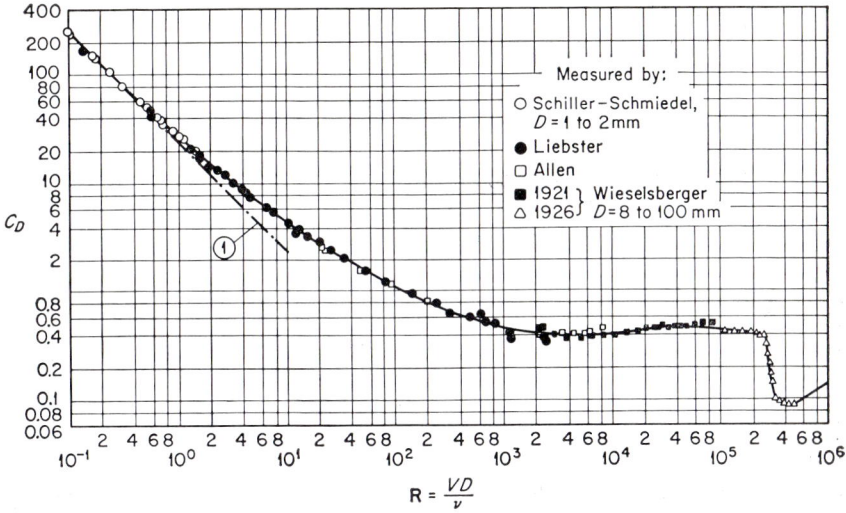

FIG. 9.5. Drag coefficient $c_D = D/(Aq)$ of the sphere in terms of the Reynolds number. Curve 1: $c_D = 24/\mathbf{R}$, theory of very slow motion. (A = cross-section area of sphere.)

Reynolds number, is connected with the transition from laminar to turbulent flow in the layer near the wall (boundary layer), which is discussed in detail in the following article.

9.5. The Boundary-layer Concept

While the friction effect is perceptible throughout the whole cross section in flow through a channel or a pipe, in many cases for flow past a body, especially a slender body, the friction effect is confined to a very thin layer in the immediate neighborhood of the boundary. While the flow slides by the boundary (Fig. 9.1a) for a frictionless fluid, in a real fluid a thin layer of the flow is retarded because of adhesion to the wall (Fig. 9.1b). This layer is called, after L. Prandtl,[1] the *boundary layer*, or friction layer.

As an example of this, in Fig. 9.6, a photograph is given of flow of water along a thin plate. Aluminum particles were strewn on the surface of the water to make the streamlines visible. The length of streak of each particle is proportional to its velocity. A thin layer immediately near the plate can be found in Fig. 9.6, in which the velocity is smaller than for larger distances from the plate. The thickness of this friction layer increases along the plate in the downstream direction.

The velocity distribution in the boundary layer for flow along a flat plate is given schematically in Fig. 9.7, where the dimensions in the direction normal to the flow have been greatly enlarged. With increasing distance from the leading edge of the plate, the thickness δ of the layer increases. This boundary layer, or friction layer, becomes thinner as the viscosity coefficient of the fluid becomes smaller. On the other hand, for very small viscosity (large Reynolds number) the frictional shear stress $\tau = \mu \, du/dy$ has a significant value in the boundary layer because of the large velocity gradient there, while the

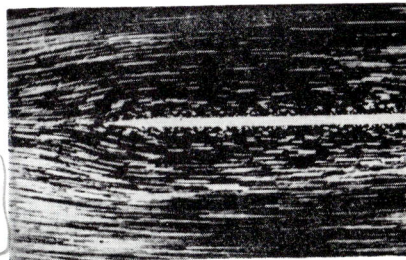

FIG. 9.6. Flow along a thin two-dimensional plate, from Prandtl-Tietjens.   Plate length l. Reynolds number $Vl/\nu = 3$.

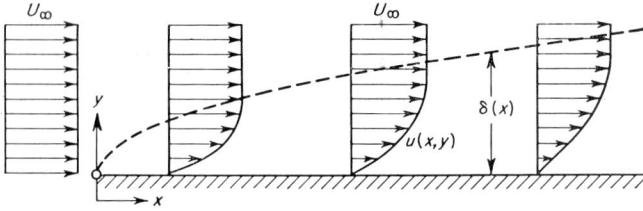

Fig. 9.7. Boundary layer along a flat plate at zero incidence (schematic).

shear stress outside of the boundary layer is very small. For theoretical considerations this allows all flows with small viscosity (large Reynolds number) to be divided into two parts: the region of thin friction layer near the wall, in which the friction forces play an important role, and the region outside of the friction layer, where the friction forces can be neglected because of their smallness and where an inviscid flow can be assumed with good approximation. This division of the flow into a frictionless external flow and a boundary layer near the body simplifies considerably the theoretical treatment of the flow with small viscosity (large Reynolds number). Before mathematical simplifications are treated, other physical features of the Prandtl boundary layer are discussed.

9.6. Separation of the Boundary Layer

The fluid particles within the boundary layer do not always remain as a thin layer lying along the entire surface. It is possible for the boundary layer to thicken appreciably downstream and for backflow to occur in the boundary layer. Thus the particles retarded in the boundary layer are carried into the external flow and are forced away from the body. This phenomenon is called *boundary-layer separation*. It occurs primarily for blunt bodies, such as circular cylinders and spheres. Separation can also occur in a highly divergent channel (diffusor). Boundary-layer separation is always associated with a high loss of energy. On the rear side of a blunt body and also in a diffusor a retarded region appears, which is called "dead water." This is shown in Fig. 9.8 for a circular cylinder. Aluminum dust was used to make the flow visible in the photograph. The pressure distribution at the rear side of the body is in this case very different from a frictionless flow, as shown in Fig. 9.4. The pressure distribution on the body surface, combined with separation of the flow, is responsible for the large drag of such blunt bodies.

In order to understand this important phenomenon of boundary-layer separation and vortex formation, the flow past a blunt body is considered. This is represented schematically in Fig. 9.9 for a circular cylinder. For ideal flow an accelerated flow with negative pressure gradient occurs on the leading surface of the body, from D to E. On the trailing surface a positive pressure gradient occurs from E to F, with retardation of the flow. A particle in the external flow moving from D to E experiences a transition from pressure energy to kinetic energy, while a particle moving from E to F experiences a transition from kinetic energy to pressure energy. A particle in the boundary layer finds itself under the effect of the same pressure distribution as in the external flow, for the boundary-layer pressure is impressed by the external flow. Such a particle going from D to E has lost so much kinetic energy through retardation

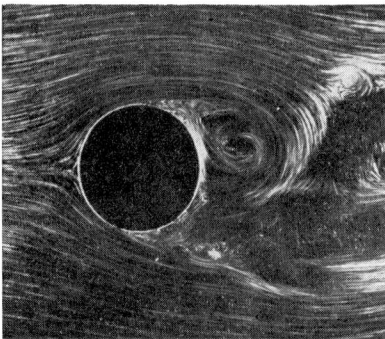

Fig. 9.8. Separated flow behind a circular cylinder, from Prandtl-Tietjens.

in the boundary layer that the remaining kinetic energy is insufficient to carry it against the positive pressure gradient from E to F. It cannot, therefore, proceed far in this region of increasing pressure. It comes to 'rest and, because of the pressure distribution of the external flow, is set into motion backward. This backflow is the beginning of separation.

Out of this consideration follows the general rule that separation of flow can never occur in the region of negative pressure gradient (accelerated flow), but only in the region of positive pressure gradient (decelerated flow). For a boundary layer flowing through a region of *positive pressure gradient*, there is an inherent tendency for separation to occur.

Whether or not separation occurs in a region of positive pressure gradient depends on the properties of the particular flow. Especially important are the magnitude of the positive pressure gradient

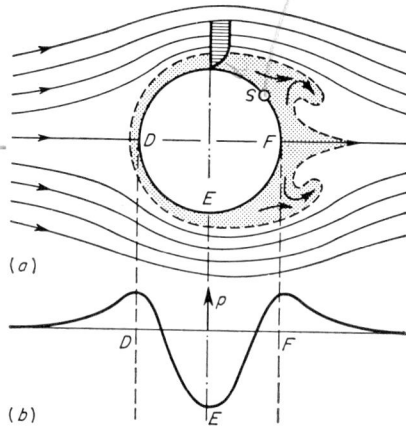

FIG. 9.9. Separation of the boundary layer and vortex formation around a circular cylinder (schematic). (S = point of separation.) (a) Flow pattern. (b) Pressure distribution.

and the condition of the flow (laminar or turbulent). A steep positive pressure gradient, as on the trailing surface of a blunt body, leads in general to separation. On the other hand, a weak positive pressure gradient, as on the trailing surface of a slender body, can be overcome without separation. In this case the accompanying effect of the external flow is sometimes sufficient to prevent backflow in the boundary layer. From this it follows that to avoid separation and to obtain a small drag the cross section of the trailing surface of the immersed body must be gradually reduced in size. A blunt leading surface of the immersed body has no important effect on the drag. This shape, favorable for low Mach numbers, is realized in the so-called *streamlined bodies* and also in airfoils.

9.7. Estimation of Boundary-layer Thickness and Frictional Resistance for Laminar Flow

In preparation for development of the equations of motion for flow in a boundary layer (Art. 9.9), an estimation of boundary-layer thickness and frictional resistance is next undertaken.

Boundary-layer Thickness. While friction forces outside of the boundary layer may be neglected in comparison with inertia forces because of the presupposed small viscosity, inside the boundary layer both forces are of the same order of magnitude. A flow is now considered along a wall coinciding with the x axis, while the y axis is taken normal to the wall (Fig. 9.7). The inertia force in the x direction per volume element is equal to $\rho u \, \partial u / \partial x$. For a body of length l, $\partial u / \partial x$ is proportional to U/l, if U is velocity of the undisturbed flow. Then the inertia force is of the order of magnitude $\rho U^2 / l$. The friction force in the x direction per volume element is equal to $\partial \tau / \partial y$, this being for laminar flow with τ as in Eq. (9.1) equal to $\mu \partial^2 u / \partial y^2$. If δ is the boundary-layer thickness, then the velocity gradient normal to the wall $\partial u / \partial y$ is of order of magnitude U/δ. Thus the friction force per unit volume is $\partial \tau / \partial y = \mu U / \delta^2$. Equating the inertia force and the friction force yields the relation $\mu U / \delta^2 = \rho U^2 / l$, or solved for the boundary-layer thickness δ,

$$\delta \sim \sqrt{\frac{\mu l}{\rho U}} = \sqrt{\frac{\nu l}{U}} \tag{9.9}$$

The remaining undetermined numerical factor in this equation is later found to be about 5, through the solution of the boundary-layer equations for a flat plate at zero incidence

(Art. 9.10). Thus for the laminar boundary layer at the end of a flat plate of length l at zero incidence

$$\delta = 5 \sqrt{\frac{\nu l}{U}} \tag{9.10}$$

The boundary-layer thickness, related to the plate length, thus becomes

$$\frac{\delta}{l} = 5 \sqrt{\frac{\nu}{Ul}} = \frac{5}{\sqrt{\mathbf{R}}} \tag{9.11}$$

in which $\mathbf{R} = Ul/\nu$ is the Reynolds number based on the plate length. From Eq. (9.9) the boundary-layer thickness is proportional to $\sqrt{\nu}$ and therefore is very small for fluids with very small viscosity. The relative boundary-layer thickness δ/l decreases with increasing Reynolds numbers as $1/\sqrt{\mathbf{R}}$, so that in approaching the limit of a frictionless fluid, $\mathbf{R} \to \infty$, the boundary-layer thickness disappears.

Frictional Resistance. With the previous result for boundary-layer thickness it is now easy to estimate the frictional resistance of a plate for laminar flow. From Newton's law of viscosity, Eq. (9.1), the shear stress at the wall is $\tau_0 = \mu(\partial u/\partial y)_0$, in which the zero subscript means the value at the wall. With the approximation $(\partial u/\partial y) \sim U/\delta$, one obtains $\tau_0 \sim \mu U/\delta$, and if the value of δ in Eq. (9.9) is inserted,

$$\tau_0 \sim \mu U \sqrt{\frac{\rho U}{\mu l}} = \sqrt{\frac{\mu \rho U^3}{l}} \tag{9.12}$$

The total frictional drag D_f of the plate is equal to $bl\tau_0$, if b is the width of the plate and τ_0 is the average shear stress. With Eq. (9.12),

$$D_f \sim b \sqrt{\rho \mu l U^3} \tag{9.13}$$

The laminar frictional resistance is therefore proportional to $U^{3/2}$ and $l^{1/2}$. The proportionality of the frictional resistance to $l^{1/2}$ is responsible for the fact that doubling the plate length does not double the resistance. The downstream half of the plate experiences less resistance than the upstream half because of the larger boundary-layer thickness downstream. Finally, the dimensionless drag coefficient in Eq. (9.6), denoted here by c_f, is solved for, setting the surface A equal to the available plate surface bl, so that one obtains from Eq. (9.13)

$$c_f \sim \sqrt{\frac{\mu}{\rho Ul}} = \frac{1}{\sqrt{\mathbf{R}}}$$

The missing numerical factor is found from the solution of the boundary-layer equations (Art. 9.10) to be 1.328. Thus one has for the resistance law of a flat plate at zero incidence for laminar flow

$$c_f = \frac{1.328}{\sqrt{\mathbf{R}}} \tag{9.14}$$

The drag coefficient is a function only of the Reynolds number for the sphere (Fig. 9.5) as well as for the flat plate at zero incidence.

Example 1. An example is given to illustrate these approximations. The laminar flow assumed here is obtained from observations up to a Reynolds number $\mathbf{R} = Ul/\nu$ of approximately 10^6. For larger Reynolds numbers the boundary layer at the plate becomes turbulent. The boundary-layer thickness at the end of a plate of length $l \doteq 3$ ft is computed for a flow of air ($\nu = 1.5 \times 10^{-4}$ ft²/sec) for a velocity $U = 50$ fps. This yields $\mathbf{R} = Ul/\nu = 10^6$, and hence, from Eq. (9.11), $\delta/l = 5 \times 10^{-3}$ and $\delta = 0.015$ ft, or 0.18 in. The drag coefficient from Eq. (9.14) is $c_f = 0.0013$ and is small if one compares it with that of the sphere in Fig. 9.5.

9.8. Turbulent Flow in the Boundary Layer

The boundary layer becomes turbulent along a wall in similar fashion as the flow through a pipe, if the boundary-layer thickness or the external velocity is sufficiently large. For the boundary layer in the vicinity of the leading edge of a flat plate at zero incidence there is always laminar flow, and under certain conditions farther downstream there is turbulent flow. The position of the transition point x_t, from laminar to turbulent, is given by observations of the critical Reynolds number based on length x.

$$\mathbf{R}_{x\ \mathrm{cr}} = \frac{Ux_t}{\nu} = 5 \times 10^5 \text{ to } 3 \times 10^6 \qquad \text{(plate)} \qquad (9.15)$$

The numerical value of this critical Reynolds number is strongly dependent on the intensity of turbulence of the external flow.[†] The smaller the intensity of turbulence is, the larger the value of the critical Reynolds number.

An especially striking phenomenon, connected with the laminar-turbulent transition in the boundary layer, occurs for blunt bodies such as circular cylinders and spheres. In Fig. 9.5 a sharp decrease of the drag coefficient is evident for the sphere with a Reynolds number VD/ν equal to about 3×10^5. This was first discovered for the sphere by Eiffel.[2] The sharp decrease in drag coefficient may be traced to the laminar-turbulent transition in the boundary layer. For a laminar boundary layer the point of separation lies on the equator of the sphere, as in Fig. 9.10a. When the boundary layer becomes more turbulent, the point of separation is caused to shift downstream (Fig. 9.10b). The turbulent boundary layer is more compatible with the positive pressure gradient at the rear surface of the sphere than the laminar boundary layer, and consequently separation for turbulent flow sets in farther downstream. As a result of this shifting of the separation point, connected with the boundary layer becoming turbulent, the region of the wake diminishes and the pressure distribution is closer to that of frictionless flow (Fig. 9.4). A considerable reduction of the pressure drag occurs for the boundary layer becoming turbulent, which appears in the drag curve for the sphere (Fig. 9.5) as a steep drop. Prandtl[3] proved the correctness of this explanation for sudden drop in the drag coefficient for a critical Reynolds number by placing a wire loop (*trip wire*) somewhat in front of the equator of the sphere. Thereby the laminar-turbulent transition was forced to take place, where otherwise it would have occurred only for an increase in Reynolds number. The photographs taken with the aid of smoke in Figs. 9.10a and b show the subcritical flow condition with a large region of dead water and large drag and the supercritical condition with a small region of dead water and small drag.

Making the boundary layer turbulent by the trip wire is *one* of the possibilities of

† With reference to intensity of turbulence, see Sec. 10.

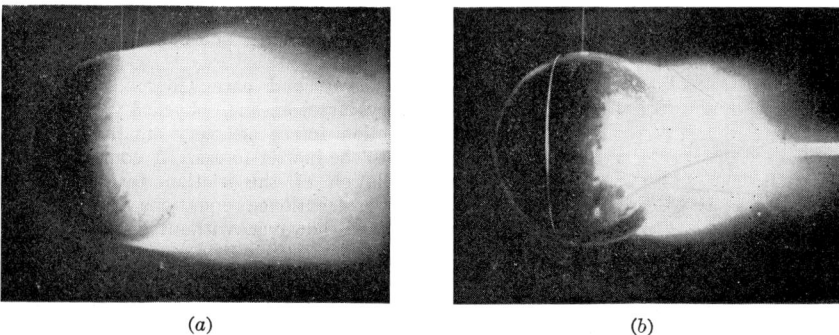

(*a*)   (*b*)

FIG. 9.10. Flow around a sphere by Wieselsberger.[4] (*a*) In the subcritical region of **R**. (*b*) In the supercritical region of **R**. The supercritical flow pattern is maintained by placing a thin wire (trip wire) on the sphere.

boundary-layer control, through which the course of the flow in a certain sense can be "steered." Other steps which in part have attained a considerable practical significance are boundary-layer suction, moving of the wall parallel to itself, and keeping the boundary layer laminar. These are considered more closely in Art. 9.14.

THE LAMINAR BOUNDARY LAYER IN INCOMPRESSIBLE FLOW

9.9. The Prandtl Boundary-layer Equations

Navier-Stokes Equations. The equations of motion of a viscous incompressible fluid, known as the Navier-Stokes equations, are obtained from the equilibrium of inertia forces, pressure forces, and friction forces (see Secs. 2 and 5 for discussion of these equations). For two-dimensional incompressible flow the Navier-Stokes equations and the continuity equation are set up in a cartesian coordinate system x, y as

$$\rho \left(u \frac{\partial u}{\partial x} + v \frac{\partial u}{\partial y} \right) = X - \frac{\partial p}{\partial x} + \mu \left(\frac{\partial^2 u}{\partial x^2} + \frac{\partial^2 u}{\partial y^2} \right) \tag{9.16}$$

$$\rho \left(u \frac{\partial v}{\partial x} + v \frac{\partial v}{\partial y} \right) = Y - \frac{\partial p}{\partial y} + \mu \left(\frac{\partial^2 v}{\partial x^2} + \frac{\partial^2 v}{\partial y^2} \right) \tag{9.17}$$

$$\frac{\partial u}{\partial x} + \frac{\partial v}{\partial y} = 0 \tag{9.18}$$

in which u and v = velocity components
$\quad\quad\quad p$ = pressure
$\quad X,\ Y$ = forces per unit volume due to gravity

In Eqs. (9.16) and (9.17) the left side represents the inertia forces while the right side contains the pressure and friction forces. Because of the adhesion of real fluid to a wall, the boundary conditions for the velocity components are

$$v_n = 0 \quad\quad \text{and} \quad\quad v_t = 0 \quad\quad \text{at the walls} \tag{9.19}$$

in which n and t refer to normal and tangential directions. Equations (9.16) to (9.18) represent a system of three equations for the three unknowns u, v, p. Because of the nonlinearity of the system, the solution of these equations is extremely difficult. Therefore terms in the equations of lesser importance should be neglected in order to facilitate the solution. Such simplifications are possible for both limiting cases of very small and very large Reynolds number. The first case (Reynolds number very small) has the physical meaning that the inertia terms are very small in comparison with the friction terms.

In this case the inertia terms in both equations of motion can be neglected. The resulting differential equations are now linear, a considerable simplification. Such flows are called *creeping motion*; they occur for very small velocities and immersed bodies of very small size.

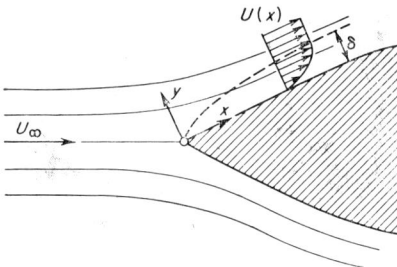

Fig. 9.11. Boundary-layer flow along a wall.

The second case (Reynolds number very large) means, physically, that the friction forces are very small compared with the inertia forces. A complete cancellation of the friction terms in the above-mentioned equations is not permitted, however, without being reduced to frictionless flow, which, as shown in Art. 9.4, yields insufficient results for the resistance problem. Rather, the simplification of the Navier-Stokes equation for the case of a very large Reynolds number requires careful consideration, if one wants to obtain physically conclusive results.

This leads to the boundary-layer theory, which has been presented in empirical form in the preceding section and whose fundamental equations are now derived from the Navier-Stokes equations.

Derivation of the Boundary-layer Equations. The simplifications in the Navier-Stokes equations which are made in the case of very small viscosity forces (very large Reynolds number) will be derived in a physically obvious fashion. A two-dimensional flow with very small viscosity past a cylindrical body is observed in Fig. 9.11, in which x is the coordinate along the surface and y is normal to the surface. The velocity near the body surface is of the order of magnitude of the undisturbed velocity U_∞. On the body, however, the velocity is equal to zero because of the condition of no slip. It is assumed that the transition from zero velocity to full velocity, existent at some distance from the surface, is made in a very thin layer of thickness δ of the so-called boundary layer. Two regions are now distinguished:

1. The *boundary layer*, in which the velocity gradient normal to the wall $\partial u/\partial y$ is very large. Here a small viscosity μ is significant, in so far as the frictional shear stress $\tau = \mu \, \partial u/\partial y$ can assume considerable value. In this layer the friction and inertia forces are of the same order of magnitude.

2. The *external flow*, which is the region outside of the boundary layer. The velocity gradients are not as large here, so that the effect of viscosity is insignificant. The flow can be closely approximated to frictionless potential flow.

The assumption is further made that the boundary-layer thickness is very small compared with a characteristic length L of the immersed body: $\delta \ll L$. It is also assumed that the Reynolds number $\mathbf{R} = U_\infty L/\nu$ is very large. If the individual terms of the Navier-Stokes equations are estimated under these conditions, it is found that the inertia and friction forces in the boundary layer are of the same order of magnitude only for the condition

$$\delta \sim \frac{1}{\sqrt{\mathbf{R}}}$$

which was shown to be true in Eq. (9.9).

If, for such an evaluation, only the largest terms are kept in Eqs. (9.16) and (9.17), one obtains the following simplified equations, which are called the Prandtl boundary-layer equations (cf. Schlichting[11]),

$$\rho \left(u \frac{\partial u}{\partial x} + v \frac{\partial u}{\partial y} \right) = -\frac{dp}{dx} + \mu \frac{\partial^2 u}{\partial y^2} \tag{9.20}$$

$$\frac{\partial u}{\partial x} + \frac{\partial v}{\partial y} = 0 \tag{9.21}$$

The boundary conditions are

$$y = 0 : u = 0 , v = 0 \qquad y = \infty : u = U(x) \tag{9.22}$$

With this simplification of the Navier-Stokes equations, the equation of motion for the y direction may be disregarded, since it contains only terms that are much smaller than those in the equation for the x direction. This follows from the fact that the pressure gradient $\partial p/\partial y$ normal to the wall in the boundary layer is equal to zero. Thus the pressure drop along the wall within the boundary layer may be found from the frictionless external flow. With the aid of the Bernoulli equation it is determined to be

$$-\frac{1}{\rho} \frac{dp}{dx} = U \frac{dU}{dx} \tag{9.23}$$

Consequently, the pressure distribution along the boundary layer is imposed by the external flow.

The mathematical simplification is considerable. Of the three original equations in u, v, p for the two-dimensional problem, one has been removed, namely, the equation of motion normal to the wall. Correspondingly, the number of unknowns has been reduced by one. The boundary-layer Eqs. (9.20) and (9.21) are a system with two unknowns,

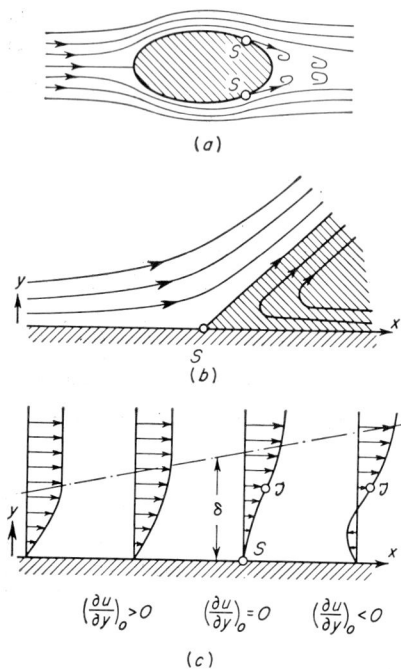

(a)

(b)

$\left(\frac{\partial u}{\partial y}\right)_0 > 0$ $\left(\frac{\partial u}{\partial y}\right)_0 = 0$ $\left(\frac{\partial u}{\partial y}\right)_0 < 0$

(c)

Fig. 9.12. Separation of the boundary layer. (S = separation point.) (a) Flow past a body with separation. (b) Behavior of the streamlines near the separation point. (c) Velocity distribution in the vicinity of the separation point. ($\mathfrak{I}$ = point of inflection.)

u and v. The pressure p is no longer to be considered as an unknown function, since it is known from the frictionless external flow.

Physical Properties of the Boundary Layer. Several important general properties can be derived from the differential equations of the boundary layer without going into their integration. An important question presents itself next: Under what conditions will separation of the flow from the wall take place? The qualitative considerations in Art. 9.6 have shown that the inherent tendency for separation of the boundary layer occurs only in the region of a positive pressure gradient (retarded flow). This is seen likewise on the basis of the boundary-layer differential equations. The course of the flow in the vicinity of a separation point is illustrated in Fig. 9.12. Backflow occurs near the wall behind the separation point S (Fig. 9.12b), which causes the flow near the separation point to be forced outside. The separation point is defined for convenience as the boundary between the forward flow and the backflow of the layer nearest the wall (Fig. 9.12c), thus:

Point of separation:

$$\left(\frac{\partial u}{\partial y}\right)_{\text{wall}} = 0 \qquad (9.24)$$

The velocity profile $u(y)$ obviously possesses a point of inflection at the separation point (Fig. 9.12a), in other words, a point where $\partial^2 u/\partial y^2 = 0$. It is further true, as is seen immediately from Eq. (9.20) considered with Eq. (9.22), that the equation for the curvature of the velocity profile at the wall is

$$\mu \left(\frac{\partial^2 u}{\partial y^2}\right)_{\text{wall}} = \frac{dp}{dx} \qquad (9.25)$$

From this follows the fact that velocity profiles in the region of a positive pressure gradient $(dp/dx > 0)$ always have a point of inflection, whereas those in the region of a negative pressure gradient $(dp/dx < 0)$ have none. The existence of a point of inflection in a laminar-boundary-layer profile is significant for the laminar-turbulent transition, which consequently is decisively influenced by the pressure gradient of the external flow. This is discussed in more detail in Arts. 9.24 to 9.28.

9.10. Boundary-layer Flow along a Flat Plate

Velocity Distribution. The simplest case of a boundary layer occurs for flow along a flat plate at zero incidence. This boundary layer at the plate was treated by Blasius[5] in his Göttingen thesis of 1907. The plate is assumed to be infinitely long. The coordinate is chosen as in Fig. 9.7. The undisturbed velocity is U_∞; it is constant along the plate, and thus the pressure gradient dp/dx is zero. The boundary-layer Eqs. (9.20) to (9.22) are simplified in this case to

$$u \frac{\partial u}{\partial x} + v \frac{\partial u}{\partial y} = \nu \frac{\partial^2 u}{\partial y^2} \tag{9.26}$$

$$\frac{\partial u}{\partial x} + \frac{\partial v}{\partial y} = 0 \tag{9.27}$$

$$y = 0 : u = 0 , v = 0 \qquad y = \infty : u = U_\infty \tag{9.28}$$

Since in this case the immersed body has no particular length, it is appropriate to assume that the velocity profiles for varying distances from the leading edge of the plate are similar. As a scale factor for y, the boundary-layer thickness $\delta(x)$ is chosen, which from Eq. (9.9) is proportional to $\sqrt{\nu x / U_\infty}$. The dimensionless coordinate y/δ is denoted by η and is set equal to

$$\eta = y \sqrt{\frac{U_\infty}{\nu x}} \tag{9.29}$$

Through the introduction of this new variable η it is possible to convert both partial differential equations, Eqs. (9.26) and (9.27), to one ordinary differential equation. The equation of continuity, Eq. (9.27), is satisfied by introducing a stream function

$$\psi(x,y) = \sqrt{\nu x U_\infty} f(\eta) \tag{9.30}$$

in which $f(\eta)$ denotes the dimensionless stream function. For the velocity components one obtains therefore

$$u = \frac{\partial \psi}{\partial y} = U_\infty f'(\eta) \tag{9.31}$$

$$v = -\frac{\partial \psi}{\partial x} = \frac{1}{2} \sqrt{\frac{\nu U_\infty}{x}} (\eta f' - f) \tag{9.32}$$

in which the prime denotes differentiation with respect to η. By inserting Eqs. (9.31) and (9.32) into (9.26) the ordinary differential equation for $f(\eta)$ is found to be

$$f \cdot f'' + 2f''' = 0 \tag{9.33}$$

with the boundary conditions

$$\eta = 0 : f = 0 , f' = 0 \qquad \eta = \infty : f' = 1 \tag{9.34}$$

The solution of this nonlinear differential equation was given first by Blasius and was improved later by others.[6]

In Fig. 9.13 the theoretical velocity distribution $u/U_\infty = f'(\eta)$ is compared with measurements by Nikuradse.[7] The similarity of the velocity profiles predicted by theory for varying distances x from the leading edge of the plate is well confirmed by the measurements. Also, the form of the measured velocity profiles is in excellent agreement with the theory. Simultaneously, the admissibility of the boundary-layer simplifications is well confirmed.

Skin Friction. The frictional resistance of the flat plate at zero incidence is easily determined from the given solution. The resistance of one side of the plate is

$$D_f = b \int_0^l \tau_0(x) \, dx = b\mu \int_0^l \left(\frac{\partial u}{\partial y} \right)_{y=0} dx \tag{9.35}$$

in which l is the length, and b is the width of the plate. The velocity gradient at the wall is, from Eq. (9.31),

$$\left(\frac{\partial u}{\partial y} \right)_{y=0} = \alpha U_\infty \sqrt{\frac{U_\infty}{\nu x}} \qquad \text{with } \alpha = f''(0) = 0.332$$

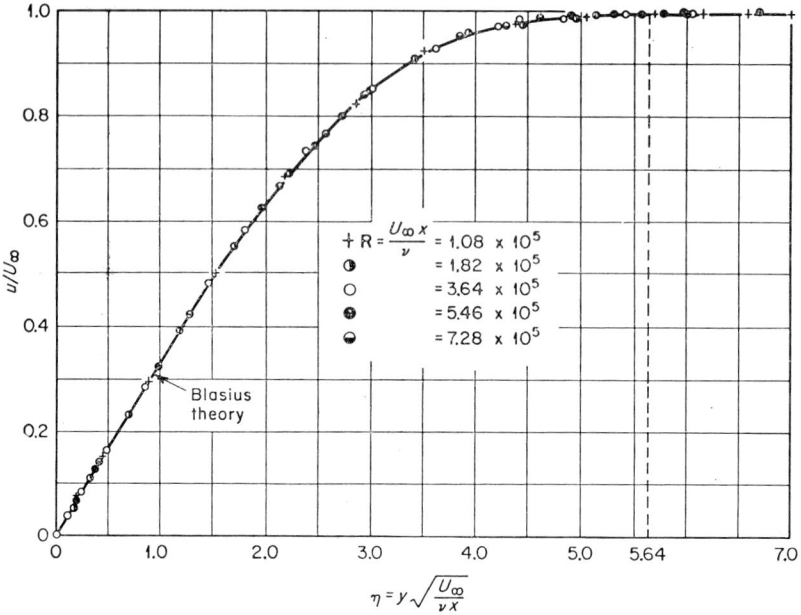

FIG. 9.13. Velocity distribution in the laminar boundary layer along a flat plate at zero incidence. Theory by Blasius,[5] measurements by Nikuradse.[7]

Consequently, the frictional resistance, from Eq. (9.35),

$$D_f = \alpha \mu b U_\infty \sqrt{\frac{U_\infty}{\nu}} \int_0^l \frac{dx}{\sqrt{x}} = 0.664 b \sqrt{\mu \rho l U_\infty^3} \qquad (9.36)$$

is in agreement with Eq. (9.13). If a dimensionless drag coefficient is introduced by

$$c_f = \frac{D_f}{bl(\rho/2)U_\infty^2} \qquad (9.37)$$

in which bl denotes the wetted area, then from Eq. (9.36),

$$c_f = \frac{1.328}{\sqrt{\mathbf{R}}} \qquad (9.38)$$

which agrees with Eq. (9.14). In this case $\mathbf{R} = U_\infty l/\nu$. Equation (9.38) represents the Blasius resistance law for the plate for laminar flow. It is given in Fig. 9.35 as curve 1. It is valid for Reynolds number up to about $\mathbf{R} = 10^6$. In the region of turbulent flow, $\mathbf{R} > 10^6$, the frictional resistance is considerably greater than that given by Eq. (9.38). For more detail refer to Art. 9.17.

The laminar law of friction has undergone extensive experimental examination. The result of the careful measurements by Liepmann and Dhawan[8] is given in Fig. 9.14, in which the local drag coefficient $c'_f = \tau_0/(\rho U_\infty^2/2)$ is plotted against the Reynolds number $U_\infty x/\nu$. Thus the local drag coefficient is

$$c'_f = \frac{0.664}{\sqrt{\mathbf{R}_x}} \qquad (9.39)$$

The measurements are in excellent agreement with the Blasius resistance law [Eq. (9.39)].

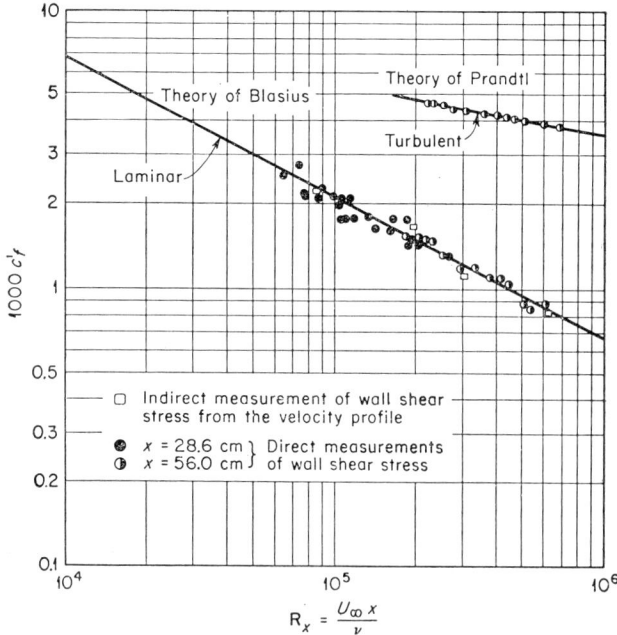

FIG. 9.14. Local skin-friction drag of the flat plate at zero incidence from indirect and direct measurements of shear stress by Liepmann and Dhawan.[8] $c'_f = \tau_0/[(\rho/2)U_\infty{}^2]$. Theory: laminar as in Eq. (9.39); turbulent as in Eq. (9. 116).

Boundary-layer Thickness, Displacement Thickness, Momentum Thickness. If the boundary-layer thickness is defined as that distance from the wall where $u = 0.99U_\infty$, then one obtains

$$\delta = 5.0 \sqrt{\frac{\nu x}{U_\infty}} \tag{9.40}$$

Another physically meaningful measurement for thickness of the boundary layer is the *displacement thickness* δ^*. By this is understood the thickness of the layer by which the potential flow is forced away from the boundary as a result of velocity reduction in the boundary layer. The deficiency of flow in the boundary layer as a result of the friction effect is

$$\int_{y=0}^{\infty} (U_\infty - u)dy$$

Consequently, the defining equation for the displacement thickness as shown in Fig. 9.15 is

$$U_\infty \delta^* = \int_{y=0}^{\infty} (U_\infty - u)\, dy \tag{9.41}$$

For the boundary layer of the plate Eq. (9.31) yields

$$\delta^* = 1.73 \sqrt{\frac{\nu x}{U_\infty}} \tag{9.42}$$

Another important measure for the thickness of the boundary layer is the *momentum thickness*, based on reduction of momentum due to frictional resistance of the plate. For the control surface given in Fig. 9.16

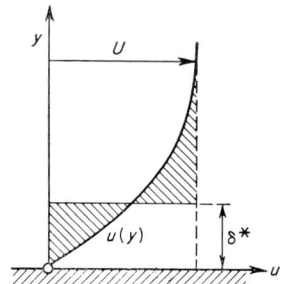

FIG. 9.15. The definition of displacement thickness of the boundary layer δ^* as in Eq. (9.41).

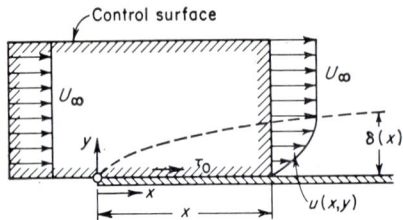

Fig. 9.16. The application of the momentum equation to the boundary layer along a flat plate at zero incidence.

the resistance of a piece of the plate of length x and width b wetted on one side is given by the momentum equation to be

$$D_f(x) = b\rho \int_{y=0}^{\infty} u(U_\infty - u)\, dy \quad (9.43)$$

in which $u(x,y)$ denotes the velocity distribution in the boundary layer at the point x. If one introduces the momentum thickness Θ into Eq. (9.43) and writes in the form $D_f(x) = \rho b U_\infty^2 \Theta(x)$, then the momentum thickness is defined by

$$U_\infty^2 \Theta(x) = \int_{y=0}^{\infty} u(U_\infty - u)\, dy \quad (9.44)$$

The calculation of $\Theta(x)$ from Eq. (9.31) gives

$$\Theta = 0.664 \sqrt{\frac{\nu x}{U_\infty}} \quad (9.45)$$

The ratio of the displacement thickness to the momentum thickness in this case is $\delta^*/\Theta = 1.73/0.664 = 2.59$.

Both quantities, displacement thickness and momentum thickness, play an important role in the boundary layer of an arbitrary body, as well as in turbulent flow.

9.11. General Properties of the Boundary-layer Equations

Dependence of the Boundary Layer on Reynolds Number. Although the boundary-layer equations represent a considerable simplification of the Navier-Stokes equations, they are still so difficult mathematically that only a few general remarks can be made about their solution. The assumptions made in deriving the boundary-layer equations are the more justified the larger the Reynolds number. Therefore the boundary-layer theory may be designated as an asymptotic integration theory of the Navier-Stokes equations for very large Reynolds numbers. The question may next be asked: In what way does the boundary layer of a certain given body depend on the Reynolds number? To this end the boundary-layer Eqs. (9.20) to (9.22) are written in dimensionless form while all velocities are referred to the undisturbed velocity and all lengths to a characteristic body length L. If each of the resulting dimensionless quantities is designated by a prime, for example, $u/U_\infty = u', \ldots, x/L = x', \ldots$, then the boundary-layer equations for two-dimensional stationary flow are

$$u' \frac{\partial u'}{\partial x'} + v' \frac{\partial u'}{\partial y'} = U' \frac{dU'}{dx'} + \frac{1}{\mathbf{R}} \frac{\partial^2 u'}{\partial y'^2} \quad (9.46)$$

$$\frac{\partial u'}{\partial x'} + \frac{\partial v'}{\partial y'} = 0 \quad (9.47)$$

with the boundary conditions

$$y' = 0 : u' = 0\,,\, v' = 0 \qquad y' = \infty : u' = U'(x')$$

Here $\mathbf{R} = U_\infty L/\nu$. From Eqs. (9.46) and (9.47) one recognizes that for a given body form the velocity distribution in the boundary layer depends on only the one parameter $\mathbf{R}$. Through a further transformation Eqs. (9.46) and (9.47) may be changed in such a way that the Reynolds number also drops out. For example, if one sets

$$y'' = y' \sqrt{\mathbf{R}} = \frac{y}{L} \sqrt{\frac{U_\infty L}{\nu}} \quad (9.48)$$

and
$$v'' = v'\sqrt{\mathbf{R}} = \frac{v}{U_\infty}\sqrt{\frac{U_\infty L}{\nu}} \qquad (9.49)$$

Eqs. (9.46) and (9.47) are transformed into

$$u'\frac{\partial u'}{\partial x'} + v''\frac{\partial u'}{\partial y''} = U'\frac{dU'}{dx'} + \frac{\partial^2 u'}{\partial y''^2} \qquad (9.50)$$

$$\frac{\partial u'}{\partial x'} + \frac{\partial v''}{\partial y''} = 0 \qquad (9.51)$$

with boundary conditions

$$u' = 0 \qquad \text{and} \qquad v'' = 0 \qquad \text{for } y'' = 0$$

$$u' = U' \qquad \text{for } y'' = \infty$$

Equations (9.50) and (9.51) no longer contain the Reynolds number. From this it follows that the solutions of these two equations, $u'(x',y'')$ and $v''(x',y'')$, are also independent of the Reynolds number. This result may be formulated so that the boundary-layer experiences solely a similar distortion for a change in Reynolds number, in such a manner that the y coordinate and the y velocity are multiplied by $(\mathbf{R})^{-\frac{1}{2}}$. In other words, the dimensionless velocity components for a given body, u/U_∞ and $(v/U_\infty) \cdot \sqrt{U_\infty L/\nu}$, are functions of the dimensionless coordinates x/L and $(y/L) \cdot \sqrt{U_\infty L/\nu}$. This property of the boundary-layer equations is called the *similarity principle with respect to the Reynolds number*.

The practical application of this principle of similarity with respect to Reynolds number is that for a given body the calculation of the boundary layer need be carried out only once, which immediately describes the nature of the boundary layer for all large Reynolds numbers for which the boundary-layer assumptions are justified as an approximation and for which the flow is laminar. This implies especially that the position of the separation point of the boundary layer is independent of the Reynolds number. Only the angle (Fig. 9.12) at which the streamline at the separation point leaves the body depends on Reynolds number, varying as $1/\sqrt{\mathbf{R}}$. The separation also remains when proceeding to the limit of a frictionless fluid, that is $\mathbf{R} \to \infty$.

The "Similar" Solutions of the Boundary-layer Equations. Another important question concerning the boundary-layer equations is: Under what conditions do "similar" solutions exist? By "similar" solutions is meant those solutions whose longitudinal component of the velocity has the property that the velocity profiles $u(x,y)$ differ at two different points x only by a scale factor for the velocity and the transverse coordinate. For such "similar" solutions, therefore, the velocity profiles $u(x,y)$ for all points x along the wall are made to coincide if they are plotted in a dimensionless representation with these scale factors. Such "similar" velocity profiles are called affine. Affinity is claimed if for two arbitrary points x_1 and x_2 the longitudinal component of the velocity $u(x,y)$ satisfies the following equation:

$$\frac{u\{x_1, [y/g(x_1)]\}}{U(x_1)} = \frac{u\{x_2, [y/g(x_2)]\}}{U(x_2)} \qquad (9.52)$$

in which $U(x)$ denotes the velocity of the potential flow, and $g(x)$ denotes the scale factor for the transverse coordinate, which is proportional to the thickness of the local boundary layer. Consideration of the "similar" solutions is particularly important with regard to the mathematical character of the solutions of the boundary-layer equations. In case there are "similar" solutions, the system of partial differential equations for the boundary layer can be transformed into one ordinary differential equation, which is a remarkable simplification.

Next, for the case of two-dimensional incompressible stationary boundary layers, the problem is examined, for which potential flows such "similar" solutions exist. This question was discussed first of all by Goldstein[9] and later by Mangler.[10] Hereafter the discussion is limited essentially to giving the result; for a detailed presentation see Schlichting.[11] Starting from the boundary-layer Eqs. (9.20) to (9.22), the continuity equation is integrated by introducing a stream function $\psi(x,y)$.

$$u = \frac{\partial \psi}{\partial y} \qquad v = -\frac{\partial \psi}{\partial x}$$

Consequently, the first equation of motion becomes

$$\frac{\partial \psi}{\partial y}\frac{\partial^2 \psi}{\partial x \, \partial y} - \frac{\partial \psi}{\partial x}\frac{\partial^2 \psi}{\partial y^2} = U\frac{dU}{dx} + \nu\frac{\partial^3 \psi}{\partial y^3} \tag{9.53}$$

with the boundary conditions

$$\frac{\partial \psi}{\partial x} = 0 \quad \text{and} \quad \frac{\partial \psi}{\partial y} = 0 \quad \text{for } y = 0$$

$$\frac{\partial \psi}{\partial y} = U \quad \text{for } y = \infty$$

If the dimensionless coordinates $\xi = x/L$, $\eta = y\sqrt{\mathbf{R}}/Lg(x)$ are introduced for the similarity transformation, as well as the dimensionless stream function,

$$f(\xi,\eta) = \frac{\psi(x,y)\sqrt{\mathbf{R}}}{LU(x)g(x)} \tag{9.54}$$

then for $f(\xi,\eta)$ the following differential equation is obtained:

$$f''' + \alpha f f'' + \beta(1 - f'^2) = \frac{U}{U_\infty}g^2\left(f'\frac{\partial f'}{\partial \xi} - f''\frac{\partial f}{\partial \xi}\right) \tag{9.55}$$

In this case the prime denotes differentiation with respect to η. Also, α and β are abbreviations for the following functions of x:

$$\alpha = \frac{Lg}{U_\infty}\frac{d}{dx}(Ug) \qquad \beta = \frac{L}{U_\infty}g^2 U' \tag{9.56}$$

in which $U' = dU/dx$. The boundary conditions for Eq. (9.55) are $f = 0$ and $f' = 0$ for $\eta = 0$ and $f' = 1$ for $\eta = \infty$.

"Similar" solutions now occur if f and f' do not depend on ξ, that is, if the right side of Eq. (9.55) disappears. At the same time, then, the coefficients α and β from the left side must also be independent of x, or in other words, they must be constants. Later conditions give certain specifications for the potential velocity $U(x)$ and the scale factor $g(x)$ of the transverse coordinate. Accordingly, one has for the stream function $f(\eta)$ the following differential equation for "similar" solutions of the boundary-layer equations:

$$f''' + \alpha f f'' + \beta(1 - f'^2) = 0 \tag{9.57}$$

with the boundary conditions

$$\eta = 0 : f = 0, f' = 0 \qquad \eta = \infty : f' = 1 \tag{9.58}$$

This equation was first given by Falkner and Skan,[12] and later the solutions were investigated more fully by Hartree.[13]

The evaluation of the two conditions given in Eq. (9.56), namely, that α and β are constant, leads to the following equations of condition for the potential flow and the scale factor of the transverse coordinate

$$U(x) = u_1 x^m \tag{9.59}$$

and

$$\eta = y\sqrt{\frac{m+1}{2}\frac{U}{\nu x}} \tag{9.60}$$

in which u_1 and m are constants. Thus these considerations result in the fact that "similar" solutions of the boundary-layer equations are obtained if the velocity distribution of the potential flow is proportional to a power of the arc length along the wall measured from the stagnation point. Such potential flows occur for a wedge-shaped body with wedge angle $\pi\beta$, as in Fig. 9.17. The wedge angle β and the exponent m are related by

$$\beta = \frac{2m}{m+1} \qquad (9.61)$$

Near a stagnation point at a plane wall $m = 1$, and consequently $\beta = 1$.

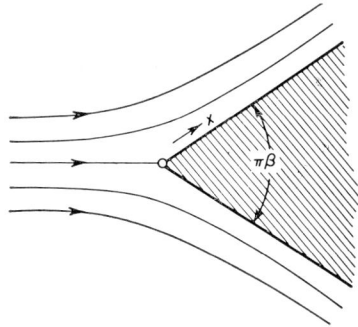

FIG. 9.17. Flow past a wedge. Near the vertex Eq. (9.59) is valid for the potential velocity distribution.

9.12. Exact Solutions

By exact solutions are meant those solutions which represent complete solutions of the boundary-layer differential equations, which may be procured either analytically or numerically. In contrast to these are the approximate solutions discussed in Art. 9.13, which are derived not from the differential equations, but from certain integral relationships, such as the momentum and energy equations. The number of exact analytical solutions is comparatively small, since in general considerable mathematical difficulties are encountered in their solution. An especially simple class of exact solutions are the "similar" solutions illustrated in the preceding article. Equations (9.59) and (9.60) are combined for the potential flow

$$U(x) = u_1 x^m$$

and for the independent variable y is introduced

$$\eta = y \sqrt{\frac{m+1}{2} \frac{U}{\nu x}} = y \sqrt{\frac{m+1}{2} \frac{u_1}{\nu}} \, x^{(m-1)/2} \qquad (9.62)$$

Consequently, the velocity components become

$$u = u_1 x^m f'(\eta) = U f'(\eta) \qquad (9.63)$$

$$v = -\sqrt{\frac{m+1}{2} \nu u_1 x^{m-1}} \left(f + \frac{m-1}{m+1} \eta f' \right) \qquad (9.64)$$

The differential equation for the stream function $f(\eta)$, already given in Eq. (9.57), becomes in the present case

$$f''' + ff'' + \beta(1 - f'^2) = 0 \qquad (9.65)$$

with the boundary conditions

$$\eta = 0 : f = 0 \,, f' = 0 \qquad \eta = \infty : f' = 1$$

The solutions of Eq. (9.65) were originally investigated by Hartree. The result is depicted in Fig. 9.18. For accelerated flow ($m > 0$, $\beta > 0$) one obtains velocity profiles without an inflection point, whereas an inflection point is obtained with velocity profiles for decelerated flow ($m < 0$, $\beta < 0$). Separation occurs for $\beta = -0.199$, from which $m = -0.091$. From this it is recognized that the laminar boundary layer endures only a very small deceleration before separation occurs.

Another class of exact solutions of the boundary-layer differential equations is obtained if one represents the potential flow $U(x)$ by a power series of the arc length x, measured from the leading-edge stagnation point, and if the velocity distribution in the boundary

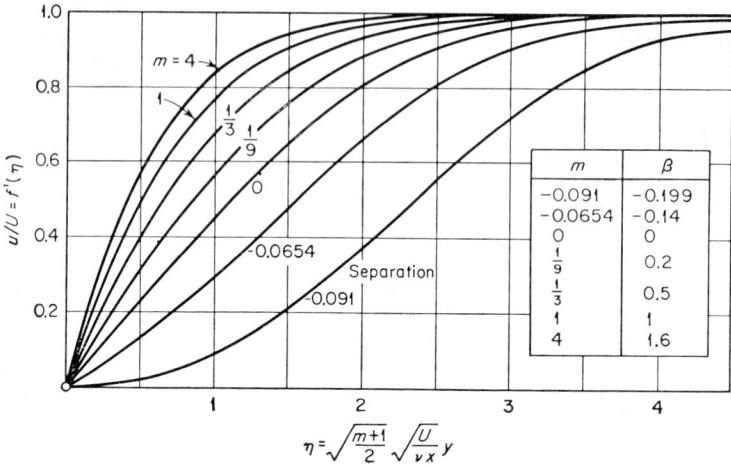

m	β
-0.091	-0.199
-0.0654	-0.14
0	0
$\frac{1}{9}$	0.2
$\frac{1}{3}$	0.5
1	1
4	1.6

$$\eta = \sqrt{\frac{m+1}{2}} \sqrt{\frac{U}{\nu x}}\, y$$

Fig. 9.18. Velocity distributions in the laminar boundary layer of the wedge flow $U(x) = u_1 x^m$ for different values of m. Relationship between m and β from Eq. (9.61).

layer is also represented by such a series, whose coefficients, however, are functions of the transverse coordinate y (Blasius series). A more detailed discussion is found, for example, in Ref. 11, chap. 9.

9.13. Approximate Solutions of the Boundary-layer Equations

The Momentum Equation of Boundary-layer Theory. The boundary layer along a flat plate at zero incidence with a constant external flow $U(x) = U_\infty = \text{const}$, as treated in Art. 9.10, is a particularly simple case, since the pressure gradient of the external flow disappears. For the general case of flow past a body, for which the pressure gradient of the external flow varies along the wall, the integration of the boundary-layer equations is considerably more difficult. Since for the general case the exact solution of the boundary-layer equation is very tedious, as illustrated in the preceding article, approximate methods have been developed. These methods are inferior to the exact solutions in accuracy, but are more convenient in the numerical calculation. The principle of such approximate methods consists in disregarding boundary-layer differential equations for every individual layer parallel to the wall, satisfying instead only an average value of the differential equations over boundary-layer thickness. Such an average value is furnished by the momentum equation of boundary-layer theory, which is obtained by integration of the boundary-layer equation over the coordinate normal to the wall.[14]

From the integration of the equation of motion (9.20), from $y = 0$ (wall) to a layer $y = h$ outside of the boundary layer, one obtains

$$\int_{y=0}^{h} \left(u\frac{\partial u}{\partial x} + v\frac{\partial u}{\partial y} - U\frac{dU}{dx} \right) dy = -\frac{\tau_0}{\rho} \tag{9.66}$$

Here the shear stress at the wall τ_0 is introduced for $\mu(\partial u/\partial y)_0$, so that Eq. (9.66) is valid for laminar as well as turbulent flow. If in Eq. (9.66) the transverse velocity from the continuity equation is replaced by $v = -\int_0^y (\partial u/\partial x)\, dy$, then one obtains after some rewriting

$$\int_0^h \frac{\partial}{\partial x}\left[u(U - u) \right] dy + \frac{dU}{dx}\int_0^h (U - u)\, dy = \frac{\tau_0}{\rho} \tag{9.67}$$

Since in both integrals the integrand disappears outside of the boundary layer, one may allow $h \to \infty$. The displacement thickness δ^* and the momentum thickness Θ, as in Eqs. (9.41) and (9.44), are introduced through the equations

$$\delta^* U = \int_{y=0}^{\infty} (U - u)\, dy \qquad \text{(displacement thickness)} \tag{9.68}$$

$$\Theta U^2 = \int_{y=0}^{\infty} u(U - u)\, dy \qquad \text{(momentum thickness)} \tag{9.69}$$

Consequently, from Eq. (9.67),

$$\frac{\tau_0}{\rho} = \frac{d}{dx}(U^2\Theta) + \delta^*\, U \frac{dU}{dx} \tag{9.70}$$

This is the momentum equation for the two-dimensional incompressible boundary layer; it is valid for laminar as well as for turbulent flow, if the appropriate formula is introduced for the shear stress at the wall τ_0.

Approximate Methods. Different approximate methods, originating from the momentum Eq. (9.70), are given for calculation of the laminar boundary layer. They are mostly rather simple in their application, but a detailed description is too extensive a project to be carried out here. Such an approximate method was first given by Pohlhausen[15] and was later simplified by Holstein and Bohlen[16] as well as by Walz.[17] Only the most important formulas are indicated here, that is, those which are necessary to carry out the calculation. For more detail the reader is referred to Ref. 11, chap. 12.

For the general case of the potential flow $U(x)$ variable along the wall, the velocity profiles are not similar. The variation of their shape along the wall is described by a shape factor as introduced by Pohlhausen:

$$\Lambda = \frac{\delta^2}{\nu} \frac{dU}{dx} \tag{9.71}$$

in which $\delta(x)$ denotes the boundary-layer thickness. All the velocity profiles in the boundary layer between the stagnation point and the separation point are expressed in terms of a one-parameter family in the form

$$\frac{u}{U} = F(\eta) + \Lambda G(\eta) \tag{9.72}$$

in which $\eta = y/\delta(x)$ denotes the dimensionless distance from the wall and $F(\eta)$ and $G(\eta)$ are both polynomials of the fourth degree:

$$F(\eta) = 1 - (1 - \eta)^3(1 + \eta) \qquad \text{and} \qquad G(\eta) = \tfrac{1}{6}\, \eta\, (1 - \eta)^3 \tag{9.73}$$

The shape factor Λ ranges from $\Lambda = 7.05$ at the leading-edge stagnation point, where $U = 0$, to $\Lambda = 0$ at minimum pressure to $\Lambda = -12$ at the separation point. In Fig. 9.19 velocity profiles are given for different values of Λ.

After the introduction of Eq. (9.72) into the momentum Eq. (9.70), the boundary-layer values of shear stress at the wall τ_0, momentum thickness Θ, and displacement thickness δ^* may all be expressed in terms of the shape factor Λ. This is the only unknown in the momentum Eq. (9.70). By carrying out this calculation one obtains an ordinary differential equation of the first order, which describes the variation of the momentum thickness along the wall. This differential equation can be integrated completely, yielding the following quadrature formula for the momentum thickness:

$$\frac{U\Theta^2}{\nu} = \frac{0.470}{U^5} \int_{x=0}^{x} U^5\, dx \tag{9.74}$$

After the growth of the momentum thickness along the wall has been determined from this equation, one obtains the other characteristic quantities of the boundary layer, namely, the shear stress at the wall τ_0 and the shape factor Λ (for determination of separation) from tables.

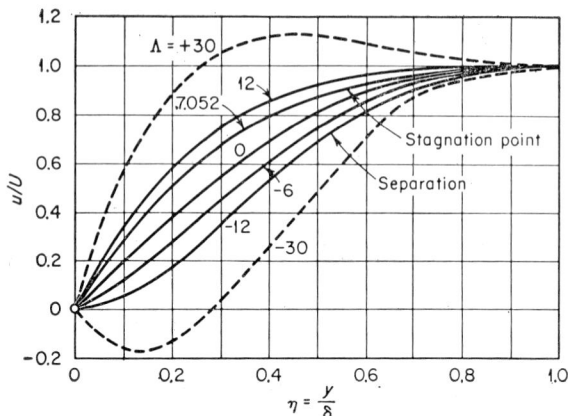

FIG. 9.19. The one-parameter family of velocity profiles of the laminar boundary layer as in Eq. (9.72) for different values of the shape factor Λ from Eq. (9.71).

As an example of such a boundary-layer calculation the results for a series of elliptical cylinders of varying slenderness a/b are depicted in Figs. 9.20 to 9.22. The cylinders were placed with the major axis parallel to the flow. The slenderness of the elliptical cylinder has the values $a/b = 1$, 2, 4, and 8. In Fig. 9.20 the velocity distribution around these four cylinders is shown as obtained from potential flow. In Fig. 9.21 the characteristic quantities of the boundary layer, the displacement thickness δ^*, the shape factor Λ, and the shear stress τ_0 at the wall, are given. As a comparison the results for the flat plate at zero incidence are also plotted here. For the circular cylinder, separation ($\Lambda = -12$) occurs for $x/l' = 0.609$, that is $\phi = 109.5°$ (l' equals the half circumference of the cylinder). With increasing slenderness the separation point moves downstream. Its position is also plotted in the velocity distribution (Fig. 9.20). The values of the displacement thickness and the shear stress at the wall for an elliptical cylinder of slenderness $a/b = 8$ differ only slightly from those of a flat plate at zero incidence (Figs. 9.21a and c). Finally, the velocity profiles for an elliptical cylinder of slenderness 4 are given in Fig. 9.22.

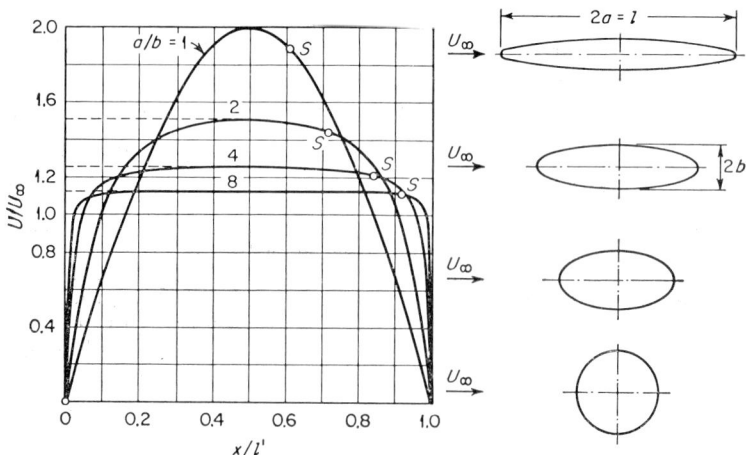

FIG. 9.20. Potential velocity distribution around elliptic cylinders of slenderness $a/b = 1, 2,$ 4, 8 placed with flow parallel to major axis. S = position of separation point. l' = one-half of circumference.

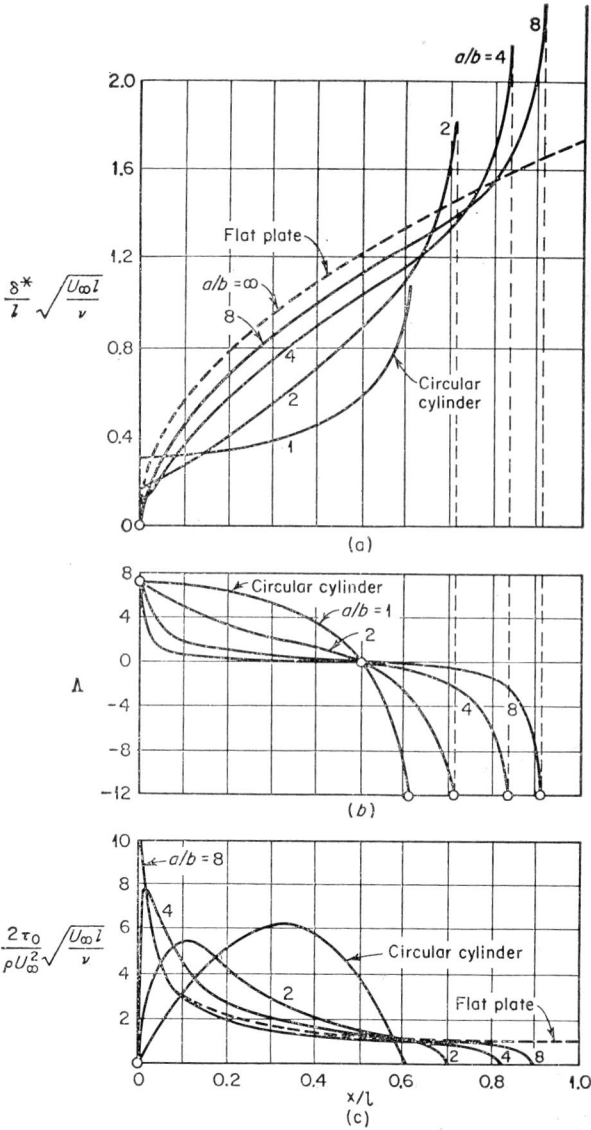

FIG. 9.21. Results of the boundary-layer calculation for the elliptic cylinder of slenderness $a/b = 1, 2, 4, 8$ as in Fig. 9.20; $l' =$ one-half of profile circumference; $l = 2a$.   (a) Displacement thickness of the boundary layer δ^*.   (b) Shape factor Λ.   (c) Shear stress at the wall τ_0.

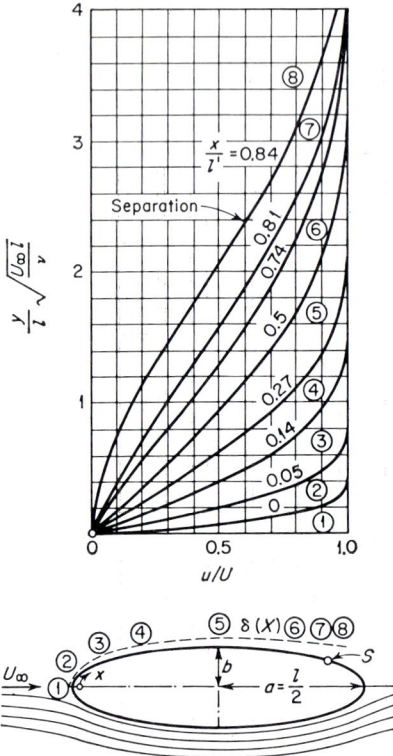

FIG. 9.22. Velocity profiles of the laminar boundary layer at the elliptic cylinder of slenderness $a/b = 4$; S = position of separation point.

Such an approximate method has also been worked out for bodies of revolution placed with their axis parallel to the flow.

9.14. Boundary-layer Control

General Remarks. A special peculiarity of flow phenomenon in the boundary layer is the fact that the entire flow past a body can be "steered" by the boundary layer. As an example of this, the trip wire on a sphere has already been discussed in Art. 9.8. Through this the laminar boundary layer is artificially made turbulent, and consequently the separation point is shifted downstream considerably. Thereby, for the sphere, there is a substantial reduction of cross section of the wake, and thus a decrease in pressure drag.

A series of further means of boundary-layer control has been developed whose fundamentals are illustrated in this article.[20] In most cases these means are concerned with avoiding separation, in order to gain thereby a reduction of drag or an increase of lift for the immersed body. However, in many cases boundary-layer control consists of changing the flow from laminar to turbulent or maintaining laminar flow. The various methods of boundary-layer control, which have been investigated mainly by experiment but also in part by theory, may be classified as follows:

1. Moving of the wall
2. Acceleration of the boundary layer
3. Suction
4. Delay of transition to turbulent flow by the provision of suitable shapes

Only a few measures are illustrated here. For a more detailed presentation see Ref. 11, chap. 13, as well as Schlichting[21] and Poisson-Quinton.[22]

Acceleration of the Boundary Layer. The most obvious method of preventing separation is to attempt to prevent the formation of a boundary layer. Since a boundary layer owes its existence to the difference between the velocity of the fluid and that of the solid wall, it is possible to avoid having a boundary layer by suppressing that difference, i.e., by causing the solid wall to move with the stream. The simplest way of achieving such a result involves the rotation of a circular cylinder. Figure 9.23 shows the flow pattern which exists about a rotating cylinder placed in a stream at right angles to its axis. On the upper side, where the flow and the cylinder move in the same direction, separation is completely eliminated. Furthermore, on

FIG. 9.23. Flow past a rotating circular cylinder.

the lower side, where the direction of fluid motion is opposite to that of the solid wall, separation is developed only incompletely. On the whole the flow pattern which exists in this case approximates very closely the case of frictionless flow past a circular cylinder with circulation. The stream exerts a considerable force (lift) on the cylinder at right angles to the mean-flow direction, and this is sometimes referred to as the Magnus effect. This force caused by rotating cylinders has been used in Flettner's rotor[23] for the propulsion of ships.

An alternative method of preventing separation consists of supplying additional energy to the particles of fluid which are being retarded in the boundary layer. This result can be achieved by discharging fluid from the interior of the body as in Fig. 9.24a, or more simply, by deriving the required energy directly from the main stream. This latter effect can be produced by connecting the retarded region to a region of higher pressure through a slot in the wing, as shown by the slotted wing in Fig. 9.24b. In either case additional energy is imparted to the particles of fluid in the boundary layer near the wall. In the case of the slotted wing[24] shown in Fig. 9.24b, the effect is produced as follows. The boundary layer formed on the forward slot A-B is carried into the main stream before separation occurs. For large angles of incidence the largest positive

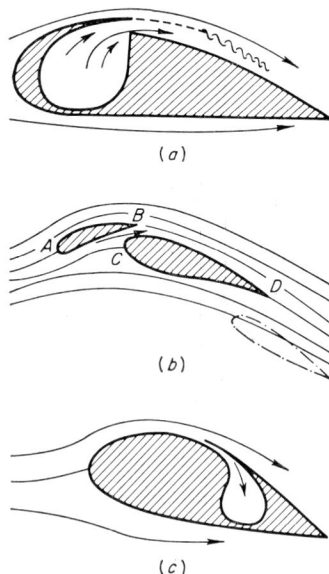

FIG. 9.24. Different arrangements for boundary-layer control. (a) Blowing out. (b) Slotted wings. (c) Suction.

pressure gradient, and consequently the greatest tendency for separation, occurs on the upper side of the forward slot. From point C onward a new boundary layer is formed, which under favorable conditions will reach the trailing edge D without separation. In this way it is possible to relegate separation to considerably larger angles of incidence and to achieve much larger lifts. Figure 9.25 shows a so-called polar diagram (lift coefficient plotted against drag coefficient) for a wing section with and without forward slot and flap. The phenomena in the slot formed by the flap near the trailing edge are, in principle, the same as those at the forward slot. The gain in lift is seen to be very considerable.

Suction. Another very effective way for boundary-layer control is suction. Suction of the boundary layer is utilized in two ways:

1. To prevent separation
2. To maintain laminar flow

In the first case the decelerated boundary-layer material is removed by suction through small slits in the body wall. If the suction is sufficiently strong, boundary-layer separation can be prevented. Suction as a measure of boundary-layer control was used by Prandtl in 1904 in his first boundary-layer work with the circular cylinder. As an example of the effect of boundary-layer suction, Fig. 9.26 shows the flow in a strongly divergent channel. Without suction there is separation because of the large positive pressure gradient. If the suction slits are opened in only one channel wall, the flow shifts to this side (Fig. 9.26b). If, however, the slits on both walls are opened, the flow is distributed across the entire cross section of the channel (Fig. 9.26c). With the aid of boundary-layer suction one obtains in the last case the streamlines of the frictionless flow. Boundary-layer suction to avoid separation has often been applied to airfoils. By applying suction, considerably greater pressure increases on the upper side of the airfoil (i.e., lower absolute pressures) are obtained at large angles of incidence and, consequently, much larger maximum lift values. Schrenk[25] investigated a large number of different arrangements of suction slits and their effect on maximum lift.

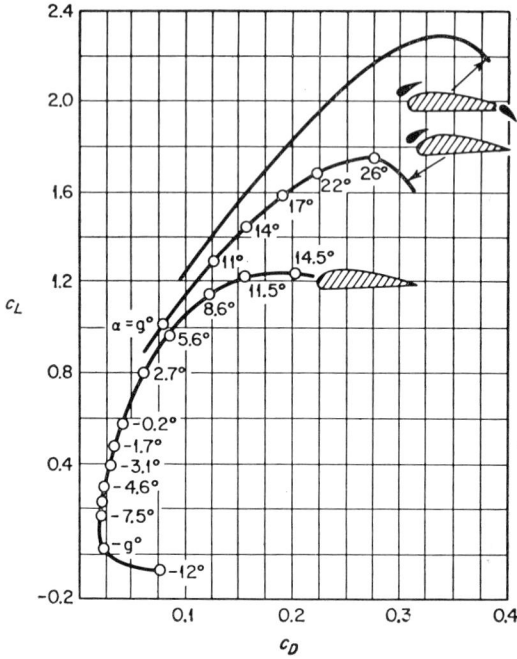

FIG. 9.25. Polar diagram of an airfoil with slot and flap.

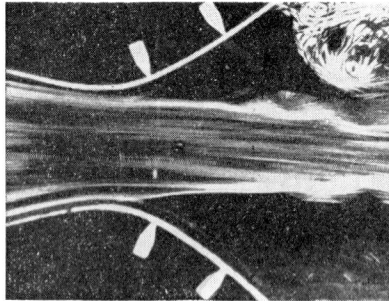

(a)

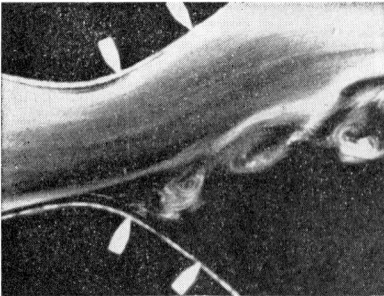

(b)

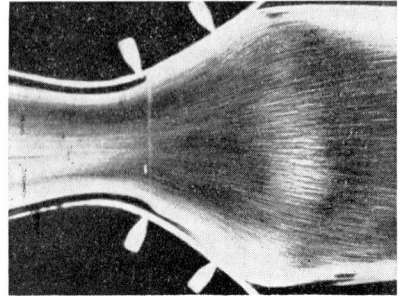

(c)

FIG. 9.26. Flow in a highly divergent channel. (a) Without suction. (b) With suction on the upper channel wall. (c) With suction on both channel walls.

In more recent times suction was also applied to reduce drag. By the use of suitable arrangements of suction slits it is possible to shift the point of transition in the boundary layer in the downstream direction, which causes the drag coefficient to decrease, because laminar drag is substantially smaller than turbulent drag. The effect of the *delay in transition* caused by suction is to reduce the boundary-layer thickness, which then becomes less prone to transition.

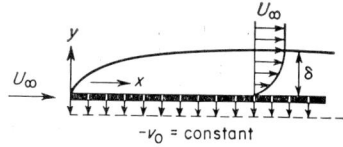

FIG. 9.27. The flat plate at zero incidence with uniform suction.

Boundary Layer at a Flat Plate with Uniform Suction. Several simple results are obtained for the laminar boundary layer with continuous suction on a flat plate at zero incidence: the uniform suction in Fig. 9.27, which can be realized with the aid of a porous wall, is so small that only fluid particles in the immediate neighborhood of the wall are sucked away. This is equivalent to saying that the ratio of suction velocity to free-stream velocity U is very small, say, $-v_0/U_\infty = 0.0001$ to 0.01. The quantity of fluid removed is $Q = (-v_0)A$, in which A is the plate area. The volume coefficient, defined by

$$Q = c_Q A U_\infty \tag{9.75}$$

is therefore equal to

$$c_Q = \frac{-v_0}{U_\infty} \tag{9.76}$$

The differential equations for the boundary layer, from Eqs. (9.20) and (9.21), are

$$\frac{\partial u}{\partial x} + \frac{\partial v}{\partial y} = 0 \tag{9.77}$$

$$u \frac{\partial u}{\partial x} + v \frac{\partial u}{\partial y} = \nu \frac{\partial^2 u}{\partial y^2} \tag{9 78}$$

with the boundary conditions

$$y = 0 : u = 0 , v = v_0 = \text{const} < 0 \qquad y = \infty : u = U_\infty \tag{9.79}$$

The condition of no slip for the flow at the wall is also retained in the case of suction, as well as the expression for the shear stress at the wall, $\tau_0 = \mu(\partial u/\partial y)_0$. The system of Eqs. (9.77) and (9.78) has a simple solution, in which the velocity distribution is independent of the current length x. By making $\partial u/\partial x \equiv 0$, it is seen from the equation of continuity that $v(x,y) = v_0 = \text{const}$, and consequently from Eq. (9.78),

$$u(y) = U_\infty(1 - e^{v_0 y/\nu}) \qquad v(x,y) = v_0 < 0 \tag{9.80}$$

The shear stress at the wall, $\tau_0 = \mu(\partial u/\partial y)_0$, becomes simply

$$\tau_0 = \rho(-v_0)U_\infty \tag{9.81}$$

and is independent of the viscosity. The present solution for a flat plate at zero incidence with uniform suction is obtained only at some distance from the leading edge, since in the case of suction the boundary-layer thickness is zero at the leading edge. For this reason this solution may be regarded as the asymptotic suction profile. Particular interest is attached to the decrease in drag caused by keeping the flow laminar with the aid of suction, and therefore to the law of friction for the plate with uniform suction, depicted in Fig. 9.28. For very large Reynolds numbers **R**, when the major portion of the plate falls within the region of the asymptotic solution, the drag is given by Eq. (9.81). In this case the local drag coefficient is

$$c'_f = \frac{\tau_0}{\rho U_\infty^2/2} = 2 \frac{-v_0}{U_\infty} = 2c_Q \tag{9.82}$$

The drag coefficient is larger for small Reynolds numbers, because the shear stress is

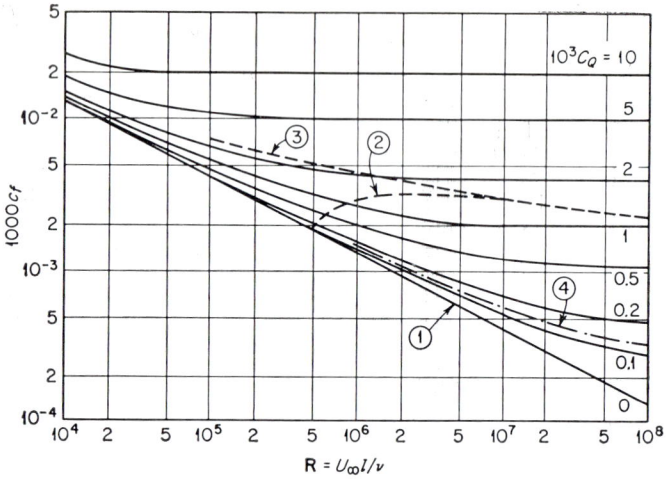

Fig. 9.28. Resistance law of the flat plate at zero incidence with uniform suction. c_Q = volume coefficient of suction as in Eqs. (9.75) and (9.76). Curves 1, 2, 3 are without suction. Curve 1, laminar; curve 2, transition from laminar to turbulent; curve 3, completely turbulent; curve 4, "optimum suction" for $c_Q = 1.2 \times 10^{-4}$.

greater over the front portion of the plate which falls within the initial region and where the boundary layer is thinner than farther downstream. The drag on a plate with a turbulent boundary layer with no suction is shown plotted in Fig. 9.28 for the purpose of comparison. The saving in drag can be deduced from this diagram if one knows the value of the smallest volume coefficient of suction which is capable of ensuring laminar conditions in the boundary layer at large Reynolds numbers. The necessary volume coefficient of suction was found by Ulrich[26] to be

$$c_{Q\ cr} = 1.2 \times 10^{-4} \qquad (9.83)$$

This value is plotted as "optimum suction" in Fig. 9.28. The difference between the curves "turbulent" and "optimum suction" is the possible saving in drag by maintaining laminar flow. In the range of Reynolds number from $R = 10^6$ to 10^8 it amounts to about 70 to 80 per cent of the drag at fully turbulent flow.

THE TURBULENT BOUNDARY LAYER IN INCOMPRESSIBLE FLOW

9.15. Fundamentals of Turbulent Flow

Mean Motion and Fluctuations. After fundamentals of the boundary layer for laminar flow have been presented, it is now appropriate that turbulent flows in the boundary layer be discussed. Flows through pipes and channels, as well as in the boundary layers of immersed bodies, are in most cases turbulent. As already mentioned in Art. 9.8, irregular fluctuations are superimposed on the principal motion, which are called mixing motion. Analysis of turbulent flow shows that at a fixed point in space the velocity and pressure do not remain constant with time but perform irregular fluctuations of high frequency. The lumps of fluid which perform such fluctuations in the direction of flow and perpendicular to it are more or less macroscopic fluid balls. By way of example it may be noted that although the velocity fluctuations in channel or pipe flow do not exceed several per cent, they nevertheless have a decisive effect on the whole motion. For experimental analysis and mathematical treatment it is convenient to split up turbulent flow into a *mean motion* and a *fluctuation*. Denoting the time average of the u

component of velocity by $\bar{u}$ and its velocity of fluctuation by u', the following equations may be written for the velocity components and pressure:

$$u = \bar{u} + u' \qquad v = \bar{v} + v' \qquad w = \bar{w} + w' \qquad p = \bar{p} + p' \qquad (9.84)$$

The time averages are formed at a fixed point in space and are given, for example, by

$$\bar{u} = \frac{1}{T} \int_{t_0}^{t_0+T} u \, dt \qquad (9.85)$$

In this connection the mean values are taken over a sufficiently long interval of time T for them to be completely independent of time. Thus, by definition, the time averages of all quantities describing the fluctuations are equal to zero.

$$\overline{u'} = 0 \qquad \overline{v'} = 0 \qquad \overline{w'} = 0 \qquad \overline{p'} = 0 \qquad (9.86)$$

The turbulent fluctuations u', v', w' cause additional stresses, which are determined with the aid of the momentum equation. Consequently, the mean motion is affected in such a way as to make it appear that the viscosity has increased. This increased *apparent viscosity* of the mean motion forms the central concept of all theoretical considerations of turbulent motion. For the stress components on an area element normal to the x axis one obtains (Ref. 11, chap. 18)

$$\sigma'_x = -\rho\overline{u'^2} \qquad \tau'_{xy} = -\rho\overline{u'v'} \qquad \tau'_{xz} = -\rho\overline{u'w'} \qquad (9.87)$$

Suitable expressions for the stress components on the area elements normal to the y and z axes may be found. These apparent stresses of turbulent flow must be added to the stresses of stationary laminar flow. Equations (9.87) were first derived by O. Reynolds from the hydrodynamic equations of motion. They are therefore called the Reynolds stresses of the apparent turbulent friction.

The stress component $\tau'_{xy} = -\rho\overline{u'v'}$ can also be interpreted as the transport of x momentum through a surface normal to the y axis. It is easily seen that the time average of the product of the velocity fluctuations $\overline{u'v'}$ is in fact different from zero, since the mean motion of a two-dimensional shearing flow is depicted in Fig. 9.29 with

$$\bar{u} = \bar{u}(y) \qquad \bar{v} = \bar{w} = 0 \qquad (9.88)$$

and with $d\bar{u}/dy > 0$. The particles in layer y traveling upward as a result of the transverse motion ($v' > 0$) come from a region where a smaller mean velocity $\bar{u}$ prevails. Since they do, on the whole, retain their original velocity $\bar{u}$, they give rise to a negative component u' in a layer y. Conversely, the particles which arrive from above the layer ($v' < 0$) give rise to a positive u' in it. On the average, therefore, a positive v' is "mostly" associated with a negative u' and a negative v' is mostly associated with a positive u'. One may thus expect that the time average $\overline{u'v'}$ is not only different from zero but also negative. The additional shear stress $\tau' = -\rho\overline{u'v'}$ is positive in this case and has the same sign as the relevant laminar shearing stress $\tau_l = \mu \, du/dy$. From the boundary conditions it follows that all turbulent components must vanish at the walls and that they are very small in their immediate neighborhood. Consequently, in every turbulent flow there exists a very thin layer next to the wall which in essence behaves like one in laminar motion. It is known as the *laminar sublayer*. In spite of its very small thickness, it is of decisive importance in the formation of skin-friction drag.

Measurements on fluctuating turbulent velocities were first carried out by Reichardt[27] for flow in a wind tunnel. Figure 9.30 shows such measurements for the turbulent

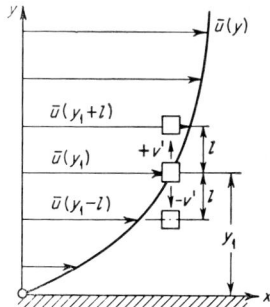

FIG. 9.29. Transfer of momentum by means of turbulent fluctuations in a two-dimensional shear flow. $l =$ mixing length.

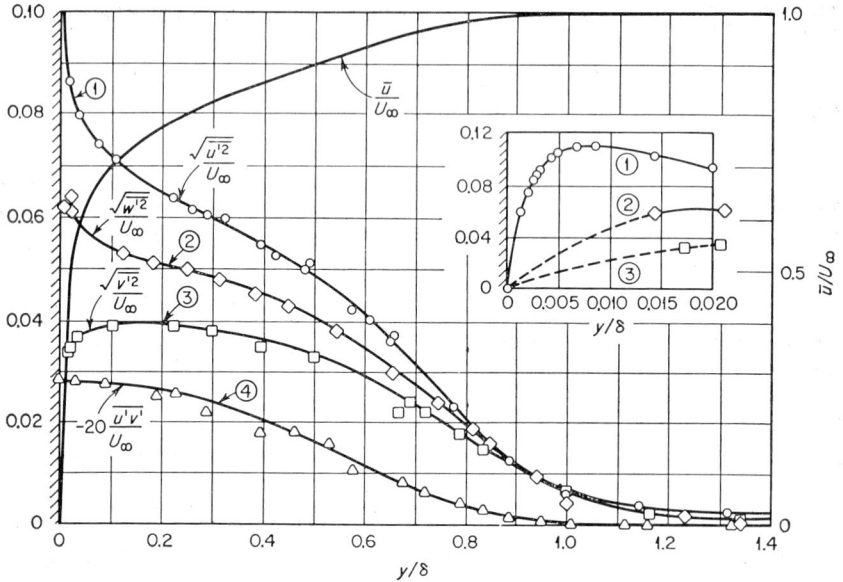

FIG. 9.30. Distribution of turbulent fluctuations in the boundary layer of a flat plate at zero incidence according to measurements by Klebanoff.[28] $\bar{u}$ = time average of the longitudinal velocity; u', v', w' are components of the turbulent fluctuations.

boundary layer on a flat plate at zero incidence by Klebanoff.[28] The longitudinal fluctuation $\sqrt{\overline{u'^2}}$ exhibits a pronounced maximum very close to the wall. The two transverse fluctuations $\sqrt{\overline{v'^2}}$ and $\sqrt{\overline{w'^2}}$ show a weaker rise than $\sqrt{\overline{u'^2}}$, but also have a maximum close to the wall. The mean value $\overline{u'v'}$ is equal to the additional turbulent shear stress τ'_{xy} except for the factor ρ.

Prandtl's Mixing-length Theory. In order to be able to make calculations of turbulent flow it is necessary to find an expression for the turbulent shear stress which relates it to the time averages of the velocity components. An expression of this kind, which has proved very useful, was first given by Prandtl[29] in 1925. It is called Prandtl's mixing-length theory and is discussed briefly here. A simple shear flow is considered, as in Fig. 9.29 and Eq. (9.88). In order to evaluate the shear-stress components

$$\tau'_{xy} = \tau' = -\rho\overline{u'v'} \tag{9.89}$$

one may now visualize the following simplified mechanism of turbulent flow, following Prandtl: as the fluid passes along the wall in turbulent motion, fluid particles coalesce into lumps which move bodily and which cling together for a given length, both in the longitudinal and in the transverse direction, retaining their momentum parallel to x. It will now be assumed that such a lump of fluid, which comes from a layer at $(y_1 - l)$ and has a velocity $\bar{u}(y_1 - l)$, is displaced over a distance l in the transverse direction. As the lump of fluid retains its original momentum, its velocity in the new lamina at y_1 is smaller than the velocity prevailing there. The difference in velocities is then

$$\Delta u_1 = \bar{u}(y_1) - \bar{u}(y_1 - l) = l\left(\frac{d\bar{u}}{dy}\right)_1$$

In this transverse motion $v' > 0$. Similarly, a lump of fluid which arrives at y_1 from the lamina at $(y_1 + l)$ possesses a velocity which exceeds that around it, the difference being

$$\Delta u_2 = \bar{u}(y_1 + l) - \bar{u}(y_1) = l\left(\frac{d\bar{u}}{dy}\right)_1$$

The velocity differences caused by the transverse motion can be regarded as the turbulent-velocity components at y_1. Hence the time average of the absolute value of this fluctuation is calculated to be

$$|\overline{u'}| = \tfrac{1}{2}(|\Delta u_1| + |\Delta u_2|) = l\left|\left(\frac{d\bar{u}}{dy}\right)_1\right| \tag{9.90}$$

Here l is the Prandtl mixing length. It is roughly analogous to the mean free path of kinetic-gas theory, with the difference that in kinetic theory it concerns itself with microscopic movements of molecules, whereas here one is concerned with macroscopic movements of lumps of fluid.

For the transverse motion one may make the assumption that v' is proportional to u'. Therefore

$$|\overline{v'}| = \text{const } |\overline{u'}| = \text{const } l\frac{d\bar{u}}{dy} \tag{9.91}$$

In order to determine the shear stress from Eq. (9.89) the mean value $\overline{u'v'}$ must be examined more closely. One now sets $\overline{u'v'} = -k\,|\overline{u'}| \cdot |\overline{v'}|$, in which k, from the above remarks, is between 0 and 1. From Eqs. (9.90) and (9.91) the following is obtained:

$$\overline{u'v'} = -\text{const } l^2 \left(\frac{d\bar{u}}{dy}\right)^2$$

If the constant is included with the still unknown mixing length and if it is further noted that the sign of τ_{turb} must change with that of $d\bar{u}/dy$, then for the turbulent shear stress from Eq. (9.89), one may write

$$\tau_{\text{turb}} = \rho l^2 \left|\frac{d\bar{u}}{dy}\right|\frac{d\bar{u}}{dy} \tag{9.92}$$

This is Prandtl's mixing-length hypothesis, which is very useful in the calculation of turbulent flows. In many cases it is possible to establish a simple relation between the mixing length l and a characteristic length of the respective flow. For example, in flows along smooth walls l must vanish at the wall itself, because transverse motions are inhibited by its presence. Prandtl's equation [Eq. (9.92)] has been successfully applied to the study of turbulent motion along walls (pipe, channel, plate) and to the problem of free turbulence (free jets, wakes).

Velocity Distribution in the Turbulent Boundary Layer. These formulas for the turbulent shear stress may be used to calculate the velocity distribution in a turbulent boundary layer. It still does not matter whether one considers the turbulent boundary layer for an immersed body, pipe, or channel. Near the wall the mixing length is set proportional to the distance from the wall y.

$$l = \kappa y \tag{9.93}$$

Here κ denotes a dimensionless constant which must be deduced from experiment. Hence, from Eq. (9.92), the turbulent shear stress is $\tau = \rho\kappa^2 y^2(du/dy)^2$, if $u(y)$ is the time average of the velocity. At this stage Prandtl introduced an additional, far-reaching assumption, namely, that the shear stress τ is constant throughout the range of the velocity, that is, $\tau = \tau_0$, in which τ_0 is the shear stress at the wall. Introducing the friction velocity

$$v_* = \sqrt{\frac{\tau_0}{\rho}} \tag{9.94}$$

the previous equation may be written in the form $v_*^2 = \kappa^2 y^2(du/dy)^2$ or $du/dy = v_*/\kappa y$. On integrating one finds

$$u = \frac{v_*}{\kappa} \ln y + C \tag{9.95}$$

Here the constant of integration C must be determined from the condition at the wall and serves to fit the turbulent-velocity distribution to that in the laminar sublayer. More simply, however, it is possible to determine C from the condition that $u = 0$ in a certain very small distance from the wall y_0, which is of the order of magnitude of the thickness of the laminar sublayer. Thus, from Eq. (9.95),

$$u = \frac{v_*}{\kappa} (\ln y - \ln y_0)$$

The thickness of the laminar sublayer is of the order of magnitude of ν/v_*. Consequently, $y_0 = \beta\nu/v_*$, in which β is a dimensionless constant. Then, from Eq. (9.95), the velocity distribution in the turbulent boundary layer is obtained in the following dimensionless form:

$$\frac{u}{v_*} = \frac{1}{\kappa}\left(\ln \frac{yv_*}{\nu} - \ln \beta\right)$$

Introducing the abbreviations

$$A = \frac{1}{\kappa} \qquad D = -\frac{1}{\kappa}\ln \beta$$

the previous equation may be written

$$\frac{u}{v_*} = A \ln \frac{yv_*}{\nu} + D \tag{9.96}$$

This is the *universal velocity-distribution law*. It is valid, as measurements show (Fig. 9.33), for flow through a pipe, as well as for the boundary layer at a flat plate at zero incidence. From measurements in smooth pipes the constants of this equation have been determined to be

$$A = 2.5 \qquad D = 5.5 \tag{9.96a}$$

Thus $\kappa = 0.4$, which seems plausible.

9.16. Some Remarks on Turbulent Flow through Pipes

A substantial contribution to the explanation of the laws of turbulent-boundary-layer flow has been furnished by the thorough experimental investigation of flow through pipes. For this reason some remarks are made here on turbulent flow through pipes.

Law of Resistance. In the investigation of flow through pipes it has become possible to combine the relationship of the pressure gradient and the quantity of flow in the pipe (law of resistance) with extensive measurements of the velocity distribution to complete an analysis of the flow. The extensive experimental data on flow resistance for turbulent flow were first arranged by Blasius[30] in accordance with Reynolds' law of similarity. For the pipe resistance coefficient λ of a smooth pipe of circular cross section of diameter D, defined by

$$\Delta p = \lambda \frac{L}{D}\frac{\rho}{2}\bar{u}^2 \tag{9.97}$$

Blasius found the following relation:

$$\lambda = \frac{0.316}{\mathbf{R}^{1/4}} \tag{9.98}$$

which is known as the Blasius formula. Here Δp denotes the pressure drop over the pipe length L; $\bar{u} = Q/(\pi D^2/4)$ denotes the average velocity over the cross section with Q the discharge; and $\mathbf{R} = \bar{u}D/\nu$ denotes the Reynolds number of the pipe. In Fig. 9.31

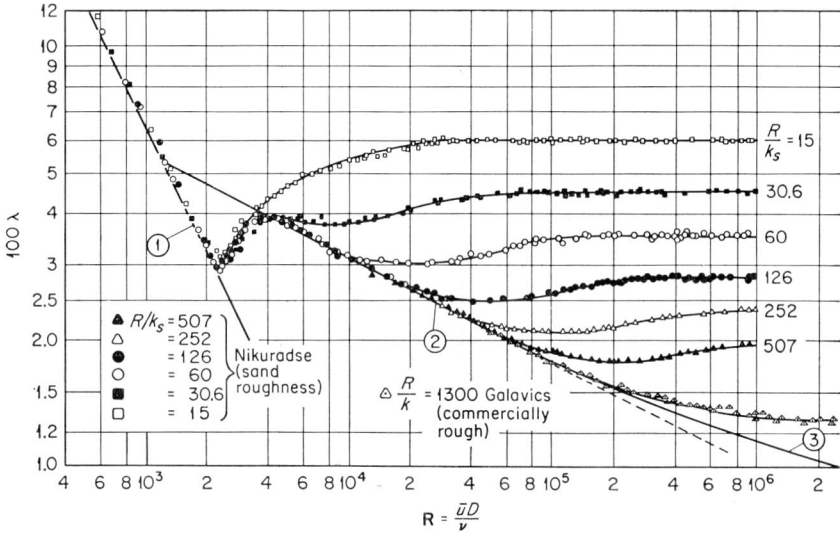

FIG. 9.31. Resistance law of smooth and rough pipes. Curve 1, laminar, $\lambda = 64/\mathbf{R}$; curve 2, turbulent, as in Eq. (9.98); curve 3, turbulent, as in Eq. (9.99). Curves 1, 2, 3 are for smooth pipes; the other curves are for rough pipes, k_S = height of roughness element.

this formula is plotted as curve 2 and is compared with measurements. It is evident that Eq. (9.98) agrees well with experimental results up to $\mathbf{R} = 10^5$. The measurements were later extended by Nikuradse[31] for larger Reynolds numbers (up to about $\mathbf{R} = 3 \times 10^6$). From these measurements and the theoretical considerations of Prandtl,[32,33] the following law of resistance was derived:

$$\frac{1}{\sqrt{\lambda}} = 2.0 \log (\mathbf{R}\sqrt{\lambda}) - 0.8 \qquad (9.99)$$

This Prandtl universal law of resistance for smooth pipes is plotted (curve 3) in Fig. 9.31. Up to $\mathbf{R} = 10^5$ it is in agreement with the Blasius law [Eq. (9.98)]. For higher Reynolds numbers the Blasius formula deviates considerably from the measurements, while Eq. (9.99) is in good agreement.

Velocity Distribution. For turbulent flow through pipes the velocity distribution as well as the law of resistance has been thoroughly investigated for large Reynolds numbers, $4 \times 10^3 < \mathbf{R} < 3.2 \times 10^6$. In Fig. 9.32 the velocity distributions are given for several Reynolds numbers in the dimensionless form u/U versus y/R, in which U is the maximum velocity in the center of the pipe and y is the distance from the pipe wall. Figure 9.32 shows that for turbulent flow the velocity is distributed substantially more uniformly over the cross section than the parabolic distribution of laminar flow. In addition, the turbulent-velocity profile becomes more uniform with increasing Reynolds number. It may be represented by the interpolation formula

$$\frac{u}{U} = \left(\frac{y}{R}\right)^{1/n} \qquad (9.100)$$

in which the exponent n varies from about $n = 6$ to $n = 10$ in the range of Reynolds number from $\mathbf{R} = 4 \times 10^3$ to 3×10^6.

According to Prandtl, there is a relation between the Blasius law of resistance and the velocity-distribution law Eq. (9.100), which makes it possible to draw conclusions from the experiments on pipe resistance of value for determining the skin friction of a flat

HANDBOOK OF FLUID DYNAMICS

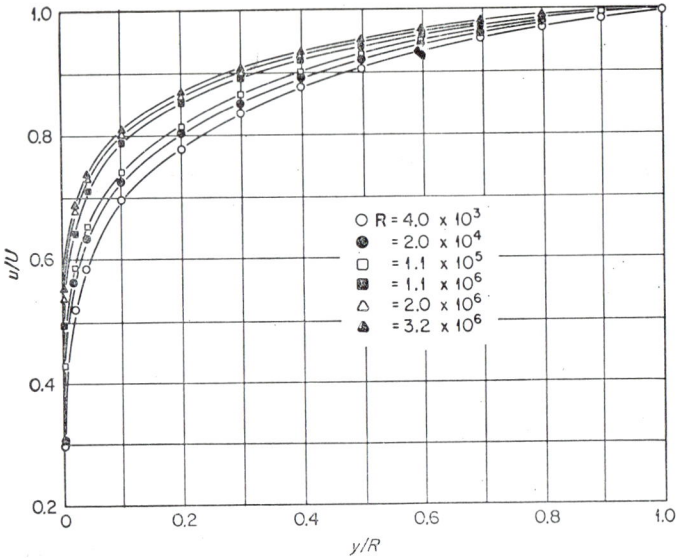

FIG. 9.32. Turbulent-velocity distribution in smooth pipes for different Reynolds numbers according to Nikuradse.[31]

plate at zero incidence. For pipe flow the following relation between pressure gradient and shear stress at the wall τ_0 is generally valid as herein:

$$\tau_0 = \frac{\Delta p}{L} \frac{R}{2} \tag{9.101}$$

By comparing Eqs. (9.101) and (9.97) the following relation between shear stress at the wall and pipe resistance coefficient is obtained:

$$\tau_0 = \tfrac{1}{8} \lambda \rho \bar{u}^2 \tag{9.102}$$

By inserting the value of λ from the Blasius law [Eq. (9.98)] into Eq. (9.102) and converting to the pipe radius by means of $D = 2R$, one obtains:

$$\tau_0 = \rho v_*^2 = 0.03325 \rho \bar{u}^{7/4} \nu^{1/4} R^{-1/4} \tag{9.103}$$

in which v_* denotes the shear-stress velocity from Eq. (9.94). Next, from Eq. (9.102) one finds $\bar{u}/v_* = 6.99(v_* R/\nu)^{1/7}$. By introducing $\bar{u}/U = 0.8$ into this equation, which proves correct for $n = 7$ and consequently for $\mathbf{R} \approx 10^5$, it is found that

$$\frac{U}{v_*} = 8.74 \left(\frac{v_* R}{\nu} \right)^{1/7} \tag{9.104}$$

If it is further assumed that this relation is valid not only for the center of the pipe $(y = R)$, but also for every distance y, one finally obtains

$$\frac{u}{v_*} = 8.74 \left(\frac{y v_*}{\nu} \right)^{1/7} \tag{9.105}$$

With this, the $\tfrac{1}{7}$-power law of velocity distribution has been derived from the Blasius law of resistance, which was shown to agree well with the measurements in a certain range of Reynolds number.

The dimensionless velocity distribution from Eq. (9.105) is plotted as curve 4 in Fig.

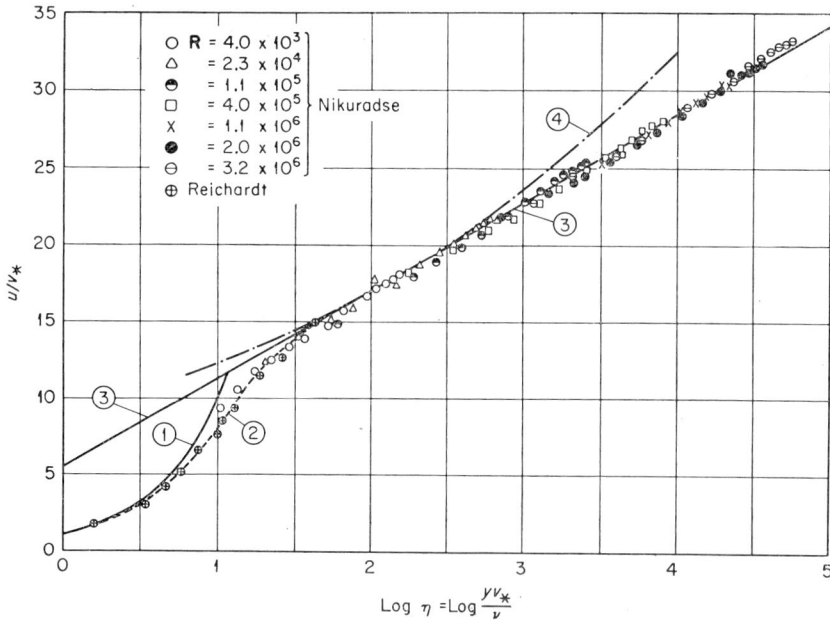

FIG. 9.33. The universal logarithmic-velocity-distribution law in smooth pipes. Curve 1, laminar; curve 2, transition from laminar to turbulent; curve 3, turbulent for all Reynolds numbers as in Eq. (9.96); curve 4, turbulent for $R < 10^5$ as in Eq. (9.105).

9.33 and is compared with experimental results. The $\frac{1}{7}$-power law agrees well with the data for Reynolds numbers up to $R = 100,000$.

With regard to a later application to the flat plate at zero incidence (Art. 9.17), the friction velocity v_*, and consequently the shear stress at the wall, may be determined [Eq. (9.104)]. One obtains $v_* = 0.150U^{7/8}(\nu/R)^{1/8}$, and thus for the shear stress at the wall $\tau_0 = \rho v_*^2$,

$$\tau_0 = 0.0225\rho U^{7/4}\left(\frac{\nu}{R}\right)^{1/4} \tag{9.106}$$

This equation is considered again in the evaluation of the frictional resistance of a flat plate at zero incidence.

For very large Reynolds numbers Fig. 9.33 shows considerable deviation of the measured velocity distribution from the $\frac{1}{7}$-power law, Eq. (9.104). The measurements for the very large Reynolds numbers are represented well by the logarithmic velocity-distribution law, Eqs. (9.96) and (9.96a), which is plotted as curve 3 in Fig. 9.33.

Rough Pipes. The resistance of rough pipes has been investigated in an especially thorough manner for granular roughnesses (sand roughnesses with size of roughness k_s) by Nikuradse.[34] The roughness of the wall in this case may be characterized by a single roughness parameter, the relative roughness k_s/R. In Fig. 9.31 the resistance coefficients of pipes roughened with sand are plotted for $R/k_s = 15$ to 500. In considering the influence of roughness on the resistance, it is necessary to differentiate three regimes:

    I. Hydraulically smooth regime:

        In this regime roughness has no effect on the resistance. $v_*k/\nu \leq 5 : \lambda = f(\mathbf{R})$.

    II. Transition regime:

        In this regime the resistance coefficient depends on the Reynolds number as well as on the relative roughness. Its value is given by $5 \leq v_*k/\nu \leq 70 : \lambda = f(\mathbf{R}, k_s/R)$.

III. Completely rough regime:

In this regime the purely quadratic law of resistance is in effect. The resistance coefficient depends only on the relative roughness. Its value is given by $v_* k/\nu \geq 70 : \lambda = f(k_s/R)$. For sand roughness in this regime

$$\lambda = \frac{1}{[2 \log (R/k_s) + 1.74]^2} \tag{9.107}$$

Physically, these three regimes may be characterized as follows: in regime I (hydraulically smooth) the protrusions are contained within the laminar sublayer; in regime II (transition regime) the protrusions extend partly outside of the laminar sublayer; and in regime III (completely rough regime) all the protrusions reach outside of the laminar sublayer.

9.17. Skin-friction Drag of a Flat Plate at Zero Incidence

The Smooth Plate. The simplest case of a turbulent boundary layer occurs on a flat plate at zero incidence. The boundary layer at a plate is very important practically, since the skin-friction drag of the flat plate at zero incidence constitutes a substantial share of the drag of turbine and blower blades and of ships, as well as of airfoils and fuselages.

Considerable difficulties are encountered in the integration of the boundary-layer differential equations with the above given expression for the turbulent shear stress. For this reason the simpler approximate method is applied, which is illustrated in Art. 9.13. For this approximate method Prandtl assumed that the velocity distribution in the boundary layer on the plate is identical with that inside the pipe. With the aid of this assumption it is possible to utilize the experimental results on flow through pipes (Art. 9.16). In the transition from the pipe to the plate the maximum velocity U in the pipe corresponds to the free-stream velocity of the plate, and the radius R of the pipe corresponds to the boundary-layer thickness δ. A system of coordinates is chosen as in Fig. 9.34, with b the width of the plate. It is further assumed that the boundary layer at the plate is turbulent from the leading edge $x = 0$.

The momentum equation is used to determine the skin friction of a plate of length x wetted on one side [Eq. (9.43)].

$$D(x) = b \int_0^x \tau_0(x')\, dx' = b\rho \int_0^{\delta(x)} u(U_\infty - u)\, dy = b\rho U_\infty^2 \Theta(x) \tag{9.108}$$

in which the second integral is to be taken over the width of the boundary layer at point x, and $\Theta(x)$ denotes the momentum thickness at point x. From Eq. (9.108) one obtains

$$\frac{1}{b}\frac{dD}{dx} = \tau_0(x) = \rho U_\infty^2 \frac{d\Theta}{dx} \tag{9.109}$$

An appropriate expression for the velocity distribution in the turbulent boundary layer is now introduced into this equation. In the simplest case the $\frac{1}{7}$-power law is chosen, as discussed for flow through pipes in Art. 9.16. On the basis of previous considerations the velocity distribution in the boundary layer on the plate in this case is found to be

$$\frac{u}{U_\infty} = \left(\frac{y}{\delta}\right)^{\frac{1}{7}} \tag{9.110}$$

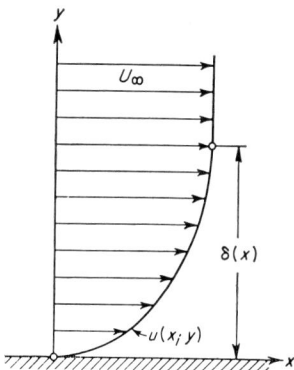

FIG. 9.34. Turbulent boundary layer on the flat plate at zero incidence (schematic).

The law for the shear stress at the wall is likewise taken from the case of flow through a pipe, Eq. (9.106); if U_∞ replaces U and δ replaces R,

$$\frac{\tau_0}{\rho U_\infty^2} = 0.0225 \left(\frac{\nu}{U_\infty \delta}\right)^{1/4} \tag{9.111}$$

The following relationship exists between the momentum thickness Θ and the boundary-layer thickness δ for the velocity distribution as in Eq. (9.110):

$$\Theta = \frac{7}{72}\,\delta \tag{9.112}$$

By inserting Eqs. (9.112) and (9.111) in Eq. (9.109) the following simple differential equation is obtained for the boundary-layer thickness $\delta(x)$:

$$\frac{7}{72}\frac{d\delta}{dx} = 0.0225 \left(\frac{\nu}{U_\infty \delta}\right)^{1/4} \tag{9.113}$$

The integration of this equation with initial condition $\delta = 0$ for $x = 0$ yields $\delta(x) = 0.37x(U_\infty x/\nu)^{-1/5}$, and consequently

$$\Theta(x) = 0.036x \left(\frac{U_\infty x}{\nu}\right)^{-1/5} \tag{9.114}$$

Thus the total skin-friction drag of a flat plate wetted on one side with width b and length l as in Eq. (9.108) is found to be

$$D = 0.036\rho U_\infty^2 bl \left(\frac{U_\infty l}{\nu}\right)^{-1/5}$$

From this it is evident that for turbulent flow the skin-friction drag is proportional to $U_\infty^{9/5}$ and $l^{4/5}$, while for laminar flow the corresponding powers are $U^{3/2}$ and $l^{1/2}$. If, finally, dimensionless coefficients for local and total drag are introduced by

$$c_f' = \frac{\tau_0}{(\rho/2)U_\infty^2} \qquad c_f = \frac{D}{bl(\rho/2)U_\infty^2} \tag{9.115}$$

respectively, then one obtains

$$c_f' = 2\frac{d\Theta}{dx} \qquad c_f = 2\frac{\Theta(l)}{l}$$

With this and Eq. (9.114) these drag coefficients are found to be

$$c_f' = 0.0576 \left(\frac{U_\infty x}{\nu}\right)^{-1/5} \tag{9.116}$$

and $\qquad\qquad c_f = 0.074(\mathbf{R})^{-1/5} \qquad 5 \times 10^5 < \mathbf{R} < 10^7 \tag{9.117}$ †

This resistance law is depicted as curve 2 in Fig. 9.35. It agrees well with measurements up to a Reynolds number $\mathbf{R} = 10^7$. As mentioned above, this resistance law is valid under the hypothesis that the boundary layer is turbulent downstream from the leading edge. In reality, if no special measures are taken, the boundary layer is laminar in front and turbulent farther downstream (Art. 9.8). The position of the transition point is determined by the intensity of turbulence of the external flow through a critical Reynolds number $(U_\infty x/\nu)_{cr} = 3 \times 10^5$ to 3×10^6. The drag reduction caused by the initial laminar boundary layer is taken into account by an additional term of the form

$$c_f = \frac{0.074}{\mathbf{R}^{1/5}} - \frac{A}{\mathbf{R}} \tag{9.118}$$

in which the constant A is taken from Table 9.2.

† In this equation the numerical factor has been changed from 0.072 to 0.074 in order to fit the experimental results better.

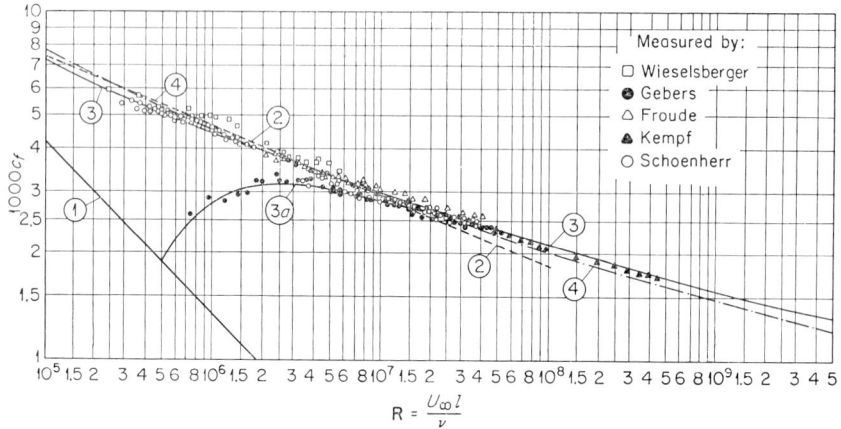

Fig. 9.35. Resistance law of the smooth flat plate at zero incidence, comparison with theory and measurements. Theoretical curves: curve 1 laminar, Blasius, as in Eq. (9.38); curve 2, turbulent, Prandtl, as in Eq. (9.117); curve 3, turbulent, Prandtl-Schlichting, Eq. (9.119) with $A = 0$; curve 3a, transition from laminar to turbulent as in Eq. (9.119); curve 4, turbulent according to Schultz-Grunow.

For larger Reynolds numbers, for which a logarithmic law replaces the $\frac{1}{7}$-power law of velocity distribution in the pipe [Eq. (9.95)], one also obtains, accordingly, another law for the plate. This resistance law has the same addition factor, as in Eq. (9.118).

$$c_f = \frac{0.455}{(\log \mathbf{R})^{2.58}} - \frac{A}{\mathbf{R}} \tag{9.119}$$

This Prandtl-Schlichting skin-friction formula for the smooth plate, plotted for $\mathbf{R}_{x\,cr} = 5 \times 10^5$ as curve 3 in Fig. 9.35, agrees with Eq. (9.118) in the lower range of Reynolds number. Its region of validity extends to about $R = 10^9$.

The effect of compressibility on the resistance law for the plate is discussed in Art. 9.22.

The Rough Plate. In most practical applications connected with the flat plate (e.g., ships, airfoils, turbine blades) the wall cannot be considered hydraulically smooth. Consequently, the flow along a rough plate is of as much practical interest as that through a rough pipe.

The relative roughness k/R of the pipe is now replaced by the quantity k/δ, in which δ denotes the boundary-layer thickness. The essential difference between the flow through a rough pipe and that over a rough plate is the fact that in a pipe the relative roughness k/R is constant, whereas along a plate k/δ decreases, because the boundary-layer thickness δ increases downstream. This circumstance causes the front of the plate to behave differently from its downstream portion as far as the influence of roughness on drag is concerned. Assuming, for the sake of simplicity, that the turbulent boundary layer begins at the leading edge of the plate, one finds completely rough flow over a certain length at the front of the plate, where k/δ is large. This forward portion is followed by the transition regime, and eventually the plate may become hydraulically smooth if it is sufficiently long. The limits between these three regions are determined by the dimensionless roughness parameter $v_* k/\nu$ (Art. 9.16).

Table 9.2. The Constant A of the Resistance Law for the Plate as a Function of the Critical Reynolds Number $\mathbf{R}_{x\,cr}$

$R_{x\,cr}$	3×10^5	5×10^5	10^6	3×10^6
A	1050	1700	3300	8700

Hydraulically smooth: $\dfrac{v_* k}{\nu} \le 5$

Transition regime: $5 \le \dfrac{v_* k}{\nu} \le 70$ (9.120)

Completely rough: $\dfrac{v_* k}{\nu} \ge 70$

The result of the calculation for pipes can be transposed to the case of rough plates in exactly the same way as for smooth plates. These calculations were carried out by Prandtl and Schlichting with the use of Nikuradse's results on rough pipes. The result for the coefficient of total skin-friction drag for sand-roughened plates is given in Fig. 9.36, in which c_f is plotted against the Reynolds number $\mathbf{R}$ with the relative roughness l/k_s as a parameter.

This diagram is applicable to roughnesses other than those discussed here, if one determines the *equivalent sand roughness*.[36]

Admissible Roughness. The amount of roughness which is considered admissible is that maximum height of roughness elements which causes no increase in drag compared with a smooth wall. The practical importance of determining the admissible roughness is very great, because it determines the amount of work, and hence the cost, of smoothing a given surface. The answer to this question depends substantially on whether the flow under consideration is laminar or turbulent. In the case of turbulent boundary layers roughness has no effect if all protuberances are contained within the laminar sublayer, whose thickness is only a small fraction of the turbulent-boundary-layer thickness. From measurements in a pipe it was found, as in Art. 9.16, that the condition for a hydraulically smooth regime is $v_* k/\nu < 5$, in which v_* is the friction velocity from Eq. (9.94). However, it is more convenient to give an admissible value of k/l for the plate. From the resistance diagram of the rough plate (Fig. 9.36) one obtains the admissible value k/l as that point where a certain curve $k/l = $ const deflects upward from the curve

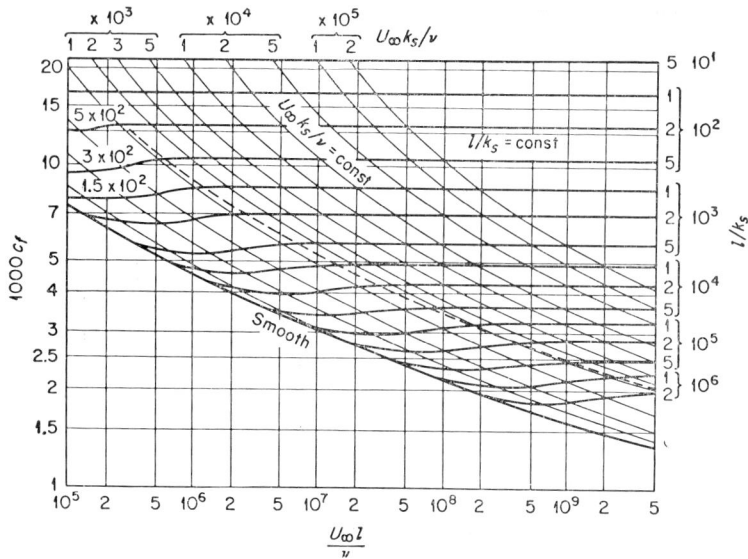

FIG. 9.36. Coefficients of frictional resistance for the sand-roughened plate according to Prandtl-Schlichting.[35]

of the smooth plate. The accompanying values of $\mathbf{R} = U_\infty l/\nu$ and $(k/l)_{\mathrm{adm}}$ are summarized in the following simple formula:

$$\frac{U_\infty k_{\mathrm{adm}}}{\nu} \leq 100 \tag{9.121}$$

From this it is seen that the admissible roughness, in general, is not dependent on the plate length; it is determined only by the velocity and the kinematic viscosity.

9.18. The Turbulent Boundary Layer with Positive and Negative Pressure Gradient

General Remarks.   The turbulent boundary layer with a pressure gradient along the wall has significance for flow through channels, as well as for flow past bodies, especially aerodynamic profiles.   A negative pressure gradient and especially a positive pressure gradient have a strong effect on the formation of a boundary layer in laminar flow as well as in turbulent flow, and particularly on their behavior in regard to separation.   For the calculation of a turbulent boundary layer several semiempirical methods have been developed which permit the calculation of the behavior of separation of the boundary layer. With the aid of these approximate methods the drag (pressure plus friction drag) on an immersed body may be determined also, in case separation plays no essential role in the proceedings.

The methods of calculation of the turbulent boundary layer are all approximate methods, which work with the momentum equation and in part with the energy equation. In contrast with the approximate methods for the laminar boundary layer, for turbulent boundary layers it is always required to introduce certain empirical assumptions into the calculation, especially those assumptions about the relation of shear stress at the wall with the form of the velocity distribution in the boundary layer.   Hereby the methods of calculation for the turbulent boundary layer attain a semiempirical character.   The first method of calculation for boundary layers with pressure gradient is due to Gruschwitz.[37] This method was improved by other authors.[38]   Later, Truckenbrodt[39] gave a simple integration method on the basis of newer measurements, which is applicable to two-dimensional as well as to axially symmetric boundary layers.   Since a complete presenta-

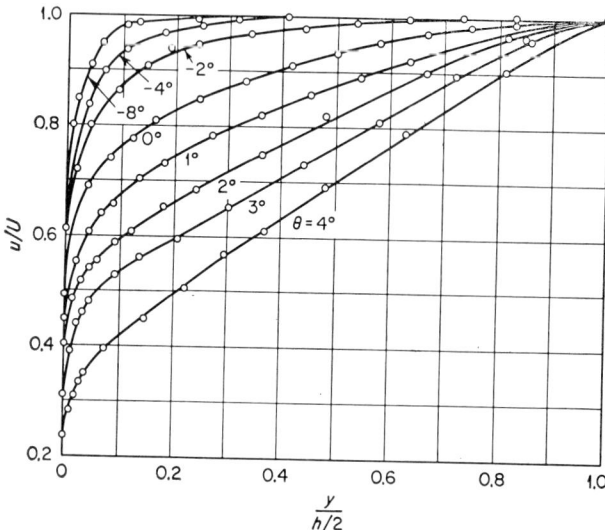

Fig. 9.37. Velocity distribution in convergent and divergent channels with two-dimensional walls according to measurements by Nikuradse[41]; θ = half of the included angle.

tion of one of these methods is too long to be included here, the discussion is limited to giving a few results. For a detailed discussion see Ref. 11, chap. 22.

Characteristic Parameters of the Turbulent Boundary Layer. Systematic measurements of turbulent boundary layers with positive and negative pressure gradient were first carried out by F. Dönch[40] and Nikuradse[41] in convergent and divergent channels with plane walls. The measured velocity distributions for several weakly convergent and divergent channels are given in Fig. 9.37 for a half included angle $\theta = -8$ to $+4°$. In convergent channels the boundary-layer thickness is substantially smaller than in a channel with parallel walls, while in the divergent part it is considerably greater and extends to the middle of the channel. The velocity distribution over the width of the channel is completely symmetric up to a half included angle $\theta = 4°$ and shows no separation phenomena. For half included angles $\theta > 4°$ separation occurs, in which the velocity distribution is very strongly unsymmetrical.

As a characteristic boundary-layer thickness the momentum-loss thickness

$$\Theta = \int_0^\delta \frac{u}{U}\left(1 - \frac{u}{U}\right)\,dy \qquad (9.122)$$

proves appropriate. In order to specify the velocity profile, which depends strongly on the pressure gradient, a velocity-profile *shape factor* is introduced. Gruschwitz chose the shape factor

$$\eta = 1 - \left[\frac{u(\Theta)}{U}\right]^2 \qquad (9.123)$$

in which $u(\Theta)$ denotes the velocity of the boundary layer at a distance $y = \Theta$. The usefulness of this shape factor for the representation of the turbulent-boundary-layer profile is shown in Fig. 9.38, which represents the measurements of Nikuradse given in Fig. 9.37, in which the plot of u/U against y/Θ is chosen. For a negative pressure gradient $\eta < 0.46$; for a positive pressure gradient $\eta > 0.46$. Separation occurs for $\eta \approx 0.8$.

A further shape factor of the turbulent boundary layer is the quantity

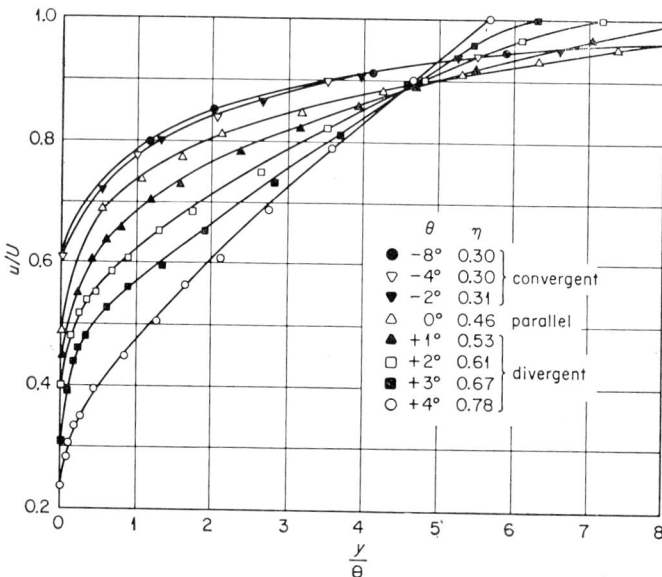

FIG. 9.38. Velocity distributions in the convergent and divergent channels of Fig. 9.37 plotting u/U against y/Θ. Θ = momentum thickness; η = shape factor as in Eq. (9.123).

$$H = \frac{\delta^*}{\Theta} \tag{9.124}$$

in which δ^* denotes the displacement thickness as in Eq. (9.41). The shape factor H occurs in the momentum equation of the boundary layer, Eq. (9.70). The measurements show that it also is useful as a shape factor of the boundary-layer profile. For the boundary layer at a plate, $H \approx 1.3$. Separation occurs for $H \approx 1.8$ to 2.6. There is a well-defined relation between the two shape factors η and H, which, if the velocity distribution is expressed in the exponential form $u/U = (y/\delta)^{1/n}$, is found from Eq. (9.123) to be

$$\eta = 1 - \left[\frac{H-1}{H(H+1)} \right]^{H-1} \tag{9.125}$$

Calculation of the Momentum Thickness. In order to determine the momentum thickness along the wall, the momentum Eq. (9.70) is written in the form

$$\frac{d\Theta}{dx} + (2 + H)\frac{\Theta}{U}\frac{dU}{dx} = \frac{\tau_0}{\rho U^2} \tag{9.126}$$

In order to be able to solve this differential equation for $\Theta(x)$, it is necessary to make assumptions about the shape factor $H = \delta^*/\Theta$ and the shear stress at the wall $\tau_0/\rho U^2$. Since H occurs only in the combination $2 + H$, it is sufficient to use a constant average value for H in calculations, for example, $H = 1.4$, which corresponds to the value for the flat plate at zero incidence. The shear stress at the wall may also be approximated. If U_∞ is replaced by $U(x)$, then these approximations, combined with Eqs. (9.111) and (9.112), result in

$$\frac{\tau_0}{\rho U^2} = \frac{\alpha}{(U\Theta/\nu)^{1/4}} \tag{9.127}$$

with $\alpha = 0.0128$. By inserting this value of τ_0 as well as the value $H = 1.4$ in the momentum Eq. (9.126), it may be integrated completely. One obtains

$$\left(\frac{U\Theta}{\nu}\right)^{1/4} = \frac{0.0160}{U^4}\left(\int_{x_u}^{x} U^4\, dx + C_1\right) \tag{9.128}$$

Here $0.0160 = \frac{5}{4}\alpha = \frac{5}{4} \times 0.0128$ and $\frac{5}{4}(2 + H) - \frac{1}{4} = 4$. The constant C_1 is to be determined from the momentum thickness at the transition point x_{tr}, where the turbulent boundary layer begins. For the flat plate at zero incidence, whose boundary layer is turbulent from the leading edge onward, Eq. (9.128) with $U = U_\infty$ and $x_{tr} = 0$ and $C_1 = 0$ is converted into Eq. (9.114).

In order to determine the separation, it is necessary to calculate the shape factor η or H along the wall. Several relationships have been pointed out by various authors, a review of which is omitted here. Separation occurs for $\eta \approx 0.8$; that is, $H \approx 2$.

Example 2. As an example of the calculation of the turbulent boundary layer, Fig. 9.39 shows the results for the suction side of an airfoil. Here the velocity distribution in the external flow is determined from a measured pressure distribution (Fig. 9.39a). The momentum thickness calculated by Gruschwitz[37] and Truckenbrodt[39] agrees well with the measured momentum thickness, as shown in Fig. 9.39b. For the shape factor (Fig. 9.39c), the calculation by Truckenbrodt agrees better with measurement than that of Gruschwitz.

The Calculation of Profile Drag. The most important use of the previously described methods of calculating the turbulent boundary layer consists of the theoretical calculation of the drag coefficient of an immersed body. This calculation is possible only if there is no substantial separation of the flow, so that the total drag consists primarily of skin friction, with a small portion of pressure drag, as is the case for slender bodies (e.g., aerodynamic profiles). Such methods of calculation for drag were first given by Pretsch[42] and Squire and Young[43] and were later extended by Truckenbrodt.[44]

From the velocity distribution in the wake at a large distance from the body one obtains the profile drag (pressure plus friction drag) by means of the momentum equation from the following integral:

$$D = b\rho \int_{y=-\infty}^{+\infty} u(U_\infty - u)\, dy \qquad (9.129)$$

Here b denotes the height of the cylindrical body, and $u(x,y)$ denotes the velocity distribution in the wake. By introducing the coefficient of profile drag c_D in $D = c_D bl(\rho/2)U_\infty^2$, and the momentum thickness of the wake at a large distance behind the body by

$$U_\infty^2 \Theta_\infty = \int_{y=-\infty}^{+\infty} u(U_\infty - u)\, dy$$

then Eq. (9.129) may be written in the form

$$c_D = 2\frac{\Theta_\infty}{l} \qquad (9.130)$$

The boundary-layer calculation, as previously given, furnishes the value of the momentum thickness Θ_1 at the trailing edge, if no separation occurs. In order to apply Eq. (9.130) for the calculation of the profile drag, a relation between the momentum thickness Θ_∞ in the wake very far behind the body and the momentum thickness Θ_1 at the trailing edge is needed. Here the potential velocity distribution at the trailing edge enters into the considerations. These relationships have been determined by Squire. Because of the detailed nature of these considerations, the reader is referred to Schlichting (Ref. 11, chap. 22). In this fashion one obtains for the drag coefficient of one side of the immersed body

$$c_D = \frac{0.074}{\mathbf{R}^{1/5}}$$
$$\left[\int_{x_{tr}/l}^{1}\left(\frac{U}{U_\infty}\right)^4 d\frac{x}{l} + C\right]^{0.8} \qquad (9.131)$$

in which $\mathbf{R} = U_\infty \cdot l/\nu$ is the Reynolds number in terms of the characteristic length l (e.g., wing chord) of the immersed body. The constant C is to be determined from the condition that the momentum thicknesses of the laminar and turbulent boundary layers are equal at the laminar-turbulent transition point. This yields

$$C = 62.5\left(\frac{\Theta_{tr}}{l}\right)^{5/4}\mathbf{R}^{1/4}\left(\frac{U_{tr}}{U_\infty}\right)^{4.25} \qquad (9.132)$$

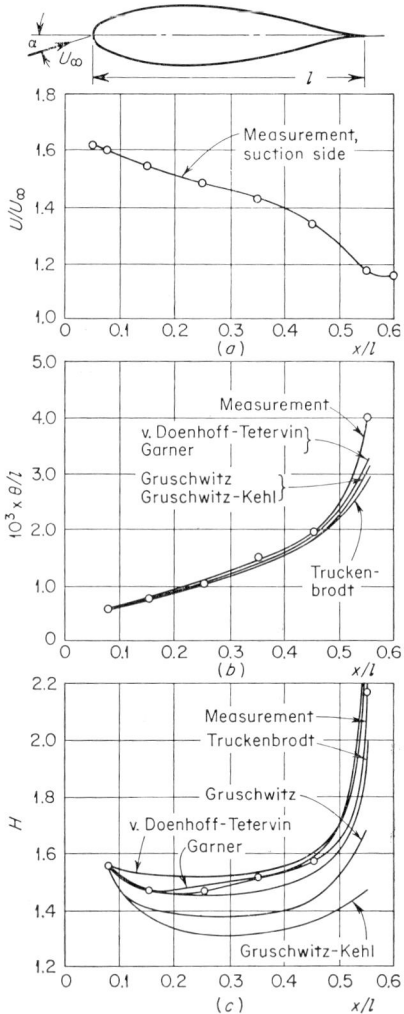

FIG. 9.39. The turbulent boundary layer on the suction side of the aerodynamic profile NACA-65 (216)-222 for angle of incidence $\alpha = 10.1°$; Reynolds number $\mathbf{R} = U_\infty l/\nu = 2.6 \times 10^6$; measurements according to von Doenhoff and Tetervin.[38] (a) Velocity in the external stream (determined experimentally), (b) momentum thickness Θ determined experimentally and by theory of different authors, (c) shape factor H determined experimentally and by theory of different authors; separation for $H \approx 2$.

in which Θ_{tr} is the momentum thickness at the transition point, and U_{tr} is the potential velocity at the transition point. The first is determined by calculating the laminar boundary layer, as in Eq. (9.74). For the flat plate at zero incidence with $U(x) = U_\infty$, Eq. (9.131) is transformed into the formula for frictional resistance of the plate, Eq. (9.117).

BOUNDARY LAYERS IN COMPRESSIBLE FLOW

9.19. General Remarks; Properties of Substances

The preceding portions of this section have been based on the flow of an incompressible fluid. A flow can, in general, be treated as incompressible if the Mach number is small compared with 1. Here the Mach number is $\mathbf{M} = w/a$, the ratio of flow velocity w to the velocity of sound a.

Some fundamentals of boundary-layer theory for compressible flow are illustrated below. This discussion leads to the fact that the effects of Reynolds number and Mach number are taken into account simultaneously. A characteristic of every compressible flow is that thermodynamic processes occur simultaneously. For supersonic velocities vigorous heating in the boundary layer takes place, which emanates from the heat caused by friction. The heating of the flowing medium by the frictional heat is confined essentially to the same thin boundary layer in which viscosity noticeably affects the flow. A *thermal boundary layer* is then formed along the immersed wall beside the velocity boundary layer. The processes in this thermal boundary layer are important because of the heat transfer from the flowing medium to the immersed body (heating or cooling of the body).

Such a thermal boundary layer is also formed for moderate stream velocities (incompressible flow), if there is a temperature difference between the body and the external flow. The variations in density and viscosity as a result of the temperature difference may be neglected for incompressible flow and moderate temperature differences. In this case the velocity boundary layer is consequently independent of the thermal boundary layer. For large velocities (compressible flow) there are such great temperature differences in the boundary layer that the variations of density and viscosity must be taken into account. Mutual interactions occur between the velocity boundary layer and the thermal boundary layer, thereby complicating the boundary-layer relationships.

Properties of Substances. The law relating pressure p, density ρ, and temperature T is given by the general equation of state of the ideal gas:

$$p = \rho g R T \tag{9.133}$$

in which R is the gas constant, which is determined from the specific heats of the gas for constant pressure c_p and constant volume c_v to be

$$R = c_p - c_v = c_p \frac{k - 1}{k}$$

with $k = c_p/c_v$ as the isentropic exponent. For air, $k = 1.4$. The speed of sound a has the value

$$a = \sqrt{k \frac{p}{\rho}} = \sqrt{kgRT} = \sqrt{(k - 1)gc_p T} \tag{9.134}$$

In air the viscosity coefficient μ increases with increasing temperature. This dependence is represented by the empirical equation

$$\frac{\mu}{\mu_0} = \left(\frac{T}{T_0}\right)^\omega \qquad \text{with } \tfrac{1}{2} < \omega < 1 \tag{9.135}$$

ω is called the viscosity exponent. Heat transfer by conduction is determined by the *conductivity* λ, which is defined by the Fourier law of heat conduction,

$$q = \lambda \frac{\partial T}{\partial n} \tag{9.136}$$

Table 9.3. Thermal Properties of Air as a Function of Temperature

(At 1 atm)

Temperature t, °F	Specific heat c_p. Btu/(lb)(°F)	Conductivity λ, Btu/(ft)(hr)(°F)	Thermal diffusivity a_1, ft²/hr	Viscosity $\mu \times 10^6$, (lb)(sec)/ft²	Kinematic viscosity $\nu \times 10^3$, ft²/sec	Prandtl number P
−50	0.246	0.0120	0.534	0.3036	0.104	0.703
0	0.240	0.0140	0.747	0.3502	0.144	0.696
100	0.240	0.0156	0.948	0.3890	0.183	0.693
200	0.241	0.0177	1.262	0.4406	0.244	0.695
400	0.245	0.0213	1.945	0.5279	0.380	0.704
600	0.251	0.0253	2.784	0.6133	0.545	0.705

in which q denotes the heat flow (quantity of heat per unit of area and time) through a surface dA with normal dn, and $\partial T/\partial n$ the temperature gradient normal to the surface element dA. Further, the following two properties are used, which are defined here:

Thermal diffusivity:
$$a_1 = \frac{\lambda}{\rho g c_p} \tag{9.137}$$

Prandtl number:
$$\mathbf{P} = \frac{\nu}{a_1} \tag{9.138}$$

The Prandtl number is dimensionless. Numerical values for the previously discussed properties are contained in Table 9.3.

9.20. The Fundamental Equations

In calculating the compressible boundary layer there are two additional variables to be determined in comparison with the incompressible boundary layer, namely, the density ρ and the temperature T. For this reason two more equations are required. These are the general equation of state for gases and the energy equation.

The *energy equation* for flow of a compressible medium is obtained by use of the first law of thermodynamics. With the introduction of the boundary-layer assumptions it is found that for two-dimensional stationary flow (Ref. 11, chap. 14),

$$\rho g c_p \left(u \frac{\partial T}{\partial x} + v \frac{\partial T}{\partial y} \right) = u \frac{dp}{dx} + \frac{\partial}{\partial y} \left(\lambda \frac{\partial T}{\partial y} \right) + \mu \left(\frac{\partial u}{\partial y} \right)^2 \tag{9.139}$$

Here the left side denotes the heat transfer by convection; on the right side the first and third terms signify heat generated by compression and friction, respectively, while the second term represents the heat transfer due to conduction.

The continuity equation and the equation of motion for a compressible boundary layer are

$$\frac{\partial(\rho u)}{\partial x} + \frac{\partial(\rho v)}{\partial y} = 0 \tag{9.140}$$

$$\rho \left(u \frac{\partial u}{\partial x} + v \frac{\partial u}{\partial y} \right) = -\frac{dp}{dx} + \frac{\partial}{\partial y} \left(\mu \frac{\partial u}{\partial y} \right) \tag{9.141}$$

Equations (9.133) and (9.139) to (9.141) are a system of four equations in the four unknowns u, v, ρ, T, while the pressure p, as in the incompressible-boundary-layer theory, is known from the potential flow.†

The boundary conditions for fluid flow in the boundary layer are, as previously,

$$y = 0 : u = 0, \quad v = 0 \qquad y = \infty : u = U(x) \tag{9.142}$$

† If the viscosity coefficient is also assumed variable, the empirical viscosity law $\mu(T)$ as in Eq. (9.135) is added to the previously mentioned four equations as an additional equation.

For the thermal boundary layer only the case of the non-heat-conducting wall (adiabatic wall) is considered here.   In this case the boundary conditions are

$$y = 0 : \frac{\partial T}{\partial y} = 0 \quad \text{and} \quad y = \infty : T = T_\infty \tag{9.143}$$

While the incompressible boundary layer of the flow of a given body is dependent only on the Reynolds number, it must be expected that the compressible boundary layer depends at least on the following dimensionless quantities: Reynolds number, Mach number, Prandtl number, and the viscosity law $\mu(T)$.

Not only because of this greater number of parameters, but also mainly because of the combining of the above four fundamental equations, is the integration of the boundary-layer equations for compressible flow more difficult than that of incompressible flow.

9.21. Frictional Heating

Adiabatic Compression.   Temperature changes brought about by dynamic-pressure variation in a compressible flow are important for its heat balance.   Therefore the temperature increase due to adiabatic compression for a frictionless flow is considered next. If the pressure and velocity in a frictionless flow vary along a streamline, then temperature changes also are connected with this.   In a simplified treatment the change of state may be regarded as adiabatic, that is, the heat conduction can be neglected.

From the energy Eq. (9.139), one obtains for frictionless flow the following equation for the change of temperature and pressure along a streamline (coordinate s), if heat conduction is neglected:

$$\rho g c_p w \frac{dT}{ds} = w \frac{dp}{ds}$$

in which $w(s)$ is the velocity along the streamline.   Integration and application of the Bernoulli equation yields

$$T - T_\infty = \frac{1}{2 g c_p} (w_\infty{}^2 - w^2)$$

For the temperature increase at a stagnation point ($w = 0$) due to adiabatic compression one obtains, consequently,

$$T_0 - T_\infty = (\Delta T)_{ad} = \frac{w_\infty{}^2}{2 g c_p} \tag{9.144}$$

This increase in temperature at a stagnation point may be expressed by the Mach number, if Eq. (9.134) is considered.   It is then found that

$$T_0 = T_\infty \left(1 + \frac{k-1}{2} \mathbf{M}_\infty{}^2 \right) = T_\infty(1 + 0.2 \mathbf{M}_\infty{}^2) \tag{9.145}$$

in which $\mathbf{M}_\infty = w_\infty/a_\infty$, the Mach number expressed in terms of the free-stream velocity, and the value 1.4 for k was inserted.   According to this, the temperature increase for a Mach number of, for example, $\mathbf{M}_\infty = 3$ amounts to about 180 per cent of the absolute temperature of the external flow.

It is next shown that temperature increases of nearly equal magnitude, as in Eq. (9.145), occur not only at the stagnation point, but along the whole immersed wall.   It is also shown that temperature increases in the boundary layer caused by frictional heat are of nearly equal magnitude to those caused by adiabatic compression.

Frictional Heat.   In order to find the temperature increase due to frictional heating, a general relation between the temperature distribution and the velocity distribution is derived from the boundary-layer equations.   The discussion is confined to the case of a flat plate at zero incidence.   The boundary-layer equations for this case, as in Eqs. (9.139) to (9.141), are

$$\frac{\partial(\rho u)}{\partial x} + \frac{\partial(\rho v)}{\partial y} = 0 \tag{9.146}$$

$$\rho\left(u\frac{\partial u}{\partial x} + v\frac{\partial u}{\partial y}\right) = \frac{\partial}{\partial y}\left(\mu\frac{\partial u}{\partial y}\right) \tag{9.147}$$

$$\rho g c_p\left(u\frac{\partial T}{\partial x} + v\frac{\partial T}{\partial y}\right) = \frac{\partial}{\partial y}\left(\lambda\frac{\partial T}{\partial y}\right) + \mu\left(\frac{\partial u}{\partial y}\right)^2 \tag{9.148}$$

with boundary conditions as in Eqs. (9.142) and (9.143).

For the case when the Prandtl number $\mathbf{P} = 1$, and for an arbitrary viscosity law $\mu(T)$, the proposition by Busemann[45] is valid: in the boundary layer the temperature is only a function of the velocity component u parallel to the wall, $T = T(u)$. Consequently, lines of constant velocity component u and the isotherms $T = $ const coincide. As cited here without proof,† the above-mentioned system of equations can be solved by use of the following expressions:

$$\frac{\mu g c_p}{\lambda} = \mathbf{P} = 1 \quad \text{and} \quad \frac{\partial^2 T}{\partial u^2} = -\frac{\mu}{\lambda} = -\frac{1}{g c_p} \tag{9.149}$$

By integrating the second equation the relation between temperature and velocity is obtained in the form

$$T(u) = -\frac{u^2}{2g c_p} + c_1 u + c_2$$

The constants of integration c_1 and c_2 are found by means of the boundary conditions (9.142) and (9.143). This gives the solution

$$T = T_\infty + \frac{1}{2g c_p}(U_\infty{}^2 - u^2)$$

Thus, for the temperature of the wall ($u = 0$), one has

$$T_W = T_\infty + \frac{U_\infty{}^2}{2g c_p} \quad (\mathbf{P} = 1) \tag{9.150}$$

After comparing this with Eq. (9.144) it is seen that in the case $\mathbf{P} = 1$ the heating of the wall by frictional heat in the boundary layer is the same as that caused by adiabatic compression at the stagnation point.

For Prandtl numbers different from 1, Eq. (9.150) is replaced by the following relationship due to Emmons and Brainerd:[46]

$$T_W = T_\infty + \sqrt{\mathbf{P}}\,\frac{U_\infty{}^2}{2g c_p} \tag{9.151}$$

which also may be written in the form

$$T_W = T_\infty\left(1 + \sqrt{\mathbf{P}}\,\frac{k-1}{2}\,\mathbf{M}_\infty{}^2\right) \tag{9.152}$$

by introducing the Mach number from Eq. (9.134). For air with $k = 1.4$ and $\mathbf{P} = 0.7$ the heating of the wall due to frictional heat is found to be

$$T_W = T_\infty(1 + 0.169\mathbf{M}_\infty{}^2) \quad (\text{air, } \mathbf{P} = 0.7) \tag{9.153}$$

The resulting heating of the wall is depicted in Fig. 9.40 in terms of the Mach number. For $\mathbf{M}_\infty = 3$, for example, the increase in temperature at the wall as a result of frictional heat amounts to about 400°C, and for $\mathbf{M}_\infty = 5$ the value is about 1200°C. The results

† In regard to this see Ref. 11, chap. 15.

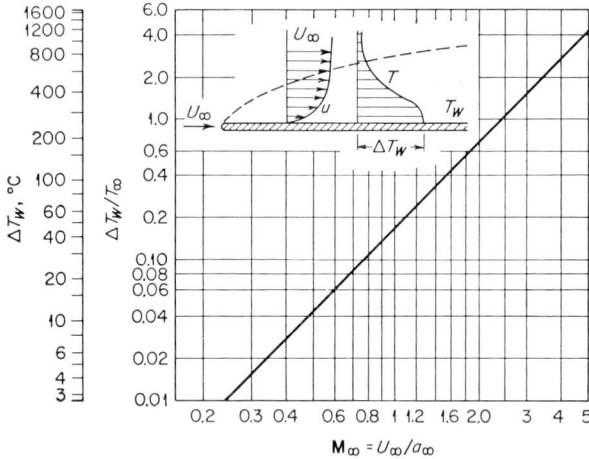

FIG. 9.40. Heating of the flat plate at zero incidence as a result of frictional heat for a non-conducting wall in terms of the Mach number for air, as in Eq. (9.153); Prandtl number $P = 0.7$, external temperature $T_\infty = 273°K$. T_W = temperature at the wall; ΔT_W = heating of the wall by frictional heat.

given in Eq. (9.152) are valid only if taken for the laminar boundary layer. However, they reproduce the relationships in the *turbulent boundary layer* if the factor $\sqrt{P} = 0.85$ is replaced by 0.88 (for air). Hence it is seen that Fig. 9.40 is also sufficiently accurate for the turbulent boundary layer.

In the more recent literature it is customary to write Eqs. (9.151) and (9.152) in the general form

$$T_W = T_\infty + r \frac{U_\infty^2}{2gc_p} = T_\infty \left(1 + r \frac{k-1}{2} M_\infty^2 \right) \tag{9.154}$$

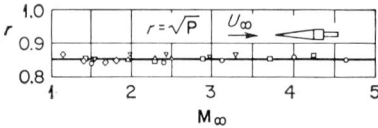

Cone angle	M_∞
○ 10°	1.5 to 4.6
□ 20°	1.4 to 4.2
▽ 40°	1.2 to 3.3
△ 60°	0.9 to 2.5
◇ 80°	1.1 to 1.8

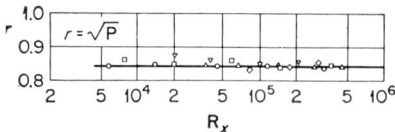

FIG. 9.41. Measured recovery factors r for laminar boundary layers on cones for supersonic velocity with various Mach numbers and Reynolds number by Eber.[47] Comparison with theory as in Eq. (9.155a).

In this equation r is called the *recovery factor*; it represents the ratio of the heating of the wall as a result of friction to the heating due to adiabatic compression as in Eq. (9.144). By comparing Eq. (9.154) with Eq. (9.152), one obtains for the recovery factor

$$r = \sqrt{P} \qquad \text{(laminar)} \tag{9.155a}$$

Hence for air,

$$r = \sqrt{0.723} = 0.851 \qquad \text{(laminar)} \tag{9.155b}$$

Measurements by Eber[47] of the recovery factor for the laminar boundary layer on wedges at supersonic velocity are given in Fig. 9.41, in terms of the Mach number as well as of the Reynolds number. The theoretical law $r = \sqrt{P}$ is well confirmed by these measurements.

9.22. The Flat Plate at Zero Incidence

The explicit calculation of the velocity and temperature distribution for the flat plate at zero incidence has been carried out in several papers by Hantzsche and Wendt[48,49] and Crocco[50] for a large number of different fluid properties and boundary conditions. The temperature and velocity distribution in the boundary layer of the flat plate for an adiabatic wall are represented in Fig. 9.42 for various Mach numbers. Here the distance from the wall is made dimensionless with $\sqrt{\nu_\infty x/U_\infty}$, in which ν_∞ denotes the kinematic viscosity in the external flow. The Prandtl number is $P = 1$, and the exponent of the viscosity law from Eq. (9.135) is $\omega = 1$. It is seen from Fig. 9.42 that the boundary-layer thickness greatly increases with increasing Mach number, especially in the region of supersonic velocity. This emanates almost exclusively from the heating of the layer near the wall and from the related large increase in volume.

Figure 9.43 shows the dependence of the friction coefficient of the flat plate for a laminar boundary layer on the Mach number for various Prandtl numbers P and viscosity exponents ω. The effect of P and ω on the friction coefficient is relatively small. For $\omega = 1$, $c_f\sqrt{R}$ is completely independent of the Mach number.

The effect of the Mach number on the friction drag of the flat plate is substantially greater for the turbulent boundary layer than for laminar flow. Some theoretical and experimental results on this are

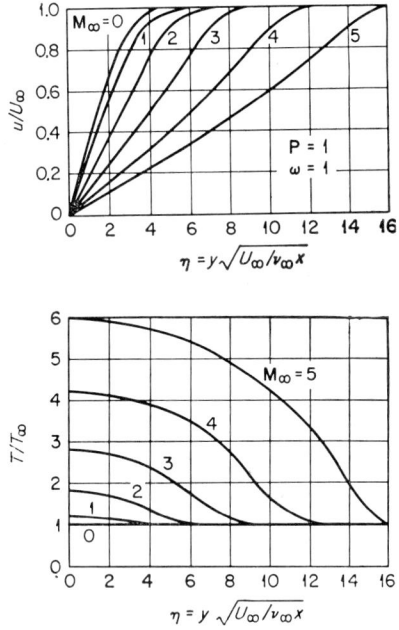

Fig. 9.42. Velocity and temperature distribution in the compressible laminar boundary layer on the flat plate at zero incidence for a heat-insulated wall, according to Crocco.[50] Prandtl number $P = 1$; $\omega = 1$; $k = 1.4$. The distance from the wall y is related to $\sqrt{\nu_\infty x/U_\infty}$.

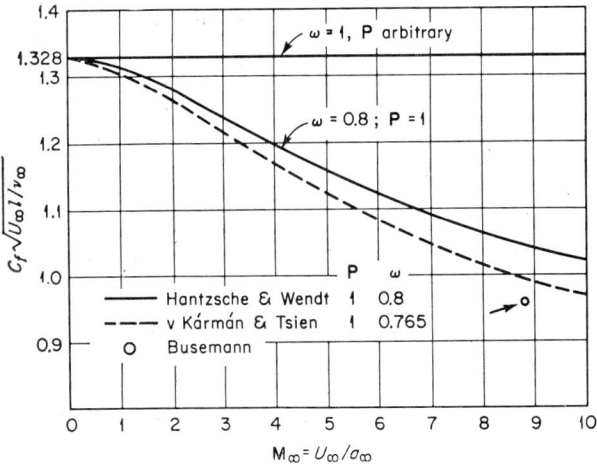

Fig. 9.43. Frictional coefficient of the flat plate at zero incidence with a compressible laminar boundary layer for an adiabatic wall.

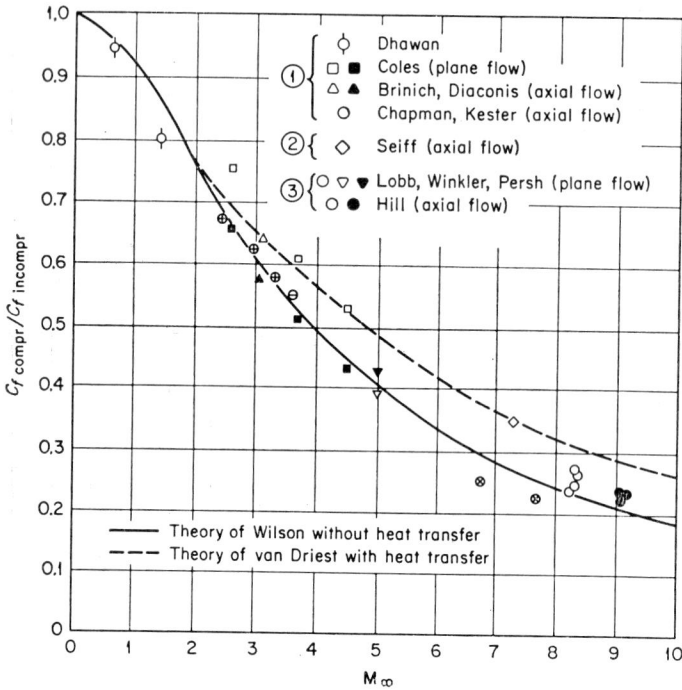

Fig. 9.44. Friction coefficient of the flat plate at zero incidence with a turbulent boundary layer in terms of the Mach number; Reynolds number $R \approx 10^7$. Comparison with theory and measurement. Theory by Wilson[75]; theory by van Driest.[76]

given in Fig. 9.44, in which it is to be noted that the theory of turbulent boundary layers in compressible flow still has a strongly empirical character, just as in incompressible flow. According to Fig. 9.44, the coefficient of friction drag of the plate decreases strongly for turbulent flow with increasing Reynolds number. The friction drag for a Mach number $M_\infty = 5$ with an adiabatic wall is about 40 per cent of that for incompressible flow. The friction drag is somewhat greater with a heat transfer from the flowing medium to the wall than for an adiabatic wall.

9.23. The Interaction of Boundary Layer and Shock Wave

If a body is placed in a flow with such a high velocity that regions with local supersonic velocity are formed near it then compression shocks occur in those places where the velocity returns from *supersonic* to *subsonic* (Fig. 9.45a). In these shock waves the pressure, density, and temperature of the flowing medium vary strongly. The steep positive pressure gradient in the shock wave has a large effect on the drag of the immersed body, since in many cases it causes a separation of the boundary layer and hence increases the pressure drag of the body. The theoretical calculation of such shock waves is still very imperfect; however, experiments indicate that the processes in the shock wave are strongly influenced by the boundary layer. The mutual interference of boundary layer and shock wave is very complicated, because on the one hand the thickness of the boundary layer varies with the Reynolds number, while on the other hand the processes in the shock wave are strongly dependent on the Mach number. Systematic experiments on the interaction of shock wave and boundary layer have been carried out by Ackeret, Feldmann, and Rott,[51] as well as by Liepmann.[52,53] The results of both investigations are as follows.

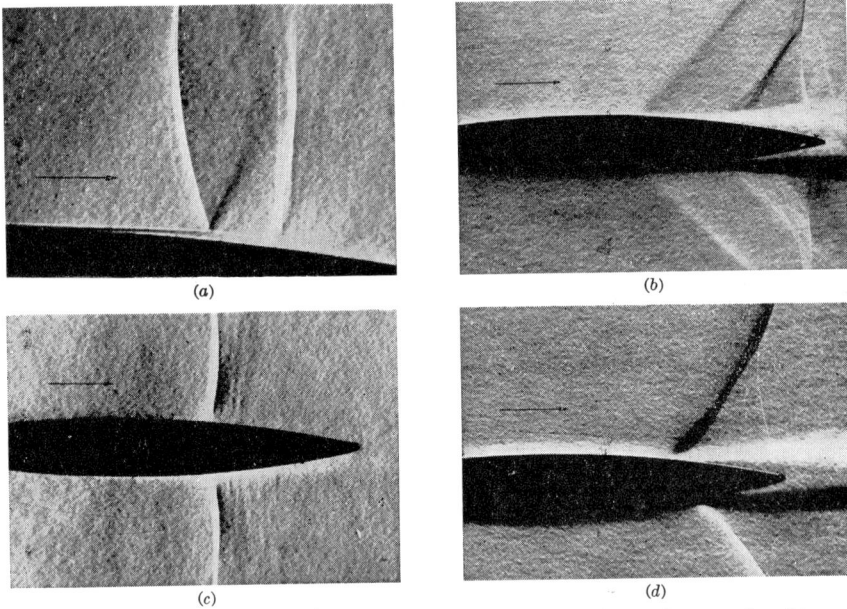

FIG. 9.45. Interaction of boundary layer and shock wave. Schlieren photographs of transsonic flow on an aerodynamic profile by Liepmann.[52] (a) Laminar boundary layer with separation in front of shock wave, reattachment behind shock wave. $M_\infty = 0.843$, $R = 8.45 \times 10^5$. (b) Laminar boundary layer with separation behind the shock wave. $M_\infty = 0.895$, $R = 8.77 \times 10^5$. (c) Turbulent boundary layer in front of the shock wave, no separation. $M_\infty = 0.843$, $R = 1.69 \times 10^6$. (d) Turbulent boundary layer with strong separation behind the shock wave. $M_\infty = 0.895$, $R = 1.75 \times 10^6$.

The appearance of the shock wave is fundamentally different, depending on whether the boundary layer is laminar or turbulent. When the boundary layer is laminar the shock-wave region is, in most cases, composed of a number of individual shock waves. Normally, a weak oblique shock appears first and is followed by a stronger normal shock, considerably farther downstream. In the case of a turbulent boundary layer, there is only one normal shock. In the boundary layer near the wall there is always a small region with *subsonic velocity*, but shock waves can be formed only in a *region of supersonic velocity*. Hence it is seen that a shock wave which occurs in the frictionless external stream cannot reach right up to the wall. It follows that in the wave region the steep pressure gradient parallel to the wall in the immediate neighborhood of the wall is smaller than in the external stream.

This very complex interaction of boundary layer and shock wave is illustrated in more detail in Fig. 9.45 by means of several schlieren photographs† of the flow past an airfoil for transsonic velocities. When studying these interactions it is possible to distinguish the following cases, as pointed out by Young:[54]

1. The approaching boundary layer is laminar and remains so beyond the shock without separation.

2. The approaching boundary layer is laminar, but separates ahead of the shock because of the adverse pressure gradient and then returns to the surface in either a laminar or turbulent state (Fig. 9.45a).

3. The approaching boundary layer is laminar and separates completely from the surface ahead of the shock and does not reattach itself to the surface (Fig. 9.45b).

† Thanks are due to Professor H. W. Liepmann of the California Institute of Technology for his permission to use the photographs in Figs. 9.45a to d and for his kindness in supplying prints for publication.

4. The approaching boundary layer is turbulent and does not separate from the surface (Fig. 9.45c).

5. The approaching boundary layer is turbulent and separates from the surface (Fig. 9.45d).

The theoretical treatment of the processes discussed here is rendered more difficult by the fact that in the region of shock waves not only parallel to the wall, but also normal to the wall, pressure gradients of considerable magnitude occur. Hereby one of the fundamental assumptions of boundary-layer theory is violated, namely, that the pressure gradient normal to the wall is very small. Furthermore, in the shock region the velocity gradient parallel to the wall $\partial u/\partial x$ is of the same order of magnitude as that normal to the wall, $\partial u/\partial y$. Consequently, the simplification of the Navier-Stokes equations based on the different order of magnitude of these two velocity gradients, which leads to the boundary-layer equations, is no longer in effect. This leads to the fact that the boundary-layer equations for flows with shock waves are not applicable without further considerations being made.

Hence for the time being it seems hopeless to compute theoretically the very complex flow processes in the boundary layer in the shock region. Rather, one can explain these processes now only by systematic experimental investigations.

TRANSITION FROM LAMINAR TO TURBULENT FLOW

9.24. Some Experimental Results

As mentioned already in Art. 9.8, flow in the boundary layer is, in general, laminar for small Reynolds numbers and turbulent for large Reynolds numbers, just as flow through pipes. The condition of the flow in the boundary layer has a great effect on the behavior of the whole flow and especially on the drag of a body. This was first recognized by Prandtl[3] on the basis of experiments by Eiffel[2] on the drag of spheres. As an example Fig. 9.10 shows the flow past a sphere with laminar and turbulent boundary layers. For turbulent flow (Fig. 9.10b) the separation point lies considerably farther downstream than for laminar flow (Fig. 9.10a). As a result the region of the wake behind the sphere is substantially smaller for a turbulent boundary layer than for a laminar flow. Consequently, the pressure distribution for turbulent flow comes considerably closer to the potential distribution than that for laminar flow. A further consequence, finally, is that the drag coefficient of the sphere is considerably smaller for a turbulent boundary layer than for a laminar boundary layer. This is recognized from Fig. 9.5, in which the plotting of the drag coefficient against the Reynolds number reveals a sharp drop in the value of the drag coefficient for the critical Reynolds number.

$$\left(\frac{VD}{\nu}\right)_{cr} = 3 \times 10^5 \qquad \text{(sphere)}$$

The laminar-turbulent transition of the boundary layer for the flat plate at zero incidence was investigated first by J. M. Burgers and van der Hegge-Zijnen,[55] and later by Hansen.[56] More recently, it has undergone thorough investigation by Dryden.[57,58,59] From the leading edge onward the boundary layer is laminar over a certain distance. Further downstream there exists a certain region where the boundary layer is being transformed from laminar to turbulent, and then farther downstream it becomes completely turbulent. The completely turbulent boundary layer begins at a distance x from the leading edge, given by

$$\mathbf{R}_{x\ cr} = \left(\frac{U_\infty x}{\nu}\right)_{cr} = 3 \times 10^5 \text{ to } 3 \times 10^6 \qquad (9.156)$$

in which the numerical value of this critical Reynolds number depends strongly on the intensity of turbulence of the external flow. It grows larger with decreasing intensity of turbulence, and conversely. The velocity profile designated by 1 in Fig. 9.46 corresponds to the laminar boundary layer. The velocity profile designated by 2 represents the completely turbulent flow with a velocity distribution which is very similar to that of

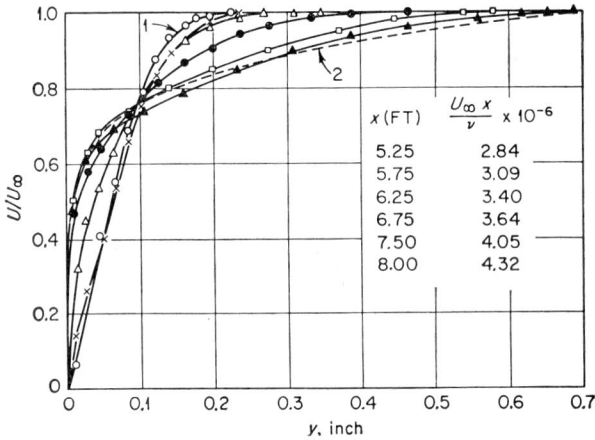

x (FT)	$\dfrac{U_\infty x}{\nu} \times 10^{-6}$
5.25	2.84
5.75	3.09
6.25	3.40
6.75	3.64
7.50	4.05
8.00	4.32

FIG. 9.46. Velocity profiles of the boundary layer at the plate in the region of the laminar-turbulent transition, according to measurements by Schubauer and Klebanoff.[60] Curve 1, Blasius profile; curve 2, 1/7-power law (boundary-layer thickness $\delta = 0.71$ in.). External velocity $U = 89$ fps. Intensity of turbulence $T = 0.03$ per cent.

turbulent flow through pipes, as in Fig. 9.32. From Fig. 9.46 it is evident that a considerable increase of velocity occurs in the region of transition from laminar to turbulent flow in the immediate neighborhood of the wall, which is subject to the strongly varying shape of the velocity distribution for laminar and turbulent boundary layers. This situation can be utilized to make a convenient measurement of the transition point (or better, of the transition region). The principle of this measurement is explained in Fig. 9.47: a static tube or an impact tube is located at a small distance from the wall. Such a pipe shows a rather steep rise of the dynamic head in relation to the total pressure, when it moves downstream through the transition region.

The laminar-turbulent transition of the boundary layer depends, besides the Reynolds number, on numerous other parameters, for example, the Mach number, the pressure gradient of the external flow along the wall, the roughness of the wall, and the heat transfer between the wall and the fluid in flow. These are discussed briefly in the following paragraphs.

The theoretical investigations of the transition of the fluid from laminar to turbulent are tied to an assumption introduced by Reynolds and Lord Rayleigh. It asserts that laminar flow, which produces a solution of the hydrodynamic differential equations for arbitrary Reynolds numbers, becomes unstable above the critical Reynolds number, and hence is transformed into turbulent flow. The stability theory of laminar flow developed from this assertion, after decades of fruitless attempts, was successfully completed about fifteen years ago. Its results have been well confirmed by measurement.

9.25. Fundamentals of Stability Theory

In the simplest case the investigations of stability are based on a two-dimensional incompressible flow with velocity

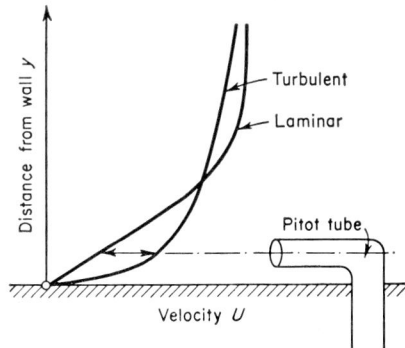

FIG. 9.47. Measurement of the laminar-turbulent transition by means of a pitot tube.

components u and v. The basic laminar flow to be investigated for stability is $U(y)$. A two-dimensional disturbance $u'(x,y,t)$, $v'(x,y,t)$ is superimposed on it. In the resulting flow the velocity components and the pressure are then

$$u = U + u' \qquad v = v' \qquad p = P + p' \qquad (9.157)$$

In the investigation of stability by the method of small disturbances it is postulated that the magnitude of the disturbances is small compared with the values of the basic flow, so that the quadratic terms of the disturbances may be neglected in comparison with the linear terms.

It is further assumed that the fundamental flow as well as the resulting motion from the superimposition of the disturbances has to satisfy the hydrodynamic equations of motion (Navier-Stokes equations). By introducing Eq. (9.157) into the Navier-Stokes equations of two-dimensional flow, Eqs. (9.16) to (9.18), one obtains the following system of equations for the disturbances:

$$\frac{\partial u'}{\partial t} + U \frac{\partial u'}{\partial x} + v' \frac{dU}{dy} = -\frac{1}{\rho} \frac{\partial p'}{\partial x} + \nu \left(\frac{\partial^2 u'}{\partial x^2} + \frac{\partial^2 u'}{\partial y^2} \right) \qquad (9.158a)$$

$$\frac{\partial v'}{\partial t} + U \frac{\partial v'}{\partial x} = -\frac{1}{\rho} \frac{\partial p'}{\partial y} + \nu \left(\frac{\partial^2 v'}{\partial x^2} + \frac{\partial^2 v'}{\partial y^2} \right) \qquad (9.158b)$$

$$\frac{\partial u'}{\partial x} + \frac{\partial v'}{\partial y} = 0 \qquad (9.158c)$$

The accompanying boundary conditions require the disturbance velocities to disappear at the boundary walls (condition of no slip).

The disturbance is assumed to be a two-dimensional progressing wave in the direction of the main stream (x direction). Thus an arbitrary disturbance may be expanded in a Fourier series each of whose terms represents a partial oscillation. The equation of continuity (9.158c) is next integrated by introducing a stream function of the disturbances $\psi(x,y,t)$. For the stream function of a partial oscillation of a disturbance, the expression

$$\psi(x,y,t) = \varphi(y)e^{i(\alpha x - \beta t)} \qquad (9.159)$$

is chosen, in which $\lambda = 2\pi/\alpha$ is the wavelength of the disturbance and $\varphi(y)$ is the amplitude function of the oscillation. The quantity $\beta = \beta_r + i\beta_i$ is complex, and β_r denotes the circular frequency of the partial oscillation, while β_i determines whether there is amplification of damping of the oscillations. For $\beta_i < 0$, damping of the oscillation takes place, hence there is stability of the main flow, whereas for $\beta_i > 0$ there is instability. Oscillations with $\beta_i = 0$ are called neutral oscillations; they define the limit of stability of the mean flow.

From Eq. (9.159) the velocity components of the disturbances are found to be

$$u' = \frac{\partial \psi}{\partial y} = \varphi'(y)e^{i(\alpha x - \beta t)} \qquad (9.160a)$$

$$v' = -\frac{\partial \psi}{\partial x} = -i\alpha\varphi(y)e^{i(\alpha x - \beta t)} \qquad (9.160b)$$

By inserting these into Eq. (9.158), the following ordinary differential equation of the fourth order is obtained for the amplitude function after eliminating the pressure:

$$(U - c)(\varphi'' - \alpha^2\varphi) - U''\varphi = -\frac{i}{\alpha\mathbf{R}} (\varphi'''' - 2\alpha^2\varphi'' + \alpha^4\varphi) \qquad (9.161)$$

This differential equation for the disturbance, which is also called the Orr-Sommerfeld equation, constitutes the starting point of the theory of stability of laminar flow. Here $c = \beta/\alpha = c_r + ic_i$ is introduced with c_r as the velocity of propagation of the wave, while c_i by its sign determines whether the oscillations grow or are damped, just as β_i. Furthermore, dimensionless quantities are introduced into Eq. (9.161), in which all lengths

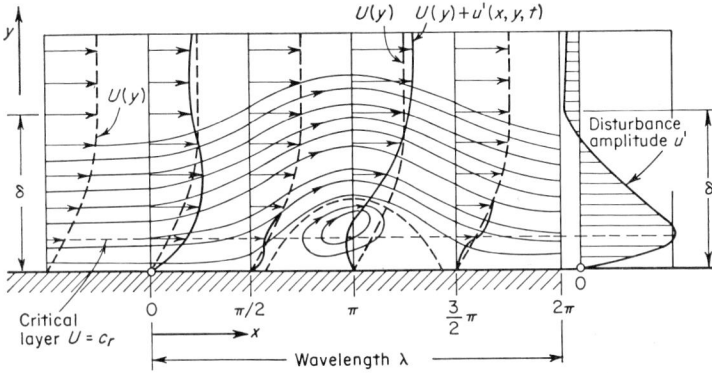

FIG. 9.48. Flow pattern and velocity distribution for a neutral disturbance of the boundary layer on the flat plate at zero incidence, by Schlichting.[64] $U(y)$ = basic flow; u' = disturbance. $U(y) + u'(x,y,t)$ = disturbed velocity distribution.

refer to a suitably chosen boundary-layer thickness δ and all velocities refer to the maximum velocity U_m of the basic flow. The prime in Eq. (9.161) denotes differentiation with respect to the dimensionless coordinate y/δ, and $\mathbf{R} = U_m \delta/\nu$ is the Reynolds number of the given basic flow. The boundary conditions of Eq. (9.161) stipulate that both components of the disturbance velocity disappear at the wall ($y = 0$) and in the external stream ($y = \infty$); consequently

$$y = 0 \quad \text{and} \quad y = \infty : u' = v' = 0 : \varphi = \varphi' = 0 \qquad (9.162)$$

To illustrate disturbances the instantaneous flow pattern and the velocity distribution of the resulting flow for the boundary layer at a flat plate are depicted in Fig. 9.48. It is evident from the flow photographs in Fig. 9.49, which show the beginning of turbulence for the boundary layer at the flat plate, that long-wave disturbances are really existent in the transition region from laminar to turbulent flow.

The problem of stability of laminar flow is an eigenvalue problem of the differential equation for disturbance, Eq. (9.161), with boundary conditions as in Eqs. (9.162). If the basic flow is given, Eqs. (9.160) contain four parameters: the Reynolds number of the main flow $\mathbf{R}$, the disturbance wavelength $\lambda = 2\pi/\alpha$, the velocity of propagation of the wave c_r, and the magnitude of decrease or increase of the disturbance c_i. From these four quantities the Reynolds number of the basic flow and the wavelength of the partial oscillation may be regarded as given. The disturbance Eq. (9.161) then supplies for every pair $(\alpha, \mathbf{R})$ an eigenfunction $\varphi(y)$ and a complex eigenvalue $c = c_r + ic_i$. Here the sign of c_i determines the stability of the main flow for a given Reynolds number and wavelength of the disturbance. The

FIG. 9.49. Boundary layer on the flat plate at zero incidence; origin of turbulence from an initial long-wavelength wave disturbance, according to Prandtl.[33]

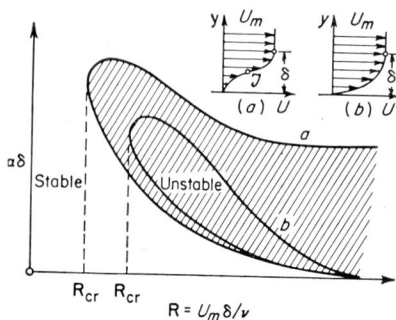

FIG. 9.50. Curves of neutral stability of a two-dimensional boundary layer for two-dimensional disturbances. (a) For velocity profiles with inflection point 3. (b) For velocity profiles without inflection point.

limiting case $c_i = 0$ gives neutral disturbances. The results of the theory of stability for a prescribed laminar flow are represented in such a way that in the $(\alpha, \mathbf{R})$ plane $c_i = 0$ is the curve which separates stable from unstable disturbances (curve of neutral stability Fig. 9.50). The point on this curve where the Reynolds number is smallest is of special interest. The tangent to the curve of neutral stability parallel to the α axis gives that Reynolds number below which all partial oscillations are damped and above which some oscillations are amplified. This smallest Reynolds number on the curve of neutral stability is the *critical Reynolds number*, or the *limit of stability of laminar flow* (instability point).

It should be noted here that one cannot expect the critical Reynolds number obtained from the investigation of stability to agree with the experimentally determined Reynolds number when the transition from laminar to turbulent takes place. The experimentally determined transition point in the boundary-layer flow along a wall lies considerably farther downstream than the theoretically determined instability point, because downstream from the instability point amplification of the unstable disturbances occurs, which leads to transition.

9.26. Results of Stability Theory (Flat Plate and Effect of Pressure Gradient)

The mathematical evaluation of the stability problem given above is exceptionally difficult. For this reason the goal of the theoretical calculation of the critical Reynolds number was not reached for some decades, in spite of the strenuous exertions.

Boundary Layer at the Plate. In connection with the investigations of Prandtl[61] and Tietjens,[62] Tollmien[63] was first successful in the theoretical calculation of the critical Reynolds number for the example of the laminar boundary layer on a flat plate at zero incidence. The result of this stability problem is given in terms of the curve of neutral stability in Fig. 9.51. From this the value of the critical Reynolds number is

$$\mathbf{R}_{cr} = \left(\frac{U_\infty \delta^*}{\nu} \right)_{cr} = 575$$

which is related to the displacement thickness of the boundary layer. According to

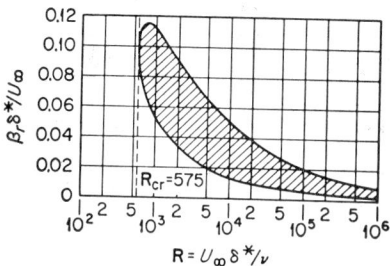

FIG. 9.51. Curves of neutral stability of the boundary layer on the flat plate at zero incidence by Tollmien.[63]

theory, disturbances with certain wavelengths are amplified above this Reynolds number while all others are damped. The wavelengths of the unstable disturbances are quite large here, while the frequency range of the unstable disturbances is very narrow.

For the flat plate at zero incidence the displacement thickness δ^* increases with the current length x as in the equation $\delta^* = 1.73 \sqrt{\nu x / U_\infty}$; see Eq. (9.42). Hence the critical Reynolds number in terms of the current length x, which corresponds to the theoretically critical Reynolds number in terms of the displacement thickness δ^*, $[(U_\infty \delta^*/\nu)_{cr} = 575]$, is $(U_\infty x/\nu)_{cr} = 1.1 \times 10^5$. It is considerably smaller than the observed critical Reynolds number, which was given above as $\mathbf{R}_{x\;cr} = 3 \times 10^5$ to 3×10^6. This must be expected, since the fully turbulent flow develops from the longitudinal-wave oscillations only after a wave-growth process that takes up a considerable length along the plate.

The first experiments to confirm the theory of stability, after years of effort, were conducted by Dryden[65] and his coworkers Schubauer and Skramstad[66] in a very-low-turbulence wind tunnel. They were successful in reducing the intensity of turbulence to a very small value of $T = 0.1$ per cent, whereas the critical Reynolds number of the plate flow had the very high value of $(U_\infty x/\nu)_{cr} = 3 \times 10^6$. For the boundary layer at the plate, the growth of some disturbance frequencies, by imposing certain disturbances of a given frequency, was found to be in very good agreement with theory. Figure 9.52 shows the comparison of the measurements of Schubauer and Skramstad with the theory of Tollmien.

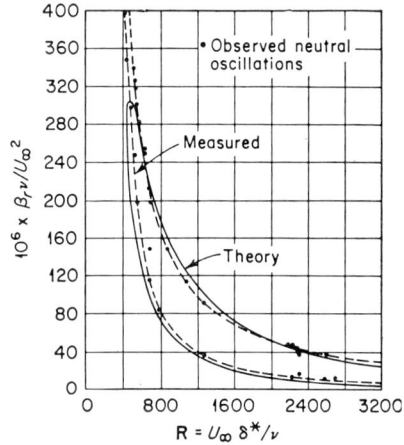

FIG. 9.52. Curves of neutral stability for neutral disturbance frequencies for the flat plate at zero incidence. Theory by Tollmien.[63] Measurements by Schubauer and Skramstad.[66]

The measured frequencies of the neutral oscillation lie very close to the theoretical curve of neutral stability. The assumption due to Reynolds, that the laminar-to-turbulent transition can be traced back to an instability of the laminar flow, is thus confirmed.

Effect of Pressure Gradient. For flow along a flat plate, the shape of the velocity profile remains constant because of the constant pressure in the external stream, but the shape of the profile varies downstream for flow past a cylindrical body, because of the effect of the pressure gradient of the external stream. In a region of positive pressure gradient the velocity profiles of the laminar boundary layer have, throughout, an inflection point of the type shown in Fig. 9.50, whereas they have none in a region of negative pressure gradient. The different shape of the velocity profile along the wall, as caused by the influence of pressure gradient, has a strong effect on the magnitude of the critical Reynolds number. Velocity profiles with a point of inflection have a considerably lower limit of stability than those without an inflection point, which was first pointed out by Tollmien.[67]

In using the Pohlhausen approximate method for calculation of the laminar boundary layer (Art. 9.13) the shape of the velocity profile is dependent on the shape factor

$$\Lambda = \frac{\delta^2}{\nu}\frac{dU_m}{dx} \qquad (9.163)$$

which has values between $\Lambda = +7.05$ at the stagnation point and $\Lambda = -12$ at the sep-

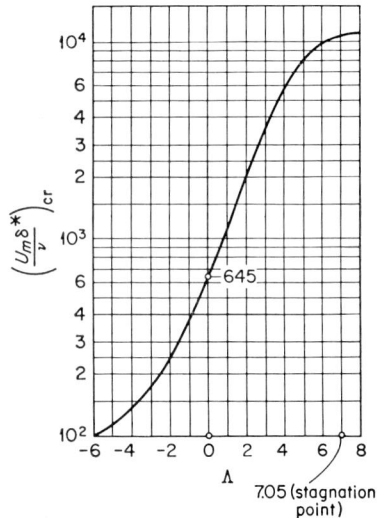

FIG. 9.53. The critical Reynolds number of boundary-layer profiles with pressure gradient in terms of the shape factor as in Eq. (9.71).

aration point. Here δ denotes the boundary-layer thickness and $U_m(x)$ denotes the velocity in the external stream. In a region of negative pressure gradient there is $\Lambda > 0$, and in a region of positive pressure gradient $\Lambda < 0$. For the one-parameter family of Pohlhausen velocity profiles, the stability calculation has been carried out by Schlichting and Ulrich.[68] Figure 9.53 shows the strong dependence of the critical Reynolds number on the shape factor Λ and consequently on the pressure gradient. A negative pressure gradient along the wall results in stabilization, and a positive pressure gradient causes strong instability. With this general stability calculation, the position of the instability point for a given body may be found relatively easily. Examples of this are given by Schlichting.[69]

9.27. Effect of Compressibility, Heat Transfer, Roughness, and Suction on the Transition

Heat Transfer. The effect of compressibility and heat transfer on the stability of laminar boundary layers has been thoroughly investigated by Lees and Lin.[70,71] The influence of compressibility on the stability of the boundary layer is small only in the case of an adiabatic wall with moderate Mach numbers (up to $\mathbf{M} = 1$). For the case of a heat-conducting wall, however, the limit of stability is strongly affected by the heat transfer between the wall and the flow. Several results are given in Fig. 9.54 for the boundary layer on a plate. The curves of neutral stability for different values of the ratio of temperature at the wall to external temperature show that extraction of heat from the boundary layer by means of cooling the wall, $T_W < T_\infty$, strongly increases the limit of stability, while heat going into the boundary layer, $T_W > T_\infty$, strongly decreases the limit of stability.

Roughness. Finally, the question should be touched upon briefly, whether the transition from laminar to turbulent is affected by the roughness of the wall. Up till

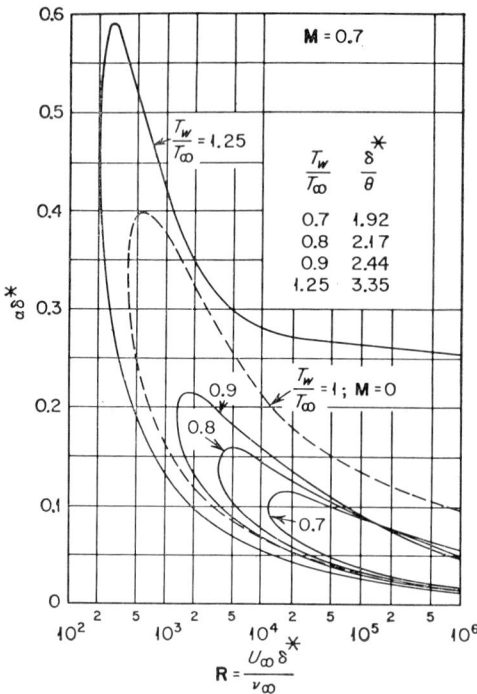

FIG. 9.54. Curves of neutral stability for the laminar boundary layer of the flat plate at zero incidence for compressible flow with *heat transfer*, according to Lees and Lin.[70] Mach number $\mathbf{M} = 0.7$; Prandtl number $\mathbf{P} = 1$. δ^*/Θ is the shape factor of the velocity profile. A cooled wall, $T_W < T_\infty$ (heat transfer from the gas to the wall), raises considerably the limit of stability, while a heated wall, $T_W > T_\infty$, lowers the limit of stability.

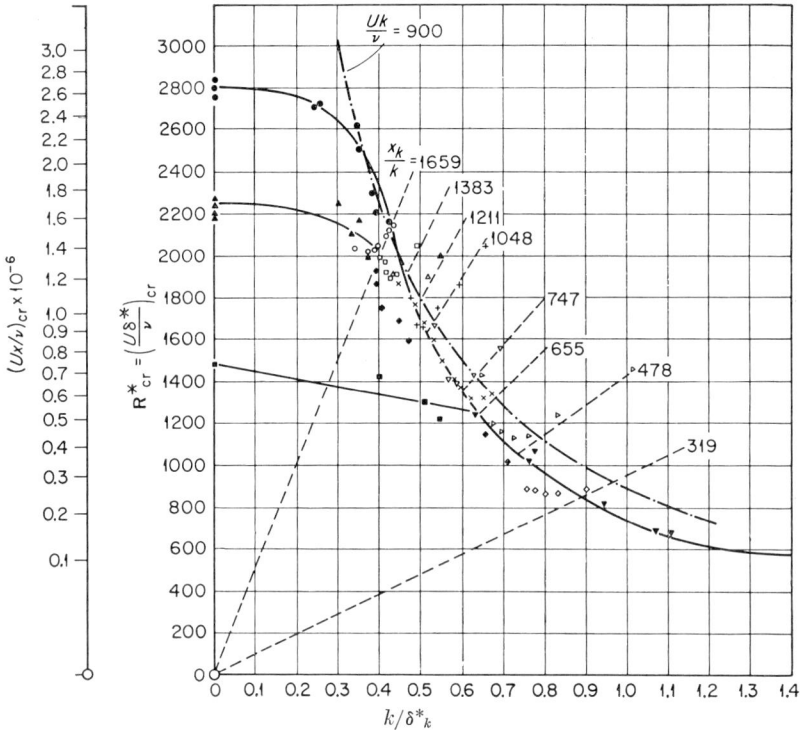

FIG. 9.55. The Reynolds number of the transition point of a boundary layer in terms of the ratio of height of roughness to boundary-layer thickness for single roughnesses (wires) in incompressible flow $R^*_{tr0} = U^* \delta_{tr}/\nu$ and $R_{x\,tr0} = Ux_{tr}/\nu$; critical Reynolds numbers of the smooth plate. The measurements are reproduced well by $Uk/\nu = 900$, as in Eq. (9.164).

now this question was not accessible to theoretical treatment; it was explained only on the basis of extended experimental investigations (Ref. 69, chap. 10). The very extensive experimental data include cylindrical (two-dimensional) roughnesses, crater-shaped (three-dimensional) single roughnesses, and roughnesses distributed on the surface.

In general, roughness of the wall favors the transition in the sense that, other things being equal, the transition in the boundary layer occurs farther upstream for a rough wall than for a smooth wall. This is evident from the theory of stability. The roughness produces additional disturbances in the laminar flow, which are already present because of the intensity of turbulence. The stronger disturbances as a whole lead to transition with less growth required than for a smooth wall.

The extensive experimental investigations on *single roughnesses* have been critically examined by Dryden,[72] as given in Fig. 9.55. In this diagram for cylindrical single roughnesses the Reynolds number of the transition point $R_{x\,cr} = (Ux/\nu)_{cr}$ is given in terms of the ratio k/δ^*_k, in which k is the height of the roughness element and δ^*_k is the displacement thickness of the boundary layer at the point of the single roughness. In this graph the experimental results from numerous different sources align themselves on *one* series of curves. The curve $Uk/\nu = 900$ is also plotted in this figure, which is obtained by means of the relation

$$\frac{U\delta^*_k}{\nu} = \frac{Uk}{\nu} \frac{1}{k/\delta^*_k}$$

The curve coincides with a large number of experimental values. It follows that the transition of the boundary layer occurs at the cylindrical roughness (wire) if

$$\frac{Uk}{\nu} \geq 900 \qquad \text{(transition at the wire)} \qquad (9.164)$$

On the other hand, according to Fig. 9.55 the transition is, practically, not affected by the wire, if $k/\delta^*_k \leq 0.3$, which is satisfied if

$$\frac{Uk}{\nu} \leq 0.5 \sqrt{\frac{Ux_k}{\nu}} \qquad \text{(hydraulically smooth)} \qquad (9.165)$$

For distributed roughness elements the position of the transition point does not vary because of the roughness as long as

$$\frac{Uk_s}{\nu} \leq 120 \qquad (9.166)$$

This limit is largely independent of whether a pressure gradient is present or not.

Suction. The limit of stability of the boundary layer is increased considerably when suction is applied, especially if the suction is distributed continuously along the wall. The suction reduces the boundary-layer thickness, but what is more important, it causes the velocity profiles to have a shape whose limit of stability is substantially higher than those of a boundary layer with an impermeable wall.

The velocity distribution in the boundary layer of a flat plate at zero incidence at a certain distance from the leading edge with uniform suction and suction velocity $v_0 < 0$ is given by

$$U(y) = U_\infty(1 - e^{v_0 y / \nu})$$

as in Eq. (9.80). For this asymptotic suction profile one obtains the following expression for the critical Reynolds number:

$$\left(\frac{U_\infty \delta^*}{\nu}\right)_{\text{cr}} = 40{,}000 \text{ to } 70{,}000 \qquad (9.167)$$

with the aid of Refs. 77 and 78. It is seen from this that the critical Reynolds number of the asymptotic suction profile is about one hundred times greater than that of the boundary layer at a plate with no suction. For more detail see, for example, Schlichting.[69]

9.28. Stability of Three-dimensional Flows

The previously discussed stability investigations were based on a two-dimensional basic flow and a likewise two-dimensional superimposed disturbance. The latter has the shape of a two-dimensional wave proceeding in the direction of the main flow. An entirely different instability is obtained, however, for flow past curved walls. For flow in the annulus between two concentric cylinders, the inner one of which is rotating while the outer one is at rest, an unstable stratification occurs as a result of the centrifugal forces, since the fluid particles in the vicinity of the inner wall are driven outward because of the larger centrifugal forces. As Taylor[79] first showed, regular vortices turning alternately right and left occur with axes along the direction of rotation (cellular vortices) for this flow from a certain Reynolds number onward. But turbulence develops only for a substantially larger Reynolds number.

An instability of three-dimensional flows similar to that of fixed walls was also found by Görtler[80] for boundary layers on concave walls.

REFERENCES

1. Prandtl, L.: Ueber Flüssigkeitsbewegung bei sehr kleiner Reibung (1904), *Verhandl. dritt. Intern. Math. Kongr.*, Heidelberg, 1904. Reprinted in "Vier Abhandlungen zur Hydrodynamik und Aerodynamik," Göttingen, 1927.
2. Eiffel, G.: Sur la résistance des sphères dans l'air en mouvement, *Compt. rend. Acad. Sci., Paris*, **155**:1597 (1912).

3. Prandtl, L.: Ueber den Luftwiderstand von Kugeln, *Göttinger Nachr.*, 1914, p. 177.
4. Wieselsberger, C.: Der Luftwiderstand von Kugeln, *ZFM*, **5**:140–144 (1914).
5. Blasius, H.: Grenzschichten in Flüssigkeiten mit kleiner Reibung, *Z. Math. u Phys.*, **56**:1 (1908).
6. Howarth, L.: On the Solution of the Laminar Boundary Equations, *Proc. Roy. Soc. (London)*, **A164**:547 (1938).
7. Nikuradse, J.: Laminare Reibungsschichten an der längsangeströmten Platte, Monographie, *Zentrale für wiss. Berichtswesen*, Berlin, 1942.
8. Liepmann, H. W., and S. Dhawan: Direct Measurements of Local Skin Friction in Low-speed and High-speed Flow, *Proc. First U.S. Natl. Congr. Appl. Mech.*, 1951, p. 869.
9. Goldstein, S.: A Note on the Boundary Layer Equations, *Proc. Cambridge Phil. Soc.*, **35**:338 (1939).
10. Mangler, W.: Die "ähnlichen" Lösungen der Prandtlschen Grenzschichtgleichungen, *ZAMM*, **23**:243 (1943).
11. Schlichting, H.: "Boundary Layer Theory," 4th ed., McGraw-Hill, New York, 1960.
12. Falkner, V. M., and S. W. Skan: Some Approximate Solutions of the Boundary Layer Equations, *Phil. Mag.*, **12**:865 (1931); *ARC Rept.* 1314, 1930.
13. Hartree, D. R.: On an Equation Occurring in Falkner and Skan's Approximate Treatment of the Equations of the Boundary Layer, *Proc. Cambridge Phil. Soc.*, **33**(2):223 (1937).
14. von Kármán, T.: Über laminare und turbulente Reibung, *ZAMM*, **1**:233 (1921); English transl. in *NACA Tech. Mem.* 1092.
15. Pohlhausen, K.: Zur näherungsweisen Integration der Differentialgleichung der laminaren Grenzschicht, *ZAMM*, **1**:252–268 (1921).
16. Holstein, H., and T. Bohlen: Ein einfaches Verfahren zur Berechnung laminarer Reibungsschichten, die dem Näherungsansatz von K. Pohlhausen genügen, *Lilienthal-Ges. Ber.* S10, pp. 5–16, 1940.
17. Walz, A.: Ein neuer Ansatz für das Geschwindigkeitsprofil der laminaren Reibungsschicht, *Lilienthal-Ges. Ber.* 141, p. 8, 1941.
18. Pretsch, J.: Die laminare Reibungsschicht an elliptischen Zylindern und Rotationsellipsoiden bei symmetrischer Anströmung, *Luftfahrt-Forsch.*, **18**:397–402 (1941).
19. Tomotika, S., and I. Imai: On the Transition from Laminar to Turbulent Flow in the Boundary Layer of a Sphere, *Aeronaut. Research Inst. Tokyo Univ. Rept.* 167, 1938; also S. Tomotika: *Proc. Phys. Math. Soc. Japan*, vol. 20, 1938.
20. Betz, A.: Beeinflussung der Reibungsschicht und ihre praktische Verwertung, *Schriften deut. Akad. Luftfahrt-Forsch.*, no. 49, 1939.
21. Schlichting, H.: Absaugung in der Aerodynamik, *Jahrb. WGL*, 1956, pp. 19–29, 1957.
22. Poisson-Quinton, P.: Recherches théoretiques et expérimentales sur le contrôle de circulation par souflage appliqué aux ailes d'avions, *ONERA publ. note tech.* 37, 1956; see also *Jahrb. WGL*, pp. 29–51, 1956.
23. Ackeret, J.: "Das Rotorschiff und seine physikalischen Grundlagen," Vandenhoeck und Rupprecht, Göttingen, 1926.
24. Betz, A.: Die Wirkungsweise von unterteilten Flügelprofilen, *Ber. Abhandl. Wiss. Ges. Luftfahrt*, no. 6, 1922. See also *NACA Tech. Mem.* 100, 1922.
25. Schrenk, O.: Tragflügel mit Grenzschichtabsaugung, *Luftfahrt-Forsch.* **2**:49 (1928); see also *ZFM*, **22**:259 (1931), *Luftfahrt-Forsch.*, **12**:10 (1935), and *Luftwissen.*, **7**:409 (1940); also *NACA Tech. Mem.* 974, 1941.
26. Ulrich, A.: Theoretische Untersuchungen über die Widerstandsersparnis durch Laminarhaltung mit Absaugung, *Schriften deut. Akad. Luftfahrt-Forsch.*, ser. B, vol. 8, no. 2, 1944.
27. Reichardt, H.: Messungen turbulenter Schwankungen, *Naturwiss.*, 1938, p. 404; see also *ZAMM*, **13**:177–180 (1933); **18**:358–361 (1938).
28. Klebanoff, P. S.: Characteristics of Turbulence in a Boundary Layer with Zero Pressure Gradient, *NACA Rept.* 1247, 1955.
29. Prandtl, L.: Ueber die ausgebildete Turbulenz, *ZAMM*, **5**:136–139 (1925), and *Verhandl. zweit. Intern. Kongr. angew. Mech.*, Zürich, 1926.
30. Blasius, H.: Das Aehnlichkeitsgesetz bei Reibungsvorgängen in Flüssigkeiten, *Forsch. Ing.-Wes.*, no. 131, 1913.
31. Nikuradse, J.: Gesetzmässigkeiten der turbulenten Strömung in glatten Rohren, *Forsch. Gebiete Ingenieurw.*, no. 356, 1932.
32. Prandtl, L.: Ueber den Reibungswiderstand strömender Luft, *Ergeb. Aerodyn. Versuchsanstalt Göttingen*, vol. 3, 1927. See also L. Prandtl: *Ergeb. Aerodyn. Versuchsanstalt Göttingen*, **1**:136, 1921.
33. Prandtl, L.: Neuere Ergebnisse der Turbulenzforschung, *Z. VDI*, **77**:105–114 (1933).
34. Nikuradse, J.: Strömungsgesetze in rauhen Rohren, *Forsch. Gebiete Ingenieurw.*, no. 361, 1933.

35. Prandtl, L., and H. Schlichting: Das Widerstandsgesetz rauher Platten, *Werft. Reed. Hafen*, pp. 1–4, 1934.
36. Schlichting, H.: Experimentelle Untersuchungen zum Rauhigkeitsproblem, *Ingr.-Arch.*, **7**:1–34 (1936), English transl. in *Proc. ASME*, **63**(9):16–31 (1937); see also *Werft. Reederei, Hafen*, vol. 99, 1936, and *Jahrb. schiffbautech. Ges.*, vol. 418, 1936.
37. Gruschwitz, E.: Die turbulente Reibungsschicht in ebener Strömung bei Druckabfall und Druckanstieg, *Ingr.-Arch.*, **2**:321–346 (1931).
38. von Doenhoff, A. E., and H. Tetervin: Determination of General Relations for the Behavior of Turbulent Boundary Layers, *NACA Rept.* 772, 1943.
39. Truckenbrodt, E.: Ein Quadraturverfahren zur Berechnung der laminaren und turbulenten Reibungsschicht bei ebener und rotationssymmetrischer Strömung, *Ingr.-Arch.*, **20**:211–228 (1952).
40. Dönch, F.: Divergente und konvergente Strömungen mit kleinen Oeffnungswinkeln, Göttingen Thesis, 1925, *Forschungsarb. Verein. deut. Ingr.*, no. 292, 1926.
41. Nikuradse, J.: Untersuchungen über die Strömung des Wassers in konvergenten und divergenten Kanälen, *Forschungsarb. Verein. deut. Ingr.*, no. 289, 1929.
42. Pretsch, J.: Zur theoretischen Berechnung des Profilwiderstandes, *Jahrb. deut. Luftfahrt-Forsch.*, **1**:61–81 (1938).
43. Squire, H. B., and A. D. Young: The Calculation of the Profile Drag of Airfoils, *Brit. ARC Rept. Mem.* 1838, 1938.
44. Truckenbrodt, E.: Die Berechnung des Profilwiderstandes aus der vorgegebenen Profilform, *Ingr.-Arch.*, **21**:176–186 (1953).
45. Busemann, A.: Gasströmung mit laminarer Grenzschicht entlang einer Platte, *ZAMM*, **15**:23–25 (1935).
46. Emmons, H. W., and J. G. Brainerd: Temperature Effect in a Laminar Compressible Fluid Boundary Layer along a Flat Plate, *J. Appl. Mech.*, **A8**:105 (1941), **9**:1 (1942).
47. Eber, G. R.: Recent Investigations of Temperature Recovery and Heat Transmission on Cones and Cylinders in Axial Flow in the NOL Aeroballistics Wind Tunnel, *J. Aeronaut. Sci.*, **19**:1–6 (1952).
48. Hantzsche, W., and H. Wendt: Zum Kompressibilitätseinfluss bei der laminaren Grenzschicht der ebenen Platte, *Jahrb. deut. Luftfahrt-Forsch.*, **1**:517–521 (1940).
49. Hantzsche, W., and H. Wendt: Die laminare Grenzschicht an der ebenen Platte mit und ohne Wärmeübergang unter Berücksichtigung der Kompressibilität, *Jahrb. deut. Luftfahrt-Forsch.*, **1**:40–50 (1942).
50. Crocco, L.: Sullo strato limite laminare nei gas lungo una lamina plana, *Rend. Math. Univ. Roma*, **5**:2 (1941).
51. Ackeret, J., F. Feldmann, and N. Rott: Untersuchungen an Verdichtungsstössen und Grenzschichten in schnell bewegten Gasen, *Inst. Aerodynamik ETH Rept.* 10, Zurich, 1946; see also *NACA Tech. Mem.* 1113, 1947.
52. Liepmann, H. W.: The Interaction between Boundary Layer and Shock Waves in Transsonic Flow, *J. Aeronaut. Sci.*, **13**:623–637 (1946).
53. Liepmann, H. W., A. Roshko, and S. Dhawan: On Reflection of Shock Waves from Boundary Layers, *NACA Rept.* 1100, 1952.
54. Young, A. D.: Boundary Layers in C. L. Howarth (ed.), "Modern Developments in Fluid Mechanics, High Speed Flow," vol. 1, pp. 375–475, Oxford, New York, 1953.
55. van der Hegge-Zijnen, B. G.: Measurements of the Velocity Distribution in the Boundary Layer along a Plane Surface, thesis, Delft, 1924. See also *Proc. First Intern. Congr. Appl. Mech.*, Delft, p. 113, 1924.
56. Hansen, M.: Die Geschwindigkeitsverteilung in der Grenzschicht an der längsangeströmten ebenen Platte, *ZAMM*, **8**:185–199 (1928); *NACA Tech. Mem.* 585, 1930.
57. Dryden, H. L.: Boundary Layer Flow near Flat Plates, *Proc. Fourth Intern. Congr. Appl. Mechanics*, Cambridge, p. 175, 1934.
58. Dryden, H. L.: Airflow in the Boundary Layer near a Plate, *NACA Rept.* 562, 1936.
59. Dryden, H. L.: Turbulence and the Boundary Layer, *J. Aeronaut. Sci.*, **6**:85, 101 (1939).
60. Schubauer, G. B., and P. S. Klebanoff: Contributions on the Mechanics of Boundary Layer Transition, *NACA Tech. Note* 3489, 1955; *NACA Rept.* 1289, 1956.
61. Prandtl, L.: Bemerkungen über die Entstehung der Turbulenz, *ZAMM*, **1**:431–441 (1921), and *Phys. Z.*, **23**:19 (1922).
62. Tietjens, O.: Beiträge zur Entstehung der Turbulenz, Göttingen Thesis, 1922, and *ZAMM*, **5**:200–217 (1925).
63. Tollmien, W.: Ueber die Entstehung der Turbulenz. I. Mitteilung. *Nachr. Ges. Wiss. Göttingen, Math.-phys. Kl.*, 1929, pp. 21–44.
64. Schlichting, H.: Zur Entstehung der Turbulenz bei der Plattenströmung, *Nachr. Ges. Wiss. Göttingen, Math.-phys. Kl.*, 1933, pp. 182–208; see also *ZAMM*, **13**:171–174 (1933).
65. Dryden, H. L.: Some Recent Contributions to the Study of Transition and Turbulent

Boundary Layers, *Sixth Intern. Congr. Appl. Mech.*, Paris, 1946; see also *NACA Tech. Note* 1168, 1947.

66. Schubauer, G. B., and H. K. Skramstad: Laminar Boundary Layer oscillations and Stability of Laminar Flow, *J. Aeronaut. Sci.*, **14**:69–77 (1947); see also *NACA Rept.* 909, 1948.

67. Tollmien, W.: Ein allgemeines Kriterium der Instabilität laminarer Geschwindigkeits-verteilungen, *Nachr. Ges. Wiss. Göttingen, Math.-phys. Kl.*, Fachgruppe I, **1**:79–114 (1935); English transl. in *NACA Tech. Mem.* 792, 1936.

68. Schlichting, H., and A. Ulrich: Zur Berechnung des Umschlages laminar-turbulent, *Jahrb. deut. Luftfahrt-Forsch.*, **1**:8–35 (1942), in detail in *Lilienthal-Ges. Ber.* S10, pp. 75–135, 1940.

69. Schlichting, H.: Entstehung der Turbulenz, in *Handbuch der Physik*, vol. 8, sec. 1, Springer, Berlin, 1959.

70. Lees, L., and C. C. Lin: Investigation of the Stability of the Laminar Boundary Layer in a Compressible Fluid, *NACA Tech. Note* 1115, 1946.

71. Lees, L.: The Stability of the Laminar Boundary Layer in a Compressible Flow, *NACA Tech. Note* 1360, 1947, and *NACA Rept.* 876, 1947.

72. Dryden, H. L.: Review of Published Data on the Effect of Roughness on Transition from Laminar to Turbulent Flow, *J. Aeronaut. Sci.*, **20**(7):477–482 (1953).

73. Homann, F.: Einfluss grosser Zähigkeit bei Strömung um Zylinder und Kugel, *Forsch Gebiete Ingenieurw.*, **7**:1–10 (1936).

74. Flachsbart, O.: Neuere Untersuchungen über den Luftwiderstand von Kugeln, *Phys. Z.*, **28**:461 (1927).

75. Wilson, R. E.: Turbulent Boundary Layer Characteristics at Supersonic Speeds, *J. Aeronaut. Sci.*, **17**:585–594 (1950).

76. van Driest, E. R.: Turbulent Boundary Layer in Compressible Fluids, *J. Aeronaut. Sci.*, **18**:145–160 (1951).

77. Bussmann, K., and H. Münz: Die Stabilität der laminaren Reibungsschicht mit Absaugung, *Jahrb. deut. Luftfahrt-Forsch.*, **1**:36 (1942).

78. Pretsch, J.: Umschlagbeginn und Absaugung, *Jahrb. deut. Luftfahrt-Forsch.*, **1**:1–7 (1942).

79. Taylor, G. I.: Stability of a Viscous Liquid Contained between Two Rotating Cylinders, *Phil. Trans.*, **A223**:289 (1923); see also *Proc. Roy. Soc.* (*London*), **A151**:494 (1935); **157**:546, 565 (1936).

80. Görtler, H.: Ueber den Einfluss der Wandkrümmung auf die Entstehung der Turbulenz, *ZAMM*, **20**:138–147 (1940).

Textbooks and Summary Presentations of Boundary-layer Theory

81. Betz, A.: Beeinflussung der Reibungsschicht und ihre praktische Verwertung, *Schriften deut. Akad. Luftfahrt-Forsch.*, no. 49, 1939.

82. Clauser, F. H.: The Turbulent Boundary Layer, in "Advances in Applied Mechanics," vol. 4, Academic Press, New York, 1956.

83. Dryden, H. L.: Fifty Years of Boundary Layer Theory and Experiment, *Science*, **121**:375–380 (1955).

84. Dryden, H. L.: Recent Advances in the Mechanics of Boundary Layer Flow, in "Advances in Applied Mechanics," vol. 1, p. 1, Academic Press, New York, 1948.

85. Eckert, E.: "Einführung in den Wärme- und Stoffaustausch," Springer, Berlin, 1959.

86. Görtler, H., and W. Tollmien (eds.): "Fünfzig Jahre Grenzschichtforschung," Festschrift in Originalbeiträgen, Braunschweig, 1955.

87. Goldstein, S. (ed.): "Modern Developments in Fluid Dynamics," vols. 1 and 2, Oxford, New York, 1938.

88. Howarth, L. (ed.): High Speed Flow, in "Modern Developments in Fluid Dynamics," vols. 1 and 2, Oxford, New York, 1953.

89. Howarth, L. (ed.): "Boundary Layer Effects in Aerodynamics," Proceedings of a Symposium at the National Physical Laboratory, London, 1955.

90. Kuerti, G.: The Laminar Boundary Layer in Compressible Flow, in "Advances in Applied Mechanics," vol. 2, pp. 21–92, Academic Press, New York, 1951.

91. Lin, C. C.: "The Theory of Hydrodynamic Stability," Cambridge, New York, 1955.

92. Moore, F. K.: Three-dimensional Boundary Layer Theory, in "Advances in Applied Mechanics," vol. 4, pp. 159–228, Academic Press, New York, 1956.

93. Pai, S. I.: "Fluid Dynamics of Jets," Van Nostrand, Princeton, N.J., 1954.

94. Pai, S. I.: "Viscous Flow Theory," vol. 1, "Laminar Flow," vol. 2, "Turbulent Flow," Van Nostrand, Princeton, N.J.

95. Prandtl, L., and O. Tietjens: "Hydro- and Aeromechanics," 2 vols., McGraw-Hill, New York, 1934.
96. Prandtl, L.: The Mechanics of Viscous Fluids, in W. F. Durand, "Aerodynamic Theory," Springer, Berlin, 1935.
97. Prandtl, L.: "Fluid Dynamics," Hafner, New York, 1952.
98. Schlichting, H.: "Boundary Layer Theory," 4th ed., McGraw-Hill, New York, 1960; see also "Grenzschicht-Theorie," 3d ed, Karlsruhe, 1958.
99. Schlichting, H.: Entstehung der Turbulenz, in *Handbuch der Physik*, vol. 8, sec. 1, pp. 351–450, Springer, Berlin, 1959.
100. Schlichting, H.: Some Developments in Boundary Layer Research in the Past Thirty Years, Third Lanchester Memorial Lecture, presented to the Royal Aeronautical Society, London, November, 1959, *J. Roy. Aeronaut. Soc.*, **64**(590):63–80 (1960).
101. Schlichting, H.: Application of Boundary Layer Theory in Turbomachinery, *J. Basic Engr.*, **D81**:543–551 (1959); see also *Siemens Z.*, **33**:429–438 (1959).
102. Schlichting, H.: Some Recent Developments in Boundary Layer Control, *Proc. First Intern. Congr. in Aeronaut.*, Madrid, **2**:563–586, September, 1958.
103. Schlichting, H., and E. Truckenbrodt: Aerodynamik des Flugzeuges, in vol. 1 (in particular chap. 4), "Strömungen mit Reibung" (Grenzschicht-Theorie), Springer-Verlag, Berlin, 1959.
104. Tollmien, W.: Grenzschicht-Theorie and Turbulente Strömungen, in W. Wien and F. Harms (eds.), "Handbuch der Experimentalphysik," vol. 4, sec. 1, Springer, Leipzig, 1931.
105. Townsend, A. A.: "The Structure of Turbulent Shear Flow," Cambridge, New York, 1956.
106. Young, A. D.: Boundary Layers (in compressible flow), contribution to Ref. 88, vol. **1**, chap. **10**.

Section 10

TURBULENCE

By

A. A. TOWNSEND, *Emmanuel College, University of Cambridge, Cambridge, England*

TURBULENCE

NATURE OF TURBULENT MOTION

10.1. Transition

If a viscous fluid flows along a channel or past an obstacle, the flow is laminar and stable to small disturbances only if the flow velocity is less than a critical value, corresponding to a critical value of the Reynolds number of the flow if the fluid has a Newtonian viscosity and is incompressible. The unstability that sets in at the critical velocity may take two forms, either leading to a steady periodic flow (e.g., the Kármán vortex street in the wake of a circular cylinder) or to a turbulent flow composed of a complicated system of eddies with no obvious regularity. If the flow becomes periodic, the periodic flow itself becomes unstable at a higher flow velocity and undergoes a transition to turbulent flow, but even if periodic flow does not occur, there may be a range of Reynolds numbers over which either laminar or turbulent flow is possible, depending on the magnitude of external disturbances of the flow. Three critical numbers may be distinguished: $\mathbf{R}_a$, above which some small disturbances of the laminar flow are amplified; $\mathbf{R}_b$, below which turbulent flow cannot be sustained; and $\mathbf{R}_c$, above which the periodic flow initiated at the first Reynolds number breaks up into turbulent motion. Approximate values of these numbers for some simple flows are given in Table 10.1.

10.2. Properties of Turbulent Flow

The most obvious property of turbulent flow is that momentum, heat, and mass are transferred across the flow at rates much greater than those of the molecular transport processes (viscosity and diffusion) that transfer these quantities in laminar flow. This is due to additional transport by motion of fluid elements across the flow and concurrent mixing of the transported quantity with neighboring fluid elements, and it may be

Table 10.1. Critical Reynolds Numbers for Shear Flows

Flow	Definition of Reynolds number	$\mathbf{R}_a$	$\mathbf{R}_b$	$\mathbf{R}_c$
Circular pipe	$U_m R/\nu$	∞	2050	
Two-dimensional channel	$U_m D/\nu$	5000	890	
Boundary layer (no pressure gradient)	$\frac{1}{\nu}\int_0^\infty (U_1 - U)\, dy$	420	?	
Circular jet	$\frac{1}{\nu}\left(2\pi \int_0^\infty U^2 r\, dr\right)^{1/2}$	*300*	*1000*	
Mixing layer	$\frac{1}{\nu U_1}\int_{-\infty}^\infty U(U_1 - U)\, dy$	*70*	*500*	*500*
Cylinder wake	$\frac{4}{\nu}\int_0^\infty (U_1 - U)\, dy$	62	200	200

NOTE: The numbers in this table have been compiled from various sources and from imprecise data. The numbers in italics should be treated with special caution.

1alitatively by assigning to the turbulent motion a particle velocity v and a
ic *mixing length* l. Considerations similar to those used in the kinetic theory
en show that the effective *eddy diffusivity* is of order vl, that is, proportional
nolds number of the turbulent motion. The occurrence of a sharp increase
or in heat and mass transfer is frequently used to determine the onset of
turbulent motion if direct observation of the fluctuations is inconvenient.

Turbulent motion, observed directly by flow-visualization techniques or by oscillo-
scopic observation of velocity fluctuations at a fixed point, appears chaotic, random,
and apparently similar to the thermal motion of gas molecules. Closer observation
shows that, unlike the molecular motion, the turbulent motion is highly anisotropic and
possesses a considerable degree of organization. In particular, almost periodic components of the motion do occur and important elements of the flow retain their identity
over comparatively long intervals of time.

10.3. Classification of Turbulent Flows

It is useful to distinguish between the following three types of turbulent flow, which
have distinct properties and need individual consideration.

Wall turbulence. Flow near a solid boundary in which the mean acceleration of the
fluid is negligible. This is found close to the solid boundaries in pipe, channel, and
boundary-layer flows.

Free turbulence. Flow remote from solid boundaries and usually surrounded by nonturbulent fluid. This is found in jets, wakes, and mixing layers and in the outer part
of boundary layers.

Convective turbulence. Flow in which potential energy is converted by mixing to
kinetic energy. The simplest example is the convectional flow between parallel horizontal planes, but turbulent flow in the annular space between concentric rotating
cylinders has similar properties.

It is interesting to note that the laminar-stability problems for these three types of
flow are essentially different, and Malkus[20] has constructed a plausible theory of turbulent shear flow which depends on the nature of the laminar-stability problem for the
flow concerned.

10.4. Notation

The general theory of turbulent flow is most conveniently carried out in rectangular
cartesian coordinates using tensor suffix notation; i.e., the coordinates of a point are
written x_i, where i may be 1, 2, or 3, corresponding to the three axes. A summation
convention is used, repetition of a free suffix denoting summation over all three possible
values, e.g.,

$$u_i u_i \equiv u_1^2 + u_2^2 + u_3^2$$

In practical flows, a particular choice of axes is always indicated. For two-dimensional
flows, $0x_1$ lies in the general direction of the mean velocity and $0x_2$ at right angles in
the direction of maximum gradient of mean velocity, and $0x_3$ is a direction of homogeneity. The suffix notation is convenient, particularly for the representation of
correlation functions, but it tends to obscure the significant differences between the
coordinate directions, and the old notation is used widely. In this, x, y, z are coordinates, u, v, w velocity components, corresponding to x_1, x_2, x_3 and u_1, u_2, u_3. At times
it is convenient to use both simultaneously [see Eq. (10.11)]. Cylindrical polar coordinates are better suited to the description of axisymmetric flows, with x measured along
the axis of symmetry, r the radial coordinate, and ϕ the directional coordinate. Symbols
used are:

U, V, W or U_1, U_2, U_3 components of mean velocity
u, v, w or u_1, u_2, u_3 components of the velocity fluctuation about the mean
$q^2 \equiv u^2 + v^2 + w^2$

P, p	mean and fluctuation of the pressure
ρ	fluid density (only in Arts. 10.26 to 10.28)
ν	kinematic viscosity
ϵ	rate of turbulent-energy dissipation [Eq. (10.3)]
$R_{ij}(\mathbf{x},\mathbf{r},\tau)$	correlation function at position $\mathbf{x}$ with space interval $\mathbf{r}$ and time interval τ
M, m	mean and fluctuation of an arbitrary scalar
$F_{ij}(n)$	longitudinal spectrum function of $u_i u_j$
L_1	integral scale
l_s	microscale
λ	Taylor microscale
l	mixing length
v_s	velocity scale of the smallest eddies
τ	total shear stress
K	Kármán constant ($= 0.41$)
d	roughness length parameter for constant-stress layer
A	constant in logarithmic profile for smooth surfaces (~ 2.3)
K_z	constant for zero-stress layer (~ 0.50)
D	half-width of channel
R	radius of pipe
$c_f = 2\tau_0/U_m^2$	resistance or friction coefficient
κ	thermometric conductivity
T, θ	mean and fluctuation of temperature
u_0, l_0, θ_0	scales of velocity, length, and temperature
α	entrainment constant
β	coefficient of thermal expansion
Q	thermometric heat emission
γ	intermittency factor
D	diffusion coefficient

GENERAL THEORY

10.5. Use of Mean Values

The velocity pattern of a turbulent flow is always changing and never repeats, so that even if it were possible to measure the complete sequence of changes, the measurements would relate only to that particular experiment. General significance can be attached only to the statistical specification of the velocity field, i.e., to the joint probability distribution function (pdf) which determines the likelihood of occurrence of any combination of velocities at points in space-time. Practical difficulties restrict our attention to a few moments of this pdf, which are usually mean values (or statistical expectations) of physical properties of the flow that are easy to measure or are of special significance. In steady flows, mean values may be obtained as averages over sufficiently long periods of time, although turbulence theory may consider either space averages or ensemble averages (Batchelor[1]).

Following Osborne Reynolds, it is usual to consider the mean motion and the mean fluid properties separately from the fluctuations from the means. In the usual notation, mean velocity and mean pressure are denoted by upper-case symbols U_i and P, while the fluctuations from these mean values are denoted by corresponding lower-case symbols u_i and p. The usefulness of this distinction between mean flow and turbulent fluctuations is that it emphasizes that energy transfer is nearly always from the mean motion to the turbulent motion, so that kinetic energy of the fluctuations is for practical purposes unavailable energy.

10.6. Momentum and Energy Equations

The turbulent motion of an incompressible fluid is described by the equation of mass conservation and by the Navier-Stokes equations of motion. Taking the mean values of these equations leads to a continuity equation for the mean flow,

$$\frac{\partial U_l}{\partial x_l} = 0 \tag{10.1}$$

and to the momentum equation for the mean flow,

$$\frac{\partial U_i}{\partial t} + U_l \frac{\partial U_i}{\partial x_l} + \frac{\partial (\overline{u_i u_l})}{\partial x_l} = -\frac{\partial P}{\partial x_i} + \nu \nabla^2 U_i \tag{10.2}$$

These differ from the corresponding equations for laminar flow only in the presence of the terms $\dfrac{\partial}{\partial x_l}(\overline{u_i u_l})$, whose effect is equivalent to the presence of an additional set of stresses, $-\overline{u_i u_j}$, the *Reynolds stresses*. These are easily seen to be virtual stresses caused by momentum flux due to turbulent movements. The central problem in the study of turbulent shear flow is the derivation of satisfactory relations between the Reynolds stresses and the mean-velocity field.

Another important equation describes the balance of turbulent kinetic energy as the sum of the rates at which it is produced by working of the mean flow against the Reynolds stresses, transferred from one part of the flow to another by convection and pressure flow and dissipated by viscous stresses to produce heat. It is

$$\frac{\partial}{\partial t}\left(\frac{1}{2}\overline{q^2}\right) + U_l \frac{\partial}{\partial x_l}\left(\frac{1}{2}\overline{q^2}\right) + \overline{u_i u_l} \frac{\partial U_i}{\partial x_l} + \frac{\partial}{\partial x_l}\left(\frac{1}{2}\overline{q^2 u_l} + \overline{p u_l}\right)$$

$$= \nu \left[\frac{\partial^2}{\partial x_l \partial x_l}\left(\frac{1}{2}\overline{q^2}\right) + \frac{\partial^2}{\partial x_i \partial x_j}(\overline{u_i u_j})\right] - \epsilon \tag{10.3}$$

in which $\epsilon = \overline{\nu(\partial u_i/\partial x_j)(\partial u_i/\partial x_j + \partial u_j/\partial x_i)}$ is the rate of conversion of turbulent kinetic energy into heat.

10.7. Boundary-layer Approximation

This approximation, due to L. Prandtl, assumes that gradients of mean quantities in the direction of the mean flow are an order of magnitude less than their gradients normal to the flow. Introducing now the usual notation for nearly rectilinear flow, the equations of mean motion, Eqs. (10.2), may be written

$$\frac{\partial U}{\partial t} + U \frac{\partial U}{\partial x} + V \frac{\partial U}{\partial y} + \frac{\partial \overline{uv}}{\partial y} = -\frac{dP_1}{dx} + \nu \frac{\partial^2 U}{\partial y^2}$$

$$P + \overline{v^2} = P_1 \tag{10.4}$$

in which P_1 depends only on x. Equation (10.3) for the turbulent kinetic energy takes the simpler form,

$$\frac{\partial(\overline{q^2}/2)}{\partial t} + U \frac{\partial(\overline{q^2}/2)}{\partial x} + V \frac{\partial(\overline{q^2}/2)}{\partial y} + \overline{uv}\frac{\partial U}{\partial y} + \frac{\partial}{\partial y}\left(\frac{1}{2}\overline{q^2 v} + \overline{pv}\right) = -\epsilon \tag{10.5}$$

These equations are for *two-dimensional flow*, i.e., with $0z$ an axis of homogeneity. For *axisymmetrical flow*, they are

$$\frac{\partial U}{\partial t} + U \frac{\partial U}{\partial x} + V \frac{\partial U}{\partial r} + \frac{1}{r}\frac{\partial(\overline{uv}r_0)}{\partial r} = -\frac{dP_1}{dx} + \frac{\nu}{r}\frac{\partial}{\partial r}\left(r\frac{\partial U}{\partial r}\right)$$

$$P + \overline{v^2} = P_1 \tag{10.6}$$

and

$$\frac{\partial(\overline{q^2}/2)}{\partial t} + U \frac{\partial(\overline{q^2}/2)}{\partial x} + V \frac{\partial(\overline{q^2}/2)}{\partial y} + \overline{uv}\frac{\partial U}{\partial r} + \frac{1}{r}\frac{\partial}{\partial r}\left[r\left(\frac{1}{2}\overline{q^2 v} + \overline{pv}\right)\right] = -\epsilon \tag{10.7}$$

The reason for the applicability of the boundary-layer approximation to turbulent flow is that the velocity fluctuations are generally an order of magnitude less than the mean velocities. When this is true, the variation with time of turbulent fluctuations observed at a fixed point is almost entirely due to the movement at the mean stream velocity of the spatial pattern of the fluctuations and hardly at all to the variation of this pattern with time. *Taylor's hypothesis* assumes that $m(x,t)$ is identical with $m(x - U\tau, t + \tau)$ if τ is not too large and that the autocorrelation function of m, $\overline{m(x,t)m(x, t + \tau)}$ is identical with the spatial correlation function in the direction of mean flow, $\overline{m(x,t)m(x - U\tau,t)}$.

10.8. Spectrum and Correlation Functions

The spatial structure of a turbulent flow may be described by spectrum and correlation functions. The general space-time correlation function,

$$R_{ij}(\mathbf{x},\mathbf{r},\tau) = \overline{u_i(\mathbf{x},t)u_j(\mathbf{x} + \mathbf{r}, t + \tau)} \tag{10.8}$$

is used in two special forms, the *spatial correlation function* with $\tau = 0$ and the *autocorrelation function* with $\mathbf{r} = 0$, the latter being identical with the spatial function with a streamwise displacement of $U\tau$. The *frequency spectrum* of the fluctuations at a fixed point, which is easily measured with standard electronic equipment, is the Fourier transform of the autocorrelation function and related to the ordinary correlation function by

$$F_{ij}(n) = \frac{4}{U} \int_0^\infty R_{ij}(r) \cos \frac{2\pi n r}{U} \, dr \tag{10.9}$$

in which r is a streamwise displacement. Conversely,

$$R_{ij}(r) = \int_0^\infty F_{ij}(n) \cos \frac{2\pi n r}{U} \, dn \tag{10.10}$$

The use of these functions is to define length scales of the turbulence. The largest, characteristic of the energy-containing eddies of the motion, is the *integral scale*,

$$L_1 = (\overline{u^2})^{-1} \int_0^\infty R_{11}(r,0,0) \, dr \tag{10.11}$$

which, by Eq. (10.9), is proportional to the spectrum function at zero frequency,

$$L_1 = \tfrac{1}{4} U(\overline{u_1^2})^{-1} F_{11}(0) \tag{10.12}$$

The smallest, characteristic of the smallest eddies of the motion, is the *microscale*, $l_s = \epsilon^{-1/4}\nu^{3/4}$, in which (see Art. 10.10)

$$\epsilon = -15\nu R''(0) = 15\nu \overline{\left(\frac{\partial u}{\partial x}\right)^2}$$

$$= 60\pi^2\nu \int_0^\infty n^2 F_{11}(n) \, dn \tag{10.13}$$

A frequently used length scale of no precise meaning is the *Taylor microscale*,

$$\lambda = \left[\frac{\overline{u_1^2}}{R''_{11}(0)} \right]^{1/2}$$

$$= U(\overline{u_1^2})^{1/2} \left[\int_0^\infty 4\pi n^2 F_1(n) \, dn \right]^{1/2} \tag{10.14}$$

These scales are related (approximately) by

$$\frac{l_s}{L_1} = 15^{3/4} \left(\frac{\lambda}{L}\right)^{3/2} \quad \text{or} \quad \frac{\lambda^2}{l_s^2} = 15^{3/2} \frac{L}{\lambda} \tag{10.15}$$

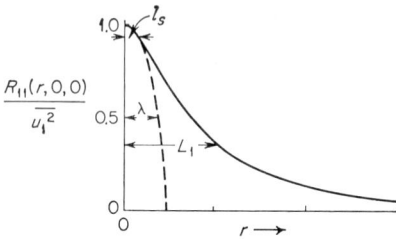

FIG. 10.1. Relative magnitudes of the length scales l_s, λ, and L_1. (The broken curve is a parabola having second-order contact with the correlation curve at $r = 0$.)

and their relation to the longitudinal correlation function $R_{11}(r,0,0)$ is indicated in Fig. 10.1

10.9. Physical Assumptions

The existence of large effective shear stresses involves a rapid conversion of mean flow energy to heat, and this is carried out by small eddies whose contribution to the Reynolds stresses and to the kinetic energy and diffusive properties of the flow is slight. The clear distinction between the large eddies that contain most of the turbulent energy and are responsible for transport effects and the small eddies that dissipate the energy by viscous work leads one to expect that the nature of the viscous-dissipation process has little effect on the large-scale motion. The important principle of *flow similarity* states that the large-scale properties of a turbulent flow (i.e., mean velocity distribution, turbulent intensities, Reynolds stresses, correlation functions, transport properties) are independent of the viscosity and the dissipation process, provided the Reynolds number of the turbulent motion is sufficiently high so that a distinction between large and small eddies is possible. These properties are then determined by the boundary conditions of the flow and are independent of the magnitude of the viscosity unless the boundary conditions of the flow themselves depend on viscous forces. The experimental evidence in favor of this principle is extensive and convincing for free turbulence and, with some minor reservations, for wall turbulence, but difficulties have been found in its application to convective turbulence (Arts. 10.24 and 10.25).

An important consequence of the principle of flow similarity is that the loss of energy from the large, energy-containing eddies to the dissipating eddies proceeds at a rate that is set by the structure of the large eddies. Dimensional considerations then show that the rate of loss, the turbulent-energy dissipation, is

$$\epsilon = C(\overline{u^2})^{3/2} L_1^{-1} \qquad (10.16)$$

in which L_1 is the integral scale defined by Eq. (10.11) and C is a constant, in theory dependent on the particular flow but approximately equal to 0.8 for many free turbulent flows.

The existence of a Reynolds stress depends on the existence of a correlation between the longitudinal and transverse components of the velocity fluctuation, and the coefficient of this correlation is necessarily less than 1. In real flows, the ratio, $|\overline{uv}|/\overline{u^2}$, is found to be nearly constant and between 0.4 and 0.5, except locally in regions of reversal in sign of the Reynolds stress. It is probable that this is a natural limit characteristic of a *structural equilibrium* attained by turbulent fluid under prolonged shear.

Using these considerations and assuming further that flow of turbulent energy from one part of the fluid to another is negligible in its consequences, it is possible to infer a relation between Reynolds stress and mean velocity gradient,

$$-\overline{uv} = l^2 \frac{\partial U}{\partial y} \left| \frac{\partial U}{\partial y} \right| \qquad (10.17)$$

which is the central result of the *momentum-transfer* form of the *mixing-length theory* (l is the mixing length, a scale of the turbulent motion whose magnitude must be estimated from other considerations). This relation can be applied consistently only to wall turbulence for which the production and dissipation of turbulent energy proceed so rapidly that flow of turbulent energy from one part of the flow to another has little effect on the turbulent motion.

10.10. Dissipation of Turbulent Energy: Local Similarity

The large-scale motion is independent of the details of the energy-dissipation process because nonlinear forces generated by interaction between eddies of different sizes usually act to create eddies one order of magnitude smaller, and continuation of this process eventually leads to eddies so small that viscous dissipation is very rapid. If the number of steps in this cascade is large, all the lower steps will have but little connection with the details of the large-scale structure of the motion and will have a structure independent of all the parameters of the large-scale motion except the rate of energy supply. This reasoning led Kolmogoroff to postulate that the small eddies of turbulence have a universal, isotropic structure that is determined by the rate of energy dissipation ϵ and by the kinematic viscosity ν. Principal results of this *theory of local similarity* are:

1. The characteristic scale of the eddies which convert turbulent energy to heat is the microscale, $l_s = \epsilon^{-\frac{1}{4}} \nu^{\frac{3}{4}}$.

2. Their characteristic velocity is $U_s = (\epsilon\nu)^{\frac{1}{4}}$.

3. The dissipating eddies are isotropic, and so

$$\epsilon = 15\nu \overline{\left(\frac{\partial u}{\partial x}\right)^2} = \frac{15}{2}\nu \overline{\left(\frac{\partial u}{\partial y}\right)^2} \tag{10.18}$$

4. The longitudinal correlation function is

$$R_{11}(r) = \overline{u_1{}^2} - C(\epsilon r)^{2/3} \tag{10.19a}$$

for $l_s^{-1} \ll r \ll L_1^{-1}$, and the spectrum function is

$$F_1(K) = \frac{4}{3(\frac{1}{3}\,!)} C\epsilon^{\frac{2}{3}} K^{-\frac{5}{3}} \tag{10.19b}$$

for $l_s^{-1} \gg K \gg L_1^{-1}$†. For further details, see Batchelor.[1]

WALL TURBULENCE

10.11. Equilibrium Layers

Wall turbulence may be simply defined as the turbulent flows that occur in the immediate neighborhood of a massive surface whose radius of curvature is large compared with the scale of the motion. Along a solid wall the mean velocity is specified and the velocity fluctuations are zero. For flow of a gas over a liquid, these boundary conditions are not satisfied exactly but the velocity fluctuations at the interface are usually much smaller than those in the bulk of the gas and it is possible, with some reservations, to ignore them. These restrictions on the motion imply the existence of a layer of fluid adjacent to the wall in which the net effects of momentum and energy transport by the mean flow are negligible and the flow is effectively homogeneous over planes parallel to the wall. To show this, integrate the momentum equation, Eq. (10.4), from the wall ($y = 0$) to $y = l$,

$$\int_0^l \frac{\partial U^2}{\partial x}\,dy - U\int_0^l \frac{\partial U}{\partial x}\,dy + (U - U_0)V_0 + \frac{dP_1}{dx}\,l = \tau - \tau_0 \tag{10.20}$$

in which U_0, V_0 are the specified velocities at the wall, and $\tau = -\overline{uv} + \nu\,\partial U/\partial y$ is the total shear stress. The first two terms are each of order $U^2 l/L$, in which L is the scale of any longitudinal inhomogeneity, while at least one of the remaining terms is of order unity. So for a suitably small value of l, the momentum balance in the layer depends only on local quantities. To this approximation, the momentum equation is

† $n! = \Gamma(n + 1) = \int_0^\infty x^n e^{-x}\,dx.$

$$V_0 \frac{\partial U}{\partial y} + \frac{\partial \overline{uv}}{\partial y} = -\frac{dP_1}{dx} + \nu \frac{\partial^2 U}{\partial y^2} \tag{10.21}$$

Similar arguments may be used to show that the energy balance depends only on local quantities and is

$$V_0 \frac{\partial (\overline{q^2}/2)}{\partial y} + \overline{uv} \frac{\partial U}{\partial y} + \frac{\partial}{\partial y} \left(\frac{1}{2} \overline{q^2 v} + \overline{pv} \right) = -\epsilon \tag{10.22}$$

In typical wall flows, the mean velocity gradient is very large close to the wall, and consequently most of the turbulent energy is produced and dissipated in a layer of thickness about one-tenth of the total flow width, sufficiently small to permit approximate validity of Eqs. (10.21) and (10.22). For this reason, the turbulent flow in this *equilibrium layer* is believed to be effectively independent of the remainder of the flow and determined by its own local parameters, τ_0, dP_1/dx, and V_0, except for a velocity of translation. Within the fully turbulent part of the flow, the principle of flow similarity (Art. 10.9) requires that viscosity have no direct effect on the mean flow, and dimensional reasoning shows that the relative mean motion is given by

$$\frac{\partial U}{\partial y} = \frac{\tau^{\frac{1}{2}}}{Ky} f \left(\frac{y}{\tau} \frac{dP_1}{dx}, \frac{V_0}{\tau} \right) \tag{10.23}$$

in which $\tau = \tau_0 + V_0 U + (dP_1/dx)y$ is the local stress at distance y from the wall. Three types of equilibrium layer may be distinguished:
1. The constant-stress layer, for which $V_0 = 0$, $\tau_0 \neq 0$
2. The zero-stress layer, for which $V_0 = 0$, $\tau_0 = 0$
3. Transpiration and suction layers, for which $V_0 \neq 0$

10.12. The Constant-stress Layer

The most common equilibrium layer is the constant-stress layer which is found in pipe, channel, and boundary-layer flows with impermeable walls and is so called because the shear stress is nearly constant within the layer. The condition for this is simply that

$$y \ll \frac{\tau_0}{\left| \dfrac{dP_1}{dx} \right|} \tag{10.24}$$

which is usually true within an equilibrium layer unless the wall stress is very small, as in a boundary layer near the point of separation. It is *not* necessary that the stress gradient $\partial \tau / \partial y$ should be zero, only that it should be small enough to allow the condition (10.24). To this approximation,

$$\tau_0 = \tau = -\overline{uv} + \nu \frac{\partial U}{\partial y}$$

$$\overline{uv} \frac{\partial U}{\partial y} + \frac{\partial}{\partial y} \left(\frac{1}{2} \overline{q^2 v} + \overline{pv} \right) = -\epsilon \tag{10.25}$$

and since $\dfrac{y}{\tau} \dfrac{dP_1}{dx}$ is negligible, Eq. (10.23) for the mean flow reduces to

$$\frac{\partial U}{\partial y} = \frac{\tau_0^{\frac{1}{2}}}{Ky} \tag{10.26}$$

Here, the constant K is an absolute constant, the same in all constant-stress layers, the *Kármán constant*. This equation integrates to

$$U = \frac{\tau_0^{\frac{1}{2}}}{K} \log \frac{y}{d} \tag{10.27}$$

in which d is a constant of integration with the dimensions of a length, whose effect is equivalent to a velocity of translation of the whole flow. This *logarithmic velocity distribution* appears to describe the mean flow over a great variety of surfaces within the fully turbulent part of the constant-stress layer (Coles[9]).

Flows with the same wall stress over different kinds of wall differ only by having different velocities of translation, represented by the length d. If the wall is *smooth*, the flow in the whole equilibrium layer including the *viscous layer* between the fully turbulent flow and the wall is determined by τ_0 and ν, and for dimensional reasons,

$$U = \tau_0^{1/2} F\left(\frac{\tau_0^{1/2} y}{\nu}\right) \tag{10.28}$$

Consistency with Eq. (10.27) requires that

$$U = \frac{\tau_0^{1/2}}{K}\left(\log\frac{\tau_0^{1/2} y}{\nu} + A\right) \tag{10.29}$$

in which A is a universal constant characteristic of flow over smooth walls, for values of $\dot{y}$ so large that the direct contribution to the stress from viscosity is small. Measurements show that Eq. (10.29) is valid for $\tau_0^{1/2} y/\nu > 30$ and that for $\tau_0^{1/2} y/\nu < 10$,

$$U = \frac{\tau_0 y}{\nu} \tag{10.30}$$

Between these values of $\tau_0^{1/2} y/\nu$, the velocity distribution changes its character and is not easily described by any simple algebraic expression. The *viscous layer*, for which $\tau_0^{1/2} y/\nu < 10$, is also known as the laminar sublayer, but the flow within it is not laminar in the usual sense. In this layer, most of the total stress is viscous stress and very little Reynolds stress but the relative turbulent intensities of fluctuations parallel to the wall are high. Laufer[8] finds that $(\overline{u^2})^{1/2} \sim 0.3U$ and $(\overline{w^2})^{1/2} \sim 0.05U$.

If the wall is not smooth but *rough*, with irregularities on a scale small compared with the thickness of the constant-stress layer, the flow at a sufficient distance from the wall is still described by Eq. (10.27) and the proper value of d now depends on the nature of the roughness. For geometrically similar roughness elements of scale s,

$$d = s\, g\left(\frac{\tau_0^{1/2} s}{\nu}\right) \tag{10.31}$$

in which the function depends on the roughness geometry but usually has the following characteristics. For small values of $\tau_0^{1/2} s/\nu$, d approaches $\nu e^{-A}/\tau_0^{1/2}$, reproducing the smooth velocity profile of Eq. (10.29), and for large values, d/s approaches a constant value. Then the flow is independent of viscosity and the value of d is the *roughness length* for the surface. The extent of the transition region between smooth and fully rough flow may be very extensive for rough surfaces without sharp projections.

10.13. The "Zero-stress" Layer

If the wall stress is very small or zero, condition (10.24) for the existence of a constant-stress layer cannot be satisfied but an equilibrium layer may still exist with defining parameters, $\partial\tau/\partial y = dP_1/dx$ and ν. Dimensional considerations then show that

$$\frac{\partial U}{\partial y} = \frac{1}{K_z}\left(\frac{1}{y}\frac{dP_1}{dx}\right)^{1/2} \tag{10.32}$$

and the velocity distribution is

$$U = \frac{2}{K_z}\left(\frac{dP_1}{dx}\right)^{1/2} y^{1/2} + C\left(\nu\frac{dP_1}{dx}\right)^{1/3} \tag{10.33}$$

Stratford[24] has produced zero-stress layers and in them $K_z = 0.50$ and the constant of integration is very small. The different values of this constant and the Kármán constant ($K = 0.41$) arise from differences in the flows, possibly related to the presence of a stress gradient in the zero-stress layer.

10.14. Equilibrium Layers with Transpiration or Suction

If the surface is porous and fluid passes through the pores with a spatial mean velocity of V_0, the flow is expected to be homogeneous over planes parallel to the surface at distances large compared with the distance between pores. Then, within the fully turbulent part of the equilibrium layer, the momentum equation is

$$\tau = -\overline{uv} + \nu \frac{\partial U}{\partial y} = \tau_0 + UV_0 \tag{10.34}$$

and the shear stress depends on the mean velocity. For small values of $V_0/\tau^{1/2}$, the layer must resemble an ordinary constant-stress layer and the local motion in the fully turbulent flow will be determined by the local Reynolds stress. Under these conditions,

$$\frac{dU}{dy} = \frac{\tau^{1/2}}{Ky} = \frac{(\tau_0 + UV_0)^{1/2}}{Ky} \tag{10.35}$$

which may be integrated to

$$\frac{(\tau_0 + UV_0)^{1/2}}{2KV_0} = \log \frac{y}{b} \tag{10.36}$$

in which b is a constant of integration. If the surface is effectively smooth, this must reduce to the universal velocity profile (10.29) for $V_0 = 0$. Consequently, the mean velocity profile for small values of $V_0/\tau_0^{1/2}$ is

$$\frac{(\tau_0 + UV_0)^{1/2}}{2V_0} - \frac{\tau_0^{1/2}}{2V_0} = \frac{1}{K}\left(\log \frac{\tau_0^{1/2}y}{\nu} + A \right) \tag{10.37}$$

In fact, most practical flows with suction or transpiration do correspond to small values of this ratio. The forms of the velocity distributions are shown in Fig. 10.2 for positive zero and negative values of V_0. It should be noticed that the suction profile (V_0 negative) has a maximum velocity of $-\tau_0/V_0$ at $y = \nu \tau_0^{-1/2} \exp - (A + K\tau_0^{1/2}/2V_0)$. Under no circumstances can the equilibrium layer extend past this point.

10.15. The Turbulent Structure of Equilibrium Layers

The constant-stress layer is the only equilibrium layer whose turbulent motion has been studied in any detail. The same reasoning that is used to derive the form of the mean velocity distribution predicts that the mean squares of the three components of the velocity fluctuations should be constant multiples of the wall stress for large values of $\tau_0^{1/2}y/\nu$ and that the length scale should be proportional to distance from the wall. The experimental results that have been obtained confirm these predictions only in part. In particular, the ratios of the turbulent intensities to the wall stress are nearly constant in any one type of flow, but the ratios, particularly that of the longitudinal component, are not the same in different types of flow (compare Laufer[16] with Klebanoff[14]). Of the scales of length defined by the various components of the correlation

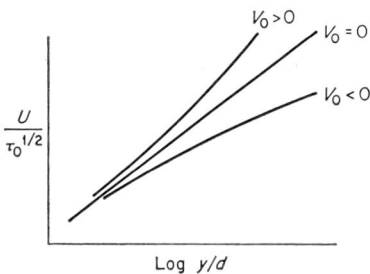

FIG. 10.2. Effects of suction and of transpiration on the velocity distribution in the equilibrium layer on a smooth surface.

function, only those based on separations in the $0z$ direction have approximately the correct behavior (Grant[12]). Length scales based on separations parallel to $0x$ are comparatively large and vary slowly in the constant-stress layer.

An interesting and important feature of the constant-stress layer is that the normal Reynolds stresses are far from being equal and, in particular, $\overline{w^2} - \overline{v^2}$ is approximately equal to $2.2\tau_0$. This means that the turbulent fluid behaves like a viscoelastic material rather than a Newtonian fluid and that secondary flows may be expected in some circumstances.

10.16. Flow in Pipes and Channels

Sufficiently far from the inlet, the flow pattern down a straight pipe of uniform section produced by a steady pressure difference becomes independent of distance from the inlet and is determined by the (uniform) pressure gradient, by the fluid viscosity, and by the pipe dimensions. The two simple forms of this flow are flow between parallel planes essentially unbounded transversely to the flow and flow in a pipe of circular section. In each case, the equations of motion may be integrated to show that the total stress is proportional to distance from the central plane or the axis and that the wall stress is related to the mean pressure gradient by

(1) $$\tau_0 = -D \frac{dP_1}{dx} \quad \text{in a channel of width } 2D$$

(2) $$\tau_0 = -\tfrac{1}{2} R \frac{dP_1}{dx} \quad \text{in a pipe of radius } R$$

Consequently, the flow is specified by the wall stress, either R or D, and the viscosity. Within the fully turbulent part of the flow, the principle of flow similarity requires that viscosity have no direct effect on the relative motion, and so the mean motion is given by

$$\frac{dU}{dy} = -\frac{\tau_0^{1/2}}{D} f'\left(\frac{y}{D}\right) \tag{10.38}$$

or in the more usual integrated form,

$$U_1 - U = \tau_0^{1/2} f\left(\frac{y}{D}\right) \tag{10.39}$$

in which U_1 is the central velocity. This result is the *defect law* for pipes and channels. As Eq. (10.39) is valid for the whole of the fully turbulent part of the flow, it must be consistent with the universal velocity distribution in the constant-stress layers. The condition for this is that

$$U_1 = \frac{\tau_0^{1/2}}{K}\left(\log\frac{y}{D} + A_c\right) \tag{10.40}$$

in which A_c is a constant characteristic of turbulent flow between parallel planes (almost identical expressions apply to pipe flow). If the flow within the viscous and transition layers can be neglected, the *resistance coefficient*, $c_f = \tau_0/(\tfrac{1}{2} U_m^2)$, and the Reynolds number based on the mean rate of flow, $\mathbf{R} = U_m D/\nu$, are related by

$$\sqrt{2}K c_f^{-1/2} = \log\left(\frac{c_f}{2}\right)^{1/2} \mathbf{R} + B_c \tag{10.41}$$

for smooth walls. If the walls are not smooth, the resistance coefficient is a function of the length d [Eqs. (10.27) and (10.31)] defined by

$$\sqrt{2}K c_f^{-1/2} = \log\frac{D}{d} + B_c - A \tag{10.42}$$

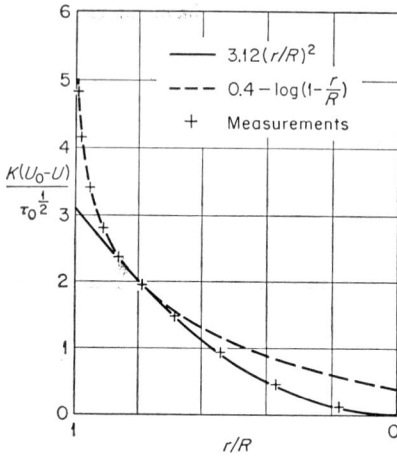

FIG. 10.3. Distribution of mean velocity in a circular pipe, showing logarithmic and parabolic sections. (*Measurements by Laufer.*[16])

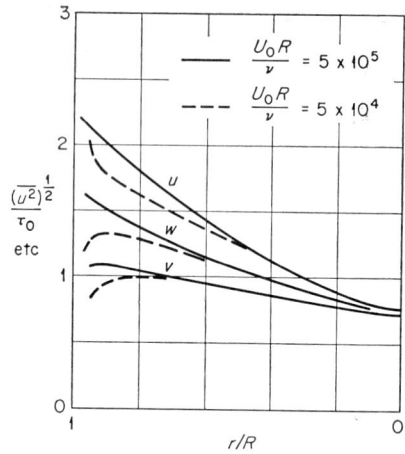

FIG. 10.4. Turbulent intensities in pipe flow. (*Measurements by Laufer.*[16])

If the flow is fully rough, d is independent of Reynolds number and so is the resistance coefficient. The form of Eq. (10.41) is such that the variation of resistance coefficient with Reynolds number is critically dependent on the magnitude of the Kármán constant K, but less dependent of the magnitude of the constant B_c, which takes different values in pipe and channel flow.

In pipes of other sections, the wall stress may vary around the perimeter with a mean value

$$\tau_m = -\frac{\text{area of cross section}}{\text{wetted perimeter}} \frac{dP_1}{dx} = -\tfrac{1}{2} R_m \frac{dP_1}{dx} \tag{10.43}$$

in which R_m is the hydraulic mean radius. These variations are considerably reduced by a secondary flow that appears, directed from the center of the pipe toward the corners and caused by the difference between the normal Reynolds stresses in the equilibrium layer, Fig. 10.3. For this reason the relation between resistance coefficient and Reynolds number in any smooth pipe is given by Eq. (10.41) with a suitable value of B_c, but since the value of B_c is not critical, the value for a circular pipe may be used with little error.

The turbulent motion in the central region of a pipe or a channel resembles free turbulence (Arts. 10.19 to 10.23) in that the intensities of the three velocity components are nearly equal and that transport of turbulent energy plays an important part in the balance of turbulent energy (Fig. 10.4). In agreement with this view, the eddy viscosity, $\nu_t = \tau/(\partial U/\partial y)$, is nearly constant outside the constant-stress layer, and the mean velocity in a circular pipe is given by

$$\frac{U_0 - U}{\tau_0^{1/2}} = \frac{1}{2} \frac{\tau_0^{1/2} R}{\nu_t} \left(\frac{r}{R}\right)^2 \tag{10.44}$$

for $r/R < 0.9$,

$$\frac{\tau_0^{1/2} R}{\nu_t} = 15$$

10.17. Flow in Convergent and Divergent Channels

The character of fully developed turbulent flow is greatly changed by comparatively small convergence or divergence of the walls. If the walls converge, the flow is accelerated, the central flow becomes more nearly uniform in velocity and less turbulent, and distinct boundary layers form at the walls and develop in a normal way. Divergence produces effects that are both more interesting and of more practical importance, and the diverging flow between two plane surfaces has been studied by Ruetenik[22] and by Milliat[21] for included angles up to 6° (Fig. 10.5). For these angles, self-preserving flows exist in which local velocities are inversely proportional to distance from line of intersection of the planes and wall stress is comparatively small. For higher angles of divergence, flow separates from one wall and becomes asymmetric and irregular, Fig. 10.6. The presence of side walls tends to induce secondary flows, and these can cause flow separation at much smaller angles of divergence than the largest angle used by Milliat, 6° included angle. Theoretical considerations, based on the concept of the zero-stress layer (see above) and the characteristics of channel flow, indicate that fully developed flow with zero wall stress will occur if the included angle is approximately 7°. It is likely that similar flows exist in conical diffusers, but the critical angle of divergence is probably less than 7°.

If a flow enters a long diffusing section, there is an extensive transition region in which the entry flow approaches the self-preserving flow (if one exists) or the irregular, separated flow, and the nature of the flow in the transition region depends strongly on the nature of the entering flow. If this is smooth and nearly uniform in velocity with very thin boundary layers, the central flow will remain nearly irrotational and with constant total head until the adverse pressure gradient causes the boundary layers to separate. The flow then becomes irregular and pressure recovery nearly ceases. For this type of entry flow, the position of separation and the pressure-recovery coefficient at separation can, in principle, be found by methods used to predict separation in turbulent boundary layers. For a given diffuser, the thinner the boundary layer the greater the pressure recovery. If the entry flow is fully developed pipe or channel flow, pressure recovery is only appreciable if a self-preserving flow is established.

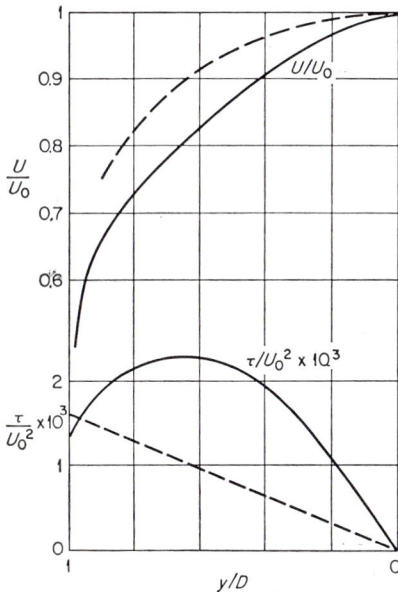

FIG. 10.5. Self-preserving flow in a divergent channel of included angle 2°. (Broken lines refer to flow in a channel of constant width.)

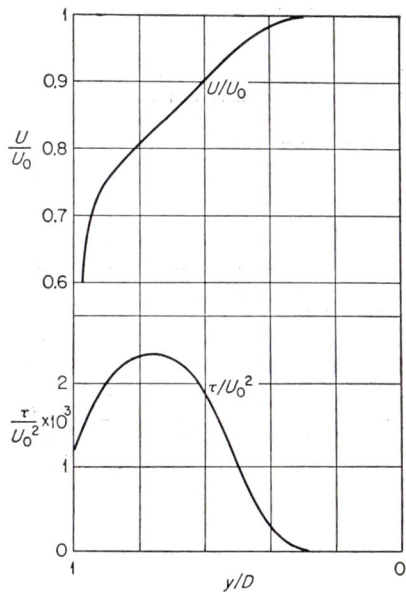

FIG. 10.6. Boundary-layer flow in a divergent channel.

10.18. Diffusion in Pipes and Channels

To a good approximation, it is possible to describe the diffusion of heat and mass in wall turbulence by the use of *Reynolds' analogy*, i.e., by assuming that the eddy-diffusion coefficients for momentum, heat, and mass are identical.

$$\nu_t = \frac{\tau}{\partial U/\partial y} = k_t = \frac{-\overline{\theta v}}{\partial T/\partial y} = D_t = \frac{-\overline{mv}}{\partial M/\partial y} \tag{10.45}$$

at all points in the fully turbulent parts of the flow. It follows that the mean temperature in equilibrium layers is given by

$$T_0 - T = \frac{Q}{K\tau_0^{1/2}} \log \frac{y}{d_0} \tag{10.46}$$

for a constant-stress layer and by analogous expressions for the other kinds of layer. The length d_0 is identical with the d of Eq. (10.27) only if the fluid Prandtl number is unity. For smooth walls,

$$d_0 = \frac{\nu}{\tau_0} e^{-A} f_n \left(\frac{\nu}{k}\right) \tag{10.47}$$

Reynolds analogy applies only in its simple form to diffusion in the $0y$ direction. If a short length of marked fluid is introduced into channel flow, it is carried along the channel and diffuses longitudinally as it goes. This process depends on interaction between the strong dispersive action of the mean velocity gradient and lateral diffusion by turbulent movements. Taylor[25] has shown that the effective *longitudinal-diffusion coefficient,*

$$D_x = \frac{1}{2} U_m \frac{d\overline{x^2}}{dt} \tag{10.48}$$

can be computed using Reynolds' analogy for the lateral diffusion and that, for flow in a circular pipe, it is approximately $10\tau_0^{1/2}R$. The lateral-diffusion coefficient varies with distance from the wall but has a maximum value of nearly $0.1\tau_0^{1/2}R$. In steady flow of water down an inclined plane, Elder[10] finds the longitudinal coefficient to be $5.9\tau_0^{1/2}h$ (h is the depth of the water), while the average value of the lateral coefficient is $0.08\tau_0^{1/2}h$. The diffusion coefficient for the $0z$ direction is $D_t = 0.23\tau_0^{1/2}h$, which is much greater than the value required by Reynolds' analogy.

FREE TURBULENCE

10.19. Development of Free Turbulent Flows

A free turbulent flow is one whose motion is substantially unaffected by the presence of solid boundaries, usually because it is surrounded by nonturbulent fluid. One essential difference between wall and free turbulence is that free turbulent flows spread laterally into the ambient fluid and the resultant inhomogeneity in the direction of flow plays an essential part in their development. Common examples of free turbulence are jets, wakes, mixing layers, convection plumes, and the outer flow in boundary layers.

The difficulty of treating an inhomogeneous developing flow is much less if the flow is *self-preserving* in structure, and flows of this sort will now be considered. A self-preserving flow is one in which the mean characteristics of the motion are similar at all transverse sections of the flow, differing only in scales of length and velocity which are functions of distance from the flow origin. In symbols,

$$U - U_1 = u_0 f\left(\frac{y}{l_0}\right)$$

$$\overline{u^2} = u_0^2 g_1 \left(\frac{y}{l_0}\right) \tag{10.49}$$

$$\overline{uv} = u_0^2 g\left(\frac{y}{l_0}\right)$$

etc., in which the functions depend on the general nature of the flow, and u_0, l_0, the scales of velocity and length, are functions of x alone. U_1 is the velocity of translation of the ambient fluid.   If the equations of motion permit the existence of a self-preserving flow consistent with the boundary conditions, it is usual to find that the real flow approximates to the self-preserving flow after a sufficient period of development. *Exactly self-preserving* flow is possible only in:

1. Mixing zones between two streams of different velocities
2. Two-dimensional or axisymmetric jets projecting into still fluid, convection plumes
3. The boundary layers in duct flow between converging planes

But *approximately self-preserving* flow is possible in condition 4:

4. Wakes of bodies, either two-dimensional or not, with finite positive or negative drag
5. Boundary layers in special kinds of longitudinal pressure gradients

The condition for approximately self-preserving flow is that the velocity variations should be small compared with the free-stream velocity.

If self-preserving flow is assumed, the length and velocity scales are related by the equation for the total linear momentum at a section of the flow,

$$\frac{d}{dx} \int U(U - U_1)\, dy + \frac{dP_1}{dx} \int \left(1 - \frac{U}{U_1}\right) dy = 0 \tag{10.50}$$

If the pressure gradient dP_1/dx is zero, as it is for most jets and wakes, this integrates to

$$\int U(U - U_1)\, dy = F \tag{10.51}$$

in which the constant F is interpreted as the (kinematic) force applied to the fluid. For axisymmetric flow,

$$2\pi \int U(U - U_1) r\, dr = F \tag{10.52}$$

A second relation between u_0 and l_0 may be found either by substituting the self-preserving forms (10.49) into the equation of mean motion (10.4) or, more conveniently, by using an *entrainment constant*.   The speed with which the turbulent flow encroaches on the undisturbed ambient fluid is the sum of the mean inward transverse (or radial) velocity at the edge of the flow and the apparent velocity of advance, $aU_1\, dl_0/dx$.   This is a characteristic of the motion and, by the assumption of self-preserving development, is a constant multiple of the velocity scale, i.e.,

$$\frac{d}{dx}(u_0 l_0) + a U_1 \frac{dl_0}{dx} = \alpha u_0 \tag{10.53}$$

for two-dimensional flow, and

$$\frac{1}{l_0}\frac{d}{dx}(u_0 l_0{}^2) + a U_1 \frac{dl_0}{dx} = \alpha u_0 \tag{10.54}$$

for axisymmetric flow.   The constants clearly depend on the definitions of the scales as well as the nature of the flow.   Table 10.2 summarizes results obtained in this way

Table **10.2.** Rates of Spread of Free Turbulent Flows

Flow	Defining quantities	l_0	u_0	θ_0
Mixing layer..............	$U_1,\ T_1 - T_0$	x	U_1	$T_1 - T_0$
Circular jet...............	$F,\ Q$	x	$F^{1/2}x^{-1}$	$QF^{-1/2}x^{-1}$
Two-dimensional jet.......	$F,\ Q$	x	$F^{-1/2}x^{-1/2}$	$QF^{-1/2}x^{-1/2}$
Wake, axisymmetric........	$F,\ Q,\ U_1$	$F^{1/3}U_1{}^{-2/3}x^{1/3}$	$(FU)^{1/3}x^{-2/3}$	$QF^{-2/3}U_1{}^{1/3}x^{-2/3}$
Two-dimensional.........	$F,\ Q,\ U_1$	$F^{1/2}U_1{}^{-1}x^{1/2}$	$F^{1/2}x^{-1/2}$	$QF^{-1/2}x^{-1/2}$

NOTE: The effective force F [Eqs. (10.51) and (10.52)] and the thermometric heat emission Q are per unit length for two-dimensional flows.

for a number of flows. Notice that, when the flow becomes self-preserving, it is determined by the force constant F and by the velocity of translation of the ambient fluid.

10.20. The Eddy-viscosity Hypothesis

The distribution of mean velocity in a self-preserving flow is not determined by assuming self-preserving development. To do this, another assumption must be made, and the most satisfactory is that the effective eddy viscosity is constant across any section of the flow. This assumption provides an excellent description of the mean-velocity profiles except near the edges of the flow, but the reasons for its validity are not well understood. If the flow is not self-preserving, the Reynolds stresses depend on the past history of rate of shear and do not depend in any simple way on the existing rate of strain.

An interesting feature of all self-preserving flows is that the "Reynolds number" based on the effective eddy viscosity is independent of position in the flow and is characteristic of the type of flow. The value of this turbulent Reynolds number, or *flow constant*, is easily computed from the mean velocity distribution, and it would be interesting to compare these constants with the critical Reynolds numbers for instability of the corresponding laminar flows. For the two-dimensional wake, these two numbers are known to be equal within the errors of measurement, but critical Reynolds numbers for other flows are not known with sufficient accuracy to be sure whether this is a general rule.

10.21. Convection Plumes

The introduction of a source of heat into a fluid in hydrostatic equilibrium in a gravitational field causes a buoyant convection plume to appear which is turbulent if the induced velocities are sufficiently high. If the density changes are small, they may be ignored except for the change in weight of the fluid, and the equations for mean velocity and mean temperature are

$$U \frac{\partial U}{\partial x} + V \frac{\partial U}{\partial y} + \frac{\partial \overline{uv}}{\partial y} = \beta g (T - T_a) + \nu \frac{\partial^2 U}{\partial y^2} \tag{10.55}$$

and

$$U \frac{\partial T}{\partial x} + V \frac{\partial T}{\partial y} + \frac{\partial \overline{v\theta}}{\partial y} = k \frac{\partial^2 T}{\partial y^2} \tag{10.56}$$

in which β is the coefficient of thermal expansion and T_a the ambient temperature. The equation for the total linear momentum [cf. Eq. (10.50)] is

$$\frac{d}{dx} \int U(U - U_1) \, dy = \int \beta g (T - T_a) \, dy \tag{10.57}$$

and for the total heat flux is

$$\frac{d}{dx} \int U(T - T_a) \, dy = -\frac{dT_a}{dx} \int (U - U_1) \, dy \tag{10.58}$$

If the development of the temperature field is also self-preserving,

$$T - T_a = \theta_0 h \left(\frac{y}{l_0} \right)$$

$$\overline{\theta v} = \theta_0 u_0 j \left(\frac{y}{l_0} \right) \tag{10.59}$$

Equations may be written down for the variation of the scales of length, velocity, and temperature. If the ambient fluid is in a state of hydrostatic, neutral equilibrium, a two-dimensional plume from a line source spreads as

$$l_0 \propto x \qquad u_0 \propto (\beta g Q)^{\frac{1}{3}} = \text{const} \qquad \theta_0 \propto Q^{\frac{2}{3}}(\beta g)^{-\frac{1}{3}}x^{-1} \qquad (10.60)$$

and the axisymmetric plume from an isolated source as

$$l_0 \propto x \qquad u_0 \propto (\beta g Q)^{\frac{1}{3}}x^{-\frac{1}{3}} \qquad \theta_0 \propto Q^{\frac{2}{3}}(\beta g)^{-\frac{1}{3}}x^{-\frac{5}{3}} \qquad (10.61)$$

(Q is the thermometric heat release per unit length for the linear source.) The general motion is very similar to that in jets, and the rates of spread are almost identical, with a semiangle of approximately 12°.

10.22. The Structure of Free Turbulence

In all free turbulent flows (Fig. 10.7), a sharply defined bounding surface separates turbulent from nonturbulent (i.e., irrotational) fluid. This surface is irregular in form and changes its shape and position by billowing movements caused by the *large eddies* of the turbulent motion and by a general advance into the irrotational fluid by a complicated process of diffusive and engulfing movements (*entrainment*), Fig. 10.8. Over a substantial part of the flow, a fixed point will lie alternately inside and outside the surface and the velocity fluctuations at that point will alternate between rapid, characteristically "turbulent" fluctuations and weaker, slow fluctuations caused by irrotational motion induced in ambient fluid by motions at the boundary (Fig. 10.9). The fraction of time that the flow is turbulent is known as the *intermittency factor* γ. It is nearly unity over the central third of a flow and decreases to about 0.2 at the outer limits of mean-velocity variation. Measurements show that most of the apparent variation of turbulent intensity is due to variation of γ and that the local properties of the main turbulent motion are nearly the same everywhere.

The large eddies of the motion by convoluting the surface of the turbulent fluid control the rate of spread into the ambient fluid, and there is some reason to suppose that the average large eddy is near a state of neutral stability, the rate of extraction of energy from the mean flow being nearly equal to the loss of energy by interaction with the smaller eddies of the main motion. Grant[5] has shown that the large eddies in wake flow closely resemble a finite section of the double row of vortices that are formed by instability of the laminar wake.

One consequence of the sharp distinction between turbulent and nonturbulent fluid is that a convected property such as heat or mass is always confined to the turbulent

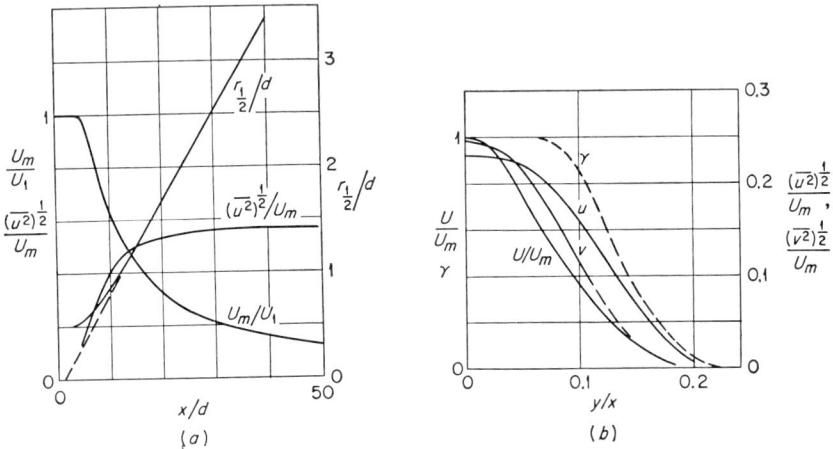

FIG. 10.7. Mean and turbulent motion in a circular jet. ($r_{\frac{1}{2}}$ is the distance from the jet axis at which the mean velocity is half its maximum value.)

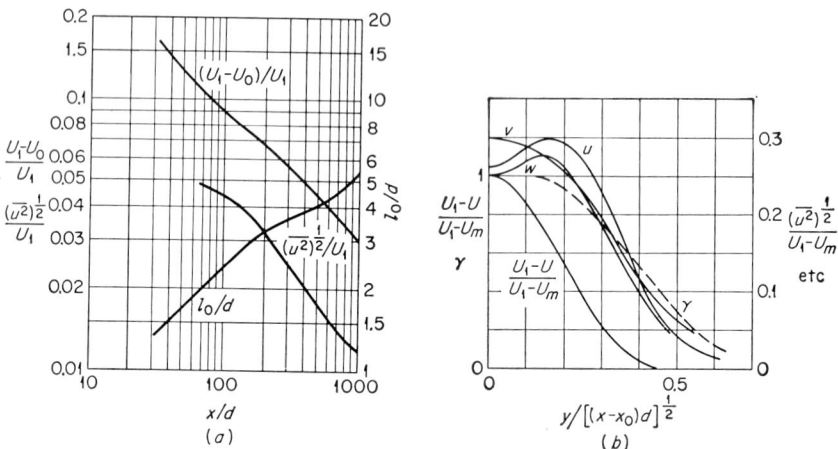

Fig. 10.8. Mean and turbulent motion in a two-dimensional wake behind a circular cylinder. (The lateral distributions of turbulent intensity, etc., refer to flow far from the cylinder, over 500 diam away.)

fluid if the Reynolds number is high. It is likely that the homogeneity of the turbulent fluid will extend to this property, and then the mean value M will be proportional to γ at any section of the flow. The same argument may be applied to the Reynolds stress, and consideration of possible departures from inhomogeneity of the turbulent fluid suggests that

$$M \propto |\overline{uv}| \qquad (10.62)$$

rather more exactly. This relation, which is only valid far from positions where the Reynolds stress changes sign, is the counterpart of Reynolds' analogy for free turbulence. In terms of effective eddy diffusivities, the ratio of the eddy diffusivities for heat and for momentum is greater than 1 and increases greatly as the edge of the flow is approached.

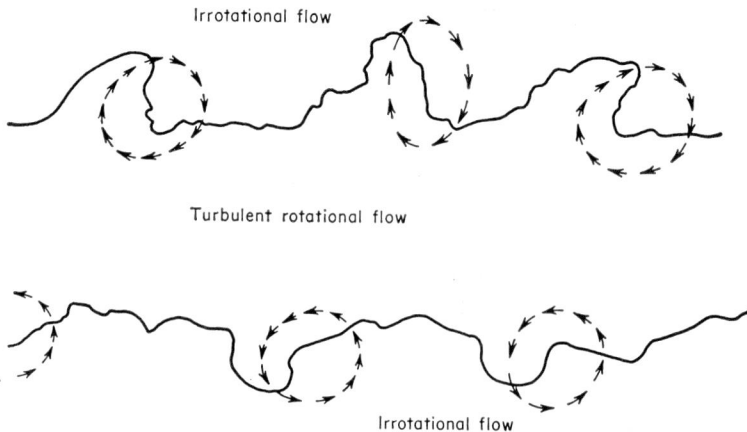

Fig. 10.9. Diagrammatic section of a turbulent wake, showing large eddies distorting the boundary between turbulent and nonturbulent fluid.

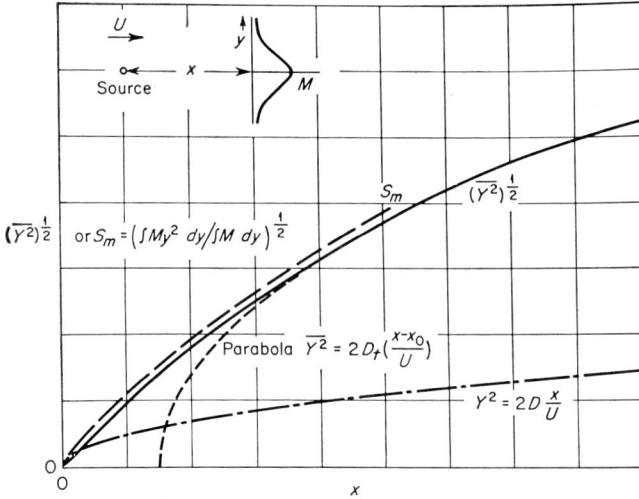

Fig. 10.10. Spread of fluid particles and of a diffusible quantity behind a line source in homogeneous, stationary turbulent flow.

10.23. Homogeneous Turbulence

Homogeneous turbulence is an ideal form of turbulence that may be approximated by the flow in a wind tunnel downstream of a uniform grid. The theory has been highly developed, partly in the hope that it would be a first step to the analytical treatment of turbulent shear flows, but in some respects homogeneous turbulence is a more difficult subject than, let us say, self-preserving free turbulence. It should perhaps be emphasized that the grid flow is in detail highly anisotropic and may not be perfectly homogeneous (Grant[12]). Some details of grid turbulence are given in Art. 10.41, and a full account in Batchelor.[1]

CONVECTIVE TURBULENCE

10.24. Flow between Concentric Rotating Cylinders

In wall and free turbulence, the mean streamlines are very nearly straight and mechanical effects due to curvature of the particle trajectories are absent. If these streamlines are curved, as in flow between rotating cylinders, mean-flow energy can be released by overturning motions if the angular momentum of the flow decreases outward, e.g., if the outer cylinder is stationary and the inner cylinder rotates. In the possibility of energy release by overturning, the stability problem resembles that of horizontally stratified fluid, vertical gradient of density corresponding with radial gradient of angular momentum, and the first mode of instability consists of a periodic array of vortex cells which grow to finite amplitude (Taylor vortices, or Bénard cells). At higher speeds of rotation, the cellular structure breaks up to a turbulent motion in which the angular momentum of the mean flow is constant except very close to the cylinders and equal to one-half the angular momentum at the inner cylinder. Most of the variation of angular momentum takes place near the wall in thin layers whose structure has not been explored in detail. At high speeds of rotation, part of the wall layer probably is a constant-stress layer but the outer part is affected by the rotation and will have a different structure.

Turbulent flow will occur at sufficiently high speeds of rotation even for the "stable" arrangement, with the inner cylinder stationary and the outer cylinder rotating, but the onset of turbulent flow is delayed and its intensity considerably reduced.

10.25. Heat Convection between Parallel Horizontal Planes

The turbulent flow between effectively infinite, horizontal planes has a close analogy with the rotating-cylinder flow and has been studied in some detail. The mean temperature hardly varies over most of the space between the planes, and within the fully turbulent part of the wall layers the temperature difference from the central temperature varies as

$$T - T_a = \left(\frac{kQ}{\beta g}\right)^{\frac{1}{2}} x^{-1} \tag{10.63}$$

The most remarkable feature of this variation is that it does not conform to the principle of flow similarity in that the viscosity and conductivity affect mean values in the fully turbulent part of the flow. The cause of this appears to be an intimate connection between the viscous layers and the whole turbulent motion, and this failure of the principle may be characteristic of convective turbulence. Although direct experimental evidence is not available in sufficient quantity, the analogy suggests that the velocity variation in the wall layers of rotating cylinder flow is of the form

$$Vr - (Vr)_a \propto (r - R)^{-1} \tag{10.64}$$

if $V/R \gg \partial V/\partial r$.

COMPRESSIBILITY AND TURBULENT FLOW

10.26. The Assumption of Incompressibility

The remainder of this section considers the motion of a Newtonian, incompressible fluid, and it is useful to consider the conditions under which the motion of a real fluid is nearly the same as that of this ideal fluid. An obvious condition is that the pressure fluctuations should be insufficient to produce an appreciable change of density. In turbulent flows, pressure fluctuations are of order $\rho \overline{q^2}$, and the condition is that $\rho \overline{q^2}$ should be much less than the bulk modulus, i.e., the Mach number of the velocity fluctuations should be small. Another condition is that expansion of the fluid due to temperature fluctuations should be small. So far as temperature fluctuations generated by the dissipation of turbulent energy are concerned, they are negligible if the Mach number is small, and temperature fluctuations due to heat transfer are negligible if the velocity $\beta H/\rho c_p$ is small compared with the velocity of sound.

10.27. Description of Compressible Turbulent Flow

The complete description of turbulent, compressible flow is even more complicated than that of ordinary turbulent flow as fluctuations of velocity, temperature, and pressure exist and interact among themselves. A useful formal separation of these fluctuations was suggested by Kovasznay.[7] It separates the velocity field into a solenoidal, rotational part and a compressible, irrotational part, each without variation of entropy. The third component is then an entropy field. These components interact with each other, but at sufficiently low Mach numbers the interactions are negligible, and the components may be identified as ordinary turbulent motion, random sound waves, and temperature fluctuations. If only two of the three components are present in appreciable quantity, it is possible to measure their intensities by use of the hot-wire anemometer.

Comparatively little is known about the details of turbulent flows at supersonic speeds, but there is no evidence that the general character of the motion is changed. For flows with free boundaries, sound energy generated by the turbulence is radiated rapidly into the surrounding fluid and the sonic component of the fluctuations is negligible within the flow. It is interesting that supersonic mixing layers spread at smaller angles than ones at low subsonic speeds, and this difference is almost certainly due to the loss of turbulent energy by sound radiation.

10.28. Sound Radiation by a Turbulent Flow

The rate of radiation of sound by a turbulent flow into the surrounding fluid can be obtained on the assumption that the turbulent velocities are so small that the turbulent motion may be considered incompressible, and the velocities associated with the sound waves small compared with the turbulent velocities. It may then be shown that the density at a point ρ is given by

$$\nabla^2\rho - \frac{1}{c_0{}^2}\frac{\partial^2\rho}{\partial x^2} + \frac{\rho_0}{c_0{}^2}\frac{\partial^2 u_i u_j}{\partial x_i \partial x_j} = 0 \tag{10.65}$$

in which the velocity of sound c_0 and the density ρ_0 refer to mean conditions. This is the ordinary wave equation for sound with the addition of the term $\dfrac{\rho_0}{c_0{}^2}\dfrac{\partial^2 u_i u_j}{\partial x_i \partial x_j}$, which represents a distribution of quadrupole sources in the turbulent part of the fluid. In homogeneous isotropic turbulence, the orientation of the sources is random and the sound is radiated uniformly in all directions with a total power

$$P \propto \rho_0 u_0{}^3 l_0{}^{-1} V \mathbf{M}^8 \tag{10.66}$$

in which $\mathbf{M}$ is the Mach number of the flow. In shear flow, most of the quadrupoles are so oriented that they radiate selectively at 45° to the direction of flow. This radiation is considerably more efficient, and the total power radiated is

$$P \propto \rho_0 u_0{}^3 l_0{}^{-1} V \mathbf{M}^5 \tag{10.67}$$

(Lighthill[17,18]).

If the theory is applied to the sound field near a turbulent jet, it is found that the acoustic efficiency, i.e., the ratio of the energy radiated as sound to the kinetic energy issuing from the jet, increases less rapidly with Mach number than is indicated by the simple theory. For jets emerging from a long pipe of internal diameter 1 in., Gerrard[11] finds that the acoustic efficiency is nearly

$$\eta = 10^{-4}\mathbf{M}^{4.2}$$

for Mach numbers between 0.3 and 1.0 and that relatively more sound is radiated in a forward direction at the higher Mach numbers. The spectrum of the sound is very flat with a broad maximum at 4000 cps almost independent of Mach number (non-dimensionally $n_{\max} = 0.3a_0/2R$). The reasons for the differences are that the sound sources are convected by the mean stream and suffer changes in frequency distribution and radiative efficiency and that the changes in the turbulent motion with Mach number are not completely described by a change in velocity scale as is assumed in the theory.

TURBULENT DIFFUSIVE PROCESSES

10.29. Diffusion by Continuous Movements

The transport of momentum that causes turbulent Reynolds stresses is an integral part of the turbulent motion, but a number of passive properties are transported by turbulent movements without affecting the motion. The most usual ones are scalar properties such as heat (in small quantities) and solutes, e.g., salt in water, water vapor in air. The equation governing the concentration of such a quantity M is

$$\frac{\partial M}{\partial t} + \mathbf{u}\cdot\operatorname{grad} M = D\,\nabla^2 M \tag{10.68}$$

in which D is the molecular diffusivity in the fluid. If D is negligibly small, the quantity is convected with the fluid and the problem reduces to the diffusion of fluid particles (a fluid particle is an imaginary particle whose velocity always is the same as the fluid at its instantaneous position), which is the subject of the theory of diffusion by continuous movements. A particle originally at the point P at time $t = 0$ is displaced a distance in time t.

$$X = \int_0^t u(t')\, dt'$$

in which $u(t')$ is the velocity at time t' of the particle that was at P at $t = 0$. Then the mean-square displacement, the *dispersion*, is

$$\overline{X^2} = \int_0^t \int_0^t \overline{u(t')u(t'')}\, dt'\, dt'' \tag{10.69}$$

in which the overbar indicates an average over many trials of the same experiment. If the turbulence is homogeneous and stationary in time, the *Lagrangian correlation function* $\overline{u(t')u(t'')}$ is a function only of the time difference; i.e.,

$$\overline{u(t)u(t + \tau)} = R(\tau)$$

and then

$$\overline{X^2} = 2t \int_0^t R(\tau)\, d\tau - 2 \int_0^t \tau R(\tau)\, d\tau \tag{10.70}$$

For short diffusion times, the variation of $R(\tau)$ from its initial value $\overline{u^2}$ is small, and then $\overline{X^2} = \overline{u^2}t^2$. For long diffusion times, the integrals may approach constant values, and then the dispersion increases as if there were a constant "eddy diffusivity" of

$$D_t = \int_0^\infty R(\tau)\, d\tau \tag{10.71}$$

This diffusivity is defined in terms of the continuous field of fluid velocity without any reference to the necessity for mixing.

The practical application of this theory is to the turbulent diffusion of heat or solute introduced as a point or a line source in a flow whose mean velocity is much larger than the turbulent-velocity fluctuations. Then the time taken for a fluid particle to move a distance x downstream from the source is nearly x/U, and its lateral dispersion is given by Eq. (10.69). As a working approximation, it may be assumed that the Lagrangian correlation function is related to the Eulerian correlation function by

$$R(\tau) = \overline{\frac{t}{u(t)u(t + \tau)}} = \overline{u(x)u(x + 1.4\sqrt{\overline{u^2}}\,\tau)} = R_1(1.4\sqrt{\overline{u^2}}\,\tau)$$

Unless the Reynolds number of the turbulence is very large, molecular diffusion will contribute appreciably to the observed spread. To a good approximation, the dispersion of a substance exceeds the fluid-particle dispersion by $2\, Dt$.

The stationary, homogeneous turbulence considered in the above theory does not exist in nature, but the results may be used if the departures from homogeneity and stationarity are small over the duration and range of the diffusion. It is also possible to modify the analysis so that it applies to flow in pipes, jets, wakes, mixing layers, and to decaying homogeneous turbulence.

10.30. Extension of Line and Surface Elements

The theory of diffusion by continuous movements can be extended to describe the relative motion of pairs or of higher numbers of particles, and then the relative dispersions depend on the initial separation. An important case is that of two particles with an infinitesimal initial separation, i.e., so small that the rate of strain is substantially the same for each particle at all times. Then the separation s increases at a rate given by

$$\frac{1}{s}\frac{ds}{dt} = \frac{\partial u}{\partial s} \tag{10.72}$$

in which u is the velocity component in the instantaneous direction of separation. Since turbulence is a diffusive process, it seems likely that the mean value of $\partial u/\partial s$ approaches a constant value ξ for long diffusion times and that

$$\bar{s} = s_0 \exp{(\xi t)} \tag{10.73}$$

Similar reasoning indicates that an infinitesimal element of surface composed of fluid particles increases in area as $\exp{(\eta t)}$. The estimated values of the constants are

$$\xi = 0.43 \left(\frac{\epsilon}{\nu}\right)^{\frac{1}{2}} \qquad \eta = 0.55 \left(\frac{\epsilon}{\nu}\right)^{\frac{1}{2}} \tag{10.74}$$

The practical importance of these results is that vectors such as magnetic field in a conducting fluid are convected by the fluid and increase in intensity in proportion to the length of the vector line, which is made up of line elements. Similarly, the gradient of a convected scalar increases in proportion to the area of the surfaces of equal intensity. These increases continue until the scale of the fluctuations becomes so small that molecular diffusion destroys the gradients as fast as they are created by the stretching of the turbulence. For a convected scalar, this occurs when the scale of the gradients becomes of order $(D^3/\epsilon)^{\frac{1}{4}}$ if $D/\nu \gg 1$ or of order $(D^2\nu/\epsilon)^{\frac{1}{4}}$ if $D/\nu \ll 1$.

10.31. Eulerian Description of Diffusion

The theory of diffusion by continuous movements is useful for describing the intermingling of fluid particles and the intensification of concentration gradients that lead to the final stage of true mixing by molecular diffusion. This approach is more useful for describing the initial stages of turbulent diffusion and for providing an understanding of the underlying mechanism of turbulent diffusion than for providing a working theory of steady-state diffusion. For this, an Eulerian description is more convenient. From Eq. (10.68) for the concentration may be derived an equation for the mean concentration at a fixed point,

$$\frac{\partial M}{\partial t} + \mathbf{U} \cdot \operatorname{grad} M + \operatorname{grad} \overline{m\mathbf{u}} = D \, \nabla^2 M \tag{10.75}$$

and an equation for the mean-square fluctuation

$$\frac{\partial}{\partial t}\left(\frac{1}{2}\overline{m^2}\right) + \mathbf{U} \cdot \operatorname{grad}\left(\frac{1}{2}\overline{m^2}\right) + \overline{m\mathbf{u}} \cdot \operatorname{grad} M + \operatorname{grad}\left(\frac{1}{2}\overline{m^2\mathbf{u}}\right) = \overline{Dm \, \nabla^2 m} \tag{10.76}$$

The terms in these equations represent transport and generation of the quantities M and $\overline{m^2}$ as in the corresponding equations for mean velocity and turbulent energy (Art. 10.9). The term on the right of Eq. (10.76) is the rate at which mean-square fluctuations are destroyed by molecular diffusion after intensification of the gradients by the turbulent motion. Analogy with the known results for the dissipation of turbulent energy by viscosity suggests that

$$E = -\overline{Dm \, \nabla^2 m} = C_m \overline{m^2}(\overline{u^2})^{\frac{1}{2}}L_1^{-1} \tag{10.77}$$

Experimentally, C_m is approximately 0.6, slightly less than the corresponding constant in Eq. (10.16). If transport of fluctuations may be neglected, it follows that

$$\overline{m\mathbf{u}} = -l_m{}^2 \left|\frac{\partial \mathbf{U}}{\partial y}\right| \operatorname{grad} M \tag{10.78}$$

which is a result of the momentum-transfer form of the mixing-length theory. It may be used with confidence only in wall-equilibrium layers, when it becomes

$$\frac{dM}{dy} = -\frac{\overline{mv}}{\tau^{\frac{1}{2}}} \frac{1}{Ky}$$

If stress and M transport are constant across the layer, this integrates to

$$M_0 - M = \frac{mv}{K\tau_0^{1/2}} \left(\log \frac{\tau_0^{1/2} u}{\nu} + A_m \right)$$

in which the additive constant A_m depends on the ability of the viscous layer to transfer M, and thus on the ratio D/ν. The quantity $\overline{mv}/\tau_0^{1/2}$ plays a similar part to the friction velocity in the logarithmic velocity profile and is called the *friction temperature* in heat-transfer problems.

10.32. Concentration Fluctuations

The field of concentration fluctuations may be described in terms of correlation or spectrum functions in the same way as the velocity fluctuations. If the diffusion has reached a steady state, it is found that the spectrum function of the fluctuations is very similar to the spectrum function of the velocity fluctuations over the range of wave number that contains most of the turbulent energy and most of the mean-square fluctuation of concentration. Wave numbers outside this range only contribute to the gradients of velocity and concentration or form part of the cascade process, and the motion and distribution of concentration are described by the theory of local similarity. If $E = -\nu \overline{m \nabla^2 m}$ is the rate of destruction of $\overline{m^2}/2$ by molecular diffusion, the theory makes the following predictions about the form of the spectrum function for the fluctuations of concentration:
If $D/\nu \gg 1$,

$$F_m(k) = C_1 E \epsilon^{-1/3} k^{-5/3} \qquad \text{if } k < \left(\frac{\epsilon}{D^3}\right)^{1/4}$$

$$= C_2 E \epsilon^{2/3} D^{-3} k^{-1/3} \qquad \text{if } \left(\frac{\epsilon}{\nu^3}\right)^{1/4} > k > \left(\frac{\epsilon}{D^3}\right)^{1/4}$$

and if $D/\nu \ll 1$,

$$F_m(k) = C_3 E \epsilon^{-1/3} k^{-5/3} \qquad \text{if } k < \left(\frac{\epsilon}{\nu^3}\right)^{1/4}$$

$$= C_4 E \epsilon^{-1/2} (\nu D^2)^{1/6} k^{-1} \qquad \text{if } \left(\frac{\epsilon}{\nu D^2}\right)^{1/4} > k > \left(\frac{\epsilon}{\nu^3}\right)^{1/4}$$

For wave numbers greater than $(\epsilon/\nu^3)^{1/4}$ or $(\epsilon/(\nu D^2))^{1/4}$, the spectrum functions approach zero very rapidly.
In general, the scattering of sound or electromagnetic waves by a turbulent medium depends on the large wave-number components of the concentration spectrum, and the theory of local similarity enables predictions of this spectrum to be made if the two dissipation rates and the properties of the fluid are known.

EXPERIMENTAL METHODS

10.33. The Hot-wire Anemometer

The most common instrument used for the study of velocity fluctuations in gases is the hot-wire anemometer (Art. 14.16). In its basic form, it is a short length of thin wire with a large temperature coefficient of resistance, commonly platinum, nickel, or tungsten. It is heated by an electric current and cooled by the stream, and the changes in the rate of heat loss as the stream velocity changes are detected and used to measure the changes. The most common system is to use a *constant current*, independent of the wire resistance, and allow the resultant temperature changes to be made evident by the changes in potential drop across the wire. The lag in response due to finite heat capacity of the wire may then be compensated by a suitable frequency response in the amplifier which is necessary to provide signals large enough to give meter readings. In the *constant-resistance* system, the heating current is adjusted continuously by associated electronic equipment to keep the wire resistance constant. If the resistance (i.e., temperature) variations are indeed negligible, no compensation for thermal lag is necessary. The constant-current system requires less complicated amplifiers and control circuits and is better suited to the measurement of very low levels of turbulent intensity, while the constant-resistance system is better suited to the measurement of large intensities.

The amplifying and measuring circuits associated with the hot-wire anemometer must respond to substantially all the frequency components of the fluctuations that are of importance. A rough approximation to the spectrum of longitudinal fluctuations is

$$F_1(n) = \frac{4L_1\overline{u^2}}{U}\left(1 + \frac{4\pi^2 n^2 L_1^2}{U^2}\right)^{-1}$$

and it follows that frequencies less than n_i include a fraction $(2/\pi)\tan^{-1}(2\pi n_i L_1/U)$ of the total energy. This may be considered negligible only if n_i is less than $0.01U/L_1$. Similarly, frequencies above n_u contain a fraction $[1 - (2/\pi)\tan^{-1}(2\pi n_u L_1/U)]$, negligible if n_u is less than $2U/L_1$. If the eddies responsible for viscous dissipation are being studied, response must be provided to a frequency of at least $(U/3L_1)(\sqrt{\overline{u^2}L_1/\nu})^{3/4}$, which may be much larger than n_u.

The small size of the hot-wire anemometer makes it a convenient instrument for the measurement of mean velocities in confined spaces, e.g., very near a wall, although its accuracy is less than that of pitot tubes. Another use is for the measurement of mean temperature and temperature fluctuations, either by using currents so small that the heating effect is negligible or by using two different heating currents.

A variant is the film anemometer, a thin layer of platinum on the apex of a quartz wedge, which is equally suited to use in liquids and gases (Ling and Hubbard[19]). Constant-resistance operation is essential. The possibility of change in sensitivity due to impact of dust has led to the use of shielded wires for measurement of mean velocities.

10.34. Diffusion Techniques

A technically simple method of investigating a turbulent flow is to introduce a source of heat or alien substance and to measure the concentration at nearby points. If the turbulence level is low, the second moment of the concentration distribution at a small distance x downstream is

$$S_y{}^2 = \frac{\overline{u^2}x^2}{U^2} + 2D\,\frac{x}{U} \tag{10.79}$$

from which the lateral turbulent intensity may be computed. If the turbulent intensity is not small, large corrections may be necessary (Batchelor and Townsend[8]).

An interesting form of diffusion instrument has been developed by Taylor[27] for use in the atmosphere. It consists of a long wire emitting heat at a uniform rate per unit length, Q. At right angles and enclosing it are a pair of temperature-sensitive wires, sufficiently long to intercept the heat wake. Assuming temperature and velocity not to vary appreciably, the resistance difference between the parallel wires will be

$$\Delta R = \sigma R_0 \frac{Q}{\rho c_p W} \tag{10.80}$$

in which R_0 = cold resistance of either wire

σ = temperature coefficient of resistance

W = velocity component normal to the three wires

10.35. Flow-visualization Techniques

A number of techniques have been used for making visible the fluid motion by introducing marking material. In water, dyes such as fluorescein or methyl blue are used, although the introduction of metallic tellurium by electrolysis from a wire is very convenient and controllable. In air, smokes are used, although heat wakes have been made visible by shadowgraph or schlieren methods. The usefulness of these methods lies in their simplicity and the possibility of observing at one time a considerable part of the flow.

SECONDARY FLOW

10.36. Secondary Flow in General

If a fluid flows along a pipe of uniform section but not necessarily straight, it is possible to satisfy the condition of continuity with any velocity distribution in which the velocity is parallel to the axis and does not vary from one section to another. The condition of continuity is still satisfied if we superimpose on the basic flow a cross flow which is also the same at all sections. This cross flow, which occurs frequently in pipe and channel flow, is called a secondary flow. The concept may be extended to developing flow by distinguishing a direction at right angles to the general directions of flow and of velocity gradient and defining the secondary flow as this velocity field and the transverse flow required to satisfy the condition of continuity. An example of this is the transverse flow in the boundary layer on an airfoil of finite span.

Prandtl has distinguished three types of secondary flow:

1. Secondary flow induced in pipes and channels with finite width by the pressure field due to curvature of the streamlines
2. Secondary flow in straight pipes and channels due to non-Newtonian behavior of turbulent fluid
3. Secondary flow caused by a strong standing wave of sound in a pipe (Fig. 10.11)

10.37. Secondary Flow in Curved Pipes and Channels

If fluid flows steadily through a pipe of constant curvature, purely axial flow is possible only if the velocity is a function only of distance from the axis of pipe curvature. This is clearly impossible, for a viscous fluid in a pipe of closed section and a secondary flow occurs, inward along the side walls and outward near the pipe center, causing an increased resistance to flow. The general nature of this and other secondary flows is

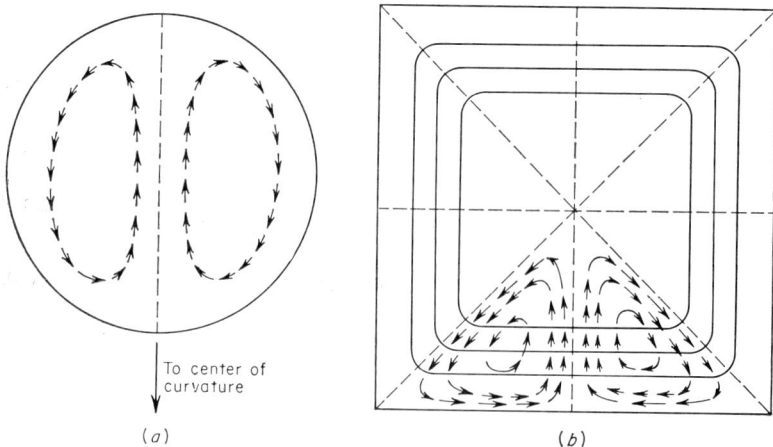

To center of curvature

(a)

(b)

Fig. 10.11. (a) First kind of secondary flow in curved pipes and channels. (b) Second kind of secondary flow in straight channels of noncircular section. (Broken lines show secondary flow, full lines are lines of equal velocity.)

easily ascertained by first assuming axial flow and inferring the body forces necessary to maintain this flow. The absence of these forces is equivalent to oppositely directed forces acting on the axial flow, and the direction of these forces will show the direction of the secondary flow. This procedure has been used to calculate the secondary flow in curved pipes at low Reynolds numbers.

10.38. Secondary Flow in Straight Channels of Noncircular Section

Flow of a viscous liquid along a straight pipe of any section can occur without second-ary flow, but turbulent flow along a pipe of any section other than circular is always accompanied by a secondary flow. Consider a pipe of square section with sides of length $2D$, two of them on the $0y$ and $0z$ axes. Then, if the flow is everywhere parallel to $0x$, the equations of mean motion in the two transverse directions may be integrated to give

$$P(y_0,D) + \overline{w^2} = P(y_0,0) \tag{10.81}$$

and
$$P(y_0,D) + \overline{v^2} = P(0,D) = P(0,y_0) \tag{10.82}$$

the paths of integration being along $y = y_0$ from $z = 0$ to $z = D$ and along $z = D$ from $y = 0$ to $y = y_0$. The symmetry of the flow requires that $P(y_0,0) = P(0,y_0)$, and so there is a pressure anomaly because $\overline{w^2} - \overline{v^2} \sim 2.2\tau_0$ within the wall equilibrium layer (Art. 10.15), which could be removed by a system of body forces acting to propel fluid from the middle of the flow toward the corners. In the absence of body forces, an oppositely directed flow occurs, fluid from the corners moving toward the middle of the walls, then toward the axis, and finally returning to the corners. The inflow to the corners substitutes fast-moving fluid for the retarded fluid that would accumulate there in laminar flow, and the general tendency is to equalize wall stress and to keep lines of constant axial velocity everywhere parallel to the nearest wall.

A similar effect occurs in the boundary layer on a flat plate of finite width. In this case, the flow is from the middle of the plate toward the free edges, but the effect is still to make more uniform the distribution of wall friction. This is done more by increasing the general level of skin friction than by reducing the friction at the edge, and it is possible that this effect is responsible for a considerable part of the increase in drag observed with flat plates of small aspect ratio.

TURBULENCE IN WIND TUNNELS

10.39. Effects of Turbulence on Model Experiments

The use of wind tunnels, ducts, and channels for the design or study of full-scale flow systems depends on the possibility of obtaining a dynamically similar flow on the scale of the testing laboratory. The conditions for this are equality of the relevant nondi-mensional parameters (Reynolds number, Mach number, etc.) and similarity of the boundary conditions, the latter including the state of the fluid supplied and in particular the intensity and nature of its turbulent motion. This raises the twin problems of adjusting the turbulent motion in the model to be a scale model of the full-scale turbulence and of reducing it to a negligible level. In wind tunnels, it is most convenient to generate a stream with a negligible level of turbulence and then, if it is needed, to provide turbulence of the required characteristics by inserting grids or other obstacles into the stream ahead of the test section.

The best-known effects of stream turbulence are the changes in the drag coefficients of spheres and of streamline bodies, and these depend on the interaction between the laminar boundary layers and the stream turbulence. If a thin plate of large aspect ratio with a tapered leading edge is placed at zero incidence to an airstream, the boundary layer may undergo transition from laminar to turbulent flow at almost any Reynolds number above 3×10^5, this minimum occurring in flows with velocity fluctuations of 5 per cent of the mean velocity and scales not more than the length of the plate. If the velocity fluctuations are extremely small (less than 0.1 per cent), transition is delayed and laminar flow may persist to Reynolds numbers of order 5×10^6. Two distinct mechanisms are involved. If the turbulent level is high, transition is probably caused by transitory separation of the laminar layer induced by adverse pressure gradients of the turbulent motion (Ref. 2, pp. 327–328), but if the level is low, Tollmien-Schlichting waves are induced by the turbulent eddies and grow until nonlinear effects lead to the production of turbulent "spots" and to transition to fully turbulent flow in the boundary layer (Schubauer[23]). Whichever mechanism is involved, the position of transition cannot be predicted from a knowledge of the turbulent intensity alone without knowing the scale. For example, so far as aircraft are concerned, the atmosphere behaves as a nonturbulent fluid whose velocity varies slowly, although the relative level of turbulence may be over 1 per cent and the effective eddy viscosity 10^5 times the molecular viscosity.

Heat transfer from a cylinder to the stream may be increased by the presence of free-stream turbulence. Van der Hegge Zijnen[13] has shown that this effect is greatest for a given turbulent intensity if the ratio L_1/D is 1.6, and it is likely that resonance occurs between the eddy-shedding mechanism and the dominant frequency of the fluctuations.

Direct interaction between turbulent boundary layers and free-stream turbulence is small, and nearly all effects may be attributed to changes in the position of transition or considered as arising from slow changes in the stream velocity.

10.40. Production of Streams with Very Low-turbulent Intensity

It is nearly impossible to arrange that the air passing through the working section of a wind tunnel has been accelerated smoothly from rest and is nonturbulent, but the fluctuations may be reduced to a very low level by a combination of two devices, *damping screens* and *stream contraction*. A damping screen is usually a woven-wire mesh whose resistance to flow is uniform over its area, although "honeycomb" forms have been used. To a good approximation, the effect on flow through one is described by the pressure coefficient for normal flow, $k = (P_1 - P_2)/\rho u^2/2$, and the refraction coefficient, $\alpha = v_2/v_1$ (Fig. 10.12). For woven-wire meshes, $\alpha = 1.1(1 + k)^{-\frac{1}{2}}$ very nearly. A screen set at right angles to a duct has two effects on the stream: (1) to reduce lateral variations of mean velocity in the ratio $(1 + \alpha - \alpha k)/(1 + \alpha + k)$, and (2) to reduce the energy of velocity fluctuations as shown in Fig. 10.13 (it has been assumed that the incident turbulence is nearly isotropic). After passage through one screen, the transverse components of the motion contain most of the turbulent energy and a second screen reduces this energy in the ratio $\alpha^2 = 1.2(1 + k)$. Note that several screens separated by intervals comparable with the scale of the turbulent motion are more effective than one with the same total-pressure coefficient.

Besides reducing the intensity of incident turbulence, a damping screen itself generates turbulence unless the Reynolds number of flow through it is very small (less than 20 if based on wire diameter and free-stream velocity). For this reason, the last of the damping screens is followed by a parallel-flow section, the *settling length*, in which the screen-produced turbulence decays to a suitably low level (usually 0.2 to 0.5 per cent). A settling length of 500 mesh lengths is usually sufficient.

The turbulence level is further reduced by passage through a contracting section which accelerates the mean flow and at the same time modifies the turbulent motion,

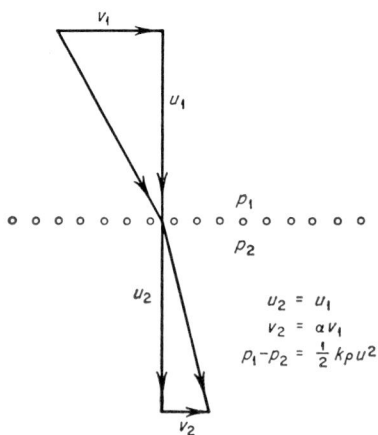

$$u_2 = u_1$$
$$v_2 = \alpha v_1$$
$$p_1 - p_2 = \tfrac{1}{2} k \rho u^2$$

Fig. 10.12. Flow through a damping screen.

decreasing the absolute energy in the longitudinal component and increasing the
energies of the transverse components. The
relative increase in energy of the mean
flow is considerably greater than the increase of the transverse components, and
the net result is a considerable reduction in
relative level. For an axisymmetric contraction, theory indicates that relative intensities are reduced in the ratios

$$\frac{(\overline{u_2^2})^{1/2}/U_2}{(\overline{u_1^2})^{1/2}/U_1} = \frac{\sqrt{3}}{2}\, c^{-2}(\ln 4c^3 - 1)^{1/2}$$

$$\frac{(\overline{v_2^2})^{1/2}/U_2}{(\overline{v_1^2})^{1/2}/U_1} = \frac{\sqrt{3}}{2}\, c^{-1/2} \qquad \text{if } c > 3$$

if the contraction is virtually instantaneous
and the turbulence entering the contraction
is isotropic. The magnitude of the *contraction ratio c* is often limited by the available
space, but it should not be less than 10.
The shape of the contracting section must
be such that local separation of the flow
does not occur.

A combination of damping screens,
settling length, and a high-ratio contraction
will reduce the level of turbulence entering
the working section to a negligible value.
The remaining motion consists in part of a
sound field arising from the boundary layers
and other fluctuating flow in the tunnel and
in part of velocity fluctuations induced by
the turbulent boundary layers on the walls.

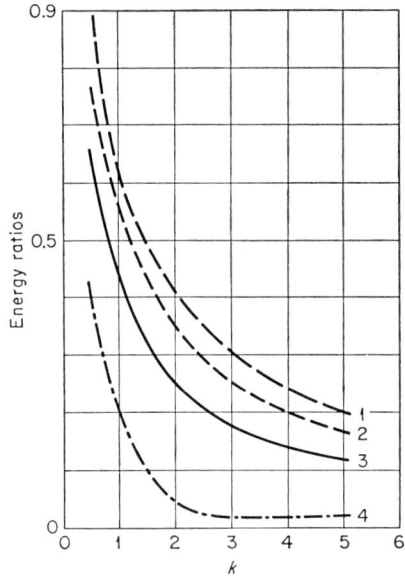

Fig. 10.13. Attenuation factors for isotropic turbulence after passage through
damping screens. Curve 1, attenuation
factor for second and subsequent screens;
curve 2, attenuation of transverse components by first screen; curve 3, attenuation of total energy by first screen; curve
4, attenuation of longitudinal component
by first screen.

In tunnels of width less than 1 ft, the rms fluctuation due to this last effect may be
as much as 1 per cent of the stream velocity. Another effect observed in small wind
tunnels is that the boundary layers on the walls generate secondary flows which are

particularly troublesome in square sections. Oblong or polygonal sections are
preferable.

The same methods can be applied to the
reduction of stream turbulence in supersonic tunnels, but entropy fluctuations
will occur if the air supply is not of uniform
stagnation temperature and these are not
affected by the damping screens and contraction.

10.41. Generation of Turbulence

A convenient method of making a
stream turbulent is to pass it through a
uniform mesh (or grid) of suitable dimensions. The most common form is
the biplane grid (two arrays of parallel,
uniformly spaced cylinders in contact
with axial directions at right angles), but

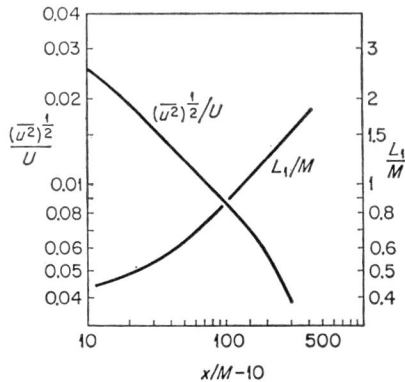

Fig. 10.14. Intensities and scales of the turbulence behind a biplane grid of mesh-diam-
eter ratio 5.33.

grids of parallel cylinders are more convenient and equally effective. This turbulent flow has been studied in great detail in connection with the theory of homogeneous turbulence (Batchelor[1]), particularly for biplane grids with spacing-diameter ratios of 4.00 and 5.33. The following results apply to grids of ratios not too different from these values. The turbulence produced is slightly anisotropic ($\overline{v^2}/\overline{u^2} \approx 0.8$), and its intensity at distance x from a grid of cylinders with diameter d is (Fig. 10.14)

$$\frac{\overline{u^2}}{U^2} = 25\left(\frac{x}{d} - 50\right)^{-1} \qquad \text{(biplane grids)}$$

or

$$= 15\left(\frac{x}{d} - 100\right)^{-1} \qquad \text{(parallel-cylinder grids)}$$

for values of x/d less than 1000. Over the same range the integral scale of the turbulence is nearly

$$L_1 = 5d\left(\frac{x}{d} - 50\right)^{1/2}$$

or

$$= 4d\left(\frac{x}{d} - 100\right)^{1/2}$$

the longitudinal correlation function is

$$R_{11}(r,0,0) = \overline{u^2}\exp\left(\frac{-r}{L_1}\right)$$

and the spectrum of the longitudinal fluctuations is

$$F_1(n) = \frac{4L_1\overline{u^2}}{U}\left(1 + \frac{4\pi^2 n^2 L_1^2}{U^2}\right)^{-1}$$

These formulas are approximate only.

REFERENCES

General

1. Batchelor, G. K.: "Theory of Homogeneous Turbulence," Cambridge, New York, 1953.
2. Goldstein, S.: "Modern Developments in Fluid Dynamics," 2 vols., Oxford, New York. 1938.
3. Hinze, J. O.: "Turbulence: An Introduction to Its Mechanism and Theory," McGraw-Hill, New York, 1959.
4. Prandtl, L.: "The Essentials of Fluid Dynamics," Blackie, Glasgow, 1952.
5. Townsend, A. A.: "The Structure of Turbulent Shear Flow," Cambridge, New York. 1956.
5a. Lin, C. C. (ed.): Turbulent Flows and Heat Transfer, "High Speed Aerodynamics and Jet Propulsion," vol. 5, Princeton University Press, Princeton, N.J., 1959.

Text

6. Batchelor, G. K.: *J. Fluid Mech.*, **5**:113 (1959).
7. Batchelor, G. K., I. D. Howells, and A. A. Townsend: *J. Fluid Mech.*, **5**:134 (1959).
8. Batchelor, G. K., and A. A. Townsend: "Surveys in Mechanics," Cambridge, New York, 1956.
9. Coles, D.: *J. Fluid Mech.*, **1**:191 (1956).
10. Elder, J. W.: *J. Fluid Mech.*, **5**:544 (1959).
11. Gerrard, J. H.: *J. Aeronaut. Sci.*, **23**:96 (1956).
12. Grant, H. L.: *J. Fluid Mech.*, **4**:149 (1958).
13. Van der Hegge Zijnen, B. G.: *Appl. Sci. Research*, **A7**:205 (1958).
14. Klebanoff, P. S.: *NACA Tech. Rept.* 1247, 1956.

15. Kovasznay, L. S. G.: *J. Aeronaut. Sci.*, **17**:657 (1953).
16. Laufer, J.: *NACA Tech. Rept.* 1174, 1955.
17. Lighthill, M. J.: *Proc. Roy. Soc. (London)*, **A211**:564 (1952).
18. Lighthill, M. J.: *Proc. Roy. Soc. (London)*, **A222**:544 (1954).
19. Ling, S. C., and P. G. Hubbard: *J. Aeronaut. Sci.*, **23**:890 (1956).
20. Malkus, W. V. R.: *J. Fluid Mech.*, **2**:521 (1956).
21. Milliat, J. P.: *Neuvième congr. intern. mécan. appl.*, Brussels, **3**:419 (1957).
22. Ruetenik, J. R.: *Johns Hopkins Univ., Dept. Mech. Eng., Rept.* I-19, 1954.
23. Schubauer, G. B.: "Boundary Layer Research," Springer, Berlin, 1958.
24. Stratford, B. S.: *J. Fluid Mech.*, **5**:1, 17 (1959).
25. Taylor, G. I.: *Proc. Roy. Soc. (London)*, **A223**:446 (1954).
26. Taylor, G. I., and G. K. Batchelor: *Quart. J. Mech. Appl. Math.*, **2**:1 (1949).
27. Taylor, R. J.: *J. Sci. Inst.*, **35**:47 (1958).

Specialized references are listed below, by subject-matter headings in the text of this section.

WALL TURBULENCE

28. Clauser, F. H.: *J. Aeronaut. Sci.*, **21**:91 (1954).
29. Clauser, F. H.: "Advances in Applied Mechanics," vol. 4, Academic Press, New York, 1956.
30. Dorrance, W. H., and F. J. Dore: *J. Aeronaut. Sci.*, **21**:404 (1954).
31. Favre, A. J., J. J. Gaviglio, and R. J. Dumas: *J. Fluid Mech.*, **3**:344 (1958).

FREE TURBULENCE

32. Corrsin, S., and A. L. Kistler: *NACA Tech. Rept.* 1244, 1956.
33. Morton, B. R., G. I. Taylor, and J. S. Turner: *Proc. Roy. Soc. (London)*, **A234**:1 (1956).

CONVECTIVE TURBULENCE

34. Townsend, A. A.: *J. Fluid Mech.*, **5**:209 (1959).

COMPRESSIBILITY AND TURBULENT FLOW

35. Kovasznay, L. S. G.: *J. Aeronaut. Sci.*, **20**:657 (1953).

TURBULENT DIFFUSIVE PROCESSES

36. Kistler, A. L., V. O'Brien, and S. Corrsin: *J. Aeronaut. Sci.*, **23**:96 (1956).

EXPERIMENTAL METHODS

37. Kovasznay, L. S. G.: *Appl. Mech. Rev.*, **12**:375 (1959).

SECONDARY FLOW

38. Townsend, A. A.: "Boundary Layer Research," Springer, Berlin, 1958.

TURBULENCE IN WIND TUNNELS

39. Ribner, H. S., and M. Tucker: *NACA Rept.* 1113, 1953.
40. Townsend, A. A.: *Quart. J. Mech. Appl. Math.*, **4**:308 (1951).
41. Stewart, R. W., and A. A. Townsend: *Phil. Trans. Roy. Soc. (London)*, **A243**:359 (1951).

Section 11

SEPARATION AND STALL

By

ROBERT C. DEAN, JR., *Thermal Dynamics Corporation, Lebanon, New Hampshire, and Dartmouth College, Hanover, New Hampshire*

SEPARATION AND STALL

11.1. Introduction

The separation of flow from the solid surfaces of fluid-handling devices is among the critical problems of fluid dynamics. The purpose of this section is to describe the physics of separation and its influence upon the operation of fluid-handling devices. Not only will available techniques of separation analysis be surveyed, but approximate engineering methods will be discussed also, in an attempt to give the reader a qualitative feel for this subject. Since the treatment of separation today is more art than science, the engineer is often forced to rely on his experience, guided by the best physical understanding at hand.

Separation, more often than not, is the limitation on the performance of any fluid-handling device, whether it be an aircraft wing or gate valve. For almost all fluid machinery, an attempt is made to design with the flow on the verge of, but not quite, separated. Under this condition, the highest performance is usually achieved. If then the working surfaces of a machine, fluid conduit, or wing are further loaded, by progressive alteration of the operating condition, separation invariably occurs. For these reasons, the prediction of the commencement of separation is of vital importance.

Many secondary effects of separation arise from its characteristic unsteadiness, which in turn engenders noise and mechanical-excitation forces. The howl of the wind, the thunder of surging turbomachinery, and the destructive effects of rotating stall in axial compressors are all due to separation. Rotating stall in axial compressors imposes a severe mechanical limitation upon the operation of a jet engine; in turn, this limitation may be a severe restriction upon the performance of the propelled aircraft. An understanding of the dynamics of separated flows is vital to analysis and control of unsteady effects.

Occasionally, separation is used to advantage. For example, it is the central mechanism of many types of acoustic generators. The rate of heat transfer in thermal-exchange equipment may be increased often by means of separation. In other devices, separation is used for control or to yield favorable characteristics. The sharp-edged orifice purposefully utilizes a separated flow to produce a flow coefficient substantially independent of Reynolds number. For these devices, also, one must be able to predict the behavior of separating or separated flow.

Without separation, a fluid would follow the solid bounding walls of a passage or body. In this unrealistic situation, fluid-dynamic design would be much simpler than in reality. The real skill in aerodynamics or in the design of fluid machinery is lodged in the prediction and control of separation.

The plan of this section is first to define separation rigorously and then to describe its manifold characteristics. Theoretical means for prediction of the onset of separation and of the behavior of separated flows are then considered. Next, the influence of separation upon the performance of fluid-handling devices is examined. Available means of controlling separation are described, as well as techniques for measurement and detection. The section closes with a bibliography of the works that provide a theoretical and empirical foundation for the subject.

Theory is derived only when not readily available elsewhere.

11.2. Notation

g_0 proportionality constant in Newton's law $F = Ma/g_0$; $[(\text{slugs})(\text{ft})]/[(\text{lb})(\text{sec}^2)]$
p pressure, psf

q $(u^2 + v^2)^{1/2}$, fps
r radius of curvature of surface, ft
u velocity in x direction, fps
U free-stream velocity, fps
v velocity in y direction, fps
w velocity in z direction, fps
x orthogonal space coordinate in plane of wall, ft
y orthogonal space coordinate in plane of wall, ft
z orthogonal space coordinate normal to wall, ft
α $\tan^{-1} u/v$, dimensionless
γ $\tan^{-1} w/q$, dimensionless
η z/δ, dimensionless
δ boundary-layer thickness (from wall to $u/v = 0.99$), **ft**
δ^* displacement thickness, ft
δ^{**} energy thickness, ft
Θ momentum thickness, ft
μ viscosity, (lb)(sec)/ft²
ν kinematic viscosity, $g_0\mu/\rho$, ft²/sec
ρ density, slugs/ft³
τ shear stress, psf

SUBSCRIPTS

0 at $z = 0$
x in x direction
y in y direction
z in z direction

11.3. Definition of Separation and Stall

In the past, there has been much confusion regarding the definition of separation. A large part of this difficulty has arisen from the fact that many persons have chosen not to identify separation until its severity causes distress. The point of distress is not absolute, but a subjective decision of the observer. To this state of mind shall be given here the term stall.[1]

Another cause of the difficulty is that in three-dimensional flows, which are common to most real situations, separation can occur without the usual flow reversal and reduction of the wall shear stress to zero. Two-dimensional definitions of separation, which commonly depend on these occurrences, are useless in three-dimensional flow. In order to eliminate confusion, a much more rigorous and general definition of separation is required.

Recently, such a definition has been developed by Eichelbrenner and Oudart[2,3] and Maskell.[4] But before defining separation according to these schemes, the concept of *limiting streamlines* must be developed. A streamline in steady flow is defined to be a stationary curve in space which is everywhere tangent to the direction of fluid motion. As the bounding wall is approached, the fluid velocity is reduced to zero by the effect of friction. Since there is no fluid motion at the wall, one cannot define strictly a streamline drawn thereon. However, in steady flow a streamline does exist at any distance from the wall, no matter how infinitesimal that distance. Therefore, in the limit one can define the flow direction of particles infinitesimally close to the wall. The so-called limiting streamlines are tangent at every point to the limiting flow direction at the wall.

Using the velocity components u, v, w, in the x, y, z directions, respectively, with x and y parallel to the plane of the wall and z normal thereto, the limiting flow direction at the wall can be defined mathematically. The flow direction in a plane parallel to the wall is

$$\tan \alpha = \frac{u}{v}$$

In order to find $(\tan \alpha)_{z=0}$ use is made of Lhopital's rule for the limit, since α must be continuous in the neighborhood of the wall:

$$\tan \alpha_0 = \lim_{z \to 0} \frac{\partial u/\partial z}{\partial v/\partial z} \tag{11.1}$$

Experience demonstrates that it is very difficult to measure the flow direction close to a wall because of the large distortions introduced by any finite probe. Fortunately, the work of Stalker[5] shows that the application of carbon black in oil or other similar material to the wall, after exposure to the flow, will produce streaks which closely represent the limiting-streamline pattern. This technique is discussed again in Art. 11.9 with pictorial examples.

Following Maskell,[4] streamlines cannot end in the fluid; they must go from infinity upstream to infinity downstream or be closed. Hence, if a limiting streamline does not form a closed loop on the bounding surface, it must join the surface at a point of attachment A and leave the surface at some subsequent point S. This latter point is called the *separation point*.

For unsteady flow, the above concept can be generalized by introducing pathlines—the trajectories of individual particles. Likewise, one can define the limiting pathlines of those particles that travel infinitely close to the wall. Where these pathlines depart from the surface at any instant is the separation point, transitory as it may be.

Within this concept of separation are included all possible cases, as shall be seen in the following paragraphs.

Ordinary and Singular Separation. In general, two types of separation may occur; they are denoted ordinary and singular.

First, consider the more common case of *ordinary separation*. Near the wall the gradient $\partial u/\partial z$ in Eq. (11.1) is proportional to the shear stress τ_x; $\partial v/\partial z$ is proportional to the shear stress τ_y (i.e., the shear stresses in the x and y coordinate directions, respectively). Therefore, since the proportionality factor is $1/\mu$ in each case,

$$\tan \alpha_0 = \lim_{z \to 0} \frac{\tau_x}{\tau_y} = \frac{\tau_{x0}}{\tau_{y0}} \tag{11.2}$$

It is clear that the shear stress in the fluid must be everywhere continuous and single-valued. As a result, unless both τ_x and τ_y go to zero simultaneously, which occurrence is called a *singular point*, Eq. (11.2) shows that α_0 is finite, single-valued, and continuous. Thus, at a separation point where two limiting streamlines meet, they both must have the same value of α_0 unless the separation point is a singular point. In order to have the same α_0, the confluent limiting streamlines must be tangent to each other in the plane of the wall, thus forming a cusp at the separation point S.

Furthermore, it can be demonstrated, in addition to the necessity of tangency between two confluent limiting streamlines, that these streamlines must also be tangent to the wall at the point of separation. This fact may be shown as follows.

The slope at a separation point of the limiting streamline in a plane perpendicular to the wall is

$$\tan \gamma_0 = \lim_{z \to 0} \frac{w}{q} = \frac{(\partial w/\partial z)_0}{(\partial q/\partial z)_0} \tag{11.3}$$

if

$$q^2 = u^2 + v^2$$

Now it can be shown at the wall that

$$\left(\frac{\partial q}{\partial z}\right)_0^2 = \left(\frac{\partial u}{\partial z}\right)_0^2 + \left(\frac{\partial v}{\partial z}\right)_0^2$$

so $(\partial q/\partial z)_0$ can be zero only if both $\tau_{x0} = \mu(\partial u/\partial z)_0$ and $\tau_{y0} = \mu(\partial v/\partial z)_0$ are simultaneously zero; in other words, only at a singular point.

In addition, it may be shown from the continuity equation that $(\partial w/\partial z)_0 = 0$ since

$$\frac{\partial u}{\partial x} + \frac{\partial v}{\partial y} + \frac{\partial w}{\partial z} = 0$$

and $(\partial u/\partial x)_0 = (\partial v/\partial y)_0 = 0$ always.

Therefore Eq. (11.3) gives these results:

$$\tan \gamma_0 = \frac{0}{(\tau_{x0}^2 + \tau_{y0}^2)^{1/2}} = 0 \qquad \text{at ordinary points} \qquad (11.4a)$$

$$\tan \gamma_0 = \frac{0}{0} \qquad \text{at singular points} \qquad (11.4b)$$

Therefore, at an ordinary separation point, the limiting streamlines joining there must be tangential to each other (cusped), tangential to the wall, and one or both wall-shear-stress components must remain nonzero.

Singular separation is the one remaining special case. Here both τ_{x0} and τ_{y0} go to zero simultaneously; as a result, the fluid has no shear at the wall. At such a point, Eq. (11.2) becomes indeterminate and the limiting flow direction can be discontinuous and many-valued.† Only at a singular point is it possible either for a limiting streamline to change direction discontinuously or for two limiting streamlines to meet in other than a cusp.

Furthermore, since $\mu(\partial q/\partial z)_0 = \tau_0 = \tau_{x0} = \tau_{y0} = 0$ at a singular point, Eq. (11.4b) shows that the inclination of the limiting streamline to the wall, γ_0, is indeterminate. Therefore, at a *singular* separation point, and only at such a point, the limiting stream-line may be inclined to the wall.

In summary, it may be seen that *ordinary-separation points* are subject to very rigid geometrical specifications, while the geometry of the limiting streamlines at a *singular-separation point* is indeterminate. The only requirement there is that the total shear-stress component in the plane of the wall must go to zero.

There is no theoretical reason apparent why lines of singular separation do not occur in fluid flow. In fact, a line of singular separation is the *only admissible condition* in two-dimensional flow, since limiting streamlines, meeting at a separation point, cannot become tangent to one another and must meet head on. In a three-dimensional flow, lines of singular separation could occur although such apparently have never been observed; however, this point has been very little investigated. Perhaps, in fact, lines of singular separation never do occur in a three-dimensional flow because of the absence of wall shear stress at the separation line. It is reasonable to expect that, in the absence of shear stress, the flow in the vicinity of the separation line would be unstable to the disturbances that are inevitably present in any real flow. Instability of the separation point is a common occurrence when a fluid is forced to flow in two-dimensional fashion. A line of ordinary separation, with its finite wall shear, appears to be a more stable condition; thus ordinary separation may be the only type that will occur in real three-dimensional flow. Isolated points of singular separation on lines of ordinary separation are observed in three-dimensional flow, particularly on planes of free-flow symmetry (Fig. 11.2d).

Stall. The last matter to be discussed under the definition of separation is the question of when separation is *stall*. The word stall is conventionally utilized to denote an unfavorable condition. The definition of whether a given condition is favorable or unfavorable depends upon the observer. Therefore stall must be a subjective term inadmissible of rigorous definition such as has been made above for separation. Usually, the concept of stall refers to the accumulation of large quantities of stagnant fluid and often to an unsteadiness associated therewith. The unsteadiness arises usually from periodic shedding of accumulated stagnant fluid.

An accumulation implies that there are not adequate means for stagnant fluid to escape. In most real three-dimensional flows, it is possible for accumulating fluid to escape in a direction normal to the main flow. Therefore accumulations of stagnant fluid are rarely seen in three-dimensional-flow situations except where some form of symmetry prevents escape. However, in two-dimensional situations, no escape route exists normal to the main flow direction. Thus, under conditions where rigorous two-dimensional flow is enforced, large accumulations of stagnant fluid can occur with the periodic shedding and unsteadiness that encourage description by the word stall. There are a few two-

† Even when τ_{x0}/τ_{y0} is indeterminate, Eq. (11.2) may have a finite limit at $z = 0$; however, by Eq. (11.4b), γ_0 may have a nonzero value, so the point should still be considered singular.

dimensional flows that do occur in practice, the most common being those involving axial symmetry.

Thus the occurrence of stall is undoubtedly related to the geometry of the flow situation and also to many other system and fluid characteristics. In any event, it should be remembered that the designation stall requires subjective judgment while the concept of separation, as defined above, is rigorous.

11.4. Characteristics of Separation

Causes of Separation. In two-dimensional-flow situations, the causes of separation can be identified easily. An examination of the role of fluid shear and pressure forces in the two-dimensional case is instructive even though this simple situation is not transferable to three-dimensional separation. In fact, for three-dimensional flows there is little understanding today of the generalities surrounding separation. Some three-dimensional laminar cases have been examined by exact or approximate analysis and separation predicted; for the common three-dimensional turbulent case, no valid analytical technique exists today.

In order to investigate two-dimensional separation, consider the simplified equation of steady motion for a particle in the boundary layer, Eq. (9.20):

$$u \frac{\partial u}{\partial x} + w \frac{\partial u}{\partial z} = -\frac{g_0}{\rho} \frac{\partial p}{\partial x} + \frac{g_0}{\rho} \frac{\partial}{\partial z} (\tau_x) \qquad (11.5)$$

From the left, the first two terms represent the acceleration of a particle, the third term the net pressure force, and the fourth term the net shear stress. Near the wall, u and v go to zero, so

$$g \frac{\partial p}{\partial x} = \left[\frac{\partial}{\partial z} (\tau_x) \right]_0$$

For laminar or turbulent flows the shear stress near the wall is proportional to the velocity gradient; therefore

$$g \frac{\partial p}{\partial x} \sim \left(\frac{\partial^2 u}{\partial z^2} \right)_0 \qquad (11.6)$$

Equation (11.6) declares that fluid shear has a regulatory effect near the wall. When the pressure gradient is adverse ($\partial p/\partial x > 0$), then the net pressure force is negative (opposite to the flow direction) and the net shear force is positive. In other words, the outer parts of the boundary layer attempt to drag the fluid near the wall against the opposing pressure force. The boundary-layer velocity profile near the wall must have an inflection point in order to produce this shearing action.

While shear effects tend to stabilize the flow, they cannot in themselves cause separation. The definition of separation (Art. 11.3) states for a two-dimensional boundary layer that the wall shear stress goes to zero at the separation point. Therefore the velocity profile must terminate perpendicular to the wall [since $\tau \alpha (\partial u/\partial z) = 0$]. This condition requires $\partial^2 u/\partial z^2$ to be greater than zero near the wall as shown in Fig. 11.1. Since $\partial^2 u/\partial z^2$ is less than zero in the outer reaches of the boundary layer, the separation profile must have a point of inflection. Now Eq. (11.6) proves that the profile described at separation can occur only if $\partial p/\partial x$ is greater than zero, in other words, if the flow is diffusing, yielding a so-called "adverse" pressure gradient. Thus an adverse pressure force on the wall particles is essential for separation of a two-dimensional boundary layer.

In three-dimensional flows, even crude generalities regarding separation cannot be specified today. While intuition argues in favor of the necessity of adverse

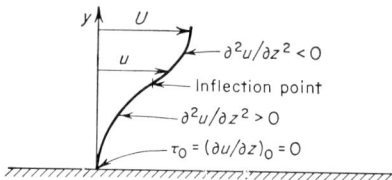

FIG. 11.1. Condition in a two-dimensional boundary layer at separation.

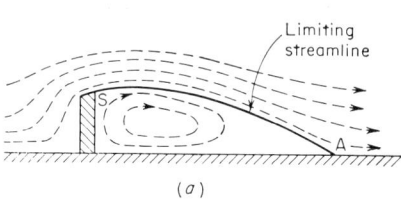

FIG. 11.2a. Closed two-dimensional separation bubble.

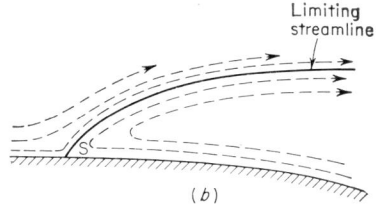

FIG. 11.2b. Open two-dimensional separation bubble.

pressure forces, there are perfectly valid cases, such as the singular separation point at the center of the vortex attached to a wall, where the pressure gradient is favorable. Undoubtedly, generalities governing three-dimensional-flow separation will be discovered in time.

Geometry of Separation. Various separation configurations are shown in Fig. 11.2. In two-dimensional separation, a "bubble" of low-velocity fluid is always formed. This bubble may be stationary, but is often unsteady. It is distinguished by interior streamlines that are closed loops (Fig. 11.2a) or that extend to infinity as illustrated in Figs. 11.2b and c.

With three-dimensional separation, a separation bubble, of closed loops or streamlines extending to infinity, may or may not be formed.

A closed three-dimensional bubble can lie in a cavity or corner or can exist even on the expanse of the wall as observed in diffusers by Kline et al.[21] These bubbles are often unstationary moving in the flow, being periodically swept away and reforming.

The physics governing the stability, the form, and the losses due to separation bubbles are not well understood today. Analytical attacks have been made such as that of Korst et al.,[56] but to date the results are uncertain. Clearly the stability and shape of separated regions depend essentially upon the ratio of the rate of supply and the rate of removal of flow-energy fluid to and from the separated region. Many factors, including particularly frictional effects and geometry, govern the balance between accumulation and removal.

This problem has been discussed qualitatively by Kline.[21] He asserts, with experimental evidence, that the gross geometry of the flow bounding walls can have a signifi-

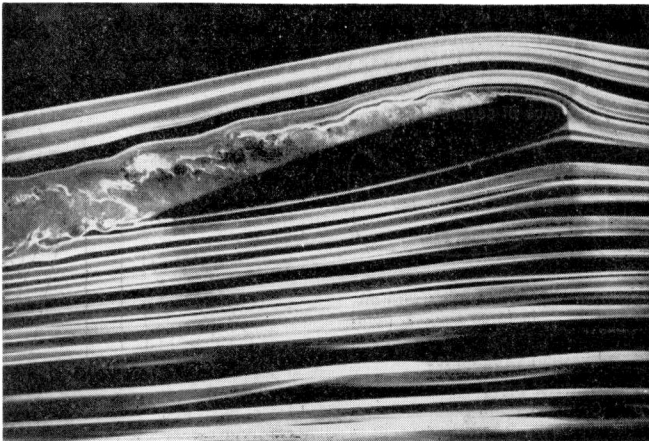

FIG. 11.2c. Open two-dimensional separation bubble on an airfoil at 14° angle of attack. (*Courtesy of F. N. M. Brown, University of Notre Dame.*)

cant influence on the nature of separation, particularly in internal flows. These geometrical influences are above and beyond the classically included influences of geometry upon the pressure distribution along the bounding walls. Kline demonstrates that the addition of solid surfaces, which do not alter the ideal-flow pressure distribution on a wall, can eliminate separation on that wall for all practical purposes.

The action of the added surfaces is produced as the flow attempts to separate; consequent alteration of the free-flow pattern is hindered by the added solid surfaces and the separation eliminated. In other words, the added surfaces make the unseparated flow more stable than the separated flow.

A simple example is a thin flat plate placed symmetrically behind a cylindrical strut. Without the trailing plate, a Kármán vortex street is formed downstream of the cylinder at proper Reynolds numbers. With the trailing plate, no vortex street forms; the flow becomes steady and the drag of the cylinder is reduced significantly (Fig. 11.23). Since the thin trailing plate would not alter the ideal-flow pressure distribution, its marked influence in reality is due to a stabilizing influence on the real separated flow. Somehow it alters the relation between the supply and removal of low-energy fluid at the separation point, thereby producing a stable balance.

Occasionally, the separated limiting-streamline sheet will form a bubble extending to infinity downstream as in Fig. 11.2d. More often, in three-dimensional flow, a bubble is not formed; instead the separated limiting-streamline sheet passes off downstream with the free flow, frequently deforming into a spiral configuration of vortices (Fig. 11.2e).

Vortex Sheets. Whenever a limiting streamline leaves a bounding surface, the situation for the free flow is equivalent to the generation of a new wall shape. As Maskell says, the separated limiting streamlines generate a skeleton over which the main flow must form a new pattern.

Separation, by diverting the boundary layer from the wall, causes sheets of vorticity to leave the wall. The vorticity contained in the boundary layer near the wall on both sides of the separation line is found, after separation, lying on each side of the stream sheet formed by the detached limiting stream lines. Immediately after separation, most of the vorticity in the separated flow is perpendicular to the free-stream velocity and parallel to the separated limiting-streamline sheet. However, because of turning of the flow before or after separation, secondary vorticity may be generated. The secondary vorticity is parallel to the direction of the main flow bounding the separated-limiting-streamline skeleton and often causes the separated limiting streamline to roll up into a vortex (Figs. 11.2e, 11.3, and 11.4).

The flow about a cylindrical strut piercing a wall boundary layer is an excellent example of vortex formation as shown in Fig. 11.3. Here separation occurred along two lines of ordinary separation divided by a singular separation point on the line of symmetry. The limiting-streamline skeleton rolls up after separation under the action of secondary vorticity and generates two large trailing vorticities. Hawthorne[7] has developed general

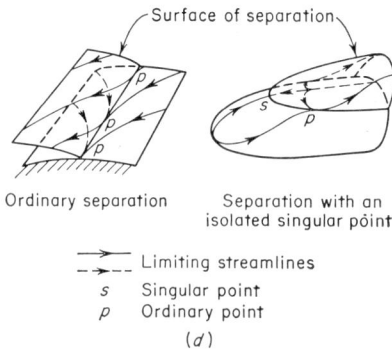

FIG. 11.2d. Modes of three-dimensional separation. (Ref. 4.)

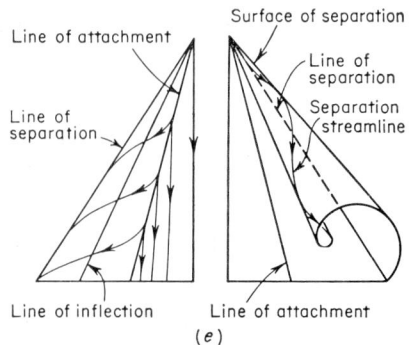

FIG. 11.2e. Three-dimensional separation on a swept wing at angle of attack. (Ref. 4.)

equations describing the generation of secondary vorticity in a curving flow; he also studied[8] the case of a strut piercing the boundary layer with the object of discovering strut shapes that lead to a minimum secondary vorticity in the downstream flow. Another example is the generation of the corner vortex commonly found in a turbine nozzle passage[9,10] (Fig. 11.4). Some investigators believe that these trailing vortices offer essential escape routes through their low-pressure cores for stagnant boundary-layer fluids. If true, trailing vortices may be important elements in the avoidance of stall.

In summary, the geometry of separated regions may be described as composed often of a bubble which is closed or extends to infinity. Vorticity is always shed into the stream at the separation point on sheets surrounding the limiting-streamline skeleton. This vorticity has an essential effect upon the shape of the downstream limiting-streamline sheet. It also affects other matters such as losses and the behavior of succeeding flow

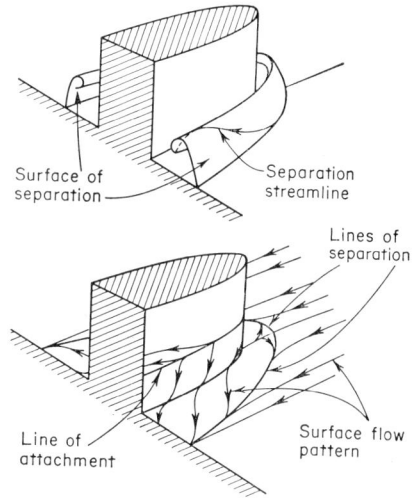

FIG. 11.3. Limiting streamlines and trailing vortices due to separation before a strut in the boundary layer. (*Ref.* 4.)

elements. The downstream configuration of the limiting-streamline skeleton, particularly as governed by vorticity, may have significant effects on the behavior of separation averting stall in many practical cases. The behavior of the limiting-streamline sheets and associated vorticity after separation must be handled by secondary-flow analysis.

Unsteadiness. Separation is the most important source of unsteadiness in fluid flow. Two types of unsteadiness may be identified: *quasi-steady*, in the sense that the

FIG. 11.4. Corner vortex in turbine nozzle cascade. (*National Aeronautics and Space Administration.*) (*Ref.* 9.)

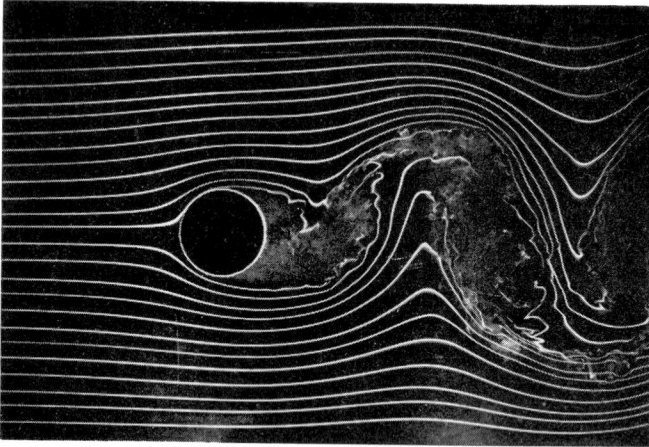

FIG. 11.5. Kármán vortex street behind a cylinder. (*Courtesy of Dr. A. M. Lippisch.*[88])

process is cyclic or its general characteristics do not alter in time, and *transient*, where the flow pattern is changing from one stable pattern, which may be unsteady, to another. Examples of the former are the fluttering aircraft wing, steady rotating stall, and the generation of Kármán vortex streets. Most of these cases involve periodic eddy shedding from a flow-bounding surface (Fig. 11.5). This is the phenomenon responsible for the galloping transmission line and much of the noise in turbomachinery. Transient separation is exemplified by an accelerating jet engine that passes through many different separated flow configurations during the process.

All these unsteadiness effects associated with separation involve the shedding of accumulated stagnant fluid. The shedding of eddies or accumulated stagnant fluid is one important fluid-dynamics problem that has not been resolved to date; in other words, without empirical data it is presently impossible to predict the frequency or size of the shed eddies and the resulting time-dependent pressure forces.

Unsteady separation is almost always self-excited. The phenomenon may involve only the fluid or, also, some vibrating solid surface.

Losses. Separation gives rise to added losses. The most important cause is the increase in shearing forces as the main flow passes over a separated region. Very little is known about this phenomenon; however, the friction factor† applying to a turbulent boundary layer on a smooth wall is about 0.005 while jets and wakes (where high-velocity fluid passes over a low-velocity region) usually demonstrate friction factors between 0.037 to 0.094. Thus a separated bubble can exert a shear force on the main flow up to twenty times higher than that of a wall. In general, it can be said today that *the losses of separated flows cannot be predicted; the loss must be measured*.

Another source of loss results from downstream influences of the separated flow. These effects include downstream mixing losses as low-energy fluid shed from the wall at separation mixes into the free flow, secondary vorticity losses which are usually small, and the influence of trailing separation bubbles and vortex sheets upon the approach flow patterns to downstream elements. Only in certain special cases can mixing losses be calculated with accuracy (Art. 11.6); means are nonexistent for analyzing the other effects.

Effects on Flow Field and Structures. Separation alters the shape of the effective flow boundaries. Alterations are produced in the pressure distributions on solid surfaces; the entry velocity triangles to the next stage of a turbomachine; the pressure

† $f = \tau/(\rho v^2/2g_0)$ if v is the relative velocity between the free flow and a wall or between the free velocities of two parallel flows.

recovery of diffusing elements; Mach-number distributions; shock locations; flow of liquids over the bounding surfaces; the trajectories of solid particles (which may lead to erosion and deposits); heat and mass transfer (e.g., recovery factors); and in lift and drag. If the separation is unsteady, as common, time-dependent pressure forces generated can excite vibration intense enough to cause failure. The best-known examples are the destructive effects of rotating stall on the blades of axial compressors, the breaking of tubes in heat exchangers due to vibration, and the failure of struts and plates immersed in flow.

Cavitation. Cavitation (Sec. 12) may cause or prevent separation. Little is known of the relationship between cavitation and separation, but since cavitation occurs near the minimum pressure point and separation often occurs just after that point, it is reasonable to expect that these two phenomena are interrelated; also, the presence of vapor bubbles in the cavitation region undoubtedly affects the fluid mechanics and occurrence of separation.

The successful use of sharp leading edges on pump blades suggests that the separation which would occur normally at small angles of attack may be delayed by cavitation.

In some cases, separation may prevent cavitation by limiting the minimum pressure achieved at the wall. For example, an ideal flow analysis of the effect of surface roughness on the cavitation characteristics of turbomachinery[11] predicts that suction specific speeds over 8,000 cannot be achieved in pumps without cavitation. However, it is suspected that separation of the flow over these wall asperities may prevent cavitation and explain the achievement of suction specific speeds up to 15,000 in commercial machinery.

Shocks. Shocks frequently cause separation, which may take the form of a permanent separation bubble extending downstream to infinity or a local closed bubble on the wall. Figure 9.45d shows a schlieren photograph of a turbulent boundary layer separated by a shock.

Although in recent years many investigators have attacked the problem of shock-wave–boundary-layer interaction and the separation engendered by shocks, this subject is still without sound analytical foundation. The basic difficulty stems from the fact that the flow deep in the boundary layer must be subsonic; as a result, shocks in the supersonic free flow cannot penetrate to the wall through the boundary layer. Not only does this situation create a problem of mixed-Mach-number flow, but the degeneration of the shock in the boundary layer leads to large differences between the pressure gradient of the free flow and that on the wall.[12,13] This effect is called *diffusion* of the pressure gradient near the wall. The resulting pressure distribution contains significant gradients normal to the wall which invalidate the simplifying assumptions leading to the Prandtl boundary-layer equations. Therefore the problem of shock-wave–boundary-layer interaction is still far from analysis.

Considerable experimental data for shock separation can be found in the literature. A few recent studies are contained in Refs. 14 to 17, in which may be found an extensive bibliography. Approximate rules for separation have been offered, such as those of Fage and Sargent,[18] which predict no separation of a turbulent layer by a normal shock if its pressure ratio is less than 1.8 (corresponding to a free-stream Mach number of 1.3). Donaldson and Lange[19] have produced a correlation for shock separation which indicates that the critical pressure rise across a shock at incipient separation is proportional to the skin-friction coefficient. Thus the critical pressure rise is a function of length Reynolds number and free-stream Mach number. Tyler and Shapiro[108] analyzed shock separation as an impulsive pressure rise and found fair agreement with the critical-pressure-rise correlation of Donaldson and Lange.

On the other hand, Kuehn[20] recently concluded:

1. "There is no single value of shock pressure rise which is suitable to predict separation. Mach number, Reynolds number, body shape, and transition locations all are important variables affecting the incipient separation pressure ratio."
2. "No theoretical method is available which will predict the onset of turbulent boundary-layer shock separation."

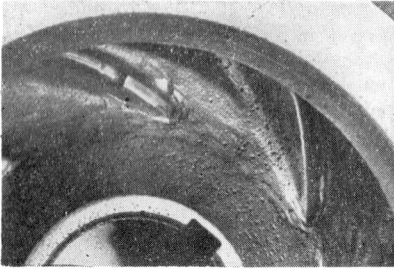

FIG. 11.6. Erosion pits produced ahead of pump blades handling abrasive slurry. (*Ingersoll-Rand Company.*)

3. "Values of pressure rise with no separation can be many times larger than the values of pressure rise at the separation point or peak pressure in the separated region, which have often been used as design criteria for the onset of separation."

4. "The general characteristics of the separated flow, which results when the conditions for incipient separation have been exceeded, are well understood for two-dimensional models, but the complete pressure distribution and size of the separated region cannot be accurately predicted by either empirical or theoretical methods."

These comments sum up well the present knowledge of the shock-separated turbulent layer. The laminar layer will almost always be separated by a shock except for very weak waves (see also Art. 9.23).

This subject is still very much an art; although the extensive literature will give the designer experience, he must resort in the end to experiment and to cut-and-try development.

Erosion-Corrosion. The accumulation at separation points of dust and dirt and liquid contained in flowing gases is a common phenomenon. Many of the characteristic erosion patterns that are seen in turbomachinery can be traced back to the geometry of the separation therein. A familiar example is the hollow scooped in the snow before a telephone pole by the wind of a blizzard. As shown in Fig. 11.6, this same phenomenon is observed around the noses of turbomachinery blading; it is also responsible for the undermining of bridge piers.

Energizing and Other Miscellaneous Effects. Finally, it is significant to note that local three-dimensional separation has been shown[21] to have an energizing effect upon a boundary-layer flow. Formation of discrete stall bubbles in a decelerating flow may be the energizing mechanism which makes it possible for a boundary layer to negotiate steep pressure rises. Other beneficial effects of separation are the increase of heat transfer from bluff bodies and the ignition of chemical reactions by flameholders which make use of the reversed flow in the permanent separation bubble to carry hot gas back for ignition of the oncoming gas mixture.

11.5. Available Theoretical Methods

Traditionally, analysis of separation divides the problem into two parts: (1) the flow up to separation and (2) the behavior of separated regions and trailing vortex sheets. Actually, these two parts are often intimately interrelated. Aircraft wings may separate first near the trailing edge, but the increased pressure gradient in the corner flow generated before the separation line will frequently cause the separation point to move upstream until it reaches the vicinity of the minimum pressure point. This strong interaction makes difficult the experimental determination of conditions at the inception of separation.

Unless the entire flow field—the shearless main flow, the shear region before separation, and the separated flow—can be handled together, iteration is required. Certain simplified cases in which the separation point is fixed by a salient edge and the pressure is assumed uniform in the separation bubble, have been solved by free-streamline methods (Art. 11.6). However, the usual case, with no separation point obvious by inspection, has not been solved completely. Analysis usually predicts the location of separation for a potential flow without separated regions; however, as pointed out above, this point need not be stable for the separated flow.

The mathematical problem of predicting separation in the usual flow situation is, first, and most importantly, the same problem as that of any turbulent shear flow where missing relations are needed between steady and unsteady properties. Second, the flow situation is nonlinear, preventing exact solutions, and too complex for complete solutions by even the largest computer. The utilization of a frontal attack attempting to solve the exact equations of motion, even in the laminar regime, has been successful only in the simplest cases. Thus the analyst must resort to empirical data for establishment of the stable flow regime and its geometry, plus extensive approximation. Even in this manner, exceedingly few cases have been attacked.

One of the most common approximations is that of Prandtl's boundary layer in which the normal pressure gradient $\partial p/\partial z$ is equal to zero. This assumption can be used only up to the separation line. Successful analysis of the separation of shear flows in which the boundary-layer assumptions cannot be made is nonexistent, as is analysis of three-dimensional separation.

Prediction of the Onset of Boundary-layer Separation. Two-dimensional Boundary Layer. Most of the classical exact and approximate two-dimensional boundary-layer solutions carry their computations to the point of separation, which is usually specified to be where the wall shear stress τ_0 is reduced to zero. However, many of these analyses become unreliable as separation is approached because of a breakdown of one or more of their assumptions. A rapid thickening of the boundary layer and curvature of the streamlines upstream of a separation point often make the boundary-layer assumption of zero-normal pressure gradient untenable. Any unsteadiness of the separation point introduces acceleration terms that are usually deleted from the classical analyses. Also, there is considerable evidence of large influences engendered by slight three-dimensionality in the flow just ahead of separation.[45,55,21]

A shift of the separation point after the onset of separation as mentioned above, of course, invalidates the predictions by altering the surface pressure distribution from that existent before separation. However, in this case, while the analysis will not predict the location of the separation once it commences, it will often indicate the flow conditions under which separation will first occur. As such, classical analyses have been useful to predict the behavior of wings (Ref. 26, p. 476), the blading of axial turbomachines,[23] and in certain other special situations.[24]

LAMINAR, EXACT SOLUTIONS. First the laminar boundary layer is considered, although the reader should be cautioned that most practical flow situations, except at low Reynolds numbers, involve separation of a turbulent boundary layer.

The boundary-layer equations for two-dimensional, incompressible laminar flow are developed in Eqs. (9.20) and (9.21) as follows:

$$u \frac{\partial u}{\partial x} + w \frac{\partial u}{\partial z} = -\frac{g_0}{\rho} \frac{\partial p}{\partial x} + \nu \frac{\partial^2 u}{\partial z^2} \tag{11.7}$$

$$\frac{\partial u}{\partial x} + \frac{\partial w}{\partial z} = 0 \tag{11.8}$$

Exact two-dimensional solutions of the laminar boundary layer are several;[27,28] most depend upon the discovery of a pressure distribution which leads to a similarity solution (i.e., the nondimensional velocity profiles are similar in shape at all stations); (Arts. 9.11 and 9.12). The very assumption of similarity automatically excludes progress of a boundary layer toward separation. Only if the separation profile is adopted is separation imminent, *everywhere*. Since, for this reason, similarity solutions are relatively unimportant to the prediction of separation, they will not be discussed further here.

A few "exact" solutions exist that do not depend on the similarity assumption. In other words, the profiles can change shape progressively to a separation profile in a decelerated flow. However, these methods do depend on series expansions and, in a rigorous sense, are not "exact."

Blasius,[27] Hiemenz,[29] and Howarth[30] developed the solution for the laminar boundary layer on a right cylinder where the potential velocity distribution on the edge of the boundary layer can be expressed as a power series in the distance from the stagnation point. This type of velocity distribution can represent well the potential or observed pressure distribution about a circular cylinder, but does not represent well the pressure distribution of slender ellipsoids or airfoils except near the leading edge. A discussion of the theory may be found in Ref. 26, page 131. Suffice to say here that Hiemenz measured separation at 81° from stagnation on a circular cylinder whereas this method using the *measured pressure distribution* predicted separation at 82°. It is interesting to note that this method with the *potential-flow distribution* about the cylinder predicts separation at 110°. The difference between calculation of the separation point based on potential and based on actual pressure distributions illustrates the sometimes large alterations of the pressure distribution due to the shape of the separation region as discussed above. Of course, alteration of separation from 110 to 81° makes a large change in the calculated drag, thus invalidating potential-flow calculations of drag on circular cylinders even if correct assumptions were made of the pressure distribution downstream of the separation, which is another serious difficulty.

Görtler[60] has contributed a number of series-type solutions for a variety of pressure distributions.

Howarth[31] has developed another "exact" series solution to the laminar-boundary-layer equations in which the potential flow is given by

$$U = U_0 - \alpha x$$

α may be positive or negative. The theory is discussed in Ref. 26, page 149. Again this is not a similar solution, but carries to a prediction of separation. It is interesting to note, incidentally, from this theory that the free-stream velocity U can be reduced only by about 12 per cent of its initial value U_0 before separation occurs. This result applies approximately to all laminar boundary layers, demonstrating their extreme propensity to separation. For this reason, devices operating with laminar layers, usually due to low Reynolds numbers, can be loaded only lightly if separation is to be avoided. Conversely, it explains why a device, such as a cascade of compressor blades, that performs well at high Reynolds numbers will usually break down to poor performance as the Reynolds number is lowered. Figure 11.7 demonstrates this effect for a valve where the flow coefficient degenerated badly with a reduction in Reynolds number.

Finally, under "exact" solutions should be mentioned step-by-step solutions which are finite-difference solutions of the laminar-boundary-layer equations (Ref. 26, p. 150). They are cumbersome and little used.

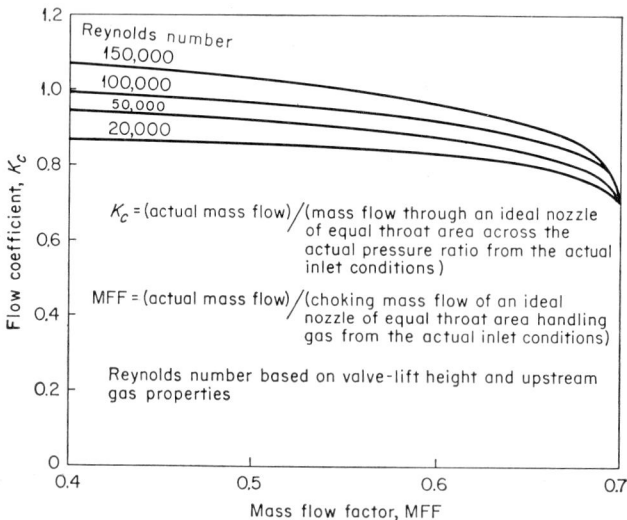

FIG. 11.7. Effect of Reynolds number on the flow coefficient of a valve. (*Ingersoll-Rand Company.*)

Similar to the rectangular two-dimensional solutions above are the solutions of axisymmetric cases (bodies of revolution), which are also two-dimensional. Boltz and Froessling have developed the theory as described in Ref. 26, page 162.

LAMINAR, INTEGRAL SOLUTION. The general problem of flow around a body of arbitrary shape cannot be solved by the exact methods above. The basic difficulty lies in our inability to handle mathematically the nonlinear partial differential equations of the boundary layer, which themselves are great simplifications of the full equations of motion of Navier and Stokes.

To circumvent this difficulty and to achieve approximate solutions, the boundary-layer equations may be integrated through the depth of the boundary layer to produce the Kármán momentum integral equations. These equations relate average properties of the boundary layer, such as the displacement or flow-continuity thickness and momentum-flux thickness to the imposed pressure distribution, wall shear stress, and initial conditions. For two-dimensional flow, laminar or turbulent, the integral equation is (Art. 9.13)

$$\frac{d\Theta}{dx} + (\delta^* + 2\Theta)\frac{1}{U}\frac{dU}{dx} = \frac{\tau_0}{\rho U^2/g_0} \tag{11.9}$$

in which Θ = momentum thickness = $\dfrac{1}{U^2}\displaystyle\int_0^\infty u(U - u)\,dz$

δ^* = displacement thickness = $\dfrac{1}{U}\displaystyle\int_0^\infty (U - u)\,dz$

U = free-stream velocity

This equation is not complete since it contains three unknowns for incompressible flow: Θ, δ^*, and τ_0. In order to produce solutions in the laminar case, only a relationship for $u = f(z)$ need be introduced, which then, for example, allows expression of τ_0 and δ^* as functions of Θ, enabling solution of Eq. (11.9).

Pohlhausen[32] developed the most widely known method of solution based on the velocity-profile assumption:

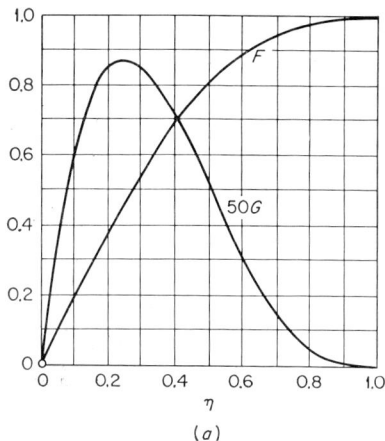

FIG. 11.8a. The functions $F(\eta)$ and $G(\eta)$. (*Ref.* 26.)

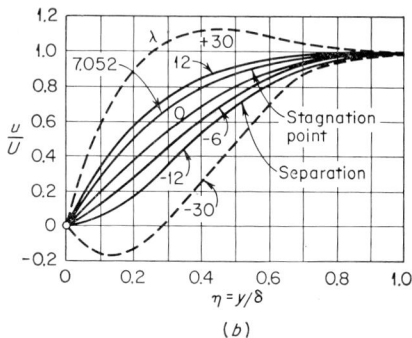

FIG. 11.8b. Velocity profiles $u/U = F(\eta) + \lambda G(\eta)$ for various values of λ. (*Ref.* 26.)

$$\frac{u}{U} = F(\eta) + \lambda G(\eta)$$

in which
$$\eta = \frac{z}{\delta}$$

$$F(\eta) = 2\eta - 2\eta^3 + \eta^4$$

$$G(\eta) = \frac{1}{6}(\eta - 3\eta^2 + 3\eta^3 - \eta^4)$$

This profile assumption satisfies the following boundary conditions:

$$z = 0 : u = 0 \qquad \nu \frac{\partial^2 u}{\partial z^2} = \frac{g_0}{\rho} \frac{\partial p}{\partial x}$$

$$z = \delta : u = U \qquad \frac{\partial u}{\partial z} = 0, \quad \frac{\partial^2 u}{\partial z^2} = 0$$

The functions F and G are shown in Fig. 11.8a. The λ parameter adds varying amounts of the G profile to the F, giving shapes as shown in Fig. 11.8b. The boundary conditions relate λ to the pressure gradient as

$$\lambda = -\frac{\delta^2}{\mu U}\left(\frac{dp}{dx}\right) = \frac{\delta^2}{\nu}\left(\frac{dU}{dx}\right)$$

The parameter λ is obviously a variable in the problem; therefore profile shapes can change toward the separation profile, which is given by

$$\lambda = -12 \qquad \text{for } \tau_0 = 0$$

The method of solution is given in Ref. 26, page 206, along with tables of integrated functions useful in application. These approximate solutions and the exact solutions mentioned above are compared also in Ref. 26 (see also Art. 9.13).

As separation is approached, the Pohlhausen method becomes increasingly uncertain; no general means of computing this uncertainty are available. Schubauer[33] measured separation on an elliptic cylinder of fineness $a/b = 2.96$, observing separation at $x/b = 1.99$. A Pohlhausen-type solution agreed well with the measured profiles up to the point of minimum pressure $x/b = 1.3$, but beyond diverged from the data and predicted no separation at all.

Newer approximate techniques developed by Thwaites,[57] Stratford,[58] and Curle and Skan,[59] depending heavily on empirically determined coefficients, greatly improve separation-point predictions. Furthermore, the resulting computational methods are far simpler than the Pohlhausen scheme.

Curle and Skan[59] arrive at a relation for separation of the two-dimensional steady laminar boundary layer

$$x^2 C_p \left(\frac{dC_p}{dx}\right)^2 = 1.04 \times 10^{-2} \tag{11.10}$$

in which x = distance from minimum pressure point
$C_p = 1 - U^2/U_m^2$ = pressure coefficient
U = local free-stream velocity
U_m = maximum free-stream velocity at the minimum pressure point

Table 11.1 compares separation predictions of this equation with 11 exact solutions for a wide variety of pressure distributions.

Note for Schubauer's ellipse that the exact solution predicts separation at $x = 1.983$ and Curle and Skan [Eq. (11.10)] at 2.01 while separation was observed at 1.99.

Actually, there is little choice in accuracy between the methods of Thwaite, Stratford, or Curle and Skan. However, the latter is far simpler to use than the others.

The evidence of Table 11.1 indicates that two-dimensional, steady laminar separation

Table 11.1

(From Curle and Skan[59])

Reference	Pressure distribution, U/U_m	Separation point, x_s	
		Exact	Eq. (11.10)
60	$(1 - x)^{-1}$	0.159	0.157
60	$(1 - x)^{-2}$	0.078	0.073
60	$(1 - x)^{1/2}$	0.223	0.218
60	$(1 - x)^2$	0.067	0.064
60	$\cos x$	0.410	0.387
60	$1 - x^3$	0.401	0.380
60	$\sin x$	1.902	1.832
60, 61	$1 - x^2$	0.271	0.271
60, 61	$1 - x^4$	0.462	0.461
62	Schubauer's ellipse	1.983	2.01
31	$1 - x$	0.120	0.121

can be predicted with great ease and accuracy by Eq. (11.10). However, it should be remembered that the *separated* pressure distribution often must be used in Eq. (11.10) to ensure a significant prediction of the stable location of the separation point.

Various techniques have been developed for the axisymmetric laminar boundary layer where the momentum integral equation takes the form

$$\frac{d\Theta}{dx} + (\delta^* + 2\Theta)\frac{1}{U}\frac{dU}{dx} + \frac{\Theta}{r}\frac{dr}{dx} = \frac{\tau_0}{\rho U^2/g_0}$$

Methods of solution similar to Pohlhausen's have been developed by Scholkemeyer,[34] Pretsch,[35] Tomotika,[36] and Rott and Crabtree.[37]

Other methods of solving the two-dimensional Kármán momentum-integral equations have been developed (Ref. 26, p. 220). In general, either the order of the velocity-profile polynomial is increased or the functional form is changed or two-parameter family profiles are adopted. The latter method requires another independent equation, which is usually the energy-integral equation

$$\frac{d}{dx}(U^3\delta^{**}) = 2\nu \int_0^\infty \left(\frac{\partial u}{\partial z}\right)^2 dz$$

if $$\delta^{**} = \frac{1}{U^3}\int_0^\infty u(U^2 - u^2)\,dz = \text{energy thickness}$$

Sutton[38] and Wieghardt[39,40] have developed such techniques, which give good results in comparison with exact solutions up to the point of separation. Walz[41] dropped the boundary condition

$$\nu\frac{\partial^2 u}{\partial z^2} = \frac{g_0}{\rho}\frac{dp}{dx}$$

and was able to use a one-parameter family of profiles to solve the momentum and energy integral equations simultaneously. This method gives better results near separation and for rapid deceleration than the Pohlhausen method.

With the various exact and approximate solutions above, it is fair to say that separation can be predicted with sufficient accuracy for engineering purposes in steady two-dimensional laminar flow. For predicting the attitude of a wing or operating point of a fluid machine where laminar separation will commence, the potential velocity distribution can be utilized, although interactions modifying the body shape with the boundary-layer-displacement thickness will improve the predictions. If the separation point is to be predicted in a stably separated flow, empirical measurements of the actual pressure distribution are usually required for accuracy because of the alteration of the free-flow geometry by the separation itself.

Turbulent Boundary Layers. The turbulent boundary layer is the common situation in fluid machines due to the disturbances which induce transition and, more particularly, since high performance usually requires that the solid surfaces be loaded as heavily as possible. For example, the allowable lift of blades operating in laminar flow without separation is on the order of one-fourth of similar conditions with a turbulent boundary layer because of the far smaller deceleration tolerance of the laminar layer. As a result, four times as many blades would be required, with a quadrupling of the drag, a large decrease of efficiency, and increase in weight and size.

It follows that a designer of fluid machinery must contend almost always with the turbulent boundary layer. Unfortunately, available means of treating the turbulent boundary layer and its separation are an order of magnitude less exact and more tenuous than means of treating the laminar layer. No such thing as an exact turbulent-boundary-layer solution exists since the relationships between fluctuating and time-average quantities are unknown. Most important, the shear stresses within a turbulent boundary layer are of the order of $10–10^3$ those due to the laminar layer and are due to cross-momentum transport produced by turbulent mixing. While some attempts have been made to model turbulent mixing, notably Prandtl's mixing-length theory, they are generally of little practical use. As a result, there are no good means for determining the shear stress of a turbulent layer as a function of profile shape, boundary-layer geometry, and so forth. This failure rules out exact solutions, of course.

One must turn to methods that circumnavigate the necessity of determining the boundary-layer shear-stress distribution. The momentum and energy integral equations do exactly this, requiring only the shear stress at the wall.

If the velocity components appearing in the Navier-Stokes equations are expressed as a time average plus a fluctuating term, and then the equations are integrated through the boundary layer, terms will appear expressing momentum transport in the direction of flow by the fluctuating components. These terms are commonly neglected, giving the momentum integral equations exactly the same form as those for laminar flow. Some investigators[73] are of the opinion that neglect of the fluctuating terms is the cause of discrepancies between predictions and data. Clauser[45] concludes, on the basis of his careful experiments, that these difficulties are due to slight three-dimensionality upstream of separation in a supposedly two-dimensional flow rather than to unsteady-flow effects. While the influence of fluctuating terms has not been resolved completely, their effect is undoubtedly far smaller than the uncertainties introduced by the various velocity-profile approximations.

In order to utilize the momentum integral equations, relationships must be found between, Θ, δ^*, and τ_0 as before. Many investigators have worked upon this problem, notably Gruschwitz,[63] von Doenhoff and N. Tetervin,[64] Truckenbrodt,[65] Wieghardt,[66] Rotta,[68,69,70] and Ross.[72] Some of these methods utilize the energy integral equation in a manner similar to that for laminar layers (see also Art. 9.18).

All the various methods for supplying the necessary auxiliary equations for Θ, δ^*, and τ_0 depend upon assumption of a velocity-profile family dependent upon one or more parameters. Empirical correlations are utilized to relate profile parameters and τ_0 to geometry, pressure distribution, Reynolds number, and so forth. Frequently the methods work well in the cases used for correlation, but are apt to break down in cases of significantly different pressure distributions.

The method of Rotta[68–70] appears today to be useful over the widest range of cases. Each of the turbulent-integral-equation methods devises its own peculiar separation criteria developed from empirical correlations. For example, the von Doenhoff and Tetervin scheme describes a one-parameter family of velocity profiles. The parameter used is the shape factor $H = \delta^*/\Theta$. Separation is specified to occur if H exceeds 1.8. Figure 11.9 illustrates various solutions for the turbulent boundary layer on a wing and comparison with experimental data. It is to be noted that all the methods are not equally successful if a critical H value is selected as the separation criterion. However, in this case, the values of H calculated with the von Doenhoff and Tetervin method varied so rapidly near separation that any critical value of H greater than 1.8 would have equally well predicted the separation point.

With these methods considerable success has been achieved in predicting the gross flow conditions or attitude of wing or cascade under which separation will first occur.

The best and most complete example of what can be done is contained in Schlicting's paper[23] describing the work of his group on the theoretical prediction of axial-compressor and turbine-cascade performance. Excellent agreement between theoretical and experimental loss and stall results was achieved. Upon application to real machines, however, the three-dimensional separation effects at the blade extremities can considerably alter blade-row performance. These influences are beyond present analysis. Nevertheless, the two-dimensional cascade behavior is fundamental to compressor and turbine design; Schlicting's work has brought this matter into the realm of theoretical treatment.

In summary of this discussion of turbulent-boundary-layer separation prediction, it can be said that fair results can be achieved on external flow devices such as wings, cascades, cylinders, and so forth. Similar success for internal flow devices such as diffusers has not been obtained. The reason may be that the development of many of the prediction methods has depended heavily on data from external flow situations which may be enough different, in pressure distribution for example, so that the results do not apply to internal flows. There seems, however, to be a more fundamental difference that is not at all well understood. This is the influence of passage geometry on flow stability that was discussed in Art. 11.4. As a result, the prediction of turbulent separation in internal flow systems is not reliable. In addition, such flows are rarely two-dimensional, which invalidates the whole idea of a two-dimensional analysis.

Before leaving the theoretical methods for the two-dimensional turbulent boundary layer, the location of transition should be discussed. Any turbulent boundary layer is preceded somewhere by a laminar layer. In ducting problems, the transition to a turbulent-boundary-layer flow often

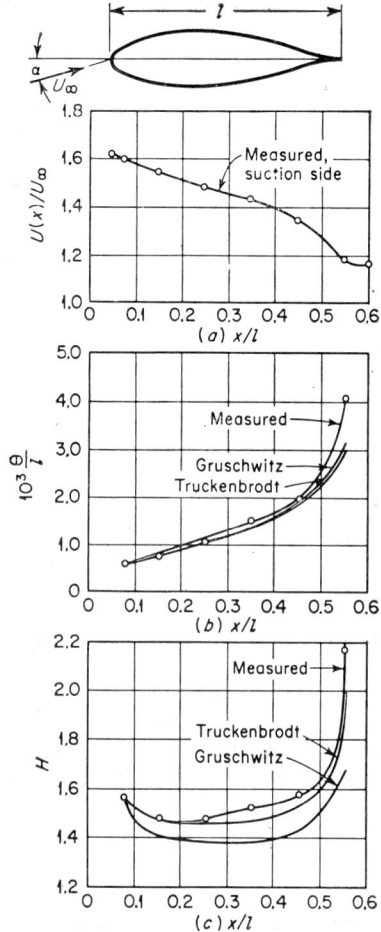

Fig. 11.9. The turbulent boundary layer on an airfoil; comparison of various computational methods with measurements. Angle of attack 10.1°, Reynolds number $= U_\infty l/\nu = 2.64 \times 10^6$. (Ref. 26, p. 476.)

occurs considerably before the region of interest for separation. Provided a reasonable estimate can be made, the theories above will not be too much affected by the exact initial values assumed. This is due to the fact that the turbulent layer adjusts quickly to local conditions and is insensitive, therefore, to conditions far upstream.

On the other hand, when the laminar layer is not far removed, such as with a flow starting at a near leading edge (e.g., an airfoil), both the laminar and the turbulent layer must be computed and matched in at least momentum thickness at the transition point. A thorough treatment of transition is contained in Arts. 9.24 to 9.26 and in Ref. 26, chaps. 16 and 17. Present transition theory is adequate in simple situations such as low-disturbance-level free flow passing over a flat plate. However, in many fluid machines large transient disturbances exist in the free flow which greatly affect the location of transition. Little can be done analytically in this situation today. In several works, such as Schlichting's,[23] transition is assumed at the minimum pressure point on the surface. This assumption appears valid, except at low Reynolds numbers.

Last, it should be mentioned that two-dimensional turbulent calculation methods for axisymmetric problems similar to the rectilinear techniques have been developed; they are reviewed in Ref. 26, page 478.

Influences of Forces and Accelerations Normal to the Surface. The influence of wall curvature and the acceleration of the coordinate system often must be considered. If pressure forces or centrifugal or Coriolis acceleration exist normal to the surface, a stabilizing or destabilizing effect is felt in the boundary layer which can greatly affect transition and the structure of turbulent boundary layer and its tendency to separate. In Newtonian coordinates, a wall curvature that is an order of magnitude smaller than a characteristic x dimension in the flow direction produces negligible effects (Ref. 26, pp. 98, 478). But many cases of practical importance fall into the large-curvature class. Also, the influence of Coriolis and centrifugal accelerations in rotating systems, such as centrifugal compressor impellers, are usually very large even if the apparent wall curvature is small.

The case of a curved duct in Newtonian coordinates best illustrates the phenomenon. Particles of relatively low energy near a concave wall cannot find equilibrium within the normal pressure gradient produced by the bulk of the flow; therefore they are accelerated against the direction of the centrifugal pressure gradient toward the center of streamline curvature. The kinetic energy of a particle may be deficient either because of low density or low velocity. Such particles, then, tend to leave the concave wall and enter the free flow, promoting mixing, transition, and the generation of turbulence. The boundary layer on a concave wall is unstable, therefore, to disturbances in the direction normal to the wall.

High-kinetic-energy particles have reversed tendencies on a concave wall. On a convex wall the entire situation is exactly reversed. The mechanism is identical with that of classical secondary flow, although in that case the fluid moves in continuous sheets, while in the present case the concept of bundles of fluid or eddies cast away from, or toward, the wall is most appropriate.

The influence of curvature (and wall rotation, which energizes near particles by drag) is clearly brought out in Fig. 11.10. The flow passed through an annular passage with inner wall rotating. The transition Reynolds number was lowered by the secondary effects from 2000 (common to ordinary pipe flow) to about 750. As another example, Kreith[43] found large differences in heat transfer on concave and convex walls, pointing out thereby the large effects introduced by induced boundary-layer mixing. Briggs[74] measured an increase in pipe-transition Reynolds number from 2000 to 15,000 upon rotating the pipe wall.

In rotating or accelerating systems of reference, the acceleration, Coriolis acceleration, and curvature of the surface, all must be considered.

Little investigation or analysis has been made of these important effects. The work of Yeh,[44] studying analytically and experimentally the turbulent structure of a boundary layer on the outer wall of a duct-convecting swirling flow, is the best available.

While induced mixing in the boundary layer might be considered to be detrimental, in fact, the evidence indicates that this influence promotes healthier boundary layers by providing an increased capability of the free flow to energize tired fluid near the

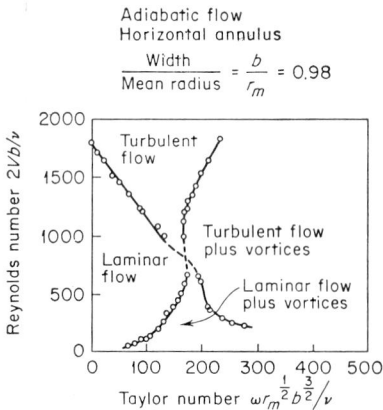

Adiabatic flow
Horizontal annulus

$$\frac{\text{Width}}{\text{Mean radius}} = \frac{b}{r_m} = 0.98$$

FIG. 11.10. Flow regimes of a narrow annular passage with inner wall rotating. Axial Reynolds number ($2Vb/\nu$; V = mean flow velocity, b = annulus width, ν = kinematic viscosity) plotted vs. Taylor number ($\omega r_m^{1/2} b^{3/2}/\nu$; ω = rotational speed, r_m = mean annulus radius). (*Ref.* 42.)

wall. It has been observed many times that turbulent boundary layers on concave stationary surfaces are far less prone to separation than those on convex surfaces even under the same pressure distribution. This explains the designer's usual lack of concern about conditions on the concave side of such devices as turbine buckets. That all the predictions, or feelings, about separation must be highly modified when large forces exist normal to the surface has been emphatically forced upon the writer by measurements of boundary-layer behavior in centrifugal impellers. Here the induced mixing effects are so strong that the boundary layers appear to bear no relationship in structure or behavior to familiar situations. Quantitative prediction of the influence of induced mixing on separation is impossible today.

Summary: Turbulent-boundary-layer Separation Prediction. In summary, it is fair to state that turbulent-boundary-layer predictions of engineering accuracy can be made today for two-dimensional flows. However, the reader is cautioned, again, that few real flows are two-dimensional. Even in well-controlled flow, such as Clauser's,[45] it is very difficult to prevent small three-dimensional effects from entering near separation, which effects can greatly alter the location of separation. Thus, while the two-dimensional theory is essential to understanding boundary-layer behavior and certainly must precede three-dimensional analysis, such flow unfortunately is a utopia rarely seen by the fluid-machine designer.

Correlation Methods. For the most important flow devices, such as aircraft wings, axial turbomachine blading, and diffusers, an approach to separation prediction has been sought with success through the use of rudimentary boundary-layer relationships coupled with systematic experimental variation of parameters.

Perhaps the best example is the NACA diffusion factor and its descendants for axial-compressor blades. Lieblein[46] has presented extensive evidence for the NACA 6500 series of blading. As is shown in Fig. 11.11, separation can be predicted well for operating conditions when the ratio of maximum suction-surface velocity to trailing-edge velocity exceeds about 2.0. The discussers of Ref. 46 indicate that Lieblein's velocity ratio also applies well to other blade shapes. The parameter of Ackeret gives similar

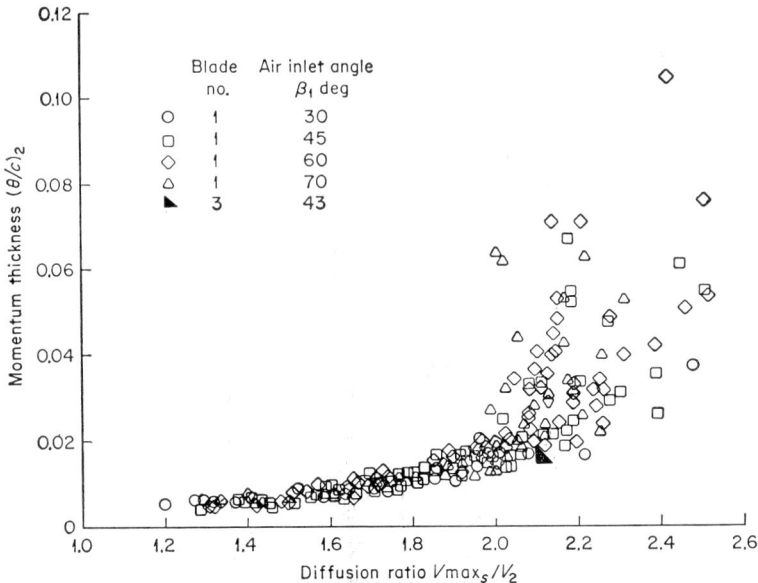

Fig. 11.11. Axial-compressor blade cascade wake-momentum thickness vs. diffusion ratio on suction surface ($V_{max\ s}$ = maximum velocity on suction surface, V_2 = cascade discharge velocity) for angles of attack greater than minimum loss. (*Ref.* 46.)

results; it simply states that the pressure rise from the minimum pressure point on the suction surface to the trailing edge must not exceed 0.7 to 0.8 of the dynamic pressure at the minimum pressure point in order to avoid separation. The success of this simple rule is demonstrated in Ref. 23. Lieblein's critical velocity ratio of 2.0 corresponds to an Ackert parameter of 0.75 for incompressible flow.

The work of Kline et al.[47] on straight-walled diffusers is another good example in point. An excellent correlation for the onset of stalling has been developed as shown in Fig. 11.14.

The reader must be cautioned that while the correlation approach can be successful, it is often very complex if many variables are involved, and the results usually apply only to the device for which they were developed. Thus this technique is of practical significance only for flow geometries that are in extensive use.

Other Techniques. The most common technique of separation prediction and control is model testing coupled with development by empirical cut and try. All good axial-compressor design today is based on extensive empirical data describing cascade behavior. Almost all the flow components of aircraft, wind tunnels, and ducting systems have been developed by this method. This approach often is necessary for engineering results, but is certainly not conducive to optimum design. An excellent example demonstrating the gains that can be achieved today, even with uncertain theories, is given by Kraft.[48] By use of potential-flow analysis, steam-turbine-blade profiles were designed that delayed transition on the blade surface and minimized diffusion; the one point gained in the efficiency of large turbines is a very significant improvement.

Another technique used by the author, but not seen elsewhere, might be called the "method of transference." The central idea is that two boundary layers should behave the same, no matter what the actual geometry of the flow device, if they start from the same initial conditions and traverse the same pressure distribution. Ignoring wall curvature, stability, and secondary effects, which sometimes may be dangerous, one is then able to take the pressure distribution from, for example, an unstalled two-dimensional diffuser and design another flow device, such as a vaned diffusing elbow, with some assurance of unseparated flow. The pressure distribution from the parent flow is specified along a wall of convenient shape, and then, by streamline-curvature methods, the other passage wall is defined. In light of the discussion above of induced mixing effects on separation, the pressure distribution on the convex wall is controlled, since it is most prone to separation, and that on the concave wall follows. If rudimentary limits, such as Ackeret's, are applied to the concave wall, trouble there probably can be avoided. While the technique has many dubious features, it has been generally successful in the writer's experience.[75] It does greatly extend the usefulness of particular experimental results, such as those of Kline et al.,[47] which results are scarce and expensive to develop.

Three-dimensional Separation. LAMINAR. A great deal of work has been done by many workers, particularly Mager,[49] Loos,[50] and Senoo,[51] on the laminar three-dimensional layer, culminating in the work of Hansen.[52] Some of these methods are approximate; some such as Hansen's are exact for similarity flows. Most of them will predict the point where limiting streamlines from two regions meet at a singular or ordinary point and separate from the wall. All, however, are boundary-layer theories and are not applicable to the flow in corners of passages, around struts piercing the boundary layer, for shear regions thick relative to the dimensions of passages, etc. In general, the three-dimensional laminar boundary layer can be analyzed approximately if sufficient effort is expended.

Regions of thick shear flow, which usually are three-dimensional, cannot be treated by boundary-layer theory. Little has been done in this area of importance to the designer. The work of Oman[53] is a good example of the situation.

TURBULENT. Separation of a turbulent three-dimensional boundary layer, the ubiquitous boundary layer of fluid machines, cannot be analyzed today except in very rare cases. However, some empirical progress has been made, particularly by Taylor[1] and Johnston,[6] who have discovered a triangular polar plot of the boundary-layer velocity components in the plane of the wall, u against v, which seems to apply to the small amount of available experimental data. However, this work is still far from a boundary-layer theory; much farther still from prediction of separation.

Johnston[6] has been able to extend the two-dimensional turbulent-boundary-layer analysis of Rotta[54] to the special three-dimensional case of a plane of symmetry in an otherwise skewed boundary layer. In other words, he was able to predict the location of a singular point on a line otherwise composed of ordinary points. His analysis adds the effects of boundary-layer divergence or convergence about the plane of symmetry.

Unfortunately, today the only rule for separation of the three-dimensional turbulent boundary layer and for thick turbulent shear flows is "suck it and see." This situation is onerous because of the commonness of such flows in practical machines and because, as mentioned in the introduction, three-dimensional effects on separation appeared to be of great importance in understanding flow behavior and in controlling separation.

11.6. Behavior of Separated Flows

In analysis of separated flows, the region up to the point of separation is usually treated first. Provided that an accurate modeling of the actual pressure distribution is available, the methods of Art. 11.5 may be applied as discussed. In certain cases, the analysis even allows the pressure distribution to be unsteady. Such treatment will work well up to the vicinity of separation. If the separated region does not thicken the boundary layer to the point where the pressure gradient normal to the wall becomes significant, then the prediction of the separation point is possible.

Again it is emphasized that the pressure distribution of a *separated* flow is usually grossly different from that of an *unseparated* flow about the same body. This fact requires empirical data for the separated flow in order that the effect of separation on the potential velocity distribution may be computed.

The second part of the problem is computation of conditions downstream of the separation point. Here, all boundary-layer assumptions break down because the shear region becomes thick, streamline curvature is often significant, and the pattern is often unsteady, with not even wall-proximity effects to restrict the kinematics.

A separated flow is usually divided into two regions: (1) flow between the separation limiting-streamline skeleton and the wall (i.e., the stalled, stagnant, or backflow region), and (2) shear flow, containing the former boundary-layer vorticity, between the free stream and the limiting-streamline skeleton. The common boundary of these regions is a zone of uncertain and unsteady shape and character.

The problem of the separated flow may be broken down further into several parts:

1. Prediction of the influence of the separated region on the free flow
2. Prediction of the forces and mass transfer between the fluid inside the separation bubble and that outside for purposes of stability analysis
3. Prediction of losses induced by the separation bubble

The first phase of the three has received the greatest attention because of its importance to the boundary layer upstream from separation, as mentioned already, and because it is the easiest phase to attack. The other two have received almost no attention; it cannot be said with any certainty, for example, what order of magnitude of drag force a separated region exerts on the free flow. These are two areas of great significance to the understanding of flow stability and losses. Until they are resolved, one must rely upon empirical data to reveal the stable flow pattern. This very difficulty has prevented analysis of the important and ubiquitous eddy-shedding problem. In the present situation, only phase 1 can be treated here.

The central idea of existing analyses is to assume constant pressure within the separation bubble on the presumption that fluid velocities therein are negligible. This assumption is borne out well by experimental observation in steady, separated flow. No similar theory exists for unsteady separation.

The constant-pressure assumption coupled with incompressibility and disregard for mass and momentum transfer between the free flow and separation bubble leads to the *free-streamline* method of Helmholtz-Kirchhoff. Considerable analysis has been made of separated and cavitated flows by this method. An excellent summary of both the theoretical and experimental work by Cornell[77] is available. Cornell includes discussion of losses, drag, and compressibility effects. It should be pointed out that these losses

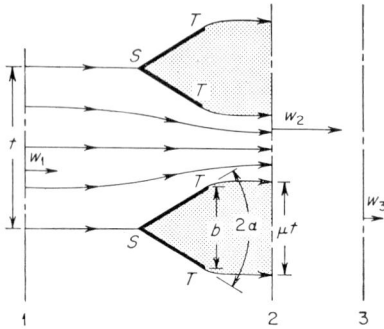

Fig. 11.12. Analytical model of steady separation of a V-gutter cascade. (*Ref. 77.*)

are due to the assumed downstream mixing of the bubble and free flow to uniform conditions and ignore the additional distributive mixing that occurs in actuality.

The Helmholtz-Kirchhoff method works best for bodies with salient edges, such as the normal disc, V-gutter cascade, and for airfoil separation from the leading edge at high angles of attack, where the separation point is known. Treatment of more streamline bodies, such as the cylinder or ellipsoid, runs into the difficulties of separation-point location mentioned in Art. 11.5. The cylinder at Reynolds numbers where a Kármán vortex sheet is shed is a very poor case, since the flow is so grossly unsteady that the free-streamline model is useless. In cases that are quasi-steady, *where the separation point is known experimentally*, the free-streamline methods can give good predictions of pressure distributions even on slender bodies.

Most of these solutions are for separation or cavitation bubbles that extend to infinity (i.e., their interiors are at the downstream static pressure). When the bubbles are finite and closed, experimental data are necessary to specify the flow model; Riabouchinsky,[78] Gilbarg and Rock,[79] and Roshko[80] treat such cases.

In order to illustrate this technique, Fig. 11.12 shows the flow model for a V-gutter cascade (flameholder). The real flow is conformally transformed into a hodograph plane in which the free streamlines (constant velocity) are semicircles. The simpler hodograph-plane flow is built up, to satisfy boundary conditions, from sources, sinks, vortices, etc., with images as required. Once completed, it is transformed back to the real plane to yield the streamline pattern and velocity distribution.

A comparison[77] of theoretical results and data is given in Figs. 11.13*a*, *b*, and *c*. Figure 11.13*a* shows that the flow geometry is well predicted; the losses—all due to downstream mixing—are also well predicted in Fig. 11.13*c*, as would be expected from the success of Fig. 11.13*a*. However, the drag prediction degenerates at low blockage, b/t, in Fig. 11.13*b*.

The latter result illustrates a general conclusion about the free-streamline theory.

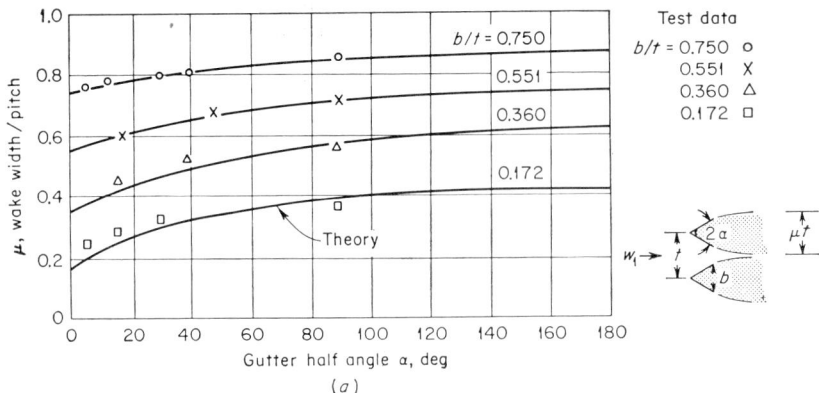

Fig. 11.13*a*. Theoretical prediction of wake width behind a V-gutter cascade and comparison with experimental data. (*Ref. 77.*)

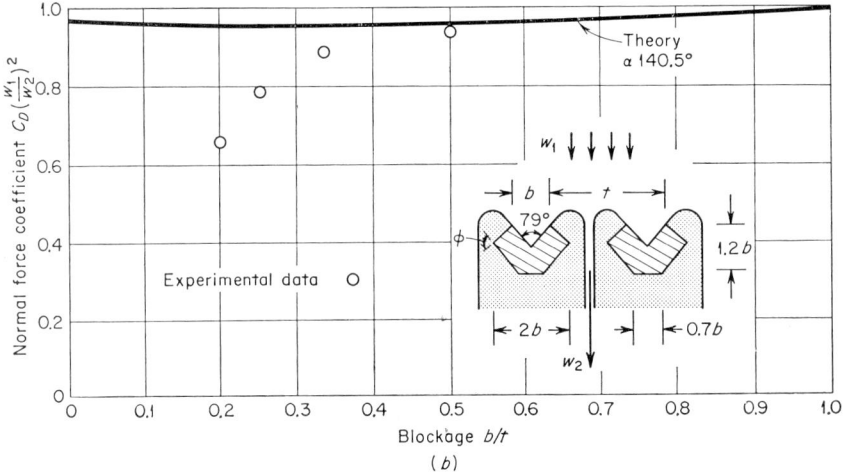

F<small>IG</small>. 11.13b. Theoretical prediction of drag force on an inverted V-gutter cascade and comparison with experimental data. (*Ref. 77.*)

The assumption of zero velocity in the separated region is most valid when small high-velocity jets pierce into a large downstream stagnant region, as is the case for the high-blockage V-gutter cascade. As the blockage and the ratio of jet to upstream velocity become less, conditions in the separated region become more significant and the theory's predictions become less accurate. The penultimate is the single disc in an infinite flow; the blockage is zero, the velocity ratio 1, and the drag prediction very bad.

No comparable free-streamline methods exist for compressible flow, but use can be made of approximate corrections to incompressible solutions or of reasonable flow-geometry assumptions in simple cases. Cornell[81] has studied compressible flow through sharp-edged screens by such techniques.

In summary of the theoretical methods for separated flow, it is fair to say that in certain cases of high blockage, high-flow velocity over the separated regions, incompressible flow, and separation from a salient edge can be treated for flow geometry, drag, and losses with good accuracy by free-streamline methods. For all other cases, there is no theory and experiment is the only resort.

11.7. Influence of Separation on the Performance of Fluid-handling Devices

Upon design of a fluid machine, one usually desires to do one or both of two things: (1) convey a fluid from one point to another with minimum losses or (2) increase or decrease the fluid enthalpy at as high

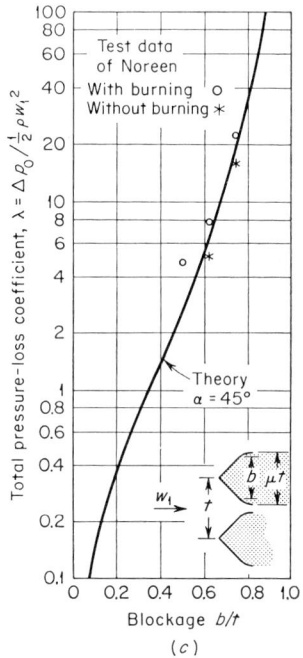

F<small>IG</small>. 11.13c. Theoretical prediction of losses generated by a V-gutter cascade and comparison with experimental data. (*Ref. 77.*)

$a\,a$ Line of appreciable-stall

$b\,b$ Transition between transitory and two-dimensional

$c\,c$ Transition from two-dimensional to jet flow

$d\,d$ Transition from jet flow to two-dimensional

$--$ Low turbulence   —— High turbulence

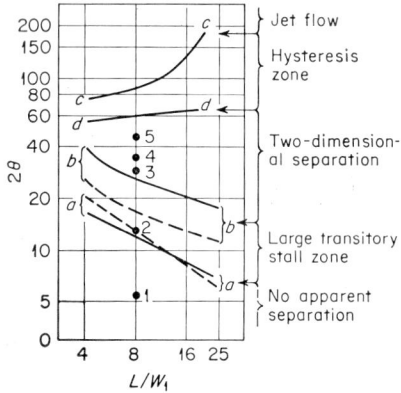

Note: Numbered points correspond to numbers on fig 11.15

FIG. 11.14. Flow regimes of two-dimensional diffusers as functions of divergence angle (2θ) and length over inlet width ratio (L/W_1). (*Ref.* 90.)

$$W_1 = 3.00''\quad L/W_1 \approx 8.0$$
$$R_{W_1} \approx 2.4 \times 10^5$$

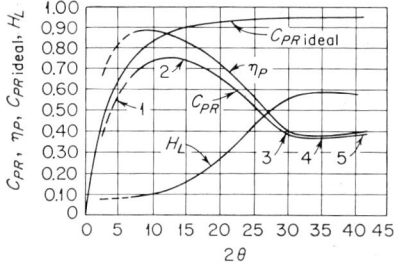

Note: Numbered points correspond to numbers on fig 11.14

FIG. 11.15. Typical two-dimensional diffuser performance (actual static pressure recovery C_{PR}, pressure recovery effectiveness $\eta = C_{PR}/C_{PR\ IDEAL}$, ideal static pressure recovery for one-dimensional flow $C_{PR\ IDEAL}$, and total pressure loss over inlet dynamic pressure H_L) plotted against divergence angle 2θ. (*Ref.* 47.)

an efficiency as possible. In order to achieve these ends, separation must be avoided.

For conveying, separation means losses and the wrong state conditions at points in the circuit where the error may mismatch associated components.

A common element in conveying systems is the diffuser. For optimum performance (minimum size or minimum losses) diffusers must be designed close to separation. Figures 11.14 and 11.15 from Kline, Abbott, and Fox[47] illustrate diffuser characteristics related to separation. Beyond the separation line aa in Fig. 11.14, point 2 in Figs. 11.14 and 11.15, not only does pressure recovery degenerate and loss soar but the flow becomes grossly unsteady. The stream in the diffuser lashes from one divergent wall to the other, producing large pressure pulsations and noise. Such disturbances may lead to mechanical failure or make the discharged flow unsuitable for use in a wind tunnel, for example.

The influence of separation on erosion and corrosion often becomes important. In separated regions, concentrated corrosive agents can accumulate; near separation points erosion is often observed. This erosion is believed to be originated by the trailing vortices associated with separation, bringing particles close to and impinging them upon the wall. Figure 11.6 shows damage ahead of a pump impeller blade; it is directly related to the separation and vortex structure produced ahead of a strut piercing a boundary layer (cf. Figs. 11.6 and 11.3).

In power-producing or power-absorbing machines, such as turbines, pumps, and compressors, separation limits performance. Not only do losses often increase drastically upon separation, but also the flow deviates from the blades, thereby reducing strongly the work extraction or input. Consideration of velocity triangles at exit from a centrifugal impeller in Figs. 11.16a and b demonstrates this effect. Although losses usually rise quite suddenly on separation, again it is found in many cases that optimum performance occurs just before or within a small distance of separation. Figure 11.17 illustrates this effect.

The onset of separation in compressors is responsible for the steep drop in output at flows slightly below the best efficiency point. Since this calamity sets the range of the machine, separation is a fundamental

concern to the designer. In addition, unsteadiness associated with separation
drives a machine with an inherently unstable performance curve into the drastic
phenomenon called surge. The transitory
separation called *rotating stall* also can
trigger surge and often breaks the blading
of a machine. Acceptability of a jet engine
is frequently determined, not at its design
point, but under partially stalled conditions, when it is attempting to accelerate
from rest.

Since separation can cause so much
difficulty (then called stall) and since
optimum machine performance is often
on the verge of or just beyond separation,
it is of fundamental importance in fluid
mechanics.

11.8. Control of Separation

Often the most desirable control of separation is avoidance by careful profile
design or development. However, this is
not always possible; under severe space
limitations, brute-force boundary-layer
control is often justified. The reduction

(a)

(b)

FIG. 11.16. Comparison of discharge-velocity
triangles for an unseparated and a separated
centrifugal impeller (*Ingersoll-Rand Company.*)

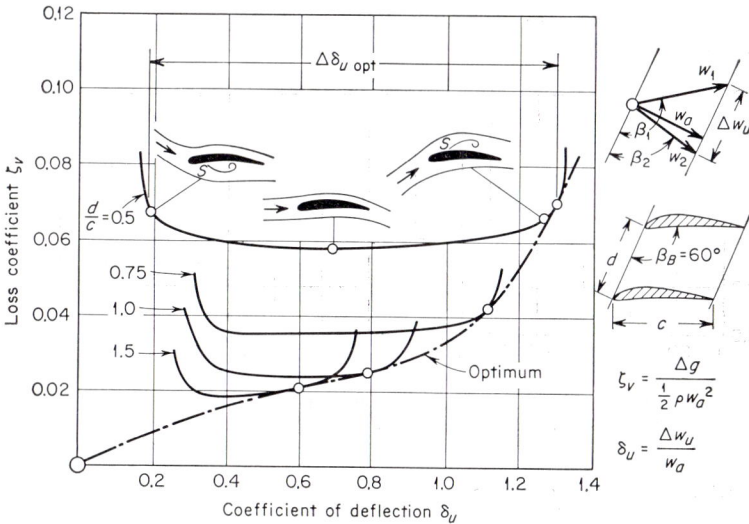

in apparatus size is often large, while the additional power required for control is not
severe in many cases. First, however, consider boundary-layer control by control of
the pressure distribution.

The most elementary law in the design of surfaces on which separation may occur is

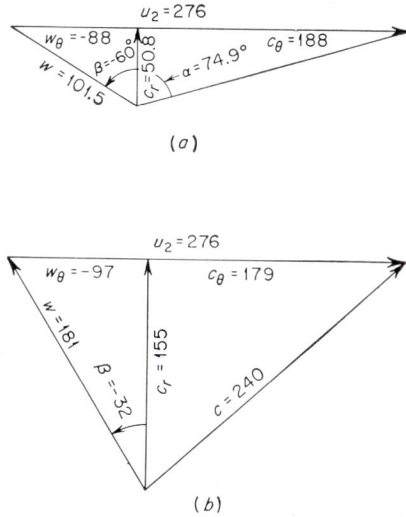

FIG. 11.17. Optimum loss coefficients of a two-dimensional cascade of axial compressor blades.
(*Ref.* 23.)

to mold the shape so that a minimum of diffusion is required. In other words, the surface should be loaded as uniformly as possible in order to avoid any undue acceleration that must later be diffused away. Even without a boundary-layer theory or separation criterion, one is often able to eliminate separation or improve range of operation before separation by applying this simple rule. Shown in Fig. 11.18 are three pressure distributions which illustrate the value of uniform loading. The profiles of Figs. 11.18a and c have equal diffusion parameters (Ackeret's), but the former carries over twice the load of the latter. In order to carry the same load (i.e., same lift coefficient), the Ackeret parameter must be raised to the verge of separation (0.75) in Fig. 11.18b in contrast to 0.60 in Fig. 11.18a. The triangular pressure distribution of Fig. 11.18b is much closer to stalling than the trapezoidal distribution of Fig. 11.18a. In addition, the smoothly loaded blade (Fig. 11.18a) for the same lift coefficient has a considerably higher critical Mach number (upstream Mach number at which the speed of sound is reached locally on the blade surface) because of the considerably lower maximum velocity on the suction surface.

The steam-turbine laminar-blade development reported by Kraft[48] is another good example of gains made by smoothing the loading without use of any boundary-layer theory or separation criteria. In the author's experience, many fluid devices can be improved by this simple approach. But some flow devices are so restricted in geometry that even the smoothest loading will not eliminate separation. In such cases, there is nothing to do but use brute-force boundary-layer control or change the over-all design restrictions.

Going one more step in sophistication, if the boundary layer could be maintained in a state of imminent separation everywhere, the highest pressure gradients could be tolerated along the surface and maximum performance or minimum size achieved. In the laminar analysis of Pohlhausen (Art. 11.5), λ would be maintained at 12. Since $[\delta^2/(\rho U^2/g_0)](dp/dx)$ is approximately equal to λ, the shortest diffusion length would result for a given change in pressure. The maintenance of the boundary layer on the verge of separation or with a range-tolerance relationship to the separation profile greatly enhances analysis, as pointed out in Art. 11.5, since the velocity profiles are similar everywhere. Clauser[45] has found experimentally pressure distributions that maintain similar turbulent profiles and has proposed design under this condition. In two-dimensional cases, this approach certainly appears to be valid and produces maximum performance; whether it can also produce satisfactory range of operation remains to be seen.

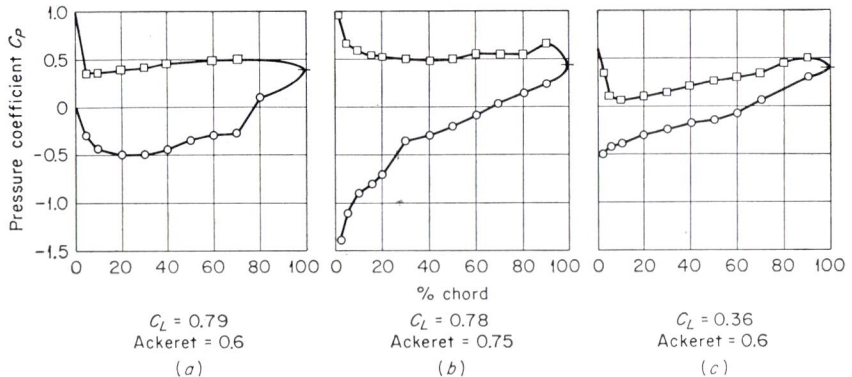

$C_L = 0.79$
Ackeret = 0.6
(a)

$C_L = 0.78$
Ackeret = 0.75
(b)

$C_L = 0.36$
Ackeret = 0.6
(c)

FIG. 11.18. Axial-compressor-blade pressure distributions of varying shape and effect on load-carrying ability and separation. (a) A trapezoidal pressure distribution produces a lift coefficient of 0.79 for an Ackeret number below separation of 0.6. (b) Triangular pressure distribution produces the same lift as (a) but with a much higher Ackeret number of 0.75 close to separation. (c) Triangular pressure distribution has the same Ackeret number as (a) but produces only 0.36 lift coefficient. (Ref. 22.)

Active-control Agents. Size and weight limitations often force configurations of flow-bounding walls that do not admit unseparated flow under any conditions. Resort may be had to active boundary-layer control devices which, in extreme form, should make the flow follow any contour. However, the expense of power increases as the flow situation becomes more extreme.

Seven agents are known for active control:
1. Boundary-layer energizing
2. Boundary-layer removal
3. Free-flow stabilization
4. Alteration of surface-pressure distribution by auxiliary bodies
5. Promotion of early transition (laminar layers only)
6. Moving walls
7. Creation of secondary flows (three-dimensional-boundary-layer effects)

BOUNDARY-LAYER ENERGIZING. These techniques are in extensive use; two classes are recognizable. The first might be called self-energizing catalyzed by some agent. The best agents discovered to date are small surface-mounted airfoils at an angle of attack and small ramplike devices. The objective of both agents is to generate trailing vortices in the boundary layer. Consequently, the airfoils or ramps terminate within the boundary layer and are called *vortex generators*. The trailing vortices are supposed to mix the boundary layer downstream, promoting momentum exchange between the free flow and the wall layers. In addition, secondary flow about the vortex generators serves to remove tired fluid from the wall and inject it into the outer parts of the boundary layer.

The best work on airfoil vortex generators is presented by Taylor[83] with the results of several applications. Such devices are under wide usage; however, their successful application is still quite an art. The ramp-type generators developed by the NACA are reported by Bursall.[84] On large flow devices, such as aircraft, vortex generators are useful and allow a considerable increase in performance. In most turbomachines, the generators become too small for practical use.

The destabilization of the boundary layer, causing induced mixing, by wall curvature, fluid swirl, or centrifugal and Coriolis forces, promotes momentum addition to the near-wall layer. This technique is rarely utilized purposefully, but can be powerful. An example is shown in Fig. 11.19 for a poppet valve. By utilizing a very slight swirl at inlet, the separating boundary layer, on the convex wall, was destabilized. The improvement in flow coefficient resulting indicates that the separation point moved downstream or was eliminated. Slight swirl in conical diffusers can improve performance, but in an angular diffuser the resulting suppression of mixing on the inner wall usually makes the situation worse. Rotation of the inner wall at speeds above local fluid swirl would allow destabilization of both walls. The author knows of few cases where this technique has been adopted purposely.

The second class of energizing control involves outside assistance to increase the boundary layer's momentum near the wall. The only successful scheme to date is blowing parallel to the wall just ahead of the separation point. If this action is done with care, significant improvements in wing performance have been achieved, as shown in Fig. 9.25. For turbomachines, Sheets[85] reports excellent results from the use of slotted blades. Nevertheless, the effect is small unless very high jet velocities are used, so this technique only works in cases of mild separation. Incidentally, jets blown

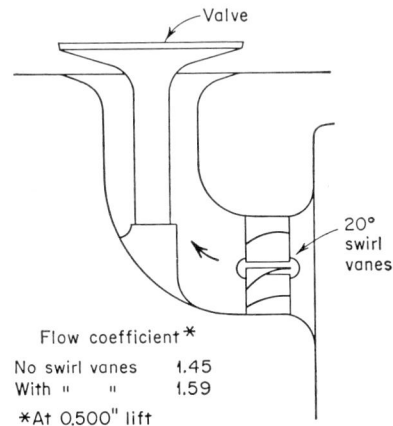

Flow coefficient *	
No swirl vanes	1.45
With " "	1.59

*At 0.500" lift

FIG. 11.19. Diffusing engine poppet valve illustrating effect of slight swirl on separation through an increase in flow coefficient. (*Ingersoll-Rand Company*.)

into laminar layers normal to the wall can induce transition and are used for such. Also such normal jets can cause early separation; this trouble is often experienced with shrouded turbomachine blade rows or impellers where leakage reenters normal to the main flow and causes separation. The addition of a downstream-projecting lip devised to reinject the leakage fluid parallel to the wall can make significant differences in performance.

It may be possible to utilize electromagnetic forces in conducting fluids to energize the boundary layers; however, it is too early to ascertain success.

BOUNDARY-LAYER REMOVAL. Suction removal of the boundary layer is an old idea and is a powerful control agent. The existing theory and some results are presented in Ref. 26, page 226. While the theory is not discussed here, it is clear that continuous removal of the tired fluid at the wall can prevent separation, for it is this low-momentum fluid that first flows backward. Figures 11.20a and b show results from using suction in a diffuser[86] and on airfoils.[87] There is an extensive literature of boundary-layer suction on wings. Suction on any other flow device has not received enough attention to produce a systematic literature, although papers on numerous particular cases may be found. Suction is also useful in delaying transition (Ref. 26, chap. 13) and has been employed to produce low-drag laminar-flow wings.

The action of a vapor condensing upon a cool surface should produce effects similar to suction, evaporation from the surface giving the reverse effect. This action may produce a large reduction in the drag of condenser tubes by moving their separation point rearward.

FREE-FLOW STABILIZATION. The unsteadiness often associated with separation is self-excited. An excellent example is the periodic eddy shedding leading to the Kármán vortex street behind a circular cylinder. Frequently, a very significant alteration in behavior of a separated region, if not elimination thereof, can be achieved by stabilization of the free flow with devices that tend to prevent alteration and unsteadiness of the flow geometry. Figure 11.21 demonstrates the influence of a downstream splitter

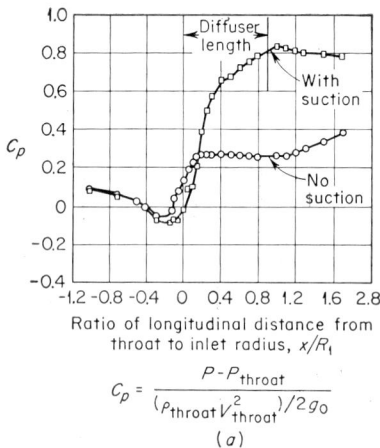

$$C_Q = \frac{Q}{VS}$$

S_f = flap deflection with respect to wing chord line, deg:

Q = suction volume flow

V = wing velocity

S = wing plane form area

$C_Q = 0.0015$ (at $\delta_f = 55°$)

$$C_p = \frac{P - P_{throat}}{(\rho_{throat} V_{throat}^2)/2 g_0}$$

(a)

(b)

FIG. 11.20a. Increase in pressure recovery of a 50° divergence angle conical diffuser by use of suction. Suction 6 per cent of through flow, inlet Mach number 0.2, diffuser area ratio = 2.0. (*Ref.* 86.)

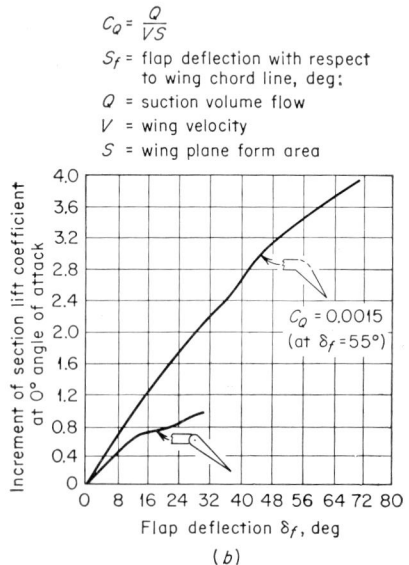

FIG. 11.20b. Increase in wing-lift coefficient produced by flap deflection with and without suction. (*Q*, suction-volume flow; *V*, wing velocity; *S*, plane-form area with wing). (*Ref.* 87.)

upon the drag of bluff bodies.[89] The flow here becomes steady with eddy shedding stopped. Figure 11.22 shows the significant effects discovered by Cochran and Kline[90] from placing simple flat vanes in a two-dimensional diffuser. Note that with both a tail splitter behind the cylinder and the single flat vane of the diffuser, only very minor alterations in the steady pressure distribution would occur since the vanes lie on a streamline of symmetry in the stationary flow. Thus the devices do not produce their effects in the same manner as those to be discussed later. They do *alter the pressure distribution of the unsteady flow*; if the flow geometry attempts to alter, these devices develop lift in such a direction as to return the streamline pattern to the steady form.

Screens and other downstream-flow restrictions can have significant stabilizing effects.[91] The action results from the fact that uniform flow produces a minimum pressure drop through the restriction. Any distortions increase the local pressure drop approximately proportional to the local mass flow squared. As a result, crosswise pressure gradients develop which tend to smooth the pattern.

While downstream resistance has strong influence, the losses through an adequate resistance are most often far too large. One interesting case in which this is not true is the interconnector between a steam turbine and condenser. The distributed sink effect of a condenser can

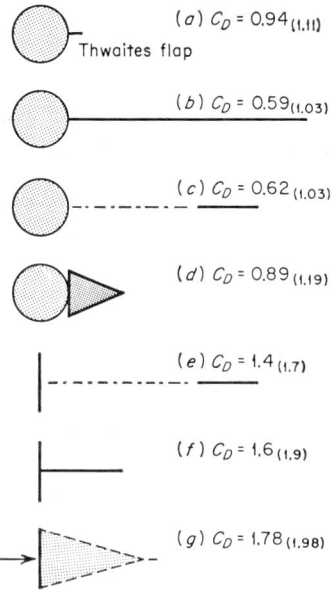

Fig. 11.21. Influence of a downstream splitter on the drag of various bluff vortex-strut-producing bodies. Numbers in parentheses indicate drag coefficient C_D without splitter. (*Ref.* 89.)

be utilized, by proper aerodynamic design, to stabilize a diffusing interconnector. Very significant increases have been achieved[92] with the diffuser-pressure-recovery

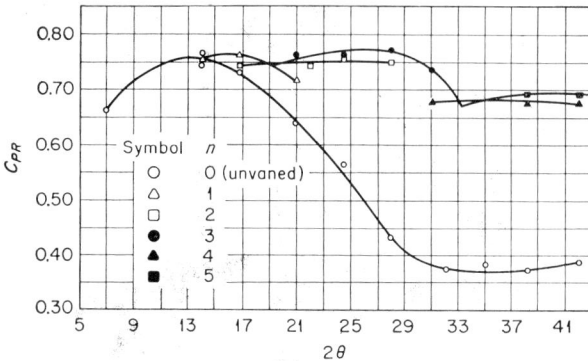

Fig. 11.22. Influence of equally spaced flat vanes in two-dimensional diffusers. Static-pressure-recovery coefficient $(\Delta P/q_1)$ vs. diffuser included angle 2θ. Length over inlet width ratio $L/W_1 = 8.0$. Reynolds number based on throat width $= 2.4 \times 10^5$.

effectiveness raised in one actual but extreme case, from close to zero to about 75 per cent.   Other investigators also have reported designs utilizing downstream resistance where losses did not overwhelm gains.[93]

Since an alteration of the free-flow geometry occurs for any unsteady separation, the proper use of stabilizers should produce significant effects.   Visualization studies prove to be the best means for development of optimum stabilizer geometry.   This is an area

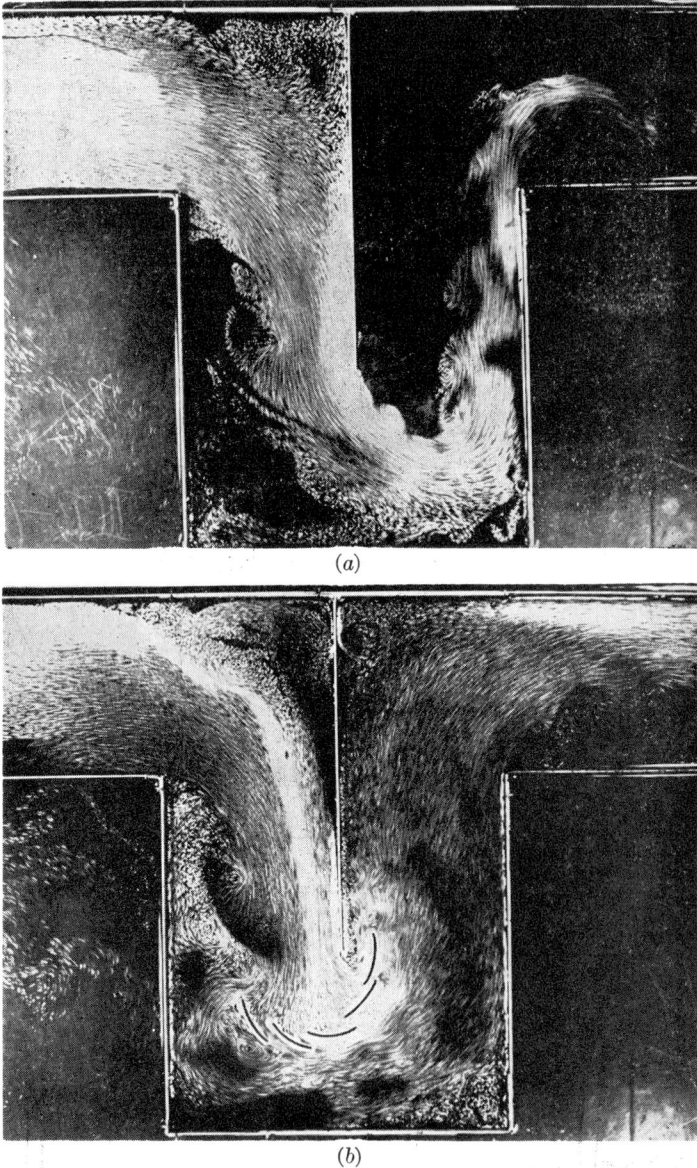

(a)

(b)

FIG. 11.23. Flow in a 180° bend (a) without and (b) with deflection vanes, illustrating the elimination of separation.   Aluminum powder on a free-water surface is used for visualization. (*Courtesy Dr. Kurt Frey.*[96])

of fluid dynamics which has been little investigated but which should yield large
rewards.

ALTERATION OF SURFACE PRESSURE DISTRIBUTION.   Separation occurs because too
much diffusion of the boundary layer is demanded; usually too much diffusion results
from asking the surface to produce an impossible lift or pressure load.   If the load cannot
be spread more evenly in order to reduce local concentrations, then more lifting surface
must be provided.

A common example is the elbow, which usually separates because of intolerable pressure gradients on the convex wall.   By the insertion of turning vanes in an elbow, more
load-bearing surface is provided, thereby reducing the load demanded of the original
walls.   Separation can be eliminated; losses usually drop markedly, although too much
added surface will actually increase losses again by increasing the total skin-friction drag.
A summary of losses, and reduction by vaning, in elbows is presented by Krober.[94] Frey[95]
presents empirical data on the use of vanes in many types of flow situations, including
heat exchanger heads.   Diffusers have been improved by vanes near the inlet corner;
for example, Frey[95] reports the case of a 90° area ratio 3 diffuser whose pressure-recovery
effectiveness was raised from 0.09 to 0.57 by insertion of three simple corner vanes.   A
carefully designed set of vanes in a diffusing elbow of area ratio 4.5 and of extremely
tight turn improved pressure-recovery effectiveness from about 0 to 75 per cent in the
author's experience.[75]

The use of auxiliary bodies to alter surface pressure distribution and prevent separation is largely an art today; however, there appears to be no reason why available analysis
could not be utilized to improve and make more certain the result.   Visualization is
very useful in development, as well shown by Frey[96] in Figs. 11.23a and b.

PROMOTION OF EARLY TRANSITION.   Should separation occur in the laminar section
of the boundary layer and it is not necessary to maintain a laminar layer, separation
may be avoided often by promoting early transition.   Various techniques exist: trip
wires fastened to the surface, pins, wedges, sand, and other types of roughness, normal
fluid jets, local concavity of the wall, free-flow disturbance by forced vibration of bodies
or unsteady flow behind bluff bodies, acoustic pressure waves, and motion of the surface
itself.   A summary is given by Morkovin.[98]

MOVING WALLS.   If the wall of a diffusing area moved with the fluid, there would
be no boundary layer to decelerate and separate.   The mechanical difficulty of this
scheme has prevented widespread application.   In a few axisymmetric cases wall rotation can be utilized to pump the boundary layer by drag forces against a pressure rise;
the external surfaces of shrouded centrifugal impellers are a case in point.   The effect
has been used by Sallou[99] in vaneless diffusers of centrifugal machines by extending the
impeller shrouds, without blades, up into the diffuser.   Beneficial effects on performance
are reported.

One unique and very interesting case is the cusp diffuser,[100] reportedly taken from the
natural phenomena that produce ice cornices.   While the wall itself does not move, an
eddy is trapped on the wall, as shown in Fig. 11.24, to produce, in effect, a moving wall.
Efficient diffusion in very short distances can be achieved; however, as might be im-
agined, the trapped eddies exhibit tendencies to escape.   This mischievousness and starting difficulties have made the device impractical, so far, for commercial use.

SECONDARY FLOW.   There is no doubt that three-dimensional effects in the boundary layer have a large influence on separation behavior.   However, since separation of a
three-dimensional boundary layer is not under-
stood, in general, it is difficult to utilize purposefully this influence.   Nevertheless, the designer and the developer of flow devices should
be aware of secondary flow as a potential control agent.   Discovery of means for analyzing
and controlling the three-dimensional turbulent
boundary layer is one of the great frontiers of
fluid mechanics.

Summary.   In summary of this discussion
of boundary-layer control, it may be stated

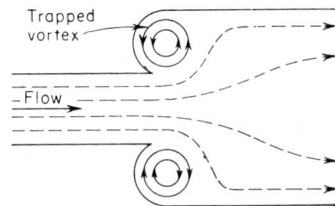

FIG. 11.24. Cusp diffuser.

that, while powerful direct-action techniques are known, they all require a considerable increase in complexity and their application is an art requiring at least some cut-and-try development. However, sophisticated use of boundary-layer control often is the only possible means of achieving high performance in tightly restricted configurations.

11.9. Experimental and Detection Techniques

The first special problem of experimentation with separation is detection of the onset. The second is the revelation of the geometry of separated regions.

Most detection schemes rely upon directional reversal of the low-velocity fluid in a separation bubble. Such methods work well for two-dimensional separation, but may be useless in three-dimensional cases. Detection in the latter case must be accomplished by revelation of the limiting-streamline pattern. As pointed out in Art. 11.3, the ubiquitous ordinary separation can occur only at a cusp; therefore, ipso facto, cusps in a limiting-streamline pattern are separation points.

The low velocity in separated bubbles implies that no pressure gradients of any magnitude can exist therein. Therefore development of a constant-pressure region on a surface where pressure gradients normally would be expected means that the flow has separated (or cavitated). Figure 11.25 shows the pressure distribution on a compressor blade at increasing angle of attack; the development of the separation bubble on the suction side near the trailing edge is clear.

So called "stall-warning" devices indicate either the drop in velocity or reversed flow associated with separated bubbles. These devices are hardly experimental instruments.

The application of tufts to the surface or the injection of smoke or particles from the surface can provide indication of a separation bubble and give an idea of its shape.

A reduction in heat and mass transfer from the surface accompanies separation. Few successful heat-transfer devices are known, but the new hot-film devices appear promising.[97] The china-clay technique,[101] depending upon the evaporation of a volatile oil from a surface coated with china clay (which becomes opaque when dry), the use of wet

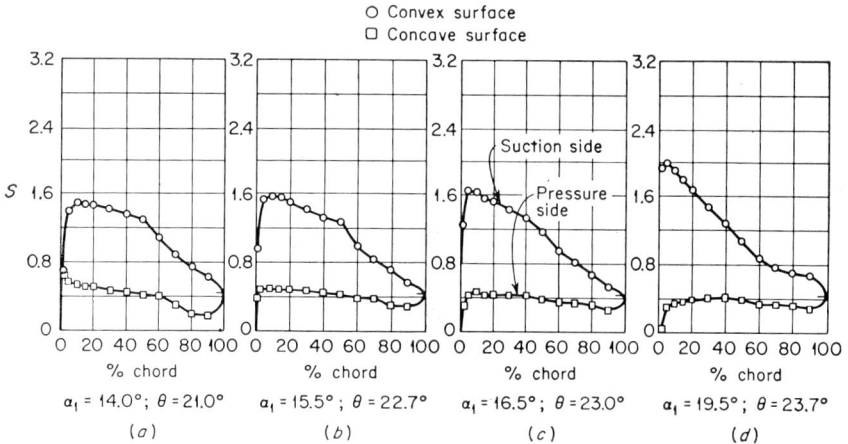

FIG. 11.25. Variation in pressure distribution about an NACA 65-(15)10 axial compressor blade at increasing angle of attack. In Fig. (d) the constant pressure region on the convex (suction) surface between per cent chord positions 70 and 90 indicates a separated region which undoubtedly extends to the trailing edge. $S = (P_{01} - P)/q_1$, P_{01} = upstream stagnation pressure, P = local surface static pressure, q_1 = upstream dynamic pressure, θ = measured air-turning angle. Air-inlet angle = 60°, solidity = 1.0. (*Ref.* 22.)

cobalt chloride–impregnated paper on the surface (producing a color change on dry-ing),[102] the use of thin naphthalene or other volatile solid coatings, all can reveal separa-tion bubbles. A word of caution is in order; these mass-transfer methods also indicate transition and are used for such. Therefore, if transition and separation occur on the same surface, great care must be exercised in interpretation.

The geometry of separation can be measured by probing with common instruments such as impact and static tubes, direction probes, hot wires, and so forth. These meth-ods are tedious and hardly successful in any but steady flow. Under proper conditions of a very steady free flow, smoke (or dye in water) can be injected into the free flow to reveal separation bubbles.[104] With considerable care to obtain a low-turbulence stream, successful smoke visualization has been achieved at 200 fps. Recently Goddard, McLaughlin, and Brown[103] reported smoke visualization of supersonic flow at 1325 fps. Unfortunately, the flow in most internal systems is too disturbed to admit the use of smoke, except in the separation bubbles themselves. An excellent example of this latter technique is presented by Sovran,[105] who revealed rotating stall cells in an axial com-pressor by smoke injection. Up to that time no other technique had revealed the geometry of the separation cell.

In disturbed flows, smoke or dust can be utilized to reveal separation if a large quantity of the tracing material can be injected suddenly. In this manner the entire through flow is clouded; since circulation from the through flow into the separation bubbles is rela-tively slow, they remain clear for a short time. Of course, high-speed recording tech-niques are essential; usually moving pictures are employed. Dust in a gas or ink in water can be suddenly injected by bursting a container in the upstream flow.[106]

Wall-shear-stress measurements could detect separation points in two-dimensional flow. However, such measurements are very difficult and uncertain, which situation, coupled with the rarity in practice of truly two-dimensional flows, makes this a minor technique.

The common three-dimensional separation without associated bubbles can be revealed today by only one technique, that is, to obtain a replica of the limiting-streamline pat-tern. The pattern can be developed on stationary surfaces by use of surface-trace techniques. Carbon black or china clay in oil is the agent for gas flows; this "gunk" is the experimental aerodynamicist's dirtiest, but also simplest and most useful, tool. In liquid flows, oil-based paint has been used; other immiscible agents should work also. On accelerating surfaces, such as rotating blading, the liquid surface-trace agents are usually so heavy that centrifugal forces cause markings not associated with the gas flow. In that event, gases have been used, for example, hydrogen sulfide on lead oxide, or ammonia on ozalid paper,[107] or leak-detection paint.[109] The gas is usually bled from the surface, but could also be injected at the inlet in certain cases.

In the past, there has been some doubt over the meaning of carbon-black surface traces. However, most experimental aerodynamicists seem to believe that, when prop-erly applied, the traces indicate the limiting-streamline pattern. Finally Stalker[5] stud-ied this problem with care and substantiated the belief. Figure 11.26 presents a selection of carbon-black data demonstrating its capabilities.

Lastly, in high-speed flows, optical techniques (the interferometer, schlieren, and shadowgraph) can reveal separation. The shadowgraph is a very simple instrument which normally shows separation bubbles best by means of its sensitivity to the asso-ciated turbulent wakes. The schlieren is next in sensitivity and is used extensively for boundary-layer–shock-interaction studies. The interferometer is not so useful because of the constancy in the separation bubble of the density to which it responds.

Other visualization techniques may be useful such as birefringent fluids that show shear distribution. This technique produces results that are often hard to interpret since separation is revealed only by the turbulent shear generated over the envelope of a bubble.

Conclusion. While the literature of separation is vast, the treatment of many aspects, unfortunately the most important aspects, is still largely an art. This adver-sity is due largely to the absence of analytical methods for the three-dimensional turbu-lent boundary layer, which lack rests on our failure to understand quantitatively the phenomena of turbulence.

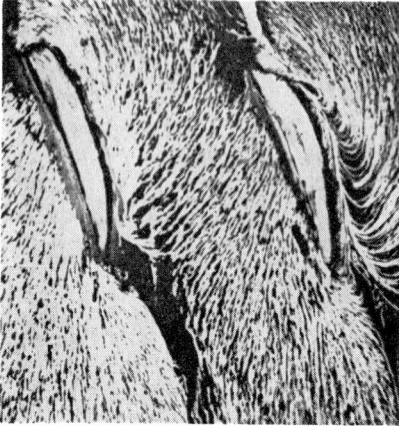

Fig. 11.26a.   Carbon-black and oil pattern showing limiting streamlines on the end wall of an axial compressor cascade.   Secondary flow overturning to the suction surface is clearly visible, as well as backflow into a separated region in the wall-suction-surface corner.   (*MIT Gas Turbine Laboratory.*)

Fig. 11.26b.   Carbon-black and oil traces of limiting streamlines on the radial-plane walls of a vaned centrifugal compressor diffuser. Swirling inlet flow was produced by the nozzles shown.   Secondary flow toward the convex side of the diffuser vanes is clearly shown, as well as backflow in the wall boundary layers ahead of the diffuser vanes.   (*MIT Gas Turbine Laboratory.*)

It is the intention of this section not only to reveal the quantitative methods available, but to give the reader a feeling for the full character of separation and for the rough engineering methods which must be used today.   The fact should be clear that much work still remains before this phenomenon, which controls all fluid-handling devices, is understood sufficiently well.

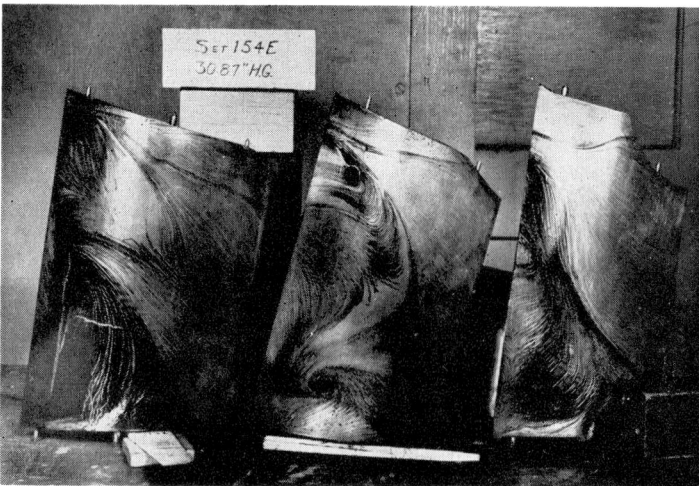

Fig. 11.26c.   Carbon-black and oil traces of limiting streamlines on a set of elbow turning vanes.   Many ordinary separation lines are clearly shown.   (*Ingersoll-Rand Company.*)

REFERENCES

1. Taylor, E. S.: The Skewed Boundary Layer, *ASME Paper* 58-A-113, December, 1958 (to be published in *Trans. ASME*).
2. Eichelbrenner, E. A., and A. Oudart: Observations sur un critère de decollement laminaire dans la couchelimite tridimensionelle, *Recherche aeronaut.* 40, 1954.
3. Eichelbrenner, E. A., and A. Oudart: Le Decollement laminaire en trois dimensions, *Recherche aeronaut.* 47, 1955.
4. Maskell, E. C.: Flow Separation in Three Dimensions, *Roy. Aircraft Establishment, Farnborough, Rept.* Aero 2565, November, 1955.
5. Stalker, R. J.: A Study of the China-film Technique for Flow Indication, *Aeronaut. Research Labs.*, Victoria, Australia, October, 1955.
6. Johnston, J. P.: The Three-dimensional Turbulent Boundary Layer, *MIT Gas Turbine Lab. Rept.* 39, May, 1957; also *ASME Paper* 59-HYD-6, *J. Basic Eng.*, September, 1960.
7. Hawthorne, W. R.: Secondary Circulation in Fluid Flow, *Proc. Roy. Soc. (London)*, **A206**:374–387 (1951).
8. Hawthorne, W. R.: The Secondary Flow about Struts and Airfoils, *J. Aeronaut. Sci.*, **21**:588 (1954).
9. Hansen, A. G., H. Z. Herzig, and G. R. Costello: A Visualization Study of Secondary Flows in Cascades, *NACA Tech. Note* 2947, May, 1953.
10. Senoo, Y.: The Boundary Layer on the End Wall of a Turbine Nozzle Cascade, *MIT Gas Turbine Lab. Rept.* 35 and *Trans. ASME*, **80**:1711 (November, 1958).
11. Holl, J. W.: The Inception of Cavitation on Isolated Surface Irregularities, *ASME Paper* 59-HYD-12, 1959.
12. Ackeret, J., F. Feldmann, and N. Rott: Untersuchungen an Verdichtungsstössen und Grenzschichten in schnell bewegten Gasen, *ETH Inst. Aerodynamics Repts.*, Zürich, no. 10, 1946; also *NACA Tech. Mem.* 1113, 1947.
13. Liepmann, H. W.: The Interaction between Boundary Layer and Shock Waves in Transonic Flow, *J. Aeronaut. Sci.*, **13**:623 (1946).
14. Chapman, D. R., D. M. Kuehn, and H. K. Larson: Investigation of Separated Flows in Supersonic and Subsonic Streams with Emphasis on the Effect of Transition, *NACA Tech. Note* 3869, 1957.
15. Bogdonoff, S. M.: Some Experimental Studies of the Separation of Supersonic Turbulent Boundary Layers, *Proc. Heat Transfer and Fluid Mech. Inst.*, sec. 5, pp. 1–23, 1955.
16. Gadd, G. S., D. W. Holder, and J. D. Regan: An Experimental Investigation of the Interaction between Shock Waves and Boundary Layers, *Proc. Roy. Soc. (London)*, **A226**:227–253 (1954).
17. Kuehn, D. M.: Experimental Investigation of the Pressure Rise Required for the Incipient Separation of Turbulent Boundary Layers in Two-dimensional Supersonic Flow, to be published by NASA.
18. Fage, A., and R. Sargent: Shock Wave and Boundary Layer Phenomena near a Flat Plate Surface, *Proc. Roy. Soc. (London)*, **A190**:1–20 (1947).
19. Donaldson, C. duP., and R. H. Lange: Study of the Pressure Rise across Shock Waves Required to Separate Laminar and Turbulent Boundary Layers, *NACA Tech. Note* 2770, September, 1952.
20. Kuehn, D. M.: Boundary Layer Separation in Supersonic Flow, *ASME Stall Symp.*, December, 1958.
21. Kline, S. J.: On the Nature of Stall, *Trans. ASME, J. Basic Eng.*, September, 1959.
22. Herrig, L. J., J. C. Emery, and J. R. Erwin: Systematic Two-dimensional Cascade Tests of NACA 65-series Compressor Blades at Low Speeds, *NACA Tech. Note* 3916, February, 1957.
23. Schlichting, H.: Application of Boundary Layer Theory in Turbomachinery, *Trans. ASME, J. Basic Eng.*, ser. D, vol. 81, no. 4, December, 1959.
24. Johnston, J. P.: The Turbulent Boundary Layer at a Plane of Symmetry in a Three-dimensional Flow, *ASME Paper* 59-A-72, 1959.
25. Schlichting, H.: "Boundary Layer Theory," McGraw-Hill, New York, 1960.
26. Schlichting, H.: "Boundary Layer Theory," McGraw-Hill, New York, 1955.
27. Blasius, H.: Grenzschichten in Flüssigkeiten mit kleiner Reibung, *Z. Math. u Phys.*, **56**:1 (1908); also *NACA Tech. Mem.* 1256.
28. Falkner, V. M., and W. Skan: Some Approximate Solutions of the Boundary Layer Equations, *Phil. Mag.*, **12**:865 (1931); also *ARC Rept. and Mem.* 1314, 1930.
29. Hiemenz, K.: Die Grenzschicht an einem in den gleichförmigen Flüssigkeitstrom

eingetauchten geraden Kreiszylinder, thesis, Göttingen (1911); *Dinglers Polytech. J.*, **32**:326 (1911).

30. Howarth, L.: On the Calculation of Steady Flow in the Boundary Layer near the Surface of a Cylinder in a Stream, *ARC Rept. and Memo.* 1632, 1935.
31. Howarth, L.: On the Solution of the Laminar Boundary Layer Equations, *Proc. Roy. Soc. (London)*, **A919**:164, 547 (1938).
32. Pohlhausen, K.: Zur näherungsweisen Integration der Differentialgleichung der laminaren Reibungschicht, *ZAMM*, **1**:252 (1921).
33. Schubauer, G. B.: Airflow in a Separating Laminar Boundary Layer, *NACA Rept.* 527, 1935.
34. Scholkemeyer, F. W.: Die laminare Reibungsschicht rotationsymmetrischen Körpen, thesis, Braunschweig, 1943.
35. Pretsch, J.: Die laminar Reibungsschicht an elliptischen Zylindern und Rotationsellipsoiden bei symmetrischer Anströmung, *Luftfahrt-Forsch.*, **18**:397 (1941).
36. Tomotika, S.: Laminar Boundary Layer on the Surface of a Sphere in a Uniform Stream, *ARC Rept. and Memo.* 1678, 1935.
37. Rott, N., and L. F. Crabtree: Simplified Laminar Boundary Layer Calculations for Bodies of Revolution and Yawed Wings, *J. Aeronaut. Sci.*, **19**:553 (1952).
38. Sutton, W. G. L.: An Approximate Solution of the Boundary Layer Equation for a Flat Plate, *Phil. Mag.*, **23**:1146 (1935).
39. Wieghardt, K.: Uber einen Energiesatz zur Berechnung laminarer Grenzschichten, *Ingr.-Arch.*, **16**:231 (1948).
40. Wieghardt, K.: On a Simple Method for Calculating Laminar Boundary Layers, *Aeronaut. Quart.*, **5**:25 (1954).
41. Walz, A.: Anwendung des Energiesatzes von Wieghardt auf einparametrige Geschwindigkeitsprofile in laminaren Grenzschichten, *Ingr.-Arch.*, **16**:243 (1948).
42. Kaye, J., and E. C. Elgar: Modes of Adiabatic and Diabatic Fluid Flow in an Annulus with an Inner Rotating Cylinder, *Trans. ASME*, April, 1958.
43. Kreith, F.: The Influence of Curvature on Heat Transfers to Incompressible Fluids, *Trans. ASME*, **77**:1247–1257 (1955).
44. Yeh, H.: Boundary Layer along Annular Walls in a Swirling Flow, *Trans. ASME*, **80**:767 (May, 1958).
45. Clauser, F. H.: Turbulent Boundary Layers in Adverse Pressure Gradients, *J. Aeronaut. Sci.*, vol. 21, no. 2, February, 1954.
46. Lieblein, S.: Loss and Stall Analysis of Compressor Cascades, *Trans. ASME, J. Basic Eng.*, ser. D, vol. 81, no. 3, September, 1959.
47. Kline, S. J., D. E. Abbott, and F. W. Fox: Optimum Design of Straight-walled Diffusers, *Trans. ASME, J. Basic Eng.*, **D81**(3):321 (September, 1959).
48. Kraft, H.: The Development of a Laminar Wing Type of Turbine Bucket, *ZAMP*, **IXB**, 1958; also *ASME Stall Symp. Notes*, 1958.
49. Mager, A.: Three-dimensional Boundary Layer with Small Cross Flow, *J. Aeronaut. Sci.*, **21**:835 (1954).
50. Loos, H. J.: A Simple Laminar Boundary Layer with Secondary Flow, *J. Aeronaut. Sci.*, vol. 22, 1955.
51. Senoo, Y.: Three-dimensional Laminar Boundary Layer in Curved Channel with Acceleration, *Trans. ASME*, **80**:1721 (November, 1958).
52. Hansen, A.: On Possible Similarity Solutions for Three-dimensional Incompressible Laminar Boundary-layer Flow over Developable Surfaces and with Proportional Main Stream Velocity Components, *NACA Tech. Mem.* 1437, September, 1958.
53. Oman, R.: Three-dimensional Laminar Boundary Layer along a Corner, Sc.D. thesis, submitted MIT, February, 1959.
54. Rotta, J.: Näherungsverfahren zur Berechnung turbulenter Benutzung des Energiesatzes, *Mitt. Max Planck Inst. Strömungs-Forsch.* no. 8, Göttingen, 1953.
55. Coles, D.: The Law of the Wake in the Turbulent Boundary Layer, *J. Fluid Mech.*, **1**:191–226 (1956).
56. Korst, H. H., Page, and Childs: Two-dimensional Jet Mixing, *Univ. Illinois Expt. Sta. Mech. Eng. Tech. Note*, 1951.
57. Thwaites, B.: Approximate Calculation of the Laminar Boundary Layer, *Aeronaut. Quart.*, **1**:245 (November, 1944).
58. Stratford, B. S.: Flow in the Laminar Boundary Layer near Separation, *ARC, R&M* 3002 (British), 1957.
59. Curle, N., and S. W. Skan: Approximate Methods for Predicting Separation Properties of Laminar Poundary Layers, *Aeronaut. Quart.*, **9**:257 (August, 1957).
60. Görtler, H.: A New Series for the Calculation of Steady Laminar Boundary Layer Flows, *Freiburg Univ. Math. Inst. Rept.*, September, 1955.

61. Tani, I.: On the Solution of the Laminar Boundary Layer Equations, *J. Phys. Soc. Japan*, vol. 4, no. 149, 1949.
62. Hartree, D. R.: A Solution of the Laminar Boundary Layer Equations, *Proc. Roy. Soc. (London)*, **A264**:542 (1938).
63. Gruschwitz, E.: Die turbulente Reibungschicht in ebener Strömung bei Druckabfall und Druckansteig, *Ingr.-Arch.*, vol. 2, no. 321, 1931.
64. von Doenhoff, A. E., and N. Tetervin: Determination of Several Relations for the Behavior of Turbulent Boundary Layers, *NACA Rept.* 772, 1943.
65. Truckenbrodt, E.: Ein Quadraturverfahren zur Berechnung der laminaren und turbulenten Reibungschicht bei ebener und rotationssymmetrischer Strömung, *Ingr.-Arch.*, **20**:211 (1952).
66. Wieghardt, K., and W. Tillman: Zur turbulenten Reibungsschicht bei Druckansteig, *UM* 6617, 1944.
67. Ludwieg, H., and W. Tillman: Untersuchungen über die Wandschubspannung in Turbulenten Reibungsschichten, *Ingr.-Arch.*, **17**:288 (1949).
68. Rotta, J.: Beitrag zur Berechnung der turbulenten Grenzschichten, *Ingr.-Arch.*, **19**:31 (1931).
69. Rotta, J.: Schubspannungsverdichung und Energiedissipation bei turbulenten Grenzschichten, *Ingr.-Arch.*, **20**:195 (1952).
70. Rotta, J.: Näherungsverfahren zur Berechnung turbulenter Benutzung des Energiesatzes, *Mitt. Max Planck Inst. Strömungs-Forsch.*, vol. 8, 1953.
71. Ringleb, F. O.: Two-dimensional Flow with Standing Vortices in Ducts and Diffusers, *ASME* 60-HYD-15, 1960.
72. Ross, D.: A New Approach to Turbulent Boundary Layer Problems, *ASCE Proc.*, vol. 81, Separate no. 604, p. 24 (1955).
73. Bidwell, J. M.: Application of the von Kármán Momentum Theorem to Turbulent Boundary Layers, *NACA Tech. Note* 2571, 1951.
74. Briggs, D. C.: Heat Transfer in Rotating Turbulent Pipe Flow, *ONR Tech. Rept.* 45, Stanford University, Sept. 30, 1959.
75. Dean, R. C., Jr.: Discussion of Optimum Design of Straight-walled Diffusers, S. J. Kline, D. E. Abbott, R. W. Fox, *Trans. ASME, J. Basic Eng.*, **D81**:329 (September, 1959).
76. Faulders, C. R.: An Aerodynamic Investigation of Vaned Diffusers for Centrifugal Compressors, *MIT Gas Turbine Lab. Rept.*, January, 1954.
77. Cornell, W. G.: Some Aerodynamic Cavity Flows in Flight Propulsion Systems, *Proc. Second Naval Hydrodynamics Symp.*, *ONR*, August, 1958.
78. Riabouchinsky, D.: On Steady Fluid Motions with Free Surfaces, *Proc. London Math. Soc.*, **19**:206–215 (1921).
79. Gilbarg, D., and D. H. Rock: *Naval Ordnance Lab. Mem.* 8718, 1945.
80. Roshko, A.: A New Hodograph for Free-streamline Theory, *NACA Tech. Note* 3168, July, 1954.
81. Cornell, W. G.: Losses in Flow Normal to Plane Screens, *Trans. ASME*, **80**(4):791–799 (1958).
82. Dean, R. C., Jr.: The Influence of Tip Clearance on Boundary Layer Flow in Rectilinear Cascades, *MIT Gas Turbine Lab. Rept.* 27-3, December, 1954.
83. Taylor, H. D.: Summary Report on Vortex Generations, *United Aircraft Research Dept. Rept.* R-05280-9, March, 1950.
84. Bursall, W. J.: Experimental Investigation of the Effects of Vortex Generators on the Maximum Lift of Symmetrical Circular-arc Airfoil Section, *NACA RML* 52G24, October, 1952.
85. Sheets, H. E.: The Slotted Blade Axial Flow Blower, *Trans. ASME*, **78**:November, 1956.
86. Holzhauser, C. A., and L. P. Hall: Exploratory Investigation of the Use of Area Suction to Eliminate Air Flow Separation in Diffusers Having Large Expansion Angles, *NACA Tech. Note* 3793, October, 1956.
87. Riebe, J. M.: A Correlation of Two-dimensional Data on Lift Coefficients Available with Blowing-, Suction-, Slotted-, and Plain-flap High-lift Devices, *NACA RML* 55D29a, October, 1955.
88. Lippisch, A. M.: Flow Visualization, *Aeronaut. Eng. Rev.*, **17**:2, 24–32, 36 (February, 1958).
89. Hoerner, S. F.: "Fluid-dynamic Drag," published by the author, 1958 (available only from author, 148 Busteed Dr., Midland Park, N. J.).
90. Cochran, D. L., and S. J. Kline: The Use of Short Flat Vanes for Producing Efficient Wide-angle Two-dimensional Subsonic Diffusers, *NACA Tech. Note* 4309, September, 1958.
91. Schubauer, G. B., and W. G. Spangenberg: Effect of Screens in Wide Angle Diffusers, *NACA Tech. Note* 1610, July, 1948.

92. Dean, R. C., Jr.: Influence of Swirl and Downstream Resistance on the Behavior of Diffusing Elements, Contribution to *ASME Stall Symp.*, 1958.
93. Hage, S. D., W. B. Anderson, V. W. Van Oruum, R. Johnson, and R. W. Flickinger: Compressor Development for Small Gas Turbines, *ASME Paper* 57-A-258, December, 1957.
94. Krober, G.: Guide Vanes for Deflecting Fluid Currents with Small Loss of Energy, *NACA Tech. Mem.* 722, September, 1933.
95. Frey, K.: Verminderung des Strömungsverlustes in Kanalen durch Leitflachen [Reduction of the Flow Loss in Channels by Means of Guiding Surfaces (Vanes)], *Forsch. Gebiete Ingenieurw.*, vol. 5, 1934.
96. Frey, K.: "Use of Flow Visualization Simplified the Solution of Many Design and Research Problems," Armour Research Foundation of Illinois Institute of Technology, 1956.
97. Ling, S. C.: Heat Transfer Characteristics of a Hot-film Sensing Element Used in Flow Measurement, *ASME J. Basic Eng.*, September, 1960.
98. Morkovin, M.: Transition from Laminar to Turbulent Shear Flow: A Review of Some Recent Advances in Its Understanding, *Trans. ASME*, 1121, July, 1958.
99. Sallou, Jean: Centrifugal Apparatus for Circulation of Fluids, Patent No. 2,845,216, July 29, 1958.
100. Hazen, D. C., R. F. Lehnert, T. F. Sweeney, and F. O. Ringleb: Preliminary Report on Circulation Control by Means of Trailing Edge Suction and the Cusp Effect, *Aeronaut. Eng. Rept.* 234, 1953.
101. Stuart, J. T., W. S. Walker, and N. Gregory: On the Stability of Three-dimensional Boundary Layers with Application to the Flow Due to a Rotating Disc, *Phil. Trans. Roy. Soc.*, **A142**:621–638 (1933).
102. Senoo, Y.: The Boundary Layer on the End Wall of a Turbine Nozzle Cascade, *MIT Gas Turbine Lab. Rept.* 35, October, 1956.
103. Goddard, V. P., J. A. McLaughlin, and F. N. M. Brown: Visual Supersonic Flow Patterns by Means of Smoke Lines, *J. Aeronaut. Sci.*, **26**(11):761 (November, 1959).
104. Hazen, C.: Some Results of the Princeton University Smoke Flow Visualization Program, *IAS Preprint* 555, June, 1955.
105. Sovran, G.: Measured and Visualized Behavior of Rotating Stall in an Axial Flow Compressor and in a Two-dimensional Cascade, *ASME Paper* 58-SA-20, June, 1958.
106. Fischer, K., and D. Thoma: Investigation of the Flow Conditions in a Centrifugal Pump, *Trans. ASME*, **5**:141 (1932).
107. Weske, J. R.: An Investigation of the Aerodynamic Characteristics of a Rotating Axial Flow Blade Grid, *NACA Tech. Note* 1128, February, 1947.
108. Tyler, R. D., and A. H. Shapiro: Pressure Rise Required for Separation in Interaction between Turbulent Boundary Layer and Shock Wave, *J. Aeronaut. Sci.*, **20**(12):858 (December, 1953).
109. Winter, P., H. R. Bilford, C. E. Jacob, and R. Kemmerer: How to Find Microscopic Leaks in Process Equipment, *Ind. Eng. Chem. Reprint* 50, May, 1958.

Section 12

CAVITATION

By

PHILLIP EISENBERG *and* **MARSHALL P. TULIN,** *Hydronautics, Inc., Rockville, Maryland*

CAVITATION

I. MECHANICS OF CAVITATION†

12I.1. Introduction

Definitions and Scope. In most engineering contexts, *cavitation* is defined as the process of formation of the vapor phase of a liquid when it is subjected to reduced pressures at constant ambient temperature. In general, a liquid is said to *cavitate* when vapor bubbles are observed to form and grow as a consequence of pressure reduction. When the phase transition is a result of pressure change by hydrodynamic means, a two-phase flow composed of a liquid and its vapor is called a *cavitating flow*. While these definitions imply a distinction between phase transitions associated with reduction of pressure, on the one hand, and addition of heat (i.e., *boiling*), on the other, heat-transfer effects may play an important role in many cases of cavitating liquids. Such effects are especially of importance in liquids near their boiling points. From a purely physical-chemical point of view, of course, no distinction need be made between boiling and cavitation, at least in so far as the question of inception is concerned, and many of the basic physical ideas regarding inception, vapor mass transfer, and condensation apply equally.

In a flowing liquid (or for a body moving through a stationary liquid), the parameter which describes the pressure conditions for similarity in the liquid-gas system is called the *cavitation number*, or *cavitation parameter*. It is a special case of the usual pressure coefficient and relates the pressure on the cavitating system (relative to the gas pressure) to the dynamic pressure. The magnitude of the cavitation number is an indication of the degree of cavitation or of the tendency to cavitate. It is defined as

$$\sigma = \frac{P - p_c}{\frac{1}{2}\,\rho U^2}$$

in which P = (absolute) static pressure at point of interest

p_c = gas pressure (vapor pressure in a two-phase, one-component flow or sum of partial pressure of vapor and other gas in a multicomponent system)

ρ = mass density of liquid

U = reference velocity

In Part I of this section, the basic questions concerning the mechanics of cavitation and some of the effects produced by cavitating flows are discussed. Of particular interest are the physical mechanisms in the inception process and the prediction of pressures required for initiation or onset of cavitation. Other essential questions to be discussed are the role of foreign-gas components entrained or dissolved in the liquid; the dynamics of cavitation bubbles during their cycle of growth, possible oscillation, final collapse, and disappearance; the conditions which determine the type of cavitation that occurs; and the transition from transient bubbles into large, quasi-steady cavity, or *supercavitating*, flows. The concurrent effects of cavitation such as noise, vibration, and damage to materials, as well as the question of modeling cavitation phenomena, are also considered. Finally, some of the more important experimental methods now used for the study of cavitation and its effects are described. Emphasis is placed on the essential ideas and data necessary to an understanding of the phenomenon as back-ground for design.

† By Phillip Eisenberg.

Fields of Interest. Cavitation has long been of interest and importance in the fields of shipbuilding and hydraulic machinery (which have been plagued with the unwanted effects—loss of efficiency, damage to materials, noise; and more recently have sought to exploit the promise of high-efficiency supercavitating flows about lifting surfaces) and in the fields of underwater signaling (background noise, acoustic power absorption) and underwater-weapon design (with its problems of drag increase and missile stability and control when cavitating). In recent years, cavitation has become of increasing interest and importance in a number of other applications and technologies. Among the latter are such diverse disciplines as chemical processing (acceleration of reactions, industrial cleaning), medicine (dysbarism and bullet wounds, speculations regarding brain trauma and concussion under blows), nuclear physics (use of bubble chambers for research on high-energy particles), and handling of highly volatile liquid rocket fuels and cryogenic liquids.

12I.2. Inception of Cavitation

The Role of Nuclei. It is now the generally accepted view that the inception of cavitation in "technical" liquids is associated with the growth of nuclei (submicroscopic in size) containing vapor, undissolved gas, or both, which are present either within the liquid or in crevices on suspended particulate matter or on bounding walls. In the case of "pure" liquids, as well as subcooled liquids such as glass, the problem is one of determining fracture strength. Earliest estimates of fracture strength of liquids were based on the hypothesis that the maximum force is that required for simultaneous separation of all atomic bonds cut by a plane surface.[1] Such estimates predict tensile strength for water of the order of thousands of atmospheres—at least an order of magnitude greater than any experimental observations. However, a liquid subject to negative pressure is in a metastable state, and vapor bubbles are observed to grow from extremely small nuclei (of the order of molecular dimensions). Such nuclei are assumed to form statistically as a result of thermal fluctuations in the interior of the liquid, with a certain (small) number reaching a critical radius for growth. When this happens, the supercritical radius continues to grow until the pressure of the system rises to the equilibrium vapor pressure. Application of the methods of nucleation theory to the nucleation of vapor bubbles in stressed liquids leads to estimates of the same order as the maximum values obtained experimentally[2]—of the order of hundreds of atmospheres for the fracture strength of liquids such as water. Various experimenters have reported values ranging from a few atmospheres to estimates as high as 1000 atm for water.[3,4] It is now recognized, however, that such wide discrepancies are associated with the gas and particulate content of the specimens, the interfacial properties of the liquid-container system, the treatment of the liquid before testing, and the experimental methods used. In the case of the liquids encountered in most practical cases (ship propulsion, hydraulic machinery, chemical processing, etc.), inception of cavitation occurs at pressures of the order of vapor pressure—again an order of magnitude less than the latter estimates. Thus cavitation onset in liquids of usual engineering interest is also associated with the growth of nuclei but of a size several orders of magnitude greater than that referred to above. Where nuclei of the order of molecular dimensions are associated with fracture-strength determination, nuclei with diameters ranging from 10^{-5} to 10^{-3} cm are required to account for observed inception in ordinary water substance. Such nuclei must contain vapor, undissolved gas, or both. On the basis of physical arguments, it is unlikely that completely dissolved gas can play a dominant role in inception, although in certain cases such dissolved gas may become important during the inception process.[5] It has been demonstrated, for example, that water, saturated with air, when "denucleated" by prior application of large pressures, exhibits fracture strength of the order of kinetic theoretical predictions.[4] It is just such evidence that substantiates the postulated requirement for large nuclei. The existence of nuclei of the sizes required for inception near vapor pressure has also been demonstrated experimentally by techniques based on the absorption of ultrasound by bubbles in resonance with the applied frequencies.[5]

Persistence and Stabilization of Nuclei. Although the need for nuclei for inception of cavitation at pressures of the order of vapor pressure is well established, there is still some difficulty in accounting for their presence and persistence. The conditions for dynamic stability of nuclei illustrate the origin of this difficulty. For static equilibrium, spherical bubbles obey the equation

$$p_v + p_g - p = 2\frac{\gamma}{r} \tag{12I.1}$$

if p_v = vapor pressure
  p_g = partial pressure of entrained gas
  p = ambient pressure
  γ = surface tension
  r = bubble radius

For constant vapor pressure, bubble growth is isothermal and $p_g = \text{const}/r^3$, so that

$$p - p_v = \frac{\text{const}}{r^3} - 2\frac{\gamma}{r} \tag{12I.2}$$

The minimum value of $p - p_v = p^*$ occurs at a radius $r = r^* = (3 \times \text{const}/2\gamma)^{1/2}$, or

$$r^* = \frac{-4\gamma}{3(p - p_v)} \tag{12I.3}$$

Thus the critical pressure is below vapor pressure, and if p is decreased slightly, the bubble is unstable and grows without bound. At pressures greater than the critical pressure, the bubble is stable and will tend to assume an equilibrium radius determined by Eq. (12I.1). However, stable bubbles will dissolve by diffusion of air out of the bubble.[6] A nucleus containing only vapor phase is in equilibrium when the radius is equal to $2\gamma/(p - p_v)$; such bubbles are, however, dynamically unstable and will either collapse or grow indefinitely if disturbed.

There is evidently little difficulty in accounting for the stabilization of nuclei (in the sense of preventing solution) in supersaturated liquids or in crevices on bounding walls. On the other hand, it has been shown that the rates of gas solution by diffusion are so large that gas bubbles will dissolve very rapidly in undersaturated solutions, and even in systems in equilibrium, in the latter case assisted by surface tension. For example, an air bubble of radius 10^{-3} cm will dissolve in saturated water in about 8 sec, and even faster if the water is undersaturated or the bubble smaller. In saturated solutions, bubbles will grow by diffusion and tend to be quickly lost at a free surface; a bubble 10^{-2} cm in diameter rises at the rate of about 1.5 cm/sec, for example. Thus if nuclei are to persist in water, some mechanism must prevent their solution or disappearance otherwise. An understanding of the mechanism or mechanisms is essential to the problems of scale effects, water-tunnel design, and the rational design of experiments.

A number of suggestions have been made to account for the nuclei in undersaturated liquids and in liquids that have been boiled, pressurized, or otherwise degassed.[7] The most common postulate is the presence of microscopic dust particles on which gas or vapor nuclei are stabilized. It has also been suggested that, in water, surface-active materials and the interaction of hydrogen and hydroxyl ions adsorbed on the surface of nuclei may play a role in certain circumstances. Another hypothesis, due to Fox and Herzfeld,[8] related to the postulate of surface-active materials, is based on the assumption that an organic skin, formed from contaminants in the liquid, surrounds the bubble and essentially acts as a rigid sphere which maintains the pressure in the bubble and prevents diffusion when the internal pressure drops to the saturation value. It is the crumbling of this shell that leads to cavitation onset. Since, according to Strasberg,[9] the growth behavior of nuclei stabilized in crevices and stabilized by organic skins would be functionally the same, it is difficult to differentiate experimentally between these postulates. Consequently, this question is far from solution.

Effect of Dissolved and Entrained Gas Content. Depending upon the magnitude of the pressure reduction and the rate of application, a bubble may grow slowly by diffusion of gas into the nucleus and contain mostly gas component. A nucleus that grows explosively contains mostly vapor phase, the diffusion time being too short for any significant increase in gas volume. The former process is simply a degassing of the liquid but has come to be called "gaseous" cavitation, especially in ultrasonically induced bubble growth.[10] The latter process, which depends upon evaporation of the liquid into the growing bubble, is a true cavitation in the sense defined above. Nevertheless, such cavitation is now sometimes called "vaporous" to distinguish between them. For cavitation to occur explosively, pressures below vapor pressure are required; for growth of nuclei by diffusion the pressures may be less than or greater than the vapor pressure, depending upon nuclei size and degree of saturation. Computations of the critical pressures have been made by Strasberg[5]; his results are shown in Fig. 12I.1. In general, it is observed that pressures less than vapor pressure are required for onset of cavitation in liquids that are saturated or undersaturated. In supersaturated solu-

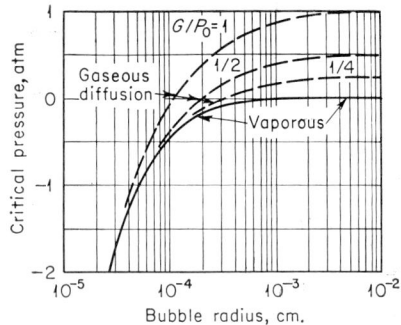

FIG. 12I.1. Critical pressure for gaseous and vaporous cavitation as a function of the radius of air-filled nuclei. The nucleus size is the size at atmospheric ambient pressure. The critical pressure is given relative to the vapor pressure. G/P_0 is the ratio of gas-saturation pressure to ambient pressure. (*After Strasberg.[5]*)

tions, as in the surface of the oceans, cavitation begins at pressures very nearly vapor pressure and degassing at pressures above vapor pressure.

Based on the calculations of Noltingk and Neppiras,[11] it may be concluded that in a true cavitation process, the inception of growth of nuclei depends only little on the duration of the pressure; the maximum size to which such nuclei will grow does, however, depend upon the time of pressure application. The maximum size does not depend to a very great extent on the initial size of the nucleus. Furthermore, explosive growth of nuclei is independent of the dissolved gas content (except in so far as the initial size is determined by the equilibrium conditions between the gas in the nucleus and ambient dissolved gas content and for those cases in which nuclei of subcritical size for onset of true cavitation first grow by diffusion to a size sufficient for cavitation to occur at that pressure).

The effect of total air content is illustrated by the results of Crump[12] obtained in experiments with a venturi nozzle having a diffuser angle of 5°. Figure 12I.2 shows that in the undersaturated liquid it was possible to obtain tensions as the relative air content α/α_s was reduced. Results in a nozzle with an abrupt expansion, however, show opposite trends in the pressures required for inception,[13] although here, too, tensions were obtained. Comparable results for sea water are shown in Fig. 12I.3; in this case, bursts of cavitation were observed at pressures well above vapor pressure. While the trends in these experiments were fairly definitive, the very large scatter of results is indicative of the need for understanding the behavior and distribution of nuclei, i.e., the mechanisms by which nuclei are stabilized and the characterization of nuclei content, e.g., a "spectrum," or description of number and distribution in size.[14] (Attempts to develop methods for such descriptions are discussed later.) It may nevertheless be expected that a relation exists between the dissolved and entrained gas content, at least in an undisturbed liquid. Some evidence for this assumption exists in the measurements of Strasberg[5] on tap water with ultrasonically induced cavitation. Since, according to the analysis of Noltingk and Neppiras,[11] the time duration of the pressure for times of the order of milliseconds has very little influence on the inception pressure, and since this is also the order of the time duration in hydraulic applications, one may compare Strasberg's results as a basis for the effect of air content on cavitation inception. These are shown in Fig. 12I.4. The data follow generally the trend predicted by Strasberg for nuclei stabilized either in crevices or by organic skins. The functional relation is $P_c = a_1 G - a_2 P_m$, if P_c is the critical pressure, G is the equilibrium or saturation pressure of the air dissolved in the water, P_m is the maximum external water pressure to

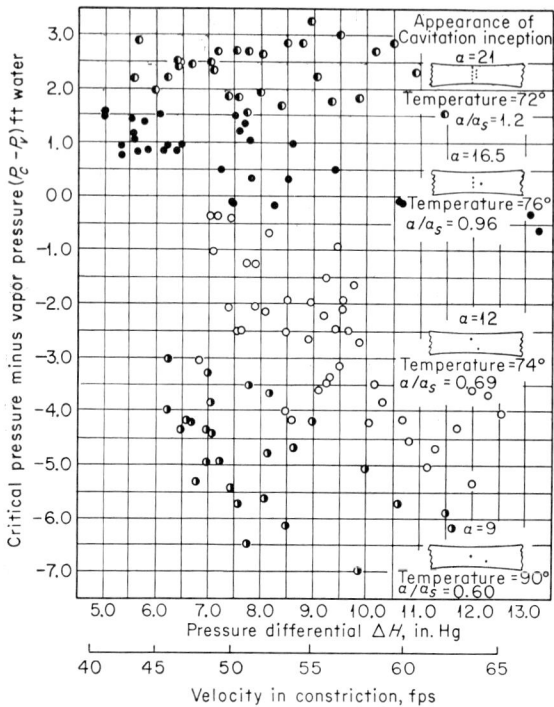

FIG. 12I.2. Critical pressures for inception of cavitation in fresh water of varying air content. (*After Crump.*[12])

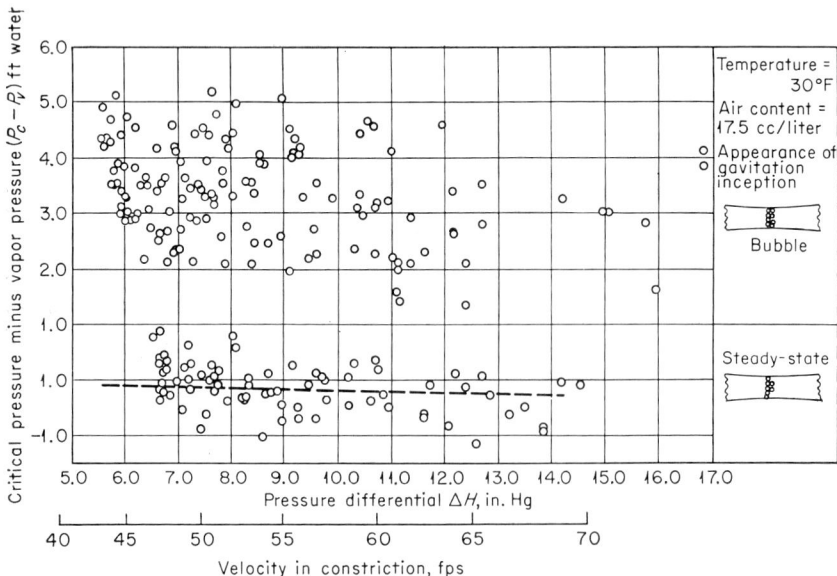

FIG. 12I.3. Critical pressures for inception of cavitation in sea water. (*After Crump.*[12])

which the cavity has been subjected, and a_1 and a_2 are numerical constants, whose values cannot be determined with present knowledge except that $a_2 + 1 > a_1 > 1$. The constant a_1, determined from the slope of the line, is approximately 4. Whether similar results would be obtained in flowing water using such ultrasonic techniques is not known. Other data on the effects of air content will be found in Ref. 15.

Boundary-layer and Turbulence Effects. Environmental factors that must be considered when attempting to predict inception include not only the average pressure conditions, but also the magnitude and duration of pressure fluctuations in turbulent regions and boundary-layer effects, including flow in zones of separation. It has been shown[7,16] that in laminar boundary layers cavitation will occur first at the boundary. In turbulent layers, it would be expected that cavitation might first occur in a region of highest turbulence intensity at a small distance from the boundary, i.e., in the regions of greatest pressure fluctuation.[7,14] In experiments with turbulent

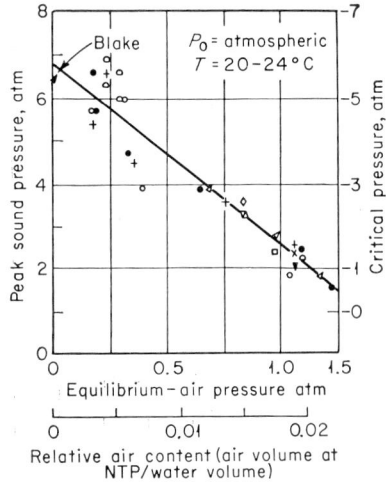

FIG. 121.4. Effect of air content on inception pressure for ultrasonic cavitation. Each plotted point represents an average of 10 to 20 measurements. Each symbol represents a different sample of water. (*After Strasberg.*[5])

boundary layers in a rectangular nozzle, Daily and Johnson[18] found that the observed onset of cavitation corresponded to a pressure drop due to turbulence of the order of 0.40 to 0.57 ft of water, in a region of favorable pressure gradient. They also observed that the maximum number of cavities occurred in the central portion of the boundary layer rather than much closer to the boundary as would have been expected[7] on the basis of experimental observations of velocity-fluctuation intensity.

Onset of cavitation in submerged jets was observed by Rouse[19] to occur at a value of $\sqrt{\overline{p'^2}}/(\frac{1}{2}\rho\overline{u'^2})$ of about 2.15, or approximately twice that corresponding to results of Daily and Johnson; here $\overline{p'^2}$ and $\overline{u'^2}$ are the turbulent-pressure and velocity fluctuations, respectively. So few data are available on either the magnitude of the turbulent-pressure fluctuations or inception in turbulent regions that little more can be said concerning the effects of turbulence on cavitation inception. However, some approximate data useful in design estimates are given here.

Critical Cavitation Numbers for Inception of Cavitation. The *critical cavitation number* σ_i is the value of σ at which cavitation inception occurs in a flowing system. When $\sigma_i > \sigma$, cavitation will not occur; thus σ_i is characteristic of the flow geometry, while σ is characteristic of the liquid-gas system. Although it has been the practice in most engineering applications to assume that cavitation will occur when the pressure drops to vapor pressure, it is clear from the foregoing discussion that this is a greatly oversimplified view. Two aspects must be kept in mind: (1) the corrections to the local pressure due to such indeterminate factors as turbulent-pressure fluctuations, and (2) the selection of the inception pressure as modified by such factors as air content. In the first case, it is usually necessary to determine the critical cavitation number on the basis of experiments or to make corrections to the critical cavitation number itself. In the second case, it is sometimes possible to select a value for inception pressure other than vapor pressure in determining the critical cavitation number; for example, on the basis of the results in Fig. 121.3, a conservative value of p_c equal to about 5 ft of sea water might be used in predicting cavitation onset in the oceans. Nevertheless, for most engineering estimates, it will be sufficient for preliminary design to assume

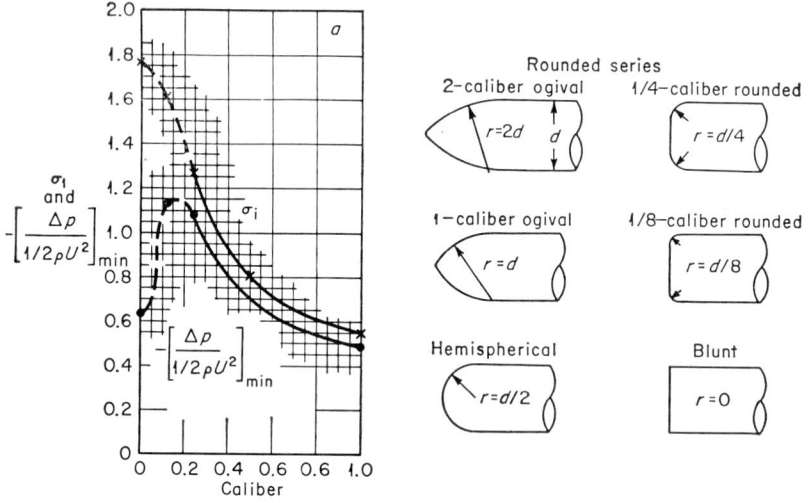

Fig. 12I.5. Critical cavitation number for a series of bodies of revolution. (*After Rouse and McNown.*[23])

vapor pressure.   Data for liquids other than water will be found in Refs. 20 to 22.

For most cases of steady, unseparated flow, the critical cavitation number may be taken as equal in magnitude to the minimum pressure coefficient; i.e.,

$$\sigma_i = -\frac{p_{min} - P}{\frac{1}{2}\rho U^2} = -C_{p_{min}}$$

if p_{min} is the minimum local pressure in fully wetted flow.   In such cases, the minimum pressure coefficient is often conveniently determined from computation of the potential

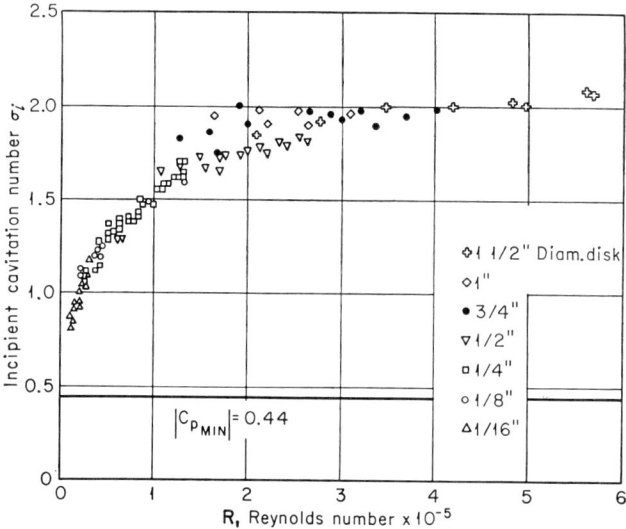

Fig. 12I.6. Critical cavitation number for a series of discs. (*After Kermeen, McGraw, and Parkin.*[16])

flow. In separated flows, cavitation will first occur not on the boundary, but in the low-pressure region developed by the vortical flow within the separation zone. Examples of the effects of local separation on the inception cavitation number are shown in Fig. 12I.5 from the experiments of Rouse and McNown.[23] In this figure are compared the minimum pressure coefficients (in fully wetted flow) with the cavitation numbers at which the nondimensional pressure distribution first showed a change. This change was attributed to microscale cavitation in locally separated regions and served to define the critical cavitation number. For onset of cavitation in jets, Rouse recommends a value of σ_i of 0.6 as representative of his experiments. Values for the onset of cavitation in the wake of sharp-edged discs are shown in Fig. 12I.6, as a function of Reynolds number based on diameter for discs ranging in diameter from $\frac{1}{16}$ to $1\frac{1}{2}$ in. Cavitation about smooth (e.g., wavy) surface roughnesses is analogous to cavitation in unseparated flows; the incipient cavitation number may be determined by taking the minimum pressure coefficient and using the boundary-layer velocity corresponding to the height of the roughness. Sharp-edged roughnesses produce cavitation in the separation zone just behind the roughness. Data on inception of cavitation about roughness elements in boundary layers will be found in Refs. 24 and 25.

121.3. Dynamics of Transient Cavities

The Hydrodynamics of Transient Cavities. Cavitation bubbles which grow from nuclei, sometimes oscillate, and eventually collapse and disappear are referred to as *transient*, or *traveling*, cavities. The life cycle of such cavities is of the order of milliseconds in the case of a transient pressure pulse—as would occur in most hydraulic machines—and depends, of course, on the frequency of ultrasound in the case of acoustically induced cavitation. The first published high-speed motion pictures of the growth and collapse of individual cavities were those of Mueller[26]; no oscillations were observed. Harvey et al.,[4] using rods withdrawn rapidly from a liquid, obtained several oscillations of the resultant cavity and attributed them to energy storage in air entrained in the bubble. Knapp and Hollander[27] showed several cycles in the oscillations of cavities in a flowing liquid and attributed the rebound primarily to the storage of energy in the liquid in elastic compression, this energy subsequently being given up in producing the outward radial velocity. However, Harrison[28] has shown that cavities formed in water of low air content do *not* rebound and concluded that only cavities containing large amounts of gas will oscillate. It may be concluded that in liquid of low air content (the upper limit is undefined), the effects of compressibility and viscosity in both the liquid and gas phases in radiating and dissipating energy are such as to allow no rebound if there is only a small amount of permanent gas in the bubble.

The motions associated with the growth and collapse of a spherical cavitation bubble have been treated in various detail by a number of writers (e.g., Refs. 29 to 33). The classical solution for a perfectly empty cavity was first given by Rayleigh[29]; for an incompressible fluid, the pressures at final collapse become infinite and a number of modifications and refinements to the theory have been carried out to investigate the effect of the properties of real fluids. Surface tension tends to increase the rate of collapse; viscous effects, compressibility effects, and the effects of entrained air (or vapor which cannot condense rapidly enough to follow the collapsing bubble walls and acts as a permanent gas), all tend to slow down the motion and hence to reduce the maximum pressures. The essential features of the motion and pressures developed during the collapse of a spherical cavity are contained in the analysis given by Gilmore,[32] and a sketch of his treatment will be given here. Gilmore assumes the Kirkwood-Bethe hypothesis[34] that in a spherically symmetric flow the quantity $r(h + \frac{1}{2}u^2)$ is propagated outward with variable velocity $c + u$; here r is the radial direction, h is the enthalpy of the liquid, u is the local velocity, and c is the local velocity of sound. (In the acoustic approximation, disturbances are assumed to propagate with the velocity c.) The equation of motion of the bubble wall is, then,

$$RU\frac{dU}{dR}\left(1 - \frac{U}{C}\right) + \tfrac{3}{2}U^2\left(1 - \frac{U}{3C}\right) = H\left(1 + \frac{U}{C}\right) + \frac{RU}{C}\frac{dH}{dR}\left(1 - \frac{U}{C}\right) \quad (12I.4)$$

in which R = radius of bubble

C = sonic velocity in liquid at bubble wall

H = enthalpy difference $\left(= \int_{p_\infty}^{P} \dfrac{dp}{d\rho} \right)$ between liquid at pressure P at bubble

       wall and at pressure p_∞ at an infinite distance from bubble

U = velocity of bubble wall

The effects of surface tension and viscosity are included in the boundary conditions by writing the pressure at the bubble wall as

$$P = P_i - 2\frac{\gamma}{R} - 2\mu\left(\frac{\partial u}{\partial r}\right)_{r=R} \tag{12I.5}$$

if P_i = pressure of internal gas

  γ = surface tension

  μ = dynamic viscosity

By using the equation of continuity for a compressible fluid and assuming the viscosity and compressibility of the liquid small,

$$P = P_i - 2\frac{\gamma}{R} - 4\frac{\mu U}{R} \tag{12I.6}$$

After assuming constant internal pressure, with surface tension and viscosity negligible, and by using empirical formulas for H and C for isentropic compression of liquids, Gilmore solved the equation of motion, retaining only terms in dU/dR and dH/dR:

$$\left(\frac{R_0}{R}\right)^3 = \left(1 - \frac{U}{3C}\right)^4 \left[1 + \frac{3p_\infty U^2}{2(p_\infty - P_i)}\right] \tag{12I.7}$$

Neglect of the term $U/3C$ yields the Rayleigh incompressible solution. As $R \to 0$, the Rayleigh theory gives $U \sim R^{-\frac{3}{2}}$ whereas the Gilmore compressible solution gives $U \sim R^{-\frac{1}{2}}$. A discussion of the Gilmore theory in connection with the sound propagated by collapsing cavities has been given by Fitzpatrick and Strasberg.[35] Mellen[36] has carried out calculations using this theory to examine the development of the shock wave, taking approximate values of $c +$ u; for example, at a radial distance of 3.6 times the initial radius R_0 of the bubble, Mellen found a peak pressure at the "shock" front of about 59 atm. He also obtained estimates of the peak pressures experimentally and found good agreement with the calculations. Schlieren photographs of the shock waves have been obtained by Güth.[37]

For spherical bubbles, the growth and collapse can be predicted with good accuracy in the region from maximum radius down to about one-fourth the maximum radius[38] using the Rayleigh theory.[29] In a superheated liquid, however, the effect of heat diffusion at the bubble wall tends to modify the growth considerably. By taking into account, approximately, the heat transfer in a small "boundary layer" at the bubble wall and using the boundary condition (12I.6), suitably modified to account for

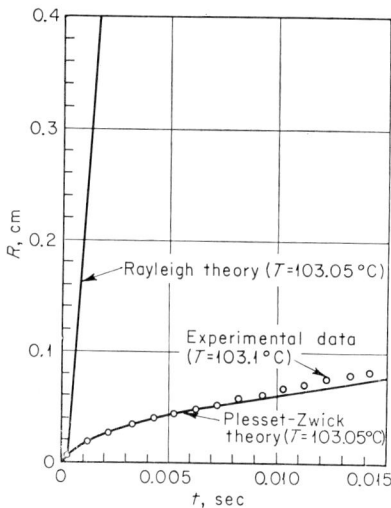

Fig. 12I.7. Effect of heat transfer on bubble growth. (*After Dergarabedian.[40]*)

the dependence of the vapor pressure on temperature, Plesset and Zwick have computed the growth of vapor bubbles in slightly superheated liquids according to the incompressible theory. Their computation has been compared with experiment by Dergarabedian,[40] whose results for one case are shown in Fig. 12I.7. The effect of local cooling in retarding growth is marked.

Pressure Developed by Collapsing Cavities. Because of the extreme complexity of the behavior of cavitation bubbles, and particularly because of the impossibility of describing in detail the properties of the liquid-gas system (size of initial bubble, air content of the bubble, vapor behavior, deformations due to instabilities of the bubble walls), it is not possible to state unequivocally the maximum pressures developed or the pressure history during the motion and collapse of such bubbles. Attempts to measure the maximum pressures in cavitated regions have been fraught with difficulty, since the rise of pressure to its maximum occurs in a time of the order of a microsecond and over a very small area. Recent experiments have given results of the order of 200,000 psi based on an analysis of

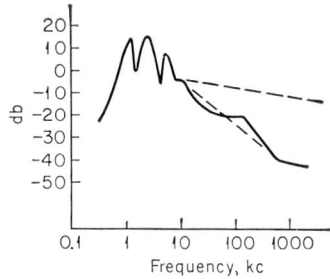

Fig. 12I.8. Measured spectrum of cavitation noise observed at a distance of 1 meter from a rod 2 in. long, $\frac{1}{16}$ in. in diameter, rotated at 4300 rpm about a transverse axis through its center. The reference level for the decibel scale corresponds to a sound pressure of 1 dyne/cm^2 in a 1-cps frequency band. The cavitation bubbles were observed to be about 1 mm in diameter; ambient pressure, approximately 1 atm. (*After Mellen.*[46])

strain waves in a photoelastic specimen exposed to cavitation.[41] Direct measurements by Jones[42] gave maximum pressures of at least 12,000 atm. Both sets of experiments were carried out with deaerated water, although the actual entrained air content is not known of course. Of particular interest, however, is that the peak pressures developed during collapse can certainly be high enough to cause mechanical damage to materials. Further discussion of the effects of entrained air, bubble instabilities, and wall effects, all of which tend to reduce the collapse rate and hence the maximum pressures, will be found in Refs. 7, 17, and 43 to 45.

Cavitation Noise. Examples of the spectrum of cavitation noise are shown in Figs. 12I.8 and 12I.9. The first was measured by Mellen,[46] using a rotating rod with cavitation occurring essentially in the wake; the latter was obtained by Jorgensen[47] with submerged cavitating water jets. At high frequencies, the spectral density varies approximately as the reciprocal of the square of the frequency (-6 db/octave) characteristic of a shock. An excellent discussion of cavitation noise will be found in Ref. 35.

121.4. Temporally Steady, or Attached, Cavities

Quasi-steady Cavity Flows; Supercavitating Flows. Following inception, cavitating flows may continue to be composed of individual transient cavities, or a large cavity, attached to the body on which cavitation has been induced, may appear immediately, particularly if the detachment point is sharply defined (as for a hydrofoil with a very sharp leading edge,

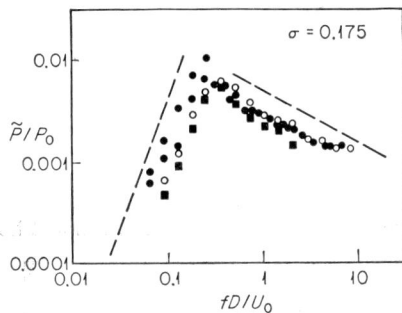

Fig. 12I.9. Measured spectrum of cavitation noise produced by a cavitating submerged water jet. $\tilde{P}$ represents the rms pressure in a half-octave band of frequency at a distance of 4 diam from the jet axis and 4 diam downstream from the orifice. The data represent different combinations of jet diameter, D ($\frac{3}{8}$, $\frac{3}{4}$, and $1\frac{1}{2}$ in.) and ambient pressures P_0 ($\frac{1}{2}$, 1, and 2 atm). U_0 is the jet velocity; f is the frequency. (*After Jorgensen.*[47])

for example). The latter cavities are quasi-steady in the sense that the cavity surface is stationary on a temporal average. The conditions for early formation of such an attached cavity are not understood, but are undoubtedly associated with the pressure gradients which influence the growth of nuclei and the rate at which the formation of vapor can be accommodated. On the other hand, a cavitating region made up entirely of transient cavities may exhibit the properties of a quasi-steady cavity in that the average envelope does not vary in time. The structure of attached cavities has been found to be very complicated.[7,17,48] In particular, it is necessary to distinguish between cavitation in a wake flow and truly free streamline flow, the relations between such flows, and the transition from one to another.

Flows with quasi-steady, or attached, cavities that are long compared with the body about which they are formed have come to be called "supercavitating" flows and are of ever-increasing importance in a multitude of engineering applications. The characteristics of such flows (lift, drag, cavity shape, etc.) are the subject of Part II of this section; here only some of the basic physical aspects of such cavity flows are discussed.

Transition to Quasi-steady Cavity Flow. It has been observed[48,16] that, for forms about which the lowest pressures coincide with a zone of separation, cavitation may first occur in more or less well defined vortices along the boundary of the separated wake. As would be expected, the average envelope does not exhibit the properties of a free-streamline flow. As the cavitation number is lowered, the cavitated region evidently exhibits the properties of both a wake flow and a free-streamline flow. In such cavities, the liquid flows along the boundary of the cavity and reenters at the downstream end. Depending on a number of factors yet but incompletely understood, the reentering fluid may fill the cavity completely and cause it to collapse, whereupon the cycle of growth, collapse, filling, and collapse reoccurs.[48,49] When the velocities are high enough, and presumably when the rate of entrainment of the reentering liquid becomes great enough, the entrained liquid is swept out of the "cavity" region, the reentrant jet has insufficient momentum to refill the cavity, and the cavity remains essentially filled only with vapor phase and air diffused from the proximate liquid. The reentrant jet still appears but is dissipated before it can fill the cavity again. Under these conditions, the trailing end of the cavity exhibits quite an unstable motion, leading to oscillating forces that are of rather low frequency and that may be the cause of rather severe vibrations in hydraulic machinery. An illustration of such cavities is shown in Fig. 12I.10; here a cavity is formed behind a disc supported from the downstream side. In the photograph taken at the high frame rate, the very rough appearance of the cavity wall is seen clearly. The appearance is characteristic of cavities in which the reentrant liquid still can fill the cavitating region and cause oscillations of the type mentioned. A number of small transient cavities may be observed being convected along the boundary of the cavity wall.

Cavity Oscillations; Associated Vibrations. The cyclic filling and emptying of cavities may be a cause of severe vibration in a cavitating machine. The only systematic investigations of the frequency of oscillations of such cavities are apparently those of Shal'nev,[50] who observed the "shedding" of cavities behind circular cylinders. He reported his results for the Strouhal number $S = fd/U$ as a function of Reynolds number and cavitation number. As would be expected, the Strouhal numbers at cavita-

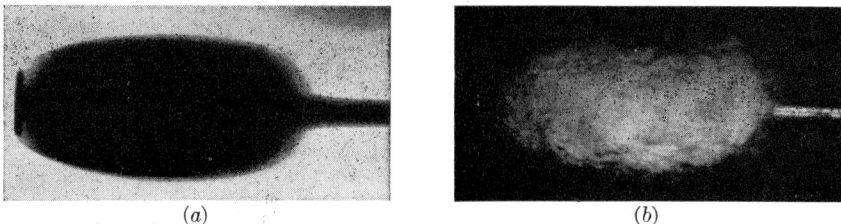

| (a) | (b) |

FIG. 12I.10. "Steady" cavity behind a disc, $\sigma = 0.188$. (a) Exposure time 2 sec. (b) Exposure time 1/10,000 sec. (*After Eisenberg and Pond.*[48] *Courtesy of the U.S. Navy, David Taylor Model Basin.*)

tion numbers near inception coincide with the values for vortex shedding in fully wetted flow, indicating simply that cavitation has occurred in the wake vortices. As the cavitation number is reduced, the Strouhal number increases to a maximum of about 0.24 at a cavitation number of 1.3, after which it again begins to fall. Knapp,[49] in experiments on bodies of revolution, simply gives periods for the emptying and filling cycle, reporting values corresponding to frequencies as high as 200 cps for a body of revolution 1 in. in diameter at 90 fps and a cavitation number of 0.348 and as low as 43 cps for a 2-in. body at 59 fps.

121.5. Cavitation Modeling and Scale Effects

Modeling Laws. For fully developed cavity flows with fixed detachment points, such as that illustrated in Fig. 12I.10, the essential modeling parameter is simply σ, defined using the actual cavity pressure p_c. Boundary-layer effects may be of importance in determining the location of the detachment point; however, for very long cavities, viscous effects will, in general, affect the gross properties (cavity shape, length, etc.) in only a minor way. With regard to the modeling laws for cavitation *inception*, the scaling parameter is again σ, but with the pressure p_c defined as the inception pressure. If cavitation occurred always when the pressure falls to a fixed pressure, usually assumed to be vapor pressure, correct scaling would be achieved if also the model and prototype flows were geometrically and dynamically similar. Because of the behavior of nuclei, the role of gas content, and the various boundary-layer and turbulence effects discussed in the foregoing, the scaling of inception is rather more complicated than is implied by this simple rule.

Scale Effects in Cavitation Inception. Scale effect in cavitation inception is among the most difficult of the problems on cavitation phenomena and, in spite of the growing knowledge of the physics of the process itself, still defies definitive treatment. While the process of bubble growth for a liquid-gas system of known or fixed properties must follow the laws of hydrodynamic similitude, the essential difficulty lies in the characterization of the systems being compared and the physical chemistry of the systems, rather than hydrodynamic similarity. Thus it is not possible a priori to characterize in detail a liquid-gas system as to number and size of nuclei without knowing precisely the mechanism which governs their origin and stability. In particular, when dealing with extrapolation to conditions for inception in prototype environments, such as rivers or the oceans, so little is known about the occurrence of gas bubbles in these complicated environments that it is not even clear what conditions must be modeled in a water tunnel, for example. Some results are, however, available for effects of scale on the inception pressures in a single liquid-gas system.

The most comprehensive attempt to date to investigate scale effects is that reported by Kermeen et al.[16] In experiments on bodies of revolution having diameters ranging from $\frac{1}{4}$ to 2 in., it was observed that the critical cavitation number depended on model size and absolute flow velocity. It was found (Fig. 12I.11) that the critical cavitation numbers for each model were below that corresponding to the minimum pressure coefficient and only approached this value as the stream velocity was increased. In these experiments, no consistent effect of total air content could be observed, in variance

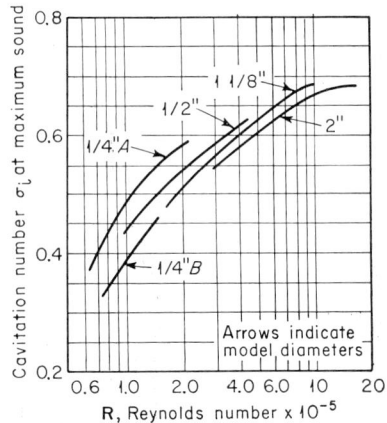

Fig. 12I.11. Cavitation number σ_i for incipient cavitation (as defined by value at which noise disappears) as a function of Reynolds number for bodies with hemispherical heads and cylindrical middle bodies. The $\frac{1}{4}$-in. A model was constructed more accurately than the $\frac{1}{4}$-in. B model. (*After Kermeen et al.*[16])

with the results of Crump (Fig. 12I.2).   The curves shown in Fig. 12I.11 were obtained by first allowing cavitation to become fully developed at cavitation numbers well below the inception value and raising the ambient pressure until cavitation disappeared. This point was defined as the *inception point*.   Attempts to observe inception by the direct procedure of approaching the critical point starting with a noncavitating system evidently resulted in so large a scatter that it was difficult to obtain accurate correlation of results.   A so-called "hysteresis" could often be observed; i.e., when approaching the inception point from a noncavitating condition, much lower critical cavitation numbers were observed than those at which cavitation disappeared.   In the latter experiments, nuclei were observed to grow *in situ* at the body surface before becoming detached and flowing into a region which eventually grew into a steady cavity.

Recent experiments by Ripken,[51,52] also on bodies of revolution, have shed further light on the effects of total and free (entrained) gas content on cavitation inception. The latter results may be summarized as follows: Cavitation inception in the form of "steady-state" cavities of rather abrupt appearance and disappearance tends to occur in water of relatively low free-gas content; cavitation inception in the form of transient bubbles tends to occur in water having a relatively high free-gas content.   So-called hysteresis effects resulted when using water of low total nuclei concentration and were not apparent in water of high free-gas content.   In the water tunnel used by Ripken, the maintenance of a high free-gas content required maintenance of a high total gas content.   However, it was noted that when changing the nuclei concentration by changing the equilibrium total gas content, there was a considerable temporal lag before stabilization of the nuclei content was achieved.   In these experiments, the response time was about 3 min; i.e., for a given total gas content and test speed, the critical incipient cavitation number achieved a fixed value only after the free-gas content was stabilized.   Furthermore, the hysteresis effects and effects of speed mentioned above were obviated by carefully allowing stabilization of the free-gas content to take place. Whether these differences are associated only with the stabilization time or are primarily a result of the differences between growth processes, i.e., slow diffusion into a nucleus or explosive growth, is not known.

Additional evidence of the effects of scale on cavitation inception has been obtained in the experiments of Jorgensen,[47] referred to above.   Jorgensen also found earlier inception for larger models (Fig. 12I.12).   He points out that this tendency is probably associated with what, in his experiments, may be designated as failure to scale spacing of the nuclei, the effect of increasing linear scale of his nozzles being equivalent to an increase of the number of nuclei available for growth.

Description of the Liquid-gas System.   It is clear from the foregoing that a complete description of the liquid-gas environment with respect to inception must depend upon a knowledge of the nuclei size-and-number spectrum.   In a given environment such as a water tunnel where the system can be maintained under fairly uniform conditions, it would in principle be possible to characterize the spectrum as well as the relations between dissolved and undissolved gas, or total gas content and free-gas content.   A number of methods are under development for just these purposes and are described in a later article.   Although the achievement of the ability to characterize the environment in such test facilities would in itself be a long step forward in furthering the research on scale effects, there still remains the question of what type of environment it is necessary to try to simulate in such facilities.

Uncertainty of Modeling Cavitation Phenomena.   If the actual situation regarding the number and size of nuclei were known, it would be possible to specify what the conditions on the model scale should be in order to achieve similarity.   However, what is meant by similarity in this situation may be quite different from that for the usual conditions for geometric and dynamic similarity.   In essence, the properties of the liquid-gas substance in model and full-scale environments have little relation to one another as far as scaling—in the sense of engineering prediction—is concerned.   Thus efforts to design model experiments must concentrate on methods of selecting liquid-gas properties that will in effect model the prototype system.   Unfortunately, very little is known of the conditions for most of the full-scale environments—the oceans, for example.   There is evidence that the surface of the oceans contains a very large population

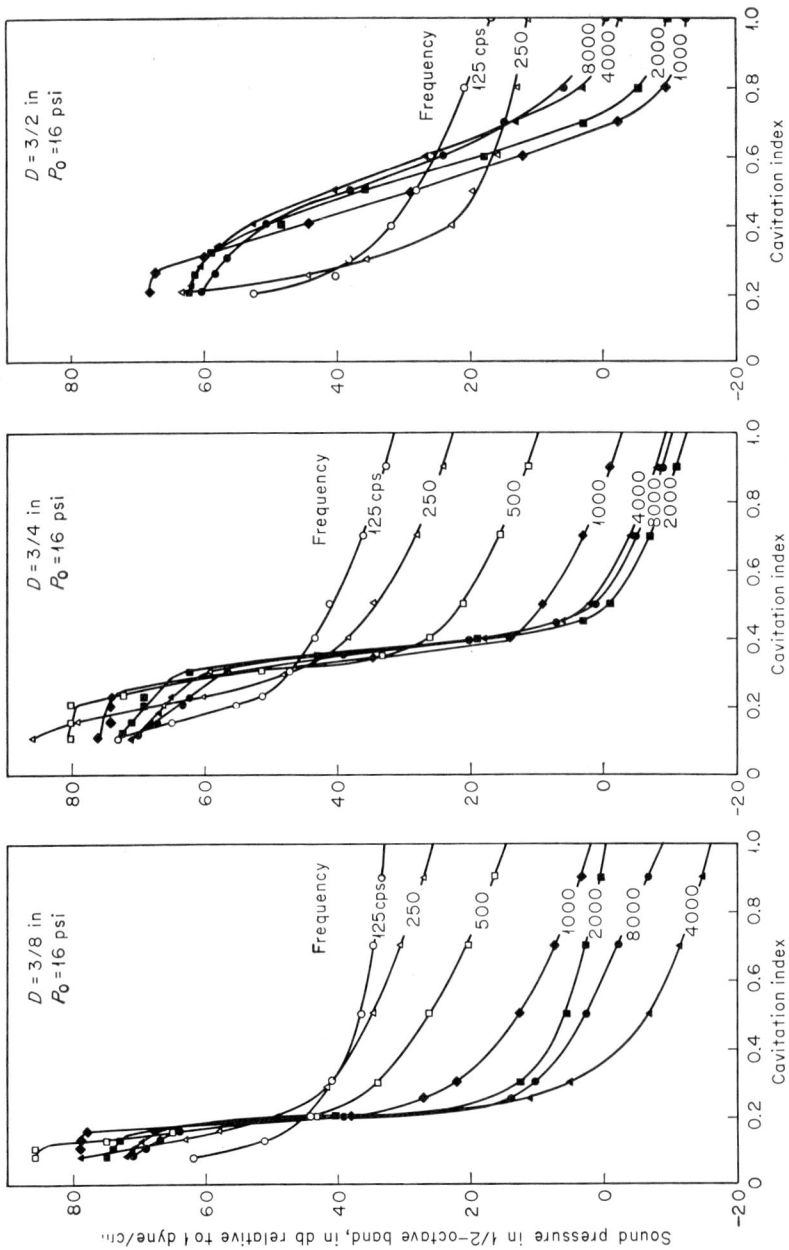

FIG. 121.12. Noise at onset of cavitation in a submerged turbulent jet at an ambient pressure of 16 psi. (*After Jorgensen.*[47])

of bubbles, and thus inception should be expected to occur earlier than in a water tunnel in which the water is not specifically nucleated in some way; most full-scale experience seems to bear out this conclusion. Indeed, it was evidence of this kind that led Crump[12] to recommend that water-tunnel experiments be conducted under supersaturated conditions in order to simulate the results he obtained in sea water.

In view of the complications of the occurrence of nuclei in environments that are not easily characterized, such as the oceans, it is not possible to make predictions of what will happen on two different scales when the liquid-gas systems are different in physical make-up as well. In addition, the effects of boundary-layer flows and of turbulence, as well as of the unsteady flow effect associated with the pressure gradients on two different scales, complicate even further the problem of achieving similarity for inception as well as for the type of cavitation that will occur. Finally, there are those possible occurrences in which nuclei smaller than critical size for vaporous cavitation grow by diffusion to critical size. In such cases, it is not unlikely that inception may be effectively prevented on a model scale and not on the prototype.[5]

121.6. Cavitation Damage and Protection

Mechanism of Cavitation Damage. Materials exposed to cavitation are subject to severe damage, especially in zones of cavity collapse. While some controversy still exists regarding the mechanism of cavitation damage, it is clear that the *onset* of damage is associated with local mechanical stressing of proximate material by the high pressures developed in the liquid surrounding cavitation bubbles. The phenomenon is a very complex one, involving a number of hydrodynamic and metallurgical variables and, in corrosive media, chemical and electrochemical effects as well. The pressures mentioned in the foregoing as representative of the maximum measured values are certainly high enough to account for brittle or fatigue failure of most materials. However, the nature of damage is so intimately related to the response of materials to mechanical stressing vs. chemical reactivity that as damage proceeds, it is often difficult to separate the effects in an unambiguous way. Inert, ductile materials show only plastic deformation for long periods of exposure, while materials that react rapidly in corrosive environments may yield corrosion products soon after exposure. In general, ductile materials at first exhibit little or no loss in weight, possessing a so-called "incubation period"; brittle materials may exhibit weight loss early in the process. The term incubation period was applied early in the history of studies of cavitation damage which were based solely on measurements of weight loss. It is a somewhat unfortunate choice of description since it implies that a certain time of exposure is required before damage can occur. Actually, it is now known that plastic deformation occurs during this period with no loss of material until actual rupture of portions of the specimen and loss of particles. Brittle materials such as cast steels, for example, lose material almost immediately, and no incubation period is observed. For certain materials there is evidence that the incubation time is proportional to the corrosion-fatigue limit.

Concurrent with the mechanical attack that occurs, a number of electrochemical and thermal effects may occur. Observations have been made which indicate rather clearly that cavitation erosion may be accelerated by the concurrent corrosive action. In such situations, the resultant damage may be described as the net result of mutually assisting effects of impingement attack in removing the products of chemical reactions, while the corrosive effects tend to produce material that is more susceptible to mechanical failure and removal of virgin material. There has also been some speculation, based on observations of discoloration of test specimens, that high temperatures—produced either in the fluid or as a result of mechanical stressing—may play a role in the cavitation-damage process.

A number of other speculations have been advanced to account for damage in cavitating liquids. These postulate that the corrosive effects not accounted for entirely by fatigue mechanisms are associated with the generation of electric currents in adjacent crystals of the material as a result of alternating mechanical or thermal stresses and deformations produced by the forces or temperatures associated with the collapse of cavities. Clearly, such mechanisms, if valid, are restricted to a certain class of materials. A complete discussion of the various postulates (mechanical, electromechanical, thermoelectric, electrochemical, mechanochemical) will be found in Ref. 53. Other pertinent background material on the mechanism of cavitation damage will be found in Refs. 15, 54, and 56 to 59.

Correlation of Material Properties and Resistance to Cavitation Damage. Correlation of cavitation-damage susceptibility or resistance of materials may be examined according to their mechanical properties, material or metallurgical properties, and their behavioral characteristics. With respect to mechanical properties, increasing resistance is exhibited with increasing hardness, ability to work-harden, increasing utlimate tensile strength, and elasticity. However, these properties alone do not define uniquely the ability of materials to withstand cavitation damage. For example, it has been shown that molybdenum, which has a hardness and tensile strength of about the same magnitude as nickel and brass, exhibits damage resistance comparable with much harder materials. Molybdenum is known to exhibit large yield lag under rapidly applied stress, so that, in view of the very short duration of the pressures applied by collapsing cavities, this behavior may indeed be expected; much more research must be carried out, however, before this conclusion can be substantiated in detail. Among the material properties that are known to be of importance in determining the resistance of material are crystal and grain structure—the finer the grain structure, the greater the resistance to damage; inclusions, which tend to reduce damage resistance; and alloy constituents, which may affect the grain structure and thus the damage resistance. Behavioral properties of importance are fatigue and corrosion-fatigue behavior—resistance to cavitation damage appears to be correlated with fatigue properties and, in corrosive media, with corrosion fatigue; and temperature dependence—materials with high strength at high temperatures exhibit good resistance to cavitation damage.

Data on the behavior of a great number of materials under cavitation attack will be found in Refs. 53 to 63. A short, representative summary of the relative resistance of metals used in hydraulic machinery has been compiled by Rheingans[64] and is shown below. The weight losses represent the losses in magnetostriction-oscillator experiments.

Alloy	Weight loss after 2 hr, mg
Rolled stellite†	0.6
Welded aluminum bronze‡	3.2
Cast aluminum bronze§	5.8
Welded strainless steel (two layers, 17 Cr, 7% Ni)	6.0
Hot-rolled stainless steel (26 Cr, 13% Ni)	8.0
Tempered, rolled stainless steel (12% Cr)	9.0
Cast stainless steel (18 Cr, 8% Ni)	13.0
Cast stainless steel (12% Cr)	20.0
Cast manganese bronze	80.0
Welded mild steel	97.0
Plate steel	98.0
Cast steel	105.0
Aluminum	124.0
Brass	156.0
Cast iron	224.0

† This material is not suitable for ordinary use, in spite of its high resistance, because of its high cost and difficulty in machining.

‡ Ampco-Trode 200: 83 Cu, 10.3 Al, 5.8% Fe.

§ Ampco 20: 83.1 Cu, 12.4 Al, 4.1% Fe.

Methods of Protection against Cavitation Damage. Protection against cavitation damage may be considered from several points of view: (1) elimination of the problem at the source, (2) use of highly resistant materials in zones of expected cavitation attack, (3) use of artificial means in which protective devices are employed as adjuncts to the system, and (4) combinations of the latter two methods. Elimination of the problem at the source implies, of course, hydrodynamic design or redesign. However, there are many cases in which it is desirable to operate under cavitating conditions for short periods of time; in such circumstances it may be necessary to employ special

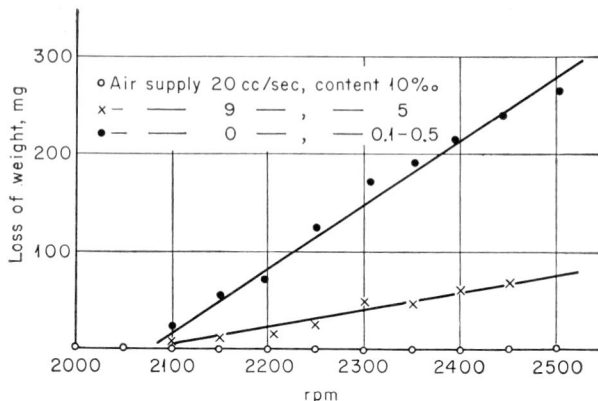

FIG. 12I.13. Effect of air injection on cavitation damage. (*After Rasmussen.*[67])

materials in the region of cavitation or imposed methods of protection. Where cavitation is expected or encountered, it has become a growing practice to use special coatings either as part of the initial installation or in repair of damaged structures. Both welded overlays and sprayed materials have been used, and data on such materials will be found in Refs. 53, 60, 63, and 64.

Of special interest are the methods that have been suggested and used for imposed protection, i.e., protection systems that are independent of the primary structure. Perhaps the earliest method of artificially protecting hydraulic machinery against cavitation damage was the use of small amounts of air injected into cavitating regions. It is not known how this suggestion came about; however, it is not unlikely that the idea originated from observations that cavitation damage was reduced in large turbines during seasons when the air content of the reservoir water was high. Air injection has been used with great success in reducing or even eliminating cavitation damage,[65,66] and the mechanism of its protective action is clearly the "cushioning" effect produced during compression by collapsing cavitation bubbles. Examples of the protective effects of air injection are shown in Fig. 12I.13 from experiments by Rasmussen.[67] These results illustrate the reduction of damage sustained by an aluminum alloy in experiments using a rotating disc in which cavitation is induced in the separation zone associated with holes drilled at the periphery. The air content in these experiments is given in

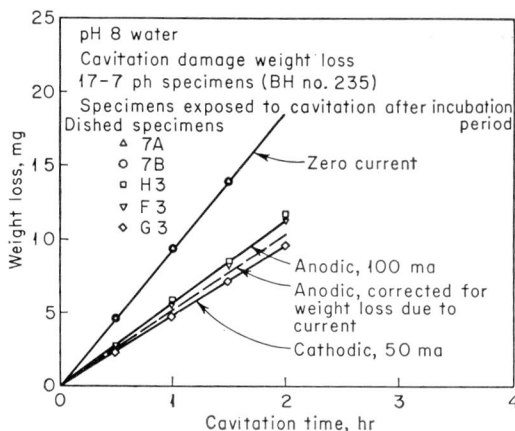

FIG. 12I.14. Comparison of cavitation-damage losses of 17-7 stainless steel in buffered distilled water with the specimen anodic and cathodic. (*After Plesset.*[69])

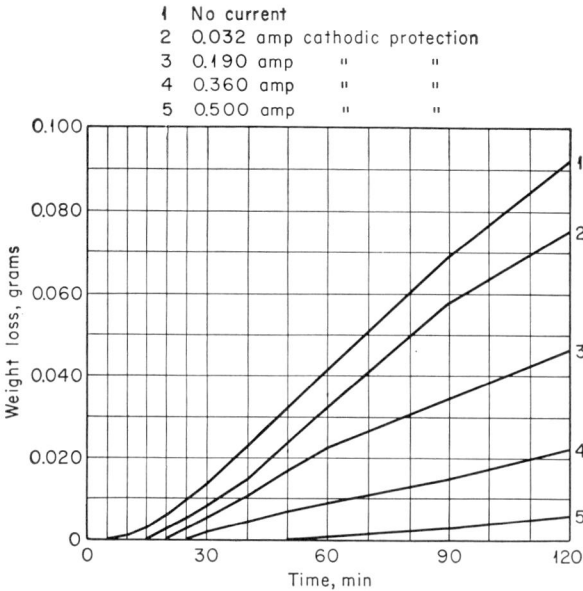

FIG. 12I.15. Cathodic protection of cast steel in sea water. (*After Leith and Thompson.*[70])

parts per thousand. The ameliorating effects of relatively small amounts of air are strikingly demonstrated. It is of interest to note that the introduction of air does not seem to produce adverse effects on most metals as far as corrosion is concerned, the reduction in primary mechanical damage being so much greater than any adverse chemical effects.

Of very recent interest are the possibilities for cathodic protection against cavitation damage. Although the use of cathodic protection was first suggested on the basis of electrochemical postulates of cavitation damage,[68] it is now quite conclusively established that the protective action is associated with evolution of hydrogen and the associated cushioning effect provided by the gas (in just the same way as in air-injection systems). Proof of the nature of cathodic protection has been given by Plesset,[69] among others, who demonstrated that protection is also obtained in an anodic system (using buffered water), in which case the evolved gas is oxygen. An example of his results is shown in Fig. 12I.14, in which are compared the protective effects of both cathodic and anodic currents. Since the valence of oxygen is just twice that of hydrogen, double the current is required in the case of the anodic system to produce an amount of gas comparable with that in the cathodic system. With the correction to the results with anodic currents for the electrolytic deposition that occurs in this case, the two cases are seen to be closely in agreement. Attempts to observe protection at currents at which no gas was evolved resulted in no observed protection, lending weight to the conclusion that protection is afforded only by the cushioning effect of the evolved gas in either case. Another example of the effect of cathodic protection is shown in Fig. 12I.15; Leith and Thompson[70] point out that the current densities were so high that hydrogen was certainly evolved during their experiments.

12I.7. Experimental Methods

It is beyond the scope of this section to describe in any detail the various experimental facilities and methods used in the investigation of the several cavitation phenomena discussed. Attention, therefore, is confined to some of the more widely used and universal facilities and methods.

Cavitation Tunnels. The cavitation tunnel is the analogue of the wind tunnel but with the primary purpose of providing a system for modeling according to the cavitation number as defined in Art. 12I.1. Thus a special feature of such facilities is the ability to reduce the ambient pressure as well as to operate at high velocities. Most tunnels may be classified in one of three catagories: (1) the closed jet, in which the test section bounds the flowing water as in a venturi tube, (2) the open jet, in which the high-velocity jet discharges into a water-filled test section, usually having a free surface at which the atmospheric pressure is controlled, and (3) the free jet, in which the jet discharges into an evacuated space used as the test section. (A description of water tunnels of conventional type and a comprehensive bibliography will be found in Ref. 71.) Of particular interest has been the development of cavitation tunnels for very small cavitation numbers (of the order of $\sigma = 0.01$). The difficult problem here is in reducing the water head on the test section. With the conventional horizontal flow tunnel, this requires either the use of very small jets, and consequently very small models, or the use of jets of very high velocity. A method of avoiding these problems is to allow the jet to fall freely, and an example of such a development is described in Ref. 72.

Most modern cavitation tunnels are designed with *resorbers*. These are simply large expansions in the tunnel circuit where the velocity is low and the pressure high. They are used to reabsorb air that has been diffused from the liquid during its passage through the low-pressure region in a cavitation experiment. While the original motivation for such resorbers was reduction of the free-air bubbles in the test section to improve the quality of photographs, interest now centers in their use to control the free-gas content. There is some question, however, of the optimum design of such resorbers; if they are too "efficient," the amount of free gas, or nuclei, may be insufficient for purposes of modeling inception. An important difficulty lies, of course, in the problem of the conditions that must be modeled (see Art. 12I.5, on scale effects in cavitation inception).

Methods of Measuring Gas Content. A number of methods have been devised for measurement of total gas content (dissolved and undissolved), of total undissolved-gas content, and of nuclei content. These will be summarized briefly; the descriptions follow generally the summary compiled by Fitzpatrick.[73]

Dissolved-gas Content. chemical tests. Perhaps the earliest method used to obtain a measure of the total gas content is the Winkler test for dissolved oxygen.[74] In this method, small quantities of manganese sulfate and alkaline potassium iodide are introduced into the sample of liquid. The dissolved oxygen oxidizes manganous hydroxide to manganic hydroxide. On acidification of the sample by addition of sulfuric acid, the latter reacts with the potassium iodide to produce free iodine in quantity proportional to the amount of dissolved oxygen in the original sample. The iodine is then titrated with a standard solution of sodium thiosulfate. Since this method determines the amount of dissolved oxygen only, the amounts of remaining gas must be inferred. Variations of the Winkler test exist, as do other chemical methods for determining the concentration of dissolved oxygen.

extraction. In the method due to Van Slyke,[75] the dissolved gases are extracted from a sample of water under a vacuum while being agitated. The extracted gases are then recompressed, and the product of pressure by volume is determined manometrically. The procedure is simple, and the accuracy is more than adequate for most water-tunnel experiments. Various modifications of the Van Slyke method have been described (e.g., Ref. 76), in some of which the sample is sprayed repeatedly into an evacuated chamber or is scrubbed in a venturi tube under low pressure.

equilibrium methods. Equilibrium methods are naturally adaptable for continuous indication of gas concentration in a water tunnel. In this type of measurement, the dissolved gases are extracted under a vacuum, but in a small chamber, in which the pressure of this extracted gas is allowed to build up to that value which, in accordance with Henry's law, corresponds to the concentration of the gas dissolved in the sample. To establish equilibrium without depleting the dissolved gas in the sample, the latter must be continuously replenished. In one type of continuously reading air-content meter,[77] the continuously flowing sample is scrubbed in a chamber in which the total pressure is maintained constant by the automatic admission of hydrogen. Thus, at equilibrium, the gas in the scrubbing chamber is a mixture of hydrogen and the gases in the flowing sample, the partial pressure of each of the latter gases being just that pressure which is in equilibrium with the sample. The gas mixture is analyzed by measurement of its thermal conductivity. In another type of continuously recording instrument depending upon establishment of an equilibrium condition, due to Fitzpatrick and Harkleroad,[78] the continuously flowing sample is sprayed into the chamber and withdrawn from the bottom at an equal rate so that the volume of the space occupied by the gas is kept constant. The gas in the chamber simply builds up, in accordance with laws of Henry and Dalton, to that mixture of gases which is in equilibrium with the dissolved gases in the incoming sample.

UNDISSOLVED-GAS CONTENT. ACOUSTIC METHODS. The presence of undissolved gas in a liquid affects the velocity of propagation and the rate of attenuation of sound. Ripken and Olson[51] have described a method of measuring the velocity of propagation of a transient pulse of sound pressure in water in which the ratio of air volume to total volume is between 10^{-4} and 10^{-2}. Measurements of the rate of attenuation of sound in a reverberant flask have been employed to detect very small concentrations of undissolved gas.[5,9] The latter method is of especial interest since it gives the opportunity of describing both the size and number of nuclei entrained in a sample of liquid.

OPTICAL METHODS. The method of optical scattering has been employed with some success in discrimination among nuclei of various sizes.[79]

Methods for Accelerated Cavitation-damage Investigations. The expensive and time-consuming experiments that of necessity result when using cavitation tunnels or venturi tubes or rotating discs for damage experiments have led to the development of laboratory devices for accelerated damage experiments. Of these, the most important has been the magnetostriction oscillator, which is still the most widely used. Such transducers possess the attributes of compactness, precise control, comparatively low initial cost, and economy of operation. Acoustic-field generators have also been used in recent years.

MAGNETOSTRICTION OSCILLATORS. Magnetostrictive effects are exhibited by ferromagnetic materials which respond to a magnetic field by a change in physical dimensions or, conversely, show a change in magnetic properties when their dimensions are changed by an external force. The type of oscillator used for cavitation-damage investigations makes use of the Joule effect, the change in length along the axis of an applied magnetic field when the field is varied. The first magnetostriction oscillator constructed specifically for cavitation tests was developed by Gaines,[80] who utilized a nickel rod in a concentric alternating field. The test specimen is fastened to the end of the rod, and high-frequency oscillations of the specimen in the test liquid are adjusted to induce accelerations high enough to produce cavitation on the face of the specimen. Since all ferromagnetic materials are temperature-sensitive, the temperature must be held below the Curie point (where all magnetic properties cease to be exhibited) by external cooling of the rod or tube which holds the specimen. Considerable effort has been devoted to the development of standardized procedures for tests with such equipment in order to ensure uniformity of comparisons between different laboratories; details will be found in Ref. 81. Typical operating frequency is of the order of 6500 cps.

ACOUSTIC-FIELD GENERATORS. A convenient way of producing intense cavitation in a liquid is to impose a focused acoustic field. An advantage of such systems for accelerated cavitation-damage testing is that damage can be obtained on specimens without introducing extraneous stresses associated with magnetostrictively induced vibrations. A very economical cavitation generator using barium titanate transducers to produce an acoustic field in a resonant container has been developed by Ellis.[57] A barium titanate ring placed on the inside of a beaker is forced to expand and contract by a sinusoidal voltage of as much as 200 volts applied to a conductive coating on its inner and outer surfaces. The operating frequencies used by Ellis range from 18 to 24 kc, depending upon the characteristics of the beaker. Another type of acousticfield generator which produces a high-frequency vibration of a piezoelectric bowl comprising part of a liquid container is described by Lichtman et al.[63]

Information concerning methods of measuring and detecting cavitation damage in the laboratory and in the field will be found in Ref. 53.

REFERENCES

1. Frenkel, J.: "Kinetic Theory of Liquids," Oxford, New York, 1946.
2. Fisher, John C.: The Fracture of Liquids, *J. Appl. Phys.*, **19**:1062–1067 (1948).
3. Temperley, H. N. V., and L. L. G. Chambers: The Behavior of Water under Hydrostatic Tension, *Proc. Phys. Soc.*, **58**:420–443 (1946).
4. Harvey, E. Newton, W. D. McElroy, and A. H. Whiteley: On Cavity Formation in Water, *J. Appl. Phys.*, **18**:162–172 (1947).
5. Strasberg, N.: The Influence of Air-filled Nuclei on Cavitation Inception, *David Taylor Model Basin Rept.* 1078, May, 1957.
6. Epstein, P. S., and M. S. Plesset: On the Stability of Gas Bubbles in Liquid-gas Solutions, *J. Chem. Phys.*, **18**(11):1505–1509 (1950).
7. Eisenberg, Phillip: On the Mechanism and Prevention of Cavitation, *David Taylor Model Basin Rept.* 712, July, 1950.
8. Fox, Francis E., and Karl F. Herzfeld: Gas Bubbles with Organic Skin as Cavitation Nuclei, *J. Accoust. Soc. Am.*, **26**(6):984–989 (1954).
9. Strasberg, Murray: "The Onset of Ultrasonic Cavitation in Tap Water," doctoral dissertation, Catholic University of America Press, Washington, D. C., 1956.
10. Blake, F. G., Jr.: The Onset of Cavitation in Liquids, *Harvard Univ. Acoust. Lab. Tech. Mem.* 12, 1949.
11. Noltingk, B. E., and E. A. Neppiras: Cavitation Produced by Ultrasonics, *Proc. Roy. Soc. (London)*, **B63**:674–685 (1950), 1032–1038 (1951).
12. Crump, S. F.: Determination of Critical Pressures for the Inception of Cavitation in Fresh and Sea Water as Influenced by Air Content of the Water, *David Taylor Model Basin Rept.* 575, October, 1949.
13. Crump, S. F.: Critical Pressures for the Inception of Cavitation in a Large-scale Numachi Nozzle as Influenced by the Air Content of the Water, *David Taylor Model Basin Rept.* 770, July, 1951.
14. Eisenberg, Phillip: A Brief Survey of Progress on the Mechanics of Cavitation, *David Taylor Model Basin Rept.* 842, June, 1953.
15. Cavitation in Hydrodynamics, *Proc. Symposium Natl. Phys. Lab.*, London, 1956.
16. Kermeen, R. W., J. T. McGraw, and B. R. Parkin: Mechanism of Cavitation Inception and the Related Scale-effects Problem, *Trans. ASME*, **77**(4):533–540 (1955).
17. Eisenberg, P.: A Critical Review of Recent Progress in Cavitation Research, in Cavitation in Hydrodynamics, *Proc. Symposium Natl. Phys. Lab. Paper* 1, London, 1956.
18. Daily, J. W., and V. E. Johnson, Jr.: Turbulence and Boundary-layer Effects on Cavitation Inception from Gas Nuclei, *Trans. ASME*, **78**(8):1695–1706 (1956).
19. Rouse, Hunter: Cavitation in the Mixing Zone of a Submerged Jet, *Houille Blanche*, 1953, pp. 9–19.
20. Grindell, A. G.: Correlation of Cavitation Inception Data for a Centrifugal Pump Operating in Water and in Sodium-Potassium Alloy (NaK), *J. Basic Eng., ASME Paper* 59-A-156, ASME annual meeting, Nov. 29–Dec. 4, 1959.
21. Salemann, Victor: Cavitation and NPSH Requirements of Various Liquids, *J. Basic Eng.*, **81**(2):167–173 (1959).
22. Jacobs, Robert R., Kenneth B. Martin, Gordon J. Van Wylen, and Bascom W. Birmingham: Pumping Cryogenic Liquids, *Natl. Bur. Standards (U.S.) Cryogenic Eng. Lab. Tech. Mem.* 36, February, 1956.
23. Rouse, Hunter, and John S. McNown: Cavitation and Pressure Distribution: Head Forms at Zero Angle of Yaw, *State Univ. Iowa Studies in Eng. Bull.* 32, 1948.
24. Shal'nev, K. K.: Kavitatsiya Nerovnostey Poverkhnosti (Cavitation of Surface Roughnesses), *Zhur. Tekhn. Fiz. USSR*, **21**(2):206–220 (1951) (*David Taylor Model Basin Transl.* 259, December, 1955).
25. Holl, J. W.: The Inception of Cavitation on Isolated Surface Irregularities, *J. Basic Eng., ASME, Paper* 59—Hyd-12, presented at Hydraulic Conference, Ann Arbor, Mich., Apr. 13–15, 1959.
26. Mueller, J.: Über den gegenwartigen Stand der Kavitationsforschung, *Naturwissenschaften*, **22**:423–426 (1928).
27. Knapp, R. T., and A. Hollander: Laboratory Investigations of the Mechanism of Cavitation, *Trans. ASME*, **70**(5):162–172 (1947).
28. Harrison, Mark: An Experimental Study of Single Bubble Cavitation Noise, *David Taylor Model Basin Rept.* 815, June, 1952.
29. Lord Rayleigh: On the Pressure Developed in a Liquid during the Collapse of a Spherical Cavity, *Phil. Mag.*, **34**:94–98 (1917).
30. Trilling, Leon: The Collapse and Rebound of a Gas Bubble, *J. Appl. Phys.*, **23**(1):14–17 (1952).

31. Poritsky, H.: The Collapse or Growth of a Spherical Bubble or Cavity in a Viscous Fluid, *Proc. First U.S. Natl. Congr. Appl. Mech.*, *ASME*, 1952, pp. 813–821.
32. Gilmore, Forrest R.: The Growth or Collapse of a Spherical Bubble in a Viscous Compressible Liquid, *Calif. Inst. Tech. Hydrodynamics Lab. Rept.* 26-4, April, 1952.
33. Flynn, Hugh G.: Collapse of a Transient Cavity in a Compressible Liquid. Part I. An Approximate Solution, *Harvard Univ. Acoust. Research Lab. Tech. Mem.* 38, 1957.
34. Kirkwood, J. G., and H. A. Bethe: The Pressure Wave Produced by an Underwater Explosion, *Office Sci. Research Develop. (U.S.) Rept.* 588, 1952. (A brief account is given in Cole, R. H.: "Underwater Explosions," pp. 305–307, Princeton University Press, Princeton, N. J., 1948.)
35. Fitzpatrick, H. M., and M. Strasberg: Hydrodynamic Sources of Sound, *Proc. Symposium on Naval Hydrodynamics, U.S. Natl. Acad. Sci.–Natl. Research Council Publ.* 515, 1957.
36. Mellen, R. H.: Spherical Pressure Waves of Finite Amplitude from Collapsing Cavities, *U.S. Navy Underwater Sound Lab. Research Rept.* 326, September, 1956.
37. Güth, W.: Zur Entstehung der Stosswellen bei der Kavitation, *Acoustica*, **6**:526–531 (1956).
38. Plesset, M. S.: The Dynamics of Cavitation Bubbles, *J. Appl. Mech.*, **16**:277–282 (1949).
39. Plesset, M. S., and S. A. Zwick: The Growth of Vapor Bubbles in Superheated Liquids, *J. Appl. Phys.*, **25**(4):493–500 (1954).
40. Dergarabedian, Paul: The Rate of Growth of Vapor Bubbles in Superheated Water. *J. Appl. Mech.*, **20**(4):537–545 (1953).
41. Sutton, G. W.: A Photoelastic Study of Strain Waves Caused by Cavitation, *J. Appl. Mech.*, **24**(3):340–348 (1957).
42. Jones, I. R.: "The Measurement of the Pressure Due to the Collapse of Cavities in Liquids," doctoral dissertation, University of Wales, Aberystwyth, England, 1959.
43. Rattray, Maurice: "Perturbation Effects in Bubble Dynamics," doctoral dissertation, California Institute of Technology, Pasadena, Calif., 1951.
44. Pennington, Ralph Hugh: Surface Instabilities on Pulsating Gas Bubbles, *Stanford Univ. Appl. Math. and Statist. Lab. Tech. Rept.* 22, May, 1954.
45. Ellis, Albert T.: Observations on Cavitation Bubble Collapse, *Calif. Inst. Technol. Hydrodynamics Lab. Rept.* 21-12, December, 1952.
46. Mellen, R. H.: Ultrasonic Spectrum of Cavitation Noise in Water, *J. Acoust. Soc. Am.*, **26**:356 (1954).
47. Jorgensen, Donald W.: Measurements of Noise from Cavitating Submerged Jets, *David Taylor Model Basin Rept.* 1126, November, 1958.
48. Eisenberg, P., and H. L. Pond: Water Tunnel Investigations of Steady-state Cavities, *David Taylor Model Basin Rept.* 668, October, 1948.
49. Knapp, R. T.: Recent Investigations of the Mechanics of Cavitation and Cavitation Damage, *Trans. ASME*, **77**(7):1045–1054 (1955).
50. Shal'nev, K. K.: Experimental Study of the Intensity of Erosion due to Cavitation, in *Cavitation in Hydrodynamics, Proc. Symposium Natl. Phys. Lab.*, London, 1956.
51. Ripken, John F., and Reuben Olson: A Study of the Influence of Gas Nuclei on Cavitation Scale Effects in Water-tunnel Tests, *Univ. Minn. St. Anthony Falls Hydraulic Lab. Rept.* 58, February, 1958.
52. Ripken, John F.: The Influence of Free Gas Content on the Inception of Cavitation on a 1.5 Caliber Ogive Mounted in a Closed Jet Water Tunnel, *Univ. Minn. St. Anthony Falls Hydraulic Lab. Advance Rept.*, 1959.
53. Eisenberg, Phillip: Cavitation Damage, chap. 5, in J. J. Harwood and N. Hackerman (eds.), "The Corrosion of Stressed Metals," Elsevier, Houston, Tex. In press.
54. Nowotny, H.: "Werkstoffzerstörung durch Kavitation," *Ver. deut. Ingenieure*, Berlin, 1942 (reprinted by Edwards Bros., Ann Arbor, Mich., 1946).
55. Kerr, S. Logan: Determination of the Relative Resistance to Cavitation Erosion by the Vibratory Method, *Trans. ASME*, **59**:373–397 (1937).
56. Mousson, J. M.: Pitting Resistance of Metals under Cavitating Conditions, *Trans. ASME*, **59**:399–408 (1937).
57. Ellis, A. T.: Production of Accelerated Damage by an Acoustical Field in a Cylindrical Cavity, *J. Acous. Soc. Am.*, **27**(5):913–921 (1955).
58. Plesset, M. S.: On Physical Effects in Cavitation Damage, in R. Grammel (ed.), Verformung und Fliessen des Festkörpers, *Proc. Colloq.*, Berlin, 1956.
59. Leith, W. C.: Cavitation Damage of Metals, *Eng. J.*, March, 1959.
60. Rheingans, W. J.: Accelerated Cavitation Research, *Trans. ASME*, **72**(5):705–719 (1950).
61. Boettcher, H. N.: Failure of Metals due to Cavitation under Experimental Conditions, *Trans. ASME*, **58**:355–360 (1936).
62. Shal'nev, K. K.: Resistance of Metals to Cavitation Corrosion in Fresh Water and Sea Water, *Doklady Akad. Nauk (USSR)*, **95**(2):229–232 (1954). (Russian.)

63. Lichtman, J. Z., D. H. Kallas, C. K. Chatten, and E. P. Cochran, Jr.: Study of Corrosion and Cavitation-erosion Damage, *Trans. ASME*, **80**(6):1325–1339 (1958).
64. Rheingans, William J.: Selecting Materials to Avoid Cavitation Damage, *Materials in Design Eng.*, 1958, pp. 102–106.
65. Cavitation in Hydraulic Structures: A Symposium, *Proc. Am. Soc. Civil Eng.*, vol. 71, no. 7, September, 1945.
66. Mousson, J. M.: Cavitation Problems and Their Effects upon the Design of Hydraulic Turbines, *Proc. Second Hydraulics Conf.*, State Univ. Iowa Bull. 27, pp. 146–170, June, 1942.
67. Rasmussen, R. E. H.: Some Experiments on Cavitation Erosion in Water Mixed with Air, in Cavitation in Hydrodynamics, *Proc. Symposium Natl. Phys. Lab.*, London, 1956.
68. Petracchi, G.: Intorno All'interpretazione del Processo di Corrosions per Cavitazione, *Metallurgica Italianna*, **41**(1):1–6 (1949).
69. Plesset, Milton S.: On Cathodic Protection in Cavitation Damage, *Calif. Inst. Tech. Eng. Div. Rept.* 85-12, July, 1959.
70. Leith W. C., and A. Lloyd Thompson: Some Corrosion Effects in Accelerated Cavitation Damage, *ASME Paper* 59-A-52, ASME annual meeting, Nov. 29–Dec. 4, 1959.
71. Robertson, J. M.: Water Tunnels for Hydraulic Investigations, *Trans. ASME*, **78**(1):95–104 (1956).
72. Silberman, Edward, and John F. Ripken: The St. Anthony Falls Hydraulic Laboratory Gravity-flow Free-jet Water Tunnel, *Univ. Minn. St. Anthony Falls Hydraulic Lab. Tech. Paper* 24, ser. B, August, 1959.
73. Fitzpatrick, H. M.: Methods of Measurement of Air Content, part II, in Phillip Eisenberg and H. M. Fitzpatrick, "Cavitation Inception and Measurement of Air Content," American Towing Tank Conference, University of California, Berkeley, Calif., 1959.
74. Griffin, R. C.: "Technical Methods of Analysis," 2d ed., p. 703, McGraw-Hill, New York, 1927.
75. Peters, John P., and Donald Van Slyke: "Quantitative Clinical Chemistry," Williams & Wilkins, Baltimore, 1932.
76. Kanellopoulos, E. V.: New Method for Measuring Gas Content of Water, *Mech. Eng. Research Lab. Fluid Rept.* 69, East Kilbride, Scotland, 1958.
77. Borden, A.: Design, Operation, and Maintenance of a Meter for Recording the Air Content of Water in the David Taylor Model Basin Water Tunnels, *David Taylor Model Basin Rept.* 549, December, 1946.
78. Fitzpatrick, H. M., and M. F. Harkleroad: A Meter for Continuous Indication of Dissolved Air in Water, *David Taylor Model Basin Rept.* 867, October, 1954.
79. Iyengar, K. S., and E. G. Richardson: The Optical Detection of Cavitation Nuclei, *Mech. Eng. Research Lab. Fluids Note* 55, East Kilbride, Scotland, 1958.
80. Gaines, N.: A Magnetostriction Oscillator Producing Intense Audible Sound and Some Effects Obtained, *Physics*, **3**(5):209–229 (1932).
81. Robinson, L. E., B. A. Holmes, and W. C. Leith: Progress Report on Standardization of the Vibratory-cavitation Test, *Trans. ASME*, **80**(1):103–107 (1958).

II. SUPERCAVITATING FLOWS†

12II.1. Introduction

This portion of this handbook concerns the flow of liquids past bodies involving trailing cavities. These cavities may be mostly filled with the vapor of the surrounding liquid, as in the case of the steam-filled cavity that is formed near and attached to a propeller blade rotating very rapidly in water, or they may be filled with a foreign gas, as in the case of the air-filled cavity which forms behind a blunt body consequent to water entry. These latter cavity flows are for obvious reasons sometimes called ventilated flows. The term supercavitating flows is, however, nowadays applied to cavity flows regardless of whether the cavity is formed as a result of cavitation or ventilation, and such is our practice here.

Supercavitating flows are of increasing engineering importance, and particularly in connection with high-speed marine propellers, hydrofoil boats, and low-head pumps and turbines. Although the topic itself is quite old, it has been the subject of especial attention during the last decade, as the dates of references reveal.

It has not been possible in the present article to deal with all aspects of supercavitating

† By Marshall P. Tulin.

flows, and attention has been centered on flows past struts, foils, and bodies of revolution, since these would seem to be of greatest general interest. Some readers will probably be disappointed in the neglect of supercavitating propellers and finite supercavitating wings and are referred particularly to certain papers in Ref. 1 which deal with those subjects.

12II.2. Struts

Cavity flows past nonlifting two-dimensional bodies are of considerable practical interest. The surface-piercing struts supporting foils on high-speed hydrofoil boats, the rudders on high-speed planing craft, and surface-piercing cables used for towing often operate in a ventilated condition. Although the cavitation number σ may in these cases vary along the strut or cable, the application of two-dimensional cavity-flow theory is still often very useful. It is further important to understand something about these symmetric and nonlifting cavity flows when dealing with problems of lifting flows.

Detachment Points. The position at which a cavity will detach from a smooth closed strut in either cavitating or ventilated flow is not simple either to estimate for engineering purposes or to calculate theoretically. It is generally assumed in theoretical studies that the detachment position is such that the curvature of the cavity and of the body is identical at the point of detachment (smooth detachment). The argument behind that assumption is generally given as follows: (1) if the detachment point were any further upstream than it is in the case of smooth detachment, the cavity would possess an infinite curvature toward the body and would thus intersect it, and (2) if the detachment point were any further downstream, then (a) the maximum velocity on the body plus cavity would be upstream of the detachment point, which is obviously not possible in a cavitating flow, and (b) the velocity gradient on the body would be, according to inviscid theory, infinitely positive (adverse) at the detachment point, implying boundary-layer separation upstream of that point (which possibility is usually ruled out).

This whole argument seems reasonably strong in the case of cavitating flows, and there exists some limited experimental evidence to confirm it in that case, but the strength of the argument in the case of ventilated flows is somewhat weak since there seems every reason to believe that boundary-layer separation must in fact occur slightly upstream of cavity detachment from a smooth body. It seems reasonable to presume that the actual position of cavity detachment for a ventilated flow will be such as to provide a just sufficient adverse gradient to separate the boundary layer slightly upstream of detachment. If that is the case, then the detachment position must depend on whether the boundary layer is laminar or turbulent ahead of that point. Since a laminar boundary layer can sustain very little adverse gradient, it may very well be that detachment at low Reynolds number occurs close to the position for "smooth" detachment as in the case of cavitating flows. There exists virtually no pertinent experimental information, and in the absence of such information it

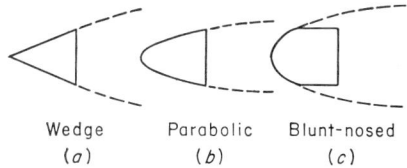

Wedge   Parabolic   Blunt-nosed
(a)   (b)   (c)

FIG. 12II.1. Blunt struts.

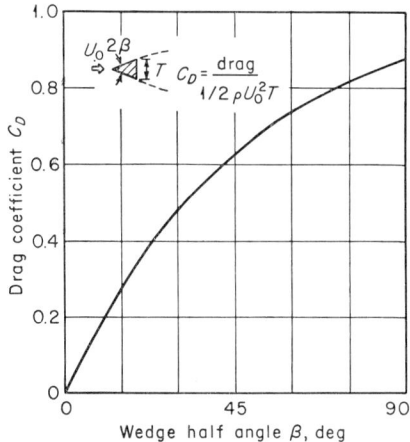

$$C_D = \frac{\text{drag}}{1/2\,\rho U_0^2 T}$$

FIG. 12II.2. Drag coefficient of wedges, $\sigma = 0$.

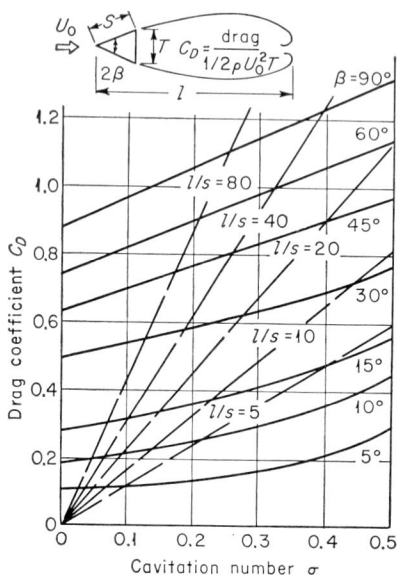

FIG. 12II.3. Drag coefficients and cavity lengths for wedges, $\sigma > 0$.

is recommended for engineering purposes that smooth detachment be assumed in all cases (except for blunt bodies), keeping in mind that detachment will at any rate occur downstream of the point so calculated and that almost certainly the drag coefficient predicted on that basis will be larger than in reality.

Blunt-based Bodies. If a body is blunt-based (not closed) and of such a shape that its thickness increases monotonically with distance downstream (such as the struts shown as Figs. 12II.1a and 12II.1b), then it will usually be valid to assume that detachment at the base will result in a maximum velocity on the cavity rather than on the body forward of the detachment point. The possible exceptions are struts which have very blunt noses, as for example the strut shown as Fig. 12II.1c.

Wedges. The wedge-shaped strut has been more extensively studied than any other particular shape, probably because its straight sides especially lend themselves to available theoretical methods. The drag coefficient for such wedges when the cavitation number σ is zero is shown as a function of the wedge half angle β in Fig. 12II.2, as given in Ref. 2.

The drag of a strut in cavity flow increases with increasing σ, and the cavity length decreases. Theoretical calculations assuming different finite cavity models reveal that for small values of σ, the drag coefficient varies as

$$C_D(\sigma) = C_D(0)(1 + \sigma) \qquad (12II.1)$$

Theoretical results obtained in a number of ways and from a variety of sources[2-6] are presented in Fig. 12II.3 for the drag of wedges as a function of wedge angle and cavitation number.

It is observed that the region of applicability of the asymptotic result [Eq. (12II.1)] depends on the wedge angle and is applicable over a very wide range of σ for the vertical plate ($\beta = 90°$) and over a relatively small range for the smallest wedge shown ($\beta = 5°$). Experimental results for drag,[4] uncorrected for possible wall effects, are in good agreement with the theory. Also presented in Fig. 12II.3 are curves of constant cavity length as estimated by theory. For small wedge angles and cavitation numbers, the following asymptotic result should be noted:

$$\frac{l}{T} = \frac{8}{\pi \sigma^2} C_D(0) \qquad (12II.2)$$

The maximum thickness of a trailing cavity decreases with increasing cavitation number, as does the cavity length. For reasonably long cavities, the trailing cavity itself will be essentially elliptic-shaped with a fineness ratio (length/thickness) dependent only on σ. The following approximate result may be used to estimate the maximum width $\bar{T}$ of the cavity:

$$\frac{l}{\bar{T}} = \frac{2\left(1 + \dfrac{\sigma}{2}\right)}{\sigma} \qquad (12II.3)$$

Equations (12II.1) to (12II.3) apply to the cavity flows past all slender struts, not only to wedges.[6] For cavitation number zero, the cavity is infinite in extent and has the asymptotic shape

$$\frac{y}{T} \sim \sqrt{\frac{2C_D x}{\pi T}} \qquad (12\text{II}.4)$$

Slender Struts with Blunt Bases. No general results are available for families of blunt-based struts other than wedges, although some partial results for parabolic struts exist.[7] However, a quite general theory for the cavity flow past thin or

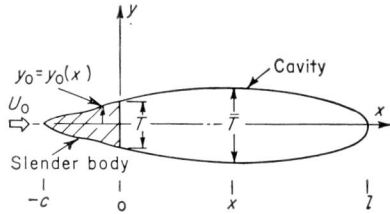

Fig. 12II.4. Cavity flow past a slender strut, $\sigma > 0$.

slender struts of arbitrary shape has been derived and should be entirely sufficient for engineering purposes in connection with struts of maximum thickness not exceeding 15 per cent of their chord.

The drag coefficient at $\sigma = 0$ for an arbitrary strut of shape $y_0 = y_0(x)$ as shown in Fig. 12II.4 may be calculated using the following result:

$$C_D(0) = \frac{2}{\pi T} \left(\int_{-c}^{0} \frac{dy_0}{dx} \frac{dx}{\sqrt{-x}} \right)^2 \qquad (12\text{II}.5)$$

The length of the cavity behind the strut is given by

$$l = \frac{4(1 + \sigma/2)}{\pi \sigma} \int_{-c}^{0} \frac{dy_0}{dx} \frac{\sqrt{l - x}}{\sqrt{-x}} \, dx \qquad (12\text{II}.6)$$

and the drag coefficient for $\sigma > 0$ by

$$\frac{D}{\rho U_\infty^2/2} = 2\sigma \sqrt{1 + \sigma} \int_{-c}^{0} \frac{dy_0}{dt} \frac{\sqrt{t}}{\sqrt{t - l}} \, dt + \frac{2l(1 + \sigma)}{\pi} \left[\int_{-c}^{0} \frac{dy_0}{dt} \frac{dt}{\sqrt{t(t - l)}} \right] \qquad (12\text{II}.7)$$

The following asymptotic results (σ small) can be derived from the above, in addition to those already given as Eqs. (12II.1) to (12II.3):

$$\bar{T} = \frac{4T}{\pi \sigma} C_D(0) \qquad (12\text{II}.8)$$

$$\frac{l}{2} - c < \bar{x} < \frac{l}{2} \qquad (12\text{II}.9)$$

Slender Parabolic Struts. The drag of struts of given length and thickness, or length and volume, depends very much on the strut shape. It has been shown[8] that slender parabolic struts are close to optimum shape with respect to drag minimization. The drag of a parabolic strut such as is shown in Fig. 12II.1b is

$$C_D(0) = \frac{\pi}{8} \frac{T}{c} \qquad (12\text{II}.10)$$

Table **12II.1.** Relative Drags of Wedge and Parabolic Struts, $\sigma = 0$

(Same length in all cases)

	Wedge	Parabola
Same thickness.................	1	0.62
Same volume..................	1	0.29
Same maximum bending stress for given bending moment........	1	0.26

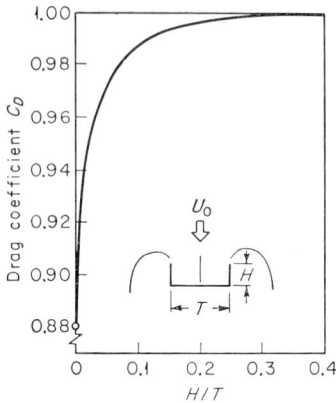

FIG. 12II.5. Drag coefficient of two-dimensional stagnation cups, $\sigma = 0$.

if the drag coefficient is based on the strut maximum thickness T and if the strut chord is c. A comparison of the relative drags of wedge and parabolic struts at zero cavitation number is shown in Table 12II.1. The superiority of the parabolic to the wedge section is noted.

The Stagnation Cup. The flat plate broadside to the flow has a drag coefficient of 0.88 as shown in Fig. 12II.2. If such a plate is fitted with a forward projecting rim at its edges, as shown in Fig. 12II.5, then its drag is increased and approaches the value unity that would obtain were stagnation pressure realized over the entire face of the cup. The effect of such a rim is very pronounced, as is shown by the theoretical results given in the figure. The stagnation cup is of practical interest since it is sometimes used in its axially symmetric form to determine the cavitation number in a high-speed water tunnel (the drag of a suitable stagnation cup closely follows the relation $C_D = 1 + \sigma$).

Closed Bodies with Smooth Detachment. *The Circular Cylinder.* The cavity flow past a circular cylinder with smooth detachment has been theoretically studied[9-11] and the results predict detachment at an angle between 55 and 56° from the nose for $\sigma = 0$ and a corresponding drag coefficient based on the cylinder diameter of approximately 0.5. The theory also indicates that both the detachment angle β_s and drag coefficient increase with σ, as shown in Fig. 12II.6.

The length of the trailing cavity decreases rapidly with increasing cavitation number, until a true cavity flow ceases to exist and the flow pattern begins to convert itself to the fully wetted condition; this happens at about $\sigma = 1.5$. The drag then tends toward its noncavitating value; this may involve a leveling off of the drag coefficient at a value of about 1.2 if the Reynolds number is sufficiently low ($\mathbf{R} < 5 \times 10^4$), or at the other extreme, a sharp drop in drag coefficient if the Reynolds number is sufficiently high[12] ($\mathbf{R} > 5 \times 10^5$).

It is to be noted that at low cavitation numbers, the theoretical detachment point moves aft very slowly with increasing σ. This result has also been obtained for slender closed bodies.[13]

ELLIPTICAL CYLINDERS. The cavity flow past elliptic cylinders with smooth detachment has been theoretically studied.[9,7] Theoretical predictions of the drag coefficient and cavity angles at the detachment point as a function of thickness ratio of the elliptic cylinders are presented in Fig. 12II.7. (The author has taken some calculated liberties with the information presented in Ref. 9 with regard to the variation of drag coefficient for small values of T/L.)

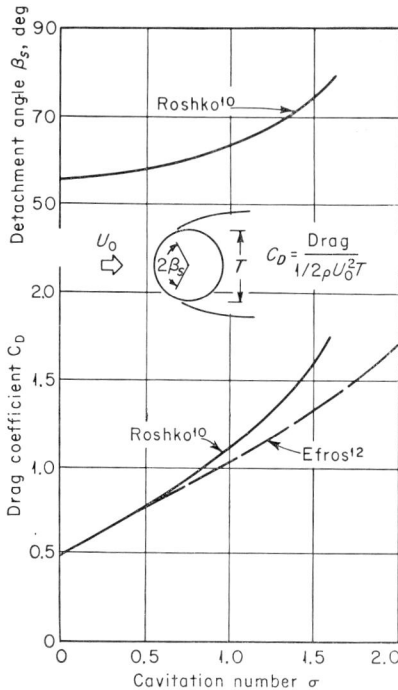

$$C_D = \frac{\text{Drag}}{1/2 \rho U_0^2 T}$$

FIG. 12II.6. Cavity-detachment angle and drag coefficient for a circular cylinder as a function of cavitation number.

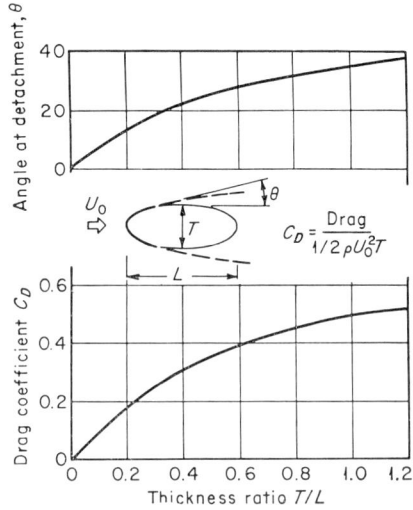

FIG. 12II.7. Drag coefficient and cavity angle at detachment for elliptic cylinders, $\sigma = 0$.

Slender Closed Struts. The linearized theory has been applied[13] to cavity flows past slender closed struts, assuming smooth detachment. Some of the important conclusions drawn were: (1) for $\sigma = 0$, the detachment-point movement with increase of thickness was of second order in the thickness; (2) for a given small thickness of strut, the movement of the detachment point with increase in σ was aft for all struts studied and was of second order in σ. This latter conclusion seems to hold for a body as thick as a circular cylinder, as was pointed out earlier (Fig. 12II.6).

The drag and detachment-point position were calculated (for small σ) for a family of closed polynomial struts, and the results are shown[13] in Fig. 12II.8.

In Figs. 12II.8 and 12II.9, the vertical ordinate of the strut is given by y_0/b and t is the horizontal coordinate; a_3 is a constant which determines the shape of struts in the polynomial family treated.

In Fig. 12II.9, the drag coefficients of three smooth closed struts of the same polynomial family are compared with the drag coefficients of three other struts for which detachment is abrupt rather than smooth. In all cases the drag coefficient is based on the maximum thickness of the strut (which is not the thickness of the strut at detachment for the smooth struts). All results are as calculated by linearized theory for $\sigma = 0$.

Wall and Free-jet-boundary Effects. The effects of walls or of a free jet boundary in a water tunnel are of considerable interest for the experimenter. A little theoretical attention has been given to cavity flows past smooth closed bodies in the presence of boundaries,[7] but the major interest has so far been in wall

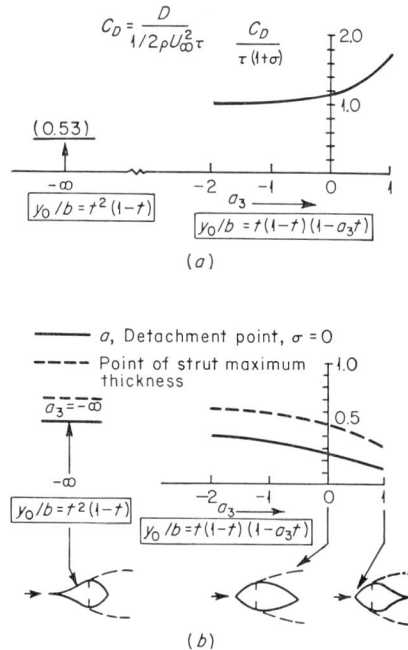

FIG. 12II.8. (a) Drag coefficient and (b) detachment-point position for family of slender polynomial struts. (Ref. 13.)

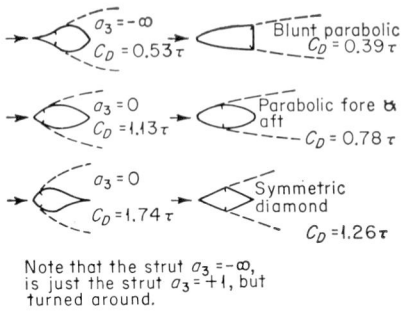

$\sigma_3 = -\infty$
$C_D = 0.53\,\tau$

Blunt parabolic
$C_D = 0.39\,\tau$

$\sigma_3 = 0$
$C_D = 1.13\,\tau$

Parabolic fore &
aft
$C_D = 0.78\,\tau$

$\sigma_3 = 0$
$C_D = 1.74\,\tau$

Symmetric
diamond
$C_D = 1.26\,\tau$

Note that the strut $\sigma_3 = -\infty$,
is just the strut $\sigma_3 = +1$, but
turned around.

FIG. 12II.9. Drag coefficients of various struts, $\sigma = 0$. (Ref. 13)

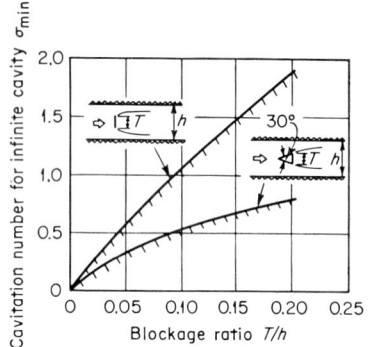

FIG. 12II.10. Choking cavitation number $\sigma_{\min}$: vs. blockage ratio T/h.

effects on flows past blunt-based bodies such as the vertical plate and wedges.[14,15] Some of the general effects are described here.

The effect of boundaries on the cavity dimensions may be very large. For a strut between solid walls, the cavity will always be lengthened relative to the unbounded condition, while the opposite effect is caused by a free jet. The lengthening effect of solid walls is so extreme that the cavity aft a given body will become infinitely long at a cavitation number greater than zero. The tunnel is then said to be choked, and further increases in speed or of reduction in σ are impossible to obtain. This choking effect is of considerable practical importance since it limits the ability of a solid-wall tunnel to operate at small cavitation numbers. The minimum cavitation number, $\sigma_{\min}$, will depend on the ratio of body thickness to tunnel height T/h and also on the drag coefficient of the body.[16] In Fig. 12II.10, the curves of $\sigma_{\min}$ versus T/h are shown for two different bodies in a two-dimensional tunnel.

In Fig. 12II.11 the opposite effect on cavity length of solid walls and free-jet boundaries are illustrated for a 30° included angle wedge[16] for a value of $T/h = 0.052$, according to linearized theory.

The effect of boundaries on the drag coefficient of a strut in cavity flow is not nearly as extreme as their effect on cavity lengths. The theoretical calculations carried out so far indicate that the effect of boundaries is invariably to reduce the drag coefficient from its unbounded value, whether solid walls or a free jet are involved. It is sometimes stated in the theoretical literature that boundary effects on drag coefficients are slight (assuming that the boundaries do not alter the cavitation number), but this conclusion does not really seem valid. Boundary effects are not important, it is true, for a vertical plate, where even in the extreme case involving a jet of width twice the plate breadth, the drag coefficient is reduced from the unbounded-stream value only about 3 per cent at $\sigma = 0$ and less for larger σ. However, the exact theory for a 30° included-angle wedge and for a free-jet width twenty times the wedge thickness reveals a drag reduction of about 17 per cent (see Ref. 17, Fig. 4a). This represents a most important effect. It is believed by the author that boundary effects in cavity

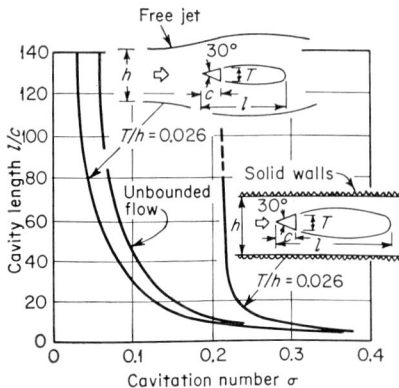

FIG. 12II.11. Cavity length vs. cavitation number for a 30° wedge in unbounded flow, in a free jet and in a solid-wall tunnel.

flows increase in magnitude as the body becomes more slender and that for many practical bodies, boundary-induced effects may be very significant and must be carefully taken into account. This is probably especially true in the case of free-jet tests at low cavitation numbers ($\sigma < 0.1$).

Gravity Effects in Strut Flows. All the theory and results discussed above refer to cavity flows without gravity effects present. If the speed of the flow is sufficiently high (or more precisely, if the Froude number based on forward speed and a body dimension are large enough), then such effects may be ignored; since cavity flows often occur in high-speed streams, such is often the case. However, it is clear that gravity effects must sometimes be taken into account.

If the acceleration of gravity is normal to the flow direction, then the cavity behind a strut will tend to drift slightly upward as a consequence of its buoyancy, the flow velocities on the upper and lower surfaces of the cavity will, of course, be different, and the symmetry of the flow will be destroyed. Linearized theory has not been applied to the case of a wedge with a vertical gravity field, but calculations for a lifting foil[18] indicate that the cavity length is only slightly affected (it decreases for the lifting foil) for Froude numbers ($\mathbf{F}_c = U_0/\sqrt{gc}$) based on the foil length c as low as 3 and cavitation numbers above 0.1; for lower cavitation numbers and longer cavities, the vertical gravity field has a larger percentile effect on cavity length. The same calculations indicate that the gravity effect on forces can be neglected for Froude numbers greater than 6.

If the acceleration of gravity is in the same plane as the flow, as it would be in a water tunnel with a vertical test section, then the cavity length may be severely affected.[19] As might be expected, a gravity force in the same direction as the flow tends to shorten the cavity while a gravity field opposing the flow direction (positive Froude number) lengthens it. The lengthening effect is such that an infinite cavity is obtained at a cavitation number greater than zero. It has been calculated, using linearized theory, that, for instance, a 30°-included-angle wedge will cast an infinite-length cavity in an unbounded stream at a cavitation number of about 0.18, at a Froude number of +10; under the same conditions a Froude number of −10 (flow direction reversed) would shorten the gravity-free cavity by only 20 per cent. However, for smaller cavitation numbers, the shortening effect becomes much more marked. The effect on strut drag of Froude number is to increase the drag for positive values and to decrease it for negative. The effect of a Froude number ±10 on the drag of a 30° included-angle wedge is about 5 per cent for small cavitation numbers. Froude numbers less than 10 will probably not be realized in water-tunnel testing, but due consideration should always be given to possible gravity effects; as is discussed later, effects on three-dimensional bodies such as bodies of revolution may be very important, especially with regard to air-entrainment rates in ventilated flows. See Refs. 18 and 19 for further information on two-dimensional effects.

Unsteady Effects on Strut Flows. Should a body in gravity flow move with variable velocity, then the cavity may generally be expected to change its shape with time. The calculation of such a time-varying flow is very difficult since the motion at any time depends on the entire history of the flow; some theory is available[20,22] but few calculations have been made. There exists, however, particular velocity-time histories which produce cavities of invariant shape behind struts or bodies of revolution, provided that the cavitation number is zero. These were first pointed out by von Kármán[23] and are of the form $U_0 = 1/(a + bt)$ if a and b are constants and t is the time variable. These relatively simple flows are of some interest since a ballistic underwater projectile may be expected to experience a velocity history of nearly such a form.

When a strut in uniform translation is given a sudden acceleration A, it experiences an acceleration-induced drag whose value at the instant of acceleration initiation may be calculated.[24,25] In the case of a vertical flat plate this drag is equal to $0.42\rho T^2 A$ if T is the breadth of the plate and ρ is the density of the liquid. It may be noted that this acceleration-induced drag is about 54 per cent of the drag experienced, in theory, by the same plate suddenly set into motion with constant acceleration but without separation of the flow about it. The added mass of a slender wedge ($\sigma = 0$) executing small streamwise harmonic motions in a uniform stream has also been determined[22] and has been found to be 11 per cent of the added mass of a fully wetted flat plate of width equal to the wedge maximum thickness. The added masses of various struts in cavity flow may perhaps be estimated for engineering purposes with the aid of these facts.

12II.3. Foils

Conventional Shapes. Conventional airfoil shapes when run under cavitating conditions suffer serious changes in their force characteristics. Furthermore, when operated at cavitation numbers sufficiently high so that the cavity is shorter than (partial cavitation) or only slightly longer than the foil itself, the forces on the foil may be subject to severe fluctuations and the foil itself to harmful cavitation erosion. The general unsatisfactory effect on lift and lift-drag ratio with decreasing cavitation number is apparent from the experimental lift and drag curves for a typical high-speed airfoil section, the NACA 66_1 - 012, shown[26] as Fig. 12II.12a. The regions in which partial cavitation exists on the top or the bottom of the foil are shown in Fig. 12II.12b. Further information on conventional airfoil shapes operating under cavitating conditions is presented in Refs. 27 and 28.

Wedges. It has been generally concluded that conventional airfoil shapes are not satisfactory for operation under cavitating conditions, for reasons illustrated by the data as shown in Fig. 12II.12. A great deal of recent interest has been given, instead, to sharp-nosed and blunt-based foils. The simplest example of such a shape is the wedge profile, and it has been much studied.

Although of little importance for use as a lifting element, the thick wedge in cavity flow may otherwise be of practical interest. When such a wedge is first inclined to the flow, an attached cavity forms at the sharp leading edge. This cavity grows in size with increasing angle of attack until it merges with the main cavity, which is attached at the blunt base. When this occurs, then only the lower side of the wedge

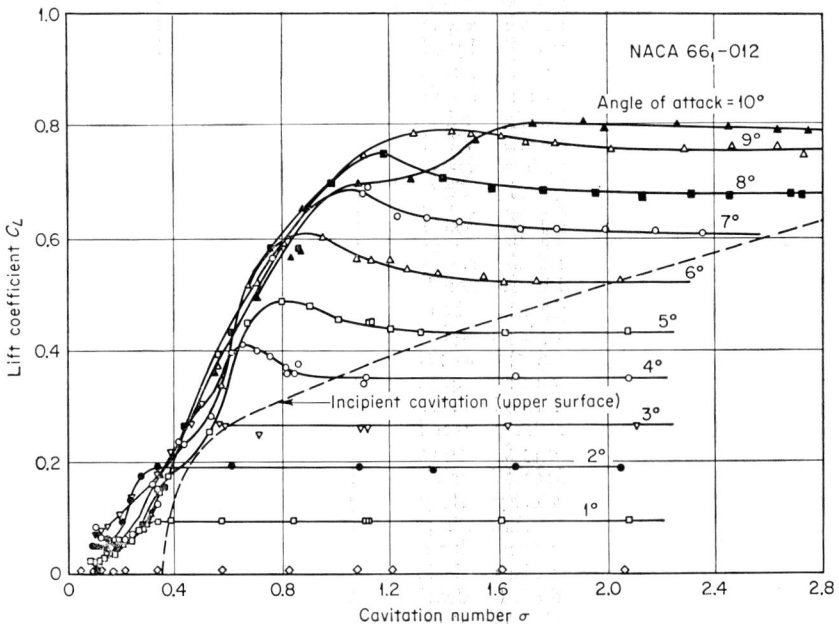

FIG. 12II.12a. Lift coefficient vs. cavitation number for NACA foil 66_1-012.   (*Ref.* 26.)

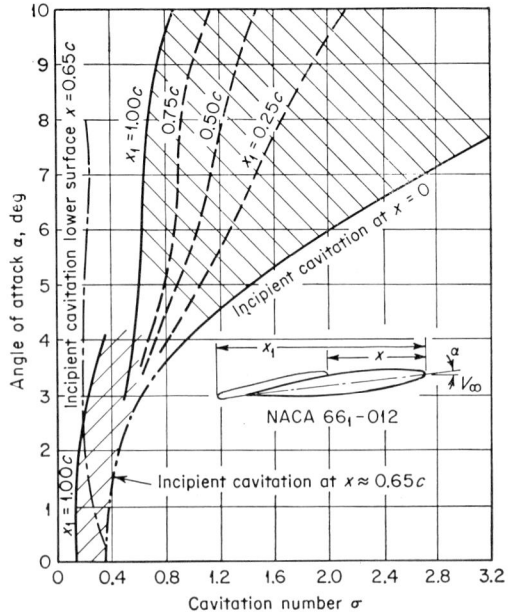

FIG. 12II.12b. Extent of cavitation on NACA foil 66_1-012 as a function of angle of attack and cavitation number. (*Ref. 26.*)

is wetted and it then, of course, experiences the same force on it as a thin flat plate of the same length and local inclination. A wedge with leading-edge cavity is shown in the photograph[4] of Fig. 12II.13.

The lift curve slopes at zero angle of attack for wedges with included angles to 90° are shown[4] in Fig. 12II.14. The drag coefficients for such wedges have previously been shown in Fig. 12II.3. Note that a wedge of included angle of about 100° develops no lift when slightly yawed and that thicker wedges actually develop negative lift. This effect is not, incidentally, caused by the existence of the nose bubble, which affects the lift at small angles of attack only to the second order in α.

The Thin Flat Plate. If the wedge is very thin, then it will behave at incidence like a thin flat plate. The lift of such a plate at zero cavitation number was calculated by Rayleigh[29] and is shown in Fig. 12II.15, together with the lift for larger values of σ as obtained by Wu[30] using the Roshko finite-cavity model.

Similar information including some experimental results is presented in Figs. 12II.16a and b, from Refs. 31 and 32.

The force on a flat-plate foil in supercavitating flow is, of course, normal to the plate, and the drag is thus simply related to the lift: $C_D = C_L \tan \alpha$. At $\sigma = 0$ and for small α, the lift-curve slope is $dC_L/d\alpha = \pi/2$; this value is just one-quarter of that for a fully wetted flat plate in theory. The lift-drag ratio of the flat plate for $\sigma = 0$ is then $L/D = \pi/2C_L$, if only the drag due to the cavity is taken into account. When the frictional drag

FIG. 12II.13. Inclined wedge in cavity flow, showing nose cavitation. (*Photo by W. A. Clayden, from Cavitating Flow about a Wedge at Incidence, J. Fluid Mech., vol 3, no. 6, March, 1958, with permission of the Controller of Her Britannic Majesty's Stationery Office.*)

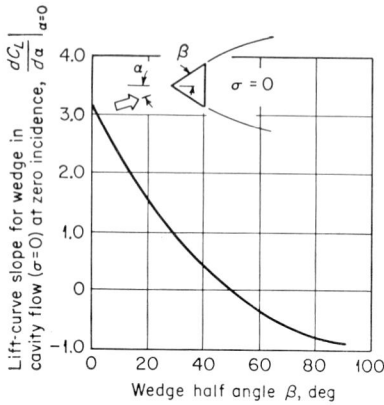

FIG. 12II.14. Lift curve slope ($\sigma = 0$ and $\alpha = 0$) for wedges.

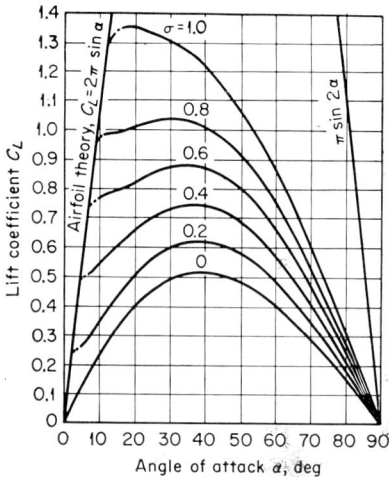

FIG. 12II.15. Theoretical lift vs. angle of attack and cavitation number for a flat-plate foil. (*Ref.* 29.)

of the lower wetted surface is additionally considered, the poor lifting efficiency of the flat plate in supercavitating flow is revealed.

Low-drag Foils. The effect of the shape of the foil bottom on lift-drag ratios was first studied in a classified publication in 1954 and then in Ref. 33, now available. It has been determined that certain positively cambered foil shapes lead to cavitation drags much lower than for the flat plate, the lift on both foils being the same. These low-drag foils are designed to have rearward-placed centers of pressure. A family of such supercavitating foils which has been tested and used in the blades of supercavitating propellers is described in Ref. 33; the bottom shape of these foils is shown in Fig. 12II.17a, and the theoretical lift-drag ratios at $\sigma = 0$ in Fig. 12II.17b. These foils are intended to operate with a cavity springing from the leading edge and with an entirely unwetted upper surface.

In Fig. 12II.17b, the symbol α' refers to the angle of attack of a particular low-drag foil, relative to the angle of attack when the foil is being operated at design lift ($C_L = C_{Ld}$). It has been recommended for design practice that values of α' approximating $1.5°$ be utilized. These foils have been designed to produce high lifting efficiencies and not to cavitate on their bottoms. The shape of the upper surface of these foils must be such that they are completely enveloped within the cavity which springs from the leading edge. The allowable shapes have been calculated, and it has been found that a foil thickness increasing approximately linearly from leading edge to trailing edge recommends itself. The maximum allowable thickness T of the section (whose chord length is c) at the trailing edge is approximately $T/c = 0.17C_L + 0.02\alpha'$, if α' is in degrees. Further detailed information on allowable foil thicknesses is presented in Refs. 34 and 35.

Theory is available to calculate the performance of arbitrary (but thin) cambered lifting foils under supercavitating conditions.[8,31,33] Of particular interest is the result obtained in the first two of these references, which very simply relates the lift, drag, and moment of a foil at $\sigma = 0$ to the lift and moments acting on an "equivalent" fully wetted foil. This result reduces the problem of estimating the performance of a supercavitating foil to an ordinary airfoil problem. No such simple results hold, unfortunately, for cavitation numbers larger than zero, but useful theory has nevertheless been developed and applied.[33]

Circular-arc Foils. The simplest cambered section is the circular arc; its lift and drag as a function of σ and angle of attack are given on page 12-37 to an approximation which should suffice for flows involving cavities at least 4 chord lengths long.

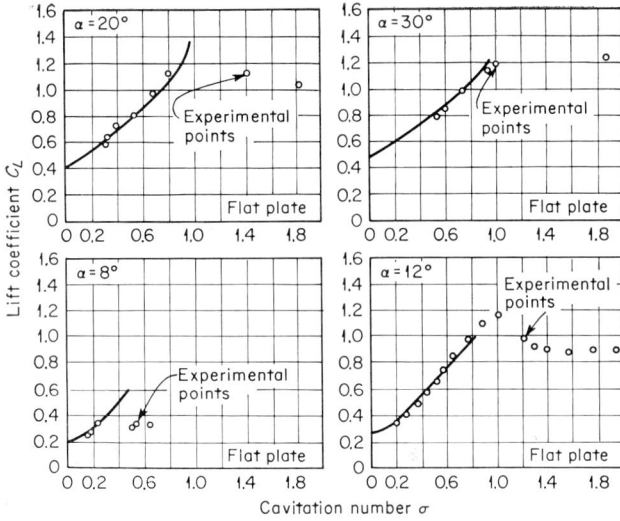

FIG. 12II.16a. The lift on flat-plate foils at four different angles of attack vs. cavitation number.

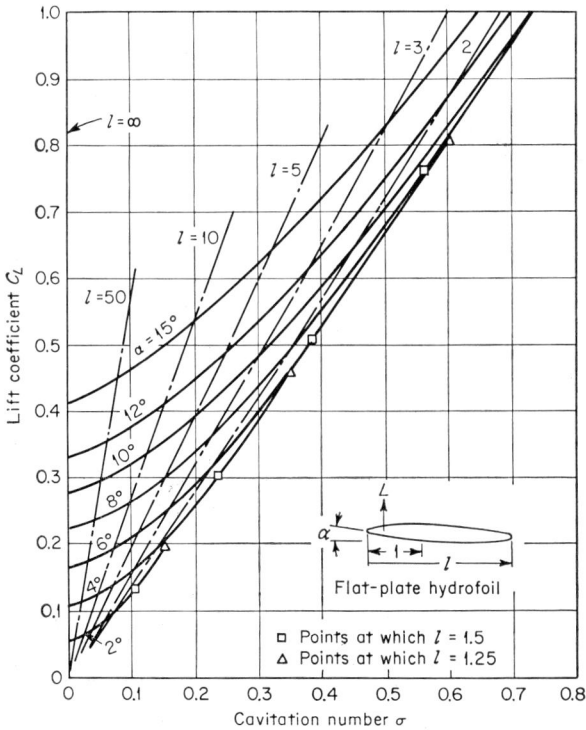

FIG. 12II.16b. Lift and cavity lengths for a flat-plate foil, according to linearized theory.

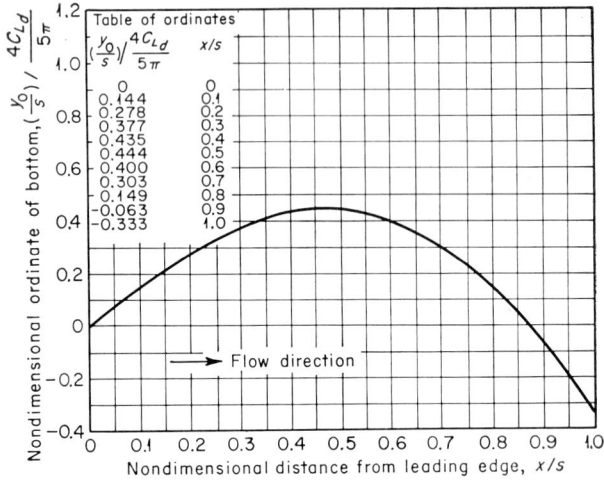

Fig. 12II.17a. Nondimensional bottom ordinates of a low-drag supercavitating foil. (*Ref.* 33.)

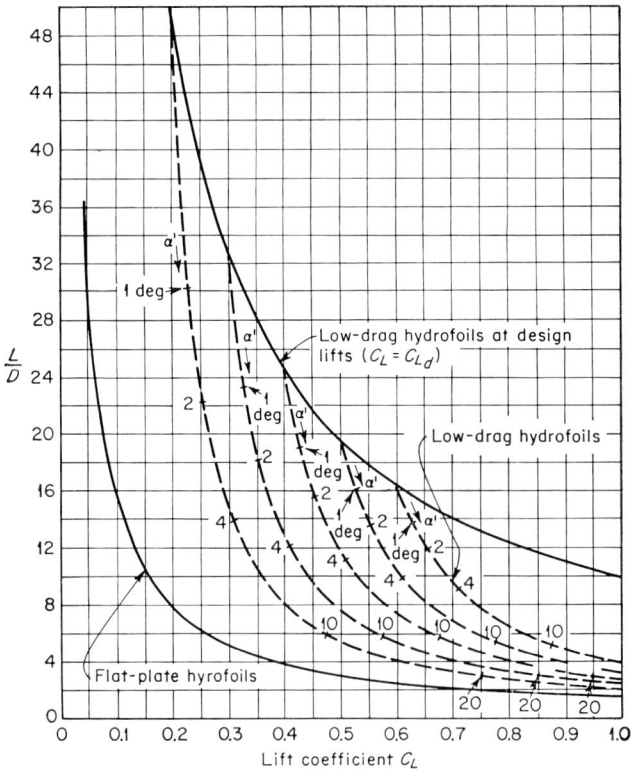

Fig. 12II.17b. Lift-drag ratios for a family of low-drag supercavitating foils. (*Ref.* 33.)

$$C_L = \frac{\pi}{2}(1 + \sigma)\left(\alpha + \frac{7\gamma}{8}\right) + \sigma^2(1 + \sigma)\frac{3\pi}{32}\frac{1}{\alpha + \gamma/4} \tag{12II.11}$$

$$C_D = \frac{\pi}{2}(1 + \sigma)\left(\alpha + \frac{\gamma}{4}\right)^2 + \sigma^2(1 + \sigma)\frac{3\pi}{32}\frac{\alpha + 7\gamma/4}{\alpha + \gamma/4} \tag{12II.12}$$

The length l of the cavity measured from the leading edge is approximately

$$\frac{l}{c} = 1 + \frac{4(\alpha + \gamma/4)^2}{\sigma^2} \tag{12II.13}$$

if c is the foil chord; α and γ are defined in Fig. 12II.18. For further details see Ref. 31.

Calculations based on nonlinear theory have been made, too, for the circular arc-foil[30] and are useful in the case in which deeply cambered foils or large angles of attack (greater than 6°, say) are involved. In that connection, it has been pointed out[36] that cambered foils operating at large angles of attack and low cavitation numbers may be treated by a combination of linearized theory for the camber effect and nonlinear theory for the angle of attack.

All the theory described above assumes cavity detachment at the foil leading edge and unwetted upper surface. For foils of greater-than-allowable thicknesses these assumptions will not apply. The consequences of operating a supercavitating foil of too great thickness are often severe. In Fig. 12II.19 are revealed the experi-

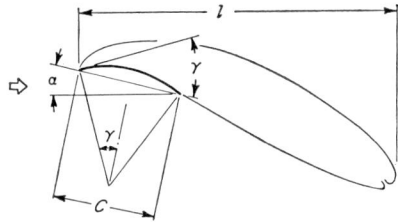

Fig. 12II.18. Schematic cavity flow past a circular arc hydrofoil.

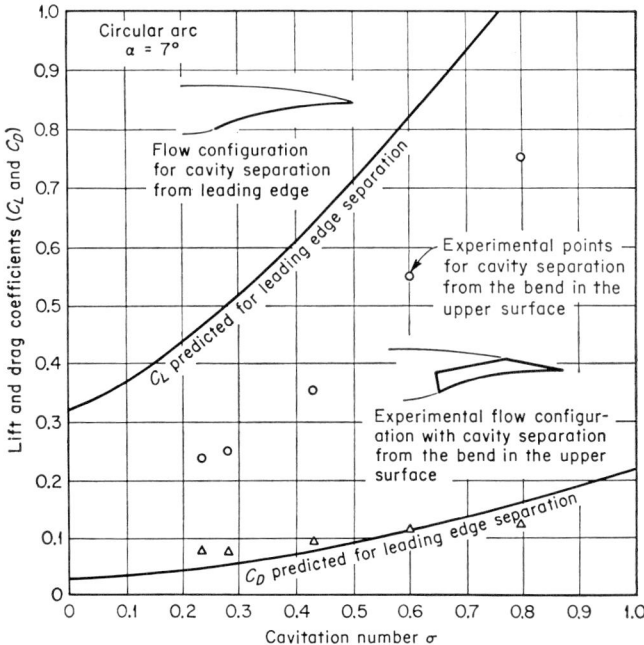

Fig. 12II.19. Measured lift and drag of a thick supercavitating foil. (*Ref.* 32.)

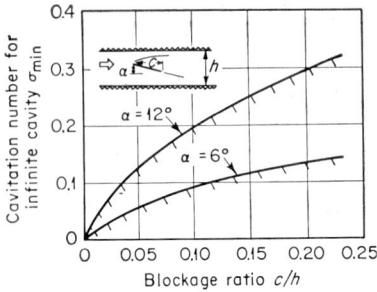

FIG. 12II.20. Choking cavitation number σ_{min}: vs. blockage ratio c/h.

mental consequences of cavity detachment not at the leading edge but at some distance aft; the loss in lifting efficiency is apparent.

The restrictions on allowable foil thickness may often cause difficulties in structural design. As an alternative to the knife-edged low-drag sections, it has been suggested that fully wetted cambered foils with a parabolic thickness distribution might prove useful.[37] Experiments reveal that properly designed foils of this type may be used at low cavitation numbers, but probably for a narrow range of angles of attack, as might be anticipated.

Wall and Free-jet-boundary Effects. As in the case of supercavitating flow past struts, the effect of boundaries on the cavity dimensions may be very large; cavity lengths on foils tested between walls will always be lengthened relative to the unbounded condition and shortened by a free jet. Tunnel choking (see the discussion of wall effects on strut flows) will occur for a lifting foil between solid walls at a cavitation number greater than zero. Theoretical values of the choking cavitation number σ_{min} for a flat-plate foil at angles of attack equal to 6 and 12° are shown for different values of the ratio of foil chord c to tunnel height h in Fig. 12II.20; the foil is in every case situated midway between the walls.

Theory indicates that the effect of the solid walls on the lift coefficient of a lifting foil placed midway between walls, the cavitation number being fixed, is not large (less than 5 per cent), the effect of the walls being to slightly reduce the lift developed. The smallness of the effect in this case seems largely due to the cancellation of the opposing effect of the upper and lower walls. If a foil lifting upward is placed above the tunnel centerline, its lift will be decreased, while the opposite effect will result should it be placed below the tunnel centerline. The different effect of walls above and below is illustrated in Fig. 12II.21, in which h_u is the distance from the foil (of chord c) to the upper wall, and h_l to the lower wall.

The effect of a free jet on a lifting foil placed midway between its boundaries is also to reduce the lift developed, but as was the case with slender struts, the free-jet effects are liable to be considerably larger than those of solid walls. As an example, both experiments and theory reveal[17] a lift reduction of 17 per cent on a flat plate inclined at an angle of attack of 8° midway between the boundaries of a free jet of width five times the foil chord at a cavitation number zero. The effect, however, became insignificant at $\sigma = 0.1$.

The effect of a free surface on the performance of a foil moving beneath it is of considerable importance in connection with the near-surface operation of hydrofoil craft. The general effect is to increase the lift over the unbounded value. A flat-plate foil at $\sigma = 0$ doubles its lift as it moves from an infinite depth to the free surface. A low-drag section developing lift through camber, however, only increases its lift about 20 per cent under the same circumstances. Although the changes of lift with submersion are particularly rapid within the last chord length of depth, theory reveals that depths even greater than 10 chords must be attained before the lift

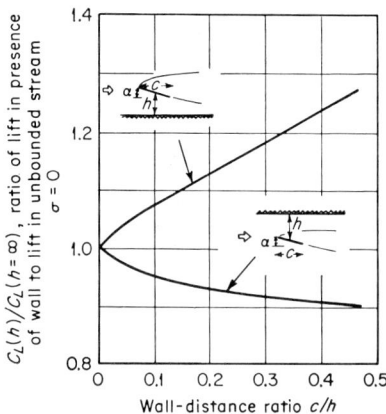

FIG. 12II.21. Lift in presence of wall vs. wall distance ratio, $\sigma = 0$.

drops to within 5 per cent of its infinite-depth value. It should be pointed out that the above remarks apply to two-dimensional (infinite-span) supercavitating hydrofoils and that the effect of finite aspect ratio is to reduce the effect of the free surface; for example, a supercavitating wing of aspect ratio 1, with flat-bottomed sections only, increases its lift by 25 per cent as it moves from infinite depth to the surface. A full discussion of these free-surface effects on foils and wings operating at low cavitation numbers is contained in Ref. 36.

Supercavitating Cascades. Lifting foils in cascade operating under supercavitating condition have been studied particularly in connection with the stalled operation of aerodynamic compressors and turbines,[38-40] the assumption being made that the flow past a completely stalled cascade is very similar to that in a "choked" supercavitating cascade. In fact, the cavity-flow theory so far applied appears to allow some reasonable predictions of high-solidity cascade performance in the completely stalled regime. A few calculations have been made for supercavitating flat plates with finite- as well as infinite-length (choked-flow) cavities, and the results of linearized theory calculations are presented in Ref. 41 for flat-plate cascades with stagger angles of 0, 30, and 60°. Just as in the case of struts or foils between solid walls, lifting cascades will throw infinite-length cavities (choke) at cavitation numbers greater than zero, thus limiting the low-cavitation-number operation of cascades. The cascade effect is to decrease the lift developed by the foil, just as in fully wetted flow, and such effects may be severe; even for a gap-chord ratio as large as 5, the lift on supercavitating flat plates in cascade may be reduced by over 10 per cent for a 0° stagger configuration and by over 30 per cent for 60° stagger.

Gravity Effects. The effect of a vertical gravity field on an infinite-span supercavitating flat plate in a horizontal flow has been studied.[18] The results of this approximate analysis indicate, however, that such gravity effects are probably not important except for small Froude numbers $\mathbf{F}$, if $\mathbf{F} = U_0/\sqrt{gc}$. The gravity effect is, as might be expected, most severe at very low cavitation numbers, where very wide cavities result, the effect increasing with the lift. For a foil lifting upward, the lift is reduced and cavities shortened by the effect of gravity; a flat-bottomed foil at 4° angle of attack operating at a cavitation number of 0.3 suffers about a 10 per cent loss in lift for $\mathbf{F} = 5$ and an insignificant loss for $\mathbf{F} = 10$. These results indicate that gravity effects of this kind are thus probably not important except for low-speed ($U_0 < 20$ fps) tests of relatively large models ($c > 2$ in.). The trailing cavities are, incidentally, apparently not caused to drift upward by the gravity field. Further quantitative information is contained in Ref. 18. The effect on a lifting foil of a gravity field in the plane of the flow has not been specifically determined, but the situation for supercavitating strut flows (see the discussion in Art. 12II.2 on gravity effect on struts) in such a field should be indicative of the magnitude of the effect to be expected.

Unsteady Effects on Lifting Foils. The lift acting on a supercavitating foil will, of course, be affected by flow unsteadiness or nonsteady motions of the foil. It is possible for the foil attitude to undergo such large changes with time that the cavity oscillates from one side of the foil to the other; such extreme effects have not been studied. If, however, the cavity oscillations are not extreme so that the cavity remains always on one side of the foil, then some predictions of the effects of unsteadiness may be made. In particular, the unsteady lift acting on a foil at $\sigma = 0$ and which is executing both small heaving and pitching motions may be determined through the superposition of the known theoretical responses to small harmonic oscillations.[21,25] These latter theoretical results indicate that the unsteady lift on a supercavitating foil ($\sigma = 0$) is very closely given by quasi-steady theory; such theory assumes that the lift at any time during the motions is identical with the value that would obtain at the instantaneous effective angle of attack (for heaving) and effective camber (in the case of pitching) and taking the lift due to added-mass effects into account. In the case of heaving motion, if the theoretical added mass is increased by about 20 per cent, then the quasi-steady theory estimates the lift due to oscillations with an accuracy better than 10 per cent even for very high frequencies of oscillation ($\omega c/U_9$ as high as 3). The meaning of this is that the lift on a supercavitating foil is insensitive to the history of the motion. This is not at all true for fully wetted foils, and the relative insensitivity of supercavitating foils to motion history is thought to be a consequence of the facts that (1) at all times the pressure at the leading and trailing edges is fixed and equal to the cavity pressure, and (2) the pressure on either side of the wake downstream of the body is the same, thus restricting the allowable strength of the wake vorticity.

The theoretical added mass of a supercavitating foil undergoing accelerations transverse to the flow direction is $\%_{16}$ of the transverse added mass of a fully wetted foil; the latter is $\rho\pi c^2/4$ if ρ is the density of the fluid and c is the foil chord.

12II.4. Bodies of Revolution

Supercavitating flows about bodies of revolution have been studied especially in connection with underwater ordnance problems, as, for example, the water entry and subsequent motions of a torpedolike body. These supercavitating flows are not as amenable to theoretical treatment as their two-dimensional counterparts, but they have been the subject of considerable experimental study.

Drag. The drag of axially symmetric bodies in cavity flow increases with body "fullness" in much the same way as the drag of struts. The drag of cones at zero cavitation number is shown in Fig. 12II.22 as obtained from approximate theory[42] and verified by experiments.[43] These results may be compared with those for wedges and presented in Fig. 12II.22.

The precise effect of cavitation number on the drag of even simple bodies of revolution with fixed detachment is not entirely understood. The drag coefficient is known[44,45] to increase asymptotically (σ approaching zero) according to Eq. (12II.1). However, the magnitude of the σ range over which this law applies must depend upon the fullness of the body, just as shown for the two-dimensional case by Fig. 12II.3. There exists some theoretical evidence[42] that for quite slender bodies the validity of Eq. (12II.1) is in fact limited to a very narrow range of cavitation numbers. In Fig. 12II.23 is shown the effect of σ on the drag of cones, according to the approximate theory of Ref. 42. These results are well summarized by the approximate relation

$$C_D(\sigma) = C_D(0) + \sigma \qquad (12\text{II}.14)$$

if the drag coefficient is based on disc area. This relationship is in contrast to the known asymptotic law as given by Eq. (12II.1). Experimental results[43,45] are somewhat in conflict, but the most recent experiments[43] are in very good agreement with the results just presented for cone angles up to 30° and in fair agreement for larger angles. Incidentally, the drag of the circular disc has been calculated most accurately by Garabedian for two cavitation numbers[46,47]; he obtained $C_D(0) = 0.827$ and $C_D(0.2235) = 1.058$; the approximate theory of Ref. 42 is in very good agreement with the first of these values and within 5 per cent agreement with the second.

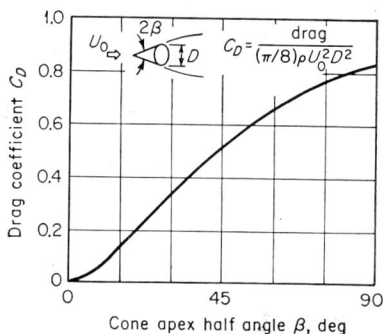

FIG. 12II.22. Drag coefficient of cones, $\sigma = 0$.

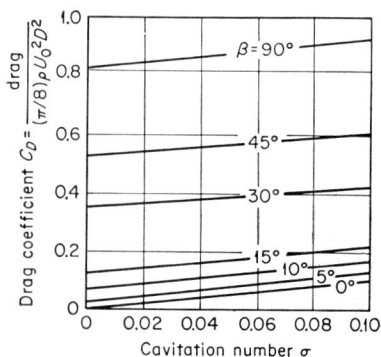

FIG. 12II.23. Cone-drag coefficient vs. cavitation number.

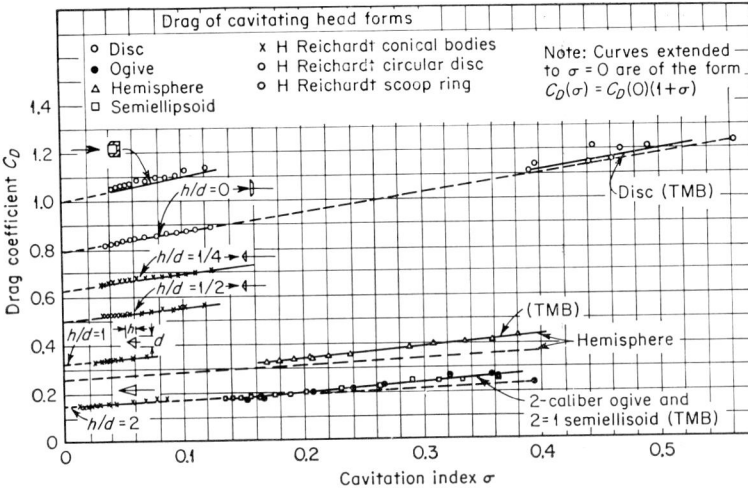

Fig. 12II.24. Measured drag coefficients for various axisymmetric bodies. (*Ref.* 49.)

Experiments on spheres in ventilated flow at low cavitation number[48] show an important influence of speed on the cavity-detachment angle and drag coefficient. The data at the highest speeds indicate a value of $C_D(0)$ of about 0.255 and a detachment angle of about 77° measured from the nose. Other data for hemispheres in cavitating flow at somewhat higher cavitation numbers are consistent with the just-quoted value of drag.[49] These hemisphere data together with a compilation of drag information on cones and other bodies are shown[49] in Fig. 12II.24.

In this figure the data of Reichardt are from Ref. 45. It is noted that the controversial extrapolation given by Eq. (12II.1) has been used in this figure. All these data are, incidentally, uncorrected for possible tunnel-wall effects.

Blunt-based axisymmetric bodies of given length-diameter ratios or of given volume (the length being fixed) will, in general, have different cavitation drag, depending on their shapes. Minimum drag bodies have been studied[8] and were found to be those forms which consist of a flat disc nose followed to the base of the body by a stream surface corresponding to the cavity shed by the nose.

Lift. The lift produced on yawed cones and discs has been measured[43,50] and the average of experimental results for the lift-curve slope at zero angle of attack is shown as Fig. 12II.25.

A resemblance may be noted between this curve and that of Fig. 12II.14, which deals with wedges. Further results[50] for the lift, moment, and drag of yawed cones and discs at $\sigma = 0.10$ are shown in Fig. 12II.26. The same reference contains similar results for a range of cavitation numbers from 0.08 to 0.16; the effect of σ on lift (measured positive in the same direction as the angle of attack) is generally slight, there being a tendency for the lift to decrease slightly with increasing cavitation number.

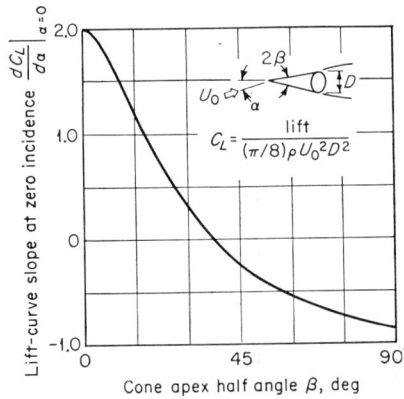

Fig. 12II.25. Cone-lift-curve slope, $\dfrac{dC_L}{d\alpha}\Big|_{\alpha=0}$ at $\sigma = 0$.

Cavity Shapes.   The asymptotic shape of axially symmetric cavities at zero cavitation number[51] is

$$\frac{r}{d} \sim \frac{(C_D)^{1/4}(x/d)^{1/2}}{(\ln x/d)^{1/4}} \tag{12II.15}$$

in which d is the body diameter.   Such cavities thus grow at a less rapid rate than in the two-dimensional case [Eq. (12II.4)].

For small σ the following asymptotic formulas have been obtained:[44,47]

$$\left(\frac{l}{d}\right)^2 \sim \frac{C_D}{\sigma^2} \ln \frac{1}{\sigma} \tag{12II.16}$$

and

$$\left(\frac{l}{\bar{d}}\right)^2 \sim \frac{1}{\sigma} \ln \frac{1}{\sigma} \tag{12II.17}$$

if l = cavity length
   d = body diameter
   $\bar{d}$ = maximum cavity diameter

These are noted to be somewhat different from their two-dimensional counterparts, Eqs. (12II.2) and (12II.3).

The Effect of Walls and Free Boundaries.   The effects of boundaries on the supercavitating flow past a body of revolution are qualitatively similar to the two-dimensional

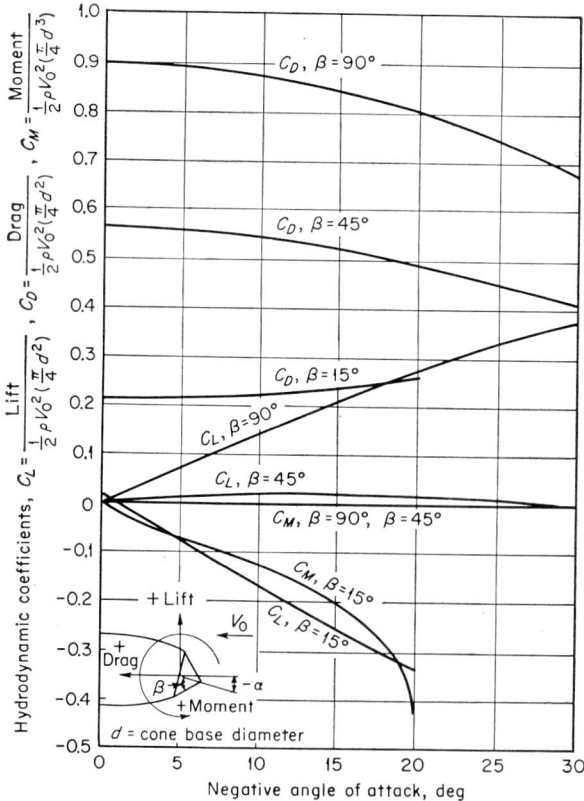

Fig. 12II.26. The lift, drag, and pitching moment for cones in cavity flow, $\sigma = 0.10$. (*Ref.* 50.)

effects described earlier in this article. Choking thus occurs in a solid-wall tunnel at some cavitation number, σ_{min}, which depends on the body size and shape; the results of approximate theory[25] are shown in Fig. 12II.27 for the case of a disc in a circular solid-wall tunnel. By comparison with the choking properties of a vertical flat plate as shown in Fig. 12II.10, the disc would seem to suffer less severe wall effects; the major reason is that the *area* blockage ratio, which is the important quantity, varies as the square of the body-tunnel diameter ratio. When a comparison of choking effects for axisymmetric and two-dimensional flows is made on the basis of area ratios, a closer accordance is obtained.

In Fig. 12II.28, the lengths of cavities shed by a circular disc in a circular solid-wall tunnel are shown. These may again be compared with some two-dimensional results (for a 30° wedge in a two-dimensional tunnel) as shown in Fig. 12II.11. No results for the disc in a

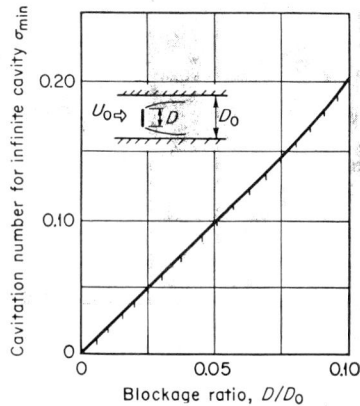

Fig. 12II.27. Choking cavitation number σ_{min} vs. blockage ratio D/D_0 for a disc in a circular tunnel.

circular free jet are presented in Fig. 12II.28, but the results of theoretical calculations[53] reveal that, just as in two dimensions, the effect of free boundaries is to shorten the cavity over the unbounded value, this effect being generally smaller by several times in magnitude than the effect of solid walls.

The extent to which the drag on an axisymmetric body is influenced by boundaries is not precisely known, it usually being assumed that the effect is unimportant. This may be quite true for blunt bodies such as the disc, but just as in two dimensions, there seems reason to believe that boundary effects on the drag of slender bodies should not be assumed negligible.

Gravity Effects on Flows about Bodies of Revolution. An interesting and important phenomenon has been observed in connection with the supercavitating flow about axisymmetric bodies in a vertical gravity field[54-56]. At low speeds (or to be more precise, at low Froude numbers $\mathbf{F}_d = U_0/\sqrt{gd}$), the cavity tends to drift upward (when the gravity field is directed downward) because of the buoyancy force acting on it; at the same time, the velocities on the top and bottom of the cavity are caused to be dif-

ferent because of the net pressure head across the cavity in the vertical direction, the velocity on the lower side being naturally the higher. It is apparently the case that this difference in velocities results in a net circulation around the body and cavity which is sometimes discharged from the end of the cavity through a trailing vortex pair. A picture of trailing vortices behind the cavity shed by a circular disc is shown in Fig. 12II.29.

The two trailing vortices, more or less aligned with the main flow, have low pressures in their cores. In the case of natural cavitation, these cores may be made visible by the core cavitation which is likely to occur; in the case of ventilated or air-fed cavities, as in Fig. 12II.29, the air from the main trailing cavity is likely to fill the low-pressure vortex cores, which may be of considerable length and may

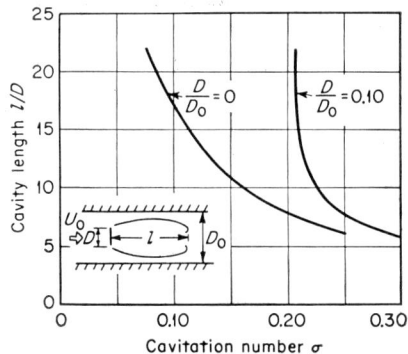

Fig. 12II.28. Cavity length vs. cavitation number for a disc in unbounded flow ($D/D_0 = 0$) and in a circular solid-wall tunnel ($D/D_0 = 0.10$).

Fig. 12II.29. View from below of trailing vortices behind a cavity shed by a disc. (*Courtesy of Taras Kiceniuk, Hydrodynamics Laboratory, California Institute of Technology.*)

even reach the water surface in the case of a body moving at not too great subsurface distances.   Especially in the latter case, it becomes necessary to feed air at a high rate to the main cavity in order to make up for the loss through the vortex-core passage to the surface.   This phenomenon involving trailing vortices does not occur in every case when a cavity flow occurs behind a body of revolution in a vertical gravity field. Experimental evidence indicates that its occurrence depends on the magnitude of the quantity $F_d\sigma$; in the case of a circular disc, when this product of Froude number and cavitation number is less than 1, then the trailing vortices and subsequent high air-supply requirements (for ventilated flows) are likely to exist, but when this product is greater than 1, then the conventional reentrant jet type of behavior is more to be expected[54-56].   This interesting phenomenon is of particular importance in connection with air-supply requirements for ventilated bodies of revolution, but its effect on the forces acting on the body is likely to be small.

The effect of a gravity field acting in the flow direction has not been studied for axisymmetric flows, but results qualitatively similar to those that occur in two-dimensions might be expected.

REFERENCES

1. *Proc. Second ONR Symposium on Naval Hydrodynamics*, Government Printing Office, 1960.
2. Arnoff, E. L.: Re-entrant Jet Theory and Cavity Drag for Symmetric Wedges, *Naval Ordnance Test Sta. Rept. 368, NAVORD Rept.* 1298, March, 1959.
3. Plesset, M. S., and P. A. Shaffer, Jr.: Cavity Drag in Two and Three Dimensions, *J. Appl. Phys.*, **19**(10):934–939 (1948).
4. Cox, A. D., and W. A. Clayden: Cavitating Flow about a Wedge at Incidence, *J. Fluid Mech.*, **3**(6):615 (1958).
5. Wu, T. Y.: A Simple Method for Calculating the Drag in the Linear Theory of Cavity Flows, *Calif. Inst. Tech. Eng. Div. Rept.* 85-5, August, 1957.
6. Tulin, M. P.: Steady Two-dimensional Cavity Flows about Slender Bodies, *David Taylor Model Basin Rept.* 834, May, 1953.
7. Birkhoff, G., H. H. Goldstine, and E. H. Zarantonello: Calculation of Plane Cavity Flows Past Curved Obstacles, *Rend. Seminar. Mat. Turin*, **13**:205–224 (1954).
8. Tulin, M. P.: Supercavitating Flow Past Foils and Struts, *Proc. 1955 NPL Symposium on Cavitation in Hydrodynamics*, Philosophical Library, New York, 1956.
9. Brodetsky, S.: Discontinuous Fluid Motion Past Circular and Elliptic Cylinders, *Proc. Roy. Soc. (London)*, **A102**:542–553 (1923).
10. Roshko, A.: A New Hodograph for Free-streamline Theory, *NACA Tech. Note* 3168, July, 1954.
11. Kawaguti, M.: Discontinuous Flow Past a Circular Cylinder, *J. Phys. Soc. Japan*, **8**(3):403–406 (1953).
12. Efros, D. A.: Construction of Free Streamline Flows by the Method of Electrical Simulation, *Rept. USSR Acad. Sci., Dept. Tech. Sci.*, 9, 1947.   Available in English as *Rensselaer Polytech. Inst. Math. Trans.* 1, 1958.

13. Tulin, M. P.: New Developments in the Theory of Supercavitating Flows, *Proc. Second ONR Symposium on Naval Hydrodynamics*, Government Printing Office, 1960.
14. Birkhoff, G., M. Plesset, and N. Simmons: Wall Effects in Cavity Flow, part I, *Quart. Appl. Math.*, vol. 8, no. 2, 1950; part II, *Quart. Appl. Math.*, vol. 9, no. 4, 1952.
15. Gurevich, M. I.: Symmetrical Cavitation Flow around a Flat Plate, Situated between Parallel Walls, *Rept. USSR Acad. Sci., Dept. Tech. Sci.*, 4, 1946. Available in English as *Rensselaer Polytech. Inst., Math. Trans.* 2, 1959.
16. Cohen, H., and R. C. Di Prima: Wall Effects in Cavitating Flows, *Proc. Second ONR Symposium on Naval Hydrodynamics*, 1960.
17. Silberman, E.: Experimental Studies of Supercavitating Flow about Simple Two-dimensional Bodies in a Jet, *J. Fluid Mech.*, **5**(3):337-354 (1959).
18. Parkin, B. R.: A Note on the Cavity Flow Past a Hydrofoil in a Liquid with Gravity, *Calif. Inst. Tech. Eng. Div. Rept.* 47-9, December, 1957.
19. Acosta, A. J.: The Effect of a Longitudinal Gravity Field on the Supercavitating Flow over a Wedge, *Calif. Inst. Tech. Eng. Div. Rept.* 79.1, May, 1958.
20. Gilbarg, D.: Unsteady Flows with Free Boundaries, *ZAMP*, vol. 3, no. 3, 1952.
21. Parkin, B. R.: Fully Cavitating Hydrofoils in Nonsteady Motion, *Calif. Inst. Tech. Eng. Div. Rept.* 85-2, July, 1957.
22. Wu, T. Y.: A Linearized Theory for Nonsteady Cavity Flows, *Calif. Inst. Tech. Eng. Div. Rept.* 85-6, September, 1957.
23. von Kármán, T.: "Accelerated Flow of an Incompressible Fluid with Wake Formation," in "Collected Works," Butterworth's Scientific Publications, London, vol. 4, pp. 396-398, 1956.
24. Gurevich, M. I.: The Impact on a Lamina with Discontinuous Streamline Flow, *Prik. Mat. Mech.*, **16**(1):116-118 (1952).
25. Wu, T. Y.: Unsteady Supercavitating Flows, *Proc. Second ONR Symposium on Naval Hydrodynamics*, Government Printing Office, 1960.
26. Kermeen, R. W.: Water Tunnel Tests of NACA 66_1-012 Hydrofoil in Noncavitating and Cavitating Flows, *Calif. Inst. Tech. Hydrodynamics Lab. Rept.* 47-7, February, 1956.
27. Kermeen, R. W.: Water Tunnel Tests of NACA 4412 and Walchner Profile 7 Hydrofoils in Noncavitating and Cavitating Flows, *Calif. Inst. Tech. Hydrodynamics Lab. Rept.* 47-5, February, 1956.
28. Numachi, F., K. Tsunoda, and I. Chida: Four Reports on Cavitation Tests of a Series of Blade Profiles, *Rept. Inst. High Speed Mech., Tohoku Univ.*, **8**:25-107 (1957).
29. Milne-Thomson, L. M.: "Theoretical Hydrodynamics," 2d ed., pp. 297-300, St. Martin's, New York, 1949.
30. Wu, T. Y.: A Free Streamline Theory for Two-dimensional Fully Cavitated Hydrofoils, *J. Math. and Phys.*, **35**(3):236-265 (1956).
31. Wu, T. Y.: A Note on the Linear and Nonlinear Theories for Fully Cavitated Hydrofoils, *Calif. Inst. Tech. Hydrodynamics Lab. Rept.* 21-22, August, 1956.
32. Parkin, B. R.: Experiments on Circular Arc and Flat Plate Hydrofoils in Noncavitating and Full Cavity Flows, *J. Ship Research*, **1**(4):34 (1958).
33. Tulin, M. P., and M. P. Burkart: Linearized Theory for Flows about Lifting Foils at Zero Cavitation Number, *David Taylor Model Basin Rept.* C-638, February, 1955.
34. Tachmindji, A. J., W. B. Morgan, M. L. Miller, and R. Hecker: The Design and Performance of Supercavitating Propellers, *David Taylor Model Basin Rept.* C-807, February, 1957.
35. Tachmindji, A. J., and W. B. Morgan: The Design and Estimated Performance of a Series of Supercavitating Propellers, *Proc. Second ONR Symposium on Naval Hydrodynamics*, Government Printing Office, 1960.
36. Johnson, V. E., Jr.: The Influence of Depth of Submersion, Aspect Ratio, and Thickness on Supercavitating Hydrofoils Operating at Zero Cavitation Number, *Proc. Second ONR Symposium on Naval Hydrodynamics*, Government Printing Office, 1960.
37. Johnson, V. E., Jr., and T. A. Rasnick: Investigation of a High-speed Hydrofoil with Parabolic Thickness Distribution, *NASA Tech. Note* D-119, November, 1959.
38. Betz, A., and E. Petersohn: Anwendung der Theorie der freien Strahlen, *Ingr.-Arch.*, **2**:190-211 (1931).
39. Cornell, W. G.: The Stall Performance of Cascades, *Proc. Second U.S. Natl. Congr. Appl. Mech.*, pp. 705-713, 1954.
40. Cornell, W. G.: Some Aerodynamic Cavity Flows in Flight Propulsion Systems, *Proc. Second ONR Symposium on Naval Hydrodynamics*, Government Printing Office, 1960.
41. Cohen, H., and C. D. Sutherland: Finite Cavity Cascade Flow, *Rensselaer Polytech. Inst. Math. Rept.* 14, April, 1958.
42. Armstrong, A. H.: Drag Coefficients of Wedges and Cones in Cavity Flow, *Armament Research Estab. Rept.* 21/54, Ft. Halstead, Kent, England, 1954.

43. Cox, R. N., and J. W. Maccoll: Recent Contributions to Basic Hydroballistics, *Proc. First ONR Symposium on Naval Hydrodynamics, Natl. Research Council Publ.* 515, 1957.
44. Garabedian, P. R.: Calculation of Axially Symmetric Cavities and Jets, *Stanford Univ. Appl. Math. and Statist. Lab. Tech. Rept.* 42, September, 1955.
45. Reichardt, H.: The Laws of Cavitation Bubbles at Axially Symmetrical Bodies in a Flow, *Minutes of Aircraft Prod. Repts. and Trans.* 766, distributed by Office of Naval Research, 1947.
46. Garabedian, P. R.: The Mathematical Theory of Three-dimensional Cavities and Jets, *Bull. Am. Math. Soc.*, **62**(3):219–235 (1956).
47. Garabedian, P. R.: The Calculation of Axially Symmetric Cavities and Jets, *Pacific J. Math.*, **6**:611–689 (1956).
48. Hsu, E. Y., and B. Perry: Water Tunnel Experiments on Spheres in Cavity Flow, *Calif. Inst. Tech. Hydrodynamics Lab. Rept.* E-24.9, April, 1954.
49. Eisenberg, P., and H. Pond: Water Tunnel Investigations of Steady State Cavities, *David Taylor Model Basin Rept.* 668, October, 1948.
50. Kiceniuk, T.: An Experimental Study of the Hydrodynamic Forces Acting on a Family of Cavity-producing Conical Bodies of Revolution Inclined to the Flow, *Calif. Inst. Tech. Hydrodynamics Lab. Rept.* E-12.17, June, 1954.
51. Levinson, N.: On the Asymptotic Shape of the Cavity behind an Axially Symmetric Nose Moving through an Ideal Fluid, *Ann. Math.*, **47**:704–730 (1946).
52. Campbell, I. J., and G. E. Thomas: Water Tunnel Boundary Effects on Axially Symmetric Fully Developed Cavities, *Admiralty Research Lab.* /R1/G/HY/18/1, Teddington, Middlesex, England, April, 1956.
53. Armstrong, A. H., and K. G. Tadman: Wall Corrections to Axially Symmetric Cavities in Circular Tunnels and Jets, *Armament Research Estab. Rept.* 7/52, Fort Halstead, Kent, England, March, 1953.
54. Swanson, W. M., and J. P. O'Neil: The Stability of an Air-maintained Cavity behind a Stationary Object in Flowing Water, *Calif. Inst. Tech. Mem. Rept.* M-24.3, September, 1951.
55. Cox, R. N., and W. A. Clayden: Air Entrainment at the Rear of a Steady Cavity, *Proc. 1955 NPL Symposium on Cavitation in Hydrodynamics*, Philosophical Library, New York, 1956.
56. Campbell, I. J., and D. V. Hilborne: Air Entrainment behind Artificially Inflated Cavities, *Proc. Second ONR Symposium on Naval Hydrodynamics*, Government Printing Office, 1960.

Section 13

MOTION OF IMMERSED AND FLOATING BODIES

By

LOUIS LANDWEBER, *State University of Iowa, Iowa City, Iowa*

MOTION OF IMMERSED AND FLOATING BODIES

13.1. Introduction

In this section the emphasis shifts from the flow about a body to its motion under the action of the forces exerted by the fluid. It is all one problem, however, since the forces are inextricably related to the flow, and the various fluid phenomena treated in the previous sections must be taken into account in determining these forces. Attention will be focused on the behavior of a single rigid body. If other moving bodies are present, only their influence on the first body will be of interest. The fluid may have rigid or free boundaries, finite or extending to infinity. It will be assumed that the fluid is incompressible.

The dynamical equations of motion of a rigid body were given by Euler about two hundred years ago. If the distribution of the fluid stresses on the body were known as a function of time, one would have a complete set of equations for investigating the stability, motions, and trajectories of the body. In principle, a complete set of equations is available in the combination of Euler's rigid-body equations and the Navier-Stokes equations. But every student of fluid mechanics knows that to solve even the equations for an inviscid fluid, for any but simple shapes, is a difficult problem; for laminar flow it is considerably more so; and that not even the simplest turbulent-flow problem has as yet been solved on the basis of the governing equations, without introducing *ad hoc* assumptions.

In dealing with rigid-body motions, only the integrated effects of the fluid pressures are needed. It suffices to determine certain gross quantities, such as force and inertia coefficients, to take the action of the fluid into account. Fortunately, it is often possible, in cases of practical interest, to estimate these quantities without the preliminary necessity of solving the flow problem completely. The procedures for accomplishing this are described in the present section. In other cases, where means for making rational estimates are not available, experimentally determined values of these quantities will be collated.

13.2. Notation

a	(1) radius of a circle
	(2) length of an elliptical forebody
	(3) wave amplitude
	(4) half width of a two-dimensional "Lewis" form
$\mathbf{a}_c$	acceleration of centroid of volume of body
a_i	coefficients of series transforming a profile into a circle
b	(1) distance between successive vortices in a row of a von Kármán vortex street
	(2) draft of a "Lewis" form
b_i	coefficients of series for complex potential
c	(1) chord of foil
	(2) phase velocity of wave
c_{rs}	coefficients of series for added mass A_{HS}
d	maximum width of a two-dimensional form
e	eccentricity of an ellipse
f	(1) frictional resistance
	(2) distance of a body axis from free surface

g	acceleration of gravity
h	(1) distance between rows of a von Kármán vortex street
	(2) depth of water
k	(1) vortex strength
	(2) height of roughness element
	(3) g/U^2
k_1	added-mass coefficient $A_{11}/\rho V\!\!\!\!-$
k_2	added-mass coefficient $A_{22}/\rho V\!\!\!\!-$
k_e	k_1 for a prolate ellipsoid
k'	added-mass coefficient $A_{55}/\rho I_y$
l	length of body
m	source strength
m_i	a source image corresponding to ϕ_i
n	frequency, cps
$\mathbf{n}$	unit vector along outward normal
n_1, n_2, n_3	components of $\mathbf{n}$ relative to body axes
n_4, n_5, n_6	components of $\mathbf{r} \times \mathbf{n}$ relative to body axes
p	pressure
p_0	ambient pressure
p_c	pressure in a cavity
$p(\omega)$	power spectrum of random variable
q_i	generalized coordinates $i = 1, 2, \ldots, 6$
$\dot{q}_i$	generalized velocities $i = 1, 2, \ldots, 6$
$\mathbf{r}$	a position vector
$\mathbf{r}_c$	position vector of centroid of volume of body
$\mathbf{r}_G$	position vector of G
s	arc length
t	time
u	velocity of vortices relative to fluid
u_0	a steady velocity in x direction
u, v, w	components of $\mathbf{v}$ relative to body axes
u_1, u_2, u_3	components of $\mathbf{v}_G$ relative to body axes
u_4, u_5, u_6	components of $\boldsymbol{\omega}$ relative to body axes
$\mathbf{v}$	velocity at a point in the fluid
$\mathbf{v}_G$	absolute velocity of G
$\mathbf{v}'$	velocity at a point within body excluding contributions from internal singularities
$\overline{v^2}$	power or square of intensity of fluctuation
$v(t)$	deviation from mean of a random variable
w	complex potential $w = \phi + i\psi$
x, y, z	axes of a rectangular cartesian coordinate system attached to body
x_0, y_0, z_0	axes of a fixed rectangular cartesian coordinate system
x_c, y_c, z_c	coordinates of centroid of volume
x_G, y_G, z_G	coordinates of origin G of body axes relative to fixed axes
z	complex variable $z = x + iy$
A	surface area
A_{ij}	added-mass matrix
A_W	waterline area
$A_{Yv}(t)$	initial admittance, response of Y to unit step function v
A_{HS}	added mass for a horizontally oscillating form
B	mass of body
B_{ij}	coefficients of quadratic forms for kinetic energy of a rigid body
C_D	drag coefficient $D/(\frac{1}{2}\rho U^2 c)$
C'_D	drag coefficient $D/(\frac{1}{2}\rho U^2 d)$ or $D/[\frac{1}{2}\rho U^2 \pi(d^2/4)]$
C_f	frictional-resistance coefficient $f/(\frac{1}{2}\rho U^2 A)$
C_{HS}	added-mass coefficient $2A_{HS}/(\pi\rho b^2)$
C_L	lift coefficient $L/(\frac{1}{2}\rho U^2 c)$
C_M	moment coefficient

C_N	normal-force coefficient $N/(\frac{1}{2}\,\rho U^2 c)$
C_p	prismatic coefficient $4 V/(\pi d^2 l)$
C_V	added-mass coefficient $2A_{22}/(\pi \rho a^2)$
C_τ	coefficient of shear stress on boundary
D	drag
E	total energy of a progressive wave per unit area of free surface
F	force per unit length of cable when tangential to stream
$\mathbf{F}$	force on a body
$\mathbf{F}_f$	Froude number $F/\sqrt{gl}$
F_i	generalized forces $i = 1, 2, \ldots, 6$
$G_{Yv}(i\omega)$	frequency-response vector
$G_{Yv}(s)$	a transfer function between input $v(t)$ and output $Y(t)$
$\overline{GM}$	metacentric height
H	draft of ship
I	designation for "imaginary part of"
I_x, I_y, I_z	moments of inertia about x, y, z axes
L	lift
L, M, N	components of $\mathbf{M}$ relative to body axes
$\mathbf{M}$	moment about G
N	normal-force component
$P_n{}^m(\mu)$	Legendre functions
$Q_n{}^m(\zeta)$	Legendre functions
$\mathbf{R}_c$	Reynolds number Uc/ν
$\mathbf{R}_x$	Reynolds number Ux/ν
R	(1) force per unit length of cable when normal to a stream
	(2) distance from origin in spherical coordinates
$R(\tau)$	autocorrelation of a random variable
$\mathbf{S}$	Strouhal number nd/U
S	area bounded by a simple closed path in complex plane
T	(1) kinetic energy of fluid
	(2) a measure of foil-thickness ratio
	(3) tension in a towing cable
U	(1) magnitude of $\mathbf{v}_G$
	(2) group velocity of a system of waves
V	volume of body
X_{u1}	a typical stability derivative $\partial x/\partial u_1$
X, Y, Z	components of $\mathbf{F}$ relative to body axes
$\overline{Y}(s)$	Laplace transform of $Y(t)$
α	(1) angle of attack
	(2) semiapex angle of a wedge
α_m	maximum wave slope
β	(1) angle of drift or yaw
	(2) camber of a foil
	(3) (central angle of a circular arc)/4
Γ	circulation
ζ	(1) a complex variable
	(2) an ellipsoidal coordinate
$\eta(x)$	ordinate of free surface, $y = \eta(x)$
θ	(1) angle of pitch or trim
	(2) angle of cable with stream
	(3) polar angle in spherical coordinates
θ'	angle between z and z_0 axes (an Eulerian angle)
λ	(1) wavelength
	(2) width-length ratio of a two-dimensional form
λ_i	stability indices
μ	an ellipsoidal coordinate
$\boldsymbol{\mu}$	doublet vector
μ_1, μ_2, μ_3	components of $\boldsymbol{\mu}$ relative to body axes

μ_i	a doublet image of ϕ_i
μ_{ij}	j component of μ_i relative to body axes
ν	kinematic viscosity
ρ	mass density of fluid
σ	(1) source distribution
	(2) ratio of area of a two-dimensional form to area of circumscribing rectangle
σ_c	cavitation number $(p_0 - p_c)/\rho U^2/2$
σ_i	a source distribution image of ϕ_i
τ_0	shear stress on boundary
τ_{ij}	stress tensor within fluid
φ	(1) angle of roll
	(2) azimuthal angle in spherical coordinates
φ'	an Eulerian angle
ϕ, ϕ_0, ϕ_i	velocity potentials
ψ	angle of yaw
ψ'	an Eulerian angle
ω	angular velocity of body
$(\Delta u_1)'$	$(u_1/u_0 - 1)$; prime denotes nondimensionalization

13.3. Kinematics and Dynamics of a Rigid Body

It is necessary to use two coordinate systems in studying the motion of a rigid body, one a right-hand rectangular cartesian coordinate system, x_0, y_0, z_0, with origin at 0, which is fixed in space, another, x, y, z, with origin at G, which is attached to the body. For most problems it will suffice to neglect the acceleration of a point on the surface of the earth, so that the fixed axes may be attached to the earth with the positive z_0 axis directed vertically downward. The x_0, y_0 axes in the horizontal plane will then generally be chosen so that the fixed and body axes coincide initially in an equilibrium attitude. The following considerations, however, do not depend upon any special selection of the fixed axes. The point G will be taken at the center of mass of the body, and the body axes will be taken to coincide with the principal axes of inertia. Whenever the geometry of the body permits, the x axis will be the longitudinal one, the y axis will be a transverse axis directed toward the right when facing in the positive x direction, and the z axis will be the normal axis directed from the top to the bottom of the body. In important classes of bodies, the zx plane will be a principal plane of symmetry.

The orientation of the body axes is specified when the nine direction cosines relating the two coordinate systems are known. In treatments of the dynamics of rigid bodies, these direction cosines are usually expressed in terms of the three independent Eulerian angles. In dealing with the important class of elongated bodies with a principal plane of symmetry, it is more useful to describe the orientation of a body in terms of an angle of pitch or trim θ, an angle of yaw ψ, and an angle of roll φ. Since in other cases it may be preferred to use the Eulerian angles, called θ', φ', ψ', to distinguish them from the previous set, the definitions and the expressions of the direction cosines and the angular velocities are given for each set.

Suppose that, instantaneously, the origins of the two coordinate systems coincide. Then the Eulerian angles θ' and φ' are the usual spherical coordinate angles of the positive z axis relative to the fixed axes, with z_0 as the polar axis, as is shown in Fig. 13.1. Similarly, θ' and $-\psi'$ are the spherical coordinate angles of the positive z_0 axis relative to the body axes. The direction cosines are then given by Table 13.1.

The pitch, yaw, and roll angles are also closely related to spherical coordinate angles. As is shown in the definition sketch (Fig. 13.2) $(\pi/2) + \theta$ and ψ are the spherical coordinate angles of the positive x axis relative to the fixed axes, with z_0 as the polar axis. Similarly $(\pi/2) - \theta$ and $(\pi/2) - \varphi$ are the spherical coordinate angles of the z_0 axis relative to the body

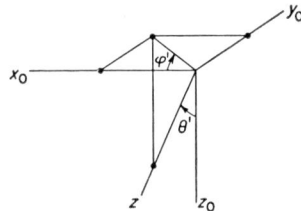

Fig. 13.1. Eulerian angles θ', φ'.

Table 13.1

	x_0	y_0	z_0
x	$\cos\theta'\cos\varphi'\cos\psi' - \sin\varphi'\sin\psi'$	$\cos\theta'\sin\varphi'\cos\psi' + \cos\varphi'\sin\psi'$	$-\sin\theta'\cos\psi'$
y	$-\cos\theta'\cos\varphi'\sin\psi' - \sin\varphi'\cos\psi'$	$-\cos\theta'\sin\varphi'\sin\psi' + \cos\varphi'\cos\psi'$	$\sin\theta'\sin\psi'$
z	$\sin\theta'\cos\varphi'$	$\sin\theta'\sin\varphi'$	$\cos\theta'$

axes with x as the polar axis, as is shown in Fig. 13.3. One could also define θ as the angle between the x axis and the $x_0 y_0$ plane, ψ as the dihedral angle between the $z_0 x_0$ and the $z_0 x$ planes, and φ as the dihedral angle between the $x z_0$ and $x z$ planes. The direction cosines are given in Table 13.2.

Let x_G, y_G, z_G denote the coordinates of G relative to the fixed coordinate system, and $\mathbf{r}_G$ the corresponding position vector. The trajectory and orientation of the body will be completely specified when x_G, y_G, z_G and the Eulerian angles are known as functions of time. Furthermore, let $\mathbf{v}_G$ denote the absolute velocity of G, with components u_1, u_2, u_3 in the moving frame, and $\boldsymbol{\omega}$ the angular velocity of the body, with components u_4, u_5, u_6, also relative to the body axes. The latter are related to the Eulerian angles by the expressions

$$u_4 = \dot{\theta}'\sin\psi' - \dot{\varphi}'\sin\theta'\cos\psi'$$
$$u_5 = \dot{\theta}'\cos\psi' + \dot{\varphi}'\sin\theta'\sin\psi' \tag{13.1}$$
$$u_6 = \dot{\psi}' + \dot{\varphi}'\cos\theta'$$

in which the dots indicate differentiation with respect to time, and the relations with the pitch, roll, and yaw angles are

$$u_4 = \dot{\varphi} - \dot{\psi}\sin\theta$$
$$u_5 = \dot{\psi}\cos\theta\sin\varphi + \dot{\theta}\cos\varphi \tag{13.2}$$
$$u_6 = \dot{\psi}\cos\theta\cos\varphi - \dot{\theta}\sin\varphi$$

Furthermore, by applying either table of direction cosines, Table 13.2, for example, the velocity components of G relative to the fixed axes may be written in the form

$$\dot{x}_G = u\cos\theta\cos\psi + v(\sin\theta\sin\varphi\sin\psi - \cos\varphi\sin\psi) + w(\sin\theta\cos\varphi\cos\psi + \sin\varphi\sin\psi)$$
$$\dot{y}_G = u\cos\theta\sin\psi + v(\sin\theta\sin\varphi\sin\psi + \cos\varphi\cos\psi) + w(\sin\theta\cos\varphi\sin\psi - \sin\varphi\cos\psi) \tag{13.3}$$
$$\dot{z}_G = -u\sin\theta + v\cos\theta\sin\varphi + w\cos\theta\cos\varphi$$

Thus, if $\mathbf{v}_G$ and $\boldsymbol{\omega}$ have been obtained as solutions of the equations of motion, the set of Eqs. (13.2) can be solved for $\theta(t)$, $\varphi(t)$, and $\psi(t)$, and these functions substituted into Eqs. (13.3) to solve for $x_G(t)$, $y_G(t)$, and $z_G(t)$.

Although the orientation of the body with respect to the relative fluid velocity is

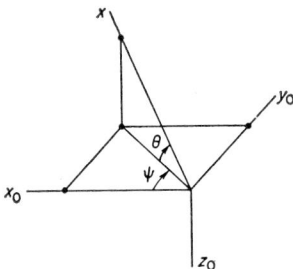

Fig. 13.2. Pitch and yaw angles θ, ψ.

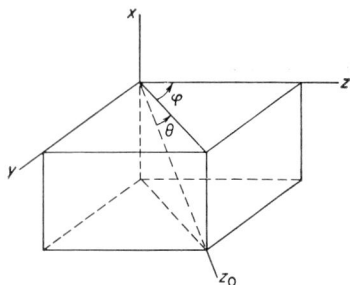

Fig. 13.3. Pitch and roll angles θ, φ.

Table 13.2

	x_0	y_0	z_0
x	$\cos\theta\cos\psi$	$\cos\theta\sin\psi$	$-\sin\theta$
y	$\sin\theta\sin\varphi\cos\psi - \cos\varphi\sin\psi$	$\sin\theta\sin\varphi\sin\psi + \cos\varphi\cos\psi$	$\cos\theta\sin\varphi$
z	$\sin\theta\cos\varphi\cos\psi + \sin\varphi\sin\psi$	$\sin\theta\cos\varphi\sin\psi - \sin\varphi\cos\psi$	$\cos\theta\cos\varphi$

specified by the velocity components u_1, u_2, u_3, it is usually expressed in terms of an angle of attack α and an angle of drift or sideslip β, defined by

$$\alpha = \arctan\frac{u_3}{u_1}$$

$$\beta = -\arcsin\frac{u_2}{U} \tag{13.4}$$

in which $U^2 = u_1{}^2 + u_2{}^2 + u_3{}^2$ (Fig. 13.4). Conversely,

$$
\begin{aligned}
u_1 &= U\cos\alpha\cos\beta \\
u_2 &= -U\sin\beta \\
u_3 &= U\sin\alpha\cos\beta
\end{aligned}
\tag{13.5}
$$

Since the body axes are coincident with the principal axes of inertia, the cross products of inertia vanish. Let B denote the mass of the body, I_x, I_y, I_z its moments of inertia about the x, y, and z axes, $\mathbf{F}$ the force acting on the body, with components X, Y, Z relative to the body axes, and $\mathbf{M}$ the moment about G, with components L, M, N, also with respect to the moving system. The dynamical equations of motion are then as follows:

or

$$
\begin{aligned}
\overline{F} &= B(\dot{\mathbf{v}}_G + \boldsymbol{\omega} \times \mathbf{v}_G) \\
X &= B(\dot{u}_1 + u_5 u_3 - u_6 u_2) \\
Y &= B(\dot{u}_2 + u_6 u_1 - u_4 u_3) \\
Z &= B(\dot{u}_3 + u_4 u_2 - u_5 u_1)
\end{aligned}
\tag{13.6}
$$

and

$$
\begin{aligned}
L &= I_x\dot{u}_4 - (I_y - I_z)u_5 u_6 \\
M &= I_y\dot{u}_5 - (I_z - I_x)u_6 u_4 \\
N &= I_z\dot{u}_6 - (I_x - I_y)u_4 u_5
\end{aligned}
\tag{13.7}
$$

13.4. Analysis of Forces Exerted by Fluid

Inviscid Fluid. An inviscid fluid exerts only normal pressures on a body, and the resulting force and moment are

$$\mathbf{F} = -\int p\mathbf{n}\,dS \qquad \mathbf{M} = -\int p\mathbf{r} \times \mathbf{n}\,dS \tag{13.8}$$

in which p is the pressure, $\mathbf{n}$ the unit vector along the outward normal, with components n_1, n_2, n_3 in the moving coordinate system, dS the area of a surface element, $\mathbf{r}$ its position vector relative to the origin G about which the moments are taken, and the integrations extend over the surface of the body.

When the body is completely immersed in the fluid, the boundary condition that the body is impermeable is expressible in the form

$$(\mathbf{v} - \mathbf{v}_G - \boldsymbol{\omega} \times \mathbf{r}) \cdot \mathbf{n} = 0 \tag{13.9}$$

in which $\mathbf{v}$ is the velocity of the fluid at a point on the body, with components u, v, w relative

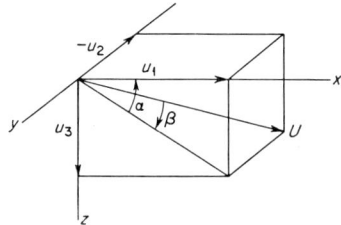

Fig. 13.4. Angles of attack and drift α, β.

to the moving coordinate system. If the flow is irrotational, the fluid velocity is expressible in terms of a velocity potential ϕ as

$$\mathbf{v} = -\mathrm{grad}\ \phi = -\boldsymbol{\nabla}\phi \tag{13.10}$$

It is convenient to obtain ϕ from the superposition of potentials corresponding to the separate velocity components, viz.,

$$\phi = \phi_0 + \sum_{i=1}^{6} u_i \phi_i \tag{13.11}$$

in which the potentials satisfy Laplace's equation and the boundary conditions

$$\frac{\partial \phi_0}{\partial n} = 0 \qquad \frac{\partial \phi_i}{\partial n} = -n_i \tag{13.12}$$

in which n is in the direction of the outward normal to the surface and n_4, n_5, n_6 are the components of $\mathbf{r} \times \mathbf{n}$ in the moving coordinate system. If these equations can be solved for $\mathbf{v}$ when $\mathbf{v}_G$ and $\boldsymbol{\omega}$ are given, the pressure would then be obtained from the Bernoulli equation, which, for the case of a system of coordinates moving with the body, assumes the form

$$\frac{p}{\rho} - gz + \tfrac{1}{2}\left[(u - u_1)^2 + (v - u_2)^2 + (w - u_3)^2\right] + \mathbf{v} \cdot \boldsymbol{\omega} \times \mathbf{r} - \frac{\partial \phi}{\partial t} = 0 \tag{13.13}$$

The force and moment due to the fluid, needed to complete the equations of motion (13.6) and (13.7), would then be given by Eqs. (13.8). This most direct procedure for obtaining the effects of the fluid is suitable for application to forms for which solutions for the six velocity potentials can be readily obtained. Because of the increasing availability of high-speed computing machines, which can perform conformal mappings or solve integral equations in a matter of minutes, it must be considered practicable to obtain such solutions for arbitrary two-dimensional forms and for bodies of revolution. Even for these classes of forms, however, this direct procedure for obtaining the force and moment may not be the best. The importance of Eqs. (13.8) lies rather in the fact that they have served as the basis for deriving other, more useful expressions for $\mathbf{F}$ and $\mathbf{M}$, which are presented in the following.

Because of the d'Alembert paradox, that a body, moving with constant velocity in an unbounded and otherwise undisturbed fluid, experiences no drag, it might be supposed that forces and moments predicted on the basis of inviscid-flow theory would be of little or no practical interest. On the contrary, it has been found that, by means of this theory, it is possible to make useful predictions of the characteristics of many practical configurations, such as airfoils, airships, submarines, and surface vessels.

Real Fluid. In a real fluid, a boundary layer and possibly a region of separated flow, around the body, and a wake behind it are present. In addition to normal pressures, the body is subjected to shear stresses, the integral of which supplies part of the drag lost in d'Alembert's paradox. The remainder of the drag is contributed by the component of the pressure integral, Eq. (13.8), in the direction of motion.

On streamlined bodies, i.e., bodies on which there is no separation, the pressure distribution on the surface differs appreciably from the inviscid-flow distribution only near the rear of the body. Even without separation the presence of a boundary layer and wake strongly modifies the flow pattern outside of these regions in the neighborhood of the rear of the body, and hence affects the pressure distribution there. This results in a pressure defect and accounts for the *viscous pressure drag* contributed by the pressure integral. When separation occurs, the viscous pressure drag is greatly increased. For streamlined bodies, the drag is principally due to the shear stresses; for bodies with marked separation, the viscous pressure drag is dominant.

In terms of the components of the symmetric stress tensor τ_{ij}, the force and moment components assume the forms of the surface integrals.

$$X = \sum_{j=1}^{3} \int \tau_{1j} n_j \, dS \qquad Y = \sum_{j=1}^{3} \int \tau_{2j} n_j \, dS \qquad Z = \sum_{j=1}^{3} \int \tau_{3j} n_j \, dS \qquad (13.14)$$

$$L = \sum_{j=1}^{3} \int (y\tau_{3j} - z\tau_{2j}) n_j \, dS \qquad M = \sum_{j=1}^{3} \int (z\tau_{1j} - x\tau_{3j}) n_j \, dS \qquad (13.15)$$

$$N = \sum_{j=1}^{3} \int (x\tau_{2j} - y\tau_{1j}) n_j \, dS$$

Here τ_{ij} denotes a force per unit area acting in the x, y, or z direction (according as $i = 1$, 2, or 3) on a surface element normal to the x, y, or z axes (according as $j = 1$, 2, or 3). In order to obtain the force and moment from these equations it would be necessary to solve the Navier-Stokes equations and the equation of continuity for the velocity and pressure field and then to obtain the τ_{ij} from their relations to the rates of strain. It is an extremely difficult problem for laminar flow, and an unsolved one for turbulent flow, to obtain an exact solution of these equations for even simple forms. By applying laminar-boundary-layer theory, it becomes possible to determine the stresses for two-dimensional and axisymmetric streamlined forms, and consequently the forces and moments on such forms, from Eqs. (13.14) and (13.15).

13.5. Forces and Moments in an Inviscid Fluid

Formulation in Terms of Added Masses.[1] In the case of a single body moving through an otherwise unbounded and undisturbed infinite fluid, it can be shown that the entire effect of the fluid may be represented by additions to the inertia of the solid. This is indicated by the expression for the kinetic energy of the fluid,

$$2T = \sum_{i=1}^{6} \sum_{j=1}^{6} A_{ij} u_i u_j \qquad (13.16)$$

in which the quantities A_{ij}, the so-called added masses, are given by

$$A_{ij} = \rho \int \phi_i n_j \, dS = \rho \int \phi_j n_i \, dS \qquad (13.17)$$

Since A_{ij} is symmetric, there are 21 added masses for a given body, of which only 15 are independent. If the body has a plane of symmetry, say, the xz plane, several of the added masses vanish and the kinetic energy assumes the simpler form

$$2T = A_{11}u_1^2 + A_{22}u_2^2 + A_{33}u_3^2 + A_{44}u_4^2 + A_{55}u_5^2 + A_{66}u_6^2$$
$$+ 2(A_{13}u_1u_3 + A_{35}u_3u_5 + A_{51}u_5u_1 + A_{24}u_2u_4 + A_{46}u_4u_6 + A_{62}u_6u_2) \quad (13.18)$$

If, in addition, the yz plane is a plane of symmetry, then Eq. (13.18) is further simplified to

$$2T = A_{11}u_1^2 + A_{22}u_2^2 + A_{33}u_3^2 + A_{44}u_4^2 + A_{55}u_5^2 + A_{66}u_6^2 + 2(A_{15}u_1u_5 + A_{24}u_2u_4)$$
$$(13.19)$$

and if the xy plane is also a plane of symmetry,

$$2T = A_{11}u_1^2 + A_{22}u_2^2 + A_{33}u_3^2 + A_{44}u_4^2 + A_{55}u_5^2 + A_{66}u_6^2 \qquad (13.20)$$

For a body of revolution with the x axis as the axis of symmetry, the expression for the kinetic energy reduces to

$$2T = A_{11}u_1^2 + A_{33}(u_2^2 + u_3^2) + A_{55}(u_5^2 + u_6^2) \qquad (13.21)$$

The force and moment exerted by the fluid on the body are given in terms of the added masses by the equations

$$X = -\frac{d}{dt}\frac{\partial T}{\partial u_1} + u_6 \frac{\partial T}{\partial u_2} - u_5 \frac{\partial T}{\partial u_3}$$

$$Y = -\frac{d}{dt}\frac{\partial T}{\partial u_2} + u_4 \frac{\partial T}{\partial u_3} - u_6 \frac{\partial T}{\partial u_1}$$

$$Z = -\frac{d}{dt}\frac{\partial T}{\partial u_3} + u_5 \frac{\partial T}{\partial u_1} - u_4 \frac{\partial T}{\partial u_2}$$

$$(13.22)$$

$$L = -\frac{d}{dt}\frac{\partial T}{\partial u_4} + u_3 \frac{\partial T}{\partial u_2} - u_2 \frac{\partial T}{\partial u_3} + u_6 \frac{\partial T}{\partial u_5} - u_5 \frac{\partial T}{\partial u_6}$$

$$M = -\frac{d}{dt}\frac{\partial T}{\partial u_5} + u_1 \frac{\partial T}{\partial u_3} - u_3 \frac{\partial T}{\partial u_1} + u_4 \frac{\partial T}{\partial u_6} - u_6 \frac{\partial T}{\partial u_4}$$

$$N = -\frac{d}{dt}\frac{\partial T}{\partial u_6} + u_2 \frac{\partial T}{\partial u_1} - u_1 \frac{\partial T}{\partial u_2} + u_5 \frac{\partial T}{\partial u_4} - u_4 \frac{\partial T}{\partial u_5}$$

More generally, if it is supposed that other boundaries are present but that only the given body is in motion, the force and moment on the body may be obtained by applying Lagrange's equations in the form

$$F_i = -\frac{d}{dt}\frac{\partial T}{\partial \dot q_i} + \frac{\partial T}{\partial q_i}$$

in which $q_i(i = 1, 2, \ldots, 6)$ are generalized coordinates that specify the position and orientation of the body and $F_i(i = 1, \ldots, 6)$ are the generalized components of the force.

Formulation in Terms of Sources and Doublets.[2] If the body of interest is moving in the neighborhood of other fixed or moving boundaries, the added masses are not constants, so that it may not be practicable to express the forces and moments in terms of them. An alternative formulation, which expresses the forces and moments in terms of the hydrodynamic singularities which may be considered to generate the flow about the body, has been found to be highly useful.

Flows that may be considered to be generated by isolated sources, sinks, and doublets and continuously distributed sources or sinks are considered. The symbol m denotes the strength of a source or sink, μ_i the ith component of the strength μ of a doublet relative to the body axes, σ the volume or area density of continuously distributed sources and sinks. Also let $\mathbf{r}_c$ and $\mathbf{a}_c$ denote the position vector and acceleration of the centroid of volume of the body.

The force on the body may be expressed in the form

$$\mathbf{F} = \rho \mathcal{V}\mathbf{a}_c - 4\pi\rho \frac{d}{dt}\left[\int \sigma \mathbf{r}\, d\mathcal{V} + \Sigma(m\mathbf{r} + \mu)\right] - 4\pi\rho \left[\int \sigma \mathbf{v}'\, d\mathcal{V} + \Sigma(m\mathbf{v}' + \mu \cdot \nabla \mathbf{v}')\right]$$

$$(13.23)$$

Here $\mathcal{V}$ denotes the volume of the body, the vector $\mathbf{r}$ the position vector of a source or sink, and $\mathbf{v}'$ the flow velocity at a doublet or an isolated or distributed source or sink, the prime indicating that the contributions to the velocity from the singularity itself and from all other singularities within the body are to be omitted. The last term in the equation may be written more explicitly in the form

$$\mu \cdot \nabla \mathbf{v}' \equiv \left(\mu_1 \frac{\partial}{\partial x} + \mu_2 \frac{\partial}{\partial y} + \mu_3 \frac{\partial}{\partial z}\right)\mathbf{v}'$$

The time derivative is an absolute one. Thus, since x is the ith component of $\mathbf{r}$ relative to the body axes,

$$\left(\frac{d\mathbf{r}}{dt}\right)_i = \frac{dx}{dt} + (\boldsymbol{\omega} \times \mathbf{r})_i$$

The indicated sums are to be taken over all the sources and doublets occurring within the body.

The first of the three groups of terms in Eq. (13.23) represents simply the inertia of the displaced fluid; the second, because it occurs as a time rate of change in a force equation, may be interpreted as a rate of change of momentum to which each source and doublet contributes in the simple manner indicated. These two groups of terms, taken together, give the inertial reaction of the fluid on the accelerating body. When the motion of the body is steady, the force is given by the last group of terms. These, and the corresponding expression for the moment given below, indicate that the forces on the body may be considered to act at the locations of the various internal singularities.

The corresponding expression for the moment on the body is

$$\mathbf{M} = \rho \overline{V} \mathbf{v}_G \times (\omega \times \mathbf{r}_c) - \rho \frac{d}{dt} \int \phi \mathbf{r} \times \mathbf{n} \, dS - 4\pi\rho \left[\int \sigma \mathbf{r} \times \mathbf{v}_G \, d\tau \right.$$

$$\left. + \Sigma(m\mathbf{r} \times \mathbf{v}' + \mu \times \mathbf{v}' + \mathbf{r} \times \mu \cdot \nabla \mathbf{v}') \right] \quad (13.24)$$

Here the vector $\mathbf{r}$ occurring in the sums denotes the position vector of a source or doublet.

Relations between Added Masses and Sources and Doublets.[2] The fact that the forces and moments can be expressed either in terms of added masses or strengths of singularities indicates that there might be a relation between these quantities. It has been found that when a rigid body is moving through a fluid, with other external boundaries at rest, the simple relation

$$A_{ij} + B_{ij} = 4\pi\rho \left(\int \sigma_i x_j \, d\tau + m_i x_j + \mu_{ij} \right) \quad i = 1, 2, \ldots, 6; \quad j = 1, 2, 3$$

$$(13.25)$$

is valid for all the added masses except the six due to rotation alone, A_{44}, A_{45}, A_{45}, A_{55}, A_{56}, A_{66}, for which it has been shown that such a simple relation does not exist. Here B_{ij} are the coefficients in the expression for the kinetic energy T_B of the displaced fluid, considered as a rigid body,

$$2T_B = \sum_{i=1}^{6} \sum_{j=1}^{6} B_{ij} u_i u_j$$

in which
$$B_{11} = B_{22} = B_{33} = B = \rho \overline{V}$$
$$B_{31} = B_{12} = B_{23} = B_{14} = B_{25} = B_{36} = 0$$
$$B_{26} = -B_{35} = B x_c \quad (13.26)$$
$$B_{34} = -B_{16} = B y_c$$
$$B_{15} = -B_{24} = B z_c$$

and x_c, y_c, z_c are the coordinates of the centroid in the moving system. The quantities σ_i, m_i, and μ_i denote the strengths of the singularities within the body corresponding to unit magnitude of the ith (linear or angular) velocity component of the body, and the subscript j denotes the jth component either of the position vector of a singularity or of the vector μ_i.

In the case of an ellipsoid rotating in an infinite fluid in which no external singularities or boundaries are present, it is possible to evaluate the missing relations between added masses and singularities. If the coordinate axes are taken along the principal axes of the ellipsoid, these relations are

$$A_{44} \cdot \frac{B_{44}}{B'_{44}} + B'_{44} = -4\pi\rho \left[\int \sigma_4 x_2 x_3 \, d\tau + \Sigma(m_4 x_2 x_3 + \mu_{42} x_3 + \mu_{43} x_2) \right] \quad (13.27)$$

in which
$$B_{44} = \rho \int (x_2{}^2 + x_3{}^2) \, d\tau \qquad B'_{44} = \rho \int (x_3{}^2 - x_2{}^2) \, d\tau$$

and similar expressions for A_{55} and A_{66}.   The coefficients A_{56}, A_{64}, and A_{45} are zero for the chosen orientation of the coordinate axes.

Equation (13.27) is also suitable as an approximation for bodies elongated along the z axis with nearly elliptical sections in planes perpendicular to this axis.   A similar approximation applies for A_{55}, but not for A_{66}.   When the sections are nearly circular, a simpler approximate relation is

$$A_{44} + B_{44} \doteq 4\pi\rho \left[\int \sigma_4 x_2 x_3 \, d\tau + \Sigma(m_4 x_2 x_3 + \mu_{42} x_3 + \mu_{43} x_2) \right] \qquad (13.28)$$

with a similar expression for A_{55}, but not for A_{66}.   Approximate relations for the mixed rotational coefficients have also been found.   A typical one of these is

$$A_{56} + B_{56} \doteq 4\pi\rho \left[\int \sigma_6 x_3 x_1 \, d\tau + \Sigma(m_6 x_3 x_1 + \mu_{63} x_1 + \mu_{61} x_3) \right] \qquad (13.29)$$

Example 1.   Consider a sphere A of radius a moving with velocity u_1 along the line of centers away from a fixed sphere B of radius b.   Let $c(t)$ be the distance between centers at a given instant.   Using the method of successive images, beginning with a doublet of strength $\mu_0 = \tfrac{1}{2} u_1 a^3$ at the center of A, one obtains for the first image in B a doublet of strength $\mu_1 = - u_1 a^3 b^3 / 2c^3$ at a distance $\xi_1 = c - b^2/c$ from the center of A.   This gives a second image in A, a doublet of strength

$$\mu_2 = \frac{u_1 a^6 b^3}{2(c^2 - b^2)^3}$$

To this order of approximation, from Eq. (13.25), the added mass A_{11} is

$$A_{11} = -B_{11} + 4\pi\rho \frac{\mu_0 + \mu_2}{u_1} = \tfrac{2}{3} \pi\rho a^3 \left[1 + \frac{3a^3 b^3}{(c^2 - b^2)^3} \right]$$

An approximation to the force on sphere A can be obtained by assuming that μ_2 is also situated at the center of A.   If v' is the velocity due to μ_1, then

$$\left(\frac{\partial v'}{\partial x} \right)_{\substack{x=c \\ y=0}} = \frac{3 u_1 a^3 b^3 c}{(c^2 - b^2)^4}$$

and Eq. (13.23) yields

$$\begin{aligned}
X &\doteq -\frac{d}{dt}(u_1 A_{11}) - 4\pi\rho(\mu_0 + \mu_2)\left(\frac{\partial v'}{\partial x} \right)_c \\
&= -\frac{d}{dt}(u_1 A_{11}) - \frac{6\pi\rho u_1^2 a^6 b^3 c}{(c^2 - b^2)^4}\left[1 - \frac{a^3 b^3}{(c^2 - b^2)^3} \right]
\end{aligned}$$

13.6. Directional Stability; Random Disturbances[3]

One of the important characteristics of a body moving through a fluid is its behavior when disturbed from a state of steady motion.   A body is said to be dynamically stable on course if, after its steady motion has been slightly disturbed from a straight course with fixed control surfaces, it resumes its motion on another straight course.   For elongated bodies with a longitudinal plane of symmetry, dynamic stability can be further classified as longitudinal stability for motion in the plane of symmetry; and as lateral stability for translation perpendicular to the plane (sideslipping) or for rotation about an axis lying in it (rolling and yawing).

The motion of a body after it is slightly disturbed from equilibrium can be determined from Eqs. (13.6) and (13.7).   Since all the linear and angular velocity and acceleration components are small, except u_1 (assuming initial steady motion with velocity u_0 in the x direction), these equations may be linearized to yield the simpler forms

$$X = B\dot{u}_1 \qquad Y = B(\dot{u}_2 + u_6 u_0) \qquad Z = B(\dot{u}_3 - u_5 u_0)$$
$$L = I_x \dot{u}_4 \qquad M = I_y \dot{u}_5 \qquad N = I_z \dot{u}_6 \qquad\qquad (13.30)$$

Dimensionless Forms. It is convenient in the stability analysis that follows to operate consistently with dimensionless expressions. A given quantity will be nondimensionalized by considering its dimensions in terms of mass, length, and time as fundamental units and dividing the mass by $\frac{1}{2} \rho l^3$, the length by l, and the time by l/u_0, in which l is the length of the body in the direction of its undisturbed motion. The nondimensionalized form of a given physical quantity will be indicated by a prime, unless explicitly defined otherwise. For example,

$$B' = \frac{B}{\rho l^3/2} \qquad I'_x = \frac{I_x}{\rho l^5/2} \qquad \left(\frac{\partial M}{\partial u_5}\right)' = \frac{\partial M'}{\partial u'_5} = \frac{\partial M/\partial u_5}{(\rho l^4/2)u_0} \qquad u'_0 = 1$$

and Eqs. (13.30) can be nondimensionalized by priming each term.

In the remainder of this treatment of directional stability all quantities will be expressed in dimensionless form. With this understood, the primes will be omitted.

Method of Stability Derivatives. Classical stability theory is based on the assumption that for small deviations from steady motion the (dimensionless) force and moment components are analytic functions of the instantaneous values of the (dimensionless) linear and angular velocity and acceleration components. This assumption has led to results of sufficient accuracy for most purposes; but since there is no a priori reason for neglecting the higher time derivatives of the velocities, these results must be considered as approximations. The nature of this approximation is shown by comparison with the exact treatment of directional stability in the following article.

According to the assumption, X, Y, Z, L, M, N are analytic functions of $u_1, u_2, \ldots, u_6, \dot{u}_1, \dot{u}_2, \ldots, \dot{u}_6$. Each of these functions is now expanded in a Taylor series about the initial values

$$u_1 = 1 \qquad u_2 = \cdots = u_6 = \dot{u}_2 = \cdots = \dot{u}_6 = 0$$

and then linearized, since the disturbances are assumed to be small. Substituting these series into Eqs. (13.30), after observing that the initial values of the forces and moments are zero, yields the set of linear differential equations:

$$X_{u1} \Delta u_1 + X_{u2} u_2 + \cdots + X_{u6} u_6 + X_{\dot{u}1} \dot{u}_1 + \cdots + X_{\dot{u}6} \dot{u}_6 = B\dot{u}_1$$
$$Y_{u1} \Delta u_1 + Y_{u2} u_2 + \cdots + Y_{u6} u_6 + Y_{\dot{u}1} \dot{u}_1 + \cdots + Y_{\dot{u}6} \dot{u}_6 = B(\dot{u}_2 + u_6)$$
$$Z_{u1} \Delta u_1 + Z_{u2} u_2 + \cdots + Z_{u6} u_6 + Z_{\dot{u}1} \dot{u}_1 + \cdots + Z_{\dot{u}6} \dot{u}_6 = B(\dot{u}_3 - u_5)$$

$$(13.31)$$

$$L_{u1} \Delta u_1 + L_{u2} u_2 + \cdots + L_{u6} u_6 + L_{\dot{u}1} \dot{u}_1 + \cdots + L_{\dot{u}6} \dot{u}_6 = I_x \dot{u}_4$$
$$M_{u1} \Delta u_1 + M_{u2} u_2 + \cdots + M_{u6} u_6 + M_{\dot{u}1} \dot{u}_1 + \cdots + M_{\dot{u}6} \dot{u}_6 = I_y \dot{u}_5$$
$$N_{u1} \Delta u_1 + N_{u2} u_2 + \cdots + N_{u6} u_6 + N_{\dot{u}1} \dot{u}_1 + \cdots + N_{\dot{u}6} \dot{u}_6 = I_z \dot{u}_6$$

in which $\Delta u_1 = u_1 - 1$. The subscript notation denotes a partial derivative of a force or moment component with respect to the subscript variable, evaluated at the initial values. The 72 quantities of this type in Eqs. (13.31) are the stability derivatives.

If the body is symmetrical about the yz plane, many of the stability derivatives vanish or become negligibly small. The following derivatives vanish because of symmetry:

1. The nine derivatives of Y, L, and N with respect to u_1, u_3, and u_5
2. The nine derivatives of X, Z, and M with respect to u_2, u_4, and u_6

The following derivatives are usually negligibly small:

1. All the acceleration derivatives except $X_{\dot{u}1}$, $Y_{\dot{u}2}$, $Y_{\dot{u}6}$, $Z_{\dot{u}3}$, $Z_{\dot{u}5}$, $L_{\dot{u}4}$, $M_{\dot{u}3}$, $M_{\dot{u}5}$, $N_{\dot{u}2}$, $N_{\dot{u}6}$, 26 in all
2. X_{u3}, X_{u5}, Z_{u1}, and M_{u1}

Although the equations can be solved without neglecting the latter group of derivatives, they will be neglected in Eqs. (13.31), which then become

$$X_{u1}\,\Delta u_1 + X_{\dot u1}\dot u_1 = B_{\dot u1} \tag{13.32}$$

$$Y_{u2}u_2 + Y_{u4}u_4 + Y_{u6}u_6 + Y_{\dot u2}\dot u_2 + Y_{\dot u6}\dot u_6 = B(\dot u_2 + u_6)$$

$$L_{u2}u_2 + L_{u4}u_4 + L_{u6}u_6 + L_{\dot u4}\dot u_4 = I_z\dot u_4 \tag{13.33}$$

$$N_{u2}u_2 + N_{u4}u_4 + N_{u6}u_6 + N_{\dot u2}\dot u_2 + N_{\dot u6}\dot u_6 = I_z\dot u_6$$

$$Z_{u3}u_3 + Z_{u5}u_5 + Z_{\dot u3}\dot u_3 + Z_{\dot u5}\dot u_5 = B(\dot u_3 - u_5)$$

$$M_{u3}u_3 + M_{u5}u_5 + M_{\dot u3}\dot u_3 + M_{\dot u5}\dot u_5 = I_y\dot u_5 \tag{13.34}$$

The equations now appear as three independent groups. The first is a longitudinal force equation for unsteady flow, taking viscous effects and virtual mass into account. Its solution is

$$\Delta u_1 = C \exp\left(\frac{X_{u1}t}{B - X_{\dot u1}}\right)$$

which, since X_{u1} and X_{u1} are negative, is a damped mode of the disturbance.

The next group, Eqs. (13.33), governs the lateral motions. In one method of solution one assumes

$$u_2 = c_2 e^{\lambda t} \qquad u_4 = c_4 e^{\lambda t} \qquad u_6 = c_6 e^{\lambda t} \tag{13.35}$$

which, substituted into Eqs. (13.33), gives the linear equations in c_2, c_4, and c_6.

$$c_2[Y_{u2} + \lambda(Y_{\dot u2} - B)] + c_4 Y_{u4} + c_6(Y_{u6} - B + \lambda Y_{\dot u6}) = 0$$

$$c_2 L_{u2} + c_4[L_{u4} + \lambda(L_{\dot u4} - I_x)] + c_6 L_{u6} = 0 \tag{13.36}$$

$$c_2(N_{u2} + \lambda N_{\dot u2}) + c_4 N_{u4} + c_6[N_{u6} + \lambda(N_{\dot u2} - I_z)] = 0$$

The necessary and sufficient condition that at least one of the coefficients c_2, c_4, c_6 not be zero is the vanishing of the *characteristic*, or *stability*, *determinant*

$$\begin{vmatrix} Y_{u2} + \lambda(Y_{\dot u2} - B) & Y_{u4} & Y_{u6} - B + \lambda Y_{\dot u6} \\ L_{u2} & L_{u4} + \lambda(L_{\dot u4} - I_x) & L_{u5} \\ N_{u2} + \lambda N_{\dot u2} & N_{u4} & N_{u6} + \lambda(N_{\dot u2} - I_z) \end{vmatrix} = 0 \tag{13.37}$$

the expansion of which gives a cubic equation for λ.

At least one of the roots of this cubic, λ_1, is real. The other two roots, λ_2 and λ_3, are either also real or complex conjugates. In the latter case the roots will be denoted by

$$\lambda_2 = \alpha + i\beta \qquad \lambda_3 = \alpha - i\beta$$

Each one of these solutions determines a particular *normal mode* of motion of the disturbed body. This is obtained by substituting a root, λ_i, for λ in any pair of the Eqs. (13.36) and solving for the ratios of c_2, c_4, and c_6. For example, from the second and third of these equations one obtains

$$\frac{c_{2i}}{[L_{u4} + \lambda_i(L_{\dot u4} - I_x)][N_{u6} + \lambda_i(N_{\dot u2} - I_z)] - L_{u6}N_{u4}}$$

$$= \frac{c_{4i}}{L_{u6}(N_{u2} + \lambda_i N_{\dot u2}) - L_{u2}(N_{\dot u2} - I_z)}$$

$$= \frac{c_{6i}}{L_{u2}N_{u4} - [L_{u4} + \lambda_i(L_{\dot u4} - I_x)](L_{u2} + \lambda_i N_{\dot u2})} \tag{13.38}$$

Substitution in Eqs. (13.35) then gives three sets of solutions for $i = 1, 2, 3$,

$$u_{2i} = c_{2i}e^{\lambda_i t} \qquad u_{4i} = c_{4i}e^{\lambda_i t} \qquad u_{6i} = c_{6i}e^{\lambda_i t}$$

from which the general solution is obtained by an arbitrary linear combination, viz.,

$$u_2 = \sum_{i=1}^{3} a_i u_{2i} \qquad u_4 = \sum_{i=1}^{3} a_i u_{4i} \qquad u_6 = \sum_{i=1}^{3} a_i u_{6i}$$

in which the constants a_i depend upon the initial conditions.

If two of the roots are equal, say, $\lambda_2 = \lambda_3$, the foregoing procedure would give only two independent sets of solutions. In this case a third set can be obtained by assuming

$$u_2 = (c_2 + d_2t)e^{\lambda_2 t} \qquad u_4 = (c_4 + d_4t)e^{\lambda_2 t} \qquad u_6 = (c_6 + d_6t)e^{\lambda_2 t} \qquad (13.39)$$

which, substituted into Eqs. (13.33), gives three linear equations with the same characteristic determinant (13.37) as before, from which the ratios of the undetermined constants in Eqs. (13.39) can be obtained. If the three roots were equal, the solutions would be assumed of the form

$$u_2 = (c_2 + d_2t + e_2t^2)e^{\lambda t}$$

and so forth. The modes are of four types, depending upon whether λ is real or complex, and have a positive or negative real part. If λ is real, a disturbance would be amplified or damped exponentially according as λ is positive or negative. If λ is complex, a mode is of the form

$$ce^{\lambda t} = ce^{\alpha t}(\cos \beta t + i \sin \beta t)$$

which indicates the real solutions $ce^{\alpha t} \cos \beta t$ and $ce^{\alpha t} \sin \beta t$. These represent amplified or damped oscillations according as α is positive or negative. If all the modes are damped, the body would have lateral stability. It has been seen that this would be the case if all the roots of the stability determinant had negative real parts.

A criterion due to Routh enables the stability of a linear system to be examined without the necessity of a complete solution for the normal modes. Let the characteristic equation, obtained by expanding the characteristic determinant, be

$$p_0\lambda^n + p_1\lambda^{n-1} + \cdots + p_n = 0 \qquad p_0 > 0 \qquad (13.40)$$

The necessary and sufficient conditions for stability for several values of n are as follows:
1. $n = 2$ p_0, p_1, p_2 positive
2. $n = 3$ p_0, p_1, p_2, p_3, and $p_1p_2 - p_0p_3$ positive
3. $n = 4$ p_0, p_1, p_2, p_3, p_4, and $p_3(p_1p_2 - p_0p_3) - p_1^2p_4$ positive

The third group of equations for the disturbed motion of a body, Eqs. (13.34), would be studied in a similar manner to investigate its longitudinal stability.

Method of Transfer Functions. The stability of a system disturbed from a state of steady motion and described by linear differential equations can be studied exactly by the method of transfer functions. If $v(t)$ is the time variation of an input disturbance and $Y(t)$ is the corresponding output of a dependent function, the transfer function for these quantities is defined by

$$\overline{Y}(s) = G_{Yv}(s)\bar{v}(s) \qquad (13.41)$$

in which $\overline{Y}(s)$ and $\bar{v}(s)$ are the Laplace transforms of $Y(t)$, $v(t)$.

$$\overline{Y}(s) = \int_0^\infty e^{-st}Y(t)\, dt \qquad \bar{v}(s) = \int_0^\infty e^{-st}v(t)\, dt$$

An expression for G_{Yv} in terms of stability derivatives can be derived by assuming that $Y(t)$ is a function of $v, \dot{v}, \ddot{v}, \ldots$, and expressible in the form of the linearized Taylor series

$$Y(t) = Y_v v + Y_{\dot{v}}\dot{v} + Y_{\ddot{v}}\ddot{v} + \cdots$$

If the initial values of $v, \dot{v}, \ddot{v}, \ldots$ are all zero, the Laplace transform of the last equation gives

$$\overline{Y}(t) = (Y_v + Y_{\dot{v}}s + Y_{\ddot{v}}s^2 + \cdots)\bar{v}$$

which, by comparison with Eq. (13.41), yields

$$G_{Yv}(s) = Y_v + Y_{\dot{v}}s + Y_{\ddot{v}}s^2 + \cdots \qquad (13.42)$$

provided the infinite series converges.

In terms of transfer functions the stability Eqs. (13.31) become

$$\sum_{i=1}^{6} G_{Xu_i}\,\bar{u}_i = B[s\bar{u}_1 - u_1(0)]$$

$$\sum_{i} G_{Yu_i}\,\bar{u}_i = B[s\bar{u}_2 - u_2(0) + \bar{u}_6]$$

$$\sum_{i} G_{Zu_i}\,\bar{u}_i = B[s\bar{u}_3 - u_3(0) - \bar{u}_5]$$

$$\sum_{i} G_{Lu_i}\,\bar{u}_i = I_x[s\bar{u}_4 - u_4(0)] \qquad (13.43)$$

$$\sum_{i} G_{Mu_i}\,\bar{u}_i = I_y[s\bar{u}_5 - u_5(0)]$$

$$\sum_{i} G_{Nu_i}\,\bar{u}_i = I_z[s\bar{u}_6 - u_6(0)]$$

a set of linear algebraic equations which can be solved for the $\bar{u}_i(s)$. The inverse transforms then give $u_i(t)$. For example, on the basis of the same assumptions and approximations as were used to derive Eqs. (13.34), the equations for investigating the longitudinal stability of an elongated body symmetrical about its xz plane become

$$\begin{aligned} G_{Zu_3}\bar{u}_3 + G_{Zu_5}\bar{u}_5 &= B[s\bar{u}_3 - u_3(0) - \bar{u}_5] \\ G_{Mu_3}\bar{u}_3 + G_{Mu_5}\bar{u}_5 &= I_y[s\bar{u}_5 - u_5(0)] \end{aligned} \qquad (13.44)$$

When the transfer functions are known, Eqs. (13.44) can be solved for $\bar{u}_3(s)$ and $\bar{u}_5(s)$ and then $u_3(t)$ and $u_5(t)$ obtained.

A transfer function can be expressed in terms of the response of a system to certain basic inputs. Thus, if the response of a quantity Y to a unit step function $v(t)$, in which

$$\begin{aligned} v(t) &= 0 \qquad t < 0 \\ v(t) &= 1 \qquad t > 0 \end{aligned}$$

is the indicial admittance $A_{Yv}(t)$, then

$$G_{Yv} = s\bar{A}_{Yv}(s) \qquad (13.45)$$

Alternatively, if $v(t)$ is the basic input

$$v = v_0 e^{i\omega t}$$

then the steady-state frequency response is

$$Y(t) = G_{Yv}(i\omega)v_0 e^{i\omega t}$$

in which $G_{Yv}(i\omega)$ is the frequency-response vector. When the latter is known, $G_{Yv}(s)$ can be obtained from it by substituting $-is$ for ω.

Motion under Random Disturbances. There are occasions, such as the motion of a ship in a seaway or the passage of an airplane through turbulent air, when the state of the medium and the response of the body are best described in a statistical manner. Only the case where the statistical properties do not change with time (stationary random variables) will be considered.

Let $v(t)$ be the deviation from the mean of a random variable, and

$$R(\tau) = \overline{v(t)v(t+\tau)} = \lim_{T\to\infty} \frac{1}{2T}\int_{-T}^{T} v(t)v(t+\tau)\,dt \qquad (13.46)$$

be its *autocorrelation*. When $\tau = 0$, the autocorrelation becomes the mean square of the fluctuation, which is called its power, or the square of the intensity. The frequency distribution of the power, or power spectrum, is then given by the Fourier cosine transform of the auto correlation

$$p(\omega) = \frac{1}{\pi} \int_0^\infty R(\tau) \cos \omega\tau \, d\tau \qquad (13.47)$$

the inversion of which yields

$$R(\tau) = \int_{-\infty}^\infty p(\omega) \cos \omega\tau \, d\omega \qquad (13.48)$$

or, when $\tau = 0$,

$$\overline{v^2} = \int_{-\infty}^\infty p(\omega) \, d\omega \qquad (13.49)$$

The suitability of $p(\omega)$ as a power-spectrum function is clearly shown by the last expression.

Now suppose that $Y(t)$ is the deviation from the mean of an output function corresponding to the random input $v(t)$. Then the output power can be expressed in terms of the frequency-response vector $G_{Yv}(i\omega)$ in the form

$$\overline{Y^2} = \int_{-\infty}^\infty |G_{Yv}(i\omega)|^2 p(\omega) \, d\omega \qquad (13.50)$$

the integrand of which gives the power spectrum of the output.

13.7. Steady Motion of Two-dimensional Forms[4]

Forms which are approximately two-dimensional often occur as appendages on three-dimensional bodies. The determinations of incompressible, irrotational two-dimensional flows are often greatly facilitated by the fortunate and unique properties that there is a 1:1 correspondence between all such flows and all analytic functions of a complex variable and that these flows can be transformed into each other.

Blasius Theorem. Let $w(z)$ be the complex potential for a steady, irrotational flow about a simple closed contour C, with $w = \phi + i\psi$, ϕ the velocity potential, and ψ the stream function, and $z = x + iy$. Then the Blasius theorem expresses the force and moment on the body in the form

$$Y + iX = -\frac{\rho}{2} \int_C \left(\frac{dw}{dz}\right)^2 dz$$
$$\qquad (13.51)$$
$$M + iN = -\frac{\rho}{2} \int_C z \left(\frac{dw}{dz}\right)^2 dz$$

in which $X + iY$ is the resultant force vector acting on the body and M is the resultant moment; N has no physical significance. Thus the forces and moments are expressed in terms of the residues of the analytic functions $(dw/dz)^2$ and $z(dw/dz)^2$.

The added mass of a contour C can also be expressed in terms of complex potentials. If the form has the translational velocity components u_1 and u_2 and the fluid is otherwise undisturbed, then the velocity potential and the kinetic energy of the fluid can be written in the forms

$$\phi = u_1\phi_1 + u_2\phi_2$$
$$2T = A_{11}u_1^2 + 2A_{12}u_1u_2 + A_{22}u_2^2$$

in which A_{11}, A_{12}, and A_{22} are added-mass coefficients defined by

$$A_{11} = \rho \int_C \phi_1 \frac{\partial x}{\partial n} \, ds \qquad A_{22} = \rho \int_C \phi_2 \frac{\partial y}{\partial n} \, ds$$

$$A_{12} = \rho \int_C \phi_1 \frac{\partial y}{\partial n} \, ds = \rho \int_C \phi_2 \frac{\partial x}{\partial n} \, ds$$

Let S be the area bounded by C, and w_1 and w_2 the complex potentials corresponding to unit velocities of the body in the x and y directions. Then the added masses are given in terms of the residues of w_1 and w_2 by the relationships

$$A_{12} - i(A_{11} + \rho S) = \rho \int_C w_1 \, dz$$

$$A_{22} + \rho S - iA_{12} = \rho \int_C w_2 \, dz \tag{13.52}$$

As an illustration of the foregoing theory, consider the complex potential

$$w = -u_1 \left(z + \frac{a^2}{z} \right) - ik \ln z$$

for steady flow about a circular cylinder of radius a, with circulation $\Gamma = 2\pi k$ in a stream of velocity u_1 in the positive x direction. Then $(dw/dz)^2 = 2iu_1k/z + \cdots$ has the residue $2iu_1k$, and hence the Blasius theorem gives

$$Y + iX = -\frac{\rho}{2}(2\pi i)(2iu_1k) = \rho u_1 \Gamma$$

or $$X = 0 \qquad Y = \rho u_1 \Gamma$$

the well-known Kutta-Joukowsky formula for the lift due to circulation.

The complex potential w_1 for the unsteady flow when the cylinder is moving with unit velocity in the positive x direction is

$$w_1 = \frac{a^2}{z} - ik \ln z$$

which has the residue $-a^2$. Hence, from Eq. (13.52), one obtains

$$F - i(A_{11} + \rho S) = -2\pi a^2 \rho i \qquad F = 0, \quad A = \rho S$$

the well-known result that the added mass of a circular cylinder is the mass of its displaced fluid.

The afore-mentioned Kutta-Joukowsky formula for the lift applies to arbitrary two-dimensional profiles. Thus, expressing the complex potential for the flow about the profile in the general form

$$w = -Ue^{-i\alpha}z + \frac{b_1}{z} + \frac{b_2}{z^2} + \cdots - ik \ln z$$

in which U is the magnitude and α the direction relative to the x axis of the incident velocity, and $\Gamma = 2\pi k$ is the circulation about the contour, application of the Blasius Eqs. (13.51) yields the result that the theoretical drag (force in the direction of the incident flow) is zero, and the lift L (force normal to the direction of the incident flow) and moment M about the origin are

$$L = \rho U \Gamma \qquad M = 2\pi \rho U I(b_1 e^{-i\alpha}) \tag{13.53}$$

in which I denotes "the imaginary part of."

It appears that the added mass, force, and moment are readily obtained when the complex potential is known. If one has been able to find a function $\zeta = f(z)$ which maps the exterior of the given profile in the z plane 1:1 into the exterior of the unit circle in the ζ plane, the complex potential for the flow about the profile in a uniform stream incident at an angle α with the x axis is given by

$$w = -U \left(\zeta e^{-i\alpha} + \frac{a^2 e^{i\alpha}}{\zeta} \right) - ik \ln \zeta \qquad \zeta = f(z) \tag{13.54}$$

Circle Theorem. When flow singularities such as sources, doublets, and vortices are also present, the foregoing result is easily generalized by observing the effect of the transformation $\zeta = f(z)$ on the positions and strengths of these singularities and then obtaining the flow about the unit circle in the presence of these modified singularities. The solution of the latter problem is given immediately by the *circle theorem* of Milne-Thomson.

If $F(z)$ is a complex potential for a flow with singularities that are situated at a distance greater than a from the origin, then the complex potential w due to the same singularities for the flow about a circle of radius a is

$$w = F(z) + \overline{F}\left(\frac{a^2}{z}\right) \tag{13.55}$$

Here $\overline{F}$ denotes the conjugate of the functional form of F; e.g., if $F(z) = z^2 + 2iz$, then $\overline{F}(a^2/z) = (a^2/z)^2 - 2i(a^2/z)$.

To illustrate the theorem, take $F(z) = ik \ln (z + h)$, the complex potential for a vortex of strength k at $x = -h$, $h > a$. Then from Eq. (13.54), one obtains

$$w = ik \ln (z + h) - ik \ln \left(\frac{a^2}{z} + h\right)$$

$$= ik \ln (z + h) - ik \left[\ln \left(z + \frac{a^2}{h}\right) - \ln z + \ln h\right]$$

The constant $ik \ln h$ may be neglected, and thus it is seen that the image of a vortex in a circle consists of a vortex of the same sense and strength at the origin and a vortex of equal strength but opposite sense at the inverse point. Then, since $(dw/dz)^2$ has poles at $z = 0$ and a^2/h and the sums of their residues is

$$\frac{4\pi i k^2 a^2}{h(h^2 - a^2)}$$

application of the Blasius theorem yields a force on the circle in the negative x direction.

$$X = -\frac{2\pi \rho k^2 a^2}{h(h^2 - a^2)}$$

Airfoil Theory. For an elongated body with a sharp trailing edge, the lift can be computed from Eq. (13.53) on the basis of the Kutta-Joukowsky hypothesis that the circulation on a two-dimensional foil adjusts itself so that the velocity at the trailing edge is finite. The values of the lift predicted by this theory are slightly too large because of the neglect of the boundary layer and wake.

Application of this hypothesis to the circular arc shown in Fig. 13.5 yields the lift coefficient

$$C_L = \frac{L}{\frac{1}{2}\rho U^2 c} = 2\pi \sin (\alpha + \beta) \sec \beta$$

Here c is the chord of the foil, α the angle of attack, and β a measure of the camber. Defining the camber as the ratio of the maximum height of the arc to its chord, it is seen to be given by $\frac{1}{2} \tan \beta$.

The circular arc in Fig. 13.5 or 13.6 may be obtained by applying a Joukowsky transformation to the circle E' with center at P and of radius PB in Fig. 13.6b. If the same transformation is applied to a slightly larger circle F' with center at D on the line BP extended and of radius DB, the resulting shape F, shown in Fig. 13.6a, is called a Joukowsky airfoil. The circular arc E is

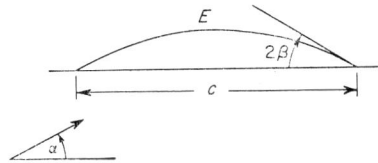

Fig. 13.5. Circular arc at angle of attack α.

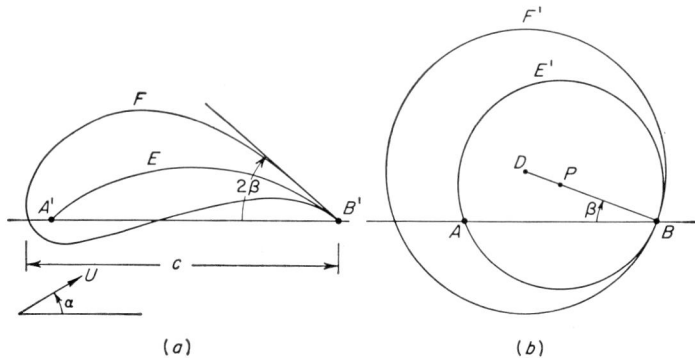

FIG. 13.6. Joukowsky airfoil mapping.

called its skeleton, the camber of which is also the camber of the foil. A measure of the thickness of the foil is the ratio $T = BD/BP$. It is found that the lift coefficient of the Joukowky foil is

$$C_L = \frac{L}{\frac{1}{2}\,\rho U^2 c} = 2\pi T \sin{(\alpha + \beta)} \sec{\beta} \qquad (13.56)$$

i.e., the lift is that of its skeleton multiplied by its thickness ratio.

When the airfoil is thin, a good approximation to the lift and moment is obtained by solving the linearized boundary-value problem. The resulting values of the lift and moment coefficients are

$$C_L = 2\pi \left(\alpha - \frac{1}{\pi} \int_0^{2\pi} \frac{dy}{dx} \cos^2{\frac{\theta}{2}}\, d\theta \right)$$

$$C_M = -\tfrac{1}{4} C_L - \frac{1}{4} \int_0^{2\pi} \frac{dy}{dx} \left[\cos{\theta} + \cos{(2\theta - \alpha)} \right] d\theta \qquad (13.57)$$

in which α is the angle of attack, and $y(x)$ is the equation of the profile.

Drag. The drag force on a body[5,6] immersed in a uniform stream depends on its shape and orientation, the Reynolds number, and the nature of the incident flow. Because of the infinite variety of shapes it is possible to consider only a few typical forms.

A SMOOTH FLAT PLATE OF LENGTH l AT ZERO ANGLE OF ATTACK IN ZERO PRESSURE GRADIENT. The drag is due to the shear stresses on the plate and is said to be frictional. If the boundary layer is *laminar* from the leading edge to a distance x along the plate and the shear stress and drag coefficients are defined by

$$C_T = \frac{\tau_0}{\frac{1}{2}\,\rho U^2} \qquad C_f = \frac{f}{\frac{1}{2}\,\rho U^2 A}$$

in which τ_0 = shear stress on wall
f = frictional resistance
A = area of plate in contact with fluid

the Blasius formulas for these coefficients are

$$C_T = \frac{0.664}{\sqrt{\mathbf{R}_x}} \qquad C_f = \frac{1.328}{\sqrt{\mathbf{R}_x}} \qquad \mathbf{R}_x = \frac{Ux}{\nu} \qquad (13.58)$$

If the boundary layer becomes *turbulent* downstream from some transition point on the plate, the relation between the shear stress and the Reynolds number (derived on the

basis of the semiempirical "inner" and "outer" laws of a turbulent boundary layer) is of
the form

$$\mathbf{R}_x - C = e^{\sigma/k}(a + b\sigma + c\sigma^2) \qquad \sigma = \sqrt{\frac{2}{C_\tau}}$$

in which a, b, c, and k are constants, and C is a parameter the value of which depends
upon the transition point, which in turn depends upon the nature of the disturbances
within and exterior to the boundary layer. When C_τ is known as a function of $\mathbf{R}_x$, C_f can
be obtained from the expression

$$C_f = \frac{1}{\mathbf{R}_x} \int_0^{\mathbf{R}_x} C_\tau \, d\mathbf{R}_x$$

An empirical formula which gives a good fit to available flat-plate resistance data in the
range $10^6 < \mathbf{R}_x < 10^{10}$ is that due to Schoenherr,

$$\frac{0.242}{\sqrt{C_f}} = \log_{10}(\mathbf{R}_x C_f) \tag{13.59}$$

The corresponding expression for the shear stress is

$$C_\tau = \frac{d}{d\mathbf{R}_x}(\mathbf{R}_x C_f) = \frac{C_f}{1 + 3.59\sqrt{C_f}}$$

STREAMLINE FORMS. Streamline forms are defined as those along which there is no
separation of flow. Since a form on which separation occurs at low Reynolds number
or in a low-turbulence stream may become separation-free at higher Reynolds numbers or
in a stream of higher turbulence, whether or not a form is streamlined depends upon
these conditions.

The drag of a streamline form is principally frictional, i.e., due to its shear stresses.
The boundary layer is laminar up to some transition point x_T (which fluctuates even
under steady conditions and can be defined only in a statistical sense), beyond which it
becomes turbulent. At Reynolds numbers $\mathbf{R}_c = Uc/\nu < 10^5$, in which c is the chord of
the profile, laminar separation occurs unless the thickness-chord ratio d/c is less than 0.1.
The experimental results of tests of various streamlined shapes, including elliptical sections, can be summarized in the empirical formula

$$C_D \doteq 2C_f\left(1 + \frac{d}{c}\right) + \left(\frac{d}{c}\right)^2 \qquad R_c < 10^5, \quad \frac{d}{c} < 0.5 \tag{13.60}$$

in which C_f is the drag coefficient for a flat plate with a laminar boundary layer, and C_D
is the drag coefficient for the profile

$$C_D = \frac{D}{\frac{1}{2}\rho U^2 c}$$

At higher Reynolds numbers turbulent separation occurs except on certain forms having
a thickness ratio $d/c < 0.4$. An approximate expression for the drag coefficient (except
for "laminar-flow" forms) is then

$$C_D \doteq 2C_f\left[1 + k\frac{d}{c} + 60\left(\frac{d}{c}\right)^4\right] \qquad \mathbf{R}_c > 10^7, \quad \frac{d}{c} < 0.4 \tag{13.61}$$

in which the value of k depends primarily upon the position of the point of maximum
thickness x_M, varying approximately from $k = 2.0$ when $x_M/c = 0.3$ to about $k = 1.2$
when $x_M/c = 0.5$, and C_f is the drag coefficient for a flat plate with a turbulent boundary
layer.

In the intermediate range of Reynolds numbers, $10^5 < \mathbf{R}_c < 10^7$, the drag coefficient
is sensitive to the pressure distribution along a particular profile and to disturbances
in the boundary layer. The turbulent shear stresses downstream from x_T tend to in-

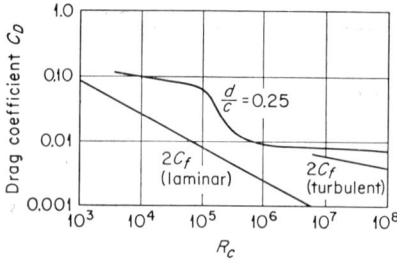

FIG. 13.7. Drag coefficients of two-dimensional forms of thickness-chord ratio $d/c = 0.25$. (*From Hoerner, Ref.* 6, *p.* 6-1.)

crease the drag coefficient; on the other hand, if laminar separation had been occurring at lower Reynolds numbers, it would now be replaced by turbulent separation or no separation, which would tend to decrease the drag. For most forms of thickness ratio $d/c > 0.10$, the drag coefficient in this range is less than that given by Eq. (13.60). A typical curve showing a composite of the measured drag coefficients vs. Reynolds number of various forms of thickness ratio $d/c = 0.25$ is shown in Fig. 13.7.

A class of forms, the laminar profiles, designed to maintain a laminar boundary layer over a large part of the surface up to high Reynolds numbers ($\mathbf{R}_c \approx 10^7$), has drag coefficients differing from Eqs. (13.60) and (13.61). These forms have their maximum thickness occurring between 40 and 65 per cent of the chord from the leading edge, a small nose radius of curvature, and negative curvature near the sharp trailing edge (Fig. 13.8). Such a shape results in a negative pressure gradient up to about the point of maximum thickness, which consequently stabilizes the laminar boundary layer to much higher Reynolds numbers than for more normal shapes. At Reynolds numbers $\mathbf{R}_c < 10^5$, the drag coefficient would be somewhat larger than that given by Eq. (13.60) because of more violent laminar separation, but at higher Reynolds numbers, exceeding $\mathbf{R}_c = 10^7$, turbulent separation would occur, but with the boundary layer still laminar ahead of the point of maximum thickness. In their range of effectiveness these forms have about half of the drag of conventional profiles of the same thickness ratio.

This advantageous property of laminar-flow profiles can be maintained only if the surface is very smooth. The permissible height of a roughness element, so as not to disturb a laminar boundary layer on a laminar-flow form, is given approximately by the relation

$$\frac{k}{c} = \frac{10^3}{\mathbf{R}_c} \qquad \text{or} \qquad \frac{Uk}{\nu} = 1000$$

More positively, it may be stated that a spherical roughness element resting on a surface will produce approximately a 20° wedge of turbulence behind it when the Reynolds number ud/ν exceeds 600, in which u is the velocity in the boundary layer at the distance d (the diameter of the spherical element) from the wall.

BLUNT FORMS. The drag of a blunt form is principally due to its pressure distribution, which differs radically from that for inviscid flow because much of the after end of such a body is immersed in a zone of separation. Separation on a body occurs either at slope discontinuities in the body profile (sharp edges) or at positions in the boundary layer where a positive pressure gradient is beginning to cause reverse flow of the slowly moving fluid near the wall. In the latter case separation occurs farther downstream in a turbulent boundary layer than in a laminar one because fresh momentum is transported to the wall by the process of the random turbulent motions.

A phenomenon observed in the flow about blunt two-dimensional forms is the periodic alternate shedding of vortices from the opposite sides at the rear of the body, forming in

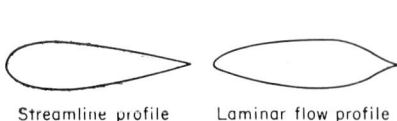

Streamline profile   Laminar flow profile

FIG. 13.8. Typical streamline and laminar-flow profiles.

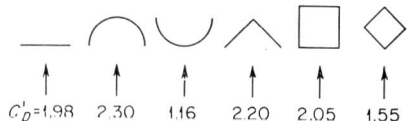

$C_D' = 1.98$ 2.30   1.16   2.20   2.05   1.55

FIG. 13.9. Drag coefficients of various blunt forms.

the wake two staggered rows of uniformly spaced vortices, called a vortex street. It was shown theoretically by von Kármán, by analyzing the stability of such an array, that the ratio of distance between the rows to the distance between successive vortices in a row, h/b, satisfies the equation

$$\cosh \frac{\pi h}{b} = \sqrt{2} \qquad (13.62)$$

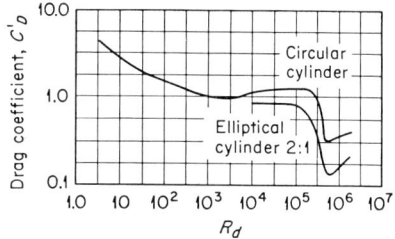

Fig. 13.10. Drag coefficient vs. Reynolds number for circular and elliptical cylinders.

which gives the approximate solution $h/b = 0.2806$, a value in very good agreement with experiment. The theory also yields an expression for the resistance coefficient of the body,

$$C'_D = \frac{D}{\frac{1}{2}\rho U^2 d} = \frac{2b}{d}\left[0.7936\,\frac{u}{U} - 0.3141\left(\frac{u}{U}\right)^2\right] \qquad (13.63)$$

in which d is the maximum width of the profile, and u is the velocity of the vortices, a result of the correct order of magnitude. It cannot be used to predict drag, however, since the values of b/d and u/U cannot yet be obtained by theory. The frequency n with which the vortices are shed is of great practical interest since the body experiences an oscillating lift as the circulation about it varies from positive to negative. Both theory and experiment show a relationship between the drag coefficient of a body and its dimensionless frequency, $S = nd/U$, called a Strouhal number. A composite empirical fit to the data from a wide range of blunt bodies is given by the formula

$$S = \frac{0.21}{C_D^{\;3/4}} \qquad (13.64)$$

In the range of Reynolds numbers $10^3 < \mathbf{R}_d < 10^8$, blunt bodies with sharp edges show little variation in drag coefficient. The coefficients for some typical cases are given in Fig. 13.9.

Blunt but rounded forms show a remarkable reduction in drag coefficient over a small range of Reynolds numbers in which transition from laminar to turbulent separation occurs. The designations "subcritical" or "supercritical" are used to indicate the Reynolds-number ranges in which laminar or turbulent separation occurs. Curves showing the variation of C'_D with R_d for a circle and a 2:1 ellipse are shown in Fig. 13.10. The variation of the drag coefficient with thickness ratio of ellipses is given for both the subcritical and supercritical ranges of Reynolds numbers in Table 13.3.

If the vortices shed by a blunt cylinder of width d cause it to oscillate, the width of the resulting vortex street is increased approximately by the double amplitude of the oscillation, $2a$, and the resulting drag is also increased approximately by the factor $1 + 2a/d$. Such vibrations commonly occur in cables situated at an angle to a stream.

The force on an element of such a cable can be obtained (as has been established experimentally) by assuming that the components of the incident velocity normal and tangential to the cable act on it independently. Thus, if the tangent to the cable is at

Table **13.3.** Drag Coefficients for Elliptical Sections

c/d	C'_D	
	Subcritical	Supercritical
1	1.17	0.40
2	0.58	0.20
3	0.42	0.12
4	0.37	0.10
6	0.30	0.10
8	0.28	0.12

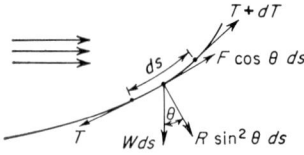

FIG. 13.11. Forces on a towing cable.

an angle θ to the incident flow, and R and F are the forces per unit length when the cable is normal and tangential to the flow, then, assuming a force variation as the square of the speed, the normal force is $R \sin^2 \theta$ and the tangential would be $F \cos^2 \theta$. Experiment indicates, however, that $F \cos \theta$ is a better fit to the data for the latter component.

The forces acting on an element of a towing cable are shown in Fig. 13.11. Here T is the tension, and W is the weight per foot of cable. The condition of equilibrium of the element yields the equations

$$\frac{dT}{ds} + F \cos \theta - W \sin \theta = 0$$

$$T \frac{d\theta}{ds} - R \sin^2 \theta - W \cos \theta = 0 \tag{13.65}$$

Also

$$\frac{dx}{ds} = \cos \theta \qquad \frac{dy}{ds} = \sin \theta$$

These four equations suffice to determine x, y, θ, and T as functions of s. The first yields immediately

$$T = T_0 - Fx + Wy$$

The other equations give

$$\ln \frac{T}{T_0} = \int_{\theta_0}^{\theta} \frac{W \sin \theta - F \cos \theta}{R \sin^2 \theta + W \cos \theta} \, d\theta$$

$$x = \int_{\theta_0}^{\theta} \frac{T \cos \theta}{R \sin^2 \theta + W \cos \theta} \, d\theta \qquad y = \int_{\theta_0}^{\theta} \frac{T \sin \theta}{R \sin^2 \theta + W \cos \theta} \, d\theta \tag{13.66}$$

Cavitation. † At sufficiently low pressures in a liquid, zones of cavitation, terminating either on the body or at some distance behind it, will be present. The pressure in the cavity is usually approximately the vapor pressure of the liquid, and the parameter characterizing the phenomenon is the cavitation number

$$\sigma_c = \frac{p_0 - p_c}{\frac{1}{2} \rho U^2}$$

in which p_0 is the ambient pressure, and p_c the cavity pressure.

Flows about sharp-edged two-dimensional forms have been treated by conformal mapping as free-streamline problems. The theoretical drag coefficients C_{D0} for wedges of semiapex angle α at zero angle of incidence are given in Table 13.4 for $\sigma_c = 0$. At other cavitation numbers, theory indicates the relation

$$C'_D = C'_{D0}(1 + \sigma_c) \tag{13.67}$$

† See Sec. 12 for more detailed discussion of cavitation.

Table 13.4. Drag Coefficients for Symmetrical Wedges ($\sigma_c = 0$)

$\alpha(deg)$	C'_{D0}	$\alpha(deg)$	C'_{D0}
15	0.28	90	0.88
30	0.49	120	0.95
45	0.64	150	0.98
60	0.75	180	1.00
75	0.83		

On round bodies cavitation begins at the point of minimum pressure, and in fact the inception cavitation number is given by

$$\sigma_i = -\left(\frac{p - p_0}{\frac{1}{2}\rho U^2}\right)_{\min} \qquad (13.68)$$

i.e., the negative of the minimum pressure coefficient for the profile. Thus, for elliptical sections and for forebodies which can be approximated by ellipses,

$$\sigma_i = -\frac{d}{a}\left(1 + \frac{d}{4a}\right)$$

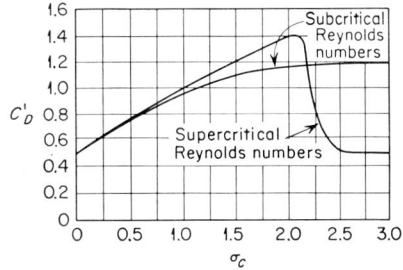

FIG. 13.12. Drag coefficients of a circular cylinder at various cavitation numbers. (*From Hoerner, Ref. 6, p. 10-8.*)

in which d is the thickness of the section, and a the length of the forebody. With decreasing cavitation number the zone of cavitation moves forward along the body. The variation of C'_D with σ_c for a circular cylinder at subcritical and supercritical Reynolds numbers is shown in Fig. 13.12. It is seen that cavitation appeared at about the theoretically predicted value of $\sigma_c = 2.0$ for supercritical flow but at a higher value for subcritical flow. On profiles with a sharp minimum-pressure peak, on the other hand, cavitation inception occurs at values less than the minimum pressure coefficient. An approximate expression for the drag coefficient of a long, thin, cavitating strut is

$$C_D = k\frac{d}{a}(1 + \sigma_c) + 2C_f\frac{a}{d} \qquad (13.69)$$

in which k depends upon the form; $k = \pi/8$ for a parabolic forebody.

The lift of foil sections is also strongly affected by cavitation. A theoretical result confirmed by experiment gives for the lift coefficient of a flat plate in supercavitating flow (one side completely immersed in the cavity), at a small angle of attack α,

$$C_L = \frac{\pi}{2}\alpha(1 + \sigma_c) \qquad \sigma_c < 0.10 \qquad (13.70)$$

At large angles of attack, the theoretical result for $\sigma_c = 0$ is that the resultant force is normal to the plate with a normal force coefficient

$$C_N = \frac{N}{\frac{1}{2}\rho U^2 c} = \frac{2\pi \sin\alpha}{4 + \pi \sin\alpha} \qquad (13.71)$$

A useful adjunct to Eq. (13.70) is the approximate theoretical formula for supercavitating flow

$$C_L = \frac{\pi}{2}\alpha + \sigma_c \qquad \sigma_c > 0.20 \qquad (13.72)$$

which is also in good agreement with experiment. The corresponding expression for the drag coefficient is

$$C_D = \frac{2}{\pi}C_L(C_L - \sigma_c) + C_f \qquad (13.73)$$

When the wetted side of the cavitating hydrofoil is cambered and the opposite side is completely immersed in a cavity, theory and experiment agree that the lift coefficient is increased with a much smaller effect on the drag coefficient. A theoretical solution by Wu[7] for arbitrary forms has given results in good agreement with experiment when applied to a circular-arc profile. The solution for a circular arc of central angle β, with $\beta < \pi/4$ and flow incident at an angle α to its chord, is as follows:

$$C_D = \frac{2\pi}{J}\left(1 + \sigma_c + \frac{\epsilon^2}{6} + \frac{\beta^2}{6}\right)\left(\sin\gamma + \frac{A_1}{2}\right)^2$$

$$C_L = \frac{2\pi}{J}\left(1 + \sigma_c + \frac{\epsilon^2}{4} + \frac{\beta^2}{6}\right)\left\{\left(\sin\gamma\cos\gamma + A_1\cos\gamma + \frac{A_2}{2}\right)\right.$$

$$+ \frac{\epsilon^2}{4}\frac{\cos\gamma}{(\sin\gamma + A_1/2)^4}\left[\left(\sin\gamma + \frac{A_1}{2}\right)^3 + \sin\gamma\left(\sin\gamma + \frac{A_1}{4}\right)\right. \qquad (13.74)$$

$$\left.\left.\left(\frac{A_1}{2} + \frac{5A_2}{4} + A_3\right)\right]\right\}$$

$$C_M = \frac{M}{\rho U^2 c^2/2} = \frac{4\pi}{J^2}\left(1 + \sigma_c + \frac{\beta^2}{3}\right)K + \mu(C_L\cos\alpha + C_D\sin\alpha)$$

in which

$$\gamma = \alpha + \frac{\delta}{2} - \frac{\epsilon^2}{4(\pi - \alpha + \beta)} - \frac{\beta}{4 + \pi\sin\alpha}\left\{\cos\alpha - \frac{\epsilon^2\cos^2(\alpha/2)}{\alpha + \beta + [(\alpha + \beta)^2 + \epsilon^2]^{\frac{1}{2}}}\right\}$$

$$\delta = \frac{\epsilon^2}{\alpha + \beta + [(\alpha + \beta)^2 + \epsilon^2]^{\frac{1}{2}}} \qquad \epsilon = \tfrac{1}{2}\ln(1 + \sigma_c)$$

$$A_1 = \beta\left[1 + \frac{\pi\sin\alpha}{8(4 + \pi\sin\alpha)}\right] + \tfrac{9}{16}\delta\left\{1 + \frac{\beta(1 + \cos\alpha)}{9[(\alpha + \beta)^2 + \epsilon^2]^{\frac{1}{2}}}\right\} + \frac{9\epsilon^2}{32(\pi - \alpha + \beta)}$$

$$A_2 = \frac{\beta}{4 + \pi(A_1 + \sin\gamma)}\left\{\cos\gamma - \frac{\epsilon^2\cos^2(\gamma/2)}{\alpha + \beta + [(\alpha + \beta)^2 + \epsilon^2]^{\frac{1}{2}}}\right\}$$

$$A_3 = \frac{1}{9}(\beta - A_1) - \frac{\gamma}{9(4 + \pi\sin\alpha)}\left\{\pi\sin\gamma + \frac{2\delta(1 + \cos\alpha)}{[(\alpha + \beta)^2 + \epsilon^2]^{\frac{1}{2}}}\right\}$$

$$J = 4 + \pi\sin\gamma + A_1(\pi + \tfrac{8}{3}\sin\gamma) + \frac{\pi}{2}A_2\cos\gamma - \tfrac{8}{15}A_3\sin\gamma$$

$$K = C_1\left\{\cos\gamma\left[\frac{5}{8} + \sin^2\gamma + A_1\left(\frac{7}{6}\sin\gamma + \frac{2}{3}\sin^3\gamma - \frac{32}{45\pi}\right)\right]\right.$$

$$+ \frac{C_1}{2}\left(\frac{\pi}{2} - \gamma\right) - A_2\left(\frac{3}{16}\sin\gamma + \frac{1}{12}\sin^3\gamma - \sin^5\gamma + \frac{64}{45\pi}\right)\bigg\}$$

$$+ \tfrac{1}{4}(A_1\cos\gamma + 2A_2)\left(1 + A_1 + \frac{A_2}{4}\cos\gamma\right)\left(1 + \frac{128}{45\pi}\sin\gamma\right)$$

$$+ \frac{A_2}{16}\cos\gamma(1 + \tfrac{5}{6}A_1)$$

$$C_1 = \sin\gamma + A_1 + \frac{A_2}{2}\cos\gamma$$

$$\mu = \frac{1}{J}\left\{2(1 - \cos\gamma) + \sin\gamma(\gamma - \sin 2\gamma) + A_1(\gamma + \tfrac{4}{3}\sin\gamma - \tfrac{3}{2}\sin 2\gamma + \tfrac{1}{6}\sin 4\gamma)\right.$$

$$+ A_2\left(\frac{\gamma}{2}\cos\gamma - \tfrac{1}{2}\sin\gamma + \tfrac{1}{6}\sin^3\gamma - 2\sin^5\gamma\right)$$

$$+ \tfrac{2}{15}A_3\sin\gamma[\cos\gamma(2 + \sin^2\gamma + 24\sin^4\gamma) - 2]\bigg\}$$

This agrees with the foregoing results for the flat plate when $\beta = 0$.

A good approximation to the lift-drag ratio for values of $\sigma_c < 0.5$ is

$$\frac{L}{D} \doteq \cot \alpha \tag{13.75}$$

for both flat and cambered profiles. The theoretical prediction that L/D decreases with σ_c is not confirmed by experiment, which shows a contrary trend.

When α, expressed in radians, is large in comparison with σ_c and β^2, Eqs. (13.74) give the simpler forms

$$C_D = \frac{2\pi}{J}\left(1 + \sigma_c + \frac{\epsilon^2}{6}\right)\left\{\cos\alpha + \frac{\epsilon^2}{4\alpha(\pi - \alpha)}\left[\frac{9\pi}{16} - (\pi - 2\alpha)\sin\alpha\right]\right\}^2$$

$$+ \frac{4\pi\beta\sin\alpha}{(4 + \pi\sin\alpha)^2}\left[1 - \frac{1}{3}\sin^2\alpha + \frac{\pi\sin\alpha\cos^2\alpha}{4(4 + \pi\sin\alpha)}\right]$$

$$C_L = \frac{2\pi}{J}\left(1 + \sigma_c + \frac{\epsilon^2}{4}\right)\left\{\sin\alpha\cos\alpha + \frac{\epsilon^2}{4\alpha(\pi - \alpha)}\left[(\pi - 2\alpha)\cos 2\alpha\right.\right.$$

$$\left.\left.+ \alpha(\pi - \alpha)\cot\alpha + \frac{9\pi}{8}\cos\alpha\right]\right\} + \frac{7\pi\beta\cos\alpha}{(4 + \pi\sin\alpha)^2}(1 + {}^{16}\!/_{21}\sin\alpha + {}^{4}\!/_{7}\sin^2\alpha)$$

in which

$$J = 4 + \pi\sin\alpha + \frac{\pi\epsilon^2}{4\alpha(\pi - \alpha)}\left[\frac{9\pi}{8} + 3.06\sin\alpha + (\pi - 2\alpha)\cos\alpha\right]$$

A linearized theory of cavitating hydrofoils, introduced by Tulin[8] in 1953, has enabled a wide range of practical problems to be treated with considerably less mathematical complexity than the more exact methods, but at some sacrifice in the range of applicability of the results.

Effect of a Free Surface. Two-dimensional forms moving steadily near the free surface of a liquid generate energy-propagating gravity waves; if they pierce the free surface, part of the body surface may be ventilated by air sucked down along the sides, or at sufficiently high Froude numbers, the liquid rising along the front of the body may shoot upward and sideways in the form of energy-dissipating spray. These phenomena influence greatly the forces and moment acting on these forms.

Suppose that the two-dimensional form is moving steadily parallel to the free surface. The lift and drag coefficients depend not only on the Reynolds number, but also on the Froude and cavitation numbers. The usual procedure for theoretical treatment of the problem is to consider the fluid as inviscid for the purpose of determining the modification of the flow about the body due to the free surface. The effects of the Reynolds and cavitation numbers are subsequently taken into account for this modified flow.

Let the origin be taken at the undisturbed level of the free surface with the x axis in the direction of motion of the body and the y axis directed vertically upward. For the equivalent case of the body at rest in a uniform stream U, the problem consists of solving Laplace's equation

$$\frac{\partial^2\phi}{\partial x^2} + \frac{\partial^2\phi}{\partial y^2} = 0$$

with the conditions

$$\frac{\partial\phi}{\partial n} = 0 \qquad \text{on the body}$$

$$\tag{13.76}$$

$$\frac{\partial^2\phi}{\partial x^2} + \frac{g}{U^2}\frac{\partial\phi}{\partial y} = 0 \qquad \text{on the free surface}$$

The latter is the linearized boundary condition derived on the assumption that the change in elevation and slope of the free surface is small and that the boundary condition may be applied at the undisturbed position of the free surface. When the velocity potential has been found, the equation of the free surface $\eta(x)$ can be obtained from

$$\eta(x) = \frac{U}{g}\left(\frac{\partial\phi}{\partial x}\right)_{y=0} \tag{13.77}$$

A two-dimensional surface disturbance can be obtained by superposition of a series of fundamental progressive waves of the form

$$\eta = a \sin\left[\frac{2\pi}{\lambda}(x \pm ct)\right] \tag{13.78}$$

in which, in a liquid of depth h, the wavelength λ and wave-phase velocity c satisfy the relation

$$c = \frac{g\lambda}{2\pi}\tanh\frac{2\pi h}{\lambda} \tag{13.79}$$

The total energy (potential and kinetic) of a progressive wave per unit area of the free surface is

$$E = \tfrac{1}{2}\,\rho g a^2 \tag{13.80}$$

A surface disturbance composed of progressive waves of varying wavelengths does not have a single-phase velocity, according to Eq. (13.79), but rather behaves as an entity moving with the so-called *group velocity* U given by

$$U = c - \lambda\frac{dc}{d\lambda} \tag{13.81}$$

This is also the rate of propagation of energy by the wave system. Substituting Eq. (13.79) in Eq. (13.81) gives the group velocity for surface waves

$$U = \frac{c}{2}\left(1 + \frac{4\pi h}{\lambda}\operatorname{csch}\frac{4\pi h}{\lambda}\right) \tag{13.82}$$

which, for infinite depth, is half of the phase velocity.

The relation between the rate at which a body does work in generating a system of surface waves and the energy in the waves yields the equation for resistance due to wave making,

$$R = E\left(1 - \frac{U}{c}\right) \quad\text{or}\quad R = E\left(\frac{U}{c} - 1\right) \quad\text{according as } \frac{U}{c} \gtrless 1$$

in which U is the group velocity. Applying Eq. (13.82) in the former case gives the expression for wave resistance,

$$R = \tfrac{1}{4}\,g\rho a^2\left(1 - \frac{2gh}{c^2}\operatorname{csch}\frac{2gh}{c^2}\right) \tag{13.83}$$

The solution for a horizontal circular cylinder of radius b athwart a stream of velocity U at a depth f to its axis is[1]

$$\eta = \frac{2b^2}{x^2 + f^2} - 4\pi k b^2 e^{-kf}\sin kx - 2kb^2\int_0^\infty \frac{k\sin mf - m\cos mf}{m^2 + k^2}\,dm \qquad x > 0$$

$$\eta = \frac{2b^2}{x^2 + f^2} - 2kb^2\int_0^\infty \frac{k\sin mf - m\cos mf}{m^2 + k^2}\,dm \qquad x < 0$$

in which $k = g/U^2$. Hence, at a great distance downstream from the cylinder, the wave becomes asymptotically

$$\eta \approx -4\pi k b^2 e^{-kf}\sin kx$$

so that, from Eq. (13.83), the wave resistance per unit length of the cylinder in deep water is

$$R = \frac{4\pi^2 g^3 b^4}{U^4} e^{-2gf/U^2} \tag{13.84}$$

Since the real flow about a circular cylinder differs considerably, because of separation, from the inviscid-flow solution, the resistance given by Eq. (13.84) must be interpreted as that of a doublet rather than that of a circular cylinder. By introducing a source behind the cylinder to simulate the wake, values of the wave resistance in better agreement with experiment have been obtained. On bodies with little or no separation, the wave resistance predicted by linearized theory should be satisfactory.

Because of the practical application to sea planes and hydrofoil boats, there is considerable interest in hydrofoils. The effect of the free surface is shown by the solution for a two-dimensional vortex of circulation Γ in infinitely deep water for which the complex potential is[9]

$$w(z) = \frac{\Gamma}{2\pi i} \ln \frac{z + if}{z - if} + \frac{\Gamma}{\pi i} e^{-ikz} \int_{\infty}^{z} \frac{e^{ik\xi}}{\xi - if} d\xi \tag{13.85}$$

in which f is the depth of the vortex, and $k = g/U^2$. The equation of the free surface, obtained from Eq. (13.85), is given by

$$\eta(x) = \frac{U}{g}\left(\frac{\partial\phi}{\partial x}\right)_{y=0} = -\frac{\Gamma}{\pi U}\int_{\infty}^{x} \frac{\xi \cos k(\xi - x) - f \sin k(\xi - x)}{\xi^2 + f^2} d\xi \qquad x > 0$$

$$= \frac{2\Gamma e^{-kf}}{U}\sin kx - \frac{\Gamma}{\pi U}\int_{\infty}^{x} \frac{\xi \cos k(\xi - x) - f \sin k(\xi - x)}{\xi^2 + f^2} d\xi \qquad x < 0$$

Thus the asymptotic-wave amplitude is zero at a great distance upstream from the vortex and given by

$$a = \frac{2\Gamma}{U} e^{-kf}$$

at a great distance downstream from it. The wave resistance can now be obtained from Eq. (13.83), but since the lift is now also of interest, it is convenient to apply the Blasius theorem, Eq. (13.51), which yields for the wave resistance R and the lift L (positive upward)

$$R = \frac{\rho g \Gamma^2}{U^2} e^{-2gf/U^2}$$

$$L = \rho U \Gamma - \frac{\rho\Gamma^2}{4\pi f} + \frac{\rho g \Gamma^2}{\pi U^2} e^{-2gf/U^2} \int_{-\infty}^{2gf/U^2} \frac{e^t}{t} dt \tag{13.86}$$

The Cauchy principal part is to be taken of the last integral, which is seen to be an exponential integral $Ei(2gf/U^2)$.

The wave resistance given by Eq. (13.86) approaches zero for very small or very large velocities and is a maximum when $U = \sqrt{2gf}$. The increment in lift due to the free surface can be expressed as a function of the Froude number $U/\sqrt{gf}$ in the form

$$\Delta L = \frac{\rho\Gamma^2}{4\pi f} F\left(\frac{U^2}{gf}\right)$$

which is positive for small values of the Froude number and negative for large ones, and vanishes when $U/\sqrt{gf} \doteq 1.57$. Since ΔL also vanishes when the Froude number is zero, it must assume a maximum at some intermediate value. This also indicates that, for a given speed, there is a depth at which the lift is a maximum.

A theory has also been developed for the case of finite aspect ratio.[10] Application to a hydrofoil of elliptical plane form and aspect ratio 6.3 indicates that the influence of the free surface on the characteristics of the hydrofoil is very small at depths greater than 2 chords. At lesser depths the wave drag increases and the induced drag (due to lift) decreases, with a resulting decrease in the drag coefficient. In the same range of depths C_L decreases steadily to about half of its value for deep submergence, but the lift-drag ratio decreases very slowly with diminishing depth until a depth of half the chord length and then decreases rapidly with reduction in depth. These characteristics indicate that depths between $\frac{1}{2}$ and 1 chord length are a favorable range of operation for hydrofoils. For the performance characteristics are nearly the same as for deep water, and the hydrofoil would be inherently stable in depth since, if it were disturbed from a depth at which the weight was in equilibrium with the lift, the changes in lift with depth would tend to return it to its equilibrium depth.

Next consider a vertical, surface-piercing strut of streamline shape at zero angle of attack. At low Froude numbers $U/\sqrt{gl}$ (l the length of the strut) the free-surface effect is negligible and the drag coefficient of the strut is due to viscosity and is the same as for deep water. With increasing Froude number the wave-drag coefficient remains small until a Froude number of about 0.3, reaches a maximum at about 0.5, and then reduces practically to zero beyond a Froude number of 3.0. At its maximum the wave drag may be from 10 to 50 times greater than the viscous drag.

At high Froude numbers the water rising about the front of a vertical, surface-piercing strut shoots outward in the form of spray, as a consequence of which, for Froude numbers $U/\sqrt{gl} > 3$, the drag of the strut is increased approximately by $0.24 \times \frac{1}{2}\rho U^2 d^2$ or by $0.12 \times \frac{1}{2}\rho U^2 d^2$, according as d/b is greater or less than 0.8, where d is the thickness of the strut and b its forebody length. Simultaneously, air is sucked down along the side (ventilation) to a depth f given by

$$- C_{p\,\text{min}} = \frac{2}{\mathbf{F}_f{}^2} \tag{13.87}$$

in which $C_{p\,\text{min}}$ denotes the minimum value of the pressure coefficient, and $\mathbf{F}_f$ is the Froude number $U/\sqrt{gf}$. The additional drag due to ventilation is approximately $\frac{1}{2}\rho g df^2$. Hence, denoting the drag coefficient of the deeply submerged strut by C_{D0}, the resultant drag coefficient for a strut extending to a depth h, for $U/\sqrt{gl} > 3$, is

$$C'_D = \frac{D}{(\rho U^2/2)hd} = C_{D0} + \binom{0.24}{0.12}\frac{d}{h} + \frac{1}{\mathbf{F}_f{}^2}\frac{f}{h} \tag{13.88}$$

in which D is the total drag of the strut.

13.8. Two-dimensional Forms in Unsteady Motion

Inertia Effects. Under certain circumstances the pressure distribution about a body in unsteady motion deviates only slightly from that for inviscid flow. This would be the case, for example, for a streamline body, for the initial flow about a body impulsively set into motion, or for a body oscillating with an amplitude small in comparison with its principal lateral dimensions. These cases have in common the condition that separation has not occurred either because of the shape of the body or because insufficient time has elapsed for separation to develop. It is then a reasonable assumption that the expressions of Art. 13.3 for the forces and moments in an inviscid fluid would give a useful approximation for the effects of acceleration in a real fluid. Thus it is desirable to know the added masses or procedures for obtaining them for bodies of various shapes.

When the complex potential for the unsteady flow about a profile is known, the added masses are immediately given by Eqs. (13.52). It is a simple matter, then, to obtain the added masses of the great variety of forms which can be derived by direct transformation from a circle. More difficult is the case of arbitrary profiles for which a function which maps the form into a circle would have to be found, at least to a close approximation.

Writing the transformation of an arbitrary profile in the z plane into the unit circle in the ζ plane in the form

$$z = \zeta + \frac{a_1}{\zeta} + \frac{a_2}{\zeta^2} + \cdots \qquad (13.89)$$

and applying Eqs. (13.52) gives for the added mass of the form moving in the x direction

$$A_{11} + \rho S + i A_{12} = 2\pi\rho(1 - a_1) \qquad (13.90)$$

Thus only the first coefficient of the mapping function needs to be found, and if this is real, $A_{12} = 0$.

Equation (13.89) is applicable when the fluid extends to infinity in all directions and is disturbed only by the translational motion of the body. More generally, if the body is also rotating, or if other stationary boundaries are present, and the complex potential has been found and expressed in the form

$$w = \frac{b_1}{\zeta} + \frac{b_2}{\zeta^2} + \cdots$$

the corresponding expression for the kinetic energy of the fluid is

$$T = \frac{\pi\rho}{2} \sum_{n=1}^{\infty} n |b_n|^2 \qquad (13.91)$$

from which the added masses can be determined.

A useful family, the so-called "Lewis" forms, the added masses of which have been thoroughly studied[11, 12] is given by the parametric equations

$$\begin{aligned} x &= (1 + a_1)\cos\theta + a_3\cos 3\theta \\ y &= (1 - a_1)\sin\theta - a_3\sin 3\theta \end{aligned} \qquad (13.92)$$

This is obtained from the unit circle by the transformation

$$z = \zeta + \frac{a_1}{\zeta} + \frac{a_3}{\zeta^3}$$

in which a_1 and a_3 are real numbers. The forms obtained for various values of a_1 and a_3 are symmetrical about the x and y axes. Their added masses are given by

$$A_{11} = \frac{\pi\rho}{2}\left[(1 - a_1)^2 + 3a_3^2\right] \qquad A_{12} = 0$$

$$A_{22} = \frac{\pi\rho}{2}\left[(1 + a_1)^2 + 3a_3^2\right] \qquad (13.93)$$

When $a_3 = 0$, the form becomes that of an ellipse of semiaxes $a = 1 + a_1$, $b = 1 - a_1$. Thus the added masses of an ellipse are

$$A_{11} = \tfrac{1}{2}\pi\rho b^2 \qquad A_{22} = \tfrac{1}{2}\pi\rho a^2 \qquad (13.94)$$

When $a_1 = 0$, the forms have a width-length ratio λ of unity. These are given in Fig. 13.13 for various values σ of the ratio of the area of the form to the area of the circumscribing rectangle. Only the lower right quarters of the profiles are shown. The added mass coefficients

$$C_V = \frac{2A_{22}}{\pi\rho a^2}$$

versus σ for various values of $\lambda = b/a$ are graphed in Fig. 13.14. The point on the graph where $C_V = 1$ represents the common value, independent of λ, for ellipses.

The added masses of rectangular sections have also been obtained theoretically. The variation of C_V with λ is shown in Fig. 13.15. The case $\lambda = 0$ corresponds to that of a flat plate moving normally to its plane.

Rotation of a two-dimensional form introduces the three additional "added masses"

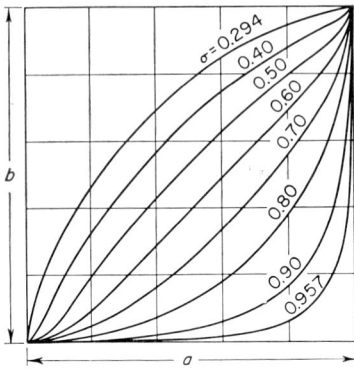

FIG. 13.13. "Lewis" forms for $\lambda = 1$.

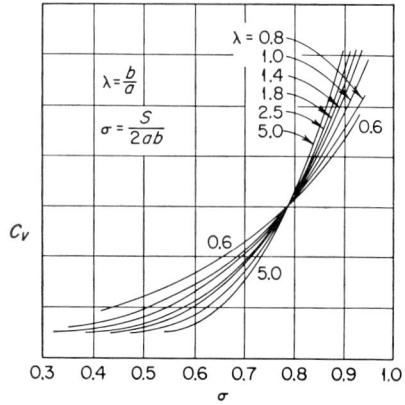

FIG. 13.14. Added-mass coefficients of "Lewis" forms for vertical motion.

A_{66}, A_{16}, and A_{26}. Proper choice of the axes (principal axes) attached to the body reduces the mixed terms A_{12}, A_{16}, and A_{26} to zero, so that it would be necessary to discuss only the additional "added mass" A_{66}, which is in fact an added moment of inertia. Since the six added masses are the coefficients of a positive definite quadratic form, their values can be readily obtained for any orientation of the axes when a set of them is known for a particular coordinate system.

The added-mass coefficient for rotation will be defined as the ratio

$$C_R = \frac{A_{66}}{\frac{1}{8}\,\pi\rho a^4}$$

which has the value of unity for a flat plate of width $2a$. For an *ellipse* with axes a and b, one obtains

$$C_R = \left[\left(\frac{b}{a}\right)^2 - 1\right]^2 \tag{13.95}$$

The coefficients for rectangular sections[13] are shown in Fig. 13.16.

The presence of a free surface may have an important effect on the added masses. If the form is moving at a high Froude number or oscillating at a high frequency, gravitational effects become negligible and the boundary condition on the free surface becomes $\phi = 0$.

First suppose that the profile is moving vertically. Then the boundary conditions are satisfied by supposing that the immersed part of the profile and its image in the free surface move together as a single rigid form in an unbounded fluid. The added mass is

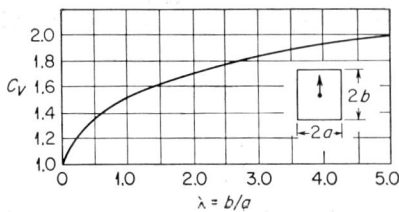

FIG. 13.15. Added-mass coefficients of rectangular sections. (*Ref.* 13.)

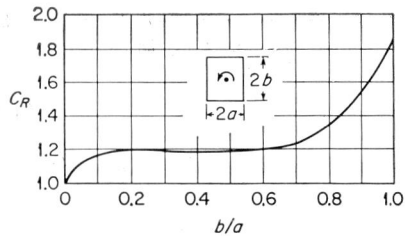

FIG. 13.16. Added moment of inertia coefficients for rectangular sections. (*Ref.* 13.)

then half of that for the double profile, and it can be derived by one of the previously described methods.

Next suppose that the profile is moving horizontally. The boundary conditions are now satisfied by supposing that the velocity of the immersed part of the profile is the negative of that of its image. The added mass is then[12]

$$
\begin{aligned}
A_{HS} = \frac{8\rho}{\pi} \Big(& c_{11}a'_1{}^2 + 2c_{13}a'_1a_3 + 2c_{15}a'_1a_5 + 2c_{17}a'_1a_7 + 2c_{19}a'_1a_9 + \cdots \\
& + c_{22}a^2_2 \quad + 2c_{24}a_2a_4 + 2c_{26}a_2a_6 + 2c_{28}a_2a_8 + \cdots \\
& \qquad\qquad + c_{33}a_3{}^2 \quad + 2c_{35}a_3a_5 + 2c_{37}a_3a_7 + \cdots \qquad (13.96) \\
& \qquad\qquad\qquad\qquad + c_{44}a_4{}^2 \quad + 2c_{46}a_4a_6 + \cdots \\
& \qquad\qquad\qquad\qquad\qquad\qquad + \cdots \Big)
\end{aligned}
$$

in which $a'_1 = a_1 - 1$, the coefficients $a_1, a_2, \ldots$, are from Eq. (13.89), and

$$
\begin{aligned}
c_{rs} &= -\frac{rs}{2(s - r)} \sum_{n=2}^{s-r} \frac{1}{(r + n)(s - n)}, \quad r,\, s \text{ odd, } n \text{ even} \\[2mm]
&= -\frac{rs}{2(s - r)} \sum_{n=1}^{s-r-1} \frac{1}{(r + n)(s - n)} \quad r,\, s \text{ even, } n \text{ odd}
\end{aligned} \Bigg\} \, r < s
$$
(13.97)

$$
\begin{aligned}
c_{ss} &= \frac{s}{4} \sum_{n=2}^{2s} \frac{1}{(s - n)^2} \quad s \text{ odd, } n \text{ even} \\[2mm]
&= \frac{s}{4} \sum_{n=1}^{2s-1} \frac{1}{(s - n)^2} \quad s \text{ even, } n \text{ odd}
\end{aligned}
$$

Values of c_{rs} up to $c_{16.16}$ are given in Table 13.5.

For the Lewis forms, Eq. (13.96) gives

$$
A_{HS} = \frac{2\rho}{3\pi} [3(1 - a_1)^2 + 6(1 - a_1)a_3 + 19a_3{}^2] \qquad (13.98)
$$

Putting $a_3 = 0$, this gives for the ellipse

$$
A_{HS} = \frac{2\rho}{\pi} b^2 \qquad (13.99)
$$

which, by comparison with Eq. (13.94), indicates that the effect of the free surface is to reduce the added mass of an elliptical section by the factor $4/\pi^2 \doteq 0.4$. Curves of the added-mass coefficient $C_{HS} = 2A_{HS}/(\pi\rho b^2)$ for the Lewis forms are shown in Fig. 13.17.

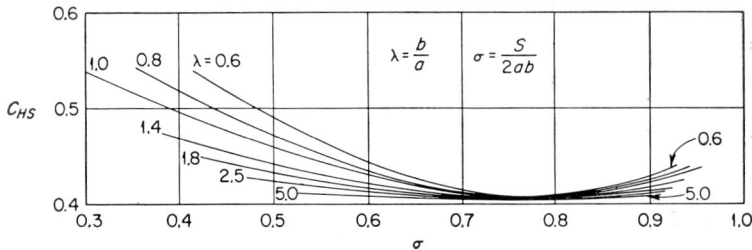

FIG. 13.17. Added-mass coefficients of "Lewis" forms for horizontal motion in a free surface.

Table 13.5. Values of c_{rs}

r \\ s	1	3	5	7	9	11	13	15
1	0.2500	−0.2500	−0.1944	−0.1612	−0.1384	−0.1222	−0.1068	−0.0996
3		1.5833	−0.2500	−0.2300	−0.2119	−0.1962	−0.1828	−0.1712
5			2.8278	−0.2500	−0.2398	−0.2288	−0.2182	−0.2082
7				4.0646	−0.2500	−0.2438	−0.2356	−0.2290
9					5.2996	−0.2500	−0.2458	−0.2406
11						6.5340	−0.2500	−0.2450
13							7.7680	−0.2500
15								9.0020

r \\ s	2	4	6	8	10	12	14	16
2	1	−0.2222	−0.2000	−0.1803	−0.1640	−0.1504	−0.1450	−0.1298
4		2.2222	−0.2400	−0.2286	−0.2162	−0.2043	−0.1934	−0.1836
6			3.4533	−0.2449	−0.2381	−0.2299	−0.2213	−0.2131
8				4.6861	−0.2469	−0.2424	−0.2367	−0.2304
10					5.9193	−0.2479	−0.2447	−0.2405
12						6.8194	−0.2485	−0.2462
14							7.9974	−0.2489
16								9.6198

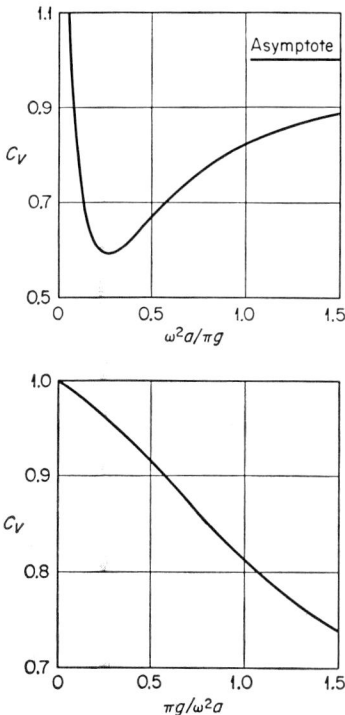

FIG. 13.18. Added mass of a vertically oscillating semi-immersed circular cylinder for various dimensionless frequencies. (Ref. 14.)

It is of interest to specify the dimensionless frequencies at which the asymptotic values of the added-mass coefficient corresponding to the free-surface boundary condition $\phi = 0$ are valid. The linearized free-surface boundary condition, of which this is a limiting case, is

$$\omega^2 \phi = g \frac{\partial \phi}{\partial y} \qquad (13.100)$$

in which ω is the angular oscillation frequency, and g the acceleration of gravity. An indication of the effect of frequency is given by Ursell's solution for a vertically oscillating, half-immersed circular cylinder[14] of radius a, which is shown in Fig. 13.18 as a graph of the added-mass coefficient C_V versus the dimensionless frequency parameter $\omega^2 a/\pi g$. The coefficient becomes infinite as the frequency approaches zero and becomes unity as the frequency approaches infinity. It is seen from the graph that $C_V = 0.98$ when $\omega^2 a/\pi g = 10$. This suggests that it would be permissible, for engineering purposes, to use the asymptotic values of added-mass coefficients for dimensionless frequencies greater than 10.

Viscous Effects. The forces due to viscosity may be modified considerably by the acceleration of a body. Acceleration may induce an earlier transition or separation than would result from steady motion at the same mean velocity. The magnitude of the effects of unsteadiness depends upon the intensity and duration of the acceleration, the time required for the formation of a wake, and the degree of streamlining of the body.

Among the infinite variety of possible unsteady motions, only a few types have been studied theoretically and experimentally. These include bodies started from rest, either impulsively or with uniform acceleration, bodies undergoing periodic motion, and bodies disturbed from a state of steady motion. Approximate solutions of the laminar-boundary-layer equations for the case of bodies started from rest have been obtained by a method of successive approximations, requiring the solution of a succession of partial differential equations resembling the equations of heat flow. Summaries of results obtained by this method are given by Goldstein[15] and Schlichting.[16] The stability of laminar boundary layers under time-dependent oscillatory disturbances has also been intensively studied.[17]

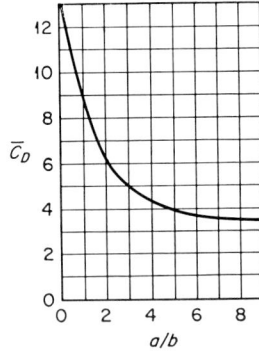

FIG. 13.19. Drag coefficient of an oscillating flat plate.

The initial rate of growth and disposition of the vorticity generated near the edges of a two-dimensional flat plate impulsively started from rest with a constant velocity normal to the plate has been computed by Anton.[18] His results have been applied by Martin[19] to obtain a mean drag coefficient

$$\overline{C}_D = \frac{\overline{F}}{\rho b U^2} = \frac{7.5}{(Ud/b)^{3/2}} \qquad (13.101)$$

in which $2b$ is the width of the plate, and $\overline{F}$ is the mean force per unit length. Martin measured the damping of a flat plate oscillating at an amplitude a normal to its plane and for small values of a/b obtained the mean drag coefficient

$$\overline{C}_D = \frac{9.15}{(a/b)^{0.59}} \qquad (13.102)$$

His experimentally determined curve is shown in Fig. (13.19). It is seen that the drag coefficients are much greater than the steady drag coefficient of 2.0. This is suggested by Martin as the explanation of the high effectiveness of bilge keels in damping the rolling of a ship.

Lifting Surfaces. Forces on lifting surfaces in unsteady motion are due to a combination of inertia effects (added masses) and circulation. If the instantaneous value of the circulation is $\Gamma(t)$, the lift due to circulation on a two-dimensional foil in a stream of velocity U is $L = \rho U \Gamma(t)$, formally the same as for steady flow. Thus the lift coefficient of a thin airfoil impulsively given an angle of attack α is initially $C_L = \pi\alpha$ due to inertia, since the circulation is initially zero. With increasing time the circulation assumes the steady-state value and the lift coefficient becomes $C_L = 2\pi\alpha$, due to circulation. This limiting value appears to be very nearly attained after a motion of about 5 chord lengths.[20]

The theory of lifting surfaces in unsteady motion involves linearizing assumptions which permit superposition of independently determined flows to determine the lift for arbitrary motion. It is also assumed that the Kutta-Joukowsky condition at the trailing edge is satisfied at all times. Theodorsen[21] studied the forces on a foil undergoing harmonic oscillations and found that the actual lift coefficient C_L was related to the quasi-steady lift coefficient C_{L0} corresponding to the instantaneous angle of attack by the relation $C_L = C(k)e^{-i\alpha(k)}C_{L0}$, in which C_L and C_{L0} are complex functions of the time, and

Table 13.6. Values of $C(k)$ and $\alpha(k)$ for an Oscillating Foil

k	0	0.05	0.1	0.3	0.5	1	4	∞
$C(k)$	1	0.921	0.859	0.688	0.624	0.550	0.505	0.500
$\alpha(k)$	0	8.2°	10.9°	15.1°	14.0°	10.5°	3.5°	0

k is the dimensionless frequency $\omega c/2U$. Here c is the chord of the foil. The variation of $C(k)$ and the phase $\alpha(k)$ are given in Table 13.6. By means of the Fourier integral, Theodorsen's solution can be applied to arbitrary unsteady flows.

13.9. Motion of Axisymmetric Bodies in an Inviscid Fluid

An axisymmetric body in steady motion in an otherwise undisturbed unbounded fluid at a zero angle of yaw experiences no forces in an inviscid fluid. When there are external boundaries, then the theory indicates the presence of forces which may often be determined, at least to an approximation, by means of the Lagally† theorem if the internal and external systems of flow singularities are known or can be estimated at each instant.

As an example, consider the force on a Rankine oval generated by a source of strength m at $x = +1$ and a sink of equal strength at $x = -1$ in a stream of velocity U in the negative x direction. Now suppose that a source of strength m' is approaching the body along the x axis. Denoting the instantaneous position of the moving source by x_s, one obtains from Eq. (13.23)

$$F \doteq 4\pi\rho m m' \left[\frac{1}{(x_s - 1)^2} - \frac{1}{(x_s + 1)^2} \right] = \frac{16\pi\rho m m' x_s}{(x_s^2 - 1)^2}$$

an attraction which for large values of x_s varies inversely as the cube of the distance. As the source approaches the body, it will become necessary to take into account its image system, which will contribute to the inertia terms in Eq. (13.23) as the strength and position of the image sources vary.

In order to apply the Lagally theorem, it is frequently necessary to estimate internal singularity distributions which are images of the external flow. This can be done exactly only in the case of a sphere by means of a recently formulated sphere theorem.[22] Suppose that an arbitrary potential flow is disturbed by a sphere. Let $\phi_0(R, \theta, \varphi)$ denote the original velocity potential and $\phi = \phi_0 + \phi_1(R, \theta, \varphi)$ the disturbed potential after the sphere of radius a at the origin is introduced. Here R, θ, φ are the spherical coordinates of a point, in which R is the distance from the origin, θ the polar angle, and φ the azimuthal angle. It is assumed that ϕ_0 has no singularities lying on or within the sphere. Then the sphere theorem states that the potential ϕ_1, such that $\partial\phi/\partial R = 0$ on the sphere, is

$$\phi_1 = \frac{a}{R} \phi_0 \left(\frac{a^2}{R}, \theta, \varphi \right) - \frac{2}{aR} \int_0^a \lambda \phi_0 \left(\frac{\lambda^2}{R}, \theta, \varphi \right) d\lambda \qquad (13.103)$$

This theorem is the three-dimensional analogue of the circle theorem, but since a transformation theory akin to that of conformal mapping does not exist, the sphere theorem cannot serve as a basis for finding image systems for other shapes.

In an axisymmetric incident flow of velocity U in the negative x direction, assume that the image system consists of a continuous distribution along the x axis of axially oriented doublets of strength $\mu(x)$ per unit length between the points a and b (Fig. 13.20) The end points a and b are selected midway between the end of the body and the center of curvature at that end. Then the distribution is to be determined as the solution of the integral equation

$$\int_a^b \frac{\mu(\xi) d\xi}{[(x - \xi)^2 + r^2(x)]^{3/2}} = \frac{U}{2} \qquad (13.104)$$

in which $r(x)$ is the equation of the body of revolution. For elongated bodies, Munk[23] has given the first approximation to a solution of Eq. (13.104), $\mu(x) \doteq -Ur^2/4$; i.e., the strength of the doublet distribution is proportional to the sec-

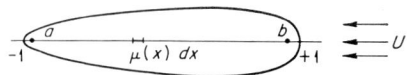

Fig. 13.20. Body of revolution with doublet distribution.

† See Art. 4.24

tional area curve.   A refinement of Munk's approximation[24] is

$$\mu(x) \doteq \frac{U}{4}\left(1 + \frac{A_{11}}{\rho V}\right) r^2(x) \tag{13.105}$$

By denoting this approximation by μ_1, a second approximation may be obtained from the iteration formula

$$\mu_2(x) = \mu_1(x) + \frac{r^2(x)}{2}\left\{\frac{1}{2} - \int_a^b \frac{\mu_1(\xi)d\xi}{[(x-\xi)^2 + r^2(x)]^{3/2}}\right\}$$

When the incident flow is normal to the axis of an elongated body, of velocity V in the negative y direction, say, the image system is given approximately by a distribution of doublets along the axis.   These doublets are oriented so that their axes are opposite in direction to that of the oncoming flow, and their strength per unit length along the axis of the body is given by

$$\mu(x) \doteq \frac{V}{4}\left(1 + \frac{A_{22}}{\rho V}\right) r^2(x) \tag{13.106}$$

Lastly, when the body is rotating in the positive sense at an angular velocity ω about the z axis, the image doublets are again oriented perpendicularly to the x axis and opposite to the direction of the relative incident flow and the strength is

$$\mu(x) \doteq \omega\left(1 + \frac{A_{22}}{\rho V}\right) xr^2(x) \tag{13.107}$$

Next suppose that the axisymmetric body is at an angle of yaw α with respect to the incident flow.   To be specific, suppose that the kinetic energy of the fluid, Eq. (13.21), is in the form

$$2T = A_{11}u_1^2 + A_{33}u_3^2$$

Then, from Eq. (13.22), one obtains the pitching moment

$$M = 2(A_{33} - A_{11})u_1u_3 \tag{13.108}$$

which exceeds values measured in a real fluid by about 10 per cent.

A commonly employed procedure for estimating the added masses of elongated bodies of revolution is to assume that they have the same values as for a prolate spheroid of the same length-diameter ratio l/d.   An empirical study of the added masses of a series of bodies of revolution, based on values computed for potential flow,[25] showed that the assumption is a good one for transverse and rotational motion but that it could lead to an error of as much as 14 per cent in the value for longitudinal motion.   An empirical formula proposed as a result of this study is

$$k_1 = \frac{A_{11}}{\rho V} = k_e\{1 + 17.0(C_p - \tfrac{2}{3})^2 + 2.49(m - \tfrac{1}{2})^2 + 0.283[(r_0 - \tfrac{1}{2})^2 + (r_1 - \tfrac{1}{2})^2]\} \tag{13.109}$$

in which k_e = added-mass coefficient for ellipsoid of same l/d
C_p = prismatic coefficient $C_p = 4V/\pi d^2 l$
m = nondimensional abscissa x_m/l corresponding to maximum ordinate
r_0, r_1 = dimensionless radii of curvature at nose and tail

$$r_0 = R_0 l/d^2 \qquad r_1 = R_1 l/d^2$$

in which R_0 and R_1 are radii of curvature.

Values of k_1 (or k_e), $k_2 = A_{22}/\rho V$, and $k' = A_{55}/\rho I_y$ for prolate spheroids, when V is volume of the spheroid and I_y its moment of inertia about the y axis,

$$V = \frac{4\pi}{3} ab^2 \qquad I_y = \frac{4\pi}{15} ab^2(a^2 + b^2)$$

obtained from the formulas (Ref. 1, pp. 154, 155)

$$k_1 = \frac{(1 - e^2)(\Lambda - 2e)}{2e - \Lambda(1 - e^2)} \qquad k_2 = \frac{2e - \Lambda(1 - e^2)}{2e(2e^2 - 1) + \Lambda(1 - e^2)}$$

$$k' = \frac{e^4[2e(3 - 2e^2) - 3\Lambda(1 - e^2)]}{(2 - e^2)[3\Lambda(1 - e^2)(2 - e^2) - 2e(6 - 7e^2)]} \qquad \Lambda = \ln\frac{1 + e}{1 - e} \quad (13.110)$$

are given in Table 13.7.

A fortunate property of the spheroid is that there is a known exact distribution of singularities for each of its degrees of freedom. This becomes apparent by application of a theorem due to Havelock[26] concerning the associated Legendre[27] functions $P_n{}^m(\mu)$, $Q_n{}^m(\zeta)$,

$$P_n{}^m(\mu)Q_n{}^m(\zeta)e^{im\varphi} = \frac{(-1)^m}{2}\left(\frac{\partial}{\partial y} + i\frac{\partial}{\partial z}\right)^m \int_{-ae}^{ae} \frac{(a^2e^2 - k^2)^{m/2}P_n(k/ae)}{[(x - k)^2 + y^2 + z^2]^{1/2}} \, dk$$

$$(13.111)$$

in which μ, ζ, φ are the ellipsoidal coordinates defined by·

$$
\begin{aligned}
x &= ae\mu\zeta \\
y &= ae(1 - \mu^2)^{1/2}(\zeta^2 - 1)^{1/2}\cos\varphi \\
z &= ae(1 - \mu^2)^{1/2}(\zeta^2 - 1)^{1/2}\sin\varphi
\end{aligned}
\qquad (13.112)
$$

a is the length of the semimajor axis and e is the eccentricity. When $m = 0$, Eq. (13.111) indicates that the left member is equivalent to a distribution of sources; when $m = 1$, it is a distribution of doublets.

Now consider the potentials for the various motions of a spheroid:[1]

$$\phi_1 = ae\left(\frac{e}{1 - e^2} - \tfrac{1}{2}\Lambda\right)^{-1} P_1(\mu)Q_1(\zeta)$$

$$\phi_2 = ae\left[\frac{e(1 - 2e^2)}{1 - e^2} - \tfrac{1}{2}\Lambda\right]^{-1} P^1{}_1(\mu)Q^1{}_1(\zeta)\cos\varphi$$

$$\phi_3 = -\phi_2\tan\varphi \qquad (13.113)$$

$$\phi_5 = a^2e^2\left[\frac{3(2 - e^2)}{2e^2}\Lambda - \frac{6 - 7e^2}{e(1 - e^2)}\right]^{-1} P^1{}_2(\mu)Q^1{}_2(\zeta)\sin\varphi$$

$$\phi_6 = -\phi_5\cot\varphi$$

Table 13.7. Values of Added-mass Coefficients for a Prolate Spheroid

l/d	k_1	l/d	k_2[†]	k'[†]
1.0	0.5000	1.	0.500	0
2.0	0.2100	1.50	0.621	0.094
3.0	0.1220	2.00	0.702	0.240
4.0	0.0816	2.51	0.763	0.367
4.5	0.0689	2.99	0.803	0.465
5.0	0.0591	3.99	0.860	0.608
5.5	0.0514	4.99	0.895	0.701
6.0	0.0452	6.01	0.918	0.764
6.5	0.0401	6.97	0.933	0.805
7.0	0.0359	8.01	0.945	0.840
7.5	0.0323	9.02	0.954	0.865
8.0	0.0293	9.97	0.960	0.883
9.0	0.0244	∞	1	1
10.0	0.0207			
11.0	0.0178			
12.0	0.0155			
13.0	0.0137			
14	0.0121			
∞	0			

† From Ref. 1, p. 155.

Comparison with Eq. (13.111) shows that each of these potentials can be considered as arising from a known axial distribution of singularities.

Effect of Free Surface. There is a considerable literature on the forces and moments on bodies of revolution moving near a free surface. For elongated bodies in steady horizontal motion, the linearized free-surface irrotational-flow theory gives results in good agreement with experiment. One begins with the same singularity distribution within the body as for the deeply immersed condition, determines the disturbance potential due to these singularities

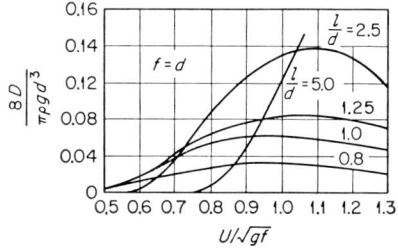

FIG. 13.21. Wave resistance of prolate spheroids at a submergence of 1 diam. (*Ref.* 29.)

which satisfies the free-surface boundary condition, and applies this to determine the force and moment on the body. An interpretation of the disturbance potential as a distribution of singularities above the free surface enables the force and moment to be determined by application of the Lagally theorem. The approximation given by this procedure appears to be adequate for the force, but as has been shown by Pond[28] and Havelock,[26] it is necessary to add to the internal singularities a system of images of the transverse flow due to the free-surface disturbance potential, in accordance with Eq. (13.106), in order to obtain a good approximation for the moment.

The wave resistance of spheroids as computed by Havelock[29] is shown in Fig. 13.21, and the moment of a Rankine ovoid[28] is shown in comparison with experimental results in Fig. 13.22.

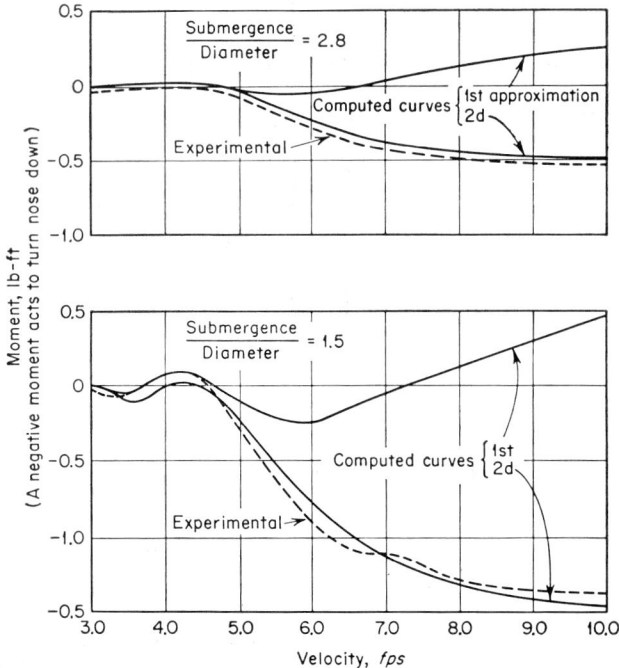

FIG. 13 22. Comparison of observed and predicted moments about center of buoyancy for 4-ft Rankine ovoid with length-diameter ratio of 10.5.

The theory yields the following expressions[30] for the force components X, Y, Z:

$$X = -\frac{k^2\rho}{2\pi} \int_{-\pi/2}^{\pi/2} |H(k\sec^2\theta,\theta)|^2 \sec^3\theta \, d\theta$$

$$Y = \rho g \mathbb{V} - \frac{\rho}{8\pi^2} \int_0^\infty \int_{-\pi}^\pi |H(\alpha,\theta)|^2 \alpha \, d\theta \, d\alpha$$

$$+ \frac{\rho k^2}{4\pi^2} \int_{-\pi}^\pi \int_{-\infty}^1 \left| H\left(\frac{k(1-\lambda)}{\cos^2\theta}, \theta\right) \right|^2 \frac{1-\lambda}{\lambda} \sec^4\theta \, d\lambda \, d\theta \quad (13.114)$$

$$Z = -\frac{k^2\rho}{2\pi} \int_{-\pi/2}^{\pi/2} |H(k\sec^2\theta,\theta)|^2 \sec^4\theta \sin\theta \, d\theta$$

in which $k = g/U^2$, and $H(\alpha,\theta)$ is a function first introduced by Kochin for the treatment of gravity-wave problems. For a source of strength m at the point ξ, η, ζ, one has

$$H(\alpha,\theta) = 4\pi m e^{\alpha\eta} e^{i\alpha(\xi\cos\theta + \zeta\sin\theta)}$$

and for a doublet of strength μ in the x direction,

$$H(\alpha,\theta) = 4\pi i\mu\alpha e^{\alpha\eta} e^{i\alpha(\xi\cos\theta + \zeta\sin\theta)} \cos\theta$$

These may be superimposed to give the H function for discrete or continuous distributions.

Added masses near a free surface have been investigated by Eisenberg[31] for the limiting cases of very large and very small Froude numbers and by Bottaccini[32] for the entire range of Froude numbers. Since the energy of the fluid, which usually serves as the basis for defining added masses, depends upon the previous history of the flow when a free surface is present, Bottaccini first defines a virtual momentum M by collecting all terms in the equation for the force acting on the body, of the form dM/dt, and then, if M contains terms of the form $u_i A_{ij}$, defines A_{ij} as an added mass corresponding to the ith component of the velocity and the jth component of the force. This is a practical point of view since these are precisely the terms that are needed for establishing the equations of motion. By applying the results of Landweber and Yih,[2] the added masses are then obtained in the following forms:

$$A_{11} = A^\circ{}_{11} + \frac{4\pi}{u_1}\rho\Sigma m'_1 x \qquad A_{22} = A^\circ{}_{22} + \frac{4\pi}{u_2}\rho\Sigma\mu'_{2y}$$

$$A_{33} = A^\circ{}_{33} + \frac{4\pi}{u_3}\rho\Sigma\mu'_{3z}$$

$$A_{55} = A^\circ{}_{55} - \frac{4\pi}{u_5}\rho\Sigma\mu^\circ{}_{5z}u'_3 \qquad A_{66} = A^\circ{}_{66} - \frac{4\pi}{u_6}\rho\Sigma\mu^\circ{}_{6z}u'_3 \quad (13.115)$$

$$A_{13} = \frac{4\pi}{u_1}\rho\Sigma\mu'_{1z} \qquad A_{23} = \frac{4\pi}{u_2}\rho\Sigma\mu'_{2z}$$

$$A_{53} = \frac{4\pi}{u_5}\rho\Sigma\mu'_{5z} \qquad A_{63} = \frac{4\pi}{u_6}\rho\Sigma\mu'_{6z}$$

in which the zero superscript indicates values corresponding to the deeply submerged spheroid, Eqs. (13.110); the primes denote that the summation is over the internal singularities of the added potential due to the free surface; the first subscript on the singularity strength indicates the velocity component with which it is associated; and the letter subscript on the doublet strengths specifies the component of the doublet vector.

The singularity distributions appearing in Eqs. (13.115) have been found by successive approximations beginning with the known distributions for the deeply submerged spheroid given by Eqs. (13.111) and (13.113). The results obtained are in the form of multiple integrals, which are tedious to evaluate. Numerical solutions have not yet been obtained except at the limiting Froude numbers. Some of Eisenberg's results are shown in Fig. 13.23.

13.10. Forces and Moments Due to Viscosity

Drag. In a real fluid it is necessary to take into account the various phenomena engendered by vorticity. First suppose that the body is moving in the direction of its axis of symmetry, so that it is subjected only to a drag force. As for the two-dimensional forms, the dimensionless magnitude of this force varies considerably with the shape of the body, the nature of the boundary layer, and the presence or absence of separation.

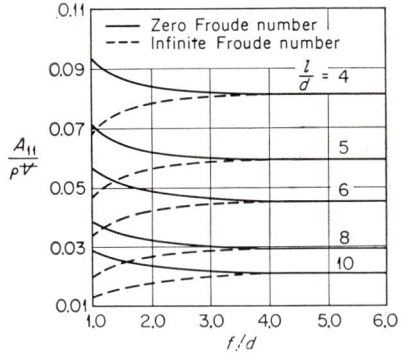

FIG. 13.23. Added-mass coefficients for motion of spheroids parallel to major axis in plane parallel to surface. (*Ref.* 31.)

For streamlined bodies various methods are available[16] for computing the shear stresses up to the point near the rear of the body where the pressure begins to deviate appreciably from the potential-flow value. Beyond this point the thickness of the boundary layer becomes too great in comparison with the radius of the section for the usual boundary-layer assumptions to apply, and it becomes necessary to retain additional terms in the Navier-Stokes equations to determine the shear stress and the pressure distribution over the rear of the body. The deviation of the latter from the potential-flow distribution yields the viscous pressure drag. Several semiempirical methods of computing the drag have been proposed.[33]

A completely rational method for computing the viscous drag of bodies of revolution has not been found, especially for the turbulent part of the boundary layer, so that reference is usually made to experiment when trustworthy values are required. Measurements of drag in a wind tunnel need to be corrected for the presence of the tunnel walls and the longitudinal pressure gradient in the tunnel by amounts which may exceed the resultant drag. Results obtained in a large towing tank would be more reliable, but little published data are available. Since the increase in drag due to the pressure defect is partly compensated by the concomitant reduction in shear stress at the rear, a first approximation should be obtainable by assuming that the drag is entirely due to the shear stresses computed on the basis of "thin" boundary-layer theory and the potential-flow pressure distribution. With these assumptions it would then be possible to apply Mangler's equations to transform the boundary-layer problem into a two-dimensional one.

Calculations indicate that the resistance of a streamlined form is proportional to the resistance of a two-dimensional flat plate of the same wetted-surface area at the same length Reynolds number,

$$C_D = \frac{D}{\frac{1}{2}\rho S U^2} = (1 + \lambda)C_f(\mathbf{R}) \qquad (13.116)$$

in which λ is very small in comparison with unity. Gertler[34] has found, however, that the difference between C_D and C_f is small, but independent of the Reynolds number. These results are based on drag measurements in a towing tank. Although the measurements were corrected for wave-making resistance assuming deep water, it is quite possible that if the wave-making resistance were recalculated for the actual tank depth and the disturbance potential

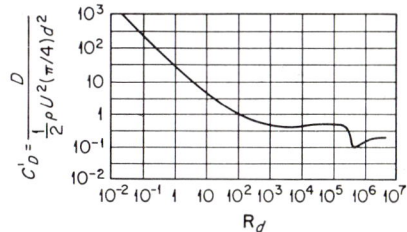

FIG. 13.24. Drag coefficients for a sphere.

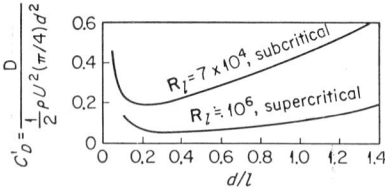

FIG. 13.25. Drag coefficients of spheroids. (*From Hoerner, Ref. 6, p. 2-12.*)

due to the presence of the rigid bottom and free surface were used to determine the effective increase in incident velocity at the submerged body, the results would be in better agreement with Eq. (13.116).

The occurrence of separation affects the drag in much the same manner as has been described for two-dimensional forms. For bodies with sufficiently blunt rear ends, there is a critical Reynolds number below or above which the separation is termed laminar or turbulent. The classical demonstration of this phenomenon is shown by the curve of C'_D against Reynolds number for a sphere in Fig. 13.24. The sphere is a member of the family of ellipsoids of revolution which for supercritical flow at sufficiently high length-diameter ratios l/d may be considered as streamlined bodies. The drag coefficients of spheroids at a subcritical Reynolds number of 7×10^4 and a supercritical Reynolds number of 10^6, as given by Hoerner,[6] are shown in Fig. 13.25. The effect of Reynolds number on the drag due to turbulent separation has been investigated experimentally by Petersohn[35] with the conclusion that the increment in drag coefficient is independent of the Reynolds number. Thus, when separation is present, Eq. (13.116) should become

$$C_D = (1 + \lambda)C_f(\mathbf{R}) + C_{DS} \tag{13.117}$$

Some additional data on the drag of deeply submerged elongated bodies of revolution will be presented in connection with the discussion of the effect of proximity of a free surface.

Lift. Measurements indicate that bodies of revolution at an angle of yaw α are also subjected to a lift force, contrary to the prediction of inviscid-flow theory. One may account for part of this lift by considering separately the boundary layer and drag due to the longitudinal and transverse components of the velocity and assuming that the combined flow and resultant force may then be obtained by superposition. This assumption has a theoretical basis for laminar boundary layers, but only an empirical one for turbulent boundary layers. This analysis accounts for a term proportional to the square of the angle of attack. It is actually found[36] that the lift coefficient is of the form

$$C_L = \frac{L}{\frac{1}{2}\rho A U^2} = a\alpha + b\alpha^2$$

if A is the area of a meridian section. The term linear in α suggests that the body also has lift due to bound vorticity as if it were a foil of low aspect ratio. Unfortunately, a theory for computing the strength of this vorticity is not available. The assumption that part of the lift is due to the drag in the transverse component of the incident velocity gives $b = C_D$, the drag coefficient for a circular cylinder, 1.2 for subcritical flow, 0.3 for supercritical flow. With an empirical value[37] for a the expression for C_L becomes

$$C_L = 0.234 \left(\frac{2V}{l^3} \right)^{0.79} \frac{l^2}{A} \alpha + C_D\alpha^2 \tag{13.118}$$

Bodies of revolution serving as vehicles or projectiles must be equipped with stabilizing and control surfaces. Their effects on the lift, drag, and moment are considerable and must be taken into account. Since these surfaces are usually present near the rear of the body, they may be immersed in part or in whole in the boundary layer or even possibly in a zone of separation. Thus the nature of the flow about the body must be considered in estimating the performance of these appendages.

Free-surface Effect. The effect of the free surface on the lift, drag, and moment has already been considered from a theoretical point of view. In actuality, the boundary layer and wake of the body affect the wave making, and the velocity field associated with the surface disturbance will in turn modify the velocity and pressure fields about

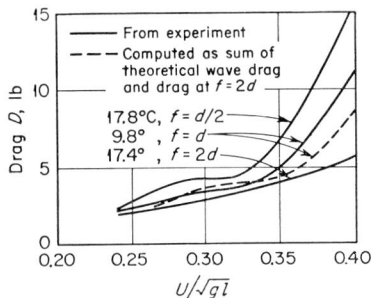

FIG. 13.26. Drag of a prolate spheroid ($l/d = 8$) moving horizontally at various depths below the free surface. (*Ref.* 38.)

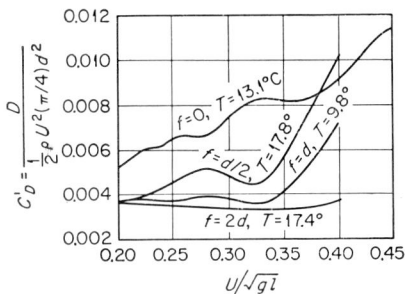

FIG. 13.27 Drag coefficients of a prolate spheroid ($l/d = 8$) moving horizontally at various depths below the free surface. (*Ref.* 38.)

the body. A comparison between the theoretical and measured values of the resistance of a prolate spheroid[38] of length-diameter ratio 8.0 is shown in Fig. 13.26. The computed values of the total resistance at a depth of 1 diam were obtained by adding the viscous drag, assumed to be given by the measured drag at a depth of 2 diam, to the computed wave resistance, neglecting the aforementioned interactions between viscous and wave effects. Curves of the measured resistance coefficient for various depths of submergence are given in Fig. 13.27. It is concluded in Ref. 38, in which tests on four forms are included, that theoretical results agree well with experiment for immersions greater than 1 diam if a displacement in the Froude numbers, resembling a "phase shift," is ignored.

Cavitation.† A projectile moving at a sufficiently high speed through a liquid will encounter cavitation, which, at small values of the cavitation number σ_c, may take the form of a solitary bubble enveloping the body and leaving only a part of the nose wetted. Under these circumstances the drag of the object may be increased considerably, and the designer must be concerned with the possibility that the stabilizing and control surfaces may become immersed in the cavity and be ineffective. The general trend of the variation of C_D with σ_c is that the drag increases gradually from its value C_{D0} at $\sigma_c = 0$ to a maximum at a σ_c value somewhat less than that for inception, and then decreases rapidly to the value of C_D for noncavitating conditions. This variation is illustrated in Fig. 13.28 for the case of a sphere. Also shown in the figure are curves for cylindrical bodies of revolution with flat, conical, and ogival noses.[39] The drag coefficients at small values of σ_c are in excellent agreement with the predictions from the theory of Plesset and Shaffer.[40]

When the body is accelerating, the Bernoulli equation for unsteady flow indicates that the incipient cavitation number is increased by

$$\Delta \sigma_i = \frac{a\phi_1}{\frac{1}{2}\rho U^2} \qquad (13.119)$$

in which a is the acceleration of the body, and ϕ_1 the velocity potential for unit axial velocity. This has been verified[39] in experiments which indicated, however, that a significant increase in the drag coefficient over the steady-state values would occur only if the dimensionless acceleration satisfies the condition $ad/U^2 > 1$, in which d is the diameter of the body. Since this condition will be satisfied only for low

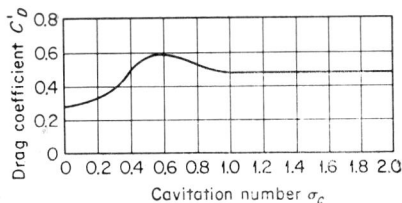

† See Sec. 12.

FIG. 13.28. Effect of cavitation on drag of a sphere and cylinders with various nose forms.

speeds, acceleration should have only a minor effect on the performance of a high-speed underwater missile.

13.11. Steady Motion of Ship Forms

First consider the steady motion of a ship on a calm sea. A ship is essentially an elongated floating body with a single plane of symmetry, the vertical longitudinal plane in its normal attitude. It is supported vertically principally by its buoyancy and partly, when in motion, in a negative sense, by dynamic pressures which affect its displacement and trim. When it is moving steadily at a zero angle of yaw, the thrust of its propulsion system is in equilibrium with the drag of the ship.

Viscous Drag. It is convenient at first to treat separately the contributions to the drag from viscosity and wave making. Viscous drag is manifested by the development of a boundary layer along the hull and the presence of zones of separated flow and a wake in which the energy of turbulence is generated and dissipated. The forces interacting with the hull consist of the tangential stresses and the normal pressures, of which part of the latter is attributable to wave making.

Very little is known about three-dimensional boundary layers, and consequently not even semiempirical methods are available for computing the viscous drag of a ship. Prediction is further complicated by uncertainty concerning the roughness of the hull. The assumption is usually made that the integrated effect of the shear stresses, the so-called frictional resistance, is equal to that of a two-dimensional flat plate of the same wetted-surface area at the same length Reynolds number. To this must be added the viscous pressure drag (or form drag) to obtain the total viscous resistance. It appears reasonable to suppose that the viscous-drag coefficient for a ship also satisfies an equation of the form of Eq. (13.117),

$$C'_D = \frac{D}{\tfrac{1}{2}\,\rho S U^2} = (1 + \lambda)C_f + C_{DS}$$

in which C_f is the drag coefficient of the equivalent flat plate and S is the actual wetted area of the ship, including the effect of the wave profile and sinkage when under way. Since these effects are difficult to estimate, a more practical form of resistance coefficient is

$$C_D = \frac{S}{S_0} C'_D = \frac{S}{S_0} [(1 + \lambda)C_f + C_{DS}] \qquad (13.120)$$

in which S_0 is the wetted-surface area at zero speed. Some empirical ship-resistance data collected by Granville[41] for smooth hulls suggest the formula

$$\lambda = 18.7 \, \frac{V^2}{l^4 H^2} \qquad 0 < \frac{V}{l^2 H} < 0.11 \qquad (13.121)$$

if H = draft of ship
  l = length of ship
  V = immersed volume of ship

The increment in the coefficient due to separation C_{DS} is difficult to estimate since it is sensitive to the shape of the stern.

The frictional resistance of a ship is increased manyfold by the roughness of its surface. These include such surface imperfections as rivet heads, butts, laps, and welds in the plating, the roughness of marine paints, and the fouling of the surface by marine growths. As the boundary layer thins with increasing speed, more of the roughness elements extend beyond the laminar sublayer, and the deviation of the frictional-resistance coefficient from that for the smooth surface continues to increase; but because of this non-uniformity of the roughness, the frictional-drag coefficient usually does not become constant (as it does for uniform sand roughness) even at the maximum speed of a ship. Experiments on marine fouling indicate that the drag of a ship may be doubled in a year on ships which spend most of their time at sea, but may be tripled in a few summer months on a ship in port.

Wave-making Resistance. A ship advancing with steady velocity in a calm sea disturbs the surface in a beautifully regular pattern which consists essentially of two systems of diverging and transverse waves generated separately by the bow and the stern. These are reasonably well in accord with Kelvin's theory of the surface disturbance by a traveling disturbance. As the speed of a ship varies, the stern wave system may partially annul the bow wave system at some speeds or reinforce it at other speeds, with the result that the curve of resistance coefficients of the ship manifests maxima and minima (humps and hollows).

The wave-making resistance of a thin ship of arbitrary shape in an inviscid liquid has been given by Michell.[42] Let $y = \pm f(x,z)$ denote the equation of the surface of the ship's hull in a coordinate system moving with the ship in the x direction at a constant velocity U. The problem is linearized in the sense that the boundary conditions on the surface of the body are assumed to apply on the centerplane of the ship, S_0, over which sources are distributed of such strength as to satisfy the boundary conditions. This results in the expression for the wave-making resistance in terms of the hull geometry, known as Michell's integral,

$$R_{\text{wave}} = \frac{4g^2\rho}{\pi U^2} \int_0^{\pi/2} \sec^3 \theta [P^2(\theta) + Q^2(\theta)]d\theta$$

$$P(\theta) = \iint_{S_0} \frac{\partial f}{\partial x} \exp\left(-\frac{gy}{U^2}\sec^2\theta\right) \cos\left(\frac{gx}{U^2}\sec\theta\right) dx\, dy \qquad (13.122)$$

$$Q(\theta) = \iint_{S_0} \frac{\partial f}{\partial x} \exp\left(-\frac{gy}{U^2}\sec^2\theta\right) \sin\left(\frac{gx}{U^2}\sec\theta\right) dx\, dy$$

Equation (13.122) has been intensively applied to determine the effect of variations of hull form upon wave resistance. An extensive bibliography is given by Wehausen.[30] In a liquid of depth h the expression for the wave resistance, given by Stretenskii,[43] is

$$R = \frac{2g\rho U}{\pi} \int_{\theta_0}^{\infty} [P^2(\theta) + Q^2(\theta)] \left[\frac{\theta}{\theta - (g/U^2)\tanh\theta h}\right]^{1/2} d\theta$$

$$P(\theta) = \iint_{S_0} \frac{\partial f}{\partial x} \frac{\cosh\theta(z-h)}{\cosh\theta h} \cos\left(\frac{x}{U}\sqrt{g\theta\tanh\theta h}\right) dx\, dy \qquad (13.123)$$

$$Q(\theta) = \iint_{S_0} \frac{\partial f}{\partial x} \frac{\cosh\theta(z-h)}{\cosh\theta h} \sin\left(\frac{x}{U}\sqrt{g\theta\tanh\theta h}\right) dx\, dy$$

in which $\theta_0 = 0$ if $U^2 < gh$

$\theta_0 \neq 0,\ \theta_0 U^2 = g\tanh\theta_0 h$ if $U^2 > gh$

Comparison of the foregoing theory with experiment on the basis of measurements of total resistance is difficult because it is not known how much of the resistance is due to viscosity. If the experiment is performed with a small model, the estimation of the viscous drag is further complicated by the uncertainty concerning the extent of the laminar boundary layer and the possibility that separation may be present. A technique for separating viscous from wave drag by means of wake measurements has been proposed by Tulin,[44] but has not yet been applied. Nevertheless, on the basis of several such comparisons, it has been concluded that the theoretical values of the wave resistance agree with the measured values within about 10 per cent, and that the predicted humps and hollows are of greater amplitude and occur at speeds about 5 to 10 per cent lower than observed. These discrepancies have been attributed by one school of thought to the approximations in the theory, viz., the linearization of the boundary conditions on the free surface and the hull and the fact that the stream surface generated by sources distributed over the plane of symmetry deviates appreciably from the actual location of the hull. Others have attributed the discrepancies to the effects of viscosity, such as the displacement thickness of the boundary layer near the stern, zones of separation, and the wake.

13.12. Unsteady Motion of Ship Forms

A ship disturbed by the action of wind and sea will undergo motions with 6 degrees of freedom: the three translational motions of surging, swaying, and heaving and the rotational ones of rolling, pitching, and yawing. These motions are superimposed on the mean course of the ship, which, for the case of a ship maneuvering under the action of its rudder, is also an unsteady motion.

Ship Maneuvering. A rudder is usually situated at the stern of a ship, in the high-velocity stream due to the propeller, in order to increase its dynamical effectiveness. The rudder is essentially a foil of aspect ratio of the order of unity, the lift on which, when it is at an angle of attack, results in a moment about the center of gravity of the ship. The ship itself will then assume an angle of attack and, if it is directionally stable, move on a circular path such that the resultant moment about the center of gravity of the forces on the hull and rudder is zero and the resultant force is mU^2/R, if m is the apparent mass of the vessel, U its tangential velocity, and R the radius of curvature of the path. An estimate of the force and moment on the hull can be obtained by treating the immersed part of the hull together with its mirror image in the water plane as a wing of low aspect ratio at an angle of attack and rotating at an angular velocity $r = U/R$. This gives the lift coefficient on the hull[45]

$$C_L \doteq \frac{\pi}{2} n\beta + \beta^2 \tag{13.124}$$

and the moment coefficient

$$C_M = \frac{M}{\frac{1}{2}\rho U^2 Al} \doteq \frac{2V}{Al}(k_1 - k_2)\beta + \frac{\pi}{4}n\beta + C_{Mr}\frac{l}{R} \tag{13.125}$$

in which A = submerged area of hull, projected on vertical plane of symmetry
$n = 2H^2/A$ = aspect ratio of double form in terms of draft H
β = drift angle
C_{Mr} = damping coefficient

$$C_{Mr} = \frac{\partial M/\partial r}{\frac{1}{2}\rho U^2 A}$$

Ship Motions. The most violent motions of a ship in a seaway are those of heaving, rolling, and pitching. Because of a combination of these motions, a vessel may capsize or be damaged by large stresses; its cargo may shift; its decks may be flooded; its speed reduced; and the passengers may become seasick. Clearly, it is desirable to design ships so that their motions will be smooth and of small amplitude even in a rough sea.

It will be supposed that a rough sea is composed of a random distribution of waves of various frequencies traveling in various directions. Let $Z(t)$ denote the vertical displacement of a point on the surface from its mean position. Then the intensity or power of the sea is given by the mean square $\overline{Z(t)^2}$, and according to Eqs. (13.47) and (13.48), the power spectrum is the Fourier cosine transform of the autocorrelation of $Z(t)$. A recently empirically derived directional power spectrum[46,47] for a fully developed sea due to a wind of velocity U is

$$p(\omega,\theta) = \frac{8}{3\pi}\frac{4.80 \times 10^4}{\omega^6}\exp\left(-\frac{2g^2}{\omega^2 U^2}\right)\cos^4\theta \qquad -\frac{\pi}{2} < \theta < \frac{\pi}{2} \tag{13.126}$$

in which ω is the angular frequency of a wave, and θ is measured from the wind direction. Integrating $p(\omega,\theta)$ over the indicated range of θ gives the Neumann power spectrum

$$p(\omega) = \frac{4.80 \times 10^4}{\omega^6}\exp\left(-\frac{2g^2}{\omega^2 U^2}\right) \tag{13.127}$$

The response of the ship to a pure harmonic wave $Z = Z_0 e^{i\omega t}$ can be expressed in the form

$$Y(t) = G_{YZ}(i\omega)Z_0 e^{i\omega t} \tag{13.128}$$

in which $G_{YZ}(S)$ is a transfer function as defined in Eq. (13.41), and $G_{YZ}(i\omega)$ is called the frequency-response vector. The power spectrum of the response or output function is then $|G_{YZ}(i\omega)|^2 p(\omega)$, and the mean square (or power) of the output is

$$\overline{Y^2} = \int_{-\infty}^{\infty} |G_{YZ}(i\omega)|^2 p(\omega) d\omega \tag{13.129}$$

as in Eq. (13.50). The foregoing relations are based on a linear theory of ship behavior in an irregular seaway.

The theoretical determination of the response of a floating body to a sinusoidal wave is a complex problem to which, because of its importance in ship design, considerable effort has been devoted. The bulk of the theoretical literature on ship motions is based on the so-called Froude-Krylov hypothesis that the kinematic boundary condition on the hull and the disturbance of the velocity potential of the wave due to the presence and motion of the ship may be neglected. This rather crude assumption was avoided in a now classical paper by John,[48] in which the motion of a floating body with no mean forward speed in a wave was treated as a linearized boundary-value problem. The case of nonzero mean speed of advance has been similarly treated by Haskind[49] and Peters and Stoker.[50] It is established in these investigations that the floating body is subjected to inertial, damping, restoring, and disturbing forces, and expressions are obtained for the added-mass and damping coefficients dependent upon the hull shape and wave frequency. The theory yields a set of linear equations for determining the amplitudes of oscillation in the 6 degrees of freedom, containing coefficients of inertia and damping which are defined as surface integrals of various velocity potentials, analogous to the definitions of the various added masses for a submerged body [Eqs. (13.17)]. Since the determination of these velocity potentials is in itself a difficult problem, simpler methods are being sought for obtaining the responses of a ship. In one approximate procedure the coefficients are derived by integrating the two-dimensional coefficients for each section of the hull. Another simplification consists of considering one degree of freedom at a time and subsequently treating the effects of coupling between degrees of freedom. An effective approach consists of replacing the oscillating ship by a distribution of harmonically pulsating sources and doublets advancing at constant speed.

A simplified form of the linearized equations of motion for pitch and heave, given in a recent summary of the subject by Weinblum,[51] is

$$(B + A_{33})\ddot{z} + N_{33}\dot{z} + \rho g A_W z = \rho g r_m A_W E_{33} e^{i(wt - \epsilon_{33})}$$
$$(I_y + A_{55})\ddot{\theta} + N_{55}\dot{\theta} + \rho g \forall \overline{GM}\theta = \rho g \alpha_m \forall \overline{GM} E_{55} e^{i(wt - \epsilon_{55})} \tag{13.130}$$

in which
B = mass of ship
A_{33} = an added mass
I_y = moment of inertia about y axis
A_{55} = added moment of inertia
θ = angle of pitch
N_{33}, N_{55} = damping coefficients
A_W = waterline area
$\overline{GM}$ = distance from center of gravity G to metacenter M for a small angular displacement about y axis
r_m = wave amplitude
α_m = maximum wave slope
E_{33}, E_{55} = exciting functions due to the wave

The omission of important cross-coupling terms between pitch and heave from these equations would cause an appreciable loss in accuracy. Nevertheless, they already serve to indicate that hydrodynamic studies of inertia, damping, and exciting forces are needed to formulate the equations of motion.[52]

A much studied but yet not fully understood motion is that of ship rolling. A simple form of the equation of rolling for a ship broadside to a regular train of waves of angular frequency ω is

$$I\ddot{\varphi} + 2k\dot{\varphi} + W\overline{GM}\varphi = W\overline{GM}\alpha_m \sin \omega t \tag{13.131}$$

in which I = apparent moment of inertia
         k = a damping coefficient
       W = weight of ship
    $\overline{GM}$ = metacentric height for rotation about x axis
      α_m = maximum slope of the wave

The problem is complicated by the fact that the inertia and damping coefficients depend upon the axis of rotation, the position of which is initially unknown. Wendel[13] determines the position of the axis on the assumption that the total kinetic energy of body and fluid is a minimum when rolling freely in comparison with the kinetic energy when restrained to roll about any other longitudinal axis. A better representation of roll damping is given by the nonlinear form $a\ddot{\varphi} + b\dot{\varphi}^2$, of which the first term is principally due to wave generation and the second to vortex formation at the bilges of a normal ship form. It has been shown theoretically by Ursell[53] and confirmed experimentally[54] that the wave damping of a rolling ship form is very sensitive to the sectional shape. The great effectiveness of bilge keels as roll dampers has recently been attributed by Martin[19] to the manyfold increase in the drag coefficient of an oscillating plate in comparison with that for steady flow (Fig. 13.19).

REFERENCES

1. Lamb, H.: "Hydrodynamics," 6th ed., Cambridge, New York, 1932.
2. Landweber, L., and C. S. Yih: Forces, Moments, and Added Masses for Rankine Bodies, *J. Fluid Mech.*, **1**(3):319 (September, 1956).
3. Etkin, B.: "Dynamics of Flight," Wiley, New York, 1959.
4. Rouse, H.: "Advanced Mechanics of Fluids," Wiley, New York, 1959.
5. Landweber, L.: The Frictional Resistance of Flat Plates in Zero Pressure Gradient, *Trans. SNAME*, 1953.
6. Hoerner, S.: "Fluid Dynamic Drag," S. Hoerner, Midland Park, N.J., 1959.
7. Wu, T. Y.: A Free Streamline Theory for Two-dimensional Fully Cavitated Hydrofoils, *Hydrodynamics Lab. CIT Rept.* 21-17, July, 1955.
8. Tulin, M. P.: Steady Two-dimensional Cavity Flows about Slender Bodies, *David Taylor Model Basin Rept.* 834, May, 1953.
9. Kotschin, N. J., L. A. Kibel, and N. W. Rose: "Theoretische Hydromechanik," vol. 1, Akademie-Verlag, Berlin, 1954.
10. Wu, T. Y.: A Theory for Hydrofoils of Finite Span, *Hydrodynamics Lab. CIT Rept.* 26-8, May, 1953.
11. Lewis, F. M.: The Inertia of Water Surrounding a Vibrating Ship, *Trans. SNAME*, vol. 37, 1929.
12. Landweber, L., and M. Macagno: Added Mass of Two-dimensional Forms Oscillating in a Free Surface, *J. Ship Research*, November, 1957.
13. Wendel, K.: Hydrodynamic Masses and Hydrodynamic Moments of Inertia, *TMB Transl.* 260, July, 1956. (Translation of Hydrodynamische Massen und Hydrodynamische Massenträgheitsmomente, *Jahrb. Schiffbautech. Ges.*, vol. 44, 1950.)
14. Ursell, F.: On the Virtual Mass and Damping of Floating Bodies at Zero Speed Ahead, *Proc. Symposium on the Behaviour of Ships in a Seaway*, Wageningen, The Netherlands, September, 1957.
15. Goldstein, S.: "Modern Developments in Fluid Dynamics," vols. 1 and 2, Oxford, New York, 1938.
16. Schlichting, H.: "Boundary-layer Theory," McGraw-Hill, New York, 1960.
17. Lin, C. C.: "The Theory of Hydrodynamic Stability," Cambridge, New York, 1955.
18. Anton, L.: Formation of a Vortex at the Edge of a Plate, *NACA Tech. Mem.* 1398. (Translation of Ausbildung eines Wirbels an der Kante einer Platte, *Ingenieur-Arch.*, vol. 10, 1939.)
19. Martin, M.: Roll Damping Due to Bilge Keels, Ph.D. dissertation, State University of Iowa, Iowa City, Iowa, 1959.
20. Wagner, H.: Dynamischer Auftrieb von Tragflügeln, *ZAMM*, **5**:17 (1925).

21. Theodorsen, T.· General Theory of Aerodynamic Instability and the Mechanism of Flutter, *NACA Tech. Rept.* 496, 1949.
22. Weiss, P.: On Hydrodynamical Images: Arbitrary Irrotational Flow Disturbed by a Sphere, *Proc., Cambridge Phil. Soc.*, vol. 40, part 3, 1944.
23. Munk, M. M.: "Fluid Mechanics," vol. 1, part II, in W. F. Durand (ed.), "Aerodynamic Theory," Springer, Berlin, 1935.
24. Landweber, L.: The Axially Symmetric Potential Flow about Elongated Bodies of Revolution, *TMB Rept.* 761, May, 1951.
25. Landweber, L., and A. Winzer: A Comparison of the Added Masses of Streamlined Bodies and Prolate Spheroids, *Schiffstechnik*, vol. 3, April, 1956.
26. Havelock, T. H.: The Moment on a Submerged Solid of Revolution Moving Horizontally, *Quart. J. Mech. and Appl. Math.*, vol. 5, 1952.
27. Jahnke, E., and F. Emde: "Tables of Functions with Formulae and Curves," Dover, New York, 1943.
28. Pond, H. L.: The Moment Acting on a Rankine Ovoid Moving under a Free Surface, *DTMB Rept.* 795, 1951.
29. Havelock, T. H.: The Wave Resistance of a Spheroid, *Proc. Royal Soc. (London)*, ser. A, vol. 131, 1931.
30. Wehausen, J. V.: Water Waves, part II, *Univ. Calif. Ser.*, 82, September, 1958. (To be published in "Handbuch der Physik," Springer, Berlin.)
31. Eisenberg, P., Asymptotic Solution for the Virtual Masses and Moments of Inertia of Prolate Spheroids near a Free Surface for Very Small and Very Large Froude Numbers, *Eighth Intern. Congr. on Theoret. and Appl. Mech.*, August, 1952.
32. Bottaccini, M. R.: The Added Masses of Prolate Spheroids Accelerating under a Free Surface, Ph.D. dissertation, State University of Iowa, Iowa City, Iowa, June, 1958.
33. Granville, P.: The Calculation of the Viscous Drag of Bodies of Revolution, *DTMB Rept.* 849, July, 1953.
34. Gertler, M.: Application of the Lap-troost Extrapolation Method to Submerged Bodies of Revolution, *DTMB Rept.* 1236, July, 1958.
35. Petersohn, E. G. M.: The Pressure Drag Due to Turbulent Separation on Bodies of Revolution with Varying Boundary-layer Thickness, *Flygtek. Försöksanstatten Rept.* 75, May, 1957.
36. Freeman, H. B.: Force Measurements on a 1/40-scale Model of the U.S. Airship *Akron*, *NACA Rept.* 430, 1932.
37. Johnson, J. L.: The Static Stability Derivatives of a Series of Related Bodies of Revolution, *DTMB Rept.* C-383, March, 1951.
38. Weinblum, G., H. Amtsberg, and W. Bock: Tests of Wave Resistance of Immersed Bodies of Revolution, *TMB Transl.* 234, September, 1950. (Translated from Versuche über den Wellenwiderstand Getauchter Rotationskörper, *Mitt. preuss. Versuchsanstalt Wasserbau u Schiffbau*, 1936.)
39. Oversmith, R. H.: Some Observations on Cavitating Flows, *Convair Rept.* ZR-659-015, March, 1959.
40. Plesset, M. S., and P. A. Shaffer, Jr.: Cavity Drag in Two and Three Dimensions, *J. Appl. Phys.*, vol. 19, no. 10, October, 1948.
41. Granville, P. S.: The Viscous Resistance of Surface Vessels and the Skin Friction of Flat Plates, *Trans. SNAME*, 1956.
42. Michell, J. H.: The Wave Resistance of a Ship, *Phil. Mag.*, ser. 5, vol. 45, 1898.
43. Stretenskii, L. N.: On the Wave-making Resistance of a Ship Moving Along in a Canal, *Phil. Mag.*, vol. 22, 1936.
44. Tulin, M. P.: The Separation of Viscous Drag and Wave Drag by Means of the Wake Survey, *DTMB Rept.* 772, July, 1951.
45. Tsakonas, S.: Effect of Appendage and Hull Form on Hydrodynamic Coefficients of Surface Ships, *Davidson Lab. Rept.* 740, July, 1959.
46. Neumann, G.: On Ocean Wave Spectra and a New Method of Forecasting Wind-generated Sea, *U.S. Army Corps Engrs.*, Beach Erosion Board, *Tech. Mem.* 43, 1953.
47. St. Denis, M.: On the Reduction of Motion Data from Model Tests in Confused Seas, *Proc. Symposium on the Behaviour of Ships in a Seaway*, Wageningen, The Netherlands, September, 1957.
48. John, F.: On the Motion of Floating Bodies, *Comm. in Pure and Appl. Math.*, no. 2, 1949; no. 3, 1950.
49. Haskind, M. D.: The Hydrodynamic Theory of Ship Oscillations in Rolling and Pitching, *SNAME Tech. Research Bull.* 1-12, 1953.
50. Peters, A. S., and J. J. Stoker: The Motion of a Ship, as a Floating Rigid Body, in a Seaway, *Comm. in Pure and Appl. Math.*, no. 10, 1957.

51. Weinblum, G. P.: Contribution of Ship Theory to the Seaworthiness Problem, *Natl. Acad. Sci. Naval Hydrodynamics Publ.* 515, 1957.
52. Weinblum, G., and M. St. Denis: On the Motions of Ships at Sea, *Trans. SNAME*, 1950.
53. Ursell, F.: On the Rolling Motion of Cylinders in the Surface of a Fluid, *Quart. J. Mech. and Appl. Math.*, vol. 2, no. 3, 1949.
54. McLeod, W. C.: Experimental Investigation of Ursell's Theory of Wave Making by a Rolling Ship, master's thesis, Dept. of Mech. and Hydraulics, State Univ. of Iowa, 1959.

Section 14

FLOW MEASUREMENT

By

R. C. BINDER, *University of Southern California, Los Angeles, California*

FLOW MEASUREMENT

14.1. Introductory Remarks

Various problems arise concerning the use of instruments for flow measurement in engineering practice and research. There are such problems as the measurement of pressure, linear velocity, and the rate of flow (volume or weight rate). A wide variety of methods and meters can be found in practice; many can be grouped into a small number of types. The present section discusses the common types of methods and devices of flow measurement.

In tackling a problem of fluid flow, there are four basic equations available for use: (1) the equation of state (a functional relation between pressure, specific weight, and temperature), (2) the equation of continuity (an accounting of mass), (3) the dynamic, or momentum, equation (force equals mass times acceleration), and (4) the energy equation (an energy and work accounting). These same equations are applicable to specific problems of flow measurement. In analyzing the action of many fluid meters, it is customary to set up a relation assuming certain ideal conditions (as no friction and uniform velocity distributions) and then use an experimentally determined calibration coefficient to take into account deviations from the ideal.

Length, time, and force are quantities that can be measured with a high degree of accuracy. It is good technique to refer all derived measurements, as velocity, weight or volume rate of flow, and pressure, as directly as possible to the basic standards of length, time, and force. For example, in order to measure the rate of flow from a pump or channel, good accuracy can be obtained by weighing the discharge or measuring the volume during a measured time interval. In many practical cases, however, convenience and economy may indicate the use of a second-choice method or instrument whose accuracy depends on a direct experimental calibration or on an assumed flow coefficient.

Various specialized details about installation, operation, and specific construction can be found in the literature (see references at the end of this section) and in current industrial catalogues. Different organizations have been sponsoring extensive programs to establish standards of flow measurement. Such standards can help in many ways, as in forming the basis of acceptance tests for turbines, compressors, fans, other machines, and equipment. New standards are published in the current literature as soon as they are developed. Participating in such activities are different international and national professional societies and different industrial associations.

The term *fluid meters* refers to various instruments, which may be classed broadly into two functional groups: (1) *quantity* meters, and (2) *rate* meters. A quantity meter shows the total amount or quantity that passes through the meter, as in number of gallons or in cubic feet. A rate meter, on the other hand, shows the rate per unit time, as gallons per minute or cubic feet per second. Each fluid meter has two distinct elements, each of which has a different function to perform. One element, called the *primary* element, is in direct contact with the fluid and is acted on directly by it. The other element, called the *secondary* element, translates the action of the fluid on the primary element into volumes, or rates of flow, and gives some indication or record of the result.

It is common to classify meters further, or more specifically, on the basis of the primary element or the physical principle involved. With a given primary element, a wide variety of secondary elements may be possible. For example, an orifice meter is a rate meter because it indicates rate of flow. This meter has two elements. The primary element is the orifice plate with a hole, and the secondary element is some form of differential pressure gauge. Various pressure-gauge arrangements are possible with the same primary element of an orifice plate.

In a quantity meter the fluid passes in successive and more or less completely isolated quantities, either in volumes or weights, by alternately filling and emptying containers of known or fixed capacities. Quantity meters may be classed into two major groups: (1) weighing, and (2) volumetric. A quantity meter may involve a reciprocating piston, a rotary (or oscillating) piston, a nutating (or wobble) disc, a rotary gear or lobe impeller, bellows, or a liquid-sealed drum.

In a rate meter the fluid passes through (or around) in a continuous stream, as contrasted with the isolated (separately counted) action of the quantity meter. Rate meters may be classed into groups, as head, area, head-area, velocity, and thermal. In the head meter there is a pressure difference developed by the primary element; this pressure difference is correlated with rate flow. Examples of head meters are the venturi, orifice, flow nozzle, pitot, and elbow. In an area meter a variation of the cross section of the stream under constant head is used as an indication of the rate of flow; the rotameter is an example. A weir is an example of a head-area meter; in this case the flow rate varies with both head and area. An example of a velocity meter is some device that is kept in continual rotation by the linear motion of the stream in which it is immersed; the primary element may be a series of rotating vanes or cups. In a thermal meter the primary element consists of a device for heating the stream and a device for measuring the resulting temperature difference; the thermal measurements are correlated with flow rate.

In some of the following, a flow measurement is discussed for both incompressible and compressible fluids. The incompressible-fluid case is presented first.

14.2. Notation

The following notation will be used:

A area, ft^2
a relative velocity, fps
B flux density, gausses
C discharge coefficient, dimensionless
c acoustic velocity, fps
c_p specific heat at constant pressure, Btu/(lb)(°F)
c_v specific heat at constant volume, Btu/(lb)(°F)
D diameter, ft
d drag force, lb
e electromotive force, volts
F buoyant force, lb
f focal length, ft
g gravitational acceleration, ft/sec^2
H height, ft
h height, ft
J conversion factor, 1 Btu equals about 778 ft-lb
K flow coefficient, dimensionless
k ratio of specific heats, $k = c_p/c_v$, dimensionless
L length, ft
l length, ft
m mass rate, slugs/sec
$\mathbf{M}$ Mach number, $\mathbf{M} = V/c$, dimensionless
P rate of heat input, Btu/sec
p pressure, psf
Q actual volume rate of flow, ft^3/sec
Q_i ideal volume rate of flow, ft^3/sec
q heat transfer, Btu/lb
R gas factor in equation $pv = RT$

r　　radius, ft
S　　distance, ft
T　　absolute temperature, °R
t　　temperature, °F
U　　peripheral speed, fps
V　　velocity, fps
V_U　tangential component of resultant velocity, fps
v　　specific volume, ft³/lb
W　　weight rate of flow, lb/sec
x　　length, ft
Y　　expansion factor, dimensionless
z　　height, ft
ρ　　density, slugs/ft³
μ　　dynamic viscosity, slugs/(ft)(sec)
γ　　specific weight, lb/ft³
ω　　angular speed, radians/sec

In the foregoing examples of units, the pound has been used only as a unit of force, and the slug as a unit of mass. A force of one pound acting on a mass of one slug is associated with an acceleration of one foot per second per second.

14.3. Measurement of Static Pressure

Pressure, or pressure intensity, is defined as force per unit area. The *static pressure* in a stream of fluid is the pressure that would act on a pressure gauge if it were moving along with the stream so as to be at rest or relatively "static" with respect to the fluid. In various flow measurements the velocity or rate of flow is correlated with static-pressure measurements.

Static pressure can be measured in various ways. Figure 14.1 shows how the static pressure at a wall can be measured, by means of a static-pressure hole, piezometer opening, or pressure tap; Fig. 14.1 illustrates a measurement with a U-tube manometer. The fluid flows past the opening or tap, but the fluid remains at rest in the hole itself if its dimensions are small enough and if the fluid in the connecting pressure-gauge system is at rest. Care must be taken to have the pressure openings at right angles to the wall and to avoid burrs. Allen and Hooper[1] present detailed information as to arrangements that will give proper static-pressure measurement.

Assuming a static incompressible fluid with a specific weight γ, a static-pressure difference Δp corresponding to the height change h, the basic relation of fluid statics is

$$\Delta p = \gamma h \qquad (14.1)$$

This relation can be applied to solve any manometer problem, simple or complex. As an illustration, consider the differential manometer in Fig. 14.2. In the leg AB is a

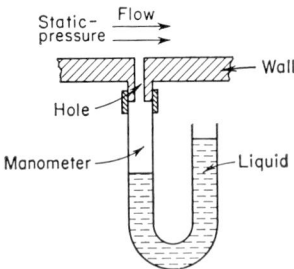

Fig. 14.1. Static-pressure measurement by means of a U-tube manometer.

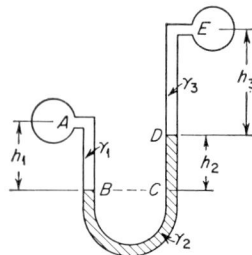

Fig. 14.2. Differential manometer.

fluid with specific weight γ_1; in the leg BD the specific weight of the fluid is γ_2; and in the leg DE the fluid specific weight is γ_3. Let p_A represent the static pressure at point A; let p_B represent the static pressure at point B; and let the static pressure at each of the other points be indicated with the corresponding subscripts. Using the basic equation of fluid statics, then the various static-pressure differences can be written as

$$p_B - p_A = \gamma_1 h_1 \tag{14.2}$$
$$p_C - p_D = \gamma_2 h_2 \tag{14.3}$$
$$p_D - p_E = \gamma_3 h_3 \tag{14.4}$$

Note that the pressure at B equals the pressure at C. These relations can be used to find the pressure difference between points A and E. By setting up relations of this sort, one can analyze any manometer measurement.

A variety of manometers are possible. One leg of a U-tube manometer may be inclined to improve the reading of small differences. A micrometer arrangement might be used to measure small changes in height. Different manometer fluids can be used. A discussion of sensitive manometers is given by Prandtl-Tietjens.[2]

The so-called bourdon tube is employed in different types of instruments for measuring pressure differences. As illustrated in Fig. 14.3, the bourdon tube is a hollow tube (made of brass or other metal) of elliptical cross section and bent in the form of a circle. One end of the bourdon tube is fixed to a frame at A, and the other end B is free to move. The free end moves a pointer by means of a linkage system. The linkage may be a rack and pinion or a helical-cam mechanism. As pressure inside the tube changes, the elliptical cross section tends to become more or less circular and the free end of the bourdon tube (point B) moves outward or inward. Movement of the free end of the bourdon tube can be indicated by an optical system. The free end can be arranged to rotate a small mirror. A light from a source can be directed to the mirror; the mirror reflects the light to a scale. A rotation of the mirror through a certain angle rotates the light beam through twice this angle. Thus an optical system can be used to give a magnified indication of the movement of the free end of the bourdon tube. A dial or pressure scale can be obtained from a calibration of the instrument. It is good technique to calibrate a gauge of this type by means of a deadweight gauge tester.[3]

The position of the free, or movable, end of the bourdon tube depends on the difference in pressure between the outside and the inside of the bourdon tube. If the outside of the bourdon tube is at atmospheric pressure, then the instrument responds to gauge pressure. Various modifications of the bourdon tube are found in practice. In some cases the tube is wound in the form of a spiral or helix with several complete turns.

There are a wide variety of pressure-measuring instruments which employ a diaphragm (or bellows). Fluid pressure acts on the diaphragm; the displacement of the diaphragm is then converted into a pressure indication. In one type of instrument the diaphragm deflection is linked mechanically to some pressure indicator, using a linkage similar to that used in bourdon gauges. Manometers, bourdon gauges, and diaphragm gauges using mechanical linkages or optical systems may be quite suitable for various pressure measurements that are steady and do not fluctuate very much. These gauges, however, may not be suitable for rapidly fluctuating pressures because of the large inertia and response delay involved. For rapidly fluctuating pressures, however, diaphragm-type instruments employing some electronic device may be suitable. Pressure-sensitive devices used for indicating pressures by electronic means can be divided broadly into four groups: (1) electrostatic devices, (2) electromagnetic devices, (3) photoelectric devices, and (4) resistance devices.

Electrostatic devices make use of the piezoelectric properties of certain crystalline substances and the variation of capacitance of a capacitor. Certain substances, as rochelle salt and quartz, possess the property of liberating small electric charges when

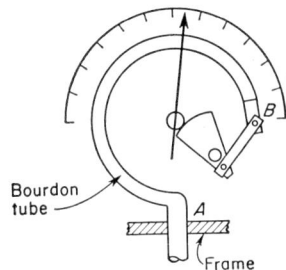

Fig. 14.3. Bourdon gauge.

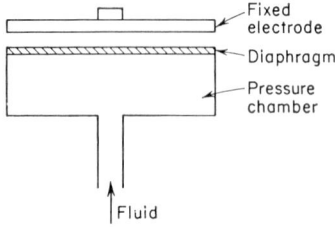

FIG. 14.4. Schematic diagram of capacitance gauge.

strained along certain axes of the crystal. The electrostatic charge produced by the applied pressure is directly proportional to the pressure. The capacitance of a capacitor may be varied by changing either the gap or the effective area of the capacitor plates. For a pressure indicator, the varying-gap method is probably a simpler design. Figure 14.4 illustrates schematically a gauge described by Ippen and Raichlen.[4] Liquid fills the pressure chamber and acts on the circular flexible diaphragm. At one end of the pressure chamber the diaphragm is firmly clamped to the chamber wall around its periphery. A fixed electrode is held a small distance away from the diaphragm separated by a thin air gap. A change in the instantaneous pressure of the liquid causes a deflection of the diaphragm. This deflection can be indicated by electronically measuring the change in capacitance between the fixed electrode and the diaphragm. The foregoing gauge was designed for use with water. Both crystal and capacitance sensing devices are used in acoustic microphones[5] where the fluid is air.

Electromagnetic devices make use of inductance changes in a magnetic system either to generate small voltages in a coil or to modulate the amplitude of an alternating current flowing in a coil. Various pressure-sensing devices are based on the change in air gap of a magnetic circuit. A diaphragm of magnetic material can be held in close proximity to one pole face of a permanent magnet so that an air gap is formed in the magnetic circuit; a coil of wire composed of a large number of turns is wound on the magnet. Pressure applied to one side of the diaphragm will deflect it, change the air gap, and thus cause a flux change. This flux change can be converted to a pressure indication.

Photoelectric devices make use of the photoelectric properties of certain materials to convert a pressure into an electrical effect. As an illustration, a beam of light from an electric filament bulb is directed toward an emission type of photo cell. The center of the diaphragm is attached to a vane that moves in front of a fixed vane and varies the area of the beam of light. Thus pressure variations at the diaphragm vary the electrical response of the photo cell, which in turn can be indicated on some instrument as a cathode-ray oscilloscope.

Resistance devices make use of the variation of electrical resistance of a material with applied strain. In one type of device, the displacement of the diaphragm acts on an unbonded-strain-gauge transducer; the use of an unbonded strain gauge reduces the mass attached to the diaphragm. This transducer is an electromechanical device that transduces minute changes of diaphragm displacement to sensible resistance changes proportional to the displacement. In a stationary frame an armature is supported in such a way as to allow free movement in the line of displacement (of the diaphragm). Wound between rigid pins in the stationary frame and in the moving armature are four windings of strain-sensitive resistance wire; these four windings comprise the four elements of a Wheatstone bridge. Figure 14.5 illustrates the circuit; R_1, R_2, R_3, and R_4 are the resistance strain elements. As the diaphragm moves the armature, two of the sets of filaments will be elongated, whereas the other two sets will be shortened. The resistance change of the filaments alters the electrical balance of the bridge to produce an electrical signal in the output circuit; this unbalance can be indicated by a galvanometer, oscilloscope, or recording instrument (G in Fig. 14.5). The galvanometer output can be calibrated to give a pressure indication.

A discussion of the measurement of fluctuating pressure is given by Wolfe.[6]

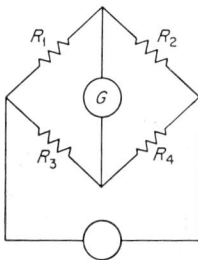

FIG. 14.5. Circuit for pressure transducer. G is indicating or recording instrument.

14.4. Pitot Tubes

Various types of pitot tubes (after Henri Pitot, 1732) are commonly used for measuring linear velocity; this is a head-rate type of meter. A pitot tube, or a similar velocity-measuring device, consists essentially of three main parts: (1) a head, or instrument, section that is inserted in the

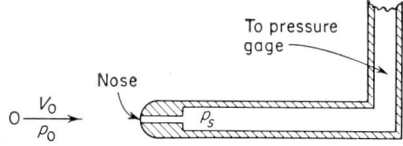

FIG. 14.6. Head of a simple pitot tube.

fluid stream, (2) the pressure-connecting lines between the head and the pressure-indicating device, and (3) the pressure-indicating device that is out of the stream. A discussion of specific details of pitot heads is given by Folsom.[7]

As shown in Fig. 14.6, V_0 is the velocity some distance ahead of a simple pitot tube. The static pressure in the upstream undisturbed fluid is p_0. The streaming fluid is brought to rest (zero velocity) at the nose or stagnation point of the head. The fluid at rest in the head of the pitot can be connected to some pressure gauge or manometer to give a measurement of the stagnation or total pressure p_s. Let γ represent the specific weight of the fluid flowing, and g gravitational acceleration. Assume incompressible frictionless flow between point 0 and the nose. Application of the momentum equation or energy equation for steady flow gives the relations

$$\frac{p_0}{\gamma} + \frac{V_0^2}{2g} = \frac{p_s}{\gamma} \tag{14.5}$$

$$V_0 = \sqrt{\frac{2g(p_s - p_0)}{\gamma}} \tag{14.6}$$

The term p_s/γ is sometimes called the "total-pressure head," or "total head"; the term $V_0^2/2g$ is sometimes called the "velocity head"; and the term p_0/γ the "static pressure head." If the difference $(p_s - p_0)$ can be measured, then the velocity V_0 can be calculated by Eq. (14.6).

In general, it is not difficult to measure the total pressure p_s accurately. A large variety of geometrical shapes are possible and have been used. Any suitable opening in a reasonable geometrical shape will provide a pressure closely approaching the total pressure; the main requirement is that the pressure opening must be placed at the stagnation point. On the other hand, it is frequently difficult to obtain an accurate measurement of static pressure or the difference $(p_s - p_0)$ in the stream. If a pitot tube is inserted in a pipe or channel, then the static pressure p_0 can be measured by means of a static-pressure opening in the pipe or channel wall (as illustrated in Fig. 14.1) provided the static-pressure distribution across the flow is constant.

The term *pitot tube* is commonly used as one involving a measurement of total pressure only. Static-pressure holes or taps can be included in a velocity-measuring instrument, as in the combined, or so-called "pitot-static," tube illustrated in Fig. 14.7. A pitot-static tube is a parallel or coaxial combination of a pitot and a static tube. Static-pressure openings are placed in the wall of the tube that is parallel to the approach flow. A differential gauge across the total-pressure and static-pressure connections would give the velocity or dynamic pressure $(p_s - p_0)$ directly. For precise work a pitot tube should be calibrated. In many cases of average engineering work, Eq. (14.6) is often used directly without any modification.

In making measurements of total pressure, it is sometimes important to use instru-

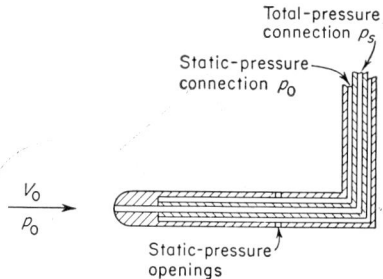

FIG. 14.7. Head of a pitot-static tube.

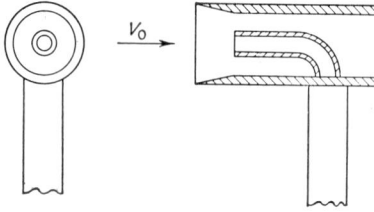

FIG. 14.8. Kiel probe.

ments that are insensitive to flow which is not in line with the pitot head, or flow at a yaw or pitch angle. Effects of the angularity of flow may be determined by calibrating a pitot. In many cases, such a calibration may be complicated, uneconomical, and undesirable. Kiel[8] devised a shielded total-pressure tube in order to meet the requirement of insensitivity to angular flow for total-pressure measurement. As illustrated in Fig. 14.8, the total-pressure tube is shielded with a concentric cylindrical tube. A shielded total-head tube is sometimes called a Kiel probe.

A number of instruments have been devised for measuring velocity in both direction and magnitude. One type of pitot, sometimes called a "direction-finding tube,"[9] can be illustrated by referring to the two-dimensional flow around a circular cylinder whose axis is perpendicular to the flow some distance ahead of the cylinder. Let p represent the pressure at any point on the surface of the cylinder. Theoretical and experimental studies show that the distribution of the pressure difference $(p - p_0)$ at each point on the surface is somewhat as indicated by the radial ordinates of Fig. 14.9. Assuming incompressible steady flow, at the stagnation point A the pressure difference $p - p_0 = \rho V_0^2/2$ in which ρ is the fluid density. The pressure difference decreases for successive points along the surface of the cylinder from point A to B (or C). At a certain critical angle (at point B or C) $p - p_0 = 0$; the pressure at the cylinder surface p equals the approach static pressure p_0. If there were a pressure opening in the surface of the cylinder at the critical angle, the pressure transmitted to a gauge would be truly static. Theory, based on incompressible frictionless flow, indicates an angle of 30°. Experimental work with real incompressible fluids shows that the critical angle is $39\frac{1}{4}°$ for an average range of turbulent flow.

Figure 14.10 illustrates a possible construction; the pitot consists of a cylindrical tube, with two pressure holes and compartments; the axis of the cylinder is perpendicular to the fluid stream. Each pressure hole is connected to one side of a differential gauge. The flow direction can be determined by a null method; the pitot tube in a stream of unknown direction can be rotated about its axis until the pressure difference is zero. In this null position the bisector of the angle between the holes gives the flow direction. A pressure reading from either compartment gives the static pressure p_0. If the cylinder is rotated about its axis so that one pressure opening is in line with the upstream flow velocity V_0, this opening will give p_s. Then the velocity can be calculated by Eq. (14.6). Thus this type of pitot can be used for measuring velocity in both direction and magnitude.

Sometimes a pitot tube is used to measure the volume (or weight) rate of flow through a pipe or channel. For an accurate measurement of such a rate of flow, pitot traverses across the channel should be made. For flow in a circular pipe, it is convenient to take pitot readings along one or more diameters at the center of concentric rings of equal area; this procedure makes possible an arithmetic averaging of the velocity read-

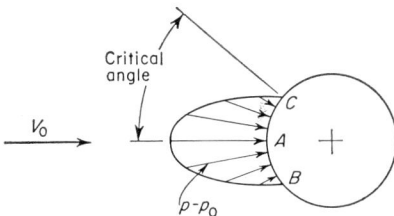

FIG. 14.9. Pressure distribution for two-dimensional flow around a circular cylinder.

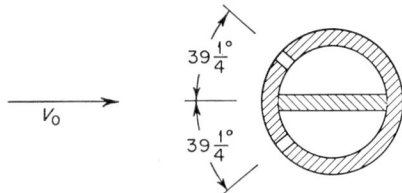

FIG. 14.10. Cylindrical or direction-finding pitot.

ings to give the mean velocity.   If the flow in a pipe is symmetrical with respect to the pipe axis, it is sometimes desired to get the rate of flow by a single reading at the center of the pipe.   Some data on the relation between the maximum velocity at the center of the pipe and the average velocity have been presented by Folsom and Iversen.[10]

14.5. Pitot Tubes in Compressible Flow

In the previous article on pitot tubes (Art. 14.4) the relations given are for incompressible flow.   In this article relations are presented for compressible flow.

Consider a gas following the relation

$$p = \rho g R T \tag{14.7}$$

in which p = static pressure
  ρ = density
  g = gravitational acceleration
  R = a gas factor depending on the gas
  T = static absolute temperature

Let V_0 represent the upstream velocity approaching a pitot, and c_0 the acoustic velocity or velocity of sound in the upstream flow.   This acoustic velocity can be calculated by either of the relations

$$c_0 = \sqrt{kgRT_0} \tag{14.8}$$

$$c_0 = \sqrt{\frac{kp_0}{\rho_0}} \tag{14.9}$$

in which the subscript zero represents the upstream condition, k is the ratio of specific heats c_p/c_v, c_p is the specific heat at constant pressure, and c_v is the specific heat at constant volume.

Imagine subsonic flow past a pitot tube, in which the upstream Mach number $\mathbf{M}_0 = V_0/c_0$ is less than unity.   A reversible adiabatic process is assumed.   For this case the velocity V_0 can be calculated by the relation

$$V_0 = \sqrt{\frac{2k}{k-1} \frac{p_0}{\rho_0} \left[\left(\frac{p_s}{p_0} \right)^{(k-1)/k} - 1 \right]} \tag{14.10}$$

in which p_s is the stagnation-point pressure on the pitot.   Note that ρ_0 in Eq. (14.10) requires a static pressure and a static temperature for computation.

Consider next the steady flow around a pitot tube (with a blunt nose) mounted in a supersonic stream in which the approach Mach number $\mathbf{M}_0 = V_0/c_0$ is greater than 1. As illustrated in Fig. 14.11, there is a short region forward of the stagnation point of the pitot in which there is a normal compression shock (detached shock).   Across this shock there is a pressure rise from the upstream static pressure p_0 to p_1 (just behind the shock) while the Mach number changes from $\mathbf{M}_0$ to the subsonic value $\mathbf{M}_1$.   This pressure rise and the relation between the corresponding Mach numbers are

$$\frac{p_1}{p_0} = \frac{1 + k\mathbf{M}_0{}^2}{1 + k\mathbf{M}_1{}^2} \tag{14.11}$$

$$\mathbf{M}_1{}^2 = \frac{\mathbf{M}_0{}^2(k-1) + 2}{2k\mathbf{M}_0{}^2 - k + 1} \tag{14.12}$$

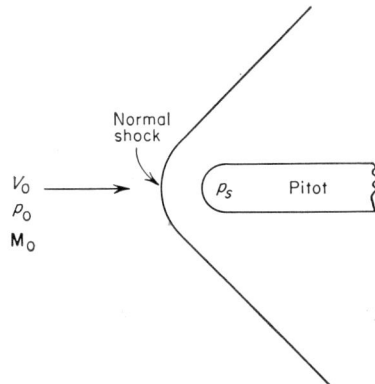

Fig. 14.11. Supersonic flow approaching a pitot.

The subsonic flow just behind the shock slows down to zero velocity at the stagnation point where the total pressure is p_s. For this subsonic flow one can use the reversible adiabatic relation, adapting Eq. (14.10):

$$\frac{p_s}{p_1} = \left[1 + \left(\frac{k-1}{2} \right) \mathbf{M}_1^2 \right]^{k/(k-1)} \tag{14.13}$$

The over-all pressure ratio is

$$\frac{p_s}{p_0} = \frac{p_s}{p_1} \frac{p_1}{p_0} \tag{14.14}$$

Combining the foregoing equations gives the over-all pressure ratio in the form

$$\frac{p_s}{p_0} = \mathbf{M}_0^2 \left(\frac{k+1}{2} \right)^{k/(k-1)} \left[\frac{2k\mathbf{M}_0^2 - k + 1}{\mathbf{M}_0^2(k+1)} \right]^{1-k/(k+1)} \tag{14.15}$$

If p_s, p_0, and k are known, then $\mathbf{M}_0$ can be calculated by the foregoing equation. Some tables, as those by Ferri,[11] are convenient for calculations of this sort.

A discussion of cylindrical, direction-finding pitot tubes for incompressible flow was given in the previous article. Measurements indicate that the change in pressure distribution on the surface of the circular cylinder is small in the range of Mach numbers up to 0.25. In this range of Mach numbers, the critical angle of $39\frac{1}{4}°$ is constant. Thus a simple cylindrical pitot tube in this range of Mach number would be suitable for direct measurements of static pressure. At the higher Mach numbers, particularly above about 0.4, the critical angle increases above that for incompressible flow.

14.6. Temperature Measurement

Various applications require a measurement of both velocity and temperature in a stream of fluid. A temperature measurement is not too difficult at relatively low velocities; at high gas velocities, however, the temperature measurement may become complicated. Consider a gas following the relation

$$p = \rho g R T \tag{14.16}$$

Picture a temperature probe as indicated in Fig. 14.12. The velocity is V_0, and the static pressure is p_0 some distance ahead of the probe. Let t_0 represent the *static temperature* in the undisturbed stream approaching the probe. Theoretically, this static temperature could be measured by an instrument moving along with the stream. In this case the instrument would be *static* with respect to the stream; this arrangement is difficult to do practically. At the stagnation point, where the fluid velocity is zero, the *stagnation*, or *total*, *temperature* is t_s.

Assume an adiabatic process (no heat transfer) between the undisturbed flow and the stagnation point. Also assume no significant change in potential energy in this flow. For this case the energy equation shows that the sum of the enthalpy change plus the kinetic-energy change is zero. For the gas under consideration, the enthalpy change is proportional to c_p times the temperature change, in which c_p is the specific heat at constant pressure. Thus an energy balance gives the relation

$$t_s - t_0 = \frac{V_0^2}{2gJc_p} \tag{14.17}$$

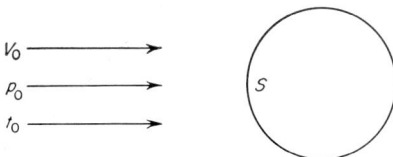

$V_0 \longrightarrow$
$P_0 \longrightarrow$
$t_0 \longrightarrow$

S

Fig. 14.12. Temperature probe in a stream.

in which J is a conversion factor. If V_0 is in feet per second, g in feet per second per second, and c_p in Btu per pound per degree Fahrenheit, then J is about 778; that is, one Btu is about 778 ft-lb.

The difference $(t_s - t_0)$ is sometimes called the *ideal adiabatic temperature rise* between the undisturbed stream and the stagnation point S. This temperature rise may be small for low velocities, and it may be large at high velocities. Because of the finite size of the temperature probe, the temperature probe may indicate a temperature t_A somewhere between the static temperature t_0 and the stagnation temperature t_s. The so-called *recovery factor* (RF) is defined as the dimensionless ratio of the actual temperature rise divided by the ideal temperature rise; that is

$$\text{RF} = \frac{t_A - t_0}{t_s - t_0} \tag{14.18}$$

The recovery factor can be determined by means of a calibration in a known flow, as that in a wind tunnel. Some values can be found in the literature.[12-14]

14.7. Venturi Meter

If a direct volumetric or weight measurement of rate of flow is not possible or convenient, then some other method requires consideration. A venturi meter, an orifice meter, nozzle, or weir can be used for measuring rate of flow; each is a head-rate type of meter.

The venturi meter (named after Venturi), as illustrated in Fig. 14.13, consists of a venturi tube and a suitable gauge system for measuring two static pressures or the pressure difference. The venturi tube includes a converging portion, a throat (or region of smallest area), and a diverging portion. The purpose of the converging portion is to increase the velocity of the fluid and to lower its static pressure. A difference of static pressure between inlet and throat is thus developed; this pressure difference is correlated with volume or weight rate of flow. In the diverging portion, or diffuser, the area of the stream is changed back to the entrance area; in this portion the velocity is reduced and the static pressure is increased. In some cases it may be desirable to have the diffuser loss as low as possible.

Different arrangements of pressure gauges and different venturi-tube proportions are found in practice. The pressure difference $(p_1 - p_2)$ can be measured by means of a U-tube differential gauge or some arrangement with one or more bourdon or other type of gauges. The throat diameter may be between one-half and one-fourth of the inlet diameter. For flow in one direction only, the included angle of the inlet cone may be about 21°, and the included angle of the outlet or diffuser cone may range from 5 to 9°. An included angle between 5 and 9° for the diverging cone usually results in a low diffuser loss. If the meter is to be used for flow in either direction, then the inlet cone and diffuser may be identical. If the head loss across the venturi tube is not important, then the gradually diverging diffuser cone is not really essential.

Using the notation shown in Fig. 14.13, assume an incompressible fluid, horizontal flow, no friction, and a uniform velocity distribution at the inlet and at the throat. Then the energy, or momentum, equation for steady flow gives the relation

$$\frac{p_1}{\gamma} + \frac{V_1^2}{2g} = \frac{p_2}{\gamma} + \frac{V_2^2}{2g} \tag{14.19}$$

The volume rate for these conditions will be called an *ideal* volume rate (as cubic feet per second) Q_i. Let A_1 represent the cross-section area at inlet where the pressure is p_1, and A_2 the area at the throat where the pressure is p_2. Using the equation of continuity for steady flow $Q = A_1V_1 = A_2V_2$ with Eq. (14.19) gives the relation

$$Q_i = \frac{A_2}{\sqrt{1 - (A_2/A_1)^2}} \sqrt{\frac{2g(p_1 - p_2)}{\gamma}} \tag{14.20}$$

For given dimensions of a meter, a measure of the static pressure difference $(p_1 - p_2)$ provides a method for determining the ideal rate of flow.

Equation (14.20) is an ideal relation; differences between this ideal and the actual flow rate can be taken into account by an experimentally determined discharge coefficient. The actual volume rate of flow Q is commonly expressed as

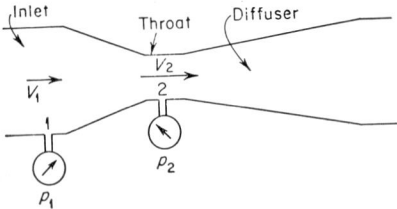

FIG. 14.13. Venturi meter.

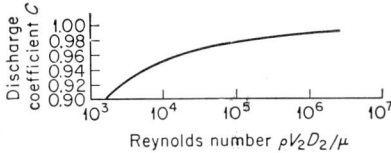

FIG. 14.14. Discharge coefficient C for venturi meters. Ratio of inlet to throat diameter from 2 to 3. (*Data adapted from Fluid Meters Report.*[15])

$$Q = CQ_i \qquad (14.21)$$

in which the discharge coefficient C is dimensionless. Dimensional analysis and dynamic similarity show that C is a function of Reynolds number. Some experimental values of C are shown in Fig. 14.14, D_2 is the internal diameter at the venturi throat, and μ is the dynamic viscosity of the fluid. Figure 14.14 is intended only to give some general idea of the magnitude of the discharge coefficient. For accurate measurements it is advisable to calibrate the venturi meter in its actual service location; it is good technique to calibrate the meter with a weighing or volumetric measurement during a measured time interval.

14.8. Flow Nozzle

The word *nozzle* refers to a channel in which the velocity increases in the direction of flow while the static pressure decreases; nozzles may be used for a variety of purposes. Usually the term *flow nozzle* refers to a nozzle placed at the end of a pipe or in a pipe for the purpose of flow measurement. As illustrated in Fig. 14.15, the flow nozzle may be regarded as a venturi meter that has been shortened and simplified by eliminating the gradually tapered diffuser on the outlet side. The final equation for the venturi meter can be used for the flow nozzle, namely,

$$Q = \frac{CA_2}{\sqrt{1 - (A_2/A_1)^2}} \sqrt{\frac{2g(p_1 - p_2)}{\gamma}} \qquad (14.22)$$

in which the subscripts 1 and 2 refer to the section indicated in Fig. 14.15, A_2 is the area of the nozzle throat, and A_1 is the area of the upstream pipe.

The rate of flow is correlated with the pressure difference $(p_1 - p_2)$. Different arrangements of pressure gauges and different shapes of nozzles are found in practice. The pressure difference can be measured by a U-tube differential manometer or by some arrangement of one or more bourdon or other types of gauges. Various organizations have sponsored research on nozzle shapes and installation details to obtain discharge coefficients that are close to unity, and constant over a range of Reynolds number.

In some cases it is convenient to group some of the terms of Eq. (14.22) into a single term. This term is called the *flow coefficient* K and is defined by the relation

$$K = \frac{C}{\sqrt{1 - (A_2/A_1)^2}} \qquad (14.23)$$

The dimensionless term $1/\sqrt{1 - (A_2/A_1)^2}$ is commonly called the *velocity-of-approach factor*. Equation (14.22) can be written in the compact form

$$Q = KA_2 \sqrt{\frac{2g(p_1 - p_2)}{\gamma}} \qquad (14.24)$$

The numerical value of the flow coeffi-

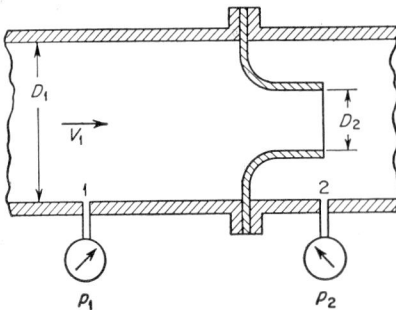

FIG. 14.15. Flow nozzle.

cient K is not an indication of accuracy. The flow coefficient K may have a value of unity or a value different from unity. Dimensional analysis and dynamic similarity show that K is a function of Reynolds number and other factors, such as nozzle dimensions and shapes. Some sample data are given in Fig. 14.16.

14.9. Orifice Meter

The orifice meter is frequently used for measuring the flow of fluids. A possible arrangement is one in which a thin flat plate is clamped between the flanges at a joint in a pipeline; the flat plate has a circular hole concentric with the pipe. As illustrated in Fig. 14.17, static-pressure

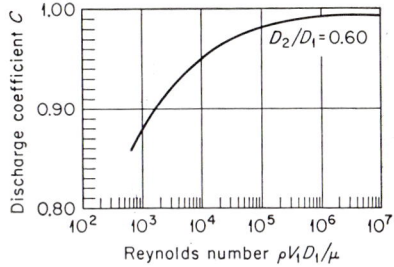

FIG. 14.16. Discharge coefficient C for ASME long-radius flow nozzle with pressure taps located 1 pipe diameter preceding and $\frac{1}{2}$ pipe diameter following inlet face of nozzle. (*Data adapted from Fluid Meters Report.*[15])

connections or taps are made at holes in the pipe wall at both sides of the orifice plate. There may be separate gauges or a differential gauge. In some arrangements, the pressure connections are integral with the orifice plate.

Using the notation of Fig. 14.17, let A_1 represent the area of the upstream pipe, let A_2 represent the area of the orifice opening, and let p_1 and p_2 represent the pressures at the indicated taps. Consider steady, incompressible flow. The previous equations for the flow nozzle can be applied to the orifice meter to give

$$Q = \frac{CA_2}{\sqrt{1 - (A_2/A_1)^2}} \sqrt{\frac{2g(p_1 - p_2)}{\gamma}} \qquad (14.25)$$

$$Q = KA_2 \sqrt{\frac{2g(p_1 - p_2)}{\gamma}} \qquad (14.26)$$

Upstream, in the approach flow in the pipe, the velocity V_1 is lower than the velocity V_2 in the jet passing through the opening or hole in the orifice plate. Because of friction, the actual jet velocity V_2 is less than the ideal jet velocity based on no friction. The ratio of the actual jet velocity to the ideal jet velocity is sometimes called the *coefficient of velocity* C_v. The streamlines curve or converge as they approach the orifice opening, bend around the edge of the hole, and continue to curve and converge beyond the orifice. At some distance from the plane of the orifice, the jet has a minimum section at which the streamlines are parallel. This minimum section of the jet is frequently called the *vena contracta*. The coefficient of contraction C_c is defined as the ratio of the minimum jet area to the orifice-opening area. Frequently the discharge coefficient C is taken as equal to the product $C_v C_c$, that is, $C = C_v C_c$.

The static-pressure connections are made at different positions. The term *vena contracta taps* indicates that the center of the upstream or inlet tap is located between $\frac{1}{2}$ and 2 pipe diameters from the upstream side of the orifice plate; a distance of 1 pipe diameter is commonly employed. The center of the downstream pressure tap is placed at the minimum-pressure position, which is assumed to be at the vena contracta. Exact tap dimensions are given in the ASME Fluid Meters Report.[15] For *flange taps*, the centers of the pressure holes are 1 in. respectively from the upstream (or inlet) and down-

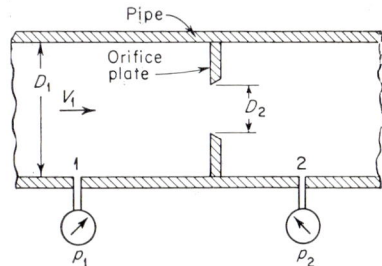

FIG. 14.17. Orifice meter.

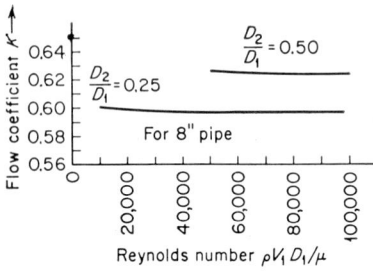

FIG. 14.18. Flow coefficient K for orifice meters with taps at $1D$ and $\frac{1}{2}D$. (*Data adapted from Fluid Meters Report.*[15])

stream (or outlet) faces of the orifice plate. For *taps at $1D$ and $\frac{1}{2}D$* the center of the inlet tap is located 1 pipe diameter preceding the inlet orifice plate, and the center of the outlet pressure tap is placed $\frac{1}{2}$ pipe diameter following the inlet face of the orifice plate. Some sample data for orifice meters are given in Fig. 14.18.

Concentric orifice plates (in which the orifice opening is concentric with the pipe) are quite common. In an eccentric orifice a circular eccentric-orifice opening is arranged so that its center is not on the axis of the pipe. In the segmental orifice, the shape of the restricting area is a segment of a circle of approximately the same diameter as that of the pipe; the orifice opening is irregular in shape.

14.10. Compressible Flow through Venturi Meter, Flow Nozzle, and Orifice Meter

In the foregoing articles 14.7 to 14.9, the relations given are for incompressible flow. In this article relations are presented for compressible flow. Let V represent the fluid velocity at any point in the flow, and c the corresponding acoustic velocity. This article will be confined primarily to subsonic flow, that is, to flow in which the Mach number $\mathbf{M} = V/c$ is less than 1.

For an incompressible fluid, the actual volume rate of flow Q can be expressed in the form

$$Q = KA_2 \sqrt{\frac{2g(p_1 - p_2)}{\gamma}} \tag{14.27}$$

Let W represent the weight rate of flow (as pounds per second). Then W can be written as

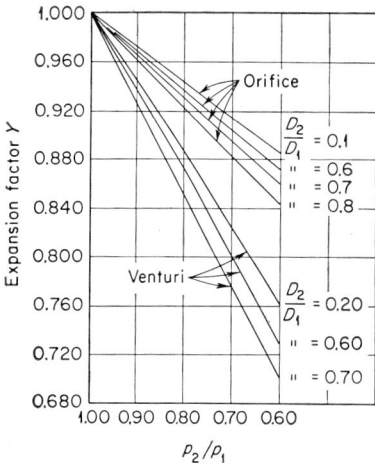

FIG. 14.19. Expansion factors vs. pressure ratio for $k = 1.4$. Orifice values are for flange and vena contracta taps. (*Data adapted from Fluid Meters Report.*[15])

$$W = KA_2\gamma \sqrt{\frac{2g(p_1 - p_2)}{\gamma}} \tag{14.28}$$

It is common practice in flow-measurement work to generalize Eq. (14.28) by multiplying the right side by a so-called "expansion factor" and by specifying the specific weight $\gamma = \gamma_1$ as that at the inlet. Let Y represent the dimensionless expansion factor. Then, for both incompressible and compressible flow, the basic relation can be written as

$$W = KA_2\gamma_1 Y \sqrt{\frac{2g(p_1 - p_2)}{\gamma_1}} \tag{14.29}$$

For an incompressible fluid, $Y = 1$. It is common to use theoretically determined values of Y for flow nozzles and venturi meters and to use experimentally determined values of Y for orifice meters. Figure 14.19 shows some values of expansion factor as a function of pressure ratio. In Fig. 14.19, p_2 and p_1 each is an absolute pressure, D_2 is the throat or orifice-opening diameter, and

D_1 is the inlet or pipe diameter. In Fig. 14.19, the curves marked "venturi" are also applied to flow nozzles.

In the orifice metering of natural gas, certain industrial groups have a particular method of organizing data. The volume rate of flow (in certain units) Q_b is expressed in the form

$$Q_b = C'\sqrt{h_w p_f} \tag{14.30}$$

where C' = orifice constant
h_w = a differential pressure
p_f = an absolute static pressure

The orifice constant C' is expressed as equal to the product of a number of different factors. These factors are basic orifice factor, pressure base factor, temperature base factor, flowing temperature factor, specific-gravity factor, supercompressibility factor, and manometer factor. Values of these factors are obtained from tables. Details are given in special reports of the industrial groups concerned.[16]

14.11. Critical-flow Nozzles and Orifices

For certain measurements it is convenient to use a short converging nozzle or an orifice of well-rounded approach in which a so-called *critical flow* exists. Meters of this sort are thus called critical-flow nozzles and critical-flow orifices.

The fluid under consideration is a gas (or superheated vapor) that follows the relation

$$p = \rho g R T \tag{14.31}$$

As illustrated in Fig. 14.20, imagine flow of this fluid through a converging tube. At the approach section 1 the static absolute pressure is p_1 and the area is so large that the velocity at section 1 (relatively speaking) is negligible with respect to the highest velocity in the channel. The channel converges to a minimum area, or *throat*, at section 2, where the fluid velocity is V_2, and the static absolute pressure is p_2. An adiabatic frictionless process is assumed; for normal nozzles and orifices, this is a good assumption. Then the velocity V_2 is given by the relation

$$V_2 = \sqrt{\frac{2k}{k-1}\frac{p_1}{\rho_1}\left[1 - \left(\frac{p_2}{p_1}\right)^{(k-1)/k}\right]} \tag{14.32}$$

in which ρ_1 is the density at section 1, and k is the ratio of specific heats c_p/c_v.

Consider first the case in which p_2 equals p_1; there is no flow through the tube. As p_2 is reduced below p_1, the velocity in the throat increases. Several features can be established by making a study of the area-velocity relation and the weight rate–pressure relation. There is a critical static pressure p_c given by the relation

$$\frac{p_c}{p_1} = \left(\frac{2}{k+1}\right)^{k/(k-1)} \tag{14.33}$$

For air at normal conditions, this critical-pressure ratio p_c/p_1 is about 0.53. The static pressure in the throat cannot be lower than the critical pressure. The highest velocity V_2 that can be reached in the throat is the acoustic velocity c_2. Thus, when the throat pressure is critical, then the throat Mach number V_2/c_2 is 1. If the pressure downstream from the throat (as outside the nozzle or orifice) is at some value below p_c, the throat pressure will be p_c. Hence, for a given inlet pressure, it is not difficult to arrange for critical pressure to exist at the throat. Knowing the throat pressure gives the velocity V_c (for p_c),

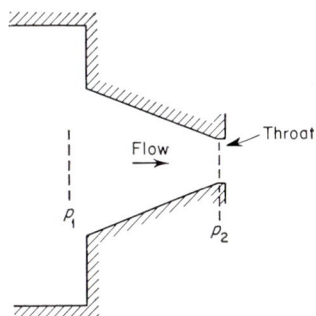

FIG. 14.20. Critical-flow nozzle.

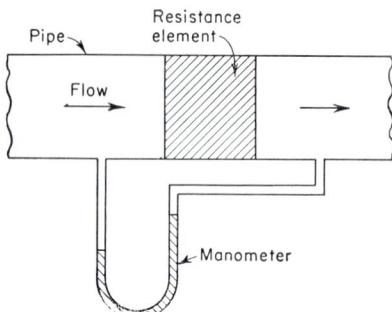

Fig. 14.21. Linear-resistance flowmeter.

$$V_c = \sqrt{\frac{2kg}{k+1} p_1 v_1} = \sqrt{\frac{kp_c}{\rho_c}} \quad (14.34)$$

if v_1 is the specific volume at inlet, and ρ_c is the fluid density at the throat. The following adiabatic relation holds

$$\frac{p_1}{\rho_1^k} = \frac{p_c}{\rho_0^k} \quad (14.35)$$

For critical conditions, knowing the velocity at the throat, the volume rate of flow or the weight rate of flow can be calculated for a known throat area, gas, and inlet conditions.

14.12. Linear-resistance Flowmeter

There is one type of fluid meter that is frequently called *linear*, or *linear-resistance*. As illustrated in Fig. 14.21, in one form of construction, this meter consists of a straight piece of tube or pipe with a porous plug or a resistance element and a differential gauge across the porous plug. In a certain flow range, the volume rate of flow through the meter is directly proportional to the pressure drop across the plug. This type of meter has characteristics that may be desirable in various applications; it indicates directly the flow rate. The flow coefficient is constant over the linear range.

For various applications, as for relatively low flow rates, a meter of this type may be constructed easily and with materials readily available. The plug or resistance element can be cotton, glass wool, steel wool, copper wool, brass screen, or some similar material. Some calibration data[17,18] are available in the literature. The resistance element may be a simple capillary tube; for laminar flow in a capillary, the pressure drop in a length of tubing is directly proportional to the volume rate.

14.13. Pipe-elbow Flowmeter

An elbow in a pipe can be used as a flowmeter. In various cases there is an elbow already in the piping system; this elbow can be converted into a meter with no additional resistance to flow. Sometimes an elbow meter can be quite convenient and economical. The dynamic or centrifugal action of the fluid, in flowing in a curved path, causes a difference in pressure between the inside and the outside curves of the elbow; the static pressure is higher on the outer curve. As illustrated diagrammatically in Fig. 14.22, pressure connections from the inner and outer curves of the elbow can be led to a differential gauge. The differential pressure is correlated with volume rate of flow.

For accurate results an elbow meter should be calibrated in its actual service location. Experimental work on elbow meters has been reported by Lansford.[19]

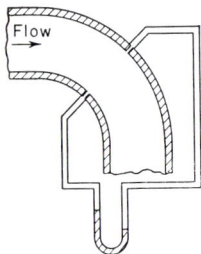

Fig. 14.22. Pipe elbow meter.

14.14. Weir

A weir can be used for the measurement of liquid flow in an open channel, in which there is a free surface. Usually the liquid measured is water. The weir, in effect, is a dam over which the liquid is made to flow. A weir is a rate meter. The weir is a head-area meter in that both the head and area vary; the area is a function of the head.

As illustrated in Fig. 14.23, the height H of the undisturbed water level above the sharp crest is correlated with the vol-

ume rate of flow through the notch in
the weir plate. The height H can be
measured with a micrometer screw with
a sharp conical point, or hook, entirely
submerged in the water; this point is
screwed up until it touches the surface, and
the height H is observed. Another method
for measuring height is to use the contact
between the water and the movable
measuring point to complete a simple
circuit and light a small lamp.

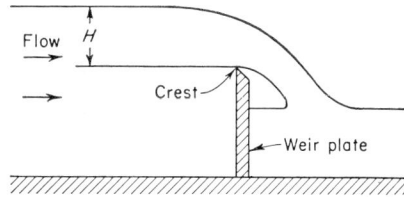

Fig. 14.23. Weir.

Figure 14.24 illustrates the front view of the flow over a rectangular weir, in which
there is a rectangular notch in the plate. Referring to Figs. 14.23 and 14.24, the *crest*,
or *sill*, is the bottom edge of the weir notch. The *crest length* is the horizontal distance
along the crest between the sides; this distance is L in Fig. 14.24. The sheet of liquid
flowing over the weir crest is called the *nappe*. The flow is said to be *free*, or *aerated*,
when the nappe falls free of the downstream face of the weir plate, as in Fig. 14.23.
The flow over the weir is *submerged* if the surface of the liquid in the downstream side
of the weir plate is not far enough below the level of the crest to permit full aeration.

Figure 14.25 shows a top view of an approach channel and weir plate. When the
width of the approach channel L_c is greater than the crest length L, the nappe will
contract; below the crest the nappe will have a minimum width less than L. This
narrowing of the nappe is called *weir contraction;* the weir is called a *contracted weir*.
For a rectangular weir, if the width of the approach channel is equal to the crest length,
there is no side contraction of the nappe, and the meter is called a *suppressed rectangular
weir*.

Sharp-crested weirs can be classified into four main groups according to the form of
notch or opening: (1) the rectangular notch, (2) the V, or triangular, notch, (3) the
circular notch, and (4) special notches. Special notches, as the trapezoidal and parabolic, are intended to have a constant discharge coefficient or to have the head directly
proportional to the rate of flow.

Refer to the rectangular weir in Fig. 14.24. The ideal velocity of a stream filament
or layer discharging from a weir notch a distance z below the undisturbed surface is

$$V_{ideal} = \sqrt{2gz} \qquad (14.36)$$

For a layer of thickness dz and a width L, the ideal volume rate of flow dQ_i for the element is

$$dQ_i = LV\,dz = L\sqrt{2gz}\,dz \qquad (14.37)$$

Integrating Eq. (14.37) between the limits $z = 0$ and $z = H$ yields

$$Q_i = \tfrac{2}{3}L\sqrt{2gH^3} \qquad (14.38)$$

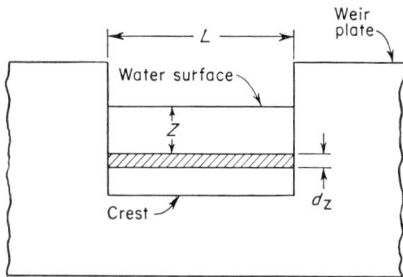

Fig. 14.24. Front view of flow over a rectangular weir.

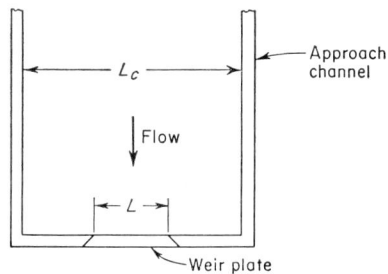

Fig. 14.25. Weir with end contractions.

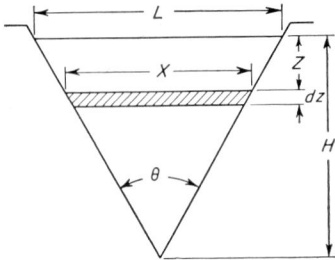

FIG. 14.26. Triangular weir.

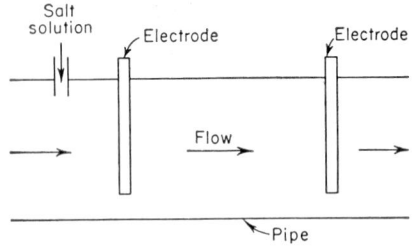

FIG. 14.27. Salt velocity method.

The ratio between the actual flow rate and the ideal is the discharge coefficient C; that is, $C = Q/Q_i$. Thus the actual flow rate Q is

$$Q = \tfrac{2}{3}CL\sqrt{2gH^3} \qquad (14.39)$$

In general, the value of C is less than 0.7. Numerical values are given in the ASME Fluid Meters Report.[15]

Figure 14.26 illustrates a triangular weir; this type of notch helps to increase the head readings at low rates of flow. The actual discharge dQ through the elementary area $x\,dz$ is

$$dQ = xC\sqrt{2gz}\,dz$$

By similar triangles, $x/L = (H - z)/H$. Then the actual total flow rate Q becomes

$$Q = C\sqrt{2g}\,\frac{L}{H}\int_0^H (Hz^{1/2} - z^{3/2})\,dz \qquad (14.40)$$

After integrating, and noting that $L = 2H \tan(\theta/2)$, the final result is

$$Q = \tfrac{8}{15}C\sqrt{2g}\tan\frac{\theta}{2}\,H^{5/2} \qquad (14.41)$$

The best method for determining the weir coefficient C is to calibrate the weir in place, under the same conditions for which it is to be used. If this plan is not possible, weir coefficients might be estimated after referring to reports of experimental investigations.[15] The discharge coefficient depends on the head H, the gravitational acceleration g, the fluid density, the fluid dynamic viscosity, and the surface tension of the interface between the fluid and the surrounding air.

14.15. Salt Velocity Method

The rate of water flow can be measured by means of the salt velocity method; this method is based on the fact that salt in solution increases the electrical conductivity of water. Salt, or a salt solution, as illustrated in Fig. 14.27, is introduced into the flow channel at some convenient point. Two electrodes are arranged at two sections, some distance apart. The flow of the solution is recorded electrically. A measurement is made of the time required for the solution to travel a measured distance. The volume flow rate is calculated from these measurements and the dimensions of the flow channel.[20]

14.16. Anemometers

There are various devices, called *anemometers*, that are used for air-flow measurements. In some anemometers there is a rotating element whose angular speed of rotation is correlated with the linear velocity of flow. The rotating element may consist

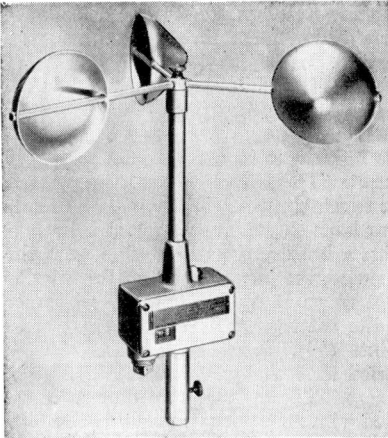

FIG. 14.28. Cup anemometer for measuring wind speed. (*Bendix Aviation Corporation, Friez Instrument Division.*)

FIG. 14.29. Anemometer. (*Taylor Instrument Co.*)

of a series of vanes (similar to a windmill) or a series of cups mounted on a shaft held in bearings. The rotating shaft is connected to some sort of revolution counter, and an observation is made of the number of revolutions in a measured time period. Figure 14.28 shows a cup anemometer for measuring wind speed; the movement of the cups, by the wind, is transmitted to the horizontal crossarms to rotate the vertical shaft. Figure 14.29 shows another anemometer using vanes; an observation is made of the number of revolutions in a measured time interval. These anemometers require calibration.

Different forms of hot-wire anemometers have been developed for the measurement of linear velocity and velocity fluctuations. In this instrument there is a wire (as platinum) of small diameter that is heated by passing an electric current through it. As air moves past the wire, the heated wire cools, and thus its electric resistance changes.

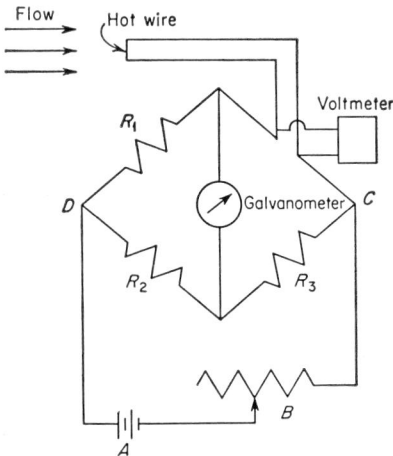

FIG. 14.30. Constant-resistance hot-wire anemometer.

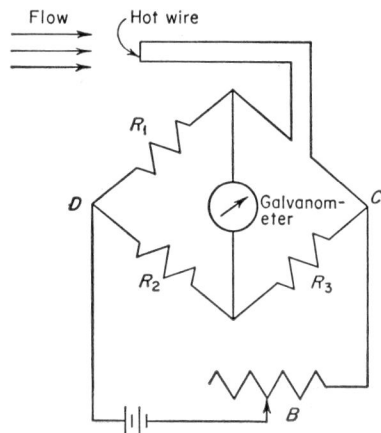

FIG. 14.31. Constant-voltage hot-wire anemometer.

The flow velocity, steady or unsteady, is correlated with certain electrical measurements.

Various circuits have been devised. Figure 14.30 illustrates the constant-resistance type. R_1, R_2, and R_3 are electric resistances in the Wheatstone-bridge circuit. The hot wire forms the remaining resistance in the bridge. B represents a variable electric resistance, and A represents a battery. With air flow past the hot wire, the temperature of the wire is kept constant by varying the resistance in the battery across the bridge (across points CD). The bridge voltage is so varied that the galvanometer deflection is zero. The voltmeter reading is correlated with air velocity by calibration.

The constant-voltage system is illustrated in Fig. 14.31. The voltage across the bridge is kept constant after the circuit is adjusted so that the galvanometer indicates zero current when the heated wire is in air at rest. As the air flows, the hot wire cools, the resistance changes, and the galvanometer deflects. The galvanometer deflection is correlated with air velocity by calibration. Details regarding hot-wire anemometers are given by Dryden, Kuethe, and Wattendorf.[21,22]

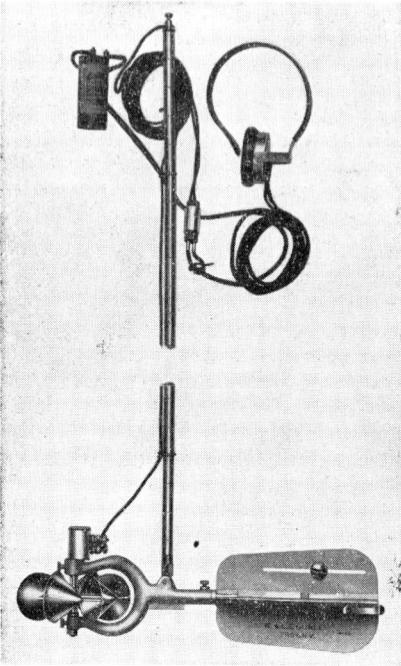

FIG. 14.32. Current meter. (*Courtesy of W. and L. E. Gurley.*)

A *current* meter, which is used for water-flow measurements, consists primarily of a rotating element whose angular speed is correlated with linear velocity. The rotating element consists of a series of cups or a series of vanes mounted on a shaft in bearings. Figure 14.32 shows a current meter. Current meters require calibration.

14.17. Volumetric Meter

In *volumetric*, or *positive-displacement*, meters, the fluid passes through the meter in successive and more or less isolated volumes. Figure 14.33 illustrates a rotary meter as an example. The two lobes, or rotors, are mounted on parallel shafts and rotate in opposite directions; a pair of timing gears, at one end of the shafts, provides the proper relative motion of the lobes. Fluid enters the inlet, fills the space between a lobe and the case, and flows from inlet to outlet. An indication of the volumetric displacement can be given by a revolution counter on the shaft of one lobe. Measuring the volumetric displacement during a measured time interval gives the rate of flow.

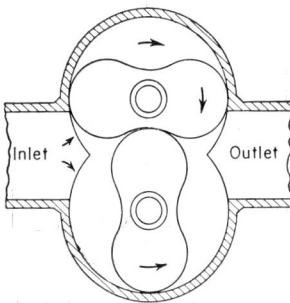

The *wobble-plate*, or *nutating-disc*, meter is another example of a volumetric meter. This meter is commonly used to measure the water supply for domestic use. As illustrated in Fig. 14.34, the movable element is a circular disc fastened to a central ball. A shaft is fastened to the ball; this shaft is always in an inclined position. The movable disc is mounted in a chamber that has a spherical side wall, a conical top surface, and a conical bottom

FIG. 14.33. Rotary meter.

FIG. 14.34. Wobble-plate meter. (*Neptune Meter Co.*)

surface; this disc is prevented from rotating about its own axis by a slot-and-guide arrangement. Water enters through an inlet in the spherical wall on one side of a partition and leaves on the other side of the partition. As the water passes through the measuring chamber (alternately above and below the disc), the disc wobbles or executes a nutating motion; in this nodding motion the shaft generates a cone with the apex down. The circular motion of the one end of this shaft rotates a set of gears that actuate the dial. The dial indication is in a volume unit, as gallons or cubic feet.

14.18. Rotameter

The *rotameter* is a device with a rotating free "float" (actually heavier than the liquid) as the indicating element. As illustrated in Fig. 14.35, a transparent tapered tube is held in a vertical position with the larger opening at the top. The fluid passes vertically upward through the tube. Inside the tapered tube is the float, which is freely suspended in the fluid. With no flow, the float rests on a stop on the lower end. With flow, the float rises toward the upper, larger diameter of the tube. There is a corresponding float position for each flow. This meter is sometimes classed as an *area* type of meter, because of the variable annular space between float and tube. This meter requires calibration.

14.19. Thermal Meter

Broadly speaking, in the field of flow measurement, the term *thermal meter* refers to an instrument in which the transfer of heat to or from the fluid is a basic part of the metering action.

FIG. 14.35. Rotameter. (*Brooks Rotameter Co.*)

Temperature probe

Heat input

p

Temperature probe

t_1

t_2

V_1

Heating element

V_2

Pipe or tube

1
2

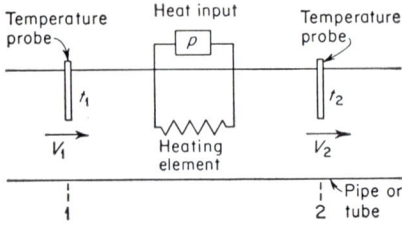

FIG. 14.36. Thermal meter.

Thermal meters may be generally classed into two groups: (1) meters in which the effect of a fluid stream on a hot body is involved, and (2) meters in which the effect of a measurable quantity of heat on a fluid stream is involved. An example of the first group is the hot-wire anemometer discussed in Art. 14.16. The second group is discussed below.

As illustrated in Fig. 14.36, imagine steady flow in a horizontal pipe between sections 1 and 2. There is a temperature probe at each section; in between the two sections is a heating element (electrical or otherwise) that adds heat to the fluid. Let q represent heat transfer per unit weight (in Btu per pound of fluid flowing), V_1 the average velocity at section 1, V_2 the average velocity at section 2, t_1 the temperature at section 1, and t_2 the temperature at section 2. An energy balance between sections 1 and 2 shows that the heat transfer to the fluid equals the change in enthalpy plus the kinetic-energy change. For a gas following the relation $p = \rho g R T$, the enthalpy change is proportional to c_p times the temperature change, in which c_p is the specific heat at constant pressure. Thus the energy equation becomes

$$q = c_p(t_2 - t_1) + \frac{V_2{}^2 - V_1{}^2}{2gJ} \tag{14.42}$$

in which J is a conversion factor. If the kinetic-energy change is small in comparison with the heat transfer, then Eq. (14.42) can be written as

$$q = c_p(t_2 - t_1) \tag{14.43}$$

Let P represent the rate of heat input to the fluid (in Btu per second); this P could be developed and determined by electrical means and measurements. In arranging the heating element, it may be necessary to insulate thermally the pipe (other than heat-input leads) so that an accurate accounting of heat rate could be made. If W is weight rate of flow (as pounds per second), then we can write

$$W = \frac{P}{q} = \frac{P}{c_p(t_2 - t_1)} \tag{14.44}$$

Thus, knowing c_p, the weight rate of flow can be measured by measuring P and the temperature difference.

14.20. Capillary-tube Viscometer

A viscometer is an instrument for measuring fluid viscosity. Considering laminar flow, the dynamic, or absolute, viscosity of a fluid is defined as the ratio between the shear stress and the corresponding rate of shearing strain. One of the best scientific methods for determining dynamic viscosity is the *capillary-tube*, or *transpiration*, method. In this method an arrangement is made for laminar flow of the test fluid through a capillary (or small-bore) tube. If the flow is laminar, then the Hagen-Poiseuille law[2] for steady flow of an incompressible fluid in a horizontal tube is

$$\mu = \frac{\pi \Delta p D^4}{128 Q l} \tag{14.45}$$

in which μ = dynamic viscosity of fluid
D = internal diameter of tube
Q = volume rate of flow
Δp = static pressure drop in tube length l

The factors on the right side of Eq. (14.45) are measured, and then the viscosity is calculated. Equation (14.45) is only accurate for laminar flow; this feature can be checked by evaluating the Reynolds number $\rho V D/\mu$, in which ρ is fluid density and V is the average velocity. The flow is laminar if this Reynolds number is equal to or is less than 2000. Details regarding different viscometers are given by Hatschek[23] and Bingham.[24]

14.21. Other Types of Viscometers

There are viscometers that involve the laminar flow of a test fluid in the annular space between two concentric cylinders. Sometimes this viscometer is called a couette type. Figure 14.37 illustrates the essential feature of a rotational viscometer. One cylinder is rotated with respect to the other. Measurements of torque, angular speed, and velocity gradient can be correlated with dynamic viscosity by theoretical analyses,[25] if the flow is laminar, and by a calibration with fluids of known viscosity. A viscometer of this type may be useful for relative measurements, as in comparing the relative action of different fluids.

The MacMichael and the Stormer instruments are commercial variations of the rotational type. In the MacMichael viscometer the outer cylinder is rotated at a certain speed and the inner cylinder is supported by a torsion wire; a measurement of angular twist of the wire is proportional to the viscous torque. In the Stormer viscometer the outer cylinder is stationary; a constant torque is applied to the inner rotating cylinder, and the angular speed of the inner cylinder is measured. In place of a cylinder sometimes a horizontal flat circular disc, or an inverted cup, is held in the fluid. Rotational viscometers are used in connection with the manufacture of paints, suspensions, and food products.

In the *falling-body*, or *falling-ball*, viscometer, a body (as a sphere) is arranged to fall steadily through a mass of the fluid to be tested. As illustrated in Fig. 14.38, let V represent the steady downward velocity of the spherical ball, w the weight of the ball, F the buoyant force of the fluid on the ball, and d the drag force of the fluid opposing the motion of the ball. Let γ_1 represent the specific weight of the ball material, γ the specific weight of the fluid, D the diameter of the sphere, and μ the dynamic viscosity of the fluid. For steady motion, the forces balance, that is,

$$w = F + d \qquad\qquad (14.46)$$

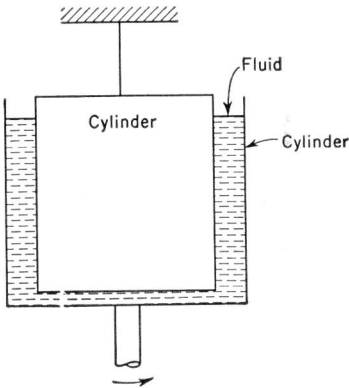

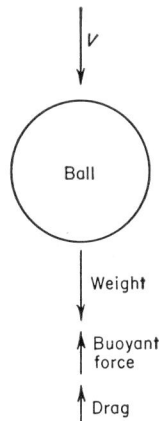

Fig. 14.37. Rotational type of viscometer.

Fig. 14.38. Falling-ball viscometer.

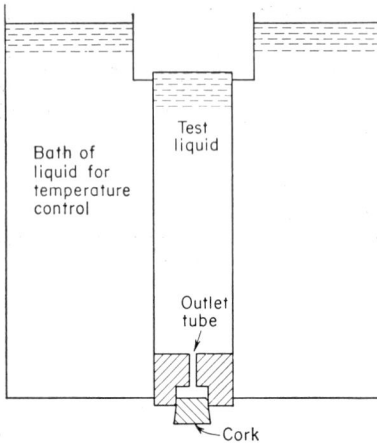

FIG. 14.39. Saybolt viscometer.

The weight w equals $\frac{4}{3}\pi(D/2)^3\gamma_1$. The buoyant force F equals $\frac{4}{3}\pi(D/2)^2\gamma$. If the flow is laminar, then Stokes' law gives the relation

$$d = 3\mu V\pi D \qquad (14.47)$$

Stokes' law holds for a Reynolds number $\rho VD/\mu$ below about 0.4. Combining Eqs. (14.46) and (14.47) gives the relation for viscosity

$$\mu = \frac{D^2(\gamma_1 - \gamma)}{18V} \qquad (14.48)$$

The various quantities on the right side of Eq. (14.48) can be measured to determine the dynamic viscosity. In an actual viscometer there may be some problems as to the effect of a wall if it is close to the ball movement. This type of viscometer can be checked and calibrated by fluids of known viscosity.

The Saybolt viscometer is used for industrial purposes, particularly for petroleum products and lubricants. Two viscometers have been standardized by the American Society for Testing Materials[26]: one the Saybolt Universal, the other the Saybolt Furol (contraction for "fuel and motor oils"). These two instruments are of the same general design, but of different dimensions. As illustrated in Fig. 14.39, the liquid to be tested is placed in the central cylinder, which has a short small-bore tube and cork at its lower end. A bath of liquid for maintaining temperature surrounds the central cylinder. After the temperature is properly established, the cork is pulled, and the time required for 60 cc of the fluid to flow out is measured. The Saybolt reading is this time of flow in seconds. See Art. 1.11 for calibration data.

14.22. Shadow and Schlieren Systems

Several good optical techniques have been devised for studying the high-velocity flow of gases. These techniques have the advantage of avoiding a disturbance of the flow by some instrument as a velocity or temperature probe.

Figure 14.40 illustrates one type of optical system. Light from some intense concentrated source at A is set at the focal point of the convex lens B. Light passing through lens B then forms a parallel beam. The compressible fluid passes through the region where the light beams are parallel. For example, the dotted lines C and D may represent the windows of a high-speed wind tunnel. The light rays passing through lens E come to a focus at point F (at a focal distance from lens E). The light rays pass to the image screen G. Say the gas in the light beam is at a uniform density; in this case the light rays will not be bent or refracted and the illumination on the image screen will be uniform. If, however, there is some mass of fluid, as at H, which has a density different from the surrounding fluid, then the light will be refracted in going from a gas with one density to a gas with another density. Definite changes in density result in definite bands of shadow or intense illumination on the image screen. A film can be placed at the image screen to get a photograph of the pattern.

Say it is desired to get a sharp image of the pattern at point H in the flow field. Let S_1 and S_2 represent the distances indicated, and f the focal length of the lens.

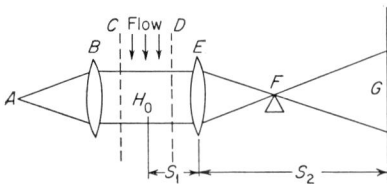

FIG. 14.40. Schlieren system

For a guide in focusing on the screen, the usual thin-lens equation can be used:

$$\frac{1}{S_1} + \frac{1}{S_2} = \frac{1}{f} \qquad (14.49)$$

There are three types of systems: (1) shadow, (2) black-white schlieren; and (3) color schlieren. In shadow system there is no knife-edge at point F. In the black-white schlieren there is a knife-edge (as a razor blade) at point F, and normal black-and-white film can be used for photographing the pattern. The knife-edge acts as an optical filter. Light rays can be bent either

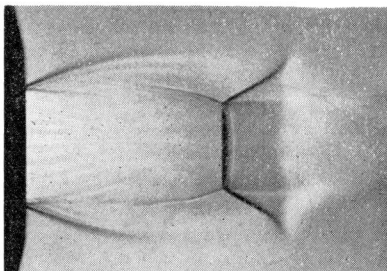

Fig. 14.41. Schlieren picture of air flow from a nozzle.

away from or toward the knife-edge; this optical filtering provides good contrast. In the color schlieren system, a series of color strips (or bands in succession) are placed at point F. As the light rays are bent in one direction or the other, the light rays pass through bands of different colors; the variation in the color on the image screen helps to differentiate density changes. Figure 14.41 shows a schlieren picture of the flow leaving a critical-flow nozzle; the schlieren system shows sharp density changes that cannot be seen with the naked eye.

A wide variety of lens systems may be used; mirrors may be used because mirrors help to avoid some of the aberrations which sometimes are found with lenses. Details are given by Barnes and Bellinger[27] and Schardin.[28]

14.23. Meters for Measuring Mass Rate

In various applications it is desirable to get a direct measurement of mass rate of flow (in slugs per second). Various meters, as the pitot, orifice, venturi, nozzle, and others, give more or less directly the volume rate of flow. In order to convert volume rate into mass rate, it is necessary to know the density of the fluid; sometimes it may be difficult to measure density accurately. Thus, in some cases, it is highly desirable to have a direct method of measuring mass rate.

A number of meters for mass rate have been devised. These meters depend on a momentum principle. Refer to Fig. 14.42. There is a runner or rotor driven by a shaft that rotates at the angular speed ω (in radians per second). Let r be the radius at any point on this runner. At this point the peripheral speed U (in feet per second) is given by the relation

$$U = r\omega \qquad (14.50)$$

Consider the case in which the fluid flows through some channel on the runner as the runner rotates. The subscript 1 will be used for quantities at runner inlet. Fluid enters the runner at a point 1 at radius r_1 with the resultant velocity V_1. The tangential component of this resultant velocity is V_{1U}. The subscript 2 will be used for quantities at runner exit. The fluid leaves the runner at a point at radius r_2, with a resultant velocity V_2. The tangential component of this resultant velocity is V_{2U}. Let m represent the mass rate of flow (in slugs per second) of the fluid passing through the runner. The runner acts on this fluid with a torque, to increase the angular momentum of the fluid. Starting from the basic dynamic equation, force equals mass times acceleration, the torque relation is

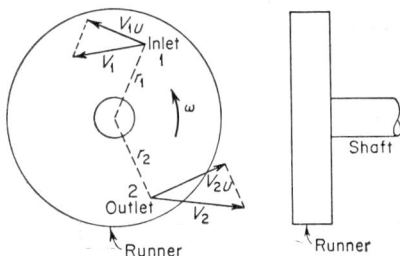

Fig. 14.42. Rotating runner.

$$\text{Torque} = m(r_2 V_{2U} - r_1 V_{1U})$$

$$m = \frac{\text{torque}}{r_2 V_{2U} - r_1 V_{1U}} \qquad (14.51)$$

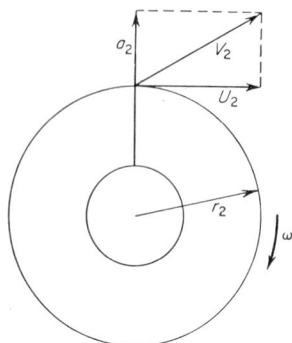

Fig. 14.43. Impeller of mass-rate meter.

If the terms on the right side of Eq. (14.51) could be measured, then a direct measurement of mass rate could be made. The problem, then, is to arrange a runner so that the measurements of torque and the other factors can be made conveniently.

Generally speaking, a runner could be arranged that resembles either a centrifugal impeller or an axial-flow runner. In the centrifugal type the relative flow is primarily in a radial direction, whereas in the axial-flow runner the relative flow is essentially at a constant radius. The centrifugal type will be illustrated as an example. The mass-rate meter involves an arrangement of a motor that drives a centrifugal impeller at a constant speed ω. The impeller is arranged with radial blades. As illustrated in Fig. 14.43, if the relative velocity at exit a_2 is in a radial direction, then the combination of U_2 and a_2 gives the resultant V_2. In turn, the tangential component of V_2 is $U_2 = r_2\omega$. If the relative velocity is radial at both inlet and at exit, then

$$V_{2U} = r_2\omega \qquad V_{1U} = r_1\omega$$

$$m = \frac{\text{torque}}{r_2{}^2\omega - r_1{}^2\omega} \qquad (14.52)$$

Thus, if the flow in the runner can be arranged in a known, suitable manner, then the mass rate can be found from a measurement of torque, radii, and angular speed. Further details can be found in the literature.[29,30]

14.24. Electromagnetic Flowmeters

The electromagnetic, or induction, flowmeter is based on the induction of an electromotive force (emf) in an electrical conductor traversing a magnetic field. Let e represent the induced voltage (in volts), L the length of the conductor, V the linear velocity of the conductor, and B the magnetic flux density (in gausses). The induced voltage, as a conductor moves relative to a magnetic field, is

$$e = C_1 BLV \qquad (14.53)$$

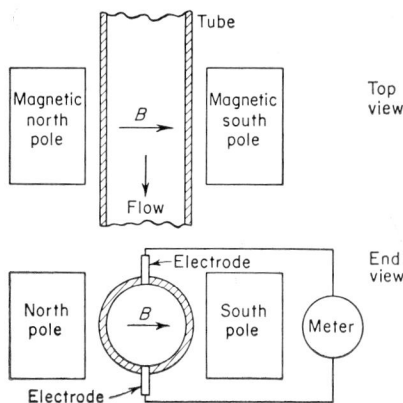

Fig. 14.44. Electromagnetic flowmeter.

in which C_1 is some constant, and the directions of B, L, and V are mutually perpendicular.

Figure 14.44 illustrates the general principle. The flow to be metered passes through a conduit or tube of nonmagnetic material; the conductivity of the pipe or tube material should be much less than that of the fluid. This fluid passes through a magnetic field. The motion of the fluid relative to the magnetic field causes a voltage to be induced in the fluid; this voltage is proportional to the average fluid velocity, and thus is proportional to the volume rate of flow. Two electrodes are imbedded in the walls of the conduit, flush with the inner conduit surface and in contact with the fluid. The voltage induced in the fluid is transferred to the electrodes; the voltage is then amplified to actuate an indicator or recorder.

The magnetic field may be either alternating or direct. For a direct field, the signal obtained is direct-current. For an alternating field, an alternating-current signal is obtained. In either case the induced voltage is given by a relation of the form in Eq. (14.53).

The electromagnetic, or induction, type of flowmeter has some advantages that are desirable in certain applications. The response of this type of meter is linear with flow rate; its calibration is independent of the type of some fluid constants (as temperature, viscosity, and density); it involves no delay in response; and its operation requires no pressure change in the fluid. The main disadvantages are that the fluid must be at least partially conducting, and the signal obtained may require electronic amplification for reliable indication. Various details are given by James[31] and Elrod.[32]

14.25. Radioactive-tracer Method

A radioactive substance, as hydrogen, for example, can be injected into a stream, and Geiger counters used to detect the passage of the substance at check points located downstream from the injection point. This radioactive-tracer method is similar to the salt velocity method; a radioactive substance is used in place of salt or a salt solution. This radioactive-tracer method can be used with gases, and no openings in the conduit are needed at the check or measuring stations.

REFERENCES

1. Allen, C. M., and L. J. Hooper: Piezometer Investigations, *Trans. ASME*, **54:** (HYD-54-1), 1932.
2. Prandtl, L., and O. G. Tietjens: "Applied Hydro- and Aeromechanics," McGraw-Hill, New York, 1934.
3. Rhodes, T. J.: "Industrial Instruments for Measurement and Control," McGraw-Hill, New York, 1941.
4. Ippen, A. T., and R. Raichlen: Turbulence in Civil Engineering: Measurements in Free Surface Streams, *Proc. ASCE Paper* HYD-1392, October, 1957.
5. Beranek, L. L.: "Acoustic Measurements," Wiley, New York, 1950.
6. Wolfe, M. O. W.: The Measurement of Fluctuating Fluid Pressures, *Aircraft Eng.*, December, 1949, p. 368.
7. Folsom, R. G.: Review of the Pitot Tube, *Trans. ASME*, October, 1956, p. 1447.
8. Kiel, G.: Gesamtdruckgerät mit grosser Unempfindlichkeit gegen Schraganströmung, *Luftfahrt-Forsch.*, **12**:75 (1935). (Translation, "Total-head Meter with Small Sensitivity to Yaw," *NACA Tech. Mem.* 775.)
9. Binder, R. C., and R. T. Knapp: Experimental Determinations of the Flow Characteristics in the Volutes of Centrifugal Pumps, *Trans. ASME*, November, 1936, p. 649.
10. Folsom, R. G., and H. W. Iversen: Pipe Factors for Quantity Rate Flow Measurements with Pitot Tubes, *Trans. ASME Paper* 48-A-35.
11. Ferri, A.: "Elements of Aerodynamics of Supersonic Flows," St. Martin's, New York, 1949.
12. Stalder, J. R., M. W. Rubesin, and T. Tendeland: A Determination of the Laminar Transitional and Turbulent Boundary Layer Temperature Recovery Factor on a Flat Plate in Supersonic Flow, *NACA Tech. Note* 2077, 1950.
13. Freeze, P. D.: Bibliography of the Measurement of Gas Temperature, *Natl. Bur. Standards (U.S.) Circ.* 513, 1951
14. King, W. W.: Measurement of High Temperatures in High Velocity Gas Streams, *Trans. ASME*, **65**:421 (1943).
15. Fluid Meters Report, American Society of Mechanical Engineers, New York, 1959.
16. Orifice Metering of Natural Gas, *Am. Gas Assoc. Gas Measurement Rept.* 3, New York, 1955.
17. Fleming, F. W., and R. C. Binder: Study of Linear-resistance Flowmeters, *Trans. ASME*, **75**(5):621, 1951.
18. Souers, R. C., and R. C. Binder: Linear-resistance Meters for Liquid Flow, *Trans. ASME*, **74**(5):837 (1952).
19. Lansford, W. M.: The Use of an Elbow in a Pipe Line for Determining the Rate of Flow in the Pipe, *Univ. Ill. Expt. Sta. Bull* 289, December, 1936.

20. Allen, C. M., and E. A. Taylor: The Salt Velocity Method of Water Measurement, *ASME Trans.*, **45**:285 (1923).
21. Dryden, H. L., and A. M. Kuethe: The Measurement of Wind Speed Fluctuations by Means of the Hot-wire Anemometer, *NACA Tech. Rept.* 320, 1929.
22. Wattendorf, F. L., and A. M. Kuethe: Investigations of Turbulent Flow by Means of the Hot-wire Anemometer, *Physics*, **5**:153 (June, 1934).
23. Hatschek, E.: "The Viscosity of Liquids," Van Nostrand, Princeton, N.J., 1928.
24. Bingham, E. C.: "Fluidity and Plasticity," McGraw-Hill, New York, 1922.
25. Schlichting, H.: "Boundary-layer Theory," McGraw-Hill, New York, 1960.
26. "Standard Method of Test for Viscosity by Means of the Saybolt Viscometer," ASTM Standards, part III, p. 216, 1939.
27. Barnes, N. F., and S. L. Bellinger: Schlieren and Shadowgraph Equipment for Air Flow Analysis, *J. Optical Soc. Am.*, **35**(8):497 (1945).
28. Schardin, H.: Das Toeplersche Schlierenverfahren, *VDI Forschungsh.* 307, July, 1934.
29. Olando, V. A., and F. B. Jennings: Momentum Principle Measures Mass Rate of Flow, *Trans. ASME*, **76**:961 (August, 1954).
30. Li, V. T., and S. Y. Lee: A Fast Responsive True Mass-rate Flowmeter, *Trans. ASME*, **74**:835 (July, 1953).
31. James, W. G.: An induction Flowmeter Design Suitable for Radioactive Liquids, *Rev. Sci. Instr.*, **22**:989 (December, 1951).
32. Elrod, H. G., Jr., and R. R. Fouse: An Investigation of Electromagnetic Flowmeters, *Trans. ASME*, **74**:589 (May, 1952).

Section 15

DIMENSIONAL ANALYSIS

By

MAURICE HOLT, *University of California, Berkeley, California*

DIMENSIONAL ANALYSIS

15.1. Introduction

To understand and describe a phenomenon in physics or mechanics, it is necessary to determine which effects and physical quantities are of importance in the phenomenon, to classify these, and to find expressions for them, based on observations or on mathematical reasoning, in terms of variables defining position in space at any given time. Dimensional analysis provides the means for the initial organization of this program of investigation and has three main functions: classification, measurement, and simplification of physical laws.

In classifying a quantity, it is convenient to analyze it in terms of a minimum number of fundamental physical quantities. In mechanics, including fluid dynamics, it is usually sufficient to take three quantities, namely, mass, length, and time, as fundamental. Once physical quantities have been classified in this way, any two different quantities can be compared by observing the extent to which each depends on the fundamental quantities.

Measurement of physical quantities starts by assigning units of measurement to the fundamental quantities. Once these are determined, dimensional analysis enables the units of measurement of any other quantity to be found from its classification in terms of the fundamental quantities.

Investigations of mechanical or physical phenomena are intended to lead to some definite law or equation relating physical quantities. Both theoretical and experimental approaches to a given problem may be used. Frequently the theoretical approach leads to some equation which is too difficult to solve by mathematical means. Other phenomena may be awkward to investigate experimentally.

Dimensional analysis is of great assistance in interpreting physical laws by both experimental and theoretical means, permitting simplification in mathematical analysis which makes governing equations more tractable or in suggesting the simplest type of experiment which can reproduce the essentials of a phenomenon in a laboratory. This point may be illustrated by two examples.

On the theoretical side the equations of motion of a compressible or viscous fluid are nonlinear and in their exact formulation impossible to solve except by numerical means. Dimensional analysis assists in selecting situations when it is possible to simplify the equations so that they can be treated by analytical means. On the experimental side it is obviously undesirable to determine the design characteristics of a supersonic transport by means of tests on a full-scale prototype. Dimensional analysis helps to organize the setting up of small-scale experiments by means of which the complete behavior of a full-size aircraft can be determined in a laboratory.

Dimensional analysis gives information about the general form of a relation between some unknown and other variables in a physical problem. It does not determine the exact form of this relation, which must be found either by solving mathematical equations governing the problem or by measurements of the unknown.

When observation and measurement are used to determine the unknown, special techniques must be employed to ensure that any experiment is a faithful reproduction of the true phenomenon.

The technique of reproducing the behavior of a phenomenon on a different and more convenient scale is known as *modeling*. In fluid dynamics modeling is always aimed at scaling down phenomena, but in other fields it may be desirable to reproduce a phenomenon on a larger scale. The conditions that a model of a phenomenon reproduces all aspects of its actual behavior on a uniformly reduced scale are known as conditions of *similitude* and are of two main kinds. *Geometrical similitude* requires that, at corresponding instants of time, the configuration in which the model phenomenon occurs is an exactly scaled down reproduction of the actual configuration. *Dynamical similitude* is more difficult to satisfy and requires that, at corresponding points in the full-scale or model configuration, the local physical behavior be identical, apart from a change in scale.

In the present short section there is space to introduce only the main features of dynamical analysis and its allied topics. A fuller treatment will be found in a number of texts[1-5,30] listed in the references at the end of this section. Particular attention is drawn to two of these. The first is the classical work by Bridgman,[1] which sets out the foundation of the subject with very sound reasoning. The second is a more recent Russian work by Sedov.[2] This is of special interest to fluid dynamicists and gives a much fuller application of dimensional methods to fluid dynamics than has ever been presented previously, at least in collected form. Furthermore, Sedov gives a systematic treatment of the concept of *self-similarity*, deduced from dimensional arguments, that is of enormous value in the theory of compressible flow. It is the basis of the theory of conical fields in supersonic flow and the theory of point explosions. A portion of this section is devoted to the description of this comparatively recent development in dimensional analysis.

The section begins with the classification of physical quantities occurring in fluid dynamics and an introduction to the concept of dimensions. Units of measurement and conversion formulas when changing from one system to another are then discussed. The following article gives a proof of the pi theorem, which is applied to various problems in fluid dynamics. Next, a general discussion of modeling and similitude is illustrated by applications in wind tunnels and water tanks. This is followed by a discussion of similitude properties in the theory of compressible flow. In a final article the use of self-similarity in the theory of explosions, boundary-layer theory, and theory of supersonic flow past conical bodies is described.

15.2. Classification and Measurement

List of Principal Symbols

c_p, c_v — specific heats
C — velocity of sound in undisturbed stream
d — typical length of body
F — $U/\sqrt{gd}$, Froude number
g — acceleration due to gravity
k — thermal conductivity
M — U/C, Mach number
p — pressure
P — $\mu c_p/k$, Prandtl number
R — Ud/ν, Reynolds number
U — undisturbed velocity of free stream
u, v, w — cartesian velocity components
V — ship volume displacement
x, y, z — cartesian coordinates
α — angle of incidence
μ — coefficient of viscosity
ρ — density
ν — coefficient of kinematic viscosity
ψ — $d/V^{1/3}$, fineness coefficient

Other symbols are defined in the text.

Dimensional and Dimensionless Quantities. All mechanical and physical quantities need to be measured in some manner. They are divided into two broad classes, depending on the form of measurement. Those which are independent of the scale or particular system of measurement used are called *dimensionless*, and those depending on such a scale are said to be *dimensional*. Examples of dimensional quantities are length, time, mass, force, and energy. Typical dimensionless quantities are angles, the ratio of two lengths, the ratio of specific heats, and so on.

Units of Measurement and Dimensional Formulas. In measuring a system of physical quantities it is customary to select certain of their number, usually those which occur most frequently and are the simplest in concept, as primary or fundamental quantities and assign to these definite units of measurement. All other quantities are then measured in units derived from these fundamental units and are called derived, or secondary, quantities.

In fluid dynamics it is usual to regard the units of length, time, and mass as fundamental. In the cgs system, which is the most common in use, the unit of length is the centimeter, the unit of time is the second, and the unit of mass is the gram. The magnitudes of these units have been established in terms of definite material standards.

The units of measurement of other physical quantities can always be expressed in terms of the fundamental units. The relationship defining a derived unit in terms of fundamental units is called the dimensions of the unit. Dimensions of physical quantities are always integral powers of the fundamental units.

The dimensions of typical quantities arising in fluid dynamics are now derived. The symbols for the fundamental units, length, time, and mass are denoted by L, T, and M, respectively. The dimensions of a typical physical quantity a will be denoted by $[a]$.

The dimensions of velocity V are, from definition,

$$[V] = \frac{L}{T}$$

while those of acceleration a are

$$[a] = \frac{L}{T^2}$$

The dimensions of force F, regarded as defined by Newton's second law, are

$$[F] = \frac{ML}{T^2}$$

The dimensions of other important quantities in fluid dynamics, pressure, and density are, by definition,

$$[p] = \frac{[F]}{[L^2]} = \frac{M}{LT^2}$$

$$[\rho] = \frac{M}{L^3}$$

The dimensions of another important quantity, the coefficient of viscosity μ, must be derived from the definition

$$\text{Frictional stress} = \mu \times \text{velocity gradient}$$

so that

$$\frac{M}{LT^2} = [\mu] \times \frac{1}{T}$$

and hence

$$[\mu] = \frac{M}{LT}$$

It follows that

$$[\nu] = \left[\frac{\mu}{\rho}\right] = \frac{L^2}{T}$$

Dimensions of further quantities arising in fluid dynamics can be evaluated in a similar manner.

15.3. Conversion Formulas

Dimensional formulas are very useful if the basic units of measurements are changed from one system to another. For example, suppose it is desired to change the units of measurement of density of water from the cgs system to the British fps system. Now

$$[\rho] = \frac{M}{L^3}$$

and the relation between the basic units in the two systems is

1 lb = 453.6 gs
1 ft = 30.48 cm

In British units, therefore,

$$\text{Density of water} = 1 \times \frac{(30.48)^3}{453.6}$$

$$= 62.3 \text{ lb/ft}^3$$

The dimensions of all the quantities discussed so far are all in the form of monomial powers $L^l M^m T^t$. This property can be shown to be true of all physical quantities.[2] It is deduced from the physical property that the ratio of two distinct values of the same derived quantity is independent of the scale used.

For simplicity, this is proved in the case of geometric quantities. Suppose that u is some geometric property such as area, volume, or second moment, which depends on three lengths x, y, z, according to the relation

$$u = f(x,y,z) \tag{15.1}$$

and suppose that u is evaluated at two different points distinguished by suffixes 1 and 2. Then u_1 and u_2 are given by Eq. (15.1). The unit of length is now diminished by a factor α. Then, although the absolute values of u_1 and u_2 will be changed in terms of the diminished units, the ratio of these quantities will remain unaltered. Accordingly,

$$\frac{u_1}{u_2} = \frac{f(x_1,y_1,z_1)}{f(x_2,y_2,z_2)} = \frac{f(\alpha x_1,\alpha y_1,\alpha z_1)}{f(\alpha x_2,\alpha y_2,\alpha z_2)} \tag{15.2}$$

whence

$$\frac{f(\alpha x_1,\alpha y_1,\alpha z_1)}{f(x,y,z)} = \frac{f(\alpha x_2,\alpha y_2,\alpha z_2)}{f(x,y,z)} \tag{15.3}$$

or

$$\frac{u_1(\alpha)}{u_1(1)} = \frac{u_2(\alpha)}{u_2(1)} = g(\alpha) \tag{15.4}$$

Equation (15.4) shows that the ratio of the numerical values of a derived quantity measured in different units of length depends only on the scale factor.

To determine the form of $g(\alpha)$, consider two different scale factors α_1 and α_2 and put $\alpha = \alpha_1/\alpha_2$, $x_2 = \alpha_2 x_1$, $y_2 = \alpha_2 y_2$, $z_2 = \alpha_2 z_2$ in Eq. (15.3). Then

$$\frac{u_1(\alpha_1/\alpha_2)}{u_1(1)} = \frac{u_1(\alpha_1)}{u_1(\alpha_2)}$$

whence

$$g\left(\frac{\alpha_1}{\alpha_2}\right) = \frac{g(\alpha_1)}{g(\alpha_2)} \tag{15.5}$$

In Eq. (15.5) differentiate with respect to α_1 and then put $\alpha_1 = \alpha_2 = \alpha$. It follows that

$$\frac{1}{g(\alpha)} \frac{dg}{d\alpha} = \frac{1}{\alpha} g'(1) = \frac{l}{\alpha} \tag{15.6}$$

if l is a constant. The integral of Eq. (15.6) gives

$$g = \alpha^l \tag{15.7}$$

since $g = 1$ when $\alpha = 1$. Equations (15.4) and (15.7) show that the length dimensions of u must be L^l, a simple power in L. The result can clearly be extended to cover the dimensions, in terms of all basic units, of any physical quantity.

15.4. The Pi Theorem

This theorem is really the kingpin in all applications of dimensional analysis and will be used repeatedly in this section. It can be stated as follows.

Suppose that, in some physical problem, one dimensional quantity u, regarded as an unknown, is expressed in terms of n other dimensional quantities $x_1, \ldots, x_n$ by a relation of the form

$$u = f(x_1, \ldots, x_n) \tag{15.8}$$

Suppose further that the first k of the variables $x_1, \ldots, x_n$ have independent dimensions. Then Eq. (15.8) can be written in the form

$$\Pi = f(1, 1, \ldots, \Pi_1, \ldots, \Pi_{n-k}) \tag{15.9}$$

where $\Pi, \Pi_1, \Pi_2, \ldots, \Pi_{n-k}$ are forms of $u, x_{k+1}, \ldots, x_n$, respectively, made dimensionless by forming suitable combinations with $x_1, \ldots, x_k$.

In words, the theorem states that any dimensional relation expressing one physical variable, the unknown, in terms of n other physical variables, of which k have independent dimensions, can be recast as a relation between the unknown in dimensionless form and $n - k$ dimensionless combinations of the remaining variables.

The pi theorem is valid only if the functional relation (15.8) is *complete*, which means that the relation is true whatever system of units is used. This property is equivalent to the principle of *dimensional homogeneity*, which applies to every equation defining some single physical law and states that each term in such an equation has the same dimensions. A complete relation must represent only one physical law or principle, and not be any combination of different laws. For example, in the theory of motion of a compressible fluid, the equation of continuity and the momentum equation are each dimensionally homogeneous, but the equation resulting from simple addition of these equations is not. Such equations are excluded in this article and in dimensional analysis generally.

To prove the pi theorem, suppose that the dimensions of $x_1, x_2, \ldots$ are written

$$X_1 = [x_1], X_2 = [x_2], \ldots \tag{15.10}$$

Then, since only the quantities $x_1, \ldots, x_k$ are dimensionally independent, the dimensions of the variables $u, x_{k+1}, \ldots, x_n$ are monomial powers of the dimensions of $x_1, x_2, \ldots, x_k$ and may be written

$$[x] = X_1{}^{l_1} X_2{}^{l_2} \cdots X_k{}^{l_k}$$
$$[x_{k+1}] = X_1{}^{m_1} X_2{}^{m_2} \cdots X_k{}^{m_k}$$
$$[x_n] = X_1{}^{z_1} X_2{}^{z_2} \cdots X_k{}^{z_k}$$

The scales of measurement of the quantities $x_1, \ldots, x_k$ are now changed by factors of $\alpha_1, \ldots, \alpha_k$, respectively. If the values of quantities in the revised units are distinguished by primes, then the following relations are satisfied:

$$x'_1 = \alpha_1 x_1 \qquad u' = \alpha_1{}^{l_1} \alpha_2{}^{l_2} \cdots \alpha_k{}^{l_k} u$$
$$x'_{k+1} = \alpha_1{}^{m_1} \alpha_2{}^{m_2} \cdots \alpha_k{}^{m_k} x_{k+1}$$
$$\cdots \cdots \cdots \cdots \cdots \cdots \cdots$$
$$x'_k = \alpha_k x_k \qquad x'_n = \alpha_1{}^{z_1} \alpha_2{}^{z_2} \cdots \alpha_k{}^{z_k} x_n$$

Equation (15.8) now becomes

$$u' = \alpha_1{}^{l_1}\alpha_2{}^{l_2} \cdots \alpha_k{}^{l_k} u$$
$$= \alpha_1{}^{l_1}\alpha_2{}^{l_2} \cdots \alpha_k{}^{l_k} f(x_1, \ldots, x_k, x_{k+1}, \ldots, x_n) \tag{15.11}$$

But using the principle of dimensional homogeneity, Eq. (15.8) also gives

$$u' = f[x'_1, \ldots, x'_k, \ldots, x'_n] \tag{15.12}$$

Hence, from Eqs. (15.11) and (15.12),

$$f[\alpha_1 x_1, \ldots, \alpha_k x_k, \alpha_1{}^{m_1}\alpha_2{}^{m_2} \cdots \alpha_k{}^{m_k} x_{k+1}, \ldots, \alpha_1{}^{z_1}\alpha_2{}^{z_2} \cdots \alpha_k{}^{z_k} x_n]$$
$$= \alpha_1{}^{l_1}\alpha_2{}^{l_2}, \ldots, \alpha_k{}^{l_k} f(x_1, \ldots, x_k, x_{k+1}, \ldots, x_n) \tag{15.13}$$

Equation (15.13) shows that the function f is homogeneous in the scales $\alpha_1, \ldots, \alpha_k$. Now choose the scales $\alpha_1, \ldots, \alpha_k$ to satisfy the relations

$$\alpha_1 = \frac{1}{x_1} \qquad \alpha_2 = \frac{1}{x_2}, \qquad \cdots, \qquad \alpha_k = \frac{1}{x_k}$$

so that, in the new units, the quantities $x'_1, \ldots, x'_k$ have value unity; i.e., they are used as units of measurement. The new values of the remaining variables are written

$$u' = \Pi = \frac{u}{x_1{}^{l_1} \cdots x_k{}^{l_k}}$$

$$x'_{k+1} = \Pi_1 = \frac{x_{k+1}}{x_1{}^{m_1} \cdots x_k{}^{m_k}}$$

$$x'_n = \Pi_{n-k} = \frac{x_k}{x_1{}^{z_1} \cdots x_k{}^{z_k}}$$

and Eq. (15.9) follows. Note that $\Pi_1, \Pi_2, \ldots, \Pi_{n-k}$ are indeed dimensionless combinations of the variables u, $x_{k+1} \cdots x_n$ with the set of k independent quantities $x_1 \cdots x_k$.

The above proof of the pi theorem is that given by Sedov.[2] A longer but not necessarily more rigorous proof is given by Bridgman.[1]

The results deduced from the pi theorem become simpler the smaller the number of quantities in excess of those with independent dimensions. If the only quantities entering the equation for an unknown are the basic parameters themselves, Eq. (15.9) reduces to

$$\Pi = f(1, 1, \ldots, 1)$$

or
$$\Pi = c = \text{const} \tag{15.14}$$

whence
$$x = c x_1{}^{l_1} \cdots x_k{}^{l_k} \tag{15.15}$$

15.5. Applications of the Pi Theorem

Every investigation of a problem in fluid dynamics, whether experimental or theoretical, should begin with a cataloguing of all the relevant quantities, whether variable or constant, entering into and influencing the problem. The next step is to pick out the principal unknown and to determine the form of the relation between this and the remaining quantities. Dimensional analysis, and particularly the pi theorem, is of great value in reducing this relation to its simplest general form, stripped of irrelevant or nonessential features. However, dimensional analysis alone does not determine the precise form

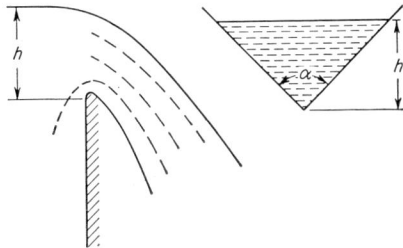

Fig. 15.1. Flow of water over a spillway.

of this relation, and this must be achieved either by experiment or by solving mathematical equations representing some physical laws. These points are best illustrated by the following examples.

Flow of Water through a Spillway.[2] Water contained behind a vertical wall, such as a dam, is free to flow through an overflow duct or spillway with a uniform triangular section of apex angle α. This is illustrated in Fig. 15.1. The floor of the spillway is horizontal, and the angle of the section is α. It is desired to determine the rate of outflow when the head of water in the spillway is of height h.

The motion of the water is due essentially to its own weight, so that for given angular spacing, the weight of water Q which flows per unit time depends on the density ρ, the height h, and acceleration due to gravity, g. The essential parameters are then

$$\rho, g, h$$

and
$$Q = f(\rho, g, h) \tag{15.16}$$

ρ, g, and h are dimensionally independent.

To express Q in terms of dimensions of ρ, g, and h,

$$[Q] = \frac{ML}{T^3}$$

$$= [\rho]^\alpha [g]^\beta [h]^\gamma$$
$$= M^\alpha L^{\beta - 3\alpha + \gamma} T^{-2\beta}$$

so that
$$[Q] = [\rho][g]^{-3/2}[h]^{5/2}$$

From the simplest form of the pi theorem it follows that

$$Q = C\rho g^{-3/2} h^{5/2} \tag{15.17}$$

in which C is a constant independent of ρ, g, and h, which is determined by experiment.

If the condition that α be constant is relaxed, it is clear that C will vary with α. If the spillway is a semicircle of radius a, then C depends on the ratio h/a.

Motion of a Body in a Fluid. The basic problem of aircraft design is that of uniform motion of a body through a fluid at rest. This is equivalent to the problem of uniform motion of a fluid past a fixed body, which is illustrated in Fig. 15.2.

If the fluid is assumed to be incompressible but viscous, then the resultant force F exerted by the fluid on the body depends on five basic parameters,

$$d, \rho, \nu, U, \alpha$$

representing a typical length of the body, the density, the kinematic viscosity, the uniform velocity of the fluid, and the angle of incidence, respectively. Then a relation exists of the form

$$F = f(d, \rho, \nu, U, \alpha) \tag{15.18}$$

The three basic parameters with independent dimensions are taken as U, ρ, and d. The combination of these with the dimensions of force is $L^{\alpha - 3\beta + \gamma} M^\beta T^{-\alpha}$, in which $\alpha - 3\beta + \gamma = 1$, $\beta = 1$, $\alpha = 2$, so that $\gamma = 1$. The combination is therefore $\rho U^2 d^2$. The dimensions of ν are L^2/T, so that the dimensionless combination of ν with U, ρ, and d is

$$\mathbf{R} = \frac{Ud}{\nu} \tag{15.19}$$

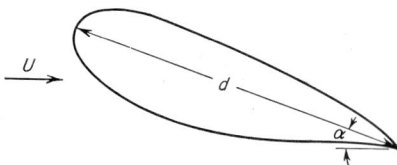

This dimensionless combination is known as the *Reynolds number*. The other dimensionless combination on the right side of Eq. (15.18) is simply α. The pi theorem then states that the dimensionless form of F satisfies the relation

$$\frac{F}{\rho\, d^2 U^2} = f(\mathbf{R}, \alpha) \tag{15.20}$$

Fig. 15.2. Uniform motion past a fixed body.

The actual dependence of f on $\mathbf{R}$ and α must be determined from wind-tunnel tests by evaluating F as a function of $\mathbf{R}$ for different angles of incidence α. Alternatively, the function can be determined from solutions of the mathematical equations of viscous incompressible motion.

The above results have to be modified when the viscous motion is very slow. In this case viscosity outweighs inertia effects and it is appropriate to discard the density ρ as a fundamental parameter and replace ν by the ordinary coefficient of viscosity μ. The basic parameters are then μ, d, and U. Since the simple product of these has the dimensions of force, the pi theorem shows that

$$F = \mu \, dU f(\alpha) \qquad (15.21)$$

In the case of a sphere, $f(\alpha)$ is a pure constant c and Eq. (15.21) reduces to Stokes' result for slow viscous motion past a sphere. Stokes found that $c = 3\pi$.

15.6. Modeling and Similitude

In the previous sections dimensional analysis was used to show that the dimensionless form of the force, exerted on a body by a uniform incompressible fluid stream, is a function of the angle of incidence α and Reynolds number $\mathbf{R}$. The remaining problem is to determine the form of this function. In the present section experimental methods of finding such functions are considered and dimensional considerations are used to determine the most convenient forms of experiment.

In general, it would be difficult to determine the law of variation of F with $\mathbf{R}$ and α by direct measurements on an aircraft in flight. Very often, of course, this information is required as design data to be available even before the aircraft is built. Accordingly, it is desirable to determine such laws by experiments reproducing the actual motions and flight conditions in a laboratory of convenient size. This simulation is known as modeling, and the conditions for satisfactory modeling are of great importance. They are essentially conditions of similitude which, when satisfied, ensure that actual flying conditions are exactly reproduced in the laboratory.

The clue to the conditions for similitude between actual motion of a body through a fluid and a satisfactory model of this motion is provided by the dimensionless character of Eq. (15.20). This equation is evidently independent of the geometric scale of the phenomenon, and the only difference which could be distinguished between the full scale and model phenomenon is possibly in the value of $\mathbf{R}$. Provided the two values of $\mathbf{R}$ are the same, the form of f on the model will be the same as that for the full-scale body.

The scaling property described is a condition of geometrical similitude. The remaining condition is one of dynamical similitude.

The conditions hold generally when modeling small-scale experiments of full-size phenomena. The two types of similitude must now be more clearly defined.

GEOMETRICAL SIMILITUDE. Two phenomena are geometrically similar if one can be derived from the other by a linear scaling with respect to a common center of similitude.

DYNAMICAL SIMILITUDE. Two phenomena are dynamically similar if the dimensionless form of each physical variable has the same value at corresponding points.

15.7. Examples of Modeling

High-speed Wind-tunnel Tests. A good example to illustrate present-day modeling techniques is found in the testing of models of aircraft or missiles in high-speed wind tunnels. Figure 15.3 shows a model in the transonic tunnel at Ames Aeronautical Laboratory.

Modeling at high subsonic or moderate supersonic speeds in air naturally requires consideration of more dimensionless parameters than in the case of incompressible low-speed flow. At such speeds compressibility, viscosity, and heat conduction must be taken into account. One effect of viscosity is to induce diffusion of vorticity, and the rate of this diffusion is μ/ρ. Heat conduction is also a diffusion effect, which takes

FIG. 15.3. Ames 14-ft transonic wind tunnel. Operates from subsonic speeds through speed of sound to low supersonic speeds. (*Courtesy of NASA, Ames Aeronautical Laboratory, Moffett Field, Calif.*)

place at a rate $k/\rho c_p$, if k is the coefficient of thermal conductivity and c_p is the specific heat at constant pressure. The ratio of these two defines a dimensionless parameter $\mu c_p/k$, known as the *Prandtl number* and denoted by **P**. When a medium is compressible, account must be taken of the finite speed of propagation of small disturbances in pressure or density and the variation of density with pressure and another thermodynamic variable. The latter is determined by the equation of state of the fluid. Up to moderate supersonic speeds air behaves like a perfect gas with constant-specific-heat ratio γ, and this dimensionless constant represents the effect of equation of state in determining conditions of dynamical similitude. The other effect of compressibility is represented by the speed of sound C of the undisturbed air. The ratio of the undisturbed-air speed to this speed U/C is a dimensionless parameter known as the *Mach number* **M**.

Summarizing, the earlier analysis in Art. 15.5 of flow of an incompressible fluid past a body can be extended to show that, in high-speed viscous air flow, the resultant force is determined by the relation

$$\frac{F}{\rho U^2 d^2} = f(\alpha, \mathbf{R}, \mathbf{P}, \mathbf{M}, \gamma) \tag{15.22}$$

The problem of modeling high-speed motion in a wind tunnel can now be appreciated. Geometrical similitude can be achieved with no more trouble than in incompressible flow, but the attainment of dynamical similitude requires the simultaneous equality of four dimensionless parameters, **R**, **P**, **M**, and γ, in flight and in the wind tunnel, respectively. Equality of **P** and γ are easy to satisfy. Provided air is used in the wind tunnel, γ will have the same value, 1.4, as in full-scale flight. Furthermore, the Prandtl number in air is usually constant, over a wide range of temperatures, with the value 0.74.

The achievement of dynamical similitude in high-speed wind tunnels·therefore requires the reproduction of full-scale flight values of **R** and **M**.

There is no difficulty in designing wind tunnels to run at a given Mach number in the subsonic or moderate supersonic range, although special precautions have to be taken to avoid blockage in the intermediate transonic range. There are two possible methods of increasing the Reynolds number to its full-scale value. The first, raising the stagnation pressure, introduces structural problems in design of model and support. The second, to reduce the kinematic viscosity by operating at very low temperatures, is more feasible, but of limited application.

In general, it is difficult to achieve precise dynamical similitude in both Mach number and Reynolds number, and the usual modeling procedure is to satisfy flight Mach number and approach the flight Reynolds number as closely as possible. A correction is then made for the departure of the wind-tunnel value of Reynolds number from its flight value. The effect of any such departure from dynamical similitude is known as the *scale effect*.

The scale effect is important even in low-speed wind tunnels. The problem in achieving full-scale Reynolds number is to compensate for the reduction in typical length d from the actual to model size. The only practical way of doing this is to decrease the kinematic viscosity. At low speeds this is achieved by increasing the tunnel density, and this is the purpose of the *compressed-air tunnel*.

This device, of course, is of no use in the compressible range, in which increases in density would have to be accompanied by undesirable increases in pressure.

In practice, scale effect is overcome by analyzing the resultant force on a body into component parts and making simplifying assumptions, based on observations, about the way in which each of these components depends on **R**, **M**, and other similitude parameters.

Suppose the body investigated is the wing of a high-speed aircraft, set at angle of incidence α in unyawed flight. Then the force on the wing is resolved into two components, the lift L, which is perpendicular to the flight direction, and the drag D, which is directly opposed to the motion. Corresponding dimensionless force coefficients

$$C_L = \frac{L}{\frac{1}{2}\,\rho S U^2} \qquad C_D = \frac{D}{\frac{1}{2}\,\rho S U^2}$$

are introduced. These are equivalent to dimensionless forces defined previously apart from a factor $\frac{1}{2}$ and the replacement of d^2 by wing area S.

The results of boundary-layer theory, based on the observed property that viscous effects are confined to the immediate neighborhood of solid bodies (and the interior of shock waves in supersonic flow), show that, at moderate angles of incidence, when separation or stalling effects are avoided, the lift is independent of Reynolds number. The drag depends on both Reynolds number and Mach number. To simplify its analysis it is assumed that the contributions to drag from these two effects are independent and can be determined in separate experiments. The assumption is justified to a good approximation provided that mixed effects such as shock-wave–boundary-layer interaction are absent. The dimensionless lift and drag coefficients can therefore be written in the form

$$\begin{aligned} C_L &= f(\alpha, \mathbf{M}) \\ C_D &= g(\alpha, \mathbf{M}) + h(\alpha, \mathbf{R}) \end{aligned} \tag{15.23}$$

The dimensionless function g is independent of Reynolds number **R** and represents the contribution to drag from Mach-number effect, called wave drag, and a contribution from circulation round the wing and associated wing-tip vortices, known as induced drag. The function h is the contribution to C_D from skin friction (shearing stresses applied to the wing surface by the fluid) and form drag, arising from boundary-layer thickening or local separation effects.

The lift coefficient can be measured directly for the required range of values of **M** and α. To determine C_D, information on the variation of h with **R**, for a range of values of α, is obtained either from low-speed tests or from theoretical estimates. The wind-tunnel value of $g + h$ is then measured directly. The flight value of C_D is then determined by subtracting the difference between wind-tunnel and flight values of the viscous-drag component h.

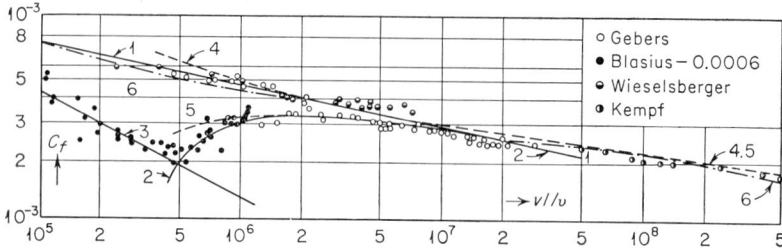

Fig. 15.4. Variations of frictional drag coefficient C_F with Reynolds number **R** on smooth flat plates. (*Ref. 7.*)

The analysis of drag (Fig. 15.4), due to viscosity effects, known as profile drag, is a subject in itself. Its measurement is subject to a scale effect resulting from absence of geometrical similitude between wind-tunnel and full-scale conditions. The flow in the boundary layer is partly laminar and partly turbulent, and the variation of profile drag with Reynolds number depends critically on the relative extents of the laminar and turbulent regimes and the position of transition from one regime to another. The contribution to drag from the turbulent boundary layer depends on the degree of roughness of the solid surface. The position of the transition point depends on the scale and level of turbulence in the undisturbed stream and, again, on the roughness of the surface. The measurement of wind-tunnel drag corresponds to full-scale conditions only provided that geometrical similitude is attained in free-stream turbulence and surface roughness. If this is not achieved, additional scale effects must be taken into account. The variation with **R** of C_F, the frictional-drag coefficient, in the case of a flat plate, is shown in Fig. 15.4. The lower curve on the left and the experimental points close to it correspond to wholly laminar flow. The uppermost curves and associated experimental points are for fully turbulent flow. On a given plate, C_F will follow the laminar curve for a certain distance and then change to the turbulent curve by a transition path such as that shown. If roughness were a factor, there would be several turbulent curves giving higher values of C_F with increasing degrees of roughness.

Hydrodynamic and Cavitation Phenomena. Many examples of modeling arise in motion on or below the surface of water. It is worthwhile to discuss two of these, ship motion[2] and cavitation.[9]

Modeling of ship motion has some features in common with modeling of supersonic aircraft flight.

A ship displaces a certain proportion of its volume of water and, in motion, generates surface waves influenced by gravitational effects.

The parameters influencing ship motion† and ship resistance are its velocity U, length L, volume displacement D, gravity g, density of water ρ, coefficient of viscosity of water μ. The resistance W is usually referred to a wetted area S, which is related to the variables already defined.

If L, U, and ρ are taken as the basic independent parameters, the dimensionless combinations of these with the remaining variables W, D, g, and μ are:

Resistance coefficient:
$$\frac{W}{\rho S U^2}$$

Fineness coefficient:
$$\psi = \frac{L}{D^{1/3}}$$

Froude number:
$$\mathbf{F} = \frac{U}{\sqrt{gL}}$$

† See Sec. 13 for discussion of hydrodynamics of ship motion.

Reynolds number:
$$\mathbf{R} = \frac{\rho U L}{\mu}$$

In modeling actual ship motion, the full-scale values of ψ, $\mathbf{F}$, $\mathbf{R}$ must be reproduced. The corresponding values of ψ will agree provided geometric similitude is achieved, but it is impossible to achieve simultaneous identity in the corresponding values of $\mathbf{F}$ and $\mathbf{R}$ in the same fluid.

To analyze ship resistance it is assumed that the effects of Froude number and fineness coefficient, on the one hand, are independent of Reynolds-number effect, on the other, so that

$$W = c_f(\mathbf{R}) \frac{\rho S U^2}{2} + c_w(\psi, \mathbf{F}) \rho g D \tag{15.24}$$

It is assumed that $c_f(\mathbf{R})$ obeys the flat-plate law, and therefore the influence of curvature and thickness on drag is neglected. Total drag is measured by towing models in tanks, and the assumed contributions from friction drag are subtracted from the observed values to give the variation of residual drag coefficient c_w with ψ and $\mathbf{F}$. The variation is given by Doyère[9] in the form of curves of c_w against ψ for different values of Froude number.

A fuller discussion of modeling of ship motion, including planing as well as displacement ships, is given by Sedov.[2]

Cavitation† is a very important phenomenon in high-speed motion of solid bodies through water such as entry of missiles from the atmosphere and motion of ship propellers. Cavitation is also important in the design of spillways and outlet works in dams. The collapse of cavitation bubbles, associated with the creation of high local pressures, can cause serious damage to propeller blades and to the concrete structure of a dam. The important dimensional quantities in underwater cavitation phenomena are the free stream pressure p_f and the vapor pressure p_v, in addition to parameters previously discussed in motion of a body through water. In the case of water entry, the atmospheric air pressure p_a replaces the vapor pressure p_v. The dimensionless parameter associated with cavitation is the *Thoma* cavitation number $\mathbf{Q} = (p_f - p_v)/(\rho U^2/2)$. The Reynolds number $\mathbf{R}$ and Froude number $\mathbf{F}$ are the other important parameters. In modeling cavitation phenomena, emphasis is laid, naturally, on reproducing the full-scale value of $\mathbf{Q}$. This can be done in cavitation tunnels, where facilities exist to vary vapor pressure, and in pressurized tanks, used to study water entry, in which the external atmospheric pressure can be varied. Modeling of cavitation and of other hydrodynamic phenomena is discussed at length by Birkhoff[11] and Birkhoff and Zarantonello.[10]

Modeling of Explosions. Explosive phenomena provide a particularly fertile field for application of modeling techniques. Full-scale explosions can be arranged only in special areas, and it is difficult to measure all quantities defining their behavior in the neighborhood of the explosion, because of the problem of designing instruments to withstand destructive effects of blast or heating. Provided certain similitude criteria are satisfied, the symmetrical detonation of a small spherical charge of a chemical explosive such as TNT or PETN will reproduce the same behavior as that of a charge with radius 1000 times as large. Unfortunately, such simple modeling is not possible in the case of fission or fusion bombs, since these must be of a certain minimum size. However, as will be seen later, nuclear explosions can be accurately described by a theoretical approach.

The quantities determining the blast effect from an explosion of a spherical charge of explosive in air are the charge energy E, the distance from the center of explosion R, the density of air, the ratio of specific heats γ, and the radius a. Application of the pi theorem shows that the peak pressure p_{max} must satisfy the relation

$$\frac{p_{max} R^3}{E} = f\left(\gamma, \frac{a}{R}\right) \tag{15.25}$$

† See Sec. 12 for discussion of cavitation.

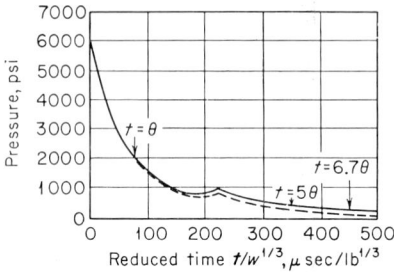

FIG. 15.5. Spherical pentolite charges. Blast-wave-pressure–reduced-time curves. Full curve, 51- and 80-lb charges. Dashed curve, 3.8-lb charges. (*Ref.* 12.)

The charge energy is proportional to the charge weight W. Equation (15.25) therefore shows that the model of an explosion can be scaled to a given full size provided that corresponding distances are scaled in proportion to $W^{1/3}$. The same law clearly applies to scaling corresponding times at corresponding points.

The validity of this scaling law in practice is seen in Fig. 15.5,[12] which compares results obtained from averaged observations of 51- and 80-lb charges of pentolite with those for 3.8-lb charges. A complete discussion of similitude properties of explosions and their applications is given by Cole.[12]

15.8. Similitude in Theory of Compressible Flow

The mathematical equations governing the motion of a compressible fluid (Sec. 8), even when viscosity and all heat-transfer effects are neglected, are nonlinear and, in general, only soluble by numerical methods. Under certain conditions, which have quite wide application, the exact equations can be approximated by simplified equations which can be solved, in part at least, by analytical means. Furthermore, the simplified equations have similitude properties not possessed by their exact counterparts. The existence of these properties means that a solution of the simplified equations can be applied to determine the flow past a whole class of bodies rather than to an isolated shape in a particular flow field.

The main prerequisite for the validity of the simplified equations is that the flow field to be determined is a small departure from a uniform flow field. This condition is satisfied in the uniform steady flow past thin wings, slender bodies, and quasi-cylindrical ducts, set at small angles of incidence to the undisturbed stream.

In deriving the simplified equations, it is usual to define a parameter τ setting the standard of smallness of the disturbance. This is chosen as the maximum-thickness–mean-chord ratio on wings and the fineness ratio on slender bodies. On sharp-nosed supersonic wings or bodies the small nose angle may be selected as the parameter τ.

The precise form of the simplified equations depends on the range of free-stream Mach number $\mathbf{M}_\infty$. When $\mathbf{M}_\infty$ is neither too close to unity nor too large, the thickness parameter τ is the only small parameter in the problem and the equations of motion can be linearized. They reduce to a distorted Laplace equation for the velocity potential in the normal subsonic range ($\mathbf{M}_\infty < 1$, $1 - \mathbf{M}_\infty$ not too small). In the normal supersonic range ($\mathbf{M}_\infty > 1$, $\mathbf{M}_\infty$ not too large and $\mathbf{M}_\infty - 1$ not too small), the potential satisfies the wave equation.

This linearization breaks down when $\mathbf{M}_\infty - 1$ is small or $\mathbf{M}_\infty$ is large. In the first case, in the transonic range, although τ is small, some combination of τ and $\mathbf{M}_\infty - 1$ is of order unity and a nonlinear term in the potential equation which can be neglected in the normal subsonic or supersonic ranges must be retained. The linearization also breaks down in the hypersonic range, where $\mathbf{M}_\infty$ is large and τ is small but $\mathbf{M}_\infty\tau$ is of order unity. In this case the disturbances to the velocity in the transverse direction are of one order larger than those parallel to the undisturbed stream direction. Furthermore, entropy gradients cannot be neglected, the flow is rotational even on a first-order theory, and the equations of motion do not reduce to a single equation for the velocity potential. In both the transonic and hypersonic cases, similitude parameters exist, and the solutions of a nonlinear differential equation or set of such equations define a whole family of flow fields.

The Prandtl-Glauert Rule.[13] The equations governing the steady irrotational motion of a uniform stream of perfect gas past a thin airfoil may be written:

Modified continuity:

$$\left(1 - \frac{(U_\infty + u)^2}{a^2}\right)\frac{\partial u}{\partial x} + \frac{uv}{a^2}\left(\frac{\partial u}{\partial y} + \frac{\partial v}{\partial x}\right) + \left(1 - \frac{v^2}{a^2}\right)\frac{\partial v}{\partial y} = 0 \qquad (15.26)$$

Irrotationality:

$$\frac{\partial u}{\partial y} - \frac{\partial v}{\partial x} = 0 \qquad (15.27)$$

Bernoulli:

$$(U_\infty + u)^2 + v^2 + \frac{2}{\gamma - 1}a^2 = q_{max}^2$$

In these equations the x axis is in the direction of the undisturbed stream, and u, v are velocity components in the x and y directions, respectively. Since the motion is irrotational and Eq. (15.27) is satisfied, a velocity potential exists. For uniform motion with velocity U_∞ past a thin airfoil of thickness ratio τ, the potential can be written

$$\Phi = U_\infty x + \varphi$$

if φ and its derivatives are of order τ. If terms of order τ^2 are neglected, Eq. (15.26) can be written

$$(1 - \mathbf{M}_\infty^2)\varphi_{xx} + \varphi_{yy} = 0 \qquad (15.28)$$

if $\mathbf{M}_\infty$ is the free-stream Mach number.

Suppose that the flow is subsonic and $\mathbf{M}_\infty < 1$. If new variables ξ, η, and φ_i defined by

$$\xi = x \qquad \eta = \beta y \qquad \varphi(x,y) = \lambda\varphi_i(\xi,\eta)$$

in which $\beta^2 = 1 - \mathbf{M}_\infty^2$, are introduced, Eq. (15.28) becomes

$$\varphi_{i\xi\xi} + \varphi_{i\eta\eta} = 0 \qquad (15.29)$$

Suppose that the equation of the airfoil is

$$y = f(x)$$

Then the surface boundary condition is

$$\frac{\partial\varphi}{\partial y} = U_\infty\frac{dv}{dx}$$

or, in terms of the reduced coordinates,

$$\frac{\partial\varphi_i}{\partial\eta} = U_\infty\frac{\partial f_i}{\partial\xi} \qquad (15.30)$$

if

$$f_i(\xi) = \frac{1}{\lambda\beta}f(x)$$

Equations (15.29) and (15.30) represent incompressible flow past an airfoil $1/(\lambda\mu)$ as thick as the original airfoil.

The pressure coefficient can be written

$$C_p(x,y) = -\frac{2\varphi_x}{U_\infty} = -\frac{2\lambda\varphi_i}{U_\infty} = \lambda C_{pi}(\xi,\eta)$$

If $\lambda = 1$, the following result is obtained, known as the *Prandtl-Glauert rule*. The pressure coefficient on a thin airfoil in subsonic flow of Mach number $\mathbf{M}_\infty$ is the same as the pressure coefficient in incompressible flow past a similar airfoil, the thickness of which is increased in the ratio $1 = \sqrt{1 - \mathbf{M}_\infty^2}$.

The Prandtl-Glauert rule leads to the definition of a similitude parameter τ/β. For uniform subsonic flow past airfoils of given shape, the surface-pressure distribution and flow pattern are the same for all airfoils with the same value of τ/β. A similar result holds in supersonic flow, with β^2 replaced by $-\beta^2$.

Transonic Similitude.   The derivation of the Prandtl-Glauert rule is not valid if the incident Mach number is too close to the critical value. In this case Eq. (15.28) does not include all the lowest-order terms and Eqs. (15.26) and (15.27) must be reexamined to derive the correct potential equation in transonic flow.

In transonic flow the x velocity component $U_\infty + u$ is close to the critical velocity a^* and it is appropriate to introduce the small variable $u' = U_\infty + u - a^*$. Then, using Bernoulli's equation, it can be shown that

$$a^2 - (U_\infty + u)^2 = -(\gamma + 1)a^* u'$$

Equation (15.26) then reduces to

$$(\gamma + 1)u' \frac{\partial u'}{\partial x} + v \left(\frac{\partial u'}{\partial y} + \frac{\partial v}{\partial x} \right) - a^* \frac{\partial v}{\partial y} = 0 \tag{15.31}$$

and Eq. (15.27) is satisfied by u' and v. From Eq. (15.31) $\partial v/\partial y$ must be of the order u'^2. Suppose that u' is of order ϵ and v of order ϵ^α, then the operator $\partial/\partial y$ must be of order $\epsilon^{2-\alpha}$, whence, from Eq. (15.27),

$$\alpha = \tfrac{3}{2}$$

If dimensionless variables

$$\xi = \frac{x}{c} \qquad \eta = \frac{\tau^{1/2} y}{c} \qquad \varphi = a^* \varphi'$$

are introduced and terms of order ϵ^3 are rejected, Eq. (15.31) reduces to

$$-(\gamma + 1) \frac{\partial \varphi'}{\partial \xi} \frac{\partial^2 \varphi'}{\partial \xi^2} + \frac{\partial^2 \varphi'}{\partial y^2} = 0 \tag{15.32}$$

If the equation of the boundary is written

$$\eta = \tau f(\xi) \tag{15.33}$$

in dimensionless form, the reduced boundary condition is

$$\frac{\partial \varphi'}{\partial \eta} = \frac{\tau \epsilon^{-3/2}}{\lambda} f'(\xi) \tag{15.34}$$

If $\lambda = 1/(\gamma + 1)$, Eqs. (15.32) and (15.34) determine all solutions of uniform transonic flow past similar shapes for which the parameter $(\gamma + 1)\tau \epsilon^{-3/2}$ has the same value. This leads to the definition of a transonic similarity parameter $(\mathbf{M}_\infty - 1)/[(\gamma + 1)\tau]^{2/3}$. This parameter was introduced by von Kármán.[14]   A slightly different parameter was proposed by Spreiter.[15]   The form of the transonic-similarity parameter shows that the reduced velocity potential in one field of uniform flow past a thin airfoil is the same as that in a field of slightly higher Mach number past a thicker airfoil. To satisfy transonic similarity in a gas of given γ, $\mathbf{M}_\infty$ must approach unity in proportion to $\tau^{2/3}$ as $\tau \to 0$. A fuller discussion of transonic similarity is given by Guderley.[16]

Hypersonic Similitude.   In hypersonic flow past a thin airfoil, the Mach number $\mathbf{M}_\infty$ is large and τ is small but

$$\mathbf{M}_\infty \tau = O(1)$$

Similitude in this type of flow has been considered by a number of authors. The following discussion is based on a complete account of the topic by Van Dyke.[17]   An exact solution for hypersonic flow past a thin wedge shows that the disturbances in the streamwise direction are $O(\tau^2)$ while those in the transverse direction are $O(\tau)$. Since $1/\mathbf{M}_\infty$ is approximately the angle of inclination of Mach lines to the stream, it is small, of order τ, and the flow field is very much confined laterally. The y coordinate is therefore expanded in the ratio $1/\tau$, and to analyze the equations of motion the following variables are introduced:

$$x' = x$$

$$y' = \frac{y}{\tau}$$

$$u = U_\infty[1 + \tau^2 u'(x',y')]$$
$$v = U_\infty \tau v'$$
$$p = p_\infty(\gamma \mathbf{M}_\infty^2 \tau^2)p'$$
$$\rho = \rho_\infty \rho'$$
(15.35)

Van Dyke shows that the equations of motion and the boundary conditions at the shock wave and surface contain only the reduced variables themselves and the adiabatic index γ. The only relation featuring $\mathbf{M}$ and τ is the upstream boundary condition

$$p' \to \frac{1}{\gamma \mathbf{M}^2 \tau^2} \qquad \text{as} \qquad x' \to -\infty$$
(15.36)

The equations of motion reduce to the following:

$$\frac{\partial u'}{\partial x'} + v'\frac{\partial u'}{\partial y'} + \frac{1}{\rho'}\frac{\partial p'}{\partial x'} = 0$$
(15.37)

$$\frac{\partial \rho'}{\partial x'} + v'\frac{\partial \rho'}{\partial y'} = 0$$
(15.38)

$$\frac{\partial v'}{\partial x'} + v'\frac{\partial v'}{\partial y'} + \frac{1}{\rho'}\frac{\partial p'}{\partial y'} = 0$$
(15.39)

$$\frac{\partial S}{\partial x'} + u'\frac{\partial S}{\partial y'} = 0$$
(15.40)

in which S is the entropy, which is related to p' and ρ' by the equation of state. As a result of the change to dimensionless variables, all the terms in these equations are $O(\tau)$. Equations (15.38) to (15.40) are uncoupled from Eq. (15.37), the only equation in which u' appears. Further, Eqs. (15.38) to (15.40) are precisely the equations for one-dimensional rotational motion of a gas in which v' is the velocity, x' is the time, and y' is the single space coordinate.

These results establish the existence of a hypersonic-similitude parameter $\mathbf{M}_\infty \tau$. For a given value of this parameter, a whole family of flow fields past thin airfoils of similar shape is determined by a single solution of Eqs. (15.37) to (15.40). This in turn corresponds to the solution of a certain problem in one-dimensional gas dynamics, which is certainly easier to solve than a corresponding problem in two-dimensional steady flow and may even be soluble analytically.

The analogy between hypersonic-small-disturbance theory and one-dimensional gas dynamics is very useful.

Similitude is of leading significance throughout the theory of hypersonic flow and is treated extensively in the work of Hayes and Probstein.[18]

15.9. Self-similarity

In earlier articles of this section similitude has been considered in terms of comparing two different flow fields which differ in scale. Similitude can also exist between two parts of the same flow field or between a complete flow pattern at one time and a corresponding pattern at a later time. Flow fields with this property are said to be *self-similar* and play a very important part in boundary-layer flow, steady supersonic flow past conical bodies, and the theory of explosions.

The advantageous property of self-similar flows is that the number of independent variables required to define them can be reduced by one from the number usually needed.

In the theory of spherical explosions the physical variables depend on the radial distance r, measured from the center of the explosion, and the time t, measured from the instant of detonation. If an explosion is self-similar, the physical variables depend only on a single independent variable, which is some combination of r and t, and the governing equations reduce to ordinary differential equations.

In certain problems of steady supersonic flow a center of similitude exists. On all spheres with this as center, the values of flow variables at corresponding points are identical. In other words, the physical variables are constant on rays through the center of similitude. It is evident that the boundaries in such problems must be generated by rays; i.e., they are conical. Unsymmetrical supersonic flow past a conical body depends on two angular variables, while the corresponding symmetrical flow depends on only one. Fields of steady supersonic flow which are self-similar are called *conical fields.* A particularly simple type of conical flow is that of uniform flow past thin conical wings, known as delta wings. This is governed by a very simple linearized theory based partly on the two-dimensional Laplace equation and partly on the one-dimensional wave equation.

Another example of a self-similar-flow solution, although it is not usually so identified, is the Blasius solution for the boundary layer in incompressible flow past a flat plate. The corresponding flat-plate boundary-layer solutions in supersonic and hypersonic flow are also self-similar. In these cases the transverse velocity profile across the boundary layer at a given distance along the plate is dynamically similar to the corresponding profile at a shorter distance.

The Blasius solution will be discussed first, then the theory of conical fields, and finally self-similar explosions.

The Blasius Solution.[19]   The equations governing the incompressible boundary-layer flow past a flat plate are (Art. 9.9)

$$u \frac{\partial u}{\partial x} + v \frac{\partial u}{\partial y} = \nu \frac{\partial^2 u}{\partial y^2}$$

$$\frac{\partial u}{\partial x} + \frac{\partial v}{\partial y} = 0 \tag{15.41}$$

if x is measured along the plate from the leading edge, and u, v are the velocity components along and perpendicular to the plate. The boundary conditions are

$$\begin{aligned} x > 0, \, y = 0 \qquad & u = v = 0 \\ y = \pm\infty \qquad & u = U_\infty \end{aligned} \tag{15.42}$$

The characteristic parameters entering the problem are U_∞, ν, x, y. From these two independent dimensionless combinations y/x, $y/\sqrt{\nu x/U_\infty}$ can be formed. In making the velocity components dimensionless it is appropriate to divide u by U_∞, in view of the second of the boundary conditions (15.42). However, the value of v never approaches U_∞ and should be expressed in terms of the other combination of U_∞, ν, and x with the dimensions of velocity, namely, $\sqrt{\nu U_\infty/x}$. The expressions for the velocity components are then of the form

$$u = U_\infty f\left(\frac{y}{x}, \frac{y}{\sqrt{\nu x/U_\infty}}\right) \tag{15.43}$$

$$v = \sqrt{\frac{\nu U_\infty}{x}} \, g\left(\frac{y}{x}, \frac{y}{\sqrt{\nu x/U_\infty}}\right) \tag{15.44}$$

The following argument, due to Sedov,[2] shows that u and v depend only on the second of the reduced variables in Eqs. (15.43) and (15.44).

Introduce dimensionless variables ξ, η, u_1, v_1 by the relations

$$x = l\xi \qquad y = \sqrt{\frac{\nu l}{U_\infty}}\,\eta \qquad u = U_\infty u_1 \qquad v = \sqrt{\frac{\nu U_\infty}{l}}\,v_1$$

in which l is an arbitrary positive length. Then Eqs. (15.41) reduce to

$$u_1 \frac{\partial u_1}{\partial \xi} + v_1 \frac{\partial u_1}{\partial \eta} = \frac{\partial^2 u_1}{\partial \eta^2}$$

$$\frac{\partial u_1}{\partial \xi} + \frac{\partial v_1}{\partial \eta} = 0 \tag{15.45}$$

The boundary conditions become

$$\xi > 0 \qquad \begin{array}{ll} \eta = 0, & u_1 = v_1 = 0 \\ \eta = \pm\infty & u_1 = 1 \end{array} \tag{15.46}$$

Equations (15.45) and (15.46) determine the solution of the problem in dimensionless form. Since the Reynolds number **R** appears nowhere in these equations, the solution must be independent of **R**. However, the revised forms of Eqs. (15.43) and (15.44) are

$$u_1 = f\left(\frac{\eta}{\xi\sqrt{\mathbf{R}}}, \frac{\eta}{\sqrt{\xi}}\right)$$

$$v_1\sqrt{\xi} = \Phi\left(\frac{\eta}{\xi\sqrt{\mathbf{R}}}, \frac{\eta}{\sqrt{\xi}}\right) \tag{15.47}$$

which depend on **R** through the variable $\eta/\xi\sqrt{\mathbf{R}}$. It follows that u_1 and $v_1\sqrt{\xi}$ are independent of $\eta/\xi\sqrt{\mathbf{R}}$ and are functions of $\eta/\sqrt{\xi}$ only.

If

$$\lambda = \frac{\eta}{\sqrt{\xi}}$$

and

$$f(\lambda) = \varphi'(\lambda)$$

it can be shown that

$$v\sqrt{\xi} = \tfrac{1}{2}\,[\lambda\varphi'(\lambda) - \varphi(\lambda)]$$

and φ satisfies the ordinary differential equation

$$2\varphi''' + \varphi\varphi'' = 0 \tag{15.48}$$

The solution of Eq. (15.48) corresponding to the boundary conditions derived from Eq. (15.46) is given in many texts on fluid dynamics.[2,18,20] It completely determines the character of boundary-layer flow on a flat plate. Similar solutions to boundary-layer flow have also been found in the incompressible case when the free-stream velocity obeys a power law in x (flow near a stagnation point)[18,20] and in hypersonic flow.[18]

Conical Flow. The equations of motion of a uniform steady supersonic stream past a cone are, in cartesian coordinates, based on the center of the cone.
Momentum (three equations):

$$\left(u\frac{\partial}{\partial x} + v\frac{\partial}{\partial y} + w\frac{\partial}{\partial z}\right)(u,v,w) + \frac{1}{\rho}\left(\frac{\partial}{\partial x}, \frac{\partial}{\partial y}, \frac{\partial}{\partial z}\right)p = 0 \tag{15.49}$$

Continuity:

$$\frac{\partial(\rho u)}{\partial x} + \frac{\partial(\rho v)}{\partial y} + \frac{\partial(\rho w)}{\partial z} = 0 \tag{15.50}$$

Entropy:

$$\left(u\frac{\partial}{\partial x} + v\frac{\partial}{\partial y} + w\frac{\partial}{\partial z}\right)S = 0 \tag{15.51}$$

State:

$$p = e^{(S-\bar{S})/c_v} \rho^{\gamma} \tag{15.52}$$

The characteristic parameters in this problem are x, y, z, U_{∞}, p_{∞}, ρ_{∞}, γ. The x component of velocity is then of the form

$$u = f(x,y,z,U_{\infty},p_{\infty},\rho_{\infty},\gamma)$$

Since no fixed fundamental length enters this problem, if x, U_{∞}, and a_{∞} (velocity of sound) are selected as fundamental parameters, the pi theorem shows that

$$\frac{u}{U_{\infty}} = F\left(\frac{y}{x}, \frac{z}{x}, \mathbf{M}_{\infty}, \gamma\right) \tag{15.53}$$

Therefore, in a given supersonic stream, the velocity components and, by similar arguments, the other physical variables depend only on the two angular variables y/x and z/x. In spherical polar coordinates r, θ, φ, the physical variables depend only on θ and φ. In axially symmetrical conical flow, i.e., uniform supersonic flow past a circular cone, the physical variables depend only on the single angular coordinate θ. In this case the equations of motion reduce to ordinary differential equations. These were integrated by Taylor and Maccoll.[21] By prescribing the free-stream Mach number and position of the attached conical shock wave, Taylor and Maccoll were able to integrate the ordinary differential equations up to a value of θ at which the normal velocity component is zero, which is the solid-cone angle corresponding to the given shock.

Spherical Explosions. Self-similar solutions are very useful in many problems of one-dimensional gas dynamics, and particularly in the theory of explosions. They provide accurate theoretical descriptions of the growth of spherical-detonation waves and of nuclear explosions. Both these phenomena can, for all practical purposes, be regarded as originating at a point center of spherical symmetry and therefore satisfy an essential condition for self-similarity.

It is remarkable that most of the basic self-similar solutions to explosion problems were developed independently and simultaneously during the last war in England, the U.S.S.R., and Germany. The solutions were developed on an *ad hoc* basis, and their publication was widely scattered. Within the last five years, however, Sedov[2] has given a connected and organized account of the subject, and a shorter treatment, not so formally based on dimensional arguments, is contained in the book on gas dynamics by Stanyukovich.[22] No formal account has yet been given in England or the United States, but most of the contributions to the field from these sources are referred to by Sedov.[2]

Sedov[2] sets out the conditions for the existence of self-similar solutions of problems in one-dimensional gas dynamics. These will be summarized here, and examples will be worked out in the cases of the spherical piston, the spherical-detonation wave, strong point explosions, and implosions, i.e., the motion of converging spherical shock waves.

The one-dimensional motion of a gas depends on two independent variables, the distance r from the plane, line, or center of similitude, and the time t, measured from the instant at which the motion begins. The physical properties of the motion are defined by three dependent variables, which may be chosen as the fluid velocity v, the pressure p, and the density ρ.

Certain constants will arise in the motion. At least one of these, a, say, must contain the mass, since both the dimensions of p and ρ contain the dimensions of mass. Without loss of generality write

$$[a] = ML^k T^s$$

Then the physical variables can be written in the form

$$v = \frac{r}{t}V \qquad \rho = \frac{a}{r^{k+3}t^s}R \qquad p = \frac{a}{r^{k+1}t^{s+2}}P \tag{15.54}$$

in which V, R, and P are functions of dimensionless combinations of r, t and other parameters in the motion.

In general there are two such dimensionless combinations, but if only one additional constant b, with dimensions independent of a, enters into the problem, there is only one combination and V, R, P are functions of a single dimensionless variable. This result follows immediately from the pi theorem. Without loss of generality it may be assumed that b is independent of the mass with dimensions

$$[b] = L^m T^n$$

Then, from the pi theorem, the dimensionless form of the relation,

$$p = f(r,t,a,b) \tag{15.55}$$

in which r, t, and a are taken as fundamental parameters, must be

$$\frac{r^{k+1}t^{s+2}}{a} p = f\left(1,1,1,\frac{b}{r^m t^n}\right) \tag{15.56}$$

which proves the result.

If a third constant c, with dimensions independent of those of a and b, entered into the problem, it would be possible to form a second dimensionless independent variable which would appear on the right of Eq. (15.56). On the other hand, if any additional constants entering into the problem each have dimensions related solely to those of a and b, then self-similarity is preserved.

A number of explosion and shock-wave phenomena satisfy these conditions for self-similarity, and a few of them will now be discussed. Firstly, the ordinary differential equations governing self-similar one-dimensional motion of a gas will be derived.

It may be assumed that $m \neq 0$, so that the dimensionless independent variable appearing on the right of Eq. (15.56) may be written

$$\lambda = \frac{r}{b^{1/m}t^\delta} \quad \text{if} \quad \delta = -\frac{n}{m} \tag{15.57}$$

The equations governing the one-dimensional unsteady motion of a perfect gas with constant specific heats are

$$\frac{\partial v}{\partial t} + u\frac{\partial v}{\partial r} + \frac{1}{\rho}\frac{\partial p}{\partial r} = 0 \tag{15.58}$$

$$\frac{\partial \rho}{\partial t} + \frac{\partial \rho v}{\partial r} + (\nu - 1)\frac{\rho v}{r} = 0 \tag{15.59}$$

$$\frac{\partial}{\partial t}\left(\frac{p}{\rho^\gamma}\right) + u\frac{\partial}{\partial r}\left(\frac{p}{\rho^\gamma}\right) = 0 \tag{15.60}$$

in which $\nu = 1$ in plane flow, $\nu = 2$ in flow with cylindrical symmetry, and $\nu = 3$ in flow with spherical symmetry.

If the expressions (15.54) are substituted and the new dependent variable

$$z = \frac{\gamma p}{R} \tag{15.61}$$

is introduced, Eqs. (15.58) to (15.60) reduce to the form

$$\frac{dz}{dV} = \frac{\{[2(V-1) + \nu(\gamma-1)V](V-\delta)^2 - (\gamma-1)V(V-1)(V-\delta) - [2(V-1) + k(\gamma-1)]z\}z}{(V-\delta)[V(V-1)(V-\delta) + (k-\nu V)z]} \tag{15.62}$$

$$\frac{d\ln\lambda}{dV} = \frac{z - (V-\delta)^2}{V(V-1)(V-\delta) + (k-\nu V)z} \tag{15.63}$$

$$(V - \delta)\frac{d \ln R}{d \ln \lambda} = [s + (k - \nu + 3)V] - \frac{V(V-1)(V-\delta) + (k - \nu V)z}{z - (V - \delta)^2} \quad (15.64)$$

if
$$k = \frac{s + 2 + \delta(k + 1)}{\gamma}$$

Sedov analyzes Eqs. (15.62) to (15.64) in great detail. Equation (15.62) is of principal interest since the integration of the other two equations can usually be regarded as simple quadratures.

To analyze Eq. (15.62) it is necessary to locate all its singular points and determine the integral curves passing through them. There are two main families of solutions of Eq. (15.62), corresponding to the following two types of problem:

1. One of the dimensional constants in the problem is a velocity.
2. One of these constants has the dimensions of energy.

Case 1 includes the problems of spherical detonation, the uniformly expanding spherical piston and implosions. The most important problem of type 2 is the nuclear explosion.

In case 1 it is appropriate to take

$$b = c \quad \text{constant velocity}$$

with dimensions LT^{-1}, and

$$\lambda = \beta \frac{r}{ct} \quad \beta = \text{a pure constant}$$

Then the remaining constant may be taken with dimensions

$$[a] = ML^{\omega-3} \quad k = \omega - 3, s = 0$$

Hence
$$\delta = 1 \quad k = \frac{\omega}{\gamma}$$

In all problems of propagation into a medium of uniform density, $\omega = 0$ and a can be taken as the constant density of the medium.

The integral curves of Eq. (15.62) in the case $\nu = 3$ (spherical motion), $\delta = 1$, and $\omega = 0$ are shown in Fig. 15.6. The equation has a node at $V = 0$, $z = 0$, a multiple node at $V = 1$, $z = 0$, a node at $V = 0$, $z = 1$, and two singular points at infinity. The curve $z = (1 - V)^2$ is not an integral curve, but corresponds to a point behind a sound wave or shock wave of zero strength. The curve, also not an integral curve,

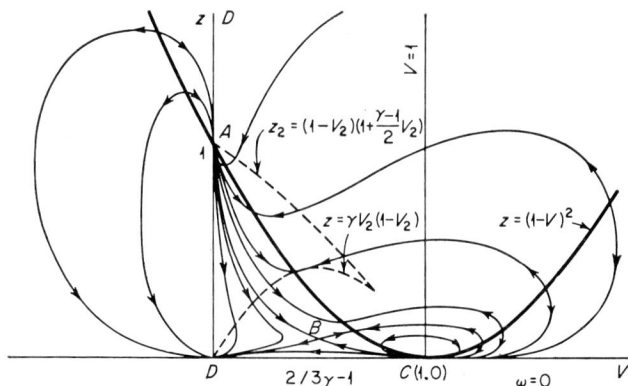

FIG. 15.6. Family of integral curves of Eq. (15.62) for $\nu = 3$, $\delta = 1$, $\omega = 0$. (*Ref. 2.*)

$$z_2 = (1 - V_2) \left(1 + \frac{\gamma + 1}{2} V_2 \right)$$

corresponds to points behind a shock wave moving into a region at rest.

The solution to a given problem reduces to finding a single path (which may be broken at isolated singularities), consisting of arcs of the family of integral curves, which satisfies all the boundary conditions of the problem. The details of this calculation can be outlined in two simple problems, spherical detonation and the spherical piston. The more complicated problem of the spherical implosion is also discussed.

Spherical Piston. A solid spherical boundary expands into a uniform atmosphere at a constant velocity U. The pressure and density in the undisturbed sphere are p_1 and ρ_1, respectively, and are nonzero. It is required to determine the disturbance after time t. Only two of the constants U, p_1, and ρ_1 are independent, and it is convenient to take

$$\lambda = \frac{r}{t} \qquad V = \frac{t}{r} v \qquad a = \rho_1$$

The piston is represented in the V, z plane by the line $V = 1$. Dimensional arguments show that the value of z at the piston must also be fixed. In Fig. 15.6, therefore, the piston is represented by the fixed point C. Conditions of rest at infinity in the undisturbed medium are defined by the point A on the z axis. The required solution in the V, z plane is therefore an integral curve connecting the points C and A. A glance at Fig. 15.6 shows that no single continuous integral curve can connect C with A. The transition can be effected only by connecting the undisturbed point at ∞, A, with the point B behind the shock, and connecting B and C with the appropriate integral curve of Eq. (15.62).

The disturbance due to the piston motion is therefore headed by a shock wave moving into the undisturbed atmosphere, followed by adiabatic compression between the shock and the piston. This problem was solved completely by Sedov[2] and Taylor,[23] working independently.

Spherical Detonation. A spherical charge of homogeneous explosive such as TNT or PETN is initiated at its center. It is required to determine the disturbance behind the spherical-detonation wave.

It is assumed that the detonated gas behaves like a perfect gas with constant γ. It is also assumed that the Chapman-Jouguet condition is satisfied so that the detonation takes place at a constant rate and proceeds at a constant detonation velocity. The latter assumption is fully confirmed by experimental evidence. Then only two independent dimensional constants enter the problem, firstly, the detonation velocity D, which depends only on the type of explosive used and the loading density, and secondly, the density ρ_1 immediately behind the detonation front, which is also fixed by the loading density.

The Chapman-Jouguet condition states that, immediately behind the detonation front, fluid particles move with sonic velocity relative to the detonation front. The motion immediately behind the detonation front therefore corresponds to a fixed point on the curve

$$z = (1 - V)^2$$

in Fig. 15.6. The complete motion in the detonated gas is then defined by the integral curve running from this curve to the node A. Within the sphere defined by the point A the gas is at rest. The form of the velocity distribution is shown in Fig. 15.7. This problem was solved independently by Taylor,[24] Zel'dovich,[25] and Döring.[26] Sedov and Yavorskaya[2] have extended the solution to deal with detonation of a nonuniform gas.

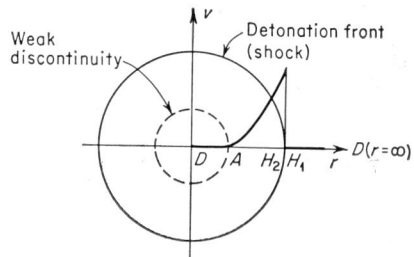

FIG. 15.7. Velocity distribution in spherical detonation solution. (*Ref. 2.*)

Spherical Implosion.   In many explosive phenomena implosions or converging spheri-cal-blast waves can develop, for example, as the result of the detonation of a spherical shell of explosive from the outside surface, or from the second shock wave in an ordinary spherical explosion of a charge of finite radius.

Ultimately, when the implosive wave is sufficiently strong and sufficiently close to its center, its motion is essentially self-similar.   Under these conditions the motion of the wave is independent of disturbances propagated from regions outside the wave and depends only on the undisturbed conditions ahead of it and the relation between velocity and radius at a given time.   If the time t is measured from the instant when the implo-sive wave contracts to its center and if R and U are the radius and velocity of the shock at this time, then, since the motion is self-similar,

$$U = \frac{dR}{dt} = \alpha \frac{R}{t}$$

in which α is a constant to be determined.   At a general point in the (t,r) plane the similarity variable is r/t^α, and the similarity solution is an integral curve of Fig. 15.6. In general, the integral curve extending from the shock point leads to a singularity on the negative characteristic through the center of the implosion.   The value of α is fixed by the condition that the integral curve passes through this singularity smoothly, without introducing infinite velocity.   The implosion problem was solved independently by Guderley[27] and Stanyukovich.[22]   Guderley's solution has been clarified and ex-tended by Butler.[28]

Nuclear Explosion.   The most important example of self-similar spherical motion of the second type is the explosion from a fission or fusion bomb.   This can be regarded as due to the instantaneous release of a given amount of energy, concentrated at a point.

Formally, three constants with independent dimensions enter this problem, the pres-sure p_1 and density ρ_1 of the undisturbed medium and the explosion energy E_0.   In view of the intensity of the explosion, it is permissible to neglect the pressure p_1 compared with the pressure behind the blast wave.

It can be shown that the similarity variable is

$$\lambda = \frac{r}{(E/\rho_1)^{1/5} t^{2/5}}$$

The motion of the shock wave can be determined without solving Eqs. (15.62) to (15.64).

The shock-wave coordinate r_2 is a function of time t.   If E, ρ_1, and t are taken as fundamental parameters, then the dimensionless combination of r_2, E, ρ_1, and t must be a constant, so that the equation

$$r_2 = \left(\frac{E}{\rho_1}\right)^{1/5} t^{2/5} \lambda^* \qquad (15.65)$$

if λ^* is a constant, defines the shock motion. This equation is accurately confirmed by obser-vation of atomic-bomb explosions.   A compari-son between Eq. (15.65) and the measured-time history of the shock front made during the first atomic-bomb explosion at Alamogordo, New Mexico, is shown in Fig. 15.8.   The motion behind the shock wave is defined by segments of integral curves of Eq. (15.62).   The curves in this case are not the same as in Fig. 15.6 since the nature and positions of the singular points are changed.   The full solution has been worked out and compared with experimental results, both by Taylor[24] and Sedov.[2]

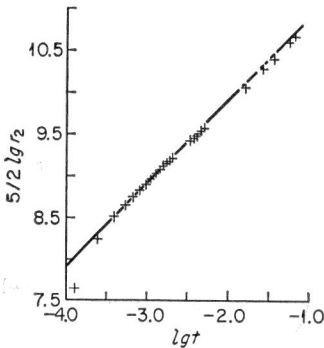

Fig. 15.8. Blast-wave path in atomic-bomb explosion. Full curve, Eq. (15.65). Experimental points, Ala-mogordo data.   (*Ref.* 24.)

REFERENCES

1. Bridgman, P. W.: "Dimensional Analysis," Yale University Press, New Haven, Conn., 1922.
2. Sedov, L. I.: "Similarity and Dimensional Methods in Mechanics" (English trans. ed. by M. Holt), Academic Press, New York, 1959.
3. Langhaar, H. L.: "Dimensional Analysis and Theory of Models," Wiley, New York, 1951.
4. Duncan, W. J.: "Physical Similarity and Dimensional Analysis," Longmans, New York, 1953.
5. Kline, S. J.: "Dimensional Analysis as a Research Tool," McGraw-Hill, New York. (In press.)
6. Howarth, L. (ed.): "Modern Developments in Fluid Dynamics, High Speed Flow," Oxford, New York, 1953.
7. Prandtl, L.: "The Physics of Solids and Fluids," part II, Blackie, Glasgow, 1936.
8. Goldstein, S. (ed.): "Modern Developments in Fluid Dynamics," Oxford, New York, 1938.
9. Doyère, C.: "Théorie du Navire," J. B. Bailliere et fils, Paris, 1927.
10. Birkhoff, G., and E. H. Zarantonello: "Jets, Wakes and Cavities," Academic Press, New York, 1957.
11. Birkhoff, G.: "Hydrodynamics: a Study in Logic, Fact and Similitude," Princeton University Press, Princeton, N.J., 1950.
12. Cole, R. H.: "Underwater Explosions," Princeton University Press, Princeton, N.J., 1948.
13. Imai, Isao: Approximation Methods in Compressible Fluid Dynamics, *Univ. Maryland Inst. Fluid Mech. and Appl. Math.* TN BN-95, 1957.
14. von Kármán, T.: The Similarity Law of Transonic Flow, *J. Math. and Phys.*, **26**:182–190 (1947).
15. Spreiter, J. R.: On Alternative Forms for the Basic Equations of Transonic Flow Theory, *J. Aeronaut. Sci.*, vol. 20, 1954.
16. Guderley, G.: "Theorie schallnaher Strömungen" (Theory of Transonic Flow), Springer, Berlin, 1957.
17. Van Dyke, M. D.: A Study of Hypersonic Small Disturbance Theory, *NASA TR* 1194, 1954.
18. Hayes, W. D., and R. F. Probstein: "Hypersonic Flow Theory," Academic Press, New York, 1959.
19. Blasius, H.: *Z. Math. u Physik.*, **56**:4–13 (1908).
20. Schlichting, H.: "Boundary Layer Theory," McGraw-Hill, New York, 1960. (English transl. by J. Kestin.)
21. Taylor, G. I., and J. W. Maccoll: in W. F. Durand (ed.), "Aerodynamic Theory," vol. 3, Springer, Berlin, 1936.
22. Stanyukovich, K. P.: "Unsteady Motion of Continuous Media" (English transl. ed. by M. Holt), Pergamon Press, New York, 1960.
23. Taylor, G. I.: *Proc. Roy. Soc. (London)*, **A186**:273–292 (1946).
24. Taylor, G. I.: *Proc. Roy. Soc. (London)*, **A200**:235–247 (1950).
25. Zel'dovich, Y. B.: *J. Expl. Theoret. Phys.*, **12**:389 (1942). (Russian.)
26. Döring, W., and G. Burkhardt: Contributions to the Theory of Detonation, *Wright Field Tech. Rept.* F-TS-1227-IA, 1949.
27. Guderley, G.: *Luftfahrt-Forsch.*, **19**:302–11 (1942).
28. Butler, D. S.: *ARDE Rept.* 54/54, Fort Halstead, Kent, England, 1954.
29. Taylor, G. I.: *Proc. Roy. Soc. (London)*, **A201**:155, 175 (1950).
30. Ipsen, D. C.: "Units, Dimensions, and Dimensionless Numbers," McGraw-Hill, New York, 1960.

Section 16

FLOW THROUGH POROUS MEDIA

By

JOSEPH G. RICHARDSON, *Humble Oil & Refining Company, Houston, Texas*

FLOW THROUGH POROUS MEDIA

INTRODUCTION

The purpose of this section is to provide a foundation for solving problems involving fluid flow through porous media. Emphasis has been placed on clearly describing the physical nature of the flow phenomena rather than developing a step-by-step mathematical treatment. Sufficient discussion is offered on the origin and simplifying assumptions involved in the equations to permit the reader to decide their applicability to his problem.

16.1. Notation

The following symbols are used in this section on flow through porous media. The usual units are indicated, but in the longer equations consistent units are assumed. In some of the shorter equations and in the example problems the units are indicated.

Symbols	Definitions	Usual units
	Properties of the medium	
k	Absolute permeability	darcys or millidarcys
k_g	Effective permeability to gas	darcys or millidarcys
k_o	Effective permeability to oil	darcys or millidarcys
k_w	Effective permeability to water	darcys or millidarcys
k_{rg}	Relative permeability to gas	fraction or per cent
k_{ro}	Relative permeability to oil	fraction or per cent
k_{rw}	Relative permeability to water	fraction or per cent
ϕ	Porosity	fraction or per cent
τ	Tortuosity factor	fraction
s	Specific surface area of medium	meters^2/g
S	Fluid saturation	fraction or per cent
$J(s)$	Dimensionless capillary pressure	dimensionless
$D(ri)$	Pore-size-distribution function	cm^2
a_p	Radius of particle	cm or ft
d	Diameter of particle	cm or ft
	Properties of the fluid	
q	Volumetric flow rate	cm^3/sec or ft^3/day
v	Superficial velocity, q/A	cm/sec or ft/day
P	Pressure	atm or psi
h	Fluid head	ft of fluid flowing
Q	Total volume of fluid	cm^3 or ft^3
F	Fraction of total fluid flowing	fraction
μ	Viscosity	centipoise
ρ	Density	g/cc or lb/ft^3
σ	Interfacial tension	dynes/cm
c	Compressibility of liquid	cc/(cc)(atm) or ft^3/(ft^3)(psi)
C	Concentration	g/cc
Z	Supercompressibility of gas	dimensionless
β	Formation-volume factor	bbl oil in reservoir/bbl in stock tank
M.Wt	Molecular weight	g/g mole
D	Diffusion coefficient	cm^2/sec or ft^2/sec
l_f	Lithology factor	dimensionless
Subscripts:		
g, o, w	Gas, oil, and water, respectively	

Symbols	Definitions	Usual units
Properties depending on both fluid and porous medium		
γ	Mobility	darcys/centipoise
M	Mobility ratio	dimensionless
K	Dispersion coefficient	cm²/sec or ft²/sec
θ	Contact angle	degrees
$\mathbf{R}$	Reynolds number	dimensionless
P_c	Capillary pressure	atm or psi
b	Klinkenberg constant	atm or psi
Geometrical properties		
A	Cross-section area	cm² or ft²
A	Angstrom	angstrom
L	Length	cm or ft
W	Width	cm or ft
H	Thickness	cm or ft
x	Distance in x direction	cm or ft
y	Distance in y direction	cm or ft
z	Distance in z direction	cm or ft
R	Radius	cm or ft
α	Angle of inclination	degrees
Other properties		
t	Time	sec or days
t_d	Dimensionless time	dimensionless
g	Acceleration of gravity	980 cm/sec² or 32.2 ft/sec²
g_c	Gravitational constant	$\dfrac{\text{g-cm}}{\text{dyne-sec}^2}$ or $\dfrac{(32.2\ \text{lb}_m)(\text{ft})}{(\text{lb}_f)(\text{sec}^2)}$
i	Current flux	amp/cm²
σ	Electrical conductivity	ohms⁻¹
V	Voltage	volts
C	Capacitance	μfarads
Subscript E	Initial conditions	

16.2. Scope

The scope of this section is principally limited to laminar flow of fluids through porous media such as reservoir rocks containing oil, water, and gas. At this point the reader might well ask: What is a porous medium? A porous medium is simply a solid with holes in it. The next logical question is: How can the nature of such a medium be described when all that can be seen is its surface and sometimes not even that? The answer is that the details of the shapes, sizes, and interconnections of the holes are seldom known, but the medium can be characterized by its average properties, such as its average resistance to flow of fluids. In Art. 16.3, a brief discussion is given on the gross or average properties of a porous solid which aid in its description.

Once the bases for characterizing the porous medium have been established, how can the flow of fluids be described? What is the relation between flow rate and pressure gradient from point to point? Again, usually only the average flow conditions can be described, not the details of the microscopic velocity variations from point to point within a given tortuous flow channel. The basic law describing the flow of fluids through porous media is Darcy's law—the equivalent of Ohm's law in flow of electric current. The discussion in Arts. 16.4 to 16.12 is confined to flow of a single fluid. The flow of slightly compressible fluids such as water and the flow of highly compressible fluids such as gas are discussed for both steady-state and unsteady-state conditions.

Articles 16.14 and 16.15 are concerned with the distribution and flow of two immiscible phases, a gas and a liquid, or two insoluble liquid phases. The first question which must be answered is: How do the fluids distribute themselves? Which fluid wets the solid? How does the resistance to fluid flow depend on the amount and distribution of the fluids within the pore spaces? These questions can be answered by interpretations of gross measurements such as capillary-pressure measurements and relative-permeability measurements. These measurements are also useful, as discussed in Arts. 16.16 to 16.24, in describing both steady-state, simultaneous flow of two fluids and the displacement of one fluid by another. The discussion in Arts. 16.25 and 16.26 of flow of two immiscible fluids is devoted to use of dimensionally scaled models to solve complex problems.

Articles 16.27 to 16.32 are concerned with flow of miscible fluids, that is, fluids completely soluble in one another. One of the obvious questions is: How do these fluids mix as they flow through the porous solid? What are the forces that govern the mixing? The role of diffusion and convection in causing the mixing is discussed. The use of scaled models in studying the displacement of one fluid by another fluid miscible with it is developed.

The material in this section should be useful to the reservoir engineer interested in recovery of oil or gas, the hydrologist interested in production and conservation of water, the soil scientist concerned with the movement of subsurface water, and the chemical engineer interested in fixed-bed reactors in the laboratory, refinery, or chemical plant. While much of the discussion is directed toward the science of reservoir engineering because of the author's interest in that particular field, the physical principles discussed apply generally.

16.3. Properties of Porous Media

Chemical Composition. The porous media of principal interest in this chapter are the rocks from underground formations that contain natural gas, oil, or water. These rocks are first classified as to their chemical composition, sandstone, limestone, chert, or serpentine. Roughly 40 per cent of the oil reserves of the world are contained in sandstone formations. Sandstone consists of grains of quartz, usually cemented together with argillaceous materials. Often hydratable materials such as montmorillonite, kaolinite, or illite clays are contained between the quartz grains in the sandstones. Roughly 60 per cent of the oil reserves of the world are contained in limestone reservoirs. By common terminology, limestone reservoirs include those formations made of limestone, calcium carbonate, and those made of dolomite, the double carbonate of calcium magnesium. Only occasionally is oil found in chert, a finely crystalline quartz, serpentine, a hydrous magnesium silicate, or in fractures in dense rocks such as granite.

Pore and Grain Structure. The pore and grain structure of rocks is usually studied by making thin sections. These are made by cementing a flat face of a core sample to a plate and grinding the sample down to a fraction of a grain in thickness. The grain structure can then be studied by transmitted light. In some cases, the shapes of the pore spaces between grains can be highlighted in thin sections by injecting Wood's metal or dyed plastic into the sample before preparing the thin section. Figures 16.1 and 16.2 are photomicrographs of thin sections of sandstone and limestone.

Another method of observing the pore structure of a rock is to impregnate it with a low-melting-point metal such as Wood's metal at high pressure. After the metal has been allowed to cool, the solid can be dissolved or broken away. The photomicrographs can be made of the pore structure. Shown in Fig. 16.3 is a photomicrograph of the pore structure of a consolidated sand. Note the tortuous, interwoven nature of the pores. The flow channels in such a medium vary continuously in direction, size, and shape.

Fig. 16.1. Thin section of a Weber sandstone. (*Ref.* 10.)

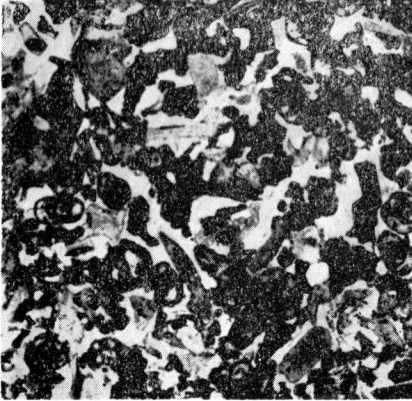

FIG. 16.2. Thin section of an Indiana limestone.

Permeability. The permeability of a porous medium is its most useful fluid-flow property. The permeability is a measure of the ease with which a fluid will flow through the medium; the higher the permeability, the higher the flow rate for a given pressure gradient. The permeability is a statistical average of the fluid conductivities of all the flow channels in the medium. This average conductivity takes into account the variations in size, shape, direction, and interconnections of all the flow channels. While obviously a number of pores or flow channels must be considered in obtaining a statistically "average" permeability, it is often convenient for mathematical purposes to consider the permeability as the property of a point in the medium. In a homogeneous medium the permeability at each point coincides with the average permeability. In a heterogeneous medium the permeability varies from point to point. Later in this article, methods of averaging permeabilities will be discussed briefly.

DEFINITION OF PERMEABILITY. The most commonly used unit of permeability is the darcy. The American Petroleum Institute defines a darcy as follows:

"A porous medium has a permeability of one darcy when a single phase fluid of one centipoise viscosity that completely fills the voids of the medium will flow through it under conditions of viscous flow at the rate of one cubic centimeter per second per square centimeter of cross-sectional area under a pressure equivalent hydraulic gradient of one atmosphere per centimeter."

FIG. 16.3. Metallic cast of pore spaces in a consolidated sand (100 ×).

For linear, horizontal, isothermal flow of a fluid, the equation is

$$q = \frac{kA}{\mu}\frac{dP}{dL} \qquad (16.1)$$

in which the common laboratory units are used:

q = flow rate, cm³/sec
k = permeability, darcys
A = cross-section area cm²
μ = viscosity, centipoises
dP/dL = pressure gradient, atm/cm

or in cgs units,

q is in cm³/sec
k is in cm²
A is in cm²
μ is in poises or dyne-sec/cm²
dP/dL is in dynes/(cm²)(cm)

Note that permeability has the units of length squared. The flow equation

$$q = \frac{6.34kA}{\mu}\frac{dP}{dL} \qquad (16.2)$$

is used for reservoir or field units in which

q is in ft³/day
k is in darcys
A is in ft²
μ is in centipoises
dP/dL is in psi/ft

Hydrologists define permeability another way. Since they are principally interested in the flow of water, their usual procedure is to include the water viscosity in the coefficient of permeability. For example,

$$q = \frac{k_p A H}{L}$$

in which k_p = coefficient of permeability
q = rate of discharge of an aquifer, gal/day at 60°F
A = cross-section area, ft²
H = difference hydraulic head, ft water
L = length of aquifer, ft

METHODS OF AVERAGING PERMEABILITIES. When a large porous medium is homogeneous, the average permeability coincides with the permeabilities of each of its small pieces. However, when the permeabilities of each of the small pieces of a medium vary, the average permeability depends on the manner in which the pieces are arranged. A clear and concise discussion of methods of averaging permeabilities is given by Cardwell and Parsons.[1] Consider a square block of uniform thickness made up of four smaller blocks as shown in Fig. 16.4. Two of the blocks have permeability k_1, and two have permeability k_2, with flow from left to right as shown. When the two permeabilities are in parallel as in a, the average permeability of the whole block is a simple-arithmetic average:

$$k_{\mathrm{av}} = \frac{k_1 + k_2}{2} \qquad \text{or} \qquad \frac{\sum\limits_{1}^{n} k_i}{n} \qquad (16.3)$$

if n is the number of blocks. When the two permeabilities are in series, the average permeability of the composite block is the harmonic mean:

$$k_{\mathrm{av}} = \frac{2}{\dfrac{1}{k_1} + \dfrac{1}{k_2}} \qquad \text{or} \qquad \frac{n}{\sum\limits_{1}^{n} \dfrac{1}{k_i}} \qquad (16.4)$$

When the permeabilities are arranged obliquely in c or are randomly distributed, no simple averaging technique applies. Cardwell and Parsons showed that the average permeability for systems illustrated by case c will always lie between the arithmetic and harmonic-mean permeabilities. Of course, in radial systems where permeabilities around the well bore are weighted more heavily, it is possible for the average permeability to exceed the volume-weighted, arithmetic-average permeability.

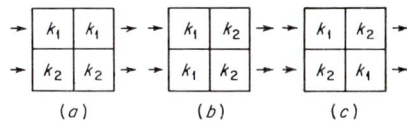

FIG. 16.4. The block composed of four squares having two different permeabilities. (*Ref.* 1.)

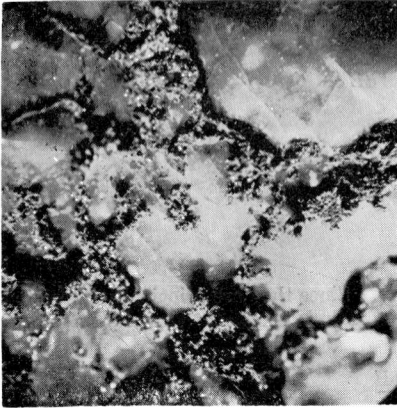

FIG. 16.5. Metal cast of solution-type porosity in limestone.

Porosity. The porosity of a porous medium is defined as the void volume, or volume of pore space divided by the total volume of the medium. Void, or pore, volumes are usually determined by measuring either gravimetrically or volumetrically the amount of liquid needed to saturate the dry medium. Pore volumes are also determined by gas-expansion methods. Bulk volumes are determined from measurements of the external dimensions of the medium or from the volume of liquid displaced by immersion of the saturated medium. Porosities are expressed as either fractions or per cent.

The average porosity of a very large porous medium such as an oil-bearing sand may be determined from the porosity of a number of small core samples of the reservoir rock. A simple-arithmetic average will suffice when sufficient samples are available to get a statistical distribution of porosities in the core samples.

TYPES OF POROSITY. Often reservoir rocks are classified as to the type of pore space that exists in the rock. The porosity in sandstones is usually that between sand grains; hence the type of porosity is referred to as *intergranular*. Some sandstones are also fractured. In limestones, one type of porosity is that between the crystals of calcite or dolomite which may be rhombohedral in shape. This shape of porosity is referred to as *intergranular*, or *intercrystalline*. Other limestone may contain crystals which are egg-shaped, or *oolitic*. Several other types of porosity occur in limestone. In some limestones, parts of the crystals have been dissolved into the ground water to form *solution* type of porosity as shown in Fig. 16.5. In others, small isolated holes have been formed to produce a *vugular* type of porosity. In still others, large channels, sometimes several feet in diameter, have been formed to produce a *cavernous* type of porosity. Also, limestone sometimes contains fracture systems which make up an appreciable part of the pore volume. This type is referred to as *fracture* porosity.

TYPICAL RANGE OF VALUES FOR POROSITY AND PERMEABILITY. The range of values commonly measured on various types of porous media has been discussed by Scheideggar.[2] The values which may be of general interest are shown in Table 16.1.

Pore Size and Pore-size Distribution. Another useful method of characterizing a porous medium is that of determining the size of its pores and the pore-size distribution. While no one single dimension can describe the size or geometric shape of the holes between sand grains or crystals of limestone or whatever the solid particles in a medium, it is convenient conceptually to visualize the holes as short circular capillary tubes.

Table 16.1. Typical Values for Permeability and Porosity for Various Porous Solids

(From Scheideggar[2])

Porous solid	Permeability, darcy	Porosity, fraction
Sand.................	2–180	0.31 –0.50
Sandstone...............	0.0000001–11	0.08 –0.40
Limestone..............	0.000001–2	0.015–0.20
Brick..................	0.0048–0.22	0.12 –0.34
Soil...................	0.29–14	0.43 –0.54
Berl saddles............	130,000–390,000	0.68 –0.83
Wire crimps............	3800–10,000	0.68 –0.76
Silica powder...........	0.013–0.051	0.37 –0.49

Then, the pressure required to force a non-wetting liquid such as mercury (Art. 16.14) into the pore spaces can be related to the radius of the pores by

$$P_c = \frac{2\sigma \cos \theta}{r} \qquad (16.5)$$

in which P_c = capillary pressure required to force nonwetting liquid into sample

r = "radius" of pore into which nonwetting liquid is just entering

σ = interfacial tension

θ = contact angle

The distribution of pore sizes can be obtained from a relation derived by Ritter and Drake.[3]

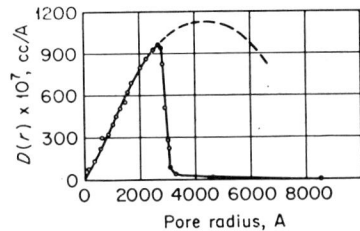

● Diatomaceous earth
● UF fritted glass

Fig. 16.6. Distribution functions for diatomaceous earth and fritted glass. (*Ref.* 3.)

$$D(r) = \frac{P_c}{r} \frac{d(V_t - V)}{dP_c} \qquad (16.6)$$

in which $D(r)$ = pore-size-distribution function

V_t = total pore volume

V = volume of nonwetting fluid injected

From an experimental curve of capillary pressure vs. the volume of mercury forced into an evacuated sample of the medium, the quantity $d(V_t - V)/dP_c$ may be determined at various values of P_c by taking the slope of the curve. Then by calculating r at each value of P_c by using Eq. (16.5), the pore-size-distribution function $D(r)$ may be calculated for each value of r by using Eq. (16.6).

Shown in Fig. 16.6 are examples of pore-size distribution for two types of materials. Note that in the fritted glass, the majority of the pores had about the same radius or slightly more than 4000 A. In other words, most of the pores were of uniform size. The diatomaceous earth had a much greater range of pore sizes, but the most frequent pore radius in this material was also slightly more than 4000 A. Of particular interest in characterizing filtering media is the maximum pore size. Shown in Fig. 16.7 is the pore-size distribution for a porous ceramic plate. Note that the medium has almost no pore spaces with radii greater than 3000 A.

Pore-size-distribution data can be used for estimating the permeabilities of rock samples.[4] Often, some insight into two-phase- and three-phase-fluid distribution and flow characteristics is gained from consideration of pore-size-distribution curves.

Surface Areas. Many porous materials contain enormous surface areas per unit volume. For instance, the surface area of the grains in a sandstone may be of the order of 30 acres/ft³ of rock. Obviously, in processes which involved adsorption of materials from the fluid flowing from the medium, knowledge of the magnitude of the surface area is essential. For packs of perfectly uniform spheres, the surface area per unit bulk volume is inversely proportional to the radius of the spheres and is readily calculated. However, in most porous materials the surface area per unit volume or specific surface must be determined experimentally.

The usual method for determining specific surfaces is from nitrogen-adsorption experi-

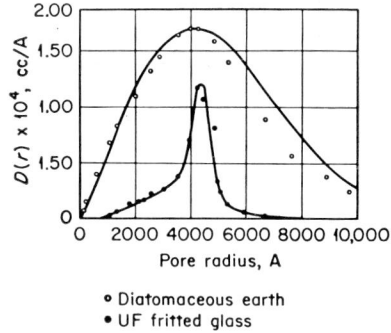

Fig. 16.7. Distribution function for porous plate. (*Ref.* 3.)

ments at constant temperatures.   The gas-adsorption techniques involve determination of the quantity of gas necessary to form a monomolecular layer on the surface.   Knowing the volume of gas in the monomolecular film, the number of gas molecules can be determined by

$$n = \frac{V_m \rho N}{M} \tag{16.7}$$

in which n = number of gas molecules
V_m = volume of gas in monomolecular film at standard conditions
ρ = density of gas at standard conditions
N = Avogadro's number
M = molecular weight of gas

The surface area of the medium is then calculated by

$$s = n\sigma = \frac{V_m \rho N}{M} \sigma \tag{16.8}$$

in which s = total surface area
σ = surface area/molecule (15.4 A^2/nitrogen molecule and 13.6 A^2/argon molecule)

The most widely accepted method of determining the volume of gas in a monomolecular film is that based on the theory of Brunauer, Emmett, and Teller.[5]   Briefly, this method consists of determining the amount of gas adsorbed on the solid surface at constant temperature for a series of pressures.   Then the BET theory (for Brunauer, Emmett, and Teller) states that

$$\frac{P}{V(P_s - P)} = \frac{1}{V_m C} + \frac{C - 1}{V_m C} \frac{P}{P_s} \tag{16.9}$$

in which V = volume of gas adsorbed measured at standard conditions
P = pressure
C = a constant depending on the gas
P_s = liquefaction pressure of gas at temperature in question

If Eq. (16.9) applies to the experiment in question, a plot of $P/V(P_s - P)$ versus P/P_s should yield a straight line with a slope of $(C - 1)/V_m C$ and an intercept of $1/V_m C$. The values of V_m and C may then be calculated.   It is also necessary that the values of C be in reasonable agreement with thermodynamic considerations, in which

$$C = \exp \frac{E_1 - E_L}{RT} \tag{16.10}$$

where E_1 = heat of adsorption of first layer of gas
E_L = heat of liquefaction
R = gas constant
T = absolute temperature

The specific surface of some common materials is shown in Table 16.2.   The data were obtained from adsorption of nitrogen at about liquid nitrogen temperature.

Electrical Properties.   Two useful electrical properties of porous rocks are the relation between water saturation and electrical resistivity and the dependence of the electrical resistivity on porosity.   Both of these properties are used in interpretation of electric logs of underground formations to determine their properties and fluid contents.   The electrical resistivity of a rock has been shown by Archie[9] to depend on water saturation according to the following relation:

$$S_w = \left(\frac{R_0}{R} \right)^{1/n} \tag{16.11}$$

Table 16.2. Typical Surface Areas for Various Solids

Porous solid	Specific surface, meters^2/g	Source
Sandstone.............	0.5 –6.0	Brooks and Purcell[6]
Limestone.............	0.05–0.5	Brooks and Purcell[6]
Silica gel.............	534	Brunauer, Emmett, and Teller[5]
Porous glass...........	123	Harris and Emmett[7]
Bone char.............	62	Loebenstein and Dietz[8]
Diatomaceous earth.....	55	Loebenstein and Dietz[8]
Monterey shale........	87	Loebenstein and Dietz[8]

in which S_w = water-saturation fraction

$\quad\quad R_0$ = resistivity of sample saturated with the water

$\quad\quad R$ = resistivity of sample at saturation S_w

$\quad\quad n$ = constant

The exponent n is usually about 2.0 for unconsolidated media and is usually about 1.9 or less for consolidated media.

The resistivity of porous media saturated with water has been shown by Winsauer et al.[10] to depend on both the porosity and tortuosity by

$$F = \frac{\tau^2}{\phi} \tag{16.12}$$

in which F = ratio of electrical resistivity of medium saturated with water to resistivity of water

$\quad\quad \tau$ = tortuosity factor, which is defined as tortuous length along which fluid or electric current must flow through medium divided by length of medium†

$\quad\quad \phi$ = porosity

FLOW OF A SINGLE FLUID

The foundation on which laminar flow of fluids through porous media rests is Darcy's law. Around the middle of the nineteenth century, while experimenting with flow of water through sand filters, Henry Darcy[11] noted that the flow rate of water was proportional to the difference in head of water across the filter. His basic equation was $q = -K(h_2 - h_1)/L$, where q is flow rate of water per unit cross-section area, K is a constant for the system, $h_2 - h_1$ is the difference in fluid head across length L. Since the work of Darcy, a number of experimenters have studied the flow of various fluids through many types of porous solids. The basic relation of Darcy has been extended to cover flow of any fluid, and as with any law, its limitations and range of applicability have been defined.

From two simple concepts—Darcy's law and the law of conservation of mass—equations can be derived to describe the isothermal, laminar flow of incompressible, slightly compressible, or compressible fluids in one, two, or three dimensions. In some cases, the equations for steady-state flow of a single fluid can be simplified into the Laplace equation. In these cases, many of the theorems of classical hydrodynamics for flow of an ideal fluid can be applied. For unsteady-state flow of slightly compressible or compressible fluids, the solutions of the equations are more complex. However, considerable literature is available for solutions of flow of fluids in one dimension. In unsteady-state flow, useful analogies with transient flow of electric current or heat can be

† Tortuosity factors are usually measured by determining the time required for ions to migrate through a given distance in the medium with a given potential gradient across the medium or by diffusion experiments. Tortuosity factors are usually estimated to be about 1.3 to 1.5 for fluid-saturated unconsolidated sands and to be in the range of 1.5 to 2.5 for consolidated sandstones saturated with a single fluid.

used to study flow in more than one dimension. Further, the advent of rapid electronic computers and numerical methods provides the means for solving many of the more difficult problems of flow in two or three dimensions. The following Arts. 16.4 to 16.12 discuss Darcy's law and the flow of a single fluid.

16.4. Darcy's Law

The concept which has become known as Darcy's law can best be developed by considering the laminar flow of a single fluid flowing in one direction through a porous medium filled with the fluid. Consider the porous medium shown in Fig. 16.8. Fluid is entering the face on the left and is emerging from the face on the right. The fluid flow is uniformly distributed across the entire cross-section area A. The direction of fluid flow is parallel with the base of the porous body, which is at an angle α with the horizontal, α being positive when the flow is upward and negative when the flow is downward. The expression which relates the flow rate to the pressure gradient is

$$q = -\frac{kA}{\mu}\left(\frac{\partial P}{\partial L} + \rho g \sin \alpha\right) \tag{16.13}$$

Stated in words, Darcy's law says that the flow rate at a given time and point along the length is proportional to the permeability of the medium, the cross-section area through which flow is taking place, and the sum of the pressure gradient at the point in question, and the gradient in hydrostatic head along the direction of flow and that the flow rate is inversely proportional to the viscosity of the fluid.

As previously stated, the permeability k is a property of the medium alone.† All the irregularities in size and shape of the pores and the complexities of the interconnections of pores are represented in the k of Darcy's law. Thus the k represents a statistical average of the fluid-flow conductivity through the cross-section area at the point in question. Conceivably, the permeability of the medium could vary from point to point along the flow path. In this case, the dependence of permeability on length would have to be taken into account in integration of Eq. (16.13).

A more general set of Darcy equations is needed when the flow is not unidirectional:

$$V_x = -\frac{k}{\mu}\frac{\partial P}{\partial x} \tag{16.14}$$

$$V_y = -\frac{k}{\mu}\frac{\partial P}{\partial y} \tag{16.15}$$

$$V_z = -\frac{k}{\mu}\left(\frac{\partial P}{\partial z} + \rho g\right) \tag{16.16}$$

in which V_x, V_y, and V_z are the superficial velocities (volumetric flow rates per unit cross-section area) in the x, y, and z directions. In applying Eqs. (16.14) to (16.16), it is convenient to visualize the permeability as a property of a point in the medium. The permeability applying to the point in question is visualized as the statistical average of the fluid-flow conductivity of the group of pore spaces surrounding the point in question. Conceivably, the permeability could be different in each direction of flow at the point in question, in which case the permeabilities in Eqs. (16.14) to (16.16) would have subscripts x, y, and z. The

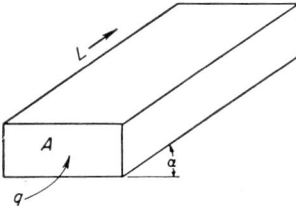

Fig. 16.8. Porous medium.

† In some cases, the fluid may react with the porous solid to swell it and change the pore structure. Examples of this are swelling of clays with water to reduce the permeability and swelling of fibers with organic solvents. Darcy's law is still applicable, but a different value of permeability may apply when fluids which react with the solid saturate the medium.

pressure gradients $\partial P/\partial x$, $\partial P/\partial y$, and $\partial P/\partial z$ are those in the x, y, and z directions at the point in question.

Restrictions on Use of Darcy's Law. INERTIAL EFFECTS. The use of Darcy's law is restricted to cases in which the flow is laminar or streamlined. In laminar flow, the individual fluid particles in a pore flow along paths roughly parallel to the walls of the pore. The laminar-flow region is at low rates of flow where inertial effects are negligible at the turns and bends of the flow channels. However, as the rate of flow increases, inertial effects eventually become important. At sharp corners of the porous solid and at points where the direction of flow changes, eddies are set up, disrupting the smooth streamlines. At still higher rates of flow, turbulence ensues throughout the flow channels and inertial forces rather than viscous forces dominate the flow behavior.

A good rule of thumb for determining the rate above which laminar flow no longer prevails in a porous medium is the rate yielding a Reynolds number greater than 1. The Reynolds number in a porous medium is defined by

$$\mathbf{R} = \frac{dV\rho}{\mu} \qquad (16.17)$$

if d is the effective particle diameter.

The relation between flow rate and pressure drop in the region in which inertial effects become important may be deduced from Fig. 16.9. The figure is a plot by Tek[12] of the Fanning friction factor vs. Reynolds number from data of Fancher et al.[13] on a number of sandstone samples. The Fanning friction factor is defined by

$$f = \frac{-\Delta P}{\rho}\,\frac{d}{2LV^2} \qquad (16.18)$$

Tek has developed an equation which is applicable to both the laminar-flow region and to at least a limited range into the region in which inertial effects become important. This equation is

$$f = \frac{d^2}{2k\mathbf{R}}\left(1 + \frac{l_f\mathbf{R}}{\phi}\right) \qquad (16.19)$$

in which l_f is a lithology factor. Equations (16.18) and (16.19) may be combined to form

$$-\frac{\Delta P}{L} = \frac{\mu V}{k} + \frac{l_f\,d\rho V^2}{\phi k} \qquad (16.20)$$

At low rates, the term involving V^2 in Eq. (16.20) is negligible, and the usual Darcy equation results. As can be noted in Fig. 16.9, the friction factor f is proportional to $1/\mathbf{R}$ for values of Reynolds numbers less than 1. In other words, Darcy's law applies for values of $\mathbf{R}$ less than 1. For Reynolds numbers greater than 1, the term in Eq. (16.20) involving V^2 becomes important. As can be noted in Fig. 16.9, Darcy's law no longer applies for most of the samples for $\mathbf{R}$ greater than 1.

KLINKENBERG EFFECT. Another restriction on the use of Darcy's law applies to flow of gases at low pressures. When the mean free path of the gas (the average distance traveled by gas molecules between collisions) becomes comparable with the radii of the pore spaces, the gas molecules no longer move in streamlines but "slip" past one another. This type of flow is called Knudsen flow when it occurs in capillaries and is commonly termed the Klinkenberg effect when it occurs in other porous media.[14] The slippage of gas results in higher flow rates than those predicted by Darcy's law. For a given gas and a given porous medium, the relation between the true permeability and that calculated from Darcy's law is given by

$$k = \frac{k_g}{1 + b/P_m} \qquad (16.21)$$

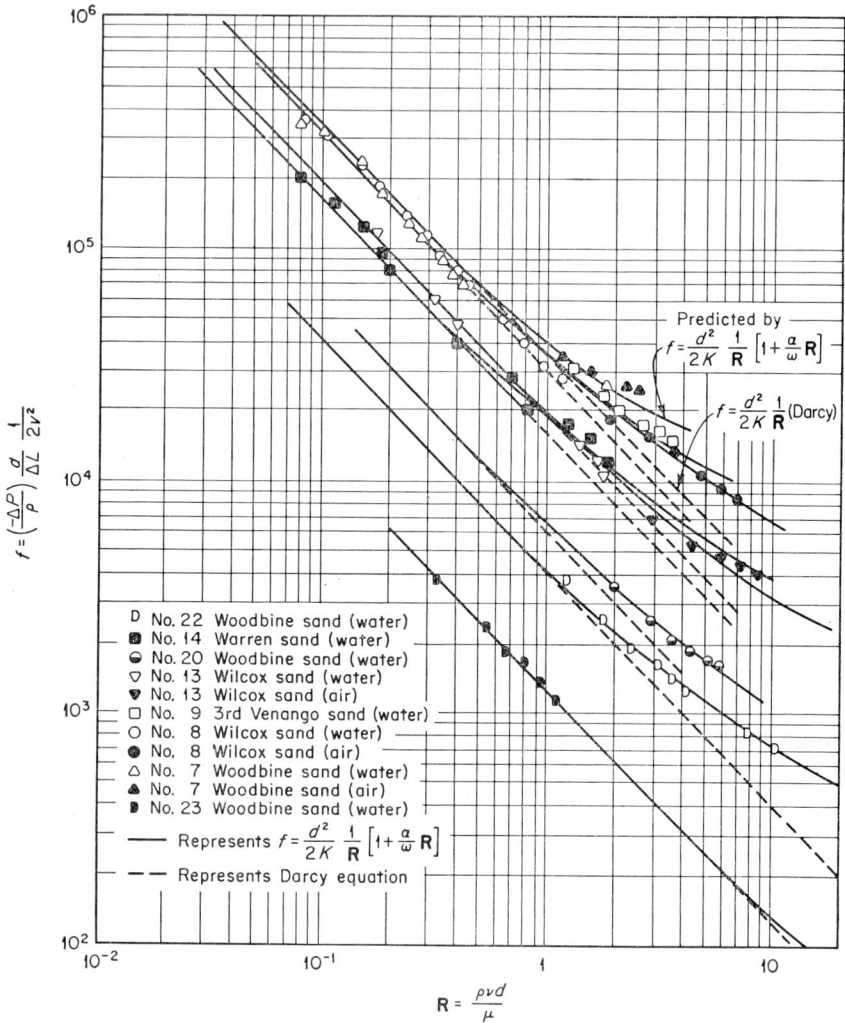

$$f = \left(\frac{-\Delta P}{P}\right) \frac{d}{\Delta L} \frac{1}{2v^2}$$

Predicted by

$$f = \frac{d^2}{2K} \frac{1}{R}\left[1 + \frac{a}{\omega} R\right]$$

$$f = \frac{d^2}{2K} \frac{1}{R} \text{(Darcy)}$$

D No. 22 Woodbine sand (water)
▣ No. 14 Warren sand (water)
◓ No. 20 Woodbine sand (water)
▽ No. 13 Wilcox sand (water)
▼ No. 13 Wilcox sand (air)
□ No. 9   3rd Venango sand (water)
○ No. 8   Wilcox sand (water)
◐ No. 8   Wilcox sand (air)
△ No. 7   Woodbine sand (water)
▲ No. 7   Woodbine sand (air)
◗ No. 23 Woodbine sand (water)

——— Represents $f = \frac{d^2}{2K} \frac{1}{R}\left[1 + \frac{a}{\omega} R\right]$

– – – Represents Darcy equation

$$R = \frac{\rho v d}{\mu}$$

FIG. 16.9. Comparison of experimental data with predictions made with Darcy and generalized Darcy equations. (*Ref.* 12.)

in which k = true permeability
           k_g = permeability calculated from Darcy's law
           b = a constant depending on both the nature of gas and on medium
           P_m = mean absolute pressure of gas

The constant b increases as the permeability of the medium (and the average radius of the pores) decreases.   Also b is greater for gases like hydrogen than for nitrogen at a given pressure and temperature because the mean free path of hydrogen is greater than that of nitrogen.

Usually, permeabilities to gas are measured at several mean pressures. A plot of k_g versus $1/P_m$ should result in a straight line with a slope of bk and an intercept at $1/P_m = 0$ of k. A typical plot of k_g versus $1/P_m$ is shown in Fig. 16.10. Note that the intercept at $1/P_m = 0$ occurs at the permeability corresponding to that measured with oil. Generally, the Klinkenberg effect is negligible at gas pressures over 100 psi and for most conditions of interest in media having permeabilities greater than 1 darcy.

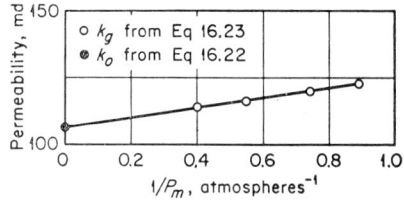

FIG. 16.10. Typical Klinkenberg plot.

16.5. Steady-state Flow

Steady-state flow occurs when the flow rate and pressure at each point in the medium are constant with time. In steady-state flow, there is no net accumulation of mass with time in any volume element of the system. The mass rate of flow of fluid into any volume element is equal to the mass rate of flow of fluid out. Many laboratory experiments are performed under steady-state conditions in packed columns. The flow through such columns is linear or one-dimensional, so linear, steady-state flow is discussed first in the following article. Then radial, steady-state flow, which is also one-dimensional, is discussed in Art. 16.7. Finally, steady-state flow in more than one dimension is discussed and a number of solutions of practical flow problems are presented. In all cases, isothermal conditions are assumed.

16.6. Steady-state Linear Flow

Incompressible Fluid. In steady-state, isothermal flow of a single, incompressible fluid in a linear system, not only is the mass flow rate in equal to the mass flow rate out, but the volumetric flow rate is also constant. The differential equation which describes linear flow of a fluid is Eq. (16.13):

$$q = -\frac{kA}{\mu}\left(\frac{dP}{dL} + \rho g \sin \alpha\right)$$

By using the material-balance concept that the volumetric flow rate is constant and after assuming that the medium has a constant permeability, it is easy to separate the variables dP and dL and integrate. The solution is

$$q = \frac{kA}{\mu}\left(\frac{P_1 - P_2}{L} - \rho g \sin \alpha\right) \tag{16.22}$$

in which P_1 = pressure at inlet
P_2 = pressure at outlet
L = length of system

Example 1. The problem is to find the flow rate of an aqueous solution through a vertical, packed tower saturated with the solution. The tower is 10 ft high, has a cross-section area of 20 ft², and has a permeability of 5 darcys. The solution has a viscosity of 1.1 centipoises and a density of 65 lb/ft³. The fluid is injected into the top of the tower, and a pressure-gauge level with the top of the tower reads 10 psig, and the one level with the bottom reads 5 psig.

Using Eq. (16.22),

$$q = \frac{kA}{\mu}\left(\frac{P_2 - P_1}{L} - \rho g \sin \alpha\right)$$

$$= \frac{\overset{\text{(ft⁴)(centipoises)}}{\overline{\text{(lb)(days)(darcys)}}} \overset{\text{darcys}}{(0.044)} \quad \overset{\text{ft²}}{(5)} \quad \overset{\text{in.²/ft²}}{(20)} \frac{\overset{\text{psi}}{144} (10-5)}{10 \;\text{ft}}}{\underset{\text{centipoises}}{1.1}}$$

$$- \frac{\overset{\text{lb/ft³}}{(65.0)} \overset{\text{ft/sec²}}{(32.2)}(-1.0)}{\underset{\substack{\text{(lb}_m\text{)(ft)} \\ \text{(lb}_f\text{)(sec²)}}}{32.2}}$$

$$= 548 \text{ ft}^3/\text{day}$$

[Note that α is negative when flow is downward; so sine $(-90°) = -1.0$.]

Compressible Fluid. The differential equation for linear flow of a single fluid, Eq. (16.13), also applies to flow of a compressible fluid such as a perfect gas. The material-balance requirement for steady-state flow is that the mass of gas in equals the mass of gas out. For a perfect gas for isothermal conditions, Boyle's law may be applied to relate the volumetric flow rate at any pressure to the constant-mass flow rate.

$$Pq = \text{const}$$

By substitution of $Pq = \text{const}$ into Eq. (16.13) and by assuming that flow is horizontal, that the medium is homogeneous, and that the viscosity of the gas is constant, the differential equation can be integrated to give

$$q_{g2} = \frac{kA(P_1{}^2 - P_1{}^2)}{2\mu_g L P_2} \tag{16.23}$$

in which subscripts 1 and 2 refer to the inlet and outlet ends of the column, respectively. It may also be shown that for flow of a nonideal gas at high pressure, if the pressure drop through the medium is sufficiently small so that the Z factor (supercompressibility of the gas) and viscosity can be considered constant and if the flow rate is measured at atmospheric pressure where $Z = 1.0$, then

$$q_{g\,1\,\text{atm}} = \frac{kA(P_1{}^2 - P_1{}^2)}{2\mu_g Z L P_{\text{atmospheric}}} \tag{16.24}$$

in which the Z factor and the viscosity are those at the high pressure.

Example 2. The problem is to find the permeability of a sand-packed tower. The tower is 30 ft long and has a cross-section area of 40 ft². Nitrogen gas having a viscosity of 0.018 centipoise is used to measure the permeability. A flow rate of 60 ft³/min is measured at the downstream end. The pressure gauges read 20 psig and 0 psig at the upstream and downstream ends of the column, respectively.

Equation (16.23) applies:

$$k = \frac{2q_g \mu_g L P_2}{A(P_1{}^2 - P_2{}^2)}$$

$$= \frac{(2)(60 \times 60 \times 24)(0.018)(30)(14.7)}{(0.044)(40)(144)[(20 + 14.7)^2 - (0 + 14.7)^2]}$$

$$= 5.5 \text{ darcys}$$

16.7. Steady-state Radial Flow

In the vicinity of a well completely penetrating a sand with uniform permeability and thickness, the flow of fluids is radial. As with flow in linear systems, Darcy's law [Eq. (16.12)] for flow of a single fluid combined with material-balance considerations yields equations for flow in radial systems.

Radial, Horizontal Flow of Incompressible Fluid. The equation for steady-state flow of an incompressible fluid in the horizontal plane is

$$q = \frac{2\pi k H(P_1 - P_w)}{\mu \ln (r/r_w)} \tag{16.25}$$

in which subscripts 1 and w refer to some point 1 in the system and the well bore, respectively, and ln denotes the natural logarithm.

Radial, Horizontal Flow of a Gas. For a perfect gas, the steady-state-flow equation is

$$q = \frac{\pi k H(P^2 - P_w{}^2)}{P_w \mu \ln (r/r_w)} \tag{16.26}$$

For a nonideal gas at high pressure, when the pressure drop is so small that the viscosity and Z factor can be assumed constant.

$$q_{1\ atm} = \frac{\pi k H (P^2 - P_w{}^2)}{P_{atmospheric}\ \mu Z \ln (r/r_w)} \qquad (16.27)$$

in which μ and Z are the viscosities and supercompressibilities at the high pressure.

16.8. Steady-state Flow in Systems of Complex-geometry

Theory. The equations for flow of a single fluid in a three-dimensional porous medium can be derived from two simple concepts, Darcy's law and the law of conservation of mass. Consider the small volume element shown in Fig. 16.11, which is dx long, dy wide, and dz thick, where z is positive vertically upward. Conservation of

Fig. 16.11. Volume element.

mass requires that the mass flowing into the volume element minus the mass flowing out of the element in a given time interval is equal to the accumulation. By taking a material balance on the element, the following equation, commonly called the continuity equation, can be derived:

$$\frac{\partial(\rho v_x)}{\partial x} + \frac{\partial(\rho v_y)}{\partial y} + \frac{\partial(\rho v_z)}{\partial z} = -\phi \frac{\partial \rho}{\partial t} \qquad (16.28)$$

For *steady-state* flow, there is no accumulation of mass (or change in density of fluid) in the volume element with time; so $\partial \rho / \partial t = 0$. Thus for steady-state flow, the continuity equation becomes

$$\frac{\partial(\rho v_x)}{\partial x} + \frac{\partial(\rho v_y)}{\partial y} + \frac{\partial(\rho v_z)}{\partial z} = 0 \qquad (16.29)$$

Substitution of the Darcy equations [Eqs. (16.14) to (16.16)] for v_x, v_y, and v_z into Eq. (16.29) results in the differential equation for steady-state flow of a single fluid in three dimensions.

$$\frac{\partial \left(\dfrac{\rho k}{\mu} \dfrac{\partial P}{dx} \right)}{\partial x} + \frac{\partial \left(\dfrac{\rho k}{\mu} \dfrac{\partial P}{\partial y} \right)}{\partial y} + \frac{\partial \left(\dfrac{\rho k}{\mu} \left[\dfrac{\partial P}{\partial z} + \rho g \right] \right)}{\partial z} = 0 \qquad (16.30)$$

For isothermal, steady-state flow of an incompressible fluid in a homogeneous sand, i.e. when ρ, k, and μ are constants, Eq. (16.30) reduces to

$$\frac{\partial^2 P}{\partial x^2} + \frac{\partial^2 P}{\partial y^2} + \frac{\partial^2 P}{\partial z^2} = 0 \qquad (16.31)$$

This is the well-known Laplace equation, which applies to many physical problems. For example, the Laplace equation applies to the steady-state flow of heat in a medium of constant thermal conductivity and to the steady-state flow of an ideal fluid.

If the flow is limited to two dimensions in the horizontal plane, the flow of a gas or a slightly compressible liquid also obeys the Laplace equation. For steady flow of a gas in the horizontal plane, substitution of $\rho = (M.Wt)P/ZRT$ into Eq. (16.30) results in

$$\frac{\partial \left(\dfrac{k[M.Wt]}{2\mu ZRT} \dfrac{\partial P^2}{\partial x} \right)}{\partial x} + \frac{\partial \left(\dfrac{k[M.Wt]}{2\mu ZRT} \dfrac{\partial P^2}{\partial y} \right)}{\partial y} = 0 \qquad (16.32)$$

which reduces to

$$\frac{\partial^2 P^2}{\partial x^2} + \frac{\partial^2 P^2}{\partial y^2} = 0$$

for isothermal flow of a gas of constant viscosity and supercompressibility factor in a medium of constant permeability. (By defining a new variable, the Laplace equation can also be obtained when μ and Z are not constant.) Similarly, for a slightly compressi-

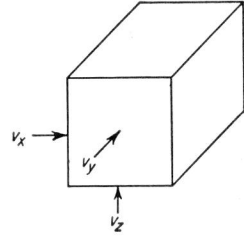

ble liquid, use of $\rho = \rho_i e^{c(P - P_i)}$, in which c is the compressibility, results in a flow equation of the form

$$\frac{\partial \left(\dfrac{k}{\mu c} \dfrac{\partial \rho}{\partial x} \right)}{\partial x} + \frac{\partial \left(\dfrac{k}{\mu c} \dfrac{\partial \rho}{\partial y} \right)}{\partial y} = 0 \qquad (16.33)$$

Equation (16.33) reduces to the form of the Laplace equation

$$\frac{\partial^2 \rho}{\partial x^2} + \frac{\partial^2 \rho}{\partial y^2} = 0 \qquad (16.34)$$

for isothermal flow of a liquid of constant viscosity and compressibility factor c in a homogeneous medium.

In solving Eqs. (16.30) to (16.33), frequent use has been made of the analogy between steady-state flow of an incompressible fluid in three dimensions or steady-state flow of a gas or compressible liquid in two dimensions and the steady-state flow of electric current.[15,16]   The equation for steady-state flow of electric current is

$$\frac{\partial \left(\sigma \dfrac{\partial V}{\partial x} \right)}{\partial x} + \frac{\partial \left(\sigma \dfrac{\partial V}{\partial y} \right)}{\partial y} + \frac{\partial \left(\sigma \dfrac{\partial V}{\partial z} \right)}{\partial z} = 0 \qquad (16.35)$$

and $i_x = -\sigma \, \partial V / \partial x$, etc., in which i_x is the current flux, σ is the electrical conductivity, and V is the voltage.

Analogue devices can be set up, such as potentiometric models filled with conductive liquids, to represent the porous medium and electrodes to represent fluid injection and production wells.   The scaling requirements for using a potentiometric model to simulate fluid flow are as follows:

1. The model and prototype are geometrically similar; that is,

$$\left(\frac{L}{W} \right)_{\text{model}} = \left(\frac{L}{W} \right)_{\text{prototype}} \qquad \text{and} \qquad \left(\frac{L}{H} \right)_{\text{model}} = \left(\frac{L}{H} \right)_{\text{prototype}} \dagger$$

The injection and production current electrodes are located in similar positions to injection and production wells.

2. The boundary conditions in model and prototype are similar; that is, the relative quantities of current injected and produced are the same as the relative quantities of fluid injected and produced from corresponding wells.

3.
$$\left(\frac{i_t L}{\sigma \, dV} \right)_{\text{model}} = \left(\frac{V_t L}{(k/\mu) \, dP} \right)_{\text{prototype}} \qquad (16.36)$$

(from the analogy between Ohm's law and Darcy's law).

Three ratios of model properties to prototype properties may be selected arbitrarily. The fourth ratio is set by Eq. (16.36).   For example:

Ratio of current flow rate to fluid flow rate:

$$\frac{i_{t \text{ model}}}{V_{t \text{ prototype}}} = R_1$$

Length ratio:

$$\frac{L_{\text{model}}}{L_{\text{prototype}}} = R_2$$

---

† Muskat[16] has shown that by adjusting the depth of fluid in a potentiometric model from point to point, account can be taken of variations in both permeability and thickness in the porous medium.   In this case, the depth of electrolyte at any given point in the model is proportional to the product of the thickness and the permeability of the porous medium at a corresponding point in the prototype.

Ratio of electric conductivity to fluid-flow conductivity:

$$\frac{\sigma_{\text{model}}}{k_{\text{prototype}}} = R_3$$

Then the relation between voltage drop in the model and pressure drop in the prototype is obtained from Eq. (16.36):

$$\frac{dV_{\text{model}}}{dP_{\text{prototype}}} = \frac{R_1 R_2}{R_3}$$

Considerable use has also been made of the analogy of the isothermal flow of an incompressible fluid in three dimensions or the flow of gases or slightly compressible liquids in two dimensions in the horizontal plane with the flow of an ideal fluid. In these cases, the theorems and principles of classical hydrodynamics[17,18] can be used to study the flow of a viscous fluid through porous media. Point sources and sinks can be used with appropriate boundary conditions to simulate injection and production wells. The principle of superposition can be used to find the effect of injection and production from several wells on the pressure at any point in the medium. Numerous examples of these applications to viscous-flow problems can be found in the excellent books of Muskat.[15,19] Besides potentiometric models, electric-resistance networks,[20] blotter models,[21] gelatin models,[22] and fluid-mapper (Hele-Shaw) models[23] have been used to solve steady-state-flow problems. In the following paragraphs some example solutions of unusual interest are given. A brief discussion of an example solution using computers and numerical methods is also given.

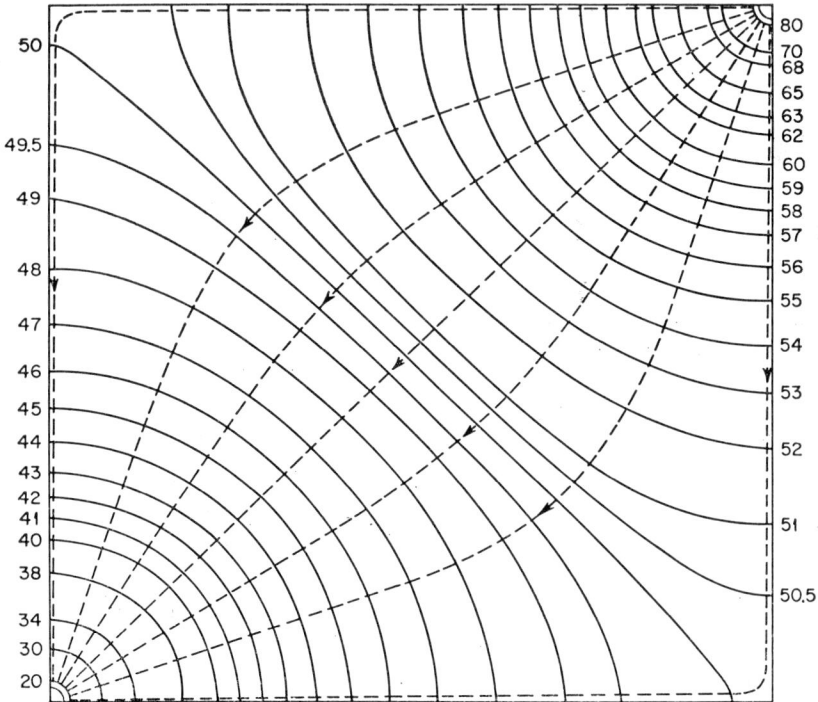

F ig. 16.12. The steady-state homogeneous-fluid equipressure contours and streamlines in a quadrant of a five-spot-network element. Numbers represent percentages of the total pressure drop. (*From Muskat and Wyckoff, Trans. AIME, 1934, in Ref. 19.*)

Steady-state Flow of a Single Fluid in Various Well Patterns. ARRANGEMENTS. The two-dimensional flow of a single fluid in the horizontal plane has been studied by Muskat.[19] Using both potentiometric models and solutions of the equations for the pressure fields, the fluid-flow resistance and fraction of the pattern swept at break-through were determined for several commonly used arrangements.

The pressure field for a five-spot pattern is shown in Fig. 16.12. The steady-state-flow capacity is given by

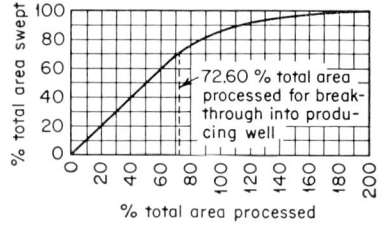

FIG. 16.13. Five-spot flood, per cent total area swept vs. per cent area processed. (*Ref.* 24.)

$$q = \frac{0.044\pi kH144(P_1 - P_2)}{\mu\beta\left(\ln\dfrac{d}{r_w} - 0.6190\right)} \qquad (16.37)$$

in which q = flow rate, ft³/day, measured at surface
k = permeability, darcys
H = thickness, ft
P = pressure, psi
μ = viscosity, centipoises
d = distance between wells, ft
r_w = well-bore radius, ft
β = formation-volume factor, bbl reservoir oil/bbl stock tank oil

The sweep efficiency at break-through for the five-spot is $E = 0.715$.

The solution of Hurst[24] for sweep efficiencies in a five-spot pattern after break-through is shown in Fig. 16.13. Hurst found a sweep efficiency of 100 per cent after injection of two displaceable volumes of fluid.

The pressure field for a staggered-line-drive pattern is shown in Fig. 16.14, and the pressure field for a direct-line-drive pattern is shown[19] in Fig. 16.15. The flow capacity for both staggered- and direct-line-drive patterns for $d/a > 1$ is given by

$$q = \frac{0.0442\pi kH144(P_1 - P_2)}{\mu\beta\left(\dfrac{\pi d}{a} - 2\ln 2\sinh\dfrac{\pi r_w}{a}\right)} \qquad (16.38)$$

The sweep efficiencies at break-through for both staggered- and direct-line-drive patterns is shown in Fig. 16.17 as functions of d/a. The d is the distance between lines of production and injection wells, and a is the distance between adjacent production or injection wells. Note that as d/a increases, the pattern efficiencies at break-through increase.

The pressure field for a seven-spot pattern[19] is shown in Fig. 16.17. The flow capacity is given by

$$q = \frac{(0.044)4\pi kH144(P_1 - P_2)}{\mu\beta\left(3\ln\dfrac{d}{r_w} - 1.7073\right)} \qquad (16.39)$$

The sweep efficiency at break-through is $E = 0.74$.

The above formulas for flow of an incompressible liquid can be adapted to flow of a gas if it is assumed that the viscosity and compressibility factor are constant during flow through the porous medium. In this case $(P_1 - P_2)$ in each equation can be replaced by $(P_1^2 - P_2^2)/2P_2$, in which q is the flow rate of gas measured at pressure P_2. Also, the lines on the pressure-field charts (Figs. 16.12 and 16.14 to 16.16) represent lines of constant $(P_1^2 - P^2)/(P_1^2 - P_2^2)$, in which P_1 is the pressure at the injection well, P_2 is the pressure at the production well, and P is the pressure at the point of interest.

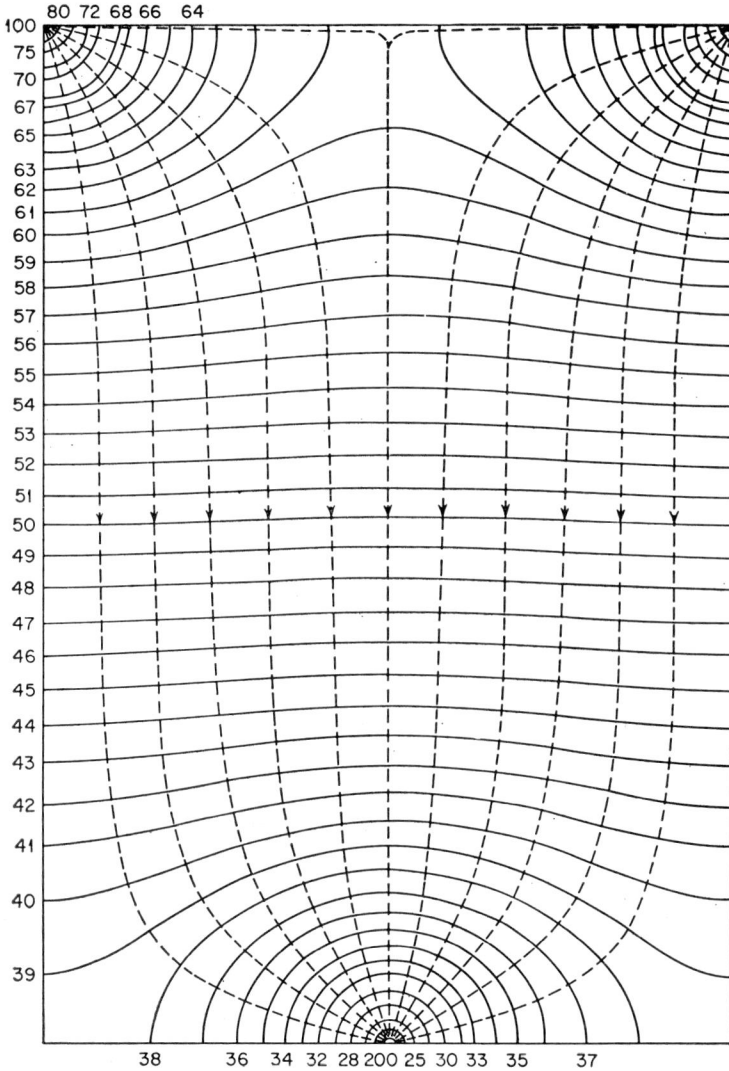

FIG. 16.14. The steady-state homogeneous-fluid equipressure contours and streamlines in a two-well element of a staggered-line-drive network. Numbers represent percentages of the total pressure drop. (*From Muskat and Wyckoff, Trans. AIME, 1934, in Ref. 19.*)

Recently, numerical methods have been applied with the aid of high-speed computers to the problem of sweep efficiencies with various pattern arrangements. One method of using computers to solve the sweep-out pattern for steady-state flow with a unit mobility ratio was described by McCarty and Barfield.[25] The equation

$$\frac{\partial}{\partial X}\left(kH\,\frac{\partial P}{\partial X}\right) + \frac{\partial}{\partial Y}\left(kH\,\frac{\partial P}{\partial Y}\right) = 0 \tag{16.40}$$

represents the two-dimensional, steady-state flow of a single incompressible fluid in a

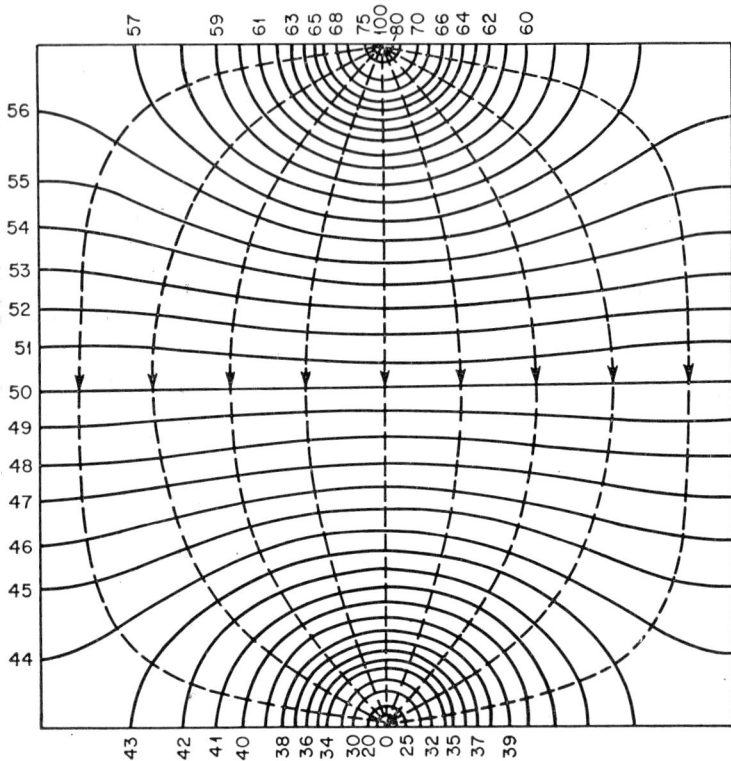

FIG. 16.15. The steady-state homogeneous-fluid equipressure contours and streamlines in a two-well element of a direct-line-drive network. Numbers represent percentages of the total pressure drop. (*From Muskat and Wyckoff, Trans. AIME, 1934, in Ref. 19.*)

porous medium in which the permeability thickness varies from place to place. The detailed description of solving the difference equations with computers described by these authors can be used to solve sweep-out patterns in cycling gas caps and in water floods in which mobility ratios are close to 1. Typical of the patterns calculated by this method are those shown in Fig. 16.18 for various times after injection is commenced in these wells.

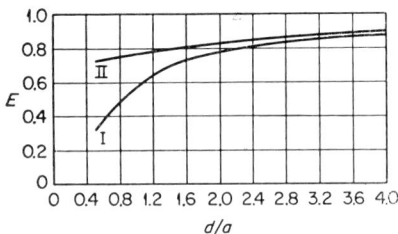

FIG. 16.16. The variation of the calculated steady-state homogeneous-fluid sweep efficiencies E of line-drive networks with $d/a =$ (distance between injection and producing lines)/(well spacing within lines). I, direct-line drive. II, staggered-line drive. (*From Muskat and Wyckoff, Trans. AIME, 1934, in Ref. 19.*)

Effects of Well Completion on Steady-state Flow of a Single Fluid. Several problems associated with completion of a well have been treated by Muskat. Those of interest here are the effects of partially penetrating wells, the effects of producing through perforations in steel liners, and the effects of producing through slotted liners on the productive capacity of a well. Muskat[19] used sinks and sources and the principle of superposition to find the pressure and flow capacities for a number of cases of interest.

The flow capacity of a partially pene-

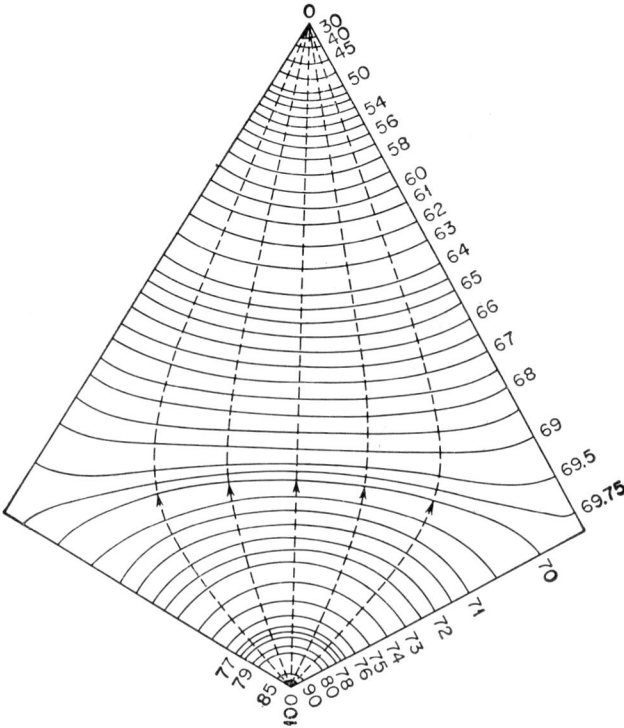

Fig. 16.17. The steady-state homogeneous-fluid equipressure contours and streamlines in a segment of a seven-spot-network element. Numbers represent percentages of the total pressure drop. (*From Muskat and Wyckoff, Trans. AIME*, 1934, *in Ref.* 19.)

trating well divided by the flow capacity of a well which penetrates the entire sand thickness is shown in Fig. 16.19. The results in Fig. 16.19 apply to wells with radii of $\frac{1}{4}$ and $\frac{1}{2}$ ft with a drainage radius of 660 ft. It can be seen that if the formation is thin compared with its drainage radius, the effects of only partially penetrating the formation are less than when the formation is thick compared with its drainage radius. Muskat also treats the case of partially penetrating wells in nonuniform sand.

The flow capacity of wells with perforations is shown in Fig. 16.20 as a function of the perforation density times the perforation radius. Note that when the perforation density times the perforation radius has a value of 1.0, the flow capacity is about 60 per cent of the capacity of an uncased hole with a radius of 3 in. This value would correspond to that in a hole with the commonly used perforation density of 4 shots/ft where the perforations had radii of $\frac{1}{4}$ in. The effect of perforation density on the flow capacity of wells in formations having lower vertical permeability than horizontal permeability is shown in Fig. 16.21.

An example of the utility of the above data is shown in the following problem.

Example 3. Given: A well is producing water from a formation 40 ft thick. The permeability of the sand is 1.5 darcys. The viscosity of the water is 0.85 centipoise at formation temperature. The well is 6 in. in diameter, and it penetrates the upper half of the formation. It produces through perforations $\frac{1}{4}$ in. in radius spaced 4 shots/ft. Assuming that the well is producing at steady-state conditions from a drainage radius of 660 ft, what is the rate of water production for a pressure drawdown of 90 psi?

Solution. The steady-state, radial-flow rate in a fully penetrating open-hole completion is given by Eq. (16.25).

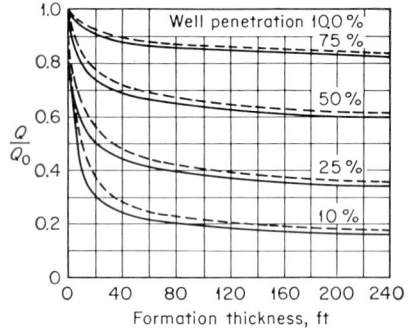

FIG. 16.19. The calculated variation of the relative steady-state homogeneous-fluid production capacities of partially penetrating wells with the formation thickness. $Q/Q_0 =$ (production capacity of partially penetrating well)/(production capacity of completely penetrating well). For solid curves, well radius $= 1/4$ ft. For dashed curves, well radius $= 1/2$ ft. External-boundary radius $= 660$ ft in all cases. (Ref. 19.)

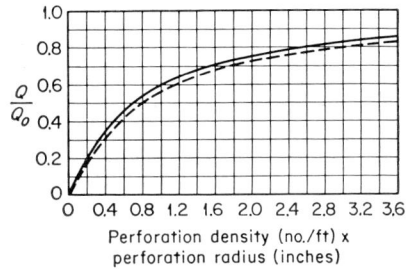

FIG. 16.20. The calculated effect of casing perforations on the steady-state homogeneous-fluid well productivity. $Q/Q_0 =$ (production capacity of cased and perforated well)/(production capacity of completely penetrating uncased well). For solid curve, casing radius $= 3$ in. For dashed curve, casing radius $= 6$ in. (Ref. 19.)

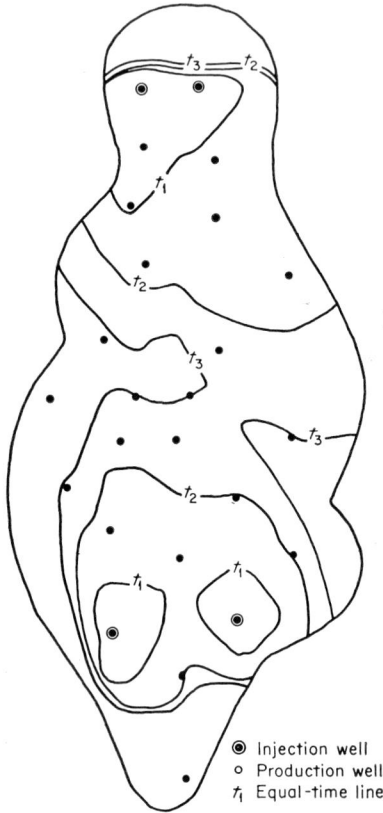

FIG. 16.18. Typical flood pattern resulting from field study. (Ref. 25.)

$$q = \frac{(0.044)2\pi kH144(P_1 - P_2)}{\mu \ln (r_a/r_w)}$$

$$= \frac{(0.044)(2\pi)(1.5)(40)(144)(90)}{(0.85)[\ln (660/0.25)]}$$

$$= 32{,}000 \text{ ft}^3/\text{day, or } 5{,}700 \text{ bbl/day}$$

From Fig. 16.19, the flow capacity of a well which penetrates 50 per cent of a 40-ft sand is 69 per cent that of a fully penetrating well. From Fig. 16.20 the flow capacity of a well with 4 shots/ft with perforation radii of $1/4$ in. is 60 per cent that of an open-hole completion.

The flow capacity of the well is then

$$q = (5700)(0.69)(0.60)$$
$$= 2360 \text{ bbl/day}$$

16.9. Unsteady-state-flow Theory

Many practical problems involve the transient or unsteady-state flow of a single fluid through a porous medium. It is easy to see how the initiation of flow in a gas well causes transient conditions in the reservoir. The first gas that flows into the well comes from lowering of the pressure and expansion of the gas adjacent to the well. As time goes by, the region in which the pressure is decreasing grows and gas flows into the well from farther and farther away, until the lateral boundaries or pressure fields from wells interfere. It can also be seen how a similar phenomenon occurs for a compressible liquid such as crude oil containing dissolved gas. Until the pressure is lowered below the saturation pressure of the oil, the initial flow of oil from a well can be described as transient flow of a single fluid from the sand. It is less obvious that unsteady-state-flow conditions are of im-

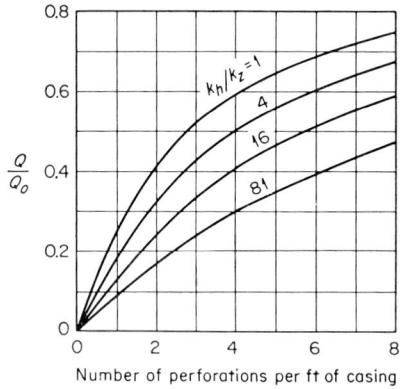

Number of perforations per ft of casing

FIG. 16.21. The calculated effect of casing perforations on the steady-state homogeneous-fluid well productivity, as a function of the perforation density, in anisotropic formations. Q/Q_0 = (production capacity of cased and perforated well)/(production capacity of completely penetrating uncased well). k_h/k_z = (horizontal permeability)/(vertical permeability); well radius = 3 in.; perforation radius = 1/4 in. (*From Trans. AIME*, 1943, *in Ref.* 19.)

portance in flow of water through underground sands. Water is only slightly compressible, the compressibility being of the order of 3×10^{-6} volume change per unit volume per pound per square inch. Nonetheless, expansion of water and the unsteady-flow process are responsible for water influx into oil sands (in the giant east Texas field, for example). In many cases, influx of water into regions drained by irrigation wells is caused by expansion and unsteady-state flow of water and not by artesian, steady-state flow of water.

As in steady-state flow, the equations for unsteady-state flow of a single compressible fluid can be derived from the law of conservation of mass and Darcy's law. The continuity equation for unsteady-state flow has been previously given:

$$\frac{\partial(\rho v_x)}{\partial x} + \frac{\partial(\rho v_y)}{\partial y} + \frac{\partial(\rho v_z)}{\partial z} = -\phi \frac{\partial \rho}{\partial t} \tag{16.28}$$

Substitution of the Darcy Eqs. (16.14) to (16.16) into Eq. (16.28) for v_x, v_y, and v_z results in the desired relation

$$\frac{\partial\left(\dfrac{\rho k}{\mu}\dfrac{\partial P}{\partial x}\right)}{\partial x} + \frac{\partial\left(\dfrac{\rho k}{\mu}\dfrac{\partial P}{\partial y}\right)}{\partial y} + \frac{\partial\left(\dfrac{\rho k}{\mu}\left[\dfrac{\partial P}{\partial z}+\rho g\right]\right)}{\partial z} = +\phi \frac{\partial \rho}{\partial t} \tag{16.41}$$

If flow is limited to two dimensions in the horizontal plane, the flow of a *slightly compressible liquid* whose density obeys the relation $\rho = \rho_i e^{c(P-P_i)}$ is described by

$$\frac{\partial\left(\dfrac{k}{\mu c}\dfrac{\partial \rho}{\partial x}\right)}{\partial x} + \frac{\partial\left(\dfrac{k}{\mu c}\dfrac{\partial \rho}{\partial y}\right)}{\partial y} = \phi \frac{\partial \rho}{\partial t} \tag{16.42}$$

If the medium is homogeneous and the viscosity and compressibility are assumed constant, Eq. (16.42) reduces to

$$\frac{\partial^2 \rho}{\partial x^2} + \frac{\partial^2 \rho}{\partial y^2} = \frac{\phi \mu c}{k} \frac{\partial \rho}{\partial t} \tag{16.43}$$

which in return can be shown to give

$$\frac{\partial^2 P}{\partial x^2} + \frac{\partial^2 P}{\partial y^2} = \frac{\phi \mu c}{k} \frac{\partial P}{\partial t} \tag{16.44}$$

when

$$c \left(\frac{\partial P}{\partial x}\right)^2 \ll \frac{\partial^2 P}{\partial x^2}$$

Flow of a gas in the horizontal plane is given by

$$\frac{\partial \left(\dfrac{k[\text{M.Wt}]}{2\mu Z RT} \dfrac{\partial P^2}{\partial x}\right)}{\partial x} + \frac{\partial \left(\dfrac{k[\text{M.Wt}]}{2\mu Z RT} \dfrac{\partial P^2}{\partial y}\right)}{\partial y} = \frac{\phi (\text{M.Wt})}{Z RT} \frac{\partial P}{\partial t} \tag{16.45}$$

which for isothermal flow in the horizontal plane in a homogeneous medium, when μ, Z, and T can be assumed constant, reduces to

$$\frac{\partial^2 P^2}{\partial x^2} + \frac{\partial^2 P^2}{\partial y^2} = \frac{\phi \mu}{kP} \frac{\partial P^2}{\partial t} \tag{16.46}$$

Solutions of Eqs. (16.41) to (16.46), given the initial and boundary conditions of the particular problem, usually require the use of high-speed computers or electrical-analogue devices. However, analytic solutions have been obtained for linear and radial flow of a slightly compressible liquid. These analytic solutions are limited to cases in which the medium is homogeneous and the fluid can be assumed to have a constant viscosity and compressibility. Fortunately, these assumptions apply in many practical problems such as transient flow of oil in a sand containing no free gas into a well suddenly placed on production or suddenly shut in, or flow of water in a large aquifer surrounding a producing oil reservoir. These solutions are presented below. Generalized computer solutions for the linear and radial flow of gas are also given. Finally, the use of electric analogues in solving two-dimensional-flow problems is discussed. Before discussing the detailed solutions, some of the principles of super-position which are useful in extending the available solutions to other cases will be discussed.

Principles of Superposition. Most of the available solutions for unsteady flow of a single fluid treat only two cases. These are for constant production rate or constant terminal pressure. Also, the solutions treat the production from only one well, or reservoir, for radial systems. Many practical problems of interest involve flow from a number of wells or flow at varying rates or terminal pressures. The following principles of superposition are useful in treating these practical problems.

1. If there are a number of wells in a reservoir of infinite extent, the pressure change at some arbitrary point caused by production from or injection into a number of wells is the sum of the pressure changes which would occur with production from or injection into each well separately.† If r_j is the distance from the point of interest to the jth well, then

$$P_i - P = \sum_{j=1}^{j=n} (P_i - P)_j \tag{16.47}$$

in which P_i is the initial, shut-in pressure, and $(P_i - P)_j$ is the pressure drawdown at the point of interest caused by injection or production in the jth well.

---

† This is strictly true only if the wells are point sources and sinks when finite pressure changes at the well caused by production or injection in other wells are negligible compared with the infinite pressure gradients caused by injection or production from the point in question. However, as a practical matter, the superposition principles also apply to actual wells of finite radius.

2. The production of fluid from a well producing with a varying terminal pressure is the sum of the production which would occur with a succession of constant-terminal-pressure drops for the appropriate time intervals. If the pressure change at the well is approximated by $P = P_i$ for $t = 0$, $P = P_1$ for $t = 0$ to t_1, $P = P_2$ for $t = t_1$ to t_2, $P = P_n$ for $t = t_{n-1}$ to t_n, and if the cumulative production for a constant terminal pressure is defined as

$$Q = Q_{\Delta P, t}$$

in which $Q_{\Delta P, t}$ is the cumulative production given as a function of the pressure change from the preceding pressure level and the time from when that pressure change decreased to the time of interest, then the total production is

$$Q_T = Q_{(P_1 - P_i, t_n)} + Q_{(P_2 - P_1, t_n - t_1)} + \cdots + Q_{(P_n - P_{n-1}, t_n - t_{n-1})} \tag{16.48}$$

3. The production of fluid from a well producing with a varying rate is the sum of the production which would occur with a succession of constant-rate changes for the appropriate time intervals. If the production rate from the well is approximated by $q = q_i$ for $t = 0$, $q = q_1$ for the interval $t = 0$ to t_1, $q = q_2$ for the interval $t = t_1$ to t_2, and $q = q_n$ for the interval $t = t_{n-1}$ to t_h, and if the pressure drop for a constant production rate is defined as

$$\Delta P = \Delta P_{\Delta q, t}$$

in which $\Delta P_{\Delta q, t}$ is the pressure drop given as function of the rate change and time from when that change occurred to the present time of interest, then the total pressure change is

$$\Delta P_T = \Delta P_{(q_1 - q_i, t_n)} + \Delta P_{(q_2 - q_1, t_n - t_1)} + \cdots + \Delta P_{(q_n - q_{n-1}, t_n - t_{n-1})} \tag{16.49}$$

16.10. Linear, Unsteady-state Flow

Flow of a Slightly Compressible Liquid. One unsteady-state-flow problem for which analytic solutions have been found is that of linear flow of a slightly compressible liquid at rest. The pressure everywhere in the medium is the initial pressure P_i. Imagine that the medium is an infinitely long right cylinder, or any solid whose lateral shape perpendicular to its main axis is constant. The fluid is withdrawn, or injected, uniformly from or into one face. In the first instant, only the pressure at the face is affected, but as time progresses, the pressure in more and more of the medium is affected.

There are two general cases of interest. In one problem fluid is either withdrawn or injected at a constant rate. In the other problem, the pressure at the production face is held constant at some value different from the initial pressure. These solutions may be found in "Handbook of Natural Gas Engineering," by Katz et al.,[26] who adapted solutions of unsteady flow of heat by Churchill[27] to those for fluid flow.

The equations for one-dimensional, isothermal flow of a slightly compressible fluid having constant viscosity and compressibility in a homogeneous medium of constant permeability are

$$\frac{\partial^2 \rho}{\partial x^2} = \frac{\phi \mu \varsigma}{k} \frac{\partial \rho}{\partial t} \tag{16.50}$$

which can be approximated by

$$\frac{\partial^2 P}{\partial x^2} = \frac{\phi \mu c}{k} \frac{\partial P}{\partial t} \tag{16.51}$$

when

$$c \left(\frac{\partial P}{\partial x} \right)^2 \ll \frac{\partial^2 P}{\partial x^2}$$

The first case of interest is that for *constant production rate* from the outflow face. The following initial and boundary conditions apply:

1. At time zero, the pressure at each point equals P_i, or $P = P_i$ for all values of x at $t = 0$.

2. For times greater than zero, the production from the face at $x = 0$ is maintained at a constant rate, or $q = q_c$ at $x = 0$ for $t > 0$.

3. Fluid is produced only from the face at $x = 0$, flow is linear, and the system is of infinite length. The solution given by Katz et al.[20] is

$$\frac{P_{i(x,t)} - Pi}{P_i} = -mP_t \tag{16.52}$$

in which m is the dimensionless linear-flow rate defined by $m = 0.1585\mu q/HkP_i$, with m positive for production and negative for injection, and

$$P_t = \frac{2t_d{}^{1/2}}{\pi^{1/2}e^{t_d/4}} - \text{erfc}\,\frac{1}{2t_d{}^{1/2}} \tag{16.53}$$

in which the dimensionless time is given by

$$t_d = \frac{6.34kt}{\mu c\phi x^2}$$

A special form of Eqs. (16.52) and (16.53) is required for $x = 0$. This relation is

$$P_{(0,t)} - P_i = \frac{2Q}{A}\left(\frac{\mu t}{6.34k\phi c\pi}\right)^{1/2} \tag{16.54}$$

The units in the above equations are:

P = pressure, psi
k = permeability, darcys
μ = viscosity, centipoises
q = flow rate, ft³/day
H = thickness of medium, ft
t = time, days
c = compressibility, vol/(vol)(psi)
x = position along length, ft
A = cross-section area

The second case of interest in linear flow of a slightly compressible liquid is that for *constant pressure* at the outflow face. The following initial and boundary conditions apply.

1. $P = P_i$ for all x at $t = 0$.
2. $P = P_1$ at $x = 0$ for $t > 0$.
3. Fluid is produced or injected only at $x = 0$, flow is linear, and the system is of infinite length.

The solution as derived by Churchill and adapted by Katz et al. to fluid flow is

$$\frac{P_{(x,t)} - P_i}{P_1 - P_i} = \text{erfc}\,\frac{1}{2t_d{}^{1/2}} \tag{16.55}$$

in which t_d is the dimensionless time as given above.

Linear, Unsteady Flow of Gas. The equation for linear, unsteady-state flow of gas in the horizontal plane is

$$\frac{\partial\left(\dfrac{k[\text{M.Wt}]}{2\mu ZRT}\dfrac{\partial P^2}{\partial x}\right)}{\partial x} = \frac{\phi(\text{M.Wt})}{ZRT}\frac{\partial P}{\partial t} \tag{16.56}$$

which reduces to

$$\frac{\partial^2 P^2}{\partial x^2} = \frac{\mu\phi}{kP}\frac{\partial P^2}{\partial t} \tag{16.57}$$

when the viscosity and compressibility factor can be assumed to be constant and the medium is homogeneous.

No analytical solutions are known to exist, even for the simpler Eq. (16.57). Solu-

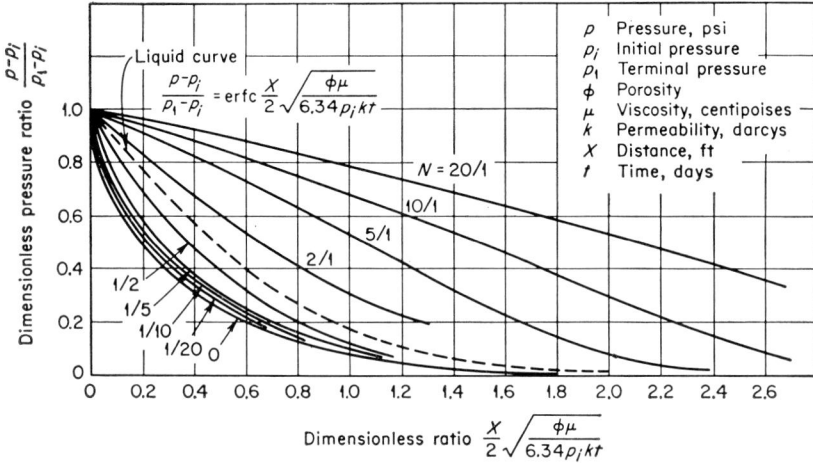

p	Pressure, psi
p_i	Initial pressure
p_1	Terminal pressure
ϕ	Porosity
μ	Viscosity, centipoises
k	Permeability, darcys
X	Distance, ft
t	Time, days

$$\frac{p-p_i}{p_1-p_i} = \text{erfc}\,\frac{X}{2}\sqrt{\frac{\phi\mu}{6.34\,p_i kt}}$$

Dimensionless ratio $\dfrac{X}{2}\sqrt{\dfrac{\phi\mu}{6.34\,p_i kt}}$

FIG. 16.22. Pressure distribution in a linear gas-flow system of infinite length. (*Ref.* 28.)

tions of difference equations based on Eq. (16.57) have been made by Aronofsky and Jenkins[28] using high-speed digital computers. Shown in Fig. 16.22 are the results of calculations for linear flow of gas in a medium of infinite length for the case where the medium was everywhere at P_i at $t = 0$, and then the pressure at the outflow face was suddenly lowered to a constant P_1. The data in Fig. 16.22 are plotted as dimensionless pressures $(P - P_i)/(P_1 - P_i)$, as functions of the dimensionless ratio $\dfrac{x}{2}\left(\dfrac{\phi\mu}{6.34kP_it}\right)^{1/2}$ in the units indicated. Increasing values of the latter dimensionless ratio can be thought of as increasing values of x, the distance from the outflow face, for a given time. The various curves in Fig. 16.22 are for various values of N, in which $N = P_i/P_1$, the ratio of the initial pressure to the pressure maintained at the outflow face. Also, shown as a dashed line is the solution of Eq. (16.55) for flow of slightly compressible liquids.

16.11. Radial, Unsteady-state Flow

Radial Flow of a Slightly Compressible Liquid. The equation for radial flow of a compressible liquid in the horizontal plane is

$$\frac{\partial\left(\dfrac{kr}{\mu c}\dfrac{\partial P}{\partial r}\right)}{\partial r} = \phi r\,\frac{\partial\rho}{\partial t} \tag{16.58}$$

This can be reduced to

$$\frac{\partial^2 P}{\partial r^2} + \frac{1}{r}\frac{\partial P}{\partial r} = \frac{\phi\mu c}{k}\frac{\partial P}{\partial t} \tag{16.59}$$

when

$$c\left(\frac{\partial P}{\partial r}\right)^2 \ll \frac{\partial^2 P}{\partial r^2}$$

for slightly compressible liquids and when it is assumed that the medium is homogeneous and the viscosity and compressibility of the liquid are constant. Analytic solutions for Eq. (16.59) have been given by Hurst[29] and later by Van Everdingen and Hurst.[30]

Solutions for Eq. (16.59) will give the pressure as a function of radius and time. Hurst and Van Everdingen used Laplace transforms to find solutions to Eq. (16.59) for several cases of interest. Since these solutions are in terms of Bessel functions, no useful purpose would be served by repeating them here. Rather, their solutions are presented in tabular form.

The first solution of interest is that for a *constant pressure* maintained at the producing well. The cumulative volume of fluid flow into a well or across a reservoir boundary is found from

$$Q_T = 2\pi\phi c r_w^2 H (P_i - P_w) Q_t \qquad (16.60)$$

in which the dimensionless fluid influx Q_t is defined by

$$Q_t = \frac{\int_0^{t_d} \left(\frac{\partial P}{\partial r}\right)_{r=r_w} dt_d}{P_i - P_w}$$

and t_d is the dimensionless time defined as

$$t_d = \frac{6.34 k t}{\phi \mu c r_w^2}$$

The following initial and boundary conditions apply:

1. At time zero, the pressure at each point is P_i, or $P = P_i$ for all r at $t = 0$.
2. For time greater than zero, the pressure at the producing well is maintained at constant pressure P_1 or $P = P_1$ at $r = r_w$ for $t > 0$.

Table 16.3. Dimensionless Fluid Influx as a Function of Dimensionless Time for Constant Well Pressure

(From Van Everdingen and Hurst[20])

t_d	Q_t				
	$r_e/r_w = 1.5$	$r_e/r_w = 3.0$	$r_e/r_w = 6.0$	$r_e/r_w = 9.0$	$r_e/r_w = \infty$
1.0×10^{-2}	0.112				0.112
2.5×10^{-2}					
5.0×10^{-2}	0.276	0.278	0.278	0.278	0.278
1.0×10^{-1}	0.395	0.404	0.404	0.404	0.404
2.5×10^{-1}	0.559	0.689	0.689	0.689	0.689
5.0×10^{-1}	0.617	1.020	1.020	1.020	1.020
1.0		1.563	1.570	1.570	1.570
2.5		2.646	2.838	2.838	2.838
5.0		3.491	4.541	4.541	4.541
1.0×10^1		3.928	7.293	7.417	7.417
2.5×10^1		4.000	12.50	14.40	1.455×10^1
5.0×10^1			15.95	22.82	2.482×10^1
1.0×10^2			17.36	32.27	4.301×10^1
2.5×10^2			17.50	39.30	9.120×10^1
5.0×10^2				39.98	16.24×10^1
1.0×10^3					29.31×10^1
5.0×10^3					11.88×10^2
1.0×10^4					21.96×10^2
5.0×10^4					9.342×10^3
1.0×10^5					17.56×10^3
5.0×10^5					7.699×10^4
1.0×10^6					14.62×10^4
5.0×10^6					6.544×10^5
1.0×10^7					12.52×10^5
5.0×10^7					5.689×10^6
1.0×10^8					10.95×10^6
5.0×10^8					5.03×10^7
1.0×10^9					9.725×10^7
5.0×10^9					4.510×10^8
1.0×10^{10}					8.747×10^8
5.0×10^{10}					4.087×10^9
1.0×10^{11}					7.948×10^9

3. There is no flow across the closed, outer boundary of the reservoir at $r = r_e$ or $q = 0$ and $\partial P/\partial r = 0$ at $r = r_e$ for all t.

The tabular solution of Van Everdingen and Hurst for this case is given in Table 16.3. Shown in this table are the dimensionless cumulative production Q_t as a function of dimensionless time t_d for various ratios of the radius of the outer closed boundary to the radius of the inner boundary across which production is taking place. Using these data and the principles of superposition, a number of practical problems can be solved as illustrated below.

Example 4. Given: The first well, radius 0.25 ft, drilled into an oil reservoir at an original pressure of 3000 psi, is placed on production. The pressure at the sand face is maintained at 2500 psi. The sand is 20 ft thick and has a permeability of 15 millidarcys and a porosity of 20 per cent. The oil has a viscosity of 0.6 centipoise and a compressibility of 1.5×10^{-5} vol/(vol)(psi). If the initial production results solely from expansion of oil, and assuming the effects of the lateral boundaries are not felt, what is the volume of oil produced in the first day?

SOLUTION. The dimensionless time is given by

$$t_d = \frac{6.34kt}{\phi\mu c r_w{}^2}$$

$$= \frac{(6.34)(0.015)(1.0)}{(0.20)(0.60)(1.5 \times 10^{-5})(0.25)^2}$$

$$= 8.45 \times 10^5$$

From interpolation in Table 16.3 for $r_e/r_w = \infty$,

$$Q_t = 1.25 \times 10^5$$

Then using Eq. (16.60),

$$\begin{aligned}
Q_T &= 2\pi\phi c r_w{}^2 H(P_i - P_w)Q_t \\
&= (6.28)(0.2)(1.5 \times 10^{-5})(0.25)^2(20)(3000 - 2500)(1.25 \times 10^5) \\
&= 1471 \text{ ft}^3, \text{ or } 262 \text{ bbl}
\end{aligned}$$

Example 5. Given: An oil reservoir, circular in shape with a radius of 3000 ft, is surrounded by a large water sand. Assume that the pressure is uniform throughout the oil sand. The pressure decline of the reservoir after being placed on production can be approximated by a step function as follows:

Time, days	Pressure, psi
0	2000
0–100	1990
100–200	1980
200–300	1970
300–400	1960
400–500	1950
500–600	1940
600–700	1930
700–800	1920
800–900	1910
900–1000	1900

The water sand is 30 ft thick and has a permeability of 500 millidarcys and a porosity of 25 per cent. The water has a viscosity of 0.72 centipoise at reservoir conditions. The effective compressibility (water plus rock) is 1×10^{-5} vol/(vol)(psi). What is the volume of water which has flowed into the oil sand at $r = 3000$ in the first 1000 days?

SOLUTION. The water influx can be found using superposition principle 2 above by summing up the influx caused by each pressure change for the time it endured. The influx caused by the pressure drop at $t = 0$ from 2000 to 1990 psi is found by first calculating the dimensionless time.

$$t_d = \frac{6.34kt}{\mu \phi c r_w{}^2}$$

$$= \frac{(6.34)(0.5)(1000)}{(0.72)(0.25)(1 \times 10^{-5})(3000)^2}$$

$$= 195.5$$

From interpolation in Table 16.3, the value of the dimensionless water influx Q_t for $t_d = 195.5$ is 74. Then the water influx caused by dropping the pressure from 2000 to 1990 psi for the time interval at $t = 0$ to the time of interest at 1000 days is obtained from Eq. (16.60).

$$Q_T = (6.28)(0.25)(1 \times 10^{-5})(3000)^2(30)(2000 - 1990)(74)$$
$$= 3.14 \times 10^6 \text{ ft}^3$$

The water influx caused by the pressure drop from 1990 to 1980 psi acting over the time from 100 to 1000 days is found in a similar manner. The dimensionless time is

$$t_d = \frac{(6.34)(0.5)(1000 - 100)}{(0.72)(0.25)(1 \times 10^{-5})(3000)^2}$$

$$= 176$$

From Table 16.3, the dimensionless influx is 68. Then

$$Q_T = (6.28)(0.25)(1 \times 10^{-5})(3000)^2(30)(1990 - 1980)(68)$$
$$= 2.89 \times 10^6 \text{ ft}^3$$

Similarly, the water influx caused by pressure drops at the later times are found. These are tabulated below:

Time interval, days	Water influx at 1000 days caused by incremental pressure drop beginning at given time, 1×10^6 ft³
0	3.14
100	2.89
200	2.64
300	2.32
400	2.04
500	1.78
600	1.48
700	1.19
800	0.87
900	0.51
	$Q_T = \overline{18.86 \times 10^6 \text{ ft}^3}$

The total water influx is the sum of the water influx caused by each incremental change, or $Q_T = 18.86 \times 10^6$ ft³, or 3,360,000 bbl. If at some later time, say, after 2000 days, it is desired to know the total water influx at that time, the water influx caused by each incremental pressure change must be recomputed using the new time interval from the time of its inception to 2000 days, which that pressure change has lasted.

Sufficient data are often available to obtain a check on the volume of water influx calculated using the unsteady-flow solutions. The volume at reservoir conditions of oil, water, and gas produced from the reservoir, the original and present pressure of the reservoir, and the compressibility of the reservoir fluids are sufficient data for a separate volumetric balance to be made to find the volume of water influx. If the value for water influx determined by volumetric balance differs from the value determined from the unsteady-state-flow solutions, the value of permeability, sand thickness, or compressibility, whichever is least well known, is adjusted so that the unsteady-state solution for the influx agrees with that from the volumetric balance.

The second solution of Eq. (16.60) of interest is that for *constant production rate* maintained at the producing well. The following initial and boundary conditions apply.

1. At time zero, the pressure at each point is P_i, or $P = P_i$ for all r at $t = 0$.
2. For time greater than zero, production of fluid from the well is maintained at a constant rate, or $q = $ const for $t > 0$ at $r = r_w$.
3. There is no flow across the closed outer boundary of the reservoir, or $q = 0$ and $\partial P/\partial r = 0$ at $r = r_e$ for all t.

The solution of Van Everdingen and Hurst[30] for this case has been listed in Table 16.4. Shown in this table are the dimensionless pressure change vs. dimensionless time for various ratios of radius of the outer boundary to that of the well, or inner boundary. The dimensionless pressure change is given by

$$P_t = \frac{6.342\pi kH(P_i - P_w)}{q\mu} \tag{16.61}$$

and the dimensionless time is as before $t_d = 6.34kt/\phi\mu cr_w{}^2$.

Table 16.4. Dimensionless Pressure Change as a Function of Dimensionless Time
for Constant Terminal Rate

(From Van Everdingen and Hurst[30])

t_d	P_t				
	$r_e/r_w = 1.5$	$r_e/r_w = 3.0$	$r_e/r_w = 6.0$	$r_e/r_w = 9.0$	$r_e/r_w = \infty$
1.0×10^{-2}	0.112	0.112	0.112	0.112	0.112
6.0×10^{-2}	0.251				
1.0×10^{-1}	0.322	0.315	0.315	0.315	0.315
2.0×10^{-1}	0.484	0.424	0.424	0.424	0.424
3.0×10^{-1}	0.644	0.503	0.503	0.503	0.503
4.0×10^{-1}	0.804	0.564	0.564	0.564	0.564
5.0×10^{-1}	0.964	0.616	0.616	0.616	0.616
6.0×10^{-1}	1.124	0.662	0.659	0.659	0.659
7.0×10^{-1}		0.703	0.702	0.702	0.702
8.0×10^{-1}		0.740	0.735	0.735	0.735
9.0×10^{-1}		0.776	0.772	0.772	0.772
1.0		0.806	0.802	0.802	0.802
2.0		1.076	1.020	1.020	1.020
3.0		1.578	1.169	1.169	1.169
4.0		1.828	1.275	1.275	1.275
5.0			1.364	1.362	1.362
6.0			1.441	1.436	1.436
7.0			1.511	1.500	1.500
8.0			1.576	1.556	1.556
9.0			1.638	1.604	1.604
1.0×10^{1}			1.698	1.651	1.651
2.0×10^{1}			2.274	1.983	1.960
3.0×10^{1}			2.846	2.244	2.147
4.0×10^{1}				2.496	2.282
5.0×10^{1}				2.746	2.388
6.0×10^{1}					2.476
7.0×10^{1}					2.550
8.0×10^{1}					2.615
9.0×10^{1}					2.672
1.0×10^{2}					2.723
2.0×10^{2}					3.064
3.0×10^{2}					3.263
4.0×10^{2}					3.406
5.0×10^{2}					3.516
6.0×10^{2}					3.608
7.0×10^{2}					3.684
8.0×10^{2}					3.750
9.0×10^{2}					3.809
1.0×10^{3}					3.860

Example 6.   Given: A number of irrigation wells are drilled into a water sand of large extent with the wells spaced over a circular area 3000 ft in radius.   The sand is 100 ft thick, has a porosity of 30 per cent, and a permeability of 20.0 darcys.   The viscosity of the water is 0.85 centipoise, and the effective compressibility factor, water plus rock, for this sand has been found from past experience in this area to be 4×10^{-5} vol/(vol)(psi).   The production rate from the wells since they were placed on production has varied approximately as follows:

Time, days	Water-production rate, 1×10^6 ft³/day
0–10	0.5
10–20	0.75
20–30	1.0
30–40	1.5
40–50	1.7
50–60	2.0
60–70	2.0
70–80	2.0
80–90	2.0
90–100	2.0

The pressure in the sand before production starts is 200 psi.   Find the pressure in the sand at the end of 100 days, assuming that the pressure within the 3000-ft radius is uniform and all the production of water is taken from the radius at 3000 ft.

SOLUTION.   The total pressure change can be found by summing up the pressure change caused by each rate change for the time interval from its inception to the time of interest.   The pressure change caused by placing the wells on production at $t = 0$ with a rate of 0.5×10^6 ft³/day, assuming that this rate is maintained 100 days, is found as follows.

The dimensionless time is

$$t_d = \frac{6.34kt}{\phi \mu c r_w{}^2}$$

$$= \frac{(6.34)(20.0)(100 - 0)}{(0.30)(0.85)(4 \times 10^{-5})(3000)^2}$$

$$= 138$$

From Table 16.4, the dimensionless pressure decrease at 100 days caused by this initial production is 2.85.

The pressure change is then

$$P_i - P_w = \frac{P_t q \mu}{(6.34)(2\pi)kH}$$

$$= \frac{(2.85)(0.5 \times 10^6)(0.85)}{(6.34)(2\pi)(20)(100)}$$

$$= 15.2 \text{ psi}$$

The additional pressure drop at 100 days caused by increasing the rate of flow to 0.75×10^6 ft³/day at 10 days is found as follows:

$$t_d = \frac{(6.34)(20.0)(100 - 10)}{(0.30)(0.85)(4 \times 10^{-5})(3000)^2}$$

$$= 124$$

From Table 16.4, the dimensionless pressure change is 2.80.   The pressure drop caused by the rate increase at 10 days is then

$$P_i - P_w = \frac{P_t(q_1 - q_i)(\mu)}{(6.34)(2\pi)kH}$$

$$= \frac{(2.80)(0.75 \times 10^6 - 0.50 \times 10^6)(0.85)}{(6.34)(2\pi)(20)(100)}$$

$$= 7.4 \text{ psi}$$

The pressure drop at 100 days is found by superposing pressure drops caused by the other incremental rate changes using Eq. (16.49). The pressure in the sand at 100 days is then $P_i - (P_i - P_w) = 200 - 58.7 = 142.2$ psi.

Time of inception of rate change, days	Rate change, 1×10^6 ft³/day	Pressure drop at 100 days caused by incremental rate change beginning at given time, psi
0	0.5	15.2
10	0.25	7.4
20	0.25	7.2
30	0.50	14.4
40	0.20	5.6
50	0.30	8.0
60	0	0
70	0	0
80	0	0
90	0	0
100	0	0
		57.8 psi

The third solution of the unsteady-state-flow, Eq. (16.60), of interest is that for the *pressure build-up* after a producing well has been shut in. The following initial and boundary conditions apply.

1. At times before $t = 0$, the well was producing at a constant rate, or $q_w = $ const for $t > 0$.
2. The pressure distribution in the reservoir had reached steady-state conditions, or $dP/dr = $ const for all r.
3. For time greater than zero, the well is shut in, or $q_w = 0$ for $t > 0$.
4. The pressure at the drainage radius is maintained constant, or $P = $ const at $r = r_e$ for all t.

The solutions obtained for this case by Miller, Dyes, and Hutchinson,[31] using high-speed computers, are shown in Fig. 16.23. Plotted on semilog paper are the dimensionless-pressure drops vs. the dimensionless time for various ratios of radius of the outer boundary to that of the producing well. Also shown as a dashed line is a solution for the boundary condition of no flow across the outer boundary for $r_e/r_w = 4000$.

The permeability of the formation can be determined from the pressure build-up at the well. Miller et al. noted that the

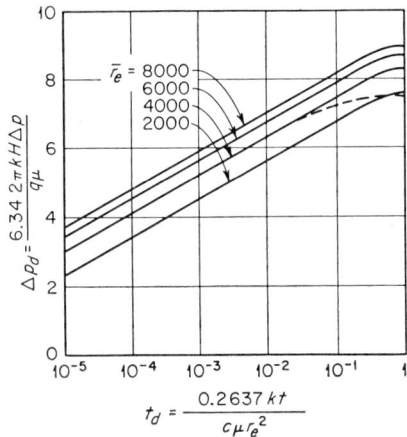

FIG. 16.23. Calculated rise in bottom-hole pressure in a shut-in well Steady-state pressure distribution obtained prior to shut-in by constant production rate. Solid lines for reservoir with constant pressure maintained at the radius of drainage. Dashed line for closed reservoir with no influx over radius of drainage and $r_e = 4000$. (*Ref.* 31.)

relations between dimensionless-pressure change and time were straight lines over most of the build-up time. The slope of the lines in Fig. 16.23 is 1.147. Substitution for the dimensionless pressure and time

$$\frac{dP_T}{d \log t_d} = \frac{kH}{0.1412q\mu} \frac{d(P_w - P_i)}{d \log t} = 1.147 \qquad (16.62)$$

and solving for the permeability gives

$$k = \frac{0.029q\mu}{mH} \qquad (16.63)$$

in which m is the slope of the pressure-build-up curve on semilog paper, or

$$m = \frac{d(P_w - P_i)}{d \log t}$$

and t = time, hr
   k = permeability, darcys
   q = flow rate, ft³/day at reservoir conditions

To measure permeability from pressure-build-up data, the well should produce at a constant rate for a period sufficient to establish steady-state-flow conditions. This condition is given[31] as

$$t_s = 1 \times 10^{-3} \frac{\phi\mu c r_e^2}{k}$$

Attempts should be made to restrict the void volume of the well so that no significant quantities of fluid flow into the well after it is shut in. To illustrate the method of calculating permeabilities from pressure build-up, Example 7 is presented.

Example 7. Given: A well produced oil at a rate of 100 bbl/day at reservoir conditions for several months. The formation had a thickness of 20 ft and a porosity of 22 per cent. The viscosity of the oil at reservoir conditions was 0.6 centipoise. The well was shut in, and the following pressure-build-up data were obtained. Find the permeability of the sand.

Time, hr	Pressure, psi
1	1920
2	1945
3	1958
4	1968
5	1977
6	1983
12	2007
24	2031

SOLUTION. The pressure-build-up data are plotted as pressure vs. log t. The data fall on a straight line. The slope of the line is

$$m = \frac{dP}{d \log t} = \frac{P_2 - P_1}{\log t_2/t_1} \quad \text{(when } P \text{ versus log } t \text{ is a straight line)}$$

$$= \frac{2007 - 1920}{\log 12/1}$$

$$= 81.3 \text{ psi/hr}$$

The permeability is

$$k = \frac{0.029q\mu}{mH}$$

$$= \frac{(0.029)(100 \times 5.615)(0.60)}{(81.3)(20)}$$

$$= 0.06 \text{ darcy, or 60 millidarcys}$$

Radial Flow of a Gas. The equation for radial flow of a gas in the horizontal plane is

$$\frac{\partial\left(\dfrac{k[\text{M.Wt}]}{2\mu ZRT}\, r\, \dfrac{\partial P^2}{\partial r}\right)}{\partial r} = \frac{\phi(\text{M.Wt})}{ZRT}\frac{\partial P}{\partial t} \tag{16.64}$$

which reduces to

$$\frac{\partial^2 P^2}{\partial r^2} + \frac{1}{r}\frac{\partial P}{\partial r} = \frac{\mu\phi}{kP}\frac{\partial P}{\partial t} \tag{16.65}$$

when the viscosity and compressibility can be assumed to be constant and the medium is homogeneous.

No analytic solutions are known to exist for these equations. However, solutions to Eq. (16.65) have been obtained by Bruce et al.[32] and by Jenkins and Aronofsky[33] using numerical methods with high-speed computers.

A solution was made for the unsteady flow of a perfect gas, i.e., viscosity is constant and $Z = 1$, in a homogeneous sand for the case of constant production rate.[32] The following initial and boundary conditions apply:

1. At time zero, the pressure at each point is P_i, or $P = P_i$ for all r at $t = 0$.
2. For time greater than zero, the production rate of gas is constant (measured at the conditions of the static pressure P_0 and reservoir temperature), or $q_{P_i,T_R} = $ const for $t > 0$.
3. There is no flow across the closed, outer boundary, or $q = 0$ and $dP/dr = 0$ at $r = r_e$.

Solutions of Eq. (16.64) for the isothermal unsteady-state flow of a perfect gas in a radial system are shown in Figs. 16.24 and 16.25. In Fig. 16.24, the dimensionless-pressure drawdown is plotted vs. dimensionless time divided by 6.34 for various ratios of radius of the external boundary to the well-bore radius. In Fig. 16.25, the reciprocal of the dimensionless-total-gas production (measured at T_R and P_i) is plotted versus di-

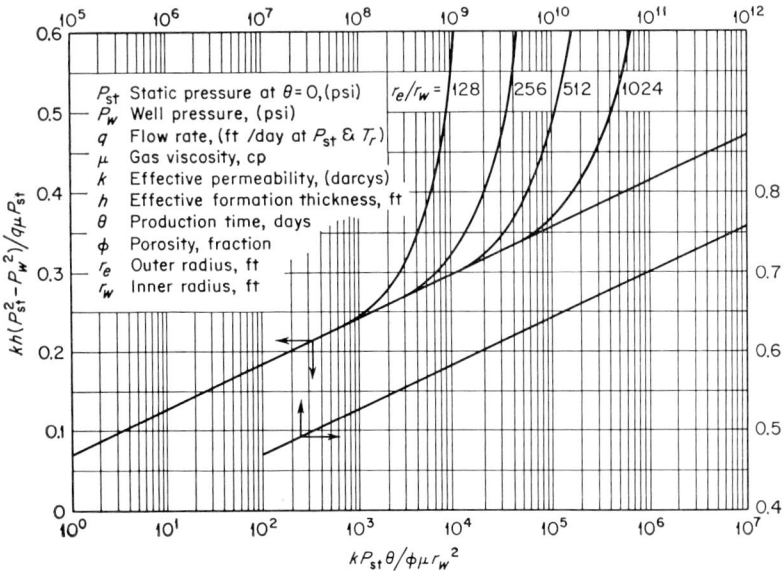

Fig. 16.24. Gas flow, constant rate.

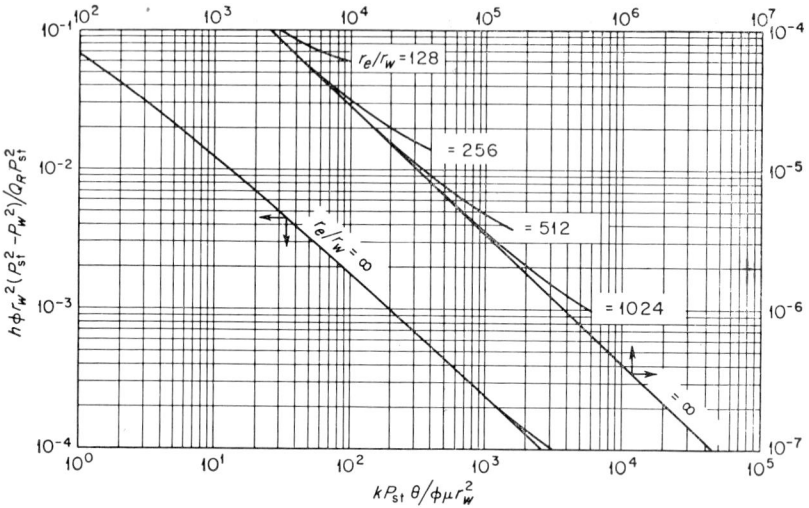

FIG. 16.25. Gas flow, constant rate.

mensionless time divided by various values of r_e/r_w. Note that for finite values of r_e/r_w, the system behaves at first as one with an infinite external radius. After the influence of the external boundary is felt, the pressure at the well changes much more rapidly with time than before. These results are useful in estimating the rate at which the pressure will decline in a producing well. It is often important to know how long a well can produce at a given rate and still maintain the pressure above a given level so that gas may be delivered to a high-pressure pipeline without recompression.

Permeabilities may be calculated from the rate at which the pressure in a gas well declines after being placed on production. The permeability may be found by calculating the dimensionless total production for several of the times and using Fig. 16.24 to obtain the permeability. If the permeability is the same for each of several consecutive times, then the calculated permeabilities are reasonable estimates of the reservoir value.

This calculation procedure is illustrated in Example 8.

Example 8. Given: A gas well in a large reservoir has been shut in sufficiently long for the pressure to build up to the static reservoir pressure of 2050 psi. The reservoir temperature is 170°F. The compressibility Z factor for the natural gas at this temperature and pressure is 0.89, and the viscosity of the gas is 0.016 centipoise. The thickness of the formation is 30 ft, and porosity is 25 per cent. The Z factor at standard conditions is 0.98.

The well has a radius of 0.25 ft. The well is placed on production at a constant rate of 2.0×10^6 ft³/day at 60°F and 14.7 psi. The pressure drawdown in the well as a function of time is given as follows:

Time, hr	Pressure, psi
1	1991
2	1958
3	1943
4	1931
5	1923
6	1918
9	1901
12	1891

Find the permeability of the formation.

SOLUTION. The volume of gas produced per day measured at the static reservoir pressure and reservoir temperature is

$$V_1 = \frac{V_2 Z_2 P_2 T_1}{Z_1 P_1 T_2}$$

$$= \frac{(2 \times 10^6)(14.7)(630)(0.89)}{(0.98)(2065)(520)}$$

$$= 1.565 \times 10^4 \text{ ft}^3/\text{day, or } 652 \text{ ft}^3/\text{hr}$$

At one hour, the quantity

$$\frac{H r_w^2 (P_i^2 - P_w^2)}{Q_T P_0^2} = \frac{(30)(0.25)(0.25)^2(2065^2 - 1946^2)}{(652)(2065)^2}$$

$$= 8.08 \times 10^{-5}$$

From Fig. 16.24,

$$\frac{k P_i t}{\phi \mu r_w^2} = 35$$

$$k = \frac{(35)(0.25)(0.016)(0.25)^2}{(2065)(\frac{1}{24})}$$

$$= 1.02 \times 10^{-4} \text{ darcy, or } 0.102 \text{ millidarcys}$$

Similarly, the permeabilities for other times are calculated. The permeability of the formation is approximately 0.12 millidarcy.

Time, hr	k, millidarcys
1	0.102
2	0.106
3	0.111
4	0.113
5	0.116
6	0.116
9	0.120
12	0.123

16.12. Unsteady-state Flow in Systems of Complex Geometry

Many practical problems involve the unsteady-state flow of fluids in more than one dimension. For example, the flow of water may be neither linear nor radial in a large aquifer containing several oil pools. In cases in which rock properties vary or geometry is complex, solutions of the unsteady-state-flow Eq. (16.44) may require the use of numerical methods and high-speed computers or use of electrical analogue devices. An analogue device known as the electric analyzer is often used when the permeability or thickness varies from point to point or when several oil fields are located in one water sand.[34]

The basic analogy is that between flow of electric current in a resistor-capacitor network charged to some constant pressure. The equation for flow of a slightly compressible fluid in a nonhomogeneous medium may be derived from Eq. (16.42) and

$$\frac{\partial \left(\frac{k}{\mu} \frac{\partial P}{\partial x} \right)}{\partial x} + \frac{\partial \left(\frac{k}{\mu} \frac{\partial P}{\partial y} \right)}{\partial y} = c\phi \frac{\partial P}{\partial t} \qquad (16.66)$$

in which the compressibility c is assumed constant.

The equation for transient flow of an electric current is

$$\frac{\partial \left(\sigma \dfrac{\partial V}{\partial x} \right)}{\partial x} + \frac{\partial \left(\sigma \dfrac{\partial V}{\partial y} \right)}{\partial y} = C \frac{\partial V}{\partial t} \tag{16.67}$$

in which C is the capacitance, and σ is the electrical conductivity.

It is obvious from inspection of Eqs. (16.66) and (16.67) that by relating fluid conductivity K/μ† to electric conductivity σ, pressure P to voltage V, and fluid-flow flux v to current flux i, as described previously in Art. 16.8, and by relating fluid compressibility in the rock ϕc to capacitance C, solutions of Eq. (16.67) using an electrical analogue device can be related to solutions of the fluid-flow problem.

An example of use of the electric analyzer is that of Rumble, Spain, and Stamm[35] in studies of flow in the aquifer of the Woodbine Basin in east Texas. These authors matched the pressure histories of a number of fields in this huge water-filled basin by trial-and-error adjustment of resistors and capacitors.

FLOW OF TWO OR MORE IMMISCIBLE FLUIDS

16.13. Introduction

To this point in discussion of flow of fluids through porous media, the porous bodies have been assumed to be filled or saturated with a single fluid. From this point on, the discussion in this section is concerned with flow of two or more fluids through the media. First, in Arts. 16.14 to 16.26, the distribution and flow of two or more immiscible fluids will be treated. By *immiscible* fluids is meant fluids that are not completely soluble in each other, so that fluid interfaces exist between them. These fluids are distinguished from *miscible* fluids, which are completely soluble in one another, so that no fluid interfaces exist. Flow of miscible fluids in porous media will be treated later in Arts. 16.27 to 16.34.

When two or more immiscible fluids are present in the interstices of a porous medium, the resistance to flow of each fluid depends not only on the amount of that fluid present, but on its distribution within the pore spaces. Thus, before delving into the laws governing two-phase flow, it behooves us to examine some of the factors affecting fluid distribution. The concept of capillary pressure is introduced in Art. 16.14, and the role of capillary forces is discussed in their role in both microscopic (within individual and between adjacent pore spaces) and macroscopic (within large bodies of the medium) fluid distribution (Art. 16.15). Introduction of the concept of relative permeability in Arts. 16.16 and 16.17 and knowledge of the factors on which relative permeabilities depend lay the groundwork for the discussions of fluid displacements. First linear or one-dimensional displacements are treated in Arts. 16.19 to 16.24. Then the theory and use of dimensionally scaled models are discussed in Arts. 16.25 and 16.26 in solving problems in flow in more than one dimension.

16.14. Capillary Pressures

Basic Concepts. One of the more important concepts in considering the distribution of immiscible-fluid phases in a porous medium is that of capillary pressure. When two phases are distributed continuously throughout a porous solid, one phase usually preferentially wets the solid. In the tiny pore spaces, a curvature will exist across the interface separating the fluids. The capillary pressure is the pressure difference across the fluid interface at a point in the medium. The capillary pressure is usually defined as the pressure in the nonwetting phase minus the pressure in the wetting phase.

$$P_c = P_{nw} - P_w \tag{16.68}$$

† As in steady-state flow, the fluid conductivity may be written as kH/μ in media in which the thickness varies.

The magnitude of the capillary pressure at any point in the medium depends on the interfacial tension and the curvature of the fluid interface at that point. This curvature depends on the sizes and shapes of the pore spaces surrounding the point in question, on the fluid saturation, and on the degree of wetting. It is visualized that the saturation at the point in question is a statistical average of that in the surrounding pores, so that both saturation and capillary pressure correspond to the same point.

For the capillary pressure to have meaning, both fluid phases must be continuous in the medium so that pressures measured on the external surface of the medium can be related to those in the medium.

In considering how a pressure difference could exist across a curved interface, it is convenient to think of a spherical bubble of gas in a liquid. The pressure in the bubble is trying to force the hemispheres apart, but the interfacial tension acting on the common periphery of the hemispheres holds them together. Since these forces are in equilibrium, it can be easily seen that the pressure in the gas above that in the liquid is given by

$$P_c = \frac{2\sigma}{r} \qquad (16.69)$$

in which P_c = pressure difference across interface (or capillary pressure)
   σ = interfacial tension
   r = radius of bubble

The manner in which wettability influences the curvature of the interface and the capillary pressure can be seen from study of the forces acting at the interface in a small vertical capillary of constant radius r. The interfacial tension σ acts at an angle θ to support the mass of fluid drawn up into the capillary against the force of gravity. At equilibrium, the interfacial forces just balance the gravitational forces, and it is easily shown that the pressure difference across the interface is

$$P_c = \Delta\rho\, gH = \frac{2\sigma\cos\theta}{r} \qquad (16.70)$$

While the pore spaces in sands do not resemble the uniform bores of capillary tubes, there is a similarity between them with respect to their capillary behavior. Consider two spherical sand grains touching each other as shown in Fig. 16.26. The capillary pressure is related to the curvature of the interface by the familiar Laplace equation

$$P_c = \sigma\left(\frac{1}{R_1} + \frac{1}{R_2}\right) = \sigma C \quad (16.70a)$$

in which C is the curvature of the interface, and R_1 and R_2 are the principal radii of curvature of the interface as shown in Fig. 16.26. (By convention, R_2, the larger radius, is negative when it falls on the opposite side of the interface from R_1, as shown here.)

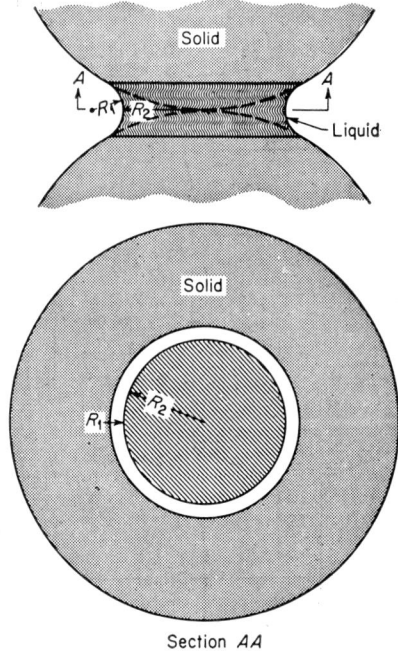

Section *AA*

Fig. 16.26. Accumulation of liquid at contact point between spherical grains. R_1 rotates in plane of paper in upper view; R_2 rotates in plane of paper in lower view. (*Ref.* 43.)

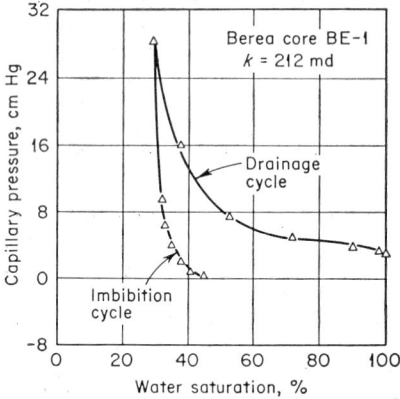

FIG. 16.27. Capillary pressure vs. water saturation, illustrating hysteresis.

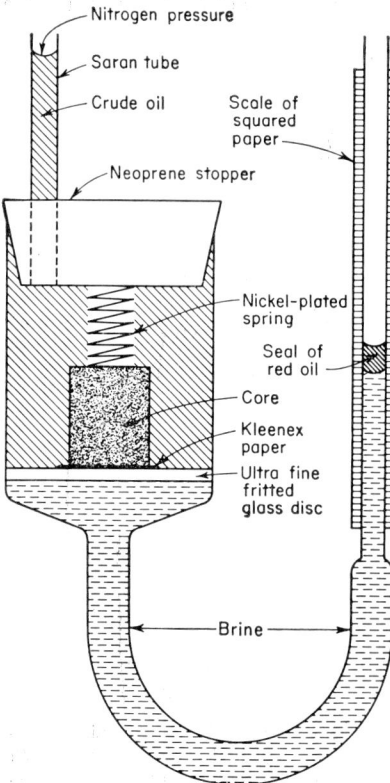

FIG. 16.28. Cross section of restored-state core-test apparatus. (*Ref.* 39.)

The wettability of the fluid-rock system enters through Young's equation.[36]

$$\cos \theta = \frac{\omega_{2s} - \omega_{1s}}{\omega_{12}} \qquad (16.71)$$

in which θ is the contact angle, ω is the free energy per unit area measured at the point of contact, and subscripts 1, 2, and s refer to fluid 1, fluid 2, and solid, respectively.

In a porous medium, the complex geometry of the particle surfaces prevents the use of a simple relation between contact angle and curvature such as $\cos \theta$, which applies in straight uniform bore capillaries.[37]

It is generally agreed, however, that the curvature of the fluid interface depends on some function of the contact angle, usually written $f(\theta)$, on the shapes and sizes of the pore spaces, on the fluid saturation, and on the saturation history.

Typical Capillary-pressure Data. A typical capillary-pressure–saturation relation for a consolidated sandstone is shown in Fig. 16.27. The upper curve is the capillary pressure between oil and water for conditions of the water phase decreasing or draining from the sample and for the water phase increasing or imbibing into the sample. There is a considerable hysteresis loop in the capillary-pressure–saturation relation. Smith[38] has shown that the geometry of the pore spaces permits a number of stable distributions of water at a given water saturation, especially at high-water saturations. These various stable distributions of water depend on the history of saturations and result in multivalued capillary pressures, depending on the method of arriving at that saturation.

Consider first the drainage capillary-pressure curve. Starting with a water-saturated sample, no oil penetrates the sand until the pressure in the oil phase exceeds that in the water by the amount required to force water from the largest pore opening exposed to oil. This capillary pressure is commonly called the *displacement pressure*. As the capillary pressure is increased, the nonwetting phase penetrates smaller and smaller pore spaces in an interconnected, interwoven network through the sand. The wetting fluid is distributed as a film over the sand grains and recedes into the smaller interstices as the capillary pressure increases. This phase also is distributed in an interwoven network, but in pore spaces smaller than these containing nonwetting fluid. As the wetting phase recedes into the smallest pore spaces, successively greater changes in capillary pressures are required to force a given amount of wetting fluid from the sample. As the capillary pressures appear to approach some minimum saturation asymmetrically, this minimum saturation is sometimes called the *irreducible minimum saturation*. There is no direct evidence, however, that any wetting-fluid saturation other than zero is a true irreducible minimum saturation.

On increasing the wetting-phase saturation from some low value, the wetting fluid occupies successively larger channels. On the imbibition cycle, the interfacial curvature is larger at a given saturation and lower capillary pressures exist across the interface. At some relatively high nonwetting-fluid saturation, the nonwetting phase breaks into discrete, discontinuous globules. This trapping of the nonwetting phase appears to coincide with the point when the capillary pressure becomes zero.

Measurement of Capillary Pressures in Porous Solids. There are a number of methods of measuring the capillary-pressure–saturation relations of porous solids. The most commonly used of these are the porous-diaphragm method,[39] the centrifuge method,[40,41] and the mercury-injection technique.[42]

A *porous-diaphragm* apparatus is shown in Fig. 16.28. A small sample of the porous solid of interest is saturated with water and placed in capillary contact with the porcelain disc sealed in the bottom of the apparatus. The apparatus is then assembled as shown in the sketch, and a gas pressure is applied to the sample. Water forced from the sample by gas flows through the porcelain disc until capillary equilibrium is attained, at which time the capillary pressure (gas pressure minus the water pressure) and water saturation are determined. Successively higher gas pressures are then applied to attain lower oil and lower water saturations. The porcelain discs used in this equipment have such small pores that no gas penetrates them over the pressure range of interest.

A *centrifuge* apparatus is shown in Fig. 16.29. The samples are placed into cups at the end of the centrifuge arms. The centrifuge is then turned on and maintained at some constant speed until no more liquid flows from the sample. The volumes of liquid in the small burettes attached to the centrifuge cups are then read with the aid of a stroboscopic light. Placing increasingly higher centrifugal forces on the small

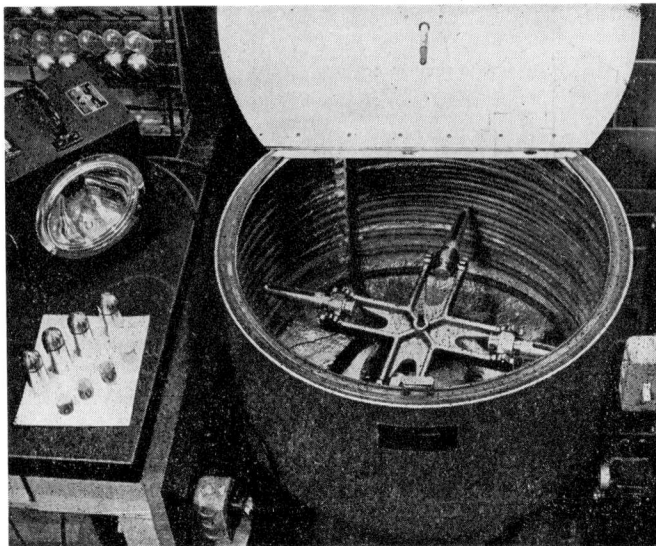

Fig. 16.29. Centrifuge showing coil, stroboscope, and two types of coreholders. (*Ref.* 41.)

core with drainage of liquid to an equilibrium condition after each increase permits a capillary-pressure saturation to be calculated for the sample. The capillary pressure existing at the inner face of the sample is given by

$$P_{c,r1} = \frac{\Delta\rho\omega^2}{2}(r_2{}^2 - r_1{}^2) \qquad (16.72)$$

in which ω = angular velocity of centrifuge
r_1 = radius of rotation to inner face of sample
r_2 = radius of rotation to outer face of sample

The saturation at the inner face of the sample can be calculated from the average saturation by

$$S_{r1} = \overline{S} + P_{c,r1}\frac{d\overline{S}}{dP_{c,r1}} \qquad (16.73)$$

in which $\overline{S}$ = average saturation
S_{r1} = saturation at inner face

Use of the last equation should be restricted to cases in which r_1/r_2 approaches unity[40] (0.8 or greater) and should also be restricted to cases when the samples are homogeneous.

A mercury-injection apparatus is shown in Fig. 16.30. The device consists of a cell into which a small dry sample of rock is placed. The cell is then evacuated to a very low pressure. Mercury is injected into the cell until the mercury is level with a graduation on the high-pressure glass capillary above the sample chamber. Then nitrogen pressure is applied in successive increments and mercury is added to maintain mercury level with the graduation on the capillary. From the volume of the cell and the volume of mercury required to fill the cell with the sample in place before any mercury enters the sample, the bulk volume of the rock can be determined. The air-mercury capillary-pressure–saturation relation is calculated from the volume of mercury forced into the sample as a function of the applied pressure of nitrogen.

Correlation of Capillary-pressure Data. A method of correlating capillary-pressure data obtained on various sands with various fluids has been discussed by Leverett.[43] Using dimensional analysis, Leverett derived a dimensionless parameter $\dfrac{P_c}{\sigma}\left(\dfrac{k}{\phi}\right)^{1/2}$, which he termed the $J(S)$ function. To include the possibility of fluid systems having different contact angles on the rock, later workers have written

$$J(S) = \frac{P_c}{\sigma f(\theta)}\left(\frac{k}{\phi}\right)^{1/2} \qquad (16.74)$$

The quantity $\dfrac{f(\theta)}{(k/\phi)^{1/2}}$ is the interfacial curvature, and the quantity $(k/\phi)^{1/2}$ is a characteristic dimension of the microscopic pore system.

The $J(S)$ function has found several uses. One important use is in correlating the capillary properties of a reservoir formation having a wide range of per-

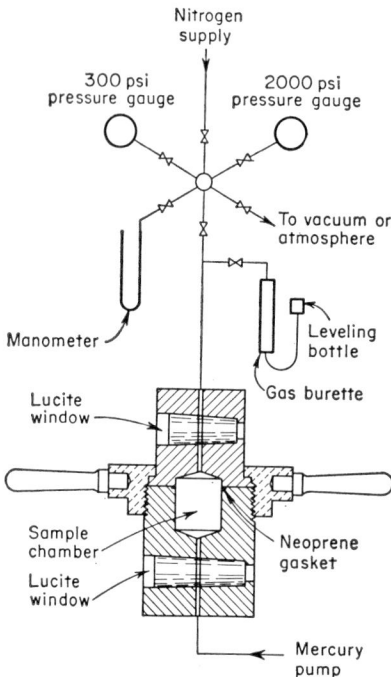

Fig. 16.30. Capillary-pressure apparatus, mercury-injection method. (*Ref.* 44.)

meabilities. The data shown in Fig. 16.31 are dimensionless capillary-pressure data[44] for limestone samples whose permeabilities ranged from 0.7 to 599 millidarcys. The correlation is useful in estimating the water saturation existing in the oil zone of this formation. Another use of the $J(S)$ function is in scaling sand-packed models to represent large sand bodies, as will be discussed later in Art. 16.25. A third use of the $J(S)$ function is in calculating the capillary-pressure–saturation relation for one fluid system from that measured with another fluid system.†

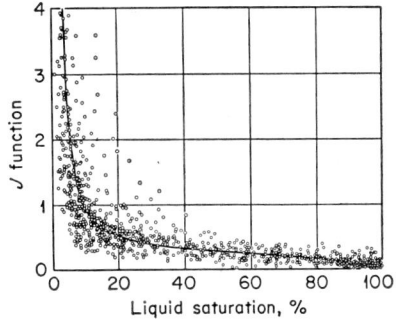

FIG. 16.31. J curve for all cores. Edwards formation–Jourdanton field. (*Ref.* 44.)

Example 9. Given: A capillary-pressure–saturation relation on a sandstone is measured with an air-mercury system. The interfacial tension of the air-mercury system is 480 dynes/cm, and the mercury has a contact angle of 140°. The interfacial tension for the oil-water system is 30 dynes/cm, and the contact angle is 30°.

Find: the capillary-pressure–saturation relation on the same sample for an oil-water system.

SOLUTION

$$J(S) = \frac{P_c(A\text{-}M)}{\sigma(A\text{-}M)\cos\theta(A\text{-}M)}\left(\frac{k}{\phi}\right)^{1/2}$$

$$= \frac{P_c(O\text{-}W)}{\sigma(O\text{-}W)\cos\theta(O\text{-}W)}\left(\frac{k}{\phi}\right)^{1/2}$$

$$P_c(O\text{-}W) = P_c(A\text{-}M)\frac{\sigma(O\text{-}W)\cos\theta(O\text{-}W)}{\sigma(A\text{-}M)\cos\theta(A\text{-}M)}$$

$$= P_c(A\text{-}M)\frac{(30)(0.866)}{(480)(0.766)}$$

$$= 0.069 P_c(A\text{-}M)$$

Thus, at any given saturation, the capillary pressure for the oil-water system is 0.0687 times that on the air-mercury capillary-pressure–saturation relation.

16.15. Fluid Distribution in Porous Media

Microscopic Distribution of Fluids. On the microscopic level, that is, within an individual or between neighboring flow channels, capillary forces control the distribution of the wetting and nonwetting phases. The wetting phase is always next to the solid and in the smaller channels. As mentioned, the magnitude of capillary forces controlling the fluid distribution depends on the interfacial tension, the fluid saturation, and on the sizes and shapes of the pore spaces. Usually in the porous rocks associated with production of oil, these interfacial forces are orders of magnitude larger than forces arising from flow of fluids through the pore spaces. Thus it is observed that capillary-pressure–saturation relations measured under dynamic conditions with two phases flowing simultaneously are identical with those measured under static conditions,[44] as illustrated in Fig. 16.32. The pressure gradients arising from the flow of fluids are usually of the order of 0.01 or 0.001 psi per sand grain even at fast laboratory rates,

---

† Another method of correlating capillary-pressure data for consolidated sandstone is to plot lines of constant capillary pressure on a plot of permeability vs. water saturation. It is generally observed that the water saturation at a given capillary pressure is inversely proportional to permeability.[45]

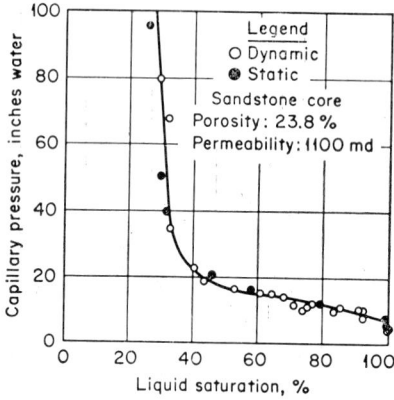

FIG. 16.32. Capillary pressures by static and dynamic methods. (*Ref.* 44.)

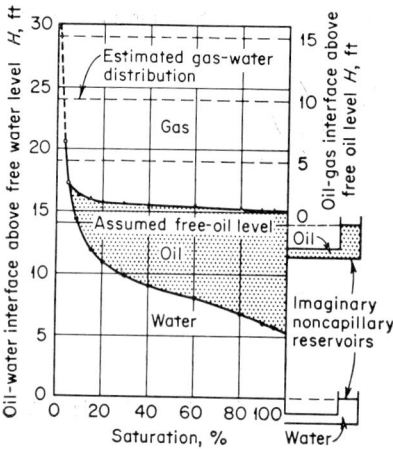

FIG. 16.33. Calculated vertical distribution of water, oil, and gas in a clean uniform sand under equilibrium conditions.

SOLUTION

$$H = \frac{P_c}{\Delta\rho g}$$

$$= \frac{(144)(10)(32.2)\dagger}{(15)(32.2)}$$

$$= 96 \text{ ft}$$

while the capillary pressures are of the order of 1.0 psi acting over distances of the order of one sand grain. Thus the flowing pressure gradients are usually too small to distort the shapes of the fluid interfaces.

Gross Distribution of Fluids. Capillary forces also play a role in the gross distribution of immiscible fluids in large sand bodies, for instance, in the distribution of water, oil, and gas in underground formations. The sands are generally believed to have been filled with water. Oil and gas migrated to the spot of accumulation and flowed to the top of the structure, causing water to drain from the rock. In geologic time, an equilibrium distribution of fluids has been reached between the capillary forces tending to hold water up in the sand body and the force of gravity pulling the water down. Capillary-pressure–saturation relations for the reservoir rock in question are used to estimate the water saturation as a function of height in the reservoir above some free-water–oil contact. Capillary-pressure–saturation relations for the fluid-rock system of the reservoir in question are converted into height above a free-water–oil contact by the equation

$$H = \frac{P_c}{\Delta\rho g} \qquad (16.75)$$

Example 10. Given: A capillary-pressure–saturation relation for the average permeability and porosity of the reservoir rock in question. The capillary pressure, corrected for the interfacial tension between the reservoir water and oil, at a water saturation of 30 per cent, is 10 psi. The density difference between the reservoir water and oil is 15 lb/ft³.

Find: the height above the water-oil contact at which a water saturation of 30 per cent exists.

Shown in Fig. 16.33 is a typical distribution of water in a petroleum-bearing rock as a function of the height above a free-water–oil contact.

Capillary forces are also important in gross movement of fluids under certain conditions of displacement of one fluid by another fluid immiscible with it. As will be discussed in more detail later, capillary forces affect the fluid distribution and flow at

† The 32.2 in the numerator is a constant with units of lbm-ft/(lbf-sec²)

the boundary where the fluids are emerging from the porous medium and also in displacement from nonuniform porous media. Generally, capillary forces cause the wetting phase to flow from regions of low capillary pressure to regions of high capillary pressure.

16.16. Simultaneous Steady-state Flow of Two or More Immiscible Fluids

The ability of two fluids to flow simultaneously through the rock depends not only on the permeability, but also on the relative amounts of the fluids filling the pore spaces. In discussing multiphase flow of fluids, the concepts of effective permeability and relative permeability are useful in describing the flow. Before proceeding, definitions of these terms are in order.

The *absolute*, or *total*, *permeability* is the permeability when the rock is completely filled or saturated with a single fluid. The absolute permeability of a rock to oil should be the same to oil, water, or gas. In some rocks, however, the presence of hydratable materials such as shales or clays, which swell when contacted by water, result in lower measured values of permeability for water than those measured for oil or gas.

The *effective permeability* to a fluid is defined as the permeability when the rock is only partly filled with the fluid. Effective permeabilities are point functions of saturation, and the saturation should always be specified with the effective permeability. For instance, the absolute permeability to water of a porous medium might be 1000 millidarcys, and the effective permeability at 70 per cent water saturation might be 100 millidarcys. As will be discussed in more detail later, effective permeabilities depend not only on the fluid saturation and pore sizes of the medium, but also on the saturation history and on rock characteristics such as the distribution of pore sizes.

The *relative permeability* is defined as the effective permeability divided by the absolute permeability. The relative permeabilities are reported as per cent relative permeability to given fluid at a certain per cent saturation of that fluid.

The equations which describe the relations between the flow rates of each phase and the pressure gradients at a given point in a porous medium when two phases are flowing linearly are

$$Q_w = \frac{-k_w A}{\mu_w}\left(\frac{\partial P_w}{\partial L} + \rho_w g \sin \alpha\right) \tag{16.76}$$

and

$$Q_{nw} = \frac{-k_{nw} A}{\mu_{nw}}\left(\frac{\partial P_{nw}}{\partial L} + \rho_{nw} g \sin \alpha\right) \tag{16.77}$$

in which k_w and k_{nw} are the effective permeabilities to the wetting and nonwetting phase at the saturation of the point in question. The pressure in the nonwetting phase is greater than that in the wetting phase by the capillary pressure at the saturation of the point in question. For cases where large saturation gradients exist at the point in question or where gravitational effects are large, the pressure gradients in the two fluids may be considerably different.

16.17. Relative-permeability–saturation Relations

Measurement of Relative Permeabilities. The utility of relative permeabilities in describing multiphase flow of fluids through a porous medium has necessitated the development of a number of methods of measuring this property of the medium. Usually, the samples of an underground formation available for study in the laboratory are small core samples 2 or 3 in. long and 2 or 3 in. wide. In such small samples, the capillary discontinuity at the outflow end can have a profound effect on the flow and distribution of two phases in the medium. All the methods of relative permeability measurement are designed to minimize the significance of this boundary, or end, effect.

The end effect arises because, as two fluids flow across the outflow face of the medium, a discontinuity in the capillary pressure occurs. Just inside the medium, the pressure between phases is different by the capillary pressure. Just outside the medium, the two fluids are the same pressure. Also, at the outflow boundary, the medium prefers to

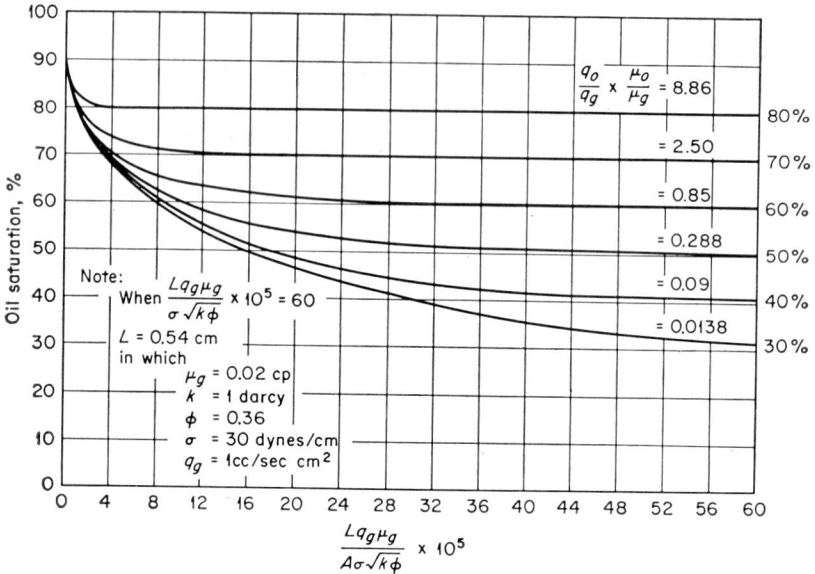

$$\frac{q_o}{q_g} \times \frac{\mu_o}{\mu_g} = 8.86$$

$$= 2.50$$

$$= 0.85$$

$$= 0.288$$

$$= 0.09$$

$$= 0.0138$$

Note: When $\dfrac{L q_g \mu_g}{\sigma \sqrt{k\phi}} \times 10^5 = 60$

$L = 0.54$ cm in which

$\mu_g = 0.02$ cp
$k = 1$ darcy
$\phi = 0.36$
$\sigma = 30$ dynes/cm
$q_g = 1$cc/sec cm^2

$\dfrac{L q_g \mu_g}{A \sigma \sqrt{k\phi}} \times 10^5$

Fig. 16.34. Saturation gradient in a core due to the boundary effect.

retain the wetting fluid which tends to pile up at the boundary. The equation describing the saturation gradients resulting from the boundary effect can be derived by combining the equations for flow of each phase [Eqs. (16.76) and (16.77)] with definition of the capillary pressure[46] [Eq. (16.68)], $P_c = P_{nw} - P_w$. The equation is

$$\frac{dS_w}{dL} = \left(\frac{q_w \mu_w}{k_w} - \frac{q_{nw}\mu_{nw}}{k_{nw}}\right)\left(\frac{1}{A}\right)\left(\frac{1}{dP_c/dS_w}\right) \qquad (16.78)$$

The distribution of saturation resulting from the end effect has been calculated for several porous media using Eq. (16.78) and the relative-permeability–capillary-pressure–saturation relations of the media. Shown in Fig. 16.34 is a typical plot of the saturation distribution as a function of the dimensionless parameter $q_o\mu_o L/A\sigma(k\phi)^{1/2}$ for various ratios of the two phases flowing. As will be discussed in more detail later, the dimensionless parameter $q_o\mu_o L/A\sigma(k\phi)^{1/2}$ is a measure of the relative importance of viscous and capillary-pressure gradients. It can be seen that increasing the flow rate compresses the saturation gradients into a smaller region near the outflow face.

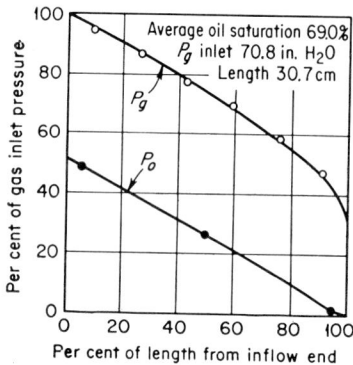

Fig. 16.35. Flowing-pressure–length relation for gas and oil in steady-state flow. (Ref. 46.)

The pressure distribution in each of the flowing phases has been measured along the length of a porous medium. Shown in Fig. 16.35 are the pressure distributions measured on a consolidated sandstone when flowing gas and oil at steady-state conditions. Note that the pressure in the oil, or wetting, phase is continuous across the outflow boundary, while the pressure in the gas, or nonwetting, phase is discontinuous. The magnitude of this pressure discontinuity is the value of the capillary pressure at the equilibrium gas saturation (the saturation at which the relative permeability to gas is zero). By increasing the total pressure drop across the sample by increasing flow rates, the errors caused by the pressure discontinuity in calculating the effective permeabilities from total pressure drops across the sample can be minimized. Thus high rates minimize the importance of both pressure discontinuities and the saturation gradients associated with the outflow boundary.

The methods of relative-permeability measurement can be divided into two classes— those that use steady-state flow conditions and those that use unsteady-state displacement of one fluid by another. Some of the more common steady-state methods are described briefly as follows.

The Penn State method[47] uses three plastic-mounted core samples pressed tightly together. The first core mixes the fluids; the middle core is the test sample; and the outflow core absorbs the saturation gradient resulting from the boundary effect.

The Hassler method[48] uses two porcelain discs pressed against the core sample. The two fluids are admitted to and removed from the sample at different, measured pressure drops. Boundary effects are avoided by maintaining the pressure drop across the sample, the same for each phase.

The Hafford method[46] uses a single porcelain disc pressed against the inflow face. The two fluids are admitted at different measured pressures. Boundary effects are made negligible by using high flow rates.

With all the above methods, two fluids are flowed through the sample until flow rates and pressure gradients are constant. Relative permeabilities are calculated using the flow rates and pressure drops. Fluid saturations are usually calculated from weight measurements.

The most rapid of the methods of measuring relative permeability are the unsteady-state methods such as the gas-drive and water-drive methods. Oil is displaced from the sample by injecting only gas or water. The volume of oil and gas or water is measured as a function of time. Relative permeability–saturation relations are calculated by the method of Welge,[49] which is discussed in Art. 16.19.

Properties of Relative-permeability–saturation Relations. Considerable research has been devoted to examining the properties of relative-permeability–saturation relations of various types of permeable media. The principal objective of this research has been to develop an understanding of the physics of the flow through rock. While it is beyond the scope of this section to describe the details of this research, the principal findings and conclusions are summarized in the following paragraphs.

A typical relative-permeability–saturation relation for a gas-oil-rock system is shown in Fig. 16.36. Though these relations vary widely from rock to rock, certain features of the curves in the figure are common to all rocks. It can be noted that at very low gas saturations, the permeability to gas is zero. As gas is injected slowly into a sand, the gas, being the nonwetting phase, prefers to enter the largest pores first. The gas is

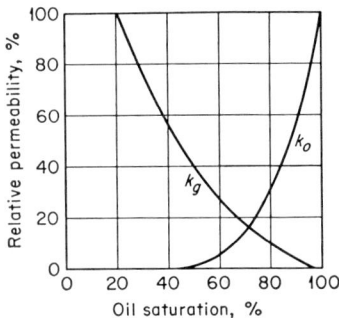

FIG. 16.36. Typical relative-permeability–saturation relation for flow of oil and gas.

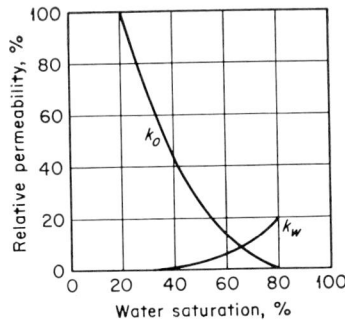

FIG. 16.37. Typical relative-permeability–saturation relation for flow of oil and water.

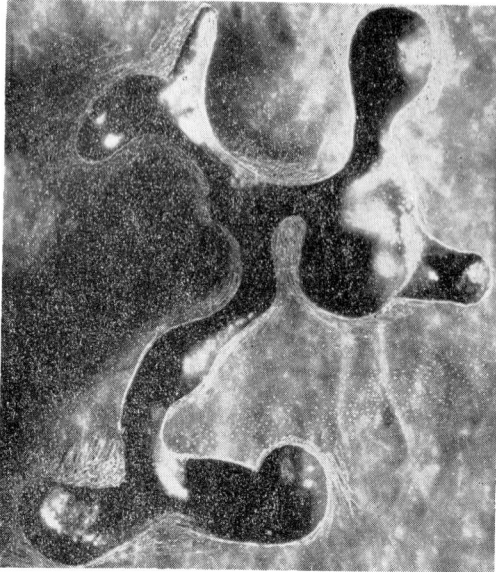

FIG. 16.38. Residual oil in sand (21 per cent saturation).

distributed as discontinuous filaments in the sand until a critical gas saturation is reached, when some of the filaments join and continuous flow of gas commences. This critical gas saturation is also referred to as the *equilibrium gas saturation*. Equilibrium gas saturations usually range from 1 to 10 per cent gas saturation and tend toward the larger value for rock with uniform pore sizes. As the gas saturation increases, the oil is displaced from successively smaller pores with the establishment of a greater network of interconnected gas-filled spaces. The permeability to gas increases with increasing gas saturation, while that to the oil which is receding into a finer and finer network decreases. At low oil saturations, the relative permeability to oil approaches zero asymptotically and the relative permeability to gas approaches 100 per cent as the oil recedes into the smallest crevices and films on the rock surface. In rock with uniform pore sizes, the relative permeability to gas and oil changes gradually with saturation.

Another useful characteristic of a permeable medium is the relative-permeability–saturation relation for a water-oil-rock system. A typical relation is shown in Fig. 16.37. While these also vary widely, depending on the rock characteristics, some of the characteristics common to all may be seen in the figure. At low water saturations when the oil, or nonwetting, phase occupies a continuous network in the larger pore spaces, the permeability to oil is 100 per cent and the permeability to water which is distributed in films and in small crevices is essentially zero. As the water saturation increases, the water occupies successively larger pore spaces, with the oil distributed in fewer and fewer of the largest spaces. Finally, at the residual oil saturation where the relative permeability to oil becomes zero, the oil network breaks into discontinuous globules or filaments. A photograph of a residual filament is shown in Fig. 16.38. Residual-oil saturations vary

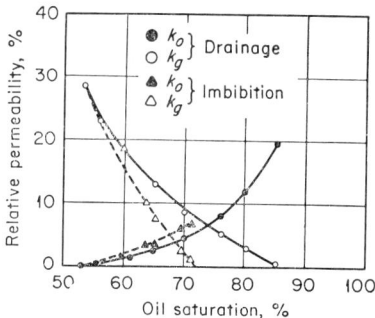

FIG. 16.39. Hysteresis–relative permeability. (*Ref.* 50.)

from 10 to 50 per cent, while relative permeabilities to water at residual-oil saturation range from 5 to 60 per cent. Residual oils are usually lowest in rocks with uniform pore sizes.

There is a hysteresis of relative permeabilities just as with capillary pressures. As previously discussed, a number of different stable distributions of fluids can exist at a given saturation, depending on the saturation history. Shown in Fig. 16.39 are relative-permeability data for drainage (wetting phase decreasing continuously from 100 per cent) and imbibition (wetting phase increasing continuously from some low value) conditions.[50] The relative permeability to the nonwetting phase at high-wetting-phase saturations is drastically affected by the saturation history.

The relative-permeability–saturation relations are independent of the flow rate over the range of interest. This is true for water-oil flow,[51] as illustrated in Fig. 16.40, or for gas-oil flow,[46] as illustrated in Fig.

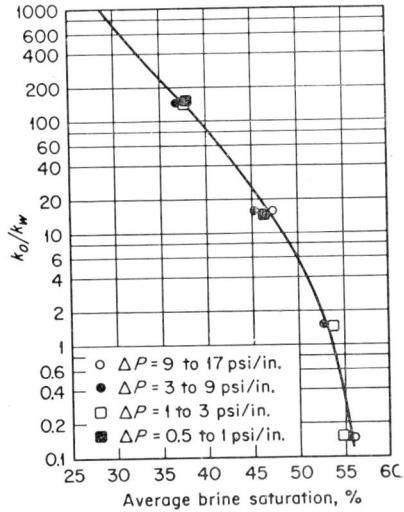

FIG. 16.40. Effect of rate on k_o/k_w-saturation relation. (*Ref. 51.*)

16.41. As previously mentioned in discussing capillary pressures, the capillary forces which control the microscopic distribution of fluids in the pore spaces are much larger than the forces causing flow by a single sand grain. Hence it is not surprising that the relative permeabilities, which are strongly dependent on the distribution of the fluids and the shapes of the fluid interfaces, are not dependent on the flow rate.

Relative permeabilities are also independent of the fluid viscosities and of the interfacial tension between the fluids over the range of practical interest[53] (Figs. 16.42 and 16.43). Also, it is generally observed that relative permeabilities calculated from unsteady-state experiments are the same as those measured in steady-state experiments,[53,46] as illustrated in Figs. 16.44 and 16.45. Relative permeabilities to gas and oil when plotted versus total liquid saturation are the same with or without a low-water saturation present, as illustrated in Fig. 16.46.

The nature of the wettability of the rock surface can affect relative-permeability–saturation relations. While the foregoing discussion has presumed a constant, known strong preference of the rock for one fluid or the other, if the surface shows little preference for one fluid or the other, if the wettability of the surface varies from point to point, or if the wettability of the surface changes during a displacement, the above remarks may not apply. While there is an incomplete knowledge of the wetting characteristics of many oil-bearing sands, effort should be made to prevent alteration of the surfaces of core samples as they come from the reservoir.[54]

Summarizing, the relative-permeability–saturation relations are independent of flow rate, fluid viscosity, and interfacial tension. By inference, they are also independent of the pressure level and the temperature.

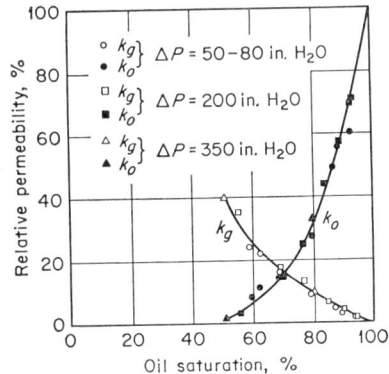

FIG. 16.41. Effect of flow rate on the relative-permeability–saturation relation. (*Ref. 46.*)

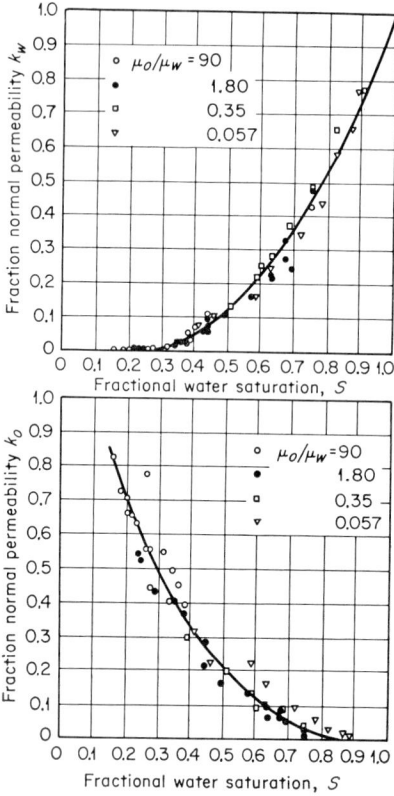

FIG. 16.42. Effect of viscosity ratio on k'_o versus S curve for 100- to 200-mesh sand. (*Ref.* 52.)

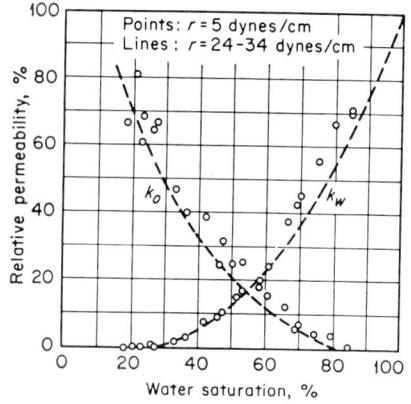

FIG. 16.43. Comparison of relative-permeability–saturation relations for two liquid pairs of widely different interfacial tension. (*Ref.* 52.)

The relative permeabilities are dependent on the saturation history and on the rock characteristics such as the pore size and the wettability. The understanding gained from study of the above factors affecting relative permeabilities is important in proper utilization of these data in the multiphase-flow calculations to be discussed next.

16.18. Immiscible Displacements in One-dimensional Systems

An understanding of the physical process of displacing one fluid from a porous medium by a second fluid insoluble, or immiscible, in the first fluid requires knowledge both of the microscopic process within the individual pore spaces and of the gross macroscopic process. In the previous article involving microscopic-flow phenomena, the role of such factors as

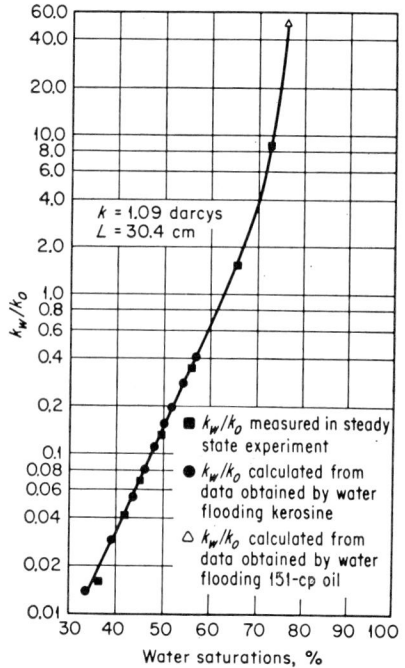

FIG. 16.44. Comparison of k_w/k_o–saturation relation measured in steady-state flow with that calculated from flooding performance. (*Ref.* 53.)

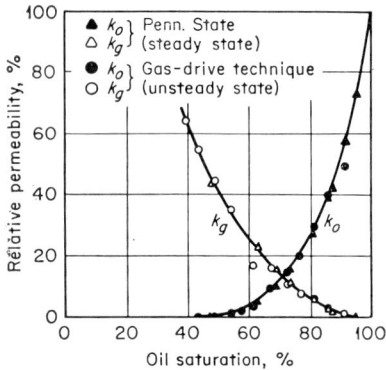

FIG. 16.45. Relative permeability obtained by steady-state and unsteady-state methods. (*Ref.* 46.)

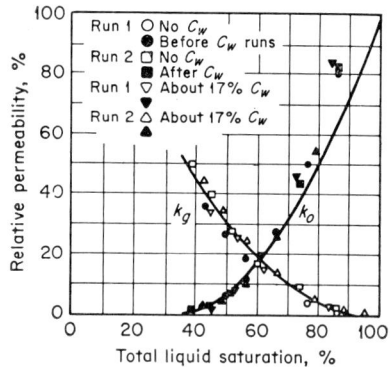

FIG. 16.46. Comparison of relative-permeability–saturation relations for a sample with and without connate water present.

flow rate and fluid and rock properties of the fluid conductivity (relative permeability) at various fluid saturations is developed. In the following articles, macroscopic phenomena are discussed.

The gross macroscopic displacement process depends not only on the fluid conductivities at various saturations, but also on an interplay among the forces acting on the fluids. These forces for laminar flow are the viscous, capillary, and gravitational forces. The viscous, or applied, forces result from the pressure gradients applied across the medium or from pressure gradients developed as fluids flow through the medium. The capillary forces result from differences in curvature of the fluid interfaces (different capillary pressures) in different parts of the medium. The force of gravity acting on coexisting fluids of different densities results in different hydrostatic pressure gradients in the fluids.

The gross-displacement behavior in a three-dimensional system is necessarily quite complex. However, as developed in Art. 16.25, the differential equations can be written and solved using dynamically scaled models. These equations can also be solved using numerical methods and high-speed computers,[55] but solutions for flow in three dimensions are quite costly with presently available machines. Before delving into discussion of displacements in three-dimensional porous bodies, considerable insight into immiscible displacement processes is obtained by studying the flow in one-dimensional, or linear, systems.

Many natural phenomena can be approximated by assuming that the flow is unidirectional. The displacement of oil by water or gas in certain types of reservoirs may sometimes be approximated by assuming that the flow is linear. Also, in many industrial and laboratory columns packed with porous materials, the flow is one-dimensional. Thus there is practical as well as academic interest in linear displacements.

The theory of linear displacements is discussed briefly in Art. 16.19. As in laminar flow of a single fluid, the basis for this theory is Darcy's law and the law of conservation of mass. In two-phase flow, the concepts of relative permeability and capillary pressure are additional factors in the flow process. Usually the linear-displacement equations are simplified to permit ready solution by assuming that the gross effects of capillarity are negligibly small.

In very long linear systems, capillary pressure gradients are negligible in laboratory columns at low rates. Experimental and numerical methods of accounting for capillary forces are given in Art. 16.20. In Art. 16.21, applications of the theory in displacement of oil by water or gas are given. Finally, in Art. 16.22, the process of spontaneous imbibition of a wetting fluid by a rock is treated for a one-dimensional system.

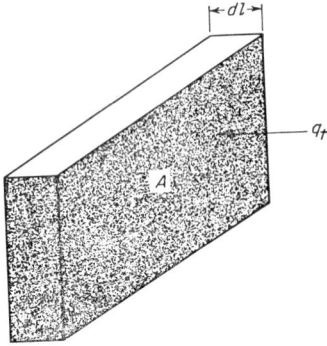

Fig. 16.47. Small element of the reservoir sand used in deriving continuity equation.

16.19. Linear-displacement Theory

Basic Equations. The theory of one-dimensional displacements was originally developed by Leverett[43] and by Buckley and Leverett.[56] In developing equations which describe the physical process of displacement of one immiscible fluid by another in a linear system, it is convenient to refer to a rectangular parallelepiped as shown in Fig. 16.47. A fluid is injected uniformly into one face as indicated, and fluid is produced uniformly from the opposite face. The assumptions in deriving the theory are as follows:

1. The flow is linear. In any plane parallel to the injection face along the length of the system, the fluids are assumed to be uniformly distributed and to be flowing with a uniform flux. No flow is permitted in the direction of the thickness.

2. The fluids are assumed to be incompressible.

By taking a material balance on a small element dL long and having a cross-section area A, a continuity equation can be derived.

$$\left(\frac{\partial S_d}{\partial t}\right)_L = \frac{-q_T}{\phi A}\left(\frac{\partial F_d}{\partial L}\right)_t \tag{16.79}$$

in which $(\partial S_d/\partial t)_L$ = rate of change of displacing-phase saturation at point of interest

q_T = total flow rate, displacing-phase flow rate plus displaced-phase flow rate

ϕ = porosity

A = cross-section area

$(\partial F_d/\partial L)_t$ = change with length of fraction of flowing stream, which is displacing fluid

The displacement equation is derived by algebraically combining Darcy's law for each fluid phase and the definition of the capillary pressure. For example, when a preferential wetting fluid such as water displaces oil, the Darcy equations are

$$q_w = \frac{-k_w A}{\mu_w}\left(\frac{\partial P_w}{\partial L} + \rho_w g \sin \alpha\right) \tag{16.76}$$

$$Q_o = \frac{-k_o A}{\mu_o}\left(\frac{\partial P_o}{\partial L} + \rho_o g \sin \alpha\right) \tag{16.77}$$

The definition of capillary pressure is

$$P_c = P_o - P_w \tag{16.68}$$

Partial differentiation of Eq. (16.68) with respect to length gives

$$\frac{\partial P_c}{\partial L} = \frac{\partial P_o}{\partial L} - \frac{\partial P_w}{\partial L} \tag{16.80}$$

Substitution of Eqs. (16.76) and (16.77) in Eq. (16.80), and noting that

$$F_w = \frac{q_w}{q_o + q_w} = \frac{q_w}{q_T} \tag{16.81}$$

and rearranging yields the displacement equation

$$F_w = \frac{1 + \dfrac{k_o A}{q_T \mu_o}\left(\dfrac{\partial P_c}{\partial L} - \Delta\rho\, g \sin \alpha\right)}{1 + k_o \mu_w / k_w \mu_o} \tag{16.82}$$

in which $\sin \alpha$ is positive when flow is in the upward direction.

This equation states that the fraction of the flowing stream which is water at any point depends on the saturation and fluid-viscosity ratio through the term $k_o \mu_w / k_w \mu_o$ and on the ratios of viscous pressure gradients $q_T \mu_o / k_o A$ to capillary pressure gradients $\partial P_c / \partial L$ and to gravitational pressure gradients $\Delta\rho\, g \sin \alpha$ in the arrangement shown.

A similar displacement equation can be derived for a nonwetting fluid such as gas-displacing oil.

$$F_g = \frac{1 - \dfrac{k_o A}{q_T \mu_o}\left(\dfrac{\partial P_c}{\partial L} - \Delta\rho\, g \sin \alpha\right)}{1 + k_o \mu_g / k_g \mu_o} \tag{16.83}$$

Taking the partial of Eq. (16.82) or (16.83) and substituting in Eq. (16.79) for $\partial F_d / \partial S_d$ yields an equation which, with proper initial and boundary conditions, would yield solutions of the displacement process. However, this equation is a second-order partial differential equation for which no analytic solution is known.

The problem is usually simplified by assuming that capillary pressure gradients are negligibly small compared with the viscous and gravitational pressure gradients.† By making this assumption, Eq. (16.82) for water-displacing oil becomes

$$F_w = \frac{1 - (k_o A / q_T \mu_o)(\Delta\rho\, g \sin \alpha)}{1 + k_o \mu_w / k_w \mu_o} \tag{16.84}$$

and Eq. (16.83) for gas-displacing oil becomes

$$F_g = \frac{1 + (k_o A / q_T \mu_o)(\Delta\rho\, g \sin \alpha)}{1 + k_o \mu_g / k_g \mu_o} \tag{16.85}$$

Now for a constant viscosity ratio, a constant angle of inclination, and a constant injection rate, the fraction of the flowing stream which is the displacing phase becomes a function of saturation alone. It is then possible to make a transformation of variables in Eq. (16.79) and show that the continuity equation can be written as

$$\left(\frac{\partial L}{\partial t}\right)_s = \frac{q_T}{\phi A}\left(\frac{\partial F_d}{\partial S_d}\right)_t \tag{16.86}$$

This equation states that the rate of movement of a particular saturation through the medium is proportional to the total flow rate times the change in composition of the flowing stream with small changes in saturation and is inversely proportional to the porosity times the cross-section area.

Methods of Solution. It is possible to solve simultaneously the continuity Eq. (16.86) and the displacement Eq. (16.84) or (16.85), given the initial and boundary conditions. One method is time-consuming because it involves a trial-and-error procedure before break-through of the displacing phase and it involves graphical integration; but the method yields a complete saturation history for all points along the flow path and also gives the recovery of the resident fluid as a function of the volume-displacing fluid injected. The other method of solution is that of Welge,[57] which involves no graphical integration and is simple and easy to apply. However, the detailed saturation history of each point is not obtained. Both methods require certain basic information. The necessary properties of the medium are porosity, permeability, relative-permeability–

† The consequences of assuming that capillary pressure gradients are negligible will be discussed in Art. 16.20.

saturation relation, length, width, thickness, and angle of dip. The necessary fluid properties are the fluid viscosities and fluid densities. In addition, the injection rate and direction of flow (updip or downdip) must be known.

Briefly, the *Buckley-Leverett* method consists of solving Eq. (16.84) or (16.85) for the fraction of displacing fluid in the flowing stream for various fluid saturations. Then, from a plot of F_d versus S_d, the slope dF_d/dS_d is determined for various saturations. Integration of the continuity Eq. (16.86) for a constant saturation yields

$$\Delta L_{sd} = \frac{q_T \, \Delta t}{\phi A} \left(\frac{dF_d}{dS_d} \right)^\dagger \tag{16.87}$$

For a given time interval from the state of the displacement, the distance moved by any given saturation can be calculated from Eq. (16.87). From plots of displacing-phase saturations versus length for various time intervals, the desired information on the displacement process can be determined. It is easy to show that the quantity of resident fluid displaced from the medium is equal to

$$Q_R = \phi A \Sigma \, \Delta S_d \, dL \tag{16.88}$$

in which Q_R is the total volume of resident fluid displaced, and ΔS_d is the saturation change in the time interval of interest in a small element of length dL. Thus, determining the area under the saturation-length curve and multiplying by ϕA yields Q_R.

Before the displacing fluid breaks through the outflow face, it is necessary to find the length of maximum advance of the displacing fluid by trial and error so that the volume of fluid injected equals the area under the saturation-length curve times ϕA. After break-through, the volume of resident fluid produced at various times is determined from graphical integration under saturation profiles and from Eq. (16.88).

The Welge[57] method is much simpler and easier to apply. Welge noted from the continuity equation that the change in fraction of water in the flowing stream with saturation at the outflow face of the medium is related to the pore volumes of water injected as follows:

$$\frac{1}{(dF_w/dS_w)_2} = Q_i \tag{16.89}$$

when Q_i is the pore volumes of water injected, and subscript 2 refers to the outflow face of the medium. Welge also showed that the saturation at the outflow face is related to the average saturation by the expression

$$S_{w \text{ av}} = S_2 - \frac{F_{w2} - 1}{(dF_w/dS_w)_2} = S_{w2} + F_{o2}Q_i \tag{16.90}$$

The displacement behavior is calculated by first computing the relation between F_w and S_w and measuring the slopes dF_w/dS_w as described in the first method. Then the relations between the saturation at the outflow face, the pore volumes of water injected, and the average saturation can be computed, using Eqs. (16.89) and (16.90). The amount of oil recovery is easily determined from the change in average saturation. The method is also useful in calculating relative-permeability–saturation relations from production data obtained from water-flooding or gas-driving core samples.

Example 11. Given: A reservoir sand 3050 ft long, 2500 ft wide, and 10 ft thick contains a 14.6 per cent initial water saturation and an 85.4 per cent oil saturation. The porosity is 30 per cent, the permeability is 2.0 darcys, a relative-permeability–saturation relation as shown in Table 16.5, and the sand is horizontal (angle of dip = 0°). The reservoir oil has a viscosity of 108 centipoises, and the viscosity of the water is 0.9 centipoise. Water is injected at a rate of 3400 ft³/day into one end of the reservoir, and oil and water are produced from the other end. Find the quantity of oil produced as a function of time and the volume of water injected.

The first step in the calculation procedure is to determine the relation between the fraction of the flowing stream that is water and water saturation. This can be deter-

---

† Under the assumptions made, dF_d/dS_d is a constant for a given saturation.

Table 16.5. F_w and dF_w/dS_w as Functions of Water Saturation

S_w	k_O	k_w	F_w	dF_w/dS_w
0.30	0.69	0.004	0.411	4.90
0.35	0.611	0.009	0.648	3.60
0.40	0.535	0.016	0.782	2.44
0.45	0.457	0.032	0.894	1.56
0.50	0.378	0.055	0.946	0.78
0.55	0.294	0.086	0.973	0.396
0.60	0.210	0.129	0.987	0.216
0.65	0.120	0.184	0.995	0.108
0.70	0.050	0.250	0.998	0.0445
0.75	0.011	0.327	0.9998	0.0160

mined from the simplified displacement equation using the relative-permeability–saturation relation and fluid viscosities. For instance, at an S_w of 30 per cent, $k_o = 0.69$ and $k_w = 0.004$.

$$F_w = \frac{1}{1 + k_o\mu_w/k_w\mu_o}$$

$$= \frac{1}{1 + (0.69 \times 0.9)/(0.004 \times 108)}$$

$$= 0.41$$

Similarly, values of F_w are calculated for other values of S_w, and a plot of F_w versus S_w is made.

The slope dF_w/dS_w is measured at various saturations. The values of F_w and dF_w/dS_w are recorded in Table 16.5.

Next the distances traveled by various saturations during a given time interval are calculated, using the continuity equation after 1350 days for $S_w = 0.30$.

$$\Delta L = \frac{q_T}{\phi A} \frac{dF_w}{dS_w} \Delta t$$

$$= \frac{3400}{(0.30)(25,000)} (4.90)(1350)$$

$$= 3000 \text{ ft}$$

The distances other saturations travel are calculated similarly and plotted in Fig. 16.48. The position of the maximum distance traveled by the water in 1350 days is found by trial and error. The total volume of water injected in that period is $(3400 \text{ ft}^3/\text{day})(1350 \text{ days}) = 4.59 \times 10^6 \text{ ft}^3$. Since water break-through has not occurred, the amount of oil displaced from the sand must equal the volume of water injected. By trial and error, the position of the front is located by making the volume of oil calculated from the area under the saturation-length plot and above the connate water saturation multiplied by the porosity and cross-section area equal the volume of water injected. The water front is found to be located at 1920 ft.

The time to water break-through is calculated to be $3050 \times 1350/1920 = 2140$ days. Additional saturation profiles are calculated and shown in Fig. 16.48 for times of 2140, 2500, 3500, 5000, 7500, 10,000, and 13,500 days.

The cumulative oil production is calculated after water break-through by multiplying the porosity times the cross-section area by the area under the saturation-length profiles and above the connate (initial) water saturation. The cumulative oil production is shown in Table 16.6 as a function of time and water injection.

Example 12. Given: A sand-packed tube 30.4 cm long with a cross-section area of 20.25 cm with a pore volume (PV) of 229 cc is prepared to contain a 14.6 per cent water saturation and an 85.4 per cent oil saturation. The viscosity of the oil is 151.5 centipoises, and the viscosity of the water is 1.26 centipoises. Water is injected into the

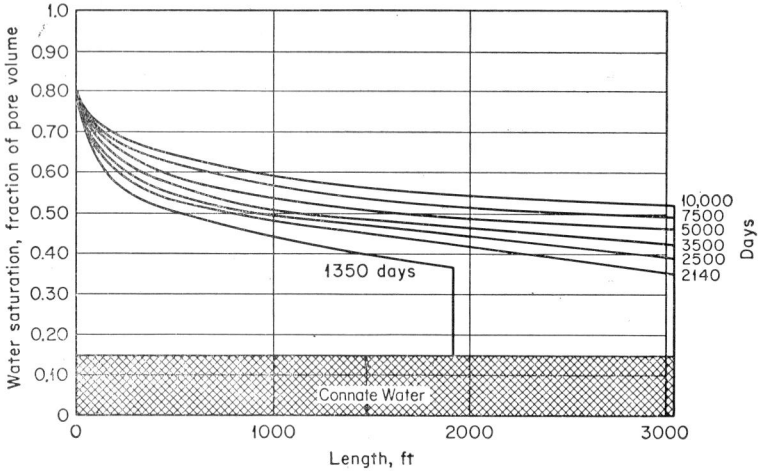

FIG. 16.48. Saturation profiles for water-displacing oil. (*Ref.* 62.)

tube to displace oil.   The volume of oil produced is given in Table 16.7 as a function of the time and volume of water injected.

The problem is to calculate the relative-permeability–saturation relation of the sand pack.

SOLUTION.   The method of Welge may be used to calculate the relative-permeability

Table 16.6. Cumulative Oil Production

Time, days	Water injected		Oil produced	
	ft³	bbl	ft³	bbl
1350	4,590,000	811,900	4,590,000	811,900
2140	7,280,000	1,290,000	7,280,000	1,290,000
2500	8,500,000	1,505,000	7,620,000	1,350,000
3500	11,900,000	2,105,000	8,270,000	1,465,000
5000	17,000,000	3,010,000	8,870,000	1,570,000
7500	25,500,000	4,510,000	9,530,000	1,690,000
10,000	34,000,000	6,020,000	10,070,000	1,780,000
13,500	45,900,000	8,110,000	10,580,000	1,870,000

Table 16.7. Oil Production as a Function of Time and Volume of Water Injected

Time, min.	Volume water injected		Volume of oil produced	
	cc	PV	cc	PV
0	0	0	0	0
37	56.4	0.246	56.4	0.246
41	65.1	0.285	64.9	0.283
49	82.0	0.358	75.0	0.328
59	102.1	0.446	79.5	0.348
81	142.0	0.62	85.0	0.371
100	177.8	0.776	88.4	0.385
120	216.3	0.945	91.5	0.400
152	285.9	1.25	96.0	0.420
180	368.5	1.61	100.0	0.437
220	512	2.24	105.2	0.459
270	749	3.27	111.4	0.486

Table 16.8. Calculation of Relative-permeability Data

Time	$S_{w\,av}$	Q_i	$F_o = \dfrac{}{dS_{av}/dQ_i}$	$Q_iF_o = \dfrac{}{S_{av} - S_2}$	S_2	$k_w/k_o = \dfrac{1 - F_o}{(\mu_o/\mu_w)F_o}$
0	0.146	0	0	0	0	0
37	0.394	0.246	0.93	0.229	0.165	0.000628
41	0.429	0.285	0.865	0.247	0.182	0.00130
49	0.474	0.358	0.375	0.134	0.340	0.0139
59	0.494	0.446	0.195	0.087	0.407	0.0344
81	0.517	0.620	0.104	0.065	0.452	0.0718
100	0.531	0.776	0.093	0.072	0.459	0.0814
120	0.546	0.945	0.070	0.066	0.480	0.111
152	0.566	1.25	0.058	0.072	0.494	0.135
180	0.583	1.61	0.041	0.066	0.519	0.195
220	0.605	2.235	0.028	0.063	0.541	0.289
270	0.632	3.27	0.020	0.065	0.567	0.408

data. First the relation between average saturation and pore volumes of water is determined from the production data. Average water saturation at any time is the sum of the pore volumes of oil produced plus the initial water saturation. Using a plot of average water saturation vs. pore volumes of water injected, the fraction of oil in the produced stream at any time is calculated from the slope of the curve. (Since dS_w is the pore volumes of oil produced with dQ volumes of total fluids, $F_o = dS/dQ$.) Then, using Welge's relation, Eq. (16.90), the saturation at the outflow face is then obtained by subtracting $S_{av} - S_2$ from the average saturation. The water-oil relative-permeability ratio at the outflow face is calculated from the form of the displacement equation

$$\frac{k_w}{k_o} = \frac{1 - F_o}{(\mu_o/\mu_w)F_o}$$

The data obtained by this procedure are shown in Table 16.8.

16.20. The Role of Capillary Forces in Linear Displacement of Oil

Capillary forces tend to cause fluid movement until the curvature at a given height is everywhere the same. If the direction of saturation change is the same at all points, the saturation at a given height in a homogeneous sand will be a constant value at equilibrium. In displacing oil with water or gas, the applied pressure gradients tend to generate a discontinuity in saturation at the displacement front. At this front, the capillary forces tend to equalize the saturations and to generate a zone of gradual change in saturation; the degree of equalization depends on the relative strengths of the capillary, viscous, and gravitational forces. Behind the front where the saturation changes are more gradual, capillary forces are of lesser importance in equalizing saturations. In their original dissertation, Buckley and Leverett saw intuitively that in very long linear reservoirs capillary effects could usually be neglected in homogeneous sands. They in effect hypothesized that only at the front would capillary forces affect the displacement and that this frontal region would usually be a negligibly small fraction of the total reservoir length.

The role of capillary forces in linear displacements was investigated theoretically and experimentally by Rapoport and Leas.[58] For displacements in linear, horizontal systems, a combination of continuity and displacement equations yields a single equation whose solution with appropriate boundary and initial conditions would describe the displacement. This equation is

$$-\frac{\phi L}{v_T}\frac{\partial S_w}{\partial t} + \frac{d}{dS_w}\left(\frac{1}{H\frac{k_o\mu_w}{k_w\mu_o}}\right)\frac{\partial S_w}{\partial x} + \frac{(k\phi)^{\frac{1}{2}}\sigma f(\theta)}{v_T\mu_o L}\left\{\frac{\partial S_w}{\partial x}\left[\frac{k_o\frac{dJ(S)}{dS_w}\frac{\partial S_w}{\partial x}}{1 + \frac{k_o\mu_w}{k_w\mu_o}}\right]\right\} = 0 \quad (16.91)$$

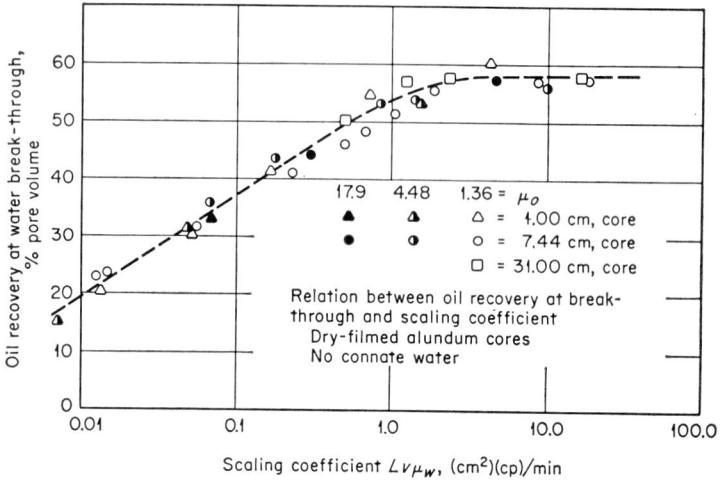

Fig. 16.49. Relation between oil recovery at break-through and scaling coefficient, drifilmed Alundum cores, no connate water. (*Ref.* 58.)

(For a more complete discussion of the origin of this equation, see Art. 16.19.) Rapoport and Leas reasoned that for a given porous medium and for given interfacial tension, contact angle, and ratio of fluid viscosities, the displacements could be scaled by the quantity $v_T \mu_o L$. For the conditions assumed, increasing the quantity $v_T \mu_o L$ increases the importance of viscous pressure gradients relative to capillary pressure gradients. These authors performed a number of displacements of oils by water at various lengths of Alundum cores which had been made oil-wet. The oil recoveries at water break-through were plotted as functions of the quantity $v_T \mu_o L$ as shown in Fig. 16.49. The oil recovery at break-through can be seen to increase with increasing values of $v_T \mu_o L$ and then to remain constant above a value of $v_T \mu_o L$ of about 2.0. This behavior was interpreted to mean that at the lower values capillary forces were smearing the displacement front, causing early water break-through. Above values of 2.0, the viscous forces dominated the displacement process and capillary forces played a negligible role in the gross fluid movement. Similar observations were later made in water-wet systems by Perkins[59] and by Kyte and Rapoport.[60] These studies corroborated the earlier intuitive observations because the value of $v_T \mu_o L$ in most reservoir displacements is usually greater than ten times the critical value where capillary forces become important.

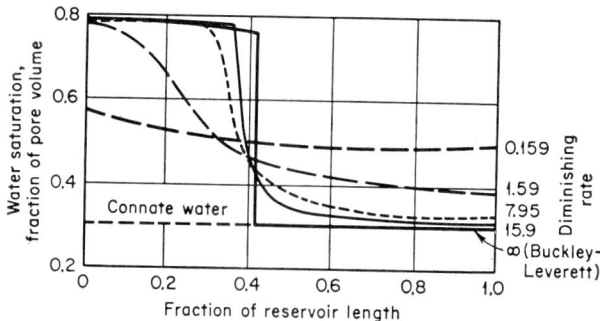

Fig. 16.50 Saturation distributions for four cases at 0.2 pore volume of water injected. (*Ref.* 55.)

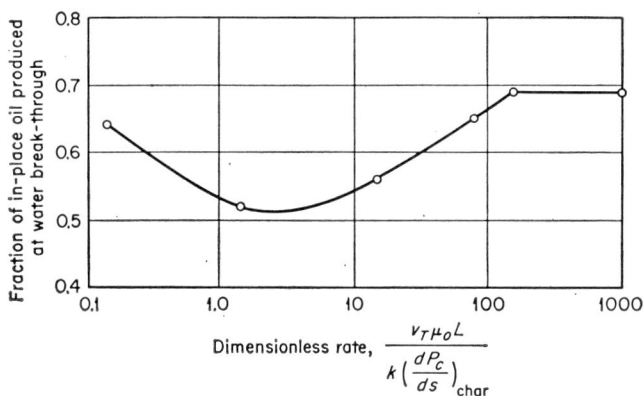

FIG. 16.51. Variation in oil recovery at water break-through as a function of dimensionless rate. (*Ref.* 55.)

Hence the term involving capillary pressure can usually be neglected in calculating displacements in long reservoir systems.

More recently, a lucid treatment of the role of capillary forces in linear water floods was presented by Douglas, Blair, and Wagner.[61]   These authors used high-speed computers to solve difference equations corresponding to Eq. (16.91). By using appropriate boundary conditions, linear displacements where calculated for a water-oil viscosity ratio of 0.5 for values of a parameter

$$\frac{v_T \mu_o L}{k(dP_c/dS)_{\text{characteristic}}}$$

which corresponds to the parameter $v_T \mu_o L/(k\phi)^{1/2} \sigma f(\theta)$ in Eq. (16.91) of 0.159, 1.59, 7.95, and 15.9.   Their calculated saturation profiles are shown in Fig. 16.50 when 0.4 pore volume of water had been injected.   Also shown is the saturation profile predicted, neglecting capillary effects.   The flat saturation profile for the dimensionless rate of 0.159 indicates the strong influence of capillary forces in equalizing saturations.   For values of dimensionless rate of 15.9, the saturation profile is approximated by the profile calculated, neglecting capillary forces.   The calculated recovery of oil at water break-through is plotted in Fig. 16.51 as a function of the dimensionless parameter

$$\frac{v_T \mu_o L}{k(dP_c/dS)_{\text{characteristic}}}$$

This plot shows the same characteristics found earlier in experiments.

16.21. Displacement Phenomena

Linear Displacement of Oil by Gas.   Recovery of oil by gas drive is most efficient when gravity plays a significant role in the displacement process.   If the reservoir sand is permeable and steeply dipping, the tendency for the gas to remain updip and for the oil to drain downward because of their density differences may result in high recoveries. Opposing the tendency for gas to float on the oil are the applied, or viscous, pressure gradients resulting from injection and production of fluids from the sand.   If the rates of injection and withdrawal are too high, little benefit may be derived from gravity drainage of the oil and gas.   A rule of thumb for estimating whether gravity segregation will improve a particular displacement may be obtained from the displacement equation

$$F_g = \frac{1 + (0.044 k_o A / q_T \mu_o)(\Delta \rho \, g \, \sin \alpha)}{1 + k_o \mu_g / k_g \mu_o}$$

$$= \frac{1 - C_1 k_{ro}}{1 + k_o \mu_g / k_g \mu_o} \tag{16.92}$$

The term $C_1 = (0.044 k_o A / q_T \mu_o)(\Delta \rho \, g \, \sin \alpha)$ is a ratio of gravitational pressure gradients to the viscous pressure gradients in the unit indicated in Example 13. A rule of thumb is that if C_1 has an absolute value of 1 or greater, gravity segregation will appreciably improve the efficiency of the displacement. The greater the value of C_1, that is, the greater the permeability and angle of dip and the lower the rate and viscosity of the oil, the higher will be the recovery of oil.

In practice, linear flow of gas and oil is probably seldom realized. The low density and low viscosity of gas tend to cause it to channel over or through the oil sand and bypass oil. These tendencies will be discussed later, in the section on displacements of oil in nonlinear systems. However, the linear-displacement theory often gives a reasonable first approximation to the recovery of oil by displacement with gas. The linear theory is also useful in developing, at least qualitatively, the role of the pertinent variables in the displacement process.

Example 13. To demonstrate the role of gravity in the linear displacement of oil by gas, a series of calculations were made, using the Welge technique discussed in Art. 16.19. The following conditions were assumed in the calculation:

Length of reservoir	10,000 ft
Width of reservoir	2000 ft
Thickness of reservoir	10 ft
Angle of dip	6°
Permeability	1.0 darcy
Porosity	0.25
Connate water saturation	0.25
Viscosity of oil	0.5 centipoise
Viscosity of gas	0.014 centipoise
Density of oil	45.5 lb/ft³
Density of gas	0.5 lb/ft³
Pressure	1000 psi
Temperature	120°F
Supercompressibility factor of gas (Z factor)	0.75
Formation-volume factor	1.25 bbl reservoir oil/bbl stock tank oil

Gas is injected updip at a rate of 500,000 ft³/day at standard conditions, and oil is produced at a rate such that the reservoir pressure remains 1000 psi.

Table 16.9. Relative permeability–Saturation

S_g	k_g	k_o
3	0	0.840
5	0.012	0.750
10	0.039	0.574
15	0.068	0.429
20	0.100	0.320
25	0.131	0.231
30	0.170	0.160
35	0.219	0.101
40	0.275	0.060
45	0.347	0.315
50	0.440	0.015

In the displacement equation,

$$F_g = \frac{1 + C_1 k_o}{1 + k_o \mu_g / k_g \mu_o}$$

$$C_1 = \frac{0.044 k_o A}{q_T \mu_o} (\Delta \rho \, g \, \sin \alpha)$$

$$= \frac{(0.044)(1.0)(25,000)(45.5 - 0.5)(1)(-0.10 \times 5)}{(500,000)(580/520)(14.7/10.5)(0.75/1)(0.5)}$$

$$= -1.71$$

Since the absolute value of C_1 is greater than 1.0, gravity segregation should be very important in the displacement.

The role of gravity segregation and the rate of displacement are demonstrated in Fig. 16.52, in which the oil recoveries have been calculated and plotted for the above case and for values of C_1 of 0, -0.855, -1.71, and -3.42. The role of gravity segregation in the displacement process may be ascertained by study of the curves in Fig. 16.52. The recovery shown for $C_1 = 0$ is that for the case in which gravity plays no role. Note that recovery of oil at gas break-through is only 15 per cent pore volume, and the recovery is only 33 per cent pore volume when 2.0 pore volumes of gas have been injected. The recoveries of 0.49, 0.54, and 0.58 of the oil in place at 2.0 pore volumes of gas injected for values of C_1 of -0.855, -1.71, and -3.42, respectively, indicate the increasing benefits of gravitational forces in causing the oil to drain downward in preference to the gas. The effect of rate of injection on recovery can also be ascertained from Fig. 16.52. At high rates of injection and production, little benefit is realized from gravity drainage of the oil.

The effect of the angle of dip on recovery is shown in Fig. 16.53. Steeply dipping sands promote the drainage of oil toward the downdip producing wells.

Other calculations have been made to illustrate the effects of the viscosity of the oil on recovery by gas drive. Shown in Fig. 16.54 are recoveries of 0.5, 1.5, and 5.0 centipoises oil. Note that the tenfold increase in viscosity of the oil from 0.5 to 5.0 centipoises reduces the recovery from 0.54 to 0.31 of the oil in place.

The properties of the reservoir rock also affect the efficiency of displacement of oil

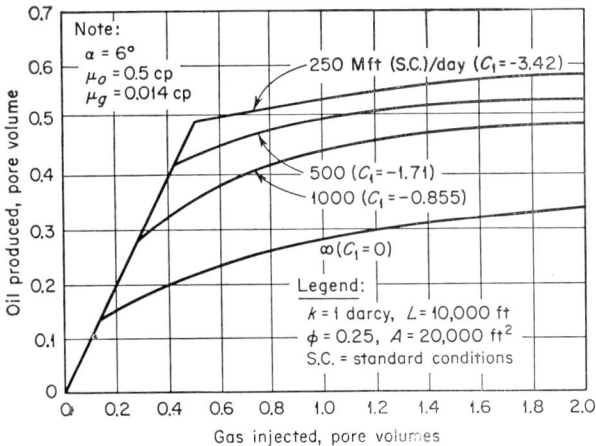

FIG. 16.52. The effect of rate of injection on recovery of oil by linear gas drive ($a = 6°$). (*Ref.* 62.)

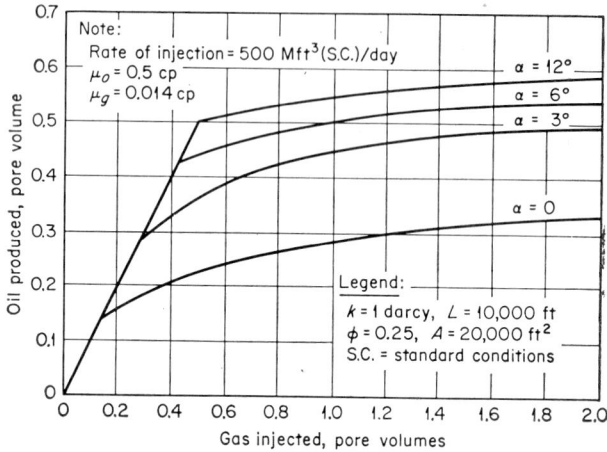

Fig. 16.53. The effect of the angle of inclination on recovery of oil by linear gas drive (constant rate of gas injection). (*Ref. 62.*)

by gas. The higher the permeability, the more effective is gravity drainage in increasing recovery in reservoirs with dip. In addition, the relative-permeability–saturation relation of some rocks is more conducive to high recoveries than that of other rocks. In rocks with uniform pore sizes, the relative permeability to oil may be 1 per cent at 60 per cent gas saturation, while in rocks with a wide range of pore sizes a relative permeability to oil may be 1 per cent at less than 30 per cent gas saturation. In the former case, recoveries by gas drive would be much higher than in the latter case.

Linear Displacement of Oil by Water. Water is usually more effective in displacing oil than is gas. As much as 80 to 85 per cent of the oil in place may be recovered by water drive, while recoveries by gas drive are seldom as high as 60 per cent. The principal reason for this higher recovery efficiency with water is that the viscosity of water is much higher than that of gas. Another reason lies in the relative-permeability–saturation relations for water-oil rock systems. In some rocks, the relative permeability to oil is 1 per cent or more when the water saturation is 80 per cent. As mentioned,

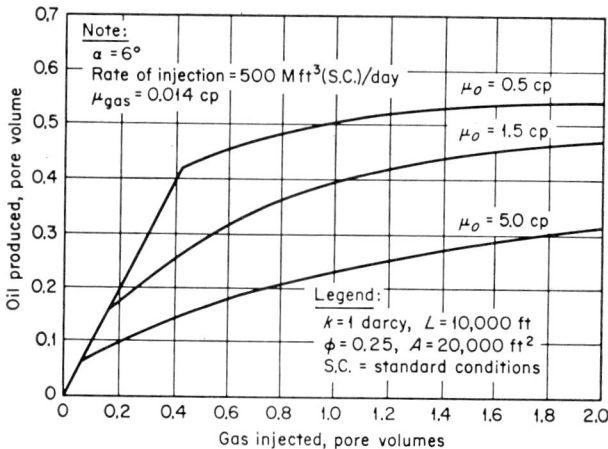

Fig. 16.54. The effect of the viscosity of the oil on recovery by linear gas drive. (*Ref. 62.*)

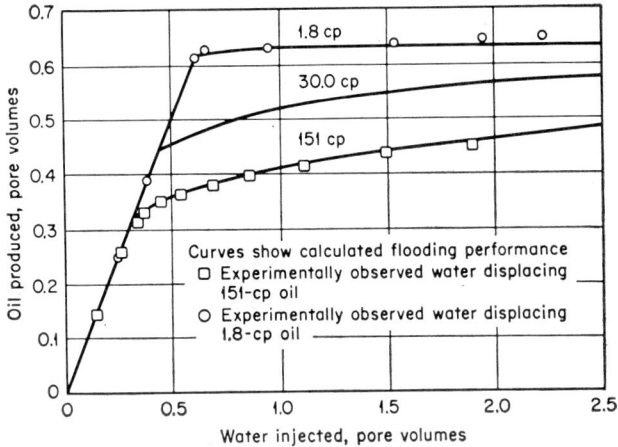

Fig. 16.55. The effect of the viscosity of the oil on recovery by water flooding.

the relative permeability to oil is 1 per cent or less in some rocks when the gas saturation is only 30 per cent.   Thus the greater relative ease with which the oil flows from
the pores of the sand when it is distributed as the nonwetting phase results in the higher
recoveries with water drive.

As with the case of gas-displacing oil, the theory of linear displacement of oil by water
does not permit channeling of water through stratified sands nor fingering and bypassing
of viscous oils.   Some of the cases where channeling occurs are discussed in Art. 16.26.
However, the linear theory is useful in examining the role of some of the variables in
the displacement process.

Gravity segregation usually does not play a major role in recovery of oil by displacement with water.   The density difference between oil and water is usually one-third or
less than that between gas and oil.   Also, recoveries by linear water drive are usually
quite high in horizontal sands where gravity segregation plays no role.

The viscosity of the oil does affect the recovery appreciably.   To illustrate qualitatively the effect of viscosity of the oil on recovery, the Welge calculation technique
was used to calculate the displacement of 1.8, 30, and 151 centipoises oil by water with a
viscosity of 1.26 centipoises.   The results of these calculations are shown in Fig. 16.55.
The oil recoveries were 0.31, 0.46, and 0.61 pore volumes at water break-through in
displacing the 151-, 30-, and 1.8-centipoises oils, respectively.   The recoveries were
0.49, 0.57, and 0.63 per cent after 2.5 pore volumes of water injected for the 151-, 30-,
and 1.8-centipoises oils, respectively.   Note that most of the recoverable oil was produced before water break-through with the 1.8-centipoises oil.   However, considerable
oil is produced after water break-through with the more viscous oils.   If enough water
were flowed through the sand, the same ultimate recovery of all the oils would be
obtained.   In practice, the cost of injecting water limits the amount which can be
flooded through a reservoir containing viscous oil.   So, as a practical matter, the
reservoir oil saturation is a function of the viscosity of the oil.

16.22. Imbibition Phenomena

If a porous medium filled with a fluid is brought in contact with a liquid which
preferentially wets the solid, some of the resident fluid will be expelled.   This spontaneous taking up of a wetting liquid by a solid is termed *imbibition*.   Examples of this
phenomena seen in everyday life are a blotter soaking up ink and expelling air from its
interstices, soil draining up water from an underground sand to replace moisture lost by
evaporation, or a dry brick on a house soaking up rain water and expelling air.   An

example of imbibition of considerable importance in recovery of oil is an oil-filled rock soaking up water and expelling oil.

In water-flooding a highly stratified reservoir sand, the tendency for water to channel through the more permeable sand is offset by imbibition of water into the tight sands, with expulsion of oil into the coarse sand. Also, in reservoir formations that are highly fractured, the tendency for water to flow preferentially through the cracks is offset by imbibition of water in the matrix blocks, with expulsion of oil into the cracks.

Both theoretical and experimental studies have been made to develop an understanding of the imbibition process.[63] These studies, described below, have given insight into the role of some of the pertinent variables such as interfacial tension, viscosities of the fluids, permeability of the rock, and the wettability of the rock.

Theory. The problem considered is that of linear, countercurrent imbibition of water into a porous medium containing a low water saturation and oil. The porous medium is a horizontal right cylinder which is completely surrounded by an impermeable surface except on one end. The open end is exposed to water at time zero. Water is drawn linearly into the medium by capillary forces. Oil flows linearly out of the sample in the opposite direction.

The equations describing the flow of water and oil at any time and at any point in the medium are obtained from Darcy's law for each phase.

$$q_w = -\frac{k_w A}{\mu_w}\frac{\partial P_w}{\partial L}$$

$$q_o = -\frac{k_o A}{\mu_o}\frac{\partial P_o}{\partial L}$$

Using the definition of capillary pressure and Leverett's $J(S)$ function and noting that $q_o = -q_w$, the equation describing the flow rate of oil at any time and point can be written.

$$q_o = -\frac{(k\phi)^{\frac12}A\sigma f(\theta)}{\mu_o}\left(\frac{k_w k_o}{1 + k_o\mu_w/k_w\mu_o}\right)\frac{dJ(S)}{dS_w}\frac{\partial S_w}{\partial L} \tag{16.93}$$

[Note the group $(k\phi)^{\frac12}A\sigma f(\theta)/\mu_o$ which appears as a parameter multiplying the groups containing relative permeabilities and capillary pressure gradients, functions of time and position.]

Equation (16.93) may be combined with the continuity equation,

$$\phi A\left(\frac{\partial S_w}{\partial t}\right)_L = \left(\frac{\partial q_o}{\partial L}\right)_t \tag{16.94}$$

By taking the partial of Eq. (16.93) with respect to length, substitution of $\partial q/\partial L$ in Eq. (16.94), substituting for length variable the fraction of the total length $\overline{L} = L/L_t$, and defining a dimensionless time $\tau = t(k/\phi)^{\frac12}\sigma f(\theta)/\mu_o L_t^2$, the differential equation describing the linear, countercurrent imbibition process is obtained.

$$\frac{\partial S_w}{\partial \tau} = -\frac{\partial}{\partial \overline{L}}\left(\frac{k_o}{1 + k_o\mu_w/k_w\mu_o}\right)\frac{dJ(S)}{dS_w}\frac{\partial S_w}{\partial L} \tag{16.95}$$

A solution of Eq. (16.95) would give values of $dS_w/d\overline{L} = 0$ for various times. Substitution of these values into Eq. (16.93) for various times would yield the cumulative oil produced from the medium as a function of time:

$$Q_o = \int_0^t q_o\,dt \tag{16.96}$$

While no attempt has been made to solve these second-order partial differential equations analytically, the role of the various variables in the imbibition process can be ascertained by study of the equations. The following observations can be made:

1. The oil-production rate is proportional to the square root of the permeability.
2. The oil-production rate is proportional to the interfacial tension.

3. The oil-production rate is proportional to some function of the contact angle. It is generally believed that the lower the contact angle, the faster the oil-production rate.

4. The oil-production rate is inversely proportional to the oil viscosity for a given viscosity ratio between the water and oil.

5. The oil production rate is a complex function of the water-oil viscosity ratio and the relative-permeability–capillary-pressure–saturation relations.

6. By study of Eq. (16.95) and noting the dimensionless time

$$\tau = \frac{t(k/\phi)^{1/2}\sigma f(\theta)}{\mu_o L^2}$$

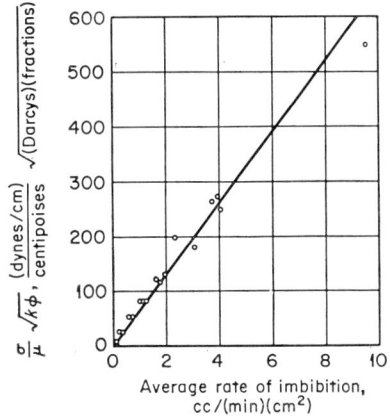

Fig. 16.56. Correlation of imbibition rates in sands. (*Ref.* 64.)

it can be seen that the fraction of the oil in place produced from porous media of various lengths is proportional to the time divided by the square of the total length of the medium, all other properties remaining constant.

Experimental Studies. The validity of the foregoing remarks on the relation between various fluid and sand properties and the imbibition rate is demonstrated by data of Leverett. Water-imbibition experiments were performed on tubes packed with sands of various permeabilities with fluids having various interfacial tensions and viscosities. Their results are shown in Fig. 16.56, which is a plot of the initial imbibition rate vs. the parameter $\dfrac{\sigma}{\mu}\left(\dfrac{k}{\phi}\right)^{1/2}$. The straight line through the data points demonstrates that the imbibition rate is proportional to the quantity $\dfrac{\sigma}{\mu}\left(\dfrac{k}{\phi}\right)^{1/2}$.

To check the relation between the fraction of oil in place produced and time, a series of imbibition tests were performed on a cylindrical sample of Berea sandstone. The initial sample, 12.5 cm long and 2.54 cm in diameter, was coated with an impermeable plastic on all sides except on one end. Water was allowed to imbibe into the sample, which initially contained a low water saturation and oil. After the imbibition test, the end of the sample was sawed off and the test was repeated on successively shorter samples of 10.6, 7.5, and 5.0 cm. The results of these tests are shown in Fig. 16.57, which is a plot of the per cent oil in place produced as a function of the time divided by the square of the total length. The data for all four lengths fall on a single curve, verifying the functional relationship implied in Eq. (16.95).

Practical Applications. One use of the imbibition theory is in designing small-scale laboratory experiments to represent the behavior in larger systems. In the following article, the theory of scaled models is developed, using some of the concepts discussed in the above discussion. Several of the practical examples of imbibition phenomena are illustrated in this section on use of models.

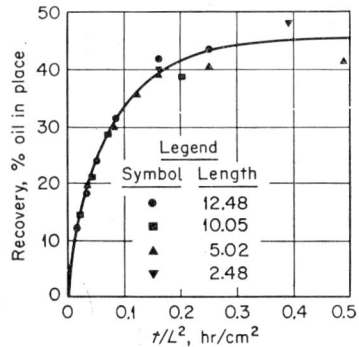

Fig. 16.57. Correlation of imbibition data on samples of different lengths.

16.23. Immiscible Displacements in Multidimensional Systems

For the general case of displacement of oil from a porous medium, the presence of injection and production wells on some kind of a pattern, the presence of strata of different permeability in communication with each other, or the presence of gravitational forces causing the less dense fluid to flow upward and the more dense fluid to flow downward result in nonlinear flow. While the differential equation can be written to describe the displacement, the equation usually cannot be solved by known analytical means. As mentioned, solutions can be made using numerical methods and high-speed computers. Also, dimensionally scaled models packed with sand can be built in which the displacement process in the larger reservoir system is duplicated in the laboratory. The laboratory measurements and observations of the displacement behavior in the model are directly related to the displacement behavior in the reservoir.

In the following articles, the general equation for displacement of oil in a three-dimensional system is developed. Then the principles of scaling are developed. The scaling criteria are developed and discussed in terms of their physical significance. The method of selecting model sand and fluid properties is illustrated using several examples. Finally, the use of models in displacements with well-pattern arrangements, with stratified sands, with capillary imbibition in fractured systems, and with gravity separation of fluids is presented.

16.24. Theory

The general equation for displacement of oil by water or gas can be developed in the manner of Rapoport[65] from the set of Darcy equations for each fluid flowing in the direction of the three principal axes and from the equation of continuity. It is assumed that the fluids are incompressible and the process is isothermal.

The equation of continuity is

$$\frac{\partial v_{xw}}{\partial x} + \frac{\partial v_{yw}}{\partial y} + \frac{\partial v_{zw}}{\partial z} = -\phi \frac{\partial S_w}{\partial t} \tag{16.97}$$

By using the definition of capillary pressure $P_c = P_o - P_w$, the pressure gradients and components of flow of the oil phase can be eliminated from the Darcy equations to yield

$$v_{xw} = \frac{v_x}{1 + k_o\mu_w/k_w\mu_o} + \frac{\partial P_c}{\partial x}\left(\frac{k_o/\mu_o}{1 + k_o\mu_w/k_w\mu_o}\right) \tag{16.98}$$

$$v_{yw} = \frac{v_y}{1 + k_o\mu_w/k_w\mu_o} + \frac{\partial P_c}{\partial y}\left(\frac{k_o/\mu_o}{1 + k_o\mu_w/k_w\mu_o}\right) \tag{16.99}$$

$$v_{zw} = \frac{v_z}{1 + k_o\mu_w/k_w\mu_o} + \frac{\partial P_c}{\partial z}\left(\frac{k_o/\mu_o}{1 + k_o\mu_w/k_w\mu_o}\right) - \Delta\rho\, g\left(\frac{k_o/\mu_o}{1 + k_o\mu_w/k_w\mu_o}\right) \tag{16.100}$$

in which $v_x = v_{xo} + v_{xw}$, etc.

After taking the partial of v_{xw} with respect to x, v_{yw} with respect to y, and v_{zw} with respect to z, by substituting Eq. (16.97), and by noting that $\partial v_x/\partial x + \partial v_y/\partial y + \partial v_z/\partial z = 0$ for incompressible fluids, the differential equation describing the displacement is

$$\phi \frac{\partial S_w}{\partial t} + \left(v_x \frac{\partial S_w}{\partial x} + v_y \frac{\partial S_w}{\partial y} + v_z \frac{\partial S_w}{\partial z}\right)\frac{d\left(\dfrac{1}{1 + k_o\mu_w/k_w\mu_o}\right)}{dS_w}$$

$$+ \frac{\partial}{\partial x}\left(\frac{\dfrac{k_o}{\mu_o}\dfrac{dP_c}{dS}\dfrac{\partial S}{\partial x}}{1 + k_o\mu_w/k_w\mu_o}\right) + \frac{\partial}{\partial y}\left(\frac{\dfrac{k_o}{\mu_o}\dfrac{dP_c}{dS}\dfrac{\partial S}{\partial y}}{1 + k_o\mu_w/k_w\mu_o}\right)$$

$$+ \frac{\partial}{\partial z}\left(\frac{\dfrac{k_o}{\mu_o}\dfrac{dP_c}{dS}\dfrac{\partial S}{\partial z}}{1 + k_o\mu_w/k_w\mu_o}\right) - \frac{\partial}{\partial z}\left(\frac{\dfrac{k_o}{\mu_o}\Delta\rho\, g}{1 + k_o\mu_w/k_w\mu_o}\right) = 0 \tag{16.101}$$

Equation (16.101) relates the rate of accumulation of water in a volume element to the effects on flow of the two phases of viscous, capillary, and gravitational forces at the point and time interval in question. At least in principle, solution of Eq. (16.101), using given initial and boundary conditions for the case in question and Darcy's law for the relation between flow rates and pressure gradients, would permit description of the displacement behavior. No known analytic method is available for solving this equation. However, the differential equation is very useful in developing scaling criteria for design of dimensionally scaled models as discussed in the following section.

Theory of Scaling. In designing a model of a larger system, the first requirement that the model must meet is that it be geometrically similar to the prototype; that is, the shape and the length-width and length-height ratios in the model must be the same as in the prototype.

This also requires that points of injection and production and boundaries across which no flow occurs be located in the same relative positions. It is desired that with injection and production of water or gas and production of oil and water or gas at the same relative rates and from the same places in the model as in the prototype will give the same displacement behavior. The additional criteria which are needed to scale the model conditions to those in the prototype to give exact similitude can be derived from the general displacement Eq. (16.101).

Equation (16.101) may be rearranged into a more meaningful form by the following method. Define the distance variables x, y, and z as fractions of the total length of the system L, $\bar{x} = x/L$, $\bar{y} = y/L$, and $\bar{z} = z/L$. Also, define the total velocities in the three principal directions as fractions of the total velocity v_T, $F_x = v_x/v_T$, $F_y = v_y/v_T$, and $F_z = v_z/v_T$. Also, Leverett's $J(S)$ function is substituted for the capillary-pressure function

$$\frac{dP_c}{dS} = \frac{\sigma f(\theta)}{(k/\phi)^{1/2}} \frac{dJ(S)}{dS}$$

Then, after multiplying Eq. (16.101) by L/v_T and by separating terms, the scaling equation results. The final equation for displacement of oil by water or gas in three dimensions is given by

$$\frac{\phi L}{v_T} \frac{\partial S_w}{\partial t} + \left(F_x \frac{\partial S_w}{\partial x} + F_y \frac{\partial S_w}{\partial y} + F_z \frac{\partial S_w}{\partial z} \right) \frac{d\left(\dfrac{1}{1 + k_o \mu_w / k_w \mu_o} \right)}{dS_w}$$

$$+ \frac{(k\phi)^{1/2} \sigma f(\theta)}{v_T \mu_o L} \left\{ \frac{\partial}{\partial \bar{x}} \left[\frac{k_o \dfrac{dJ(S)}{dS_w} \dfrac{\partial S_w}{\partial \bar{x}}}{1 + k_o \mu_w / k_w \mu_o} \right] + \frac{\partial}{\partial \bar{y}} \left[\frac{k_o \dfrac{dJ(S)}{dS_w} \dfrac{\partial S_w}{\partial \bar{y}}}{1 + k_o \mu_w / k_w \mu_o} \right] \right.$$

$$\left. + \frac{\partial}{\partial \bar{z}} \left[\frac{k_o \dfrac{dJ(S)}{dS_w} \dfrac{\partial S_w}{\partial \bar{z}}}{1 + k_o \mu_w / k_w \mu_o} \right] \right\} - \frac{k \, \Delta\rho \, g}{v_T \mu_o} \left[\frac{\partial}{\partial \bar{z}} \left(\frac{k_o}{1 + k_o \mu_w / k_w \mu_o} \right) \right] = 0 \quad (16.102)$$

Equation (16.102) forms a basis for selecting model sand and fluid characteristics so that a displacement in the model will exactly duplicate that in the prototype. Note that the equation contains parameters $\phi L/v_T t$, $(k\phi)^{1/2}\sigma f(\theta)/v_T \mu_o L$, $k \, \Delta\rho \, g/v_T \mu_o$, and μ_w/μ_o (other implied parameters relating to geometric similarity are the length-height ratio L/H and length-width ratio L/W of the model). Note also that for a given viscosity ratio $\dfrac{\mu_w}{\mu_o}$, $\dfrac{1}{1 + k_o \mu_w / k_w \mu_o}$ and $\dfrac{dJ(S)}{dS_w}$ are functions of saturation alone. It can now be seen by inspection that solutions of Eq. (16.102) will satisfy both model and prototype if the following are true:

1. The model and prototype are geometrically similar.
2. The model and prototype have similar initial and boundary conditions.
3. The model and prototype have the same values for the parameters $(k\phi)^{1/2}\sigma f(\theta)/v_T \mu_o L$, $k \, \Delta\rho \, g/v_T \mu_o$, and μ_w/μ_o with times given by $\phi L/v_T t$.

4. The model and prototype have the same relative permeability and dimensionless capillary-pressure–saturation relations.

When all the above conditions are met, a displacement of oil from a laboratory model will usually be an exact miniature of the displacement in the larger system. An additional criterion is sometimes required when the displacing fluid is more mobile than the displaced fluid. The additional criterion for this latter case is discussed in Art. 16.25.

The requirement for geometric similarity was briefly discussed previously. Also implied in this requirement is that the distribution of permeabilities and of impermeable layers or areas be similar. For instance, if the reservoir sand consisted of two layers of equal thickness but with one sand twice as permeable as the other, the model should have two layers of equal thickness with one layer twice as permeable. If an impermeable shale barrier separated the two sands in the reservoir, then the model should contain an impermeable barrier located similarly.

The requirement for similar initial and boundary conditions was also discussed briefly before as to location of wells, lateral boundaries, and relative injection and production rates. It is also required that the initial gross distribution of water, oil, and gas saturation be the same in the model as in the prototype. For instance, if the reservoir has an initial gas saturation uniformly distributed through the sand, so should the model.

The significance of several of the parameters in the scaling equation will develop additional understanding of the displacement process. The group $\phi L/v_T t$ relates the time to pore volumes of fluid injected, $v_T/\phi L$ or $q_T/\phi A L$. At similar times, the same fraction of a pore volume of fluid is injected into or produced from the model and prototype. The dimensionless group $(k\phi)^{1/2}\sigma f(\theta)/v_T\mu_o L$ is a measure of the ratio of capillary forces to viscous forces. Having this dimensionless group the same means that capillary imbibition has equal importance in model and prototype. For example, if water tries to channel through a permeable stratum in the reservoir but is restrained by imbibition of water into an adjacent tight sand, this effect can be duplicated in the model if the parameter $(k\phi)^{1/2}\sigma f(\theta)/v_T\mu_o L$ is the same. The group $k \Delta\rho \, g/v_T\mu_o$ is a measure of the ratio of gravitational forces to viscous forces. Having this group the same gives equal opportunity in model and prototype for two fluids with different densities to separate as they flow through the sand. For instance, in displacing oil with water, the tendency for water to sink to the bottom of the sand and flow only through the lower part is scaled by the group $k \Delta\rho \, g/v_T\mu_o$. The parameter μ_w/μ_o is a measure of the relative ease with which the two fluids flow. It is not necessary to have the viscosities of the oil and water the same in the model and prototype; just the ratio of viscosities.

The foundation has already been laid in Art. 16.16 for discussion of similarity of relative permeability and dimensionless-capillary-pressure–saturation relations in model and prototype. It was shown that the relative-permeability–saturation relations were independent of the viscosities of the fluids, the rate of flow (provided the flow rate is sufficiently low so that flow is in the laminar region), the density of the fluids, and the interfacial tension (over the range 5 to 30 dynes/cm). Also, the relative permeability and dimensionless-capillary-pressure–saturation relations depend on pore-size distribution and not pore size nor absolute permeability, provided the pore sizes are not too large. Leverett et al.[64] have shown that these relations become dependent on sand-grain size only for particles larger than those which will pass through a 20-mesh screen. Thus considerable freedom is had in selecting sand and fluid systems for the models.

Design of Scaled Models. In building models to represent large reservoir systems, the first question which must be faced is: What size should the model be? The model size is usually that which is small enough so that the cost of the equipment is reasonably low and time required for experiments is practical, but large enough so that the necessary scaling criteria can be met and the experimental precision can fall within desired limits. The next question which must be faced is: What sand and fluid system should be used? It is often desirable to use as permeable a sand as possible which has the desired relative-permeability and capillary-pressure characteristics. Fluid pairs with high viscosities and with as high a density difference as possible are usually chosen, with the precaution that the wetting characteristics of the fluids on the rock simulate those of the reservoir-rock–fluid system. The interfacial tension is then adjusted to the required

Table 16.10. Rock and Fluid Properties of Example Reservoir

Radius of well bore.................. 0.25 ft
Distance between injection wells...... 1320 ft
Sand thickness...... .... 26 ft
Permeability...................... 150 millidarcys
Porosity..... . ... 22 per cent
Angle of dip. ... . 0°
Viscosity of oil.................... 4.0 centipoises
Density of oil...................... 52 lb/ft³
Viscosity of water.................. 0.8 centipoise
Density of water................... 63 lb/ft³
Interfacial tension.................. 30 dynes/cm
Rate of water injection............. 200 bbl/day

value, making sure that any surfactant added to the fluids does not change the wetting characteristics of the sand.

Example 14. Given: To illustrate the design of models, a typical case is assumed. A reservoir containing a homogeneous sand is to be water-flooded with a regular pattern of injection and production wells. The repeated pattern of wells consists of four injection wells on the corner of a square area 40 acres in extent surrounding one production well in the center of the square. The reservoir rock and fluid properties are given in Table 16.10.

SOLUTION. The length of the side of the model is chosen to be 4 ft. Since the model must be geometrically similar to the prototype, it must have the same shape as the reservoir elements, with four injection wells on the corners and one producing well in the center. Also for geometric similarity, the model thickness must be $(4/1320) \times 26 =$ 0.0778 ft, or 0.945 in., and the radii of the wells must be 0.009 in. The model is packed with a 200-darcy sand having a porosity of 34 per cent and the same relative permeability and dimensionless capillary-pressure characteristics as the reservoir. An aqueous solution having a viscosity of 5 centipoises and a density of 70 lb/ft³ is prepared. Since the viscosity ratio must be the same in the model as in the reservoir, mineral oils are blended to make an oil having a viscosity of $5 \times 4.0/0.8 = 25$ centipoises. The density of the oil is 54 lb/ft³.

Applying the criterion that gravitational forces be of the same importance in the model and prototype,

$$\left(\frac{k \, \Delta\rho \, g}{v_T \mu_o} \right)_{\text{mod}} = \left(\frac{k \, \Delta\rho \, g}{v_T \mu_o} \right)_{\text{res}}$$

$$\frac{(200)(70 - 54)(1)}{(v_{T\,\text{mod}})(25)} = \frac{(0.150)(63 - 52)(1)}{(v_{T\,\text{res}})(4)}$$

$$\frac{v_{T\,\text{mod}}}{v_{T\,\text{res}}} = 310$$

Applying the criterion that capillary forces be of the same importance in model and prototype,

$$\left[\frac{(k\phi)^{1/2}\sigma f(\theta)}{v_T \mu_o L} \right]_{\text{mod}} = \left[\frac{(k\phi)^{1/2}\sigma f(\theta)}{v_T \mu_o L} \right]_{\text{res}}$$

$$\frac{(200 \times 0.34)^{1/2}(\sigma_{\text{mod}})(1)}{(v_{T\,\text{mod}})(25)(4)} = \frac{(0.150 \times 0.22)^{1/2}(30)(1)}{(v_{T\,\text{res}})(4)(1320)}$$

$$\frac{v_{T\,\text{mod}}}{v_{T\,\text{res}}} = 80\sigma_{\text{mod}}$$

From above,

$$\frac{v_{T\,\text{mod}}}{v_{T\,\text{res}}} = 310$$

$$\sigma = \frac{310}{80} = 3.86 \text{ dynes/cm}$$

The interfacial tension of the model fluids must be adjusted to 3.86 dynes/cm to scale capillary forces in the model (with this low an interfacial tension, care must be taken to see that no emulsification occurs in the model sand).

The injection rate in the model is given by

$$\frac{q_{T\ \mathrm{mod}}}{q_{T\ \mathrm{res}}} = \frac{(v_{T\ \mathrm{mod}})(A_{\mathrm{mod}})}{(v_{T\ \mathrm{res}})(A_{\mathrm{res}})}$$

$$\frac{q_{T\ \mathrm{mod}}}{200} = (310)\left(\frac{4}{1320}\right)\left(\frac{0.0778}{26}\right)$$

$$q_{T\ \mathrm{mod}} = 0.57\ \mathrm{bbl/day,\ or\ } 1.05\ \mathrm{cc/sec}$$

The relation between model and reservoir times is given by

$$\left(\frac{\phi L}{v_T t}\right)_{\mathrm{mod}} = \left(\frac{\phi L}{v_T t}\right)_{\mathrm{res}}$$

$$\frac{(0.34)(4)}{(310 v_{T\ \mathrm{mod}})(t_{\mathrm{mod}})} \quad \frac{(0.22)(1320)}{(v_{T\ \mathrm{res}})(t_{\mathrm{res}})}$$

$$\frac{t_{\mathrm{mod}}}{t_{\mathrm{res}}} = 1.51 \times 10^{-5}, \text{ or } 1 \text{ sec in model} = 0.765 \text{ day in reservoir}$$

16.25. Instability Phenomena

In displacing a fluid from a porous medium, under certain conditions the interface separating the displacing and displaced fluid will be on the gross scale smooth and even. This surface is usually referred to as the *displacement front*. Under other conditions, the displacement front will become irregular, with channels, or *fingers*, of the injected fluid penetrating and bypassing the resident fluid. In the latter case, the process is said to be *unstable*. The instability may arise from several causes.

One type of instability can occur when the displacing phase is more mobile than the displaced phase. This situation is described by stating that the mobility ratio is unfavorable. The *mobility ratio* M is defined as the mobility of the displacing fluid, $\gamma_1 = k_1/\mu_1$, divided by the mobility of the resident fluid, $\gamma_2 = k_2/\mu_2$, or

$$M = \frac{\gamma_1}{\gamma_2} = \frac{k_1/\mu_1}{k_2/\mu_2}$$

For unfavorable mobility ratios, unless the rate of displacement is less than certain critical rates below which gravitational or capillary forces can stabilize the displacement, the process will be unstable.

A second type of instability results for displacements with favorable mobility ratios. At low rates when displacing a less dense fluid downward or a more dense fluid upward, gravity can cause the front to become unstable. This type of instability also occurs when displacing a denser, less mobile fluid in the upward direction. In these cases a certain critical rate must be exceeded to obtain a stable displacement.

The criterion for obtaining stable displacements utilizing gravitational forces is discussed next. Also, the scaling criterion, in addition to those given in Art. 16.24, required when capillary forces are important in tending to stabilize displacements with unfavorable mobility ratios, is discussed.

Stabilization by Gravitational Forces. When a high-mobility, low-density fluid displaces a less mobile but denser fluid downward through a permeable medium, the gross displacement front will be smooth and even if the rate is sufficiently low. If the rate is increased above some critical rate, indentations, or fingers, may appear at the front and grow. At still higher rates, channeling may dominate the displacement process, with no semblance of a uniform front observable.

The critical rate below which no channeling occurs in a homogeneous medium was first derived by Hill,[66] who was studying refining of sugar. The significance of this critical rate can best be understood by considering the simple mathematical model illustrated in Fig. 16.58. Shown is a two-dimensional porous medium with flow in the downward direction, with the displacement front having a protuberance.† The critical rate is that at which the displacement front will maintain its shape. Using Darcy's law for each fluid and requiring that in the region of the protuberance both the linear velocities and pressure gradients in the displacing fluid equal those in the displaced fluids, the critical rate is obtained.

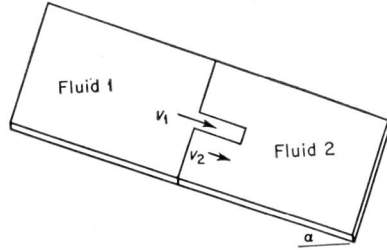

FIG. 16.58.
Displacement with fluid channeling.

$$V_{cr} = \frac{-(\rho_1 - \rho_2)\sin\alpha}{\mu_2/k_2 - \mu_1/k_1} \qquad (16.103)$$

in which subscripts 1 and 2 refer to the resident and displacing fluids, respectively, and $\sin\alpha$ is negative when flow is downward.

At all rates below the critical rate given by Eq. (16.103), gravitational forces will cause any bulges at the front to diminish in size until the front becomes even. At rates above the critical value, the viscous forces predominate, with the displacing fluid preferring to channel through the bulge. At rates above the critical value, the channel will grow in length.

A similar instability results in displacing a less dense, less mobile fluid in the upward direction. The critical rate below which gravity can prevent channeling is also given by Eq. (16.103).

Stabilization by Capillary Forces. When water displaces a viscous oil from a porous medium, the water may tend to channel in horizontal sands or in displacements in nonhorizontal sands when the rate exceeds the critical rate given by Eq. (16.104). In these cases, capillary action may tend to disperse the water laterally from the channels and in some cases prevent their growth. Chuoke, Van Muers, and Van der Poel[67] added an additional criterion that for instability to occur, the displacement front must contain deformations with wavelengths greater than a critical wavelength given by

$$\lambda_{cr} = 2\pi \left[\frac{\sigma^*}{(\mu_2/k_2 - \mu_1/k_1)(V - V_{cr})} \right]^{1/2} \qquad (16.104)$$

in which σ^* is an effective interfacial tension which depends on the interfacial tension and the wettability of the medium, and V_{cr} is given by Eq. (16.103).

Channels having lateral dimensions less than λ_c will not grow because of lateral capillary action. The wavelength of maximum instability is $(3)^{1/2}\lambda_c$. According to these authors, when the wavelength of maximum instability is of the order of the lateral dimensions of the medium, the ratio λ_{max}/D, in which D is the greater lateral dimension, must be scaled. This requirement is that

$$\frac{\lambda_{max}}{D} = C \left[\frac{\sigma}{(\mu_2/k_2 - \mu_1/k_1)(V - V_{cr})D^2} \right]^{1/2} \qquad (16.105)$$

in which C is a constant, depending on the medium and the wettability of the medium. The value of C is determined experimentally. Values of C for neutral sands are reported to be of the order of 30. For water-wet sands, values of C greater than 200 have been observed.

When λ_{max}/D is much less than 1.0, channeling dominates the process to such an extent that the behavior is insensitive to changes in values of λ_{max}/D. In this case, exact scaling is not required, but λ_{max}/D must be small in both model and prototype.

---

† Even in homogeneous sand packs or uniformly permeable rocks there exist small local regions having permeabilities different from the average. Channeling is believed to originate in such regions.

When λ_{max}/D is much greater than 1.0, capillary action prevents channeling. Again, exact scaling is not required, but λ_{max}/D must be much greater than 1.0 in both model and prototype. In the region of 1, changes in λ_{max}/D change the behavior, so that exact scaling is required. These additional scaling requirements must be met along with those given in Art. 16.24.

Stabilization by Viscous Forces. Another type of instability may occur when the displacing fluid is more dense and less mobile than the resident fluid and the direction of flow is downward. At very low rates, gravitational forces tend to cause the denser fluid to bypass the resident fluid. Although above a critical rate, viscous forces result in a uniform displacement front. This critical rate, the value of which must be exceeded for a stable front, is given by

$$V_{cr} = \frac{-(\rho_2 - \rho_1)\sin\alpha}{\mu_2/k_2 - \mu_1/k_1} \tag{16.106}$$

The same criterion applies to upward displacement when the displacing fluid is less dense and less mobile than the resident fluid.

16.26. The Use of Scaled Models in Systems of Complex Geometry

In many practical problems involving displacement of oil, the geometry of the system is so complex that the flow does not approximate the linear-flow case for which solutions are sometimes possible. Although the differential equation can be written which describes the displacement of oil in a three-dimensional system of arbitrary geometry, the equation cannot be solved by known analytical means. In many cases, solutions of this three-dimensional displacement equation can be obtained by use of dimensionally scaled laboratory models. In these sand-packed models, the viscous, gravitational, and capillary forces can be adjusted to have the same relative importance in the model as in the prototype. In a properly scaled model, the laboratory results faithfully duplicate the behavior in the prototype, but on a miniature dimensional scale and in a compressed time scale.

The scaled model is the most powerful tool available for study of complex displacement phenomena. In fact, most of the knowledge of the physics of flow of fluids through porous media has been derived from models of one kind or another. A good example is the use Darcy made of the sand-packed columns to find the relation between flow rate and head of water. Models are extremely valuable as research tools in studying physical processes. It is possible to study the role of one parameter by systematically changing the parameter in repeated experiments, holding all others constant. Also, observations of displacements in visual models often provide an insight into the physical processes involved which is difficult to gain in any other way.

One purpose of this article is to illustrate the utility of scaled models in solving several types of complex flow problems. The second, and perhaps more important, purpose is to summarize some of the knowledge gained from a number of model studies already made. Three different types of flow problems are considered. These are the gravity underrunning or overriding of high-density or low-density injection fluids, flow through stratified sands, and two- and three-dimensional studies with various well-pattern arrangements.

Gravity Overriding or Underrunning. The force of gravity may have a significant effect on the displacement of oil by gas or water in horizontal, permeable sands at low rates. The gas, because of its lower density, tends to float to the top of the sand and to override the oil, flowing through only the upper part of the sand interval. The converse is true when water displaces oil. The water, because it is more dense than oil, may sink to the bottom of the sand interval and try to flow under the oil. When the mobility of the water is less than that of the oil, the viscous forces resulting from the flow of fluids through the sand oppose the underrunning and tend to maintain a uniform front. The capillary forces also try to maintain a uniform water saturation throughout the sand thickness at each point as the water front progresses.

Some of the qualitative effects of gravity in displacement of oil by water from horizontal sands were studied, using a sand-packed Lucite model.[68] The model was 6 ft

Table **16.11**. Properties of Model and Prototype Used in Studies
of Gravity Underrunning

Property	Symbol	Model	Prototype
Permeability	k	213,000 millidarcys	85 millidarcys
Porosity	ϕ	0.37	0.37
Wettability	$f(\phi)$	1 (strongly water-wet)	1 (strongly water-wet)
Length	L	6 ft	300 ft
Sand thickness	H	½ ft	25 ft
Angle of dip	α	0°	0°
Viscosity of oil	μ_o	1.8 centipoises	1.8 centipoises
Viscosity of water	μ_w	0.89 centipoise	0.89 centipoise
Viscosity of gas	μ_g	0.018 centipoise	0.018 centipoise
Density difference (water-oil)	$\Delta\rho_{w-o}$	0.2 g/cc	0.2 g/cc
Density difference (oil-gas)	$\Delta\rho_{o-g}$	0.8 g/cc	0.8 g/cc
Interfacial tension (water-oil)	σ_{w-o}	37 dynes/cm	37 dynes/cm
Interfacial tension (oil-gas)	σ_{o-g}	28 dynes/cm	28 dynes/cm
Linear rate of advance	v_T	$(2500q/A)_{res}$	$(q/A)_{res}$
Time	t	$1/125,000t_{res}$	t_{res}

long, 6 in. wide, and ⅜ in. thick. It was packed uniformly with a 20–30–mesh Ottawa sand to have a permeability of 212 darcys and a porosity of 37 per cent. The model sand, fluid, and flow properties were scaled, using the procedure discussed in the preceding section to represent a reservoir sand 300 ft long and 25 ft thick, having a permeability of 85 millidarcys. Using this procedure, the viscous, gravitational, and capillary forces have the same relative values in the model as in the prototype, and a displacement in the model will duplicate that in the reservoir, but on a smaller scale. The model and prototype characteristics are presented in Table 16.11.

Two water floods were made on the model prepared to contain a 13 per cent initial water saturation and an 87 per cent oil saturation. The first flood corresponded to a linear rate of advance of 0.047 ft/day in the prototype, and the second flood simulated a rate of 0.10 ft/day in the prototype. The shapes of the flood fronts at the two rates are illustrated in Fig. 16.59. At the lower rate, 0.047 ft/day, the gravitational forces cause the water to tend to flow under the oil. The flood front has a considerable slope, with the front spread out over about 100 ft on the prototype. Notice that the front is actually rather blunt on its leading edge at the bottom of the sand. This bluntness results from the action of capillary forces, which cause some of the water to flow upward into the oil sand bypassed by the underrunning water. At the higher rate, 0.10 ft/day, the flood front is rather steep. The viscous forces have become

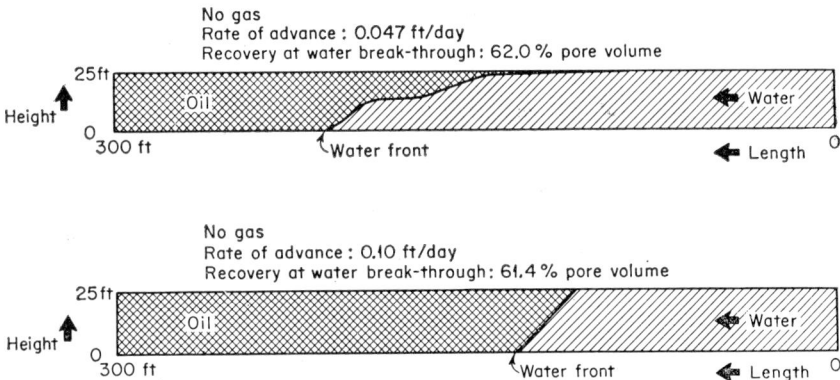

No gas
Rate of advance : 0.047 ft/day
Recovery at water break-through: 62.0 % pore volume

No gas
Rate of advance : 0.10 ft/day
Recovery at water break-through: 61.4 % pore volume

Fig. 16.59. The effect of rate on the flooding conformance of a uniform sand where gravitational segregation is important. (*Ref.* 68.)

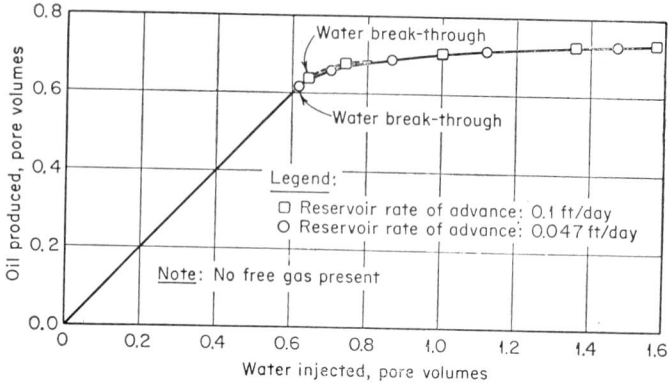

FIG. 16.60. The effect of rate on production characteristics of a uniform sand where gravitational segregation is important. (*Ref.* 68.)

predominant at this rate. The water tends to displace the oil with a more pistonlike flood front. The oil produced as a function of water injected for these two experiments is shown in Fig. 16.60. Water break-through occurred slightly earlier at the lower rate. Break-through was at 62 per cent pore-volume oil recovery at a rate of 0.047 ft/day, while break-through occurred at 64.1 per cent pore-volume oil recovery at 0.10 ft/day. However, no noticeable difference in recovery after water break-through exists in this particular case.

The effect of an initial free-gas saturation on the gravity underrunning of water was simulated in another experiment. It had been postulated that the presence of a zone of high gas saturation overlying an oil sand may cause the water to channel through the gas sand because of the high mobility of the gas. Therefore the model was prepared to contain a 37 per cent initial gas saturation, a 50 per cent oil saturation, and a 13 per cent water saturation. The gas was distributed in the sand by flooding with gas with the model in a flat position and then turning the model on its edge. Gravity segregation of the gas and oil resulted in a region of high gas saturation in the upper third of the sand and a region of high oil saturation containing a trapped gas saturation in the lower two-thirds of the sand. A water flood was made simulating a rate of 0.047 ft/day in the prototype. It was observed that water underran the oil just as when no gas was present. A comparison of the displacement fronts with and without free gas present is shown in Fig. 16.61. The shape of the displacement in the upper part of the sand was displaced by oil, which was in turn displaced by water. No channeling

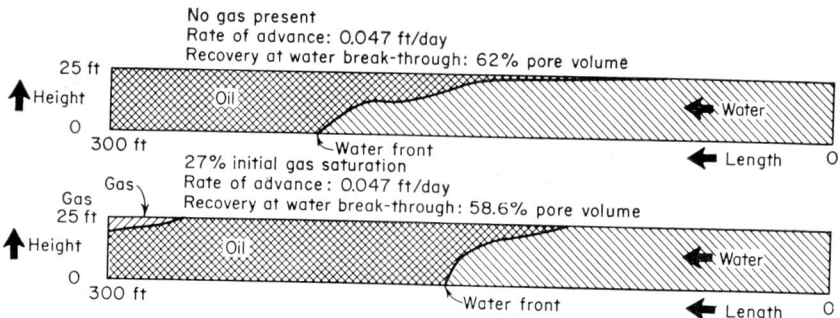

FIG. 16.61. The effect of the presence of an initial gas saturation on the flooding conformance of a uniform sand where gravitational segregation is important. (*Ref.* 68.)

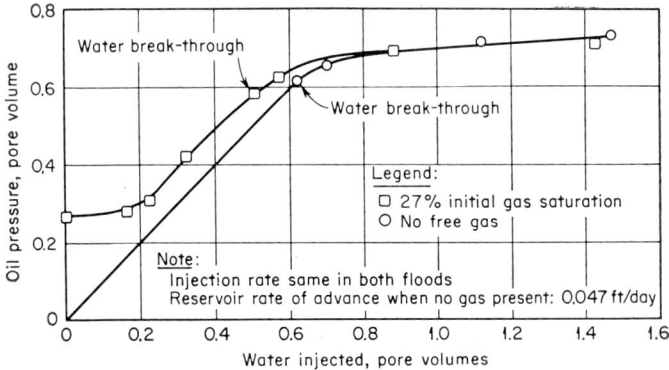

FIG. 16.62. The effect of the presence of gas on the production characteristics of a uniform sand where gravitational segregation is important. (*Ref.* 68.)

of water through the gas sand was observed. The oil recovery obtained by water flooding with and without free gas present is shown in Fig 16.62. Water breakthrough was slightly higher than when no gas was present.

An original and comprehensive study of gravity segregation in frontal drives was performed by Craig et al.[69] These authors studied both underrunning of water and overriding of gas. The scaling criteria presented by these authors introduced new concepts in scaling models to represent reservoir systems. Their scaling criteria, which must be the same in the model and prototype, are

$$R_a = \frac{L}{H} \left(\frac{k_H}{k_L} \right)^{1/2} \tag{16.107}$$

$$R_b = \frac{k_{r1}/\mu_1}{k_{r2}/\mu_2} \tag{16.108}$$

$$R_c = \frac{v_T \mu_o L}{k_L^{1/2} \sigma \cos \theta} \tag{16.109}$$

$$R_d = \frac{v_T \mu_o L}{(k_L k_H)^{1/2} \Delta \rho \, g} \tag{16.110}$$

The scaling criterion $R_a = \frac{L}{H} \left(\frac{k_H}{k_L} \right)^{1/2}$ requires that the ratio of effective length to height be the same in both model and prototype. This permits modeling of reservoir sands that are uniformly anisotropic; that is, the medium has a constant permeability in the vertical direction which is different from the constant permeability in the horizontal direction. To illustrate how this scaling group might be useful, consider a reservoir sand having a permeability in the vertical direction one-fourth that in the horizontal direction. Then a model which is packed with sand having the same permeability in all directions should have a length-height ratio one-half that of the prototype.

The scaling group $R_b = \frac{k_{r1}/\mu_1}{k_{r2}/\mu_2} = M$ states that the mobility ratio in the model should be the same as in the prototype. This criterion is intended to replace the more correct but more restrictive scaling criteria discussed in Art. 16.24 requiring that the relative-permeability–saturation relations and viscosity ratios in the model equal those in the prototype. In two-dimensional-pattern floods, it has been found that when a saturation gradient exists behind the flood front, the effective mobility of the displacing phase is that at the average saturation behind the front. It was found that the results of the pattern floods with miscible fluids in which the mobility ratios are simply the ratio

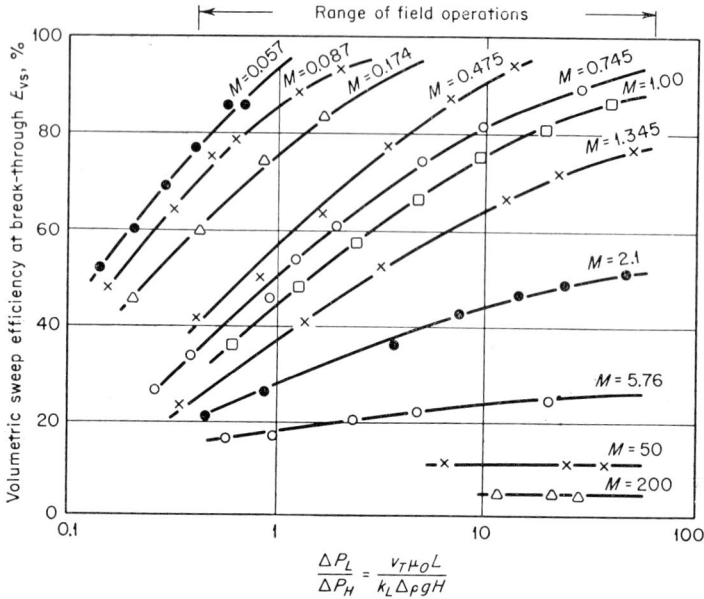

FIG. 16.63. Volumetric sweep efficiency at break-through—linear uniform systems. (*Ref.* 69.)

of viscosities agreed with results of floods with immiscible fluids having the same mobility ratio.

The other two scaling groups used by Craig et al. are R_c, which is a measure of the ratio of viscous to capillary pressure gradients, and R_d, which is a measure of the ratio of viscous to gravitational pressure gradients. These are similar to scaling criteria previously discussed. In addition to the four scaling criteria mentioned above, the initial and boundary conditions must be the same in model and prototype.

A large number of experiments were performed using models which were rectangular parallelepipeds in shape. These models were from 10 to 66 in. long, with length-height ratios ranging between 4.1 and 66. Some of the models were made of Lucite and packed uniformly with unconsolidated sand. Other models were constructed using a consolidated sandstone cut from outcrop sands. A large number of displacements were made over a range of rates using gas, water, and solvents to displace oil. In all these tests, the models were horizontal. In each experiment, the volume of sand contacted at break-through of the displacing fluid was determined from measurements using the profiles of the displacement front at break-through.

It was found that the underrunning or overriding of the injected fluid is particularly severe at low rates in displacements with high mobility ratios. Once the injected fluid is concentrated in one part of the sand interval by gravity segregation, its tendency to channel through that part of the sand is greatly enhanced when it has a high mobility compared with that of the oil. The results of all the displacements were correlated by plotting the volumetric sweep efficiency at break-through vs. the ratio $\Delta P_L/\Delta P_H = v_T\mu_o L/k_L \Delta\rho\, gH$† as shown in Fig. 16.63. The volumetric sweep efficiency is defined as the per cent of the total sand volume actually swept or invaded by the injected field. The parameter $v_T\mu_o/k_L \Delta\rho\, gH$ has the sense of being the ratio of the viscous pressure drop across the sand in the horizontal direction to the gravitational pressure drop in

† This group was obtained by combining two scaling groups $\dfrac{L}{H}$ and $\dfrac{v_T\mu_o}{k_L \Delta\rho g}$. While in the above case, the new group satisfactorily correlated the results, the procedure of combining two scaling groups into one is not generally correct.

the vertical direction at the start of a displacement. It can be seen in Fig. 16.63 that even when the mobility ratio is favorably low, for example, water-flooding with $M = 0.057$, underrunning of the water can result in bypassing of much of the sand at water breakthrough if the horizontal sand is thick and permeable and the rate is sufficiently low. When the mobility ratio is higher, for example, in gas-flooding with a mobility ratio of 2.1, overriding at low rates can result in the gas contacting only 20 per cent of a horizontal sand at break-through.

When the sands are dipping, gravitational forces have the opposite effect to that

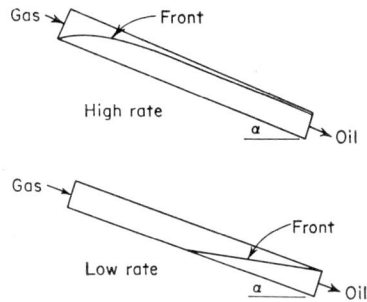

FIG. 16.64. Shapes of fronts.

noted in horizontal sands. Volume of sand swept by gas injected at the crest of a structure or by water injected at the base of a structure is greater at low rates than at high rates. Lindley and Gaskell[70] have performed a number of gas floods in Lucite models packed uniformly with unconsolidated sands. The permeability was 44 darcys, and the porosity was 34 per cent. The model was $17\frac{3}{4}$ ft long, 0.69 in. thick, and 0.83 in. wide. Displacements were made with the model having 2.5, 5.0, and 10.0° dip for oil-gas viscosity ratios of 18 and 92.

It was found that injecting gas updip at low rates, the gas-oil front proceeded downdip almost horizontally. At higher rates of flow, the gas tended to channel over the top of the sand as shown in Fig. 16.64. The recoveries of oil at gas break-through are shown in Fig. 16.65, plotted as a function of the ratio of viscous to gravitational pressure gradients $v_T \mu_o / k \, \Delta\rho \, g \sin \alpha$. It can be seen in Fig. 16.65 that when displacing the oil having a viscosity 92 times that of the gas, all the data at different angles of dip fall on a single curve. Very high recoveries are obtained at low rates, but recovery at gas break-through decreases rapidly with rate. The recoveries obtained in displacing an oil only 18 times as viscous as the gas are also shown in Fig. 16.65. Recoveries are higher than with the more viscous oil, but the same qualitative dependence on rate is indicated.

The recoveries obtained in these experimental models have been compared with those predicted using the linear-displacement calculation (Fig. 16.66). The reason for this disagreement is believed to result from drainage of oil vertically downward from regions swept by gas, with subsequent flow of oil in a region of higher saturation along

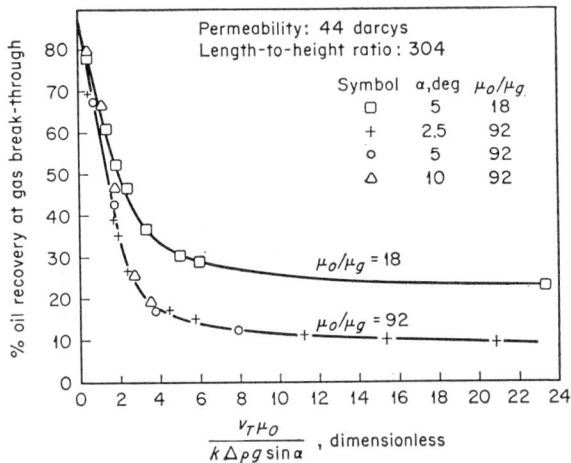

FIG. 16.65. Oil recovery at gas break-through vs. viscous-gravitational pressure-gradient ratio.

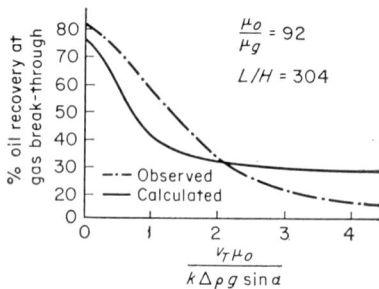

FIG. 16.66. Comparison of calculated with observed break-through recoveries.

the bottom of the sand interval. This two-dimensional character of the flow is not permitted in the linear theory. For values of $v_T \mu_o / k\, \Delta\rho\, g \sin\alpha$ greater than 2.0, the observed recoveries are less than those calculated. Since these rates are over twice the critical rate for stability, it is believed that channeling and bypassing of the oil, not permitted in the linear theory, result in the poor recovery efficiency.

These experimental results were also compared with those predicted using the theory of Martin.[71] This theory permits separation by gravity and overriding of the oil sand by gas. Good agreement was obtained below values of $v_T \mu_o / k\, \Delta\rho\, g \sin\alpha$ of 0.8, but the predicted and observed behavior diverged widely above values of 0.8.

Flow through Stratified Sands. One of the most important but complex problems in production of oil is in calculating the flow through stratified sands. In many cases the degree and kind of stratification control whether a secondary recovery method will succeed or fail. But unfortunately, the nature of the stratification is usually the least well known of all the reservoir characteristics. Some reservoirs are composed of several strata that are laterally continuous and fairly uniform throughout the extent of the pool.[72] Each stratum may have a different permeability than neighboring strata, and the strata may or may not be in intimate contact. In some cases, layers of shale of very low permeability separate the sand members, while in other cases there is no shale and free communication prevails between sands. Each layer may be fairly homogeneous, or it may vary widely in permeability both laterally and vertically. Obviously, an infinite number of kinds and degrees of stratification exist. Only a few of the more simple cases are treated here to illustrate the qualitative effects of stratification on the efficiency with which oil is displaced. A few qualitative studies of the case in which the sands are in communication are discussed below, and the case for isolated parallel strata is treated next.

In scaling a model to represent a particular stratified reservoir prototype, a necessary condition is that the model have the same relative distribution of permeabilities as the reservoir; that is, if the reservoir has a sand distributed over the lower half of the interval which is twice as permeable as the upper half, the model must have a sand distributed in the lower half of the thickness twice as permeable as the upper half. If $k_a, k_b, \ldots, k_n$ are the permeabilities at different points in the reservoir, then the model must have different permeabilities at corresponding points according to the following criterion:

$$\left(\frac{k_b}{k_a}\right)_{\text{mod}} = \left(\frac{k_b}{k_a}\right)_{\text{res}}, \ldots, \left(\frac{k_n}{k_a}\right)_{\text{mod}} = \left(\frac{k_n}{k_a}\right)_{\text{res}}$$

All other scaling criteria discussed in Arts. 16.24 and 16.25 also apply.

To illustrate some of the qualitative characteristics of displacement of oil from stratified sands and the scaling procedure, a model study was performed.[68] The reservoir sand of interest was 300 ft long and 25 ft thick. The formation contained two layers of 12.5 ft thick each with free communication between layers. One stratum had a permeability of 67.5 millidarcys, and the other had a permeability of 450 millidarcys. A sand-packed Lucite model was scaled to represent this reservoir. The model was 6 ft long, 6 in. thick, and ⅜ in. wide. Two sand layers having the same permeability ratio as those in the prototype 450/67.5 = 6.66 were packed into the model. These layers were each 6 ft long, 3 in. thick, and ⅜ in. wide and had permeabilities of 22,000 and 3300 millidarcys. Since it was desired to study only the effects of stratification, gravitation forces were made negligible by placing the model on its flat side during displacements. The model and prototype characteristics are shown in Table 16.12.

Water floods were made on the model at several rates of flow with and without free

Table **16.12.** Properties of Stratified Model and Prototype

Property	Symbol	Model	Prototype
Length	L	6 ft	300 ft
Thickness	H	0.5 ft	25 ft
Angle of dip	α	0°	0°
Permeability of first sand	k_1	22,000 millidarcys	450 millidarcys
Permeability of second sand	k_2	3300 millidarcys	67.5 millidarcys
Viscosity of oil	μ_o	1.8 centipoises	1.8 centipoises
Viscosity of gas	μ_g	0.018 centipoise	0.018 centipoise
Viscosity of water	μ_w	0.89 centipoise	0.89 centipoise
Interfacial tension (water-oil)	σ_{w-o}	37 dynes/cm	37 dynes/cm
Interfacial tension (oil-gas)	σ_{o-g}	28 dynes/cm	28 dynes/cm
Linear rate of advance	v_T	350 $v_{T\ res}$	$v_{T\ res}$
Time	t	$1/17{,}500 t_{res}$	t_{res}

gas present. In the first cases, the model was prepared to contain a low water saturation and oil with no free gas present. Water floods were conducted at rates simulating 0.18 and 0.51 ft/day in the prototype. Shown in Fig. 16.67 are the profiles of the water front in the model just before water break-through. At the higher rate, water channeled farther ahead through the permeable sand but did not even approximate the factor of 6.66 obtained from a ratio of permeabilities of the sands. Note that even at the higher rate, the movement in the coarse sand is only 20 per cent greater than that in the tight sand. The explanation of this behavior lies in the capillary-imbibition phenomenon. As water tries to channel through the coarse sand and bypass oil in the less permeable sand, the water is imbibed into the tight sand with expulsion of oil into the more permeable sand. The power of the capillary forces is vividly demonstrated by the rate at which water and oil are exchanged by the two sands. At 0.18 ft/day, the capillary action results in an almost uniform rate of advance even though one sand is 6.66 times more permeable. The recovery obtained at the two rates is shown in Fig. 16.68. While water break-through occurred at the higher rate when 0.530 pore volume of oil had been recovered compared with 0.605 at the lower rate, recoveries after injection of 0.80 pore volume of water were practically independent of rate.

The effect of the presence of free gas on displacement of oil from stratified sands is qualitatively shown in Fig. 16.69. The model contained an initial gas saturation of 37 per cent before water-flooding at 0.51 ft/day. Most of this gas was concentrated in the more permeable sand. As the water flood progressed, an oil bank built up, displacing gas down the coarse sand. At the water-oil flood front, the selective exchange of water for oil by capillary imbibition again retarded the channeling of water through the coarse

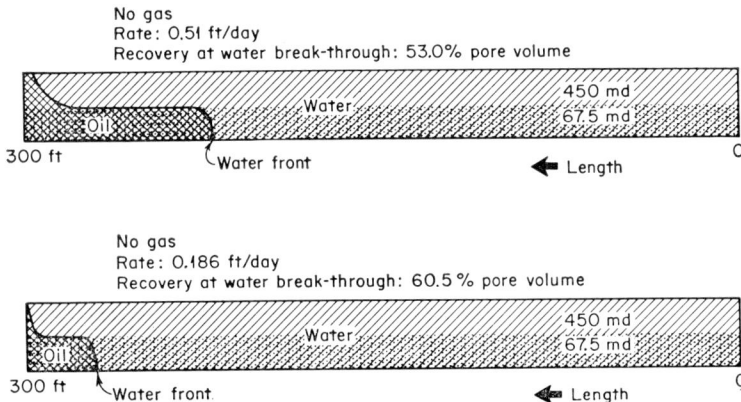

Fig. 16.67. The effect of rate on the flooding conformance of a stratified reservoir. (*Ref.* 68.)

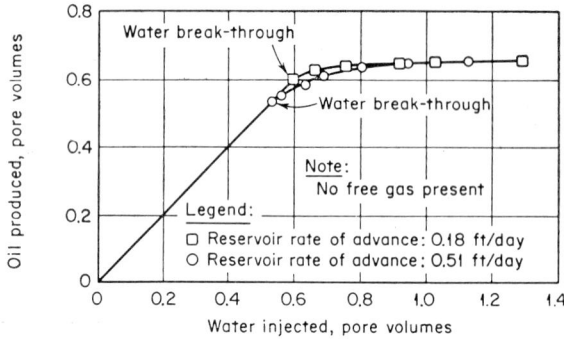

FIG. 16.68. The effect of rate on the production characteristics of a stratified reservoir. (*Ref.* 68.)

sand. While the high-mobility gas was being displaced in the coarse sand, slightly more rapid channeling of water was observed than when no gas was present. Recovery of oil at water break-through was 0.472 pore volume when gas was present and 0.53 pore volume when no gas was present. However, the recovery at 0.8 pore-volume water injection was slightly higher when gas was present.

Gravity segregation and location of the sands also affect the recovery of oil from stratified sands. If the tight sands are on the bottom of the reservoir, both gravitational and capillary forces offset the tendency for water to channel through the more permeable sands. If the coarse sands are on the bottom, both gravitational and viscous forces cause water to prefer to flow through the permeable sand and only the capillary force acts to offset channeling. Thus it is expected that higher recoveries may be obtained in water-flooding formations which have the tight sands on the bottom than in those where the tight sands are on the top.

The second case of interest is that when sands are separated by *impermeable* barriers. When shale barriers separate the sand members in a stratified reservoir, the benefits of capillary imbibition and cross flow caused in some cases by gravitational forces are no longer obtained. A rigorous treatment of the case for displacement of oil by water with no cross flow would involve solution of the three-dimensional displacement equation for each sand member with the boundary conditions that free communication existed between strata only in the injection wells and in the production wells and that the fraction of the total flow into each member at any time is proportional to the fraction of total fluid conductance. It is obvious that if the mobility of the water is dif-

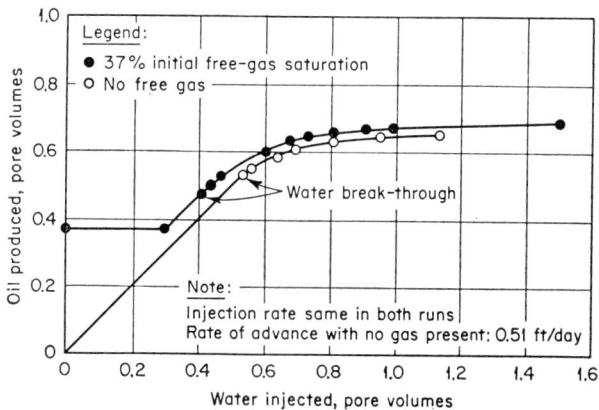

FIG. 16.69. The effect of the presence of a free-gas saturation on the production characteristics of a stratified reservoir. (*Ref.* 68.)

ferent from that of the oil, the fraction of the total flow entering the most permeable sand will change with time. Initially, the water enters each sand in proportion to the fraction $k_1H_1 / \sum\limits_{i=1}^{i=n} k_iH_i$ in which the permea-

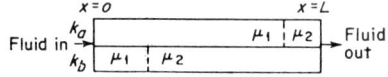

Fig. 16.70. Sketch of stratified sand.

bility-thickness product for the sand in question is divided by the sum of the permeability-thickness products for all the sands. However, as the flood progresses, water advances farthest in the most permeable stratum. If the mobility of the water is higher than that of the oil, the fluid conductivity of the most permeable sand increases faster than in the less permeable sands. In this case, the fraction of the total flow entering the most permeable sand increases with time. If the mobility of the water is less than that of the oil, the fraction of the total flow entering the most permeable sand decreases with time. If the mobilities of the water and oil are equal, the fraction of water entering each sand does not change with time. The last case has been discussed by Stiles.[73]

A simple mathematical model is used to illustrate qualitatively the effects of different permeability ratios of the sand members and the effects of different mobility ratios on recovery. The model consists of two sand members as shown in Fig. 16.70 having permeabilities of k_a and k_b. Flow is assumed to be linear and horizontal. Fluid of viscosity μ_1 displaces fluid of viscosity μ_2, and the mobilities behind the flood front are assumed to be constant k_{1a}/μ_1 and k_{1b}/μ_1 in the two sands. The pressure drop across both sands is ΔP, which is constant. The equation relating the position of the front in each sand before break-through is

$$\frac{\phi}{2}\left(\frac{\mu_1}{k_1} - \frac{\mu_2}{k_2}\right)X^2 + \phi\left(\frac{\mu_2}{k_2}\right)XL = \Delta Pt$$

At break-through in the coarse sand, the position of the front in the tight sand is given by

$$\frac{\phi}{2}\left(\frac{\mu_1}{k_{1b}} - \frac{\mu_2}{k_{2b}}\right)X_b{}^2 + \phi\left(\frac{\mu_2}{k_{2b}}\right)X_bL = \frac{\phi}{2}L^2\left(\frac{\mu_1}{k_{1a}} - \frac{\mu_2}{k_{2a}}\right) \qquad (16.111)$$

Equation (16.111) has been solved for several mobility ratios for permeability ratios of 2, 5, and 10. It was assumed that the strata were of equal thickness and porosity. The results of these calculations are shown in Fig. 16.71, in which the volumetric sweep efficiency at break-through in the coarse sand is plotted vs. the mobility ratio. It can be seen that when the mobility ratio is unfavorable and the permeability ratio is high, practically none of the tight sand is swept at break-through. For example, for a mobility ratio of 10, permeability ratio of 10, only 51.4 per cent of the sand is swept at break-through. Since all the coarse sand is swept, this means that only 2.8 per cent of the tight sand is swept. Better sweep efficiencies are obtained for lower mobility ratios and as the ratio of permeabilities approaches 1.0.

In many reservoir sands, the permeabilities are thought to vary both laterally and vertically with varying degrees of communication between members. In such cases, displacement of oil will be more efficient than that predicted, assuming that the various permeabilities encountered in a well bore are laterally continuous, with no communication between layers.

Areal Pattern Studies. In planning fluid-injection programs for recovery of oil from a

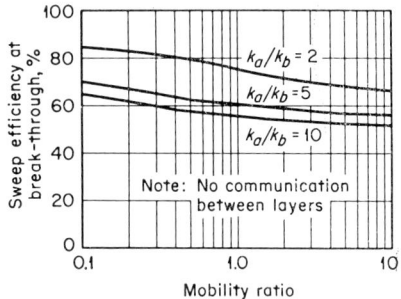

Fig. 16.71. The effect of mobility ratio of sweep efficiencies in stratified sands.

reservoir, one of the factors at the control of the operator is the pattern of injection and production wells. In selection of a particular pattern with a given number of wells, the aim is to recover the most oil with the least amount of fluid injected. Stated another way, the aim is to contact the largest fraction of the reservoir volume with the least amount of fluid injection. The injection and production wells are small in comparison with the reservoir dimensions. The maximum diameter of the wells is usually about 6 in., while the oil-producing formation may extend for miles. Particularly when flooding with low-viscosity fluids, the injected fluid tends to flow preferentially along the lines joining injection and production points. Some of the corner areas may not be swept unless a large volume of fluid is injected. Thus one of the necessary pieces of information in planning successful injection programs is the fraction of the reservoir contacted as a function of the well-pattern arrangement, the mobility ratio of the fluids, and the volume of fluid injected.

Most of the early knowledge of the effects of well-pattern arrangements on flow of fluids resulted from the pioneering work of Muskat[15] (Art. 16.8). This work was concerned with the steady-state flow of a single fluid and can be used to determine the fraction of pattern area swept at break-through, with incompressible fluids having a mobility ratio of 1. Hurst[24] (Art. 16.8) later extended the work of Muskat by treating production after break-through in a five-spot pattern for a mobility ratio of 1. More recently the work of Dyes et al.[74] and that of Craig et al.[75] have extended the knowledge of pattern efficiencies to include a range of mobility ratios at and subsequent to break-through. These studies were concerned with the two-dimensional aspects of pattern flooding; that is, they were concerned with the fraction of the pattern area swept and did not consider the effects of gravity segregation or permeability stratification. Additional work of Craig et al.[69] included the effects of gravity segregation in five-spot-pattern floods.

The pattern studies of Dyes et al.[74] were conducted using miscible fluids to simulate oil and water or gas. As already discussed, capillary effects can be quite large in small models unless high rates or very low interfacial tensions are used. Rather than scale the capillary effects, these authors eliminated them by use of miscible fluids. They assumed that capillary imbibition would be of negligible importance in affecting fluid movement over large reservoir distances when effects of gravity and permeability stratification are negligible, as in thin, homogeneous sands. Their technique may be illustrated by discussion of their five-spot-pattern studies. A uniform porous plate 5 in. square and 1/4 in. thick was used to simulate one-fourth of a repeated five-spot pattern. An injection well in one corner of the model represented one-fourth of an injection well, while the producing well on the opposite corner represented one-fourth of a producing well. The plate was sealed on all sides with a ceramic glaze. The model was saturated with oil, and another oil with the desired viscosity was injected with a constant-rate pump to the resident oil. The area of the pattern swept by the injected fluid was measured from X-ray shadowgraphs taken at various times during the displacement. The region swept by the injected fluid contained an X-ray absorbing tracer. The basic result of these measurements was the pattern area swept as a function of the volume of fluid injected, such as that shown in Fig. 16.72.

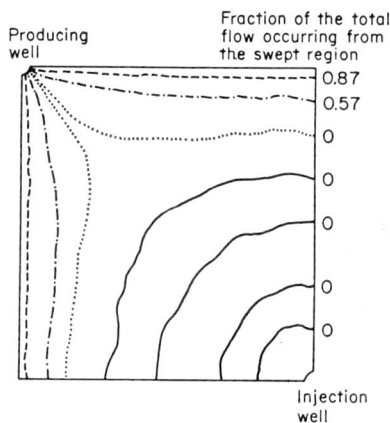

Fraction of the total flow occurring from the swept region

0.87
0.57
0
0
0
0
0

Producing well

Injection well

Fig. 16.72. Sweepout patterns at successive times during flood of a five-spot pattern at mobility ratio of 1.06. (*Ref.* 74.)

Pattern studies were made for a range of mobility ratios from 0.059 to 9.5. Five-spot direct-line-drive and staggered-line-drive patterns (Art. 16.8) were studied. In the line-drive patterns, the distance between injection or producing wells was 1. The

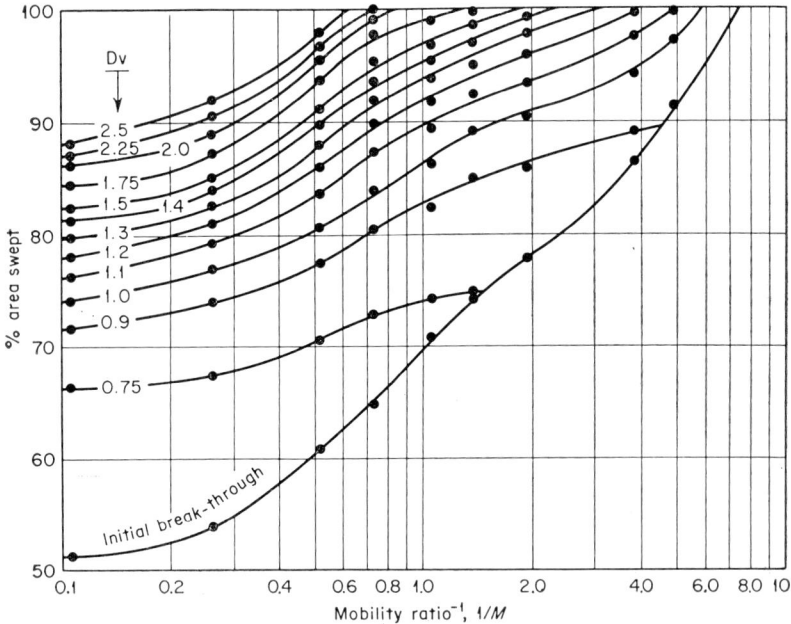

FIG. 16.73. Effect of mobility ratio on the displaceable volumes injected for the five-spot pattern. (*Ref.* 74.)

results of these investigations are shown in Figs. 16.73 to 16.75. The per cent area swept is presented as a function of the reciprocal of the mobility ratio for various displaceable volumes injected for the three-pattern arrangements studied. The mobility ratio is defined by

$$M = \frac{(k_1/\mu_1 + k_2/\mu_2)_{\text{swept}}}{(k_1/\mu_1 + k_2/\mu_2)_{\text{unswept}}} \tag{16.112}$$

which is the sum of the mobilities of the fluid flowing in the swept region divided by that sum in the unswept region. (In the miscible displacements used in this study, all the oil is displaced from the region swept by the invading fluid, and the mobility ratio reduces to the viscosity of the oil divided by that of the injected fluid.) The displaceable volumes injected are defined as volume of fluid injected divided by the product of the pore volume on the pattern area and the fractional change in saturation which occurs in the pattern area. (In miscible displacement all the oil is displaced so that the displaceable volume is the volume of fluid injected divided by the pore volume. In immiscible displacements, the displaceable volume is the volume injected divided by the pore volume times the initial oil saturation minus the residual oil saturation in the pattern.) The additional information presented in Figs. 16.76 to 16.78 is the per cent area swept as a function of ψ_s, which is the fraction of the produced fluids coming from the pattern area and of the reciprocal of the mobility ratio. The authors noted that the fronts become very irregular and the areas swept difficult to discern when the displacing phase was much less viscous than the oil, so data for reciprocal mobility ratios less than 0.5 were considered only approximate.

The use of these data may be illustrated by Example 15.

Example 15. Given: An oil-producing formation is developed on a regular five-spot pattern with 40 acres included within each four injection wells. The sand thickness is 10 ft. The permeability is 100 millidarcys, and the porosity is 22 per cent. The formation contains an initial water saturation of 30 per cent and 70 per cent oil satura-

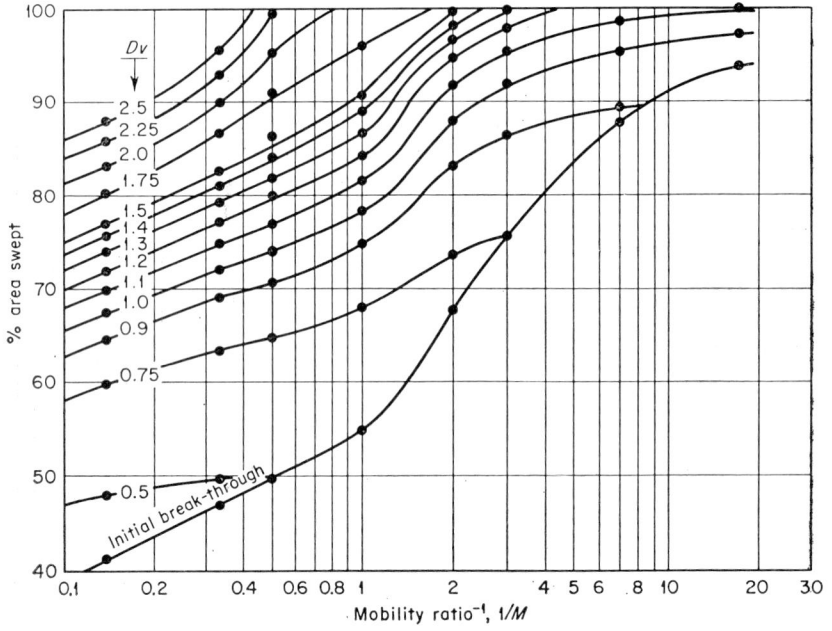

FIG. 16.74. Effect of mobility ratio on the line drive (square pattern).   (*Ref.* 74.)

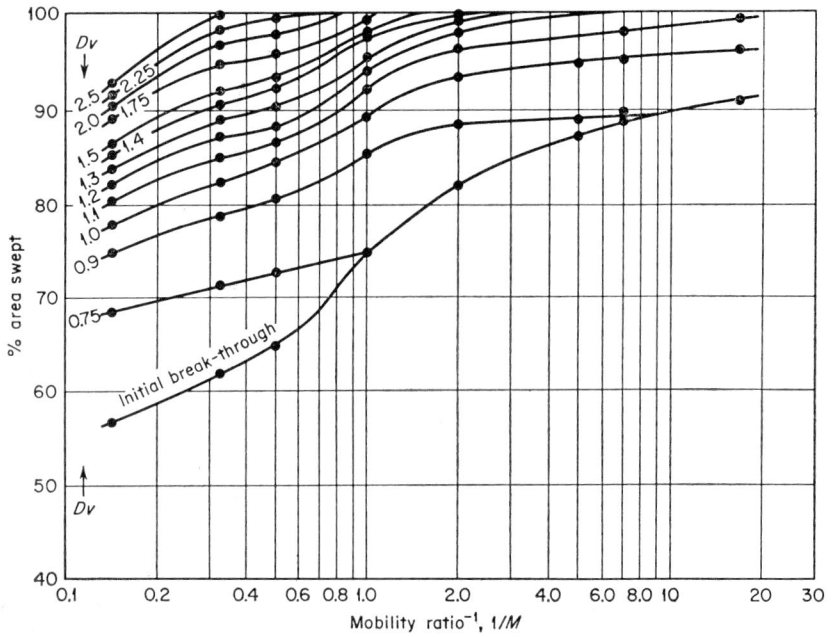

FIG. 16.75. Effect of mobility ratio on the displacement volumes injected for the staggered-line drive.   (*Ref.* 74.)

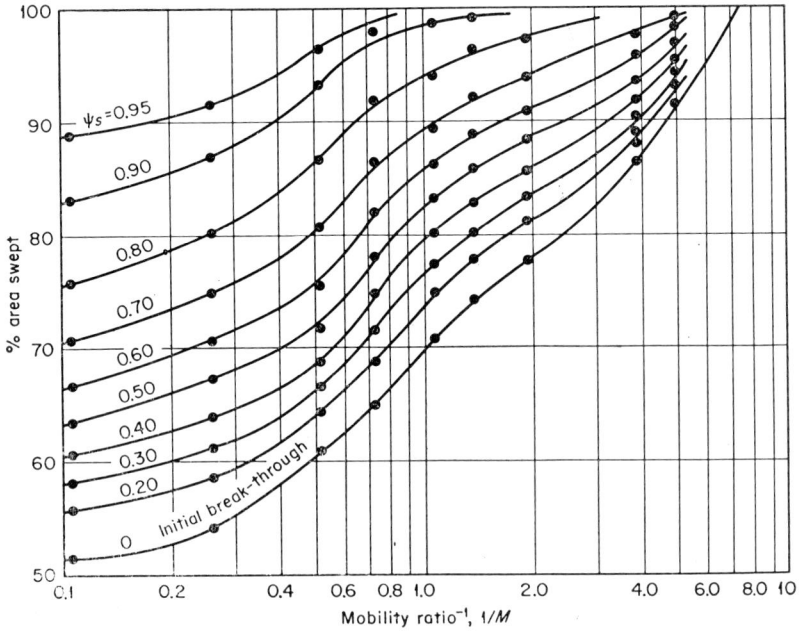

Fig. 16.76. Effect of mobility ratio on oil production for the five-spot pattern. (*Ref.* 74.)

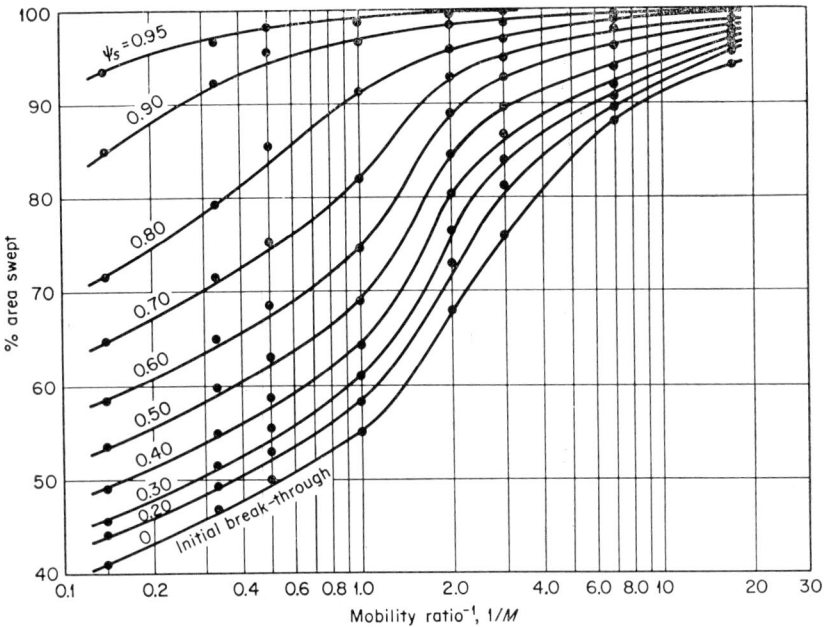

Fig. 16.77. Effect of mobility ratio on oil production for the direct-line drive (square pattern). (*Ref.* 74.)

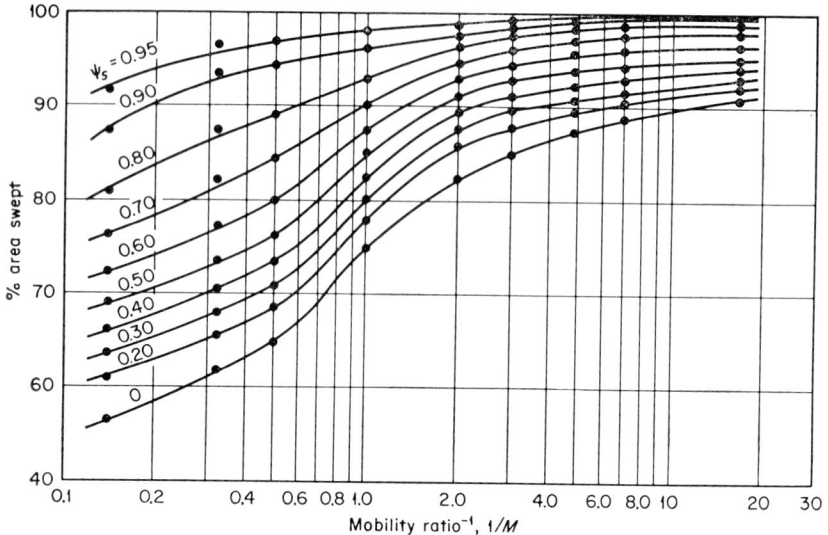

FIG. 16.78. Effect of mobility ratio on oil production for the staggered-line drive. (*Ref.* 74.)

tion. The oil has a viscosity of 1.4 centipoises, and the water has a viscosity of 0.7 centipoise at reservoir conditions. Linear water-flooding tests on cores from the reservoir indicate that all the recoverable oil is produced at water break-through, the residual oil saturation is 20 per cent, and the relative permeability to water is 50 per cent at residual-oil saturation.

Find: The amount of oil recovered from each producing well at water break-through and the ultimate recovery and volume of water injected to an economic limit of 95 per cent water in the produced stream.

SOLUTION. The volume of recoverable oil in the pattern area at reservoir conditions is

$$\text{Volume recoverable oil} = (40)(43,560)(10)(0.22)(0.50)$$
$$= 1,920,000 \text{ ft}^3$$

The mobility ratio is given by

$$M = \frac{k_1/\mu_1}{k_2/\mu_2} = \frac{0.5/0.7}{1.0/1.4} = 1.0$$

From Fig. 16.73 the per cent area swept at break-through in a five-spot for a mobility ratio of 1.0 is 70 per cent. Therefore the recoverable oil at break-through is $Q_o = (1,920,000)(0.70) = 1,343,000 \text{ ft}^3$ at reservoir conditions.

From Fig. 16.76, 99+ per cent of the pattern is swept when 95 per cent of the produced stream is water. Most of the recoverable oil in the pattern, or 1,920,000 ft³ at reservoir conditions, has been produced. The volume of water required can be read from Fig. 16.78 by interpolation as 1.9 displaceable volumes. The volume of water injected is

$$\text{Volume H}_2\text{O injected} = (1.9)(1,920,000)$$
$$= 3,650,000 \text{ ft}^3 \qquad \text{at reservoir conditions}$$

Additional two-dimensional studies were made by Craig et al.[75] of the areal sweep efficiencies in five-spot patterns for gas and water floods. In these studies gas and water were used to displace oil from a uniform slab of consolidated sandstone 4 in. square and ¾ in. thick. The scaling criterion used by these authors was

$$\left(\frac{v_T \mu_o L}{\sigma \cos \theta}\right)_{\text{mod}} = \left(\frac{v_T \mu_o L}{\sigma \cos \theta}\right)_{\text{res}}$$

This criterion as discussed in Art. 16.24 is a measure of the ratio of viscous-capillary pressure gradients when the model and prototype are made from the same rock. In their water-flooding tests, isopropyl alcohol was added to the oil and water to reduce the interfacial tension to a low value. Water floods made over a range of rates corresponding to 0.15 to 9.1 bbl/day/ft of formation thickness showed no effect of rate on recovery. Gas floods were made at rates corresponding to 3.5 to 21 M ft³/day/ft at 500 psi. In both water and gas floods, the area swept was measured from X-ray shadowgraphs made using X-ray absorbing tracers in either the oil or injected fluid.

The sweepout patterns observed in floods with two mobility ratios are shown in Fig. 16.79. When the injected fluid had a mobility 1.41 times greater than that of the oil, it tended to nose into the producing well, leaving unswept regions in the corner of the pattern area. Only 82.2 per cent of the pattern was swept when the produced water-oil ratio was 2.0. When the injected fluid had a mobility only 0.396 that of the oil, more of the corner areas were contacted. About 95.6 per cent of the pattern area was contacted when the water-oil ratio was 4.7.

It was found that the areal sweep efficiencies obtained with water or gas could be correlated with the results of Dyes et al.[74] obtained with miscible fluids. The method of correlation consisted of defining the mobility ratio as the mobility of the displacing phase at the average saturation in the swept region divided by the mobility of the oil in the unswept region, or

$$M = \frac{k_1/\mu_1}{k_2/\mu_2} \tag{16.103}$$

The data obtained with gas or water displacing oil are compared with the data of Dyes et al. in Fig. 16.80. The agreement between the two methods of determining areal sweep efficiencies is excellent.

The results obtained by Craig et al.[75] for the areal sweep efficiency after break-through are shown in Fig. 16.81. Plotted on semilog paper in Fig. 16.81 are the areal sweep efficiencies vs. the volume of fluid injected divided by the volume injected at break-through for floods with a range of viscosity ratios. It was found that all the lines for the various viscosity ratios were parallel in this plot. This implies that if the areal

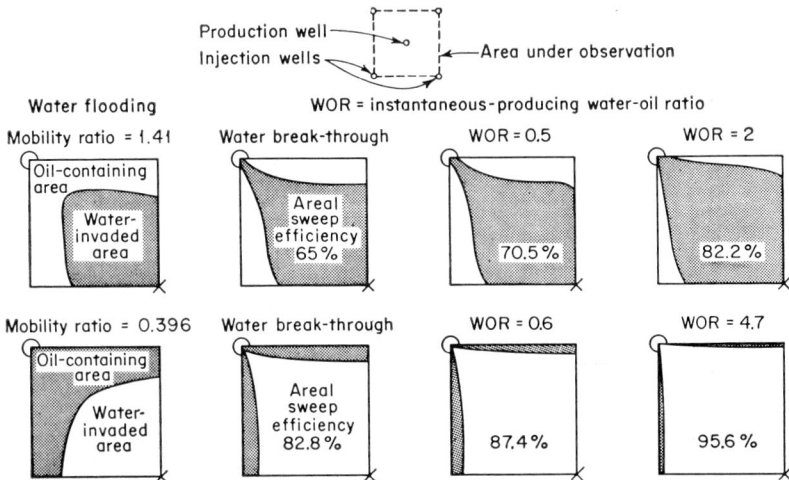

Fig. 16.79. X-ray shadowgraphs of flood-progress five-spot pattern. (*Ref.* 75.)

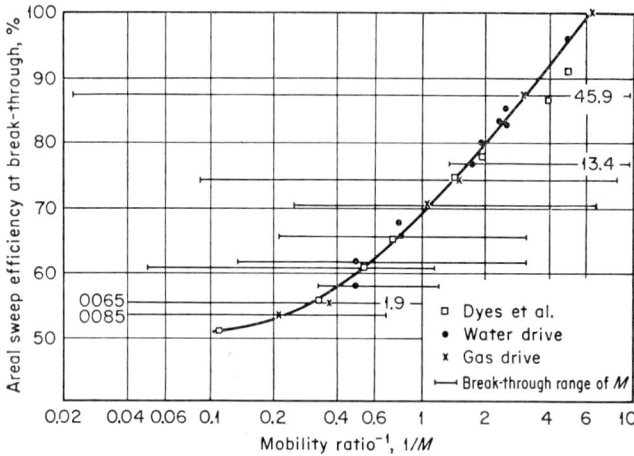

FIG. 16.80. Areal sweep efficiency at break-through—five-spot well pattern. (*Ref.* 75.)

sweep efficiency at break-through is known, the sweep efficiency for any volume injected after break-through can be found by constructing a line parallel to those in Fig. 16.81 and passing through the areal sweep efficiency at break-through for the flood of interest.

The detailed method of Craig et al. in applying their results to calculation of the water-flooding performance is too lengthy to include here. However, the highlights of their method are mentioned to illustrate the principles involved. The oil produced at break-through is determined in the following manner. First a linear displacement calculation is made using relative-permeability–saturation relations and viscosity data for the information in question. The Buckley-Leverett or Welge calculation procedures previously discussed in Art. 16.19 are used to determine the average water saturation and recovery at break-through in a linear flood. Then the relative permeability to water at the average water saturation at break-through is used to calculate the mobility ratio. This value of M is used to find the areal sweep efficiency at break-through,

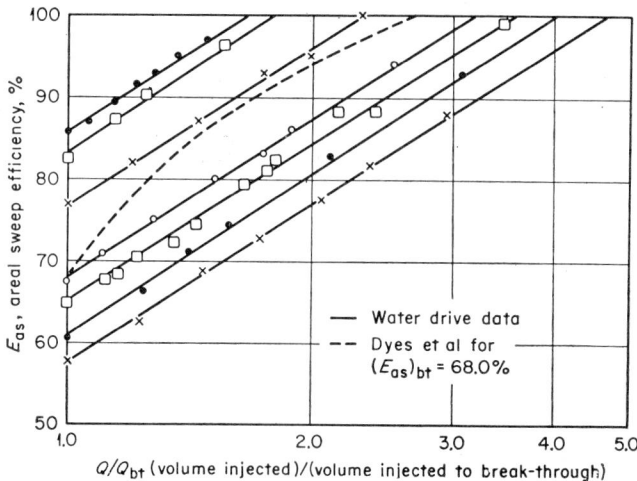

FIG. 16.81. Increase in areal sweep efficiency after break-through. (*Ref.* 75.)

as will be seen from Fig. 16.80. The oil recovery at break-through is the product of the fraction of the area swept, the fraction pore-volume oil recovery obtained from the linear calculation, and the pore volume of the pattern. Subsequent to break-through, the increase in pattern area with continued injection can be determined using Fig. 16.81 by the method already discussed. The oil recovery from the area already invaded subsequent to break-through is calculated in small time increments using the linear-calculation procedure to obtain the fraction-saturation change and using Fig. 16.81 to f nd the pattern swept. Account is taken after each increment of the pore-volume increase in the swept area. The recovery from newly invaded areas in each time increment is obtained by assuming that the oil saturation is that at the flood front in the linear displacement calculation. The total oil production in each time increment is the sum of that from the previously swept area plus that from the newly invaded area.

The above two-dimensional-pattern studies permit some qualitative conclusions regarding the areal sweep efficiencies in pattern floods:

1. The areal sweep efficiency at break-through is strongly dependent on the mobility ratio: the greater the mobility ratio, the less the areal sweep efficiency. For very unfavorable mobility ratios, i.e., those greater than 10, the areal sweep efficiency at break-through may be less than 50 per cent.

2. For the three patterns examined, the five-spot and the particular staggered-line-drive and direct-line-drive patterns investigated ($d/a = 1$), the areal efficiency is not too dependent on the particular pattern chosen.

3. Although the pattern efficiency may be low at break-through for a high mobility ratio, considerable oil can be economically produced after break-through. For example, in a five-spot flood with $M = 10$, only 51 per cent of the pattern is swept at break-through. More than 88 per cent of the pattern has been swept at practical abandonment conditions when 5 per cent of the produced stream is oil.

4. For favorable mobility ratios, i.e., those less than 1.0, almost 100 per cent of the pattern area is swept at practical abandonment conditions.

Some of the *three-dimensional* aspects of pattern flooding concern the tendency for water to underrun or gas to override the oil sand because of gravity effects and the tendency for water to channel through permeable strata. Gravity segregation in five-spot floods of uniform, horizontal sands has been studied by Craig et al.[69] Two sizes of models were used, packed uniformly with sand, to represent one-eighth of a five-spot pattern. One model was 46 in. between wells and 4 in. thick; the other was 29 in. between well bores and 3 in. thick. The models were scaled using the criterion that the model and prototype have the same product of length-thickness ratio times the ratio of viscous to gravitational pressure gradients at a point midway between wells. This criterion is

$$\frac{\Delta P_L}{\Delta P_H} = \frac{q_T \mu_o}{4 k_L \, \Delta\rho \, g H^2}$$

This criterion has the sense of being the ratio of viscous pressure drops between wells to the gravitational pressure drop in the vertical direction.

Gravity underrunning of the water was appreciable over the range of rates and mobility ratios studied. Particularly at lower rates with mobility ratios greater than 1.0, the tendency for the water to underrun and bypass oil was noticeable. The results of this study are summarized in Fig. 16.82, which is a plot of the volumetric sweep efficiency at break-through as a function of $\Delta P_L/\Delta P_H = q_T \mu_o/4 k_L \, \Delta\rho \, g H^2$.† Volumetric

† The data in Fig. 16.82 are for two model sizes, one 40 in. between wells and 4 in. thick and the other 29 in. between wells and 3 in. thick. While the volumetric sweep efficiencies at break-through for both models correlated in Fig. 16.82 with the parameter $\dfrac{q_T \mu_o}{4 R_L \, \Delta\rho \, g H^2}$, the L/H ratio for the two models was practically the same, 9.67 in one case and 10.0 in the other. Thus the agreement between results of the two models does not mean that these data can be applied to L/H ratios other than 10. It is possible that in thin sands in which capillary forces would tend to prevent underrunning, different curves would result for different ratios of viscous to capillary pressure gradients. The authors note that each case should be studied individually when capillary forces are important.

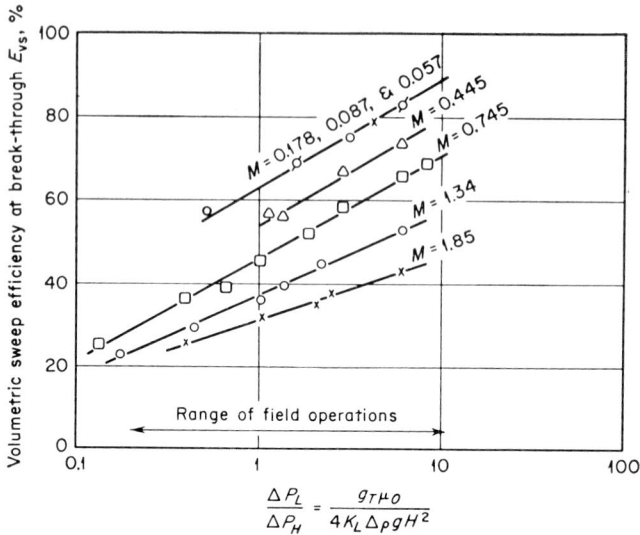

FIG. 16.82. Volumetric sweep efficiency at break-through—five-spot uniform systems. (*Ref.* 69.)

sweep efficiencies for a number of mobility ratios are included. The effects of gravity underrunning causing early water break-through may be illustrated by Example 16.

Example 16. Consider a mobility ratio of 1.85 and a $\dfrac{\Delta P_H}{\Delta P_L} = 10$. From Fig. 16.82 the volumetric sweep efficiency at break-through is about 46 per cent. If one assumed that no gravity effects were involved, the areal sweep efficiency at break-through for a mobility ratio of 1.85 is seen in Fig. 16.80 to be about 60 per cent. The error resulting from ignoring gravitational effects in this example is $(60 - 46)/46 \times 100 = 30$ per cent.

FLOW OF MISCIBLE FLUIDS

16.27. Introduction

The subject of Arts. 16.27 to 16.33 is the flow of miscible fluids through porous media. Miscible fluids are defined here as those completely soluble in one another. If two fluids are mixed together in any proportion and a single-phase, homogeneous mixture always results, the two fluids are said to be miscible in one another. Understanding the flow of miscible fluids through porous media has considerable importance in recovery of oil from underground formations. Many new methods of recovery of oil involve displacement of the oil by fluids miscible with the oil. For instance, liquefied petroleum gases containing propane and butane are used to flush oil from underground formations. In refinery processes, solvents are used to displace fluids from packed towers and fixed-bed reactors. The flow of water or a single fluid through a sand is a special case of flow of miscible fluids, that in which the displaced and displacing fluid have the same viscosity and density.

As in studies of the flow of immiscible fluids, the scope of the discussion is limited to the laminar-flow regime as defined in Art. 16.4.† Understanding of the physics of the

---

† For studies of miscible displacement when inertial effects are important, see papers by Bernard and Wilhelm,[76] Aris and Amundson,[77] Kramers and Alberda,[78] and McHenry and Wilhelm.[79]

flow processes of miscible fluids can best be achieved by considering the processes on two levels. On the first level, the microscopic phenomena are those associated with the flow within a given pore space or between neighboring pore spaces. On the second level, the macroscopic phenomena are those associated with the gross movement of fluids through large sand bodies.

On the microscopic level, a porous medium can as a first approximation be visualized to contain a number of flow channels or filaments. Each filament varies continuously in size and shape and undulates as it moves generally in a direction parallel with that of its neighbors. Locally these neighboring flow channels may move together and abut in holes between sand grains; or the neighboring channels may move apart as they wriggle around sand grains. But generally, the neighboring flow filaments move parallel to one another from regions of high pressure to regions of low pressure.

In displacing a fluid from a porous medium with a miscible fluid, the velocity variations across a given filament tend to make the injected fluid move fastest at the center of the filament. However, lateral diffusion within the flow filament tends to prevent bypassing of resident fluid. Also, diffusion between filaments at the junctures where they abut tends to prevent bypassing caused by differences in velocities between filaments. Thus the mixing or intermingling of injected and resident fluid results from an interplay between convective forces and diffusional forces. This interplay between convection and diffusion has been treated by Taylor[80] for flow of fluids of equal viscosity and density in small-diameter single straight capillaries. Later, Aris[81] removed limits on the velocity ranges considered by Taylor. More recently, Blackwell[82] has studied experimentally the mixing process in single straight capillaries to include fluids of different viscosities and densities. Later, data for mixing in porous media have been correlated using dimensionless parameters suggested by studies of the microscopic mixing processes in single capillaries.[83,84]

On the macroscopic level, the gross movement of miscible fluids is influenced by three kinds of forces. The first of these is the viscous, or applied, force, which causes both the injected and resident fluids to move generally from regions of high pressure to regions of low pressure. The second kind of force is the gravitational force, which tends to cause the low-density fluid to rise to the top of the sand. The third kind of force is the diffusional force, which tends to equalize concentration differences within the porous medium. The three-dimensional-flow behavior of miscible fluids has not yet been solved mathematically. Most of the knowledge of the gross displacement behavior of miscible fluids has been learned by experimentation. Scaled models have been used to study the role of diffusional and gravitational forces.

The following articles summarize some of the knowledge gained in studies of microscopic and macroscopic flow of miscible fluids through porous media.

16.28. Microscopic Flow in Single Straight Capillaries

The simplest porous medium is the single straight capillary of circular cross section. For laminar flow of a single fluid in the capillary, it is possible to find the velocity at any point in a capillary of radius a by the equation

$$v = v_0 \left(1 - \frac{r^2}{a^2} \right) \qquad (16.113)$$

in which v_0 is the velocity at the center.

Consider for a moment the case in which the rate is so high or the capillary is so large that diffusion is negligible. If a fluid were injected into the capillary to displace another fluid having the same viscosity and density, the injected fluid would move fastest along the center of the capillary. At break-through of the injected fluid, only one-half of the resident fluid would be displaced. The position of the injected resident-fluid interface at break-through is given by

$$x_r = L \left(1 - \frac{r^2}{a^2} \right) \qquad (16.114)$$

The different velocities at the different radii result in spreading the interfaces over the entire length of the capillary. This process is termed *convection*.

When diffusion becomes important in the displacement process, a completely different picture results. The radial-velocity variations again try to spread the fluid interface along the length of the capillary. However, radial diffusion tends to eliminate radial-concentration variations. Actually, for low rates in small capillaries, radial diffusion may be so fast compared with the convective mixing that no radial-concentration variations exist. The classic work of Sir Geoffrey Taylor[80] has treated this latter situation. By taking a small tubular volume element dx long and dr thick, a material balance can be made to account for the concentration change in the element caused by radial diffusion, longitudinal diffusion, and convection. The equation resulting is

$$D\left(\frac{\partial^2 c}{\partial z^2} + \frac{1}{z}\frac{\partial c}{\partial z} + \frac{\partial^2 c}{\partial x^2}\right) = \frac{\partial c}{\partial t} + v_0(1 - z^2)\frac{\partial c}{\partial x} \qquad (16.115)$$

when

$$z = \frac{r}{a}$$

By using the boundary condition that $\partial c/\partial z = 0$ at $z = 1$, a general solution of Eq. (16.115) for values of c at all values of z, r, and t would describe the displacement process. However, no general solution is known.

Taylor found solutions for the following limited case:

1. Longitudinal diffusion was of negligible importance, so the term $\partial^2 c/\partial x^2$ could be dropped from Eq. (16.115).

2. The time required for radial concentrations to be eliminated by radial diffusion is short compared with the time required for convection to cause appreciable radial-concentration variations; that is, the concentration can be assumed to be uniform across a given cross section.

Stated mathematically, these conditions are

$$\frac{4L}{a} \gg \frac{a\bar{v}}{D} \gg 6.9$$

in which $\bar{v}$ is the average velocity.

After making these assumptions, it was found that the process by which a miscible fluid displaces another of equal viscosity and density could be visualized, as follows. Relative to a plane which moves with the average velocity, the injected and resident fluids mix as if by diffusion but with a dispersion coefficient—an effective diffusion coefficient—given by

$$K_T = \frac{a^2\bar{v}^2}{48D} \qquad (16.116)$$

K_T will hereafter be referred to as the Taylor diffusivity. For the case where the miscible fluid is injected at constant rate at concentration C_0 into a tube initially filled with the resident fluid, the concentration of the injected fluid is given by

$$\frac{C}{C_0} = \tfrac{1}{2} + \tfrac{1}{2}\,\mathrm{erf}\left[\frac{x_1/2}{(K_T t)^{\frac{1}{2}}}\right] \qquad (x_1 < 0) \qquad (16.117)$$

and

$$\frac{C}{C_0} = \tfrac{1}{2} - \tfrac{1}{2}\,\mathrm{erf}\left[\frac{x_1/2}{(K_T t)^{\frac{1}{2}}}\right] \qquad (x_1 > 0) \qquad (16.118)$$

The 50 per cent concentration level moves with the average velocity of the stream. The length of the transition zone between the 90 and 10 per cent concentration levels of this injected fluid is given by

$$\Delta L = 3.62(K_T t)^{\frac{1}{2}} \qquad (16.119)$$

By including diffusion in the direction of flow, Aris[81] was able to show theoretically that in small capillaries at low rates, the mixing between injected and resident fluid can be described by an effective dispersion coefficient

$$K_{\text{eff}} = D + K_T = D + \frac{a^2 \bar{v}^2}{48D} \quad (16.120)$$

that is, the dispersion coefficient is the sum of the molecular diffusivity and the Taylor diffusivity. This work removed the lower limit on rates imposed by Taylor. The theoretical conclusions of Aris have been verified by Blackwell,[82] who performed a number of displacements in a capillary 101 cm long with an inside radius of 0.0271 cm. The agreement shown in Fig. 16.83 between the measured dispersion coefficients and those calculated using Eq. (16.120) is excellent. Thus, at very low rates in small capillaries, $a\bar{v}/D < 1.0$, the mixing between the invading and resident fluid is governed by molecular diffusion in the direction of flow. At intermediate rates, $1 < a\bar{v}/D < 10$, both longitudinal diffusion and the Taylor-type mixing resulting from the interplay between radial diffusion and convection contribute to the mixing. At still higher rates, $a\bar{v}/D > 10$, the Taylor-type mixing predominates. At very high rates,

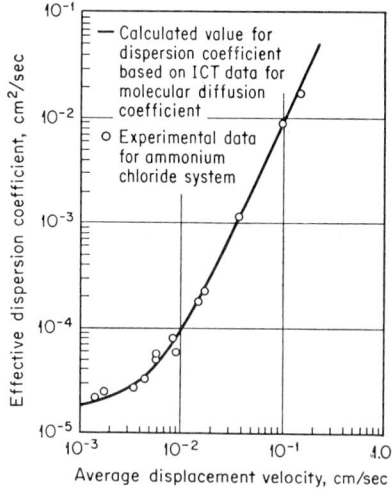

Fig. 16.83. Dispersion coefficient for fluids with equal viscosities and densities. (*Ref.* 82.)

convection dominates the flow until turbulence ensues, at which time inertial forces dominate the flow.[79] In all but the latter case, the concentration is uniform at a given length along the capillary. The displacement of the resident fluid is complete. The process proceeds with a widening transition zone as the front moves down the capillary.

Similar behavior has been observed for displacement of fluids of different viscosities. Shown in Fig. 16.84 are experimental results obtained for three pairs of fluids having different viscosities. Note that the dispersion coefficients increase as the square of the velocity in the Taylor region, just as do those for 1:1 viscosity ratios. The amount of

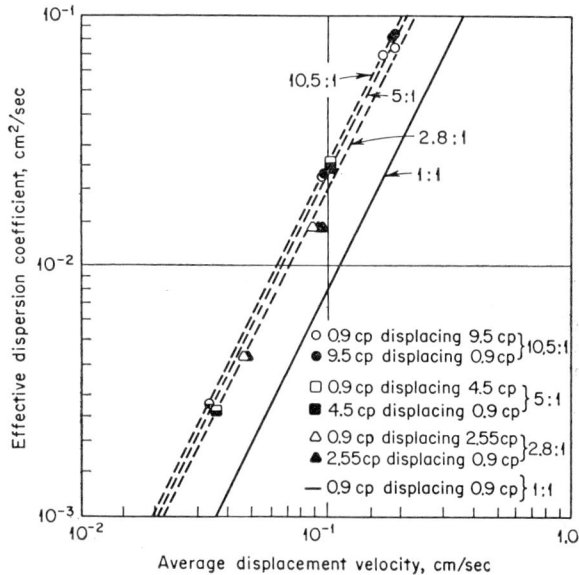

Fig. 16.84. Dispersion coefficient for fluids with unequal viscosities–equal densities. (*Ref.* 82.)

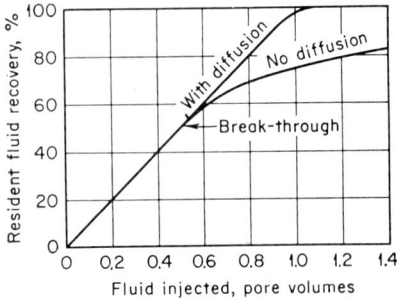

FIG. 16.85. Effect of diffusion on recovery from capillary.

mixing was the same whether the low-viscosity fluid was the displaced or displacing fluid. The dispersion coefficients for unequal viscosity fluids can be approximated by the formula

$$K_{\text{eff}} = \frac{a^2 \bar{v}^2}{48 D_{\text{av}}} \qquad \frac{a\bar{v}}{D} > 10 \qquad (16.121)$$

if D_{av} is an average molecular diffusivity found by displacement experiments in capillaries.[82]

These findings concerning slow flow through small capillaries when diffusion (either radial or longitudinal or both) is important show that displacements of miscible fluids can be very efficient. Rather than needle down the center of the capillary along the streamline of maximum velocity, the displacement may be almost pistonlike. This is illustrated in Fig. 16.85, which shows that almost 100 per cent of the resident fluid is recovered where one pore volume has been injected. Also shown in Fig. 16.85 is the displacement that would occur if diffusion were ignored. Note that break-through occurred at 50 per cent recovery and only 75 per cent of the resident fluid had been recovered at one pore volume.

These findings provided a basis for attacking the problems or understanding the more complicated cases of displacement of miscible fluids from sands. These will be discussed next.

16.29. Microscopic Mixing Processes in Porous Media

The mixing process when a miscible fluid in laminar flow displaces another from a sand is considerably more complicated than that in single straight capillaries. Similarities to flow in capillaries exist, since velocities are low near the walls and highest in the center of the pores. This, the basic process of convection arising from velocity variations and radial diffusion, is common to both single capillaries and sands. Differences between the two arise from the geometrical complexities of the sand. The flow channels through the sand change rapidly in size, shape, and direction. At frequent intervals adjacent flow channels may flow side by side through a hole between sand grains. A particle of fluid moving in the contour of a hole may find itself near the wall as the stream is diverted around a sand grain. This would give additional mixing above that observed in capillaries. Also, the velocity variations between adjacent streamlines with equalization of concentrations by diffusion in the holes where the filaments abut would give additional mixing. Over the range of interest in this discussion, mixing at the junctures occurs by molecular diffusion and not by eddy diffusion resulting from inertial effects, because the Reynolds numbers are usually quite small, 0.01 or less, so that inertial effects can be ignored.

In flow through porous sands, two kinds of mixing are of interest. Mixing in the direction of flow is termed *longitudinal* mixing, and mixing perpendicular to the direction of flow is called *lateral* mixing. Both of these are important in miscible displacements in porous media, and they will be discussed separately below.

Longitudinal Mixing. The process by which miscible fluids in laminar-flow mix in the direction of flow has been studied experimentally by a number of investigators.[85–88] A variety of miscible-fluid pairs, gases and liquids, having the same viscosity and density, have been used in a variety of sand-packed apparatus over a wide range of rates. Most of these data were correlated into a consistent picture by putting the effective dispersion coefficient divided by the molecular diffusivity vs. the dimensionless parameter $a_p v/D$ as shown in Fig. 16.86, in which a_p is the average sand-particle radius and v

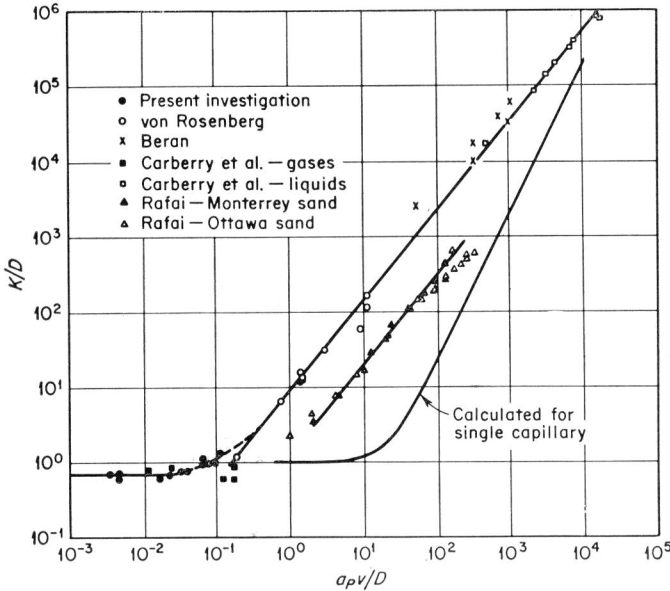

Fig. 16.86. Correlation of dispersion coefficients. (*Ref.* 83.)

is defined as the average velocity of the front, $v = q/\phi A$. The parameter $a_p v/D$ has the sense of being the ratio of the convective force, causing transport in the longitudinal direction, to the diffusional force, causing transport in the lateral direction. Even though the data in Fig. 16.86 cover a 10^7 range of $a_p v/D$, most of the data fall on a single curve. At values of $a_p v/D$ less than 0.04, the dimensionless dispersion coefficient is independent of the rate or particle size and has a value of 0.67. In this range of $a_p v/D$, the process of mixing is dominated by molecular diffusion in the direction of flow. Since the diffusion occurs along tortuous paths, the effective dispersion coefficient is the molecular diffusivity divided by the tortuosity factor. A reasonable tortuosity factor for the unconsolidated sands of interest here is 1.5. Hence $K = D/1.5$, or $K/D = 1/1.5 = 0.67$.

For values of $a_p v/D > 0.5$ in Fig. 16.86, most of the data fall on a single line whose slope is 1.17 on the log-log paper. The equation of this line is

$$K_L/D = 8.8 \left(\frac{a_p v}{D} \right)^{1.17} \qquad (16.122)$$

In this range of rates and particle sizes, the mixing process is primarily one of convection arising from velocity variations with rapid lateral diffusion within each pore invaded or between adjacent pores. In this range longitudinal molecular diffusion is of little importance. This is not to say that diffusion plays no role in the process, however. For within each pore invaded, lateral diffusion results in complete displacement of the resident fluid. As in the single capillary, the process by which a miscible fluid displaces another fluid of equal viscosity and density from a sand can be visualized as pistonlike. All the resident fluid is displaced, with a transition zone between the two growing as the displacement front proceeds down the column. The length of this mixing zone between the 90 and 10 per cent concentration levels off. The invading fluid is given by

$$L = 3.62(K_L t)^{\frac{1}{2}} \qquad (16.119)$$

Table **16.13.** Typical Mixing-zone Lengths for Reservoirs

Rate, ft/day	Length of mixing zone, ft		
	$L = 100$ ft	$L = 1000$ ft	$L = 10,000$ ft
0.1	4.0	12.7	40
0.5	1.8	5.7	18

NOTES: (1) The value of D was assumed to be 5×10^{-8} ft²/sec. (2) L is the length of the reservoir.

K_L is determined from Fig. 16.86 for the rate, particle size, and molecular diffusivity of interest.[†]

Typical mixing-zone lengths are shown for conditions when longitudinal diffusion controls the mixing in Table 16.13. It can be seen that the length of the mixing zone decreases as the rate increases. The transition zone increases as the square root of the distance traversed by the front.

When convection affects the longitudinal mixing $a_p v/D > 0.5$, the length of the transition zone is only slightly affected by rate. This can be seen in Table 16.14, where typical values for transition zones in the direction of flow are shown for conditions usually encountered in the laboratory. However, again the length of the mixing zone increases as the square root of the distance traveled.

Lateral Mixing. Mixing in the laminar-flow regime between the injected and resident fluids in the directions perpendicular to the direction of flow has received little study in the literature. However, Blackwell[84] has recently presented data on the lateral mixing between fluids of equal viscosity and density in unconsolidated sands. When two fluids are flowing parallel to one another through a porous medium, the fluids tend to mix by molecular diffusion across the interface separating them. Also, at high rates, the wriggle of the flow filaments as they follow tortuous paths around sand grains with subsequent interchange of the fluids by diffusion in the junctures imparts lateral mixing between fluids. The data on lateral mixing are shown in Fig. 16.87 in a plot of K_T/D versus the dimensionless parameter $a_p v/D$. Also shown in Fig. 16.87 for comparison are longitudinal dispersion coefficients. The data are for several types of sands. The band of values shown by the fine dots are for longitudinal mixing. The band covered by coarse dots represents the range of values measured for lateral mixing. The upper curve in each region represents data for fine sands, and the lower curve represents that for coarse sands.

It can be seen that for small values of $a_p v/D$, the lateral dispersion is governed by molecular diffusion. The value of K_T/D of 0.67 in this region is that one would expect for molecular diffusion along a tortuous path with a tortuosity factor of 1.5. Molecular diffusion controls the lateral dispersion for a larger range of rates than it does with the longitudinal dispersion. As can be seen, the lateral-dispersion coefficients are equal

[†] The data for the unconsolidated sand packs correlated in Fig. 16.86 do not necessarily apply to other types of porous media, as noted in the discussion of lateral mixing. Where it is of sufficient importance, data should be taken on the medium of interest and plotted in a similar manner.

Table **16.14.** Typical Mixing-zone Lengths for Laboratory Models

Rate, ft/day, laboratory	Length of mixing zone, ft					
	For 20–30–mesh sand			For 120–270–mesh sand		
	$L = 1$ ft	$L = 10$ ft	$L = 100$ ft	$L = 1$ ft	$L = 10$ ft	$L = 100$ ft
1	0.33	1.0	3.3	0.14	0.46	1.4
10	0.37	1.1	3.7	0.10	0.31	1.0
50	0.40	1.2	4.0	0.10	0.32	1.0
100	0.41	1.3	4.1	0.11	0.34	1.1

NOTES: (1) The value of D was assumed to be 2×10^{-8} ft²/sec. (2) L is the length of the model.

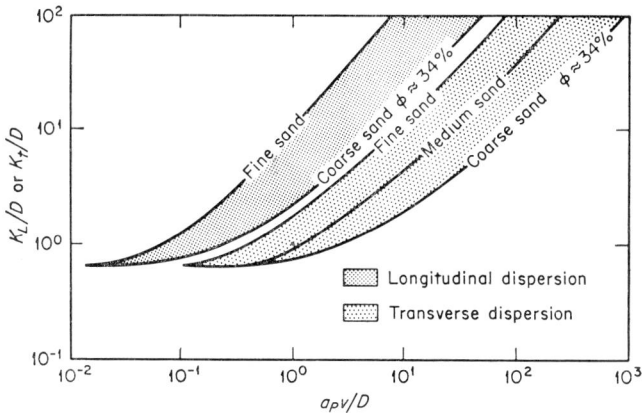

Fig. 16.87. Range of dispersion coefficients for various sand sizes on packing conditions. (*Ref.* 84.)

to the molecular diffusivity divided by the tortuosity factor for values of $a_p v/D$ less than 1.2. For values of $a_p v/D > 10$, the lateral dispersion results primarily from an interplay between lateral convection caused by the tortuous flow paths and diffusion at the junctures. The lateral-dispersion coefficients are about $\frac{1}{24}$ those in the longitudinal direction for values of $a_p v/D > 10$, for all the sands investigated. The higher dispersion coefficients in the finer sands are attributed to bridging and packing irregularities. It is believed that coarse sands or uniform spheres can be packed more uniformly, and hence dispersion coefficients for these media would be approximated by the lower curves for the two types of mixing.

16.30. Macroscopic Phenomena

The gross flow characteristics of miscible fluids has received considerable study during the past few years because of the potential importance of solvent floods in recovery of oil. The injected solvent displaces all the oil from the pores invaded by the fluid. Lateral diffusion is sufficiently rapid over the width of a pore space to ensure that no oil is left behind once the solvent enters the pore. The problems arise from the large differences in density and viscosity of the oil and solvent. The solvents used are usually propane or butane injected as a liquid bank or dissolved in high concentrations in natural gas. In some cases, high-pressure methane is a solvent for the oil. These fluids always have a much lower viscosity and density than the oil. The solvent tends to channel and to bypass oil sands unless advantage can be taken of the dip of the sand and gravity segregation.

Diffusion, instead of capillary imbibition, is involved along with viscous and gravity forces in flow of miscible fluids. Diffusion tends to equalize any concentration differences that exist within the porous medium and could conceivably offset the tendency for a low-viscosity solvent to channel and bypass oil. Thus in studying solvent flooding processes in the laboratory, the models must have diffusion properly scaled. Also in production of chemicals involving miscible displacements with reactions or adsorption in packed columns, it is important that bench-scale reactors have been properly scaled as to diffusional effects.

In the following articles, the principles of scaling miscible displacements are discussed. Later the use of models to study several gross-flow phenomena is treated.

16.31. Theory of Models in Miscible Displacements and Principles of Scaling

Principles of scaling models to simulate miscible displacements in larger systems are similar to the principles used in scaling immiscible displacements discussed in Art.

16.24. While a displacement equation similar to that for immiscible displacements [Eq. (16.101)] has not been formulated for miscible fluids, similarities between the processes may be used to formulate most of the scaling criteria. The main difference between scaling miscible and immiscible displacements is that diffusional forces instead of capillary forces must be scaled in the former. The scaling requirements for miscible flow not involving diffusion can be written at once from those already developed for immiscible flow. The scaling requirements follow.

1. The model and prototype must be geometrically similar; that is, the L/H and L/W ratios must be the same in the model and prototype. Also, the angle of inclination of the two must be the same. Any regions of different permeability must be similarly located, and the ratios of the permeabilities in these localized regions to the average permeability must be the same in model and prototype.

2. The model and prototype must have similar initial and boundary conditions; that is, wells for injection and production must be located similarly. Impermeable boundaries must be in similar positions. The relative fractions of fluids injected and produced must be the same in the two and in the same scaled time sequences. Initial gas-, oil-, and water-saturation distributions must be the same in model and prototype.

3. The ratio of viscosities of the fluids must be the same in model and prototype; that is,

$$\left(\frac{\mu_o}{\mu_s}\right)_{\text{mod}} = \left(\frac{\mu_o}{\mu_s}\right)_{\text{prototype}} \tag{16.123}$$

in which subscripts o and s are for oil and solvent, respectively.

4. The ratio of viscous to gravitational pressure gradients must be the same in model and prototype. This requirement is met when

$$\left(\frac{v_T \mu_o}{k\,\Delta\rho\,g}\right)_{\text{mod}} = \left(\frac{v_T \mu_o}{k\,\Delta\rho\,g}\right)_{\text{prototype}} \tag{16.124}$$

in which v_T is the total linear flow rate defined as $v_T = (q_o + q_s)/A$.

5. The model and prototype times are related through the equation of continuity. The times are related through

$$\left[\frac{\phi L(1 - S_{wi})}{v_T t}\right]_{\text{mod}} = \left[\frac{\phi L(1 - S_{wi})}{v_T t}\right]_{\text{prototype}} \tag{16.125}$$

6. The microscopic displacement process must be the same in the model and prototype. For exact scaling, the model and prototype should both operate in the region of $a_p v/D < 0.04$, where mixing is controlled by molecular diffusion or else at the same $a_p v/D$. However, it was seen in discussion of the microscopic-flow behavior that all the resident fluid is displaced from the pores invaded over a considerable range of rates and pore sizes. Lateral diffusion of solvent and oil over the short distances involved in a pore space invaded by solvent results in a clean sweep of oil from the pore space. Thus exact scaling of $a_p v/D$ is not necessary.

7. Gross mixing between the solvent and oil should be of the same importance in the model and prototype. This requirement can be stated

$$\left(\frac{L^2}{K_L t}\right)_{\text{mod}} = \left(\frac{L^2}{K_L t}\right)_{\text{prototype}} \tag{16.126}$$

$$\left(\frac{H^2}{K_T t}\right)_{\text{mod}} = \left(\frac{H^2}{K_T t}\right)_{\text{prototype}} \tag{16.127}$$

$$\left(\frac{W^2}{K_T t}\right)_{\text{mod}} = \left(\frac{W^2}{K_T t}\right)_{\text{prototype}} \tag{16.128}$$

in which K_L, K_T = longitudinal and transverse dispersion coefficients defined in Art. 16.29
L, H, W = length, thickness, and width, respectively
t = time

These parameters have the sense of being the rate of transport of a particle of fluid by flow of convection relative to the rate of transport by molecular diffusion or mixing.

The last of these scaling requirements are often the most difficult to meet in practice. Exact scaling of the mixing usually requires that the model be quite long and that the sand particles be small. Often, however, practical considerations such as the space available limits the model size. And considerations such as the time available affect the sand and fluid characteristics and, through the other scaling criteria, the rates. In some cases, failure to scale the mixing in the direction of the length or width may not cause serious errors. In the reservoir, these mixing zones are usually of the order of 1 or 2 per cent of the length or width, and they may not appreciably affect the gross flow behavior. Hence larger fractional mixing zones (up to 10 per cent of the length) may be permitted in the laboratory models without appreciably affecting the behavior. However, in the direction of the reservoir thickness, the mixing zone may be of the same order of magnitude as the thickness, e.g., 10 to 50 ft. Mixing in the direction of the thickness may have a profound effect on the displacement behavior. Hence mixing in this direction should be scaled. Fortunately, as can be seen in Fig. 16.87, lateral mixing is dominated by molecular diffusion over a larger range than is longitudinal mixing. This gives a correspondingly wider selection of model conditions of rates, sand-grain sizes, and molecular diffusivities in scaling mixing in the direction of the thickness. In the following articles, the study of a number of miscible-flow problems using scaled models is discussed.

16.32. Miscible Displacements in Homogeneous Sands

Viscous Fingering. One of the most serious problems in displacing oil from a porous medium with solvent is the tendency for the solvent to channel. In the usual case, the viscosity of the solvent is one-tenth or less that of the oil. Even if the displacement front is smooth or even at the injection face, local permeability variations tend to let the solvent form small perturbations on the front. The local regions in which the solvent has forged ahead of the main front are regions of lower resistance to flow. So additional solvent tends to flow into these regions. Thus solvent may form and grow from local permeability variations. The viscous forces tend to propagate these solvent channels. Hence the term viscous fingering is descriptive of the cause and appearance of solvent channels. In horizontal sands, the force of gravity acts on the low-density solvent to cause it to tend to flow to the top of the sand. Gravity cannot act to stabilize the displacement front or prevent the channeling in horizontal sands. If the rate were sufficiently low, lateral diffusion might offset the tendency for the low-viscosity solvent to channel and bypass oil.

Viscous fingering and the role of lateral diffusion in stabilizing miscible displacements have been studied in sand-packed models.[89,83] The models used by Blackwell et al.[83] were 6 ft long and $\frac{3}{8}$ in. thick with widths of $\frac{1}{2}$, 6, and 24 in. These models were packed with uniform sand to be as homogeneous as possible. To study the fingering process in the absence of gravitational effects, solvents having the same density as the oils were used to displace the oils. The viscosities of the solvents ranged from that of the oil to $\frac{1}{375}$ that of the oil. The displacement rates ranged from 0.5 ft/day to over 900 ft/day.

When a solvent having the same viscosity as the oil is used to displace the oil, a uniform, pistonlike displacement front is observed. Depending on the microscopic mixing process, a short mixing zone between the oil and solvent exists. Uniform shape of the front is an indication of the homogeneity of the sand. When the solvent has a lower viscosity than the oil, channeling of the solvent is always observed. A number of small needlelike fingers are seen to form very close to the inlet face of the sand. A few of these fingers then get slightly ahead and begin to grow more rapidly than their neighbors. The subsequent growth of these larger fingers is dictated by the pressure fields set up by them and the lateral boundaries of the models. Typical experimental displacement patterns when a low-viscosity solvent displaces oil are shown in Figs. 16.88 and 16.89. When the mobility ratio, μ_o/μ_s, is low as in Fig. 16.88, the channeling is less severe than when the mobility ratio is high.

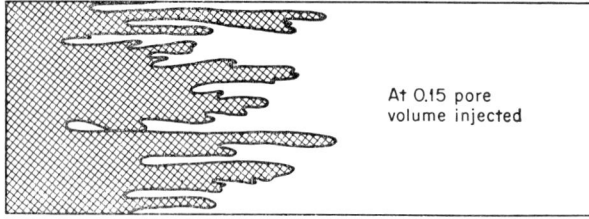

Fig. 16.88. Displacement front for mobility ratio of 20. (*Ref.* 83.)

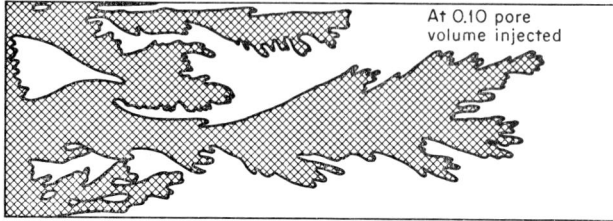

Fig. 16.89. Displacement front for mobility ratio of 383. (*Ref.* 83.)

The role of diffusion in stabilizing miscible displacements may be discerned from the experiments performed over a range of rates. Shown in Fig. 16.90 are recoveries at break-through as functions of rate of displacement. The solvent had a viscosity $\frac{1}{93}$ that of the oil, but the densities were equal. Note that with the wider models, the recovery was independent of rate over the range of rates investigated. Diffusion of solvent into the oil bypassed by solvent channels was too slow over the range of rates studied to affect the displacement behavior. A different result was obtained in the model only $\frac{1}{2}$ in. wide, where recovery at break-through decreased with rate. The fingers which formed initially in the $\frac{1}{2}$-in.-wide model could be seen to grow for a while and then merge together by diffusion. At high rates the distance traveled by these fingers before they merged was greater. Once the fingers merged, the mixed zone whose viscosity graded from that of the solvent to that of the oil was observed to move pistonlike down the column.

The results illustrated in Fig. 16.90 have several important implications on recovery of oil from reservoirs by solvent flooding. The models can be scaled to represent large reservoirs, using the criteria of geometric similarity and of lateral mixing as having the same importance, W^2/K_T, and using an effective dispersion coefficient for the reservoir of five times that in the laboratory. The three models represent reservoir prototypes 6000 ft long, 31.2 ft thick, and 41.6, 500, and 2000 ft wide. The scaled rates of advance in the prototypes are $\frac{1}{200}$ those in the model. The prototype only 41.6 ft wide is not a realistic reservoir; it is usually manyfold wider. The observation that diffusion in the direction of the width did not affect the displacement behavior in

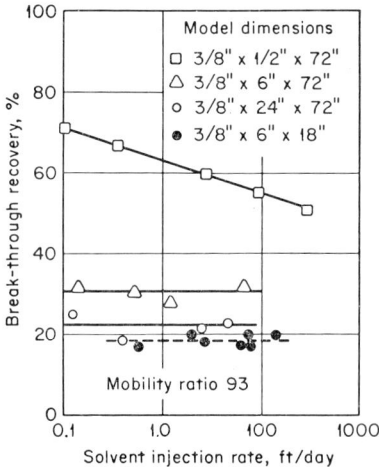

Fig. 16.90. Effect of injection rate on recovery at break-through. (*Ref.* 83.)

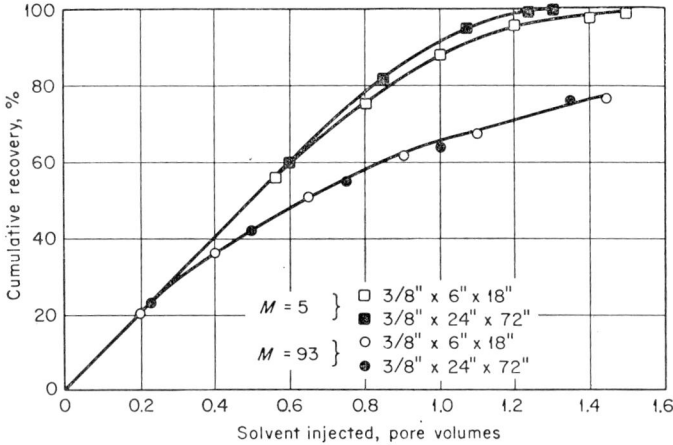

Fig. 16.91. Effect of model dimensions on cumulative recovery. (*Ref.* 83.)

models representing realistic prototypes 500 and 2000 ft wide means that diffusion in the direction of the width will not be of aid in improving solvent floods in the reservoir. The effect of the model geometry on recovery is also illustrated by the results in Fig. 16.90, which is a plot of oil recovery at solvent break-through vs. mobility ratio for the models of three widths. Better recoveries are obtained from long narrow models than from long wide models. In the narrow models, the solvent channels fill a larger fraction of the model width because they grow laterally and feel the influence of the lateral boundaries early in the displacement. In the wider models, the influence of the lateral boundaries is not felt until late in the displacement. Thus it is important in designing models to represent larger systems to preserve geometric similarity.

The effect of the mobility ratio on oil recovery in miscible displacements from homogeneous sands with no gravitational effects is illustrated in Fig. 16.91. Channeling becomes more severe and recoveries less as the oil becomes more viscous. However, considerable oil is recovered after break-through when the more viscous oils are displaced. For instance, when the oil is 375 times more viscous than the solvent, recovery at break-through is only 13 per cent, but recovery after injection of 1.0 pore volume of solvent is 45 per cent.

The causes of the phenomenon of viscous fingering are best illustrated by a series of two-dimensional calculations that have been made using an IBM 704 computer.[90] These calculations were made assuming several arbitrary shapes of the displacement front for low-viscosity solvent displacing oil. The Laplace equation

$$\frac{\partial^2 p}{\partial x^2} + \frac{\partial^2 p}{\partial y^2} = 0$$

and the Darcy equations

$$v_x = -\frac{K}{\mu}\frac{\partial p}{\partial x} \quad \text{and} \quad v_y = -\frac{K}{\mu}\frac{\partial p}{\partial y}$$

were solved in both the region in which solvent was flowing and in the region in which oil was flowing. The following boundary conditions were used:

1. No flow across the lateral walls.
2. Injection of solvent uniformly across the inflow face at constant rate and production of oil uniformly from the outflow face at constant rate.
3. The pressure was continuous across the boundary separating the fluids.
4. The velocities were continuous across the boundary separating the fluids.†

† The correct boundary condition is that the velocities normal to the boundary are continuous. However, it is believed that the errors introduced by using the condition that the velocity is continuous at the boundary introduced negligible errors in this case.

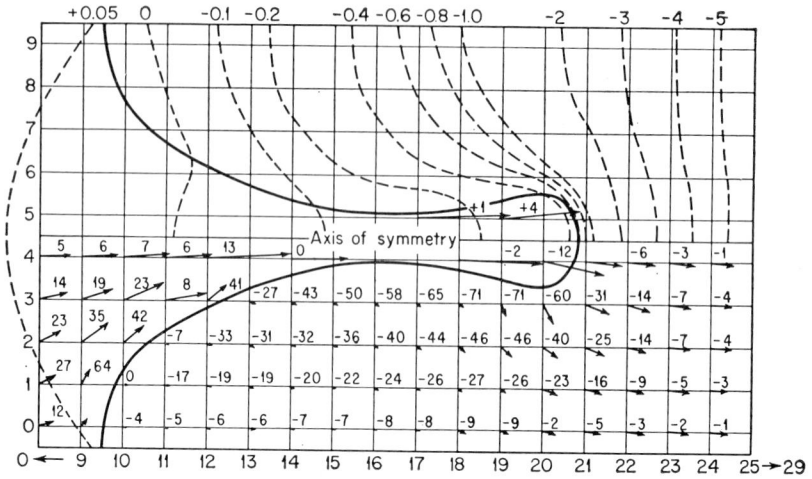

FIG. 16.92. Calculated velocity and pressure profiles in and around channels of low-viscosity solvent in homogeneous sand. Mobility ratio: $M = 150$. Arrows indicate velocity.

The results of one set of these calculations is shown in Fig. 16.92 for a finger shape similar to one observed in a sand-packed model. The length of the arrows represents the magnitude of the velocity, while the direction of the arrow represents the direction of flow. The lines of equal pressure are also shown in the figure. At the base of the finger, the solvent flow is directed toward the axis of the finger, since this represents a

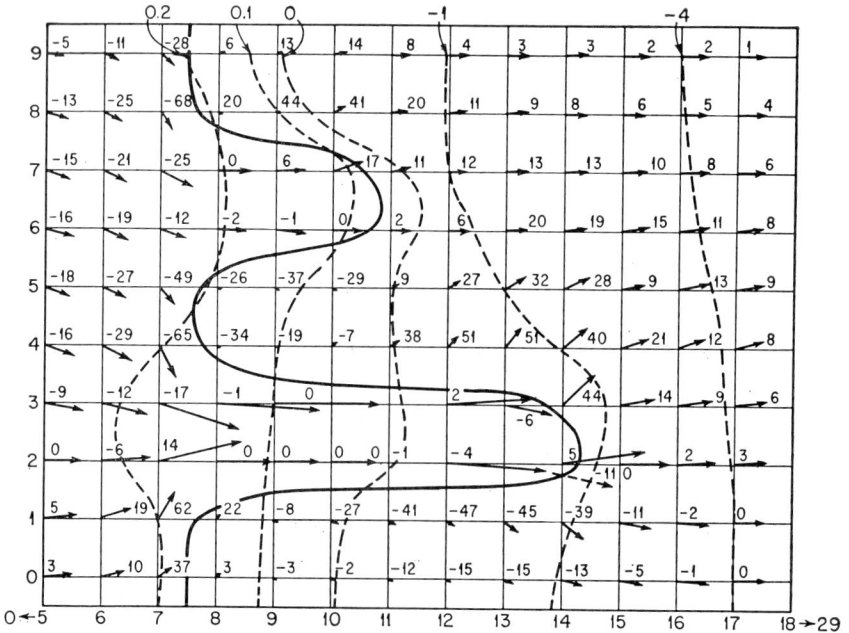

FIG. 16.93. Calculated velocity and pressure profiles in and around channels of low-viscosity solvent in homogeneous sand. Mobility ratio: $M = 80$. Arrows indicate velocity.

path of smaller resistance. In the stem of the finger, the velocities are highest and are directed along the axis of the finger. The pressure gradients in the oil phase are lowest in the region which has been bypassed by solvent and are greatest at the head of the solvent channel. At the head, there is a slight tendency for the solvent to flow later-ally or for the head to "mushroom," but the predominant tendency is for the channel to propagate itself in the forward direction.

The velocity and pressure fields set up by two solvent channels of equal length are shown in Fig. 16.93. The interesting fact to note concerning these channels is that since they were closer to the center than to the walls, the channels tend to repel each other. In Fig. 16.94 are shown the velocity and pressure fields set up when one finger is twice the length of the other. In this situation, the pressure field set up by the longer channel has slowed the forward growth of the shorter channel. The longer channel is growing faster than the shorter one and is tending to move toward the center of the model away from the closer wall.

These calculations effectively illustrate the cause of viscous fingers. The fingers grow because the solvent tends to flow through the path of least resistance. While local permeability variations initiate the process, the subsequent growth of the solvent chan-nels is dictated by the pressure fields set up by the viscous flow of fluids through the porous medium and by the boundary conditions imposed on the medium.

Gravity Overriding in Horizontal Sands. The prior discussion has been concerned with the viscous flow of solvent and oil when no gravitational forces are present. In actual solvent displacements, the solvent usually has a density less than that of the oil. In displacing oil from horizontal sands by solvent, gravitational forces cause the solvent to seek the top of the sand and flow over the oil. Once the solvent is concentrated at the top of the sand, the viscous forces abet the flow of additional low-viscosity solvent through this region of low resistance to flow.

Gravity overriding has been studied in sand-packed Lucite models and in models of consolidated sand. These models were the same rectangular parallelepiped previously

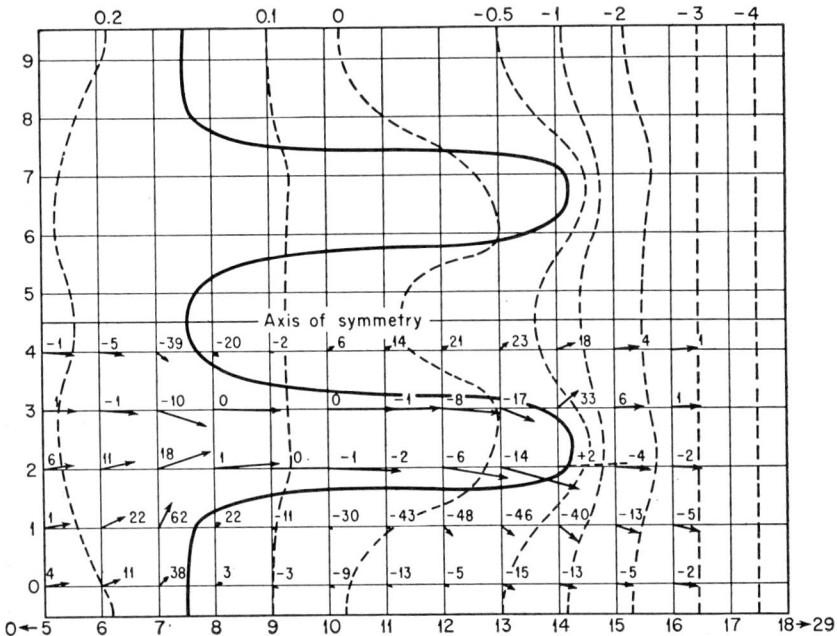

FIG. 16.94. Calculated velocity and pressure profiles in and around channels of low-viscosity solvent in homogeneous sand. Mobility ratio: $M = 80$. Arrows indicate velocity.

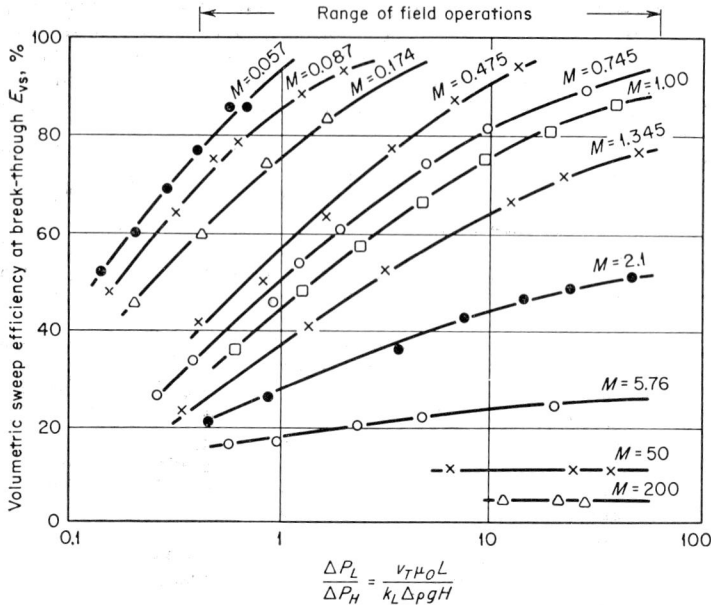

Fig. 16.95. Volumetric sweep efficiency at break-through—linear uniform systems. (*Ref.* 69.)

discussed in discussions of gravity overriding in immiscible displacements.[69] The results of displacements over a range of rates have been correlated in Fig. 16.95. Recoveries at break-through are plotted against the parameter

$$\frac{\Delta P_L}{\Delta P_H} = \frac{v_T \mu_o L}{k_L \, \Delta \rho \, gH}$$

which has the sense of being the initial ratio of the viscous pressure drop in the horizontal direction to the gravitational pressure drop in the vertical direction. The mobility ratios of interest in solvent floods are those shown in Fig. 16.95 from $M = 1.0$ to $M = 200$. For all mobility ratios, recoveries were lower at the lower rates. It can be seen that for high, unfavorable mobility ratios, gravity overriding of the solvent results in almost complete bypassing of the oil. For instance, when the mobility ratio was 200, the oil recovery at solvent break-through was only 5 per cent. It should be emphasized that the models used in these studies were so thick that diffusion of solvent down into the oil being bypassed was negligible.

A limited amount of data is available for cases where diffusion in the direction of the thickness was important in the displacement of oil from horizontal sands.[91] Displacements were conducted at several rates in a model in which mixing in the vertical direction was scaled to represent that in a thin reservoir sand. The model and prototype characteristics are shown in Table 16.15.

The results of displacements conducted at rates representing those in the prototype of 0.105, 0.35, and 1.05 ft/day are shown in Fig. 16.96. The data are plotted as oil recovery vs. the pore vs. volume of solvent injected. It can be seen that better recoveries are obtained at low rates. Recoveries at break-through were 54, 42, and 34 per cent of the oil in place at rates of 0.105, 0.35, and 1.05 ft/day, respectively. While at first glance these results seem in conflict with those in Fig. 16.95, the explanation for this behavior lies in the diffusion of solvent downward into the oil. Gravitational and viscous forces tend to cause the solvent to override and bypass oil more easily at the lower rates, but molecular diffusion downward tends to offset the bypassing. The

Table **16.15.** Model and Prototype Characteristics in Gravity-overriding Experiments

Property	Symbol	Model	Prototype
Permeability	k	190,000 millidarcys	125 millidarcys
Porosity	ϕ	0.305	0.20
Length	L	63 in.	2100 ft
Width	W	6 in.	200 ft
Thickness	H	$\frac{3}{8}$ in.	12.5 ft
Angle of dip	α	0°	0°
Viscosity of oil	μ_o	6.8 centipoises	0.55 centipoise
Viscosity of solvent	μ_s	0.33 centipoise	0.027 centipoise
Density difference	$\Delta\rho$	21.8 lb/ft³	21.8 lb/ft³
Molecular diffusivity	ΔP_D	1.5 cm²/sec	7.5×10^{-5} cm²/sec
Linear rate of advance	v_T	122 $v_{t\ \text{res}}$	$v_{t\ \text{res}}$
Time	t	$1/3200 t_{\text{res}}$	t_{res}

slower the rate, the more time for diffusion and the better the recovery. These results point out the importance of scaling diffusional mixing in the direction of the reservoir thickness in modeling recovery of oil from reservoirs by solvent flooding.

Gravity Segregation in Sands with Dip. When the flow is in the downward direction, the force of gravity may act to improve the solvent displacement. If the low-density solvent is injected at a rate below a critical rate given by

$$v_{T\ \text{cr}} = \frac{K\,\Delta\rho\,\sin\,\alpha}{\mu_o - \mu_s} \qquad (16.129)$$

the displacement of oil will be pistonlike.† No channeling of the solvent will occur at rates below this critical rate because gravity segregation will float the solvent upon the oil.

The role of gravity segregation in miscible displacements in sands with dip is illustrated in Fig. 16.97. Experiments were performed by injecting solvent at the updip end of a model over a range of rates. At rates below the critical rate of 0.2 ft/day given by Eq. (16.129), 100 per cent recovery of the oil was obtained at break-through.

No channeling was observed at these low rates. When the rates exceeded the critical rate, solvent channels were observed to form and grow. When the rate was six times the critical rate, channeling was as severe as in horizontal sands with no gravitational

† See Art. 16.25 for a more complete discussion of the origin of Eq. (16.129).

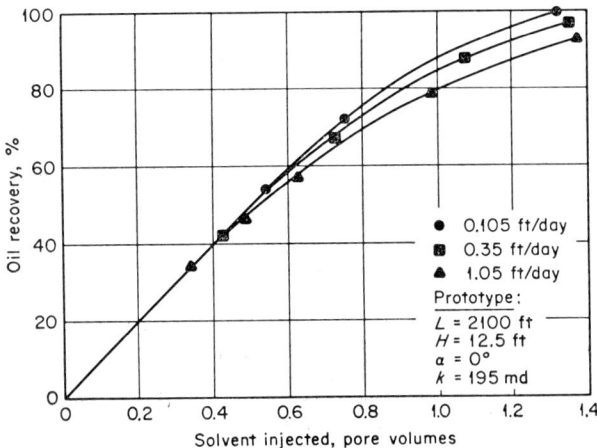

Fig. 16.96. Effect of rate in horizontal sands when vertical diffusion is important.

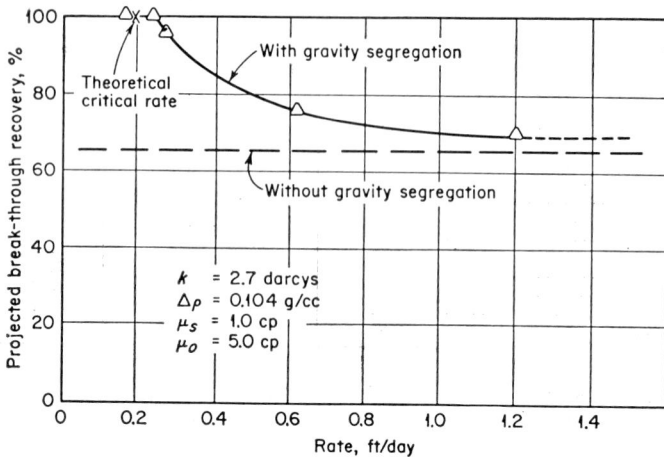

Fig. 16.97. Effect of rate on recovery at break-through with gravity segregation. (*Ref.* 83.)

effects. At over six times the critical rate, recoveries at solvent break-through were only slightly higher than those observed in displacements with the same mobility ratio, but with no density differences between the solvent and oil. Obviously, where economic consideration permits, solvent floods in the reservoir should be conducted at rates less than the critical rate.

16.33. Miscible Displacements in Stratified Sands

When the medium is not homogeneous but contains sands of different permeabilities, the channeling tendencies of low-viscosity solvents are intensified. If the sands are distributed as parallel strata of different permeabilities, the low-viscosity solvent tends to selectively flush the coarse sand and bypass the tight sand. If the permeability varies both horizontally and vertically, the solvent tends to channel through a path of least resistance in the sand. An infinite number of kinds and degrees of stratification exist. Two cases will be treated here to demonstrate the qualitative features of miscible displacement of oil from stratified sands.

Flow in Parallel Strata of Different Permeabilities. The displacement of oil from stratified sands by solvents is best treated by scaled models. The tendency of solvent to channel in homogeneous sands superimposed on the preference to channel through the permeable stratum presents an imposing mathematical problem. Simplified mathematical approaches are possible, however, if one assumes that flow is linear and horizontal, the displacement is pistonlike in each stratum, and there is no cross flow between strata, i.e., there is an impermeable barrier between strata.† In this case, a break-through in the most permeable stratum, the distance traveled in the less permeable strata, can be calculated from

$$\frac{\phi(\mu_1 - \mu_2)X_b{}^2 + 2\phi\mu_2 X_b L}{2k_b} = \frac{\phi(\mu_1 - \mu_2)L^2}{2k_a} \qquad (16.130)$$

in which subscripts 1 and 2 refer to the displacing and displaced fluids, respectively; subscripts a and b refer to the more permeable and less permeable strata, respectively; and X_b is the distance traveled in the less permeable sand.

When the viscosity of the displacing phase is equal to that of the resident fluid, the distance traveled in the less permeable sand is

† See Art. 16.26 and Fig. 16.72 for more complete description of the mathematical model.

$$X_b = \frac{k_b}{k_a} L \qquad (16.131)$$

However, this simplified mathematical approach leaves much to be desired in that miscible displacements are not piston-like when the viscosity of the injected fluid is less than that of the oil. The most reliable method of finding the displacement behavior for a particular fluid and sand system is to perform displacements in models.

To illustrate flow of miscible fluids in parallel sands, consider miscible displacements performed using a model containing two sands. The model was $72 \times 6 \times \frac{3}{8}$ in. and was packed with two 3-in.-wide

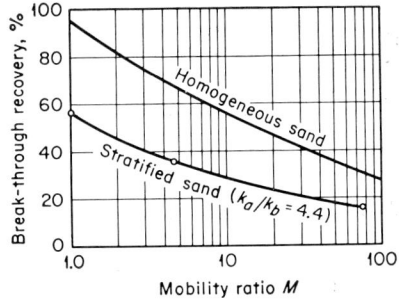

Fig. 16.98.
Effect of mobility ratio on recovery.

sand strata in communication with each other. One stratum had a permeability of 190 darcys, and the other a permeability of 43 darcys. Solvents having the same density as the oil to eliminate gravitational effects were used. The oils had viscosities of 1, 4.6, and 75 times that of the solvent. It was observed that with the adverse mobility ratio of 75, much of the solvent which initially entered the tighter sand crossed into the more permeable stratum near the oil-solvent front advancing in the tight sand. This resulted in poor recoveries for the solvent flood. A comparison of the recovery at break-through as a function of mobility ratio for displacements in the stratified sand with those for homogeneous sands is shown in Fig. 16.98. Note that

Table **16.16.** Permeability Pattern for Segmented-stratified Model

Layer	Segment											
	A	B	C	D	E	F	G	H	I	J	K	L
1	9.5	33.0	16.2	9.5	41.5	56.0	16.2	41.5	33.0	9.5	33.0	41.5
2	56.0	16.2	41.5	56.0	16.2	33.0	6.5	16.2	9.5	56.0	6.5	16.2
3	6.5	41.5	33.0	6.5	33.0	41.5	9.5	6.5	56.0	33.0	41.5	9.5
4	41.5	6.5	56.0	33.0	6.5	9.5	41.5	56.0	6.5	16.2	56.0	33.0
5	16.2	56.0	9.5	16.2	56.0	6.5	33.0	9.5	16.2	41.5	9.5	6.5
6	33.0	9.5	6.5	41.5	9.5	16.2	56.0	33.0	41.5	6.5	16.2	56.0

the recovery in the stratified sand is only about 60 per cent that in the homogeneous sand for any given mobility ratio.

Flow in Segmented Stratified Sands. If the reservoir sands vary both horizontally and vertically and the sands are in communication, the displacement characteristics of miscible fluids may be better than if the permeability were constant in the horizontal direction. To study this possibility a model 6 ft long, 3 in. high, and ¼ in. thick, containing the permeability distribution shown in Table 16.16, was prepared.

The model contained twelve segments, each of which contained six strata of different permeabilities. The strata were arranged so that the permeability in a given layer was not the same in that layer in the adjacent segment. Miscible floods were

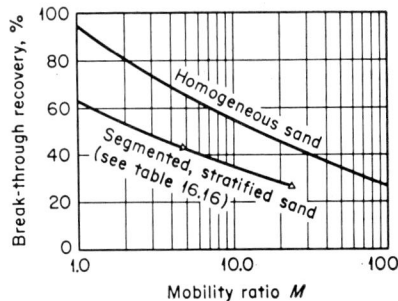

Fig. 16.99.
Effect of mobility ratio on recovery.

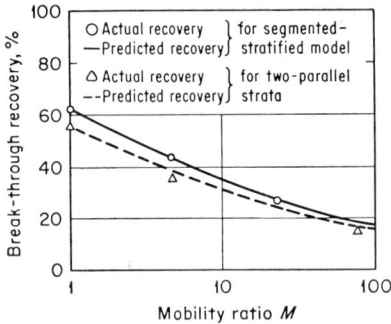

FIG. 16.100. Comparison of predicted with actual recoveries at break-through for stratified models. (*Ref.* 83.)

conducted with mobility ratios of 1, 4.6, and 23. For a mobility ratio of 1.0, the recovery at break-through was 62 per cent. Using Eq. (16.130), one would predict a break-through recovery of only 48 per cent if the strata were continuous instead of randomly arranged. Recoveries at break-through in the segmented-stratified model are compared with those in homogeneous sands in Fig. 16.99 for various mobility ratios. Again the recovery in the stratified sand is appreciably less than that in the homogeneous sand.

A method of predicting the displacement behavior of miscible floods is suggested by the data in Figs. 16.98 and 16.99. If the recovery at break-through in a stratified sand is known or can be determined, this value can be used to calculate the recovery in the stratified sand for other mobility ratios.

Example 16. Given: The recovery at break-through in a stratified sand having a length-width ratio of 12 is 50 per cent for a mobility ratio of 1. It is desired to know the recovery from the stratified sand for a mobility ratio of 100. The recovery at break-through for a mobility ratio of 100 is 19 per cent for a length-width ratio of 12 in a homogeneous sand, as read from Fig. 16.84. The recovery in the stratified sand for a mobility ratio of 100 is equal to 19 per cent × 0.50 = 9.5 per cent.

The agreement between the observed recoveries at break-through and those predicted by the above method for two sets of model data is shown in Fig. 16.100. While this prediction method is empirical, it may be useful in some engineering calculations.

16.34. Areal Pattern Studies

The high, unfavorable mobility ratios characteristic of many solvent floods result in low pattern efficiencies. The effect of mobility ratio on pattern efficiencies has been previously discussed in studies of flow of immiscible fluids. These same data may be applied to miscible fluids with the precaution that the use of data obtained in small homogeneous models with no gravity effects may be optimistically high.

Five-spot Patterns. The areal sweep efficiencies measured in small two-dimensional models of five-spot patterns have been previously presented in Art. 16.26 in Figs. 16.73 and 16.76. These data go only as high as mobility ratios of 10. Even at mobility ratios of 10, fingering and channeling had made the experimental techniques difficult to apply. The areal sweep efficiency for a mobility ratio of 10 is shown to be 51 per cent, but the actual volume of sand swept in a reservoir-pattern flood with solvent would be expected to be only a fraction of this, depending on the importance of gravity overriding and permeability stratification.

Line-drive Patterns. The maximum areal sweep efficiency of miscible floods in staggered-line drives or direct-line drives, in which the ratios of the distances between lines of producing and injection wells to the distance between producers are equal, may be estimated from Figs. 16.74, 16.75, 16.77, and 16.78. Again the effects of fingering, stratification, and gravity overriding will decrease recoveries below those shown in the figures.

REFERENCES

1. Cardwell, W. T., Jr., and R. L. Parsons: *Trans. AIME*, **160**:34 (1945).
2. Scheideggar, A. E.: "The Physics of Flow through Porous Media," Macmillan, New York, 1957.
3. Ritter, L. C., and R. L. Drake: *Ind. Eng. Chem., Anal. Ed.*, **17**:782 (1945); **17**:787 (1945).

4. Burdine, N. T., L. S. Gournay, and P. P. Reichertz: *Trans. AIME*, **189**:195 (1950).
5. Brunnauer, S., P. H. Emmett, and E. Teller: *J. Am. Chem. Soc.*, **60**:309–319 (1938).
6. Brooks, C. S., and W. R. Purcell: *Trans. AIME*, **195**:289 (1952).
7. Harris, B. L., and P. H. Emmett: *J. Phys. and Colloid Chem.*, **53**:811 (1953).
8. Loebenstein, W. V., and V. R. Dietz: *J. Research Natl. Bur. Standards*, **46**:54 (1951).
9. Archie, G. E.: *Trans. AIME*, **146**:54 (1952).
10. Winsauer, W. O., H. M. Shearin, P. H. Masson, and M. Williams: *Bull. AAPG*, **36**(2):253 (1952).
11. Darcy, H.: "Les Fontaines publiques de la ville de Dijon," Victor Dalmint, Paris, 1856.
12. Tek, M. R.: *Trans. AIME*, **210**:336 (1957).
13. Fancher, G. H., J. A. Lewis, and K. B. Barnes: *Penn. State Coll. Mineral. Ind. Expt. Sta. Bull.*, **12**:65 (1933).
14. Klinkenberg, L. J.: "Drilling and Production Practices," API, p. 200, 1941.
15. Muskat, M.: "Flow of Homogeneous Fluids through Porous Media," McGraw-Hill, New York, 1937.
16. Muskat, M.: *Trans. AIME*, **179**:216 (1949).
17. Lamb, H.: "Hydrodynamics," 6th ed., Cambridge, New York, 1932.
18. Streeter, V. L.: "Fluid Dynamics," McGraw-Hill, New York, 1948.
19. Muskat, M.: "Physical Principles of Oil Production," McGraw-Hill, New York, 1949.
20. Nobles, M. A., and H. B. Janzen: *Trans. AIME*, **213**:356 (1958).
21. Wyckoff, R. D., and H. G. Botset, *Physics*, **5**:265 (1934).
22. Swearingen, J. S.: *Oil Weekly*, **96**:30 (Dec. 25, 1939).
23. Hele-Shaw, H. S.: *Trans. Inst. Naval Architects*, **39**:145 (1897).
24. Hurst, W.: *Petrol. Engr.*, **25**:B-40 (April, 1953).
25. McCarty, D. G., and E. C. Barfield: *Trans. AIME*, **213**:139 (1958).
26. Katz, D. L., D. Cornell, R. Kobayashi, F. H. Poettmann, C. F. Weinaug, J. A. Vary, and J. R. Elenbaas: "Handbook of Natural Gas Engineering," McGraw-Hill, New York, 1959.
27. Churchill, R. V.: "Modern Operational Mathematics in Engineering," McGraw-Hill, New York, 1944.
28. Aronofsky, J. S., and R. Jenkins: *Proc. First U.S. Natl. Congr. Appl. Mech.*, Ann Arbor Mich., 1952,. p. 763.
29. Hurst, W.: *Physics*, January, 1934.
30. Van Everdingen, A. F., and W. Hurst: *Trans. AIME*, **186**:305 (1949).
31. Miller, C. C., A. B. Dyes, and C. A. Hutchinson, Jr.: *Trans. AIME*, **189**:91 (1950).
32. Bruce, G. H., D. W. Peaceman, H. H. Rachford, Jr., and J. D. Rice: *Trans. AIME*, **193**:79 (1953).
33. Aronofsky, J. S., and R. Jenkins: *Trans. AIME*, **201**:149 (1954).
34. Bruce, W. A.: *Trans. AIME*, **151**:112 (1943).
35. Rumble, R. C., H. H. Spain, and H. E. Stamm, III: *Trans. AIME*, **192**:B-31 (1951).
36. Young, Thomas: *Phil. Trans. Roy. Soc. London*, 1805, p. 65.
37. Purcell, W. R.: *Trans. AIME*, **189**:369 (1950).
38. Smith, W. O.: *Physics*, **4**:425 (1933).
39. Bruce, W. A., and H. J. Welge: Presented at API Division of Production, Amarillo, Tex., May 22–23, 1947.
40. Hassler, G. L., and E. Brunner: *Trans. AIME*, **160**:114 (1945).
41. Slobod, R. L., A. Chaml ers, and W. L. Prehn, Jr.: *Trans. AIME*, **192**:127 (1951).
42. Purcell, W. R.: *Trans. AIME*, **186**:39 (1949).
43. Leverett, M. C.: *Trans. AIME*, **142**:152 (1941).
44. Brown, H. W.: *Trans. AIME*, **192**:67 (1951).
45. Schilthuis, R. J.: *Trans. AIME*, **127**:199 (1938).
46. Richardson, J. G., J. K. Kerver, J. A. Hafford, and J. S. Osoba: *Trans. AIME*, **195**:187 (1952).
47. Morse, R. A., P. L. Terwilliger, and S. T. Yuster: *Oil Gas J.*, **46**(16):109 (Aug. 23, 1947).
48. Hassler, G. L., E. Brunner, and T. J. Deahl: *Trans. AIME*, **155**:155 (1944).
49. Welge, H. J.: *Trans. AIME*, **195**:91 (1952).
50. Osoba, J. S., J. G. Richardson, J. K. Kerver, J. A. Hafford, and P. M. Blair: *Trans. AIME*, **192**:47 (1951).
51. Geffen, T. M., W. W. Owens, D. R. Parrish, and R. A. Morse: *Trans. AIME*, **192**:99 (1951).
52. Leverett, M. C.: *Trans. AIME*, **132**:149 (1939).
53. Richardson, J. G.: *Trans. AIME*, **210**:114 (1957).
54. Richardson, J. G., F. M. Perkins, Jr., and J. S. Osoba: *Trans. AIME*, **204**:86 (1955).
55. Douglas, J., Jr., D. W. Peaceman, and H. H. Rachford, Jr.: A Method for Calculating Multi-dimensional Immiscible Displacements, presented at meeting of SPE of AIME, Dallas, Tex., Oct. 4–7, 1959.

56. Buckley, S. E., and M. C. Leverett: *Trans. AIME*, **146**:107 (1942).
57. Welge, H. J.: *Trans. AIME*, **195**:91 (1952).
58. Rapoport, L. A., and W. J. Leas: *Trans. AIME*, **198**:139 (1953).
59. Perkins, F. M., Jr.: *Trans. AIME*, **210**:409 (1957).
60. Kyte, J. R., and L. A. Rapoport: *Trans. AIME*, **213**:423 (1958).
61. Douglas, J., Jr., P. M. Blair, and R. J. Wagner: *Trans. AIME*, **213**:96 (1958).
62. Hocott, C. R.: *Producers Monthly*, **21**(10):38 (August, 1957); **21**(11):20 (September, 1957).
63. Graham, J. W., and J. G. Richardson: *Trans. AIME*, **216**:65 (1959).
64. Leverett, M. C., W. B. Lewis, and M. E. True: *Trans. AIME*, **146**:175 (1942).
65. Rapoport, L. A.: *Trans. AIME*, **204**:143 (1955).
66. Hill, S.: Génie chemique, *Chem. Eng. Sci.*, I(6):246 (1952).
67. Chuoke, R. L., P. Van Muers, and C. Van Der Poel: The Instability of Slow, Immiscible Viscous Liquid-liquid Displacements in Permeable Media, presented at Annual Fall Meeting AIME, Petroleum Branch, Houston, Tex., October, 1958.
68. Richardson, J. G., and F. M. Perkins, Jr.: *Trans. AIME*, **210**:114 (1957).
69. Craig, F. F., Jr., J. L. Sanderlin, D. W. Moore, and T. M. Geffen: *Trans. AIME*, **210**:275 (1957).
70. Lindley, D. C., and M. H. Gaskell: Private communication from unpublished work.
71. Martin, J. C.: *Trans. AIME*, **213**:202 (1958).
72. Buckley, S. E.: "Petroleum Conservation," American Institute of Mining, Metallurgical, and Petroleum Engineers, New York, 1951, p. 81.
73. Stiles, W. E.: *Trans. AIME*, **186**:9 (1949).
74. Dyes, A. B., B. H. Caudle, and R. A. Erickson: *Trans. AIME*, **201**:81 (1954).
75. Craig, F. F., Jr., T. M. Geffen, and R. A. Morse: *Trans. AIME*, **204**:7 (1955).
76. Bernard, R. A., and R. H. Wilhelm: *Chem. Eng. Progr.*, **46**:233 (1950).
77. Aris, R., and N. R. Amundson: *AIChE J.*, **3**:280 (1957).
78. Kramers, H., and G. Alberda: *Chem. Eng. Sci.*, **2**:173 (1953).
79. McHenry, K. W., and R. H. Wilhelm: *AIChE J.*, **3**:83 (1957).
80. Taylor, G. I.: *Proc. Roy. Soc. (London)*, **A219**:186 (1953); **223**:446 (1954); **225**:473 (1954).
81. Aris, R.: *Proc. Roy. Soc. (London)*, **A235**:67 (1956).
82. Blackwell, R. J.: An Investigation of Miscible Displacement Processes in Capillaries, presented to the AIChE local section in Galveston, Tex., 1957.
83. Blackwell, R. J., J. R. Rayne, and W. M. Terry: *Trans. AIME*, **217**:1 (1959).
84. Blackwell, R. J.: Laboratory Studies of Microscopic Dispersion Phenomena, presented at AIChE-SPE meeting, San Francisco, Calif., Dec. 6–9, 1959.
85. Carberry, J. J., and R. H. Bretton: Axial Dispersion in Flow through Fixed Beds, presented to AIChE meeting in Chicago, 1957.
86. Ebach, E. A.: Ph.D. dissertation, University of Michigan, Ann Arbor, Mich., 1957.
87. Rifai, M. N.: Ph.D. dissertation, University of California, Berkeley, Calif., 1956.
88. Beran, M. J.: Ph.D. dissertation, Harvard University, Cambridge, Mass., 1955.
89. Oferinga, J., and C. Van Der Poel: *Trans. AIME*, **201**:310 (1954).
90. Peaceman, D. W.: Private communication.
91. Rayne, J. R.: Private communication.

Section 17

TWO-PHASE FLOW

By

M. R. TEK, *University of Michigan, Ann Arbor, Michigan*

TWO-PHASE FLOW

17.1. Introduction

Problems of two-phase flow have been of continuing interest to many industries for a long time. In a large variety of engineering installations such as pipelines, chemical reactors, heat exchangers, boilers, condensers, two-phase flow conditions are of common occurrence. In oil- or natural-gas-production operations, the transportation of oil and gas together in a common pipe from oil field to process plant frequently proves to be an economically sound practice. Recent trends in oil-production practices have resulted in centrally located separators and stock-tank batteries and longer gathering pipelines through which more than one phase flows. In the examples cited above, as well as in many other engineering applications such as process piping for two-phase flow, design of boiler and partial-condenser tubes, etc., optimization of pipe sizes has become an important design factor.

When two or more mutually immiscible phases flow simultaneously through a pipe, the usual engineering problem encountered involves the prediction of the relationships between the flow rates and pressure drops as affected by fluid properties, pipe geometry, the flow regimes, and the flow patterns. In other problems equally significant challenges are presented in areas where optimum design characteristics are desired to bring about satisfactory mixing, separation, heat, and mass-transfer conditions.

The literature contains a large number of publications dealing with specific aspects of multiphase-flow problems. Key references and sources of more detailed information or derivations are listed at the end of this section.

One of the more generally accepted solutions to problems of two-phase flow through pipe was published by Lockhart and Martinelli[1] and Martinelli et al.[2] The correlation proposed by Lockhart and Martinelli is based on the hypothesis that the pressure drop for simultaneous flow of two phases is equal to the pressure drop which would occur if one of the phases were flowing alone, multiplied by a predictable factor. This factor was correlated as a function of the ratio of single-phase pressure drop of the liquid to the single-phase pressure drop of the gas phase for a specified flow regime. There have been several attempts to improve the correlation developed by Lockhart and Martinelli. As a result, several modifications of their basic approach have been developed and proposed.[3-5] Alves[6] demonstrated that several flow patterns may coexist for the various flow regimes classified by Lockhart and Martinelli. A modification of Lockhart and Martinelli procedure based on turbulent-liquid–turbulent-gas-flow regime has been developed by Ovid Baker.[4] The basic flow regimes considered originally by Lockhart and Martinelli were obtained by combining laminar or turbulent flow in both liquid and gas phases. One major difficulty and disadvantage of applying the correlation of Lockhart and Martinelli to practical engineering calculations has been the need to know the particular flow regime before deciding on the appropriate correlation chart. Bergelin, Gazeley, et al. presented a correlation for predicting gas-phase pressure drop for stratified and annular flow patterns.[7-9] Treatment of each of the two phases as a pseudo single-phase fluid has been suggested and applied with some success to flow-rate–pressure-drop calculations by several investigators.[10,11] The problems associated with simultaneous flow of liquid and gas are treated for various conduits and flow containers. Available theory, correlations, and example problems are given for two-phase flow through horizontal vertical and inclined pipe. Multiphase-flow problems, where more than two phases are transported through pipes, and the flow, formation, and stability of sprays and bubbles are described separately. In the subsection related to flow of sprays and bubbles, the fundamentals of the fluid mechanics of spray formation, the prediction of particle sizes, the description of spray-producing equipment, the properties of sprays, and the mechanics of liquid drops and gas bubbles in continuous fluids are discussed.

The problems of simultaneous flow of liquids and solids are treated at the end of this section. This section includes a summary of the dynamics of particles submerged in fluids and the basic principles of sedimentation along with applications to fluidization and pneumatic conveying. Examples and design problems are given in transport of dispersed solids by continuous liquid phase.

17.2. Notation

A	inside cross-section area of the pipe, ft²
a	(1) numerical constant, dimensionless
	(2) half thickness of a two-dimensional liquid jet, cm
B_i	intercept of the formation-volume factor, pressure curve at $P = 0$ axis, vol/vol
b	a parameter used in two-phase horizontal flow, dimensionless
C_i	proportionality constant between volume of a particle and the cube of its average diameter, dimensionless
c	volume-fraction solids in a slurry, dimensionless
D	internal diameter of pipe (ID), in. or ft
D'	pipe ID, ft
D_t	tube diameter, ft
d	diameter of a drop, cm
d_{av}	average diameter of particle from screen analysis, ft
d_p	particle diameter, ft
d_s	diameter of a sphere having the same volume as a given particle, ft
F	formation-volume factor, ratio of barrels of liquid at pressure P to barrels of liquid at standard conditions, dimensionless
F_d	drag force on a particle, lb$_f$
$\mathbf{F}$	Froude number, dimensionless, $\mathbf{F} = u_f{}^2/d_P g$
f	Moody friction factor, dimensionless
f'	two-phase f factor, dimensionless
f_D	drag coefficient, dimensionless
f_g	Fanning friction factor, dimensionless
f^*_P	friction factor for solids flow, dimensionless
G	specific mass velocity, (lb/hr) (ft²)
G_G	specific gravity of gas (air = 1.0)
G_M	specific mass velocity of the two-phase mixture, (lb/hr) (ft²)
G_W	specific gravity of produced water (pure water = 1.0), dimensionless
G'_G	specific mass velocity of the gas phase, (lb/sec) (ft²)
G_L	(1) specific gravity of the liquid ($G_L = 1.0$ for pure water), dimensionless
	(2) specific mass velocity of the liquid phases, (lb/sec) (ft²)
G_{mf}	specific mass velocity for minimum fluidization
G_o	specific gravity of stock-tank oil (water = 1.0), dimensionless
g	acceleration of gravity, cm/sec² or ft/sec²
g_c	32.174
h	length of vertical flow string in reference to a horizontal datum, ft
K	mass flow ratio between gas and liquid phases, dimensionless
K'	a numerical constant, dimensionless
L	pipe length, ft; also pipe length, miles
$\overline{lw}$	lost work, ft-lb$_f$/lb$_m$
M	total mass of the two-phase mixture associated with each barrel of flowing liquid lb$_m$/bbl liquid flow
N	number of hills, dimensionless
$\mathbf{N}_{vi}$	a dimensionless viscosity group $= \mu_d/\sqrt{v\rho_d\sigma d}$
n	characteristic ratio of specific surfaces, dimensionless
n_f	slope of the formation-volume factor, pressure curve, vol/(vol psia)

n_s slope of the solubility curve, (ft³/bbl) (psia)

P_0 pressure base, psia

P_1 upstream pressure, psia

P_2 downstream pressure, psia

P_c pseudo-critical pressure, psia

$_pP_r$ pseudo-reduced pressure, dimensionless

$_pT_r$ pseudo-reduced temperature, dimensionless

Q volumetric flow rate, cfm; also gas-phase flow rate, measured at temperature T_0, pressure P_0, std ft³/hr (used in Weymouth equation)

Q' flow rate of the gas phase, std M ft³/day (Clinedinst equation)

Q_L liquid flow rate, bbl/day

R producing gas-oil ratio, ft³ gas/bbl stock-tank oil

R' solids-liquid mass ratio, dimensionless

Re   two-phase Reynolds-number function, dimensionless

R   Reynolds number, dimensionless

r (1) a parameter used in two-phase horizontal flow, dimensionless
      (2) radius of liquid drop, cm

S solubility of gas in oil at pressure P, std ft³/bbl

S_{g-o} gas-oil ratio, ft³ gas measured at standard conditions (14.65 psia and 60°F) per bbl of liquid measured at stock tank

S_i intercept of the solubility pressure curve at $P = 0$, ft³/bbl

s a parameter used in two-phase horizontal flow, dimensionless

T average pipeline temperature, °R

T_0 temperature base, °R

u_f superficial fluid velocity, fps or cm/sec

u_g superficial velocity of gas, fps

u^*_p fully accelerated particle velocity, fps

V_H hindered settling velocity, cm/sec or fps

V_m specific volume of the two-phase mixture associated with one barrel of flowing liquid, ft³/bbl

$\overline{V}_m$ integrated average volume of gas, oil, and water per each barrel of produced oil, ft³/bbl

V_w water-production rate, ft³/bbl stock-tank oil

v average velocity, fps; also velocity of liquid jet relative to gas phase, cm/sec

v_g superficial velocity of the gas phase, fps or cm/sec

v_m terminal velocity of a particle, cm/sec or fps

W_G specific mass velocity of gas phase, (lb$_m$/sec) (ft²)

W_L specific mass velocity of liquid phase, (lb$_m$/sec) (ft²)

$\overline{W}$ shaft work, ft-lb$_f$/lb$_m$

W*   Weber number, dimensionless, $\mathbf{W} = \rho_a\lambda^* v^2/\sigma$

X (1) a dimensionless parameter in two-phase flow $X = \sqrt{(\Delta P/\Delta L)_L}/\sqrt{(\Delta P/\Delta L)_G}$
      (2) volume-fraction fluid in a slurry, dimensionless

Z compressibility factor, dimensionless

Z_0 compressibility factor of the gas at temperature and pressure bases T_0 and P_0, dimensionless

Δ denotes incremental quantity

ΔL length of pipe, ft

ΔP pressure drop, psi

ΔP_L liquid-phase pressure drop, psf

ΔP_t pressure drop in pneumatic conveying through horizontal pipe

$(\Delta P)_{TP}$ two-phase pressure drop, psf

δ particle average diameter, ft

ϵ (1) absolute roughness of the pipe, ft
      (2) porosity, dimensionless

ϵ_{mf} minimum-fluidization voidage, dimensionless

λ^* disturbance wavelength of maximum instability, cm

η efficiency, dimensionless

ρ	density of the two-phase mixture at pressure P and temperature T, lb_m/ft^3
ρ_a	density of gas phase, g/cc
ρ_b	bulk density of suspension, lb/ft^3 or g/cc
ρ_e	effective density of immersed particles, lb/ft^3
ρ_L	density of the liquid lb/ft^3
ρ_m	mean density of two-phase slurry, lb/ft^3
ρ_s	solid density, lb/ft^3
μ_b	bulk viscosity of the suspension, $lb_m/(ft)(sec)$ or $g_m/(cm)(sec)$
μ_G	viscosity of the gas phase, $lb_m/(ft)(sec)$
μ_L	viscosity of the liquid phase, $lb_m/(ft)(sec)$
Σ	denotes summation
σ	surface tension, dynes/cm
ψ	sphericity, dimensionless
ϕ	(1) slurry-density factor ρ_e/ρ_L, dimensionless
	(2) denotes function of
ϕ_L	a correlating parameter, dimensionless

SUBSCRIPTS

av	denotes average value
c	refers to continuous phase; also denotes critical condition
d	refers to dispersed phase
G	denotes gas phase
g-o	denotes gas-oil ratio
H	refers to hindered condition
o	denotes standard or base condition
i	denotes the running index in a summation
L	denotes liquid phase
ll	denotes liquid-phase-laminar, gas-phase-laminar
lt	denotes liquid-phase-laminar, gas-phase-turbulent
r	denotes reduced condition
s	denotes solid
TPH	denotes two-phase condition corrected for hilly terrain
tl	denotes liquid-phase-turbulent, gas-phase-laminar
tt	denotes liquid-phase-turbulent, gas-phase-turbulent
w	denotes water
1	denotes upstream terminal of pipe
2	denotes downstream terminal of pipe

SIMULTANEOUS FLOW OF LIQUID AND GAS

The engineering problems involving simultaneous flow of liquid and gas may be classified from the standpoint of geometry of the conduit through which the flow is taking place. Horizontal and vertical two-phase flow through pipe, inclined two-phase flow, and more-than-two-phase flow through pipe are considered separately. At the end of this section the engineering information available on the flow of sprays and bubbles, on disintegration of liquid jets, and on dispersed systems is treated along with suitable applications such as design of spray-producing equipment.

Most commonly encountered multiphase-pipe-flow problems involve the prediction of pressure-drop–flow rate relations for a variety of different flow conditions. Horizontal, vertical, or oblique flow of liquid and gas phases through pipe or the simultaneous flow of three immiscible phases through pipe provide most of the cases encountered in engineering practice.

17.3. Horizontal Two-phase Flow

The general problem of predicting the pressure drop in a multiphase-flow system is a very complicated one. One of the main difficulties is due to the fact that numerous flow patterns of widely different geometry and mechanics may coexist. The flow patterns

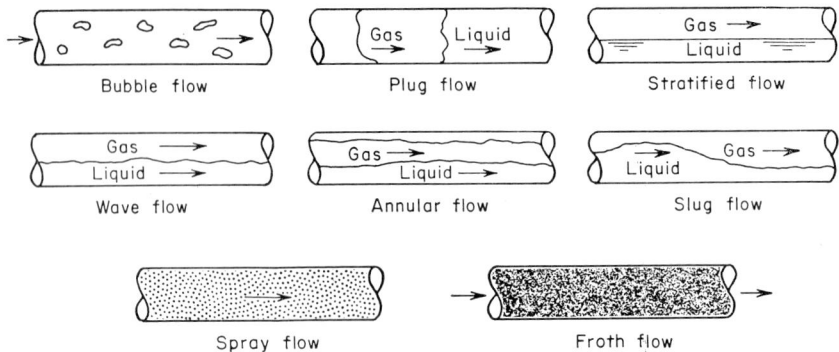

Fig. 17.1. Typical two-phase-flow patterns.

usually encountered in multiphase flow are sketched in Fig. 17.1. These various flow patterns are usually referred to as

Bubble flow	Annular flow
Plug flow	Slug flow
Stratified flow	Spray flow
Wave flow	Froth flow

With the possible exception of stratified flow, these various flow patterns are common to horizontal, vertical, or inclined flow. These various flow patterns not only impose unstable, basically unsteady, and intricate geometry to the system, but also critically affect the relative magnitudes of several force systems which are active to varying extents. The classical approach of attempting to solve the Navier-Stokes equations appears almost hopelessly devoid of any promise of success, not only because of analytical difficulties stemming from their nonlinear nature, but also because of virtual impossibility of expressing the ever-changing boundary conditions. The necessity of including in a general formulation of the problem, the interfacial and gravitational forces along with viscous, inertia, and pressure forces further complicates the theoretical approach. These difficulties and the additional difficulty that direct mathematical solution did not seem likely to give hope of practical success led several investigators to adopt semiempirical approaches to the problem. In some of these attempts the combination of experimental facts and data available on two-phase-flow systems with ideas from the well-established theory of single-phase flow through pipe yielded research results of practical utility and theoretical significance. These are highlighted by the methods of Martinelli et al. and Bertuzzi, Tek, and Poettmann. These methods will be described to the reader in enough detail to facilitate their practical application in actual problems.

17.4. Lockhart and Martinelli Procedure

The procedure for the calculation of two-phase pressure drops through horizontal pipe proposed by Lockhart and Martinelli may be summarized as follows:

1. By assuming that liquid and gas phases are flowing alone through the pipe, calculate single-phase pressure drops for both liquid and gas phases.

2. Calculate the dimensionless parameter X from

$$X = \sqrt{\frac{(\Delta P/\Delta L)_L}{(\Delta P/\Delta L)_G}} = \sqrt{\frac{\Delta P_L}{\Delta P_G}} \qquad (17.1)$$

Several specific equations and some general procedures for the calculation of single-phase liquid or gas pressure drops are available in Secs. 3 and 8 or in the literature. For example, in the oil industry the single-phase pressure drop for the gas is usually calculated from the Weymouth or Clinedinst equation.[12] These equations in oil- and gas-production field units are given in the following:

$$Q = 3.22 \frac{T_0}{P_0} \left[\frac{(P_1{}^2 - P_2{}^2)D^5}{G_G T L f Z_a} \right]^{0.5} \qquad (17.2)$$

Equation (17.2) is the modified form of the early Weymouth equation in which the effect of the nonideality of the gas is included through the average compressibility factor Z_a. In Eq. (17.2):

Q = flow rate of gas measured at temperature T_0 and pressure P_0, std ft³/hr
L = length of pipe, miles
D = internal diameter of pipe (ID), in.
P_1 = upstream pressure, psia
P_2 = downstream pressure, psia
G_G = gas gravity (air = 1.0)
T = average pipeline temperature, °R
Z_a = average compressibility factor (in Weymouth's original equation Z = 1.0)
f = friction factor

The Clinedinst equation also takes account of the deviation of natural gas from ideal behavior:

$$Q' = 3973.0 \frac{Z_0 T_0 P_c}{P_0} \left[\frac{D'^5}{G_G T L f} \left(\int_0^{P_{r,1}} \frac{P_r}{Z} dP_r - \int_0^{P_{r,2}} \frac{P_r}{Z} dP_r \right) \right]^{0.5} \qquad (17.3)$$

in which Q' = flow rate of gas phase, std M ft³/day
Z_0 = compressibility factor at temperature and pressure bases T_0 and P_0
T_0 = temperature base, °R
P_0 = pressure base, psia
P_c = pseudo-critical pressure, psia
D' = pipe ID, ft
T = flowing temperature, °R
P_r = pseudo-reduced pressure, dimensionless

and the numerical values of the integral functions $\int_0^{P_r} \frac{P_r}{Z} dP_r$ are obtained from tables published in the literature.[12]

The single-phase liquid pressure drop may also be computed from suitable friction-factor–Reynolds-number charts by using the Bernoulli, or flow, equation with appropriate units. An equation frequently used in the oil industry with the oil field units is

$$\Delta P_L = \frac{34 \times 10^{-10} f Q_L{}^2 L \rho_L}{g_c D'^5} \qquad (17.4)$$

in which f = Moody friction factor, dimensionless
Q_L = liquid flow rate, bbl/day
ρ_L = liquid density, lb/ft³
ΔP_L = liquid-phase pressure drop, psf
g_c = 32.174, conversion factor, lb$_m$/slug

3. Once the X factor has been computed and the Reynolds numbers calculated for both liquid and gas phases as if they were flowing separately and fully alone through the pipe, from the magnitudes of these Reynolds numbers Table 17.1 is used to determine the flow regime which must apply.

4. Once the correct flow regime and the correlating factor X are established, the chart given in Fig. 17.2 may be used. In Fig. 17.2 ϕ_L or ϕ_G are the final correlating parameters permitting the calculation of two-phase pressure drops once X, the flow regime, and single-phase pressure drops have been determined. The curves labeled ϕ_L are used along

Table 17.1. Flow Regimes for Two-phase Flow

Flow regime	Reynolds numbers	
	Gas phase, R_G	Liquid phase, R_L
Liquid-turbulent–gas-turbulent........	>2000	>2000
Liquid-laminar–gas-turbulent..........	>2000	<1000
Liquid-turbulent–gas-laminar	<1000	>2000
Liquid-laminar–gas-laminar	<1000	<1000

with the single-phase liquid pressure drops and ϕ_G curves with the gas-phase pressure drops. Once ϕ_L is read from the appropriate correlating curve, the following equations defining ϕ_L may be used to determine the two-phase pressure drop.

$$\left(\frac{\Delta P}{\Delta L}\right)_{TP} = \phi^2 \left(\frac{\Delta P}{\Delta L}\right)_{L \text{ or } G} \tag{17.5}$$

$$(\Delta P)_{TP} = \phi^2 (\Delta P)_{L \text{ or } G} \tag{17.6}$$

In making two-phase-flow calculations using the Lockhart and Martinelli procedure, one may choose to determine the two-phase pressure drop either from the single-phase liquid or single-phase gas pressure drops. Each method gives the same answer.

Example 1. A 2-in. horizontal oil-gathering line carries crude oil at a rate of 440 bbl/day simultaneously with natural gas of 0.65 sp gr at a rate of 16,680 std ft³/hr. The discharge pressure of the pipeline, which is 1000 ft long, is 35 psig. It is desired to compute the pressure distribution along the pipeline by the Lockhart and Martinelli method. The average flowing temperature of the pipeline is 70°F. The density of the crude oil is 50 lb$_m$/ft³.

Viscosity of the natural gas = 0.014 centipoise at 50 psia and 70°F
Viscosity of the crude oil = 0.6 centipoise at 50 psia and 70°F

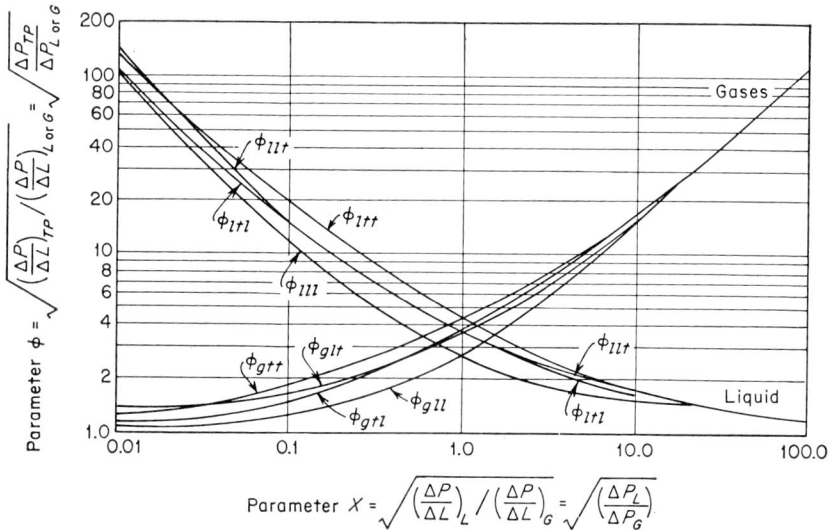

FIG. 17.2. Correlation for horizontal two-phase flow. (*Lockhart and Martinelli*[1,2] *procedure.*)

SOLUTION. 1. First, liquid- and gas-phase Reynolds numbers must be calculated.

$$D = \frac{1.995}{12} \text{ ft} \qquad A = \frac{\pi}{4}\frac{1.995^2}{144} = 2.17 \times 10^{-2} \text{ ft}^2$$

$$\mathbf{R}_L = \frac{50 \times 400 \times 5.61 \times 1.995}{24 \times 12 \times 3600 \times 2.17 \times 10^{-2} \times 0.6 \times 0.000672}$$

Since 1 centipoise $= 0.000672 \text{ lb}_m/(\text{ft})(\text{sec})$,

$$\mathbf{R}_L = 2.47 \times 10^4$$

$$\mathbf{R}_G = \frac{0.076 \times 0.65 \times 16{,}680 \times 1.995}{3600 \times 2.17 \times 10^{-2} \times 12 \times 0.014 \times 0.000672}$$

$$\mathbf{R}_G = 1.86 \times 10^5$$

From Table 17.1 it can be concluded that the flow regime to be used is turbulent-turbulent, i.e., liquid-turbulent and gas-turbulent.

2. Calculate single-phase pressure drop for liquid, using Eq. (17.4).

$$(\Delta P)_L = \frac{34 \times 10^{-10} f Q_L{}^2 L \rho_L}{g_c D'}$$

$$Q_L = 400 \text{ bbl/day}$$

The absolute roughness and the relative roughness of the pipeline may next be determined from standard tables or charts as

$$\frac{\epsilon}{D'} = 0.003$$

for $\quad \dfrac{\epsilon}{D'} = 0.003$ at $\mathbf{R} = 2.47 \times 10^4 \quad f = 0.0263 \quad$ from Moody chart (Fig. 3.9)

$$L = 1000 \text{ ft}$$

$$\rho_L = 50 \text{ lb/ft}^3$$

$$(\Delta P)_L = \frac{34 \times 10^{-10} \times 0.0263 \times \overline{400}^2 \times 1000 \times 50}{32.17 \times (1.995/12)^5} = 175 \text{ psf}$$

$$= 1.21 \text{ psi}$$

3. Calculate $(\Delta P)_G$.
From Eq. (17.2),

$$Q = 3.22 \times \frac{520}{14.7}\left[\frac{(P_1{}^2 - P_2{}^2)D^5}{G_G T L f Z_a}\right]^{0.5}$$

for $\epsilon/D = 0.003$ at $\mathbf{R} = 1.86 \times 10^5$ and $f = 0.018$.

The pseudo-critical pressure and temperature for a natural gas of 0.65 sp gr may be determined from charts of the "Handbook of Natural Gas Engineering"[12] as $_pP_r \cong 50/668 = 0.075$; $_pT_r = 530/375 = 1.41$ at $_pP_r = 0.075$ and $_pT_r = 1.41$, $Z = 0.995$. (The charts giving the Z factor for the natural gas as a function of reduced temperature and pressure are also in Ref. 12.)

From Eq. (17.2),

$$16{,}680 = 3.22 \times \frac{520}{14.7}\left[\frac{(P_1{}^2 - \overline{50}^2)\overline{1.995}^2}{0.65 \times 530 \times 0.018 \times (1000/5280) \times 0.995}\right]^{0.5}$$

which gives $P_1 = 57.4$ psia.

Therefore $(\Delta P)_G = 57.4 - 50 = 7.4$ psi

$$X = \sqrt{\frac{1.21}{7.4}} = 0.404$$

From Fig. 17.2,

$$\phi_L \cong 7.5$$
$$(\Delta P)_{TP} = \phi^2 (\Delta P)_L \qquad \text{Eq. (17.6)}$$
$$(\Delta P)_{TP} = 56 \times 1.21 = 67.9 \text{ psia}$$

If instead of the $(\phi_L)_{tt}$ curve the $(\phi_G)_{tt}$ curve was used,

$$\phi_G \cong 3.0$$
$$(\Delta P)_{TP} = (3)^2 \times 7.4 = 66.6 \text{ psi}$$

which is approximately equal to the result obtained with the calculations based on single-liquid-phase pressure drop.

For the calculation of the pressure distribution along the pipe, first take $\Delta L_1 = 250$ ft.

$$(\Delta P)_L = \frac{1.21 \times 250}{1000} = 0.303 \text{ psi}$$

For the gas flow, single-phase pressure drop is computed as before:

$$\left[(P^2_{250} - \overline{50}^2) \times 27 \times \frac{1000}{250} \right]^{\frac{1}{2}} = 146.3$$

$$P_{250} = 51.9$$

$$(\Delta P)_G = 51.9 - 50 = 1.9 \text{ psi}$$

$$X = \sqrt{\frac{0.302}{1.9}} = 0.398$$

$$(\phi_L)_{tt} = 7.5$$
$$(\Delta P)_{TP} = (7.5)^2 \times (\Delta P)_L = 56 \times 0.304 = 16.9 \text{ psi}$$
$$(P_{250})_{TP} = 50 + 16.9 = 66.9 \text{ psia}$$

Next take:

$$(\Delta L)_2 = 250 \text{ ft} \qquad (\Delta P)_L = 0.302 \text{ psia}$$

$$P^2_{500'} - P^2_{250'} = \frac{(146.3)^2}{108} = 198$$

$$P^2_{500} = P^2_{250} + 198$$
$$P_{500} = 70.5 \text{ psia}$$
$$(\Delta P)_G = 70.5 - 69 = 1.5 \text{ psi}$$

$$X = \sqrt{\frac{0.302}{1.5}} = 0.449$$

$$(\phi_L)_{tt} \cong 7.0$$
$$(\Delta P)_{TP} = 49 \times 0.302 = 14.8$$
$$(P_{500})_{TP} = 66.9 + 14.8 = 81.7 \text{ psia}$$

By repeating the same procedure,

$$\Delta L_3 = 250 \text{ ft} \qquad (\Delta P)_L = 0.302 \text{ psi}$$
$$P^2_{750'} - P^2_{500'} = 374$$
$$P_{750'} = 83 \text{ psia}$$
$$(\Delta P)_G = 83 - 81.7 = 1.3 \text{ psi}$$

$$X = \sqrt{\frac{0.302}{1.3}} = 0.483$$

Table 17.2. Summary of Results on Example 1

L, ft	$P, psia$
1000	107.53
750	94.85
500	81.7
250	67.9
0	50

$$(\phi_L)_{tt} \sim 6.6$$
$$(\Delta P)_{TP} = (6.6)^2 \times 0.302 = 13.15$$
$$(P_{750})_{TP} = 81.7 + 13.15 = 94.85 \text{ psia}$$

Finally,

$$\Delta L_4 = 250 \text{ ft} \qquad (\Delta P)_L = 0.302 \text{ psi}$$
$$P^2_{1000'} - P^2_{750} = 198$$
$$P_{1000} = 96 \text{ psia}$$
$$(\Delta P)_G = 96 - 94.85 = 1.15$$

$$X = \sqrt{\frac{0.302}{1.15}} = 0.51$$

$$(\phi_L)_{tt} = 6.5$$
$$(\Delta P)_{TP} = (6.5)^2 \times 0.302 = 12.68 \text{ psi}$$
$$(P_{1000})_{TP} = 94.85 + 12.68 = 107.53 \text{ psia}$$

The summary of results of the pressure-profile calculations is given in Table 17.2

17.5. Two-phase f'-factor Method

The concept of two-phase f' factor has been used by many. The most recent and generally accepted correlation was published by Bertuzzi, Tek, and Poettmann.[10] The proposed method eliminates the need to establish a flow pattern by a somewhat arbitrary criterion for predicting the flow patterns. This is based upon the fact that the same variables that determine the flow patterns and regimes must also determine the particular pressure-drop-flow-rate relation. The two-phase f'-factor method treats the two phases as a pseudo fluid phase having the density equal to the density of the mixture. The two-phase f' factor is correlated against a special two-phase Reynolds-number function. The development is based on a total-energy balance for the flowing two-phase mixture under steady-state conditions.

The two-phase f' factor is defined by the following relation:

$$f' = \frac{2g_c D \overline{lw}}{4v^2 L} \tag{17.7}$$

in which f' = two-phase f factor, dimensionless
         D = inside diameter of the pipe (ID), ft
         $\overline{lw}$ = lost work, ft-lb$_f$/lb$_m$
         v = average velocity of the two-phase mixture, fps
         L = pipe length, over which the pressure drop is occurring, ft

The correlating parameter is the two-phase Reynolds-number function, which is defined by the following relation:

$$\text{Re} = \left(\frac{DW_G}{\mu_G}\right)^a \left(\frac{DW_L}{\mu_L}\right)^b \tag{17.8}$$

if

$$a = \frac{K}{K+1} \tag{17.9}$$

$$b = e^{-0.1K} \tag{17.10}$$

and W_G = gas-phase mass velocity, $lb_m/(ft^2)(sec)$
    W_L = liquid-phase mass velocity, $lb_m/(ft^2)(sec)$
    K = mass flow ratio between gas and liquid phases, dimensionless

It is important to note that the coefficients a and b of the gas- and liquid-phase Reynolds numbers are specifically chosen functions of K so that for all-liquid or all-gas flow the given correlation would inherently reduce to the well-known and established single-phase friction-factor–Reynolds-number correlation.

As K approaches infinity, for all-gas flow

    a will approach the limit of 1
    b will approach the limit of 0
$\mathbf{R}_G{}^a \times \mathbf{R}_L{}^b$ will approach $\mathbf{R}_G$

On the other hand, if K approaches zero, for all-liquid flow

    a will approach 0
    b will approach 1
$\mathbf{R}_G{}^a \times \mathbf{R}_L{}^b$ will approach $\mathbf{R}_L$

For these limiting conditions the two-phase f' factor will approach the single-phase f factor because the mixture densities will approach the single-phase densities. The functional relation between the two-phase f' factor and the two-phase Reynolds-number function is of the form:

$$f' = \phi \left[\left(\frac{DW_G}{\mu_G} \right)^a \left(\frac{DW_L}{\mu_L} \right)^b \right] \tag{17.11}$$

This correlation is given in Fig. 17.3. In this figure the curves A, B, C, and D and A', B', C', and D' permit the determination of the f' factor for each value of the Reynolds-number function and the gas-liquid mass ratio K. Once the f' factor is determined from application of the flow equation, or Bernoulli's equation, for the particular flow system, the lost work or pressure drop may be determined. It is important to note that, as indicated in Fig. 17.3, it is possible to have more than one value of f' for each value of two-phase Reynolds-number function and gas-liquid mass ratio over a range of $\mathbf{R}_G{}^a\mathbf{R}_L{}^b$ values. The reason for this is mainly attributed to the possibility of several flow pat-

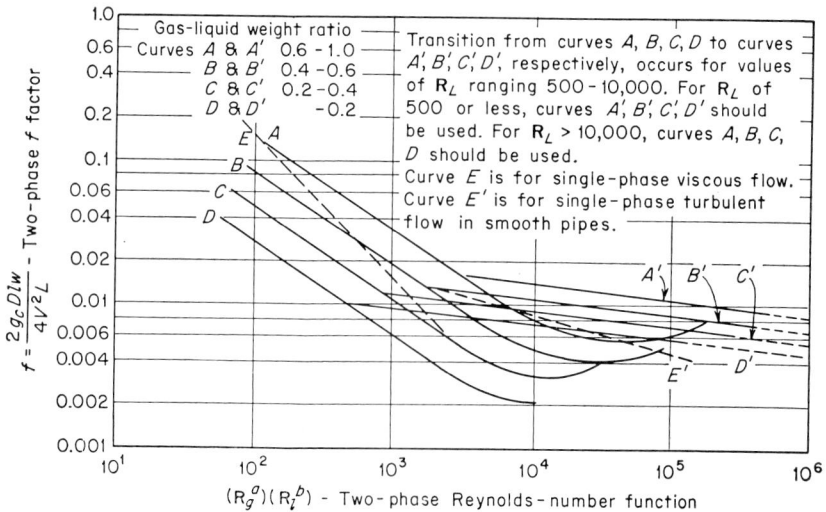

Fig. 17.3. Correlation for horizontal two-phase flow. Two-phase f-factor method. (*Ref.* 10.)

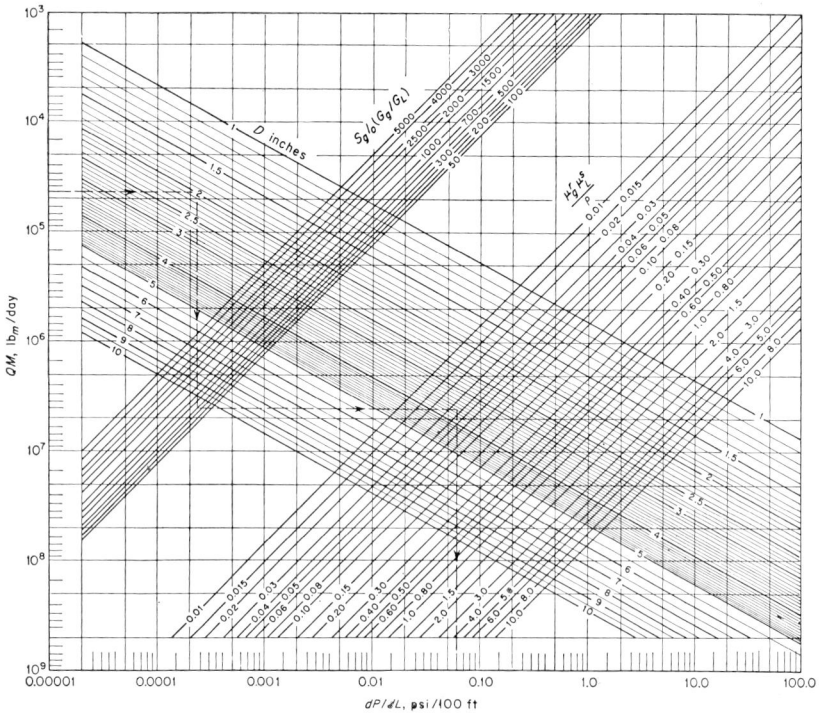

FIG. 17.4. Chart for estimating pressure drop for horizontal multiphase fluid flow in pipes. (*Ref.* 10.)

terns existing for the same value of Re at the range of transition from one set of curves to the other. The data available on several systems further indicate that at high values of the Reynolds-number function, the correlation becomes more independent of the flow pattern for a given gas-liquid mass ratio. The transition from the lower curves to the upper ones corresponding to the same gas-liquid mass flow ratio occurs for the range of R_L between 500 and 10,000.

Figure 17.4 is a working chart developed in order to facilitate horizontal two-phase pressure-drop calculations by the correlation described above. While Fig. 17.4 is developed for natural gas–crude oil horizontal-flow calculations and in oil field units, it applies equally well to other horizontal-two-phase-flow systems. The two-phase pressure drop for horizontal flow may be computed by using the direct-correlation chart (Fig. 17.3) or graphically by using the chart in Fig. 17.4. To illustrate the use of these two figures an example problem is included on each at the end of this article.

The procedure for graphical determination of two-phase pressure gradients is included below.

Knowing the pipe diameter, liquid and gas flow rates, or gas-liquid mass ratio, specific gravities of the gas and liquid, the flowing temperature, entrance or exit pressure, and the viscosities of the gas and liquid, the pressure gradient dP/dL may be graphically computed, using Fig.17.4, as follows:

1. Determine QM. Q is the number of barrels of liquid flowing per day. The quantity M represents the total number of pounds-mass of the two-phase mixture associated with one barrel of flowing liquid. The quantity M can be computed from the following equation:

$$M = (5.61)(62.4)G_L + 0.0764G_G S_{g\text{-}o} \tag{17.12}$$

in which G_L = specific gravity of liquid (G_L = 1.0 for water)
     G_G = specific gravity of the gas, molecular weight of gas divided by 29 (G_G = 1.0 for air)
     S_{g-o} = cubic foot of gas measured at standard conditions (14.65 psia and 60°F) per barrel of liquid

The quantity QM represents total mass flow rate of the two phases together in pounds-mass per day.

2. Draw a horizontal line from the location of the computed QM value on the vertical scale until the intersection with appropriate pipe diameter in inches with the family of straight lines labeled D.

3. From the intersection with the D lines, draw a vertical line until the intersection with the family of lines labeled $S_{g-o}(G_G/G_L)$ at the appropriate value of $S_{g-o}(G_G/G_L)$.

4. From the intersection with the above gas-liquid ratio lines draw a horizontal line and extend until the intersection with the third family of lines labeled $(\mu_G{}^r \mu_L{}^s)/\rho$, at the computed value of $(\mu_G{}^r \mu_L{}^s)/\rho$. In order to compute the latter quantity, the following equations must be used:

$$r = 0.12 \frac{K}{K+1} \tag{17.13}$$

$$s = 0.12 e^{-0.1K} \tag{17.14}$$

and μ_G = viscosity of gas, $\mathrm{lb}_m/\mathrm{(ft)(sec)}$
     μ_L = viscosity of liquid, $\mathrm{lb}_m/\mathrm{(ft)(sec)}$
     ρ = density of mixture at pressure P and temperature T, $\mathrm{lb}_m/\mathrm{ft}^3$

The density of the mixture ρ may be computed from

$$\rho = \frac{M}{V_m} \tag{17.15}$$

If V_m = specific volume of the mixture associated with one barrel of flowing liquid,

$$V_m = 5.61 F + \frac{P_a T_{\mathrm{av}} Z}{P T_a}(S_{g-o} - S_s) \tag{17.16}$$

in which F = ratio of barrels of liquid at pressure P to barrels of liquid at standard conditions, formation-volume factor
     P_a = base pressure, 14.65 psia
     T_{av} = average flowing temperature, °R
     T_a = base temperature, 520°R
     S_s = solubility of gas in liquid, std ft³ gas/bbl liquid

In problems in which the solubility of the gas in the liquid phase is negligible, such as in simultaneous flow of air and water in Eq. (17.16), $F = 1$, $S_s = 0$, and

$$V_m = 5.61 + \frac{P_a T_{\mathrm{av}} Z}{P T_a} S_{g-o} \tag{17.17}$$

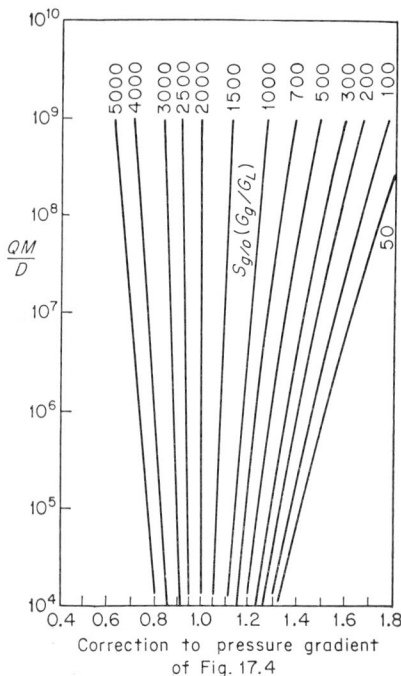

FIG. 17.5. Multiplication correction to Fig. 17.4. (*Ref.* 10.)

5. Once the intersection of the horizontal line with the lines of physical-property function $(\mu_g{}^r \mu_L{}^s)/\rho$ is obtained, a ver-

tical line from this intersection reads the pressure gradient dP/dL in pounds per square inch per 100 ft on the lower horizontal scale.

Limitations of the Graphical Procedure.   In using Fig. 17.4 the liquid-phase Reynolds number should be greater than 10,000.   Because of some additional simplifications introduced in developing the chart of Fig. 17.4, once the quantity dP/dL is calculated as indicated above, it must be multiplied by a correction factor determined according to the values of $S_{g\text{-}o}(G_G/G_L)$ and QM/D.   Figure 17.5 is a chart permitting the calculation of this correction factor.

Example 2.   Example 1, given in the preceding section, will now be solved by the two-phase f'-factor method.   The solution given in the following is based upon the use of the chart given in Fig. 17.3.

1. Calculate the gas-liquid mass ratio:

$$\text{Gas-phase mass flow rate} = 16{,}680 \times 0.076 \times 0.65 = 824 \; \text{lb}_m/\text{hr}$$
$$\text{Liquid-phase mass flow rate} = (400/24) \times 5.61 \times 50 = 4675 \; \text{lb}_m/\text{hr}$$
$$K = 824/4675 = 0.176 < 0.2 \qquad (\text{curve } D \text{ or } D' \text{ will be used})$$

2. Calculate the two-phase Reynolds-number function $\mathbf{R}_G{}^a\mathbf{R}_L{}^b$.

$$a = \frac{K}{1+K} = \frac{0.176}{1.176} = 0.150$$

$$b = e^{-0.1K} = e^{-0.0176} = 0.984$$
$$\mathbf{R}_G = 1.86 \times 10^5$$
$$\mathbf{R}_L = 24{,}700$$
$$\text{Re}_{G}{}^a \times \text{Re}_L{}^b = (1.86 \times 10^5)^{0.150} \times (24{,}700)^{0.984}$$
$$= 1.27 \times 10^5$$

Since $\mathbf{R}_L > 10{,}000$, the curve D' will be used.   For $\text{Re} = 1.27 \times 10^5$,

$$f' = 0.0055$$

$$= \frac{2a_cD\overline{(lw)}}{4v^2L} \qquad \text{Eq. (17.7)}$$

For horizontal flow with approximately no change in kinetic energy,

$$\overline{lw} = -\frac{\Delta P}{\rho} \tag{17.18}$$

Consequently,

$$f' = \frac{2g_cD(-\Delta P)}{4v^2L\rho}$$

$$-\Delta P = \frac{4\rho v^2 L f'}{2g_cD}$$

$$= \frac{2 \times 12}{32.17 \times 1.995}\rho v^2 L f'$$

$$= \frac{2 \times 12 \times 250 \times 0.0055}{32.17 \times 1.995}\rho v^2$$

$$= 0.413(\rho v)v$$

$$\rho v = G_M \; \text{lb}_m/(\text{ft}^2)(\text{sec}) \qquad A = 0.0218 \; \text{ft}^2$$

$$= \frac{4675 + 824}{3600 \times 0.0218} = 72 \; \text{lb}_m/(\text{ft}^2)(\text{sec}) \; \text{specific mass velocity}$$
of two phases as a mixture

$$-\Delta P = 0.413 \times 72v$$

$$v = \frac{W}{\rho A}$$

If W denotes the mass flow rate of the mixture, and ρ the mass density of the mixture,

$$v = \frac{5499}{0.0218 \times 3600\rho} \cong \frac{72}{\rho}$$

The density of the two-phase mixture may be computed from the densities of each of the phases and the gas-liquid mass ratio. A material balance based upon 1.176 lb mixture yields

$$\frac{1.176}{\rho} = \frac{0.176}{\rho_G} + \frac{1}{\rho_L}$$

The density of the gas phase may be computed from

$$\rho_G = \frac{29 G_G}{ZRT} P \qquad Z_{\mathrm{av}} \cong 0.995 \qquad\qquad (17.19)$$

$$= \frac{29 \times 0.65}{0.995 \times 1544 \times 530} (P \times 144) \qquad \text{with } P \text{ in psia}$$

$$= 3.38 \times 10^{-3} P$$

$$\frac{1.176}{\rho} = \frac{0.176}{3.38 \times 10^{-3} P} + \frac{1}{50}$$

which gives

$$\rho = \frac{0.198 P}{8.8 + 3.38 \times 10^{-3} P}$$

In substituting this value of ρ in the equation giving $-\Delta P$ in terms of v:

$$144(-\Delta P) = 0.413 \times 72 + \frac{72}{0.198 P} (8.8 + 3.38 \times 10^{-3} P)$$

Therefore

$$-\Delta P = 75 \frac{8.8 + 3.38 \times 10^{-3} P}{P}$$

Now for $\Delta L = 250$ ft if one approximately calculates $-\Delta P$ or P_{250} from the above equation,

$$P_{250} - 50 = 75 \frac{8.8 + 3.38 \times 10^{-3}(P_{250} + 50)/2}{(P_{250} + 50)/2}$$

This last expression generates a quadratic equation in P_{250},

$$P^2_{250} - 0.0250 P_{250} - 3541.2 \cong 0$$

which may be readily solved for P_{250}, yielding

$$P_{250} = \frac{0.250 \pm \sqrt{0.0625 + 14164.8}}{2}$$

$$P_{250} = 59.6 \text{ psia}$$

It must be recognized that the above calculation of P_{250} is only approximate. Another method of approximately calculating ΔP, and consequently P_{250} from $P_0 = 50$ psia, may be developed from the equation

$$-\Delta P \cong 75 \frac{8.8 + 3.38 \times 10^{-3} P}{P}$$

for $P_{\mathrm{av}} \cong P = 50$ psia.

$$-\Delta P = 75 \times \frac{8.969}{50}$$

$$= 13.45 \text{ psi} \qquad \text{for 250 ft of pipeline}$$

Therefore $P_{250} = 50 + 13.45 = 63.45$ psia.

Now repeating the same procedure, this time treating $P = 63.45$ psia, the average pressure

$$P_{500} = 63.45 + 75 \times \frac{8.8 + 3.38 \times 10^{-2} \times 63.45}{63.45}$$

$$= 74.1 \text{ psia}$$

and
$$P_{750} = 74.1 + 9.15 = 83.25 \text{ psia}$$
$$P_{1000} = 83.25 + 8.18 = 91.43 \text{ psia}$$

Example 3. Example 1, given in the preceding sections, is next solved by the graphical procedure, using the charts in Figs. 17.4 and 17.5.

STEP 1. Determine the product QM.

$$Q = 400 \text{ bbl/day}$$
$$M = 350.1 G_L + 0.0764 G_G S_{g\text{-}o}$$
$$= 329.7 \text{ lb}_m/\text{bbl liquid}$$
$$QM = 400 \times 329.7 = 131{,}880 \text{ lb}_m/\text{day}$$

This value establishes the starting point on Fig. 17.4.

STEP 2. The pipe diameter 2 in. (1.995 ID) locates point 2 on Fig. 17.4.

STEP 3. The gas-liquid mass-ratio function locates point 3 on Fig. 17.4 if $S_{g\text{-}o}(G_G/G_L) = 1000 \times 0.65/0.80 = 812.5$.

STEP 4. This step involves location of point 4, which establishes the pressure gradient for a given pressure. Point 4 is determined from the physical-property function $\mu_G^r \mu_L^s/\rho$. Since this function varies with pressure, it is best to calculate the function for several pressures and tabulate corresponding pressure gradients in preparation for steps 5 and 6. As a first approximation, fluid viscosities at the outlet conditions were used. Usually, if the pressure drop is less than 100 psi, change in fluid viscosities with pressure can be neglected and Eq. (17.17) can be used for calculating V_m.

$$a = \frac{K}{K+1} = 0.151$$

$$b = \frac{1}{e^{0.1K}} = \frac{1}{e^{0.0176}} = 0.980$$

$$r = 0.12a = 0.018 \qquad s = 0.12b = 0.118$$
$$\mu_G = 0.014 \text{ centipoise} = 9.4 \times 10^{-6} \text{ lb}_m/(\text{ft})(\text{sec}) \qquad \text{at } 75°F \text{ and } 50 \text{ psia}$$
$$\mu_L = 0.6 \text{ centipoise} = 4.0 \times 10^{-4} \text{ lb}_m/(\text{ft})(\text{sec}) \qquad \text{at } 75°F \text{ and } 50 \text{ psia}$$
$$\mu_G^r = (9.4 \times 10^{-6})^{0.018} = 0.812$$
$$\mu_L^s = (4.0 \times 10^{-4})^{0.118} = 0.397$$
$$\mu_G^r \mu_L^s = 0.322$$

$$\rho = \frac{M}{V_m} = \frac{329.7}{V_m}$$

$$V_m = 5.61 + \frac{P_a T_{av}}{T_a} S_{g\text{-}o} \frac{Z}{P}$$

$$= 5.61 + \frac{(14.65)(535)(1000)}{520} \frac{Z}{P}$$

$$= 5.61 + 15{,}073 \frac{Z}{P}$$

The NGSMA manual[13] or the "Handbook of Natural Gas Engineering"[12] can be used for establishing Z, the compressibility factor for the gas. If it is necessary to use Eq. (17.16), the generalized correlations of Standing[14] can be used for estimating gas solubility and formation-volume factor. Estimates of hydrocarbon liquid viscosity may be made by the method of Katz and Bicher[15] or by the Beal method.[16] Estimates of gas viscosity may be made by the method of Kobayashi,[17] as seen in Table 17.3.

Table 17.3. Summary of Calculations for Graphical Determination of Two-phase Pressure Drops

QM	131,880	131,880	131,880	131,880	131,880	131,880
D	1.995	1.995	1.995	1.995	1.995	1.995
$S_{g-o}(G_G/G_L)$	812.5	812.5	812.5	812.5	812.5	812.5
$\mu_G{}^r \mu_L{}^s$	0.322	0.322	0.322	0.322	0.322	0.322
M	329.7	329.7	329.7	329.7	329.7	329.7
Z	0.99	0.99	0.99	0.985	0.985	0.98
P, psia	50	60	70	80	90	100
V_m	304.50	254.31	218.79	191.19	170.57	153.32
ρ	1.084	1.296	1.507	1.724	1.933	2 150
$\mu_G{}^r \mu_L{}^s/\rho$	0.297	0.248	0.214	0.187	0.167	0.150
dP/dL, psi/100 ft	5.7	4.6	4.0	3.6	3.25	3.0

STEP 5. This step involves a correction to the estimated gradients determined by step 4. Figure 17.5 is used for this correction.

$$\frac{QM}{D} = 131,880 \times \frac{12}{1.995} = 793,260$$

$$S_{g-o}G_G/G_L = 812.5$$

$$\text{Correction} = 1.21$$

STEP 6. Table 17.4 shows the incremental integration to give the pressure distribution along the pipe.

A plot of P versus L cumulative gives a value of 97 psia at the pipe terminal. Since the pressure drop throughout the length of pipe is only 47 psi, taking into account variation in fluid viscosities and gas solubility with pressure will give no significant difference in pressure drop.

Based on the calculations given on Tables 17.3 and 17.4 the final results on two-phase-flow pressure distribution along the pipe is given in Table 17.5.

The final P versus $L_{\text{cumulative}}$ plot is given in Fig. 17.6. The results of approximate calculations previously given on this problem by Lockhart and Martinelli procedure and generalized two-phase f'-factor method are also plotted on Fig. 17.6 to illustrate the accuracy and agreement between the three methods.

17.6. Vertical Two-phase Flow

Two-phase flow through vertical pipes occurs in many engineering installations. In the petroleum industry one prominent example is provided by the vertical flow strings of gas wells producing water. For oil wells flowing naturally, the pressure drop during the vertical ascent through the flow string will cause the natural gas to come out of solution and flow simultaneously with the oil. Two-phase flow through vertical pipes

Table 17.4. Summary of Pressure-gradient Corrections

P	50	60	70	80	90	100
dP/dL, psi/100 ft	5.7	4.6	4.0	3.6	3.25	3.0
Correction	1.21	1.21	1.21	1.21	1.21	1.21
$(dP/dL)_{\text{corrected}}$	6.9	5.6	4.8	4.4	3.9	3.6

Table 17.5. Summary of Pressure-distribution Calculations for Two-phase Flow

P	50	60	70	80	90	100
ΔP	0	10	10	10	10	10
dP/dL	6.9	5.6	4.8	4.4	3.9	3.6
$(dP/dL)_{\text{av}}$		6.25	5.2	4.6	4.15	3.75
ΔL	0	160	192	217	241	267
$L_{\text{cumulative}}$	0	160	352	569	810	1077

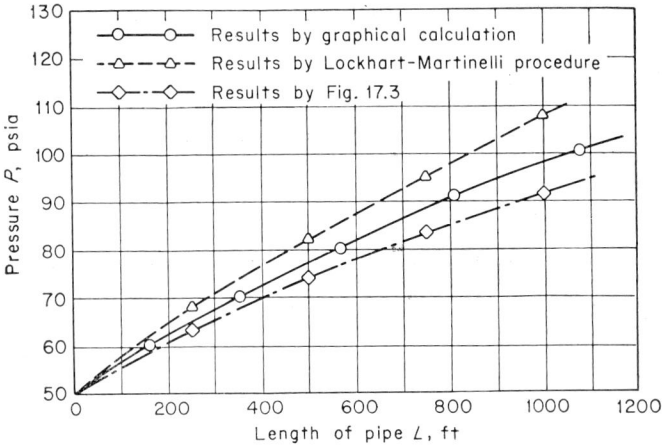

Fig. 17.6. Two-phase-flow pressure distribution calculated by Lockhart and Martinelli and two-phase f-factor methods (Example 1).

becomes particularly important in design, installation, and operation of gas-lift equipment. An understanding of two-phase-flow conditions in such vertical-flow equipment provides the necessary information on where to inject the gas, the pressure at which the injection should take place, and the energy required to lift the oil, as well as the effect of production rate, tubing size, and other physical parameters. In chemical-process engineering and in mechanical- and nuclear-engineering applications, equipment such as heat exchangers, boilers, partial condensers, and reactors frequently encounter conditions of two-phase vertical flow.

A considerable amount of theoretical and experimental work is available on many phases of this problem in the literature. One of the most prominently accepted practical solutions to the problem has been given by Poettmann.[18] The basic features of Poettmann's correlation may be summarized as follows:

1. Treatment of the two phases as a pseudo single phase
2. Use of flowing mixture densities rather than *in situ* mixture densities
3. Use of field data on two-phase flow systems
4. Restriction to highly turbulent flow conditions
5. Inclusion of change of solubility of gas in the liquid phase as affected by the pressure level

The correlation essentially consisted of developing a vertical two-phase f' factor from field data available on 49 flowing and gas-lift wells. The two-phase f' factor for vertical flow was defined according to the following equation:

$$f' = \frac{2g_c(\overline{lw})D}{4v^2(h_2 - h_1)} = \frac{7.413 \times 10^{10}(\overline{lw})D^5}{Q^2\overline{V}_m{}^2(h_2 - h_1)} \tag{17.20}$$

in which $\overline{lw}$ denotes the lost work, or the energy dissipated into heat to the surroundings as a result of flow irreversibilities. In the above equation,

D = inside diameter of pipe, ft
$\overline{lw}$ = lost work, ft-lb$_f$/lb$_m$
Q = liquid flow rate, bbl/day
$\overline{V}_m$ = specific volume of liquid-gas mixture, ft³ mixture/bbl flowing liquid; integrated average value
$h_2 - h_1$ = vertical length of flow string, ft

The term $\overline{V}_m$ is a pressure-integrated average value defined by

$$\overline{V}_m = \frac{\int_{P_2}^{P_1} V_m dP}{P_1 - P_2}.$$ (17.21)

V_m = volume of mixed gas, oil, and water at pressure P per each barrel of produced stock-tank oil

The value of V_m may be computed from

$$V_m = 5.61F + \frac{P_0 T_{\mathrm{av}} Z}{PT_0} (R - S) + V_w$$ (17.22)

in which F = formation-volume factor of oil, i.e., barrels of reservoir oil per barrel of stock-tank oil; F is a function of pressure at average flowing temperature

S = solubility of gas in oil at pressure P, std ft³/bbl

T_{av} = arithmetic average temperature of flow string, °R

V_w = water-production rate, ft³/bbl stock-tank oil

P = pressure, psia

P_0 = base pressure at which standard gas is measured, psia

T_0 = base temperature at which standard gas is measured, °R

Z = compressibility factor of gas in vertical pipe at pressure P and temperature T_{av}

R = producing gas-oil ratio, ft³ gas/bbl stock-tank oil

Quite often the formation-volume factor and gas-solubility data are such that they can be represented as linear functions of the pressure, at least over limited ranges of pressures under consideration. Under these circumstances, the specific volume of the mixture V_m can be calculated from

$$V_m = 5.61 n_f P + 5.61 B_i + \frac{P_0 T_a Z}{T_0} \left(\frac{R}{P} - n_s - \frac{S_i}{P} \right) + V_w$$ (17.23)

in which n_f = slope of formation-volume-factor–pressure curve, vol/(vol psia)

B_i = intercept of formation-volume-factor–pressure curve at $P = 0$ axis, vol/vol

n_s = slope of solubility curve, ft³/(bbl)(psia)

S_i = intercept of solubility curve, ft³/bbl

After using Eq. (17.23) and by evaluating the integrated mean of Eq. (17.21), $\overline{V}_m$ can be evaluated.

$$\overline{V}_m = 2.805 n_f (P_1 - P_2) + 5.61(B_i + V_w) + \frac{P_0 T_a}{T_0(P_1 - P_2)}$$

$$\left[(R - S_i) \int_{P_{r2}}^{P_{r1}} \frac{Z}{P_r} dP_r - n_s P_c \int_{P_{r2}}^{P_{r1}} Z \, dP_r \right]$$ (17.24)

if P_c denotes the pseudo-critical pressure.

Tables are provided in the literature[12] for evaluation of $\int \frac{Z}{P_r} dP_r$ and $\int Z \, dP_r$ terms.

In the above, the subscripts denote the terminal points of the two-phase-flow pipe, the flow going from 1 to 2.

In Poettmann's work the two-phase f' factor was correlated against

$$D\rho v = 1.4737 \times 10^{-5} \frac{MQ}{D}$$ (17.25)

in which M = total mass, in pounds of gas, oil, and water associated with one barrel of stock-tank oil flowing through the system.

The quantity M, total mass flow per barrel of oil flow, can be computed from

$$M = 5.61 \times 62.4 G_0 + 0.0764 G_G R + 62.4 G_W V_w \qquad (17.26)$$

In Eq. (17.26),

G_G = specific gravity of gas (air = 1.0)
G_0 = specific gravity of stock-tank oil (water = 1.0)
G_W = specific gravity of produced water (water = 1.0)
V_w = water-production rate, ft³/bbl stock-tank oil

The correlation of f' versus $\rho v D$ is given in Fig. 17.7.

In using this figure to make direct vertical two-phase-flow calculations, one must first determine the abscissa:

$$D\rho v = \frac{1.4737 \times 10^{-5} MQ}{D}$$

read off the corresponding value of f', determine $\overline{(lw)}$ from Eq. (17.20) defining f', and finally calculate the pressure drop from the flow equation knowing lost work $\overline{lw}$ and flow conditions. It must be recognized that in the above procedure, in computing lost work

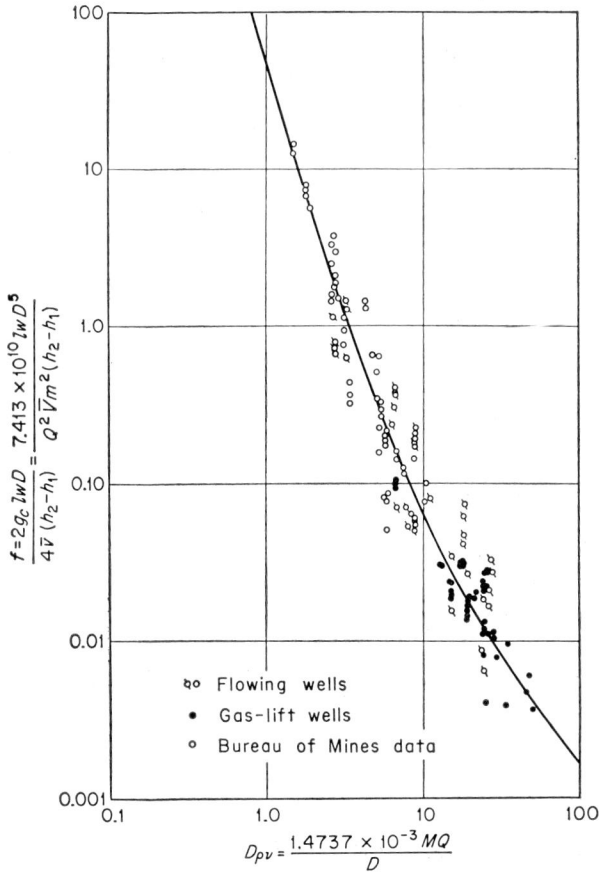

FIG. 17.7. Correlation of field data on flowing and gas-lift wells. (*Ref.* 18.)

from $\overline{lw}$, $\overline{V}_m$, which is a function of pressure, must be determined. This need to estimate the terminal pressures to calculate the pressure drop necessitates a trial-and-error procedure, which is illustrated in the examples.

Simplification for Gas-Water Systems. In order to solve problems in which solubility shrinkage effects are nonexistent or negligible, such as in natural gas and water flow, the equations above may be simplified in eliminating references to oil, formation-volume factor, and solubility. When the gas and liquid in simultaneous flow are inert with respect to mutual solubility effects, some of the equations discussed above take on the following simplified forms:

$$M = 5.61\rho_L \times 62.4 + 0.076 G_G R \tag{17.27}$$
$$R = \text{gas-liquid ratio, std ft}^3 \text{ gas/bbl liquid}$$
$$G_G = \text{specific gravity of gas (air} = 1.0)$$

Equation (17.22) for V_m becomes

$$V_m = 5.61 + \frac{14.73}{520}\frac{T_{\mathrm{av}}RZ}{P} \tag{17.28}$$

when $F = 1.0$, $S = 0$, and $V_w = 5.61$ ft^3/bbl liquid, the basis used in defining R and M.

In this particular case, the equation giving the mean specific volume of the flowing mixture reduces to

$$\overline{V}_m = 5.61 + \frac{14.73 T_{\mathrm{av}} R}{520(P_1 - P_2)}\int_0^{P_1}\frac{Z}{P_r}\,dP_r - \int_0^{P_2}\frac{Z}{P_r}\,dP_r \tag{17.29}$$

If the length of the vertical pipe is small, so that Z values do not vary a great deal around a mean value, then Eq. (17.29) may be further simplified.

$$\overline{V}_m = 5.61 + \frac{14.73 T_{\mathrm{av}} Z_{\mathrm{av}} R}{520(P_1 - P_2)}\ln\frac{P_1}{P_2} \tag{17.30}$$

and the equation giving the mean density becomes

$$\bar{\rho} = \frac{M}{V_m} = \frac{5.61 \times \rho_L \times 62.4 + 0.0764 G_G R}{5.61 + \dfrac{14.73 T_{\mathrm{av}} Z_{\mathrm{av}} R}{520(P_1 - P_2)}\ln\dfrac{P_1}{P_2}} \tag{17.31}$$

Example 4. A natural-gas storage well is producing 4 MM ft^3 (millions of cubic feet) of natural gas per day through a 2-in. ID vertical pipe 2000 ft long. Along with the gas produced, due to water encroachment in the storage area, water is being produced at the rate of 150 bbl/MM ft^3. The mean well-bore temperature is 60°F. Calculate the total pressure drop for this well when the well-head pressure is equal to 600 psig. The specific gravity of the natural gas is 0.6.

SOLUTION

STEP 1. Calculate $D\rho v$.

From Eq. (17.25),

$$D\rho v = 1.4737 \times 10^{-5}\frac{MQ}{D}$$

$$M = 5.61 \times 62.4 + 0.076 \times 0.6R \qquad \text{Eq. (17.27)}$$
$$R = 10^6/150 = 6.67 \times 10^3$$
$$M = 5.61 \times 62.4 + 0.076 \times 0.6 \times 6.67 \times 10^3$$
$$= 654 \text{ lb/bbl of water flow}$$
$$Q = 150 \times 4 = 600 \text{ bbl/day}$$
$$QM = 600 \times 654 = 392{,}400 \text{ lb mixture/day}$$

$$D\rho v = 1.4737 \times 10^{-5} \times \frac{392{,}400}{\frac{2}{12}}$$

$$= 34.8$$

STEP 2. $f' = 0.007$ from Fig. 17.6.

STEP 3.   Calculate $\overline{lw}$ from Eq. (17.20).

$$\overline{lw} = \frac{f'Q^2\overline{V}_m{}^2(h_2 - h_1)}{7.413 \times 10^{10} \times D^5}$$

$$\overline{V}_m = 5.61 + \frac{14.73T_{av}RZ_{av}}{520(P_1 - P_2)} \ln \frac{P_1}{P_2} \qquad \text{(approximately)}$$

$$P_2 = 614.7 \text{ psia}$$

Assume $P_1 = 700$ psia.

$$P_{av} = 657.3$$

Pseudo-critical pressure and temperature for natural gas of specific gravity 0.6 (from Ref. 12):

$$P_c = 670 \text{ psia}$$
$$T_c = 360°\text{R}$$

Pseudo-reduced pressure and temperature for the natural gas at

$$P_{av} = 657.3 \text{ psia} \qquad T_{av} = 520°\text{R}$$
$$P_r = 657.3/670 = 0.98$$
$$T_r = 520/360 = 1.445$$

Z at P_r and T_r from Ref. 12:

$$Z_{av} = 0.89$$

$$\overline{V}_m = 5.61 + \frac{14.73 \times 520 \times 6.67 \times 10^3}{520 \times (700 - 614.7)} \ln \frac{700}{614.7}$$

$$= 162.41 \text{ ft}^3/\text{bbl water}$$

$$\overline{lw} = \frac{0.007 \times 600 \times 600 \times 162.4 \times 162.4 \times 2000}{7.413 \times 10^{10} \times 32/(12)^5}$$

$$= 13,950$$

From the flow equation in Ref. 12,

$$\int_1^2 \frac{dP}{\rho} + \Delta \frac{v^2}{2g_c} + \Delta \frac{g}{g_c} h = -\overline{w} - \overline{lw}$$

By neglecting the kinetic-energy term, by having $\overline{w} = 0$, and by using average $\rho = \bar{\rho}$,

$$\frac{\Delta P}{\bar{\rho}} + (h_2 - h_1) = -\overline{lw}$$

$$\frac{P_2 - P_1}{\bar{\rho}} + (h_2 - h_1) = -\overline{lw}$$

$$P_1 - P_2 = \bar{\rho}[\overline{lw} + (h_2 - h_1)]$$

$$\bar{\rho} = \frac{M}{\overline{V}} = \frac{654}{162.4} = 4.02 \text{ lb/ft}^3 \text{ (mixture density)}$$

$$\Delta P = 4.02(13,950 + 2000) \text{ psf}$$

$$= \frac{4.02 \times 15,950}{144} = 446 \text{ psia}$$

$P_{1\,calc} = 614.7 + 446 = 1063.4$ psia as compared with 700 psia assumed.

Next assume $P_1 = 980$, and repeat preceding calculations.

$$P_{av} = \frac{614.7 + 981}{2} = 797.35 \text{ psia}$$

$$P_r = \frac{797.4}{670} = 1.21$$

$$T_r = 1.445 \qquad \text{(same as before)}$$

$$Z_{av} = 0.87 \text{ at } P_r \text{ and } T_r$$

$$\overline{V}_m = 5.61 + \frac{14.73 \times 520 \times 6.67 \times 10^3 \times 0.87}{520 \times (670.5 - 614.7)} \ln \frac{980}{614.7}$$

$$= 115.61 \text{ ft}^3 \text{ mixture/bbl water}$$

$$\overline{lw} = \frac{0.007 \times 600 \times 600 \times 115.61 \times 115.61 \times 2000}{7.413 \times 10^{10} \times 32/(12)^5}$$

$$= 7060$$

$$\bar{\rho} = \frac{654}{115.61} = 5.65 \text{ lb/ft}^3 \text{ (mixture density)}$$

$$\Delta P = \frac{5.61(7060 + 2000)}{144}$$

$$= 353 \text{ psi}$$

$$P_{1 \text{ calc}} = 614.7 + 353 = 967.7 \text{ psia}$$

which is approximately equal to the assumed value of 980 psia.

17.7. Flow of More Than Two Phases through Pipe

There are several engineering installations in which the simultaneous flow of more than two phases occurs through pipes. In the oil industry, lifting and transportation of natural gas, crude oil, or condensate and water from producing wells is a typical example of such installations. When large amounts of wet gas are handled through pipelines along with a second liquid phase, usually water or oil, quite often it becomes necessary to inject glycol in order to depress the hydrate-forming temperature. The method of calculation for vertical flow of oil, water, and gas through vertical pipe is given by Poettmann and Carpenter.[18]

This treatment is described in detail in the preceding chapter. A correlation for horizontal flow of air, gas-oil, and water through pipe has been published by Sobocinski and Huntington.[19] Figure 17.8 represents the correlation for three-phase-flow pressure-drop calculations as proposed by Huntington and Sobocinski.[19] The friction factor f'_g is defined in the same manner as Schneider[20] for two-phase flow and correlated versus $G'_L \mu_L / G'_G \mu_G$.

The quantities G'_L and G'_G are specific mass flow velocities, respectively, for both liquid phases and the gas phase. The three-phase friction factor f'_g is defined by the following equation:

$$f'_g = \frac{(\Delta P/\Delta L)g_c D \rho_G}{2G'^2_G} \qquad (17.32)$$

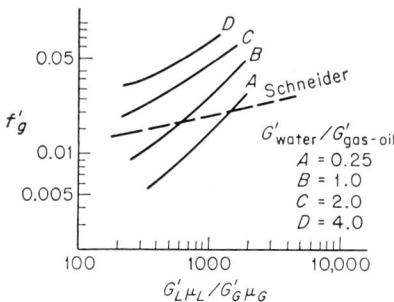

FIG. 17.8. Friction-factor correlation for three-phase flow. (*Ref.* 19.)

The combined viscosity of both liquid phases is computed by μ_L = mass-fraction water $\times \mu_{water}$ + mass-fraction gas-oil $\times \mu_{gas\text{-}oil}$. As indicated in Fig. 17.7, the correlating curves A, B, C, and D are for specific water to gas-oil liquid ratios.

17.8. Two-phase Flow through Inclined Pipe

There is not a great deal of information in the literature on cases intermediate to horizontal and vertical two-phase flow. Data on systematic experiments with an oblique two-phase-flow system have been published by Brigham, Holstein, and Huntington.[21] This work indicates that for small deviations from a horizontal plane, wave, cresting, and semiannular flow will exhibit the same pressure drop at all slopes and may be predicted with reasonable engineering accuracy by Martinelli et al[1,2] or White[22] correlations.

An empirical relation developed by Baker[23] was found useful in designing two-phase-flow pipelines over hilly terrain.

$$\Delta P_{TPH} = \Delta P_{TP}(\text{for horizontal pipe}) + \frac{1.6NH\rho_L}{144v_g^{0.7}} \qquad (17.33)$$

in which　ΔP_{TP} = calculated two-phase pressure drop for horizontal pipe, psi
　　　　ΔP_{TPH} = pressure drop corrected for hilly terrain, psi
　　　　　　N = number of hills
　　　　　　H = average height of hills, ft
　　　　　　ρ_L = density of liquid phase, lb_m/ft^3
　　　　　　v_g = superficial gas velocity through pipeline

Equation (17.33) is entirely empirical and should be used only in reference to conditions under which it was developed. The correlations on two-phase vertical and horizontal flow given in the preceding chapters are of more general nature and should at least provide sounder basis for estimating upper and lower limits for problems involving inclined two-phase flow through pipes.

FLOW OF SPRAYS AND BUBBLES

The problems associated with the flow of sprays and bubbles are two-phase-flow problems in which considerations of fluid and particle dynamics, stability, and statistical representation become important. The generation of sprays has been the subject of permanent interest and intensified research for a long time. Mainly because sprays and bubbles are indigenous to widely different areas of engineering research and practice, there has been no centralized or concerted attack on the subject. Perhaps because the generation, behavior, and properties of sprays appear incidental to solutions of problems posed by several engineering systems, spray literature may be found pertaining to combustion, jet-engine injectors, spray-producing equipment, nozzles, spray drying, manufacture of granulated products, meteorology, and many other areas of diversified engineering interest.

The basic problem of formation of sprays is one which belongs to the field of stability of liquid free surfaces. There have been several basic studies in fluid mechanics of spray formation, dating all the way back to Lord Rayleigh.[24]

17.9. Fluid Mechanics of Spray Formation

The literature is abundant with a wealth of information on the subject of disintegration of liquid jets, stability of free surfaces, and various modes of formation of drops. Excellent reviews of the literature are available on this subject.[25–28]

There are several modes and mechanisms of disintegration by which sprays of discrete, small particles are generated from a continuous liquid phase. In practically all the different modes of disintegration the pressure energy of the continuous liquid phase is first converted into kinetic energy of a jet, which subsequently becomes subject to breakup phenomena. Inertial forces, mechanical impact, surface shear, aerodynamic effects, and surface tension are the important causes leading to the formation of drops torn from the main body of the fluid. The mathematical model most widely used to idealize and simulate the disintegration phenomena consists of a cylindrical jet perturbed at its surface by a wavelike disturbance. When such a wave disturbs the free surface of the jet, a triple set of force systems become effective. The gravitational and the surface-tension forces tend to oppose the original disturbance. The induced-pressure condition near the wave, on the other hand, tends to amplify the magnitude of the wave. As a result of the interplay between these three force fields, the free surface may become stable or unstable. When certain conditions required for instability are fulfilled, the surface wave begins to grow in amplitude. The conditions of instability are mathematically derived[29] as a relation between the geometric, physical, and flow properties of the jet, the receiving medium, and the original wavelike disturbance. Figures 17.9 to 17.12 illustrate the surface instability associated with the growth of waves ultimately leading to the breakup of a liquid jet in the form of a hollow cone.

17.10. Prediction of Average Particle Size from a Hollow-cone Spray

An equation is given in the literature[29] for predicting the approximate average size of drops to be obtained from a spray produced by a hollow-cone or swirl-chamber nozzle.

$$r \cong 1.06 \left(\frac{2a \mathbf{W}^* \sigma}{\rho_a v^2} \right)^{\frac{1}{2}} \qquad (17.34)$$

in which r = radius of particle, cm

$\mathbf{W}^* = \rho_a \lambda^* v^2 / \sigma$, dimensionless Weber number

λ^* = wavelength of maximum instability, cm

σ = surface tension, dynes/cm

ρ_a = density of gas phase, g/cc

v = velocity of jet (liquid phase relative to gas phase), cm/sec

a = half thickness of liquid sheet breaking up into drops, cm

When the density of the gas phase is small compared with the density of the liquid phase, York, Stubbs, and Tek[29] have shown that $\mathbf{W}^* \cong 9$. This simplifies Eq. (17.34) to

$$r \cong 1.06 \left(\frac{18 a \sigma}{\rho_a v^2} \right)^{\frac{1}{2}} \qquad (17.35)$$

It must be noted that these equations will predict an approximate statistical average value for the particle size of drops obtained from hollow-cone or swirl-chamber nozzles. The mathematical model resorted to is idealized and also represents one predominant breakup mechanism out of many.

17.11. Spray-producing Equipment

Several technical papers and articles are available in the literature on design and characteristics of spray-producing equipment. There are many ways to classify the nozzles and atomizers. From the standpoint of their operating characteristics, the more commonly used types of nozzles are:

Air-atomizing nozzles   Variable-area nozzles
Simplex nozzles   Swirl-chamber nozzles
Duplex nozzles   Injectors
Fixed-pintle nozzles   Flow dividers
Moving-pintle nozzles

The nozzles listed above basically fulfill two important functions in spray production:

Production of spray
Flow metering

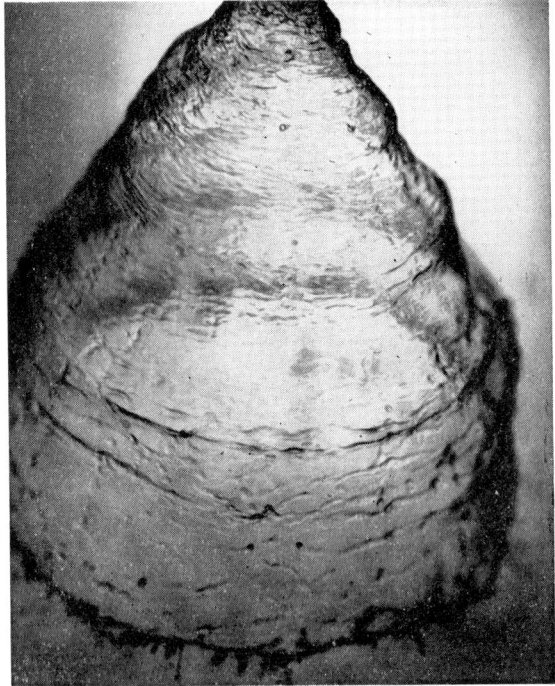

FIG. 17.9. Liquid sheet from swirl-chamber spray nozzle. Flow rate 100 lb/hr. Magnification 6×. (*Ref.* 29.)

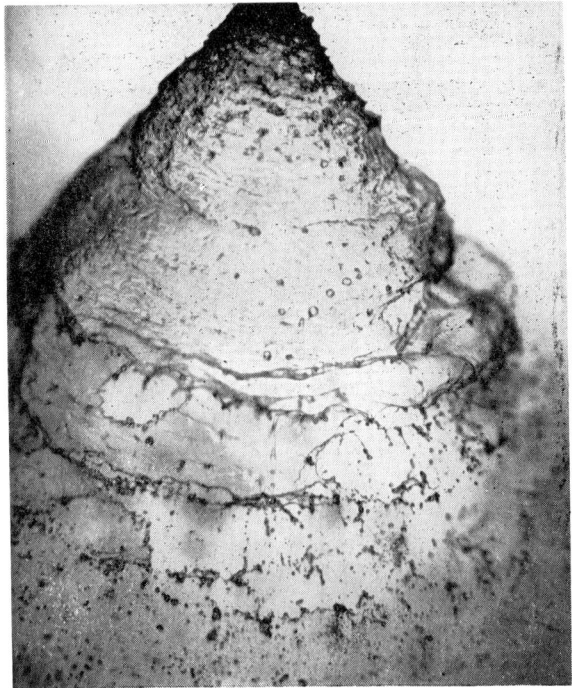

FIG. 17.10. Disintegration of water sheet from swirl-chamber spray nozzle. Flow rate 200 lb/hr. Magnification 6×. (*Ref.* 29.)

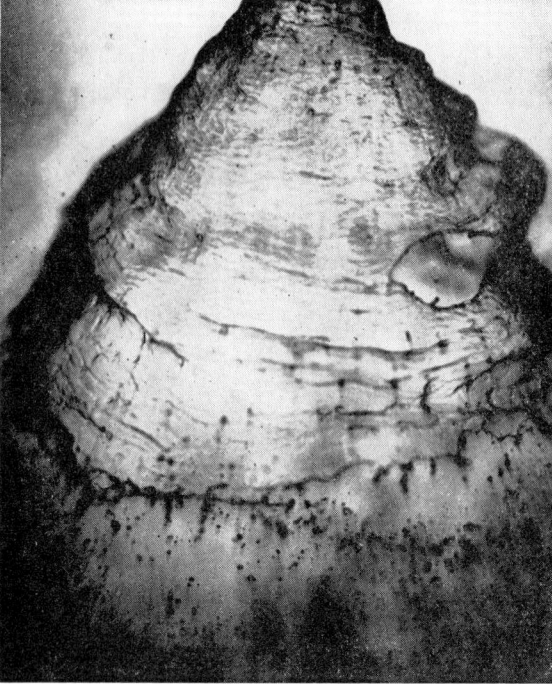

FIG. 17.11. Wave growth on water sheet from swirl-chamber spray nozzle. Flow rate 150 lb/hr. Magnification 6×. (*Ref.* 29.)

FIG. 17.12. Disintegration of water sheet from swirl-chamber spray nozzle. Flow rate 150 lb/hr. Magnification 6×. (*Ref.* 29.)

For further information and detail on fluid mechanics of spray formation and hydraulics of nozzle flow, the reader is referred again to existing literature surveys compiled on the subject.[25-28]

17.12. Properties of Sprays

The most important and characteristic property of a spray is probably the size distribution. There are several analytical techniques available for determining the particle-size distribution of sprays. The use of electronic probe detectors, light-scattering equipment, and silhouette flash photography are among the more recent techniques used in determining particle-size distributions of sprays.

From a statistical viewpoint, the particle-size distribution is usually expressed in a mean value and a standard deviation around the mean value. There are several average, or mean, values defined after some basic property of the individual particle and the aggregate system. Arithmetic, surface, mass, and specific-surface mean diameters are used in many phases of spray-analysis work.

Spatial distribution is the property of a spray describing the concentration of particles in the space around the spraying device. The penetration of a spray marks the linear distance corresponding to the maximum travel of sprayed particles.

The cone angle measures the extent of conical dispersion obtained from a cylindrical or conical jet emerging from a nozzle.

17.13. Stability and Breakup of Liquid Drops

The problem of stability and breakup of drops is encountered in the operation of fractionators, in the study of spray formation, in the behavior of dispersions, and in many other related areas. The stability of drops exposed to the flow field of a continuous gaseous medium has been studied by Hinze[30] and many others.[31-33] Hinze's theoretical and experimental work indicates that the relation between the size of a drop and the size of a turbulent eddy in its vicinity is important to the stability criterion, which determines whether the drop will break up into smaller satellite drops or not. Depending upon the nature of the flow field around the drop, whether viscous shear flow or turbulent flow, the deformation and ultimate breakup of an individual drop depend upon the numerical value of the Weber number and a dimensionless viscosity group $\mathbf{N}_{vi}$. According to Hinze, the breakup will occur when the Weber number exceeds a critical value. The critical Weber number depends on the particular deformation and the flow pattern around the drop. When the flow in the receiving medium is viscous, the critical Weber number may have a minimum value of 0.5 or larger, depending upon the ratio of viscosities between the two phases. For drops subject to turbulent flow in the gas stream, the value of critical Weber number depends on the value of the viscosity group $\mathbf{N}_{vi}$.

These dimensionless parameters, $\mathbf{W}$ and $\mathbf{N}_{vi}$, are defined by the following equations:

$$\mathbf{W} = \frac{\rho_c v^2 d}{\sigma} \qquad (17.36)$$

$$\mathbf{N}_{vi} = \frac{\mu_d}{\sqrt{\rho_d \sigma d}} \qquad (17.37)$$

In the preceding equations ρ_c denotes the density of the continuous phase, v the maximum relative velocity, d the drop diameter, σ the surface tension, and ρ_d the density of the drop.

17.14. Flow of Gas Bubbles in Continuous Liquid Phase

The motion of gas bubbles moving uniformly in various liquids has been investigated by several authors.[34] A stability criterion predicting whether the ascent will be in rectilinear or oscillatory motion and drag coefficient vs. Reynolds-number data are available in the literature.

SIMULTANEOUS FLOW OF FLUIDS AND SOLIDS

17.15. Introduction

In many engineering problems mutual effects of relative flow between solids and fluids are of interest. In reference to problems encountered in multiphase flow, while it is somewhat arbitrary to discern between solid-liquid and solid-gas flow, these two areas will be discussed separately after a brief review of fundamental concepts of immersed-particle mechanics. A vastly different number of engineering unit operations, such as classification, jigging, tabling, sedimentation, separation, contacting, fluidization, and others too numerous to list completely, are based upon the applications of solid-fluid flow.

When the dynamics of one or several particles immersed in a fluid is considered, it becomes immaterial whether the fluid is moving past the solid or the solid is moving through the fluid. When a solid is immersed in a stream of real fluid, because of viscous shear and friction, a force is required in order to maintain the relative flow between the solid and the fluid. By virtue of the principle of action and reaction, the force exerted by the solid on the fluid must be equal and opposite to the force exerted by the fluid on the solid. This force is called the drag force. There are two other forces acting on any particle immersed in a fluid. These are gravity and buoyancy. The gravity force is vertical downward and equal to the weight of particle. The buoyant force is in the opposite direction to gravity force and is equal to the weight of fluid displaced. The drag force is in the direction of relative flow between the solid and the fluid. Quite often the gravity and buoyancy forces are combined algebraically, resulting in a force called net submerged weight. The gravity and buoyancy are independent of the relative velocity of the solid with respect to fluid. The drag force is a function of the relative velocity between the solid and the fluid. When all three forces acting on a particle are in balance, the particle preserves its motion with no further acceleration and reaches a terminal velocity. The correlations permitting the calculation of drag forces and terminal velocities for various systems are given in the next article.

17.16. Dynamics of Particles Submerged in Fluids

The following equation may be used in predicting the terminal velocity of a solid particle settling through a fluid:

$$v_m = \sqrt{\frac{4(\rho_s - \rho_L)gd}{3\rho_L f_D}} \qquad (17.38)$$

in which v_m = terminal velocity, fps

ρ_s and ρ_L are, respectively, density of solid and fluid, $\mathrm{lb}_m/\mathrm{ft}^3$

g = acceleration of gravity; $g = 32.17$ ft/sec^2

d = diameter of particle, ft

f_D = dimensionless drag coefficient, function of Reynolds number corresponding to motion of fluid relative to particle (see relationship between drag coefficient and Reynolds number, Fig. 17.13)

The drag coefficient f_D is defined by the equation

$$F_D = f_D \rho_L A \frac{v^2}{2} \qquad (17.39)$$

if F_D denotes the drag force and A the cross-section area exposed to relative flow between the solid and fluid phases. The Reynolds number is usually calculated by the following equation:

$$\mathbf{R} = \frac{\rho_L v d_s}{\mu} \qquad (17.40)$$

d_s in this equation denotes the diameter of a sphere having the same volume as the particle. For a spherical particle, $d_s = d$. The average particle diameter is usually

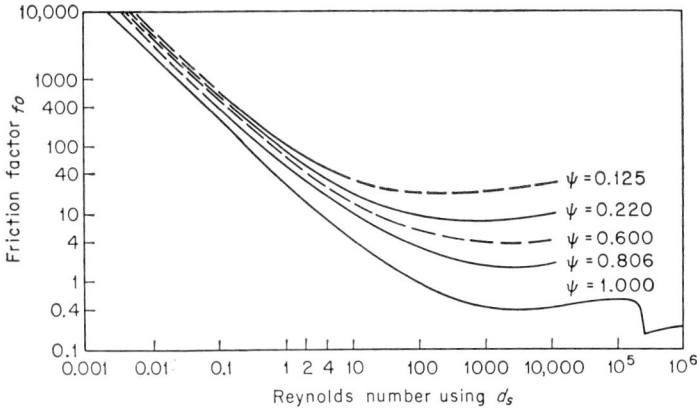

FIG. 17.13. Friction factor, or drag coefficient, vs. Reynolds number of different sphericities. (*Ref. 47.*)   (*Reprinted with permission from G. G. Brown and Associates, Unit Operations, 1950, John Wiley & Sons, Inc.*)

obtained from the screen analysis of the particles.   If the particles are nonspherical, the effect of shape becomes important.   This shape effect is taken into account in Fig. 17.13 by a factor, ψ, called the "sphericity."[47]

The sphericity is defined as the ratio between the surface area of a sphere having the same volume as the particle and the actual surface area of the particle.   By obtaining d_{av} from the screen analysis and ψ, the diameter of the sphere having the equivalent volume may be computed from the following equation:

$$d_s = \frac{d_{av}}{n\psi} \qquad (17.41)$$

In Eq. (17.41) above, n is a parameter defined as the ratio of the specific surface of the particle and the specific surface of a sphere having the same diameter as the particle. The value of n may be estimated from the average particle diameter, using the curves on Fig. 17.14 for different materials indicated on the figures.   Table 17.6 is useful in estimating the sphericity of particles having typical geometric shapes.

Equation (17.38) is general and applies for both laminar and turbulent flow around the particles.   It is, however, restricted to nonhindered settling, i.e., when the particle is settling freely without interference from other particles.

In using Eq. (17.38), it must be noted that if the quantity v_m is the unknown, since it appears implicitly also in f_D through the Reynolds number, a trial-and-error procedure usually becomes necessary to solve for v_m.

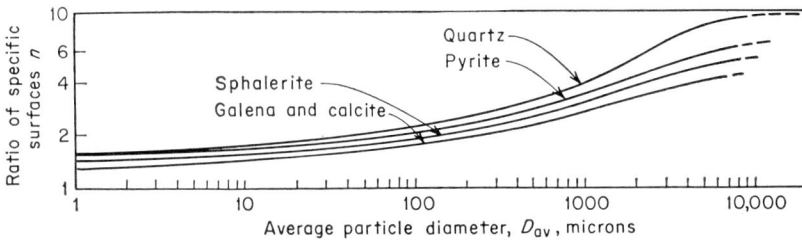

FIG. 17.14. Ratio n of specific surfaces as a function of average diameter of particles D_{av} for quartz, pyrite, sphalerite, calcite, and galena.   (*Ref. 47.*)   (*Reprinted with permission from G. G. Brown & Associates, Unit Operations, 1950, John Wiley & Sons, Inc.*)

Table 17.6. Sphericity and the Value of d_s Related to Screen Size

Shape	Sphericity	d_s/d_{av}
Sphere..........................	1.00	1.00
Octahedron.....................	0.847	0.965
Cube...........................	0.806	1.24
Prisms:		
$a \times a \times 2a$...................	0.767	1.564
$a \times 2a \times 2a$.................	0.761	0.985
$a \times 2a \times 3a$.................	0.725	1.127
Cylinders:		
$h = 2r$.......................	0.874	1.135
$h = 3r$.......................	0.860	1.31
$h = 10r$......................	0.691	1.96
$h = 20r$......................	0.580	2.592
Discs:		
$h = 1.33r$.....................	0.858	1.00
$h = r$........................	0.827	0.909
$h = r/3$......................	0.594	0.630
$h = r/10$.....................	0.323	0.422
$h = r/15$.....................	0.254	0.368

If the flow of fluid with respect to the solid is laminar, the equation for v_m is simplified and may be obtained directly from the Stokes law.

$$v_m = \frac{(\rho_s - \rho_L)gd^2}{18\mu} \qquad (17.42)$$

For the condition of hindered settling, Eq. (17.42) becomes

$$v_H = v_m \frac{(\rho_s - \rho_b)gd^2}{18\mu_b} \qquad (17.43)$$

if ρ_b = bulk density of suspension
μ_b = bulk viscosity of suspension
v_H = hindered-terminal-settling velocity

The bulk viscosity of the slurry may be computed from the fluid viscosity μ_L and the volume fraction X of the fluid in the slurry by the equation

$$\frac{\mu_B}{\mu_L} = \frac{10^{1.82(1-X)}}{X} \qquad (17.44)$$

This relationship has been developed for spherical particles.[36]

17.17. Fluidization

The fluidization of solids by fluids is a process of somewhat intermediate characteristics between the flow of solids through fluids and flow of fluids through solids. When a fluid is passed upward through a bed of granular solids, in order to maintain flow and overcome friction a certain amount of pressure drop must be available across the length of the bed. When this pressure drop approaches the weight of the bed per unit cross-section area, the individual granules become disengaged from one another and the bed begins to resemble a liquid in the state of boiling at its free surface. It appears that the bed has been "rendered fluid," i.e. fluidized. In the area of fluidization some additional basic concepts and characteristic states must be defined.[37] When the particles contained in a bed are immobile, the granular system is usually called a *fixed bed*. In a fixed bed the particles support and contact one another. In a *moving bed* the particles remain in mutual contact but move as a whole in relation to a fixed reference system. When the rate of fluid flow through a bed reaches the point where the particles begin to move, the condition of the bed is usually referred to as *insipient fluidization,* or *onset of fluidization.* A bed which has been brought beyond the point of insipient fluidization is called a *dense-phase fluidized bed.* When the fluid velocity through the bed is just above the value required for the onset of fluidization, the system remains in a *quiescent* fluidized state. In a quiescent fluidized state there is little or no mixing between particles. For higher fluid velocities, a substantial amount of mixing between solids takes place. This state is known as a *turbulent fluidized bed.* For considerably higher fluid velocities the bed expands to a condition of great solids dilution with continuous net transport of solids. This state is usually referred as a *dispersed suspension,* or *dispersed phase.* In dispersed phase, the solids move with respect to the conduit, with no upper boundary.

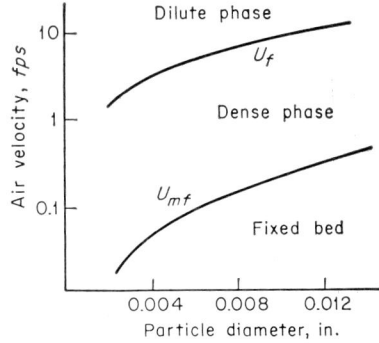

Fig. 17.15. Typical fluid velocity ranges encountered in the fluidization spectrum. (*Ref.* 37, *p.* 19.)

The historical background of fluidization is presented in detail in a very recent and excellent book by Max Leva.[37] It is believed that the earliest recorded application of fluidization is published by Brötz.[38] The first patents on fluidization were issued to Phillips and Bulteel[39] in 1910. The first large-scale application of fluidization in the United States dates back to the catalytic cracking process in 1940. The large success and widespread acceptance of the catalytic cracking process precipitated a large amount of fundamental and applied research effort during the last decade on many phases of fluidization. The pressure drop necessary to bring about insipient fluidization in a dense-phase fluidized bed may be computed from the following equation:

$$\Delta P = L(1 - \epsilon)(\rho_s - \rho_F) \tag{17.45}$$

if L is the bed height, in ft, and ϵ is the porosity of the bed, volume-fraction voids. ρ_s and ρ_F are, respectively, solid and fluid densities. The ranges of fluid velocity required for a typical spectrum of fluidization from fixed bed to dense phase and dilute phase are illustrated on Fig. 17.15.

While no distinction has been made in the foregoing between gas and liquid phases as fluidizing media, there are some differences observed in performance. The fluidization with liquid phase is usually termed *particulate,* while fluidization with gas is commonly referred to as *aggregative.* The aggregative fluidization results in a much more heterogeneous bed than particulate fluidization.

According to Wilhelm and Kwauk,[40] if the Froude number $\mathbf{F} = u^2/d_p g < 1.0$, particulate fluidization will prevail, and if $\mathbf{F} > 1.0$, aggregative fluidization will prevail.

The pressure-drop fluid-flow-rate diagrams for ideally fluidizing solids and moderately channeling solids are given in Fig. 17.16. The minimum pressure drop at point C is associated by the "unlocking" of solid particles, which occurs at the threshold of insipient fluidization.

Various phases of phenomena in fluidization have been summarized in their proper sequence by Fig. 17.17, originally proposed by Reboux.[41]

Calculation of the Pressure Drop in a Fixed Bed. A generalized correlation for pressure drops through fixed beds was proposed by Ergun.[42]

$$\frac{\Delta P}{L} g_c = 150 \frac{(1 - \epsilon)^2}{\epsilon^3} \frac{\mu u_0}{d_p^2} + 1.75 \frac{1 - \epsilon}{\epsilon^3} \frac{G u_0}{d_p} \tag{17.46}$$

if u_0 = superficial velocity through the bed, fps
G = fluid mass velocity, (lb)/(hr)(ft²)

When the porosity ϵ, viscosity μ, and particle size d_p are known, the fixed-bed pressure drop may be computed by using Eq. (17.46) for different values of G and u. It may be

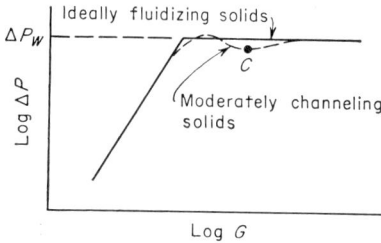

FIG. 17.16. Typical pressure-drop–fluid-flow-rate diagram for ideally fluidizing and moderately channeling solids. (*Ref.* 37.)

noted that the first term on the right-hand side represents energy loss to viscous shear while the second term is essentially related to inertial or turbulent losses.

Determination of Minimum Fluidization Velocity. The mass flow rate of the fluid required for the onset of fluidization is given by[37]

$$G_{mf} = \frac{0.005 d_p{}^2 g_c \rho_F (\rho_s - \rho_F) \psi^2 \epsilon_{mf}{}^3}{\mu(1 - \epsilon_{mf})} \quad (17.47)$$

in which ψ represents the sphericity (defined earlier) and ϵ_{mf}, the minimum fluidization voidage. Equation (17.47) is not general and applies only to the cases in which the flow of fluid through the packed system is laminar. It is, however, quite realistic since most gas-solid systems begin to fluidize for Reynolds numbers approximately less than 10.

The Expanded Bed. Bed expansion up to a voidage of about 80 per cent may be predicted by equations given by Leva.[37] The motion of individual particles in an expanded bed follows characteristics of hindered settling. The behavior of gas-solid expanded beds deviates markedly from idealized behavior. Methods for estimating the expanded-bed height are also given in detail by Leva.[37] The nonideal behavior is known to be partially due to aggregative fluidization, which may be eliminated to some extent through the use of adequately designed baffles. The use of the baffles, on the other hand, is known to introduce segregation of the particles.

Dilute Phase—Moving Solids Fluidization—Pneumatic Conveying. Dilute phase is characterized by low-ratio solids-gas flow. In systems fluidized by gas the dense phase is separated from the disperse, or dilute, phase by a slugging zone. This is an unstable zone where the bed density becomes extremely sensitive to gas rate. The porosity defining the slugging zone ranges approximately from 75 to 95 per cent. Limiting velocities required to assure net transport of solids in vertical or horizontal transfer lines are quite uncertain.

In pneumatic conveying the total pressure drop due to combined gas and solid flow in horizontal pipe may be approximately calculated by a correlation proposed by Hinkle.[43]

$$\Delta P_t = \frac{f_g u_g{}^2 \rho_F L}{2 g_c D_i} \left(1 + \frac{f^*_p u^*_p R'}{f_g u_g} \right) \quad (17.48)$$

in which f_g = Fanning friction factor
f^*_p = a solids-flow friction factor
u_g = superficial gas velocity, fps
u^*_p = fully accelerated particle velocity, fps
R' = solids-gas weight ratio

Fully accelerated particle velocity u^*_p may be estimated from the following equation:

$$u^*_p = u_G \left[1 - 1.41 d_p{}^{0.3} \left(\frac{\rho_s}{62.3} \right)^{0.5} \right] \quad (17.49)$$

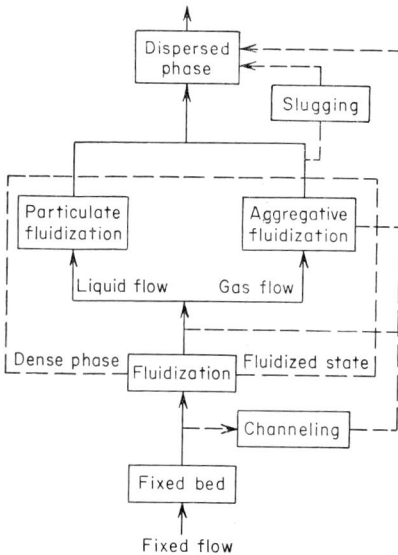

FIG. 17.17. Phases and phenomena in fluidization. (*Ref.* 41.)

The term f^*_p may be calculated from the following equation:

$$f^*_p = \frac{3\rho_F f_D D_j}{2 d_p \rho_s} \left(\frac{u_o - u^*_p}{u^*_p} \right)^2 \qquad (17.50)$$

if f_D is the drag coefficient (Fig. 17.13).

The range of variables for which Eqs. (17.48) to (17.50) may be used is given by Leva[37] as follows:

Air velocity u_g 66 to 119 fps
Particle diameter d_p 0.014 to 0.33 in.
Solids density ρ_s 65.3 to 113 lb_m/ft^3
Solids loading   up to about 5 lb_m solids/lb_m air

17.18. Flow of Dispersed Solids in Continuous Liquid Phase

When a dispersed solid phase is in suspension in a pipe filled with a liquid, the resulting mixture is often called a *slurry*. In general, if the suspended solid particles are less than 1 μ in diameter, the suspension is referred to as a *colloidal* solution. According to some investigators,[44] the slurries may be classified in two main categories:

Settling slurries
Nonsettling slurries

Sand in water, salt in benzene, and clay in drilling mud are typical examples of settling slurries. Paper pulp is a good example of a nonsettling slurry.

A practical problem commonly encountered in the study of solid-liquid flow is turbulent mixing of two immiscible phases. This is a problem usually encountered in reactor dynamics and fluidized transport operations. Mixing of the two immiscible phases is accomplished by pumping the mixture at a rate which results in a sufficiently high degree of turbulence. The momentum transfer present in a highly turbulent field provides individual eddies with sufficient energy to maintain the particles in their trajectories superimposed on the main-stream velocities in spite of the gravitational pull. In turbulent mixing, if the Reynolds number is high enough, the eddies will have enough energy to maintain the system in a constantly agitated state. This is sometimes referred to as Reynolds-number mixing.

When the mechanics of a settling slurry is considered, the difference in density between the two phases is often high enough so that the gravitational effects are of the same order of magnitude as the inertial effects. Under these conditions the Froude number becomes a critical parameter, as important as the Reynolds number. The mechanics of eddy currents which emanate in all directions in a turbulent-flow field provides the driving potential which maintains the particles in suspension. The dimensionless parameters affecting the turbulent mixing are:

δ/D particle- to pipe-diameter ratio
R   Reynolds number
F   Froude number

The problem of distribution and mixing of solids in turbulent slurry flow has been studied by Spells[45] and Johnstone.[46]

In solid-liquid slurry flow through horizontal pipe, according to Spells, as the flow velocity of the slurry is increased:

1. At very low velocities the particles will settle out by free or hindered settling.
2. When a minimum velocity is reached and surpassed, there will be no gradual settling but there will exist a concentration gradient in the vertical direction in a cross-section of the horizontal pipe.
3. When "the standard velocity" is reached, the net horizontal transport will be accomplished with adequate mixing and no appreciable concentration gradient.

According to Spells, the magnitude of flow velocity or Reynolds number required for maintaining turbulent mixing of solid-liquid slurries may be computed from the following relation:

$$\frac{\rho_L v^2}{\rho_e g \delta} = K' \left(\frac{\rho_m v D}{\mu} \right)^{0.775} \tag{17.51}$$

in which ρ_L = density of liquid, $\mathrm{lb}_m/\mathrm{ft}^3$
       ρ_e = effective density of immersed particles, $\mathrm{lb}_m/\mathrm{ft}^3$
       $\rho_e = \rho_s - \rho_L$
       v = minimum or standard velocity, fps
       g = 32.17 ft/sec^2
       δ = mean particle diameter (mass-mean), ft

In systems where individual particle diameters are distributed over a wide range, the mass-mean diameter may be computed from the screen-analysis data by:

$$\delta = \sqrt[3]{\frac{\Sigma X_i}{C\Sigma X_i / C_i D_i{}^3}} \tag{17.52}$$

if X_i = mass fraction of size range D_i
       D_i = average particle diameter, obtained from averaging oversize and undersize screen apertures, ft
C or C_i = proportionality constant between volume of a particle and cube of its average diameter
       K' = a numerical constant found experimentally to be equal to 7.22 for "minimum velocity" and 21.31 for "standard velocity"
       ρ_m = mean density of slurry, $\mathrm{lb}/\mathrm{ft}^3$

When density of the solids and liquid is known, along with volume-fraction solids in slurry, the density of the mixture may be computed from the following equation:

$$\rho_m = c\rho_s + (1 - c)\rho_L \tag{17.53}$$

in which c is the volume-fraction solids in the slurry. Equation (17.51) is recommended for mean diameters between 50 and 500 μ.

Based exactly on Spell's work and conclusion, the following design equation has been given by Lowenstein:[44]

$$D = \frac{0.231 Q^{0.38}}{(K\phi\delta)^{0.31}(\rho_m/\mu)^{0.24}} \tag{17.54}$$

in which D = pipe or conduit diameter, ft
       Q = volumetric flow rate, cfm
       ϕ = slurry density factor, ρ_e/ρ_L
       μ = liquid viscosity, centipoises
       K = 232 for minimum velocity
          = 685 for standard velocity

For a specified volume flow rate, with known physical properties for the slurry and its constituents, Eq. (17.54) permits calculation of the appropriate design diameter.

Since the ratio δ/D is one of the important dimensionless scale-up parameters of slurry flow, it must be recognized that a relationship of the form

$$\mathbf{F} = K'(R_c)^d$$

should hold for each value of δ/D. Spell's correlation of

$$\mathbf{F} = K'(\mathbf{R})^{0.775}$$

applies for δ/D ratio of about 1.64×10^{-4}, say, between 10^{-4} and 10^{-3}.

Example 5. In order to perform hydraulic fracturing of a natural oil-producing formation, it is desired to pump a slurry of sand and water through a horizontal pipe 1 ft in diameter. The slurry has 80 per cent volume-fraction water. The mass-mean diameter of the sand particles in the mixture is equal to 100 μ. The specific gravity of the sand is 2.34. The temperature of the flow system is 60°F. The horizontal pipe extending from the hydraulic fracturing pumps to well inlet has a total aggregate equivalent length of 250 ft (including equivalent lengths of all auxiliary equipment such as valves, tees, elbows, etc.). The pressure at the pump inlet is approximately atmospheric. The pressure at the exit end of the horizontal pipe is specified at 500 psig. Calculate the power required of the pump drive motor at 80 per cent over-all efficiency for pumping the slurry without settling in the horizontal pipe.

Viscosity of water = 1 centipoise
Relative roughness of pipe ϵ/D = 0.00015

SOLUTION. According to Spell's correlation Eq. (17.51),

$$\rho_L \frac{v^2}{\rho_e g \delta} = K' \left(\frac{\rho_m v D}{\mu} \right)^{0.775}$$

Solving with respect to v:

$$v = \left[K' \left(\frac{\rho_m D}{\mu} \right)^{0.775} \frac{\rho_e g \delta}{\rho_L} \right]^{1/1.225}$$

$K' = 21.31$ for standard velocity

$\rho_m = c\rho_s + (1 - c)\rho_L$
$\quad\;\; = 0.20 \times 62.4 \times 2.34 + 0.80 \times 62.4$
$\quad\;\; = 79.2 \text{ lb}_m/\text{ft}^3$

$D = 1 \text{ ft}$

$\mu = 1 \text{ centipoise}$

$\rho_e = \rho_s - \rho_L = 146 - 62.4 = 83.6 \text{ lb}_m/\text{ft}^3$

$g = 32.17 \text{ ft/sec}^2$

$\delta = 0.010/30.45 = 3.28 \times 10^{-4} \text{ ft}$

$\rho_L = 62.4 \text{ lb}_m/\text{ft}^3$

$$v = \left[21.31 \times \left(\frac{79.2 \times 1}{1} \right)^{0.775} \times \frac{83.6 \times 32.17 \times 3.28 \times 10^{-4}}{62.4} \right]^{1/1.225}$$

$$= 5.95 \text{ fps}$$

By knowing the average velocity, the flow equation, or Bernoulli equation, may be applied between the terminal points of the horizontal pipeline to determine the power required

$$\frac{\Delta P}{\rho} + \Delta(\text{KE}) + \Delta(\text{PE}) = -\bar{w} - \overline{lw} \qquad (17.49)$$

$\Delta(\text{KE}) = 0 \qquad$ no kinetic energy change between points 1 and 2

$\Delta(\text{PE}) = 0 \qquad$ no potential energy change between points 1 and 2

and $\bar{w}$ denotes the shaft work supplied by the pump in ft-lb$_f$/lb$_m$.

From the above relation,

$$-\bar{w} = +\overline{lw} + \frac{\Delta P}{\rho} = +\frac{f\Sigma l v^2}{2g_c D} + \frac{\Delta P}{\rho} \qquad \text{ft-lb}_f/\text{lb}_m$$

$$\text{HP}_{\text{act}} = \frac{1}{\eta_{\text{eff}}} \left(+\frac{f\Sigma l v^2}{2g_c D} + \frac{\Delta P}{\rho_m} \right) \frac{A v \rho_m}{550}$$

in which η_{eff} = over-all efficiency of pump-drive-motor combination
$\qquad \Sigma l$ = over-all equivalent length of pipe plus accessories
$\qquad \rho_m$ = density of slurry

In order to calculate f,

$$\mathbf{R} = \frac{\rho_m v D}{\mu} = \frac{79.2 \times 5.4 \times 1}{1 \times 0.000672} = 6.36 \times 10^5$$

At $\epsilon/D = 0.00015$, $f = 0.022$ roughly estimated from friction-factor–Reynolds-number chart at $\mathbf{R} = 6.36 \times 10^5$

$$= \frac{1}{0.80} \left[\frac{0.022 \times 250 \times (5.4)^2}{2 \times 32.17 \times 1} + \frac{500 \times 144}{79.2} \right] \frac{\pi}{4} \times 1 \frac{5.4 \times 79.2}{550}$$

$$= 695 \text{ hp required}$$

REFERENCES

1. Lockhart, R. W., and R. C. Martinelli: Proposed Correlation of Data for Isothermal Two-phase, Two-component Flow in Pipes, *Chem. Eng. Progr.*, **45**:39–48 (1949).
2. Martinelli, R. C., L. M. K. Boelter, T. M. Taylor, E. G. Thomsen, and E. H. Morin: Isothermal Pressure Drop for Two-phase, Two-component Flow in a Horizontal Pipe, *Trans. ASME*, February, 1944, pp. 139–151.
3. Baker, O.: Simultaneous Flow of Oil and Gas, *Oil Gas J.*, **53**(12):185–195 (1954).
4. Chenoweth, J. M., and M. W. Martin: A Pressure Drop Correlation for Turbulent Two-phase Flow of Gas Liquid Mixtures in Horizontal Pipes, *Petrol. Refiner*, **34**:151 (1955).
5. Reid, R. C., A. B. Reynolds, A. J. Diglio, I. Spiewak, and D. H. Klipstein: Two-phase Pressure Drops in Large Diameter Pipes, *AIChE J.* **3**(3):321–324 (1957).
6. Alves, G. E.: Co-current Liquid-gas Flow in a Pipeline Contractor, *Chem. Eng. Progr.*, **50**:449–456 (1954).
7. Bergelin, O. P., and C. Gazely: "Co-current Gas-Liquid Flow. I. Flow in Horizontal Tubes," Heat Transfer and Fluid Mechanics Institute, Berkeley, California, 1949.
8. Bergelin, O. P., P. K. Kegel, F. G. Carpenter, and C. Gazely: Co-current Gas-Liquid Flow. II. Flow in Vertical Tubes, Heat Transfer and Fluid Mechanics Institute, Berkeley, California, 1949.
9. Bergelin, O. P.: Flow of Gas Liquid Mixtures, *Chem. Eng.*, **56**:104 (1949).
10. Bertuzzi, A. F., M. R. Tek, and F. H. Poettmann: Simultaneous Flow of Liquid and Gas through Horizontal Pipes, *Trans. AIME*, **207**:17 (1956).
11. Benjamin, M. W., and J. G. Miller: Flow of a Flashing Mixture of Water and Steam through Pipes, *Trans. ASME*, **64**:657 (1942).
12. Katz, D. L., et al.: "Handbook of Natural Gas Engineering," p. 305, McGraw-Hill, New York, 1959.
13. "NGSMA Engineering Data Book," 7th ed., Natural Gasoline Supply Men's Association, Tulsa, Okla., 1957.
14. Standing, M. B.: "Volumetric and Phase Behavior of Oil Field Hydrocarbon Systems," Reinhold, New York, 1952.
15. Bicher, L. B., and D. L. Katz: *Ind. Eng. Chem.*, **31**:426 (1943).
16. Beal, C.: *Trans. AIME*, **165**:94 (1946).
17. Kobayashi, R., N. L. Carr, and D. B. Burrows: *Trans. AIME*, **201**:264 (1954).
18. Poettmann, F. H., and P. G. Carpenter: The Multiphase Flow of Gas Oil and Water through Vertical Flow Strings, *API Drill Prod. Practice*, 257, 1952.
19. Sobocinski, D. P., and R. L. Huntington: Concurrent Flow of Air, Gas Oil and Water in a Horizontal Line, *Trans. ASME*, **80**:1, 252 (1958).
20. Schneider, F. N., et al.: Horizontal Two-phase Oil and Gas Flow, *Pipeline Ind.*, **1**:47–51 (1954).
21. Brigham, W. E., E. D. Holstein, and R. L. Huntington: How Uphill and Downhill Flow Affect Pressure Drop in Two-phase Pipelines through Hilly Country, *Oil Gas J.* **55**(45):145 (1957).
22. White, P. D., and R. L. Huntington: Horizontal Co-current Two-phase Flow of Fluids in Pipelines, *Petrol. Eng.*, **27**:615 (1955).
23. Baker, O.: *Oil Gas J.*, **55**(45):150 (1957).
24. Rayleigh, Lord (J. W. Strutt): "Theory of Sound," 2d ed., Macmillan, London, 1894.
25. Giffen, E., and A. Muraszew: "The Atomization of Liquid Fuels," Chapman & Hall, London, 1953.
26. Marshall, W. R., Jr.: Atomization and Spray Drying, *AIChE Nomograph Ser.*, **50**:2 (1954).
27. Ranz, W. E.: On Sprays and Spraying, *Penn. State Univ. Dept. Eng. Research, Bull.* 65, 1956.

28. Injection and Combustion of Liquid Fuels, *WADC Tech. Rept.* 56-344, *ASTIA Document* AD 118142, March, 1957.
29. York, J. L., H. E. Stubbs, and M. R. Tek: The Mechanism of Disintegration of Liquid Sheets, *Trans. ASME*, **75**:1279 (1953).
30. Hinze, J. O.: Fundamentals of the Hydrodynamic Mechanism of Splitting in Dispersion Processes, *AIChE J.*, **1**:3, 289 (1955).
31. Hinze, J. O.: *Sixth Intern. Congr. Appl. Mech.*, 1946.
32. Hinze, J. O., *Appl. Sci. Research*, **A1**:263 (1948).
33. Tamotika, S.: *Proc. Roy. Soc. (London)*, **A146**:302 (1936).
34. Davies, R. M., and G. I. Taylor: The Mechanics of Large Bubbles Rising through Extended Liquids in Tubes, *Proc. Roy. Soc. (London)*, **A200**:375 (1950).
35. Saffman, P. G.: On the Rise of Small Air Bubbles in Water, *J. Fluid Mech.*, **1**:249 (1956).
36. Steinour, H. H.: The Rate of Sedimentation, *Ind. Eng. Chem.*, **36**:618, 840, 901 (1944).
37. Leva, Max: "Fluidization," McGraw-Hill, New York, 1959.
38. Brötz, W.: *Chem. Engr. Tech.*, **24**(2):60–81 (1952).
39. Leva, Max, M. Weintraub, M. Grummer, M. Pollchik, and H. H. Storch: *U.S. Bur. Mines Bull.* 504, 1951.
40. Wilhelm, R. H., and M. Kwauk: *Chem. Eng. Progr.*, **44**:201 (1948).
41. Reboux, P.: "Phénomènes de fluidisation," pp. 53–58, Association Française de Fluidisation, Paris, June 11, 1956.
42. Ergun, Sabri: *Chem. Eng. Progr.*, **48**:89–94 (1952).
43. Hinkle, B. L.: Ph.D. thesis, Georgia Institute of Technology, Atlanta, Ga., 1953.
44. Lovenstein, J. G.: Design So Solids Can't Settle Out, *Chem. Eng.*, **66**:1 (1959).
45. Spells, K. E.: *Trans. Inst. Chem. Eng. (London)*, **33**(2):79–82 (1955).
46. Johnstone, R. E., and M. W. Thring: "Pilot Plants, Models and Scale-up Methods in Chemical Engineering," pp. 119–120, McGraw-Hill, New York, 1957.
47. Brown, G. G., et al.: "Unit Operations," Wiley, New York, 1950.

Section 18

SEDIMENTATION

By

ALVIN G. ANDERSON, *University of Minnesota, Minneapolis, Minnesota*

SEDIMENTATION

18.1. Introduction

Sedimentation as used in this section is a term describing the interaction of a moving fluid and an assemblage of discrete particles in motion or capable of being put into motion. The dynamics of sediment transport has been developed largely in connection with the erosion, transport, and deposition of soil or rock particles on the land and in rivers and streams where its greatest economic importance lies. The significant changes in the configuration and character of land surfaces and water courses give rise to problems of considerable magnitude. Large expenditures have been made to develop means of preventing or lessening the erosion which is inherent in many agricultural processes. The control of sediment and the prevention of scour is an important part of the design of hydraulic structures.

Although sediment-transport phenomena are closely identified with streams, their application is by no means limited to this field. They are basic to many industrial processes where solids are transported by fluids or where different kinds of solids need to be mixed or separated. An important field of application is the transport of solids by winds. Many solutions of the problem of transport as obtained in the field of stream control are of direct application to other phases of technology, and for this reason the discussion in this section is based primarily upon the dynamics of sediment transport as developed in this discipline.

18.2. Notation

A	area
A_L	distance of deposit area measured in d_s
A_3	constant
A_*	constant in Einstein bed-load equation
a	thickness of jet; distance from bed where $C = C_a$
B_*	constant in Einstein bed-load equation
b	breadth of channel
C	mean concentration in pipe transport
C_a	concentration at elevation a from bed
C_d	coefficient of drag for spheres
C_y	concentration at elevation y from bed
D	pipe diameter
d	depth of open-channel flow
d'	thickness of layer in DuBoys equation
d_i	diameter of particle
d_s	diameter of sediment particle
d_{35}	diameter of particles of which 35 per cent is finer
d_{90}	diameter of particles of which 90 per cent is finer
f	Darcy friction factor for water-sediment mixture
f_w	Darcy friction factor for clear water
$f(B)$	mathematical description of bed configuration
G_B	bed-load-transport rate in weight dry per second per unit width
g	acceleration due to gravity
$g(B)$	local transport rate as function of bed configuration
$g(S)$	rate of sediment supply to a reach

I_1 integral in Einstein suspended-load equation
I_2 integral in Einstein suspended-load equation
i_B fraction of bed load of given size d_s
i_b fraction of bed material of given size d_s
i_i fraction of a sample of size d_i
K_s equivalent particle diameter for friction
L lift force on bed particle
l mixing length
N_d number of particles deposited per second
N_e number of particles eroded per second
n (1) Manning roughness coefficient
        (2) number of layers in DuBoys equation
n_b Manning roughness coefficient due to bed
n'_b Manning roughness coefficient due to particles
n_w Manning roughness coefficient due to banks
P (1) wetted perimeter
        (2) fraction of bed covered by movable particles
        (3) integral in Kalinske suspended-load equation
p probability of a particle being eroded
p_s probability of a particle being eroded per second
Q fluid discharge
Q_s sediment volumetric discharge
q_s sediment volumetric discharge per unit width
R hydraulic radius
R_b hydraulic radius of bed
R'_b hydraulic radius with respect to particles
R''_b hydraulic radius with respect to bed waves
R_w hydraulic radius of banks
S_e energy slope
S'_b energy slope due to particles
t (1) variable of integration
        (2) time
t_1 exchange time of bed particles
$\overline{U}$ mean velocity
u instantaneous velocity near bed level
$\bar{u}$ mean velocity near bed level
u_c critical velocity for initiation of movement
$u_{\max}$ maximum velocity at surface
u_* shear velocity
u_s velocity of particles moving along the bed
u_t threshold velocity for initiation of movement of wind-blown particles
V mean velocity of flow in closed conduit
V_f fall velocity of particle in still water
W weight of submerged particle
x lateral extent of scour hole
y variable distance from bed
y_a average saltation height of wind-blown sand
y' distance from bed where velocity is zero
z exponent in suspended-sediment equation
α_1 area shape factor
α_2 distance from bed measured in particle diameters
α_3 volume shape factor
β constant of proportionality in $\epsilon_s = \beta\epsilon_m$
γ specific weight of fluid
γ_s specific weight of sediment
δ thickness of laminar sublayer
ϵ_m diffusion coefficient for momentum transport
ϵ_s diffusion coefficient for sediment suspension

η (1) variable lift factor
        (2) friction coefficient in DuBoys equation
η_0 root-mean-square value of η
η_* η measured in terms of η_0
θ function in Kalinske bed-load equation
λ (1) wavelength
        (2) particle step measured in diameters d_s
ν kinematic viscosity
ρ density of fluid
ρ_s density of sediment particles
σ standard deviation of velocity fluctuations
σ_s standard deviation of particle distribution
τ_0 bed shear
τ_b bed shear
τ'_b bed shear due to particles
τ''_b bed shear due to sediment waves
τ_c critical shear for initiation of movement of particles
τ_y shear at elevation y above bed
ψ shear parameter in Einstein bed-load equation
ψ' sediment parameter in DuBoys equation
Φ transport parameter in Einstein bed-load equation
ϕ function of

18.3. Hydraulic Properties of Sediments

In so far as transport phenomena are concerned, sediments may be broadly classified as noncohesive and cohesive sediments. As the term implies, noncohesive sediments are those consisting of discrete particles, the movement of which depends only upon the physical properties of the individual particles such as size, shape, and density and upon their relative position with respect to other particles. Sands and gravels of stream beds or beaches that have been previously transported or deposits laid down by wind or water fall into this class, as would industrial products consisting of discrete particles. Cohesive sediments, on the other hand, are those whose resistance to erosion depends primarily upon the strength of the cohesive bond between the particles. This resisting force may far outweigh the influence of the physical characteristics of the individual particles. In its initial state a sediment may be cohesive in character and be highly resistant to movement, but once the bond is broken, it becomes a noncohesive sediment in relation to further transport. This class includes residual soils containing clay or other cohesive materials. Other deposits may change to this classification through chemical or physical reaction after having been previously transported as a noncohesive sediment. In the broad sense it might also include soils bound together by a root network or protected by a vegetative cover.

Because of the greater possibility of characterizing the properties of noncohesive sediments and relating these properties to the transport process, progress in the development of the transport mechanism has been limited largely to these sediments. The significant hydraulic properties of noncohesive sediments are size, shape, and density and the variations of these properties within the sediment aggregation. The settling velocity serves to combine, in some respects, these properties into a single parameter that is useful to characterize directly its reaction to the flow. Flocculation is sometimes important in the case of fine sediments and may be a major factor in determining the effective settling velocity.

Natural sediments are irregular in shape, and therefore the definition of size as a single length or diameter must be made arbitrarily or according to some convenient method of measurement. Three such definitions[1] are in common use: (1) the *sieve diameter*, the size of sieve opening through which the given particle will just pass; (2) the *sedimentation diameter*, the diameter of a sphere of the same specific gravity and the same terminal-settling velocity as the given particle in the same sedimentation fluid; and (3) the *nominal diameter*, the diameter of a sphere of the same volume as the given particle. Sands are commonly analyzed by sieving, although sizing by means of settling-velocity measurement is often used in connection with suspended-sediment samples. The sizes of silts and clays are generally expressed in sedimentation diameters. The nominal diameter is useful in defining the size of large particles for which the volume can be easily measured. These definitions of size have the same values for spheres, and the differences of these measures depend upon the shape of the particles.[2]

In a particular sediment the sizes of the individual particles may vary over a wide range; consequently it is convenient to describe the sediment as a whole by statistical measures. The common method is to determine the fraction or weight of sediment within a series of size classes by sieving through a nest of sieves or other means and plotting a cumulative size-frequency curve of the fraction or per cent by weight greater than a certain size against the logarithm of the size. From such curves the median size (50 per cent size) can be read and the variation in size determined. In many natural sands the size distribution is nearly log-normal, and hence a cumulative size-frequency curve will yield approximately a straight line on log-probability plotting paper from which the median size, geometric mean size, and the standard deviation from the mean can easily be determined.[3] Figure 18.1 is a cumulative size-frequency curve, plotted on semilog and log-probability paper, for a typical sediment.

The shape of natural particles involves both sphericity and roundness. Sphericity is defined as the ratio of surface area of a sphere of the same volume as the particle to the surface area of the particle. Roundness of a particle is defined as the average radius of curvature of the individual edges to the radius of the largest circle inscribed within the cross section of the grain. According to these concepts, a cube, for example, has a relatively high sphericity and low roundness while a cylinder can have a low sphericity and a high degree of roundness. Many natural sands which consist predominantly of quartz or feldspar have a relatively high degree of sphericity, and because of the difficulty of measuring these parameters, their influence on the transport process is neglected except when the shape departs radically from the spherical.

The density of the sediment particles plays an important role in transport phenomena and consequently must be determined for the particular sediment involved. The aver-

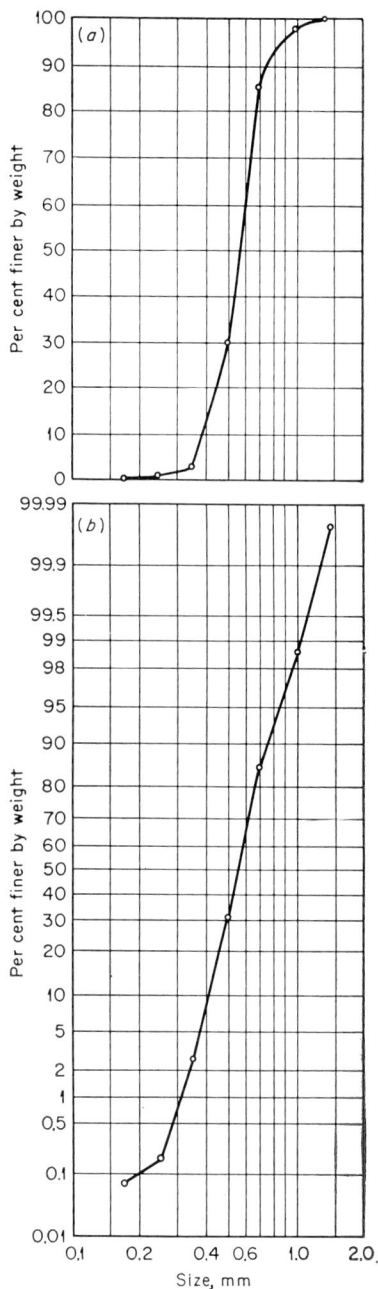

Fig. 18.1. Cumulative size-distribution curve for typical sediment sample. (a) Semilogarithmic plot. (b) Probability plot.

HANDBOOK OF FLUID DYNAMICS

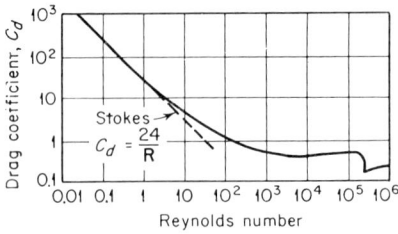

FIG. 18.2. Drag coefficient for spheres as function of Reynolds number.

age specific gravity of natural sediments is very close to that of quartz and is often taken as 2.65 for purposes of calculation.

The fall velocity of a particle in a fluid depends upon the size, shape, and density of the particle and on the viscosity and density of the fluid. When a sphere falls through a still fluid at its terminal speed, the drag on the sphere is equal to the submerged weight of the sphere. For this condition,

$$\tfrac{1}{6}\pi d_s{}^3(\rho_s - \rho)g = C_D \frac{\pi}{4} d_s{}^2\rho \frac{V_f{}^2}{2} \quad (18.1)$$

or

$$V_f{}^2 = \frac{4}{3}\frac{1}{C_D} g d_s \frac{\rho_s - \rho}{\rho} \quad (18.2)$$

in which V_f = fall velocity of a sphere of diameter d_s
ρ_s, ρ = densities of sphere and fluid, respectively
g = acceleration due to gravity
C_D = drag coefficient, a function of particle Reynolds number defined as
$\mathbf{R} = V_f d_s/\nu$, if ν = kinematic viscosity of fluid

The variation of C_D as a function of $\mathbf{R}$ is shown in Fig. 18.2. The drag coefficient in the Stokes range, that is $\mathbf{R} < 0.1$, is given by $C_D = 24/\mathbf{R}$. When this expression is substituted into Eq. (18.2), the fall velocity becomes that given by the Stokes law,

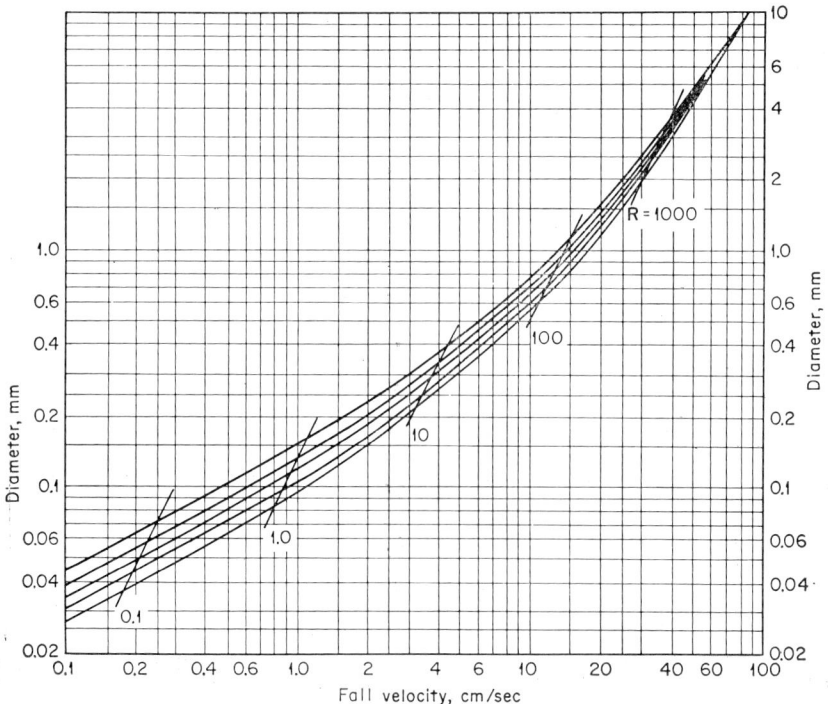

FIG. 18.3. Fall velocity of quartz spheres in water.

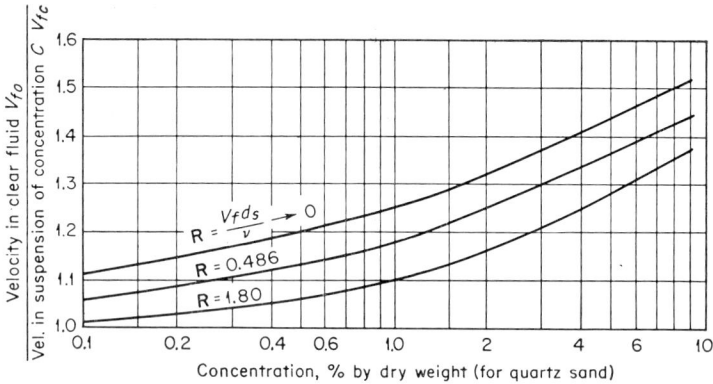

FIG. 18.4. Effect of concentration on fall velocity. (*After McNown and Lin.*[4])

$$V_f = \frac{1}{18} \frac{g d_s^2}{\nu} \frac{\rho_s - \rho}{\rho} \tag{18.3}$$

For larger values of **R**, the drag coefficient cannot be expressed analytically; however, the fall velocity for spheres of given density and size may be calculated with the aid of Eq. (18.2) and Fig. 18.2. To aid in such calculations, curves for the fall velocity of spheres in terms of the diameter may be prepared, such as Fig. 18.3, which shows the fall velocity of quartz spheres in water. If the settling velocity of a nonspherical particle is measured, substitution of the measured settling velocity into Eq. (18.2) permits computation of the sedimentation diameter of the particle.

The fall velocity given by Eq. (18.2) is for a single sphere falling in an infinite fluid. For a number of particles uniformly dispersed in the fluid, the fall velocity is less than that for a single particle and becomes smaller as the concentration of particles increases. This relationship is shown in Fig. 18.4 after McNown and Lin.[4]

18.4. Sediment-transporting Capacity

The *sediment-transport capacity* of a moving fluid is the maximum rate at which the moving fluid can transport a particular sediment aggregation. This condition requires that a sufficient quantity of the sediment be available to satisfy the transporting capacity. If this is not so, the flow will transport all that is available or fed into the flow, and hence the rate of transport will be independent of the flow conditions. In natural streams both conditions may exist because of the wide range of particle sizes entering the stream system. The larger sizes down to some minimum size will be similar to those already composing the bed so that the transport rate can be adjusted to the capacity rate of the flow. The finer fractions which are more easily kept in suspension are not so likely to be found in the bed. Consequently, that portion of the total load that consists of sizes found in the bed is transported at the capacity rate, while that portion made up of sizes that are smaller than any found in the bed may be transported at less than the capacity rate. It is transported mostly in suspension and is carried through the flow section with the fluid with little or no contact with the bed. As a result, the transport of this portion is independent of the flow and depends only on conditions extraneous to the flow. Since this fine material is essentially washed through the channel, it has been given the name *wash load* to distinguish it from the *bed-material load*, which is derived from the bed and whose transport is prescribed by the local flow conditions.[5] Consequently, all particles of the total load that are not found in significant quantities in the bed must be classified as wash load. This limiting size can be determined by a size analysis of the bed material.

With reference only to the bed-material load, an alluvial channel may be defined as one in which the bed is composed of sediment of the same type as that being transported. In an alluvial channel the bed configuration and the flow characteristics are interdependent.   If for any reason a local change in transport rate occurs, there will be a corresponding local change in bed elevation.   An increase in the rate will result in a local scour, and a decrease in the rate will result in a local deposition.   This condition can be expressed symbolically[6] by

$$\frac{df(B)}{dt} = g(B) - g(S) \tag{18.4}$$

if 　　B = a mathematical description of bed boundary
　$df(B)/dt$ = local rate of scour or deposition
　　$g(B)$ = local transport rate as a function of bed geometry
　　$g(S)$ = transport rate or supply into region under consideration

Equation (18.4) should describe the rate of erosion caused by an obstruction in the flow, such as a bridge pier, for example.   Here, because of the local boundary change, the local transport rate is greater than the supply rate.   As the scour proceeds it would be expected that $g(B)$ would gradually decrease until it was again equal to $g(S)$, at which time $df(B)/dt$ would equal zero and the scour hole would be stabilized.   An alluvial stream in equilibrium would correspond to the case where $g(B) = g(S)$ so that $df(B)/dt = 0$.
To apply Eq. (18.4) to a specific situation, the transport rate as a function of the boundary geometry and the flow conditions must be known.   In most instances involving local bed changes, such functions are not available, so recourse must be had to experimentation for the solution.   Some success has been attained, however, in establishing these functions for a stable bed, for which $df(B)/dt = 0$, and for uniform flow.   A discussion of the various aspects of the transport phenomena and the application of Eq. (18.4) will be undertaken in the following sections.

18.5. Description of the Transport Process

If one considers an assemblage of discrete particles immersed in a moving fluid such that they, having a specific weight greater than that of the fluid, form the lower boundary or bed, certain forces are generated by the fluid upon the particles.   In Fig. 18.5 some of these forces are shown schematically as they might be applied to a particular particle. A characteristic velocity profile in the neighborhood of the bed is also shown.   The velocity profile represents the temporal mean velocity at each point and shows the characteristic decrease in velocity as the boundary is approached.   Because of the irregularity of the boundary, elevations are measured from an arbitrary datum.   Superimposed upon this temporal mean-velocity field are the turbulent-velocity fluctuations in three mutually perpendicular directions which may or may not cause instantaneous local modifications of velocity field about the particle.

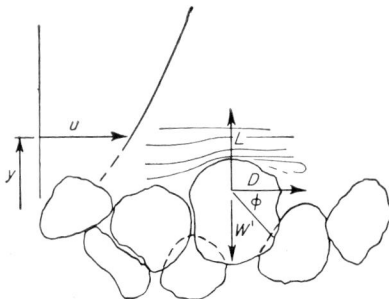

Fig. 18.5. Diagram showing forces on typical particle on stream bed.

As the flow passes the particle, the streamlines are deflected upward and around the particle and form a wake downstream.   The size of the wake depends upon the point of separation of the local boundary layer developed on the particle, which in turn depends upon the shape of the particle and the local Reynolds number.   As a result of the mean-velocity field, forces are generated on the particle which may be decomposed into a drag force in the direction of the mean velocity and a lift force perpendicular to the mean velocity.   The drag force is composed of a skin-friction drag and a form drag, and its location with respect to the center of gravity of the particle depends upon the relative magnitude of the two effects, which again depends upon the local Reynolds number and the shape and relative position of the particle. If the form drag predominates, the resultant drag force will pass through a point approaching the center of gravity of the exposed portion of the particle. The effect of the skin-friction component is to raise the point of application toward the top of the grain.

The lift force is the resultant of the pressure difference between the upper and lower sides of the particle. On the upper side the pressure is reduced below the static pressure by virtue of the curvature of the streamlines and increased velocity around the particle. On the lower side of the particle, since the flow through the interstices of the bed is small, the pressure approaches the static pressure of the flow. The lift force is normally directed upward. When the turbulent-velocity fluctuations are superimposed upon the mean-velocity field, it is clear that the lift and the drag are fluctuating quantities both in magnitude and in location of the point of application. In fact, it is conceivable that at certain instants either one or both might be reversed in direction.

The force-resisting motion is the submerged weight of the particle plus any downward-force component caused by contact with other particles near it in the bed. The submerged weight depends upon the size, shape, and density of the particle. In an aggregation of natural particles, the shape, and particularly the size, can vary over a wide range. In addition, the degree of exposure to the fluid forces depends upon the relative position of the particle in the bed and can vary from that of being completely exposed on the surface to that of being completely submerged in the bed. Consequently, considering the flow characteristics also, the force systems that determine the motion of the particles are complex functions of time, space, and the distribution of the properties that make up the aggregation.

Referring again to Fig. 18.5, the movement of the indicated particle will depend upon the instantaneous relative magnitudes of the forces acting and may occur in one of several ways. If the moment of the resultant of the lift and drag about the point of contact is greater than the moment of the submerged weight about the same point, the particle will be rolled from its initial position to some point downstream where the combination of forces, including its own momentum, is such that it is once more stable. If the lift force at any instant becomes larger than the submerged weight, the particle will be lifted bodily from the bed and carried upward. The drag force on the particle in the turbulent stream above the bed will tend to carry it downstream. As the particle leaves the bed, there will be a tendency for the flow pattern around the particle to be equalized, with a subsequent decrease in the lift and a tendency for the particle to again fall back to the bed. The combination of the longitudinal motion due to the drag and the vertical motion from the bed and back to the bed due to the lift will result in a downstream trajectory to a point where the particle may stop or bounce to make a second step or hop. This procedure may then continue until it finally returns to the bed at a point where it will be stable. On the other hand, when it is lifted from the bed and carried up into the turbulent-velocity field, the velocity fluctuations may at that instant be of such a magnitude and direction that the particle is transported further in an upward direction, and its consequent motion will depend upon the turbulent pattern of the moving fluid and its intensity in relation to the weight of the particle. It is apparent that the character of the motion that the particle undergoes depends upon the interaction of the characteristics of the fluid motion with the properties of the sediment particles. In a particular situation, all three types of motion involving different particles may occur in a continuous variation from no movement of some particles to nearly permanent suspension of others. These three types of motion have been designated[7] as rolling or sliding, saltation, and suspension.

The quantity transported by these three processes depends to a certain extent upon the relative magnitudes of the fluid properties to the sediment properties. It has been shown[8] that the height above the bed to which sand particles in air might be carried in the saltation process is about 800 times as high as that of similar sand particles in water. Therefore, for sediment transport in water, as between rolling and saltation, saltation is negligible and transport near the bed occurs primarily by sliding or rolling. On the other hand, for wind-blown sand, saltation predominates and the rolling process is secondary. It has been found convenient to classify the movement of sediment on the basis of mode of transport as bed load and suspended load where bed load (rolling and saltation) is that portion of the total load that takes place on or near the bed where both the transport and the flow pattern are influenced by the presence of the bed, and suspended load is that part occurring relatively far from the bed and is governed by the fully developed turbulence field.

In addition to the transport of individual particles, a complexity arises in the interaction of particles with each other and its effect on the flow. This interaction manifests itself by the formation of sediment waves, or bars, on the channel bed. The character of these waves as observed in laboratory channels may perhaps best be described by observing the sequence of forms that develop as the mean velocity over the bed is increased. If initially the bed is smooth and a flow of low velocity is introduced such that particles of various sizes and at various locations are moved by rolling or saltation, a series of small irregular sand ripples appears. As the velocity increases, the ripples increase in size and take on a characteristic appearance. They have a long, relatively flat upstream face and an abrupt downstream face. The sediment particles are transported along the upstream face to the crest, and then roll down the downstream face or are carried a short distance beyond the crest by the flow. The downstream face assumes essentially the angle of repose of the particles. Sand waves of this type are called *dunes*. They move slowly downstream, and in time the various patches of dunes that form on the bed coalesce and readjust themselves until a single system is formed. With a further increase in velocity the sediment transport becomes more intense and the waves increase in both amplitude and length and tend toward a more longitudinally symmetrical profile. When the velocity is still further increased, a point is reached where the waves disappear, the bed becomes smooth again, and sediment transportation is quite intense. A final change occurs when the velocity is again increased and waves of a rather transient character are again formed. These tend to move upstream by accretion on their upstream face. They grow to a maximum size and then disappear, only to reappear a short time later. Waves of this type have been called *antidunes* because of the tendency toward upstream motion.

Sediment waves, particularly of the dune type, have been clearly observed in laboratory channels and natural streams. In channels of good alignment and uniform cross section they have an opportunity to form and develop in a systematic sequence. In natural channels that are subjected to irregular changes in alignment, cross section, and roughness, the wave patterns are deformed, in some cases so as to be hardly recognizable. As a result of the occurrence of sediment waves and other irregularities of the bed, the delineation of magnitude and direction of the velocities, and hence the forces, become confused and the force system acting on the bed becomes more difficult to evaluate.

SEDIMENT TRANSPORT IN ALLUVIAL CHANNELS

Although the suspension of particles derived from the bed is generated by the same forces that determine the movement of those particles which move close to the bed, their subsequent movement is determined by the turbulent field far from the bed. It is therefore convenient to consider the two parts separately and consider first the initiation of movement and transport rate of those particles that are near the bed. The movement of bed load results from the action of the fluid forces on the bed particles as suggested in Fig. 18.5 and hence requires the determination of these forces as functions of the general flow pattern. The evolution of bed-load equations has been one of gradual refinement in the delineation of these forces and their effect on the bed particles.

18.6. Hydraulics of Alluvial Channels

The shear on the bed of an alluvial channel depends upon the relationship between the flow, the channel geometry, and the boundary resistance. The requirements of a stable bed and equality between the transport rate and the supply imply that the flow is essentially uniform throughout the reach under consideration.

The mean velocity under these circumstances can be expressed by the Manning equation

$$\overline{U} = \frac{1.49}{n} R^{2/3} S_e^{1/2} \tag{18.5}$$

wherein $\quad\quad \overline{U}$ = mean velocity

$R = A/P$ = hydraulic radius of cross section of area A whose wetted perimeter is P

S_e = energy slope

n = roughness coefficient, a factor which describes over-all resistance to flow and represents cumulative effect of all boundary elements such as banks and bed that contribute to dissipation of flow energy

The mean boundary shear along the wetted perimeter can be written for uniform flow by equating the fluid-weight component in the direction of flow to the total resistance, so that the mean unit shear is

$$\tau_0 = \frac{\gamma A S_e}{P} = \gamma R S_e \tag{18.6}$$

in which γ is the specific weight of the fluid When the boundary is composed of sections of different roughness geometry, the unit shear τ_0 taken over the total wetted perimeter is the mean of the component shears due to the separate components, each taken over its proportionate part of the total perimeter. If the channel is very wide so that the sidewall or bank influences are small compared with those of the bed, the hydraulic radius approaches the mean depth and the mean bed shear can be approximated by

$$\tau_0 \approx \gamma \, d \, S_e \tag{18.7}$$

For narrower channels where the wall or bank friction cannot be neglected, it becomes necessary to separate the total shear into its component parts in order to determine that part of the total shear which is due to the bed resistance. By Eq. (18.6) the over-all mean shear is proportional to the product of the hydraulic radius and the slope. Presumably this product is composed of products of components of the variables. The division of the total shear is considerably simplified, however, if it is assumed that either the hydraulic radius or the slope is common to all the elements and the other is then distributed among the elements in accordance with their relative influence on the total shear. Both methods have been used. The concept is perhaps more easily visualized if, as Einstein[9] proposed, the slope, which is the rate of energy loss in foot-pounds for each pound of fluid, is taken as constant for all the fluid units and that each unit contributes its energy to one type of roughness only. In this way the cross-section area can be divided among the various roughness elements in proportion to the energy that each dissipates; that is, the energy in a certain portion of the total cross section would be dissipated on the channel walls and the energy of the remaining portion would be dissipated on the bed. If it is further assumed that the mean velocity in each component part of the total area is equal to the mean velocity of the channel as a whole, the respective hydraulic radii of proportionate areas pertaining to the walls and the bed can be determined by the application of the Manning equation to the component parts separately; that is,

$$R_w = \left(\frac{\overline{U} n_w}{1.49 S_e^{1/2}} \right)^{3/2} \tag{18.8}$$

and

$$R_b = \left(\frac{\overline{U} n_b}{1.49 S_e^{1/2}} \right)^{3/2} \tag{18.9}$$

if n_w and n_b are the roughness coefficients characteristic of the channel walls and channel bed, respectively. If n_w is known or estimated from the character of the banks or walls, R_b can be computed from the relationships $A = A_w + A_b$ and $R_w = A_w/P_w$ and $R_b = A_b/P_b$. If data are available for several discharges, n_w and n_b can be determined by solution of simultaneous equations. By having the value of R_b, the unit shear on the bed can be written analogously to Eq. (18.6) as

$$\tau_b = \gamma R_b S_e \tag{18.10}$$

The shear τ_b represents the total shear on the bed, and if the bed were a plane surface composed of sediment particles, it would be the shear that is effective in transporting sediment. The bed, however, is not in general flat and even, but contains sediment waves or bars that form and grow as the flow increases. The bed shear may then be considered as being composed of two parts: (1) the shear generated by friction over the sediment particles, and (2) the shear resulting from the pressure forces on the sand waves. This separation is based upon the supposition that the part of the total energy transformed into turbulence energy at the particle surface is effective in moving the particles, while the energy transformation by the waves occurs at a considerable distance from the bed particles and is not effective in transporting the sediment. When several types of roughness, one of which is considerably larger than the other, are superimposed along a common perimeter, Einstein and Banks[10] found that the total shear was the sum of the contributions of the separate elements. The total shear on the bed can be written as

$$\tau_b = \tau'_b + \tau''_b \qquad (18.11)$$

if τ'_b is the shear due to flow over the sediment particles, and τ''_b is the shear due to pressure drag created by the waves. By utilizing the concept of the division of the area of flow into two parts, each contributing its energy to only one type of roughness, and since the roughnesses are superimposed on a common perimeter, the hydraulic radius of the bed can also be divided into two parts, so that

$$\gamma R_b S_e = \gamma R'_b S_e + \gamma R''_b S_e$$

and from which
$$R_b = R'_b + R''_b \qquad (18.12)$$

in which R'_b is the hydraulic radius pertaining to the sediment particles, and R''_b is the hydraulic radius pertaining to the sediment waves or bars.

For flow over a plane boundary composed of uniform particles, the roughness coefficient in the Manning equation depends upon the size of the particles and can be expressed as

$$n = C_1 d_s^{1/6} \qquad (18.13)$$

Then, again utilizing the concept that the mean velocity of each part of the cross section is equal to the mean velocity of the entire cross section and after using Eq. (18.13), the Manning formula in terms of the hydraulic radius pertaining to the sediment particles can be written as

$$\overline{U} = \frac{1.49}{\sqrt{g}C_1} \left(\frac{R'_b}{d_s}\right)^{1/6} \sqrt{gR'_b S_e}$$

from which
$$\frac{\overline{U}}{\sqrt{\tau'_b/\rho}} = C_2 \left(\frac{R'_b}{d_s}\right)^{1/6} \qquad (18.14)$$

in which
$$\sqrt{\tau'_b/\rho} = u'_* = \sqrt{gR'_b S_e}$$

When the bed is composed of a mixture of various sizes of particles, the choice of effective size of sediment that represents the bed as a whole probably depends upon the distribution of sizes. A number of different effective sizes have been proposed, ranging from the 50 per cent size to the 90 per cent size. Good results have been obtained[9] when the effective particle size was taken as that size at which 65 per cent by weight is finer. For this effective size, Eq. (18.14), the Manning-Streckler equation is

$$\frac{\overline{U}}{\sqrt{\tau'_b/\rho}} = 7.66 \left(\frac{R'_b}{d_s}\right)^{1/6} \qquad (18.15)$$

An alternative equation for the shear on the sediment particles based on the logarithmic velocity distribution of Prandtl–von Kármán is

$$\frac{\overline{U}}{\sqrt{\tau'_b/\rho}} = 5.75 \log\left(12.2 \frac{R'_b}{d_s}\right) \qquad (18.16)$$

From Eqs. (18.13) and (18.15) the boundary shear τ'_b that is effective in transporting the sediment particles can be obtained. This shear is the temporal mean shear acting on the particles that form the bed and is effective in creating the drag and lift on the individual particles.

18.7. Concept of Critical Tractive Force

From what has been said, the critical boundary shear, or critical tractive force, is rather indeterminate. It is defined as that value of the shear, or tractive, force at which there will be a general beginning of movement. Because of variations in the shear due to turbulence and variations in the size and exposure of the sediment particles, the inception of movement of particular particles may vary considerably. However, the range of mean shear required to initiate movement is sufficiently narrow in general to justify the usefulness of the critical-tractive-force concept. The value of the mean shear for the beginning of movement may be estimated by visual observation of the condition of general movement or by extrapolating the curve showing the transport rate as a function of the bed shear to the condition of zero transport and by evaluating the mean shear for this condition.

A number of attempts have been made to develop a relationship of the critical tractive force in terms of the properties of the particles and the character of the bed. Shields[11] considered the forces acting on the particles much as shown in Fig. 18.5. The drag tending to move the particles can be described by

$$D = C_d A \rho \frac{u^2}{2}$$

if A is the exposed area of the grain characterized by a shape factor α_1, and d_s^2 is the diameter squared. The drag coefficient depends also on the shape factor and the local Reynolds number, $u d_s / \nu$, if ν is the kinematic viscosity of the fluid. The mean drag force in functional form is then

$$D = \phi_1 \left(\alpha_1 \frac{u d_s}{\nu} \right) \rho d_s^2 u^2 \tag{18.17}$$

By assuming that the flow is turbulent, the velocity in the neighborhood of the bed particles can be described by the Prandtl–von Kármán logarithmic velocity-distribution equation in the form

$$\frac{u}{\sqrt{\tau_0/\rho}} = 5.75 \log \frac{y}{d_s} + f \left(\frac{d_s \sqrt{\tau_0/\rho}}{\nu} \right) \tag{18.18}$$

which is valid for both hydraulically smooth and rough boundaries and in which the particle diameter has been substituted for the roughness parameter K_s. The critical velocity around the particle u_c, which characterizes the effect of the velocity profile, is presumed to occur at an elevation y, proportional to the particle size; that is, $y = \alpha_2 d_s$. By using Eq. (18.18) after substituting this value of y, the critical velocity can be described by

$$u_c = \sqrt{\frac{\tau_0}{\rho}} \left[5.75 \log \alpha_2 + \phi \left(\frac{d_s \sqrt{\tau_0/\rho}}{\nu} \right) \right] \tag{18.18a}$$

or

$$u_c = \sqrt{\frac{\tau_0}{\rho}} \, \phi_2 \left(\alpha_2, \frac{d_s \sqrt{\tau_0/\rho}}{\nu} \right) \tag{18.19}$$

The mean drag on the particle is then

$$D = \phi_1 \left[\alpha_1, \frac{d_s}{\nu} \sqrt{\frac{\tau_0}{\rho}} \, \phi_2 \left(\alpha_2, \frac{d_s \sqrt{\tau_0/\rho}}{\nu} \right) \right] \rho d_s^2 \frac{\tau_0}{\rho} \phi_2^2 \left(\alpha_2, \frac{d_s \sqrt{\tau_0/\rho}}{\nu} \right)$$

or

$$D = \phi_3 \left(\alpha_1, \alpha_2, \frac{d_s \sqrt{\tau_0/\rho}}{\nu}, \tau_0 d_s^2 \right) \tag{18.20}$$

The weight of the particle immersed in the fluid, resisting movement, is simply

$$W = \alpha_3(\gamma_s - \gamma)d_s^3 \tag{18.21}$$

if α_3 is a volumetric shape factor, and γ_s and γ are specific weights of the sediment particles and the fluid, respectively.

At incipient movement the drag force is proportional to the particle weight, so that

$$\phi_3\left(\alpha_1, \alpha_2, \frac{d_s\sqrt{\tau_c/\rho}}{\nu}\right)\tau_c d_s^2 = \alpha_3(\gamma_s - \gamma)d_s^3$$

wherein τ_c takes on the character of a critical shear and the proportionality constant is combined with α_3. It follows then that

$$\frac{\tau_c}{(\gamma_s - \gamma)d_s} = \phi_4\left(\alpha_1, \alpha_2, \alpha_3, \frac{d_s\sqrt{\tau_c/\rho}}{\nu}\right) \tag{18.22}$$

Now, if the bed consists of particles of uniform size and essentially of the same shape, the factors α_1, α_2, and α_3 are constants, and Eq. (18.22) reduces to

$$\frac{\tau_c}{(\gamma_s - \gamma)d_s} = \phi\left(\frac{d_s\sqrt{\tau_c/\rho}}{\nu}\right) = \phi_1\left(\frac{d_s}{\delta}\right) \tag{18.23}$$

since $\delta = 11.6\dfrac{\nu}{\sqrt{\tau_c/\rho}}$ is the thickness of the laminar sublayer.

The results of experiments by Shields and others are shown in Fig. 18.6. A smooth curve drawn through the data shows the dependency of the critical tractive force upon the ratio of the particle size to the thickness of the laminar sublayer. The minimum value of the parameter $\tau_c/(\gamma_s - \gamma)d_s$ occurs when $d_s/\delta \approx 1$, that is, when the drag is due largely to skin friction on the particle. For larger values of d_s/δ, the parameter approaches a constant of 0.06.

By following much the same procedure in describing the drag force on the particles, White[12] considered that the tractive force was distributed among those grains that rested on top of the bed and introduced a factor which served as an estimate of the distribution

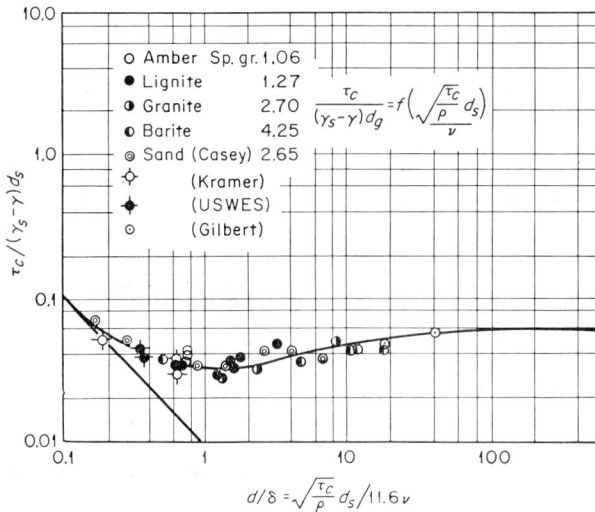

FIG. 18.6. Critical tractive force for bed particles. (*After Shields.*[11])

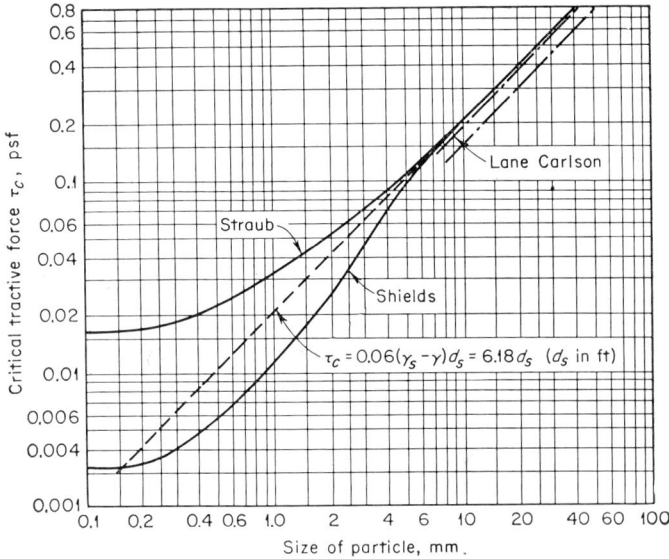

Fig. 18.7. Critical tractive force for quartz particles in water.

of the movable particles. Kalinske[17] showed that on the basis of turbulent-velocity fluctuations, the critical tractive force for the movement of uniform particles could be considerably less than the mean.

When applied to quartz particles in water, by substituting the appropriate specific weights, Eq. (18.23) can be rewritten for the critical tractive force in terms of the particle size only. This relationship has been plotted in Fig. 18.7. Superimposed on Fig. 18.7 are the results of Straub[15] and some results by Lane and Carlson[13] observed for coarse gravel that formed the bed of several irrigation canals.

18.8. Bed-load Transport

A bed-load equation relates the rate of transport of material on or near the bed to the flow for the condition of capacity transport. The flow characteristic involved in the transport rate is usually the boundary shear acting upon the particles. The history of sediment-transport mechanics represents a more or less continuous evolution of steps to more adequately describe these forces and their interactions with the particles.

DuBoys Equation. One of the earliest attempts to relate the transport rate to the flow conditions was that of DuBoys[14] in 1879. Although the development was based upon assumptions regarding the character of movement no longer tenable, the resulting equation with experimentally determined coefficients has found wide application because of its simplicity. It has been found useful to discover general trends and the approximate influence of various changes upon the transport regime.

It was presumed that transport took place as a series of superposed layers that approximated a particle diameter d' in thickness and that the speed of the successive layers decreased linearly from a maximum for the surface layer to zero for the nth layer. The speed of the surface layer was then $(n - 1)\Delta u_s$ if Δu_s is the incremental change in speed of the successive layers. The weight rate of transport per unit width is then equal to the product of the specific weight of the sediment, the total thickness of the layers, and the mean velocity of the layers; that is,

$$G_B = \gamma_s n d' \frac{(n - 1)\Delta u_s}{2} \qquad (18.24)$$

The resistance of the layers, which depends upon the submerged weight of the moving layers and a friction coefficient between the layers, is equal to the existing tractive force acting on the surface layer, or

$$\tau_0 = \eta(\gamma_s - \gamma)nd' \tag{18.25}$$

If the flow conditions were such that the boundary shear on the bed surface were just sufficient to move the first layer, a critical tractive force representing the lower limit of movement would exist, that is,

$$\tau_c = \eta(\gamma_s - \gamma)d' \tag{18.26}$$

and from which

$$n = \tau_0/\tau_c \tag{18.26a}$$

Substitution of this definition of n into Eq. (18.24) gives the transport rate in pounds per second-dry per unit width as

$$G_B = \frac{\gamma_s d' \,\Delta u_s}{2\tau_c^2}\,\tau_0(\tau_0 - \tau_c) = \psi'\tau_0(\tau_0 - \tau_c) \tag{18.27}$$

The constants ψ' and τ_c are functions of the particle size. Equation (18.23) and Fig. 18.7 show that τ_c increases with the particle size, therefore ψ', according to Eq. (18.27), should decrease with the grain size. Consequently, for a given tractive force τ_0, the transport rate decreases as the size of the sediment increases. The values of ψ' and τ_c must by the very nature of the development be determined by experiment. By thus examining the results of various experiments, Straub[15] evaluated the critical tractive force τ_c and the sediment parameter ψ' by fitting Eq. (18.27) to the experimental data in the regions of most interest and comparing these values with the size of sediment used in each case. The results are tabulated below and plotted in Fig. 18.8.

ds, mm	⅛	¼	½	1	2	4
τs, psf	0.0162	0.0172	0.0215	0.0316	0.0513	0.089
ψ', ft³/(lb²)(sec)	134	79.8	47.8	28.4	17.0	10.2

The critical tractive force τ_c is also plotted in Fig. 18.7, with the Shields curve, for comparison.

Meyer-Peter and Müller Equation. Subsequent to Straub's evaluation of the constant in DuBoys' equation, numerous other empirical equations have been proposed,

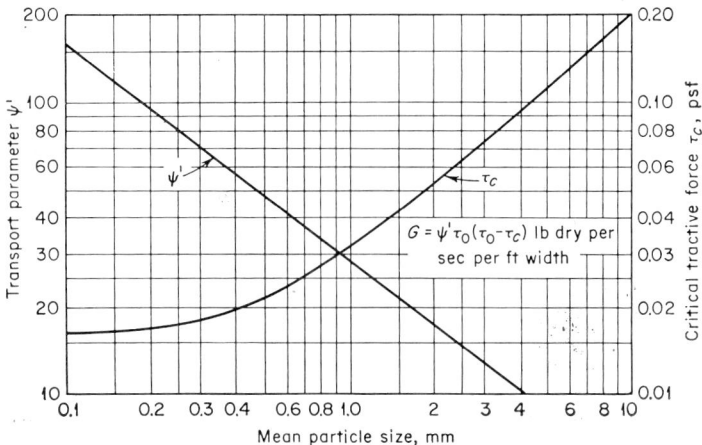

FIG. 18.8. Transportation parameter and critical tractive force for DuBoys bed-load equation. (*After Straub.*[15])

most of which are of the DuBoys type. The variation in the equations is probably due to the difficulty of accounting for and measuring the many variables involved. In the process, however, a better understanding of the phenomenon was gained. The formula of Meyer-Peter and Müller[16] represents the latest attempt to include the essential variables and to develop an inclusive empirical equation. It is based upon a large number of experiments covering a wide range of hydraulic conditions. The analysis of these data led to an equation that can be expressed in the notation used here as

$$\left(\frac{n'_b}{n_b}\right)^{3/2} \gamma R_b S_e = 0.047(\gamma_s - \gamma)d_s + 0.25\left(\frac{\gamma}{g}\right)^{1/3}\left(\frac{\gamma_s - \gamma}{\gamma}\right)^{2/3} G_B^{2/3} \tag{18.28}$$

if
$$n_b = \frac{\overline{U}}{1.49 R_b^{2/3} S_e^{1/2}} \tag{18.29}$$

and
$$n_b' = 0.034 d_{90}^{1/6} \tag{18.30}$$

In addition to terms previously defined, d_{90} is the size of bed particles, of which 90 per cent by weight are finer, measured in feet; $d_s = \Sigma(d_i i_i)$ is the effective particle size; i_i is the fraction of bed particles of size d_i; and G_B is the transport rate in pounds-dry per second per foot width.

In Eq. (18.28), the factor $(n'_b/n_b)^{3/2}$ represents the portion of the total bed shear that is effective in moving the bed particles [Eq. (18.9)]. The division of the bed shear is accomplished by dividing the slope S_e into two parts, the slope S'_b necessary to overcome the particle resistance and the slope S''_b to overcome the resistance of the bars and other irregularities. Then, using the Manning formula with the assumption that the velocity is distributed uniformly over the entire cross section,

$$\frac{S'_b}{S_e} = \left(\frac{n'_b}{n_b}\right)^2 \tag{18.31}$$

Meyer-Peter and Müller found, however, that $(n'_b/n_b)^{3/2}$ fit the data better than Eq. (18.31), so they proposed using the ratio to the three-halves power. They concluded also that the 90 per cent size of the particle mixture was the size that was effective in establishing the particle resistance. For a plane bed, $n'_b/n_b = 1$.

By recognizing that the left-hand term in Eq. (18.28) represents the shear, or tractive, force on the grains and that the first term on the right is equivalent to the critical tractive force τ_c, given by Eq. (18.23), Eq. (18.28) can be reduced to

$$G_b = K(\tau_b - \tau_c)^{3/2} \tag{18.32}$$

if
$$K = 8\left(\frac{g}{\gamma}\right)^{1/2}\frac{\gamma_s}{\gamma_s - \gamma}$$

which is somewhat similar to the tractive-force equation of DuBoys.

Kalinske Equation. The DuBoys and Meyer-Peter equations and other similar ones assumed that the shear acting on the bed particles was a constant and equal to the average value. However, as pointed out in Art. 18.5, the fluid forces acting on the particles fluctuated with respect to time because of the fluid turbulence. Kalinske[17] attempted to evaluate the effect of the turbulent fluctuations on the fluid velocity near the particles, and thus the fluid forces.

The average transport rate by weight depends upon the number and size of the particles being moved and the average speed with which they move. Any single particle at any instant will have a speed equal to

$$u_s = b(u - u_c) \tag{18.33}$$

if u is the instantaneous fluid velocity at the particle level, and u_c is a critical fluid velocity, that is, the velocity of the fluid that is required to initiate movement of the particle. The constant b should have a value near unity. Since u varies with time, the particle velocity will also vary with time. If the number of uniform particles per unit area of the bed available for movement is $P/\alpha_1 d_s^2$, in which P is the fraction of the bed covered by these particles and α_1 is the shape factor, the mean transport rate in pounds per second, dry weight, per unit width of the bed will be

$$G_B = \alpha_3 \gamma_s d_s{}^3 \bar{u}_s \frac{P}{\alpha_1 d_s{}^2} = \alpha P \gamma_s d_s \bar{u}_s$$

or

$$\frac{G_B}{\bar{u} d_s \gamma_s} = \alpha P \bar{u}_s / \bar{u} \qquad (18.34)$$

in which $\alpha = \frac{2}{3}$ for uniform spheres
$\bar{u}$ = mean velocity at particle level
$\bar{u}_s$ = mean velocity of particles

Since $\bar{u}$ is the mean velocity near the particles, it can be expressed approximately by $\bar{u} = C\sqrt{\tau_0/\rho}$ if C has a value near 11.   Consequently, Eq. (18.34) can be approximated by

$$\frac{G}{u_* d_s \gamma_s} = \frac{2.5 \bar{u}_s}{\bar{u}} \qquad (18.35)$$

if P is taken as 0.35, and $u_* = \sqrt{\tau_0/\rho}$.
  By assuming that the velocity fluctuations are normally distributed, the mean value of $u_s = (u - u_c)$ for all values of $u > u_c$ is

$$\bar{u}_s = \int_{u_c}^{\infty} (u - u_c) f(u)\, du \qquad (18.36)$$

in which $f(u)$ is the instantaneous velocity-frequency distribution and $\int_{-\infty}^{\infty} f(u)\, du = 1$.
Integration of Eq. (18.36) after dividing by $\bar{u}$ leads to

$$\frac{\bar{u}_s}{\bar{u}} = \phi\left(\frac{u_c}{\bar{u}}\right) = \theta\left(\frac{\tau_c}{\tau_0}\right) \qquad (18.37)$$

since $u_c/\bar{u}$ can be expressed as $(\tau_c/\tau_0)^{1/2}$.   The function θ depends upon the magnitude of the velocity fluctuations.   A value of $\sigma/\bar{u} = \frac{1}{4}$ was taken by Kalinske as typical of the turbulent intensity of natural streams and was used to evaluate θ.   Substitution of Eq. (18.37) into Eq. (18.35) gives the transport rate as

$$\frac{G}{u_* d_s \gamma_s} = 2.5 \theta\left(\frac{\tau_c}{\tau_0}\right) \qquad (18.38)$$

which has been plotted in Fig. 18.9.

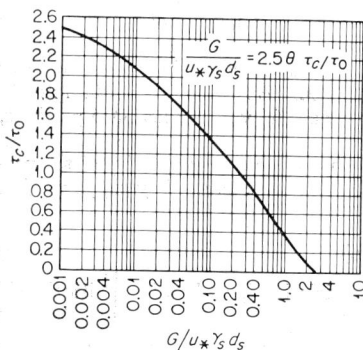

Fig. 18.9. Kalinske transport function.

The analysis of several sand mixtures led Kalinske to propose the median size of the mixture as the effective particle size to be used in Eq. (18.38).   Comparison with measurements of the transport rate indicates that Eq. (18.38) agrees reasonably well over a large portion of the range but indicates rates that are too low in the region of high transport rates.

Einstein Equation.   It was shown in Fig. 18.5 that a particular particle on the bed will move if the fluid force at any instant was greater than the resistive force.   Since these forces on the particle vary both with respect to time and space, the movement of any particular particle depends upon the probability that at a particular time and place the dynamic forces exceed the resistive force.

Under these circumstances the critical tractive force represents some average value of the shear for which the probabilities of movement are sufficiently large to indicate appreciable movement. Instead of dealing with the concept of a critical tractive force, Einstein[18] considered the dependence of the probabilities of movement or deposition on the flow characteristics.

Based upon experiment, he concluded that particles are transported along the bed in a series of steps the length of which on the average is proportional to the particle size and that the particle is deposited on the bed after performing one or more of these steps. The rate of deposition per unit area then depends upon the transport rate past a given section and the probability that the dynamic forces are such that the particle may be deposited. On the other hand, the rate of erosion from this area depends upon the number and properties of particles in the unit area and the probability that the hydrodynamic force on each particle is sufficiently large to move it. For the bed to be stable, the rate of deposition must be equal to the rate of erosion.

The number of particles that are deposited per unit area per second can be expressed as

$$N_d = \frac{q_B i_B}{\gamma_s \alpha_3 d_s^3 A_L d_s} \tag{18.39}$$

in which q_B = transport rate in dry weight of all particles moving through a cross section per unit width

      i_B = fraction of q_B of size d_s

      $\alpha_3 d_s^3$ = volume of each grain

      $A_L d_s$ = length of area one unit wide in which all particles have been deposited

It can be shown[18] that

$$A_L d_s = \frac{\lambda d_s}{1 - p} \tag{18.40}$$

if λ is a constant, and p is the probability of eroding a particle, which also corresponds to the fraction of the bed on which at any time the force on a particle of diameter d_s is sufficient to move it.

The number of particles eroded from the bed per unit area per second is

$$N_e = \frac{i_b p}{\alpha_1 d_s^2 t_1} \tag{18.41}$$

in which i_b = fraction of area composed of particles of size d_s and projected area is $\alpha_1 d_s^2$

      p = probability of being eroded as given above

      t_1 = time over which exchange is taking place

Einstein concluded that the time of exchange should be a characteristic of the particle only and proposed a time proportional to the time required for the particle to fall in still fluid a distance equal to its diameter, so that, from Eq. (18.2),

$$t_1 = A_3 \frac{d_s}{V_f} = A_3 \left(\frac{d_s}{g} \frac{\rho}{\rho_s - \rho} \right)^{1/2}$$

Then
$$N_e = \frac{i_b p}{\alpha_1 d_s^2 A_3} \left(\frac{g}{d_s} \frac{\rho_s - \rho}{\rho} \right)^{1/2} \tag{18.42}$$

Since $N_d = N_e$, the probability of a particle of size d_s being eroded can be written from Eqs. (18.39), (18.40), and (18.42) as

$$\frac{p}{1 - p} = \frac{\alpha_1 A_3}{\alpha_3 \lambda} \frac{i_B}{i_b} \frac{q_B}{\gamma_s} \left(\frac{\rho}{\rho_s - \rho} \right)^{1/2} \left(\frac{1}{g d_s^3} \right)^{1/2} = A_* \phi \tag{18.43}$$

if
$$\phi = \frac{q_B}{\gamma_s} \left(\frac{\rho}{\rho_s - \rho} \right)^{1/2} \left(\frac{1}{g d_s^3} \right)^{1/2}$$

and
$$\frac{i_B}{i_b} = 1$$

The probability p in Eq. (18.43) is the probability of a particle being eroded, and hence is also the probability that the dynamic forces on the particle exceed the particle's submerged weight. The submerged weight is

$$W = \alpha_3(\gamma_s - \gamma)d_s{}^3 \qquad (18.21)$$

The dynamic force acting on the particle varies with time in accordance with the velocity near the particle and can be expressed in terms of the mean value as given in Eq. (18.20) and a parameter η that varies with time about a mean of zero. Assuming the bed to be hydraulically rough so that the velocity is independent of d_s/δ,

$$L = \phi(\alpha_1, \alpha_2)\tau^d d_s{}^2(1 + \eta) \qquad (18.44)$$

By writing τ_0 as the shear on the particles alone and after assuming that the bed is hydraulically rough, the fluctuating lift is

$$L = \phi(\alpha_1, \alpha_2)\tau'_b d_s{}^2(1 + \eta) = A\gamma R'_b S_e d_s{}^2(1 + \eta) \qquad (18.44)$$

Then the probability that the lift is greater than the weight, that is, $W/L < 1$, can be expressed as the probability that

$$|1 + \eta| > \frac{\alpha_3(\gamma_s - \gamma)d_s{}^3}{A\gamma R'_b S_e d_s{}^2} \qquad (18.45)$$

or

$$|1 + \eta| > B_* \psi$$

if B_* is a constant and

$$\psi = \frac{\rho_s - \rho}{\rho}\frac{d_s}{R'_b S_e}$$

If η varies in accordance with the normal-error curve, the probability that η, in terms of its standard deviation η_0, is such that erosion occurs is

$$p = 1 - \frac{1}{\sqrt{\pi}}\int_{-B_*\psi - 1/\eta_0}^{B_*\psi - 1/\eta_0} e^{-t^2}\,dt \qquad (18.46)$$

if t is only an integration variable. By combining Eqs. (18.43) and (18.46) to eliminate p, the transport equation becomes

$$1 - \frac{1}{\sqrt{\pi}}\int_{-B_*\psi - 1/\eta_0}^{B_*\psi - 1/\eta_0} e^{-t^2}\,dt = \frac{A_*\phi}{1 + A_*\phi} \qquad (18.47)$$

The constants, determined by experiment, are $A_* = 43.5$, $B_* = 0.143$, and $1/\eta_0 = 2$. In order to facilitate its use, Eq. (18.47) is plotted in Fig. 18.10 in terms of ϕ and ψ.

For mixtures of a wide range of sizes corrections to ϕ and ψ are introduced[18] to take into account the interference effect of larger particles on the movement of the finer particles and for the thickness of the laminar sublayer with respect to the particle size.

Comparison of Bed-load Equations. In the various bed-load equations that have been developed, there are certain similarities in the expressions used to describe the forces and resistances. Chien[19] has shown, for example, that the Meyer-Peter formula when expressed in terms of ϕ and ψ agrees very well with the Einstein formulation. He has shown that in terms of ϕ and ψ the Meyer-Peter formula can be written as

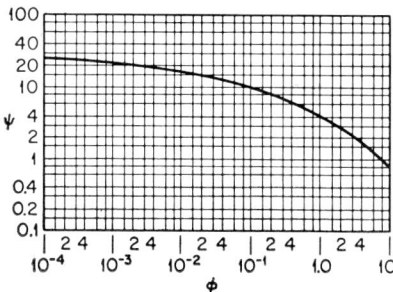

FIG. 18.10. Einstein transport function.

$$\phi = \left(\frac{4}{\psi} - 0.188\right)^{3/2} \qquad (18.48)$$

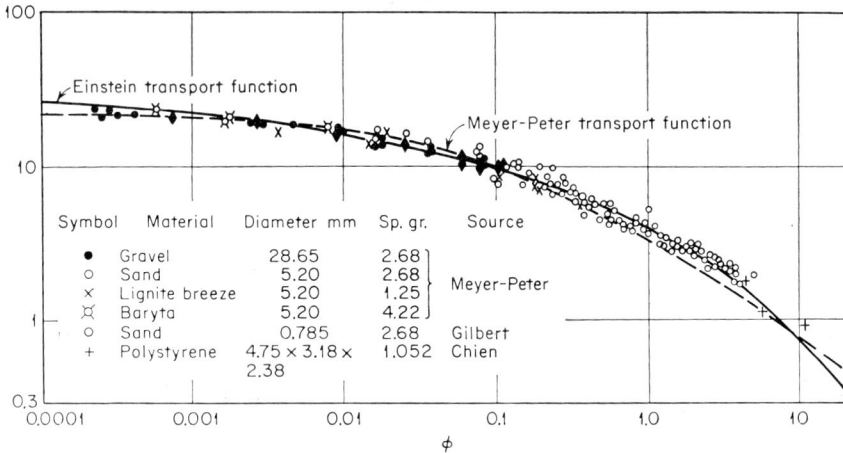

Fig. 18.11.   A comparison of the Einstein and the Meyer-Peter transport functions.   (*After Chien.*[19])

Chien's[19] comparison of the two equations with some experimental data is shown in Fig. 18.11.   It has already been shown that the Meyer-Peter equation can be reduced to one of the DuBoys type.

By the nature of the problem, particularly the difficulty of measuring transport rates in nature, the development of bed-load equations and the mechanics of transport have been limited to laboratory experiment.   A few attempts have been made to obtain reliable field measurements[20, 21] to verify the proposed equations.

18.9. Suspended-load Transport

Particles are transported as suspended load when the forces as shown in Fig. 18.5 are such that the particle is lifted from the bed and carried into a region where the turbulent-velocity components may carry it farther into the flow.   Its subsequent motion while being suspended is independent of the bed and is governed by the turbulence pattern of the flow.   A particular particle will be carried upward when the upward vertical components exceed the fall velocity and downward when the fall velocity exceeds the turbulent components.   There is thus a continual interchange of particles leaving and returning to the bed.

In addition to the particles derived from the bed, other particles, particularly very fine particles, that enter the reach are easily kept in suspension so that there is little interchange with the bed.   This wash load, however, is also distributed in accordance with the turbulent fluctuations.

In a wide-open channel where the flow can be considered two-dimensional, only the vertical velocity components are significant in the distribution of sediment particles in a vertical section.   Consider a horizontal section a distance y from the bed.   Although the mean velocity is parallel to this section, the vertical turbulent-velocity components carry fluid through the section both in an upward and downward direction.   On the average, the upward components are equal to the downward components, and consequently through a unit area the fluid-flow rate in the upward direction is equal to the downward flow rate.   Sediment particles that are entrained in the fluid are also transported through the section with the fluid.   As in the case of the mixing-length theory of turbulence, it is assumed that the fluid containing the sediment particles moves an average distance l before it loses its identity.   The flow in the upward direction can then be assumed to originate at a distance $l/2$ below the horizontal section, while that moving downward originates an equal distance above the section.   If the concentration of particles of a given size at the horizontal section is C_y, then, as a first approximation, the concentration at the upper level is $C_y + (l/2)dc/dy$ and that at a point $l/2$ below the section is $C_y - (l/2)dc/dy$. Now superimposed upon the velocity of the fluid carrying the sediment particles is the settling velocity of the particles which is in the downward direction, so that the upward speed of the particles is the difference between the fluid velocity and the settling velocity while in the downward direction the particle speed is the sum of these velocities. For an equilibrium to exist, that is, for the time average of the sediment concentration to be a constant at a particular section above the bed, the sediment-transport rate upward through the section must be equal to the corresponding transport rate downward. Hence

$$\left(C_y - \frac{l}{2}\frac{dc}{dy} \right)(v' - V_f) = \left(C_y + \frac{l}{2}\frac{dc}{dy} \right)(v' + V_f)$$

or
$$C_y V_f + v'\frac{l}{2}\frac{dc}{dy} = 0 \tag{18.49}$$

Both v' and l are unknown as such and may be combined into a single variable representing the diffusion coefficient for the sediment. Then

$$C_y V_f + \epsilon_s \frac{dc}{dy} = 0 \tag{18.50}$$

in which ϵ_s, which is composed of the vertical velocity components and the mixing length, is a function of y. Since the sediment particles are transported with the fluid masses, it might be expected that the diffusion coefficient for the sediment is similar to that for momentum transport, although the magnitude of ϵ_m, the momentum-diffusion coefficient, depends upon the correlation of the longitudinal and transverse velocity fluctuations while ϵ_s depends only on the vertical components. The momentum-diffusion coefficient ϵ_m is defined by

$$\tau_y = -\rho\epsilon_m \frac{du}{dy} \tag{18.51}$$

if τ_y is the shear at a distance y from the bed, and du/dy is the velocity gradient. Since the shear is linearly distributed, the shear at y can be written in terms of the boundary shear on the bed as

$$\tau_y = \tau_0 \frac{d - y}{d} \tag{18.52}$$

By assuming the velocity profile as described by the Prandtl–von Kármán velocity defect law,

$$\frac{u - u_{\max}}{u_*} = \frac{1}{K}\ln\frac{y}{d} \tag{18.53}$$

in which $u_{\max}$ = maximum velocity at surface
$u_* = \sqrt{\tau_0/\rho}$
K = von Kármán constant

the velocity gradient is

$$\frac{du}{dy} = \frac{u_*}{Ky} \tag{18.54}$$

After using Eqs. (18.52) and (18.54) in Eq.(18.51), the diffusion coefficient becomes

$$\epsilon_m = Ku_* \frac{d - y}{d} y \tag{18.55}$$

If it is assumed that $\epsilon_s = \beta\epsilon_m$, Eq. (18.50) becomes

$$C_y V_f - \beta K u_* \frac{d - y}{d} y \frac{dc}{dy} = 0 \tag{18.56}$$

which upon integration from a to y gives the sediment concentration as a function of y in the form

$$\frac{C}{C_a} = \left(\frac{d-y}{y} \frac{a}{d-a} \right)^z \tag{18.57}$$

if C_a is the concentration at the level $y = a$, and the exponent

$$z = \frac{V_f}{\beta K u_*} \tag{18.57a}$$

Equation (18.57) is integrated from a level $y = a$, which may be near the bed because at $y = 0$ the equation gives an infinite concentration. Although Eq. (18.57) describes the distribution of sediment particles, the magnitude of the concentration is related to that at the level $y = a$ and must be determined by other means, such as sampling. The equation shows that for a given shear, the smaller the value of V_f, and hence the sediment size, the more uniformly is the sediment distributed throughout the vertical, and the larger the sediment particles the greater is the decrease of concentration in the upper levels of the flow. It also follows that for a given particle size, the greater the boundary shear, the more uniform is the sediment distribution. The equation is valid at neither the bed nor the water surface. At the bed, the equation indicates an infinite concentration, whereas the actual concentration depends upon the bed-load transport rate. Hunt[22] improved the relationship by taking into account the volume occupied by the sediment. This becomes significant near the bed where the concentrations are high. The character of the distribution and the results of measured distribution as presented by Vanoni[23] are shown in Fig. 18.12. It shows the agreement of measurement with Eq. (18.57) except that the values of the exponent z in Fig. 18.12 indicate that β is greater than unity and increases with an increase in z. This indicates that the sediment is more uniformly distributed than is suggested by Eq. (18.57).

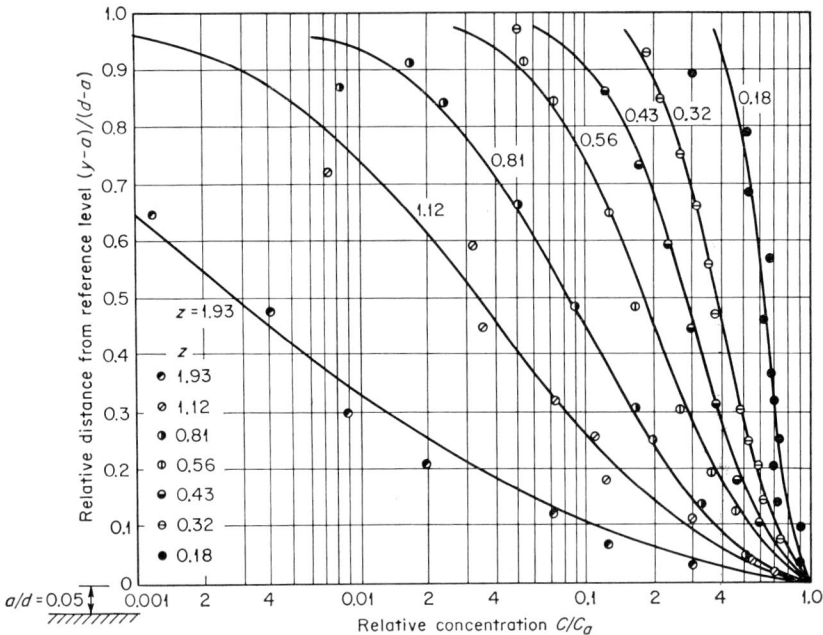

FIG. 18.12. Distribution of suspended sediment. (*After Vanoni.*[23])

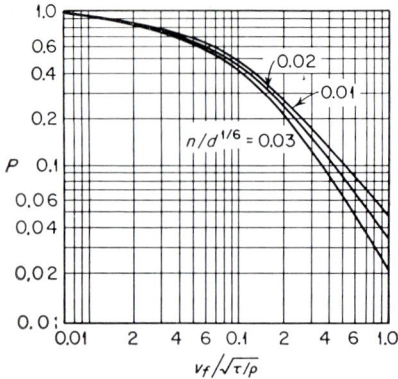

$n/d^{1/6} = 0.03$

$v_f/\sqrt{\tau/\rho}$

FIG. 18.13.   Kalinske suspended-load function.

The total suspended-load transport involves the integration of the product of the velocity and concentration over the depth of flow, or

$$q_s = \int_0^d Cu\,dy \qquad (18.58)$$

In order to simplify the integration, Lane and Kalinske[24] suggested that ϵ_s be defined as a constant equal to its mean value. Then

$$\epsilon_s = \frac{d\,u_*}{15}$$

Equation (18.57) then becomes

$$\frac{C}{C_a} = e^{-15\frac{y-a}{d}\frac{V_f}{u_*}} \qquad (18.59)$$

By using the logarithmic velocity distribution and Eq. (18.59) in Eq. (18.58), the total suspended-load transport becomes

$$q_s = qC_a e^{15\frac{a}{d}\frac{V_f}{u_*}} P \qquad (18.59a)$$

in which q is the discharge per unit width, and P the integral in terms of V_f/u_* and $n/d^{1/6}$, with n the Manning roughness coefficient. See Fig. 18.13.

Einstein[18] carried out the integration indicated by Eq. (18.58), using the more exact Eq. (18.57) and the logarithmic velocity distribution, giving the total suspended-load transport as

$$q_s = 11.6u_*C_a a\left[2.3\log_{10}\frac{y}{K_s}\cdot(I_1 + I_2)\right] \qquad (18.60)$$

I_1 and I_2, which are integrals involving the relative distance from the bed, and the exponent z were evaluated by Einstein.

18.10. Transport by Wind

Transport of sediment by wind is in many respects quite similar to the transport by water. The differences that exist are largely due to the difference in density between air and water. The principles are the same in both cases. In some respects, however, the variables that influence the phenomena cover a wider range of values in, for example, the wind structure, surface variations, and soil properties.

In nature the problems are generally those involving the removal of soil particles from the earth's surface by the moving wind and their consequent deposition. In this case the term $df(B)/dt$ in Eq. (18.4) is not strictly zero; however, the change in bed elevation compared with the area involved and the thickness of the wind stream is so small that it may be neglected as a factor in altering the flow pattern over the bed. Consequently, the problem becomes one of finding the transport function $g(B)$ in terms of the fluid motion and the sediment particles.

The movement of soil particles is similar to that described for water in that movement occurs as bed load or surface creep, saltation, and suspension. The relative proportions moved by the saltation process are much greater in the case of wind-blown particles than in water and consequently cannot be neglected in determining the transport rate. The characteristics of the saltation process have been described[25] as a bouncing along the bed. In general, the grains rise vertically from the bed with a high degree of rotation, gain forward momentum from the air stream, and return to the bed at a relatively flat angle, where by impact it or other grains are again projected into the air stream. The horizontal distance traveled may be 10 to 15 times the height of rise. The angular velocity of the particles is gained upon impact with other grains either upon the bed or by collision above the bed.

As for particles in water in open channels, the particles will move when the drag forces overcome the resistive forces. The dynamic force is a function of the velocity in the neighborhood of the grain and can be described by the boundary shear generated by the wind velocity. In contrast to the flow in an open channel, however, the mean boundary shear cannot be calculated from the fluid-weight component in the direction of flow, but must be determined from the velocity profile directly. It has been found[26] that the wind velocity profile in the neighborhood of the ground surface can be described by the von Kármán–Prandtl velocity-distribution law,

$$u = \frac{2.3}{K} u_* \log \frac{y}{y'} \tag{18.61}$$

if u = average wind velocity at elevation y above the surface
$u_* = \sqrt{\tau_0/\rho}$ = shear velocity in which τ_0 is shear stress
ρ = fluid density
K = von Kármán universal constant
y' = value of y where $u = 0$

(The value of y' has been considered to be one-thirtieth of the height of the roughness elements. In field measurements, however, it has been found that y' may be equal to a major portion of the roughness element.)

Over drifting-sand surfaces Bagnold[25] found that the velocity profile could best be described by

$$u = 5.75 u_* \log \frac{y}{y'} + u_t \tag{18.62}$$

if u_t is the velocity at y' required to move the sand particles. Other measurements[26] give other values of y' and u_t. In addition, the wind profiles as measured by Zingg suggest that a value of $K = 0.375$ is required to obtain reasonable agreement between the measured shear stress and that computed from the velocity profile. Typical profiles near the surface level for a stabilized surface and for a drifting-sand surface as measured by Zingg[26] in a wind tunnel are plotted in Fig. 18.14.

As suggested by Eqs. (18.61) and (18.62), the shear stress that is effective for the movement of sand particles can be determined from the velocity profile over the surface. By utilizing a procedure similar to Shields'[11] for the critical shear, Bagnold[25] developed an expression for the "threshold" velocity:

$$u_t = \sqrt{\frac{\tau_c}{\rho}} = A \left(\frac{\rho_s - \rho}{\rho} \, g d_s \right)^{\frac{1}{2}} \tag{18.63}$$

and found by visual observation that A was equal to 0.1 for nearly uniform sand of diameter > 0.2 mm. Chepil[27] obtained for soils classes ranging from 0.10 to 3.0 mm values of A varying between 0.09 to 0.11. Also from tunnel experiments of air flow over stable beds and over drifting sand, Zingg[26] deduced a value of 0.116 for A. The results of Shields for the critical shear for sediment particles in water correspond to values of A from 0.187 to 0.245. The reason for the higher values obtained using water as against those using air is not readily apparent, but may be due to a higher level of turbulence in the airstreams. Field measurements indicate a wide range of turbulence intensity. Using the standard deviation σ of the velocity fluctuation, values of $\sigma/\bar{u}$ varying over a range of 5 : 1 have been measured. This implies consequent relatively large instantaneous variations in the local shear.

The height to which saltating grains will rise after they have been put into motion will depend upon the particle size and the wind shear. By sampling the saltating particles at various elevations above the bed for different flow conditions, Zingg[26] found empirically that the mean height of saltation could be described by

$$y_a = 92.5 d_s^{\frac{3}{2}} \tau_0^{\frac{1}{4}} \tag{18.64}$$

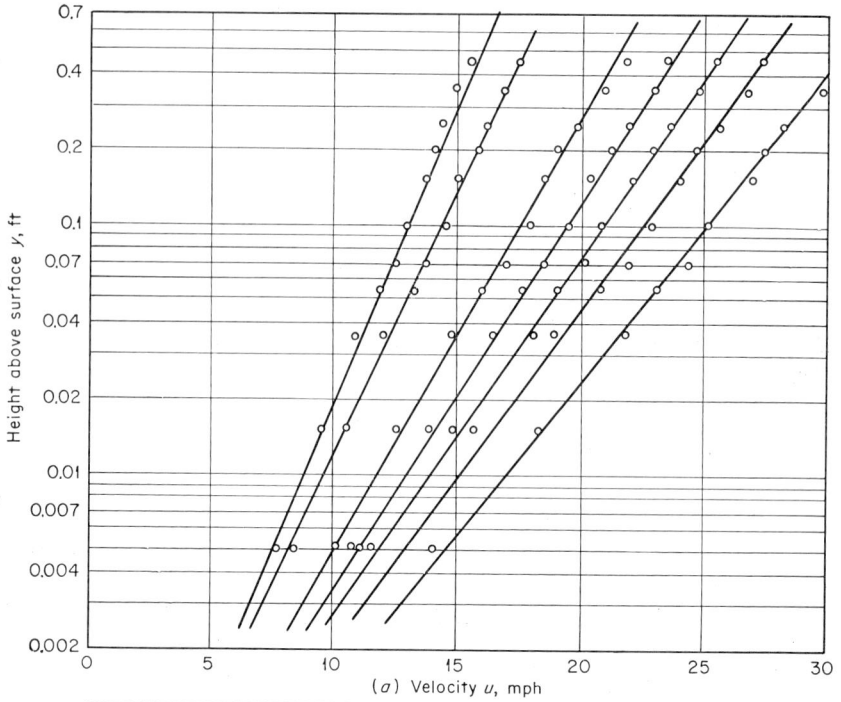

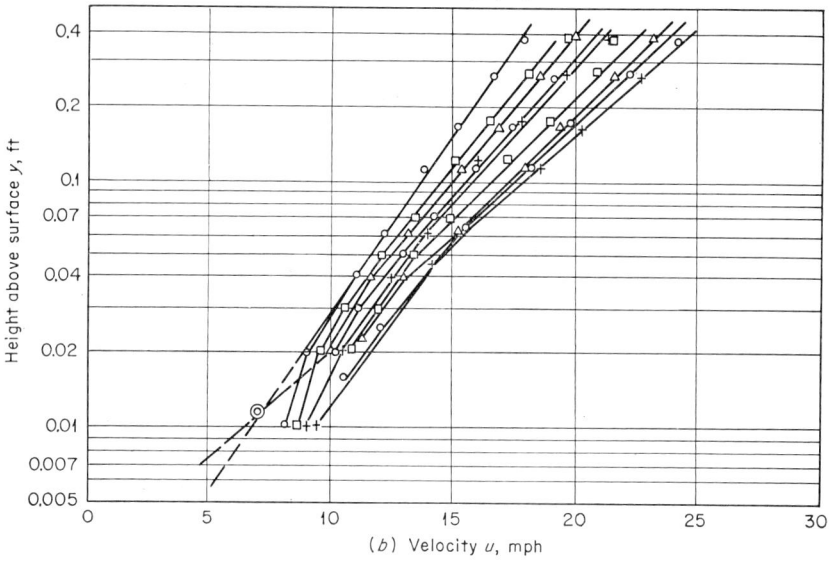

FIG. 18.14. Velocity profiles over (a) stabilized and (b) drifting-sand surfaces. (*After Zingg.*[26])

if y_a = mean height, ft

d_s = particle diameter, mm

τ_0 = average surface shear, psf

By integrating the rate of transport at various heights Zingg then estimated that the total transport rate in pounds per foot width per hour could be described by the empirical equation

$$q_T = 175 \times 10^3 d_s^{\frac{3}{4}} \tau_0^{\frac{3}{2}}$$ (18.65)

in which, again, d_s is the sediment size in millimeters, and τ_0 is the boundary shear in pounds per square foot.

APPLICATIONS OF TRANSPORT MECHANICS

The previous sections dealt with the transport of sediment in alluvial channels in equilibrium; that is, the transport rate was equal to the sediment-transporting capacity of the channel. For this condition the rate was a function of the sediment properties and the flow conditions. Of interest and of considerable importance are those cases in which the transport rate is less than the capacity rate as may exist in a closed conduit or where changes in flow boundaries occur, with the resulting readjustment of the bed regime. The solutions for problems of this type must in many cases be obtained by experiment.

18.11. Transport in Closed Conduits

The transport of discrete particles by fluids in closed conduits has many industrial applications, ranging from dredging operations where the material transported is heterogeneous in both size and quality to the transport of fine carefully graded products in industrial processes. In many respects such transport is analogous to the transport in open channels and includes both capacity transport and less-than-capacity transport.

For a given concentration of sediment in a given conduit, the transporting capacity may be exceeded for a low velocity. Some of the particles will settle out and form a deposit on the bed, over which some particles will be transported as bed load. If the rate of feed remains constant, the bed will increase in depth, since the rate of supply exceeds the local transport rate in accordance with Eq. (18.4). With increasing velocity the transport rate will increase until it is equal to the supply. The deposit on the bed will then be stable. Additional increases in velocity will cause the deposit to degrade until the bed is swept clear and all the sediment is transported in suspension. Above this point the suspended load is analogous to the wash load in alluvial channels and is independent of the flow characteristics. This sequence of events is shown in Fig. 18.15, which is typical of turbulent flow in rough pipes for which the friction factor is a constant. At the low velocities the slope of the hydraulic grade line decreases with increasing velocity until a minimum is reached, after which it increases and approaches that for clear water. The minimum values of the slope represent the velocity at which all the particles are moving in suspension or saltation and no deposits are left on the bed.[28] At velocities less than this, particles are being transported over a bed consisting of deposited particles.

Both types of motion are significant in different applications. The region with velocities less than the nondeposit critical is important in the design of conduits utilized for drainage purposes where the deposition of sediment would be detrimental. The region above this critical is of importance for the design of systems for the transport of particles in industrial processes.

An analytical solution for the transport function in pipes is not available, so recourse is had to experiment to delineate the significant variables and their effect on the phenomenon. Durand[28] has reported an extensive series of experiments dealing with the nondeposit phase covering a wide range of conduit sizes, particle sizes, and concentrations. A systematic analysis of the data revealed that for sediment larger than 0.2 mm transported in horizontal circular conduits, the friction factor for the mixture could be computed from

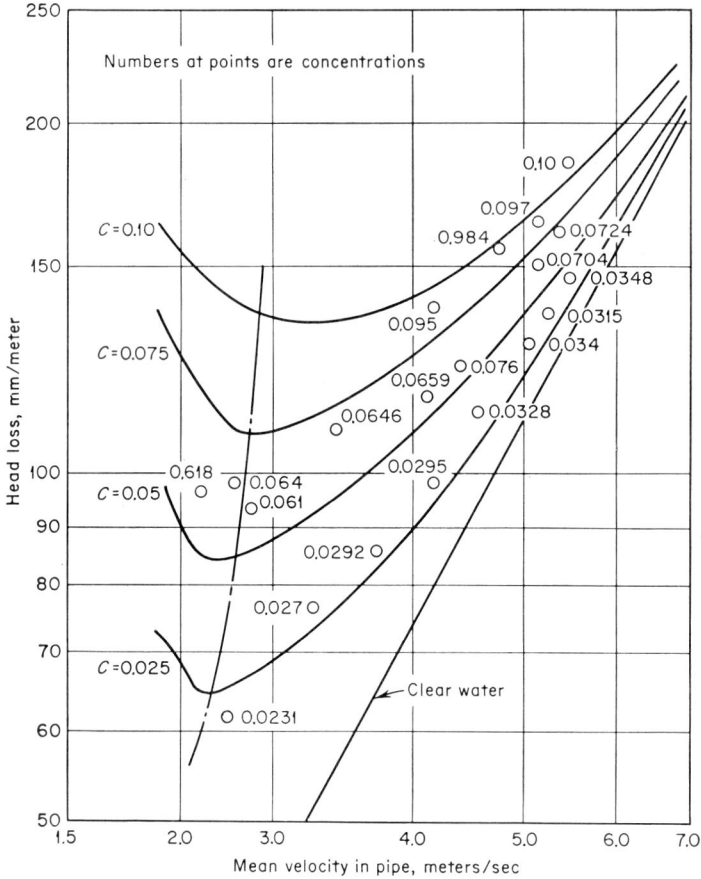

FIG. 18.15. Effect of concentration of suspensions on head loss in pipes. (*After Durand.*[28])

$$f = f_w \left[1 + 82 \left(\frac{gD}{V^2} \frac{\rho_s - \rho}{\rho} \right)^{\frac{3}{2}} \frac{C}{C_d^{\frac{3}{4}}} \right] \tag{18.66}$$

if f_w is the Darcy friction factor for clear water in a pipe of diameter D and velocity V; C, the concentration, is the ratio of the volume of particles per unit volume of particles and water; ρ_s and ρ are the densities of the particles and water, respectively; and C_d [Eq. (18.2)], the drag coefficient of the particle falling through still water, is the measure of the particle size being transported. For mixtures of various sizes of particles, the equivalent diameter is equal to the weighted average diameter.

Craven[29] studied the case where a deposit formed on the bed as characteristic of a drainage conduit and found that no permanent deposit of sediment would occur if the factor

$$\frac{Q}{D^2 d_s^{\frac{1}{2}} \left(g \frac{\rho_s - \rho}{\rho} \right)^{\frac{1}{2}}} > 2.5 \tag{18.67a}$$

in which Q is the pipe discharge.

In most drainage installations the conduit runs only partly full. For such conditions the objective is generally to design the installation so that deposits of the incoming sediment will not occur. For this situation Ambrose[30] found that the conduit would stay clear if the factor

$$\frac{Q}{D^2 Q_s^{1/6} g^{2/5} \left(\dfrac{\rho_s - \rho}{\rho}\right)^{2/5}} > 2.9 \tag{18.67b}$$

in which Q_s is the volume rate of transport into the culvert.

18.12. Channel Contractions

If the width of a channel transporting sediment is changed, corresponding changes will occur in the bed regime. The effect of channel contractions in increasing the depth in the contracted section is of considerable importance in river regulation, and the problem lies in relating the increase in depth to the degree of contraction. Equation (18.4) is applicable to this situation. Initially, the contraction will increase the local rate of transport, with a consequent reduction in bed elevation, since $g(B)$ will be greater than $g(S)$. With the passage of time and as the depth in the contracted section increases, the transport rate will decrease and approach the supply rate. At this time $df(B)/dt$ will approach zero and the new regime will be stabilized.

The stabilized condition was treated by Straub[15]. It was assumed that the contracted portion was sufficiently long so that normal flow was established in both the contracted and uncontracted sections. The discharge, as required by continuity, is the same in both sections, as is the rate of transport for the stabilized regime. Using the Manning discharge equation for wide channels and assuming equal roughness in each section,

$$Q = \frac{1.49}{n} b_1 d_1^{5/3} S_1^{1/2} = \frac{1.49}{n} b_2 d_2^{5/3} S^{1/2} \tag{18.68}$$

The transport rate in the two sections was described by the DuBoys Eq. (18.27), so that for equilibrium,

$$g(B) = \psi' b_1 \tau_1 (\tau_1 - \tau_c) = \psi' b_2 \tau_2 (\tau_2 - \tau_c) \tag{18.69}$$

if τ_1 and τ_2 are the bed shears in the uncontracted and contracted sections, respectively. By combining Eqs. (18.68) and (18.69), the ratio of the depths in the two sections becomes

$$\frac{d_2}{d_1} = \left(\frac{b_1}{b_2}\right)^{3/7} \left\{ \frac{-\tau_c/\tau_1 + [(\tau_c/\tau_1)^2 + 4(1 - \tau_c/\tau_1) b_1/b_2]^{1/2}}{2(1 - \tau_c/\tau_1)} \right\}^{3/7} \tag{18.70}$$

Equation (18.70) has been plotted in Fig. 18.16, which shows that the contracted depth is relatively independent of τ_c/τ_1 and can be closely approximated for moderate values of b_1/b_2 and over an appreciable range of τ_c/τ_1 by

$$\frac{d_2}{d_1} = \left(\frac{b_1}{b_2}\right)^{9/14} = \left(\frac{b_1}{b_2}\right)^{0.642} \tag{18.71}$$

Equation (18.70) has been compared with both laboratory and field observations with reasonably good results.

18.13. Effect of Channel Obstructions

The term channel obstructions is used to include any object or structure that disrupts the uniform flow and thus the equilibrium transport conditions of the channel. A channel contraction is an instance of a channel obstruction, although the contraction discussed in the previous section was assumed to be long enough for the

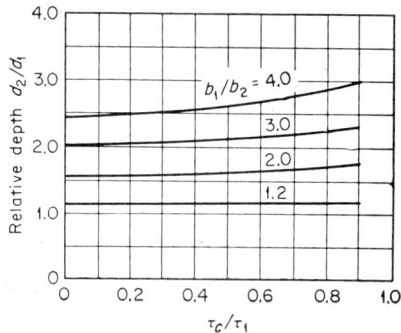

Fig. 18.16. Relative depth in contractions.

establishment of uniform flow. In the sense used here, the channel obstruction would be limited to the entrance and exit of the contraction where the flow is nonuniform. Within this category are included such obstructions as bridge piers and abutments, outlet and intake works of hydraulic structures, local channel works, and natural channel irregularities.

The disruption of the uniform flow pattern caused by these abrupt changes in boundary geometry must necessarily introduce changes in bed configuration to conform to these changes. This process is described by Eq. (18.4), which states that the rate of scour is equal to the difference between the local transport rate and the supply rate. In discussing the nature of scour, Laursen[6] promulgated certain scour characteristics and limiting conditions upon the solution of Eq. (18.4) in the present application. In general, the enlargement of the scoured area will result in a reduction of velocity along the boundary and therefore a reduction in the transport capacity. This implies a limit to the extent of scour when the local transport rate is reduced to that of the supply. Further, if the supply rate is zero, the limit of the scour is reached when the local transport capacity reaches zero, a value which is approached asymptotically. The application of Eq. (18.4) in general depends upon the establishment of mathematical functions to describe the bed geometry, transport rate, and supply rate as functions of the flow properties and time. In general, in the absence of such functions, recourse must be had to experiment to determine empirically the integral of Eq. (18.4); that is,

$$f(B) = \phi[g(B), g(S), t] \tag{18.72}$$

The transport rate depends upon the flow pattern and properties of the sediment. The flow pattern in turn will depend on the boundary geometry, including the bed configuration, the characteristic velocities, and the fluid properties. By utilizing the procedures of dimensional analysis, Eq. (18.72) might be written as

$$f_1(B) = \phi_1\left(\frac{V}{V_f}, \frac{V_f t}{a}, \sigma_s, \frac{Va}{\nu}, \frac{V^2}{ga}, g(S), \frac{b}{a}, \ldots\right) \tag{18.73}$$

in which $f_1(B)$ is a dimensionless function describing the bed configuration, the velocity V is taken as characterizing the flow pattern, and a is a characteristic length describing its spatial aspects. Additional geometric ratios may be needed to describe the geometry of the system, or additional dimensionless kinematic variables may be needed to describe the flow pattern. The fluid properties enter in a characteristic Reynolds number and characteristic Froude number, and the sediment properties for noncohesive sediments are characterized by the mean settling velocity and standard deviation of the settling velocity. For cohesive sediments a critical scouring velocity would be required compared with which the settling velocity and standard deviation may be negligible. The supply rate $g(S)$ is a dimensionless parameter describing the rate of supply, if any, into the scoured area. It should be realized that terms descriptive of the flow pattern may also be functions of time, and the particular meaning assigned to each variable must be determined for each situation.

Understanding of the scour phenomenon has been aided considerably by investigations of the scour caused by relatively simple flow patterns, such as submerged jets in which the flow can be more simply described by size and velocity of the jet. In experiments of this kind, Eq. (18.73) can be greatly simplified. The supply rate is usually zero, the flow pattern is characterized by the size and velocity of the jet, the sediment is usually relatively uniform and noncohesive and can be described by the mean settling velocity, and since the jet is submerged and of relatively high velocity, the pattern will be relatively independent of the Reynolds and Froude numbers. If the scour pattern remains similar as the scour progresses, it can be described by a single parameter relating its size to the size of the jet. Equation (18.73) can then be written simply as

$$\frac{X}{a} = \phi_2\left(\frac{V}{V_f}, \frac{V_f t}{a}\right) \tag{18.74}$$

if X represents the lateral extent of the scour hole. Some results of Laursen's experiments utilizing a submerged jet plotted in Fig. 18.17 in accordance with Eq. (18.74)

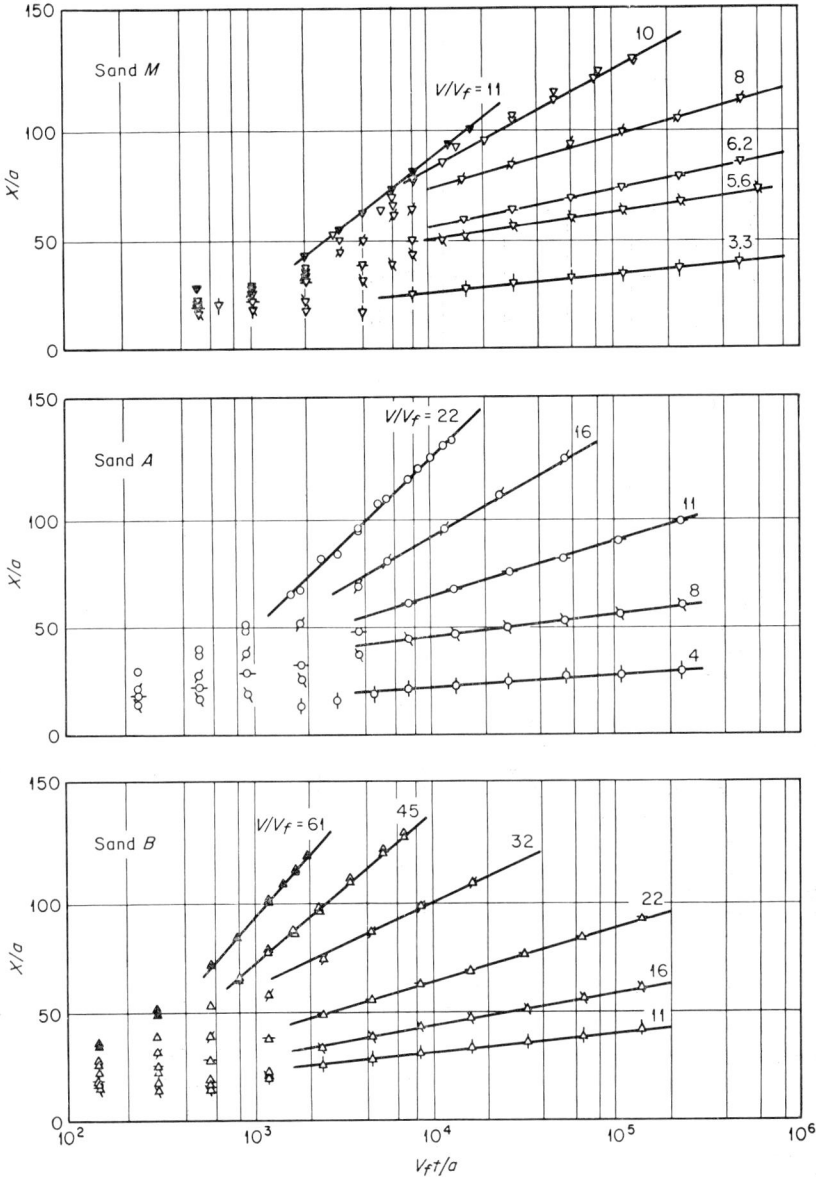

Fig. 18.17. Scour due to horizontal submerged jet. (*After Laursen.*[31])

show a separate curve for each value of V/V_f during the formative stage. Although the experiments apparently were not carried far enough to reach a limit in size, the logarithmic function of time suggests an asymptotic approach to the limit. It is the limiting, or equilibrium, extent of scour that is of practical importance. Under such circumstances, experiment and Eq. (18.74) indicate that the significant factors are the geometry of the structure, the flow pattern, and the sediment characteristics only; that is

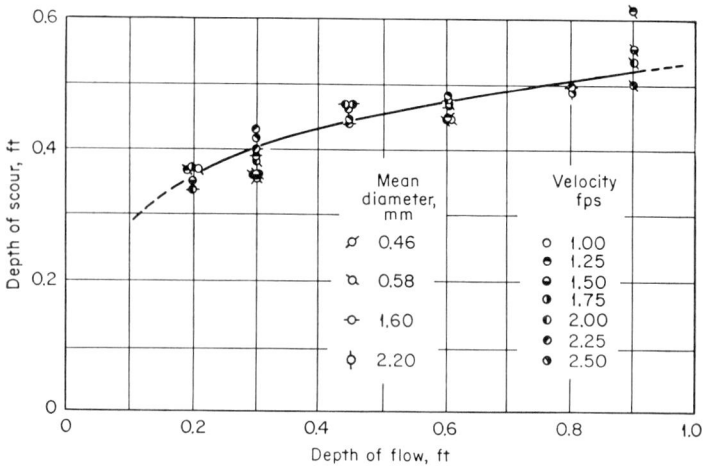

FIG. 18.18. Depth of scour around bridge piers.   (*After Laursen.*[31])

$$f_1(B) = \phi_2 \left(\frac{V}{V_f} \right) \tag{18.75}$$

In the usual case of flow from a hydraulic structure or around an obstruction such as a bridge pier where the complexities of the flow pattern preclude the use of a single variable to represent the kinematics of the flow, recourse is had to model studies. In this way scour patterns caused by different designs may be compared. An extensive study of the problem of scour around bridge piers by means of hydraulic models made by Laursen and Toch[31] included measurement of the scour depth for a rather wide range of mean velocities and sediment sizes. A significant general result was that the equilibrium depth of scour appeared to depend only upon the initial depth of flow and to be independent of both the mean velocity and the sediment size. These results are given in Fig. 18.18. The explanation given for this independence was that since the supply rate and the transport capacity in the scour hole were appreciable, the size of sediment will have little effect on the existing balance of transport capacities and the size of the scour hole will depend only on the flow pattern as defined by the boundary geometry. This conclusion is qualitatively corroborated by Eq. (18.71) pertaining to a long contraction, which shows that for a given boundary change as exemplified by the ratio b_1/b_2, the depth of scour depends only on the antecedent depth, even for appreciable values of τ_c/τ_1 (the smaller the ratio τ_c/τ_1, the greater is the transport rate).

In many structures, however, the supply of sediment is cut off, that is, $g(S) = 0$. The equilibrium, or limit, condition is that the transport rate in the scour hole is also zero. The extent of scour should then be a function of the erosive forces as determined by some characteristic velocity. In this case, also, the extent of scour is relatively independent of the sediment size. Blaisdell,[32] using the same sediment in two similar models—one three times as large as the other—found that the relative scour patterns were very nearly identical, whereas in other models of different design but of the same scale, the equilibrium scour pattern was considerably different. A general conclusion to be drawn from these studies is that an equilibrium scour pattern exists and its magnitude is primarily a function of the flow pattern as determined by the boundary geometry and initial energy. It is independent of the sediment properties provided that the initial-flow energy is sufficiently large to initiate movement of the particles.

18.14. Formation of Sediment Waves

One of the factors that affect the transport rate was the formation of sediment waves, or bars, on the channel bed. The mechanism by which sediment waves can be generated on the bed is not well understood. One concept suggested by Inglis[33] is that the waves are initiated by small irregularities in the bed which exist even if the bed is, on the average, a plane surface. A particle or small accumulation of particles projecting from the mean surface will give rise to a trailing vortex, the increased local velocities of which move more of the particles, which are already on the verge of movement. These tend to be deposited downstream out of the range of the initial vortex and form a new accumulation, which in turn serves to generate a new vortex. In the end, a series of ridges are formed which spread both laterally and longitudinally. If such a series of ripples are formed at various locations, their growth will tend to cover the entire bed. As the flow is increased, these ripples are reformed and assume wavelengths and amplitudes consistent with the flow characteristics.

Liu[34] ascribed the generation of ripples to the creation of a vortex sheet at the effective interface of the moving fluid and the movable bed. In the region near the bed where the velocity is high, the roll-up of the vortex will modify the configuration of the bed, which at that time is at the point of movement and hence is relatively unstable. The parameters that characterize both the properties of the sediment and the flow in the bed region were found to be u_*/V_f, which represents a ratio of the scouring force to the resisting force, and $u_* d_s/\nu$, the Reynolds number of the particle, which characterizes the flow. Data describing conditions for ripple formation, plotted in Fig. 18.19, show a high degree of correlation between various experiments. Superimposed on this plot is the mean curve developed by Shields to represent the critical tractive force taken from Fig. 18.6. It is apparent that the formation of ripples occurs almost simultaneously with the initiation of particle movement. Whatever the mechanism of ripple formation, whether due to an initial bed irregularity or to the instability of a vortex sheet at the interface, the results apparently can be correlated as in Fig. 18.19.

After the waves have been developed, observation indicates that the form, spacing, and speed are apparently governed by the velocity and transport rate and follow a particular sequence of changes as the flow is increased. This sequence was described previously. The phenomenon of sediment waves is an example of the operation of the equation of continuity defined by Eq. (18.4). When applied to the two-dimensional case over a region of the same order as the wavelength, it can be written as

$$\frac{\partial \eta}{\partial t} + \frac{\partial q_s}{\partial x} = 0 \qquad (18.76)$$

if η is the bed elevation with respect to some datum such as the mean elevation, and $\partial q_s/\partial x$ is the rate of change of transport rate with distance along the bed. If it is as-

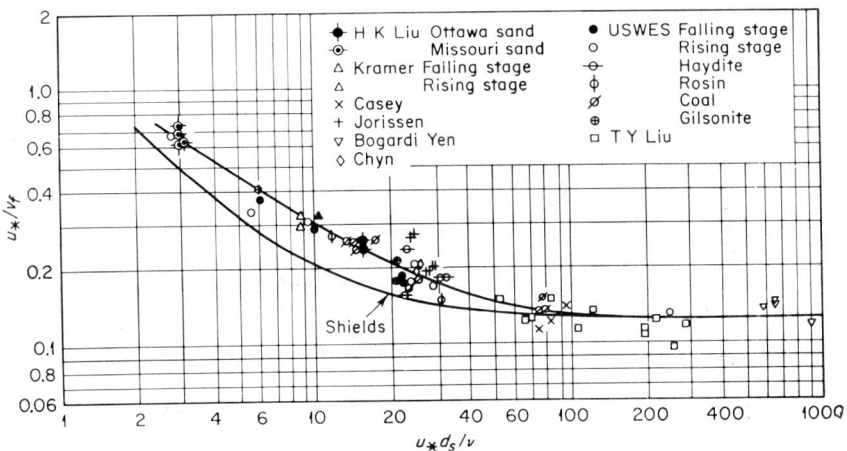

FIG. 18.19. The formation of bed waves in movable beds in open channels. (*After Liu.*[34])

sumed that the transport rate is proportional to the fluid velocity near the bed, Eq. (18.76) reduces to the Exner equation,

$$\frac{\partial \eta}{\partial t} + K \frac{\partial u}{\partial x} = 0 \tag{18.77}$$

The solution of Eq. (18.77) depends on establishing u as a function of x. Starting with the Inglis concept of ripple formation, Anderson[35] obtained a solution that related the relative wavelength to the Froude number of the flow in the form

$$\frac{2\pi d}{\lambda} \left[\tanh \frac{2\pi d}{\lambda} - \frac{2}{\sinh (4\pi d/\lambda)} \right] = \frac{gd}{\overline{U}^2} \tag{18.78}$$

if d is the depth, and λ is the wavelength. This solution indicates that the wavelength increases with velocity and hence with increased transport rate. For great depths or for wind-formed dunes, Eq. (18.78) reduces to

$$\lambda = 4\pi \frac{\overline{U}^2}{2g} \tag{18.79}$$

which shows that such waves depend upon velocity only. However, the velocity gradient near the ground has not been taken into account. Von Kármán[36] developed a similar equation from dimensional considerations in which

$$\lambda \simeq \sqrt{C_f} \frac{2U^2}{g} \tag{18.80}$$

if C_f is the friction coefficient of the wind with respect to the ground.

Little work has been done in relating the sediment wave amplitude to the flow. This property along with the wavelength is significant in establishing the resistance to flow offered by the bed waves. Since the wave shape, height, and length vary with the flow conditions, as does the rate of transportation, Einstein and Barbarossa[9] reasoned that the portion of the total resistance that is contributed by the bed waves should be a function of the same parameter that establishes the transport rate. This relation was expressed by

$$\frac{\overline{U}}{(gR'_bS_e)^{1/2}} = f(\psi) = f\left(\frac{\rho_s - \rho}{\rho} \frac{d_{35}}{R'_bS_e} \right) \tag{18.81}$$

Data from a number of rivers could be approximately correlated by this means.

REFERENCES

1. Lane, E. W.: Report of the Subcommittee on Sediment Terminology, *Trans. Am. Geophys. Union*, **28**:936–938 (December, 1947).
2. Subcommittee on Sedimentation Inter-Agency Committee on Water Research: Some Fundamentals of Particle Size Analysis, *Univ. Minn., St. Anthony Falls Hydraulic Lab., Rept.* 12, December, 1957.
3. Otto, George H.: A Modified Logarithmic Probability Graph for the Interpretation of Mechanical Analyses of Sediments, *J. Sediment. Petrol.*, **9**(2):62–76 (August, 1939).
4. McNown, J., and P-N. Lin: Sediment Concentration and Fall Velocity, *Proc. Second Midwestern Conf. on Fluid Mech.*, Ohio State University, 1952, pp. 401–411.
5. Einstein, H. A., A. G. Anderson, and J. W. Johnson: A Distinction between Bed Load and Suspended Load in Natural Streams, *Trans. Am. Geophys. Union*, **21**(2):628–633 (1940).
6. Laursen, E. M.: Observations on the Nature of Scour, *Proc. Fifth Hydraulics Conf.*, State University of Iowa, June 9–11, 1952.
7. Gilbert, G. K.: The Transportation of Debris by Running Water, *U.S. Geol. Survey Prof. Paper* 86, 1914.
8. Kalinske, A. A.: Criteria for Determining Sand-transport by Surface-creep and Saltation, *Trans. Am. Geophys. Union*, **23**:639–643 (1942).
9. Einstein, H. A., and N. Barbarossa: River Channel Roughness, *Trans. ASCE*. **117**:1121–1146 (1952).

10. Einstein, H. A., and R. B. Banks: Fluid Resistance of Composite Roughness, *Trans. Am. Geophys. Union*, **31**:603–610 (1950).
11. Shields, A.: Anwendung der Aehnlichkeits Mechanik und der Turbulenzforschung auf die Geschiebebewegung, *Mitt. preuss. Versuchanstalt Wasserbau u. Schiffbau*, 1936.
12. White, C. M.: The Equilibrium of Grains on the Bed of a Stream, *Proc. Roy. Soc. (London)* **A174**:322–338 (1940).
13. Lane, E. W., and E. J. Carlson: Some Factors Affecting the Stability of Canals Constructed in Coarse Granular Materials, *Proc. Minn. Intern. Hydraulics. Conv.*, IAHR-ASCE: pp. 37–48, September, 1953.
14. DuBoys, P.: Le Rhône et les rivières à lit affouillable, *Ann. ponts et chaussées*, ser. 5, **18**:141–195 (1879).
15. Straub, L. G.: The Missouri River, 73d Cong., 2d Sess., H. D. 238, p. 1135, 1935.
16. Meyer-Peter, E., and R. Müller: Formulas for Bed-load Transport, *Proc. Third Meeting Intern. Assoc. Hydraulic Research*, Stockholm, 1948, pp. 39–64.
17. Kalinske, A. A.: Movement of Sediment as Bed in Rivers, *Trans. Am. Geophys. Union*, **28**:615–620 (1947).
18. Einstein, H. A.: The Bed-load Function for Sediment Transportation in Open Channel Flow, *U.S. Dept. Agr. Tech. Bull.* 1026, 1950.
19. Chien, Ning: The Present Status of Research on Sediment Transport, *Trans. ASCE*, **122**(2824):833–884 (1956).
20. Einstein, H. A.: Bed-load Transportation in Mountain Creek, *U.S. Dept. Agr. Tech. Publ.* 55 SCS, 1944.
21. Colby, B. R., and C. H. Hembree: Computations of Total Sediment Discharge, Niabrara River near Cody, Wyoming, *U.S. Geol. Survey, Water Supply Paper* 1357, 1955.
22. Hunt, J. N.: The Turbulent Transport of Suspended Sediment in Open Channels, *Proc. Roy. Soc. (London)*, **A224**(1158):322–335 (1954).
23. Vanoni, V. A.: A Summary of Sediment Transportation Mechanics, *Proc. Third Midwestern Conf. on Fluid Mech.*, 1953, pp. 129–160.
24. Lane, E. W., and A. A. Kalinske: Engineering Calculations of Suspended Sediment, *Trans. Am. Geophys. Union*, **22**:603–607 (1941).
25. Bagnold, R. A.: "The Physics of Blown Sand and Desert Dunes," p. 265, Morrow, New York, 1943.
26. Zingg, A. W.: Wind Tunnel Studies of the Movement of Sedimentary Material, *Proc. Fifth Hydraulics Conf.*, State University of Iowa, 1952, pp. 111–135.
27. Chepil, W. S.: Dynamics of Wind Erosion. II Initiation of Soil Movement, *Soil Sci.*, **60**:475–480 (December, 1945).
28. Durand, R.: Basic Relationships of the Transportation of Solids in Pipes: Experimental Research, *Proc. Minn. Intern. Hydraulics Conv.*, Minneapolis, September, 1953, pp. 89–103.
29. Craven, J. P.: The Transportation of Sand in Pipes: Full-pipe Flow, *Proc. Fifth Hydraulics Conf.*, State University of Iowa, June, 1952, pp. 67–76.
30. Ambrose, H. H.: The Transportation of Sand in Pipes: Free Surface Flow, *Proc. Fifth Hydraulics Conf.*, State University of Iowa, June, 1952, pp. 77–86.
31. Laursen, E. M., and A. Toch: A Generalized Model Study of Scour around Bridge Piers and Abutments, *Proc. Minn. Intern. Hydraulics Conv.*, Minneapolis, September, 1953, pp. 123–131.
32. Blaisdell, F. W.: The Use of Sand Beds for Comparing Relative Stilling Basin Performance, *Trans. Am. Geophys. Union*, pt. II, 1942, pp. 633–639.
33. Inglis, C. C.: Bed Ripples and Bed Dunes, *Central Water Power Irrigation and Navigation Research Sta. Research Publ.* 13, Poona, India, 1949, pp. 459–467.
34. Liu, H. K.: Discussion of Present Status of Research on Sediment Transport by Ning Chien, *Trans. ASCE*, **121**:877–881 (1956).
35. Anderson, A. G.: The Characteristics of Sediment Waves Formed by Flow in Open Channels, *Proc. Third Midwestern Conf. on Fluid Mech.*, University of Minnesota, Minneapolis, 1953, pp. 379–395.
36. Von Kármán, T.: Sand Ripples in the Desert, *Technion Yearbook*, 1947.

Section 19

TURBOMACHINERY

By

THEODORE BAUMEISTER, *Columbia University in the City of New York, New York*

19–1

TURBOMACHINERY

19.1. Introduction

The application of fluid-dynamic principles to the design of fluid-acceleration machinery, or turbomachinery, involves an understanding of jet and vane relationships and their modification as imposed by the restrictions of commercially acceptable apparatus. The broad principles are adapted in the following pages to the performance of pumps, fans, compressors, propellers, turbines, and couplings, with emphasis on the characteristic curves, design details, equipment proportions, and the essential behavior of real machinery.

The reader is referred to Secs. 9 to 11 for further information on boundary-layer growth, turbulence, and separation and stall phenomena of importance in design of turbomachinery.

19.2. Notation

a	area, ft^2
ahp	air horsepower
C	coefficient
C_c	contraction coefficient
C_d	discharge coefficient $= C_c C_v$
C_D	drag coefficient
C_H	head coefficient
C_L	lift coefficient
C_M	torque coefficient
C_N	nozzle coefficient $= C_v{}^2$
C_{nP}	specific speed, power basis, dimensionless
C_{nQ}	specific speed, capacity basis, dimensionless
C_P	power coefficient
C_Q	capacity coefficient
C_T	thrust coefficient
C_v	velocity coefficient $= \sqrt{C_N}$
c_p	specific heat, constant pressure
c_v	specific heat, constant volume
D	(1) diameter, ft
	(2) drag, lb
d	density
E	energy, ft-lb/sec
E_F	fluid energy, ft-lb/sec
E_R	rotor energy, ft-lb/sec
F	force, lb
F_i	impulse force
F_r	reaction force
$\mathbf{F}$	Froude number
f	(1) friction factor
	(2) function
G	weight flow, lb/sec
g	gravitational acceleration, ft/sec^2 (32.2)
H	head, ft

h	(1) enthalpy, Btu/lb
	(2) head, in. of water
hp	horsepower
K	constant
kw	kilowatts
kwh	kilowatthours
L	(1) length, ft
	(2) lift, lb
M	torque, moment, lb-ft
M	Mach number
m	(1) mass, slugs
	(2) mean hydraulic depth, ft
N	(1) speed, rpm
	(2) number of stages
N_s	specific speed, capacity basis $= 17,200 C_{nQ}$
N'_s	specific speed, power basis $= 270 C_{nP}$
n	speed, rps
P	(1) power, ft-lb/sec
	(2) pressure, psfa
	(3) pitch
p	pressure, psia
Q	(1) capacity, cfs
	(2) heat, Btu
	(3) discharge, gpm
R	(1) gas constant, $PV = RT$
	(2) radius, ft
R_p	ratio of pressures
R	Reynolds number
r	radius, ft
S	surface
s	(1) entropy, Btu/(lb)(deg)
	(2) normal component of absolute velocity v, fps
shp	shaft horsepower
T	(1) temperature, abs, °R
	(2) thrust, lb
t	(1) temperature, scale, °F
	tangential component of absolute velocity v, fps
u	absolute tip, bucket, rotor velocity, fps
V	volume
$\overline{V}$	specific volume, ft³/lb
v	(1) velocity, fps
	(2) absolute velocity (fluid and casing), fps
W	work, ft-lb
w	relative velocity (fluid and rotor), fps
$\bar{w}$	weight density, lb/ft³ $= \rho g$
whp	water horsepower
Z	elevational head, ft
α	(1) vane angle
	(2) angle of attack
β	nozzle angle
Δ	increment
η	efficiency
κ	isentropic exponent $= c_p/c_v$
μ	absolute viscosity, lb-sec/ft²
π	3.14159
ρ	mass density, slugs/ft³
σ	cavitation factor

ϕ (1) function of
       (2) speed ratio $= u_1/v_1$
ω angular velocity, radians/sec

SUBSCRIPTS

i, f initial and final for a machine; generic
1, 2   (1) entering and leaving a runner or impeller
       (2) heel and tip
0   theoretical or ideal values
i impulse
p primary
r reaction
s (1) static
       (2) secondary
t (1) total
       (2) tangential
v velocity

PRINCIPLES

19.3. Theoretical Jet and Vane Relations—Impulse and Reaction Force

The force F of a jet, by Newton's second law of motion, is

$$F = \rho a v^2 = \frac{\bar{w}}{g} a v^2 = \frac{Gv}{g} \tag{19.1}$$

and the kinetic energy ΔE_F of the fluid is

$$\Delta E_F = \frac{Gv^2}{2g} \tag{19.2}$$

If the fluid issues from a nozzle as in Fig. 19.1, with zero or negligible velocity of approach and final velocity v, the energy can also be expressed in terms of the impulse force F_i as

$$\Delta E_F = F_i \frac{v - 0}{2} \tag{19.3}$$

in which F_i is from Eq. (19.1). By Newton's third law of motion there is an equal and opposite reaction force F_r such that

$$F_r = -F_i = -\frac{Gv}{g} \tag{19.4}$$

19.4. Work Done by Jet Impinging on Moving Vanes

The force, or thrust, acting on a series of moving vanes (Fig. 19.2) is

$$\text{Force} = \frac{Gv}{g} - \frac{Gu}{g} = \frac{G}{g}(v - u) \tag{19.5}$$

if v and u are the absolute jet and vane velocities, respectively. The work done on the vanes (or the energy absorbed by the rotor), ΔE_R, is

$$\Delta E_R = \frac{G}{g}(v - u)u \tag{19.6}$$

From Eq. (19.6), ΔE_R will be zero when $u = 0$ and also when $u = v$. ΔE_R will be a maximum when $u = v/2$; that is,

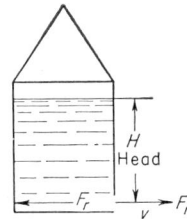

FIG. 19.1. Water escaping from a swinging bucket to illustrate impulse and reaction forces of the issuing jet.

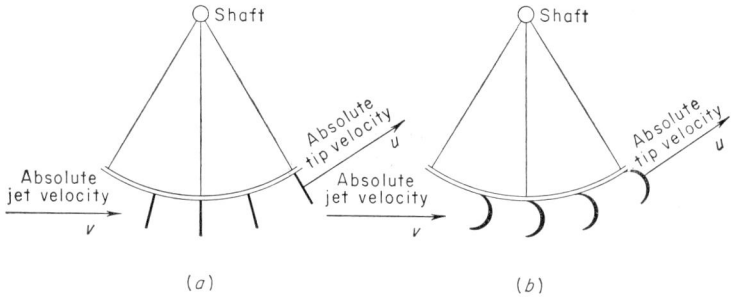

Fig. 19.2. Jet impinging on a series of vanes: (a) Flat vanes, (b) curved vanes.

$$\Delta E_R = \frac{G}{g}\left(v - \frac{v}{2}\right)\frac{v}{2} = \frac{1}{2}\frac{Gv^2}{2g} \tag{19.7}$$

and the efficiency,

$$\eta = \frac{1}{2}\frac{Gv^2/2g}{Gv^2/2g} = 0.5 \tag{19.8}$$

This is the maximum efficiency obtainable with the simple impulse principle and a series of flat blades (Fig. 19.2a). With complete (180°) reversal of the jet (Fig. 19.2b), the impulse force is $(G/g)\,(v - u)$ acting through the first 90° of deflection, followed by a reaction force in the same direction, and is $(G/g)(v - u)$ for the second 90° of deflection. The aggregate force on the rotor is

$$\text{Force} = 2\frac{G}{g}(v - u) \tag{19.9}$$

the energy absorbed is

$$\Delta E_R = 2\frac{G}{g}(v - u)u \tag{19.10}$$

and the efficiency, with $u = v/2$, is

$$\eta = \frac{2\dfrac{G}{g}\left(v - \dfrac{v}{2}\right)\dfrac{v}{2}}{Gv^2/2g} = 1.0 \tag{19.11}$$

With complete reversal of the jet and effective utilization of both the impulse and reaction forces, the efficiency can thus approach 100 per cent as a limit.

19.5. Work Done by Reaction of a Jet from a Moving Nozzle

If the nozzle is free to move, as in the Barker's mill of Fig. 19.3, instead of fixed in position, as in Fig. 19.2, the reaction force is used directly to turn the shaft on which the nozzle is mounted. The vector difference between the relative jet velocity w and the absolute nozzle velocity u is the absolute jet velocity v, and reaction force F_r is

$$F_r = \frac{Gv}{g} = \frac{G(w - u)}{g} \tag{19.12}$$

The rotor energy ΔE_R is

$$\Delta E_R = \frac{G(w - u)}{g}u \tag{19.13}$$

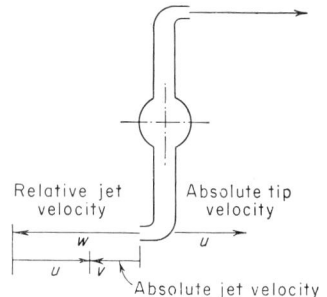

Fig. 19.3. Barker's mill; reaction-type jet device.

and the fluid energy ΔE_F is

$$\Delta E_F = \frac{G(w^2 - u^2)}{2g} \qquad (19.14)$$

The efficiency η is the ratio of these two quantities, or

$$\eta = \frac{2u}{w + u} \qquad (19.15)$$

This will be a maximum ($\eta = 1.0$) when the residual absolute velocity v is zero or when the jet velocity is equal to the nozzle velocity.

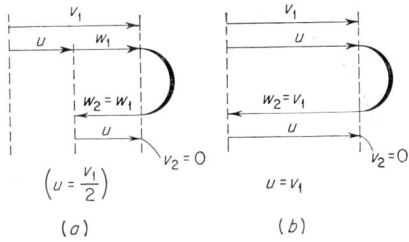

FIG. 19.4. Velocity vector diagrams for idealized (a) impulse- and (b) reaction-turbine blading; 180° jet reversal.

19.6. Vector Relationships for Impulse and Reaction Principles

The analyses given for the devices of Figs. 19.2 and 19.3 indicate some confusion in the definition of *impulse* and *reaction*, as applied to turbines. Half the work done in the curved vane device of Fig. 19.2b is by impulse and half by reaction. In the Barker mill of Fig. 19.3, all the work done is by reaction. The distinguishing feature of the latter is the presence of a moving nozzle. In accepted turbine practice, a reaction turbine is one which has moving nozzles, and an impulse turbine has stationary nozzles only. A reaction unit is thus characterized by a pressure drop and consequent acceleration of the fluid across the moving element. It may also have stationary nozzles for the fluid to reach the moving element, as in the customary axial-flow reaction steam turbine. The ideal vector relationships for the case of frictionless flow with 180° reversal of the jet, in the typical axial-flow construction, is shown in Fig. 19.4, where, for zero residual absolute velocity v_2, the blade speed is one-half the jet speed for the true impulse turbine and equal to the jet speed for the reaction turbine. The ideal reaction stage must have a blade speed $\sqrt{2}$ times that of the ideal impulse stage to do the same amount of work.

Figure 19.5 illustrates the more realistic vector relationships as experienced on axial flow turbines where the jet reversal is less than 180°. In the construction of these diagrams, the flow is frictionless and the fluid is accelerated in a stationary nozzle to an absolute velocity v and approaches the wheel at a nozzle angle β_1. The entrance angle α_1 must accommodate the relative jet velocity w_1 and the absolute blade velocity u_1. The fluid moves through the wheel passage without friction to give a right triangle for the exit vector diagram where the absolute exit fluid velocity v_2 is a minimum and the angle $\beta_2 = 90°$. The same exit triangle is employed for the three types of

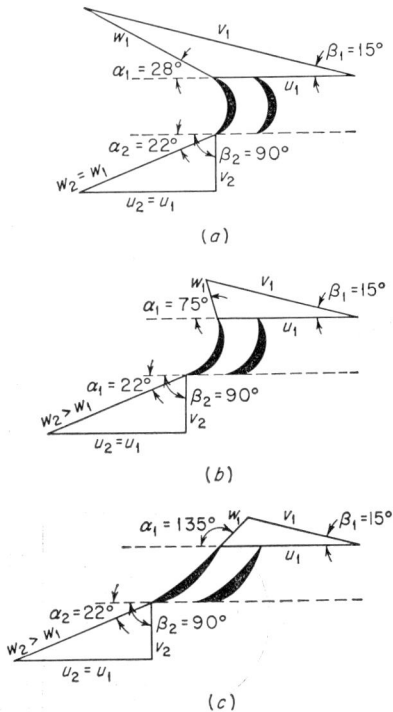

FIG. 19.5. Vector diagrams for (a) impulse- and (b and c) reaction-turbine blading; jet reversal less than 180°; speed ratio equals 0.49 for (a), 0.88 for (b), and 1.22 for (c).

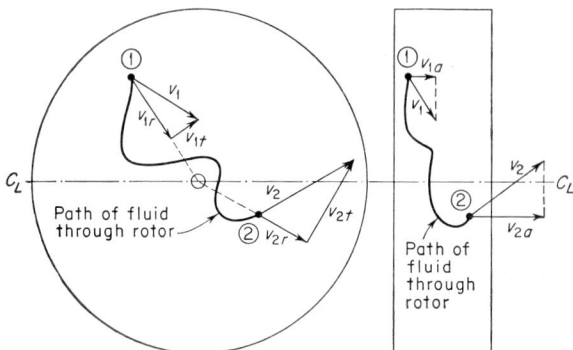

FIG. 19.6. General case of fluid path through a moving wheel: (1) is point where fluid enters and (2) where fluid leaves.

blading illustrated in Fig. 19.5, with $\beta_2 = 90°$, $\alpha_2 = 22°$, $u_2 = u_1$, values constant for all cases. Likewise, the entrance nozzle angle β_1 is fixed at 15°, but the entering absolute velocity magnitude v_1 is altered to accommodate the three entering blade angles α_1 of 28, 75, and 135°, with suitable values of relative velocity w_1. There are considered to be no friction losses. In Fig. 19.5a, the conditions of a true impulse turbine are illustrated with all fluid acceleration in the fixed nozzles, $w_2 = w_1$, and a speed ratio $u_1/v_1 = 0.49$ with a jet reversal of 143°. Figure 19.5b is representative of some reaction steam-turbine stages where the entrance vane angle α_1 has been increased to 75°, there is a pressure drop across the moving blades (nozzles) so that $w_2 > w_1$ and approximately equal to v_1, and the speed ratio $u_1/v_1 = 0.88$. Figure 19.5c illustrates the conditions of the propeller-type hydraulic runner where the entrance vane angle α_1 has been increased to 135°, there is greater acceleration across the moving blades, and the speed ratio $u_1/v_1 = 1.22$. These three vector cases demonstrate the latitude available in the selection of velocity relations and the wide variation in the extent of reaction which can be employed.

19.7. Euler Equation of Energy Transfer

If, in Fig. 19.6, fluid enters the rotor at point 1 with absolute velocity v_1 and leaves at point 2 with absolute velocity v_2, then, regardless of the path through the rotor, the change in angular momentum between entrance and exit will theoretically determine the work done by the fluid on the moving rotor, if a prime mover, and the work done on the fluid by the moving rotor, if a pump. Under conditions of steady, uniform, continuous flow and turning speed, for a pump or fan,

$$\text{Change in momentum} = \frac{G}{g}(v_2 - v_1) \tag{19.16}$$

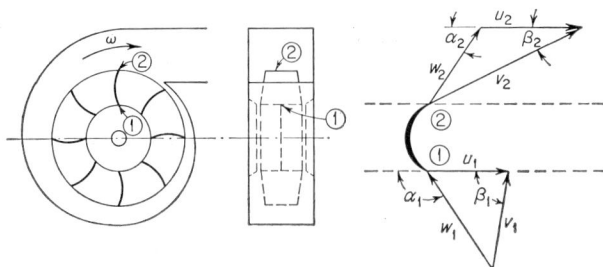

FIG. 19.7. Vector diagrams for radial-flow pump or fan (centrifugal type): (1) entrance, (2) exit.

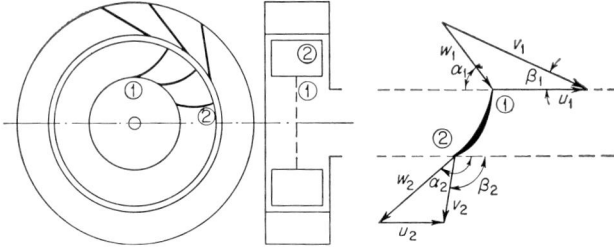

FIG. 19.8. Vector diagrams for radial-inward-flow (Francis) type of turbine: (1) entrance,
(2) exit.

and

$$\text{Change in moment of momentum} = \frac{G}{g}(r_2 v_{2t} - r_1 v_{1t}) \qquad (19.17)$$

in which v_{1t} and v_{2t} are the tangential components of velocity and r_1 and r_2 are the radii.
The work done by the rotor, ΔE_R, with angular velocity ω, is

$$E_R = \frac{G\omega}{g}(r_2 v_{2t} - r_1 v_{1t}) \qquad (19.18)$$

or, as $u = \omega r$,　　　　　　　$$\Delta E_R = \frac{G}{g}(u_2 v_{2t} - u_1 v_{1t}) \qquad (19.19)$$

This is the Euler equation, applicable to all fluid-acceleration-machinery performance.
If applied to a turbine or other prime mover, the work will be negative and

$$-\Delta E_R = \frac{G}{g}(u_1 v_{1t} - u_2 v_{2t}) \qquad (19.20)$$

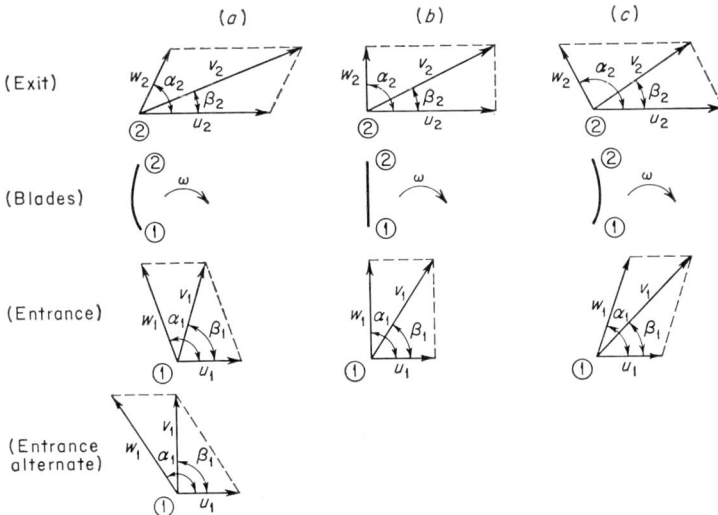

FIG. 19.9. Vector diagrams for various types of radial-flow (centrifugal) pumps and fans:
(a) forward-curved, (b) radial, (c) backward-curved blades; (1) entrance (heel), (2) exit (tip).

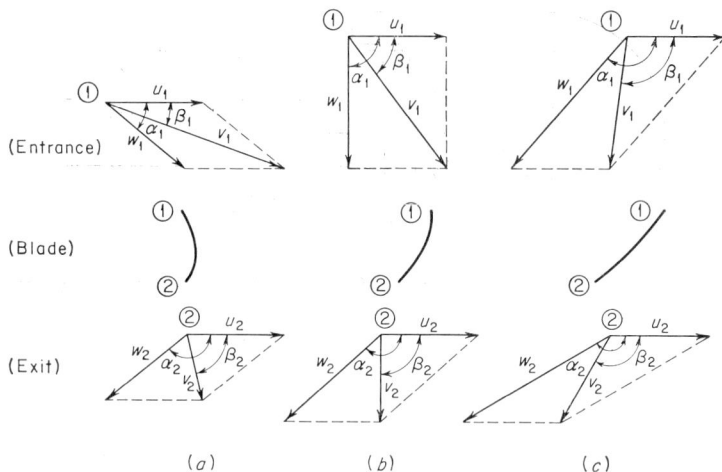

FIG. 19.10. Vector diagrams for various types of axial-flow impulse turbines: (1) entrance, (2) exit.

The Euler equation can be applied to cases of two-dimensional flow, as in Fig. 19.7 for a centrifugal pump or fan, with outward radial flow, and Fig. 19.8 for an inward radial-flow turbine.   Many factors limit the utility of the Euler equation in the performance of real machines, to wit, absence of two-dimensional flow patterns; substitution of pulsating nonuniform flow patterns in passages; flow paths not rigorously defined by nozzle angles, blade angles, and vectors; and effects of fluid viscosity, turbulence, friction, shock, impact, eddies, whirls, internal leakage, recirculation, and all like phenomena of fluid dynamics.   The complexities are so great that they defy analysis, and the Euler equation must be used with discretion.

In the use of vector diagrams and the Euler Eqs. (19.19) and (19.20), confusion can be largely avoided by the employment of vector parallelograms as illustrated in Figs. 19.9 and 19.10, where α is the angle between the absolute bucket velocity u and the relative velocity w, and β is the angle between the absolute bucket velocity u and the absolute fluid velocity v. Angles may often, accordingly, be greater than 90°, but adherence to these definitions should avoid confusion.

19.8. Euler Equation as Applied to Radial-flow Fans and Pumps

From the trigonometry of Fig. 19.9, the Euler Eq. (19.19) for rotor energy resolves to

$$\Delta E_R = \frac{G}{g}\left(\frac{u_2{}^2 - u_1{}^2}{2} + \frac{v_2{}^2 - v_1{}^2}{2} + \frac{w_1{}^2 - w_2{}^2}{2}\right) \tag{19.21}$$

If the flow G is made equal to 1 lb/sec, then the rotor energy from the equation becomes foot-pounds per pound, or in reduced dimensions, the theoretical head in feet, so that

$$\text{Theoretical head} = \left(\frac{u_2{}^2 - u_1{}^2}{2g} + \frac{v_2{}^2 - v_1{}^2}{2g} + \frac{w_1{}^2 - w_2{}^2}{2g}\right) \tag{19.22}$$

The first and third terms represent the gain in static energy on passage through the wheel, and the second term represents the gain in kinetic energy, which may be partially converted to the static form in the surrounding casing.   These terms can be related to the phenomena of the forced vortex and free radial flow.   Further, if the entrance vector diagram shown as alternate (Fig. 19.9a) with no velocity of spin at entrance to the rotor, then the tangential component v_{1t} of the absolute velocity vector v_1 becomes zero and Eq. (19.20) resolves to

$$\text{Theoretical head} = \frac{u_2 v_{2t}}{g} \qquad (19.23)$$

19.9. Euler Equation as Applied to Axial-flow Impulse Turbines

From the trigonometry of Fig. 19.10, the Euler Eq. (19.20) for rotor energy per pound of fluid flowing resolves for true axial flow ($u_1 = u_2$) to the form

$$-\Delta E_R = \frac{1}{2g}\left[(v_1{}^2 - v_2{}^2) + (w_2{}^2 - w_1{}^2) \right] \qquad (19.24)$$

The work done on the rotor is made up of the change in kinetic energy and the reaction effect of the fluid. It may be further developed to the form

$$-\Delta E_R = \frac{u}{g}\,(w_1 \cos \alpha_1 - w_2 \cos \alpha_2) \qquad (19.25)$$

If the blading is symmetrical $\alpha_1 = 180 - \alpha_2$, and with no friction and no acceleration in the blade passages,

$$-\Delta E_R = \frac{2u}{g}\,(v_1 \cos \beta_1 - u) \qquad (19.26)$$

By differentiation of this expression with respect to u, the maximum work output will obtain when

$$u = \frac{v_1 \cos \beta_1}{2} \qquad (19.27)$$

and substitution in Eq. (19.26) gives

$$-\Delta E_{R\,\text{max}} = \frac{v_1{}^2 \cos^2 \beta_1}{2g} \qquad (19.28)$$

As the energy input is $v_1{}^2/2g$,

$$\text{Maximum blading efficiency} = \cos^2 \beta_1 \qquad (19.29)$$

Or, ideally, with an axial-flow impulse turbine with symmetrical blades, the efficiency is solely a function of the nozzle angle; the smaller the angle, the higher the efficiency. The same conclusion can be demonstrated for the ideal Parsons-type reaction turbine.

19.10. Characteristic Curves

The over-all performance of turbomachinery is most conveniently and practically expressed by graphs, generally called characteristic curves. These curves may be plotted on many alternative bases, but they must relate items such as (1) speed, (2) flow rate, (3) pressure change, (4) power, and (5) fluid properties. Theoretically, it should be possible to develop algebraic relationships, like the Euler equation, among these variables and all the design elements which influence equipment performance. Practically, however, this is not possible, and the graph or characteristic is the realistic way

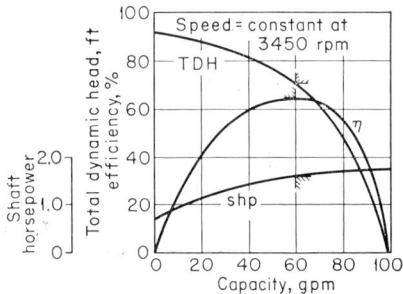

FIG. 19.11. Characteristics of a general-service centrifugal pump: capacity, 60 gpm; head, 70 ft; speed, 3450 rpm; $N_s = 1150$; power, 1.6 shp.

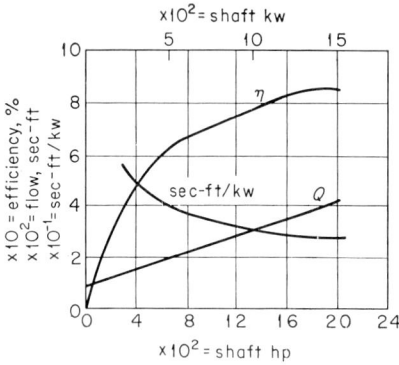

FIG. 19.12.   Characteristics of a hydraulic turbine: head, 50 ft; power, 2000 shp; speed, 240 rpm, $N_s = 80$; speed ratio, 0.62.

of expressing the relationships. Graphical methods thus supplant algebraic equations for definition of the relationships in mathematical terms. The basis of plotting varies with the kind of equipment because experience has demonstrated preferred bases for each type of machine. Figures 19.11 and 19.12 thus show typically the characteristics for (1) the centrifugal pump and (2) the hydraulic turbine. It is essential to recognize that characteristic curves are exactly definitive and that it is impossible to make a turbomachine operate at any point not on its characteristic curves.

For a centrifugal pump (Fig. 19.11), the standard graph shows capacity (gpm) as the independent variable with head, power (shp), and efficiency as dependent variables all at constant speed (rpm) and with

cold water ($< 85°$F).

For a hydraulic turbine (Fig. 19.12), the standard graph shows power (shp) as the independent variable with water flow (sec-ft), efficiency, and water consumption (sec-ft/kw) as dependent variables, all at constant head and constant speed (rpm).

19.11. Laws of Performance

There are several relationships, or laws, which permit the data of the characteristics to be adapted to other speeds or sizes of units. These laws are summarized in Table 19.1. They apply, ideally, to a given point on the efficiency curve, e.g., peak efficiency. The first column shows the influence of speed n on the capacity Q, head H, and power P for a given unit. The second column shows the influence of size (measured by wheel diameter D) on an entire series of similar or homologous units when operating at constant speed (rpm).

19.12. Coefficients of Performance

The six laws of Table 19.1 can be combined to give a series of coefficients of performance which can, for convenience, be made dimensionless by selection of a suitable consistent system of units as follows:

Capacity coefficient:
$$C_Q = \frac{Q}{nD^3} \tag{19.30}$$

Head coefficient:
$$C_H = \frac{Hg}{n^2D^2} \tag{19.31}$$

Power coefficient
$$C_P = \frac{Pg}{\bar{w}n^3D^5} \tag{19.32}$$

Table **19.1**. Laws of Performance

	For a given unit	For a series of similar units (at the same rpm or rps)
Capacity...............	$Q \propto n$	$Q \propto D^3$
Head..................	$H \propto n^2$	$H \propto D^2$
Power.................	$P \propto n^3$	$P \propto D^5$

If the D term is eliminated between Eqs. (19.30) and (19.31), a coefficient called specific speed C_{nQ} (on the volume basis) results, or

$$C_{nQ} = \sqrt{\frac{C_Q}{C_H{}^{1.5}}} = \frac{nQ^{0.5}}{H^{0.75}g^{0.75}} \qquad (19.33)$$

If D is eliminated between Eqs. (19.31) and (19.32), another specific speed coefficient, C_{nP} (on the power basis) results, or

$$C_{nP} = \sqrt{\frac{C_P}{C_H{}^{2.5}}} = \frac{nP^{0.5}}{\bar{w}^{0.5}H^{1.25}g^{0.75}} \qquad (19.34)$$

In current American engineering practice these dimensionless coefficients are not generally used but hybrid units are employed for C_{nQ} and C_{nP}, respectively, as

$$N_s = \frac{\text{rpm} \times \text{gpm}^{0.5}}{\text{head}^{0.75}} \qquad \text{for pumps} \qquad (19.35)$$

where $N_s = 17{,}200\,C_{nQ}$

and
$$N'_s = \frac{\text{rpm} \times \text{shp}^{0.5}}{\text{head}^{1.25}} \qquad \text{for hydraulic turbines} \qquad (19.36)$$

where $N'_s = 270\,C_{nP}$

19.13. Speed Ratio

Another term, speed ratio ϕ, is frequently used and is defined as

$$\phi = \frac{u}{\sqrt{2gH}} = 2.22\sqrt{\frac{1}{C_H}} \qquad (19.37)$$

19.14. Dimensionless Coefficients

The actual characteristics (Figs. 19.11 and 19.12) can be applied to an entire series of similar units by expressing performance on the dimensionless-coefficient basis (Figs. 19.13 and 19.14). By the principles of dynamic similarity, it can be demonstrated, for example, for a series of similar pumps or fans, that

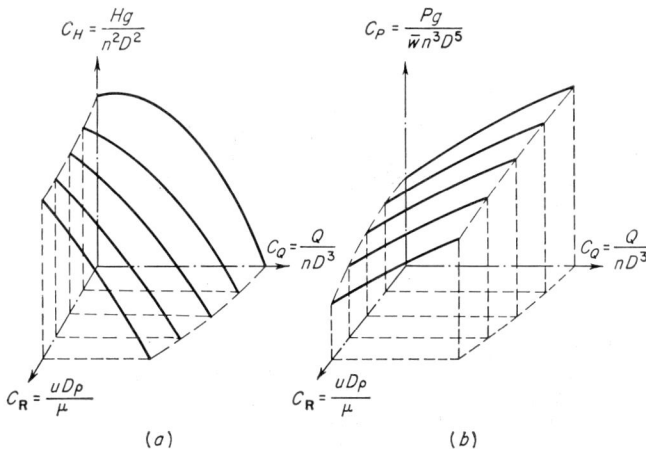

Fig. 19.13. Dimensionless-coefficient characteristics of a series of similar centrifugal pumps plotted on three coordinate bases; (a) head, (b) horsepower.

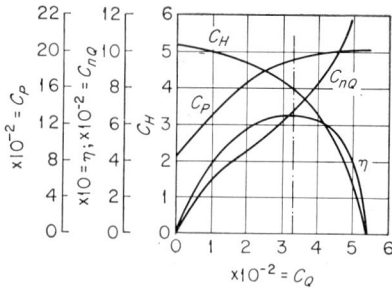

FIG. 19.14. Dimensionless-coefficient characteristics of a general-service centrifugal pump (cf. Fig. 19.11).

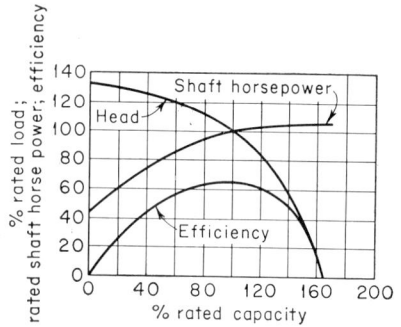

FIG. 19.15. Percentage characteristics of a general-service centrifugal pump (cf. Fig. 19.11).

$$Q = \phi(D^a n^b H^c \rho^d \mu^e g^f) \tag{19.38}$$

$$C_Q = \frac{Q}{nD^3} = \phi\left(\frac{Hg}{n^2D^2}\right)\left(\frac{\mu}{nD^2\rho}\right) \tag{19.39}$$

$$P = \phi'\,(Q^a D^b n^c H^d \rho^e \mu^f g^g) \tag{19.40}$$

and

$$C_P = \frac{P}{\rho n^3 D^5} = \frac{Pg}{\bar{w}n^3D^5} = \phi'\left(\frac{Q}{nD^3}\right)\left(\frac{Hg}{n^2D^2}\right)\left(\frac{\mu}{nD^2\rho}\right) \tag{19.41}$$

In Eqs. (19.39) and (19.41), the term Hg/n^2D^2 is the head coefficient C_H and the term $\mu/nD^2\rho$ is the Reynolds number. A three-dimensional plot (Fig. 19.13) shows these relations graphically for a representative series of similar pumps. The usual characteristic curves (Figs. 19.11, 19.12, and 19.14) are plotted in a single plane and represent the projection of a locus on the surfaces of graphs like Fig. 19.13 on that plane. These projections presuppose the applicability of the fluid-acceleration-machinery laws of Table 19.1. When their applicability is no longer rigorously or practically acceptable, then the Reynolds criterion must be incorporated and a three-dimensional plot (Fig. 19.13) or a series of characteristics at different speeds (Fig. 19.18) substituted.

19.15. Percentage Characteristics

Another form of plotting the characteristic curves for a series of similar units is the percentage basis as in Fig. 19.15. The values obtaining at the point of maximum efficiency are called the rated, or 100 per cent, values, and all other performances are referred to them as a base. These percentage characteristics are useful in the comparison of relative, rather than absolute, performance criteria. Sometimes the relationships are based on shutoff or wide-open conditions rather than peak efficiency.

CENTRIFUGAL PUMPS

19.16. Types

A centrifugal pump is essentially a rotor with blades disposed more or less radially and mounted to turn in a *volute* (spiral) or concentric (*diffuser*) casing (Figs. 19.16 and 19.17). The fluid enters axially through the eye of the impeller (single or double inlet) and is accelerated centrifugally through the blade passages into the volute or diffuser where kinetic energy is converted to static pressure energy. The impeller may be *open* or *closed* (shrouds); the pump shaft may be *vertical* or *horizontal;* the pump may be *single-* or *multistage* (Figs. 19.16 and 19.17); casings may be *split* (Fig 19.16), *drum-type* (Fig.

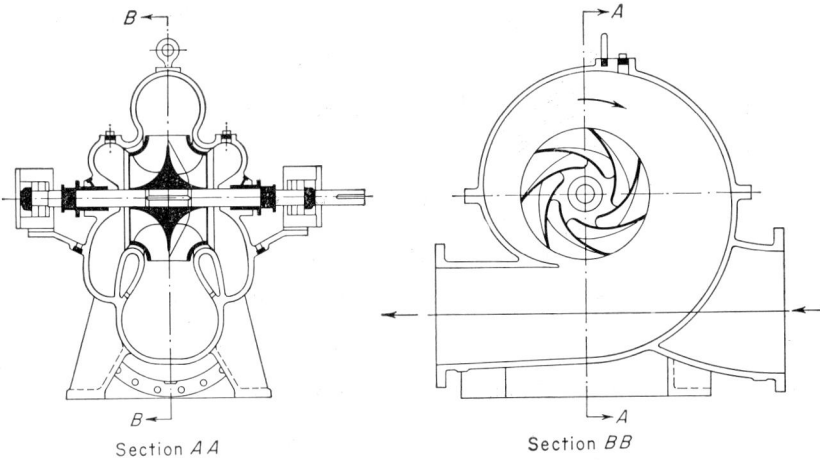

Section *AA*   Section *BB*

Fig. 19.16. Sections showing single-stage, double-inlet, volute-type centrifugal pump.

19.17), or *ring-type;* the pump may be *right-* or *left-hand* (as viewed from the driven end); *discharge* and *suction* connections may be *horizontal* or *vertical, bottom* or *top, upward* or *downward.*

19.17. Performance Terms

Capacity Q of a pump is a volume flow rate, such as gallons per minute or cubic feet per second. Specifications and tests are based on cold water ($<85°F$) with standard water ($60°F$) having a density of 62.37 lb/ft³ (0.01603 ft³/lb).

Head H is measured in feet of fluid (cold water unless otherwise specified), and conversion from pressure is

$$\text{Head, ft} = \text{pressure, psi} \times 2.304 \times \text{sp gr} \tag{19.42}$$

The head is the net useful head, generally called total dynamic head (TDH), and is rigorously determined under the test codes with all allowances for test arrangements, friction losses, positions of gauges, and velocity head.

Horsepower P is the theoretical water horsepower:

$$\text{whp} = \frac{\text{capacity (gpm)} \times \text{head (ft)} \times \text{sp gr}}{3960} \tag{19.43}$$

The input horsepower (shp) to the shaft is best measured by a dynamometer.

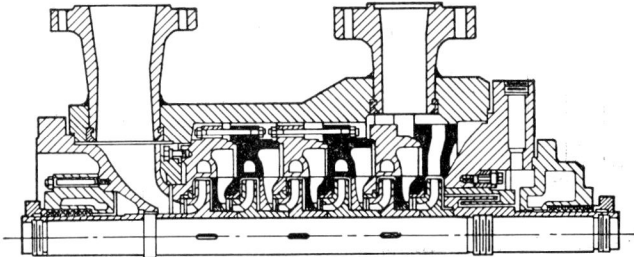

Fig. 19.17. Half section of a six-stage, high-pressure, centrifugal boiler-feed pump.

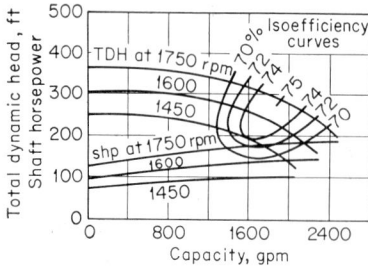

FIG. 19.18. Characteristic curves for a two-stage centrifugal pump at several speeds.

Pump efficiency η is the ratio of whp to shp.

Pump sizes are usually designated by the nominal pipe diameter of the discharge (foreign practice frequently uses the suction diameter) and

$$\text{Approx. rated pump capacity, gpm} = (\text{discharge pipe diam., in.})^2 \times 20 \qquad (19.44)$$

19.18. Performance

Characteristic curves (Figs. 19.11, 19.13 to 19.15, and 19.18) best express performance. They are different from the theoretical characteristics predicated on the Euler equation [Eqs. (19.21) to (19.23)]. Comparative performances of several selected types of pumps are shown in Fig. 19.19 and Table 19.2. The range of dimensionless coefficients at the point of maximum efficiency, predicated on a single-stage, single-inlet impeller, is 0.01 to 0.3 for C_{Qi}, 3.7 to 4.7 for C_H, and 0.1 to 1.5 for C_p. Peak pump efficiency ranges generally between 0.5 and 0.9, and tip speeds seldom exceed 150 fps. The nature of the characteristics (Fig. 19.19) is equally important with the numerical values of performance. Thus some head characteristics are steep (curve 4) and therefore suitable for parallel operation of pumps, while other characteristics are drooping (curve 1). There are varying degrees of self-limiting horsepower characteristics.

19.19. Suction Conditions

The performance of a pump is more sensitive to suction conditions than any other external influence. Suction conditions are primarily the responsibility of the pump user rather than the pump designer. The limits of suction lift are practically fixed as specified in Fig. 19.20 and are altered by items such as temperature, vapor pressure, gas entrained or in solution, system tightness, and length of (and fittings in) suction line. The curves clearly demonstrate that with water above 160°F no rational installation should attempt a negative head. The positive head may range to 50 ft or more as on a pump handling water at 200 to 400°F for heads of 3000 to 4000 ft. In vacuum service the suction pressure approaches the vanishing point and the extreme sensitivity of the pump to suction submergence is shown in Fig. 19.21.

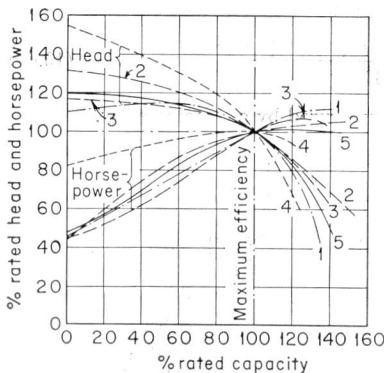

FIG. 19.19. Comparative characteristics of some selected centrifugal pumps; percentage basis.

19.20. Design Details

Blades of centrifugal pumps are always curved backward against the direction of rotation to reduce the ill effects of cavitation with α_2 ranging from 90 to 160°. The higher vane angles give greater steepness to the head characteristic (Fig. 19.19).

The number of blades usually ranges between six and twelve and must be selected to assure motion of the fluid in the desired direction and will vary with the diameter of the impeller eye and the radial depth of the blades.

Casing design varies from a simple scroll to a concentric diffuser with or without guide vanes. The casing with two cutoff points diametrically opposite reduces the radial forces and shaft diameter.

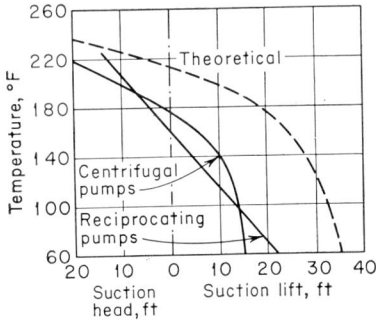

FIG. 19.20. Theoretical and practical suction lifts and heads for pumps handling water at various temperatures. Based on sea-level conditions, saturated water, pumps in reasonable state of repair.

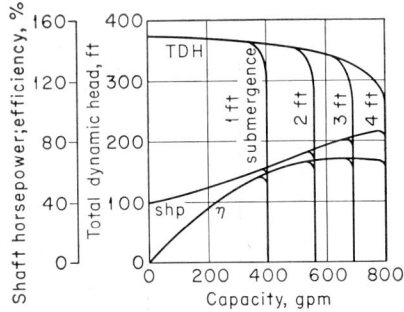

FIG. 19.21. Effect of submergence on the characteristics of a three-stage, steam-condenser hot-well, centrifugal pump.

A single-inlet impeller (Fig. 19.17) experiences an axial thrust toward the inlet end. This may be corrected by use of (1) double-suction impellers (Fig. 19.16); (2) opposed single-inlet impellers; (3) hydraulic balancing drums or disks; and (4) thrust bearings.

Packings, labyrinths, and glands are needed to reduce shaft leakage, both internal and external.

Ordinarily the temperature rise of the fluid on passage through a pump is negligible, but for high heads and large powers (e.g., 3000 ft and 1000 hp) the pump must not be allowed to churn with zero flow. Recirculation limits the temperature rise to some predetermined value, e.g., 25 to 50°F.

19.21. Specific Speed, N_s, C_{nQ}

Some representative specific-speed data are given in Table 19.2 and Figs. 19.22 and 19.23. Specific speed, Eqs. (19.33) and (19.35), is a unique criterion which rigorously defines the performance of a whole series of homologous pumps. When a discreet value

Table **19.2.** Comparative Dimensionless Coefficients of Selected Centrifugal Pumps

Pump number	1	2	3	4	5
Pump description:					
No. of stages	2	1	6	1	1
No. of inlets per stage	1	1	1	2	1
Rated rpm	1700	3450	3500	1750	425
Rated gpm	190	60	1400	1875	15,000
Rated head	230	70	3400	57	22
Rated shp	20	1.6	1500	31.5	110
Service	General	General	Boiler feed	General	Circulating
N_s	650	1150	1165	2600	3600
Shutoff:					
C_H	5.0	5.2	5.5	5.6	4.4
C_P	0.057	0.085	0.14	0.55	0.73
Maximum efficiency point:					
C_H	4.7	3.9	4.7	3.7	3.7
C_Q	0.014	0.033	0.045	0.16	0.31
C_P	0.12	0.19	0.31	0.67	1.51
$\eta, \%$	57	65	69	86	75
C_{nQ}	0.038	0.067	0.068	0.15	0.21
Wide-open:					
C_Q	0.021	0.054	0.065	0.22	0.47
C_P	0.13	0.20	0.32	0.50	1.50

NOTE: All coefficients are on the single-stage, single-inlet basis.

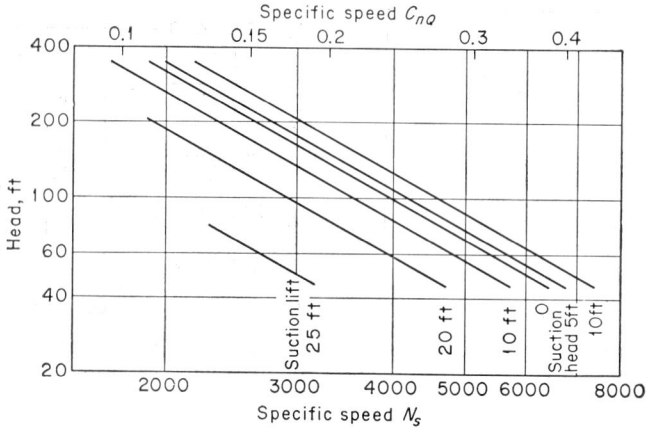

FIG. 19.22. Upper limit of specific speeds for double-suction, single-stage centrifugal pumps. Sea level; temperature, 80°F. (*Hydraulic Institute.*)

is given, the reference is generally to the peak of the efficiency curve. Specific speed is the single most useful criterion for pump selection since it relates the prime variables of head, capacity, and speed. Figure 19.22 is an "experience curve," which demonstrates the selection barriers in any problem of pump choice. The specific speed is a function of the width-diameter ratio of the impeller (Fig. 19.23), and with decreasing values of the ratio the specific speed decreases. A pump which has a low value of width-diameter ratio is more nearly a true centrifugal than an axial-flow type.

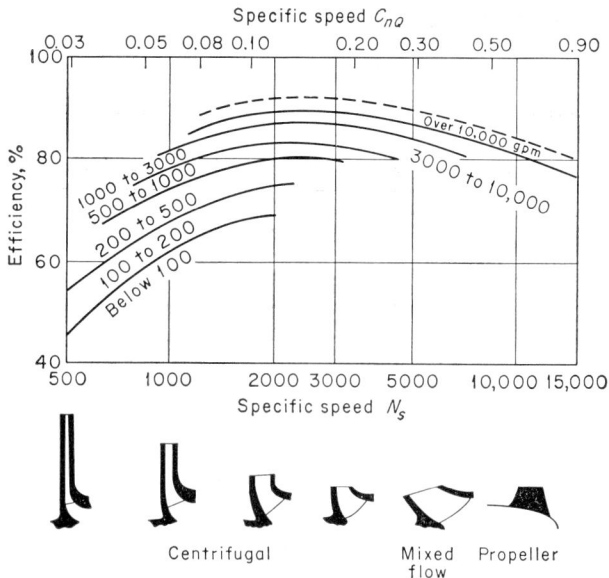

FIG. 19.23. Specific-speed–efficiency curves for centrifugal, propeller, and mixed-flow pumps. (*Adapted from "Pumps: A Power Handbook," Power, October* 1954.)

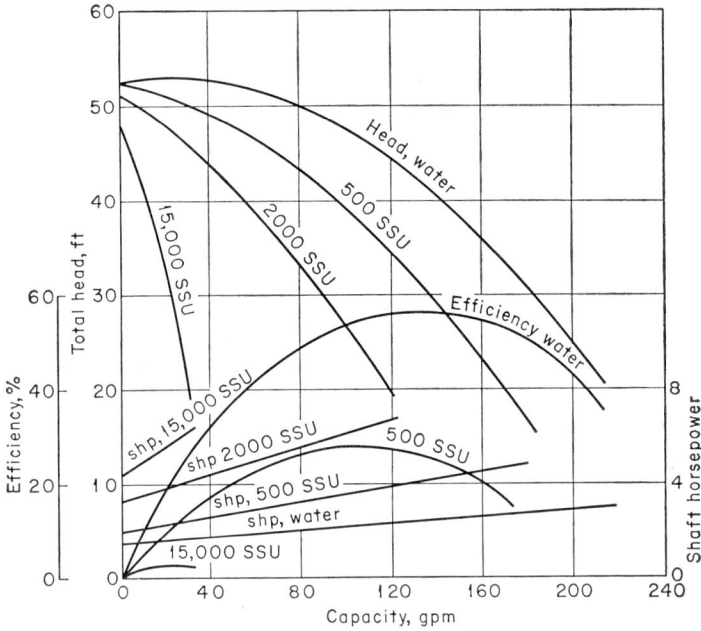

Fig. 19.24. Effects of viscosity change on centrifugal-pump characteristics.

19.22. Effects of Fluid Viscosity

The influence of change in fluid viscosity on the performance of a centrifugal pump is typified by the characteristic curves of Fig. 19.24.

CENTRIFUGAL FANS

19.23. Types

The prior discussion of centrifugal pumps is largely applicable to fans because the compression ratio of the gas is so small (density change less than 5 to 10 per cent) that

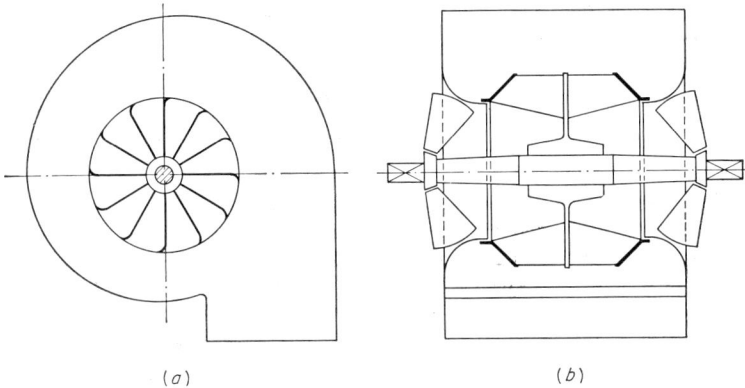

Fig. 19.25. Double-inlet, double-width centrifugal fan, backward-curved blades, inlet vane control.

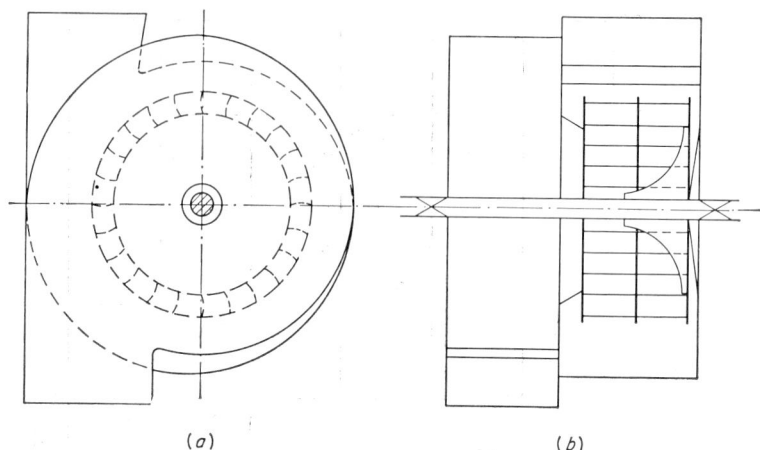

(a)   (b)

FIG. 19.26. Single-inlet, single-width centrifugal fan, forward-curved blades, inlet scroll.

the fluid can be considered noncompressible in effect. The structural elements are essentially similar, but diffuser rings and concentric casings are seldom used. Fans may be *single-* or *double-inlet* and *single-* or *double-width* (Figs. 19.25 and 19.26). If the load is on the discharge side, the unit is often called a *blower* (Fig. 19.25), and if on the suction side, an *exhauster* (Fig. 19.26). The fan may have a *free inlet* or be equipped with *inlet guide vanes* (Fig. 19.25). Fans are often identified by the type of *blade curvature* (Fig. 19.27). *Conveying fans* handle gases laden with a wide assortment of solid particles such as dust, soot, cinders, fly ash, lint, and sawdust. While fans and pumps have many features in common, there are wide differences, largely the consequence of the economic conditions prevailing in the commercial markets. With fans, the horsepower involved in many applications is small and precludes elaborate design and manufacturing techniques for the reduction of operating costs. Price and investment are frequently of dominating significance. Glands, sealing rings, balancing drums, polished shrouds, and polished impeller surfaces are not prevalent on fans. Pumps follow steam-turbine practice in design and workmanship, but the fan user generally is satisfied with the more liberal standards of the plate shop and the foundry.

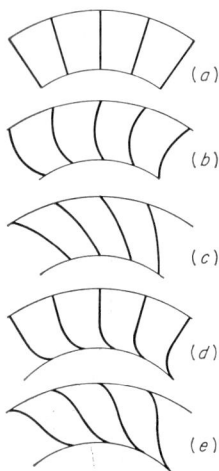

FIG. 19.27. Blade curvature for centrifugal fans: (a) radial, steel plate, or paddlewheel; (b) forward-curve or multivane; (c) backward-curve or high-speed; (d) radial-tip; (e) reverse curve.

19.24. Performance Terms

Capacity Q is given as cubic feet per minute. Density is widely variable with gases, so that performance is always predicated, unless otherwise noted, on standard air, defined as air at 68°F, 29.92 in. barometer, 50 per cent relative humidity, density 0.07488 lb/ft³, specific volume 13.35 ft³/lb.

Head is measured in inches of water (h_w) for manometric convenience but should, for rigorous analysis, be measured in feet of fluid (H) flowing, with conversion by

$$H = \frac{h_w \times \text{density of water}}{12 \times \text{density of fluid}} \qquad (19.45)$$

For standard air, H is equivalent to 69.5 ft for 1 in. of water.

Head may be static (h_s), velocity (h_v), or total (h_t), with $h_t = h_s + h_v$. Conversion is by

$$v,\ \text{fpm} = 1096.2\ \sqrt{h_w \times \bar{w}_g} \qquad (19.46)$$

in which h_w is inches of water, and $\bar{w}_g$ is the density of the fluid flowing. For standard air, $v = \sqrt{4000h_w}$. Commercial duct velocities range to 4000 fpm, and when the equivalent velocity head is compared with the static pressure, the former is often far from negligible. Hence, in recording the head developed by a fan, there is the reasonable inclination to include the velocity head and use total head h_t to measure performance. As velocity head is not usable in overcoming a connected-system resistance, static pressure h_s is generally preferred for expressing fan performance. In certain conveying fan applications, however, the total pressure is usable for impact propulsion of solid particles.

The theoretical horsepower, ahp, required, on the basis of a noncompressible fluid, is given by

$$\text{ahp} = \frac{\text{capacity (cfm)} \times \text{head (in. water)}}{6348} \qquad (19.47)$$

The head may be static or total to give two alternative values of ahp, the latter, of course, being larger.

Fan efficiency η is the ratio of the ahp to the horsepower input on the fan shaft (shp) and may be expressed as

$$\text{Static fan efficiency} = \frac{\text{ahp (static)}}{\text{shp}} \qquad (19.48)$$

or

$$\text{Total fan efficiency} = \frac{\text{ahp (total)}}{\text{shp}} \qquad (19.49)$$

The static-efficiency characteristic will be zero at shutoff and wide-open conditions, with an intermediate peak. The total efficiency is zero only at shutoff.

19.25. Performance

Representative characteristic curves and dimensionless-coefficient data are given in Figs. 19.28 to 19.31 and Table 19.3. Head characteristics range from rising (forward-

Table **19.3.** Comparative Dimensionless Coefficients of Selected Centrifugal Fans

Fan number	1	2	3	4	5	6
Type	Steel plate	Pressure blower	Radial tip	Forward curve	Backward	Backward (axial inlet)
Width and inlet	DWDI	SWSI	DWDI	SWSI	DWDI	SWSI
Rated cfm	150,000	1500	23,000	32,000	117,000	5000
Rated head, in.	9.3	4.2	5.7	1.5	13.9	4.5
Rated rpm	360	1800	900	213	1160	1750
Rated power	350	1.8	31.5	11.5	338	5.7
Shutoff:						
C_H	6.3	5.7	5.4	11.2	3.8	5.1
C_P	0.44	0.7	0.89	7.0	0.78	1.5
Maximum efficiency point:						
C_H	6.3	3.9	5.7	10.8	3.6	5.3
C_Q	0.17	0.19	0.40	1.2	0.42	0.82
C_P	1.6	1.4	3.5	20.0	2.0	7.0
$\eta,\%$	66	54	66	65	75	62
C_{nQ}	0.11	0.16	0.17	0.19	0.25	0.26
Wide-open:						
C_Q	0.43	0.33	0.95	3.3	0.75	1.5
C_P	3.4	2.0	6.5	74	1.5	10

NOTE: All coefficients are on the single-width, single-inlet basis. DWDI = double-width, double-inlet.

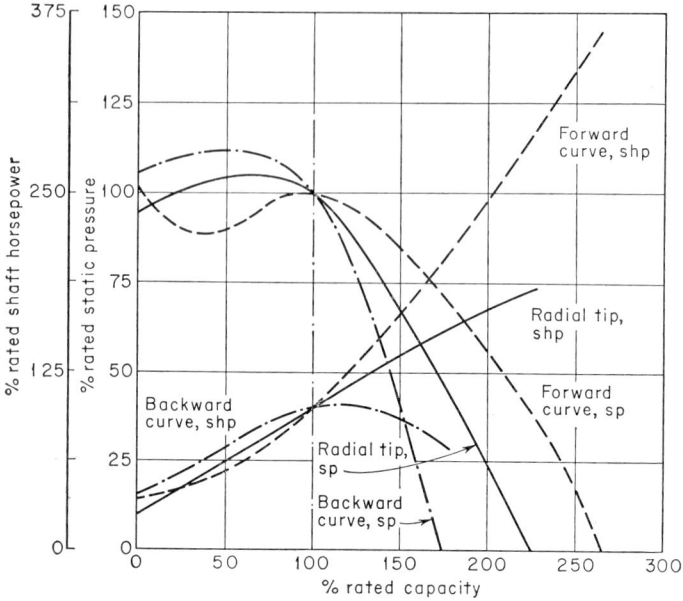

Fig. 19.28. Comparative characteristics for selected centrifugal fan types; percentage basis.

curved blades) to falling (backward-curved blades). The horsepower characteristics range, respectively, from concave upward to concave downward. The steep head and self-limiting horsepower characteristics are essential for good parallel operation of fans. Shutoff values of head range between 95 and 105 per cent of rating, while horsepower is from 20 to 40 per cent of rating. The shutoff head coefficient ranges from 3.8 to 11.2 (Table 19.3) compared with 4.4 to 5.6 for pumps (Table 19.2); backwardly curved blade fans range from 3.8 to 5.1 and are in close agreement with pumps, where backwardly curved blades are used exclusively. The range of specific speed C_{nQ} is 0.11 to 0.26 on fans and 0.038 to 0.21 on pumps. Tip speeds will be as high as 10,000 to 20,000 fpm for the maximum pressure services. Efficiency may be as low as 50 per cent, but will exceed 80 per cent on the largest well-designed and well-constructed units. If the fluid density is changed, as by barometric pressure or temperature, then the performance of a fan can be estimated by the fact that the head in feet of fluid pumped will remain constant but manometric heads will be altered in accordance with the gas laws.

19.26. Suction Conditions

Fans, like pumps, are exceedingly sensitive to inlet conditions. If the load is on the discharge side of the fan, then a free radial bellmouthed entry may be employed. If the fan serves as an exhauster, the suction connecting piece will vitally influence the performance and could easily curtail the head and cut the capacity in half. Some manufacturers accordingly prefer a contrarotation spiral inlet (Fig. 19.26) as most foolproof. Inlet guide vanes (Fig. 19.25) may be employed for purposes of

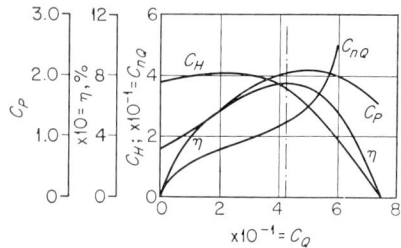

Fig. 19.29. Dimensionless-coefficient characteristics for a selected centrifugal fan with backwardly curved blades.

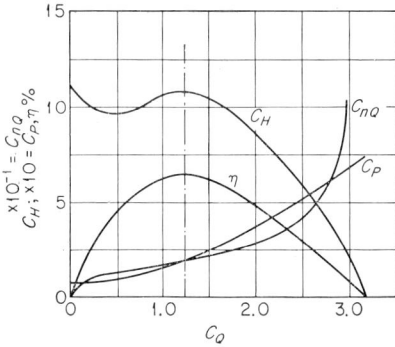

Fig. 19.30. Dimensionless-coefficient characteristics for a selected centrifugal fan with forwardly curved blades.

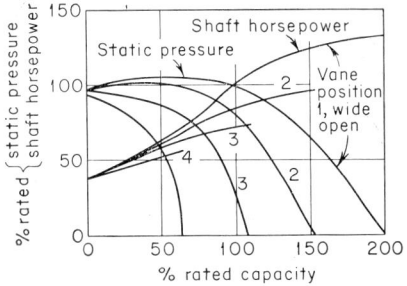

Fig. 19.31. Characteristic curves of a centrifugal fan with inlet vane control; percentage basis.

flow regulation and give good power savings compared with simple dampering and avoid the need for a variable-speed drive (cf. Fig. 19.31).

19.27. Design Details

The blade angle of 90° at heel and tip for the paddlewheel fan may be altered so that α_1 is made 120 to 135° for a scoop action at the heel. The tip angle α_2 will range from 60° on a forward-curve fan to 120 to 160° on a backward-curve fan. One practical economic solution uses flat blades set at 45°, approximately.

The number of blades ranges from six on some paddlewheel fans to sixty or seventy on some forward-curve multivane designs. The optimum number is fixed by the fluid-dynamic requirement of acceleration of all the fluid to the desired magnitude and direction. If the blades are radially shallow, the number must be increased. Radial depth ranges from 0.05 to $0.35D_2$. The axial length of the blades follows from the desire to avoid throttling within the wheel passages.

Structurally, the blades are most frequently made of plate and are riveted, welded, or bolted to center plates, shrouds, spiders, and reinforcing rings. The largest fans may employ airfoil sections.

The discharge casing is a scroll (Fig. 19.32) following a formulation

$$R_s = R_2(1 + K\alpha) \tag{19.50}$$

in which R_s = radius of spiral at any point
 R_2 = radius of fan wheel at tip
 α = angle of advance, radians, measured from point where scroll, if extended, would intersect wheel-tip circle
 K = an experimentally determined constant ranging between 0.08 and 0.2

The cutoff point may be located with a large radial clearance (± 10 per cent of the wheel diameter) and with a large wheel exposure when viewed along the discharge-opening axis. On small fans the cross-section form of the case is circular, but on large fans it is built up of plate and is rectangular. The double scroll, as

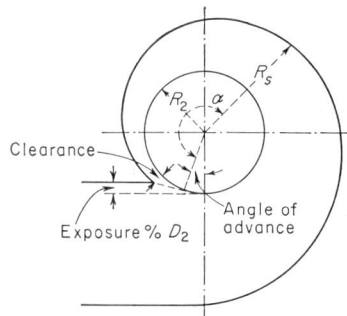

Fig. 19.32. Scroll-casing dimensions for a centrifugal fan.

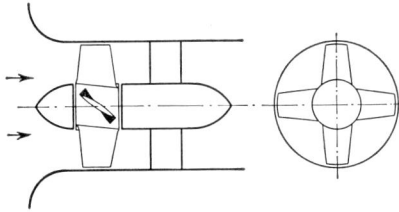

FIG. 19.33. Single-stage axial-flow fan.

on pumps, is employed on large units to improve radial loading and permits of a lighter shaft construction.

PROPELLER PUMPS AND FANS

19.28. Types

The fluid screw can be used to move a gas or liquid against an incidental resistance as with a pump or fan or to provide an axial thrust for propulsion of an attached vehicle or vessel. In the former application, its effectiveness for a given power input is measured by the quantity of fluid moved, and in the latter, by the magnitude of the thrust developed. A *casing* (Figs. 19.33 to 19.35) is needed for the development of static pressure. The *casingless* device, like a desk fan, is essentially a stirrer. *Single-stage* (Fig. 19.33) and *multistage* units are available. *Guide vanes* (Figs. 19.33 and 19.34), fixed or movable, are frequently employed. Impeller blades are seldom movable because the economics of variable pitch is doubtful. *Mixed-flow* units (Fig. 19.35) incorporate some radial flow, with the maximum latitude of choice between centrifugal- and axial-flow features.

19.29. Performance

The characteristics as typified by Figs. 19.36 to 19.39 best show the performance of axial-flow units. Figure 19.36 demonstrates comparatively the performance of centrifugal and axial pumps. No centrifugal pump can offer the steep head and horsepower characteristics of the propeller units. Shutoff head and horsepower can be several times the rated head and the rated horsepower. More power is uniquely required at light loads than at heavy load. This can lead to overmotoring for continued partial-load operation. Starting procedure requires a wide-open damper rather than the closed damper for centrifugal units. Because neither the propeller nor centrifugal designs are self-priming, the propeller pump must be mounted in a submerged position and started wide-open, while the centrifugal pump can be placed above the level of the sump, primed with the discharge valve closed, and started at the shutoff point on the characteristic. Figures 19.37 to 19.39 show the performance characteristics on the dimensionless-coefficient basis for representative pumps and fans. The absolute values should be compared with those of Figs. 19.23, 19.29, and 19.30 and Tables 19.2 and 19.3 to identify the particular variations for the full range of centrifugal-, axial-, and mixed-flow designs.

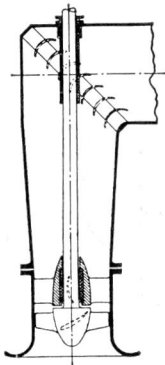

FIG. 19.34. Single-stage axial-flow pump.

19.30. Design Details

Performance is most substantially influenced by blade pitch (Fig. 19.39), when geometric pitch P is the distance the fluid screw would advance in one revolution if there were no slip, or

$$P = 2\pi R \times \tan \alpha_1 \tag{19.51}$$

in which R is the radius at which the blade angle α_1 is measured. Pitch ratio is the quotient of pitch P and diameter D. Capacity is substantially altered by pitch, and head to a lesser extent, and there is a wide range of pitch for which the peak efficiency is only modestly altered (Fig. 19.39). Blades with airfoil sections give maximum efficiency, but plates, flat or warped, are frequently adequate for the economical construction of fans. Camber similarly may be dictated by structural-strength requirements. With the prevalent warped surfaces, outlet-inlet pitch

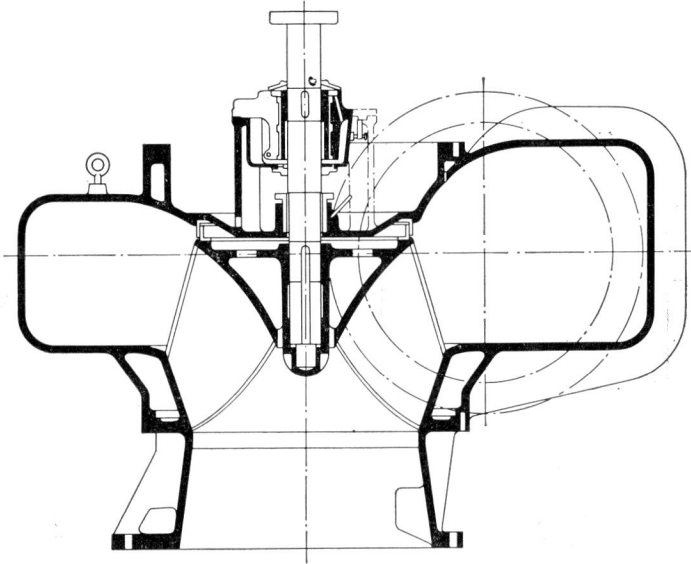

Fig. 19.35. Open mixed-flow-impeller volute-type pump.

ratio is of the order of 1.4:2.0. Blade form, number, and proportions have been an inventor's paradise. Blade number has ranged from 2 to 60, but modern aerodynamics has demonstrated the difficulties of interference among multiple planes so that modern designs use the minimum number of blades with good aspect ratios. Capacity and head are increased with greater projected area ratio, so that solidity often exceeds unity. The contribution from the blade portion near the hub is small or dubious, so that many units use short radial depth blades on a large-diameter hub.

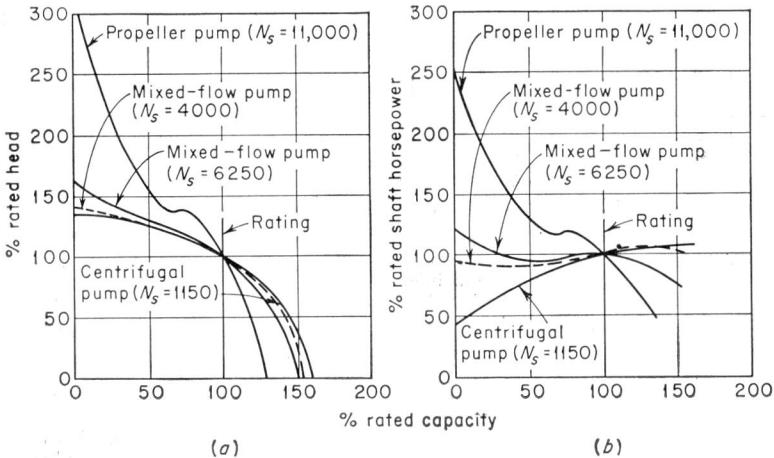

Fig. 19.36. Comparative head and horsepower characteristics of some propeller, centrifugal, and mixed-flow pumps; percentage basis.

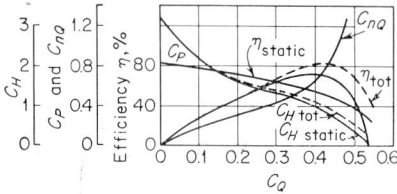

FIG. 19.37. Dimensionless-coefficient characteristics for a selected axial-flow blower.

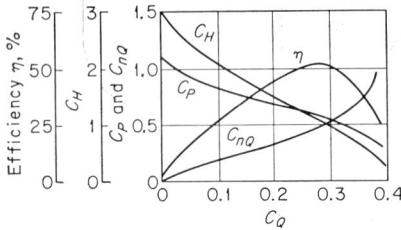

FIG. 19.38. Dimensionless-coefficient characteristics for a selected four-stage axial-flow pump.

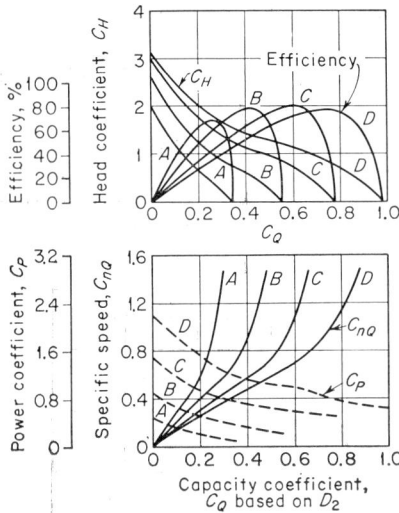

FIG. 19.39. Dimensionless-coefficient characteristics of a selected axial-flow fan as influenced by pitch. (*Note:* $D_2 = 12$ in.; 4000 rpm; two blades; 0.635, projected area ratio.)

Fan	$\dfrac{P_i}{D_2}$	$\dfrac{P_o}{D_2}$	$\dfrac{P_o}{P_i}$
A	0.33	0.56	1.67
B	0.525	0.85	1.67
C	0.75	1.25	1.67
D	1.00	1.67	1.67

The casings on units for development of static pressure may have an evasé diffuser section (15 to 20° divergence and 2:1 area ratio), or a plain cylindrical tube may be used. The slip stream leaving the impeller has a helical path, so that guide vanes are prevalent. They are especially needed on the multistage units to give the necessary straightening effect between stages. Counterrotation has been employed on some two-stage fans, but the complexity of the mechanism is usually a deterrent. Adjustable guide vanes are rarely used, as are inlet guide vanes.

19.31. Specific Speed, C_{nQ}, N_s

Specific-speed limitations are illustrated by Figs. 19.22, 19.23, and 19.40. The axial-flow pumps give the highest values ($N_s = 10,000$ to 20,000), while the centrifugal units give the lowest values ($N_s = 500$ to 1000). The mixed-flow units are intermediate, so that there is the widest opportunity for design and selection. The axial-flow designs are the true high-speed units, and the characteristics show the feature of maximum head delivered and horsepower required at minimum loads.

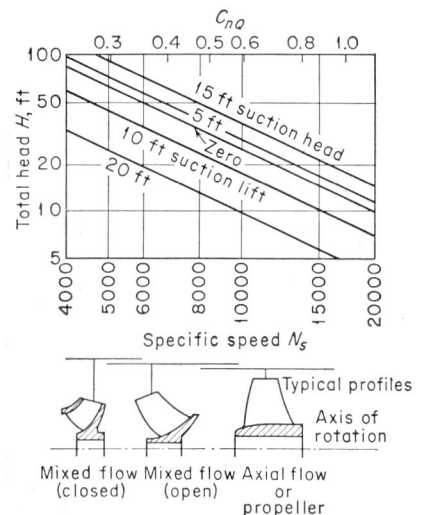

FIG. 19.40. Upper limit of specific speeds for single-stage, single-suction, mixed-flow, and axial-flow pumps. Sea level; temperature, 85°F. (*Hydraulic Institute.*)

TURBOCOMPRESSORS

19.32. Types

Turbocompressors are of the *centrifugal* (Figs. 19.41 and 19.42) or *axial* (Fig. 19.43) type. They are extensions of fans into the area where compressibility (density change greater than ±10 per cent) of the gas cannot be neglected. The laws of thermodynamics must be substituted for the laws of hydraulics. If the necessary compression cannot be accomplished in a *single stage* (Fig. 19.41), then a *multistage* (Figs. 19.42 and 19.43) construction is employed, with the over-all compression ratio generally limited to something less than 10:1. *Horizontal* shaft construction prevails. With multistage units the *casing* is usually *split* with a horizontal parting plane through the shaft. The heat of compression may be partially transferred through *intercoolers* between selected stages, especially with higher ratios of compression on centrifugal

FIG. 19.41. Centrifugal supercharger.

units. Water-cooled *jackets* and diaphragms between stages are often employed on centrifugal units, but cooling to the ambient prevails on axial units. *Blade curvature* on centrifugal units is backward or radial; *diffusers* are with or without stationary guide vanes; *concentric* and *volute cases* are employed. *Governing* may be at constant or variable speed for constant pressure or constant volume. *Variable speed* is especially suited to turbine drive. *Turbine drive* avoids the limitations of synchronous speeds and step-up gears.

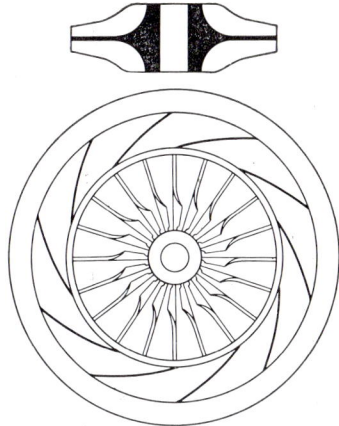

19.33. Performance Terms

Capacity is generally expressed as cubic feet per minute measured at the suction conditions, and if dealing with atmospheric conditions, the definition is in terms of free (ambient) air. The dimensionless coefficient C_{nQ} will vary with each stage of a multistage machine, and when used to identify the unit in its entirety it is that of the first stage.

Head, or pressure, is usually expressed in inches of mercury or pounds per square inch because of the magnitudes of the pressures involved.

Horsepower. Several recognizable standards used for evaluating horsepower of compressors include the following:

1. The isothermal standard (Fig. 19.44) is predicated on Boyle's law for perfect gases

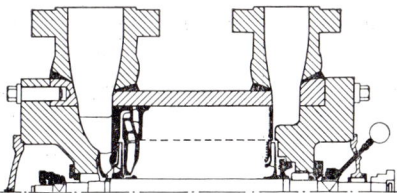

FIG. 19.42. Vertically split, multistage centrifugal compressor (half section).

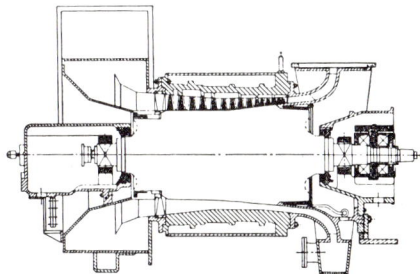

FIG. 19.43. Multistage axial compressor.

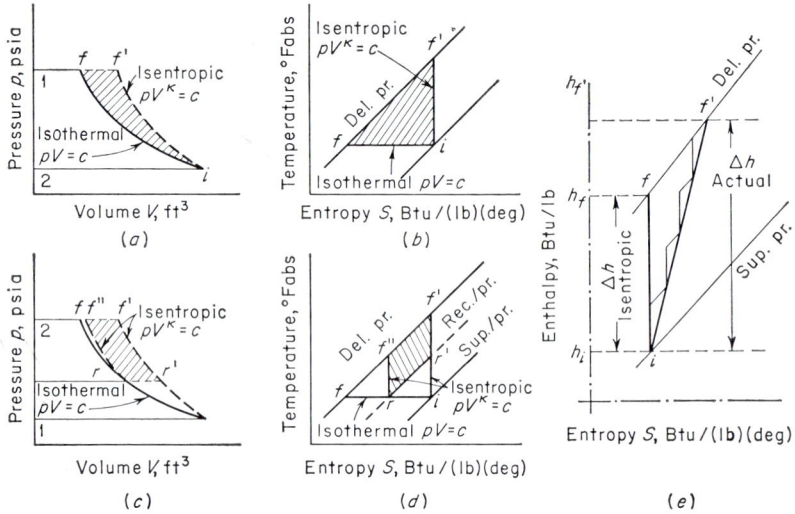

FIG. 19.44. Pressure-volume, temperature-entropy, enthalpy-entropy diagrams for various compressor performance standards: (*a* and *b*), single-stage; (*c* and *d*), two-stage, perfect intercooling; (*e*) isentropic and actual compression in a multistage turboblower.

and gives the theoretical minimum power requirements for any gas in any kind of compressor.

$$\text{Isothermal work, ft-lb} = P_i V_i \ln \frac{P_f}{P_i} \tag{19.52}$$

$$\text{Isothermal hp/100 cfm supply gas} = \frac{p_i}{2.292} \ln \frac{p_f}{p_i} \tag{19.53}$$

in which subscripts i, f = initial and final conditions, respectively
$\quad\quad\quad\quad\quad\quad P$ = absolute pressure, psf
$\quad\quad\quad\quad\quad\quad p$ = absolute pressure, psi
$\quad\quad\quad\quad\quad\quad V$ = volume, ft^3

2. The isentropic standard, often erroneously called the "adiabatic" standard (Fig. 19.44), is the other important perfect-gas standard in which there is no transfer of heat to or from the surroundings and with no internal friction.

$$\text{Isentropic work, ft-lb} = \frac{\kappa}{\kappa - 1} P_i V_i \left[\left(\frac{P_f}{P_i} \right)^{(\kappa - 1)/\kappa} - 1 \right] \tag{19.54}$$

$$\text{Isentropic hp/100 cfm supply gas} = \frac{\kappa}{\kappa - 1} \frac{p_i}{2.292} \left[\left(\frac{p_f}{p_i} \right)^{(\kappa - 1)/\kappa} - 1 \right] \tag{19.55}$$

if $\kappa = c_p/c_v$, the ratio of the specific heats at constant pressure and constant volume. The power required on the isentropic standard is larger than the isothermal (larger area, Fig. 19.44*a*).

3. The multistage isentropic standard (Fig. 19.44*c*) with perfect intercooling between stages:

$$\text{Ideal work, ft-lb} = \frac{\kappa}{\kappa - 1} P_i V_i \left[(R_{p1})^{(\kappa - 1)/\kappa} + (R_{p2})^{(\kappa - 1)/\kappa} + \cdots + N \right] \tag{19.56}$$

$$\text{Ideal work, hp/100 cfm supply gas} = \frac{\kappa}{\kappa - 1} \frac{N p_i}{2.292} \left[\left(\frac{p_f}{p_i} \right)^{(\kappa - 1)/N\kappa} - 1 \right] \tag{19.57}$$

if N = number of stages, and R_p = ratio of compression. The power will be a minimum if best receiver pressure prevails at the intercooling points and defined as

$$\text{Best } R_p \text{ per stage} = \sqrt[N]{P_f/P_i} \qquad (19.58)$$

4. The performance with the properties of real gases is most conveniently and accurately evaluated by the use of a Mollier (h-s) chart and the general energy equation in which (Fig. 19.44e)

$$\text{Work of the cycle, Btu/lb} = h_{\text{final}} - h_{\text{initial}} \qquad (19.59)$$

with h = enthalpy, Btu/lb.

If the initial and final conditions are connected by an isentropic line ($s_f = s_i$), then the result is for an ideal Rankine cycle ($h_f - h_i$). If there are internal losses, then the final enthalpy is larger and the work is given by the difference ($h'_f - h_i$). If heat is extracted, as with a jacket system, then this energy must also be supplied through the compressor shaft.

5. The shaft horsepower is the actual energy input to the compressor shaft.

Compression efficiency is defined as the ratio of theoretical horsepower to actual, or shaft, horsepower. The theoretical horsepower may be any one of the theoretical values defined above. The isothermal standard is applicable equally to all types of machines, but it is furthest removed from reality. Reference is frequently made to the isentropic standard where for convenience the ideal isentropic temperature rise, $T_i(R_p)^{(\kappa-1)/\kappa} - T_i$, is divided by the actual temperature rise to give efficiency. T_i is the initial temperature absolute. Over-all efficiency is sometimes employed and calls for use of input horsepower to the driver instead of shaft horsepower.

19.34. Performance

Representative performance and dimensional data are given in Figs. 19.45 to 19.48 and Tables 19.4 and 19.5. Characteristic curves best define the performance, but there is one sharp difference when compared with similar curves for pumps and fans: the unstable part of the curves in the light-load region. This phenomenon of instability, hunting, pumping, or surging is inconsequential with fans but is so troublesome with turboblowers that no unit can be operated below the limit of stability without flow reversal and blowback. Its effects are determined by the compression ratio, the compressor type, the number of stages in the unit, the slope of the head characteristic, the rate of flow, and the volume and proportion of the connected system. For example,

Table 19.4. Selected Turboblowers and Turbocompressors—Performance Data

Blower no.	1	2	3	4	5	6
Service application	Aircraft engine supercharger	Multistage	Blast-furnace blower	High-pressure air compressor	Gas-turbine compressor	Gas-works blower
Compressor type	Centrifugal	Centrifugal	Centrifugal	Centrifugal	Axial	Centrifugal
Number of stages	1	7	5	13	20	1
Fluid	Air	Air	Air	Air	Air	Gas: $w = 0.05$ $\kappa = 1.33$
Capacity, cfm	2000	1000	30,000	15,000	40,000	15,000
Supply pressure, psia	15	15	15	15	15	14.7
Discharge pressure, psia	25	24	45	115	60	20.4
Ratio of compression, R_p	1.67	1.6	3.0	7.67	4	1.4
Speed, rpm	25,000	3500	3000	3000	5000	14,000
Shaft horsepower	104	60	3130	3600	5400	470
Compression efficiency, %:						
Single-stage adiabatic	70	55	81	75	81	72
Isothermal	65	51	69	55	66	68
Energy added per stage, ft-lb/lb	15,000	1400	7500	6000	2400	15,000

Table 19.5. Comparative Performance of Selected Axial-compressor Types

After Ponomareff

Capacity = 24,000 cfm; suction conditions = 14.7 psia, 70°F; $R_p = 4$; $\Delta h = 61.5$ Btu/lb ($\Delta T = 256°$) theoretical

	Symmetrical	Nonsymmetrical	Vortex
Compressor type:			
Speed, rpm....................	15,750	8750	5000
Number of stages............	10	18	22
R_p per stage.................	1.149	1.08	1.062
Attainable efficiency, %........	82	87	86
First stage:			
Tip diameter, in.............	16	19	24.5
Base diameter, in.............	10	11.5	15
Blade height, in..............	3.0	3.75	4.63
Tip speed, fps.................	1100	725	535
Axial velocity, fps............	525	335	200
Last stage:			
Tip diameter, in.............	16	19	24.5
Base diameter, in.............	14	16	21.25
Blade height, in..............	1.0	1.5	1.63
Tip speed, fps.................	1100	725	535
Axial velocity, fps............	475	275	195

If the head characteristic, as with forward-curve centrifugal impellers (Fig. 19.28), shows more than one flow volume for the same developed head, the unit is unable to select the proper light-load value. Flow reversal results, with consequent hunting and surging because of the fluid elasticity and high compression. Figure 19.48 shows the stable-operating range, wider with centrifugal- than with axial-flow units.

19.35. Design Details, Centrifugal-type Compressors

The head developed per stage is of the order of 10,000 to 12,000 ft-lb/lb, or 12 to 15 Btu/lb. Blades are either of the straight radial or backwardly curved type because of the wider stable-operating capacity range. The backward-curve vane gives the lowest head coefficient C_H, so requires the maximum speed for a specified service. Blade speed seldom exceeds 1200 to 1500 fps, and structural design is as stringent as with steam turbines. The ordinary plate work of much fan practice is unsuited. Rotative speeds may range to 30,000 and 40,000 rpm. This is in excess of electric motor speeds, so that direct drive favors the use of a gas or steam turbine. Blade proportions are more nearly akin to those found on pumps than on fans. Axial length is from 0.02 to 0.2D_2, and radial depth from 0.1 to 0.4D_2. In multistage units, to accommodate the increased fluid density of successive stages with homologous wheels, $D_2 \propto (1/\bar{w})^{0.33}$. A stepped construction for groups of stages is an economic solution. Thrust bearings and balancing drums are used to counterbalance the axial-end thrust on the shaft. A diffuser, with or without fixed guide vanes, and a concentric case is usual construction. On high-pressure compressors ($R_p > 6$), water-cooled jackets, diaphragms, and intercoolers may be used.

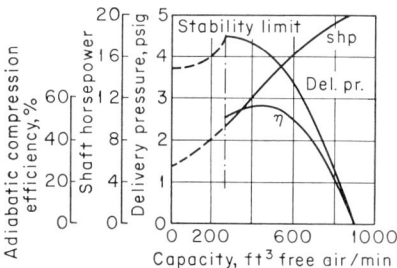

Fig. 19.45. Characteristics of a seven-stage centrifugal compressor: 3600 rpm; $D_2 = 18$ in.

19.36. Design Details, Axial-type Compressors

The axial compressor has many structural similarities to the multistage steam turbine. There are alternate rows of fixed and moving blades, radially shallow (0.05 to 0.15 × pitch diameter); aspect

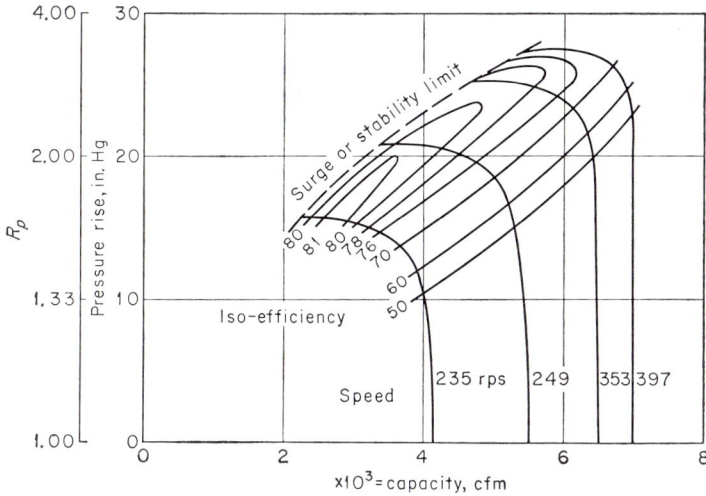

FIG. 19.46. Characteristics of a centrifugal-supercharger, axial-inlet, radial-engine collector case: impeller diameter, 13 in.; constant discharge pressure, 40 in. Hg abs. (*Adapted from Campbell and Talbot.*)

ratio 0.5 to 3.0; moving buckets mounted on periphery of a drum-type rotor. The compressor must convert kinetic to static energy in the blade passages, so diffusers instead of nozzles are prevalent. Airfoil sections are used to give maximum efficiency as demanded, typically, by gas-turbine applications. The basic recognizable types are illustrated by the vector diagrams of Fig. 19.49 as (1) symmetrical, (2) nonsymmetrical, and (3) vortex, with different degrees of diffuser and nozzle action in the stationary and moving passages. Each of these types has merits and limitations, as reflected in the data of Fig. 19.50 and Table 19.5, with consequent wide potential range for impeller diameters, speed, number of stages, weight, floor space, stress loading, reliability,

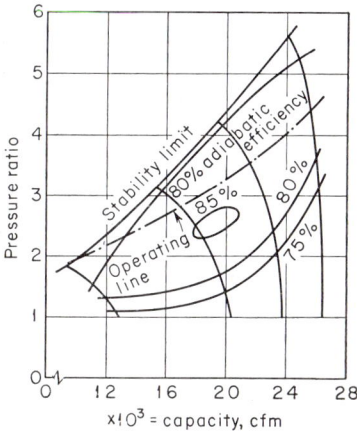

FIG. 19.47. Characteristics of a multi-stage axial compressor. Air supplied at 14.7 psia and 70°F. (*Adapted from Ponomareff.*)

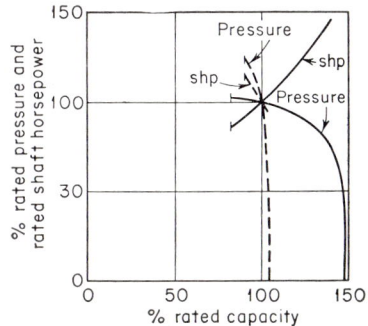

FIG. 19.48. Comparative characteristics of centrifugal and axial compressors in stable region; percentage basis. Solid lines, centrifugal; broken lines, axial.

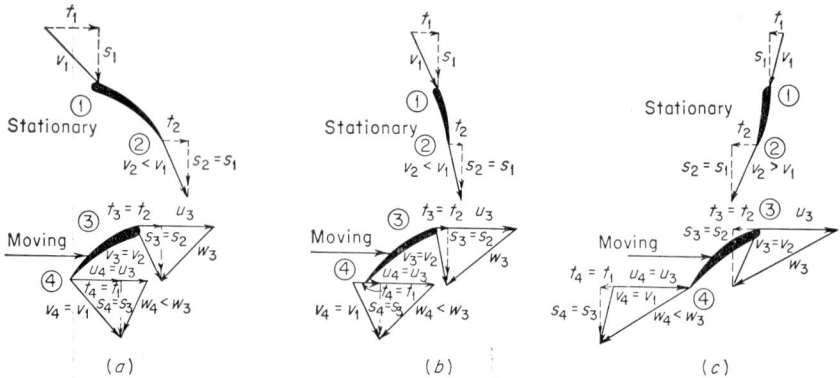

FIG. 19.49. Vector diagrams for axial-compressor types: (a) symmetrical, (b) nonsymmetrical, (c) vortex.

life, and efficiency. Blade speeds seldom exceed 1200 fps, and the energy added per stage lies between 2500 and 6000 ft-lb/lb or 3 and 8 Btu/lb. The number of stages is usually less than 25 or 30.

PROPELLERS

19.37. Types

The *propeller* (Figs. 19.51 and 19.52) is an application of the principle of the *fluid screw* to the translatory motion of a connected vessel or vehicle. The basic principle is similar to the motion of a nut advancing along the screw thread of a bolt. The pitch of the blades determines the extent of the advance, but when working on an elastic fluid, like water or air, the absence of solid rigidity means that there will be slip. In any event, there is an acceleration of the fluid by the rotating screw, with the fluid entering axially and discharging in a helical path, the slip stream. This phenomenon may be employed as:

1. A propeller for aircraft or ships; in the former, the screw advances in an infinite mass of air and an axial thrust is developed to offset the drag of the connected vehicle; in the latter, the screw operates near the surface of the water and the submergence head is the force bringing the fluid to the rotor and preventing cavitation.

2. A propeller, disc, or axial-flow pump or fan (cf. Arts. 19.28 to 19.31) where the objective is to move the maximum amount of fluid against the imposed resistance head.

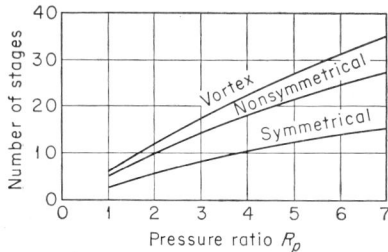

FIG. 19.50. Number of stages required to develop various pressure ratios with different types of axial compressors. (*Adapted from Ponomareff.*)

A casing is added for the generation of static pressure, and multistage constructions are common.

3. A windmill, where a high-velocity air stream impinges on vanes to turn the rotor and overcome the connected resistance.

4. A power brake on an airplane when in a power dive where thrust and torque may be positive or negative as fixed by the forward velocity of the airplane.

Propellers for airplanes are usually mounted in a *tractor* position to take advantage of a free unobstructed inlet condition, while for ships the *pusher* position is preferred for protection against submerged obstacles. *Fixed-blade* propellers dominate

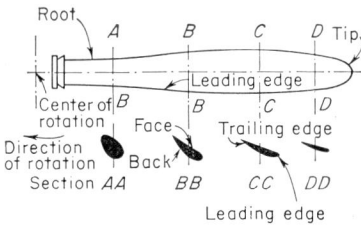

FIG. 19.51. Aircraft propeller blade.

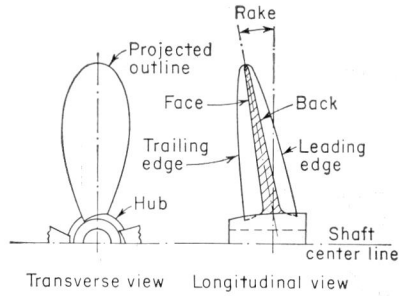

FIG. 19.52. Ship propeller blade.

marine practice, while *feathering* propellers are dominant in aircraft service. A few *counterrotation* propellers have been employed on aircraft applications, but the complexity is generally great.

19.38. Performance and Terms

The characteristic curves of Fig. 19.53 show basically the over-all relationship between forward speed (fps or knots) as the independent variable and thrust (lb), torque (lb-ft), power (hp or ft-lb/sec), and efficiency as the dependent quantities. Figure 19.53 gives data for typical aircraft and ship propellers of 9-ft diameter. Propellers for seagoing ships may absorb as much as 50,000 or 75,000 hp, with speeds below 500 rpm, while aircraft propellers are limited to capacities of about 3000 hp and speeds between 1000 and 2000 rpm.

Dimensionless characteristics are preferred for most analytical purposes, and several coefficients are usually employed, as follows:

1. Slip function V/nD is used instead of forward speed V and is the consequence of analysis of the motion of a blade element as in Fig. 19.54, where the velocity vector AC is the resultant of the forward velocity V and the peripheral velocity πnD. If the geometric pitch angle is θ, the angle of attack of the blade element α will change with each

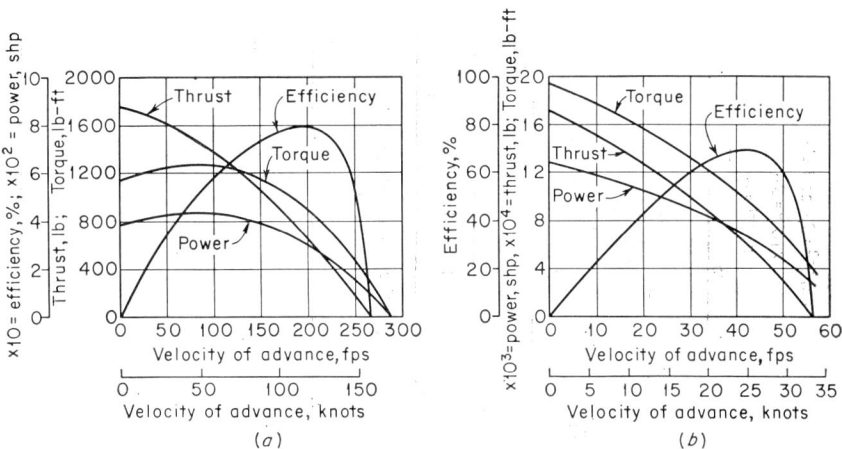

FIG. 19.53. Selected propeller characteristics; (a) Aircraft, $D = 9$ ft, two blades, pitch ratio, 0.8 at $0.67R$, 1800 rpm. (*Adapted from Weick.*) (b) Marine, $D = 9$ ft, four blades, pitch ratio = 0.9, 360 rpm. (*Adapted from Rossell and Chapman.*)

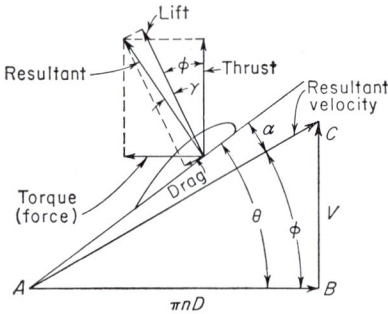

FIG. 19.54. Force diagram of a fluid screw element.

new value of AC. The value of the lift and drag of the airfoil, and consequently the thrust and torque of the propeller, are vitally affected by the angle of attack. The angle of attack is thus critically determined by the relative lengths of the vectors V and πnD, or by the ratio of these vectors. This ratio is critical in the performance of fluid screws. It is customary to omit the π item, thus defining slip function $= V/nD$. The nominal slip S is defined by $(1 - S) = V/np$, if $p =$ the nominal geometric pitch, in feet measured at some standard diameter such as $0.67D$.

2. Thrust coefficient C_T is derived from

$$T = C_T \rho n^2 D^4 \qquad (19.60)$$

in which C_T will be dimensionless if T is in pounds, ρ in slugs per cubic foot, n in revolutions per second, and D in feet.

3. Torque coefficient C_M is derived from

$$M = C_M \rho n^2 D^5 \qquad (19.61)$$

if $M =$ torque at shaft, lb-ft.

4. Power coefficient C_P is derived from

$$P = C_P \rho n^3 D^5 \qquad (19.62)$$

if $P =$ shaft horsepower, ft-lb/sec.

5. Propeller efficiency η is the ratio of energy output reflected in thrust and speed to the energy input in shaft horsepower, or

$$\eta = \frac{TV}{\text{shp} \times 550} = \frac{C_T}{C_P} \frac{V}{nD} \qquad (19.63)$$

6. Speed-power coefficients, like specific speed on pumps and turbines, are useful in propeller selection and eliminate the D dimension between C_P and slip function, thus

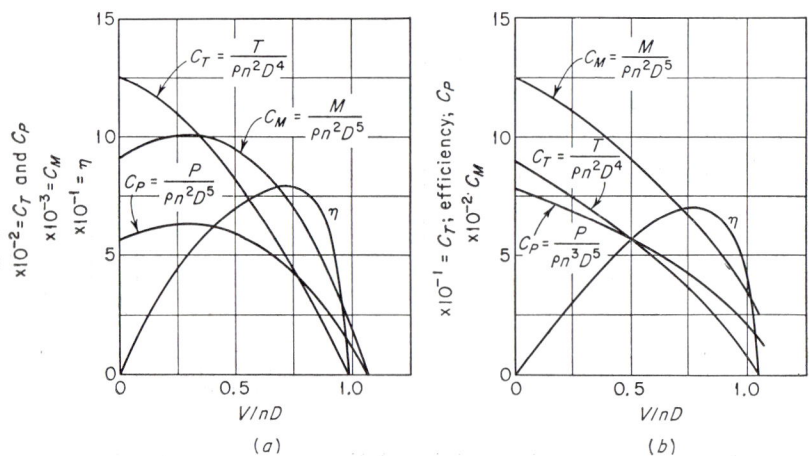

FIG. 19.55. Dimensionless-coefficient characteristics for selected propellers: (a) aircraft, (b) marine (cf. Fig. 19.53).

Speed-power coefficient $= \dfrac{C_P}{(V/nD)^5} = \dfrac{Pn^2}{\rho V^5}$ (19.64)

Sometimes the reciprocal or the square root or the fifth root of Eq. (19.64) is employed.

19.39. Dimensionless Characteristics

Dimensionless characteristics which show some of the relationships between the different performance coefficients are given in Fig. 19.55 and are computed from the actual airplane- and marine-propeller characteristics of Fig. 19.53. The fact that the thrust must become zero before the torque becomes zero can be demonstrated from the trigonometry of Fig. 19.54 if $T = L \cos \phi - D \sin \phi$ and $M = L \sin \phi + D \cos \phi$.

19.40. Design Details

Pitch is a substantial influence on performance (Fig. 19.56) and gives higher thrust coefficients and efficiencies with the same value of slip function and increasing pitch angles for a representative aircraft propeller. The cruising and full-power regions use, generally, a pitch ratio from 0.6 to 1.3 (blade angles 10 to 30° at 0.75R). Grading curves show that little thrust is contributed by the hub section and that body interference is a maximum in this region.

Blade area has a similar effect on thrust and torque of a propeller, as does blade area on lift and drag of an airfoil; e.g., lift $= C_L \rho S v^2 / 2$. Fluid density ρ and velocity v are not amenable to manipulation in applying a propeller, so that area S is the one factor readily available to the designer. Aspect ratio dictates use of multiple blades, but blade multiplicity alters peak efficiency because of interference.

Tip speed must be held below sonic velocity (1000 ± fps) to avoid loss of thrust at supersonic speeds on aircraft propellers. Cavitation is significant on ship propellers, and acceleration must not exceed the value set by finite submergence. Noise and vibration become pronounced with high tip speeds.

Clark Y, or some reasonable modification, sections are generally used for air screws with the face (slip-stream side) flat and the back cambered for structural strength. Aspect ratio is usually about 6, with a leading straight edge and maximum blade width at 0.6 to 0.8 tip radius. Marine propellers use much greater blade widths since the velocities are very much lower and it is necessary to increase area for requisite thrust with minimum over-all diameter.

19.41. Selection

Propeller selection is one of the most difficult problems in fluid-acceleration machinery because of the many basic variables which must be related and the modification of basic performance data required by the proximity of a hull, fuselage, nacelle, or wing. The feathering, or adjustable-pitch, propeller has simplified the problem. The nature of the complexity is reflected in the data of Fig. 19.57, where it is necessary to predict the drag curve for the airplane. This must be

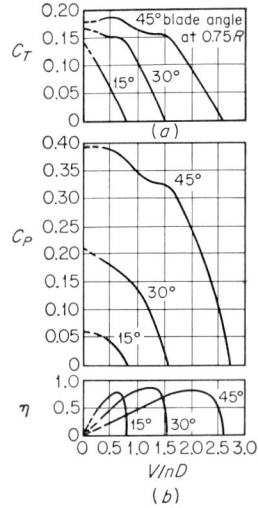

FIG. 19.56. Effect of blade angle on propeller characteristics. (*Adapted from NACA Rept. 640*).

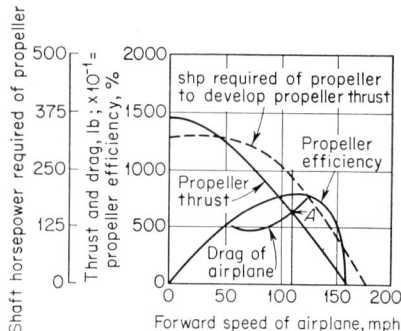

FIG. 19.57. Selection curves for an aircraft selection application.

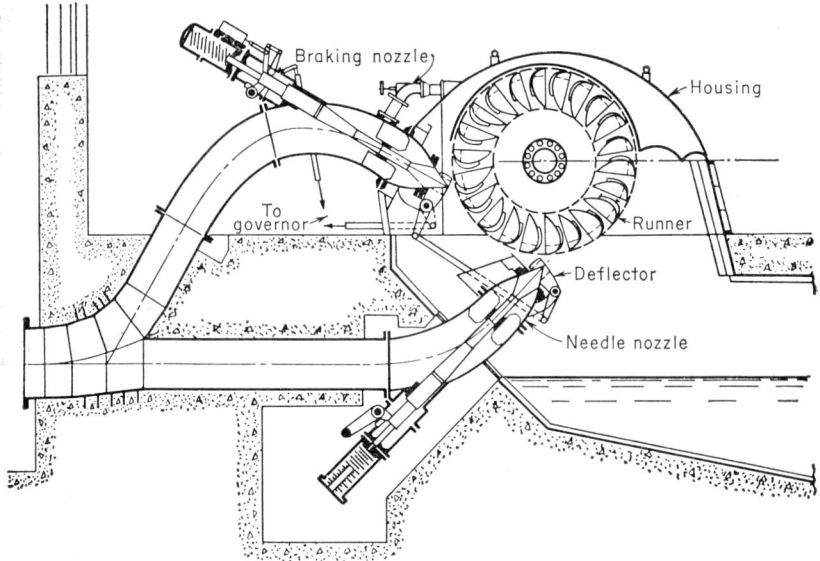

FIG. 19.58. Impulse (Pelton) hydraulic turbine, section.

matched by the thrust of the chosen propeller, as at point A. Any error in prediction of either the drag or thrust curve will shift the point A, and efficiency will be sacrificed. An appreciation of this exacting requirement serves to explain the occasional need to replace ship or airplane propellers with a second, better selection.

HYDRAULIC TURBINES

19.42. Types

The old-style water wheels which directly utilized the weight effect of an elevated water supply have been superseded by hydraulic turbines which operate on the impulse

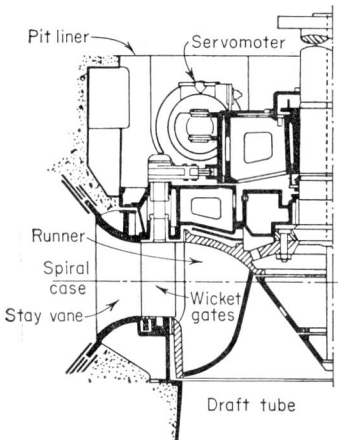

FIG. 19.59. Reaction (Francis) hydraulic turbine, half section.

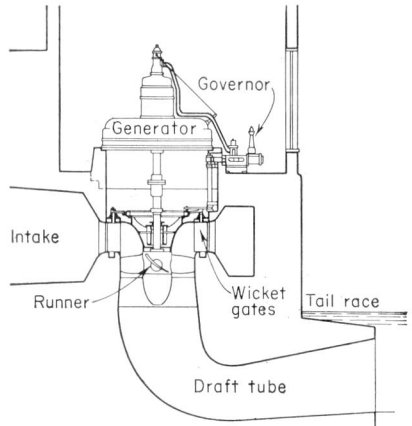

FIG. 19.60. Reaction (Smith-Kaplan) hydraulic-turbine installation, section.

or reaction principle (Art. 19.6 and Fig. 19.5). The *impulse* (*Pelton*) unit (Fig. 19.58) has all available energy converted to kinetic form in one, two, or at most four stationary nozzles, with the energy absorbed in reversing buckets mounted on the wheel. The *reaction* units (Figs. 19.59 and 19.60) run full of water, submerged, with a draft tube and a continuous column of water from headrace to tailrace. There is some fluid acceleration in stationary nozzles followed by acceleration through the moving nozzles of the rotor. The *draft tube* produces a negative pressure in the runner with the *propeller*, or *Kaplan*, units (Fig. 19.60) as suction runners, while the *Francis* (Fig. 19.59) inward-flow units act as pressure runners. All sorts of *mixed-flow* units (Fig. 19.61) give intermediate degrees of rotor pressure drop and fluid acceleration. Reaction runners use *vertical* shafts for better accommodation of the draft tube, while Pelton units usually have a *horizontal* shaft. Kaplan units employ adjustable propeller blades as well as adjustable stationary nozzles in the gate ring. Pelton runners are preferred for *high head* service (1000+ ft). Francis runners for *medium heads* (500± ft), and propeller, or Kaplan, units for *low heads* (100 ± ft).

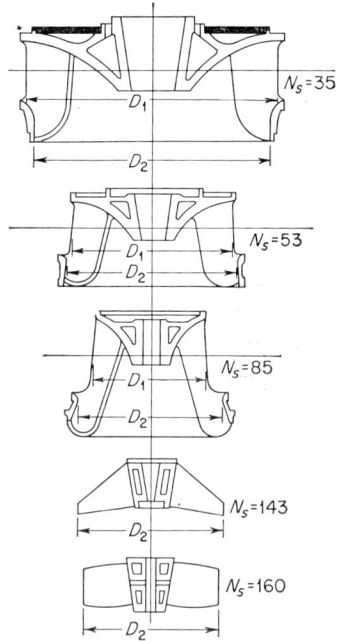

Fig. 19.61. Hydraulic-turbine runners of equal power but different specific speeds.

19.43. Performance

Figure 19.12 shows the most convenient characteristic form where speed and head are constant and power is the independent variable. Characteristics may be on the actual, percentage, or dimensionless-coefficient basis. Figure 19.62 shows complete characteristics on the last basis. Speed ratio ϕ is frequently used instead of head coefficient C_H [Eq. (19.37)], and specific speed C_{nP} or N'_s is on the power basis [Eqs. (19.34) and (19.36)].

19.44. Design Details

The vector triangles of Fig. 19.5 show, in simplified form, the basic arrangements for impulse and reaction turbines. Except possibly for the Pelton wheel, in which all the acceleration is accomplished in the stationary nozzle (discharge coefficient 0.98 over a wide operating range with the needle construction) and 160 to 170° jet reversal in the moving buckets, it is necessary to use a three-dimensional analysis for a proper interpretation of flow phenomena. Speed ratio ϕ ranges from 0.45 on Pelton units to 1.3 on propeller units, with the intermediate range devoted to Francis and mixed-pressure reaction designs. Table 19.6 gives some representative dimensional and performance data. Specific speed is a minimum on the Pelton units and for a constant ratio of wheel diameter to jet diameter is solely a function of the number of jets, to wit, with diameter ratio = 12, $N'_s = 4.42n$, $C_{nP} = 0.0163n$, and with ratio = 7, $N'_s = 7.5n$, $C_{nP} = 0.028n$, where n = the number of jets per wheel.

Reaction water-wheel types are of the widest diversity (Fig. 19.61), ranging from the true inward-radial-flow (Francis) designs, where $N'_s = 35$, $C_{nP} = 0.13$, $\phi = 0.7$, to propeller, or Kaplan, runners, where $N_s = 160$, $C_{nP} = 0.6$, $\phi = 1.2$. Other pertinent representative dimensional data are given in Table 19.6. Efficiencies in excess of 90 per cent are standard and reflect the exact understanding of fluid dynamics which is incorporated in the design of commercial units. Extension of model m to prototype p

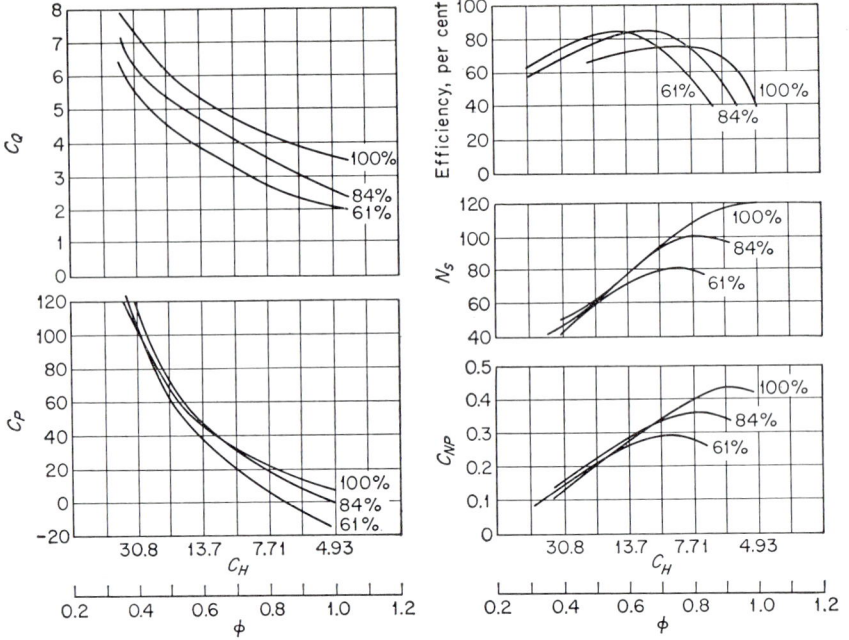

Fig. 19.62. Dimensionless-coefficient characteristics for a selected reaction turbine at various gate openings, 61, 84, and 100 per cent.

data is by equations such as the Moody [Eq. (19.65)] and Camerer [Eq. (19.66)] expressions:

$$\eta_p = 1 - (1 - \eta_m)\left(\frac{D_m}{D_p}\right)^{1/4}\left(\frac{H_m}{H_p}\right)^{1/10} \tag{19.65}$$

$$\eta_p = 1 - (1 - \eta_m)\frac{1.4 + 1/D_p}{1.4 + 1/D_m} \tag{19.66}$$

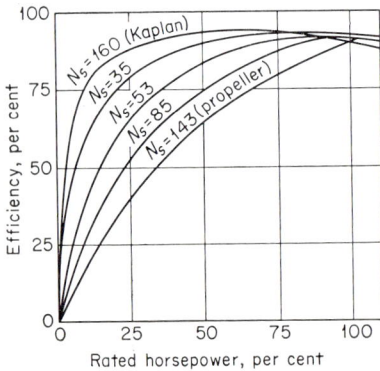

Fig. 19.63. Selected water-wheel efficiency characteristics.

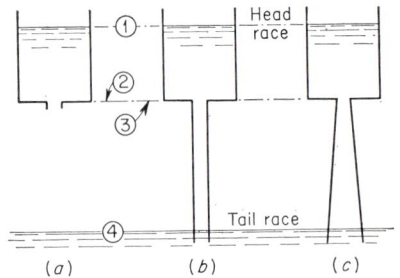

Fig. 19.64. Schematic diagram of draft-tube principles.

Table 19.6. Dimensions and Performance Data of Some Selected Hydraulic Turbines

	Reaction (Francis) units		
Wheel type.................................	1	2	3
Specific speed:			
N'_s..	12–17	35–45	80–100
C_{nP}..	0.045–0.063	0.13–0.17	0.3–0.37
Speed ratio ϕ..............................	0.6	0.7	0.9
Nozzle angle β_1, deg.......................	15	30	45
Vane angle α_1, deg.........................	60	90	125
Width-diameter ratio B/D.................	0.03	0.12	0.6

Impulse (Pelton) units	
Jet reversal, deg...............................	160–170
Wheel diameter $D_w \div$ jet diameter D_j.............	(7–14) to 1
Speed ratio ϕ................................	0.42 to 0.46
Bucket speed u, fps...........................	100 to 300
No. of jets per wheel..........................	1–4
Jet diameter, in., approximate maximum...........	12
Specific speed, over-all range:	
N'_s...	3–12
C_{nP}..	0.011–0.045
Specific-speed, single-wheel, single-jet $(D_w/D_j = 12)$:	
N'_s...	4.42
C_{nP}..	0.0165
Specific-speed, single-wheel, single-jet $(D_w/D_j = 7)$:	
N'_s...	7.5
C_{nP}..	0.0278

Figure 19.63 gives comparative efficiency characteristics for a selected group of turbines. The Kaplan designs with their feathering blades and adjustable wicket gates give the maximum range of sustained efficiency. Propeller units, on the other hand, give a sharp peak to the efficiency curve, but can be simplified in construction and made lower in price by substitution of fixed rotor blades and cylindrical gates.

19.45. Draft Tubes

Draft tubes are a component element of all reaction-turbine installations and serve many purposes, e.g., to utilize the full site head between headrace and tailrace; to place the unit safely above tail water even with flood conditions; and partially to regain kinetic energy in the water, leaving the discharge side of the runner in a helical-flow pattern. Figure 19.64 serves to demonstrate the basic conditions where, in part *a*, discharge is to atmosphere and the head below the orifice (runner) is lost; in part *b*, the full head is made available by the tail pipe; and in part *c*, the divergent section will regain some of the velocity energy leaving the runner. In any event, the physical height of draft tube must be less than the atmospheric-pressure equivalent to retain the unbroken column of liquid between headrace and tailrace.

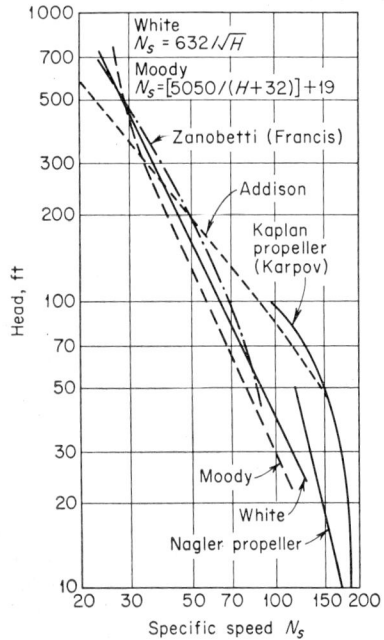

Fig. 19.65. Specific speed-head experience curves for hydraulic turbines.

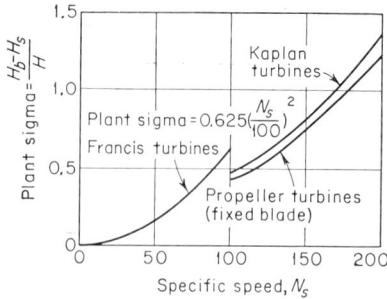

FIG. 19.66. Values of plant sigma cavitation coefficient. (*Adapted from Rogers, ASCE, December,* 1937.)

19.46. Selection and Cavitation

There are severe limitations on the practical selection of a hydraulic turbine for a given site as defined by (1) specific-speed experience curves (Fig. 19.65) and (2) cavitation coefficients (Fig. 19.66). Figure 19.65 shows the former as prescribed by several authorities. Cavitation manifests itself by pitting of runner parts. Material selection will help reduce wear by erosion and chemical corrosion. Improperly designed wheels and installations are subject to hydraulic cavitation, and pitting from this cause is not corrected by material selection. In the runner passages, at or near the exit, absolute pressures may get so low as to be less than the vapor pressure. Bubbles or cavities form, which on subsequent collapse damage the parts by violent mechanical action. Excessive maintenance costs can be avoided if the absolute pressure is prevented from dropping below a predetermined satisfactory minimum. Installation conditions must comply with the practical standard (Fig. 19.66) of plant sigma σ, defined as $\sigma = (H_b - H_s)/H$, if H_b = barometric water column, H_s = greatest height above tail water at which cavitation does not occur, H = total effective head on turbine, all measured in feet.

STEAM AND GAS TURBINES

19.47. Types

Steam and gas turbines, like hydraulic turbines, operate on the *impulse* or *reaction* principle (Fig. 19.5), but to accommodate the supersonic jet velocities to acceptable bucket speeds, rpm, and wheel diameters, *multistage* constructions prevail. The basic problem for the designer is to give the most effective reconciliation among the items of jet speed, bucket speed, strength speed, and use speed. From the fluid-dynamic viewpoint, a turbine is essentially a series of calibrated nozzles with the flow cross-section areas becoming progressively larger through the machine. Impulse turbines may be (1) *velocity-staged* (*Curtis*) (Fig. 19.67c) with multiple rows of moving blades and sta-

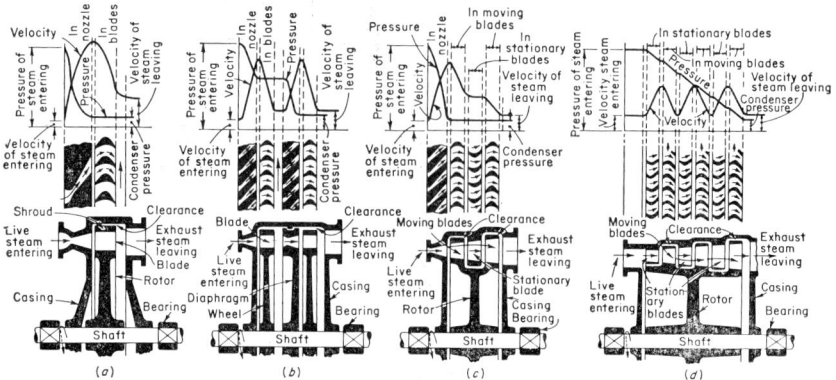

FIG. 19.67. Basic steam-turbine types: (*a*) simple impulse (DeLaval), (*b*) pressure-staged impulse (Rateau), (*c*) velocity-staged impulse (Curtis), (*d*) reaction (Parsons).

Fig. 19.68. Tandem compound double-flow, multistage, condensing steam turbine (half section). (*General Electric Co.*)

tionary blades following a row of nozzles, or they may be *reentry* type with a single row of moving blades, or (2) *pressure-staged (Rateau)* (Fig. 19.67*b*) with a cellular construction (Fig. 19.69), where each cell is in reality a *DeLaval* type (Fig. 19.67*a*) and operates at its own pressure. *Reaction (Parsons)* (Fig. 19.67*d*) turbines have both stationary and moving nozzles in alternate rows and are usually built with a *drum*-type rotor instead of *wheel*-type. The *Ljungström* design is a *radially outward* flow unit with alternate rings of oppositely turning nozzles instead of *axial* flow as with Parsons units. *Single* or *multicylinder* or *barrel, tandem* or *cross-compound, single* or *multiple shaft,*

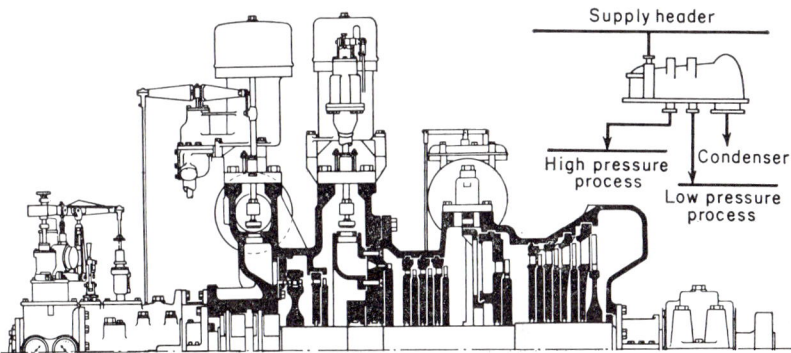

Fig. 19.69. Condensing double-automatic constant-pressure industrial-type steam turbine (half section). (*General Electric Co.*)

single or *double case, extraction* or *nonextraction, constant* or *variable speed, condensing* or *noncondensing, regulated* or *unregulated bleed pressures, marine, central station,* or *industrial* are all names which serve to identify turbines by customary features. *Horizontal shafts* are standard with steam turbines, but *vertical shafts* are standard with hydraulic turbines. Figures 19.68 to 19.70 illustrate representative steam and gas turbines.

19.48. Performance and Terms

Over-all performance is generally shown by characteristic curves (Figs. 19.71 and 19.72) with steam consumption and engine efficiency as a function of power output all at constant speed, steam pressure, steam temperature, and exhaust pressure. Steam

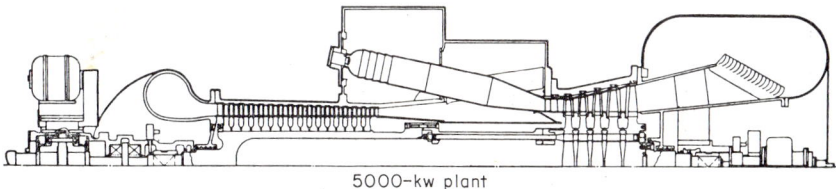

5000-kw plant

Fig. 19.70. Single-shaft gas turbine, half section.

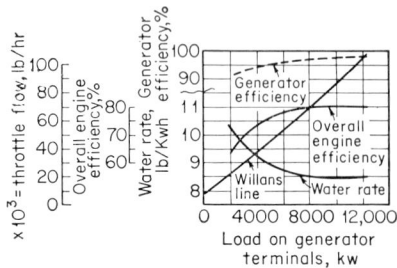

FIG. 19.71. Water rate, Willans line, and efficiency characteristics of a 10,000-kw steam-turbine–generator unit.

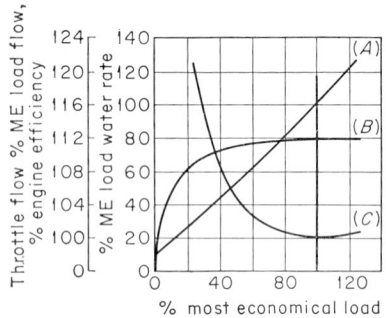

FIG. 19.72. Percentage characteristics of a steam-turbine–generator: (A) throttle flow, (B) engine efficiency, (C) water rate.

consumption may be expressed as water rate, pounds per kilowatthour or pounds per hour (Willans line). Some approximate correction factors are given in Table 19.7. Engine efficiency is defined as the ratio of the actual work to the Rankine-cycle work and is most conveniently evaluated by the use of the Mollier chart (Fig. 19.73). The ideal work

$$\Delta h = h_i - h_f \tag{19.67}$$

in which the initial and final enthalpies are related by an isentropic expansion. The actual work will be less than this and may or may not include bearing and generator losses. Similarly, the ideal work may or may not include throttle losses at entrance or leaving losses at exit.

The state line (Fig. 19.73) shows graphically the conditions of the fluid in each stage of the turbine for various flow rates. The steeper the line, the closer it approaches the

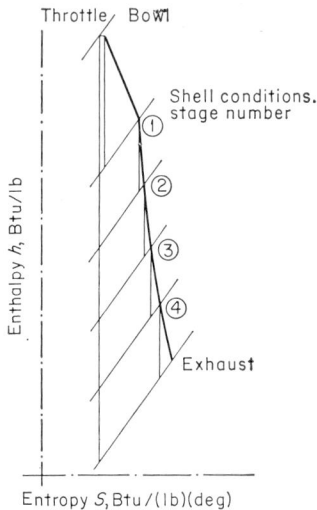

FIG. 19.73. State line or condition curve for a steam turbine as plotted on a Mollier chart.

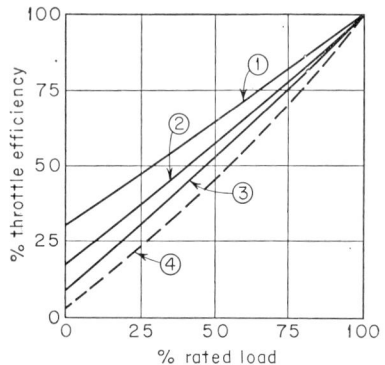

FIG. 19.74. Comparative Willans lines for several steam turbines, percentage basis: (1) throttle-governed auxiliary turbine, (2) throttle-governed central-station turbine, (3) nozzle-governed central-station turbine, (4) marine turbine.

Table 19.7. Some Approximate Correction Factors for Water Rates of Steam Turbines

(Applicable to parameter changes less than ±10 per cent)

Item	Factor, %	Note
Steam pressure	1–1.5 per 10 psi	Higher on small turbines and low pressures
Superheat	0.5–1.0 per 10°F	Lower with higher superheats
Vacuum	5–10 per 1 in. Hg abs	Higher with high vacuum
Positive exhaust pressure	2–3 per 1 psi	Atmospheric exhaust pressure
Speed	1 per 100 rpm	3600-rpm turbine

isentropic ideal. The line is steeper with superheated than with wet steam and with large passages as opposed to small passages.

The pressure on any stage is approximately proportional to the weight flow below that stage.

Performance curves may be plotted on percentage bases as in Figs. 19.72 and 19.74. The curves on steam consumption will show discontinuities on valve openings, but the Willans lines of Fig. 19.74 can be considered straight and continuous for many estimating purposes. The intercept on the latter ranges from 4 to 30 per cent of the most efficient value.

Engine efficiencies are a function of size, design conditions, and operating conditions (Figs. 19.75 and 19.76). The wide latitude in efficiency is reflected in the investment and operating costs which are permissible.

19.49. Design Details

The inefficiency reflected in the state lines (Fig. 19.73) is the aggregate of many losses, e.g., nozzle, blade, interstage leakage, disc friction, windage, fanning, throttle, and exit (Table 19.8).

The actual jet velocity is found from the ideal Rankine cycle, enthalpy drop (Btu/lb) [Eq. (19.67)], by introducing a velocity coefficient C_v or the nozzle efficiency η_n:

$$\text{Actual jet velocity, fps} = C_v \times 223.8 \sqrt{\Delta h} = 223.8 \sqrt{\eta_n \, \Delta h} \qquad (19.68)$$

The numerical value of C_v or η_n is always high (Fig. 19.77). If expansion is beyond the critical (back pr < 0.5 init pr), the nozzle must theoretically have a diffuser section follow-

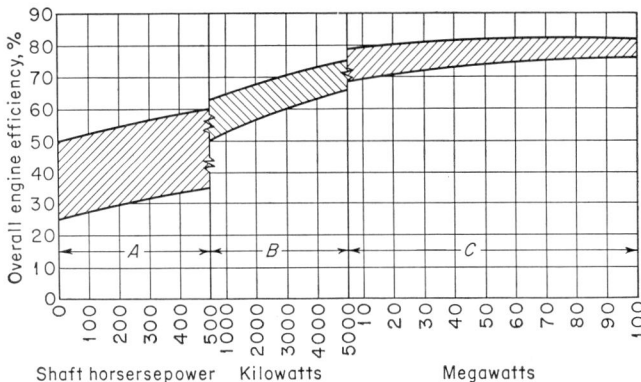

Fig. 19.75. Engine efficiencies for representative steam turbines: region A for auxiliary units, B for industrial units, C for central-station units.

Table 19.8. Dimensions and Performance Data of Some Selected Steam Turbines

Turbine type	Impulse, velocity-staged	Impulse, pressure-staged	Reaction
Nozzle angle β_1, deg...............	10–30	10–30	10–30
Vane angle α_1, deg.................	15–30	15–30	70–80
Vane angle α_2, deg.................	18–24 1st row	15–30 HP end	
	25–40 2d row	$(3–5° > \alpha_1)$	
		50° max. LP end	
Nozzle efficiency, %...............	0.89–0.93	0.95–0.99	
Blading efficiency, %..............	0.75–0.85	0.88–0.93	0.85–0.92
Stage efficiency, %................	0.6–0.7	0.7–0.9	0.7–0.9
Speed ratio......................	0.20–0.23 (2-row)	0.40–0.46	0.75–0.90
Blade height, in..................	0.5–3	0.5–30	0.5–30
		(0.01 to 0.3 PD)	(0.01 to 0.3 PD)
Axial length, in..................	0.5–2	0.75–4	0.35–2.0
Blade pitch, in...................	0.3–1	0.3–1	0.2–1
Max. pitch diameter, ft..........	6	10±	10±
Tip speed at PD, fps..............	300–600	300–1500	300–1500

ing the throat. The ratio of mouth to throat areas favors underexpansion rather than overexpansion (Fig. 19.78). Diffuser angles are usually less than 20°, with a linearly uniform increase in diameter. Some turbine designs (e.g., Rateau) will use no diffuser section, with expansion limited to the critical or a little beyond. Nozzles are usually constructed of blades or buckets (Fig. 19.5). Nozzle angles (β_1) are 10 to 30°. For good hydraulic mean depth, impulse turbines may use partial circumferential admission but reaction turbines must use full circumferential admission.

For symmetrical impulse blades and a nozzle angle of 10 to 20°, the ideal blading efficiency is from 88 to 97 per cent [Figs. 19.5, 19.10, and Eq. (19.29)]. Shock, eddy, impact, and friction losses $(w_2 < w_1)$ lead to lower actual blading efficiencies (Fig. 19.79). On reaction turbines the blading and nozzle efficiencies are usually combined with the results often called stage efficiency.

Blade heights, axial-blade lengths, and blade pitch are essentially the combination of experience on successful designs and good aerodynamics. Blade heights are never less than 0.5 in. Tip speeds are as high as 1800 fps on some gas turbines, 1200 fps on long-life steam-turbine exhaust ends, and 500 to 1000 fps as standard general practice. Long blades [30(54) in. max at 3600(1800)rpm] may have a length equal to one-third the pitch diameter, and for equal effectiveness along their entire length they must be warped surfaces. Structural considerations usually dictate aspect ratio.

Entrance angles (α_1) of moving blades range from a minimum of 15° on some impulse turbines to a maximum of 80 or 90° on reaction units. Exit angles (α_2) may be as small as 15° for maximum jet reversal and to reduce velocity carryover, or they may be as large as 50° to handle maximum volumes of flow.

Leaving (exit) loss from the last stage of a turbine shows a minimum value for some particular flow (Fig. 19.80) where the absolute velocity v_2 assumes a position perpendicular to the bucket velocity u_2 (Fig. 19.5). The leaving loss also includes the fluid-dynamic losses through the exhaust annulus and hood, with the axial exhaust showing the minimum over-all loss.

Leakage losses are minimized by the use of glands, packings, and labyrinths and may range as high as 5 per cent on any stage with a turbine in poor repair. Disc and windage losses are proportional to $n^3 D^5 \bar{w}$, if n = speed, D = diameter,

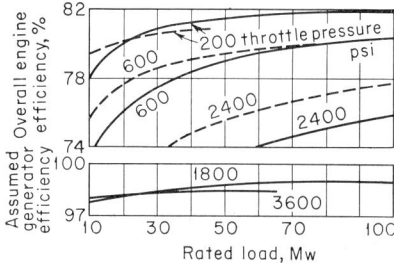

FIG. 19.76. Engine efficiencies of selected large steam-turbine–generators: 300° superheat, 4 per cent exhaust loss, 1.25 per cent mechanical loss; full lines, 1800 rpm, broken lines, 3600 rpm. *(Adapted from Warren.)*

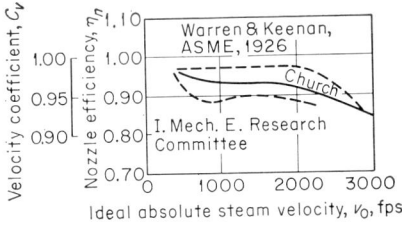

FIG. 19.77. Impulse-turbine-nozzle efficiencies.

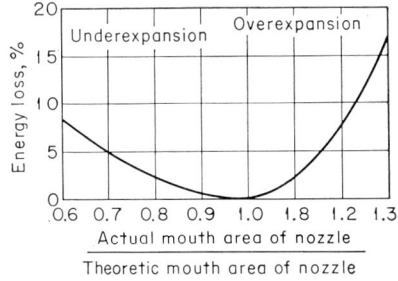

FIG. 19.78. Effect of under- and overexpansion on turbine-nozzle losses. (*Adapted from Church and Steinmetz.*)

$\bar{w}$ = fluid density. Stage efficiency reflects all these component items and is defined as the ratio of the actual work output on a stage to the isentropic drop for that stage. Bearing losses are external to the turbine and do not appear as reheat in the steam.

19.50. Axial Thrust

In the impulse turbine the relative velocity w_2 leaving a stage is smaller than the entering velocity w_1, because of friction with resulting axial thrust. If the exit-blade angle α_2 is made some 5° larger than the entering angle α_1, the thrust will be largely offset. In the reaction turbine there is a pressure drop and consequent acceleration across any moving blade row, with a resultant axial thrust of considerable magnitude. Balancing pistons and divided or double-opposed flow are common corrective devices. In any event, a thrust bearing must be included primarily to meet the imbalance of starting and stopping conditions.

19.51. Governing and Regulation

The common methods of governing either throttle the steam supply to the first stage or cut out nozzles at the front end. The latter gives a wider range of load for maximum

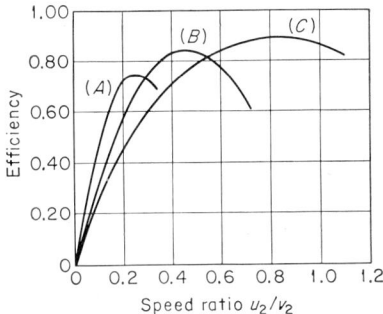

FIG. 19.79. Blading efficiency vs. speed ratio: (*A*) actual for a two-row Curtis stage with nozzle angle 20°, symmetrical blades; (*B*) actual for a single-row impulse stage with nozzle angle 20°, symmetrical blades; (*C*) actual combined nozzle and blading efficiency for a Parsons reaction stage with nozzle and angle 15°. (*Adapted from Church.*)

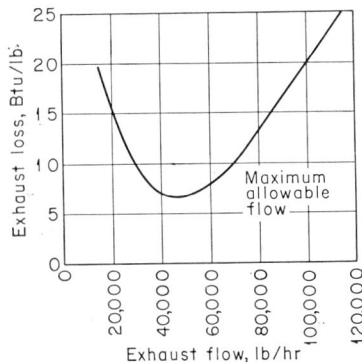

FIG. 19.80. Exhaust loss curve for a condensing turbine at 1 in. Hg abs; actual loss = curve reading × engine efficiency; exhaust loss at any exhaust pressure from $G_{corrected} = G_{actual} \times$ sp $val_{actual}/580$, where G is weight flow.

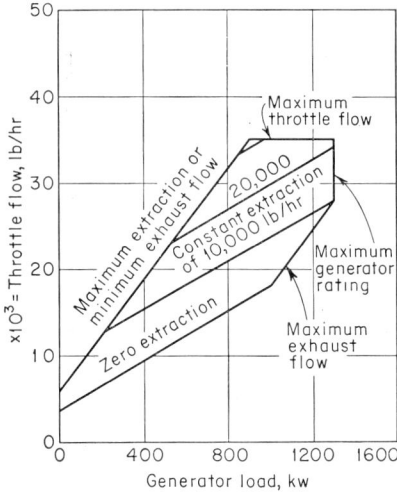

FIG. 19.81. Willans lines for an automatic-extraction turbine-generator.

economy on the use of steam. Sometimes a bypass is incorporated, with throttle governing, wherein the steam is introduced at a lower stage with heavy flows. Stationary turbines usually show minimum water rate at two-thirds to three-quarters load, but marine turbines may demand a lower load for maximum economy. With industrial turbines, where a constant-pressure bleed point (Fig. 19.69) is often specified for process or heating purposes, an internal throttle (grid valve) is employed. The resulting performance of such a unit is typified by the characteristics of Fig. 19.81.

FLUID COUPLINGS

19.52. Types

The hydrokinetic coupling is essentially a centrifugal pump impeller and a hydraulic turbine runner in series in a circuit for the control of output speed, power, and torque. Accompanying advantages of its use include simpler parts alignment of driver and driven member, rapid declutching and rapid speed control, reduced shock loads and torsional-vibration transmission, power saving, and better maintenance. Essential elements of a *coupling* are shown in Fig. 19.82, where a vortex is set up between the two elements of the torus, and if the primary shaft operates at a constant speed, the sec-

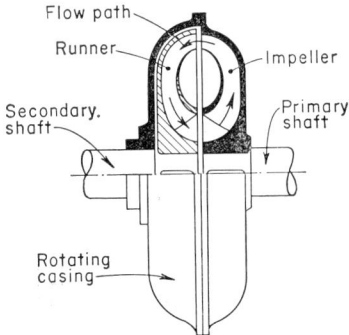

FIG. 19.82. Fluid coupling.

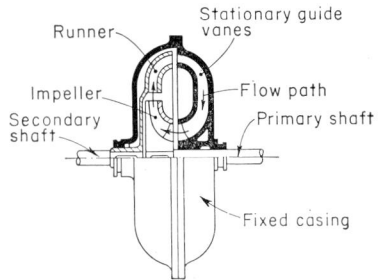

FIG. 19.83. Fluid torque converter.

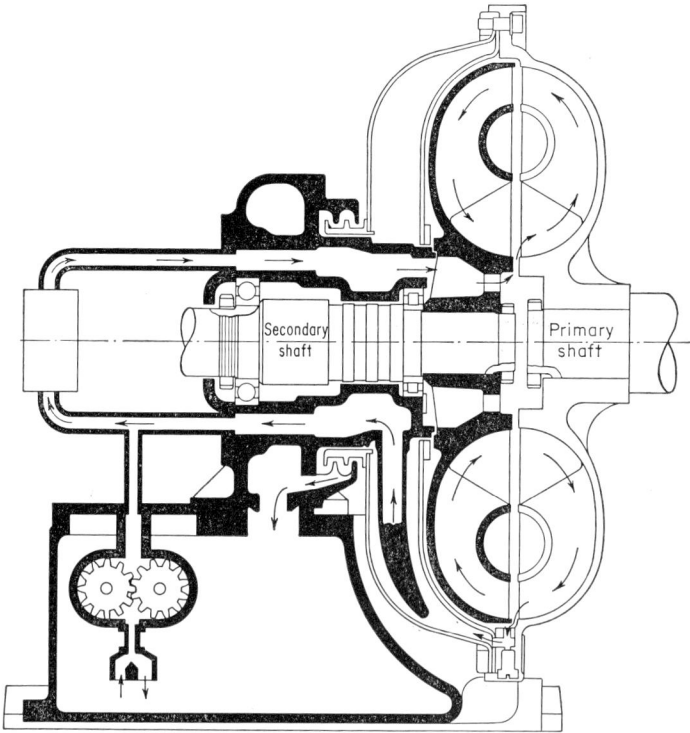

Fig. 19.84. Variable-filling, scoop-tube coupling.

ondary shaft can run at any speed from standstill to within 2 per cent of the primary shaft speed. The primary and secondary shaft torques are equal in the mechanism of Fig. 19.82, but if the torque is to be modified, then a *torque converter* (Fig. 19.83) with a set of stationary guide vanes between the two moving elements must be incorporated. Some constructions are a combination of the coupling and converter features. Fluid

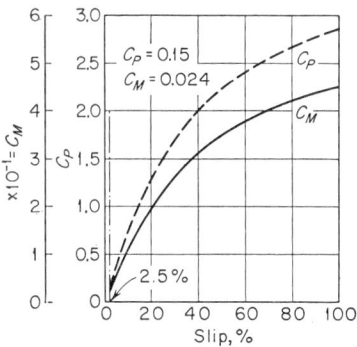

Fig. 19.85. Dimensionless-coefficient characteristics of a selected hydraulic coupling.

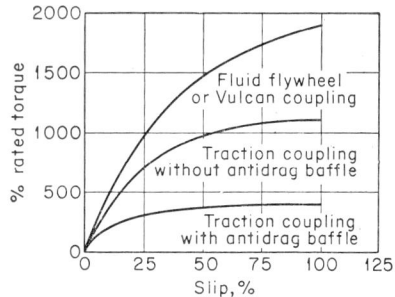

Fig. 19.86. Percentage characteristics of a selected hydraulic coupling.

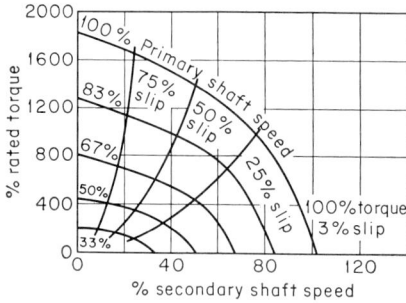

Fig. 19.87. Torque characteristics of a selected hydraulic coupling, percentage basis.

couplings may be constant-filling or variable-filling, as with a scoop-tube construction (Fig. 19.84). Losses may be dissipated as heat through the casing to the ambient for small traction-type applications, but with large powers a circulatory cooling system with pumps and heat exchangers is necessary (Fig. 19.84).

19.53. Performance (Couplings)

The purpose of a coupling, resolved to its simplest terms, is to vary the speed n_s of the secondary shaft s when the primary shaft p is operating at a given speed n_p by controlling the slip between the two shafts. The torque M is constant ($M = M_p = M_s$) for a true coupling (Fig. 19.82) despite efforts to use vanes of various curvatures. This constancy does not alter the applicability of characteristic curves (Figs. 19.85 to 19.87). It means that input and output torque has one distinct value for a given coupling operating at a given speed and slip. If some other torque is desired for the given coupling, either the primary speed n_p or the slip must be altered, when slip is defined by

$$\text{Slip} = \frac{n_p - n_s}{n_p} \tag{19.69}$$

Efficiency η is the ratio of power output P_s to power input P_p, or

$$\eta = \frac{P_s}{P_p} = \frac{M_s W_s}{M_p W_p} = \frac{W_s}{W_p} = \frac{n_s}{n_p} \tag{19.70}$$

By combining Eqs. (19.69) and (19.70), the important conclusion is that the efficiency of a coupling is equal to 1 minus the slip, a relationship which holds for all degrees of filling. The inefficiency represented by the slip will appear as heat which must be removed (1) by an external cooling system (Fig. 19.84) if the losses are high, as with many constant-speed drivers, or (2) by dissipation to the ambient if the losses are small, as with an automotive application where the driver speed can be varied and the slip kept low.

The same rules apply for expressing coupling performance as apply with pumps and turbines, so that characteristic curves on the actual, percentage, or coefficient bases are most significant. Figures 19.85 to 19.87 show some representative curves. The power C_P and torque C_M coefficients are defined by

$$C_P = \frac{Pg}{n^3_p D^5 \bar{w}} \tag{19.71}$$

and

$$C_M = \frac{Mg}{n^2_p D^5 \bar{w}} \tag{19.72}$$

if D is the diameter. The graphs show that with a constant primary speed, the torque and power increase rapidly with slip but taper off as the stall point is approached. The slip curves express efficiency, because, as pointed out above, efficiency is the complement of slip.

19.54. Design Details

Many attempts have been made to improve on the torque-equality feature of couplings by variation in blade design details, but practice has standardized on flat radial blades for both impeller and runner. While high fluid density will decrease the bulk

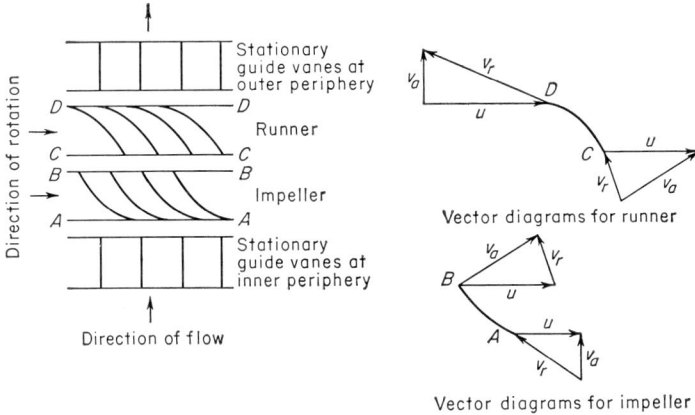

Fig. 19.88. Vector diagrams for a torque converter.

and diameter of a coupling, the requirements of good lubricating properties, noncorrosiveness, low viscosity, low freezing point, high boiling point, chemical stability, and low over-all cost usually lead to the selection of a typical turbine oil of 150 to 300 SSU at 100°F maximum viscosity. Traction automotive couplings usually have capacities below 500 hp, but variable-filling couplings, suitable for direct connection to electric motors, are built in sizes ranging to 20,000 hp.

19.55. Performance (Torque Converter)

If the control of speed of the secondary shaft is to be accompanied by amplification of torque, then a converter (Fig. 19.83) which contains a set of stationary guide vanes in the fluid circuit must be used. Typical vector diagrams are illustrated in Fig. 19.88, where the designer has ample latitude of choice to alter the resultant characteristic performance curves (Fig. 19.89). The primary shaft speed n_p is constant (and therefore primary torque M_p is constant), so the graph uses secondary shaft speed n_s as the independent variable. Percentage values are replotted in Fig. 19.90, using speed ratio as the independent variable. For the converter shown, the secondary torque M_s is

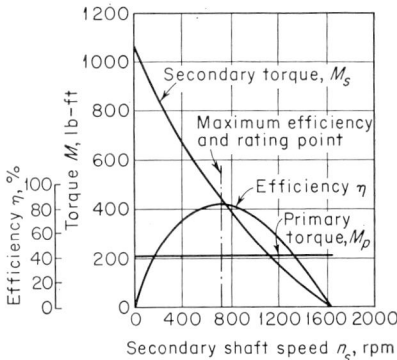

Fig. 19.89. Actual characteristics for a selected torque converter: primary shaft speed n_p, constant at 1800 rpm.

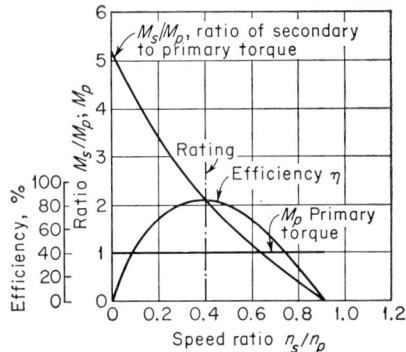

Fig. 19.90. Relative characteristics for a selected torque converter.

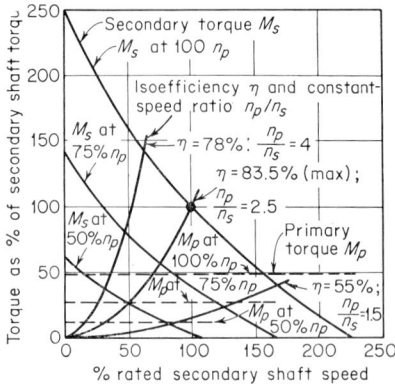

FIG. 19.91. Percentage characteristics for a selected torque converter.

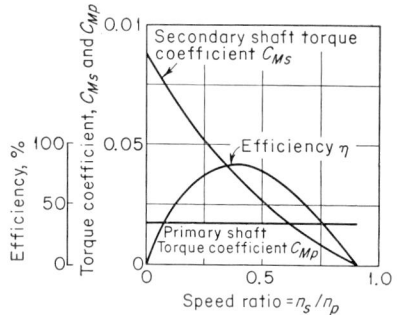

FIG. 19.92. Dimensionless coefficients for a selected torque converter.

more than double M_p at the point of maximum efficiency and five times as great at stall. (Efficiency $= P_s/P_p = M_s n_s/M_p n_p$.)

A nest of percentage characteristics can be drawn as in Fig. 19.91, using the value of secondary torque M_s at 100 per cent n_p and the point of maximum efficiency as the rating base. The M_s values slope sharply downward, while the M_p curves are horizontal. The isoefficiency curves also signify constant-speed ratios, n_p/n_s. If the customary rules are applied to the data, the results can be expressed as a set of dimensionless-coefficient curves (Fig. 19.92) to give absolute, instead of relative, performance values. The torque coefficients C_{Mp} and C_{Ms} (primary and secondary) are defined as

$$C_{Mp} = \frac{M_p g}{n^2_p D^5 \bar{w}} \qquad (19.73)$$

and

$$C_{Ms} = \frac{M_s g}{n^2_p D^5 \bar{w}} \qquad (19.74)$$

where all values are in feet, pounds, seconds.

19.56. Design Details

Torque converters for marine application, with both ahead and astern circuits for reversibility, are built in sizes as large as 20,000 hp and a speed reduction from 1000 or 1500 rpm to propeller speed and a torque conversion of some 5:1 at 85 per cent efficiency. This efficiency is too low for competitive purposes, so that a hydraulic coupling, with 97 to 98 per cent efficiency and reduction gears in series, is usually preferred.

Multiple stages, with or without automatic shifting from a converter to a coupling condition, are used in some applications. With rail service, high starting torque is required so the converter feature may be used until a predetermined speed (e.g., 50 per cent) is reached, when there is an automatic changeover to the coupling circuit. This is an attempt to utilize the inherent advantages of the two basic types of hydrodynamic gear.

REFERENCES

1. Addison, H.: "Treatise on Applied Hydraulics," Wiley, New York, 1945.
2. *ASME Power Test Codes*, New York.
3. Baumeister, T.: "Fans," McGraw-Hill, New York, 1935.
3a. Baumeisler, T. (ed.): "Marks' Mechanical Engineers' Handbook." McGraw-Hill, New York, 1958.

4. Binder, R. C.: "Advanced Fluid Dynamics and Fluid Machinery," Prentice-Hall, Englewood Cliffs, N.J., 1951.
5. Church, E. F.: "Steam Turbines," McGraw-Hill, New York, 1950.
6. Church, A. H.: "Centrifugal Pumps and Blowers," Wiley, New York, 1944.
7. Eck, B.: "Ventilatoren," Springer, Berlin, 1957.
8. Gibson, A. H.: "Hydraulics and Its Application," Constable, London, 1952.
9. Glauert, H.: "Aerofoil and Airscrew Theory," Cambridge, New York, 1948.
10. Hunsaker, J. C., and B. G. Rightmire: "Engineering Applications of Fluid Mechanics," McGraw-Hill, New York, 1947.
11. Kearton, W. J.: "Steam Turbine Theory and Practice," Pitman, New York, 1948.
12. Kearton, W. J.: "Turbo-blowers and Compressors," Pitman, New York, 1926.
13. Keller, C. (Marks): "Axial Flow Fans," McGraw-Hill, New York, 1937.
14. Lorenz, H.: "Neue Theorie und Berechnung der Kreiselraeder," Oldenbourg, Munich, 1906.
15. Moss, S. A., W. R. Foote, and C. W. Smith: Energy Transfer between a Fluid and a Rotor for Pump and Turbine Machinery, *Trans. ASME*, vol. 64, 1942.
16. Newman, L. E.: "Modern Turbines," Wiley, New York, 1944.
17. Rossell, H. E., and L. R. Chapman: "Principles of Naval Architecture," SNAME, New York, 1939.
18. Rouse, H., and J. W. Howe: "Basic Mechanics of Fluids," Wiley, New York, 1953.
19. Salisbury, J. K.: "Steam Turbines and Their Cycles," Wiley, New York, 1950.
20. Shepherd, D. G.: "Principles of Turbomachinery," Macmillan, New York, 1956.
21. Shepherd, D. G.: "An Introduction to the Gas Turbine," Van Nostrand, Princeton, N.J., 1949.
22. Spannhake, W.: "Centrifugal Pumps, Turbines, and Propellers," Technology Press, Cambridge, Mass., 1934.
23. Stepanoff, A. J.: "Centrifugal and Axial Flow Pumps," Wiley, New York, 1957.
24. Stodola, A. (Lowenstein): "Steam and Gas Turbines," McGraw-Hill, New York, 1927.
25. Weick, F. E.: "Aircraft Propeller Design," McGraw-Hill, New York, 1930.
26. Wislicenus, G. F.: "Fluid Mechanics of Turbomachinery," McGraw-Hill, New York, 1947.

Section 20

FLUID TRANSIENTS IN ENGINEERING SYSTEMS

By

HENRY M. PAYNTER, *Massachusetts Institute of Technology, Cambridge, Massachusetts*

FLUID TRANSIENTS IN ENGINEERING SYSTEMS

20.1. Introduction

The dynamic phenomena encountered in the confined flow of fluids through pipes, ducts, and other conduits connecting two or more regions of space are treated in this section.

It is not possible to move fluids in any fashion except with the expenditure of some available energy. This necessity has a profound influence upon the basic design of the transporting geometry. For example, in the case of pipelines carrying petroleum or natural gas, pumping stations must be located at frequent intervals to replace the energy lost in pipe friction.

However, at this point the steady-state problem is not of primary interest. Rather, the circumstances surrounding any *changes* from a steady-flow regime are considered. The dominant features of these modes are manifestations of the conservation principles of mass and momentum, customarily associated with the notions of surge and water hammer.

The term *water hammer* is commonly used to cover all pressure transients in hydraulic pipelines that demonstrate both inertial and elastic effects, while the word *surge*, in hydraulics at least, generally refers to the inertial effects, alone. Here the word "water hammer" is used as a synonym for fluid transients, to cover all such phenomena, and, whenever a distinction must be made between elastic and inertial effects, reference is made to them as such. These points are clarified in the discussion of the elastic and rigid analyses below.

A Thumbnail History of Water-hammer Research. The Russian physicist, Nicolai Egorovich Joukowsky, and the Italian engineer, Lorenzo Allievi, working independently, first demonstrated at the turn of the century that the phenomenon commonly known to engineers as water hammer was an acoustic wave action and thus fell completely within the scope of the classical wave equation of mathematical physics.

Therefore, credit for the first efforts to solve water-hammer problems mathematically would appear to belong to Euler, who investigated the wave equation around 1775 in connection with the problem of the circulation of the blood. This was followed by work on the propagation of sound waves and other acoustic phenomena in unconfined water by Savart (1825) and Cagnard de la Tour (1835). Wertheim (1848) found that the actual velocity of sound through water confined in conduits was less than the theoretical formula $c = \sqrt{B/\rho}$, which was correctly attributed by Helmholtz that same year to the elastic deflections of the pipe walls.

Thomas Young (1808) had earlier considered the problem of a rigid liquid column surrounded by elastic pipe walls, again in connection with the blood circulation problem. His work was verified by detailed experiments conducted by E. H. Weber and W. Weber (c. 1830) using water and rubber hose. The only complete link to this past research seems to be the studies of Korteweg (1878) who reconciled the effects of elasticity of *both* the fluid and the pipe and first gave the accurate formula for the velocity of sound in a thin-walled pipe [Eq. (20.34)].

Historically, the first purely mathematical solutions to the partial differential equation known as the *wave equation*

$$\frac{\partial^2 u}{\partial t^2} = c^2 \nabla^2 u$$

were obtained about the same time by d'Alembert, Euler, and Daniel Bernoulli (c. 1750) in connection with the problem of the vibrations of a musical string. This work was generalized by Fourier in the early 1800s, followed by the extensions of the wave equation to two- and three-dimensional cases by Poisson and Liouville in the early nineteenth century, when solutions were obtained for elastic waves in fluids. The first studies of the nonlinear problem of sound waves of finite amplitude propagated in air were made independently by Riemann and Earnshaw (1860), the former introducing the method of characteristics (Art. 20.4).

Water hammer, as such, was first studied by Michaud (1878), who discussed various means of alleviating the effects but without associating the problem with the prior work on sound waves. This crucial connection may be attributed to Joukowsky[1] in 1897, who carried out an impressive series of complementary experiments to verify his theories and who developed the now classic Joukowsky formula for the water-hammer pressure change due to sudden velocity change [Eq. (20.108)]. His experimental results indicated that the reflections of branch pipes influenced the pressures, but he did not develop adequate analysis to treat these effects.

The masterful work of Allievi[2] in 1904 and 1913 reviewed all previous studies, again rediscovering and redeveloping many of these earlier formulas, but here establishing the relationships for slow valve closures based upon an idealized throttle with a constant discharge coefficient. Although he concentrated his attention on obtaining pressure-time curves and maximum rise and drop in pressure due to *linear* valve stroking, all his techniques apply equally well to more general throttle conditions. In fact, his generally useful relation [Eq. (20.119)] is known throughout the world as "Allievi's equation."

Contemporary with the work of Allievi were the European studies of Boulanger, Boussinesq, A. H. Gibson, Rateau, and de Sparre.

The first studies of water hammer originating in the United States were those made by R. D. Johnson (1915), who developed a rigid theory, and by N. R. Gibson (1920), who established an elastic theory without knowledge of the prior work of Allievi and other contemporary European writers. In a discussion of the Gibson paper, E. E. Halmos first introduced American hydraulic engineers to the work of Allievi, pointing out that the (N. R.) Gibson and Allievi results were identical and also that the value for the limiting pressure in slow linear closures [Eq.(20.119)] was identical for both the rigid and the elastic theories. Halmos made another significant contribution to American art with his translation of Allievi's treatise which appeared in 1925.[26]

Since this pioneering work there has been a copious amount of theoretical and experimental study devoted to the problem of water hammer down to the present day, the major portion of which merely gives corroboratory evidence to support theoretical results when they are suitably modified to meet field conditions, and much of which has always been a rediscovery or restatement of previously derived relationships. Many valuable studies have been made, applying these theories and techniques to particular problems with noteworthy success. Much of this work was summarized and reported at the two International Symposia on Water Hammer sponsored by the Water Hammer Committee of the ASME in 1933 and in 1937, as well as in many subsequent isolated papers.

If nothing else has been learned in the exhaustive and detailed attention that has been given to single aspects of this one problem, it is now certainly realized that no single formula is so useful in the treatment of water-hammer problems as a thorough understanding of the basic assumptions and working principles. It is with this experience-proved precept in mind that the ideas of this section are developed.

20.2. Notation

The notation of this section basically follows that employed in Sec. 2 and in most other places in this handbook. The following list summarizes both standard symbols and special nomenclature.

a wave velocity in tube
A area
B liquid bulk modulus

B	valve opening
c	acoustic plane-wave celerity
C	capacitance
$\mathcal{C}$	pipeline specific capacitance
D	diameter
D	differential operator $= d/dt$
D_i	inside diameter
D_o	outside diameter
e	wall thickness
E	pipe elastic modulus
f	pipe stress factor
f	Darcy friction factor
$\mathbf{F}$	generalized phase-delay operator
h	head increment $= \mathbf{z}^2 - 1$
$\mathbf{h}$	per-unit pressure variable $= \mathbf{z}^2 = P/P_0$
i	interval time
I	pipeline total inertance
$\mathcal{I}$	pipeline specific inertance $= I/L$
$\mathcal{K}$	pipe elastic characteristic (Allievi's ρ) $\equiv Z_0 Q_0 / P_0$
L	length
$\mathfrak{N}$	relative closure time (Allievi's θ) $\equiv T_v/2T$
P	fluid-pressure measure
$\mathbf{P}$	pressure vector
P_0	reservoir pressure
P_t	pressure in tank
Q	pipe-flow variable
$\mathbf{Q}$	flow vector
Q_d	demand or drive flow
Q_0	flow upset
Q_t	tank inflow
R	resistance characteristic
$\mathbf{R}$	resistance function
s	distance
$\mathcal{S}$	dimensionless tank parameter
t	time
T	total wave transmission time down pipe
T_p	half-period time
U	intrinsic pressure variable
$\mathbf{U}$	intrinsic pressure vector
u^+	positive relative surges $= P^+/Z_0 Q_0$
u^-	negative relative surges $= P^-/Z_0 Q_0$
$\mathbf{u}(t)$	per-unit pressure
$\mathfrak{U}$	stored momentum
$\mathbf{v}$	per-unit flow
V	intrinsic flow variable
$\mathbf{V}$	intrinsic flow vector
$\mathcal{V}$	stored volume
$\mathcal{Y}(D)$	specific admittance operator
$\mathcal{Y}^+$	positive surge function
$\mathcal{Y}^-$	negative surge function
Z_0	pipeline characteristic impedance
$\mathcal{Z}(D)$	specific impedance operator
Ψ	impedance relation

20.3. Fundamental Concepts and Principles

Flow Variables. The majority of practical cases of unsteady flow can be treated employing the concept of one-dimensional flow along a mean filament (Sec. 3). In such

Table 20.1. Conjugate Flow Variables

Variable	Defining relations	
	Liquids	Gases
Pressure P......	Stagnation pressure, $p + wz + \rho V^2/2$	Total head, $pv + z + V^2/2g$
Flow Q.........	Volume flow AV	Weight flow wAV

cases the behavior of the fluid may be described in terms of the values of a conjugate pair of variables P, Q. At each point along the filament the P variable is taken to measure the fluid "pressure" and the Q variable, the fluid "flow." It is particularly convenient if the fluid pressure P and flow Q are defined for liquids and for gases as indicated in Table 20.1.

Thus in each case the pressure P variable satisfies the Bernoulli energy equation in the steady state while the flow Q variable satisfies the continuity equation.

Power Flow. So defined, the specification of P and Q at any pipe section completely determines the instantaneous transport of fluid available energy or *power flow* across the section since

Power flow:
$$\mathbf{P}(t) \equiv P(t) \cdot Q(t)$$

Any such section with the *power state* (P,Q) known provides us with a *power bond* which is conveniently symbolized with a long dash (—) in direct analogy to the ordinary chemical bond.

In these terms the common situation involving a flow from a tank through a pipe to a valve discharging to the atmosphere may be depicted as the bond diagram

$$\text{Tank} \frac{P_1}{Q_1} \text{Pipe} \frac{P_2}{Q_2} \text{Valve}$$

in which the two bonds are shown corresponding to the power states (P_1,Q_1) and (P_2,Q_2). It is often helpful to associate these bonds with the actual flanged or threaded connections of the several parts. Thus the physical assembly of an actual hydraulic system has its conceptual counterpart in the establishment and interconnection of corresponding power bonds between the primitive elements such as tanks, pipes, and valves.

The Concept of Friction Joints. An actual length of fluid piping may be conceived as having all shearing and form resistance and other forms of energy loss concentrated or lumped at the upstream and/or downstream end, in the fashion

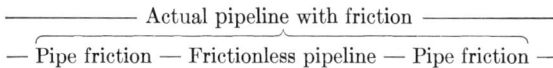

——————— Actual pipeline with friction ———————

— Pipe friction — Frictionless pipeline — Pipe friction —

Clearly, if this situation is assumed to hold for a sufficiently large number of appropriately small pipe segments, any actual pipeline may be approximated in this fashion to an arbitrary degree of accuracy. The particular joints or sections at which all pipe friction is assumed to be concentrated have been called *friction joints*.

It is important to realize that, while certain forms of viscous loss may sometimes be handled in other analytical fashions, the use of friction joints (or disguised equivalents thereof) becomes mandatory for turbulent losses and other nonlinear friction terms.

20.4. Characteristic Variables and Plane-wave Propagation

Remarks. The case of a *uniform frictionless pipeline* carrying a liquid or gas is first considered. This could be represented by the bond diagram

$$\frac{P_a}{Q_a} \text{ Uniform frictionless pipeline } \frac{P_b}{Q_b}$$

Historically, this problem has been analyzed in terms of pressure and velocity (p, V) variables but the relation of these results to p, Q variables is indicated. The performance relations for such pipelines are represented both in *operational form* as *transmission relations*, with the same results as in Sec. 21, and in the form of characteristic relations involving *time-difference equations*, which are generalizations of the Allievi equation

Principles Governing Fluid Behavior in a Frictionless Pipe. Based upon the discussion of fundamentals presented in Sec. 2, it is possible to write a conjugate pair of governing equations for unsteady conservative fluid motion.

In the absence of both nonpotential body forces and viscous forces, Eq. (2.41) becomes

$$\frac{D\mathbf{V}}{Dt} = -\frac{1}{\rho}\nabla p \tag{20.1}$$

while the continuity equation, Eq. (2.32), yields

$$\frac{D\rho}{Dt} = -\rho\nabla \cdot \mathbf{V} \tag{20.2}$$

These two relations are both written here in terms of *substantial derivatives* as described in Sec. 2.

By introducing the substitutions

$$c^2 = \frac{\partial p}{\partial \rho} \tag{20.3}$$

$$U = \int \frac{dp}{\rho c} \tag{20.4}$$

the conjugate pair may be expressed in the standard canonical form

Conservation of momentum: $\dfrac{D\mathbf{V}}{Dt} + c\,\nabla U = 0$ $\qquad$ (20.5)

Conservation of matter: $\dfrac{DU}{Dt} + c\,\nabla \cdot \mathbf{V} = 0$ $\qquad$ (20.6)

One-dimensional Motion. The conjugate vectorial equations above reduce to simple scalar relations for one-dimensional motion in an st plane. The flow variables would be written

$$U = U(s, t) \tag{20.7}$$

$$\mathbf{V} = V(s, t) \tag{20.8}$$

$$\text{grad } U = \quad \nabla U = \frac{\partial U}{\partial s} \tag{20.9}$$

$$\text{div } \mathbf{V} = \nabla \cdot \mathbf{V} = \frac{\partial V}{\partial s} \tag{20.10}$$

Equations (20.5) and (20.6) become for these conditions

$$\frac{\partial V}{\partial t} + V\frac{\partial V}{\partial s} + c\frac{\partial U}{\partial s} = 0 \tag{20.11}$$

$$\frac{\partial U}{\partial t} + V\frac{\partial U}{\partial s} + c\frac{\partial V}{\partial s} = 0 \tag{20.12}$$

If the left-hand sides of these two equations are added and subtracted, respectively, there results

$$\frac{\partial(V + U)}{\partial t} + (V + c)\frac{\partial(V + U)}{\partial s} = 0 \tag{20.13}$$

$$\frac{\partial(V - U)}{\partial t} + (V - c)\frac{\partial(V - U)}{\partial s} = 0 \tag{20.14}$$

These very useful results may now be physically interpreted in terms of the characteristic variables

$$\mathcal{P} = V + U \tag{20.15}$$

$$\mathcal{Q} = V - U \tag{20.16}$$

as the following conditions:

The $\mathcal{P}$ characteristic	*The $\mathcal{Q}$ characteristic*
$\mathcal{P} = V + U = $ constant	$\mathcal{Q} = V - U = $ constant
along the ray or path	along the ray or path
$ds = (V + c)dt$	$ds = (V - c)dt$
propagating *downstream*	propagating *upstream*

These results were first obtained by B. Riemann in 1859 for finite plane waves in *air*, but are generally valid for liquids and gases alike, and are not restricted to any particular *pressure-density* relationship.

This method of dealing with wavelike phenomena is generally known as the *method of characteristics* and is fundamental to most practical analytical techniques, regardless of their special origins and evolutions.

Physically, the earlier substitution

$$c = \sqrt{\frac{\partial p}{\partial \rho}} \tag{20.3b}$$

is now readily interpreted as a *propagation velocity* or *wave celerity*.

For *gases* undergoing a transient polytropic process, $p/\rho^n = $ const, the celerity becomes

$$c^2 = \frac{\partial p}{\partial \rho} = \frac{np}{\rho}$$

or

$$c = \sqrt{\frac{np}{\rho}} \tag{20.17}$$

and therefore depends upon the local instantaneous *state* of the fluid.

So-called *sonic* or *acoustic* waves correspond to the situation in which

$$dp \ll p_0$$
$$d\rho \ll \rho_0 \tag{20.18}$$

and thus where the behavior may be considered incrementally linear.   Then

$$c = c_0 = \sqrt{\frac{np_0}{\rho_0}} \tag{20.19}$$

which is usually taken as constant throughout the flow.

For *liquids* the celerity depends upon the bulk modulus of elasticity B in the form

$$c^2 = \frac{\partial p}{\partial \rho} = \frac{B}{\rho_0}$$

or

$$c = \sqrt{\frac{B}{\rho}} \tag{20.20}$$

and is almost always nearly constant even for wide variations in pressure, so long as the minimum pressure remains above the vapor pressure for the particular substance.

Just as the parameter c is separately evaluated for gases and for liquids, so too is the potential variable U.

For gases undergoing polytropic change, U could be evaluated in the fashion

$$U = \int^\rho \frac{c \, d\rho}{\rho} = \frac{2c_0}{n-1}\left(\frac{\rho}{\rho_0}\right)^{(n-1)/2} = \frac{2c_0}{n-1}\left(\frac{p}{p_0}\right)^{(n-1)/2} \tag{20.21}$$

while, for liquids, U is determined as

$$U = \int \frac{dp}{\rho c} = \frac{1}{\rho c} \int dp = \frac{p}{\rho c} \tag{20.22}$$

The foregoing results are summarized in Table 20.2.

It should be clear now that a strict analogy exists between sound waves in gases, such as air, and elastic waves in liquids, such as water. Thus it is surprising to consider that the former phenomenon was well understood nearly a century before the latter.

The Wave Equations. For many circumstances involving fluids the *acoustic* assumption is valid, wherein $c = c_0 = $ const. Moreover, particularly for liquid flows, the flow velocity is usually materially less than the wave celerity ($V \ll c$), in which case the flow is said to be *subsonic*. Whenever a one-dimensional flow is both *acoustic* and *subsonic*, the conjugate conservation laws become

$$\frac{\partial V}{\partial t} + c_0 \frac{\partial U}{\partial s} = 0 \tag{20.23}$$

$$\frac{\partial U}{\partial t} + c_0 \frac{\partial V}{\partial s} = 0 \tag{20.24}$$

Upon differentiating both equations by t and by s in turn, there result the four relations

$$\frac{\partial^2 V}{\partial t^2} = c_0 \frac{\partial^2 U}{\partial t \, \partial s} = 0 \qquad \frac{\partial^2 V}{\partial s \, \partial t} + c_0 \frac{\partial^2 U}{\partial s^2} = 0 \tag{20.25}$$

$$\frac{\partial^2 U}{\partial s \, \partial t} + c_0 \frac{\partial^2 V}{\partial s^2} = 0 \qquad \frac{\partial^2 U}{\partial t^2} + c_0 \frac{\partial^2 V}{\partial t \, \partial s} = 0 \tag{20.26}$$

Multiplying the lower left equation and dividing the lower right equation each by c_0 and subtracting each from the equation above yields

$$\frac{\partial^2 V}{\partial t^2} = c_0{}^2 \frac{\partial^2 V}{\partial s^2} \qquad \frac{\partial^2 U}{\partial t^2} = c_0{}^2 \frac{\partial^2 U}{\partial s^2} \tag{20.27}$$

These equations for V and for U are in the classical form of the *wave equation*, which was first expressed in this fashion in 1747 by d'Alembert for the vibrating-string problem. Much lore useful to understanding fluid transient behavior derives from the rich mathematical and physical literature devoted to Eqs. (20.23) and (20.24).

Wave Propagation and Water Hammer in Pipes. The previous results were based upon the assumption of plane-wave propagation in an unbounded fluid medium, while the fluid transient problems here considered involve flow confined in a pipe. As stated at the outset in Art. 20.3, the power-state variables useful for such cases are P and Q. While in the paragraphs above both liquids and gases have been considered, henceforth attention is confined primarily to elastic liquids, alone, flowing in pipes and conduits. The transient phenomenon associated with such cases has historically been called water hammer as indicated earlier.

Thus for this situation it is convenient to convert the one-dimensional conjugate equa-

Table 20.2. Characteristic Parameters

Item	Gases	Liquids
Velocity V........	V	V
Celerity c.........	$\sqrt{\dfrac{n p_0}{\rho_0}}$	$\sqrt{\dfrac{B}{\rho}}$
Potential U.......	$\dfrac{2c_0}{n-1}\left(\dfrac{p}{p_0}\right)^{(n-1)/2n}$	$\dfrac{p}{\rho c}$

tions in U, V variables into corresponding relations for the pipe-flow (P, Q) variables.

Wave Velocity in a Pipe. It is first necessary to establish the fact that the wave velocity in a tube, here denoted by a, is distinct from, and always less than, the plane-wave celerity c. For this it is helpful to return to a restatement of the conservation relations, under the subsonic assumption $V \ll a < c$.

Under these conditions the substantial derivative is not significantly different from the local derivative; that is

$$\frac{D}{Dt} \cong \frac{\partial}{\partial t} \tag{20.28}$$

Then the two conjugate laws may be written

Conservation of	Pressure gradient	Fluid inertia

Momentum:

$$-\frac{\partial P}{\partial s} = \rho \frac{\partial V}{\partial t} \tag{20.29}$$

Mass:

$$-\frac{\partial V}{\partial s} = \frac{1}{\rho}\frac{\partial \rho}{\partial t} + \frac{1}{A}\frac{\partial A}{\partial t} \tag{20.30}$$

Velocity gradient	Fluid compressibility	Wall elasticity

The second term on the right-hand side is made necessary by the possibility of elastic deflection of the pipe walls under the transient internal pressures. The two elastic terms may be separately and jointly related to the pressure as follows:

$$\frac{1}{\rho}\frac{\partial \rho}{\partial t} = \frac{1}{B}\frac{\partial P}{\partial t} \tag{20.31}$$

$$\frac{1}{A}\frac{\partial A}{\partial t} = \frac{2}{C}\frac{\partial C}{\partial t} = \frac{f}{E}\frac{\partial P}{\partial t} \tag{20.32}$$

$$\therefore \quad \frac{1}{\rho}\frac{\partial \rho}{\partial t} + \frac{1}{A}\frac{\partial A}{\partial t} = \frac{1}{B}\left(1 + f\frac{B}{E}\right)\frac{\partial P}{\partial t} \tag{20.33}$$

in which B = fluid bulk modulus, psf
E = pipe elastic modulus, psf
f = pipe stress factor, dimensionless
C = pipe circumference or perimeter, ft

Table 20.3 gives values for the stress factor f corresponding to some of the commonly encountered conduits.

In a directly analogous fashion to the earlier definition of c

$$a^2 = \frac{B/\rho}{1 + f(B/E)}$$

or

$$a = \frac{c}{\sqrt{1 + f(B/E)}} \tag{20.34}$$

Table 20.3. Stress Factors for Fluid Conduits

Conduit	Dimensions	Stress factor f
Thin-wall circular pipe.......	Diameter D Wall thickness e	$\dfrac{D}{e}$
Thick-wall circular pipe.......	Inside diameter D_i Outside diameter D_0	$2\dfrac{D_0^2 + D_i^2}{D_0^2 - D_i^2}$
Circular tunnel.............	$D_0 \to \infty$	2

Table 20.4. Effective Wave Velocity a for Several Liquids

The table gives values of a in feet per second

Liquid	Value of E/f, psi				
	∞ Celerity c	800,000	400,000	200,000	100,000
Water.........	4720	4025	3568	2895	2360
Crude oil.......	4840	4274	3870	3317	2682
Gasoline.......	4068	3742	3483	3094	2595

This is a generalization of the Helmholtz-Korteweg result and clearly demonstrates how pipe elasticity reduces the effective wave velocity. Table 20.4 has been prepared for several fluids at standard conditions and with various values of E/f. As indicated, the value $E/f = \infty$ corresponds to the acoustic velocity c.

By using the parameter a, the continuity equation may be written in the form

$$-a\frac{\partial V}{\partial s} = \frac{\partial U}{\partial t} = \frac{\partial}{\partial t}\left(\frac{P}{\rho a}\right) = \frac{1}{\rho a}\frac{\partial P}{\partial t} \tag{20.35}$$

which is identical with Eq. (20.24) *but with a replacing c.*

Thus one may anticipate that pressure U and velocity V waves will propagate up and down a confined flow as in unconfined fluids but with an effective wave speed a, which is inevitably reduced below the acoustic celerity c.

Parenthetically, it is interesting to note that the transient flow of energy into the walls for liquids has the same qualitative effect upon reducing propagation velocity as the transient outflow of energy in the form of heat in the case of gases. Thus since a high-frequency disturbance in gas pipelines tends to be adiabatic ($n = \gamma$) and low frequency, isothermal ($n = 1$), one might expect that high-frequency acoustic waves in pipes propagate at values of a which approach c with increasing frequency. This phenomenon is discussed briefly in Art. 20.7 in connection with dispersion and scattering of water-hammer waves.

Relation between Power Variables and Characteristic Variables. The variables P, Q may now be directly related to the wave variables U, V through the identities

$$P = \rho a U$$
$$Q = AV \tag{20.36}$$

or, conversely

$$U = \frac{P}{\rho a}$$
$$V = \frac{Q}{A} \tag{20.37}$$

Principally for historical reasons, it is of interest to express these results in traditional forms. Following Allievi, it has been customary to use (head h, velocity V) variables. These are related to U, V as follows:

$$\text{Head } h = \frac{a}{gU} \tag{20.38}$$

$$\text{Velocity } V = V$$

This identification makes it possible to review all historical literature in the terms of this section.

Pipeline Inertance and Capacitance. It is now possible to write both conservation relations in an alternative symmetrical form of great utility, namely,

$$-\frac{\partial P}{\partial s} = g \cdot \frac{\partial Q}{\partial t} = gD \cdot Q \tag{20.39}$$

$$-\frac{\partial Q}{\partial s} = e \cdot \frac{\partial P}{\partial t} = eD \cdot P \tag{20.40}$$

if g = pipeline specific inertance $= \rho/A$
   e = pipeline specific capacitance $= A/\rho a^2$

For a length of uniform constant cross section A and length L, define

I = pipeline total inertance $= g \cdot L \tag{20.41}$

C = pipeline total capacitance $= e \cdot L \tag{20.42}$

Pipeline Characteristic Impedance and Travel Time.   Another generally useful way to relate Eqs. (20.39) and (20.40) to the previous wave relations is through introduction of the *pipeline characteristic impedance* Z_0, which is defined as

$$Z_0 = \sqrt{\frac{g}{e}} = \sqrt{\frac{I}{C}} = \frac{\rho a}{A} \tag{20.43}$$

This number, together with the *wave travel* time T down a pipe of length L, namely,

$$T = L\sqrt{g \cdot e} = \sqrt{I \cdot C} = \frac{L}{a} \tag{20.44}$$

constitutes the two measures which are certainly the most important constants in water-hammer analysis, as is evidenced in the following discussion.

It is also important to note the useful converse relations

$$T \cdot Z_0 = \sqrt{I \cdot C \frac{I}{C}} = I \tag{20.45}$$

$$\frac{T}{Z_0} = \sqrt{I \cdot C \frac{C}{I}} = C \tag{20.46}$$

These parameters permit three additional useful transformations between U, V variables and P, Q variables, namely,

I. Pressure scaling $U = \qquad P \qquad P = \qquad U \tag{20.47}$

$V = \quad Z_0 \cdot Q \qquad Q = \quad \frac{1}{Z_0} \cdot V$

II. Flow scaling $U = \quad \frac{1}{Z_0} \cdot P \qquad P = \quad Z_0 \cdot U \tag{20.48}$

$V = \qquad Q \qquad Q = \qquad V$

III. Power scaling $U = \quad \frac{1}{\sqrt{Z_0}} \cdot P \qquad P = \sqrt{Z_0} \cdot U \tag{20.49}$

$V = \sqrt{Z_0} \cdot Q \qquad Q = \quad \frac{1}{\sqrt{Z_0}} \cdot V$

Note that only for transformation III is the power state given by the *unscaled* product; that is

$$\mathbf{P} = U_3 \cdot V_3 \tag{20.50}$$

but

$$\mathbf{P} = Z_0 \cdot U_2 \cdot V_2 \tag{20.51}$$

$$= \frac{1}{Z_0} \cdot U_1 \cdot V_1$$

The State-characteristic Plane and Graphical Representations.   By returning now to the characteristic relations Eqs. (20.13) and (20.14), it is helpful to interpret them *physically* for a pipeline of length L, in the fashion

$$\frac{U_a}{V_a}\underset{T=L/a}{\overset{\leftarrow L \rightarrow}{\xrightarrow{\text{pipeline}}}}\frac{U_b}{V_b} \tag{20.52}$$

Figure 20.1 depicts the field of state characteristics corresponding to Eqs. (20.13) and (20.14).   The time-dependency may now be reasoned as follows:

For the $\mathcal{P}$ characteristic of this pipe one would write that the $\mathcal{P}$ state for station b at time t is that for station a at an earlier time $(t - T)$.   Thus

$$\mathcal{P}_b(t) = \mathcal{P}_a(t - T) \tag{20.53}$$

or

$$U_b(t) + V_b(t) = U_a(t - T) + V_a(t - T) \tag{20.54}$$

Similarly, the $\mathcal{Q}$ state at station a is at time t the same as the $\mathcal{Q}$ state of station b at the earlier time $(t - T)$, or

$$\mathcal{Q}_a(t) = \mathcal{Q}_b(t - T) \tag{20.55}$$

or

$$U_a(t) - V_a(t) = U_b(t - T) - V_b(t - T) \tag{20.56}$$

However, both relations may be more compactly represented, using the operational substitution

$$e^{-TD} \cdot X(t) = \mathbf{\Delta} \cdot X(t) = X(t - T) \tag{20.57}$$

if $e^{-TD} = \mathbf{\Delta}$ is the time delay, or time translation, operator. Corresponding to Eqs. (20.53) and (20.55), there now results

$$\mathbf{\Delta}\mathcal{P}_a = \mathcal{P}_b \tag{20.58}$$

$$\mathcal{Q}_a = \mathbf{\Delta}\mathcal{Q}_b \tag{20.59}$$

A time sequence of states at both ends of the pipe may then be related as indicated

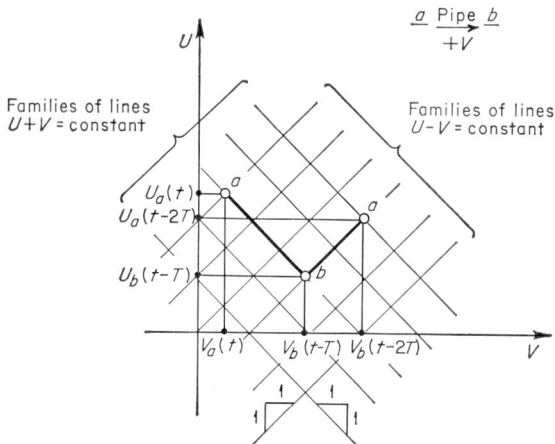

Fig. 20.1.   Characteristic lines.

Table 20.5

Section k	Length L_k, ft	Area A_k, ft^2	Inertance L_k/A_k, ft^{-1}	Capacitance $L_k \cdot A_k$, ft^3
1	1000	100	10.00	100,000
2	500	80	6.25	40,000
3	200	40	5.00	8,000

Take $\rho = 2$ slugs/ft^3 and $c^2 = 10^7$ ft^2/sec^2 $\qquad \sum = 21.25$ ft^{-1}	$\sum = 148,000$ ft^3
$I = \rho \sum \dfrac{L_k}{A_k} = 2 \times 21.25$ $\qquad\qquad = 42.5$	$C = \dfrac{1}{\rho c^2} \sum (L_k A_k) = \dfrac{148 \times 10^3}{20 \times 10^6}$ $\qquad\qquad = 7.4 \times 10^{-3}$

in the graphical construction of Fig. 20.1. Of course, if it is more convenient, P, Q scales may be used on the UV plane with no change in method but merely a corresponding change in the scaled *slopes* of the characteristic lines. These slopes are clearly ± 1 for the (U,V) set of characteristic variables.

Historically, in the field of water-hammer analysis credit for originating the graphical treatment has been traditionally shared by Ottmar Schnyder, Louis Bergeron, and R. W. Angus, but the first comprehensive use of graphical methods in connection with the method of characteristics must clearly be attributed to Junius Massau[3] in 1889. This little-known work has remained obscure despite a recent translation by H. Putman,[3b] which clearly indicates the universality of the tool. The most accessible book on particular practical applications is that of Bergeron,[4] which is shortly to appear in English translation.

Later articles demonstrate the striking advantage of this graphical characteristic technique, particularly for intuitive visualization purposes.

Composite and Other Nonuniform Pipelines. Frequently pipelines are constructed with sections which vary over the length of the pipe. It is always possible to calculate the total inertance and total capacitance of such pipes from the formulas:

Continuous   Discrete
variation   variation

Inertance: $\qquad\qquad I = \rho \int_0^L \dfrac{1}{A}\, ds \quad = \rho \sum_k \dfrac{L_k}{A_k}$ $\qquad\qquad\qquad$ (20.60)

Capacitance: $\qquad C = \dfrac{1}{\rho a^2} \int_0^L A \cdot ds = \dfrac{1}{\rho a^2} \sum_k (L_k \cdot A_k)$ $\qquad\qquad$ (20.61)

A sample tabulation of such a situation involving a pipe composed of a sequence of three uniform pipes of different section is indicated in Table 20.5.

For all such variable section pipelines, the conjugate pair of governing equations would be written as

$$-\frac{\partial P}{\partial s} = g(s) D \cdot Q \qquad\qquad (20.62)$$

$$-\frac{\partial Q}{\partial s} = \mathcal{C}(s) D \cdot P \qquad\qquad (20.63)$$

20.5. Transmission Characteristics of Pipelines

Transmission Relations. The results of the previous article may now be compactly summarized in terms of simple *operational* relations, which hold for any length of uniform frictionless pipe. Later in this section the mechanics of handling compound and branching pipe systems is discussed.

The characteristic relations for a pipe as derived above may be rewritten in terms of the delay operator $\Delta = e^{-TD}$

Upstream end   Downstream end

$$\Delta U_a + \Delta V_a = \quad U_b + V_b \tag{20.64}$$

$$\Delta U_a - \Delta V_a = \Delta^2 U_b - \Delta^2 V_b \tag{20.65}$$

If these equations are both added and subtracted, two important transmission relations are obtained.

$$2\Delta U_a = (1 + \Delta^2)U_b + (1 - \Delta^2)V_b \tag{20.66}$$

$$2\Delta V_a = (1 - \Delta^2)U_b + (1 + \Delta^2)V_b \tag{20.67}$$

Canonical Transmission Equations. Dividing these last two equations by 2Δ

$$U_a = \frac{1 + \Delta^2}{2\Delta} U_b + \frac{1 - \Delta^2}{2\Delta} V_b \tag{20.68}$$

$$V_a = \frac{1 - \Delta^2}{2\Delta} U_b + \frac{1 + \Delta^2}{2\Delta} V_b \tag{20.69}$$

By recognizing the identities

$$\cosh TD = \frac{e^{TD} + e^{-TD}}{2} = \frac{1 + e^{-2TD}}{2e^{-TD}} = \frac{1 + \Delta^2}{2\Delta} \tag{20.70}$$

$$\sinh TD = \frac{e^{TD} - e^{-TD}}{2} = \frac{1 - e^{-2TD}}{2e^{-TD}} = \frac{1 - \Delta^2}{2\Delta} \tag{20.71}$$

permits the writing of Eqs. (20.68) and (20.69) in the standard form

$$U_a = (\cosh TD) \cdot U_b + (\sinh TD) \cdot V_b \tag{20.72}$$

$$V_a = (\sinh TD) \cdot U_b + (\cosh TD) \cdot V_b \tag{20.73}$$

This form is used extensively in Sec. 21, in terms of P, Q variables.

Sinusoidal Inputs and Frequency Response. If one wishes to determine the response of any pipeline to a sinusoidal variation in flow and/or pressures, it is necessary to substitute only $j\omega$ for D in these last equations.

Since then

$$\cosh TD = \cosh j\omega T = \cos \omega T \tag{20.74}$$

$$\sinh TD = \sinh j\omega T = j \sin \omega T \tag{20.75}$$

finally universal relationships between the upstream vectors U_a, V_a and the downstream vectors U_b, V_b are obtained in the form

$$U_a = (\cos \omega T) \cdot U_b + j(\sin \omega T) \cdot V_b \tag{20.76}$$

$$V_a = j(\sin \omega T) \cdot U_b + j(\cos \omega T) \cdot V_b \tag{20.77}$$

Pressures at Interior Points of a Uniform Pipe. It is frequently necessary to determine the pressures at one or more intermediate stations between the terminals of a pipeline of constant properties. This may be readily accomplished using the transmission characteristics presented above.

Consider the pipeline divided into two sections

$$\frac{P}{Q} \text{ Pipe section } \overset{\overset{\displaystyle T_x}{\longleftarrow}}{\frac{P_x}{Q_x}} \text{ Pipe section } \frac{P_0}{Q_0} \tag{20.78}$$

$$\overset{}{\underset{\displaystyle T}{\longleftarrow}}$$

Here (P,Q) is the power state at one terminal, (P_0,Q_0) the state at the opposite terminal, station 0, and (P_x,Q_x) the state at the internal station x. The total transmission time is T, and T_x $(\leq T)$ is the transmission time from station 0 to station x.

By using Eq. (20.72), one may write

$$P_x = (\cosh T_x D)P_0 + (Z \sinh T_x D)Q_0 \qquad (20.79)$$

$$P = (\cosh TD)P_0 + (Z \sinh TD)Q_0 \qquad (20.80)$$

If delivering to, or receiving from, a reservoir of constant pressure, one can always take $P_0 \equiv 0$. In this case, dividing Eq. (20.79) by Eq. (20.80) gives

$$\frac{P_x}{P} = \frac{\sinh T_x D}{\sinh TD} \qquad (20.81)$$

For low frequencies (where $TD \to 0$), this yields the physically intuitive result

Low frequencies: $\qquad \dfrac{P_x}{P} \to \dfrac{T_x}{T} = \dfrac{L_x}{L} \qquad (20.82)$

if L_x is the length to station x, and L is the total length. Thus, for example, the mid-point of a pipe terminating in a constant pressure will tend to have one-half the pressure variation at the other terminal.

However, this result does not hold for high-frequency disturbances. The more general relation may be derived from Eq. (20.81) using time-delay operators, whence

$$\frac{P_x}{P} = \frac{\mathbf{\Delta}}{\mathbf{\Delta}^x} \cdot \frac{1 - \mathbf{\Delta}^{2x}}{1 - \mathbf{\Delta}^2} = \frac{\mathbf{\Delta}^{1-x} - \mathbf{\Delta}^{1+x}}{1 - \mathbf{\Delta}^2} \qquad (20.83)$$

if $\mathbf{\Delta}^u \equiv \exp{(-T_u D)}$. This relation can then be interpreted in the time domain as

$$P_x(t) = P_x(t - 2T) + P(t + T_x - T) - P(t - T_x - T) \qquad (20.84)$$

Thus, given any $P(t)$, $P_x(t)$ may be found for any x.

Abrupt and Gradual Nonuniformities. A general variable-section conduit can always be considered as a finite or infinite sequence of small elements, as indicated in Fig. 20.2. Each small section may be considered as two small lengths of uniform pipe with equal transmission times. The properties and corresponding surge impedance of one half section are taken as that at the *beginning* of the physical element, while the parameters of the other half section are those corresponding to the *end* of the physical element. It is then clear that, as the lengths and corresponding transmission times shrink to zero, this model becomes exact; however, often only one or very few sections are required to accurately represent typical pipelines for design and operating purposes. Moreover, if the pipeline has a finite number of section and/or property discontinuities, the above method leads to a technique directly analogous to the method of "Dedekind cuts" in number theory, wherein irrational numbers are approximated from above and below by the nearest rational numbers.

For *gradual* changes in characteristics where the variations in $Z(s)$ and $a(s)$ are small over a change in distance s comparable to one wavelength of the fundamental pressure transient, it has been found that the behavior is similar to that of a uniform pipeline with the same total transmission time. However, the characteristic variables $U(s, t)$ and $V(s, t)$ are now defined by

$$U(s, t) \equiv \frac{P(s, t)}{\sqrt{Z_0(s)}} \qquad (20.85)$$

$$V(s, t) \equiv Q(s, t) \cdot \sqrt{Z_0(s)} \qquad (20.86)$$

Thus it is that the variations in pressure and flow along the pipe vary directly and inversely with the square root of the relative characteristic impedance level.

This fundamental relationship was first obtained by George Green[5] in 1837 as the

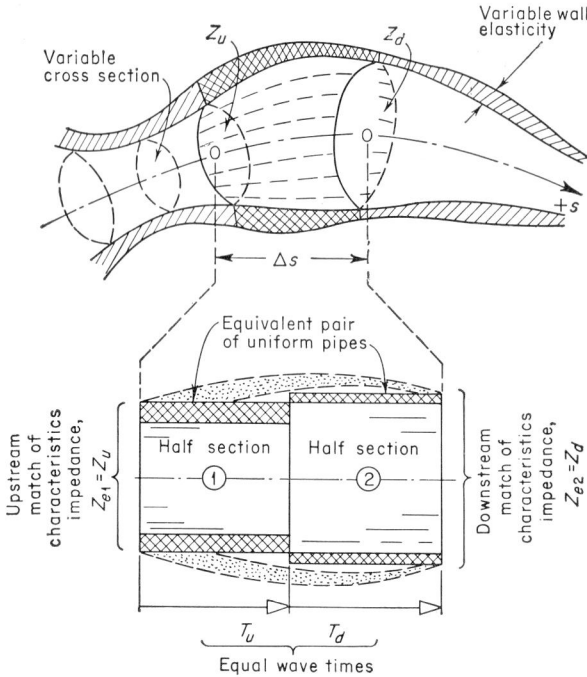

Fig. 20.2. Pipeline of variable characteristics.

classical "Green's law" for gravity waves in shallow canals of variable section. This work was applied specifically to the water-hammer problem by Giuseppi Evangelisti[6] and further discussed and generalized by the writer.[7]

A practical example of the use of Green's law for engineering estimates may be indicated by calculating the pressure surge resulting from the complete sudden shutoff at the small end (station 0) of a tapered pipe.

The Green's law estimate is obtained from the formula

$$\frac{P(s)}{P_0} \cong \sqrt{\frac{Z(s)}{Z_0}} \tag{20.87}$$

or, since $P_0 = Z_0 \cdot Q_0 = \rho a_0 Q_0 / A_0$, and with $a(s) = a_0 = \text{const}$, gives $Z_0/Z(s) = A(s)/A_0 = [D(s)/D_0]^2$, or

$$P(s) \cong \frac{\rho a_0 Q_0}{A_0} \cdot \frac{D_0}{D(s)} \tag{20.88}$$

Table 20.6. Relative Surge Pressures in a Tapered Pipe

Abrupt flow stoppage, linear flare in diameter

Station	Diameter	Calculated relative head rise	
		Exact results	Green's law
0	1.00	1.00	1.00
1	1.20	0.82	0.83
2	1.40	0.69	0.71
3	1.60	0.60	0.63
4	1.80	0.53	0.56
5	2.00	0.47	0.50

Table 20.6 compares the exact results calculated for a pipe with a linear diametrical flare or taper with the Green's law estimate for the same case.   The approximate results are everywhere within 10 per cent of the exact values and are obtained with great ease.

20.6. The Terminal Impedance of Pipelines

Remarks.   The *terminal impedance* of a fluid system involves the determination of the (P,Q) relationship at a terminal port as indicated

Given: $$\frac{P}{Q}\ \text{Fluid system}$$ (20.89)

Then: $$\Psi(P,Q) = 0$$ (20.90)

This impedance relation Ψ is of universal importance in expressing the interaction of the particular element or subsystem upon the other elements of a complex engineering system.

Input Impedance of a Pipe Connected to a Reservoir.   One is here concerned primarily with frictionless pipes connected at one end to a constant-pressure reservoir. Flow may be either *positive* $(+)$ *into* the reservoir or *negative* $(-)$ *out of* the reservoir. This situation can be indicated by the bond diagram

$$\frac{P_a}{Q_a}\text{Pipeline} \overset{\underset{\text{Constant}}{}}{\underset{}{}} \frac{P_b}{}\text{Reservoir}$$ (20.91)

For convenience and simplicity all pressures are measured as *changes* from reservoir pressure, in which case P_b is considered to be zero.

From the transmission Eqs. 20.72 and 20.73 by setting $P_b(t) = 0$, one can immediately write

$$U_a = (\sinh TD) \cdot V_b$$ (20.92)

$$V_a = (\cosh TD) \cdot V_b$$ (20.93)

Elimination of V_b from these relations yields

$$U_a(t) = (\tanh TD) \cdot V_a(t)$$ (20.94)

For water-hammer analysis it is convenient to substitute the power-state variables P, Q for the characteristic variables U, V.   Thus one obtains

$$P_a(t) = Z_0 \cdot \tanh TD \cdot Q_a(t)$$ (20.95)

The expression $Z_a = Z_0 \tanh TD$ represents the terminal impedance of a uniform frictionless pipeline connected to a constant-pressure reservoir.

Slow changes in flow correspond to $D \to 0$, while very fast changes imply that $D \to \infty$. Therefore

Slow changes: $D \to 0$ $Z_a \to Z_0 T \cdot D = I \cdot D$ (20.96)

Fast changes: $D \to \infty$ $Z_a \to Z_0 \cdot 1 = \sqrt{\dfrac{I}{C}}$ (20.97)

These results imply that, when the flow changes gradually, the inertial (I) effects will dominate, while, for abrupt changes in flow such as occur with sudden valve closures, the surge impedance Z_0 is most significant.   This spectral difference, so to speak, has tended to cause much confusion in the application of special results.

When Eq. (20.95) is interpreted in the time domain, a modified Allievi equation results

$$P_a(t) + P_a(t - 2T) = Z_0 \cdot [Q_a(t) - Q_a(t - 2T)]$$ (20.98)

This particular time-difference equation is perhaps the most useful single relation in the entire theory of water hammer.

Similarly, specializing Eq. (20.95) for the frequency response yields

$$Z_a = \mathbf{j} \cdot Z_0 \cdot \tan \omega l \tag{20.99}$$

Since $Z_0 \cdot \tan \omega T$ is always *real*, this relation indicates that the pressure vector **P** will *always* be at right angles to the flow vector **Q**. This must necessarily include the low-frequency limit, when, as $\omega \to 0$,

$$Z_a \to \mathbf{j} \cdot Z_0 \cdot \omega T = \mathbf{j}\omega T \tag{20.100}$$

The variation in the *magnitude* of input impedance with frequency is merely

$$\frac{Z_a}{Z_0} = \tan \omega T \tag{20.101}$$

and therefore has characteristic frequencies which give

(a) Nulls or zeros at $\omega T = k \cdot \pi$

(b) Resonances or poles at $\omega T = \dfrac{2k+1}{2} \cdot \pi$ $k = 0, 1, 2, \ldots$ (20.102)

Gradual Flow Changes. The significance of the terminal impedance may best be appreciated in terms of some examples. First consider an arbitrary case in which the flow *from* the reservoir is gradually reduced from an initial steady flow ($Q_a = -Q_0$) to a final zero flow ($Q_a = 0$), according to a cosine law in a time $2\mathfrak{N}T$. Then, for

$$t \leq 0 \qquad Q_a(t) = -Q_0 \tag{20.103}$$

$$0 \leq t \leq 2\mathfrak{N}T \qquad Q_a(t) = -Q_0 \cdot \cos\left(\frac{\pi}{4}\frac{t}{\mathfrak{N}T}\right) \tag{20.104}$$

$$2\mathfrak{N}T \leq t \qquad Q_a(t) = 0 \tag{20.105}$$

The resultant pressure rise as the relative closure time $\mathfrak{N}$ is varied is indicated in Fig. 20.3. It is directly evident that the maximum pressure *increases* with
1. *Increasing* characteristic impedance Z_0
2. *Decreasing* relative closure time $\mathfrak{N}$

The "sawtooth afterwaves," after the flow has reached zero at the terminal a, are characteristic of the *elastic* nature of the phenomenon and testify to the presence of the transient surge flows.

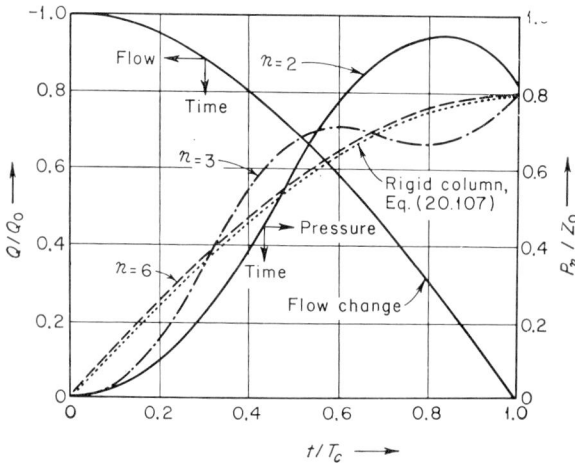

Fig. 20.3. Water hammer from gradual flow change.

On the other hand, for sufficiently slow rates of flow change ($D \to 0$), the basically *inertial* terms will dominate. Under these conditions the following impedance relation would hold approximately

$$P_a(t) \cong ID \cdot Q_a(t) = I \frac{dQ_a}{dt} \qquad D \to 0 \qquad (20.106)$$

For the same assumed deceleration law, the surge pressures may be determined by direct differentiation to give

$$0 \le t \le 2\Re T \qquad P_a(t) = Z_0 T \frac{\pi}{4\Re T} \sin\left(\frac{\pi}{4} \frac{t}{\Re T}\right) = \frac{\pi}{4} \frac{Z_0}{\Re} \sin\left(\frac{\pi}{4} \frac{t}{\Re T}\right) \qquad (20.107)$$

This result for the same three values of $\Re$ is compared to the elastic-wave analysis of the previous example, in Fig. 20.3.

Abrupt Flow Change. Consider now the case where $0 \le \Re \le 1$, that is, where the flow is brought to zero at station a within one round-trip wave interval. This corresponds to the conditions of Joukowsky's original experiments and analysis, and is generally said to be a *sudden* or *abrupt* flow change.

In the limiting case, the deceleration is *instantaneous*, and the pressure will instantaneously rise to the Joukowsky value

$$\Delta P = Z_0 \Delta Q = \frac{\rho a}{A} \cdot \Delta Q \qquad (20.108)$$

The rest of the time history for this instantaneous case is most rapidly determined by considering the terminal impedance in operational-delay form, namely,

$$\frac{\Delta P}{\Delta Q} = Z_0 \tanh TD = Z_0 \frac{1 - \boldsymbol{\Delta}^2}{1 + \boldsymbol{\Delta}^2} \qquad (20.109)$$

This may be expanded simply to obtain

$$\frac{\Delta P}{Z_0 \Delta Q} = (1 - \boldsymbol{\Delta}^2)(1 - \boldsymbol{\Delta}^2 + \boldsymbol{\Delta}^4 - \boldsymbol{\Delta}^6 + \cdots) \qquad (20.110)$$

which may be interpreted as an alternating square wave of period $4T$ as indicated in Fig. 20.4.

It is clear that for this case an inelastic analysis would have nothing sensible to say regarding the transient fluctuations in pressure. If a uniform pipe connected to a reservoir must be designed for sudden stoppage, the safest value of pressure rise to use for design is the value

$$\Delta P_m = Z_0 \Delta Q$$

However, it must be emphasized that pressures even in excess of this value can arise if the pipe is not uniform or is but a part of a complex flow network.

20.7. Water-hammer Pressures from Valve Stroking

Introduction. As indicated at the outset of this section it was to the typical situation of pipelines with a reservoir at one end and a valve at the other that Joukowsky and Allievi directed their primary attention.

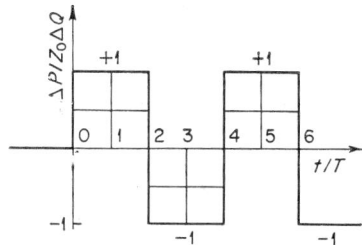

Fig. 20.4. Water hammer from sudden flow change.

For nearly all general studies of this sort, the following bond diagram may be assumed

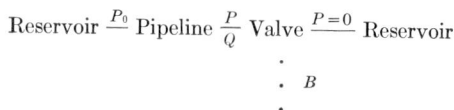

$$\text{Reservoir} \xrightarrow{P_0} \text{Pipeline} \xrightarrow{\frac{P}{Q}} \text{Valve} \xrightarrow{P=0} \text{Reservoir}$$

$$\cdot \ B$$

in which the flow is normally from left to right and the downstream reservoir is assumed zero for convenience.

Conventionally, the reasonable assumption has been made that the relation between flow Q and pressure P is of the form

$$Q = B\sqrt{P} \tag{20.111}$$

or, equivalently,

$$P = \frac{1}{B^2} \cdot Q^2 = K \cdot Q^2 \tag{20.112}$$

The *variable* B measures the effective "flow area," and throughout the ensuing discussion it is assumed that this may be freely varied through appropriate valve stroking.

Flow Establishment after a Sudden Valve Opening.   Consider the physical situation

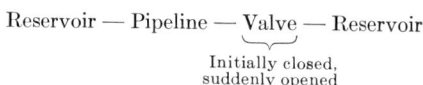

$$\text{Reservoir} - \text{Pipeline} - \underbrace{\text{Valve}} - \text{Reservoir}$$

Initially closed,
suddenly opened

For simplicity, friction in the pipe may be included as a downstream friction joint combined with the valve characteristic.   Figure 20.5 depicts the graphical solution for two values of the surge characteristic $\mathcal{K} \equiv Z_0 Q_0 / _2 P_0$, namely,

(*a*)	$\mathcal{K} > 1$	(Fig. 20.5*a*)
(*b*)	$\mathcal{K} < 1$	(Fig. 20.5*b*)

It is clearly evident that only for the first case (large $\mathcal{K}$) can the accelerated flow be considered inelastic.   The relation between this result and the response, assuming a rigid column, namely,

$$Q(t) = Q_0 \tanh\left(\frac{t}{T_f}\right) \tag{20.113}$$

is indicated in Fig. 20.5, in terms of the inertia time constant, $T_f = 2\mathcal{K}T$.

Inertial Water Hammer.   From the previous case it is evident that, for $\mathcal{K} \equiv Z_0 Q_0 / 2 P_0$ sufficiently large, the fluid behavior becomes inelastic.   In the limiting case, the fluid column may be treated as a rigid inertial body, using Eq. (20.96), and the corresponding pressure transient is called *inertial water hammer.*

Under these conditions, the governing relations are the following:

$$I\frac{dQ}{dt} = P_0 - P \tag{20.114}$$

$$Q = B\sqrt{P} \tag{20.115}$$

By introducing dimensionless per-unit quantities through the substitutions

$$p \equiv \frac{P}{P_0} \qquad q \equiv \frac{Q}{Q_0} \qquad b \equiv \frac{B}{B_0} \qquad z \equiv \sqrt{p} \qquad t \equiv \frac{tP_0}{IQ_0} \tag{20.116}$$

these equations may be combined to yield

$$\frac{dq}{dt} = z\frac{db}{dt} + b\frac{dz}{dt} = z^2 - 1 \tag{20.117}$$

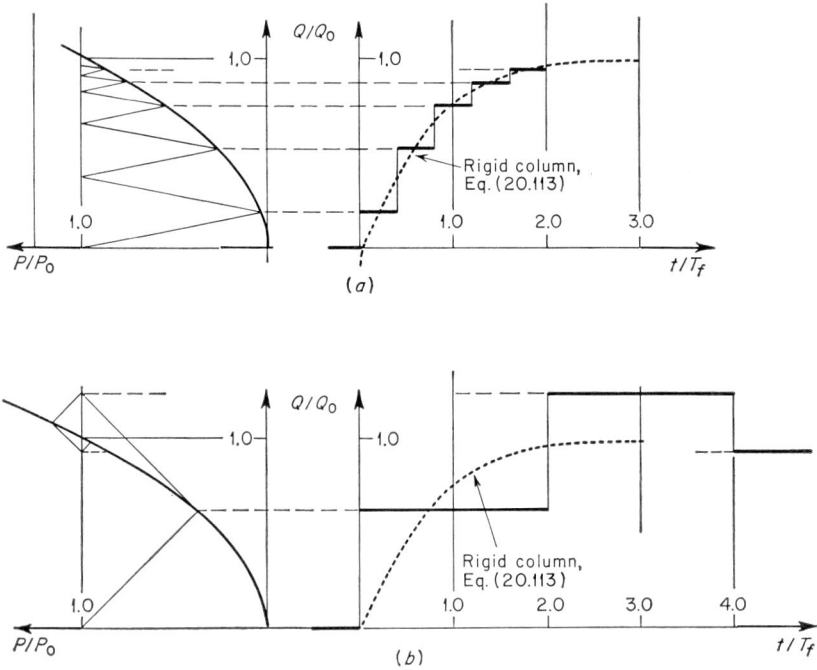

FIG. 20.5. Flow establishment after a sudden valve opening.

This classical equation for inertial water hammer due to valve stroking originated with R. D. Johnson. In principle, given any valve-stroking function $B(t)$, the values of **b** and $d\mathbf{b}/dt$ could be determined for each instant. From these, the middle and right-hand terms of Eq. (20.117) could be solved as a time-varying linear differential equation in $z(t)$. However, in practice, only the simplest types of valve strokes yield analytical results. If, on the other hand, some arbitrary stroking curve is specified, the elastic analysis next below is actually much simpler to carry out. Nevertheless, useful results may be derived from Eq. (20.117) as will be indicated.

Elastic Water-hammer Equations. Allievi first introduced into the characteristic wave relations appropriate terms for the valve motion. Beginning with Eq. (20.98) in per-unit form, namely,

$$h(t - 2T) + h(t) = 2\mathfrak{K}[\mathbf{q}(t - 2T) - \mathbf{q}(t)] \tag{20.118}$$

he merely made the replacements $\mathbf{z}^2 - 1 = h$, $\mathbf{bz} = \mathbf{q}$, and $i \equiv t/2T$, to obtain the now familiar Allievi *interval equation:*

$$\mathbf{z}^2_{i-1} + \mathbf{z}_i^2 - 2 = 2\mathfrak{K}(\mathbf{b}_{i-1}\mathbf{z}_{i-1} - \mathbf{b}_i\mathbf{z}_i) \tag{20.119}$$

It must be strongly emphasized that this relation holds not only for integral values of the "interval time" i, *but also for fractional values as well!* From this fact, given $B(t)$, the entire pressure history may be obtained in very direct fashion.

In terms of the further substitution

$$m \equiv \mathfrak{K}\mathbf{b} \tag{20.120}$$

the Allievi interval equation becomes

$$\mathbf{z}^2_{i-1} + \mathbf{z}_i^2 - 2m_{i-1}\mathbf{z}_{i-1} + 2m_i\mathbf{z}_i - 2 = 0 \tag{20.121}$$

This quadratic relation may be readily solved for z_i in terms of known values of m_i, m_{i-1}, and z_{i-1}, with the following result where $c_i \equiv 2 + 2m_{i-1}z_{i-1} - z^2_{i-1}$:

$$z_i = \sqrt{m_i^2 + c_i} - m_i \qquad (20.122)$$

Thus with the aid of a table of squares and roots, the water-hammer pressure for an arbitrary valve stroking has been calculated as indicated in Table 20.7.

However, in many practical problems involving water hammer due to valve stroking, the head variations are *necessarily* kept small enough to permit the approximation

$$q = b\sqrt{1 + h} \cong b(1 + \tfrac{1}{2}h) \qquad (20.123)$$

This reduces the per-unit Allievi equation

$$h_{i-1} + h_i = 2\mathcal{K}(q_{i-1} - q_i) \qquad (20.124)$$

to the approximate form, with $m = \mathcal{K}b$,

$$h_{i-1}(1 - m_{i-1}) + h_i(1 + m_i) \cong 2(m_{i-1} - m_i) \qquad (20.125)$$

which may be readily solved for h_i as

$$h_i \cong A_i - B_i h_{i-1} \qquad (20.126)$$

in which $A_i = \dfrac{2(m_{i-1} - m_i)}{1 + m_i}$ $\qquad (20.127)$

$B_i = \dfrac{1 - m_{i-1}}{1 + m_i}$ $\qquad (20.128)$

This formula (20.126) has a marked advantage over the more exact Eq. (20.122) since it may be solved accurately using a pocket slide rule. An approximate solution based on Eq. (20.126) is presented in Table 20.8 for the same case treated previously in Table 20.7. This is also plotted in Fig. 20.6.

Linear Valve Motion. A very useful and instructive case results when the valve is stroked in such a way that the time rate of change of area dB/dt is constant. Such linear opening and closing motion was the basis of the exhaustive analysis by Allievi of the limiting and extremum pressures.

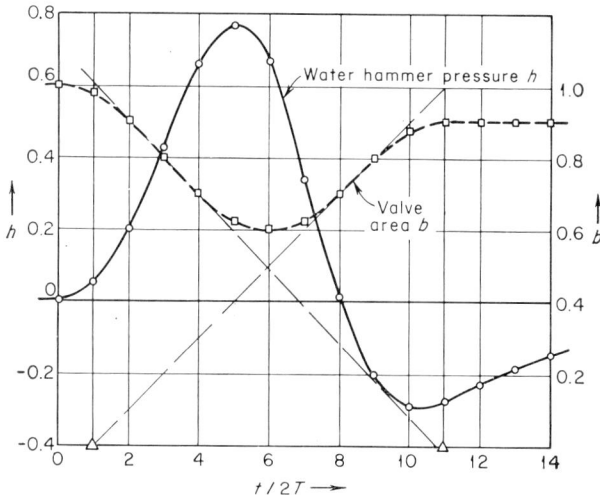

Fig. 20.6. Water hammer from valve stroking.

Table 20.7. Elastic Water-hammer Pressure

Based upon Eq. (20.122):

$$h_i = z_i^2 - 1$$
$$z_i = \sqrt{m_i^2 + c_i} - m_i$$

(1) i	(2) m_i	(3) $2m_i z_i$	(4) $2 + m_i z_i$	(5) $-z_i^2$	(6) $c_i = 2 + 2m_{i-1}z_{i-1} - z_{i-1}^2$	(7) m_i^2	(8) $m_i^2 + c_i$	(9) $\sqrt{m_i^2 + c_i}$	(10) m_i	(11) $z_i = \sqrt{m_i^2 + c_i} - m_i$	(12) z_i^2	(13) $h_i = z_i^2 - 1$
0	10.00	20.00	22.00	1.00	21.00	100.00	121.00	11.000	10.000	1.000	1.000	0
1	9.75	19.95	21.95	1.05	21.00	95.06	116.06	10.773	9.750	1.023	1.047	0.047
2	9.00	19.72	21.72	1.02	20.90	81.00	101.90	10.095	9.000	1.095	1.199	0.199
3	8.00	19.09	21.09	1.42	20.52	64.00	84.52	9.193	8.000	1.193	1.423	0.423
4	7.00	18.02	20.02	1.65	19.67	49.00	68.67	8.287	7.000	1.287	1.656	0.656
5	6.25	16.90	18.90	1.76	18.37	39.06	57.43	7.578	6.250	1.328	1.764	0.764
6	6.00	15.49	17.49	1.66	17.14	36.00	53.14	7.290	6.000	1.290	1.664	0.664
7	6.25	14.40	16.40	1.33	15.73	39.06	54.79	7.402	6.250	1.152	1.327	0.327
8	7.00	14.06	16.06	1.01	15.07	49.00	64.07	8.004	7.000	1.004	1.008	+0.008
9	8.00	14.25	16.25	0.79	15.05	64.00	79.05	8.891	8.000	0.891	0.794	-0.206
10	8.75	14.75	16.75	0.71	15.46	76.56	92.02	9.593	8.750	0.843	0.711	-0.289
11	9.00	15.32	17.32	0.72	16.04	81.00	97.04	9.851	9.000	0.851	0.724	-0.276
12	9.00	15.82	17.82	0.77	16.60	81.00	97.60	9.879	9.000	0.879	0.773	-0.227
13	9.00	16.21	18.21	0.81	17.05	81.00	98.05	9.902	9.000	0.902	0.814	-0.186
14	9.00				17.40	81.00	98.40	9.920	9.000	0.920	0.846	-0.154

Table 20.8. Approximate Elastic Water-hammer Pressure

Based upon Eq. (20.126):

$$h_i \cong A_i - B_i h_{i-1}$$

$$\mathcal{K} = \frac{Z_0 Q_0}{2P_0} = 10$$

(1) i	(2) b_i	(3) $m_i = \mathcal{K} b_i$	(4) m_{i-1}	(5) $\Delta m_i = m_{i-1} - m_i$	(6) $m_{i-1} - 1$	(7) $m_i + 1$	(8) $-B_i = \dfrac{m_{i-1} - 1}{m_i + 1}$	(9) $A_i = \dfrac{2\Delta m_i}{m_i + 1}$	(10) $-B_i h_{i-1}$	(11) h_i
0	1.000	10.00	10.00	0	+9.00	11.00	....	0	0	0
1	0.975	9.75	10.00	0.25	9.00	10.75	....	0.04	0	0.04
2	0.900	9.00	9.75	0.75	8.75	10.00	0.80	0.15	0.03	0.18
3	0.800	8.00	9.00	1.00	8.00	9.00	0.89	0.22	0.16	0.38
4	0.700	7.00	8.00	1.00	7.00	8.00	0.88	0.25	0.34	0.59
5	0.625	6.25	7.00	0.75	6.00	7.25	0.83	0.21	0.49	0.70
6	0.600	6.00	6.25	0.25	5.25	7.00	0.75	0.07	0.53	0.60
7	0.625	6.25	6.00	-0.25	5.00	7.25	0.69	-0.07	0.41	0.34
8	0.700	7.00	6.25	-0.75	5.25	8.00	0.66	-0.19	0.22	0.03
9	0.800	8.00	7.00	-1.00	6.00	9.00	0.67	-0.22	0.02	-0.20
10	0.875	8.75	8.00	-0.75	7.00	9.75	0.72	-0.15	-0.14	-0.29
11	0.900	9.00	8.75	-0.25	7.75	10.00	0.78	-0.05	-0.23	-0.28
12	0.900	9.00	9.00	0	8.00	10.00	0.80	0	-0.22	-0.22
13	0.900	9.00	9.00	0	8.00	10.00	0.80	0	-0.18	-0.18
14	0.900	9.00	9.00	0	8.00	10.00	0.80	0	-0.14	-0.14

Consider a linear valve motion governed by the following law:

$$B(t) = B_0 \left(1 \pm \frac{t}{T_v} \right) \tag{20.129}$$

in which valve *opening* corresponds to the plus sign; *closure*, to the minus sign.

In per-unit terms this becomes

$$\mathbf{b}(t) = 1 \pm \frac{t}{T_v} \tag{20.130}$$

For valve *closure* in the inelastic case this may be conveniently expressed in the form

$$\mathbf{b} = 1 - r\mathbf{t}$$

$$\frac{d\mathbf{b}}{d\mathbf{t}} = -r \tag{20.131}$$

if $r \equiv T_v/T_i$, $\mathbf{t} \equiv t/T_i$, and $T_i \equiv IQ_0/P_0$ is the inertia time constant described previously. Valve *opening* may then be associated with negative values of r.

For elastic analysis Eq. (20.130) may be reduced to the form

$$\mathbf{b}_i = 1 + \mathfrak{R} \cdot i \tag{20.132}$$

if $\mathfrak{R} = T_v/2T$ is a measure of the number of round-trip intervals required to produce 100 per cent change in valve area.

Limiting Pressures. If the values of $\mathbf{b}$ and $d\mathbf{b}/d\mathbf{t}$ are substituted into the inelastic Eq. (20.117), there results the equation

$$r\mathbf{z} + (1 - r\mathbf{t}) \frac{d\mathbf{z}}{d\mathbf{t}} = \mathbf{z}^2 - 1 \tag{20.133}$$

If an extremum in pressure exists, then, necessarily, $d\mathbf{z}/d\mathbf{t} \equiv 0$, with the resulting condition

$$\mathbf{z}^2 - r\mathbf{z} - 1 = 0 \tag{20.134}$$

The corresponding value for the maximum or minimum per-unit head increment, $h_m \equiv \mathbf{z}^2 - 1$, is given by

$$h_m = r \sqrt{1 + \frac{r^2}{4}} + \frac{r^2}{2} \tag{20.135}$$

if valve *closure* corresponds to $+r$, and *opening* to $-r$.

The significance of this relation also carries over into the elastic case, for if it is recognized that, for closure

$$\mathbf{b}_{i-1} - \mathbf{b}_i = \frac{1}{\mathfrak{R}} \tag{20.136}$$

then in Eq. (20.119) the condition

$$\mathbf{z}_{i-1} = \mathbf{z}_i = \mathbf{z}_m \tag{20.137}$$

results in

$$\mathbf{z}_m{}^2 - \frac{\mathfrak{K}}{\mathfrak{R}} \mathbf{z}_m - 1 = 0 \tag{20.138}$$

which is identical with Eq. (20.134) since

$$\frac{\mathfrak{K}}{\mathfrak{R}} = \frac{Z_0 Q_0/2P_0}{T_v/2T} = \frac{Z_0 T \cdot Q_0/P_0}{T_v} = \frac{I(Q_0/P_0)}{T_v} = r \tag{20.139}$$

Thus the asymptotic pressure change for linear valve motion is identical, whether we consider the fluid elastic or inelastic.

A graphical presentation of Eq. (20.135) is given in Fig. 20.7.

Pressure History with Linear Stroking. The resulting equation when the relations of 20.131 are substituted into Eq. (20.117) can be integrated with the result obtained by Johnson, namely,

$$h\left(\frac{t}{T_v}\right) = \frac{1}{4}\left[\frac{a - bc(1 - t/T_v)^n}{1 + c(1 - t/T_v)^n}\right]^2 - 1 \tag{20.140}$$

in which $a = \sqrt{4 + r^2} + r$

$b = \sqrt{4 + r^2} - r$

$c = \dfrac{a - 2}{b + 2}$

$n = \sqrt{\dfrac{4 + r^2}{r}}$

A very accurate approximation for Eq. (20.140) may be written for valve closure, namely,

$$h\left(\frac{t}{T_v}\right) \cong h_m\left[1 - (1 - t/T_v)^{2/h_m}\right] \tag{20.141}$$

if $h_m(r)$ is the limiting pressure rise given in the previous paragraphs. Some representative cases are indicated in Fig. 20.7.

Elastic vs. Inertial Effects. The principal conclusions to be drawn from the previous paragraphs are the following:

1. Elastic effects in water hammer may be considered as deviations about the basic inertial phenomena which are described by the rigid analysis.
2. These deviations become very small for large $\mathfrak{K}$ (low heads) and large $\mathfrak{N}$ (short pipelines, slow closures) so that in such cases the water may be considered effectively inelastic.
3. Both formulations lend themselves readily to straightforward solution techniques once the terminal velocity-time curve is specified or determined.
4. Thus for both analyses the pressure-time curves in any particular case depend primarily on the nature of the velocity variation.
5. If the valve-stroking curve is specified, an elastic analysis will usually be simpler to carry out.

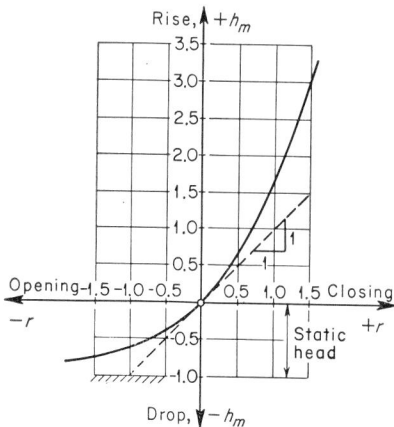

FIG. 20.7. Limiting water-hammer pressures.

Consideration of the Effects of Pipe Friction. The simple pipe under consideration thus far was assumed to have no friction or other loss in energy. But in every actual installation some energy is lost even under steady conditions of operation; during transient changes there is considerable evidence of increased viscous friction losses together with other types of energy dissipation and dispersion, including acoustic radiation into the region surrounding the pipe. These losses are now discussed, and the modifications which they introduce in the dissipation-less treatment previously outlined are pointed out.

Flow through a pipe is always subject to the effects of fluid friction arising from viscosity and turbulence. Under steady flow, this loss of available energy manifests itself as a sloping pressure gradient; to each value of flow there corresponds a particular steady gradient, which is linear for a uniform pipe. From this fact one might expect that, when the pipe flow changes with time, the pressure gradient must also change with time, not only due to dynamic changes brought about by the transient effects treated above, but also simply from change in friction loss throughout the pipe. Particularly for slow-momentum changes in long pipes, this friction term may be as significant as the inertial component in the determination of the dynamic gradient.

When elastic effects are also considered in the calculation of the dynamic gradient, a number of additional factors must be dealt with. First, as indicated above, the flow is no longer the same throughout the pipe at any instant, causing the friction gradient to vary from section to section. Furthermore, these fluctuations in flow may have high-frequency components even for gradual terminal changes, and there is experimental and theoretical evidence that friction and other forms of energy dissipation depend sensibly upon the rates of change of velocity. Indeed, most test results clearly demonstrate the presence of such dispersion or scattering losses, since the higher harmonics in the velocity and pressure transients attenuate more rapidly than the lower harmonics. This latter phenomenon is discussed later under anelastic effects.

Returning to the case of pipe friction, while a pair of equations can, in fact, be written to account for distributed friction loss, namely,

$$-\frac{\partial P}{\partial S} = \mathcal{g}\,\frac{\partial Q}{\partial t} + \mathbf{R}(Q) \tag{20.142}$$

$$-\frac{\partial Q}{\partial S} = \mathcal{e}\,\frac{\partial P}{\partial t} \tag{20.143}$$

the resistance term $\mathbf{R}(Q)$ is generally nonlinear in Q, making impossible analytic solutions such as those obtained above for the frictionless case. Thus, for purely practical reasons, one is forced into one of the two conventional alternatives:

1. Linearization of the resistance term but preserving the distribution over space or
2. Lumping the resistance term but preserving the nonlinearity with flow

In the former case analysis starts with the relations

$$-\frac{\partial P}{\partial S} = \mathcal{g}\,\frac{\partial Q}{\partial t} + \Re Q \tag{20.144}$$

$$-\frac{\partial Q}{\partial S} = \mathcal{e}\,\frac{\partial P}{\partial t} \tag{20.145}$$

These equations have been applied specifically to water-hammer problems by F. M. Wood, G. R. Rich, and W. T. Rouleau, among others, but they have also been studied in exhaustive detail for nearly a century in connection with RLC electric transmission lines, beginning with the classic researches of Oliver Heaviside. Therefore, many solutions for various parametric and boundary conditions can be found in readily available literature. However, little attention has yet been given to the valve-terminated case except for the frequency response; that is, the behavior under sinusoidal valve stroking, which employs methods similar to those of Art. 20.6.

In the case of alternative 2, the most practical recourse is to employ "loss junctions" or *friction joints* as indicated in Art. 20.3. Even if only one friction joint is used, at least the steady flow can be computed accurately. Moreover, if the pipe is terminated at one end in a valve, the single friction joint may be absorbed into the valve characteristic.

A useful rule of thumb to indicate the number of friction joints required to characterize accurately high-frequency response is simply the following: *The spacing between adjacent friction joints should be no larger than the wavelength of the highest-frequency disturbance of significance.* This is the same rule as cited elsewhere for the representation of a compound pipe. It is then obvious that no finite number of friction joints can more than roughly characterize the surge-friction change due to large and abrupt stoppages of flow. However, since under these conditions the surge pressures are usually many times larger than the friction swings, this limitation is usually overlooked in practice.

Anelastic Fluid Behavior and Dispersion Losses. From a phenomenological stand-point, it is not a priori reasonable to assume a purely static relationship between pressure changes ΔP and density changes $\Delta \rho$ of a fluid under dynamic conditions. Logic would dictate a more complete (albeit linear) form such as

$$a_0 \, \Delta\rho + a_1 \, \Delta\dot{\rho} + a_2 \Delta\ddot{\rho} + \cdots = b_0 \Delta P + b_1 \, \Delta\dot{P} + b_2 \, \Delta\ddot{P} + \cdots \qquad (20.146)$$

in which the dots indicate time derivatives, and the coefficients are in general undeter-mined. This relationship may be indicated in equivalent operation form

$$\left(\sum_{k=0}^{\infty} a_k D^k \right) \Delta\rho = \left(\sum_{k=0}^{\infty} b_k D^k \right) \Delta P$$

with $D = d/dt$ denoting the differential operator.

Historically, only the very simplest of the infinitude of possibilities for Eq. (20.146) have been considered analytically or have been employed as descriptive models for re-ducing experimental data. However, for some time it has been recognized how arbitrary such idealizations have been; this awareness has become widespread since the advent of generalized continuum mechanics and rheology.

Consider, for example, the next approximation beyond the classical, namely, that with a_0, a_1, b_0, b_1, nonzero, and with all the rest of the a_k and b_k assumed vanishingly small. The coefficient a_1 is directly related to what has been termed the second coefficient of viscosity.

If such anelastic, frequency-dependent effects are to be taken into account, it is first necessary to generalize the specific inertance and capacitance terms in the conjugate conservation relations. This may be done by defining a specific impedance operator $z(D)$ and a specific admittance operator $y(D)$, such that the following relations are as-sumed to hold:

$$-\frac{\partial P}{\partial s} = z(D) \cdot Q \qquad (20.147)$$

$$-\frac{\partial Q}{\partial s} = y(D) \cdot P \qquad (20.148)$$

Then Eqs. (20.39) and (20.40) are merely the specializations of Eqs. (20.147) and (20.148), respectively, with

$$z(D) \to \mathit{s} \cdot D \qquad y(D) \to \mathrm{c} \cdot D \qquad (20.149)$$

which may now be considered as low-frequency approximations of the more general case.

The corresponding surge impedance and propagation operator are also frequency-de-pendent and become

$$Z_0 \equiv \sqrt{\frac{zL}{yL}} = \sqrt{\frac{z}{y}} = Z_0(D) \qquad (20.150)$$

$$\Gamma \equiv \sqrt{zL \cdot yL} = L\sqrt{zy} = \Gamma(D) \qquad (20.151)$$

Again, these reduce to the earlier results since

$$Z_0 \to \sqrt{\frac{ID}{CD}} = \sqrt{\frac{I}{C}} = Z_0$$

$$\Gamma \to \sqrt{ID \cdot CD} = (\sqrt{I \cdot C})D = TD \qquad (20.152)$$

One may continue to use the concept of characteristic variables, provided only that the two characteristic relations are interpreted in an operational sense. Thus with

$$\mathcal{P} = P + (z_0 * Q) \qquad (20.153)$$

$$\mathcal{Q} = P - (z_0 * Q) \qquad (20.154)$$

and

$$\mathbf{F} = \exp\left[-\Gamma(D)\right] \tag{20.155}$$

the generalization of $\mathbf{\Delta} = \exp(-TD)$, the characteristic equations between an upstream station a and a downstream station b become

$$\mathcal{P}_b = \mathbf{F} * \mathcal{P}_a \tag{20.156}$$

$$Q_a = \mathbf{F} * Q_b \tag{20.157}$$

The generalized phase-delay operator $\mathbf{F}$ is nearly always a *monotone process*.[8,9] As such, simple approximations may be used for practical computations.

For example, the principal effects of anelastic dispersion on water hammer may be accounted for by a simple modification of Allievi's equation. In place of the usual relation, when $U_0 = 0$,

$$U(t) + V(t) = V(t - 2T) - U(t - 2T) \tag{20.158}$$

one may substitute the expression

$$U(t) + V(t) = \sum_k c_k[V(t - 2T_k) - U(t - 2T_k)] \tag{20.159}$$

with the following conditions and definitions:

c_k = weighting coefficient ≥ 0, with the normalizing condition, $\sum_k c_k = 1$

T_k = component delay, with the normalizing condition, $\sum_k c_k T_k = T$

This technique can account for the frequency-dependent anomalous dispersion and may be matched accurately to any experimental data such as Figs. 20.19 and 20.20. The dramatic effects on afterwaves of a mere 10 per cent dispersion are evidenced in Fig. 20.8, where a solution using the constants

$$c_1 = c_2 = \tfrac{1}{2} \qquad T_1 = 0.9T \qquad T_2 = 1.1T$$

is compared with the previous result obtained in Fig. 20.3 for $\mathfrak{N} = 2$.

Concluding Remarks. The above discussion completes the brief treatment of the developments by Allievi, Johnson, and others on the basic water-hammer equations for a simple pipe, and the application of these equations to cases of linear operation of an idealized quadratic valve. In Art. 20.9 an examination is made of how these solutions are modified when actual engineering installations are considered, where the pipe is generally not of the simple lossless type, and where the terminations are necessarily more

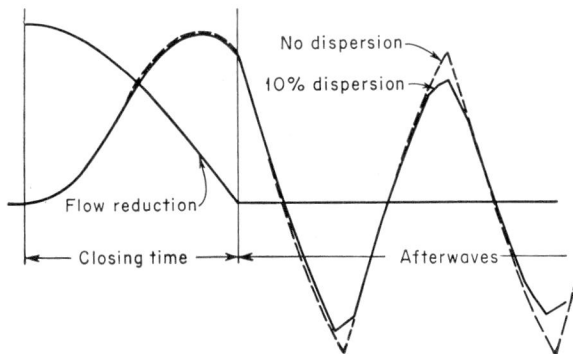

Fig. 20.8. Dispersion.

complex than the idealized forms treated above. However, some of the simple formulas developed for linear gate motion have more general utility in estimating the maximum rise or drop in pressure from a knowledge of the extreme or limiting stroking rates. Figures 20.19 and 20.20 indicate the two cases, one opening, one closing, in which the pressures calculated from the previous formulas, based upon *equivalent time* of opening or closing, are fair approximations to the actual pressure extremes, which have been calculated as the basis of the given nonlinear gate-time curve.

20.8. Surge Chambers for Pressure Regulation

Introductory Remarks. Some form of supplemental fluid capacitance, in addition to the fluid elasticity, is generally required whenever the transient pressure changes due to normal flow variations in a fluid pipeline are in excess of allowable limits. This circumstance will frequently arise for long pipelines even under normal rates of acceleration or deceleration.

In pumping systems an air chamber is often used for this ballasting purpose, while in hydroelectric developments surge tanks are commonly employed. Other more complex systems of these and similar devices are called for under special circumstances. However, here attention is restricted to a few simple examples of analysis and design problems involving surge tanks and air chambers.

It is helpful to keep in mind the qualitative analogy existing between the mass oscillations of a pipe equipped with a surge vessel and the same pipe with its elastic capacity alone; the bond diagrams for these situations would appear:

Surge problems:

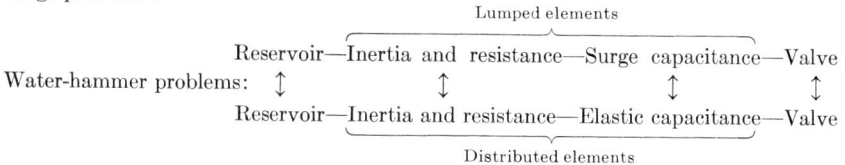

Lumped elements

Reservoir—Inertia and resistance—Surge capacitance—Valve

Water-hammer problems:　↕　　　　↕　　　　　↕　　　　↕

Reservoir—Inertia and resistance—Elastic capacitance—Valve

Distributed elements

The essential difference between the two systems lies in the fact that the surge system involves lumped elements with a dominant single oscillatory frequency, while the water-hammer mode involves distributed behavior with an infinite set of harmonic frequencies. However, many of the general comments made before still apply. This is particularly true of the essential parameters and properties.

The physical situation treated in this article is depicted by the bond diagram:

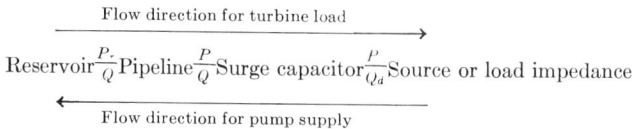

Flow direction for turbine load

Reservoir$\frac{P}{Q}$Pipeline$\frac{P}{Q}$Surge capacitor$\frac{P}{Q_a}$Source or load impedance

Flow direction for pump supply

Physical Basis of Undulating Surges. Surge chambers and surge tanks have been used as pressure-stabilizing devices in the flow lines of hydroelectric plants and pumping stations for more than fifty years. Knowledge of the basic design factors and operating features was greatly enhanced by the early analytical and experimental work of Johnson and Durand in the United States, A. H. Gibson in England, and Thoma, Braun, Pressel, Calame, Gaden, and other investigators on the Continent during the period 1905 to 1930.

Specifically, the purpose of a surge tank in the fluid transmission systems of hydroelectric plants is to provide a point of pressure relief when the turbine load is suddenly decreased and demand flow reduced, and, on the other hand, to supply a volume of water close to the unit when the load, and demand flow, is suddenly increased. Under steady operating conditions the water level in the surge tank remains constant at an elevation corresponding to the friction-gradient level at the base of the tank, but, whenever the discharge to the turbine is changed, the inertia of the conduit water column gives rise to a pressure differential jointly proportional to the inertance of the column and the rate of acceleration as indicated previously. However, this accelerating head is now represented by the instantaneous difference between friction-gradient level and tank-surface level.

The ensuing undulating behavior may also be interpreted on an energy basis: The surging action reflects the continuous, cyclic transformation of kinetic energy into potential, and the reverse. Of course, friction in the conduit and throttling action in the tank will tend to attenuate these oscillations. However, the variation of demand (or supply) flow with tank level due to plant impedance will produce effects on surges which can sometimes lead to instability. Moreover, if the load oscillates or pulsates in approximate synchronism with the natural period of the tank surges, the resultant amplitudes may augment to a final steady swing of considerable magnitude.

Representation of the Pipeline. For all practical problems involving mass oscillation between two variable-level reservoirs, the significant frequencies are so low that the pipeline may be considered as an inelastic column of liquid. Under these conditions, taking into account the steady-state friction loss in the pipe, one might write for the governing equation

$$P_r - P = I \cdot \frac{dQ}{dt} + \mathbf{R}(Q) \tag{20.160}$$

Typically, for engineering projects, the resistance function $\mathbf{R}$ could be represented by a square-law damping of the form

$$\mathbf{R}(Q) = R|Q|Q \tag{20.161}$$

It is clear that Eq. (20.160) is precisely the same as the low-frequency terminal impedance treated in Art. 20.6. High-frequency behavior of surge-tank systems must be treated taking elastic behavior into account.

Types of Surge Vessels. As mentioned above, the two most common forms of surge capacitors involve either

1. Simple or composite storage of the flowing fluid in a free-surface vessel (or vessels) connected to the pipe directly or through a throttle or
2. Similar storage of the flowing liquid but confined under air or other gas pressure

These two types of devices are generally called *surge tanks* and *air chambers*, respectively.

In any case, the pressure head P in the chamber is related to the stored volume of liquid $\mathcal{V}$ by a capacitance relation of the form

$$\mathcal{V} = \mathbf{C}(P) \tag{20.162}$$

This relation is ordinarily monotonic-nondecreasing, with increasing pressure corresponding to increasing stored liquid.

If the generalized surge vessel is provided with a throttle to the atmosphere having a resistance $\mathbf{R}_a$ and another throttle to the pipeline with a resistance $\mathbf{R}_t$, as indicated in Fig. 20.9, all commonly used chambers can be classified by the following scheme:

Name	Resistance	
	$\mathbf{R}_a$	$\mathbf{R}_t$
1. Simple surge tank..............................	Zero	Zero
2. Throttled surge tank (restricted orifice tank)......	Zero	Finite
3. Air-throttled tank.............................	Finite	Zero
4. Air chamber..................................	Infinite	Zero
5. Throttled air chamber.........................	Infinite	Finite

The differential surge tank introduced by R. D. Johnson is a composite of tank 1 with tank 2 in the form

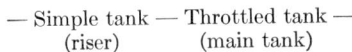

— Simple tank — Throttled tank —
(riser)   (main tank)

To atmosphere

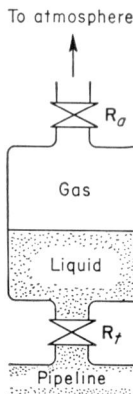

FIG. 20.9. General-
ized surge tank.

while the comparable differential air tank would have the form

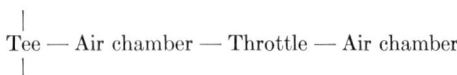

$$\text{Tee} \longrightarrow \text{Air chamber} \longrightarrow \text{Throttle} \longrightarrow \text{Air chamber}$$

All the above throttled tanks introduce a shunt damping or resistance term which markedly reduces surge amplitudes and attenuates the oscillations when the throttle is properly sized. In order to represent this effect, it is necessary to introduce the *tank inflow* Q_t defined by the relations

$$Q_t \equiv \frac{d\mho}{dt} \qquad \text{or} \qquad \mho \equiv \int^t Q_t \, dt \qquad (20.163)$$

Then the pressure *in* the tank P_t may always be related to the pressure P below the tank in the pipe by the expression

$$P - P_t = \mathbf{R}_t(Q_t) \qquad (20.164)$$

If the throttle has zero resistance and is therefore "absent" or nonexistent, $P \equiv P_t$. Otherwise, a transient pressure differential will always exist between the pipe and the chamber.

The nature of the throttling characteristics $\mathbf{R}_t$ and $\mathbf{R}_a$ depends on the geometry of the throttling devices. These questions are discussed briefly later.

By considering the unthrottled simple cylindrical surge tank as the prototype case, then, with $\mho$ measured in cubic feet and P in feet, the capacitance relation becomes

$$\mho = \mathbf{C}(P) = C \cdot P = A \cdot P \qquad (20.165)$$

if $C = A$, the horizontal sectional area (in square feet) of the tank. In similar fashion all capacitance can be measured in "area" (square foot) units, for either surge tanks or air chambers. While $A(Z) = A(P)$ is a satisfactory way of describing the variation with a level of a nonuniform tank, a simpler approach is to return to the capacitance relation and deal directly with the variation in volume $\mho$ with level P. In this way the treatment of noncylindrical surge tanks and air chambers becomes strictly equivalent.

The Phenomenon of Mass Oscillations. One is now in a position to treat the transient behavior of a liquid pipeline provided with a throttled surge vessel of some sort. Following the developments above, the governing equations of motion become

$$P_r - P = I \frac{dQ}{dt} + \mathbf{R}(Q)$$

$$Q - Q_d = Q_t = \frac{d\mho}{dt} \qquad (20.166)$$

$$P - P_t = \mathbf{R}_t(Q_t)$$

These relations may be solved analytically only for the very simplest of situations. At first thought such drastic oversimplifications might appear to have little or no value; however, this is definitely not the case. By systematically treating certain dominant attributes to the exclusion of the others, a better understanding of the nature of the surge problem is approached.

In particular, if resistance ($\mathbf{R}$) and throttling ($\mathbf{R}_t$) effects are eliminated and if the fluid momentum $\mathfrak{U}$ is introduced, in which

$$\mathfrak{U} \equiv I \cdot Q \qquad (20.167)$$

then the above relations take on a canonical form of great value, namely,

$$P_r - P = \frac{d\mathfrak{U}}{dt} \qquad \mathfrak{U} = \int^t (P_r - P)\, dt$$

or

$$Q - Q_d = \frac{d\mathfrak{V}}{dt} \qquad \mathfrak{V} = \int^t (Q - Q_d)\, dt$$

(20.168)

These may be *divided* to eliminate time, resulting in the *phase* or *energy* equation in the three alternative forms

$$\frac{d\mathfrak{U}}{d\mathfrak{V}} = \frac{P_r - P}{Q - Q_d}$$

or
$$(P_r - P)d\mathfrak{V} = (Q - Q_d)d\mathfrak{U} \qquad (20.169)$$

or
$$(Q - Q_d)d\mathfrak{U} + (P - P_r)d\mathfrak{V} = 0$$

These phase equations govern the vibratory behavior that characterizes surge problems as can be seen below in the following discussion.

Lossless Surges in a Cylindrical Vessel. The undulatory behavior of a constant capacitance chamber such as a vertical surge tank of constant cross section may now be investigated. In all such cases the chamber capacitance relation becomes

$$\mathfrak{V} = \mathbf{C}(P) = C \cdot P \qquad (20.170)$$

if the constant capacitance C is measured in terms of an effective area A.

The conjugate conservation relations now become

$$I\frac{dQ}{dt} = P_r - P$$

$$C\frac{dP}{dt} = Q - Q_d$$

(20.171)

while the phase equation, Eq. (20.169), yields

$$(Q - Q_d)(I\, dQ) + (P - P_r)(C\, dP) = 0 \qquad (20.172)$$

In this last equation consider a circumstance where $Q_d = P_r = 0$. Then

$$I \cdot Q \cdot dQ + C \cdot P \cdot dP = 0$$

$$\tfrac{1}{2}I \cdot Q^2 + \tfrac{1}{2}C \cdot P^2 = \text{const} = E_0$$

(20.173)

or

The lower form reflects the law of conservation of energy since

Kinetic energy	$= \tfrac{1}{2}IQ^2$
Potential energy	$= \tfrac{1}{2}CP^2$
Total energy	$= \text{KE} + \text{PE} = \text{const}$

(20.174)

in the absence of energy-dissipative terms.

Equation (20.173) is the equation for an *ellipse* which can always be affinely transformed into a *circle*, in this case through the simple expedient of a scale change. This normalizing procedure involves the use of the *surge impedance* Z_0 if

$$Z_0 \equiv \sqrt{\frac{I}{C}} \qquad (20.175)$$

by direct analogy to the treatment leading to Eq. (20.43). One again has a choice of scales identical with those given by expressions (20.47), (20.48), and (20.49).

If one chooses a per-unit *flow* scaling $\mathbf{v} = Q/Q_0$ represented by relation (20.48), one merely divides the pressure P by the surge impedance Z_0 times Q_0 to obtain

$$\mathbf{u} = \frac{P}{Z_0 \, Q_0}$$

$$\mathbf{v} = \frac{Q}{Q_0}$$

(20.176)

A step change in Q_r from Q_0 to zero would give the results indicated in Fig. 20.10.

The phase diagram at the left is merely the circle corresponding to the energy-conservation relation

$$\mathbf{u}^2 + \mathbf{v}^2 = 1$$

(20.177)

The temporal variations of per-unit pressure $\mathbf{u}(t)$ and per-unit flow $\mathbf{v}(t)$ are depicted by the left-hand curves. These are governed by the equations

$$\mathbf{u} = \sin \frac{2\pi t}{T_0}$$

$$\mathbf{v} = 1 - \cos \frac{2\pi t}{T_0}$$

(20.178)

if

$$T_0 = 2\pi \sqrt{I \cdot C}$$

(20.179)

is the period of a frictionless surge system with inertance I and capacitance C.

Thus it is that the parameters $\sqrt{I/C}$ and $\sqrt{I \cdot C}$ play the same role as normalizing constants in surge phenomena as they do in water-hammer problems.

The pressure extrema occur whenever $\mathbf{v} \equiv 0$ and have the values

$$\mathbf{u}_e = \pm 1 \qquad \mathbf{u}_{\max} = +1 \qquad \mathbf{u}_{\min} = -1$$

(20.180)

In physical terms these correspond to the values

$$P_{\max} = +Z_0 \cdot Q_0 \qquad P_{\min} = -Z_0 \cdot Q_0$$

(20.181)

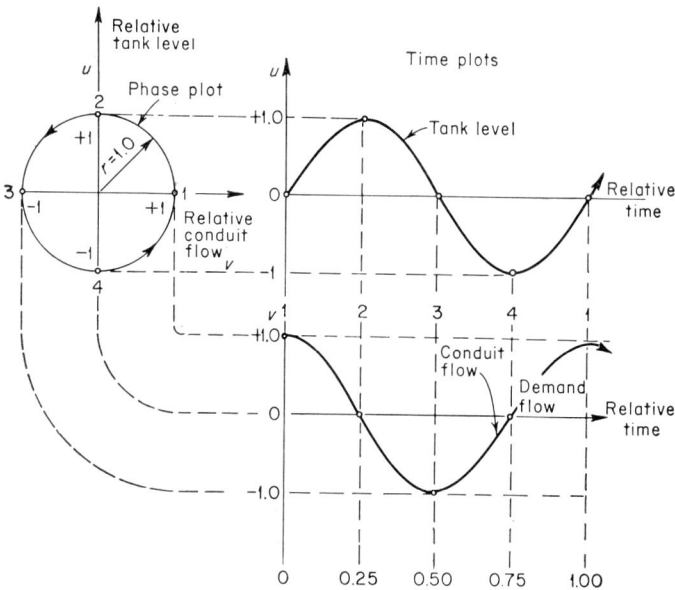

FIG. 20.10. Frictionless surges.

in which it must be emphasized that the reservoir pressure P_r has been taken identically zero.

Lossless Surges with a Variable Capacitance. For the variable-capacitance case it is particularly advantageous to write the governing equations in the mixed form

$$I \cdot \frac{dQ}{dt} = P = S(\mathcal{V})$$

$$\frac{d\mathcal{V}}{dt} = Q - Q_d = Q_t \qquad (20.182)$$

in which $S(\mathcal{V})$ is the nonlinear storage relation giving the pressure corresponding to any stored liquid volume.

The corresponding phase-energy equation becomes

$$S(\mathcal{V}) \cdot d\mathcal{V} + I \cdot Q_t \cdot dQ = 0 \qquad (20.183)$$

In the case of a step change in a load flow from Q_0 to zero, the volume will change from $\mathcal{V}_0$ to $\mathcal{V}_e$ if $\mathcal{V}_e$ is an extremum given by

$$\int_{\mathcal{V}_0}^{\mathcal{V}_e} S(\mathcal{V}) \cdot d\mathcal{V} = \frac{I}{2} Q_0^2 \qquad (20.184)$$

for which graphical plots permit ready solutions.

Of course, this result gives the same answer as before for a tank with constant capacitance C if $S(\mathcal{V}) = \mathcal{V}/C$, namely, $\mathcal{V} = C \cdot P$:

$$\frac{1}{2C} \mathcal{V}_e^2 = \frac{C}{2} P_e^2 = \frac{I}{2} Q_0^2 \qquad (20.185)$$

Air-chamber Surges. An application of the previous result concerns behavior of air chambers upon sudden change in demand flow. If all losses are neglected, the governing equations may be taken as the following

$$I \frac{dQ}{dt} = P_0 - P$$

$$-\frac{d\mathcal{V}}{dt} = Q - Q_d \qquad (20.186)$$

$$\frac{P}{P_0} = \left(\frac{\mathcal{V}_0}{\mathcal{V}}\right)^n$$

In this last equation $\mathcal{V}$ is the *air* (*not* liquid) volume, n is the polytropic exponent, normally between 1.0 and 1.4, and the reservoir pressure P_0 and the tank pressure P are both on an absolute scale.

For a step change in Q_d from Q_0 to zero, solution of the energy Eq. (20.184) will give the corresponding extreme upsurges and downsurges. The results are conveniently represented in terms of a per-unit pressure variable **h** if

$$\mathbf{h} \equiv \frac{P}{P_0} \qquad (20.187)$$

together with a dimensionless tank parameter $\mathbb{S}$ defined as

$$\mathbb{S} \equiv Z_0 \frac{Q_0}{P_0} \qquad (20.188)$$

The surge impedance Z_0 is here defined about the equilibrium point $(P_0, \mathcal{V}_0)$ as

$$Z_0 = \sqrt{\frac{I}{C_0}} = \sqrt{I \left(\frac{n P_0}{\mathcal{V}_0}\right)} = Z_0(n) \qquad (20.189)$$

The resultant solution to the system (20.186) yields the relations
For $n = 1$ (isothermal):

$$S = \sqrt{2\left(\ln \mathbf{h} + \frac{1}{\mathbf{h}} - 1\right)} \tag{20.190}$$

For $n \neq 1$ (nonisothermal):

$$S = \sqrt{2n\left[\frac{1}{n-1}\mathbf{h}^{(n-1)/n} + \left(\frac{1}{\mathbf{h}}\right)^{1/n} - \frac{n}{n-1}\right]} \tag{20.191}$$

These relations are plotted in Fig. 20.11. From the graphs it may be noted that over a very wide range the per-unit surge $\mathbf{h}$ with $S = Z_0 Q_0 / P_0$ and $Z_0 = Z_0(n)$ is only weakly dependent on the value of n. As indicated, this fact permits very close approximation by the formulas

$$\frac{P_{\max}}{P_0} = \mathbf{h}_{\max} \cong \exp S$$

$$\frac{P_{\min}}{P_0} = \mathbf{h}_{\min} \cong \exp(-S) \tag{20.192}$$

The corresponding air volumes are then determined as

$$\frac{\mathcal{V}_{\max}}{\mathcal{V}_0} = \left(\frac{1}{\mathbf{h}_{\min}}\right)^{1/n} \cong \exp \frac{S}{n}$$

$$\frac{\mathcal{V}_{\min}}{\mathcal{V}_0} = \left(\frac{1}{\mathbf{h}_{\max}}\right)^{1/n} \cong \exp\left(\frac{-S}{n}\right) \tag{20.193}$$

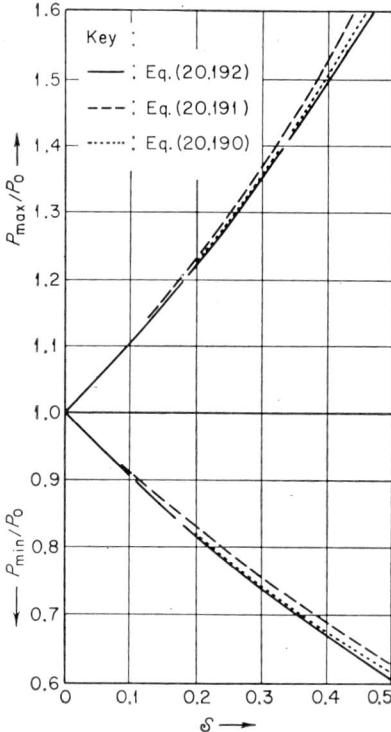

FIG. 20.11. Air-chamber surges.

By way of a practical example, consider a tank for a pumping plant with an initial compressed volume of $\mathcal{V}_0 = 4800$ ft³ under a pressure head $P_0 = 100$ ft at the end of a pipeline 3220 ft long and 10 ft² in sectional area. By assuming a polytropic exponent $n = 1.2$, then the following parameters can be found:

$$I = \frac{L}{gA} \qquad = \frac{3220}{32.2 \times 10} = 10 \text{ sec}^2/\text{ft}^2 \tag{20.194}$$

$$C_0 = \frac{\mathcal{V}_0}{nP_0} \qquad = \frac{4800}{1.2 \times 100} = 40 \text{ ft}^2 \tag{20.195}$$

$$Z_0 = \sqrt{\frac{I}{C_0}} \qquad = \sqrt{\frac{10}{40}} \qquad = 0.5 \text{ ft/cfs} \tag{20.196}$$

$$T = \sqrt{I \cdot C_0} = \sqrt{10 \times 40} = 20 \text{ sec} \tag{20.197}$$

If the flow is suddenly reduced from $Q_0 = 44$ cfs to zero, the parameter S becomes

$$S = \frac{Z_0 Q_0}{P_0} = \frac{0.5 \times 44}{100} = 0.22 \tag{20.198}$$

From Fig. 20.11 or Eq. (20.191), the corresponding maximum and minimum levels can be determined as follows:

$$\frac{P_{\max}}{P_0} = 1.25 \qquad P_{\max} = 125 \text{ ft}$$

$$\frac{P_{\min}}{P_0} = 0.80 \qquad P_{\min} = 80 \text{ ft} \tag{20.199}$$

The corresponding pressure-time curves of undamped oscillations in an air chamber may be very closely approximated by a "cnoidal" wave relation

$$P(t) \cong P_{\min} + (P_{\max} - P_{\min})\text{cn}^2\left(\frac{Kt}{T}\bigg|\, k\right) \tag{20.200}$$

if cn $(y|k)$ is the Jacobian elliptic function "cosam" with argument y, modulus k, and quarter period $K = K(k)$. The value of the modulus k may be estimated by the formula

$$k^2 \cong 1 - \frac{P_{\min}}{P_{\max}} \tag{20.201}$$

For example, consider the previous case in which $P_{\min} = 80$ ft, $P_{\max} = 125$ ft, and $T = 20$ sec; then

$$k^2 = 0.36 \tag{20.202}$$

$$k \ = 0.6 \tag{20.203}$$

$$K = 1.95 \tag{20.204}$$

and the time curve is as indicated in Fig. 20.12. This is plotted using readily available tables.[10]

Quadratic Friction in a Cylindrical Surge Tank. First consider the effects of quadratic friction $\mathbf{R}(Q) = R|Q|Q$ on the level extrema in a simple surge tank upon sudden stoppage of demand or drive flow Q_d.

By defining a friction parameter

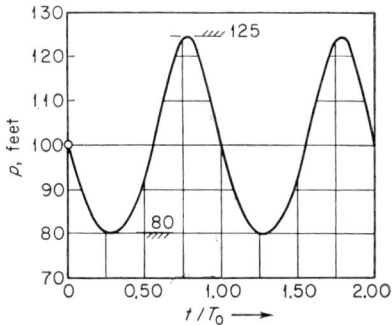

FIG. 20.12. Pressure-time curve.

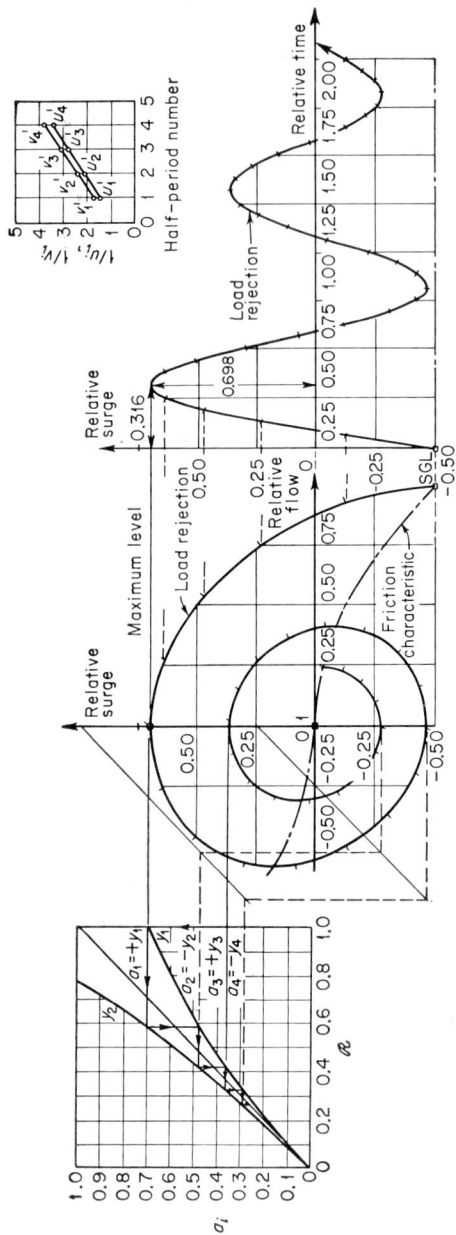

FIG. 20.13. Load-rejection surges.

$$\mathcal{R} = \frac{2RQ_0^2}{Z_0 Q_0} = \frac{2R}{Z_0} Q_0 \tag{20.205}$$

the phase equation for this case, in terms of normalized values, becomes

$$-\frac{d\mathbf{v}}{d\mathbf{u}} = \frac{\mathbf{u} + (\mathcal{R}/2) \cdot |\mathbf{v}|\mathbf{v}}{\mathbf{v}} \tag{20.206}$$

This may be rearranged in the form

$$-\frac{d\mathbf{f}}{d\mathbf{u}} = \mathbf{u} + (\mathcal{R} \ \text{sgn} \ \mathbf{v})\mathbf{f} \tag{20.207}$$

with $\mathbf{f} \equiv \mathbf{v}^2/2$. During any given "half cycle," the sign of the per-unit flow $\mathbf{v}$ will remain constant, either positive or negative. For $\mathbf{v}$ positive, $\text{sgn} \ \mathbf{v} = +1$, and the following linear differential equation applies

$$\frac{d\mathbf{f}}{d\mathbf{u}} + \mathcal{R}\mathbf{f} = -\mathbf{u} \tag{20.208}$$

having the complete analytical solution

$$\mathcal{R}^2\mathbf{f} = 1 - \exp\left[-\mathcal{R}\left(\mathbf{u} + \frac{\mathcal{R}}{2}\right)\right] - \mathcal{R}\mathbf{u} \tag{20.209}$$

For the first maximum (in the turbine case), $\mathbf{v} = \mathbf{f} = 0$ and $\mathbf{u} = \mathbf{u}_m$.

$$\exp\left[-\mathcal{R}\left(\mathbf{u}_m + \frac{\mathcal{R}}{2}\right)\right] = 1 - \mathcal{R}\mathbf{u}_m \tag{20.210}$$

$$-\frac{\mathcal{R}^2}{2} = \ln(1 - \mathcal{R}\mathbf{u}_m) + \mathcal{R}\mathbf{u}_m \tag{20.211}$$

or
$$\mathcal{R} = \sqrt{-2[\ln(1 - \mathcal{R}\mathbf{u}_m) + \mathcal{R}\mathbf{u}_m]} \tag{20.212}$$

It is useful to define the right side of this transcendental expression as the positive surge function $\mathcal{Y}^+$ and also define a complementary negative surge function $\mathcal{Y}^- \equiv \mathcal{Y}^+(-\mathbf{u}_m)$. Thus the two functions, $\mathcal{Y}^+$ and $\mathcal{Y}^-$, in which

$$\mathcal{Y}^+ = \sqrt{-2[\mathcal{R}\mathbf{u}_m + \ln(1 - \mathcal{R}\mathbf{u}_m)]} \tag{20.213}$$

$$\mathcal{Y}^- = \sqrt{2[\mathcal{R}\mathbf{u}_m - \ln(1 + \mathcal{R}\mathbf{u}_m)]} \tag{20.214}$$

are plotted at the left side of Fig. 20.13. As can be seen in the figure, these surges oscillate and attenuate, resulting in a series of alternating but decreasing amplitudes. The successive extreme values of pipe flow $\mathbf{v}_m$ and tank level $\mathbf{u}_m$ can be found by a "staircase" construction between the functions $\mathcal{Y}^+$ and $\mathcal{Y}^-$ as indicated in Fig. 20.13.

A very useful approximation for the first extrema follows directly from Eq. (20.212) and is given by

$$\mathbf{u}_1 \cong \frac{1}{1 + \frac{1}{3}\mathcal{R} + \frac{1}{10}\mathcal{R}^2} \tag{20.215}$$

For the example of Fig. 20.14, with $\mathcal{R} = 1$, this gives $\mathbf{u}_1 \cong 0.698$, which happens to be the exact value to three decimal places.

It is also interesting to note that, as a result of the square-law damping process, the attenuation envelope is *hyperbolic*,

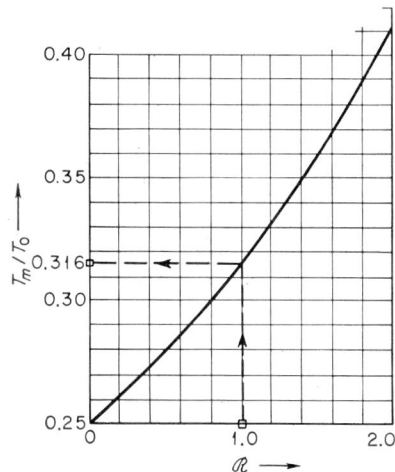

FIG. 20.14. Time to first surge.

resulting in the fact that the *reciprocals* of the level and flow extrema, namely,

$$\frac{1}{\mathbf{u}_m} \quad \text{and} \quad \frac{1}{\mathbf{v}_m}$$

plot linearly as indicated on the figure cited.

As can be seen in Fig. 20.14, the time T_m to the first extremum is no longer $\frac{1}{4}T_0 = (\pi/2)T$ as in the frictionless case but is now increased with increasing $\Re$. This effect is indicated in Fig. 20.14 and may be closely approximated by the formula

$$T_m \cong \left(1 + \frac{\Re}{5} + \frac{\Re^2}{16}\right) \cdot \frac{1}{4} \cdot T_0 \tag{20.216}$$

Similarly, the half-period times T_p between alternate positive and negative surges $\mathbf{u}^+$ and $\mathbf{u}^-$ are always slightly greater than the frictionless value $\frac{1}{2}T_0 = \pi T$. This augmentation can be accurately reflected by the approximate formula

$$T_p \cong \left[1 + \left(\frac{\Re(\mathbf{u}^+ + \mathbf{u}^-)}{10}\right)^2\right]\frac{1}{2} \cdot T_0 \tag{20.217}$$

Nevertheless, it should be pointed out that for any practical case this last correction will be less than 3 per cent!

It should be evident from these results that the more general situation of surge-tank transients resulting from arbitrary variations in flow disturbance $Q_d(t)$ does not lend itself to any type of exact or simple analytical treatment. While many special cases are worked out in the voluminous literature on this problem, most of these cases are best handled by direct computational methods beginning with the fundamental dynamic relations.

However, an outstandingly useful set of tables and accompanying analyses for the system of Eq. 20.206 was produced during the early work of W. E. Milne[11] in this field.

Limiting Positive Surge. The previous analytical results display one very unusual property for surge vessels on pipes with quadratic friction, namely: *There is a maximum possible surge rise above the reservoir surface which the tank level cannot exceed, regardless of the magnitude or nature of the load change.*

This is readily found to be the value

$$\Re\mathbf{u}_{m1} \equiv 1 \tag{20.218}$$

or, in physical terms, since $P_m = \mathbf{u}_m \cdot Z_0 \cdot Q_0$,

$$P_{m1} = \frac{Z_0^2}{2R} = \frac{I}{2CR} = \frac{I/R}{2C} \tag{20.219}$$

or, with D and A the pipe diameter and area, respectively, f the Darcy friction factor, and C the tank area,

$$P_{m1} = \frac{D/f}{C/A} \quad \text{ft} \tag{20.220}$$

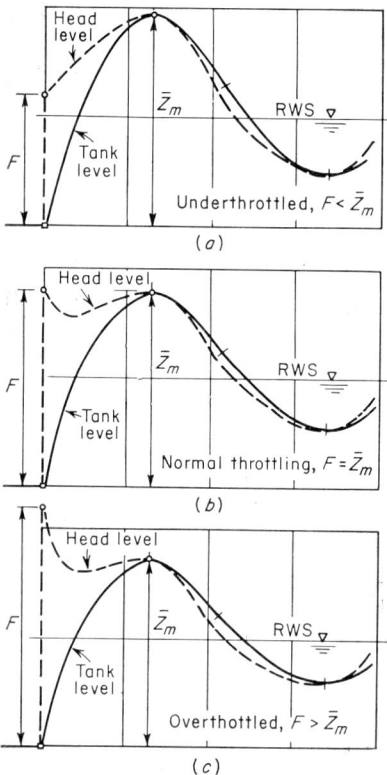

(a)

(b)

(c)

Fig. 20.15. Degrees of throttling.

If the top of the tank is placed above this

level, there will be no spillage, even under the worst conditions of resonance. However, in most instances it is not economical to design tanks for such contingencies, and the above result is better employed to protect against inadvertent overdesign. For example, a surge tank designed to be marginally stable according to the classical Thoma criterion would have a limiting positive surge just equal to the gross static head.

Throttled Surge Tanks. It was R. D. Johnson in 1915 who first promulgated the insertion of an orifice restriction or throttle between the surge vessel and the pipeline. Not only does this furnish extra damping action, but it also results in smaller tank-level excursions as well as pressure fluctuations, provided that *normal throttling* is used as indicated in Fig. 20.15*b*.

The throttle for such tanks is frequently "shaped" to produce different head losses for flow into than for flow out of the tank.

Preliminary design and analysis of such tanks is fundamentally based on a prototype "frictionless" case in which all damping action is assumed to occur in the throttle R_t with the pipeline assumed frictionless ($R = 0$).

For the turbine case the governing equations become

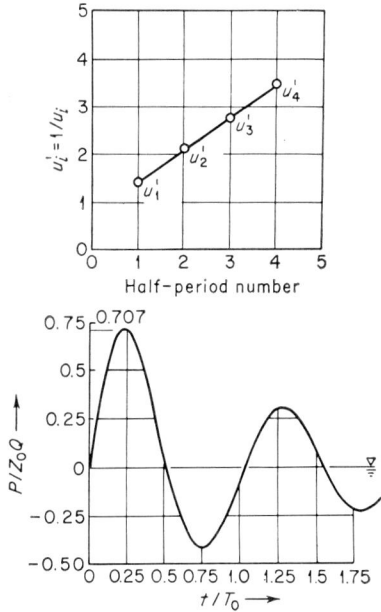

FIG. 20.16. Throttled surge tank.

$$I \frac{dQ}{dt} = -P \tag{20.221}$$

$$C \frac{dP_t}{dt} = Q - Q_d = Q_t \tag{20.222}$$

$$P = P_t + R_t |Q_t| Q_t \tag{20.223}$$

It follows very directly from these equations that if the throttle resistance constant R_t is given the value

$$R_t = \frac{Z_0}{\sqrt{2} \cdot Q_0} = \frac{\sqrt{I/2C}}{Q_0} \tag{20.224}$$

in which Q_0 is the magnitude of the design change in flow, or "flow upset," the unique solution depicted in Fig. 20.16 results for a step change in demand of magnitude Q_0. It is evident that this solution gives a maximum surge which is 70.7 per cent of the undamped surge in a time 90 per cent of T_m, and the oscillation is adequately damped even in a frictionless pipe.

These damped alternating surges after the first maximum are governed by identical laws with those discussed previously for quadratic friction in the pipeline. However, now the alternate surges may be tabulated once and for all as the values

$$
\begin{aligned}
^+u_1 &= 0.7071 \\
^-u_2 &= 0.4197 \\
^+u_3 &= 0.2998 \\
^-u_4 &= 0.2339
\end{aligned}
\tag{20.225}
$$

and so forth, whose reciprocal values plot linearly as indicated in Fig. 20.16.

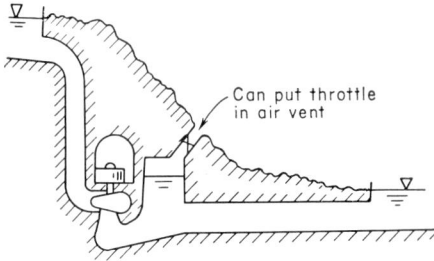

FIG. 20.17. Underground plant.

The Air-throttled Tank. Particularly for the type of underground power plants or pumping stations indicated in Fig. 20.17, it is practical to build a tailrace tank with throttling action provided by an air valve, having resistance R_a, which may also be conveniently "activated" or control-modulated for additional damping and stabilization.

For the same rated throttling loss, the area ratios between gas and liquid throttles ratios would vary as the square root of the density ratios; that is

$$\frac{A_g}{A_l} = \sqrt{\frac{\rho_g}{\rho_l}} \qquad (20.226)$$

Then for air and water with $\rho_{air} = 0.0024$ and $\rho_{water} = 1.94$, the area ratio becomes

$$\frac{A_{air}}{A_{water}} = 0.035 \quad \text{or 3.5 per cent} \quad (20.227)$$

This can represent a substantial saving in cost for what frequently proves to be superior behavior.

Figure 20.18 depicts a comparative study by Peralta[12] on the MIT model surge tank of an air-throttled tank designed to produce behavior comparable to that of a conventional throttled tank. Note, however, that pipe friction is obviously not negligible, and due allowance must be made for this in the sizing of the throttle.

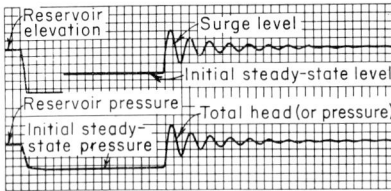

Simple surge tank,
full-load rejection

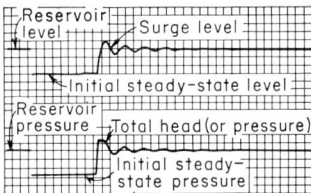

Restricted orifice surge tank
full-load rejection

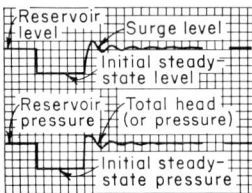

Throttled air-flow surge tank
full-load rejection

FIG. 20.18. Air-throttled surge tank.

20.9. Experimental Results

Test Data. A very significant series of experimental verifications of water-hammer analysis were conducted as part of the German wartime effort and reported in a document edited by Toelke.[13] In particular, the pressure transients associated with gate motions in a small hydroelectric plant in Baden were carefully instrumented and recorded, and the data reduced with great care and precision. This situation is used as an example of the computational methods required in a practical application.

The following plant data pertain to this case:

Steel pipeline:

Equivalent uniform length:	$L = 429$ ft
Equivalent uniform diameter:	$D = 2.62$ ft
Resultant mean area:	$A = 5.4$ ft²
Mean wall thickness:	$e = 0.20$ ft
Over-all friction factor:	$f = 0.026$

Hydraulic conditions (water):

Rated static head:	$P_0 = 230$ ft
Rated steady flow:	$Q_0 = 23.0$ cfs

The corresponding required transmission parameters follow readily

Inertance:

$$I = \frac{L}{gA} = \frac{429}{32.2 \times 5.4} = 2.47 \ \text{sec}^2/\text{ft}^2 \qquad (20.228)$$

Capacitance:

$$C = \frac{gAL}{a^2} = \frac{32.2 \times 5.4 \times 429}{(3575)^2} = 0.00585 \ \text{ft}^2 \qquad (20.229)$$

Propagation velocity:

$$a = \frac{c}{\sqrt{1 + \dfrac{B}{E}\dfrac{D}{e}}} = \frac{4720}{\sqrt{1 + 0.756}} = 3575 \ \text{fps} \qquad (20.230)$$

Therefore surge impedance

$$Z = \sqrt{\frac{I}{C}} = 20.5 \ \text{ft/cfs} \qquad (20.231)$$

and propagation time

$$T = \sqrt{I \cdot C} = 0.12 \ \text{sec} \qquad (20.232)$$

The pressure transients are here computed corresponding to but two of the many experimental results reported in the cited reference. These involved the following conditions:

Valve closure (test 40):	Initial steady flow:	$Q_1 = 11.3$ cfs
	Final steady flow:	$Q_2 = 1.3$ cfs
	Valve closing time:	$T_v = 0.91$ sec
Valve opening (test 49):	Initial steady flow:	$Q_1 = 1.3$ cfs
	Final steady flow:	$Q_2 = 23.0$ cfs
	Valve opening time:	$T_v = 1.58$ sec

For these cases the test data indicated an essentially linear variation of valve area with time. As discussed in Art. 20.7, the stroke of a valve is generally not linearly related to the flow area, so that even linear stroking motions by no means ensure linear area changes. Therefore, precaution must be taken in generalizing the case treated here to other situations.

Experimental Results. For many cases of opening and closing valve motions, time histories of pressures at several points along the pipe were measured and recorded, using a number of precision instruments at each station. In this way the highly reliable curves indicated in Figs. 20.19 and 20.20 were obtained, with the following designations

Figure 20.19: Valve closure —test 40
Figure 20.20: Valve opening—test 49

Approximate Computed Results. An approximate computation of the pressure transients is now carried out to check against these results, by using the method of Eq. (20.126) and Table 20.8.

It is further assumed that the actual valve motion here gives an effectively linear variation in area with time and that the valve stroking is therefore completely specified by the three numbers Q_1, Q_2, T_v.

For the approximate computation scheme employed, the corresponding numbers become

Closure:	$m_1 = 0.500$	$m_2 = 0.060$	$\mathfrak{N} = 3.75$
Opening:	$m_1 = 0.060$	$m_2 = 1.020$	$\mathfrak{N} = 6.50$

Tables 20.9 and 20.10 give the corresponding approximate computed values, which are also plotted as points on Figs. 20.19 and 20.20, respectively.

Table 20.9. Water-hammer Pressure for Valve Closure

Approximate calculations for test 40

(1) i	(2) m_i	(3) m_{i-1}	(4) $\Delta m_i = m_{i-1} - m_i$	(5) $m_{i-1} - 1$	(6) $m_i + 1$	(7) $-B_i = \dfrac{m_{i-1}-1}{m_i+1}$	(8) $A_i = \dfrac{2\Delta m_i}{m_i+1}$	(9) $-B_i h_{i-1}$	(10) h_i	(11) P, ft	(12) t, sec
0	0.500	0.500	0	−0.500	1.500	−0.333	0	0	0	0	0
.25	0.470	0.500	+0.030	−0.500	1.470	−0.340	+0.041	0	+0.041	+ 9.4	0.06
.5	0.440	0.500	0.060	−0.500	1.440	−0.347	+0.083	0	+0.083	+19.1	0.12
.75	0.410	0.500	0.090	−0.500	1.410	−0.355	+0.128	0	+0.128	+29.2	0.18
1	0.382	0.500	0.118	−0.500	1.382	−0.362	+0.170	0	+0.170	+39.1	0.24
.25	0.354	0.470	0.116	−0.530	1.354	−0.392	+0.171	−0.016	+0.155	+35.7	0.30
.5	0.324	0.440	0.116	−0.560	1.324	−0.423	+0.176	−0.035	+0.141	+32.4	0.36
.75	0.294	0.410	0.116	−0.590	1.294	−0.457	+0.179	−0.058	+0.121	+27.8	0.42
2	0.266	0.382	0.116	−0.618	1.266	−0.488	+0.183	−0.083	+0.100	+23.0	0.48
.25	0.236	0.354	0.118	−0.646	1.236	−0.523	+0.191	−0.081	+0.110	+25.3	0.54
.5	0.206	0.324	0.118	−0.676	1.206	−0.560	+0.195	−0.079	+0.116	+26.7	0.60
.75	0.178	0.294	0.116	−0.706	1.178	−0.600	+0.197	−0.073	+0.124	+28.5	0.66
3	0.148	0.266	0.118	−0.734	1.148	−0.640	+0.206	−0.064	+0.142	+32.7	0.72
.25	0.118	0.236	0.118	−0.764	1.118	−0.683	+0.211	−0.075	+0.136	+31.2	0.78
.5	0.090	0.206	0.116	−0.794	1.090	−0.728	+0.213	−0.084	+0.129	+29.6	0.84
.75	0.060	0.178	0.118	−0.822	1.060	−0.775	+0.222	−0.094	+0.128	+29.4	0.90
4	0.060	0.148	0.088	−0.852	1.060	−0.804	+0.165	−0.114	+0.051	+11.7	0.96
.25	0.060	0.118	0.058	−0.882	1.060	−0.832	+0.109	−0.113	−0.004	− 0.9	1.02
.5	0.060	0.090	0.030	−0.910	1.060	−0.859	+0.057	−0.111	−0.054	−12.4	1.08
.75	0.060	0.060	0	−0.940	1.060	−0.887	0	−0.114	−0.114	−26.2	1.14
5	0.060	0.060	0	−0.940	1.060	−0.887	0	−0.045	−0.045	−10.3	1.20
.25	0.060	0.060	0	−0.940	1.060	−0.887	0	+0.004	+0.004	+ 0.9	1.26
.5	0.060	0.060	0	−0.940	1.060	−0.887	0	+0.048	+0.048	+11.0	1.32
.75	0.060	0.060	0	−0.940	1.060	−0.887	0	+0.101	+0.101	+23.2	1.38
6	0.060	0.060	0	−0.940	1.060	−0.887	0	+0.040	+0.040	+ 9.2	1.44
.25	0.060	0.060	0	−0.940	1.060	−0.887	0	−0.003	−0.003	− 0.7	1.50
.5	0.060	0.060	0	−0.940	1.060	−0.887	0	−0.043	−0.043	− 9.9	1.56
.75	0.060	0.060	0	−0.940	1.060	−0.887	0	−0.089	−0.089	−20.5	1.62
7								−0.035	−0.035	− 8.1	1.68

20–44

Table 20.10. Water-hammer Pressures for Valve Opening

Approximate calculations for test 49

(1) i	(2) m_i	(3) m_{i-1}	(4) $\Delta m_i = m_{i-1} - m_i$	(5) $m_{i-1} - 1$	(6) $m_i + 1$	(7) $-B_i = \dfrac{m_{i-1}-1}{m_i+1}$	(8) $A_i = \dfrac{2\Delta m_i}{m_i+1}$	(9) $-B_i h_i$	(10) h_i	(11) P, ft	(12) t, sec
0	0.060	0.060	0	−0.940	1.060	−0.89	0	0	0	0	0
.5	0.134	0.060	−0.074	−0.940	1.134	−0.83	−0.131	0	−0.131	−30.2	0.12
1	0.208	0.060	−0.148	−0.940	1.208	−0.78	−0.245	0	−0.245	−56.5	0.24
.5	0.282	0.134	−0.148	−0.866	1.282	−0.68	−0.231	+0.089	−0.142	−32.5	0.36
2	0.356	0.208	−0.148	−0.792	1.356	−0.59	−0.218	+0.145	−0.073	−16.8	0.48
.5	0.430	0.282	−0.148	−0.718	1.430	−0.50	−0.207	+0.071	−0.136	−31.2	0.60
3	0.504	0.356	−0.148	−0.644	1.504	−0.43	−0.197	+0.031	−0.166	−38.2	0.72
.5	0.578	0.430	−0.148	−0.570	1.578	−0.36	−0.188	+0.049	−0.139	−32.0	0.84
4	0.652	0.504	−0.148	−0.496	1.652	−0.30	−0.179	+0.050	−0.129	−29.7	0.96
.5	0.726	0.578	−0.148	−0.422	1.726	−0.24	−0.171	+0.033	−0.138	−31.7	1.08
5	0.800	0.652	−0.148	−0.348	1.800	−0.19	−0.164	+0.025	−0.139	−32.0	1.20
.5	0.874	0.726	−0.148	−0.274	1.874	−0.15	−0.158	+0.021	−0.137	−30.5	1.32
6	0.948	0.800	−0.148	−0.200	1.948	−0.10	−0.152	+0.014	−0.138	−31.7	1.44
.5	1.020	0.874	−0.146	−0.126	2.020	−0.06	−0.145	+0.008	−0.137	−30.5	1.56
7	1.020	0.948	−0.072	−0.052	2.020	−0.03	−0.071	+0.004	−0.067	−15.4	1.68
.5	1.020	1.020	0	+0.020	2.020	+0.01	0	+0.001	+0.001	0	1.80
8	1.020	1.020	0	0.020	2.020	+0.01	0	......	0		
.5	1.020	1.020	0	0.020	2.020	+0.01	0	0	0		

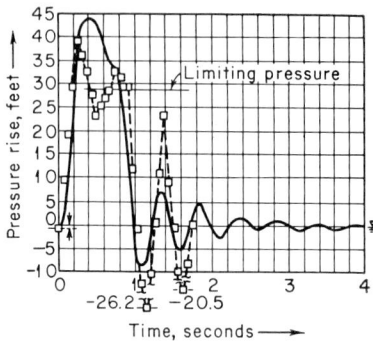

Fig. 20.19. Water-hammer pressure for valve closure.

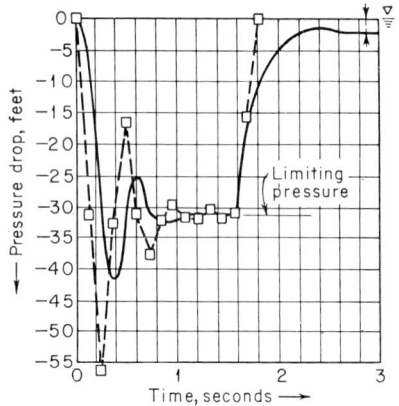

Fig. 20.20. Water-hammer pressure for valve opening.

As may be seen, the general agreement is excellent, and additional complications in analysis do not yield proportional benefits in accuracy. Thus the results are fairly typical of the level of agreement between computed and experimental results for these problems.

The anelastic filtering action is clearly evident and may be completely accounted for by the procedure of Eq. (20.159), but this deviation has no appreciable effect upon the peak magnitudes of the initial pressure swings, and the computations neglecting dispersion will produce design figures generally on the safe side.

Values of the limiting pressures using Eq. (20.135) or Fig. 20.7 are indicated on Figs. 20.19 and 20.20. These results are determined as follows:

Closure: $\qquad r = \dfrac{0.500 - 0.060}{3.75} = +0.117 \qquad h_m = +0.124$

$$P_m = 0.124 \times 230 \quad = +28.5 \text{ ft}$$

Opening: $\qquad r = \dfrac{0.060 - 1.020}{6.50} = -0.148 \qquad h_m = -0.137$

$$P_m = -0.137 \times 230 = -31.5 \text{ ft}$$

REFERENCES

1a. Joukowsky, N. E.: Ueber den hydraulischer Stoss in Wasserleitungsroehren, *Mém. acad. sci. St. Petersbourg,* IX (8e) sér., 1898.
1b. Translation of the above paper by Miss Olga Simin as: Water Hammer, *Proc. Am. Water Works Assoc.,* **24**:341–424 (1904).
2a. Allievi, L.: Teoria generale del moto perturbata dell acqua nei tubi in pressisne, *Ann. soc. ing. ed architetti italiani Milano,* 1903. Teoria del colpo d'ariete, *Atti coll. ing. ed architetti Milano,* 1913.
2b. Translation of the last paper above by E. E. Halmos as: Theory of Waterhammer, printed by Riccardo Garoni, Rome, 1925. (Sponsored and distributed by the ASCE-ASME.)
3a. Massau, Junius: Mémoire sur l'integration graphique des equations aux dérivées partielles, *Ann. assoc. ingrs. sortis des écoles speciales de Gand,* **23**:95–214 (1900).
3b. Translation of the above paper by Henry J. Putman as: Unsteady Flow, Rocky Mountain Hydraulic Laboratory, Allenspark, Colorado, 1948.
4. Bergeron, L.: "Du coup de belier en hydraulique au coup de foudre en électricité, methode graphic générale," Dunod, Paris, 1950.

5. Green, G.: On the Motion of Waves in a Variable Canal of Small Depth and Width, *Trans. Cambridge Phil. Soc.*, vol. 6, 1837.

6. Evangelisti, G.: Sul calcolo del colpo d'ariete nelle condotte forzate a caratteristoche variabili, *Energia elettrica*, vol. 16, December, 1939.

7. Paynter, H. M., and F. D. Ezekiel: Waterhammer in Nonuniform Pipes as an Example of Wave Propagation in Gradually Varying Media, *Trans. ASME*, **80**(7):1585–1595 (1958).

8. Ezekiel, F. D., and H. M. Paynter: Firmoviscous and Anelastic Properties of Fluids and Their Effects on the Propagation of Compression Waves, ASME Paper 59-HYD-19, 1959.

9. Paynter, H. M.: "Regelungstechnik: Moderne Theorien und ihre Verwendbarkeit," chap. 7, pp. 243–250, R. Oldenbourg-Verlag, Muenchen, 1957.

10. Milne-Thomson, L. M.: "Jacobian Elliptic Function Tables," Dover, New York, 1950.

11a. Milne, W. E.: Damped Vibrations. General Theory Together with Solutions of Important Cases, *Univ. Oregon Publ.*, vol. 2, no. 2, August, 1923.

11b. Milne, W. E.: Tables of Damped Vibrations, *Univ. Oregon Publ.*, vol. 1, no. 1, March, 1929.

11c. Milne, W. E.: "Tables of Derivatives for Damped Vibrations," Oregon State College Monographs, Corvallis, Oregon, December, 1935.

12. Peralta, L. A.: Investigation of an Air Throttled Surge Tank, M.S. thesis, MIT (unpublished), August, 1956.

13. Toelke, Friedrich: "Veroeffentlichungen zur Erforschung der Druckstossprobleme," Springer, Berlin, 1949.

Section 21

CONVERSION, TRANSMISSION, AND CONTROL OF FLUID POWER

By

J. L. SHEARER, *Massachusetts Institute of Technology, Cambridge, Massa-chusetts*

CONVERSION, TRANSMISSION, AND CONTROL
OF FLUID POWER

21.1. Introduction and Notation

This section deals with the most important aspects of fluid dynamics, which are involved in modulating the flow of power from a prime source of energy to a load. Major emphasis is placed on interacting systems and the unsteady flows of matter and energy which most frequently occur as system components interact in response to varying inputs. The topics have been organized and presented to expedite the formulation of functional relationships, often in the form of differential equations, which will be helpful to engineers and scientists in formulating a rational basis for the design of hydraulic and pneumatic systems.

Notation is as follows:

A area, in.^{2}
A_o area of orifice opening, in.^{2}
A_p cross-section area of pipe, in.^{2}
A_s area of passage leading to the poppet seat, in.^{2}
b viscous-friction coefficient, lb-sec/in.
C_d discharge coefficient
C_d coefficient for friction dependent on speed, dimensionless
C_f coefficient for friction dependent on pressure, dimensionless
C_p specific heat at constant pressure, in.^{2}/(sec^2)(°F)
C_s coefficient for leakage due to pressure, dimensionless
C_v specific heat at constant volume, in.^{2}/(sec^2)(°F)
C_1 $g\sqrt{2k/R(k-1)}$, 2.06 (°R)$^{1/2}$/sec for air
D (1) diameter, in.
       (2) differential operator, derivative with respect to time, sec^{-1}
D_r displacement per radian, in.^{3}/radian
E Young's modulus of elasticity of pipe material, psi
E_k kinetic energy, in.-lb
E_p potential energy, in.-lb
E_{tot} total energy stored in reservoir, in.-lb
E_u total internal energy of a mass of fluid
e specific total internal energy, in.-lb/(lb-sec^2/in.) = in.^{2}/sec^2
F force, lb
f friction factor (from Stanton diagram)
g acceleration due to gravity, 386 in./sec^2
h specific enthalpy, in.-lb/(lb-sec^2/in.) = in.^{2}/sec^2
K_r total resistance coefficient for line, lb-sec^2/in.^{6}
k ratio of specific heats c_p/c_v, 1.4 for air
k_a steady-state gain of system
k_b steady-state load sensitivity of system
k_e elasticity coefficient of pipe, in.^{5}/lb
k_s servomotor steady-state gain
k_1 flow sensitivity of valve, in.^{2}/sec
k_2 change of volume flow due to change of load pressure, in.^{5}/lb-sec
k_3 compliance of fluid, in.^{5}/lb
L length of pipe, in.

l height above datum, in.

m mass of fluid, lb-sec^2/in.

P pressure, psi

Q volume rate of flow, in.^{3}/sec

R gas constant, 2.47×10^5 in.^{2}/(sec^2)(°R) for air

T shaft torque, in.-lb

T_c friction torque independent of pressure and speed, in.-lb

T_e $L\sqrt{\rho/\beta_e}$, propagation time for wave to travel length of pipe, sec

T_s absolute temperature of air supply, °R

u specific internal energy, in.-lb/(lb-sec^2/in.) = in.^{2}/sec

V velocity, in./sec

$\mathcal{V}$ volume, in.^{3}

v specific volume, in.^{4}/lb-sec

W weight rate of flow, lb/sec

X valve position, in.

Y distance from end of cylinder to piston, in.

Y_s characteristic admittance of the line, $\sqrt{A^2/\rho\beta_e}$

Z_s characteristic impedance of the line, $\sqrt{\rho\beta_e/A^2}$

β_e equivalent bulk modulus, psi

γ normalized valve displacement

Δ prefix symbol denoting small change

ζ damping ratio of system

ζ_s servomotor damping ratio

η efficiency, per cent

$\dot{\theta}$ shaft speed, radians/sec

μ absolute viscosity of hydraulic fluid, lb-sec/in.^{2}

ρ density, lb-sec^2/in.^{4}

ϕ (1) pump stroke, radians

        (2) dimensionless parameter

ω_n natural frequency of system, radians/sec

ω_{ns} servomotor natural frequency, radians/sec

POWER CONVERSION—PUMPS AND MOTORS

Most pumps will operate with varying degrees of success as motors, and most motors will operate similarly as pumps. The term pump is taken here to designate a unit which operates primarily as a device to convert mechanical power to fluid power. Similarly, a motor is a device operating primarily to convert fluid power to mechanical power and thus includes turbines as well as positive-displacement motors. Since positive-displacement units are employed much more frequently in fluid-power-control systems, and since the characteristics of hydrokinetic devices such as compressors and turbines are discussed in detail in another section of this book (Sec. 19), major emphasis is placed on positive-displacement pumps and motors here.

21.2. Basic Types of Positive-displacement Pumps and Motors

Ram (Single Piston). A single piston operating in a cylinder constitutes a very effective pump or motor in which the mechanical power consists of the rectilinear motion of the piston shaft with an axial stress or force and the fluid power consists of fluid flow displaced under pressures by the piston and flowing through the ports of the motor. When both sides of the piston are exposed to fluid under pressure, the unit is referred to as a double-acting ram. Figure 21.1 illustrates three types of ram motor frequently used in the control of the linear motion of a mechanical load.

Rotary Hydraulic Pumps and Motors. Of the three basic types of rotary unit, multiple-piston, gear, and vane, the multiple-piston type has been the most frequently chosen type of motor for high-pressure (up to 5000 psi) applications because of high power-weight ratio, large torque-inertia ratio, low leakage, and good over-all efficiency

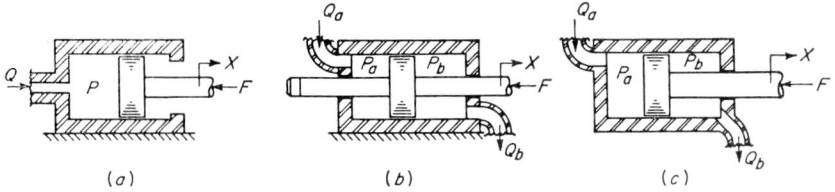

FIG. 21.1. Three types of ram. (a) Single-acting. (b) Double-acting, equal area. (c) Double-acting, differential area.

characteristics. Both gear and piston units have been frequently used as high-pressure pumps for similar reasons, the gear units being specially designed to prevent excessive leakage but resulting in mechanical-friction effects which make them less suitable as motors. At lower pressures (up to 1000 psi), vane-type units have proved to be very effective as either pumps or motors and considerably less expensive to manufacture. Figures 21.2 to 21.4 are photographic illustrations of typical gear, vane, and piston units.

Rotary pumps and motors are used both for continuous and intermittent conversion of power with reversible-shaft rotation. Hydraulic fluids such as mineral-base or synthetic-base oils are usually employed which have the viscosity and lubricity characteristics required by the intricate, highly loaded mechanisms of these units.

21.3. Performance Characteristics

When they are available, the performance characteristics of hydraulic pumps and motors are usually given for operation with one of the port pressures equal to zero (atmospheric pressure). Although this condition exists in a large fraction of the applications of these units, many of the high-performance-control applications involve operation with considerable pressures acting simultaneously on both ports.

The difference in performance between a given unit operating with one pressure equal to zero and the same unit operating with both ports at elevated pressures is greatest for multipiston units, the degree of this difference depending also on detailed features of each particular design. The breakaway and static running friction in multipiston pumps and motors is usually greater when both ports are at elevated pressures because of greater bearing loads. On the other hand, gear and vane units, because of character-

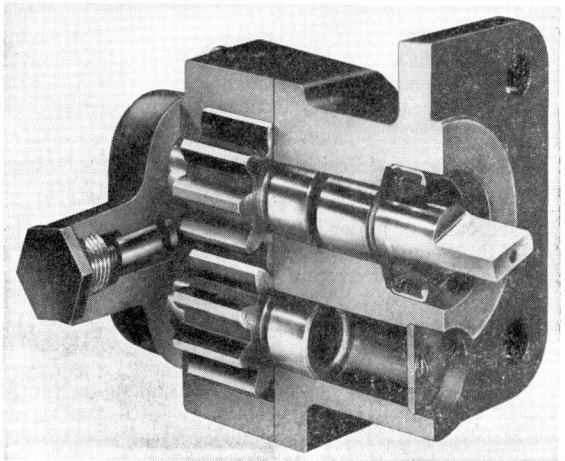

FIG. 21.2. Photograph of spur gear pump. (*John S. Barnes Corp., Rockford, Ill.*)

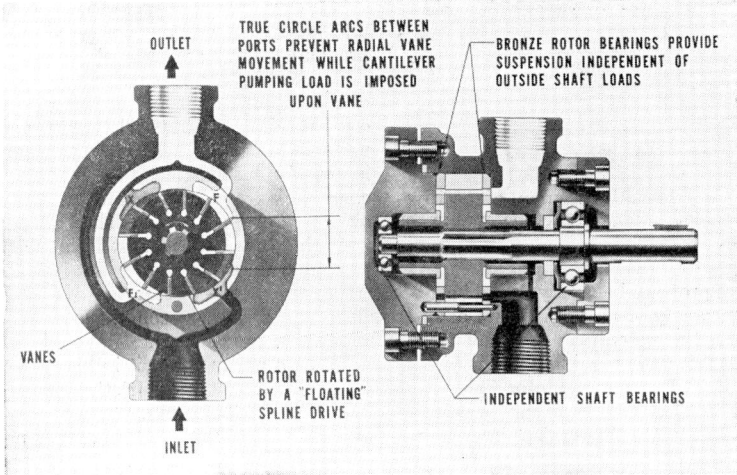

Fig. 21.3. Balanced vane pump. Pumping pressures which would otherwise produce bearing loads are canceled out by equal and opposing pressure areas (ports $F = F_1$, and ports $X = X_1$). (*Vickers, Inc., Detroit.*)

istics inherent in their designs, do not exhibit so much dependence of breakaway and static running friction on elevated-port pressures. External leakage is, of course, related to the pressures of both ports and seems to be most pronounced in gear and vane units.

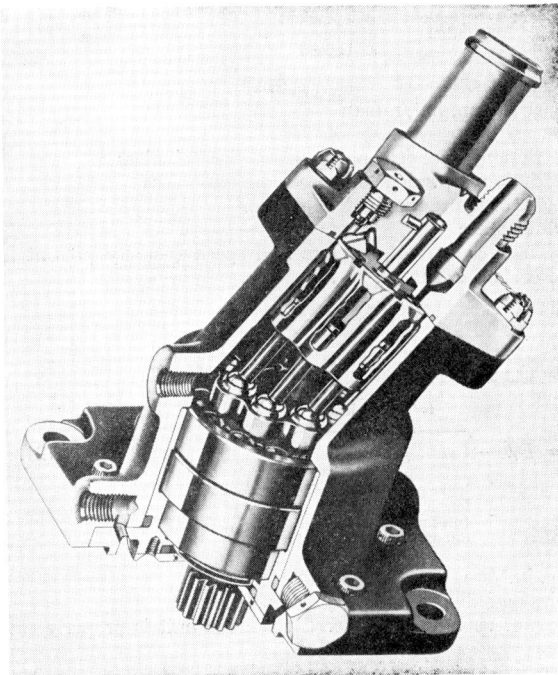

Fig. 21.4. Photograph of axial piston pump. (*Vickers, Inc., Detroit.*)

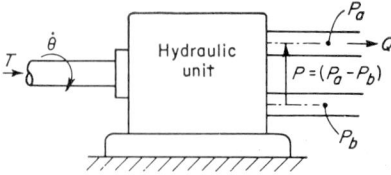

FIG. 21.5. Schematic diagram of positive-displacement rotary hydraulic pump or motor.

The characteristics presented here are for units operating with one port at atmospheric pressure. They are useful in a qualitative sense; that is, they reveal significant features of a pump or motor and enable the user to compare data qualitatively on competitive units in order to help decide which unit is best for his particular application. The characteristics of most commercially available pumps and motors show departures from the somewhat idealized characteristics presented here. Yet the idealized characteristics prove to be a very useful base of reference and means of carrying out simplified dynamic analyses of performance of systems incorporating these components. In each instance, the potential user is advised to request as much specific detailed data as possible from the manufacturer before incorporating a particular unit in his system.

Idealized Pump and Motor Characteristics. These result when friction and leakage are treated as simple linear functions of speed and/or pressure. The reader who wishes to explore this subject in greater detail is referred to published material, notably by Wilson[1] on positive-displacement pump and motor characteristics.

The idealized equations for torque and flow of a positive-displacement hydraulic pump are as follows (for example, when $\dot\theta$, T, Q, and P are all positive in Fig. 21.5):

PUMP TORQUE

$$T = T_{ideal} + T_{friction}$$

$$= D_r P + \overbrace{C_f D_r P + C_d D_r \mu \dot\theta + T_c}^{\text{total friction torque}} \tag{21.1}$$

$\quad$ ideal $\quad$ pressure- $\quad$ speed- $\quad$ friction
$\quad$ torque $\quad$ dependent $\quad$ dependent $\quad$ independent
$\qquad\qquad$ friction $\qquad$ friction $\qquad$ of pressure
$\qquad\qquad\qquad\qquad\qquad\qquad\qquad$ and speed

in which T = shaft torque, in.-lb
$\quad D_r$ = displacement per radian, in.^{3}/radian
$\quad P$ = pump pressure, psi
$\quad C_f$ = coefficient for friction dependent on pressure, dimensionless
$\quad C_d$ = coefficient for friction dependent on speed, dimensionless
$\quad \mu$ = absolute viscosity of hydraulic fluid, lb-sec/in.^{2}
$\quad \dot\theta$ = shaft speed, radians/sec
$\quad T_c$ = friction torque independent of pressure and speed (usually present in shaft seals and certain bearings), in.-lb

PUMP FLOW RATE

$$Q = Q_{ideal} - Q_{loss}$$

$$= D_r \dot\theta - \overbrace{C_s D_r P/\mu - \qquad Q_c}^{\text{total flow loss}} \tag{21.2}$$

$\qquad\qquad\qquad$ leakage $\qquad\qquad$ cavitation
$\qquad\qquad\qquad$ loss $\qquad\qquad\qquad$ loss (usually
$\qquad\qquad\qquad$ (pressure- $\qquad\qquad$ speed-
$\qquad\qquad\qquad$ dependent) $\qquad\qquad$ dependent)

in which Q = pump flow rate, in.^{3}/sec
$\quad C_s$ = coefficient for leakage due to pressure, dimensionless
$\quad Q_c$ = cavitation loss (not usually encountered when the unit is properly employed), in.^{3}/sec

Similarly, the equations for torque and flow of a positive-displacement motor are as follows (for example, when T and P are positive and $\dot{\theta}$ and Q are negative in Fig. 21.5):

MOTOR TORQUE

$$T = T_{\text{ideal}} - T_{\text{friction}}$$

$$= \underset{\substack{\text{ideal} \\ \text{torque}}}{D_r P} - \underset{\substack{\text{pressure-} \\ \text{dependent} \\ \text{friction}}}{C_f D_r P} + \underset{\substack{\text{speed-} \\ \text{dependent} \\ \text{friction}}}{C_d D_r \mu \dot{\theta}} - \underset{\substack{\text{friction} \\ \text{independent} \\ \text{of pressure} \\ \text{and speed}}}{T_c} \qquad (21.3)$$

MOTOR FLOW RATE

$$Q = Q_{\text{ideal}} + Q_{\text{leakage}}$$

$$= \underset{\substack{\text{ideal} \\ \text{torque}}}{D_r \dot{\theta}} - \underset{\substack{\text{leakage} \\ \text{(only pres-} \\ \text{sure-depend-} \\ \text{ent)}}}{C_s D_r P / \mu} + \underset{\substack{\text{cavitation loss} \\ \text{(usually speed-} \\ \text{dependent)}}}{Q_c} \qquad (21.4)$$

By incorporating the sign of the shaft speed, $(\dot{\theta}/|\dot{\theta}|)$, the pump and motor equations may be realized from a single pair of generalized equations for a positive-displacement unit:

Torque:

$$T = D_r P + \frac{\dot{\theta}}{|\dot{\theta}|} C_f D_r P + C_d D_r \mu \dot{\theta} + \frac{\dot{\theta}}{|\dot{\theta}|} T_c \qquad (21.5)$$

Flow rate:

$$Q = D_r \dot{\theta} - C_s D_r \frac{P}{\mu} - \frac{\dot{\theta}}{|\dot{\theta}|} Q_c \qquad (21.6)$$

Complete sets of torque and flow characteristics based on the generalized equations are shown in Fig. 21.6, illustrating operation not only as a pump or motor but also

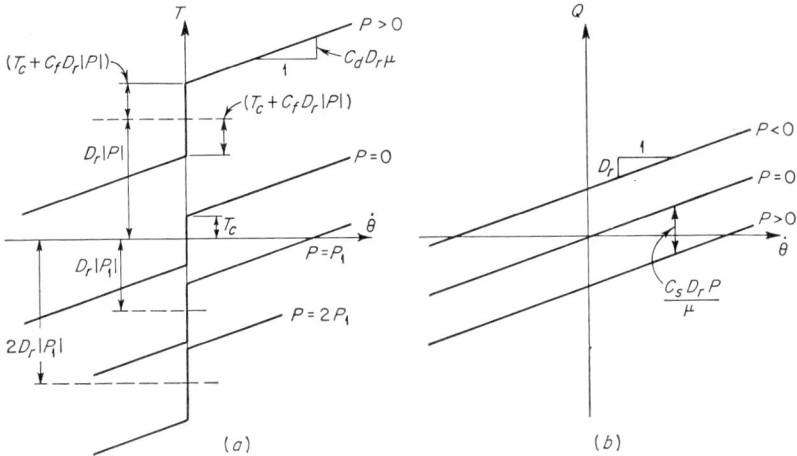

FIG. 21.6. Idealized characteristics of positive-displacement rotary pumps and motors. (a) Torque vs. speed at various constant pressures. (b) Flow vs. speed at various constant pressures.

as a complete dissipator of energy (i.e., it receives both hydraulic and mechanical power simultaneously and all input power is dissipated by leakage and friction). Figure 21.7 illustrates the various segments of the torque- and flow-characteristic graphs which represent pump, motor, or complete dissipational operation.

Real Pump and Motor Characteristics. These may be expected to depart to some degree from the preceding idealized characteristics, and the designer is cautioned to seek all possible test data from the manufacturer in order to determine how well the idealized characteristics approximate the real characteristics.

As noted previously, friction torque may be influenced as much by values of both port pressures as it is by the difference in port pressures. In units where distortion is caused by internal pressures, the working clearances are sometimes changed and one may

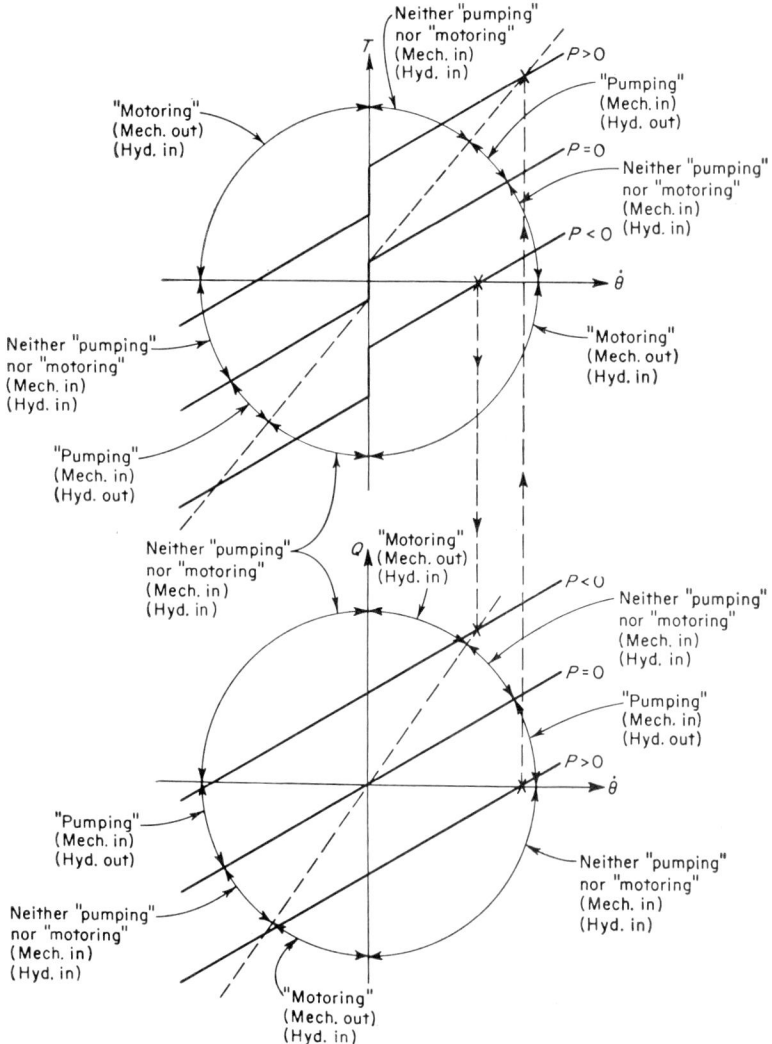

Fig. 21.7. Torque-speed graph and flow-speed graph segmented to delineate various regimes of operation of a positive-displacement unit.

expect very unusual changes of friction torque with pressure ranging from very high power-law *increase* of friction torque with increasing pressure (i.e., P^n, $n > 1$) to *decrease* of friction torque with increasing pressure (i.e., P^n, $n < 0$). Friction torque has also been found to vary nonlinearly with respect to speed because of such things as turbulent-windage losses due to high-speed churning of case fluid by rotating members and large temperature rise of fluid in small clearance spaces between ports in relative motion at high speed. Shaft misalignments, improper mounting, and improper design of external bearings can also result in unanticipated friction torques which may vary with pressure.

In units which start, stop, and reverse frequently, especially motors, breakaway friction is an important factor in the operation of the unit. Breakaway friction frequently exceeds the very-low-speed running friction by a factor of 2 or more, yet it is seldom given as part of the manufacturer's technical data. When precise control functions are to be accomplished with a hydraulic motor, it is important to employ a motor with low breakaway friction.

Leakage is sometimes nonlinearly related to pressure because of the existence of orifice-type rather than capillary-type leakage paths or because of capillary leakage paths in clearance spaces which change with pressure due to pressure distortion. Leakage has also been observed to vary with speed as well as with pressure, especially in multiple-piston units because of *thermal-wedge* effects.[2] In addition to internal leakage between the high- and low-pressure areas in positive-displacement units, external leakages from each of the pressure areas to the areas inside the housing, sometimes called external leakage, can be important. In the event that both the ports are at elevated pressures, the external-leakage effects may exceed the internal-leakage effects. The external leakage that occurs in units operating with one port pressure at zero is usually included with internal leakage because the casing is connected directly with the zero pressure port. This means that units of this kind cannot normally be operated with reversed pressure drop unless they are of special design having high-pressure housings and special shaft seals.

The reader who is interested in a more detailed treatment of positive-displacement pump and motor characteristics is referred to the work reported by Wilson.[1]

Efficiency. Although efficiency is not always the most important factor involved in the choice of a pump or motor, a knowledge of the peak efficiency of a given unit and the range of operating conditions which result in operation near the peak efficiency can be very helpful to the system designer. Efficiency can be an important deciding factor between two units which otherwise have substantially similar desired characteristics. It should be noted that friction and/or leakage may be needed in some systems to provide essential damping through energy dissipation. Because friction and leakage reduce pump and motor efficiency, it is seen that high-efficiency requirements may be at odds with dynamic-stability requirements of the systems employing these units.

Mechanical efficiency is determined by the amount of friction torque in relation to the ideal torque and is defined as follows:

For a pump:

$$\eta_{mp} = \frac{T_{\text{ideal}}}{T_{\text{ideal}} + T_{\text{friction}}} = \frac{1}{1 + T_{\text{friction}}/D_r P} \tag{21.7}$$

For a motor:

$$\eta_{mm} = \frac{T_{\text{ideal}} - T_{\text{friction}}}{T_{\text{ideal}}} = 1 - \frac{T_{\text{friction}}}{D_r P} \tag{21.8}$$

Volumetric efficiency is determined by the amount of leakage flow in relation to the ideal flow and is defined as follows:

For a pump:

$$\eta_{vp} = \frac{Q_{\text{ideal}} - Q_{\text{leakage}}}{Q_{\text{ideal}}} = 1 - \frac{Q_{\text{leakage}}}{D_r \dot{\theta}} \tag{21.9}$$

For a motor:

$$\eta_{vm} = \frac{Q_{\text{ideal}}}{Q_{\text{ideal}} + Q_{\text{leakage}}} = \frac{1}{1 + Q_{\text{leakage}}/D_r \dot{\theta}} \tag{21.10}$$

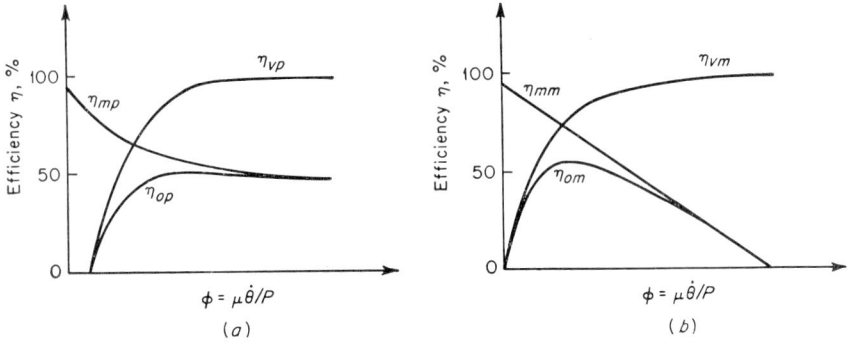

FIG. 21.8. Typical efficiency characteristics. (a) For a pump. (b) For a motor.

Over-all efficiency is determined by the amount of power lost in relation to the power supplied and is defined as follows:

For a pump:

$$\eta_{op} = \frac{\mathrm{HP}_{in} - \mathrm{HP}_{loss}}{\mathrm{HP}_{in}} = \frac{\mathrm{HP}_{out}}{\mathrm{HP}_{in}} = \frac{PQ}{T\dot\theta}$$

$$= \frac{P\eta_{vp}Q_{ideal}}{(1/\eta_{mp})T_{ideal}\dot\theta} = \frac{\eta_{vp}D_rP\dot\theta}{(1/\eta_{mp})D_rP\dot\theta}$$

$$= \eta_{vp}\eta_{mp} \tag{21.11}$$

For a motor:

$$\eta_{om} = \frac{\mathrm{HP}_{in} - \mathrm{HP}_{loss}}{\mathrm{HP}_{in}} = \frac{\mathrm{HP}_{out}}{\mathrm{HP}_{in}} = \frac{T\dot\theta}{PQ}$$

$$= \frac{\eta_{mm}T_{ideal}\dot\theta}{P(1/\eta_{vm})Q_{ideal}} = \eta_{mm}\eta_{vm}\frac{D_rP\dot\theta}{D_rP\dot\theta}$$

$$= \eta_{m}\eta_{vm} \tag{21.12}$$

It is seen in each case that the over-all efficiency is the product of the mechanical efficiency and the volumetric efficiency. When the unit has torque and flow characteristics which correspond closely to the idealized characteristics discussed earlier, it is possible to define all the efficiencies in terms of a single dimensionless parameter ϕ, which is defined as follows:

$$\phi = \frac{\mu\dot\theta}{P}$$

if μ = viscosity of hydraulic fluid
  $\dot\theta$ = shaft speed
  P = pressure difference across ports

The graphs shown in Fig. 21.8 illustrate a typical set of efficiency curves showing how the mechanical, volumetric, and over-all efficiencies vary with the dimensionless parameter ϕ. When the torque and flow characteristics of a given unit do not correspond well with the idealized characteristics discussed earlier, it is usually not possible to express the efficiencies as functions of a single dimensionless parameter such as ϕ.

21.4. Physical Characteristics

In addition to the performance characteristics that have just been discussed, there are a number of physical characteristics of hydraulic pumps and motors which are worthy of note.

Power per Unit Weight or per Unit Volume. One very useful figure of merit for an energy-conversion device is the power per unit weight of the device. Occasionally power per unit volume is also used. As contrasted with electric generators and motors which employ relatively large amounts of magnetic- and electrical-conducting and insulating materials which work at very low stress levels, hydraulic pumps and motors use alloy steels that are usually very highly (but safely) stressed. As a result, weight and volume of high-pressure hydraulic-power conversion units are much less than for electric-power conversion units of the same power rating. The magnitude of the difference of power-per-unit-weight factor for hydraulic and electric units is usually at least a factor of 10. Important exceptions to this factor often are subfractional horsepower units, where it is necessary to employ rather low hydraulic pressures in order to have a hydraulic unit that is large enough to be manufactured with conventional manufacturing facilities. In this case, subfractional horsepower electric units are large enough in relation to their power-handling capability to be readily made in most cases. Thus at very low power levels in the order of several watts, it is possible to have electric-energy conversion units with a power-weight ratio that is competitive with a hydraulic conversion unit of the same power rating.

At power levels above 0.1 hp (or about 100 watts), the power-weight ratio for fixed-displacement hydraulic pumps and motors is usually in the range of 1 to 3 hp/lb.

Inertia of Moving Parts. When a hydraulic unit is to be employed in systems requiring rapid acceleration, the effective moment of inertia of the moving parts of the unit at the rotating shaft is often an important factor in relation to the maximum torque available to accelerate these moving parts. The torque-inertia ratio of hydraulic pumps and motors is usually at least a thousandfold greater than the torque-inertia ratio of electric motors and generators of the same power ratings. Nevertheless, some systems require the largest torque-inertia ratio attainable with hydraulic units.

Torsional Stiffness of Drive Shaft. Although the drive shafts of commercially available hydraulic units may be expected to have sufficient strength to transmit all loads that are commensurate with their normal operating conditions, the torsional stiffness of some drive shafts may not be sufficiently high to make it possible to meet desired speed-of-response requirements when driving high-inertia loads. Backlash in spline-shaft connections can also be troublesome from the control-system point of view.

Trapped Volumes. The volume of hydraulic fluid trapped between the pipe connections and the acting members of a pump or motor has proved in many instances to be an important factor limiting the speed of response (time constants or natural frequency) in systems with high-inertia loads because of fluid compressibility. The existence of dead-end passages and air pockets which cannot be readily bled of air is even more serious because of the much greater compressibility of air which tends to accumulate in these places. The analysis of the effects of fluid compliance on system performance is discussed in a later portion of this section (Arts. 21.15, 21.16, and 21.18).

21.5. Variable-displacement Pumps and Motors

When positive-displacement units are designed to make it possible to vary the displacement D_r by external means through a shaft or actuating mechanism, one can then control the rate or manner of conversion of energy. In the case of a variable-displacement pump running at constant speed, increasing the displacement results in increasing the flow delivery from the pump, with the result that at a given maximum working pressure, the maximum rate of generation of hydraulic power is increased. In the case of a variable-displacement motor running with a constant flow input, increasing the displacement results in decreasing the speed of the motor, with the result that the torque developed for a given pressure increases.

Variable-displacement units are more complex and more costly than fixed-displacement units of the same power ratings. The degree of complication required to provide variable displacement may be seen by comparing Figs. 21.9 and 21.10 with Figs. 21.3 and 21.4.

The performance characteristics of variable-displacement pumps or motors are similar in many respects to the characteristics of a fixed-displacement pump or motor, especially

FIG. 21.9. Photograph of variable-displacement vane pump. *(Racine Tool and Machine Co., Racine, Wis.)*

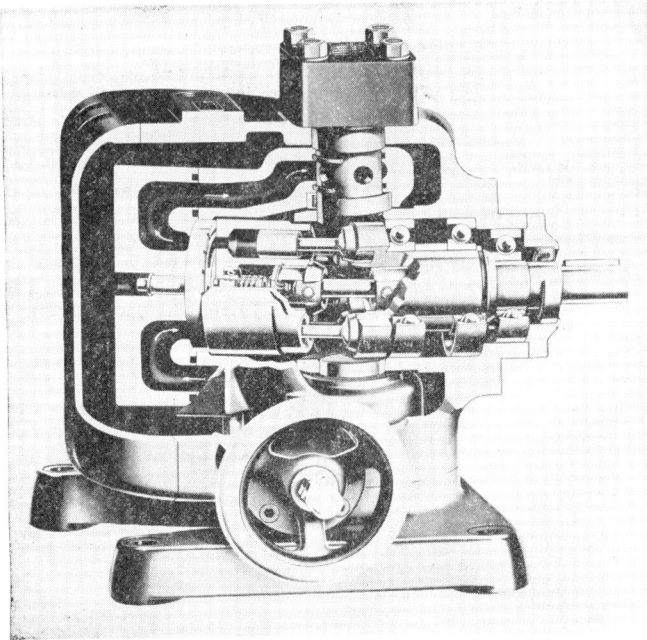

FIG. 21.10. Photograph of variable-displacement axial piston unit. *(Vickers, Inc., Detroit, Mich.)*

when the variable-displacement unit is operating at maximum displacement. A variable-displacement unit operating with only a small fraction of its maximum displacement is relatively inefficient because the leakage and friction losses do not vary appreciably with displacement.

The forces required to actuate a variable-displacement mechanism are usually of the order of 10 to 1000 lb; hence if fast response is required, an appreciable amount of power must be provided to vary the displacement. This power is usually supplied by a hydraulic amplifier or positioning servomechanism.

Variable-displacement pumps are widely used in constant-pressure variable-flow hydraulic-power supplies, in variable-speed hydraulic transmissions, and in high-power-level hydraulic servomotors for servomechanism systems.

ENERGY STORAGE

Although energy storage might not at first glance seem to be an important aspect of the transmission and control of fluid power, it would be impossible to discuss the important fluid-dynamics problems in this field without being deeply concerned with the energy stored in working fluids and the mechanical elements in contact with them. Indeed, the rate of change of the energy stored in system components is one of the most important phenomena involved in dynamic systems.

21.6. Energy Stored in Working Fluids

There are four basic types of fluid-energy storage that are of importance in fluid-power-control systems (excluding systems in which nuclear reactions take place): potential energy (due to position in a force field), kinetic energy (due to momentum), elastic energy (change of volume due to pressure), and thermal energy (change in temperature due to heat flux or shear work). Although two or more of these phenomena usually occur simultaneously in a given system, each phenomenon is discussed separately here, but in such a way that it can be included in a general system analysis.

Potential energy of a fluid is important whenever that fluid is moved from one level to another in a force field such as a gravitational field. The potential energy of a given mass of the fluid is equal to the integral of the product of the force due to the field times an increment of level evaluated between some reference or datum level and the level at which the fluid exists. In the case of the earth's gravitational field within a few miles of the surface of the earth, the force field is practically constant and the potential energy of a unit mass is equal to its weight times its height above datum. And since its weight is equal to its mass times the acceleration due to gravity g

$$E_p = mgl$$
$$= \text{potential energy, in.-lb}$$

if m = mass of fluid, lb-sec^2/in.

g = acceleration due to gravity, in./sec^2

l = height above datum, in.

Reservoirs and open surge tanks offer the best examples of systems where potential energy may be stored in significant amounts. The stored fluid is usually a liquid of much greater density than air, so that the pressure of the air does not vary appreciably around the tank and may be neglected. Two types of reservoir or tank are shown in Fig. 21.11, the first having a cross-section area A which varies with height y and the second being cylindrical with constant area A at all heights. The total potential energy stored in such tanks is given by

$$E_p = \int_0^l \rho g A y \, dy \tag{21.13}$$

in which ρ = mass density of liquid, lb-sec^2/in.^{4}

g = acceleration due to gravity, 386 in./sec^2

A = cross-section area of tank at level y, in.^{2}

dy = increment in level y, in.

l = level of surface of liquid in tank, in.

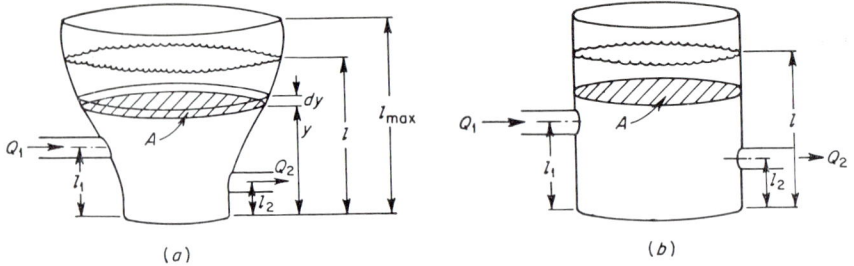

Fig. 21.11. Schematic diagrams of reservoirs. (a) Reservoir with nonuniform cross section. (b) Reservoir with uniform cross section.

The value of ρ is nearly constant when the fluid is a liquid. (An exception to this might be found when great level differences are involved, such as penetrating very deeply into an ocean.) For the case when A is constant, as in Fig. 21.11b, the total potential energy is given by

$$E_p = \rho g A \frac{l^2}{2} \tag{21.14}$$

Energy Equation—Rate of Change of Stored Energy. By applying the energy equation (based on conservation of energy) to the cylindrical reservoir,

$$\rho Q_1 h_1 - \rho Q_2 h_2 = \rho Q_1 \left(\frac{P_1}{\rho} + e_1 \right) - \rho Q_2 \left(\frac{P_2}{\rho} + e_2 \right) = \frac{dE_{\text{tot}}}{dt}$$

in which Q_1 = volume rate of flow into reservoir, in.^{3}/sec
           Q_2 = volume rate of flow out of reservoir, in.^{3}/sec
           P_1 = pressure of fluid entering reservoir, psi
           P_2 = pressure of fluid leaving reservoir, psi
           ρ = fluid density, lb-sec^2/in.^{4}
           h = specific enthalpy, in.-lb/(lb-sec^2/in.) = in.^{2}/sec^2
           e = specific total internal energy, in.^{2}/sec^2
    $E_{\text{tot}} = E_p + E_u = \rho g A l^2/2 + \rho A u l$ = total internal energy stored in reservoir, in.-lb

After noting that $P_1 = \rho g(l - l_1)$, $P_2 = \rho g(l - l_2)$, $e_1 = g l_1 + u$, $e_2 = g l_2 + u$ and that the specific internal energy u due to elastic and thermal effects is constant here, one finds†

$$\rho Q_1 [g(l - l_1) + g l_1 + u] - \rho Q_2 [g(l - l_2) + g l_2 + u] = \rho g A l \frac{dl}{dt} + \rho A u \frac{dl}{dt}$$

or

$$Q_1 - Q_2 = A \frac{dl}{dt} \tag{21.15}$$

Continuity Equation. This result can be verified by applying the continuity equation (based on conservation of matter) to the reservoir. It simply says that the rate at which fluid accumulates in the reservoir is equal to the net rate of flow into the reservoir, a fact which should be intuitively obvious to the reader. Thus storage of liquid in a reservoir under these highly simplified conditions may be thought of either as a problem involving storage of potential energy or a problem involving the storage of fluid.

Kinetic Energy. Kinetic energy is important when a mass of fluid is accelerated from one velocity to another. In some instances only the conditions before and after the acceleration are important. In many fluid-dynamics problems, however, it is

---

† It is also assumed here that kinetic-energy effects are negligible throughout. For a more thorough discussion of internal energy, see J. H. Keenan, "Thermodynamics," pp. 17–40, Wiley, New York, 1941.

necessary to analyze the events which occur during the acceleration as well. Kinetic energy is the integral of the product of accelerating force times an increment of distance evaluated over the total distance moved, i.e. the mechanical energy required to accelerate from zero velocity to a final velocity condition. Expressed mathematically, this becomes

$$E_k = \int_0^s m \frac{dV}{dt}\, ds \qquad (21.16)$$

in which E_k = kinetic energy of mass of fluid, in.-lb
          m = mass of fluid, lb-sec²/in.
          V = velocity of fluid mass, in./sec
    dV/dt = acceleration of fluid mass, in./sec²
        ds = incremental distance moved by mass of fluid, in.

By making use of the fact that

$$\frac{dV}{dt} = \frac{dV}{ds}\frac{ds}{dt} = \frac{V\,dV}{ds}$$

one can then express the integral of Eq. (21.16) in terms of V:

$$E_k = m \int_0^V V\, dV = \frac{mV^2}{2} \qquad (21.17)$$

Pipes and fluid-flow passages are good examples of systems in which stored kinetic energy is frequently important. Considering a stream tube in which the velocity is constant across a section normal to the direction of flow (Fig. 21.12), the kinetic energy of the fluid in the tube may be evaluated as follows:

$$E_k = \int_0^L \frac{\rho A V^2}{2}\, ds$$

in which all parameters are defined in Fig. 21.12 or have been defined earlier in this section. The area A and velocity V are each, in general, functions of s.

When the area A is constant along the stream tube and the fluid density is constant, the velocity V is also constant along the tube. The kinetic energy of the fluid in the tube may then be expressed by

$$E_k = \frac{\rho A V^2 L}{2} \qquad (21.18)$$

An interesting and useful case in which the area of the tube varies along its length is when the area increases linearly with length so that $A = A_1 + ks$. From continuity, it is noted that if the fluid is incompressible, $V = V_1 A_1/(A_1 + ks)$, making it possible to express the kinetic energy by

$$E_k = \frac{\rho}{2} V_1^2 A_1^2 \int_0^L \frac{ds}{A_1 + ks}$$

which, when integrated, gives

$$E_k = \frac{\rho V_1^2 A_1^2 \ln (A_2/A_1)}{2k} \qquad (21.19)$$

Another frequently encountered situation is that of *flow in a pipe with a fully developed velocity profile.* In this case, the kinetic energy of a fluid having uniform density along the pipe is given by

$$E_k = \rho \int_0^L \left(\int_0^A \frac{V^2}{2}\, dA \right) ds \qquad (21.20)$$

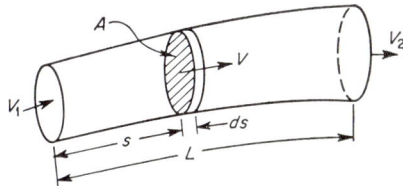

FIG. 21.12. Stream tube with one-dimensional flow.

and it is necessary to know the velocity for each increment in area dA before the integral over the area can be evaluated.   For the case of fully developed laminar flow having a *parabolic velocity profile*, $V = V_{\max}[1 - (r^2/R^2)]$, one finds

$$E_k = \rho \int_0^L \left[\int_0^R V_{\max}^2 \left(1 - \frac{r^2}{R^2} \right)^2 \pi r \, dr \right] ds$$

which, when integrated, gives

$$E_k = \frac{\rho V_{\max}^2 L}{2} \frac{\pi R^2}{2} = \rho V_{\max}^2 \frac{LA}{4} \qquad (21.21)$$

which is just one-half of the kinetic energy that would be obtained if the velocity were equal to $V_{\max}$ across the entire area [Eq. (21.18)].

Accelerated Flow.   In order to gain an understanding of events that occur during a period of acceleration such as might occur during a transient, one may apply the energy equation to the flow passage, giving for the case of negligible friction and heat transfer

$$\rho_1 Q_1 h_1 - \rho_2 Q_2 h_2 = \frac{dE_{\text{tot}}}{dt} = \frac{d}{dt} (E_k + E_u)$$

in which all parameters have been previously defined or given in the nomenclature.   The general case of compressible unsteady flow is rather complicated, but there are many important problems in which the flow is incompressible but unsteady and in which the length of the passage is short enough to neglect wave-propagation effects.   One such case is that of a uniform straight tube with unsteady incompressible frictionless flow. In this case, $\rho_1 = \rho_2$, $Q_1 = Q_2$, and

$$\rho Q \left[\frac{P_1}{\rho} + e_1 - \left(\frac{P_2}{\rho} + e_2 \right) \right] = \frac{d}{dt} (E_k + E_u)$$

Here it may be noted that $e_1 = e_2 = u + (V^2/2) + gl$, $E_k = \rho A V^2 L/2$, and $E_u = \rho A L u = $ const, making it possible to simplify the above equation to give

$$P_1 - P_2 = \rho L \frac{dV}{dt} \qquad (21.22)$$

if $P_1 - P_2$ is the pressure difference between the ends of the passage.   Another form of this equation is often used, employing the flow rate Q instead of the velocity V to describe *accelerated flow in a passage:*

$$P_1 - P_2 = \frac{\rho L}{A} \frac{dQ}{dt} \qquad (21.23)$$

Elastic Energy.   The energy stored in a fluid because of its elasticity (compressibility) is important when the rate of storage of elastic energy is a significant fraction of the major power flow in the system.   It is also of prime concern when the compliance of the fluid interacting with a moving mass results in an oscillatory mode of operation having a resonant frequency of the same order of magnitude as the frequency of an input disturbance to the system.   Thus elastic-energy storage is most important in the *unsteady-state* operation of many fluid power-control systems.   Elastic energy is that part of the internal energy of the fluid which is due to work done on the boundaries of the fluid in compressing it.   Paddlewheel or shear-type work is not included in this definition and is assumed to be zero in this discussion.   Thermal effects due to heat flow, shear work, or paddlewheel work are not within the scope of this section, except for the case of isothermal compression of a gas in which heat-transfer effects are allowed to hold the gas temperature constant during the compression.

The total internal energy of a mass of fluid E_u is given by

$$E_u = mu$$

if $m = $ mass of fluid, lb-sec^2/in.
$\quad u = $ specific internal energy, in.-lb per lb-sec^2/in. $= $ in.^{2}/sec^2

When this mass of fluid undergoes an increase in pressure, an amount of elastic energy is stored which is equal to the work done on the fluid as it is compressed. Expressed mathematically, this becomes

$$E_e = E_{u2} - E_{u1} = \int_{u_1}^{u_2} m \, du = m \int_{v_1}^{v_2} - P \, dv \tag{21.24}$$

in which v = specific volume, in.^{4}/lb-sec.

In order to evaluate this integral, it is necessary to know how P and v are related and to know the upper and lower limits of integration. The relationship between P and v is expressed in the equation of state for the fluid.

The equation of state for a liquid at a given temperature† is given in the form

$$\rho = \rho_0 \left[1 + \frac{P - P_0}{\beta} + k_a(P - P_0)^2 + k_b(P - P_0)^3 + \cdots \right] \tag{21.25}$$

in which the subscript 0 denotes a constant reference state and in which the higher-order terms $k_a(P - P_0)^2$, etc., are small enough to be negligible in most engineering problems. Thus one may write

$$\rho = \rho_0 \left(1 + \frac{P - P_0}{\beta} \right) \tag{21.26}$$

or

$$d\rho = \rho_0 \frac{dP}{\beta} \tag{21.27}$$

in which β is known as the bulk modulus of elasticity, lb/in.^{2}

Since $\rho v = 1$, $d\rho/\rho_0 = -dv/v_0$, one may substitute in Eq. (21.27) to obtain the desired relationship between P and v:

$$dv = -v_0 \frac{dP}{\beta} \tag{21.28}$$

The integral in Eq. (21.24) may now be expressed completely in terms of P to give the *elastic energy stored in compressing a liquid*:

$$E_e = \frac{mv_0}{\beta} \int_{P_0}^{P} P \, dP = \frac{mv_0}{2\beta} (P^2 - P_0^2) \tag{21.29}$$

Thus the elastic energy stored in a mass of *liquid* varies as the difference of the squares of the final and initial pressures.

The equation of state for a gas is closely approximated by the perfect-gas relation if the gas is not at a state near its liquid phase or critical point:

$$P = \rho R T \tag{21.30}$$

if R = gas constant, in.^{2}/(sec^2)($^\circ$R), 2.47×10^5 for air.

In the special case when the gas is *compressed isothermally* (just enough heat is removed as it is compressed to hold its temperature constant), the relationship between P and v becomes

$$dv = -\frac{RT \, dP}{P^2} \tag{21.31}$$

When the gas is compressed without heat flow or shear work, the *isentropic relationship* between pressure and volume is used.

$$Pv^k = \text{const} = P_0 v_0^k \tag{21.32}$$

† The temperature change caused by adiabatic compression of a liquid is usually so small that it may be neglected. If the temperature change is appreciable, it will affect the density because of thermal expansion, and then a more comprehensive equation of state of the form $\rho = f(P,T)$ must be employed. See J. F. Lee and F. W. Sears, "Thermodynamics," pp. 206–210, Addison-Wesley, Reading, Mass., 1955.

if k = ratio of specific heats, c_p/c_v, from which one may solve for dv.

$$dv = -\frac{v\,dP}{kP} = -P_0^{(1-k)/k}RT_0\frac{dP}{kP^{(k+1)/k}} \tag{21.33}$$

After employing Eq. (21.24), expressions for E_e may be integrated for the *isothermal compression* and the *isentropic compression* of a perfect gas:

Isothermal compression:

$$E_e = m\int_{v_1}^{v_2} - P\,dv = mRT\int_{P_0}^{P}\frac{dP}{P} = mRT\ln\frac{P}{P_0} \tag{21.34}$$

Isentropic compression:

$$E_e = m\int_{v_1}^{v_2} - P\,dv = mP_0^{(1-k)/k}\frac{RT_0}{k}\int_{P_0}^{P}\frac{dP}{P^{(k+1)/k}}$$

$$E_e = \frac{mRT_0}{P_0}\left[1 - \left(\frac{P_0}{P}\right)^{1/k}\right] \tag{21.35}$$

Unsteady Flow with Elastic-energy Storage—Negligible Momentum (Kinetic-energy), Heat Transfer, and Friction Effects. The elastic energy stored in fluid in the lines, passages, and chambers of fluid power-control systems is especially important when flow rates and pressure are changing rapidly. Although this elastic effect is more pronounced in pneumatic systems, it is also important in many hydraulic systems where fast dynamic response is required. Lines, passages, and working chambers of various kinds are places where fluid compliance can often be considered, to the exclusion of momentum and friction effects. In some cases, the boundaries of the system containing the fluid are also elastic or movable in some other way. The following example includes the effects of moving walls.

Consider the system composed of an elastic pipe, a cylinder with rigid walls, and a moving piston as shown in Fig. 21.13, which receives a fluid flow at rate Q. If momentum and friction effects can be neglected, the fluid pressure P will be uniform throughout the system. The volume of the elastic pipe may be given by

$$\mho_p = A_pL = \mho_{pi} + k_eP \tag{21.36}$$

in which $\mho_p$ = volume of fluid in pipe, in.^{3}
          A_p = cross-section area of pipe, in.^{2}
          L = length of pipe, in.
          $\mho_{pi}$ = initial volume of pipe at zero pressure, in.^{3}
          k_e = elasticity coefficient of pipe, in.^{5}/lb
          P = system pressure, psi

and the volume of the chamber in the cylinder is

$$\mho_c = A_cY \tag{21.37}$$

if $\mho_c$ = volume of fluid in cylinder, in.^{3}
    Y = distance from end of cylinder to piston, in.

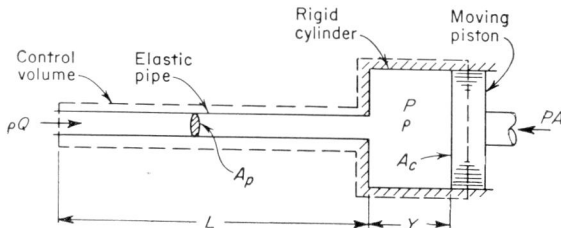

FIG. 21.13. Unsteady flow in a system having compliance due to fluid compressibility and elastic-pipe walls

Applying the unsteady-flow energy equation to the control volume shown in Fig. 21.13 gives

$$\rho Q\left(\frac{P}{\rho} + e\right) - P\frac{d}{dt}(\mathcal{V}_p + \mathcal{V}_c) = \frac{dE_u}{dt} \tag{21.38}$$

Because of negligible kinetic and potential energy effects, $e = u$. Employing Eqs. (21.36) and (21.37), Eq. (21.38) becomes

$$\rho Q\left(\frac{P}{\rho} + u\right) - k_e P\frac{dP}{dt} - A_c P\frac{dY}{dt} = \frac{d}{dt}(\rho \mathcal{V}u) \tag{21.39}$$

if $\mathcal{V} = \mathcal{V}_p + \mathcal{V}_c$. But

$$\frac{d}{dt}(\rho \mathcal{V}u) = \rho \mathcal{V}\frac{du}{dt} + \rho u\frac{d\mathcal{V}}{dt} + \mathcal{V}u\frac{d\rho}{dt} \tag{21.40}$$

and for a liquid

$$\frac{du}{dt} = -P\frac{dv}{dt} = \frac{v_0 P}{\beta}\frac{dP}{dt} \tag{21.41}$$

while

$$\frac{d\rho}{dt} = \frac{\rho_0}{\beta}\frac{dP}{dt} \tag{21.42}$$

also

$$\frac{d\mathcal{V}}{dt} = k_e\frac{dP}{dt} + A_c\frac{dY}{dt} \tag{21.43}$$

By combining Eqs. (21.39) to (21.43),

$$\rho Q\left(\frac{P}{\rho} + u\right) = k_e P\frac{dP}{dt} + A_c P\frac{dY}{dt} + \rho \mathcal{V}v_0\frac{P}{\beta}\frac{dP}{dt} + \rho u k_e\frac{dP}{dt} + \rho u A_c\frac{dY}{dt} + \mathcal{V}u\frac{\rho_0}{\beta}\frac{dP}{dt}$$

After noting that $\rho_0 \approx \rho$ because liquids are only slightly compressible and that $\rho_0 v_0 = 1$,

$$Q = \left(k_e + \frac{\mathcal{V}}{\beta}\right)\frac{dP}{dt} + A_c\frac{dY}{dt} \tag{21.44}$$

The relationship between input flow rate Q, system pressure P, and piston position Y, expressed by this differential equation, is typical of the dynamic relationships between system variables that are encountered in control systems. In this case, the important effects are elastic-energy storage in the liquid working fluid and in the pipe walls and energy conversion by means of the ram motor.

When the working fluid is a perfect gas, the analysis following Eq. (21.39) is somewhat different and may proceed as follows.

Since for a perfect gas, $P = \rho RT$, $u + P/\rho = h = C_p T$, and $u = C_v T$, one may write for the case when no heat flows to the system,

$$\rho Q C_p T - k_e P\frac{dP}{dt} - A_c P\frac{dY}{dt} = \frac{d}{dt}(\rho \mathcal{V}C_v T) = \frac{C_v}{R}\frac{d}{dt}(P\mathcal{V}) \tag{21.45}$$

It should be noted that the temperature of the incoming flow is taken equal to the temperature in the system, a reasonable assumption if the system does not rapidly undergo large pressure changes. By recognizing that

$$\frac{d(P\mathcal{V})}{dt} = P\frac{d\mathcal{V}}{dt} + \mathcal{V}\frac{dP}{dt} = P\left(k_e\frac{dP}{dt} + A_c\frac{dY}{dt}\right) + \mathcal{V}\frac{dP}{dt}$$

by substitution in Eq. (21.45),

$$\rho Q C_p T = k_e P\frac{dP}{dt} + A_c P\frac{dY}{dt} + \frac{C_v}{R}\left[A_c P\frac{dY}{dt} + (\mathcal{V} + k_e P)\frac{dP}{dt}\right]$$

which can be simplified, by making use of $R = C_p - C_v$, to give

$$Q = \left(k_e + \frac{\mathcal{V}}{kP}\right)\frac{dP}{dt} + A_c\frac{dY}{dt} \tag{21.46}$$

The similarity between Eq. (21.46) obtained for the case of a gaseous working fluid and Eq. (21.44) obtained for the case of a liquid working fluid should be noted. It may be seen by comparing terms that the effective bulk modulus of a gaseous working fluid when it is compressed adiabatically is simply equal to kP. Thus air at 2000 psi is about 100 times more compliant than water. Note also that elasticity of the pipe wall, expressed by k_e, has the same effect as the fluid compressibility factor $\mathcal{V}/kP$.

Momentum effects in the fluid in the pipe were negligible in this case because the pipe was relatively short and of large enough diameter to minimize the kinetic energy stored in the fluid. If it had been necessary for some special reason to employ a very small-diameter pipe, then the above analysis would have to be modified to take the kinetic energy into account, such as through the use of Eq. (21.18) or Eq. (21.21). In the case of a very small-diameter pipe, friction in the flow would also be important.

If a very long pipe were to be used, then it is very likely that both kinetic-energy- and elastic-energy-storage effects would have to be considered because of distributed mass and compliance along the pipe, resulting in the need to consider the wave-propagation characteristics of the line.

Unsteady Frictionless Flow in a Pipe with Distributed Mass and Compressibility. In longer lines where wave-propagation characteristics may be important, both kinetic-energy and elastic-energy effects occur simultaneously along the pipe in such a way that the flow rate and pressure are functions of both time and location along the pipe. For the purposes of generality, the ensuing analysis is based on a pipe having elastic walls.

By considering the events which occur in a small elemental control volume of length dx in the uniform pipe of length L shown in Fig. 21.14, one may apply the continuity equation to give

$$-\frac{\partial \rho\, VA}{\partial x}\, dx = \frac{\partial \rho A}{\partial t}\, dx$$

or

$$-\left(VA\frac{\partial \rho}{\partial x} + \rho A\frac{\partial V}{\partial x} + \rho V\frac{\partial A}{\partial x}\right) = A\frac{\partial \rho}{\partial t} + \rho\frac{\partial A}{\partial t} \tag{21.47}$$

From the equation of state of a compressible fluid,

$$d\rho = \frac{\rho}{\beta}\, dP \tag{21.48}$$

and for a thin-walled elastic pipe,

$$dA = \frac{A}{E(D_o/D_i - 1)}\, dP \tag{21.49}$$

in which D_o = outside diameter of pipe, in.
$\quad\quad D_i$ = inside diameter of pipe, in.
$\quad\quad E$ = Young's modulus of elasticity of pipe material, psi

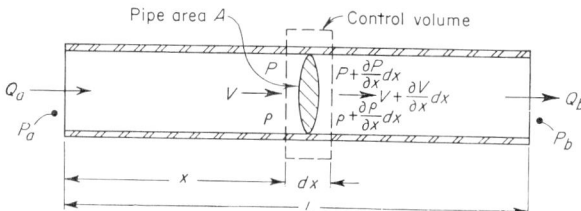

FIG. 21.14. Unsteady, frictionless flow with distributed mass and compressibility in a uniform elastic pipe.

After combining Eqs. (21.47), (21.48), and (21.49),

$$-\left[\frac{1}{\beta} + \frac{1}{E(D_o/D_i - 1)}\right] V \frac{\partial P}{\partial x} - \frac{\partial V}{\partial x} = \left[\frac{1}{\beta} + \frac{1}{E(D_o/D_i - 1)}\right] \frac{\partial P}{\partial t}$$

By defining an equivalent bulk modulus β_e such that

$$\frac{1}{\beta_e} = \frac{1}{\beta} + \frac{1}{E(D_o/D_i - 1)} \qquad (21.50)$$

one may then write

$$-\frac{V}{\beta_e} \frac{\partial P}{\partial x} - \frac{\partial V}{\partial x} = \frac{1}{\beta_e} \frac{\partial P}{\partial t} \qquad (21.51)$$

By applying the momentum equation to the same control volume, one obtains

$$-A \frac{\partial P}{\partial x} dx = \frac{\partial(\rho V^2 A)}{\partial x} dx + \frac{\partial(\rho V A)}{\partial t} dx \qquad (21.52)$$

The combination of Eqs. (21.52), (21.48), and (21.49) yields

$$-\left(1 + \frac{\rho V^2}{\beta_e}\right) \frac{\partial P}{\partial x} = \rho \frac{\partial V}{\partial t} + 2\rho V \frac{\partial V}{\partial x} + \frac{\rho V}{\beta_e} \frac{\partial P}{\partial t} \qquad (21.53)$$

In many problems, the velocity V is always small enough to be negligible, even though appreciable power is being transmitted at velocity V, so that the two basic equations, (21.51) and (21.53), may be simplified to give

Continuity:
$$-\frac{\partial V}{\partial x} = \frac{1}{\beta_e} \frac{\partial P}{\partial t} \qquad (21.54)$$

Momentum:
$$-\frac{\partial P}{\partial x} = \rho \frac{\partial V}{\partial t} \qquad (21.55)$$

This pair of simultaneous partial differential equations, often known as the wave equations, describes the traveling wave phenomena observed in a pipe of this kind. In working with such a transmission line it is often sufficient to consider the pressure and flow effects at each end of the line and to determine the functional relationships between P_a, Q_a, P_b, and Q_b (Fig. 21.14). This transmission line is considered simply as an element having four variables, as shown by the block diagram of Fig. 21.15. Experience has shown that any two of these variables may be considered as physically independent (inputs) as long as they do not both occur at the same end of the transmission line. In other words, it is physically impossible to arbitrarily vary both P_a and Q_a simultaneously by external means, but it is physically possible to arbitrarily vary P_a simultaneously with P_b or Q_b by external means (i.e. as inputs to the system). The other two variables must be considered, of course, as outputs.

There are two different forms in which the solutions of the wave equations may be expressed. The first is a set of four differential equations involving hyperbolic sine and hyperbolic cosine functions:

$$P_b = (\cosh \Gamma)P_a - (Z_s \sinh \Gamma)Q_a \qquad (21.56)$$

$$Q_b = -(Y_s \sinh \Gamma)P_a + (\cosh \Gamma)Q_a \qquad (21.57)$$

$$P_a = (\cosh \Gamma)P_b + (Z_s \sinh \Gamma)Q_b \qquad (21.58)$$

$$Q_a = (Y_s \sinh \Gamma)P_b + (\cosh \Gamma)Q_b \qquad (21.59)$$

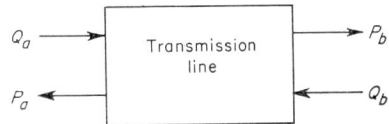

Fig. 21.15. Block-diagram representation of transmission line.

in which $\quad \Gamma = L\sqrt{\rho/\beta_e}D$

$\qquad D \equiv$ differential operator $\partial/\partial t$

$\qquad Y_s =$ characteristic admittance of the line, $\sqrt{A^2/\rho\beta_e}$

$\qquad Z_s =$ characteristic impedance of the line, $\sqrt{\rho\beta_e/A^2}$

The second form of solution is a set of four time-difference equations:

$$Y_s[P_b(t - 2T_e) + P_b(t) - 2P_a(t - T_e)] = Q_b(t - 2T_e) - Q_b(t) \qquad (21.60)$$

$$Z_s[Q_b(t - 2T_e) + Q_b(t) - 2Q_a(t - T_e)] = P_b(t - 2T_e) - P_b(t) \qquad (21.61)$$

$$Y_s[P_a(t - 2T_e) + P_a(t) - 2P_b(t - T_e)] = Q_a(t) - Q_a(t - 2T_e) \qquad (21.62)$$

$$Z_s[Q_a(t - 2T_e) + Q_a(t) - 2Q_b(t - T_e)] = P_a(t) - P_a(t - 2T_e) \qquad (21.63)$$

in which $\quad T_e = L\sqrt{\rho/\beta_e} =$ propagation time for wave to travel length of pipe, sec

$\sqrt{\beta_e/\rho} =$ velocity of sound in fluid in elastic pipe, in./sec

The above results apply when the fluid is gaseous if the pressure changes are small and if the isentropic relationship between P and ρ is used:

$$\left.\frac{\partial P}{\partial \rho}\right|_s = kRT = \text{(speed of sound in gas)}^2$$

When large pressure variations occur with gases, shock waves occur, so that the flow is no longer frictionless; also V may no longer be negligible in Eqs. (21.51) and (21.53); and the above solutions may then be only very crude approximations of the actual behavior of the line.

Response of Frictionless-distributed-parameter Hydraulic-transmission Line to a Step Change in Pressure. Consider the problem of finding how Q_a and Q_b vary with time in the system shown in Fig. 21.14 after a step change in P_a is made with P_b held constant. The time-difference Eqs. (21.60) and (21.62) give the desired relationships of Q_a and Q_b to P_a and P_b so that a set of time response plots such as that shown in Fig. 21.16 results. It is seen that the flow rate Q_a changes immediately when the step change in P_a occurs, while Q_b does not change until T_e sec later. Moreover, the pressure wave which required T_e sec to travel down the line, resulting in the change in Q_b at time t equal to T_e, requires another T_e sec to travel back to the a end, again increasing Q_a, etc. The time-difference equations have also been very useful in the preparation of graphical solutions of hydraulic transient problems.

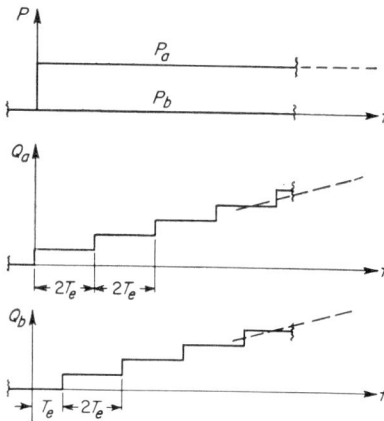

FIG. 21.16. Time variation of flow rates at each end of a frictionless-distributed-parameter line for a step change in pressure at one end.

POWER TRANSMISSION

The transmission of useful power by means of a working fluid is accomplished primarily through the flow of fluid at high pressure. In the case of a liquid working fluid, the energy stored in the fluid due to pressure is small, and power transmission is mostly due to the use of the liquid as a sort of "shaft" transmitting power by virtue of its displacement under a state of stress. In the case of a gaseous working fluid, the energy stored in the fluid because of pressure is appreciable, and if a means is provided for extracting this energy, it can represent a significant fraction of the total power transmitted by the moving stream. Otherwise the gas acts much as a liquid would in providing a sort of "shaft" for the transmission of power. The transmission of power by virtue of thermal energy is not within the scope of this section, since this is more of a thermodynamic problem. Because line losses tend to increase as nearly the square of flow velocity, relatively low-flow velocities are used, and thus the kinetic energy stored in the working fluid is small, if not negligible. The major problems associated with the transmission of fluid power are related to the mechanical or physical characteristics of the pipe and to the fluid-flow characteristics within the passages enclosed by the pipe and fittings.

21.7. Mechanical Considerations

Because relatively high pressures are involved and because the consequences of transmission-line failure are often very serious, *mechanical strength* of the pipe and fittings is a very important factor. Factors of safety from 3 to 5 are frequently employed, based on estimated working pressure. Fatigue is usually an important factor because of the cyclic variation of fluid pressure which usually occurs in the line. Steel is usually preferred over copper, aluminum, and nonferrous alloys because it has an endurance limit. It is frequently difficult to predict the worst possible pressure surges that might occur; loading effects are not always well enough defined, and mechanical loading due to mounting misalignments can frequently give trouble. Whenever possible, it is advisable to make a thorough dynamic system analysis to determine how high peak pressure surges may go.

A certain amount of bending flexibility is desirable to minimize the effects of misalignments. In some instances, where a great deal of flexibility is required to allow for relatively large motions, steel-wire-reinforced rubber hoses are employed.

The elasticity of the pipe or hose wall (expansion due to pressure) is sometimes important because of its effect on over-all system dynamic response.

When fluid-power lines are not properly anchored at key points, they will readily respond to sources of vibration, and in some instances failure has been attributed to stresses induced by large-amplitude mechanical vibrations, especially in mobile equipment, aircraft, and missiles.

A wide variety of commercially available fittings are employed to facilitate the use of standard pipe, seamless tubing, and flexible hoses for fluid-power transmission lines. Additional factors of safety are often required for certain fittings because of stress concentrations due to threaded joints and/or unusual shapes.

21.8. Fluid-flow Considerations

Because weight and cost are very important factors, and because fluid-power transmission lines are usually rather short, the smallest feasible diameter is employed for a given line and the rated flow is turbulent. However, since the pressure drop increases with nearly the square of the flow rate, liquid velocities are usually limited to 200 in./sec and gas velocities are usually limited to 2000 in./sec. The higher gas velocities are allowable because of the much lower densities and viscosities of gases as compared with liquids.

When the line is mostly a straight run with a minimum of sharp turns and sudden changes of diameter, the pressure drop may be estimated from the well-known friction-factor equation.

$$P_1 - P_2 = 4f \frac{L}{D} \rho \frac{V^2}{2} \tag{21.64}$$

in which P_1 = upstream pressure, psi
$\quad P_2$ = downstream pressure, psi
$\quad f$ = friction factor (from Stanton diagram)
$\quad L$ = pipe length, in.
$\quad D$ = pipe diameter, in.
$\quad \rho$ = fluid density, lb-sec^2/in.^{4}
$\quad V$ = average fluid velocity in pipe

Table 21.1. Loss Coefficients for Fittings

Fitting	Pipe ID range, in.	Loss coefficient K range
45° standard elbow........................	0.4–12.0	0.45–0.2
90° standard elbow........................	0.4–12.0	0.9 –0.4
45° miter bend...........................	0.4–12.0	0.35–0.17
90° miter bend...........................	0.4–12.0	1.7 –0.8
90° sweep bend ($R_s/D = 4$)	0.4–12.0	0.32–0.15
Sudden expansion to much larger pipe.........	Any size	1.0
Sudden contraction to much smaller pipe.......	Any size	0.5
Other fittings such as check valves, wide-open valves, tees, and special fittings.............	Seek manufacturer's data	Seek manufacturer's data

Because the friction factor f tends to vary inversely with the Reynolds number $\rho VD/\mu$ to the one-fourth power for flow in a pipe, the pressure drop in this case tends to vary as the 7/4 power of the rate of flow through a given pipe.

When there are several sharp turns, sudden enlargements, etc., the pressure drop for each may be estimated by the following equation:

$$P_1 - P_2 = K\rho \frac{V^2}{2}$$

(21.65)

in which K is a loss coefficient ranging from 0.2 to 2.0, depending on the geometry of the bend or enlargement. Table 21.1 may be used for the purposes of making rough estimates.

Thus the pressure drop across a fitting or sudden change in pipe diameter tends to vary as the second power of the rate of flow through a given line. When the effects of pipe friction and the fitting losses are of the same order of magnitude, the pressure drop for a complete line is seen to vary with about the 1.9 power of the flow rate, and the power lost (proportional to pressure drop times flow rate) thus varies with about the 2.9 power of the flow rate.

21.9. Dynamic-response Characteristics

In general, fluid-power transmission lines are flow passages with distributed mass, compliance, and frictional resistance to flow. The case of frictionless flow with distributed mass and compliance has been analyzed and is discussed in Art. 21.6. When one attempts to include the effects of friction, especially the type of nonlinear friction encountered with turbulent flow, one is hampered by the lack of mathematical solutions of the resulting partial differential equations.

It is fortunate, at least from the point of view of ease of analysis, that friction effects occur predominantly at the ends of the line because of fittings at those locations. In any event, it is customary to consider the friction effects to be concentrated at the terminal points. When this is done, the line is characterized by the use of three elements: an inner element which includes the effects of mass and compliance and two outer elements, each comprising half of the total resistance effect of the line as shown in Fig. 21.17.

Strictly speaking, the distributed-parameter representation of the inner element is the most accurate. However, if it is never subjected to frequencies higher than its lowest natural frequency, a lumped-parameter approximation such as that shown schematically in Fig. 21.18 may be used.

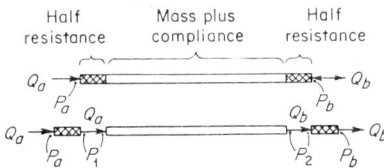

Fig. 21.17. Schematic diagram illustrating how transmission-line resistance is lumped at ends.

A convenient way to represent the mass-compliance portion of the transmission line is with a block diagram such as that given in Fig. 21.19 which reveals each of the four distinct dynamic-transfer characteristics required to describe this part of the transmission line. Each of these dynamic-trans-

Table **21.2.** Dynamic-transfer Characteristics for Frictionless Transmission Line

(Used in connection with Fig. 21.19)

Symbol	Distributed-parameter characteristic	Lumped-parameter characteristic
G_{1a}	$\dfrac{Z_s(e^{T_eD} + e^{-T_eD})}{e^{T_eD} - e^{-T_eD}}$	$\dfrac{\beta_e}{ALD}\dfrac{1 + \rho L^2 D^2/2\beta_e}{1 + \rho L^2 D^2/4\beta_e}$
G_{2a}	$\dfrac{2Z_s}{e^{T_eD} - e^{-T_eD}}$	$\dfrac{\beta_e}{ALD}\dfrac{1}{1 + \rho L^2 D^2/4\beta_e}$
G_{2b}	$\dfrac{-Z_s(e^{T_eD} + e^{-T_eD})}{e^{T_eD} - e^{-T_eD}}$	$\dfrac{-\beta_e}{ALD}\dfrac{1 + \rho L^2 D^2/2\beta_e}{1 + \rho L^2 D^2/4\beta_e}$
G_{1b}	$\dfrac{-2Z_s}{e^{T_eD} - e^{-T_eD}}$	$\dfrac{-\beta_e}{ALD}\dfrac{1}{1 + \rho L^2 D^2/4\beta_e}$
ω_n	$\dfrac{\pi}{L}\sqrt{\dfrac{\beta_e}{\rho}}, \dfrac{2\pi}{L}\sqrt{\dfrac{\beta_e}{\rho}}, \dfrac{3\pi}{L}\sqrt{\dfrac{\beta_e}{\rho}}, \ldots$	$\dfrac{2}{L}\sqrt{\dfrac{\beta_e}{\rho}}$

in which $Z_s = \sqrt{\rho\beta_e/A^2}$, lb-sec/in.^{5}

$T_e = L\sqrt{\rho/\beta_e}$, sec

β_e = equivalent bulk modulus, psi

ρ = mass density of fluid, lb-sec^2/in.^{4}

L = line length, in.

A = cross-section area of line, in.^{2}

fer characteristics is given in Table 21.2 for the line with distributed mass and compliance and for the line with lumped mass and compliance.

The transfer characteristics in Table 21.2 for the distributed parameter line are derived from Eqs. (21.57) and (21.59), and the transfer characteristics for the lumped-parameter approximation are derived by means of a simple dynamic analysis of the system shown in Fig. 21.18.

The accuracy with which the lumped-parameter characteristics approximate the distributed-parameter characteristics is readily determined by employing appropriate series expansions for the exponentials of the distributed-parameter characteristics, substituting $j\omega$ for D in each expression and comparing them for the values of ω at which the system may be expected to operate. The natural frequencies ω_n are also given in the above table. As long as the inputs Q_a and Q_b do not vary at frequencies in excess of $1/T_e$, the lumped-parameter approximation is reasonably good (maximum amplitude error of about 12 per cent). Since the effective surge impedance of the lumped-parameter approximation exactly matches the surge impedance Z_s of the distributed-parameter system, one can artificially increase the natural frequency of the lumped-parameter approximation by the factor $\pi/2$ and thus produce a lumped-parameter characterization that is quite good for input frequencies up to $2/T_e$. Obviously, if the input vary at frequencies in excess of $2/T_e$, the distributed-parameter model must be used.

When the inputs vary at frequencies that are very low with respect to $1/T_e$, the effects of fluid mass are negligible and the pressures P_1 and P_2 are very nearly the same.

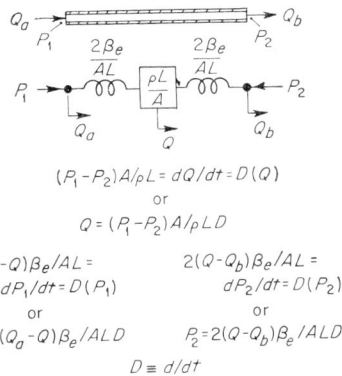

$$(P_1 - P_2)A/\rho L = dQ/dt = D(Q)$$

or

$$Q = (P_1 - P_2)A/\rho LD$$

$$2(Q_a - Q)\beta_e/AL = \qquad 2(Q - Q_b)\beta_e/AL =$$
$$dP_1/dt = D(P_1) \qquad dP_2/dt = D(P_2)$$

or

$$P_1 = 2(Q_a - Q)\beta_e/ALD \qquad P_2 = 2(Q - Q_b)\beta_e/ALD$$

$$D \equiv d/dt$$

Fig. 21.18. Lumped-parameter approximation of mass-compliance portion of transmission line.

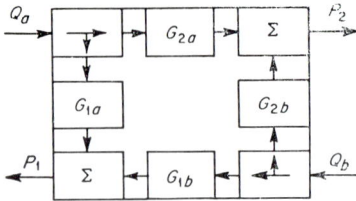

FIG. 21.19. Block diagram showing dynamic-transfer characteristics of mass-compliance portion of transmission line.

In this case, the equations developed in Art. 21.6 for a line with compliance may be used. For example, Eq. (21.44), adapted to this use, gives

$$Q_a - Q_b = \frac{AL}{\beta_e} \frac{dP}{dt} \qquad (21.66)$$

if $P = P_1 = P_2 = $ pressure throughout line, lb/in.^{2}

Functional Block Diagrams for Analogue-computer Studies. When a fluid-power transmission line is incorporated in a complex system, it is often useful to be able to simulate all the components of the system with an analogue computer through the use of operational block diagrams. The block diagrams shown in Fig. 21.20 have been prepared to simulate, respectively, the dynamic-response characteristics of a frictionless-distributed-parameter hydraulic transmission line and its lumped-parameter approximation. Also shown is the simple operational block diagram that may be used

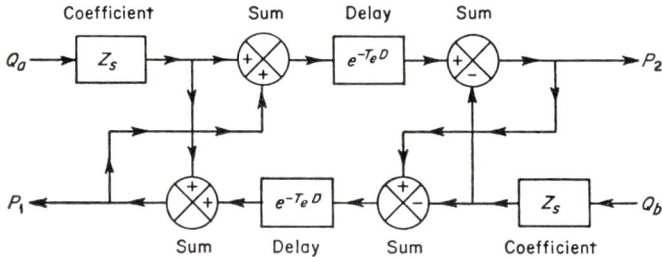

(a)

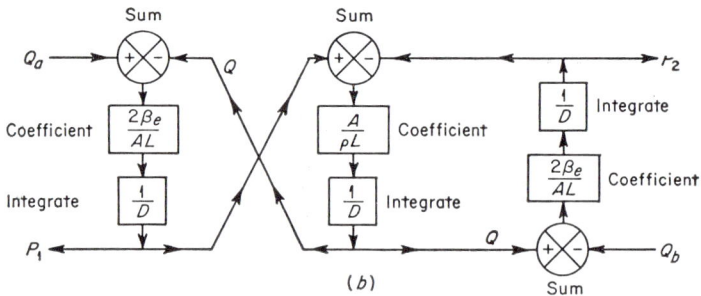

(b)

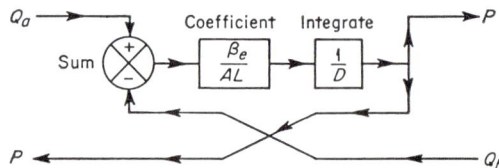

(c)

FIG. 21.20. Operational block diagrams of frictionless transmission lines. (a) Distributed-parameter line. (b) Lumped-parameter line. (c) Lumped-parameter line with negligible mass.

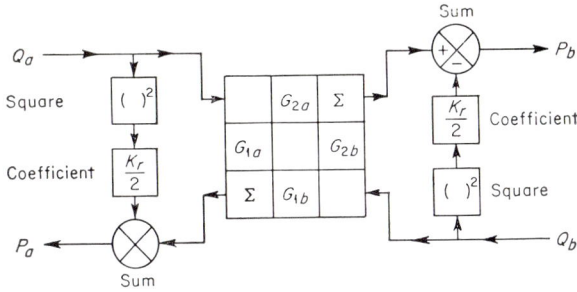

FIG. 21.21. Functional block diagram showing the dynamic interaction of a mass-plus-compliance line with nonlinear flow resistances lumped at ends.

when the effects of distributed mass are negligible. Each of the functional components employed in the construction of these diagrams is readily simulated by a corresponding analogue-computer component employing input and output signals (usually voltages) analogous to the real physical variables such as flow and pressure shown in Fig. 21.20. For the interested reader Refs. 2, 5, and 6, at the end of this section, provide a more detailed discussion of analogue computation.

Mass-plus-compliance Transmission Line with Friction Effects Lumped at the Ends. When the resistance characteristics are lumped at the ends of the frictionless transmission line as shown in Fig. 21.17, the half resistances may be described by the following equations:

$$P_a - P_1 = \frac{K_r}{2} Q_a^2 \tag{21.67}$$

$$P_2 - P_b = \frac{K_r}{2} Q_b^2 \tag{21.68}$$

if $K_r = (\rho/2A^2)(\Sigma K_{\text{loss}})$ = total resistance coefficient for line, lb-sec^2/in.^{6}

By combining Eqs. (21.67) and (21.68) with the equations represented by the block diagram of Fig. 21.19, one finds

$$P_a = \frac{1}{2}K_r Q_a^2 + G_{1a}Q_a + G_{1b}Q_b \tag{21.69}$$

$$P_b = G_{2a}Q_a + G_{2b}Q_b - \frac{1}{2}K_r Q_b^2 \tag{21.70}$$

a pair of differential equations that are linear except for the terms which contain Q_a^2 and Q_b^2. Figure 21.21 illustrates this system by means of a functional block diagram which employs operational components corresponding to analogue-computer components. Of particular note are the nonlinear components used to square the flows Q_a and Q_b, respectively. The existence of this nonlinear effect means that transient or frequency analysis of this system is limited to situations in which the flows Q_a and Q_b undergo only "small" changes from some constant values Q_{ai} and Q_{bi}.

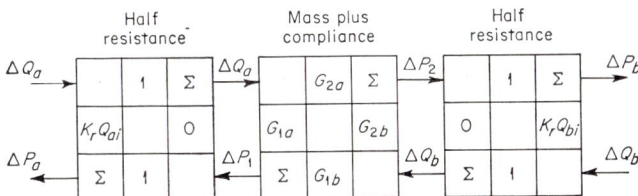

FIG. 21.22. Functional block diagram illustrating dynamic interactions when flow changes are small.

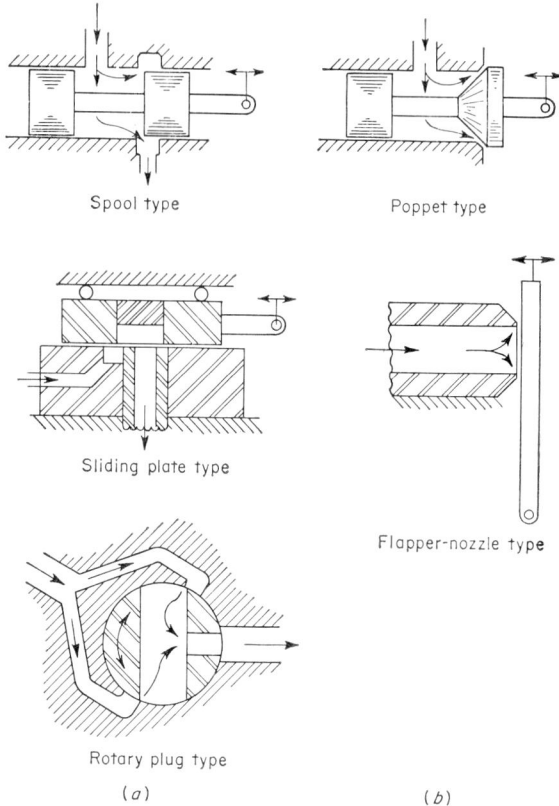

Spool type

Poppet type

Sliding plate type

Flapper-nozzle type

Rotary plug type

(a)

(b)

Fig. 21.23. Basic types of variable orifice. (a) Shear-seal type. (b) Seating type.

When only such small changes occur, one may "linearize" Eqs. (21.67) and (21.68) by differentiation and allowing the differential to be finite but small. Thus

$$\Delta P_a - \Delta P_1 = K_r Q_{ai}(\Delta Q_a) \tag{21.71}$$

$$\Delta P_2 - \Delta P_b = K_r Q_{bi}(\Delta Q_b) \tag{21.72}$$

When the fluid is a liquid, the mass-plus-compliance portion of the line is linear, its performance with small changes is the same as for large changes of all variables, and the system may be described by the functional block diagram shown in Fig. (21.22). When the fluid is a gas, the preceding analyses of the line behavior are limited to cases when only small changes occur (see discussion near the end of Art. 21.6). The dynamic performance of gas lines when large changes occur is beyond the scope of this section.

CONTROL VALVES

Control valves are widely used to modulate the flow of fluid power because they offer a means of bringing about a large change in flow of fluid power through the use of a small amount of energy to stroke the valve. Control is usually† accomplished through the use of variable orifices, which act as variable-resistance elements. The two basic types of variable orifice, shear-seal type and seating type, are illustrated in Fig. 21.23. In

† A notable exception to this statement is the jet-pipe valve which is described briefly at the end of this section.

some instances, a single orifice can provide the necessary control, while in other instances two or more orifices are needed. Of greatest interest to the designers of control systems employing control valves are *flow-pressure-opening (stroke) characteristics* and *stroking-force characteristics* of the various types of valves. The characteristics of a given valve operating with a gaseous fluid are usually quite different from those with a liquid fluid, and in both cases the characteristics are rather nonlinear.

21.10. Single-orifice Valves

Single-orifice valves are used for one-way-flow control.

A single-orifice *hydraulic valve* (liquid working medium) has a flow rate vs. pressure drop characteristic which is very nearly parabolic. Departure from a true parabola occurs when the valve is very nearly closed and is due to friction effects, which become important at low Reynolds numbers $(\rho V D/\mu)$.† As long as the Reynolds number is above 250, the well-known orifice equation holds if the liquid does not have entrained or dissolved gases in it.

$$Q = C_d A_o \sqrt{\frac{2(P_u - P_d)}{\rho}} \qquad (21.73)$$

in which Q = volume rate of flow, in.^{3}/sec
  C_d = discharge coefficient
  A_o = area of orifice opening, in.^{2}
  P_u = upstream pressure, psi
  P_d = downstream pressure, psi
  ρ = mass density of fluid, lb-sec^2/in.^{4} (for water, $\rho = 10^{-4}$ lb-sec^2/in.^{4}; for mineral oils, $\rho = 8 \times 10^{-5}$ lb-sec^2/in.^{4})

The discharge coefficient for "sharp-edged" configurations is about 0.63, and for configurations with chamfering, rounding, etc., it can be as large as 0.8 or 0.9. Normalized load flow vs. normalized load pressure characteristics for a single orifice controlling the flow through a load are shown in Fig. 21.24. It is always preferable to employ the valve downstream of the load to prevent loss of control which would occur if the valve were upstream and closed so rapidly that the coasting motor would act like a pump and cause cavitation of the fluid between the valve and motor.

A single-orifice *pneumatic valve* (gaseous fluid) has characteristics which differ considerably from those of a hydraulic valve because of the very compressible nature of the fluid, which leads to a "choked-flow" condition when the pressure drop is greater than that for critical (sonic) flow. Because of the much lower viscosity of most gases as compared with liquids, viscous effects are seldom noticed in pneumatic valves even at small openings. The much greater compressibility of gases leads to the use of weight

† See Ref. 2, chap. 7, pp. 178–184.

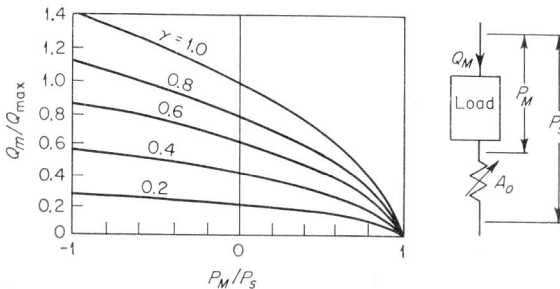

Fig. 21.24. Normalized load flow vs. normalized load pressure for a single-orifice hydraulic valve controlling the flow through a load. $\gamma = A_o/A_{o\,max}$. $Q_{max} = C_d A_{o\,max}\sqrt{2P_s/\rho}$.

rate of flow rather than the use of volume rate of flow in describing the flow characteristics of pneumatic valves. The orifice equation for a gas holds if the flow is not choked.

$$W = C_d A_o C_1 \frac{P_u}{\sqrt{T_u}} \left(\frac{P_d}{P_u}\right)^{1/k} \sqrt{1 - \left(\frac{P_d}{P_u}\right)^{(k-1)/k}} \qquad (21.74)$$

in which W = weight rate of flow of gas, lb/sec
     $C_1 = g\sqrt{2k/R(k-1)}$, 2.06 $(°R)^{1/2}$/sec for air
     k = ratio of specific heats c_p/c_v, 1.4 for air
     g = acceleration of gravity, 386 in./sec^2
     R = gas constant, 2.47×10^5 in.^{2}/(sec^2)(°R) for air
     C_d = discharge coefficient, usually 0.8 to 1.0
     A_o = area of orifice opening, in.^{2}
     P_u = upstream pressure (absolute), psi
     P_d = downstream pressure (absolute), psi

The flow is said to be choked when the pressure ratio P_d/P_u is less than the critical value given by

$$\left(\frac{P_d}{P_u}\right)_{cr} = \left[\frac{2}{k+1}\right]^{k/k-1} \qquad 0.528 \text{ for air}$$

When the flow is choked, $P_d/P_u < (P_d/P_u)_{cr}$,

$$W = C_d A_o C_2 \frac{P_u}{\sqrt{T_u}} \qquad (21.75)$$

It is seen that the flow can be expressed by a single equation of the following form:

$$W = C_d A_o C_2 \frac{P_u}{\sqrt{T_u}} f_1 \frac{P_d}{P_u} \qquad (21.76)$$

if $C_2 = g\sqrt{\dfrac{k}{R}\left(\dfrac{2}{k+1}\right)^{(k+1)/(k-1)}}$ 0.532 $(°R)^{1/2}$/sec for air

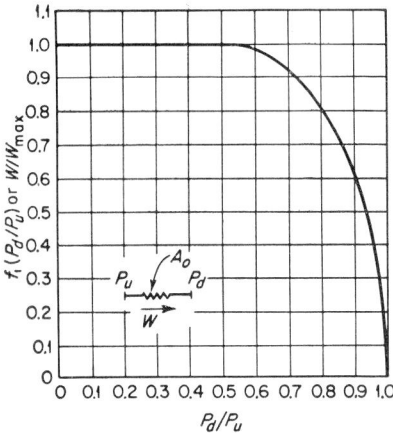

FIG. 21.25. Graphical representation of $f_1(P_d/P_u)$ for the case of air flowing through an orifice. $W_{max} = C_d A_o (0.532) P_u/\sqrt{T_u}$.

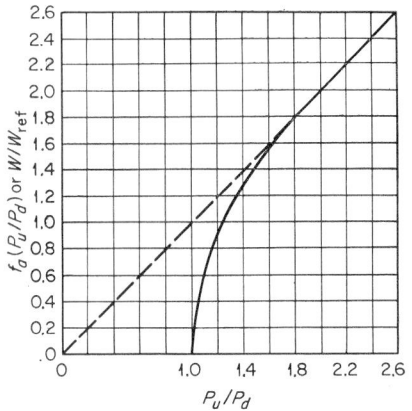

FIG. 21.26. Graphical representation of $f_a(P_u/P_d)$ for the case of air flowing through an orifice. $W_{cr} = C_d A_o (0.532) P_d/\sqrt{T_u}$.

and $f_1(P_d/P_u)$ is given by

$$f_1 \frac{P_d}{P_u} = \begin{cases} \left(\frac{C_1}{C_2}\right)\left(\frac{P_d}{P_u}\right)^{1/k} \sqrt{1 - \left(\frac{P_d}{P_u}\right)^{(k-1)/k}} & \text{for subcritical flow} \\ 1 & \text{for supercritical or choked flow} \end{cases}$$

which is shown graphically in Fig. 21.25 for air. This function is identical with the function A^*/A for subcritical flow given in the "Gas Tables."[7] The graph given in Fig. 21.25 may also be interpreted as representing the ratio W/W_{max} for a given orifice with a given constant upstream pressure. It is important to note that the downstream pressure does not affect the flow when it is less than $(P_d/P_u)_{cr}$ times P_u, that is, when the flow is choked. In some instances, it is valuable to have a similar curve showing how the flow through an orifice varies with the pressure ratio (P_u/P_d) when P_d is held constant. In this case, it can be shown that

$$W = C_d A_o C_2 \frac{P_d}{\sqrt{T_u}} f_a \left(\frac{P_u}{P_d}\right) \tag{21.77}$$

in which the function $f_a(P_u/P_d) = (P_u/P_d)f_1(P_d/P_u)$ is given graphically for air in Fig. 21.26. This curve may also be interpreted as the ratio W/W_{ref} for a given orifice with a given constant downstream pressure, where W_{ref} is the critical flow which would pass through the orifice if its upstream pressure was P_d.

Normalized load flow vs. normalized load pressure characteristics for a single orifice controlling the flow through a load are given in Fig. 21.27 for the cases of valve upstream

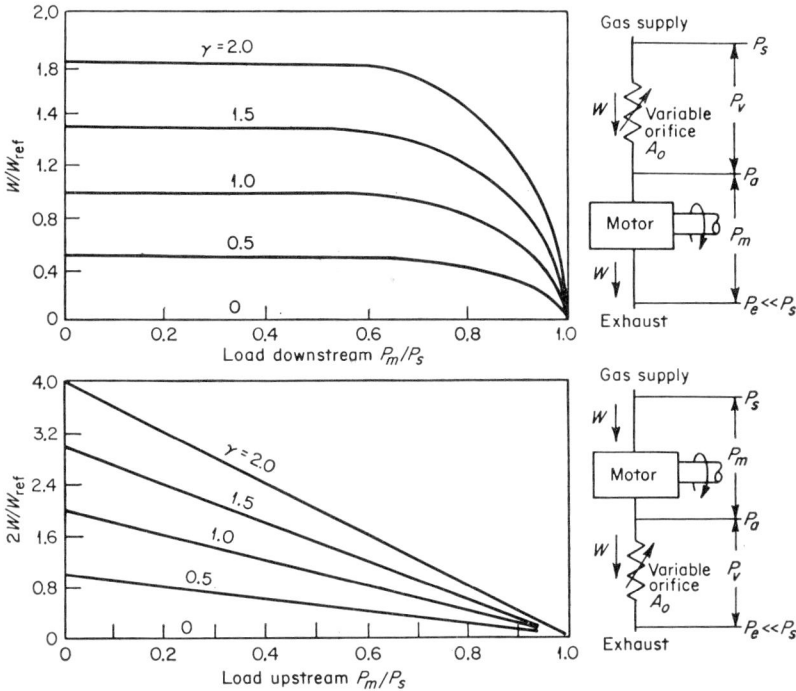

Fig. 21.27. Normalized load flow vs. normalized load pressure for a single-orifice pneumatic valve controlling the flow of air through a load. $\gamma = A_o/A_{o\,ref}$. $W_{ref} = C_d A_{o\,ref}(0.532)P_s/\sqrt{T_s}$. T_s = absolute temperature of air supply, °R.

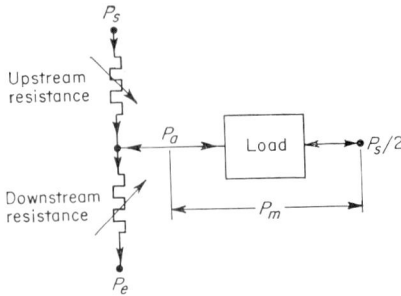

of the motor and valve downstream of the motor when the gas is air. It is assumed that the temperature of gas entering the orifice from the load is equal to supply temperature T_s.

The stagnation temperature of the gas leaving an orifice is usually very nearly the same as the stagnation temperature of the gas entering the orifice.

21.11. Three-way Valves

In order to facilitate bidirectional control, two orifices are arranged as shown schematically in Fig. 21.28. In some cases both orifices are variable, one increasing while the other decreases, and vice versa. In other cases, one of the orifices is fixed.

The ideal characteristics of *three-way hydraulic control valves* may be obtained by mathematically or graphically combining the characteristics of two single orifices. Figure 21.29 gives the characteristics of some frequently employed types of three-way hydraulic valves when the supply pressure is constant. For the interested reader, Ref. 2, chap. 7, provides a more thorough discussion of hydraulic three-way valves. Measured three-way-valve characteristics agree reasonably well with the theoretical curves shown in Fig. 21.29, the greatest difference appearing in the case of the closed-center valve with no overlap (Fig. 21.29b) near its center position. It is impossible with presently known manufacturing techniques to make a spool valve with zero radial clearance, perfectly sharp corners at the metering orifices, and perfect alignment of the corners of the metering orifices; hence the discrepancies near null. In valves of this kind, all flow passages leading to and from the orifices should have cross-section areas at least three times as large as the maximum orifice area, otherwise the resistance characteristics of the passages may alter the valve characteristics seriously.

The ideal characteristics of *three-way pneumatic control valves* may be obtained by methods similar to those used in obtaining characteristics of three-way hydraulic valves. Figure 21.30 gives the characteristics of some frequently employed types of three-way pneumatic valves when the supply pressure is constant. Reference 2, chap. 8, provides a detailed discussion of pneumatic-valve characteristics. The characteristics of the most carefully manufactured closed-center pneumatic valves depart from the ideal characteristics more than the case of hydraulic valves because of the effects of leakage past clearance spaces in addition to the other causes mentioned for hydraulic valves. As in the case of hydraulic valves, generous passage areas should be provided leading to and from the orifices.

21.12. Four-way Valves

Even more effective bidirectional control can be achieved if four orifices are combined as shown schematically in Fig. 21.31. With this scheme, the valve is capable of driving the load either way without the need for another source of pressure or force on the other side of the motor, which was required in the case of a three-way valve. In some cases only the downstream orifices are variable, but better control is usually attainable with all four orifices variable.

The ideal characteristics of *four-way hydraulic control valves* may be obtained for the case of a symmetrical load (equal flow rates at both ports of the motor) by mathematically or graphically combining the characteristics of four single orifices or by combining the characteristics of two three-way valves. Figure 21.32 gives the characteristics of some frequently employed types of four-way valves. The schematic diagram shown in Fig. 21.33 is included to help define the parameters used in parts b to d of

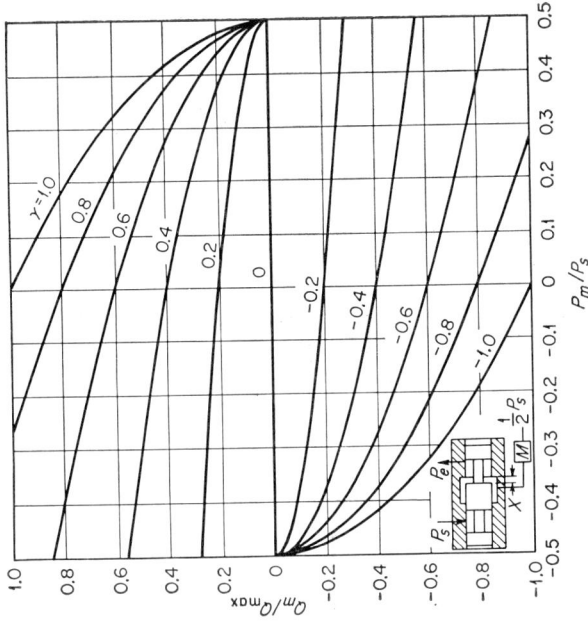

$\gamma = X/X_{max} = A_o/A_{o\,max}$
X = valve displacement
X_{max} = maximum valve displacement
$Q_{max} = 0.625A_{o\,max}\sqrt{P_s/\rho}$ = maximum no-load flow to motor
$A_{o\,max}$ = maximum orifice area

Q_m = flow to motor
P_m = pressure drop across motor
P_s = supply pressure (constant)
ρ = fluid density

(b)

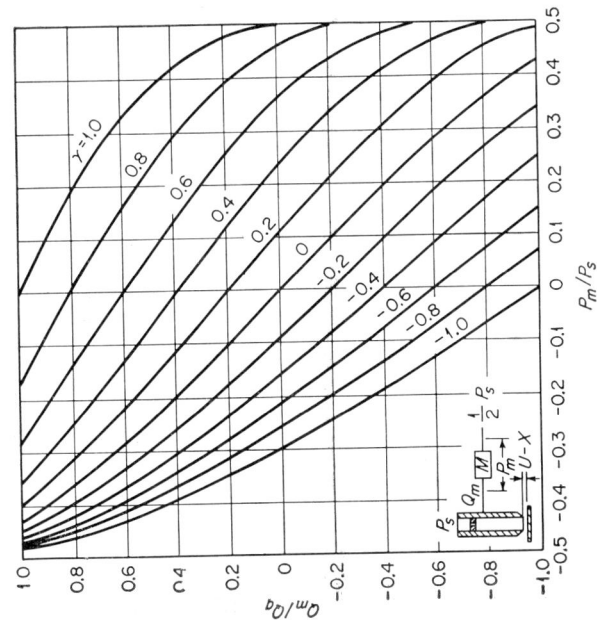

$\gamma = X/U$
X = flapper displacement
U = flapper initial separation
$Q_q = 0.625A_o\sqrt{P_s/\rho}$ = quiescent flow to valve
A_o = area of each orifice when valve is centered

Q_m = flow to motor
P_m = pressure drop across motor
P_s = supply pressure (constant)
ρ = fluid density

(a)

Fig. 21.29. Characteristics of three-way hydraulic valves with constant supply pressure. (a) Fixed upstream orifice, variable downstream orifice. (b) Variable upstream orifice, variable downstream orifice, closed center, neither underlap nor overlap.

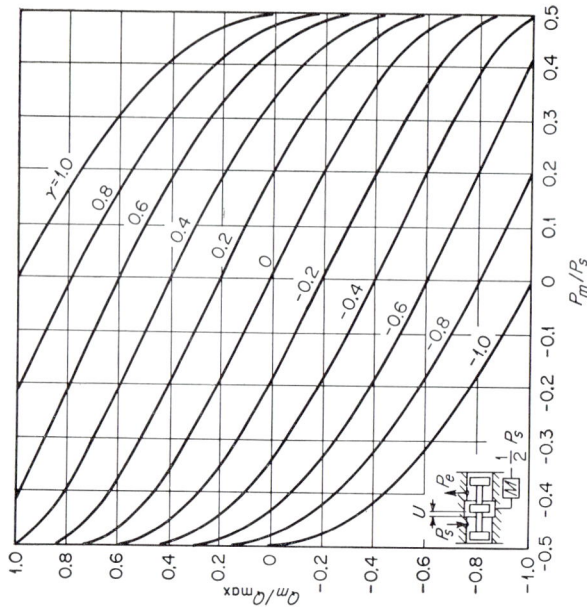

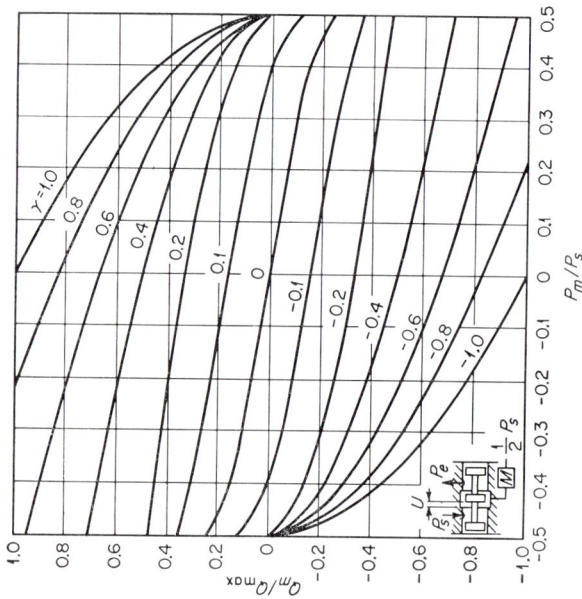

γ = X/U
X = valve displacement
U = valve underlap
Q_{max} = $1.25A_o\sqrt{P_s/\rho}$ = maximum no-load flow to motor = quiescent flow to valve
A_o = area of each orifice when valve is centered

Q_m = flow to motor
P_m = pressure drop across motor
P_s = supply pressure (constant)
ρ = fluid density

(d)

γ = X/X_{max}
X = valve displacement
X_{max} = maximum valve displacement
$Q_{o\,max}$ = $0.625A_{o\,max}\sqrt{P_s/\rho}$ = maximum no-load flow to motor
$A_{o\,max}$ = maximum orifice area
U = valve underlap

Q_m = flow to motor
P_m = pressure drop across motor
P_s = supply pressure (constant)
ρ = fluid density

(c)

Fig. 21.29 (Continued). Characteristics of three-way hydraulic valves with constant supply pressure. (c) Variable upstream orifice, variable downstream orifice, partly open center, $U = 0.2X_{max}$. (d) Variable upstream orifice, variable downstream orifice, fully open center, $U = 1.0X_{max}$.

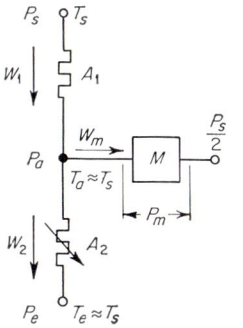

$$P_e = 0.1 P_s$$
$$W_{ref} = C_d A_{ref} (0.532) P_s / \sqrt{T_s}$$
$$A_{ref} = A_{2\,max} = 2 A_1$$
$$\gamma = A_2 / A_{ref}$$
$$W_{1\,max} = 0.5 W_{ref}$$

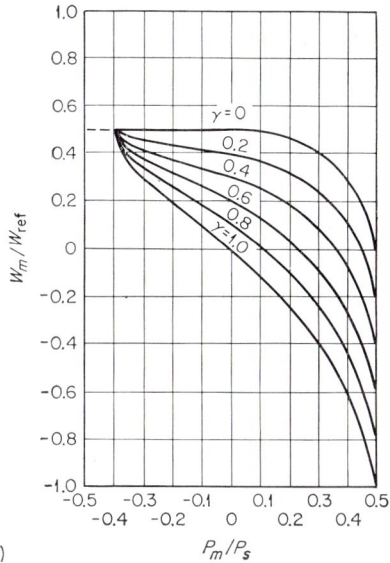

(a)

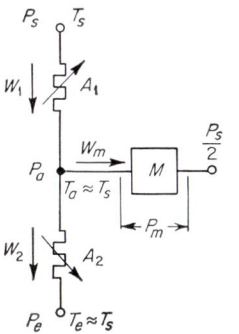

$$P_e = 0.1 P_s$$
$$W_{ref} = C_d A_{ref} (0.532) P_s / \sqrt{T_s}$$
$$A_{ref} = A_{1\,max} = A_{2\,max}$$
$$\gamma = \begin{cases} A_1/A_{ref}, & A_2 = 0 \\ 0, & A_1 = A_2 = 0 \\ -A_2/A_{ref}, & A_1 = 0 \end{cases}$$
$$W_{1\,max} = W_{ref}$$

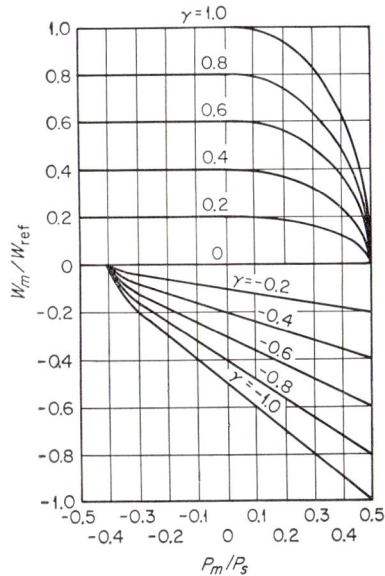

(b)

FIG. 21.30. Characteristics of three-way pneumatic valves with constant supply pressure. (a) Fixed upstream orifice, variable downstream orifice. (b) Variable upstream orifice, variable downstream orifice, closed center (neither underlap nor overlap).

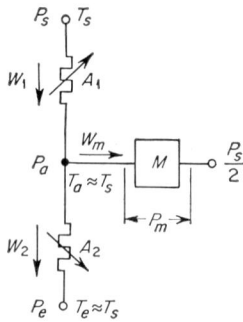

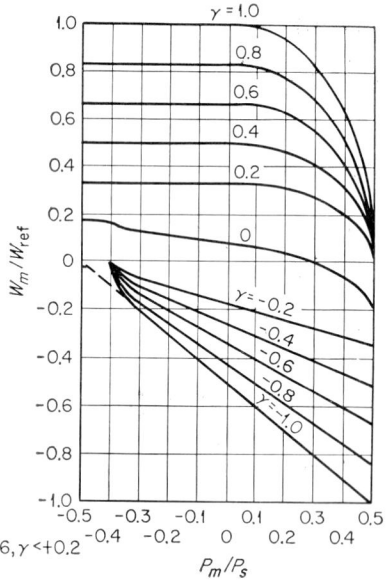

$P_e = 0.1 P_s$

$W_{ref} = C_d A_{ref} (0.532) P_s / \sqrt{T_s}$

$A_{ref} = A_{1\,max} = A_{2\,max}$

$$\gamma = \begin{cases} (6A_1 - A_{ref})/5A_{ref}, & A_1 > A_{ref}/6 \\ 0, & A_1 = A_2 = A_{ref}/6 \\ -(6A_2 - A_{ref})/5A_{ref}, & A_2 > A_{ref}/6 \end{cases}$$

or

$$A_1 = \begin{cases} (1+5\gamma)A_{ref}/6, & \gamma > -0.2 \\ 0, & \gamma < -0.2 \end{cases}, \text{ and } A_2 = \begin{cases} (1-5\gamma)A_{ref}/6, & \gamma < +0.2 \\ 0, & \gamma > +0.2 \end{cases}$$

(c)

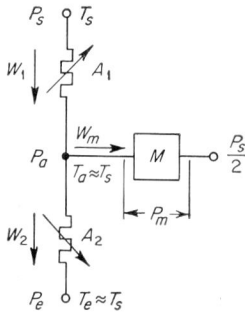

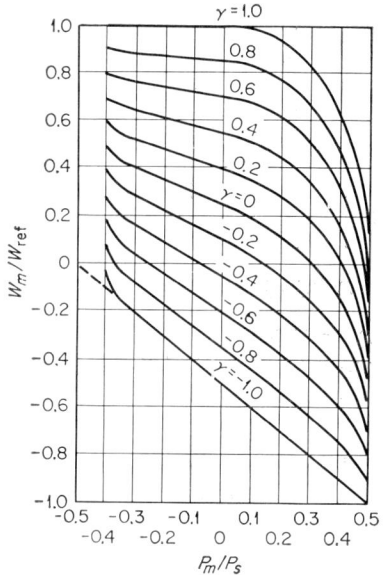

$P_e = 0.1 P_s$

$W_{ref} = C_d A_{ref} (0.532) P_s / \sqrt{T_s}$

$A_{ref} = A_{1\,max} = A_{2\,max}$

$A_1 = (\gamma + 1) A_{ref}/2$

$A_2 = (\gamma - 1) A_{ref}/2$

$W_{1\,max} = W_{ref}$

(d)

Fig. 21.30 (*Continued*). Characteristics of three-way pneumatic valves with constant supply pressure. (c) Variable upstream orifice, variable downstream orifice, partly open center. (d) Fixed upstream orifice, variable downstream orifice, fully open center.

Fig. 21.32. *These curves may not be used when the flows to and from the motor are not the same.*

The ideal characteristics of *four-way pneumatic control valves* depend considerably on the nature of the motor being driven. However, once the type of the motor is known, one may combine the characteristics of two three-way pneumatic valves into a single set of four-way-valve characteristics for the particular motor being employed.

21.13. Jet-pipe Valves

Although the concept of variable resistance to fluid flow and the combination of variable resistances into control-valve configurations are of paramount importance, another type of control valve, known as the jet-pipe valve, is finding increased use in fluid-power control systems. This device, shown in Fig. 21.34, is obviously a control valve, but it is difficult to delineate clearly one or more distinct variable-resistance elements in this valve. It might be more proper to classify it as

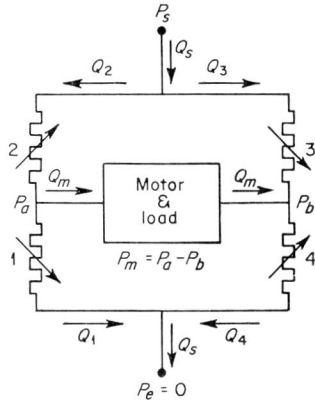

Fig. 21.31. Schematic arrangement of four orifices into a four-way valve to further facilitate bidirectional control.

an energy-conversion device employing a means of varying the way in which fluid power is delivered to a load. Fluid power is supplied at constant high pressure and low velocity, converted to a jet having low pressure and high velocity, directed in a controllable manner at one or more receiving holes connected to the load and reconverted to variable pressure and variable flow rate to the load. Power dissipation obviously occurs to an appreciable degree in the process of reconverting the constant power of the jet to modulated flow of power to the load. Yet it is not really correct to refer to this process as a variable-resistance process. For the purposes at hand, it seems sufficient to call it a dissipatory controlled conversion device.

Hydraulic-jet-pipe control valves have been used for many years in industrial control systems, notably by Askania.† The exact nature of the physical phenomena which occur in hydraulic jet pipes seems to be very complicated and seems to have eluded attempts to make either a precise analysis or to visualize a reasonably simple model of what occurs during the process of dissipatory controlled conversion of hydraulic power.

It has been found from experience that the best maximum power to the load condition is obtained with a jet pipe of the kind shown in Fig. 21.34 when the area of each of the receiving holes A_r is about twice the area of the jet stream A_j. The separation s between the jet pipe and the receiving block has little effect on the characteristics as long as it is between 1 and 20 jet diameters. In order to attain the best sensitivity, it is important to keep the receiving holes as close together as possible.

A typical set of pressure-flow-stroke characteristics for a hydraulic-jet-pipe valve is shown in Fig. 21.35. These characteristics are comparable in many respects with the first quadrant characteristics of a four-way-flapper-valve configuration shown in Fig. 21.32a. However, the jet pipe offers the advantage of better pressure recovery with zero-load flow and better flow recovery with zero-load pressure drop. It should be noted that flow recovery is here based on supply flow Q_s, which is twice the maximum no-load flow to the motor Q_{max} in the case of the flapper valve.

Pneumatic-jet-pipe valves have not been used as much as hydraulic-jet-pipe valves, and a reasonable theory describing their operation seems to be even more obscure. The situation in a pneumatic-jet-pipe valve is complicated by the very compressible nature of the flow, which results in sonic velocities and rapid expansion of the "jet stream" in the region between the jet pipe and the receiving block. Reid[8] has found that if the spacing s is kept small (less than one-fifth the diameter of the jet-pipe nozzle-

† Formerly Askania Regulator Company, Chicago, Ill., but now known as General Precision Instruments, division of General Precision, Inc., Chicago, Ill.

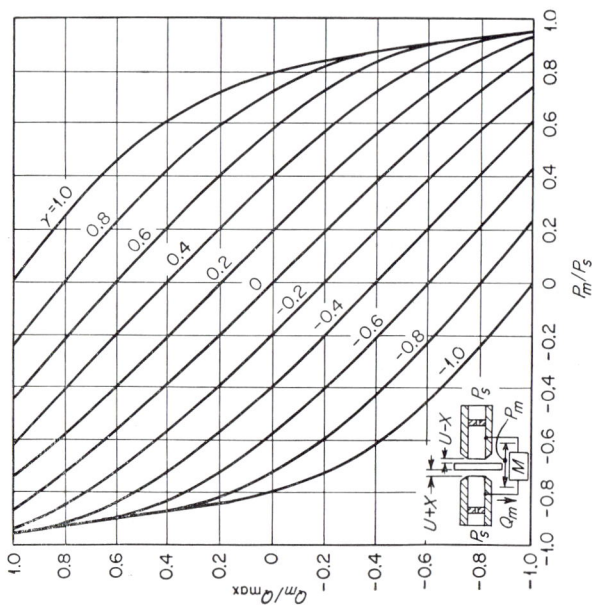

$\gamma = X/U$
X = valve displacement
U = valve underlap
$Q_{max} = 0.625 A_o \sqrt{P_s/\rho}$ = maximum no-load flow to motor
A_o = area of each orifice when valve is centered

Q_m = flow to motor
P_m = pressure drop across motor
P_s = supply pressure (constant)
ρ = fluid density

(a)

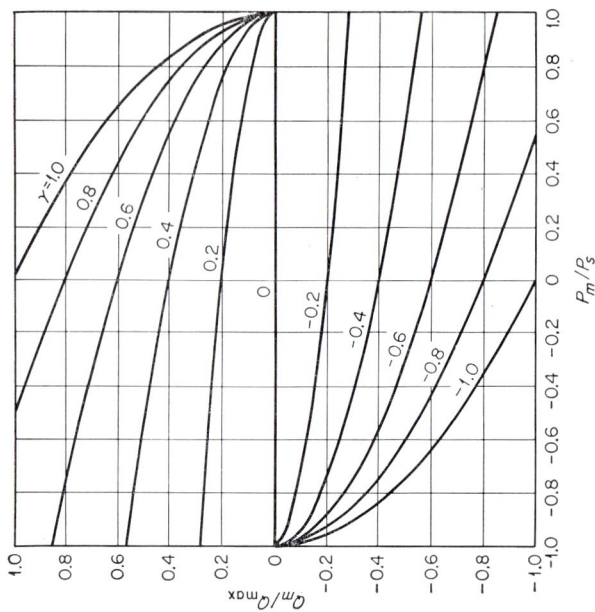

$\gamma = A_o/A_{o\,max} = X/X_{max}$
X = valve displacement
X_{max} = maximum valve displacement
$Q_{max} = 0.625 A_{o\,max} \sqrt{P_s/\rho}$ = maximum no-load flow to motor
$A_{o\,max}$ = maximum orifice area

Q_m = flow to motor
P_m = pressure drop across motor
P_s = supply pressure (constant)
ρ = fluid density

(b)

FIG. 21.32. Characteristics of four-way hydraulic valves with constant supply pressure. (a) Fixed upstream orifices, variable downstream orifices. (b) Variable upstream orifices, variable downstream orifices, closed center (neither overlap nor underlap).

21–38

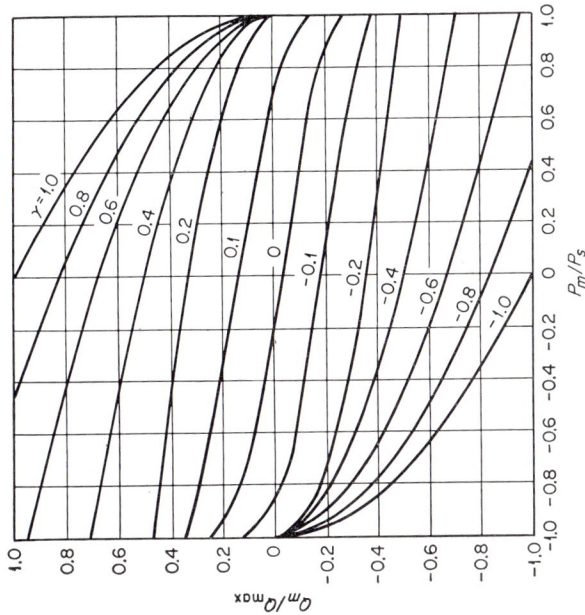

$\gamma = X/X_{max}$ Q_m = flow to motor
X = valve displacement P_m = pressure drop across motor
X_{max} = maximum valve displacement. P_s = supply pressure (constant)
$Q_{max} = 0.625 A_{o\,max} \sqrt{P_s/\rho}$ = maximum no-load flow to motor
$A_{o\,max}$ = maximum orifice area ρ = fluid density
U = valve underlap

(c)

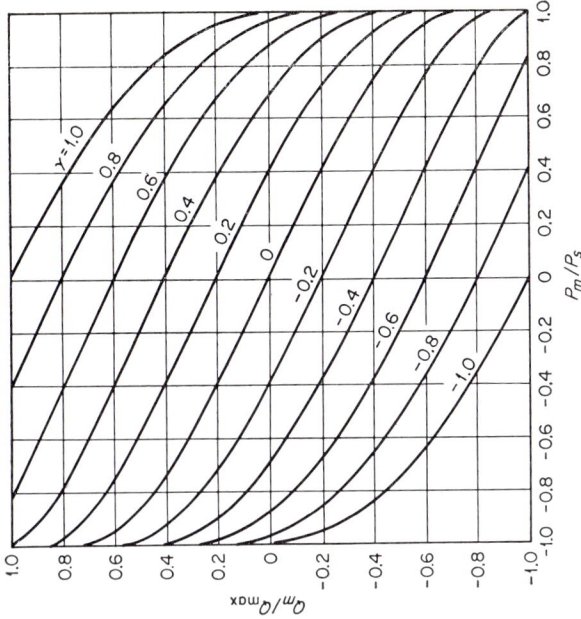

$\gamma = X/U$ Q_m = flow to motor
X = valve displacement P_m = pressure drop across motor
U = valve underlap P_s = supply pressure (constant)
$Q_{max} = 1.25 A_o \sqrt{P_s/\rho}$ = maximum no-load flow to motor = quiescent flow
A_o = area of each orifice ρ = fluid density
     when valve is centered

(d)

Fig. 21.32 (Continued). Characteristics of four-way hydraulic valves with constant supply pressure. (c) Variable upstream orifices, variable downstream orifices, partly open center, $U = 0.2X_{max}$. (d) Variable upstream orifices, variable downstream orifices, fully open center, $U = 1.0X_{max}$. (Note: See Fig. 21.33 schematic in connection with b to d.)

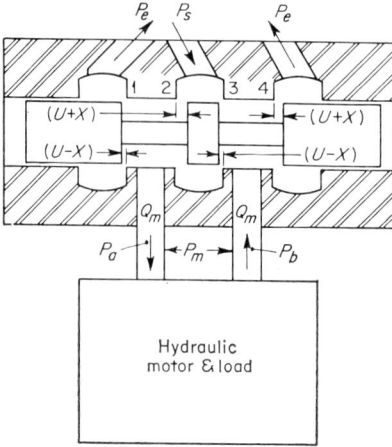

Fig. 21.33. Schematic cross section of spool-type four-way valve.

hole diameter), the best maximum power-recovery capability occurs when the area of each of the receiver holes is about twice the jet-pipe nozzle area, which is about the same area ratio as for a hydraulic-jet-pipe valve.

A typical set of pressure-flow-stroke characteristics is shown in Fig. 21.36. The important parameters of the valve are illustrated schematically in Fig. 21.37. It is important to note that the shapes of the normalized characteristics of a jet-pipe valve seem to be more strongly influenced by having different constant supply pressures than in the case of hydraulic-jet-pipe valves.

A continuing program of basic research work on jet-pipe valves is now active in the Dynamic Analysis and Control Laboratory at the Massachusetts Institute of Technology.

21.14. Actuating Forces of Valves

The forces which must be overcome in stroking valves are of three kinds: forces due to pressure and shear stresses of the fluid being controlled, forces due to friction effects between moving parts of the valve, and forces required to accelerate the mass of the moving parts of the valve.

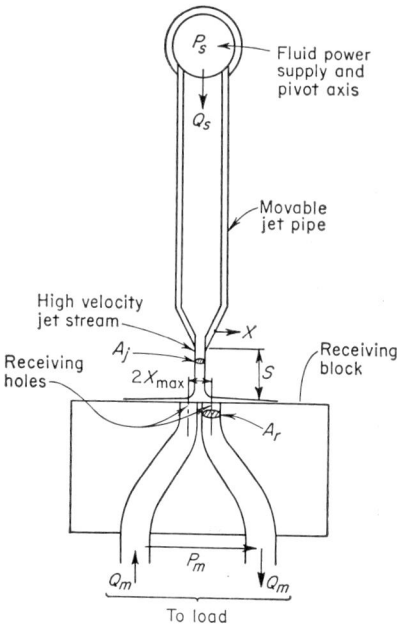

Fig. 21.34. Schematic diagram of jet-pipe valve.

Fluid-flow forces occur because of areas of the moving part or parts of a valve that are exposed to the pressure forces normal to the surfaces and shear forces tangential to the surfaces.

A *hydraulic slide valve* of the type shown in Fig. 21.38 exhibits a fluid-flow force tending to close it that is proportional to the product of the orifice area, the pressure drop across the orifice, and the cosine of the entrance or exit angle θ and which may be expressed as follows:

$$F_1 = 1.2A_o(P_u - P_d) \cos \theta \quad (21.78)$$

When the flow is unsteady, there is also an unsteady force due to the rate of change of flow in the flow length L. The sign of this force depends on the direction of the flow. When the pressure drop across the valve is steady, the unsteady flow force is given by

$$F_2 = \rho L \frac{dQ}{dt} \qquad (21.79)$$

and the force opposes the motion when the flow is in the same direction as the valve-piston motion. The force aids the motion when the flow is in the opposite direction to the valve-piston motion.

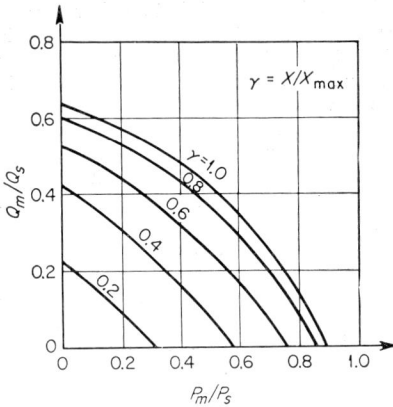

FIG. 21.35. Typical set of pressure-flow-stroke characteristics of a hydraulic jet-pipe valve. See Fig. 21.34.

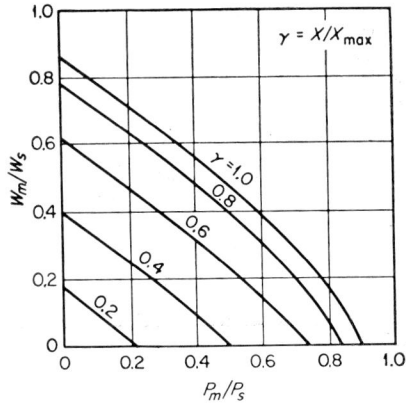

FIG. 21.36. Typical set of pressure-flow-stroke characteristics of a pneumatic jet-pipe valve. See Fig. 21.37.

Both of the forces discussed above can be reduced considerably by proper design of the valve. The reader is referred to the literature[2] for a detailed discussion of spool-valve design.

A *flapper-nozzle* valve exhibits a fluid-flow force that is proportional to the pressure drop across the valve. In the case of such a valve having a very sharp edge on the so-called nozzle, the force is given by

$$F_f = (P_u - P_d)A_n \qquad (21.80)$$

if A_n is the area of the nozzle passage, as long as the distance between the flapper and the nozzle is less than one-fifth the diameter of the nozzle and the flow leaving the valve follows the flapper. Norwood[9] has found that the exhaust flow sometimes leaves along the nozzle chamfer in pneumatic flapper valves, and when it does, the force F_f may be as much as 25 per cent greater than that found from Eq. (21.80). When the nozzle has a flat region at its end rather than a sharp edge, the force F_f is also greater than that found from Eq. (21.80) because of the effects of friction causing a pressure gradient along the flapper in the region where the nozzle flat is adjacent to it. In pneumatic flapper valves, it has been found that supersonic flow may exist in this region between the nozzle flat and the flapper.

A *poppet valve* exhibits a fluid-flow force that is proportional to the pressure drop across the valve. In the case of such a valve having a very sharp edge on the seat, the force is approximated by

$$F_p = (P_u - P_d)A_s \qquad (21.81)$$

if A_s is the area of the passage leading to the poppet seat.

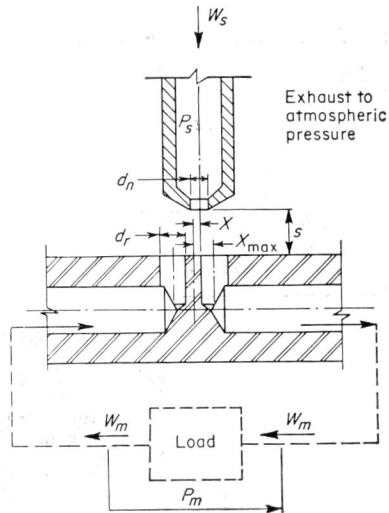

Data:

$P_s \approx 500$ psia
$d_r/d_n = 1.4$
$S/d_n \approx 0.2$
$d_n \approx 0.030$ in.
$W_s =$ supply weight rate of flow, approx 0.02 lb/min
$W_m =$ weight rate of flow through load
$P_m =$ pressure across load

FIG. 21.37. Schematic diagram of pneumatic jet-pipe valve for use in connection with Fig. 21.36.

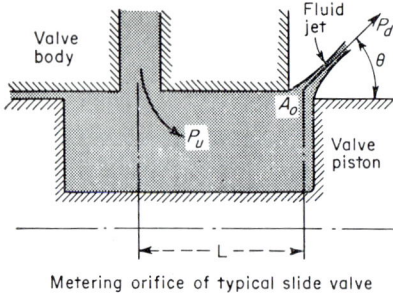

Metering orifice of typical slide valve

FIG. 21.38. Sectional schematic of slide-valve orifice.

It should be noted that the downstream pressure P_d acting on the poppet is strongly affected by the nature of the flow leaving the orifice and swirling around in the downstream chamber.[10] Stone[10] also found that important shear forces exist on the conical surface of the poppet because of the high-velocity flow past it and that these forces also tend to open the valve. On the other hand, the falling pressure in the region of the orifice results in a reduction of the opening force given in Eq. (21.81). This reduction in the opening force, sometimes referred to as a *closing force*, is similar in nature to the flow force F_1 in a slide valve.

DYNAMIC INTERACTIONS IN CONTROL SYSTEMS

The earlier parts of this section have dealt primarily with the dynamic characteristics of fluid-power control-system components. In order to illustrate some of the more important aspects of the dynamic interactions between components in complete systems, this part deals with some complete systems of general interest and importance in the field of fluid-power control.

21.15. Constant-pressure Control with a Variable-displacement-pump Power Supply

Many hydraulic control systems require a source of fluid power capable of delivering the required flow rates at a nearly constant supply pressure. Because positive-displacement pumps are normally required to supply the high pressures needed in hydraulic control systems, and because a positive-displacement pump running at constant speed is more nearly a constant-flow source than it is a constant-pressure source, it is customary either to bypass (and waste) part of the pump flow or to employ a variable-displacement pump to establish control over the pressure as the load-flow-rate requirement changes. A conventional air-charged hydraulic accumulator is usually employed to facilitate the control of supply pressure and to make it possible to supply short-term peak-load requirements that may exceed the maximum delivery of the pump.

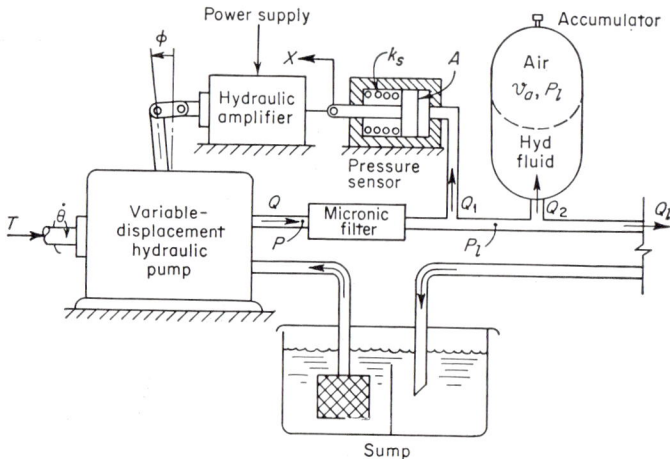

FIG. 21.39. Pressure-controlled hydraulic power supply.

The system shown schematically in Fig. 21.39 is typical of the systems which employ *pressure-compensated* hydraulic pumps. The pump shaft is driven at very nearly constant speed by an a-c motor or similar prime source of power. In order to attain the best possible pressure regulation, the pressure sensor is connected downstream of the micronic filter. The output motion X of the pressure-sensor piston is applied to a hydraulic amplifier which adjusts the pump stroke to maintain the desired pressure established by the setting of the pressure-sensor spring k_s. The inlet strainer is of coarse mesh and exhibits negligible pressure drop. The accumulator is precharged with enough air so that it is about half filled with oil when the line pressure P_l is at its desired value. The load flow rate Q_l is an input to this system because it is to be considered as completely determined by events occurring external to this system.

Basic Equations of System Components. The basic equations of the components of this system are derivable from first principles or attainable from measured characteristics.

The *pump flow rate* is given by

$$Q = D_r \dot{\theta} - \frac{C_s D_r P}{\mu}$$

but since the displacement D_r of the pump is directly related to stroke angle ϕ, $D_r = k_p \phi$, and one may write

$$Q = k_p \dot{\theta} \phi - \frac{C_s D_r}{\mu} P \qquad (21.82)$$

The *micronic filter* offers very nearly linear resistance to flow through it.

$$P - P_l = R_f Q \qquad (21.83)$$

In describing the *pressure sensor*, it will be assumed as a first approximation that negligible force is required at the input to the hydraulic amplifier and that the mass of the pressure-sensor piston is small enough to be neglected. The mass and compliance of the hydraulic fluid in the line to the sensor are also negligible because the line is short. The pressure sensor may then be described by the following two equations:

$$A P_l = F_i + k_s X \qquad (21.84)$$

if F_i is the initial spring-compression force when $X = 0$ and

$$Q_1 = A \frac{dX}{dt} \qquad (21.85)$$

The *hydraulic amplifier* may be considered to a first-order approximation as a first-order lag, and since the maximum pump-stroke angle is less than $10°$, one may write

$$\tau \frac{d\phi}{dt} + \phi = -k_a X \qquad (21.86)$$

The *accumulator* stores energy by virtue of its pneumatic spring (hydraulic fluid compressibility is negligible in comparison with air in this case), and it is described by

$$Q_2 = \frac{\mathcal{V}_a}{k P_l} \frac{dP_l}{dt} \qquad (21.87)$$

[see Eq. (21.46) also].

The *continuity equation* applied to the line between the micronic filter and the load-flow terminus yields (with pipe walls having negligible compliance)

$$Q_2 = Q - Q_1 - Q_l \qquad (21.88)$$

The system is completely described dynamically by the set of Eqs. (21.82) to (21.88). Of these equations, only Eq. (21.87) is nonlinear. However, since the pressure P_l is to be controlled to a very nearly constant value $P^*_l = F_i/A$, and since one is primarily

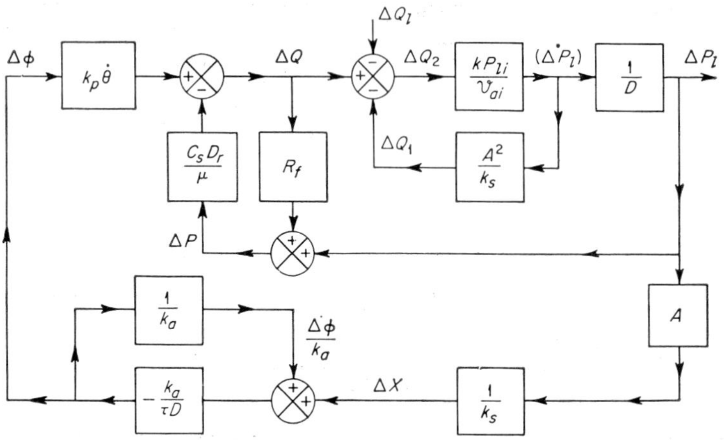

Fig. 21.40. Operational block diagram of pressure-controlled hydraulic power supply.

concerned with dynamic changes which occur when the accumulator is approximately half full of hydraulic fluid, Eq. (21.87) will be linearized to give

$$Q_2 = \mathcal{V}_{ai} \frac{A}{k} F_i \frac{dP_l}{dt} \tag{21.89}$$

for small changes of $\mathcal{V}_a$ and P_l from their normal operating values.

An excellent over-all view of the important dynamic interactions which may occur in this system is provided by the operational block diagram shown in Fig. 21.40. This block diagram may be thought of as a sort of pictorial representation of all the basic differential equations of the system, and it may be directly employed in carrying out an electronic-analogue simulation of the system.

The equations of this system may also be combined mathematically to give a single over-all differential equation relating the pressure P_l to the load flow Q_l:

$$\left[\left(\frac{\mathcal{V}_{ai}}{kP_{li}} + \frac{A^2}{k_s} \right) \tau D^2 + \left(\frac{\mathcal{V}_{ai}}{kP_{li}} + \frac{A^2}{k_s} + \frac{C_s D_r \tau}{\mu + C_s D_r R_f} \right) D \right.$$
$$\left. + \frac{k_p \dot\theta k_a A \mu + k_s C_s D_r}{k_s(\mu + C_s D_r R_f)} \right] (\Delta P_l) = -(\tau D + 1)(\Delta Q_l) \tag{21.90}$$

Mathematical solution of Eq. (21.90) reveals how the pressure P responds to changes in the flow Q under unsteady conditions as well as under steady conditions of operation. Of prime importance during unsteady operation are characteristic response times (time constants and/or natural frequency) and degree of stability (tendency to oscillate or go out of control) of the system. Steady-state errors in system pressure P_l due to steady-load-flow changes are also of great concern in the final choice of system parameters. The actual solution of Eq. (21.90) and determination of response times and degree of stability are beyond the scope of this section. The reader interested in this aspect of the problem is referred to the literature.[2]

The steady-state load sensitivity is readily found by setting all derivatives in Eq. (21.90) equal to zero and by solving for $(\Delta P_l/\Delta Q_l)_{ss}$:

$$\left(\frac{\Delta P_l}{\Delta Q_l} \right)_{ss} = \frac{k_s(\mu + C_s D_r R_f)}{k_p \dot\theta k_a A \mu + k_s C_s D_r} \tag{21.91}$$

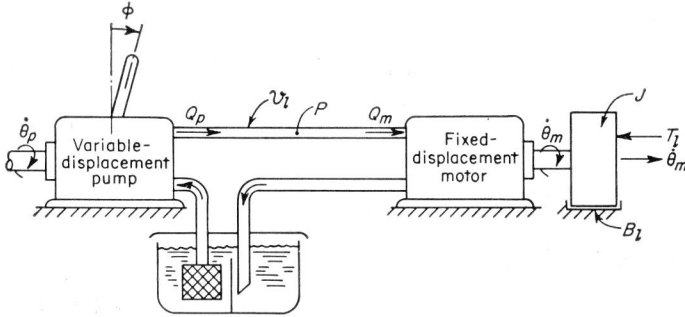

Fig. 21.41. Pump-stroke-controlled variable-speed drive (unidirectional).

21.16. Unidirectional Hydraulic Variable-speed Drive

When a variable-displacement unit is connected to a fixed-displacement unit, a variable-speed transmission results. The variable-displacement unit is most frequently the pump which is often driven at constant speed by a prime source of power. Such an arrangement is shown in Fig. 21.41. This system, in the form shown, is suitable for driving the load in only one direction. The line between the outlet of the pump and the inlet of the motor transmits fluid under pressure from the pump to the motor. The return line from the motor is at atmospheric or sump pressure. The motor speed tends to be proportional to the stroke angle ϕ of the pump. However, elastic-energy storage in the fluid in the pressurized line, leakage in the pump and motor, inertia in the load, and external load torques, all cause departures from a true proportionality between output speed and pump stroke.

This variable-speed drive is ineffective whenever the load torque is reversed, so that the load tends to drive the motor, because the return line from the motor cannot be pressurized and the line from the pump outlet to the motor inlet cannot sustain a negative pressure (because of cavitation).

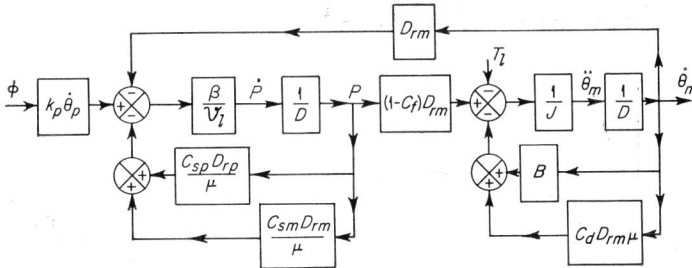

k_p = pump-displacement coefficient, in.^{3}/radian^2
C_{sp} = slip (leakage) coefficient of pump
C_{sm} = slip (leakage) coefficient of motor
D_{rm} = displacement of motor, in.^{3}/radian
C_f = static friction coefficient of motor (pressure dependent)
C_d = dynamic friction coefficient of motor (speed dependent)
μ = viscosity of hydraulic fluid, (lb)(sec)/in.^{2}

In analysis let $k_1 = k_p\,\dot\theta_p$; $k_2 = (C_{sp}D_{rp} + C_{sm}D_{rm})/\mu$; $k_3 = \mathcal{V}_l/\beta$

$$B_{tot} = B + C_d D_{rm}\mu$$

Fig. 21.42. Operational block diagram of unidirectional hydraulic variable-speed drive.

Assuming that the motor shaft always rotates in the same direction and that power is always being delivered by the motor to the load, this system may be readily analyzed for its steady-state and dynamic characteristics. The operational block diagram shown in Fig. 21.42 describes all the basic physical phenomena occurring in this system in a manner similar to that employed in the preceding discussion of a pressure-controlled hydraulic power supply. The individual basic equations will not be written here because of space limitations.

When all the basic equations are properly combined, one may derive a single differential equation relating output speed $\dot{\theta}_m$ to pump stroke ϕ and external load torque T_l as follows:

$$[k_3 J D^2 + (k_2 J + k_3 B_{\text{tot}})D + k_2 B_{\text{tot}} + (1 - C_f)D_{rm}^2]\dot{\theta}_m$$
$$= k_1(1 - C_f)D_{rm}\phi - k_2\left(\frac{k_3}{k_2}D + 1\right)T_l \quad (21.92)$$

This equation may also be written in the following form:

$$\left(\frac{D^2}{\omega_n^2} + \frac{2\zeta D}{\omega_n} + 1\right)\dot{\theta}_m = k_a\phi - k_b\left(\frac{k_3}{k_2}D + 1\right)T_l \quad (21.93)$$

in which

$$\omega_n = \sqrt{\frac{k_2 B_{\text{tot}} + (1 - C_f)D_{rm}^2}{k_3 J}} \quad \text{natural frequency of system, radians/sec}$$

$$\zeta = \frac{k_2 J + k_3 B_{\text{tot}}}{2\sqrt{k_3 J[k_2 B_{\text{tot}} + (1 - C_f)D_{rm}^2]}} \quad \text{damping ratio of system}$$

$$k_a = \frac{k_1(1 - C_f)D_{rm}}{k_2 B_{\text{tot}} + (1 - C_f)D_{rm}^2} \quad \text{steady-state gain of system, radians/(sec/radian)}$$

$$k_b = \frac{k_2}{k_2 B_{\text{tot}} + (1 - C_f)D_{rm}^2} \quad \text{steady-state load sensitivity of system,}$$
$$\text{radians/(sec/in.-lb)}$$

$$D = \frac{d}{dt} \text{ derivative with respect to time, sec}^{-1}$$

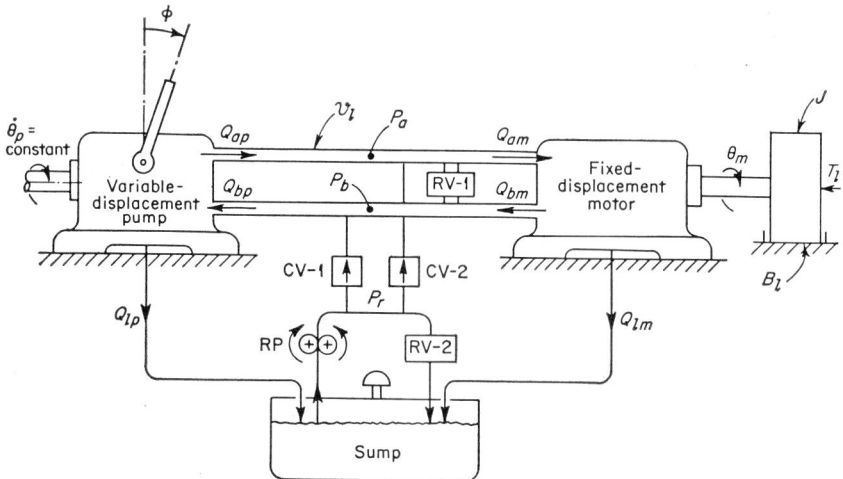

FIG. 21.43. Pump-stroke-controlled variable-speed drive (reversible).

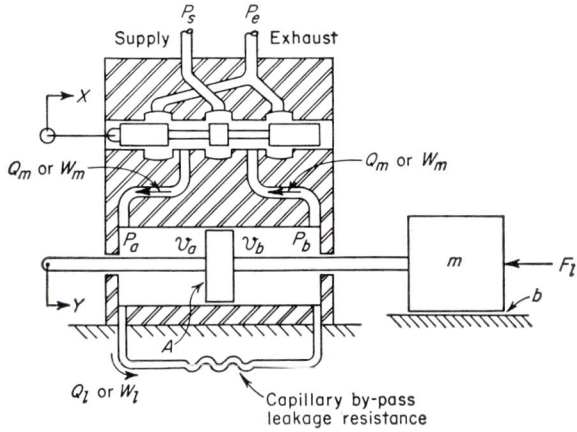

FIG. 21.44. Schematic diagram of valve-controlled ram.

Capillary by-pass leakage resistance

21.17. Reversible Variable-speed Hydraulic Drive

When it is necessary to drive the load in either direction or to be able to allow power to flow either to or from the load, the system shown in Fig. 21.41 must be modified as shown in Fig. 21.43 in order to make it possible to have pressure at either port of the motor and pump. The replenishing system consisting of pump, low-pressure relief valve, and check valves serves to maintain a minimum pressure in either line, thereby keeping the lines always filled with hydraulic fluid and ready to act to transmit fluid power in either direction. As long as one line is at constant pressure and the motor is rotating in one direction, the previous analysis of a unidirectional drive may be used to describe the performance of this system. However, when the pressure in both lines changes and when the direction of motor rotation changes, the analysis becomes much more complicated.[2]

21.18. Hydraulic and Pneumatic Valve-controlled Drives

A valve-controlled hydraulic drive requires less stroke and lower force at the input than a variable-displacement pump drive of comparable power output; for example, to deliver 10 hp to the load, the latter needs about plus or minus 0.5-in. stroke at a maximum force of about plus or minus 200 lb, while a valve needs only a plus or minus 0.030-in. stroke at a maximum force of plus or minus 50 lb.

Valve-controlled pneumatic drives for high-power levels have been developed for pressure levels up to 2000 psi and temperatures (short time operation) up to 2400°F.

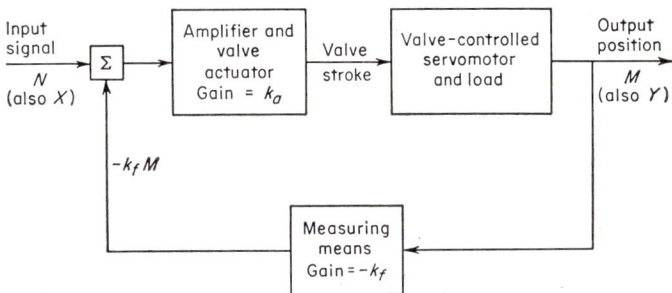

FIG. 21.45. Ram-positioning servo system.

Table 21.3. Hydraulics vs. Pneumatics for Valve-controlled Drive

(System shown schematically in Fig. 21.44)

Factor	Hydraulic fluid	Compressed gas
Over-all system complexity..........	Pump, pressure control, sump, filter, and heat exchanger	Multistage compressor with interstage cooling, pressure control, filter, dryer (no return line)
Working fluid.........	High-quality mineral-base oils with additives, water-base solutions, synthetic liquids (all expensive—some flammable)	Air, nitrogen, products of combustion
Efficiency.............	Seldom over 60 per cent	Seldom over 30 per cent
Over-all size..........	Approximately the same for a given supply pressure	Approximately the same for a given supply pressure
Ease of energy storage..	Air- or spring-loaded accumulator	Simple tank
Lubrication of moving parts........	Usually good—sticking valves usually due to poor design or dirty fluid	Small amounts of grease help seals to last; air has negligible lubricating qualities
Susceptibility to moisture............	Will not attack corrosion-resistant materials—small amounts of water will eventually dissolve traces of acids or salts in mineral-base oils and attack corrosive materials. Regular change of working fluid generally recommended at fixed intervals of time	Corrosion-resistant materials recommended throughout pneumatic systems because of combination of small amounts of moisture and other contaminants in atmosphere. Small amounts of water can freeze valves and render them inoperable below 32°F
Susceptibility to contamination (various kinds of dirt)	Closely fitted valves (0.0002 in. clearance) stick very easily except when best dirt filters are used. Oil has "washing" action that dislodges particles that would adhere to walls	Less trouble than with oil. Foreign particles seem to drop out of air before it gets to valve. Little "washing" action apparent with air. Dirty combustion products are troublesome
Ease of manufacture....	Valves usually require great care. Precision machining usually required throughout	Same as hydraulic, but valves need more care and tight seals are difficult to attain
Safety of operation.....	Leakage of flammable fluids a fire hazard. High-velocity jet can pierce skin and cause blood poisoning. Fluid can cause serious eye inflammations. Not explosive	Flying debris from a rupture can be very dangerous. Explosions possible when small amounts of volatile fuel such as oil are present in air—not with pure nitrogen
Temperature sensitivity	Most hydraulic fluid viscosities change greatly with temperature changes. Unequal expansion of dissimilar materials can give serious trouble. (Some "orifices" behave as orifices only when fluid viscosity is low.) If temperature is too high, fluid vaporizes; if too low, it solidifies	Since viscosity of most gases is much less than that of hydraulic fluids, relatively little trouble can be expected from viscosity changes. Same trouble as with hydraulic systems when dissimilar materials work together. Neither liquefaction nor freezing is common
Valve-stroking forces...	Both steady and dynamic flow forces are often significant. Sticking due to dirt or lateral forces (pressure unbalanced) is common in control valves	Neither steady nor dynamic flow forces are often significant because of low fluid density. Steady flow force can cause high velocity (1000 fps) at throat of control valve. Lateral forces very troublesome because of lack of lubrication. Sticking due to dirt seems less troublesome
Pressure range........	50–5000 psig	5–3000 psig
Relative speed of response.........	Usually better than any other means of control at same output power level	Not as good as same system with hydraulic fluid; better than electric drive at same power
Dry friction acting on output shaft......	Can cause excessive steady errors in a position servomechanism, especially when an open-center valve is used	Steady errors in position servomechanism more serious than in some hydraulic drives. Can also cause large low-frequency phase shift
Quiescent-power drain..	Usually less than 10 per cent of maximum output power with a closed-center valve. Up to 100 per cent with open-center valve	Up to 20 per cent of maximum output power with closed-center valve. Up to 100 per cent of maximum output power with open-center valve
Rotary motors for continuous control...	Many types commercially available. Some work at pressures up to 5000 psig	Few available—none at pressures above about 100 psig

Though the dynamic performance of such drives is good, their static performance and low-frequency performance are sometimes hampered by coulomb friction in the valve or in the motor and its load.

Hydraulic vs. Pneumatic Operation.   The relative merits of operating a valve-controlled ram with hydraulic (liquid) and pneumatic (gaseous) fluids are given in Table 21.3.

In order to demonstrate and compare various factors involved in the design of valve-controlled ram (servomotor) systems, consider that the system shown in Fig. 21.44 is to be used to position a 500-lb mass within a maximum stroke of plus or minus 3 in. in a system like that in Fig. 21.45.   Assume that the measuring means and the amplifier and valve actuator have negligible lags (possible with simple linkages, but generally not with electric transducers).

System specifications: a maximum load acceleration of 500 in./sec² at zero velocity with a 500-lb external opposing load; a maximum steady velocity of 3 in./sec with a steady 500-lb external opposing load; a fluid supply pressure of 800 psi; a stand-by power loss (load motionless, external load zero) not to exceed 0.5 hp.   The mass-loaded servomotor should have a damping ratio of at least 0.5 to make possible the best closed-loop performance.[2]

Ram-area Calculation.   If the valve is displaced far enough from its neutral position, the full supply pressure is available to move the ram when its velocity is low.   Based on acceleration and external-load specifications, summing forces (Newton's second law) gives

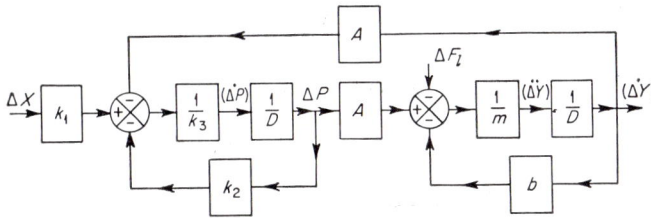

Nomenclature | Description

A ——— Ram area, in.²
b ——— Viscous friction on output shaft, $15.9 + 1.5 = 17.4$ (lb)(sec)/in.
D ——— Symbol denoting derivative with respect to time, sec⁻¹
F_l ——— External load force, lb
g ——— Acceleration due to gravity, 386 in./sec²
k ——— Ratio of specific heats, C_p/C_v
m ——— Load mass, $500/386 = 1.36$ (lb)(sec)²/in.
P_i ——— Initial pressure in ram chambers (when $F_l = 0$), lb/in.²
P_m ——— Pressure difference across motor, lb/in.²
P_s ——— Supply pressure, lb/in.²
Q_m ——— Volume flow rate to motor, in.³/sec
R ——— Gas constant (for air: 2.47×10^5) in.²/(sec)²(°F)
T_s ——— Gas-supply temperature, °F abs
$\mathcal{V}_i$ ——— Initial volume of each ram chamber, in.³
W_m ——— Weight rate of flow to motor, lb/sec
X ——— Valve position, in.
Δ ——— Prefix symbol denoting small change
ρ ——— Fluid density, (lb)(sec)²/in.⁴

k_1
k_2 Hydraulic: $\begin{bmatrix} [\partial Q_m/\partial X] \\ [\partial Q_m/\partial P_m + \partial Q_l/\partial P_m] \\ [\mathcal{V}_i/2\beta] \end{bmatrix}$ Pneumatic: $\begin{bmatrix} (RT_s/gP_i)[\partial W_m/\partial X] \\ (RT_s/gP_i)[\partial (W_m + W_l)/\partial X] \\ [\mathcal{V}_i/2kP_i] \end{bmatrix}$
k_3

Fig. 21.46. Detailed operational block diagram of valve-controlled ram system.   (Schematic in Fig. 21.44.)

$$P_s A = m \frac{d^2Y}{dt^2} + b \frac{dY}{dt} + F_l$$

or, at zero velocity,

$$A = \frac{(1.3)(500) + 0 + 500}{800} = 1.44 \text{ in.}^2$$

A commercially available equal-area double-acting cylinder with a net working area of 1.50 in.² and a total stroke of 6.5 in. has a measured viscous-damping coefficient of 1.5 lb-sec/in. Load damping measures 15.9 lb-sec/in. Thus the pressure across the ram, P_m, that is needed for 3 in./sec maximum steady velocity with 500-lb external opposing load is

$$P_m A = b \left(\frac{dY}{dt} \right)_{\text{max}} + F_{l\,\text{max}}$$

or

$$P_m = \frac{(17.4)(3) + 500}{1.50} = 368 \text{ psi}$$

Dynamic Analysis. A linearized dynamic analysis, based on small changes of all variables from initial steady operating conditions with the ram centered, yields a basic set of equations which are described by the operational block diagram of Fig. 21.46. The complete set of equations may be combined mathematically to give the following relationship between ram output motion Y and the two inputs X and F_l:

$$\left(\frac{k_3 m}{k_2 b + A^2} D^2 + \frac{k_2 m + k_3 b}{k_2 b + A^2} D + 1 \right) \Delta \dot{Y} = \frac{k_1 A \, \Delta X - (k_3 D + k_2) \, \Delta F_l}{k_2 b + A^2} \quad (21.94)$$

This equation may also be written in the same form as Eq. (21.93):

$$\left(\frac{D^2}{\omega_{ns}^2} + \frac{2 \zeta_s D}{\omega_{ns}} + 1 \right) \Delta \dot{Y} = k_s \, \Delta X - k_b \left(1 + \frac{k_3 D}{k_2} \right) \Delta F_l \quad (21.95)$$

in which $\omega_{ns} = \sqrt{\dfrac{k_2 b + A^2}{k_3 m}}$　　servomotor natural frequency, radians/sec

$$\zeta_s = \frac{k_2 m + k_3 b}{2 \sqrt{k_3 m (k_2 b + A^2)}} = \frac{\pi_a + \pi_b}{2 \sqrt{\pi_a \pi_b + 1}}$$　　servomotor damping ratio (Fig. 21.47)

$$k_s = \frac{k_1 A}{k_2 b + A^2}$$　　servomotor steady-state gain, in./(sec/in.)

$$k_b = \frac{k_2}{k_2 b + A^2}$$　　servomotor steady-state load sensitivity, in./(sec/lb)

The closed-loop differential equation relating output position change ΔM to input signal change ΔN and external-load-force change ΔF_l (Fig. 21.45) is

$$\left(\frac{D^3}{\omega_{ns}^2} + \frac{2 \zeta_s D^2}{\omega_{ns}} + D + k_a k_s k_f \right) \Delta M = k_s k_a \, \Delta N - k_b \left(1 + \frac{k_3 D}{k_2} \right) \Delta F_l \quad (21.96)$$

and under steady-state conditions,

$$(\Delta M)_{ss} = \frac{1}{k_f} (\Delta N)_{ss} - \frac{k_b}{k_a k_s k_f} (\Delta F_l)_{ss}$$

or

$$(\Delta M)_{ss} = \frac{1}{k_f} (\Delta N)_{ss} - \frac{k_2}{k_1 A k_a k_f} (\Delta F_l)_{ss} \quad (21.97)$$

Although k_f can usually be readily chosen to meet most requirements, the product $k_1 k_a k_f$ must be chosen carefully. Large values of $k_1 k_a k_f$ reduce the steady-state load

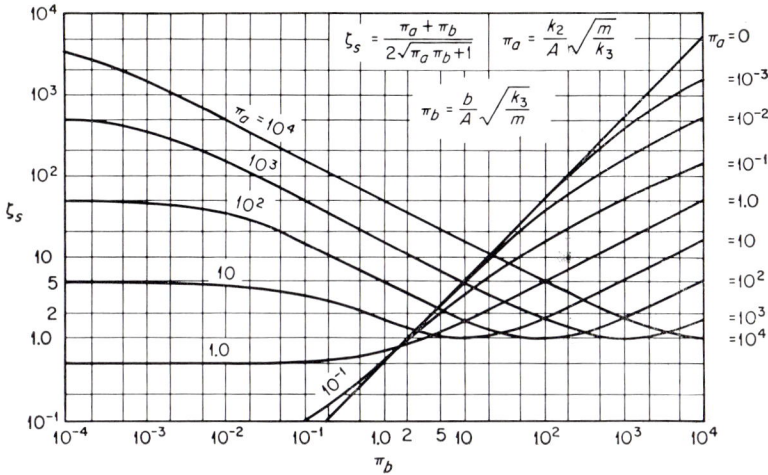

FIG. 21.47. Graph giving servomotor damping ratio ζ_s as a function of dimensionless parameters π_a and π_b.

sensitivity of the closed-loop system but also frequently lead to system instability.[2] The system will usually be stable if

$$K_l = k_a k_s k_f = \frac{k_1 k_a k_f A}{k_2 b + A^2} \tag{21.98}$$

does not exceed $0.45\omega_{ns}$.

In Table 21.4 a comparative analysis of hydraulic and pneumatic systems is made.

Table 21.4. Comparative Analyses—Hydraulic and Pneumatic

Hydraulic

For hydraulic oil, the fluid compliance is

$$k_3 = \frac{\mathcal{U}_i}{2\beta}$$

if β is the bulk modulus of pure hydraulic fluid (no entrained air) which has a value of about 2.5×10^5 psi. One may then calculate a value for π_b:

$$\pi_b = \frac{b}{A}\sqrt{\frac{k_3}{m}} = \frac{17.4}{1.5}\sqrt{\frac{4.87}{2(2.5 \times 10^5)(1.36)}}$$

$$= 3.18 \times 10^{-2}$$

From the graph of Fig. 21.47, for a servomotor damping ratio $\zeta_s = 0.5$,

$$\pi_a = 1.0 = \frac{k_2}{A}\sqrt{\frac{m}{k_3}}$$

from which one may determine k_2.

$$k_2 = \pi_a A \sqrt{\frac{k_3}{m}} = (1.50)(2.5 \times 10^{-3})$$

$$= 3.75 \times 10^{-3}\,\text{in.}^5/\text{lb-sec}$$

As defined in Fig. 21.46,

$$k_2 = \frac{\partial Q_m}{\partial P_m} + \frac{\partial Q_l}{\partial P_m}$$

Pneumatic

For air, the fluid compliance is

$$k_3 = \frac{\mathcal{U}_i}{2kP_i}$$

In contrast to a hydraulic four-way valve which has initial balanced ram pressure $P_i = 0.5P_s$, an open-center pneumatic valve has a $P_i \approx 0.8P_s$, as may be readily seen from Fig. 21.30d. Thus

$$P_i = (0.8)(800) = 640 \text{ psia}$$

(Note that absolute pressures must be used in working with pneumatic valves.)

By solving for π_b,

$$\pi_b = \frac{b}{A}\sqrt{\frac{k_3}{m}} = \frac{17.4}{1.5}\sqrt{\frac{4.87}{(2)(1.4)(640)(1.36)}}$$

$$= 0.518$$

From Fig. 21.47, for $\zeta_s = 0.5$, $\pi_a \approx 0.5$, from which k_2 may be determined.

$$k_2 = \pi_a A \sqrt{\frac{k_3}{m}} = (0.5)(1.5)(4.47 \times 10^{-2})$$

$$= 3.35 \times 10^{-2}\,\text{in.}^5/\text{lb-sec}$$

As defined in Fig. 21.46,

$$k_2 = \frac{RT_s}{gP_i}\left(\frac{\partial W_m}{\partial P_m} + \frac{\partial W_l}{\partial P_m}\right)$$

Table 21.4. Comparative Analyses—Hydraulic and Pneumatic (*Continued*)

Hydraulic

If the leakage past the ram is zero,

$$\frac{\partial Q_l}{\partial P_m} = 0 \quad \text{and} \quad k_2 = \frac{\partial Q_m}{\partial P_m}$$

From Fig. 21.32d, it is seen that

$$\frac{\partial (Q_m/Q_{max})}{\partial (P_m/P_s)} = \frac{1}{2}$$

for operation around the normal quiescent condition (the origin of this figure). Thus

$$\frac{\partial Q_m}{\partial P_m} = \frac{Q_{max}}{2P_s}$$

and

$$k_2 = \frac{\partial Q_m}{\partial P_m} = \frac{(0.625)A_o}{\sqrt{P_s\rho}}$$

The density ρ of hydraulic oil is approximately 8×10^{-5} lb-sec^2/in.^{4} Using the given supply pressure of 800 psi, the area A_o of each of the control-valve orifices when it is centered is

$$A_o = \frac{k_2\sqrt{P_s\rho}}{0.625}$$

$$= \frac{(3.75 \times 10^{-3})\sqrt{64 \times 10^{-3}}}{0.625}$$

$$= 1.52 \times 10^{-3} \text{ in.}^2$$

The quiescent supply flow to the valve is

$$Q_q = 2(0.625)A_o\sqrt{\frac{P_s}{\rho}}$$

$$= 2(0.625)(1.52 \times 10^{-3})\sqrt{10^7}$$

$$= 6.02 \text{ in.}^3/\text{sec}$$

The quiescent power loss is given by

$$\text{HP} = \frac{P_sQ_q}{6600} = \frac{6.02}{8.25}$$

$$= 0.73 \text{ hp}$$

which exceeds the specified 0.5 hp. Hence A_o must be reduced by about one-third to 1.0×10^{-3} in.^{2} A bypass capillary can be designed to give $\partial Q_l/\partial P_m = 1.25 \times 10^{-3}$ in.^{5}/lb-sec and to provide the required value of $k_2 = 3.75 \times 10^{-3}$ in.^{5}/lb-sec.

The maximum hydraulic power which must be supplied to the valve is

$$\text{HP}_{max} = \frac{P_sQ_{m\,max}}{6600}$$

$$= \frac{P_sC_dA_{o\,max}}{6600}\sqrt{\frac{P_s}{\rho}}$$

in which

$$A_{o\,max} = \frac{A(dY/dt)_{max} + (\partial Q_l/\partial P_m)P_{m\,max}\sqrt{\rho}}{C_d\sqrt{P_s - P_{m\,max}}}$$

The maximum power thus computed is about 0.75 hp. However, it is well to provide at least 100 per cent extra maximum flow capacity ($A_{o\,max}$) in the valve to provide for transient peak demands. An accumulator is frequently employed in order to meet infrequent peak flows without using a large pump.

Pneumatic

If the leakage past the ram is zero, the term $\partial W_l/\partial P_m = 0$, and

$$k_2 = \frac{RT_s}{gP_i}\frac{\partial W_m}{\partial P_m}$$

Because this is a four-way valve (two three-way valves operating push-pull), the value for $\partial W_m/\partial P_m$ will be just half that found from Fig. 21.30d for operation about its null position.

$$\left(\frac{\partial W_m}{\partial P_m}\right)_{4\text{-way}} = \frac{1}{2}\frac{W_{ref}}{P_s}\left(\frac{\partial(W_m/W_{ref})}{\partial(P_m/P_s)}\right)_{3\text{-way}}$$

Thus

$$\frac{\partial W_m}{\partial P_m} = \frac{(0.67)C_dA_{ref}(0.532)}{2\sqrt{T_s}}$$

and since

$$k_2 = \frac{RT_s}{gP_i}\frac{\partial W_m}{\partial P_m} = 3.35 \times 10^{-2}$$

the value of A_{ref} may be determined.

$$A_{ref} = \frac{2\sqrt{T_s}\,gP_ik_2}{(0.67)C_d(0.532)RT_s}$$

By using $C_d \approx 0.8$, $g = 386$ in./sec^2, $R = 2.47 \times 10^5$ in.^{2}/(sec^2)($^\circ$F), and $T_s = 530^\circ$F abs,

$$A_{ref} = \frac{(2)(386)(640)(0.0335)}{(0.67)(0.8)(0.532)(2.47 \times 10^5)(23)}$$

$$= 1.03 \times 10^{-2} \text{ in.}^2$$

It should be noted that A_{ref} as defined in Fig. 21.30d is twice the area of each orifice when the valve is centered. Thus W_{ref} is the quiescent supply flow to the four-way valve.

$$W_q = W_{ief} = \frac{C_dA_{ref}(0.532)P_s}{\sqrt{T_s}}$$

$$= \frac{(0.8)(0.0103)(0.532)(800)}{\sqrt{530}}$$

$$= 0.152 \text{ lb/sec}$$

The stand-by power required to isothermally compress this flow rate continuously from 15 to 800 psia is found from

$$\text{HP} = \frac{W_qRT_s(\ln 800 - \ln 15)}{6600g}$$

$$= \frac{(0.152)(2.47 \times 10^5)(530)(6.7 - 2.7)}{(6600)(386)}$$

$$= 31.2 \text{ hp}$$

which exceeds the allowable steady quiescent power drain by a factor of more than 60! This means that the pneumatic valve must be a very nearly closed-center valve (Fig. 21.30b). Damping can be provided by a capillary passage or porous-flow resistance between the two ends of the ram having

$$\frac{\partial W_l}{\partial P_m} = \frac{gP_i}{RT_s}k_2$$

$$= \frac{(386)(640)(0.0335)}{(2.47 \times 10^5)(530)}$$

$$= 6.32 \times 10^{-5} \text{ (lb)/(sec·psi)}$$

Table 21.4. Comparative Analyses—Hydraulic and Pneumatic (*Continued*)

Hydraulic	*Pneumatic*

Hydraulic

Dynamic response of the closed-loop servo system is determined partly by the dynamic characteristics of the hydraulic servomotor and partly by the loop gain $K_l = k_a k_s k_f$. The servomotor's natural frequency is

$$\omega_{ns} = \sqrt{\frac{(3.75 \times 10^{-3})(17.4) + (1.5)^2}{(9.75 \times 10^{-6})(1.3)}}$$

$$= 428 \text{ radians/sec} \qquad (68.2 \text{ cps})$$

When the maximum allowable value of loop gain is used,

$$K_l = (0.45)\omega_{ns} = 192 \text{ sec}^{-1}$$

the speed of response will be about the best attainable with this type of control.[2]

The value of the feedback gain k_f is determined by the desired steady-state relationship between ΔM and ΔN [Eq. (21.97)].

$$k_f = \frac{(\Delta N)_{ss}}{(\Delta M)_{ss}}$$

The valve flow sensitivity $k_1 = \partial Q_m/\partial X$ is determined by the port width of the orifices in the valve and the supply pressure. If the valve has rectangular ports (constant port width),

$$k_1 = 2C_d w \sqrt{\frac{P_s}{\rho}}$$

if w = port width, in.

The choice of amplifier-and-valve-actuator gain k_a depends on the allowable value for loop gain K_l and upon the values chosen for k_f and k_1. From Eq. (21.98),

$$k_a = \frac{(k_2 b + A^2)K_l}{k_1 k_f A}$$

and the final choice of the values for k_a and k_1 is usually a compromise between conflicting factors encountered in the design of the components involved.

The steady-state load sensitivity may be readily computed [Eqs. (21.97) and (21.98)].

$$\left(\frac{\Delta M}{\Delta F_l}\right)_{ss} = -\frac{k_2}{k_1 k_a k_f A}$$

$$= -\frac{k_2}{K_l(k_2 b + A^2)}$$

$$= -\frac{3.75 \times 10^{-3}}{(192)[(3.75 \times 10^{-3})(17.4) + (1.5)^2]}$$

$$= -8.7 \times 10^{-6} \text{ in./lb}$$

The response of the output shaft to a step change in input signal will overshoot by about 20 per cent, and the time to first crossover† will be

$$T_1 \cong \frac{2.5}{\omega_{ns}} \cong \frac{2.5}{428} \cong 5.85 \times 10^{-3} \text{ sec}$$

Pneumatic

The maximum pneumatic power which must be supplied to the valve may be calculated from the peak flow W_{mp} needed for a ram velocity of 3 in./sec when P_a is about 700 psia (i.e., when $F_l = 500$ lb).

$$W_{mp} = \frac{P_a g A}{RT}\left(\frac{dY}{dt}\right)_{max} = \frac{(700)(386)(1.5)(3.0)}{(2.47 \times 10^5)(530)}$$

$$= 9.3 \times 10^{-3} \text{ lb/sec}$$

The power required to compress air isothermally to 800 psia at this rate is

$$\text{HP} = \frac{W_{mp} R T_s(\ln 800 - \ln 15)}{6600 g}$$

$$= \frac{(9.3 \times 10^{-3})(2.47 \times 10^5)(530)(4)}{(6600)(386)} = 1.91 \text{ hp}$$

It is seldom necessary to compress air at this peak rate because of the tremendous storage capacity of even relatively small tanks in the supply system.

Dynamic response of the closed-loop servo system is determined partly by the dynamic characteristics of the pneumatic servomotor and partly by the loop gain $K_l = k_a k_s k_f$.

The servomotor's natural frequency is

$$\omega_{ns} = \sqrt{\frac{(3.35 \times 10^{-2})(17.4) + (1.5)^2}{(2.48 \times 10^{-3})(1.3)}}$$

$$= 9.2 \text{ radians/sec} \qquad (1.46 \text{ cps})$$

so that the maximum allowable loop gain is

$$K_l = (0.45)(9.2) = 4.13 \text{ sec}^{-1}$$

The value of the feedback gain k_f is determined by the desired steady-state relationship between ΔM and ΔN [Eq. (21.97)].

$$k_f = \frac{(\Delta N)_{ss}}{(\Delta M)_{ss}}$$

The valve flow sensitivity $k_1 = \partial Q_m/\partial X$ is determined by the port width of the orifices in the valve and the supply pressure. If the valve has rectangular ports (constant port width), the characteristics shown in Fig. 21.30b may be used to determine k_1, assuming $A_1 = wX$, if w = port width.

The choice of amplifier-and-valve-actuator gain k_a depends on the allowable value for loop gain K_l and upon the values chosen for k_f and k_1. From Eq. (21.98),

$$k_a = \frac{(k_2 b + A^2)K_l}{k_1 k_f A}$$

and the final choice of values for k_a and k_1 is usually a compromise between conflicting factors encountered in the design of the components involved.

The steady-state load sensitivity may be readily computed [Eqs. (21.97) and (21.98)]

$$\left(\frac{\Delta M}{\Delta F_l}\right)_{ss} = -\frac{k_2}{k_1 k_a k_f A} = -\frac{k_2}{K_l(k_2 b + A^2)}$$

$$= -\frac{3.35 \times 10^{-2}}{(4.13)[(3.35 \times 10^{-2})(17.4) + (1.5)^2]}$$

$$= -3.61 \times 10^{-3} \text{ in./lb}$$

The response of the output shaft to a step change in input signal will overshoot by about 20 per cent, and the time to first crossover† will be

$$T_1 \cong \frac{2.5}{\omega_{ns}} \cong \frac{2.5}{9.2} \cong 0.27 \text{ sec}$$

† See Ref. 2.

Thus the "compliance" $(\Delta M / \Delta F_l)_{ss}$ of the pneumatic system is about 1000 times as great as the comparable hydraulic system, and the response time is about 50 times as long as the hydraulic system.

REFERENCES

1. Wilson, W. E.: "Positive Displacement Pumps and Fluid Motors," Pitman, New York, 1950.
2. Blackburn, J. F., G. Reethof, and J. L. Shearer: "Fluid Power Control," Technology Press, Cambridge, Mass., 1960.
3. Keenan, J. H.: "Thermodynamics," Wiley, New York, 1954.
4. Lee, J. F., and F. W. Sears: "Thermodynamics," Addison-Wesley, Reading, Mass., 1955.
5. Korn, G. A., and T. M. Korn: "Electronic Analog Computers," 2d ed., McGraw-Hill, New York, 1956.
6. Paynter, H. M. (ed.): "A Palimpsest on the Electronic Analog Art," G. A. Philbrick Researches, Inc., Boston, 1955.
7. Keenan, J. H., and J. Kaye: "Gas Tables," Wiley, New York, 1948.
8. Reid, K. N., Jr.: Optimum Design Parameters of a Pneumatic Jet-pipe Valve, presented at International Federation of Automatic Control Congress at Moscow, June 27–July 7, 1960; published by Butterworth's Scientific Publications, London, 1960. (A condensed version with a somewhat different title is Basic Characteristics of a Pneumatic Jet-pipe Valve, Institute of Radio Engineers, Boston Section, 313 Washington St., Newton, Mass., The NEREM Record, 1960.)
9. Shearer, J. L.: Resistance Characteristics of Control Valve Orifices, *Proc. Brit. Inst. Mech. Engrs. Symposium on Automatic Control*, London, Jan. 5–7, 1960.
10. Stone, James A.: Discharge Coefficients and Steady Flow Forces for Hydraulic Poppet Valves, *Trans. ASME*, **82**, ser. D (1): 144–154 (March, 1960).

Section 22

LUBRICATION MECHANICS

By

DUDLEY D. FULLER, *Columbia University in the City of New York, New York*

LUBRICATION MECHANICS

22.1. Introduction

When fluid films are confined to thin slots, grooves, and crevices and when pressure gradients and flow are induced, these films develop remarkable and sometimes unbelievable physical properties. The films may range from only about $\frac{1}{5}$ to 3 or 4 mils in thickness, yet under certain conditions pressures have been generated in them as high as 20,000 psi. The film pressures acting against the confining walls of the slot produce the very well known fluid-film bearing. Much of our industrial life would grind to a stop without the load-carrying action of these fluid films. Every kilowatt of electricity, for example, that is produced by the public utilities is generated by machinery using such bearings. Every ship at sea is propelled by the oil-film pressures in its thrust bearings. The oil film literally pushes the ship through the water. Every truck, tractor, bus, and automobile runs as a result of this action in its bearings. And for thousands of other machines of every kind, this fundamental action is indispensable.

Where this pressure is self-induced by the relative sliding motion of the walls of the slot, the action is called hydrodynamic lubrication. This is the most common type of fluid-film lubrication and is the most useful in terms of the number of existing applications.

In the past the classical concept of hydrodynamic lubrication has been limited to that of the converging geometric wedge as found in the tilting-pad bearing, or in the plain, cylindrical journal bearing having some clearance. This is indeed an unnecessary and highly undesirable restriction of the use of this theory since pressure films can be and are induced by many different geometries. This generalization will be pointed out. The lubricants, as well, need not be limited to conventional oil. Bearings have been run successfully, for example, on water, alcohol, liquid refrigerants, mercury, red-fuming nitric acid, molten metal, gasoline, grease, slurries, and a number of gases, including air.

This type of lubrication, hydrodynamic lubrication, is described in the first part of this section (Arts. 22.3 to 22.5).

In the second part of this section (Arts. 22.6 to 22.8) another form of fluid-film lubrication is considered. This may be used in special instances in which there is very little relative motion of the walls of the bearing or perhaps even none. It may be more desirable then to introduce the lubricant into the clearance space from some external high-pressure source. The pressure in the film is therefore not self-induced, but is externally induced. This is known as externally pressurized lubrication, or hydrostatic lubrication.

An early application of this type of lubrication was to the 200-in. Hale optical telescope on Mount Palomar. Perhaps an even more spectacular application is to the bearings of the mammoth radio telescope erected at Green Bank, W.Va., by the Associated Universities. This structure weighs 5 million pounds and cradles a parabolic dish 140 feet in diameter. The hydrostatic bearings must restrain this telescope even when it is subjected to 100-mph winds. This and other aspects of hydrostatic lubrication will be described in the second part of this section.

22.2. Notation

a eccentricity, radial clearance $\times$ eccentricity ratio, in.
b (1) length of slot in hydrostatic journal bearing, in.
        (2) width of tilting-pad bearing, perpendicular to motion, in.
c radial clearance in journal bearing, in.

d	diameter of journal bearing, in.
h	film thickness, in.
h_0	minimum film thickness, in.
h^*	film thickness at point of maximum pressure, in.
h_1	film thickness at leading edge of tilting-pad bearing, in.
k_p	pressure function for hydrodynamic lubricant film
l	length of journal bearing, in.; also length of tilting-pad bearing in direction of motion
ln	logarithm to the base e
m	clearance ratio for journal bearings, radial clearance/radius
m'	slope parameter of tilting-pad bearing
p	pressure at any point in lubricant film, psi
q_x, q_z	unit flow volume per unit of width along x and z coordinate axes
r	shaft radius, in.
u	linear sliding velocity, in./sec
v	linear velocity in the lubricant film
x, y, z	coordinate axes
A	load-carrying factor for hydrodynamic journal bearings, $(132/n)\ (1000m)^{\frac{1}{2}}$ (P_{av}/ZN)
F	friction force, lb
F_R	friction force on runner, lb
F_S	friction force on shoe, lb
K_{fB}	friction factor for bearing of journal bearing
K_{fJ}	friction factor for shaft of journal bearing
K_{fR}	friction factor for runner of tilting-pad thrust bearing
K_{fs}	friction factor for shoe of tilting-pad thrust bearing
K_p	load-carrying function
M_B	friction moment on bearing, in.-lb
M_J	friction moment of journal, in.-lb
N	speed, rpm
O	center of cylindrical bearing
O'	center of journal or shaft
P_{av}	average pressure based on projected area, psi
P_0	supply pressure for hydrostatic bearings, psi
Q	flow volume, in.³/sec
R	journal-bearing radius; also outer radius of hydrostatic step bearing; in.
R_0	recess radius in hydrostatic step bearing, in.
$\mathbf{R}$	Reynolds number
V	linear sliding velocity, in./sec
W	load, lb
Z	lubricant viscosity, centipoises, dyne-sec/cm² $\div$ 100
β	angle between line of action of applied load and leading edge of load-carrying film in a journal bearing
ϵ	eccentricity ratio, film thickness/radial clearance
η	side-leakage factor, hydrodynamic bearings
θ	angular coordinate
μ	lubricant viscosity, reyns, lb-sec/in.²
ν	kinematic viscosity, in.²/sec
τ	shear stress in lubricant film, F/A
ω	angular rotational velocity of journal, radians/sec

22.3. Hydrodynamic Lubrication

Because of the generally small dimensions of bearings and their films, the distinctive unit employed in this country, for lubrication work, is the inch. For greater convenience on small dimensions, one-thousandth of an inch, or the mil, is used. For describing surface roughness of bearings or extremely thin lubricating films, one-millionth of an inch, or the microinch, is employed.

Table 22.1. Typical Fluid Viscosities at 70°F

Fluid	Centipoises	Reyns, 1×10^{-7}	Microreyns
Honey (approx.).............	1500	2175	217.5
SAE 50 (heavy).............	800	1160	116
Glycerin....................	500	725	72.5
SAE 30 (medium)..........	300	435	43.5
Olive oil...................	100	145	14.5
SAE 10 (light).............	70	101	10.1
SAE 5 (X light)............	32	46.5	4.65
Ethylene glycol............	20	29	2.9
Mercury...................	1.5	2.17	0.217
Turpentine................	1.45	2.1	0.21
Water.....................	1.00	1.45	0.145
Octane....................	0.54	0.78	0.078
Air.......................	0.018	0.026	0.0026

Lubrication analysis requires the use of either absolute viscosity or kinematic viscosity. As defined by Sir Isaac Newton, the shear force in thin films under laminar steady-state conditions is

$$F = \mu A \frac{V}{h} \qquad (22.1)$$

in which μ = absolute viscosity
A = swept shear area
V = linear relative sliding velocity of solid surfaces enclosing film
h = film thickness

Solving for μ:

$$\mu = \frac{Fh}{AV} \qquad (22.2)$$

The unit of absolute viscosity, which reflects the usefulness of the inch, is called the *reyn*, after Sir Osborne Reynolds. It has the dimensions lb-sec/in.² This is a large unit, and recently a unit one-millionth the size of the reyn has been suggested and appropriately called the *microreyn*. In the cgs system the unit of absolute viscosity is the dyne-sec/cm², called the *poise*, after the French physician Poiseuille. Since the poise is also a large unit, the *centipoise*, or one-hundredth part of a poise, is commonly used. The size of the centipoise is well matched to the magnitude of absolute viscosity of common liquids, so that the viscosity of water at room temperature is measured as one centipoise. The microreyn is about the same order of size as the centipoise.

Table 22.1 lists typical fluid viscosities at 70°F.

The hydrodynamic theory of lubrication, like all other theories, is restricted by the assumptions that were made in its derivation. A thorough understanding of these assumptions is required for a proper appreciation of the range of applications in which the hydrodynamic theory can be properly used. These assumptions are generally as follows:

1. Laminar-flow conditions prevail, and the liquids are consistent with Newton's definition of viscosity. (The liquids are Newtonian.)

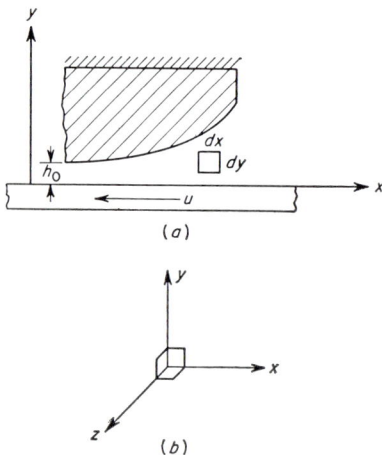

Fig. 22.1. Geometry of converging fluid wedge.

2. Inertia forces resulting from acceleration of the liquid are small as compared with the viscous shear forces and may be neglected.

3. The fluid is incompressible. This means that the volume flowing past any section in unit time will be constant.

4. The pressure in the film is a function only of x (Fig. 22.1). This means that the pressure across the film in the y direction is a constant. This is a valid assumption since the load-carrying hydrodynamic films are very thin. They are of the order of 0.001 in. in thickness.

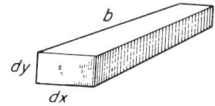

FIG. 22.2. Unit volume of hydrodynamic film.

5. The velocity in the film is a function of both x and y.

6. The viscosity of the liquid as it passes through the bearing remains constant. With many bearings, if the average of the inlet and exit viscosities is used, the results are found to have little error. This assumption permits a great simplification in the analysis.

Consider, then, some general geometric form as shown in Fig. 22.1a. The upper part is fixed, and the lower part is moving in the negative x direction with constant velocity u. The bearing is of infinite width in the z direction perpendicular to both the x and y axes (Fig. 22.1b). This means, then, that there is no flow in the z direction.

The differential fluid element dx, dy, and of width b, in the z direction, as shown in Fig. 22.2, has certain forces acting on it. The equilibrium of forces in the x direction will now be expressed using Fig. 22.3.

Pressure on the right face of area $b \, dy$ will be p. Pressure on the left face will be $p + (dp/dx)dx$. The shear stress on the bottom of the differential element of area $b \, dx$ is τ. The shear stress on the top of the element is $\tau + (\partial\tau/\partial y)dy$ (Fig. 22.3). The equation for summation of forces in the horizontal direction is then

$$\left(p + \frac{dp}{dx} dx\right) b \, dy + \tau b \, dx - \left(\tau + \frac{\partial \tau}{\partial y} dy\right) b \, dx - pb \, dy = 0$$

or

$$\frac{dp}{dx} = \frac{\partial \tau}{\partial y} \tag{22.3}$$

From Eq. (22.1),

$$F = A\mu \frac{dv}{dy}$$

$$\tau = \frac{F}{A} \qquad \tau = \mu \frac{dv}{dy}$$

But in this application v is a function of both x and y. So

$$\tau = \mu \frac{\partial v}{\partial y}$$

and

$$\frac{\partial \tau}{\partial y} = \mu \frac{\partial^2 v}{\partial y^2}$$

Substituting in Eq. (22.3),

$$\frac{dp}{dx} = \mu \frac{\partial^2 v}{\partial y^2} \tag{22.4}$$

Equation (22.4) may be obtained directly from the Navier-Stokes equations when all body forces acting on the fluid elements are dropped out except for those forces resulting from viscous shear and from the pressure that is generated as a result of viscous shear. It is also necessary to assume that the density of the lubricant is constant. One must recognize that $\partial^2 v/\partial x^2$ and $\partial^2 v/\partial z^2$ are very much smaller than $\partial^2 v/\partial y^2$ and may be appro-

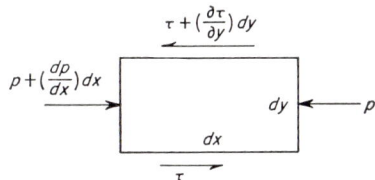

FIG. 22.3. Force equilibrium on unit volume of hydrodynamic film.

priately neglected. Equation (22.4) then results. To obtain the velocity distribution in the y direction, integrate twice with respect to y. dp/dx is a constant as far as y is concerned.

$$v = \frac{1}{2\mu}\frac{dp}{dx} y^2 + C_1 y + C_2 \qquad (22.5)$$

To evaluate the constants of integration, the boundary conditions are

$$v = -u \qquad y = 0$$
$$v = 0 \qquad y = h$$

By evaluating the constants and after substituting into Eq. (22.5),

$$v = \frac{1}{2\mu}\frac{dp}{dx}(y^2 - hy) + u\left(\frac{y}{h} - 1\right) \qquad (22.6)$$

Equation (22.6) represents the velocity distribution in the liquid film and is the superposition of a parabolic velocity function (as represented by the first parenthesis) and a linear velocity function (as represented by the last parenthesis).

As the pressure varies along the length of the film, it must reach a maximum at some point. At the same instant, the rate of change of pressure with respect to x will be zero, or $dp/dx = 0$ (Fig. 22.4). By substituting $dp/dx = 0$ in Eq. (22.6)

$$v = u\left(\frac{y}{h} - 1\right) \qquad \text{a linear relationship}$$

The particular film thickness at the point of maximum pressure is identified by the symbol h^*. To evaluate dp/dx examine the continuity of flow. The flow passing any section is

$$Q = \int_0^h vb\, dy$$

By substituting Eq. (22.6),

$$Q = b\int_0^h \frac{1}{2\mu}\frac{dp}{dx}(y^2 - hy)\, dy + u\left(\frac{y}{h} - 1\right) dy$$

$$= b\left(-\frac{1}{12\mu}\frac{dp}{dx}h^3 - \frac{uh}{2}\right) \qquad (22.7)$$

Q is constant because of no side flow and continuity of flow, and at h^*, where $p_{\max}$ exists, $dp/dx = 0$. Substituting in Eq. (22.7),

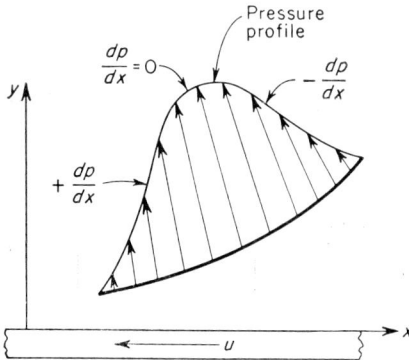

FIG. 22.4. Pressure profile in hydrodynamic film.

$$Q = -\frac{u}{2} bh^* \qquad (22.8)$$

By equating Eqs. (22.7) and (22.8),

$$-\frac{u}{2} bh^* = b \left(-\frac{1}{12\mu} \frac{dp}{dx} h^3 - \frac{uh}{2} \right)$$

and after simplifying,

$$\frac{dp}{dx} = 6\mu u \left(\frac{h^* - h}{h^3} \right) \qquad (22.9)$$

This is a perfectly general relationship, and as long as h can be described in terms of x, this equation will predict the build-up of pressure for any geometric shape or configuration, whatever it may be. Examples of ten typical shapes are given in Fig. 22.5.

Type a. This geometric shape is typical of the journal bearing and will be described in detail. If no arbitrary pressure-draining grooves are cut in the load-carrying area, this type of bearing builds up a film with tremendous carrying power, and with suitable selection of variables it can sustain average pressures well above 2500 psi. Theoretically, the load-carrying capacity increases as the film thickness decreases and will rise to a hypothetical value of infinity as the film thickness reduces to zero. But thermal and elastic distortions, as well as variations in surface finish, limit the minimum fluid-film thickness to a practical value of 0.0001 in. (one ten-thousandth of an inch) or, in very extreme cases, one-half of this amount, or five hundred-thousandths of an inch (0.00005 in.).

Type b. This is the classical shape for the tilting-shoe bearing as typified by the Kingsbury and by the Michell thrust bearing and is described in detail later (Art. 22.4). The same action is achieved by the spring-supported type (Fig. 22.6).

As is shown schematically in Fig. 22.6, the load-carrying shoe is free to tip and establish its own equilibrium angle with the moving runner and is held elastically in position by a nest of helical springs.

Types c **to** h. In Fig. 22.5, profiles c to h have been analyzed by Purday[2] for pressure build-up under comparable conditions. It is interesting to observe that one shape is just about as effective as another in building up fluid-film pressure, with shape h actually producing the maximum peak pressure. This particular profile was discussed first by Lord Rayleigh[3] in 1918, when he made a very significant announcement. He pointed out that the existence of hydrodynamic pressure films was not predicated alone on the wedge-shaped clearance space, but could be developed by an assortment of clearance shapes. He then analyzed the action of various clearance profiles and determined that the shape for maximum load-carrying capacity was simply two flat parallel surfaces, one having a dam of rectangular cross section (Fig. 22.5h). Not until 1950 did any further literature appear developing this idea of Rayleigh's, when Archibald applied it to a sector-shaped thrust bearing[4] and later to a journal bearing.[5]

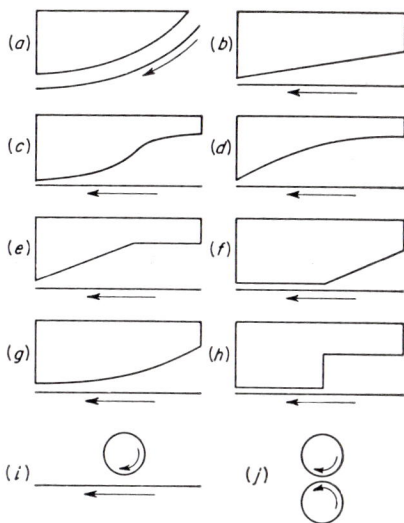

Fig. 22.5. Ten typical geometrics that have been analyzed for the formation of hydrodynamic films.

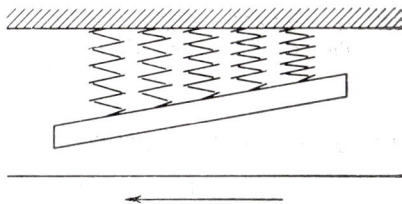

Fig. 22.6. Spring-supported tilting-shoe bearing.

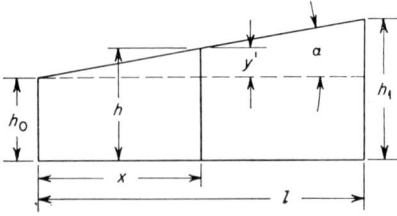

FIG. 22.7. Geometry of converging wedge.

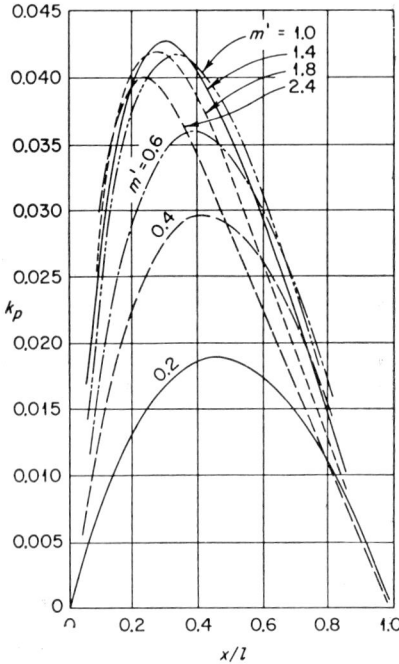

FIG. 22.8. Plot of pressure coefficients for slider bearing.

Types i and j. These have also been analyzed, and the results may be found in the literature.[6,7]

22.4. Hydrodynamic Theory Applied to Tapered Wedge and Tilting Pad

Now that the general nature of Eq. (22.9) has been discussed in terms of a variety of geometric profiles, the tapered wedge is examined and its hydrodynamic variables quantitatively analyzed.

Where the wedge is bounded by plane surfaces as shown in Fig. 22.7,

$$h = h_0 + y'$$

$$\frac{y'}{h_1 - h_0} = \frac{x}{l}$$

$$y' = \frac{x}{l} (h_1 - h_0)$$

and then

$$h = h_0 + \frac{x}{l} (h_1 - h_0)$$

or

$$h = h_0 \left(1 + m' \frac{x}{l} \right) \qquad (22.10)$$

where

$$m' = \frac{h_1}{h_0} - 1 \qquad (22.11)$$

Physically, m' will usually vary in the range from 0.5 to 2.0, with most values around $m' = 1$. With $m' = 1$, $h_1 = 2h_0$, or the leading-edge film thickness is twice the trailing-edge film thickness. Also h^* in Eq. (22.9) can be replaced by $C^* h_0$, $h^* = C^* h_0$, with, of course, $C^* > 1$. By substituting in Eq. (22.9),

$$\frac{dp}{dx} = 6\mu u \frac{C^* h_0 - h_0[1 + m'(x/l)]}{h_0^3[1 + m'(x/l)]^3} \qquad (22.12)$$

By integrating and by solving for p,

$$p = \frac{6\mu u l}{m' h_0^2} \left\{ \frac{C^*}{-2[1 + m'(x/l)]^2} + \frac{1}{1 + m'(x/l)} + D \right\} \qquad (22.13)$$

The constant of integration D and the constant C^* can be evaluated from the physical boundary conditions that when

$$x = l \qquad p = 0$$

$$x = 0 \qquad p = 0$$

The pressure function (22.13) then becomes

$$p = \frac{6\mu u l}{m' h_0^2} \left\{ \frac{2m' + 2}{-2(2 + m')[1 + m'(x/l)]^2} + \frac{1}{1 + m'(x/l)} - \frac{1}{2 + m'} \right\} \qquad (22.14)$$

or

$$p = \frac{6\mu u l}{h_0^2} k_p \qquad (22.15)$$

Table 22.2. Values of k_p

x/l	$m' = 0.6$	$m' = 0.8$	$m' = 1.0$	$m' = 1.2$	$m' = 1.4$	$m' = 1.6$	$m' = 1.8$	$m' = 2.0$
0	0	0	0	0	0	0	0	0
0.1	0.0185	0.0220	0.0248	0.0269	0.0285	0.0297	0.0306	0.0312
0.2	0.0294	0.0340	0.0370	0.0390	0.0402	0.0408	0.0410	0.0408
0.3	0.0348	0.0390	0.0414	0.0426	0.0429	0.0426	0.0419	0.0410
0.4	0.0360	0.0393	0.0408	0.0411	0.0406	0.0396	0.0384	0.0370
0.5	0.0341	0.0364	0.0370	0.0366	0.0356	0.0343	0.0328	0.0312
0.6	0.0299	0.0313	0.0312	0.0304	0.0292	0.0278	0.0263	0.0248
0.7	0.0240	0.0246	0.0242	0.0233	0.0220	0.0208	0.0187	0.0182
0.8	0.0168	0.0170	0.0165	0.0156	0.0147	0.0137	0.0127	0.0118
0.9	0.00876	0.00869	0.00831	0.00780	0.00725	0.00672	0.00591	0.00574
1.0	0	0	0	0	0	0	0	0

if

$$k_p = \frac{1}{m'} \left\{ \frac{2m' + 2}{-2(2 + m')[1 + m'(x/l)]^2} + \frac{1}{1 + m'(x/l)} - \frac{1}{2 + m'} \right\}$$

Thus a pressure profile can be plotted, using Eq. (22.14) for all values of k_p and any combination of the operating variables. Values for k_p are listed in Table 22.2 and are plotted in Fig. 22.8.

If the pressure distribution is known, the load-carrying capacity can be evaluated by summing up the effect of the pressure all along the shoe.

$$P_{av} = \frac{1}{l} \int_0^l p \, dx$$

By substituting the value of p from Eq. (22.14) and after integrating,

$$P_{av} = \frac{6\mu u l}{h_0^2} \left[\frac{1}{(m')^2} \ln (1 + m') - \frac{2}{m'(2 + m')} \right] \tag{22.16}$$

or

$$P_{av} = \frac{6\mu u l}{h_0^2} K_p \tag{22.17}$$

if K_p is the bracketed term in Eq. (22.16). The load-carrying capacity is the product of the average pressure and the area (bl), or

$$W = \frac{6\mu u l^2 b}{h_0^2} K_p \tag{22.18}$$

Also

$$h_0 = \sqrt{\frac{6\mu u l}{P_{av}} K_p} \tag{22.19}$$

Values of K_p are listed in Table 22.3. It will be observed that K_p and the load-carrying capacity of the bearing are very insensitive to changes in m', the slope of the tapered land, or the angle of inclination of the shoe, as the case may be.

Pivot Position of Tilting Shoe. An analysis of stability for the hinged shoe shows that the pivot point should be somewhat to the rear of the middle of the shoe, closer to the

Table 22.3

m'	K_p
0.6	0.0235
0.7	0.0247
0.8	0.0255
0.9	0.0261
1.0	0.0265
1.2	0.0267
1.4	0.0265
1.5	0.0263
2.0	0.0246

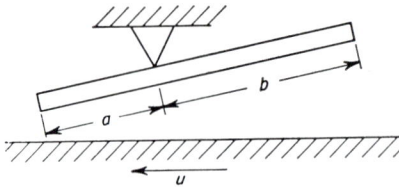

FIG. 22.9. Representation of pivoted shoe.

trailing edge. In Fig. 22.9, b should be longer than a for stability with the direction of motion shown. It is possible to compute a theoretical pivot position in terms of the variables of operation in order to obtain a maximum film thickness under the shoe. However, since many of the variables, such as oil temperature and viscosity, for example, are not under exact control, these refinements of analysis are hardly justified in most instances. Good results have been obtained by placing the pivot point at a position five-ninths of the length of the shoe from the leading edge and four-ninths from the trailing edge. If the direction of sliding may ever be reversed, the pivot position must be at the mid-point of the shoe. Theoretically, with the shoe pinned in this manner, it should never lift off the runner and form a tapered wedge, but designs of this kind often operate very well. This is probably the result of a small amount of bending or buckling of the shoe, forming a slightly convex profile. It has been clearly shown that if the surface of a tilting pad is deliberatedly made convex, it will carry a predictable load even when pivoted at the center point. Thus convex distortions due to elastic or thermal causes will also produce a significant load-carrying capacity.[8-10]

Effect of Side Flow. Equations (22.17) and (22.18) have been developed for the shoe where the width b is large as compared with the length l. This means there is no flow in the z coordinate direction (Fig. 22.1b), and consequently no drop in pressure in this direction. As will be shown, these equations can be applied with sufficient accuracy to real bearings only if the width is at least four times the length. If the width is less than the ratio of 4:1, a modification of the derivation must be used to allow for the loss in load-carrying capacity because of side flow and reduction of pressure.

The pattern of pressure for a bearing, assuming no flow in the z direction, would resemble Fig. 22.10. With side leakage, however, the pressure pattern would correspond

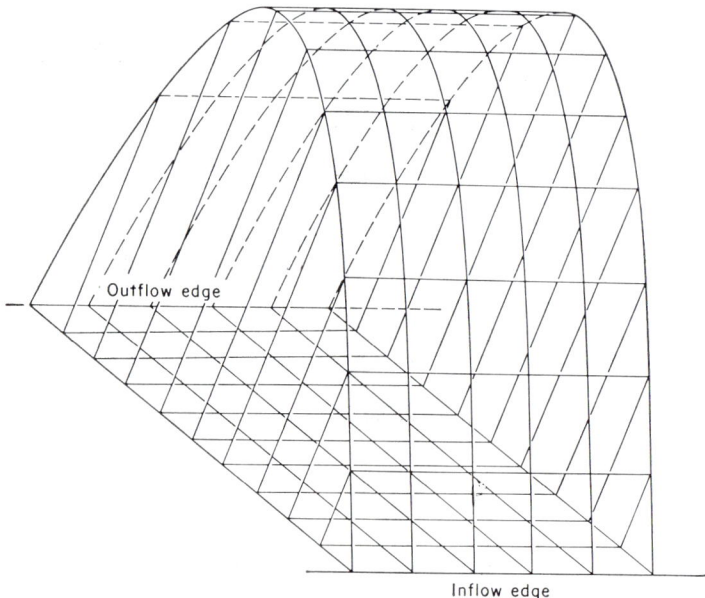

FIG. 22.10. Pressure pattern in slider bearing without side flow. (*Ref.* 11.)

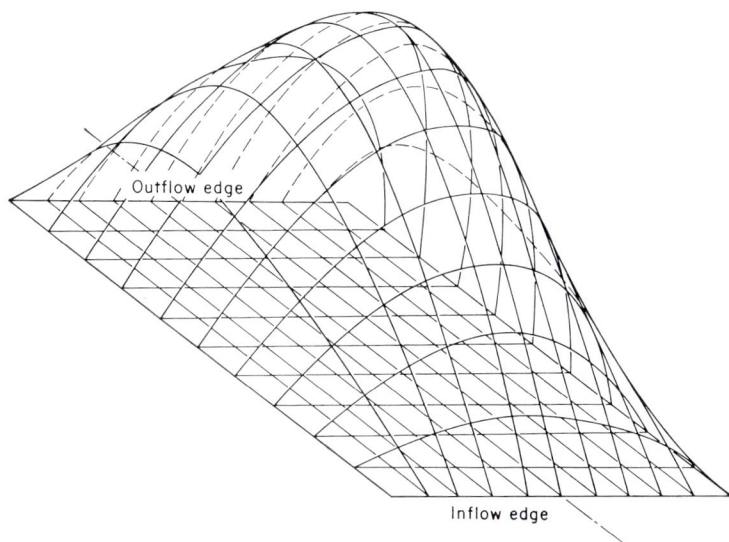

FIG. 22.11. Pressure pattern in slider bearing with side flow.   (*Ref.* 11.)

more closely to Fig. 22.11, and the loss in load-carrying capacity is clearly evident.

In the previous derivation for a plane of infinite width, Eq. (22.4) was developed. With side leakage the dependency of the pressure p on both the x and z coordinates must be recognized. Therefore Eq. (22.4) is modified.

$$\frac{\partial p}{\partial x} = \mu \frac{\partial^2 v_x}{\partial y^2}$$

and

$$\frac{\partial p}{\partial z} = \mu \frac{\partial^2 v_z}{\partial y^2}$$

if v_x is the component of fluid velocity in the x direction, and v_z is the component of the fluid velocity in the z direction. To establish the basic equations for hydrodynamic action, including side leakage, a differential cube can be considered of dimensions dx, dz and of height h, the total height of the fluid film, extending from the moving surface to the stationary surface (Fig. 22.12). The volume of fluid going into this element equals the volume flowing out at any instant.

q_x is a unit flow in the x direction of cubic inches per second per linear inch of face width, and q_z corresponds to the unit flow in the z direction per linear inch. The volumes entering or leaving all four possible faces of the element are shown in Fig. 22.12. For continuity of flow, the volume entering the element equals the volume that is leaving, or

$$q_x \, dz + q_z \, dx = \left(q_x + \frac{\partial q_x}{\partial x} \, dx \right) dz + \left(q_z + \frac{\partial q_z}{\partial z} \, dz \right) dx$$

$$= q_x \, dz + \frac{\partial q_x}{\partial x} \, dx \, dz + q_z \, dx + \frac{\partial q_z}{\partial z} \, dx \, dz$$

$$\frac{\partial q_x}{\partial x} = -\frac{\partial q_z}{\partial z} \tag{22.20}$$

From Eq. (22.7),

$$Q = b \left(-\frac{1}{12\mu} \frac{dp}{dx} h^3 - \frac{uh}{2} \right)$$

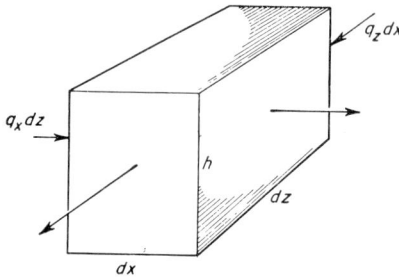

FIG. 22.12. Flow through elemental volume of height h.

Division by b will convert this into an equation for the unit flow, cubic inches per second per inch of width. Also, recognizing that p is now a function of both x and z, Eq. (22.7) can be rewritten as

$$q_x = \left(-\frac{1}{12\mu} \frac{\partial p}{\partial x} h^3 - \frac{uh}{2} \right) \quad (22.21)$$

Since there is no sliding motion in the z direction, the flow in that direction will result only from the pressure difference that is acting. q_z will therefore correspond to the flow through a slot formed by two flat plates resulting from a pressure differential.

As applied to this derivation,

$$Q_z = \frac{bh^3}{12\mu} \frac{\partial p}{\partial z}$$

After dividing by b to obtain the unit flow, cubic inches per second per linear inch,

$$q_z = \frac{h^3}{12\mu} \frac{\partial p}{\partial z} \quad (22.22)$$

By substituting Eqs. (22.21) and (22.22) in Eq. (22.20),

$$\frac{\partial}{\partial x} \left(-\frac{1}{12\mu} \frac{\partial p}{\partial x} h^3 - \frac{uh}{2} \right) + \frac{\partial}{\partial z} \left(\frac{h^3}{12\mu} \frac{\partial p}{\partial z} \right) = 0$$

or

$$\frac{\partial}{\partial z} \left(\frac{h^3}{\mu} \frac{\partial p}{\partial z} \right) - \frac{\partial}{\partial x} \left(\frac{h^3}{\mu} \frac{\partial p}{\partial x} \right) = \frac{\partial}{\partial x} (6uh) \quad (22.23)$$

Equation (22.23) is the Reynolds equation in three dimensions. There is no general solution for this equation. The difficulties in getting an exact solution for any real bearing are very great and in many cases impossible, with our present knowledge of mathematics. However, alternative, and at times more approximate, methods have been used to force the Reynolds differential equation to yield the information that was needed.

One of the most useful of these approximate methods is that employing the electrical analogue. It is well known that the laws of viscous flow in fluids are closely analogous to those of flow of electricity in conducting substances, and the equations which express them are very similar. Fluid pressures correspond to electrical potential, and velocities correspond to current. Kingsbury[12] and Needs,[13] by using an electrolytic bath, devised a method to produce a model of a hydrodynamic oil film in a bearing and have evaluated, for many cases, the effect of side flow on the reduction of pressure and load-carrying capacity.

Table 22.4

b/l	η
¼†	0.060
⅓	0.090
½	0.185
⅔	0.278
1	0.440
1½	0.550
2	0.680
4	0.835
5¾	0.920
∞	1.000

† Narrow ski-like shoe.

For bearings with the tapered geometric wedge, the modifications of load-carrying capacity and film thickness can be made by introducing the factor η. These values are shown in Table 22.4. They are for the case of $m' = 1$, $(h_1 = 2h_0)$ and approximate very well other possible inclinations of the shoe.

Equations (22.18) and (22.19) would then be modified to become

$$W = \frac{6\mu u l^2 b \eta}{h_0^2} K_p \qquad (22.24)$$

and

$$h_0 = \sqrt{\frac{6\mu u l \eta}{P_{av}} K_p} \qquad (22.25)$$

Example 1.   The use of Eqs. (22.24) and (22.25) may be illustrated by an example involving a thrust bearing for a typical hydroelectric generator.

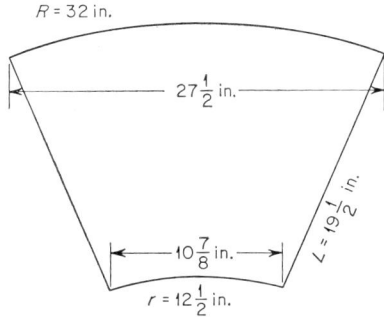

$R = 32$ in.

$27\frac{1}{2}$ in.

$10\frac{7}{8}$ in.

$L = 19\frac{1}{2}$ in.

$r = 12\frac{1}{2}$ in.

FIG. 22.13. Dimensions of one of the shoes of the thrust bearing. (*Courtesy of American Institute of Electrical Engineers.*)

Operating Data

Static load, lb	503,000
Running load, lb	703,000
Rotor speed, rpm	150
Oil viscosity, SSU at 100°F	200
Operating temperature, °F	100
Bearing diameter, in	64
Number of shoes	6
Mean diameter of shoe circle, in	44.5
Load per shoe, lb	117,100

Figure 22.13 shows a detail of one shoe of this thrust bearing. At 150 rpm and with an oil of 200 Saybolt seconds at 100°F (53.4×10^{-7} reyn), the minimum oil-film thickness may be calculated using Eq. (22.25). Mean length of shoe $(27.5 + 10.875)/2 = 19.2$ in; width of shoe, 19.5 in; average pressure on shoe, $117,100/386$ in.^{2} or 303 psi. By assuming that the shoe is square and $b/l = 1$, the value of $\eta = 0.44$. With a mean diameter of the shoe circle of 44.5 in., the linear velocity at the mean diameter is 349 in./sec. From Table 22.3, $K_p = 0.0265$. Then, in Eq. (22.25),

$$h_0 = \sqrt{\frac{6 \times 53.4 \times 10^{-7} \times 349 \times 19.2 \times 0.44 \times 0.0265}{303}}$$

$$= \sqrt{8.26 \times 10^{-6}}$$

$$= 0.0029 \text{ in.}$$

Friction in Slider Bearings.   It is important to find the total frictional resistance resulting from the relative motion of the runner with respect to the stationary shoe. The friction force results, of course, from the viscous shear of the lubricant film.

The frictional force on an element of length dx and with b (Fig. 22.14) is, from Eq. (22.1),

$$dF = \mu \, dA \, \frac{\partial v}{\partial y}$$

but

$$dA = b \, dx$$

So

$$dF = \mu b \, dx \, \frac{\partial v}{\partial y} \qquad (22.26)$$

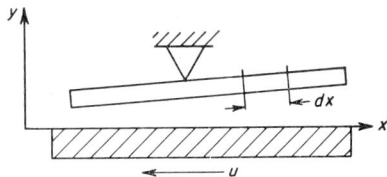

FIG. 22.14. Differential friction element on shoe face.

but since the velocity $v = \dfrac{1}{2\mu}\dfrac{dp}{dx}(y^2 - hy) + u\left(\dfrac{y}{h} - 1\right)$ from Eq. (22.6),

$$\frac{\partial v}{\partial y} = \frac{1}{2\mu}\frac{dp}{dx}(2y - h) + \frac{u}{h}$$

Then, by substituting in Eq. (22.26),

$$dF = b\left[\frac{1}{2}\frac{dp}{dx}(2y - h) + \frac{\mu u}{h}\right]dx \tag{22.27}$$

There will be two values of friction: first at the runner where $y = 0$, and second at the stationary shoe where $y = h$. Consider first the friction of the runner identified by letting $y = 0$. Then, in Eq. (22.27),

$$dF_R = b\left(-\frac{1}{2}\frac{dp}{dx}h + \frac{\mu u}{h}\right)dx \tag{22.28}$$

Now from Eqs. (22.10) and (22.12), by substituting in Eq. (22.28) and after performing the integration,

$$F_R = \mu b l\frac{u}{h_0}\left[\frac{4}{m'}\ln(1 + m') - \frac{6}{2 + m'}\right] \tag{22.29}$$

or

$$F_R = \mu b l\frac{u}{h_0} \times K_{fR} \tag{22.30}$$

if K_{fR} is the factor enclosed by brackets in Eq. (22.29).

The friction on the shoe can be obtained by letting $y = h$ in Eq. (22.27) and proceeding in the same manner described above.

$$F_S = \mu b l\frac{u}{h_0}\left[\frac{6}{2 + m'} - \frac{2}{m'}\ln(1 + m')\right] \tag{22.31}$$

or

$$F_S = \mu b l\frac{u}{h_0}K_{fs} \tag{22.32}$$

if K_{fs} is the bracketed term of Eq. (22.31). Table 22.5 lists values of K_{fR} and K_{fs} in terms of m'. It will be observed that the apparent frictional drag on the shoe is less than the frictional drag on the runner. As the shoe inclination becomes steeper, the apparent discrepancy becomes larger. However, this can be easily resolved. It can be shown that if the component of hydrodynamic film force that acts in the horizontal direction is added to the frictional drag on the shoe, this sum will then equal the frictional drag on the runner.

Example 2. As an illustration of the use of Eq. (22.30), Feifel cites data taken from a thrust-bearing test.[14] The unit had six shoes each, with an area of 120.5 in.^{2} Each shoe was approximately 11 in. square. Total load, 268,000 lb. Load per shoe,

Table 22.5

m'	K_{fs}	K_{fR}
0.6	0.741	0.826
0.7	0.706	0.810
0.8	0.673	0.796
0.9	0.643	0.784
1.0	0.614	0.773
1.2	0.534	0.753
1.4	0.514	0.736
1.5	0.492	0.729
2.0	0.401	0.697

44,600 lb. Average pressure on shoe, $44,600/120.5 = 370$ psi. Speed, 152.7 rpm. Mean diameter of shoe circle, 50.5 in. Outside diameter of shoe circle, 61.5 in. Linear velocity at mean diameter, $u = \pi \times 50.5 \times 152.7/60 = 404$ in./sec. Oil viscosity at 86°F operating temperature, 0.721×10^{-5} reyn. Assuming $m' = 1$, $K_p = 0.0265$. Also for a "square" shoe, $\eta = 0.44$. Therefore, in Eq. (22.25),

$$h_0 = \sqrt{\frac{6 \times 0.721 \times 10^{-5} \times 404 \times 11 \times 0.44 \times 0.0265}{370}}$$

$$= \sqrt{6.06 \times 10^{-6}}$$

$$= 0.00246 \text{ in. minimum film thickness}$$

Then, in Table 22.5 for $m' = 1$, $K_{fR} = 0.773$, and in Eq. (22.30),

$$F_R = \frac{0.721 \times 10^{-5} \times 11 \times 11 \times 404}{0.00246} \times 0.773 = 110.7 \text{ lb}$$

at the mean radius of the shoe circle. Since the load on each shoe is 44,600 lb, the coefficient of friction is

$$f = \frac{F_R}{W}$$

$$= \frac{110.7}{44,600} = 0.00248$$

The measured coefficient of friction from the actual test was 0.00216. This is an excellent check, considering the extent of the assumptions that must be made in order to arrive at a theoretical estimate.

22.5. Hydrodynamic Theory Applied to the Journal Bearing

This is the type of bearing in which a sleeve of bearing material is wrapped partially or completely around a rotating shaft or journal and is designed to support a radial load.

It is usually possible to design a journal bearing to operate with its rubbing surfaces separated by a fluid lubricant film and still carry a substantial load. Under these conditions, the friction losses in the bearing are generally very low and, if the lubricant is free of abrasive matter, wear becomes vanishingly small.

The approach is to be concerned first with the minimum film thickness in the bearing as it is running. This is a safety consideration. If the film becomes too thin, metal-to-metal contact will be initiated and under many circumstances the bearing will destroy itself. Primary concern therefore is with the minimum film thickness between the shaft and the bearing.

The friction loss must also be evaluated so that an estimate can be made of the heat that is being generated in the bearing. In this way the amount of heat that must continuously be removed from the bearing can be determined so that the bearing may be maintained at a reasonable steady-state level.

Figure 22.15 shows a schematic view of a journal bearing, with a greatly exaggerated clearance, running at some angular speed ω under the action of a load W. When starting, with metallic contact between the shaft and the bearing at a point under the load, the shaft will start to run up the right side of the bearing to-

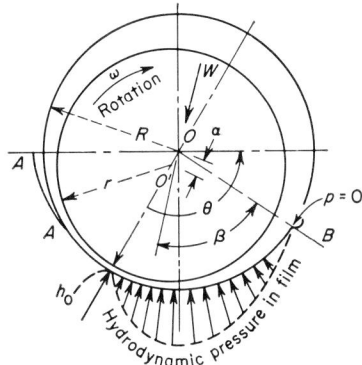

FIG. 22.15. Journal in 360° full bearing.

ward point B. After rising a few degrees of arc, it will enter a region where oil comes between the bearing and the journal. Slip will begin. Then as the journal comes up to speed, it will revolve faster and faster and build up a wedge-shaped film, which will then place the journal in the position shown in Fig. 22.15.

A polar diagram of film pressures is shown representing the extent of the arc of actual load-carrying lubricant film. The leading edge of the film may be established by an oil-distribution groove, such as at B, by a relief such as AA, or by the actual limit of the bearing itself as in a partial bearing (Fig. 22.16).

The trailing edge of the load-carrying film is considered as terminating at the point of closest approach between the shaft and bearing (Fig. 22.15). Beyond this point the clearance space is no longer converging, but begins to diverge. The film thickness at the point of closest approach is designated as h_0. A negative pressure will be established in the crown of the bearing and will contribute very little to the load-carrying function of the bearing since the positive oil-film pressures are generally many orders of magnitude larger than these negative pressures. Point O represents the center of the bearing, and O' the center of the shaft. The radius of the shaft is r, and the radius of the bearing R. Distance between O and O' is indicated by a and is the eccentric distance. The ratio of a for the actual operating conditions to the radial clearance in the bearing is called the eccentricity ratio ϵ. For light loads and high operating speeds the center of the shaft and the bearing coincide and a approaches zero. The eccentricity ratio also approaches zero. For heavy loads or extremes of operation, such as low speed or very low viscosity, the journal becomes more eccentric in the bearing and the distance a increases. The limit is where the journal just begins to make metallic contact with the bearing, or the distance a equals the radial clearance. The eccentricity ratio is then 1. Equation (22.9) is employed and applied to the converging geometric wedge of the journal bearing. It is necessary to express h as a function of the radial clearance and the angle θ. h^* is the film thickness at the point of maximum pressure.

The radial clearance in the bearing is c, which equals mr, if m is the clearance modulus of the bearing in inches per inch. The value of m will usually range between 0.0005 and 0.003, with typical values for industrial-type bearings running from 0.001 to 0.0025.

The value of dx in Eq. (22.9) is replaced by $r\,d\theta$ (Fig. 22.15). Also

$$h + a \cos\theta = mr$$

but

$$a = \epsilon mr$$

so

$$h + \epsilon mr \cos\theta = mr$$

$$h = mr(1 - \epsilon \cos\theta) \tag{22.33}$$

Also

$$h_0 + a = mr$$

$$h_0 = mr(1 - \epsilon) \tag{22.34}$$

Also let h^* be replaced by K^*mr (K^* will always be less than 1) and

$$u = \omega r$$

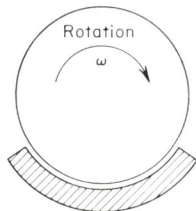

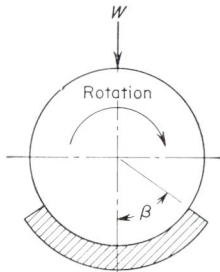

<table>
<tr><td>Fig. 22.16. Journal in partial bearing.</td><td>Fig. 22.17. Partial bearing showing angle β between line of action of load W and leading edge of bearing.</td></tr>
</table>

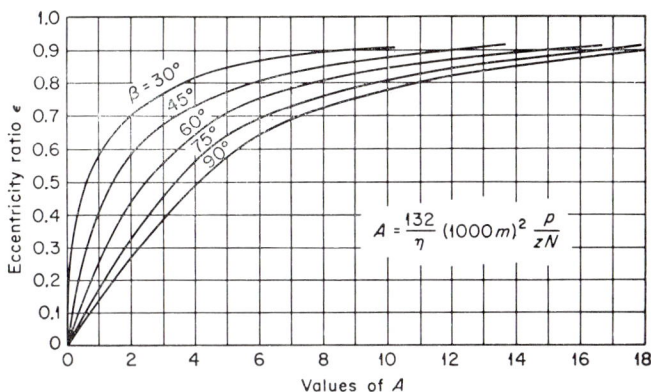

FIG. 22.18. Load-carrying factor for journal bearings.

After substituting in Eq. (22.9),

$$\frac{dp}{d\theta} = \frac{6\mu\omega}{m^2} \frac{K^* - (1 - \epsilon \cos \theta)}{(1 - \epsilon \cos \theta)^3}$$

or

$$p = \frac{6\mu\omega}{m^2} \left[\int \frac{K^* \, d\theta}{(1 - \epsilon \cos \theta)^3} - \int \frac{d\theta}{(1 - \epsilon \cos \theta)^2} \right] \qquad (22.35)$$

This can be integrated in closed form, using as a boundary condition that $p = 0$ when $\theta = 0$. However, the resultant expression is so cumbersome that it does not represent a workable solution to the problem. Instead, Karelitz[15,16] evaluated Eq. (22.35) by a process of numerical and graphical integration, in the process of which the term K^* was replaced by an equivalent form containing the physical parameter β. This is the angle between the line of action of the applied load W and the leading edge of the bearing, as shown in Fig. 22.17. Actually, for centrally loaded bearings, 2β would be the entire physical arc of the bearing. Thus a 120° partial bearing would have $\beta = 60°$. For a 180° partial bearing, $\beta = 90°$. As far as load-carrying capacity is concerned, a complete 360° bearing would be the same as a 180° partial bearing and β would also equal 90°.

The results of this numerical and graphical integration are shown in Fig. 22.18, in which the load-carrying function A is plotted against values of eccentricity ratio ϵ, for different values of β. Load-carrying function A is given as

$$A = 132(1000m)^2 \frac{P}{ZN} \qquad (22.36)$$

The previous analysis has been based on the absence of lubricant flow along the axis of the journal. Thus in Fig. 22.19, flow is considered only in the circumferential direction, the direction of $r \, d\theta$. No flow is assumed in the z direction. To actually have no flow in the z direction, the bearing dimension l must be infinitely long. This is the same condition described previously for the tilting-pad bearing. Once again, any effort to evaluate the performance of a cylindrical journal bearing including the effect of flow in the z direction (side flow) brings one up against the Reynolds differential Eq. (22.23).

The Kingsbury-Needs electric-analogue

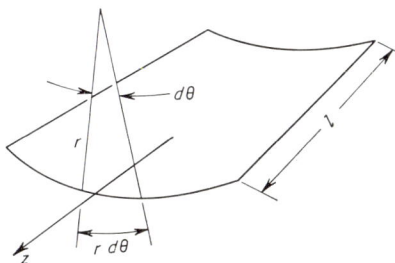

FIG. 22.19. Film area in partial bearing.

solution again provides useful data on reduction of pressure and load-carrying capacity because of side flow.

The same symbol η can be used, so that for the infinite bearing with no end flow or side leakage, $\eta = 1$. For bearings of finite length then, η will always be less than 1 and can be applied to the general equations for load capacity of infinite bearings as a reduction factor since side leakage bleeds off some of the pressure in the lubricant film and the resultant load-carrying capacity of the bearing is correspondingly reduced.

Equation (22.36) is rewritten as

$$A = \frac{132}{\eta}(1000m)^2 \frac{P_{av}}{ZN} \tag{22.37}$$

Values of η are shown in Fig. 22.20 plotted against l/d ratio and values of eccentricity ratio ϵ. The use of the two diagrams (Figs. 22.18 and 22.20) permits the analysis of the majority of industrial-type bearings and has proved to be of great value. The method of use is extremely simple and fast, and experience has shown it to be accurate. The method of solution is one of trial and error, but the results are sharply convergent, so that seldom are more than two trials needed.

Example 3. As an example of the use of Figs. 22.18 and 22.20, let us calculate the expected eccentricity and minimum film thickness for a journal bearing, with data taken from Barber and Davenport.[17] This is for a complete journal bearing (360°): $N = 1600$ rpm; $p_{av} = 271$ psi; average viscosity of the oil film, 54 centipoises; bearing length, 2.375 in.; shaft diameter, 2.504 in.; l/d ratio, 0.95; diametral clearance, 0.0094 in.; measured eccentricity ratio, 0.81; corresponding minimum film thickness, 0.0009 in.

$$m = \frac{\text{diametral clearance}}{\text{diameter}} = \frac{0.0094}{2.504} = 0.00375$$

It is necessary first to assume a value for the eccentricity ratio ϵ. Suppose the first

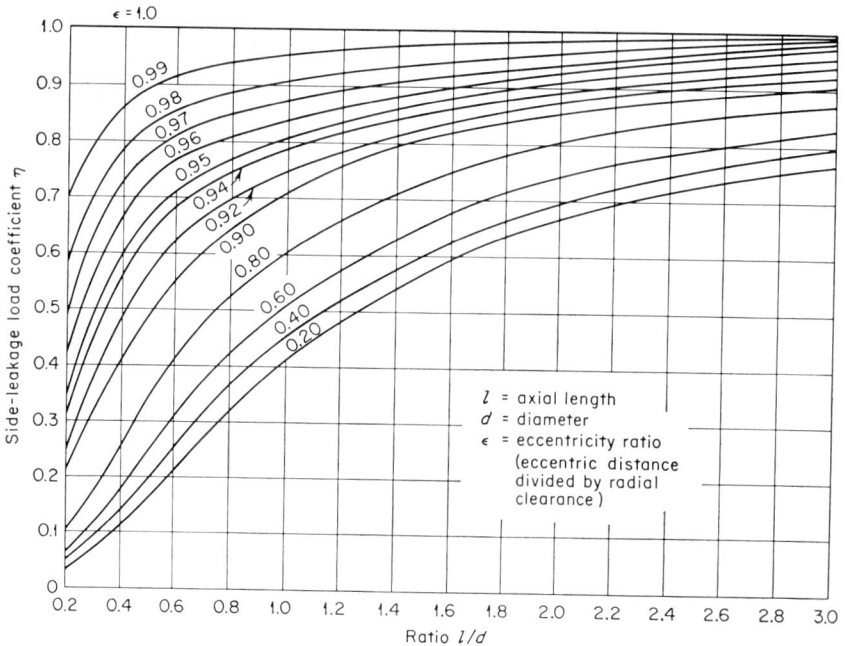

FIG. 22.20. Side-leakage factors for journal bearings.

estimate is 0.7. Then in Fig. 22.20, the side-leakage chart, with $l/d = 0.95$ and $\epsilon = 0.7$, the value of η is approximately 0.54.

Next, from Eq. (22.37), calculate the value of A.

$$A = \frac{132}{0.54}(3.75)^2 \frac{271}{54 \times 1600}$$

$$= 10.8$$

Now in Fig. 22.18, entering with $A = 10.8$ and rising to intersect the curve for $\beta = 90°$ (corresponding to a 180° partial bearing or a complete 360° bearing), the value of eccentricity ratio ϵ that is obtained is 0.8. This does not agree with the first estimate of $\epsilon = 0.7$. Repeat the process, now using $\epsilon = 0.8$. In Fig. 22.20 for $l/d = 0.95$ and $\epsilon = 0.8$, the value of η is 0.58. Evaluation of A from Eq. (22.37) is then 10.0. Once again in Fig. 22.18 with $A = 10.0$, value of ϵ is 0.79. This is very close to 0.8, and the calculation need not be carried further. Thus the estimated value of eccentricity ratio ϵ is 0.8. The measured value is 0.81.

The minimum film thickness h_0 is then, from Eq. (22.34),

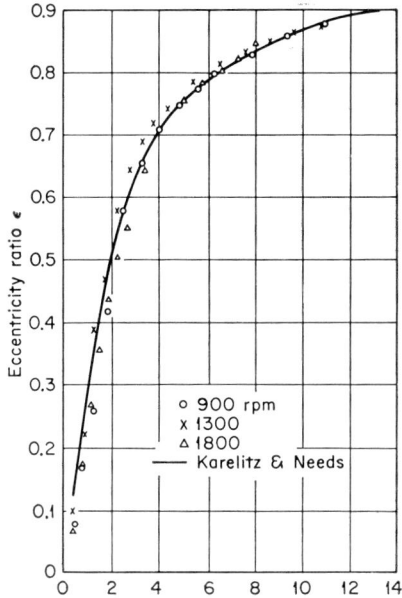

Fig. 22.21. Values of A for 360° bearing ($l/d = 1$).

$$h_0 = mr(1 - \epsilon)$$
$$= 0.00375 \times 1.252(1 - 0.8)$$
$$= 0.00094 \text{ in.}$$

The method of solution outlined has proved to be exceedingly accurate in the prediction of the eccentricity ratio and minimum film thickness. Figure 22.21 shows correlation between very precise experimental data for a 360° journal bearing having an l/d of 1 and the corresponding theoretical curve for the performance of this bearing. The theoretical curve was obtained by using the Karelitz-Needs method as derived and demonstrated above. The data were taken by M. I. Smith at Columbia University.[18]

Friction in Journal Bearings. No analysis of journal bearings can be considered complete until an evaluation of the probable friction and power losses has been made. This estimate is then weighed against the expected heat-dissipating capacity of the bearing. All the heat generated in the bearing from friction must be removed in order for the unit to reach some steady-state operating temperature. The design of many bearings has unfortunately not included a proper evaluation of this vital heat-balance condition, and consequently it is quite common to observe bearings that are properly designed from the hydrodynamic-oil-film point of view, but fail badly from overheating.

Using a method similar to that employed for evaluating the friction loss in a tilting-pad bearing, one arrives at Eq. (22.38), which expresses the friction moment acting on the journal as

$$M_J = \frac{\mu l r^2 N}{m} \times K_{fJ} \qquad (22.38)$$

if, for a 360° bearing,

$$K_{fJ} = \frac{\pi^2}{30}\left[\frac{2}{\sqrt{1 - \epsilon^2}} + \frac{3\epsilon^2}{(2 + \epsilon^2)\sqrt{1 - \epsilon^2}}\right] \qquad (22.39)$$

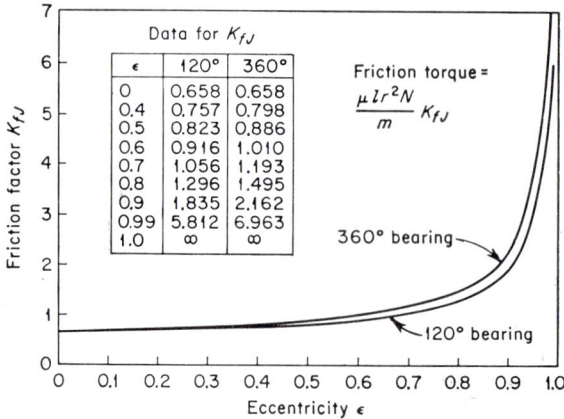

Data for K_{fJ}		
ϵ	120°	360°
0	0.658	0.658
0.4	0.757	0.798
0.5	0.823	0.886
0.6	0.916	1.010
0.7	1.056	1.193
0.8	1.296	1.495
0.9	1.835	2.162
0.99	5.812	6.963
1.0	∞	∞

Friction torque = $\dfrac{\mu l r^2 N}{m} K_{fJ}$

Fig. 22.22. Friction factors for torque on journal bearing.

Values of K_{fJ} from Eq. (22.39) and also values for a 120° partial bearing with a complete cap over the journal are shown in Fig. 22.22.

The friction torque on the bearing is less than that of the journal. This can be explained in a manner similar to that used for the shoe and runner of the tilting-pad bearing. For the journal bearing, equilibrium of moments can be established if the off-center effect of the applied load is considered, acting at some eccentric distance relative to the center of the bearing (Ref. 1, pp. 233–235). It is relatively simple to measure the friction torque on the bearing itself, but a true indication of the friction loss in the unit is not obtained until a correction is made and the offset effect of the applied load is included. The total resulting friction moment, bearing plus offset moment, will then equal the friction torque on the journal. For computation purposes K_{fJ} for the journal should be used.

Example 4. To illustrate the use of Eq. (22.38), consider a 360° journal bearing, 1 in. in diameter by 1 in. long. Clearance modulus, $m = 0.0016$. Speed, 1800 rpm. Load, $W = 802$ lb. Oil viscosity at a film temperature of 110°F is 24 centipoises. If the Karelitz-Needs method of analysis is used, it should be found that the eccentricity ratio ϵ is 0.8 and the minimum film thickness h_0 is 0.00016 in.

In Fig. 22.22, the value of K_{fJ} is 1.495 for a 360° bearing. After substituting in Eq. (22.38),

$$M_J = \frac{24 \times 1.45 \times 10^{-7} \times 1 \times (0.5)^2 \times 1800}{0.0016} \times 1.495$$

$$= 1.46 \text{ in.-lb}$$

This result can also be expressed in whatever units may be most convenient, such as coefficient of friction, for example, or when coupled with the speed of rotation, Btu per minute, friction horsepower, etc.

It may be noticed that in Fig. 22.22, for lightly loaded bearings where the eccentricity ratio approaches zero, the value of K_{fJ} approaches 0.658. This permits Eq. (22.38) to be rewritten as

$$M_J = \frac{0.658 \mu l r^2 N}{m} \qquad (22.40)$$

It will be noticed in Fig. 22.22 that Eq. (22.40) may be used with reasonable accuracy to predict friction losses in journal bearings up to eccentricity ratios of about 0.5. This is a great convenience.

All the calculations of friction thus far have assumed that laminar-flow conditions prevail in the lubricant film. In most cases this assumption is valid, but in some circumstances where the speeds are high, the film thickness and clearance fairly large, or

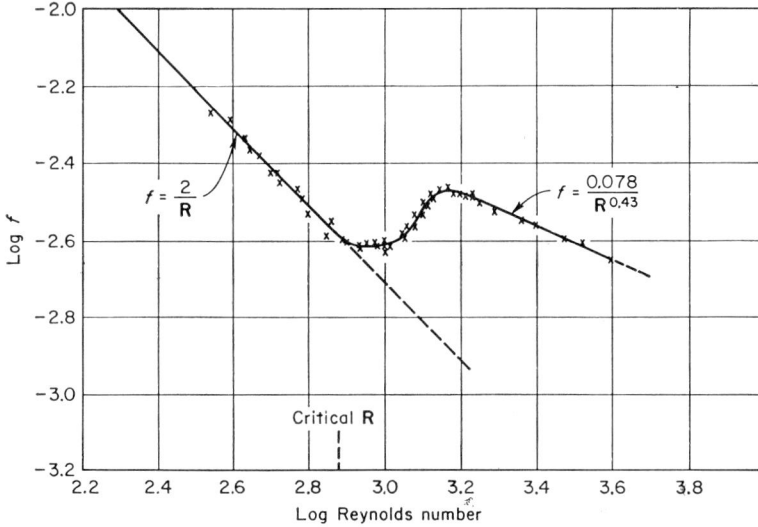

FIG. 22.23. Friction as a function of Reynolds number (unloaded journal bearing $l/d = 1$). (*Ref.* 18.)

the kinematic viscosity of the lubricant relatively low, it is quite possible to produce a breakdown of laminar flow in the bearing clearance space. As for other situations dealing with fluid flow, the Reynolds number again serves as a sensitive measure of when laminar conditions begin to break down. If the Reynolds number for a journal bearing is defined as $\mathbf{R} = uh/\nu$, in which h is the radial clearance or film thickness in the bearing (for lightly loaded operating conditions), it has been shown experimentally that for Reynolds numbers between 800 and 1000, laminar-flow conditions will start to deteriorate. Figure 22.23 is a plot of experimental results obtained at Columbia University,[18] showing a plot of friction factor against Reynolds number in the classical fluid-mechanics tradition. A striking resemblance is seen to the friction-factor plots for pipe flow. A turbulent regime is shown at the right side of the plot, a laminar regime to the left, and a familiar transition zone in the center. Friction in a bearing is of course greatly increased if laminar-flow conditions give way to turbulent flow.[19] The same conditions have been observed in tilting-pad thrust bearings.[20]

22.6. Hydrostatic Lubrication

One of the most outstanding and useful recent developments in the field of lubrication has been the introduction of a type of fluid-film lubrication known as hydrostatic lubrication. Here lubricant is forced into the clearance space of the bearing from an external high-pressure source. The pressure in the film is therefore not self-induced but externally induced. The bearing surfaces are kept separated at all times even if these surfaces are stationary, and relative sliding motion does not exist.

The rigidity or stiffness of the lubricant film is a matter of analysis, and such stiffness can be one of the specifications of the design. Bearings have been designed with a film rigidity of from 25 to 30 million pounds per inch and, in one unusual case for a large radio telescope, has been as high as 300 million pounds per inch. This means that the actual oil film in the clearance space of the bearing has the same rigidity or stiffness as a cube of steel 10 in. on a side! Thus, where positioning or alignment of rotors or gimbals is vital, this type of bearing can provide the necessary rigidity and can in fact often produce a bearing film that is stiffer than the metal structure that contains it.

An additional feature of hydrostatic lubrication, and one of vital significance in some

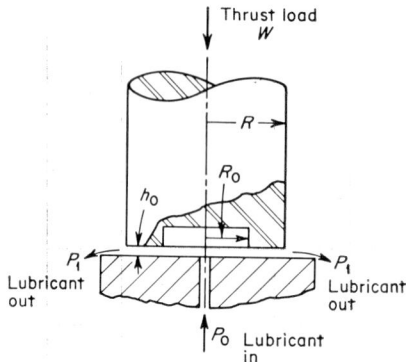

Fig. 22.24. Schematic diagram of step bearing.

applications, is the unbelievably low friction that can result. With the Hale telescope on Mount Palomar in California, the over-all coefficient of friction for the entire supporting system of the million-pound structure is about 0 000004, for normal operation. Even lower values can be achieved. On the cradle of an electric dynamometer weighing 130(lb, a coefficient of friction[21] is reported of 0.000,000,75. Actually, for these and like applications, it can be assumed realistically that the coefficient of friction is approaching zero.

Mathematical analysis of these bearings is straight-forward, and the resultant equations relating the variables of viscosity, pressure, film thickness, and oil flow can be conveniently applied to their design. As an example, the significant equations are derived for the circular hydrostatic thrust bearing having a single circular recess. Figure 22.24 is a schematic representation of such a bearing. It is frequently called a *step* bearing.

The radius of the shaft is R, and there is a recess at the bottom of the shaft having a radius R_0. Inlet lubricant pressure is P_0, supplied at the center of the bearing. The lubricant flows radially outward through an annulus of depth h_0 and escapes at the periphery of the shaft at some pressure P_1, which may often be atmospheric pressure.

In order to evaluate the load-carrying capacity, it is first necessary to determine the rate of change of pressure as the oil flows outward over the step. Figure 22.25 represents, in the top view, a plan of the bearing with a differential annulus of length $2\pi r$ and depth dr through which the oil is flowing. This is, in effect, a differential slot. The expression for the flow of an incompressible viscous fluid through a slot of infinite width is

$$Q = \frac{\Delta P b h^3}{12\mu l}$$

Applied to the differential slot this equation becomes

$$Q = -\frac{dp\,2\pi r h_0{}^3}{12\mu\,dr} \qquad (22.41)$$

The minus sign is used since dp/dr is negative. By rewriting and after integrating,

$$p = -\frac{6\mu Q}{\pi h_0{}^3}\ln r + C \qquad (22.42)$$

The constant C is evaluated by considering the boundary conditions that $p = 0$ when $r = R$. The pressure p at any radius r then becomes

$$p = \frac{6\mu Q}{\pi h_0{}^3}\ln\frac{R}{r} \qquad (22.43)$$

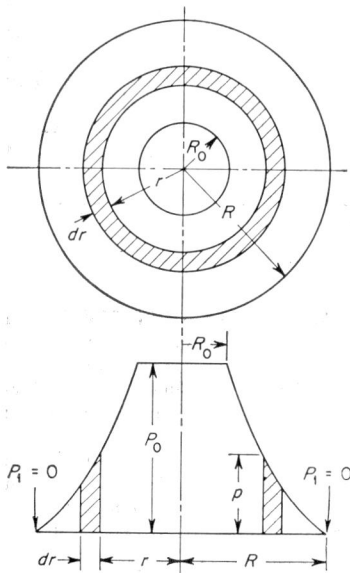

Fig. 22.25. Plan view (upper) and radial pressure distribution (lower) of a step bearing.

From this equation the required inlet pressure P_0 can be evaluated by setting $r = R_0$.

$$P_0 = \frac{6\mu Q}{\pi h_0{}^3} \ln \frac{R}{R_0} \tag{22.44}$$

It may be noted that the quantity of flow needed to maintain a predetermined film thickness is given by transposing Eq. (22.44) to read

$$Q = \frac{P_0 \pi h_0{}^3}{6\mu \ln (R/R_0)} \tag{22.45}$$

Now the load-carrying capacity can be evaluated. The lower view in Fig. 22.25 shows a profile of the pressure distribution. The total load-carrying effect will be the sum of the forces exerted by the inlet pressure P_0 acting on the area of the recess of radius R_0 and by the variable pressure p acting on the sill area of the bearing. Expressed mathematically,

$$W = P_0(\pi R_0{}^2) + \int_{R_0}^{R} p(2\pi r \, dr)$$

By inserting p from Eq. (22.43),

$$W = P_0 \pi R_0{}^2 + \frac{12\mu Q}{h_0{}^3} \int_{R_0}^{R} \left(\ln \frac{R}{r} \right) r \, dr$$

By integrating, by inserting the limits, and after substituting for Q from Eq. (22.45),

$$W = \frac{P_0 \pi}{2} \frac{R^2 - R_0{}^2}{\ln (R/R_0)} \tag{22.46}$$

This equation is valid even when the recess is eliminated, in which case R_0 becomes the radius of the inlet oil-supply pipe and the equation is still determinate.

Example 5. A typical combination thrust and guide bearing is shown in Fig. 22.26. The thrust bearing is of the hydrostatic step type. Thrust load is 101,000 lb; outside diameter of bearing 16 in.; diameter of recess 10 in. After substituting these values in Eq. (22.44),

$$101,000 = \frac{P_0 \pi}{2} \frac{8^2 - 5^2}{\ln (8/5)}$$

$$P_0 = 774 \text{ psi}$$

Film thickness in the bearing should be from 0.001 to 0.010 in., to protect the surfaces from metal-to-metal contact and to allow passage of harmful grit that may find its way into the system. The film thickness determines the oil flow for a given viscosity and pressure.

In the foregoing example, if the film thickness is to be maintained at 0.006 in. with an oil equivalent to SAE 20 at 130°F, what quantity will be pumped in gallons per minute? Oil viscosity is 29.24 centipoises, or 42×10^{-7} reyn. By using Eq. (22.45),

$$Q = \frac{774\pi(0.006)^3}{6 \times 42 \times 10^{-7} \times 0.470} = 43.9 \text{ in.}^3/\text{sec}$$

Converting to gallons per minute,

$$Q = 43.9 \times 60/231 = 11.35 \text{ gpm}$$

The total energy losses in such a bearing are made up of (1) the viscous friction on the step due to rotation of the shaft and (2) the energy required to force or pump the lubricant radially outward through the film space. The first part is simple viscous shear on the step and is proportional to the rotational speed of the shaft. The slower the shaft speed, the smaller this effect becomes, and at standstill it vanishes.

The second part, or *pump work*, is a constant for any given volume of flow and pressure difference and is independent of shaft speed. In forcing lubricant through the clearance over the annulus, against the viscous resistance to flow, work is done. The energy in-

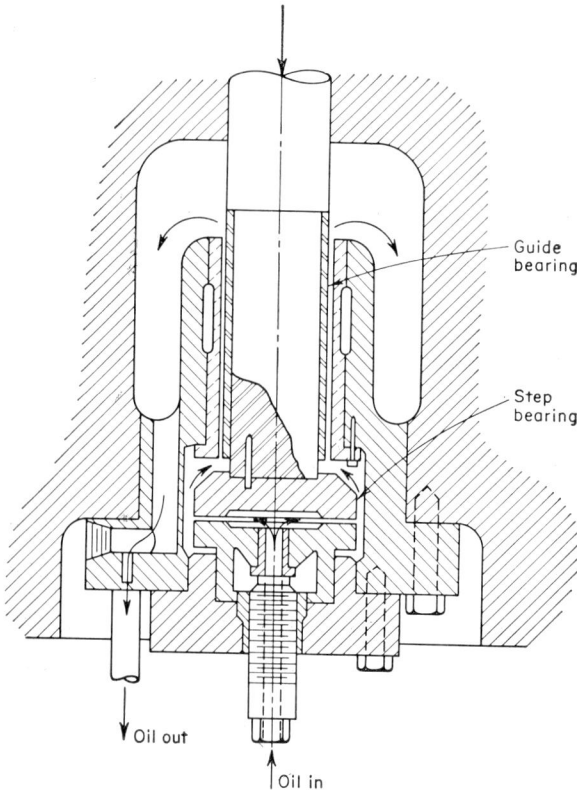

FIG. 22.26. Application of hydrostatic lubrication to a step bearing.

volved is equal to the product of Q and the pressure difference ΔP. Thus energy $= Q\,\Delta P$ in.-lb/sec. This can then be converted to whatever units are convenient.

22.7. Hydrostatic Lubrication Applied to Journal Bearings

Sleeve bearings of the oil-film type, after being brought up to speed, operate with a high degree of efficiency and reliability. However, difficulties arise when the rotational speed of the journal is too low to maintain a complete hydrodynamic oil film. This condition is especially noticeable at starting, stopping, and reversing or whenever the operating speed falls below a certain minimum. When this occurs, the oil film is ruptured, frictional drag increases, and metal-to-metal contact develops, rapidly worsens, and leads to wear of the bearing material.

This condition can be eliminated by introducing high-pressure oil to the area between the bottom of the journal and the bearing (Fig. 22.27). If the pressure and quantity of flow are in the correct proportions, the shaft, whether it is rotating or not, will be raised and supported by an oil film. Frictional drag may drop to one-tenth or even less, and in certain kinds of heavy rotational equipment, where available torque is low, this may mean the difference between starting or not starting.

Figure 22.28 illustrates a shaft of radius r being floated in a bearing of radius R by a lubricant pumped through slot S at pressure P_0, the supply pressure of the pump. Oil flows up the sides until it reaches the relief at some angle θ_1, where the pressure is approximately atmospheric.

It may be assumed that end leakage is negligible, that is, oil flow along the length of the

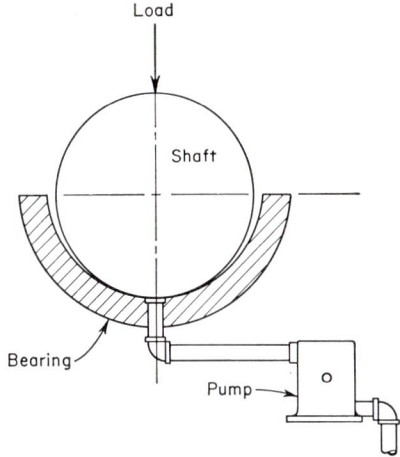

FIG. 22.27. Schematic diagram of hydro-static lift.

journal is small compared with that up and around the sides of the journal. This condition is closely realized in a clearance bearing when the slot is shorter than the length of the bearing.

Consider flow up one side through an elemental slot of length $r\,d\theta$ and width b. With laminar conditions, the flow through a slot of infinite width is given by

$$q = \frac{\Delta P h^3 b}{12\mu l}$$

As applied to the elemental slot, ΔP is replaced by dp and l is replaced by $r\,d\theta$. Also inasmuch as θ increases as the oil-film pressure decreases, the equation becomes

$$q_1 = -\frac{dp\,h^3 b}{12\mu r\,d\theta}$$

Here the film thickness h is not a constant, but depends upon the angular position θ and the eccentricity of the journal in the bearing. When the shaft has settled in the bearing and has made metal-to-metal contact, the eccentricity ratio, which may be denoted by ϵ, is 1. When the shaft and bearing are concentric, the eccentricity ratio ϵ is zero. The radial clearance built into the bearing can be called mr, where m is a clearance modulus varying from about 0.0005 to roughly 0.003 in./in., and r is the radius of the journal. Thus, for a journal with radius 5 in. and clearance modulus 0.003 in./in., the radial clearance in the bearing is 5×0.003, or 0.015 in.

By referring again to Fig. 22.15, if distance a is small compared with r (this is the usual case) and h is the film thickness at any angular position θ, then

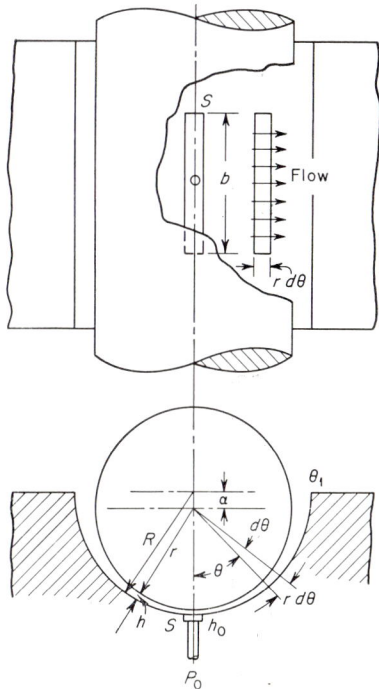

FIG. 22.28. Schematic diagram of hydro-static lift.

$$h = mr - a \cos \theta$$

but

$$a = \epsilon mr$$

Therefore

$$h = mr(1 - \epsilon \cos \theta)$$

By substituting in equation for q_1,

$$q_1 = -\frac{dp \; bm^3 r^3 (1 - \epsilon \cos \theta)^3}{12 \mu r \; d\theta}$$

ϵ	A	B
0	24.00	18.85
0.1	28.14	23.18
0.2	33.75	29.00
0.3	41.62	38.24
0.4	53.30	52.70
0.5	72.00	77.90
0.6	105.1	127.5
0.7	173.4	245.5
0.75	237.0	343.5
0.8	359.8	634.0
0.85	613.0	1258
0.9	1321	3355
0.91	1615	4340
0.92	2074	5810
0.93	2620	8040
0.94	3533	11,750
0.95	5040	18,380
0.96	7800	32,050
0.97	13,740	65,300
0.98	30,600	179,000
0.99	121,200	348,200
1.00	∞	∞

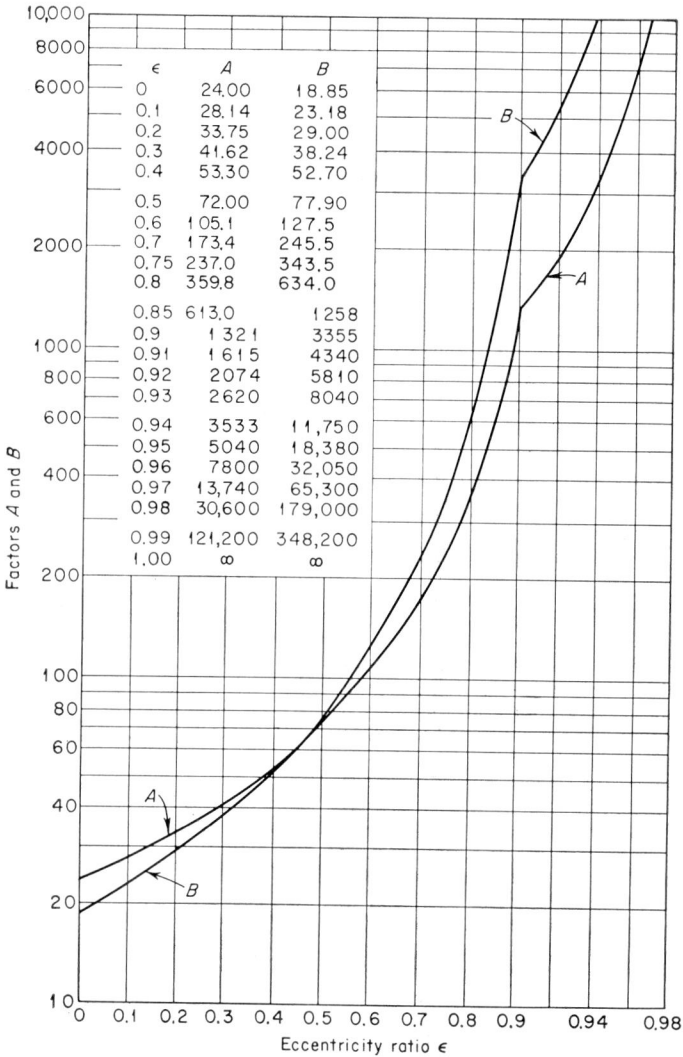

FIG. 22.29. Tabular and plotted values of the constants in the oil-lift equations for pressure and load-carring capacity of the bearing.

After separating the variables,

$$dp = \frac{-12\mu q_1}{bm^3r^2} \frac{d\theta}{(1 - \epsilon \cos \theta)^3}$$

and

$$p = \frac{-12\mu q_1}{bm^3r^2} \int \frac{d\theta}{(1 - \epsilon \cos \theta)^3}$$

General solution of this equation is

$$p = \frac{-12\mu q_1}{bm^3r^2} \left[\frac{\epsilon \sin \theta(4 - \epsilon^2 - 3\epsilon \cos \theta)}{2(1 - \epsilon^2)^2(1 - \epsilon \cos \theta)^2} + \frac{2 + \epsilon^2}{(1 - \epsilon^2)^{5/2}} \arctan \left(\frac{1 + \epsilon}{\sqrt{1 - \epsilon^2}} \tan\frac{\theta}{2} \right) + D \right]$$

$$(22.47)$$

The constant of integration can be evaluated by setting $p = 0$ when $\theta = \theta_1$, the angle of relief. When $\theta_1 = 90°$, as in a 180° bearing, the constant D becomes

$$D = -\left[\frac{\epsilon(4 - \epsilon^2)}{2(1 - \epsilon^2)^2} + \frac{2 + \epsilon^2}{(1 - \epsilon^2)^{5/2}} \arctan \frac{1 + \epsilon}{\sqrt{1 - \epsilon^2}} \right]$$

The inlet pressure P_0 of the oil-lift groove can now be evaluated for the 180° bearing by letting $\theta = 0$ in Eq. (22.47), which leads to

$$P_0 = \frac{\mu q_1}{bm^3r^2} B \qquad (22.48)$$

if the term B is given by the following equation:

$$B = 12\left[\frac{\epsilon(4 - \epsilon^2)}{2(1 - \epsilon^2)^2} + \frac{2 + \epsilon^2}{(1 - \epsilon^2)^{5/2}} \arctan \frac{1 + \epsilon}{\sqrt{1 - \epsilon^2}} \right]$$

Values of B have been calculated and are listed on Fig. 22.29, which also includes a plot of these points. The significance of the subscript 1 on q is to indicate that q_1 represents the flow up one side of the bearing only. Because of symmetry, the total flow will be twice this value.

To evaluate the load-carrying capacity, the pressure distribution must be calculated (Fig. 22.30). At position θ, the pressure is p. It acts on area $r\,d\theta\,b$ and produces a force toward the center of the journal. The vertical component of this force, $pr\,d\theta\,b \cos \theta$, will act vertically upward and carry part of the load W. The total load W will be sustained by the summation of all these small vertical forces acting on the lower surface of the journal. Expressed algebraically for the general case, this becomes

$$W = 2 \int_0^{\theta_1} br\,d\theta\,p \cos \theta$$

in which p is substituted from Eq. (22.47). For the 180° bearing with $\theta_1 = 90°$, the integration eventually simplifies to the following:

$$W = \frac{\mu q_1}{m^3r} A \qquad (22.49)$$

if

$$A = 12\frac{2 + 3\epsilon - \epsilon^3}{(1 - \epsilon^2)^2} \qquad (22.50)$$

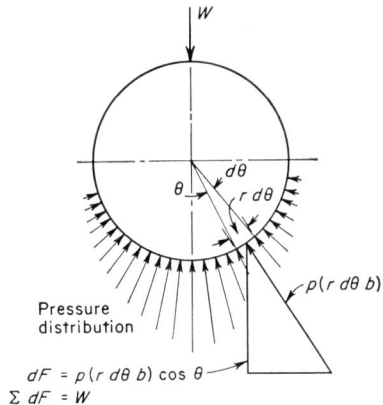

Pressure distribution

$dF = p(r\,d\theta\,b) \cos \theta$
$\Sigma\,dF = W$

FIG. 22.30. Load-carrying capacity is summation of vertical components of pressure forces acting on lower surface of journal.

Numerical values of A are tabulated and plotted on Fig. 22.29. By solving for q_1 from Eq. (22.49),

$$q_1 = \frac{1}{A} \frac{Wm^3 r}{\mu} \tag{22.51}$$

The expression for minimum film thickness in terms of eccentricity of shaft is, from Fig. 22.28, $h_0 + a = mr$, which may be written $h_0 = mr - \epsilon mr$, or

$$h_0 = mr(1 - \epsilon) \tag{22.52}$$

After solving for ϵ, the eccentricity ratio

$$\epsilon = 1 - \frac{h_0}{mr} \tag{22.53}$$

Example 6. A 4.000-in.-diameter journal rests in a bearing of diameter 4.012 in. SAE 30 oil at 100°F is supplied under pressure through a groove at the lowest point of the bearing. Length of bearing is 6 in.; length of groove is 3 in.; and load on bearing is 3600 lb. What inlet pressure and oil flow are needed to raise the journal (a) 0.002 in. and (b) 0.004 in.?

SOLUTION. Radial clearance $= mr = \frac{1}{2}(4.012 - 4.000) = 0.006$ in.; hence the clearance modulus is $m = 0.006/2 = 0.003$ in./in. and the eccentricity ratio, from Eq. (22.53), is $\epsilon = 1 - (0.002/0.006) = 0.667$. Viscosity for SAE 30 at 100°F is 152×10^{-7} reyn (lb-sec/in.²).

From Fig. 22.29, for $\epsilon = 0.667$, A will be 140, and B will be 183. By substituting values in Eq. (22.51),

$$q_1 = \frac{3600 \times (0.003)^3 \times 2}{140 \times 152 \times 10^{-7}}$$

$$= 0.091 \text{ in.}^3/\text{sec (one side)}$$

or

$$Q = \frac{0.091 \times 2 \times 60}{231} = 0.0478 \text{ gpm (total)}$$

From Eq. (22.48),

$$P_0 = \frac{0.091 \times 183 \times 152 \times 10^{-7}}{3 \times 2^2 \times (0.003)^3} = 784 \text{ psi}$$

By repeating the same procedure for $h_0 = 0.004$ in., $\epsilon = 0.334$, $A = 44.5$, $B = 42$, $q_1 = 0.2896$ in.³/sec, $Q = 0.1505$ gpm, and $P_0 = 566$ psi.

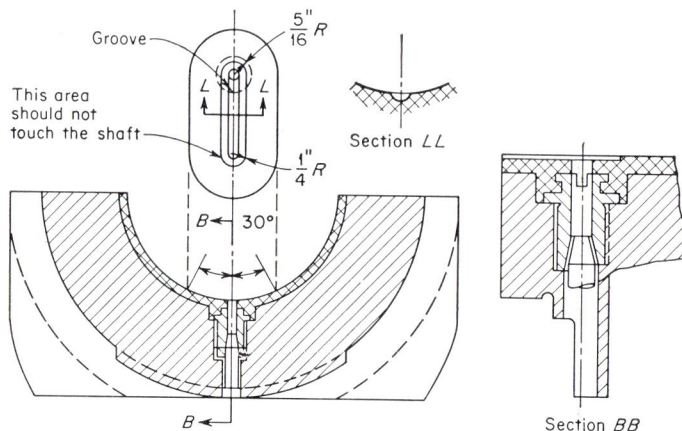

FIG. 22.31. Detail of a 5- by 10-in. bearing with oil lift, showing the proportions of the groove. (*Drawing, courtesy of Westinghouse Electric Corp.*)

Obviously, the closer the shaft is to the center of the bearing, the smaller is the pressure required and the larger is the oil flow.   Some designers prefer a constant-displacement pump with adequate pressure and volume capacity.   Others use high-pressure spur-gear pumps   The pressure capacity of the pump should be greater than that calculated by the foregoing method for the reason that, as the shaft begins to lift from the bearing, the initial eccentricity ratio being 1, it progressively moves through eccentricity ratios of 0.9, 0.8, 0.7, etc., and in passing through these large eccentricity ratios, higher pressures are momentarily needed than for lower values, such as 0.6, 0.5, 0.4, etc.

Figure 22.31 shows details of a hydrostatic lift as applied to a bearing 5 in. in diameter by 10 in. long.

22.8. Solutions for Hydrostatic Bearings Obtained by the Use of an Electric Analogue

It is obvious that the solution derived above for the journal bearing is somewhat approximate in that it neglects flow of the lubricant along the axis of the bearing.   Flow was only assumed to take place up and around the sides of the journal in a circumferential direction.   To allow for flow in both the circumferential and axial directions introduces further mathematical complications.   Actually, any shape of a hydrostatic bearing other than the most simple is difficult to analyze if an exact solution is desired.

However, since the thickness of the fluid film in a hydrostatic bearing is frequently constant and if the relative sliding velocity of the bearing surfaces is zero, certain simplifying assumptions can be made in the Reynolds Eq. (22.23), so that it takes the general form

$$\frac{\partial}{\partial x}\left(\frac{h^3}{12\mu}\frac{\partial p}{\partial x}\right) + \frac{\partial}{\partial y}\left(\frac{h^3}{12\mu}\frac{\partial p}{\partial y}\right) = 0 \tag{22.54}$$

There is then a direct analogy between this equation and that which governs the relationship between resistance and voltage distribution in a two-dimensional electric field, or

$$\frac{\partial}{\partial x}\left(\frac{1}{k}\frac{\partial E}{\partial x}\right) + \frac{\partial}{\partial y}\left(\frac{1}{k}\frac{\partial E}{\partial y}\right) = 0$$

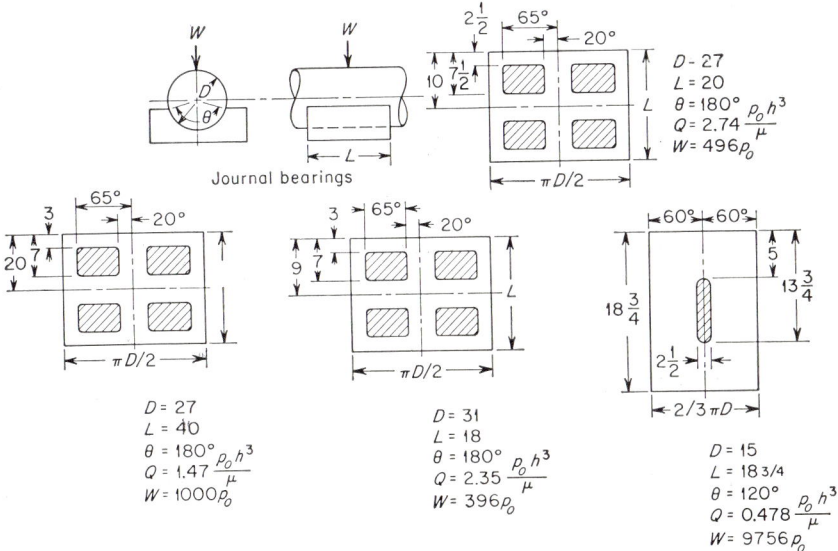

Fig. 22.32. Field-plotter solutions for hydrostatic journal bearings.   (*Ref.* 22.)

Thrust bearings

$Q = 0.488 \dfrac{p_0 h^3}{\mu}$

$W = 177.8 p_0$

$Q = 0.732 \dfrac{p_0 h^3}{\mu}$

$W = 199.5 p_0$

$Q = 0.129 \dfrac{p_0 h^3}{\mu}$

$W = 60.1 p_0$

$Q = 0.633 \dfrac{p_0 h^3}{\mu}$

$W = 213 p_0$

Note: All recesses 1 in. diameter

$Q = 0.33 \dfrac{p_0 h^3}{\mu}$

$W = 106 p_0$

$Q = 2.03 \dfrac{p_0 h^3}{\mu}$

$W = 549.9 p_0$

$Q = 0.905 \dfrac{p_0 h^3}{\mu}$

$W = 531 p_0$

Note: Recess corners 1 in. radius

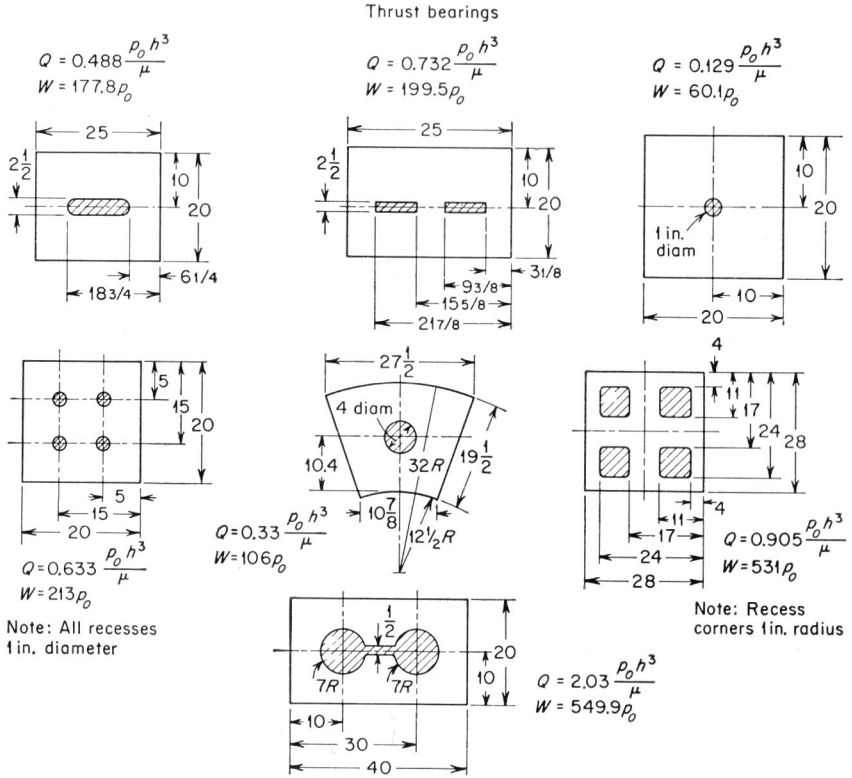

FIG. 22.33. Field-plotter solutions for hydrostatic thrust bearings. (*Ref.* 22.)

If the resistivity k is constant, then an electrolytic sheet of constant thickness will be a valid analogy for the hydraulic pressure field, assuming that the film thickness and viscosity are constant. Consequently, a plot of voltage distribution E, obtained from a developed model of the fluid film in a hydrostatic bearing, will also be a plot of the pressure distribution in that film.[22]

The results of such determinations on a number of different geometries are shown in Fig. 22.32 for journal bearings and Fig. 22.33 for thrust bearings.

These figures show load and flow equations obtained by the use of the electric-analogue field plotter.

Dimensions for the journal bearings are in inches unless otherwise noted and are given for only one quadrant of symmetrical models. The shapes shown are developed views of the curved surfaces. In all figures, the crosshatched areas are the high-pressure recesses.

The thrust bearings are flat pads, and their dimensions are given in inches.

REFERENCES

1. Fuller, D. D.: "Theory and Practice of Lubrication for Engineers," Wiley, New York, 1956.
2. Purday, H. F. P.: "An Introduction to the Mechanics of Viscous Flow," Dover, New York, 1949.
3. Rayleigh, Lord: Notes on the Theory of Lubrication, *Phil. Mag.*, **35**:1–12 (1918).

4. Archibald, F. R.: A Simple Hydrodynamic Thrust Bearing, *Trans. ASME*, **72**:393–400 (1950).
5. Archibald, F. R.: The Stepped Shape Film Applied to a Journal Bearing, *J. Franklin Inst.*, **253**:21–27 (1952).
6. Cameron, A.: Hydrodynamic Lubrication of Rotating Disks in Pure Sliding: A New Type of Oil Film Formation, *J. Inst. Petrol.*, **37**:471–486 (1951).
7. Heidebroeck, E.: On the Theory of Fluid Friction between Sliding and Rolling Surfaces, *Forsch. Gebiete Ingenieurw.*, **6**:161–168 (1935). (In German.)
8. Abramovitz, S.: Theory for a Slider Bearing with a Convex Pad Surface: Side Flow Neglected, *J. Franklin Inst.*, **259**:221–223 (1955).
9. Raimondi, A. A., and J. Boyd: The Influence of Surface Profile on the Load Capacity of Thrust Bearings with Centrally Pivoted Pads, *Trans. ASME*, **77**:321–330 (1955).
10. Gross, W. A.: A Gas Film Lubrication Study. Part I. Some Theoretical Analyses of Slider Bearings, *IBM Journal*, **3**:237–255 (1959).
11. Michell, A. G. M.: "Lubrication," Blackie, Glasgow, 1950.
12. Kingsbury, A.: On Problems in the Theory of Fluid-film Lubrication, with an Experimental Method of Solution, *Trans. ASME*, **53**:59–75 (1931).
13. Needs, S. J.: Effects of Side Leakage in 120 Degree Centrally Supported Journal Bearings, *Trans. ASME*, **56**:721–732 (1934) and **57**:135–138 (1935).
14. Feifel, E.: Test Bed for Large Thrust Bearings, *Z. Ver. deut. Ingr.*, **69**:679–682 (1925). (In German.)
15. Karelitz, G. B.: Charts for Studying the Oil Film in Bearings, *Trans. ASME*, **47**:1101–1122 (1925).
16. Karelitz, G. B.: Performance of Oil Ring Bearings, *Trans. ASME*, **52**:57–70 (1930).
17. Barker, E. M., and C. C. Davenport: Investigation of Journal Bearing Performance, *Penn. State Coll. Bull.* 42, 1933.
18. Smith, M. I., and D. D. Fuller: Journal-bearing Operation at Superlaminar Speeds, *Trans. ASME*, **78**:469–474 (1956).
19. Wilcock, D. F.: Turbulence in High-speed Journal Bearings, *Trans. ASME*, **72**:825–834 (1950).
20. Abramovitz, S.: Turbulence in a Tilting Pad Thrust Bearing, *Trans. ASME*, **78**:7–11 (1956).
21. Potts, P. S.: Hydrostatic Bearings Minimize Friction in Cradle Dynamometer, *Machine Design*, **24**:180–184 (1950).
22. Loeb, A. M.: The Determination of the Characteristics of Hydrostatic Bearings through the Use of the Electric Analog Field Plotter, *ASLE Trans.*, **1**:217–224 (1958).

Section 23

THERMAL-JET AND ROCKET-JET PROPULSION

By

M. J. ZUCROW, *Purdue University, Lafayette, Indiana*

THERMAL-JET AND ROCKET-JET PROPULSION

23.1. Introduction

The basic operating principle of all known methods for propelling a body in a fluid medium is the *reaction principle* formulated by Sir Isaac Newton (1642–1727); it states that *to every action there is an equal and opposite reaction*. In a dynamical system a reaction force is produced in one direction by accelerating a mass in the opposite direction. In applying the reaction principle to the propulsion of a body in a fluid medium, the momentum of a working fluid is increased in the direction opposite to that desired for the propelled body, and the *reaction* to the time rate of increase in the momentum of the fluid produces a *propelling force* termed the *thrust*, acting in the desired direction of motion for the propelled body. The basic differences between the known means for propelling bodies in fluid media are those pertinent to the methods and devices employed for increasing the rate of flow of momentum of the working fluid.

In a conventional propulsion method, such as propeller propulsion, the working fluid is caused to flow around and over the surfaces of the propelled body. *Jet propulsion* differs from such methods in that the increase in the rate of flow of momentum of the working fluid produces a high-speed fluid jet, termed the *propulsive jet*, which is ejected from *within* the propelled body. In the abstract, at least, there are no restrictions on the character of the fluid that can be employed for the propulsive jet. The selection of the most appropriate fluid is governed, however, by the conditions pertinent to the propulsion problem. Thus for the propulsion of bodies through the earth's atmosphere, one finds that only two types of fluids are particularly suitable for creating the propulsive jet.

1. There is the propulsive jet formed by heating compressed atmospheric air, usually by burning a liquid fuel in it, the fuel-air ratio depending upon the desired gas temperature. An engine for producing such a propulsive jet is called a *thermal-jet engine*.

2. There is the propulsive jet formed from the high-pressure, high-temperature gases generated by reacting appropriate chemicals in a suitable device, no air from the atmosphere being consumed in creating the propulsive jet. Such a propulsive jet is called a *chemical rocket jet*. From a broad point of view, a rocket jet is one formed by ejecting matter, excluding atmospheric air, in the form of a high-speed jet from within a body. Thus the jet formed by heating a working fluid in a nuclear reactor, a jet of ions, a jet consisting of the plasma produced by an electric arc, and the like, are rocket jets. The discussions of rocket jets will be confined to those produced by *chemical rocket engines*.

Thermal-jet engines may be segregated into three basic types: (1) ramjet engines, (2) pulsejet engines, and (3) turbojet engines.

Chemical rocket engines may be grouped into two broad classes which are based on the physical characteristics of the chemicals consumed in creating the propulsive jet. Each material consumed in the *rocket motor*, the component wherein the chemical reaction takes place, is termed a *propellant*. Thus there are (1) liquid-propellant rocket engines and (2) solid-propellant rocket engines.

Only the basic types of thermal-jet and chemical rocket engines will be discussed. It is possible, however, to have combinations of the different thermal-jet engines and of the different rocket engines and also combinations of thermal-jet engines with rocket engines.

In the application of jet propulsion to propelling bodies on (or in) water, it is most convenient to use the surrounding water for producing the propulsive jet. That mode of propulsion is termed *hydraulic-jet propulsion*. The basic characteristics of hydraulic-jet propulsion will be discussed.

23.2. Notation

a	acoustic speed, fps
a_0	acoustic speed, in the free-stream air, fps
a_o	stagnation (or total) acoustic speed, fps
A	cross-section area
A_C	cross-section area of case surrounding solid-propellant grain
A_e	area of exit cross section of exhaust nozzle
A_G	cross-section area of solid-propellant grain
A_m	maximum cross-section area of ramjet engine
A_P	port area for a solid-propellant rocket motor
A_t	area of throat cross section of exhaust nozzle
A^*	critical cross-section area of a passage where the velocity is sonic (isentropic flow)
c	burning-rate exponent for a solid propellant
c_p	specific heat at constant pressure, Btu/(lb) (°F)
c_v	specific heat at constant volume, Btu/(lb) (°F)
c^*	V_j/C_F = characteristic velocity for a rocket motor, fps
C_d	discharge coefficient
C_D	drag coefficient
C_F	$F/A_t p_c$ = thrust coefficient for a rocket motor
C_{Fg}	$F_g/q_0 A_m$ = gross-thrust coefficient for a ramjet engine
C_w	$\dot{W}/A_t p_c$ = weight-flow coefficient for a rocket motor
D	drag force
D_i	$\dot{m}_a V$ = ram drag for a thermal-jet engine, lb
E	energy
E_f	calorific value of a fuel
E_k	kinetic energy
E_p	calorific value of a rocket-propellant combination
E_P	potential energy
E_{in}	rate at which energy is furnished to a propulsion system, ft-lb/sec
f	$\dot{m}_f/\dot{m}_a$ = fuel-air ratio
f'	f/η_B = fuel-air ratio for an ideal combustor
F	thrust (due to the internal flow for the engine), lb
F_j	$\dot{m}_2 w$ = jet thrust, lb
F_p	$(p_e - p_0)A_e$ = pressure thrust, lb
F_g	F = gross thrust for a ramjet engine, lb
$F_g SFC$	$g\dot{m}_f 3600/F_g$ = gross-thrust specific-fuel consumption for a ramjet engine, lb fuel/(hr) (lb gross thrust)
g	acceleration due to gravity, ft/sec²
h	static specific enthalpy, Btu/lb
Δh_n	enthalpy change for exhaust nozzle, Btu/lb
H	stagnation (total) specific enthalpy, Btu/lb
ΔH_c	calorific value of a fuel
ΔH_p	calorific value of a propellant combination
I	specific impulse, sec
I'	theoretical specific impulse, sec
I_a	$F/g\dot{m}_a$ = specific thrust or air specific impulse, lb-sec/lb air
J	mechanical equivalent of heat
k	c_p/c_v = specific-heat ratio
K_n	S_c/A_t = propellant area ratio of a solid-propellant rocket motor
K_P	A_P/A_t = port-to-throat area ratio
L^*	$\mathcal{U}_c/A_t$ = characteristic length for a rocket motor
m	mass in general, or net mass of a rocket-propelled body excluding all propellants and auxiliary fluids, slugs
m_p	mass of rocket propellants at the beginning of the powered flight, slugs
$\dot{m}$	dm/dt = mass rate of flow, slugs/sec
$\dot{m}_a$	mass rate of air induction for a thermal-jet engine, slugs/sec

$\dot{m}_f$	mass rate of fuel consumption, slugs/sec
$\dot{m}_o$	mass rate of oxidizer consumption, slugs/sec
$\dot{m}_p$	$\dot{m}_o + \dot{m}_f$ = mass rate of propellant consumption for a rocket engine, slugs/sec
$\dot{m}_2$	mass rate of flow of fluid ejected from the exhaust nozzle of a propulsion system, slugs/sec
$\overline{m}$	$1545/R$ = molecular weight of gas
$\mathbf{M}$	V/a = Mach number
M	mass of rocket-propelled system at any instant during the powered flight, slugs
p	static pressure, psia
p_c	static pressure of gas at entrance to exhaust nozzle of a rocket motor, psia
p_e	static pressure in the exit cross section A_e of an exhaust nozzle, psia
p_o	static pressure in the atmosphere surrounding the propelled vehicle, psia
P	$p\left(1 + \dfrac{k-1}{2}\mathbf{M}^2\right)^{k/(k-1)}$ = total (stagnation) pressure corresponding to the Mach number $\mathbf{M}$, psia
$\mathcal{P}$	propulsive power, ft-lb/sec
$\mathcal{P}_L$	leaving loss, ft-lb/sec
$\mathcal{P}_T$	thrust power, ft-lb/sec
q	$\rho V^2/2 = kp\mathbf{M}^2/2$ = dynamic pressure, psf
q_0	dynamic pressure of the free-stream air, psf
Q	heat added from external sources
$\dot{Q}_i$	volumetric flow rate, cfs
Q_i	heat supplied to an actual combustor
Q'_i	heat supplied to a loss-free combustor
r	(1) $\dot{m}_o/\dot{m}_f$ = mixture ratio for a rocket engine
	(2) linear burning rate for a solid propellant, in./sec
R	$1545/\overline{m}$ = gas constant, ft-lb/(lb)(°F)
s	specific entropy, Btu/(lb)(°F)
S	surface area
S_c	area of burning surface of a solid-propellant grain
t	static temperature, °R
t_c	static temperature of gases in combustion chamber, °R
t_e	static temperature in exit section of exhaust nozzle, °R
t_p	static temperature of solid propellant prior to ignition, °R
t_t	static temperature in throat cross section of exhaust nozzle, °R
T	total (stagnation) temperature, °R
T_c	total temperature of gases entering the exhaust nozzle of a rocket motor, °R
T_2	total temperature of air at entrance to air compressor of a turbojet engine (Fig. 23.3), °R
T_3	total temperature of the air discharged from air compressor of a turbojet engine (Fig. 23.3), °R
T'_3	total temperature of air discharged from an isentropic compressor operating between the same pressure limits as the actual compressor, °R
T_4	total temperature of gases entering the turbine of a turbojet engine (Fig. 23.3), °R
T_5	total temperature of gases discharged from turbine of a turbojet engine (Fig. 23.3), °R
T'_5	total temperature of gas discharged from an isentropic turbine operating between the same pressure limits as actual turbine, °R
$TSFC$	$3600g\dot{m}_f/F$ = thrust specific fuel consumption for a turbojet engine, lb/(hr)(lb thrust)
v	$1/\gamma$ = specific volume, ft³/lb
V	velocity, fps
V_c	velocity of gases at entrance section of exhaust nozzle, fps
V_e	velocity of gases crossing exit section A_e of exhaust nozzle, fps
V_j	effective jet (or exhaust) velocity, fps
V_p	velocity of propelled body at the end of the powered flight (cutoff velocity), fps
V_t	velocity of gases crossing throat section A_t of exhaust nozzle

V_{bi}	ideal burned velocity for rocket-propelled vehicle, fps
V_{ex}	x-component (coincident with longitudinal axis) of velocity of the exhaust jet ejected from a rocket motor, fps
V'	isentropic velocity, fps
V'_e	isentropic exit velocity, fps
υ	volume
w	velocity of exit gases relative to walls of exhaust nozzle, fps
W	weight, lb
W_E	dry weight of complete rocket engine, lb
W_f	weight of fuel, lb
W_o	weight of oxidizer, lb
W_p	weight of rocket propellants, lb
W_S	structural weight of rocket-propelled body, lb
W_U	weight of useful load (payload), lb
$\dot{W}$	$dW_p/dt = g\dot{m}_p$ = weight rate of propellant consumption, lb/sec
$\dot{W}_f$	$dW_f/dt = g\dot{m}_f$ = weight rate of fuel flow, lb/sec
$\dot{W}_g$	$dW_g/dt = g\dot{m}_g$ = weight rate of gas flow, lb/sec
$\dot{W}_o$	$dW_o/dt = g\dot{m}_o$ = weight rate of oxidizer flow, lb/sec
$\dot{W}_{sp}$	$\dot{W}/F = g/V_j$ = specific propellant consumption, lb/(sec)(lb thrust)
z	altitude, ft
z_c	altitude traversed by rocket-propelled vehicle by coasting after all the propellants have been consumed, ft
z_p	altitude attained by a rocket-propelled vehicle at any instant during the powered flight, ft
Z_c	$\Theta_c - 1$ = compression factor
Z_t	$1 - \Theta_t$ = expansion factor
α	(1) $T_4/t_0 = \alpha_d\alpha_1$ = cycle temperature ratio for a turbojet engine
	(2) T_6/t_0 = cycle temperature for a ramjet engine
	(3) divergence half angle of exit cone of exhaust nozzle (Fig. 23.4)
α_d	T_2/t_0 = temperature ratio for diffusion system of thermal-jet engine
γ	$1/v$ = specific weight, lb/ft³
γ_p	specific weight of propellant combination, lb/ft³
δ	$P/14.7$ = corrected pressure for a thermal-jet engine
ϵ	A_e/A_t = area ratio for an exhaust nozzle
ϵ_P	propellant loading ratio
ζ	m_p/M_0 = propellant mass ratio
η	efficiency
η_B	f'/f = combustion efficiency for a thermal-jet engine
η_c	$(T'_3 - T_2)/(T_3 - T_2)$ = isentropic efficiency for a compressor
η_d	$(T'_2 - t_0)/(T_2 - t_0)$ = isentropic efficiency for a diffuser
η_n	ϕ^2 = isentropic efficiency for a nozzle
η_P	$\mathcal{O}_T/(\mathcal{O}_T + \mathcal{O}_L)$ = ideal propulsive efficiency
η_t	$(T_4 - T_5)/(T_4 - T'_5)$ = isentropic efficiency for a turbine
η_{th}	$\mathcal{O}/E_{in}$ = thermal efficiency of a propulsion engine
θ	$T/519$ = corrected temperature for a thermal-jet engine
Θ_c	$(P_3/P_2)^{(k-1)/k}$ = compressor pressure-ratio parameter
Θ_d	$(P_2/p_0)^{(k-1)/k}$ = diffuser pressure-ratio parameter
Θ_n	$(P_7/p_0)^{(k-1)/k}$ = nozzle pressure-ratio parameter
Θ_t	$(P_4/P_5)^{(k-1)/k}$ = turbine pressure-ratio parameter
λ	$\frac{1}{2} + \frac{1}{2}\cos\alpha$ = divergence coefficient for an exhaust nozzle with a conical divergence section
ν	speed ratio
ρ	γ/g = density, slugs
τ	time
τ_p	duration of powered flight
Φ_p	M_0/m = vehicle mass ratio
Ψ^*	$[2/(k + 1)]^{1/(k-1)} [k/(k + 1)]^{1/2}$ = critical value of flow factor
Ω	$\sqrt{k}\,[2/(k + 1)]^{(k+1)/2(k-1)}$

SUBSCRIPTS

0	free stream
1	entrance to subsonic diffuser
2	exit from subsonic diffuser
3	entrance to combustion chamber
4	entrance to turbine of turbojet engine
5	exit from turbine of turbojet engine
6	entrance to tailpipe of turbojet engine
7	entrance to exhaust nozzle of turbojet engine
8	throat section of exhaust nozzle of turbojet engine
9	exit section of exhaust nozzle of turbojet engine
O	atmosphere
B	combustion chamber (burner)
c	compression
e	exit section of exhaust nozzle
f	fuel
o	oxidizer
p	propellant
t	throat

SUPERSCRIPTS

'	(prime) denotes state is reached by an isentropic process
*	refers to *critical section* where the gas velocity is *sonic*, excepting c^*, the characteristic velocity, and L^*, the characteristic length, for a rocket motor

BASIC TYPES OF THERMAL-JET ENGINES

23.3. The Ramjet Engine

Figure 23.1 illustrates schematically the essential features of a ramjet engine for propelling a body at supersonic flight speeds. It comprises a supersonic diffuser (0–1) which is followed by a subsonic diffuser (1–2), a combustion chamber (3–6), and an exhaust nozzle (6–7). If one assumes a *relative coordinate system*† the propulsion system is stationary and the air flows toward the engine with the flight speed V_0, and the propulsive jet is ejected from the engine with the velocity V_7 *relative to the walls of the ramjet engine.*

The function of the supersonic and subsonic diffusers is to convert into a pressure rise, called the *ram pressure,* the largest possible fraction of the kinetic energy associated with the air entering the engine. The ramjet engine typifies those thermal-jet engines which induct atmospheric air continuously and compress it entirely by diffusion.

† A relative coordinate system is assumed in all the discussions which follow.

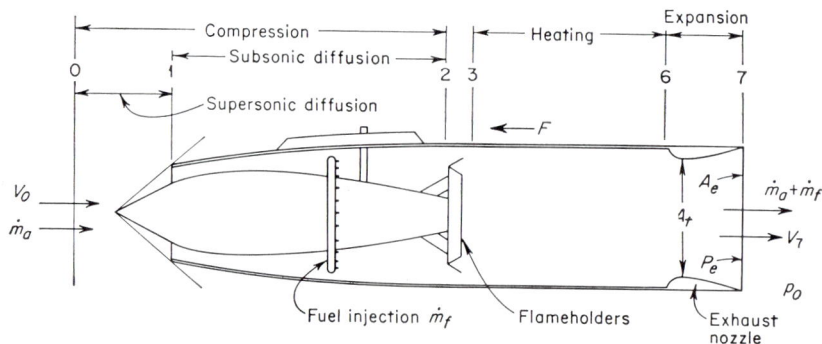

FIG. 23.1. Schematic arrangement of a supersonic ramjet engine.

In operation of the engine, atmospheric air enters the engine after being decelerated and compressed by the supersonic diffuser; the air is then further compressed in the subsonic diffuser. As a consequence of the diffusion, the temperature of the air is increased as well as its static pressure. The compressed air leaving the diffusion system flows into the combustion chamber, which contains flameholders for stabilizing the combustion process; fuel is injected into the air at an appropriate location upstream from the flameholders. The air is heated in the combustion chamber to a high temperature, approximately 3800°F, by the continuous combustion of a fuel in the air. Liquid hydrocarbon fuels are most generally used, but other fuels can also be burned. The hot gaseous products of combustion are then expanded as they flow through the exhaust nozzle and are ejected into the atmosphere with the relative velocity V_7, which is larger than V_0. Thus the momentum flow through the engine is increased from $\dot{m}_a V_0$ at its entrance to $(\dot{m}_a + \dot{m}_f)V_7$ at its exit, with the result that a thrust F is developed in the direction of flight.

It is important that the diffusion process reduces the Mach number of the air entering the combustion chamber, denoted by $\mathbf{M}_3$, to a value low enough to prevent blowing out the flame. Theory and experience indicate that $\mathbf{M}_3$ for a conventional supersonic ramjet engine should not be appreciably larger than approximately $\mathbf{M}_3 = 0.2$. The combustion process in the combustion chamber is not quite isobaric; there are pressure drops due to wall friction, the obstruction of the flameholders, and to the increase in the momentum of the working fluid as a result of the heat addition.

The ramjet engine cannot function until a definite ram pressure is obtained at the entrance to the combustion chamber. Consequently, it cannot operate at zero flight speed. To put it into operation it must therefore be *launched*, or *boosted*, by some auxiliary means, such as *booster rockets*, to a high enough flight speed for it to develop sufficient thrust for accelerating the vehicle it propels to the design flight Mach number.

Since it is an *air-consuming* engine, the maximum operating altitude of the ramjet engine is limited. Moreover, its field of operation appears to be in the supersonic speed range, from approximately $\mathbf{M}_0 = 2$ to possibly $\mathbf{M}_0 = 6$, the upper speed being limited by the degree to which the hot-metal parts of the engine can be kept at a sufficiently low temperature so that they can withstand the stresses imposed upon them. The stagnation temperatures become very large as the flight Mach number exceeds $\mathbf{M}_0 = 6$, as can be seen from the following equation:

$$T = t(1 + 0.2\mathbf{M}_0{}^2)$$

in which T = stagnation temperature
$\quad\quad\ t$ = atmospheric temperature
$\quad\ \mathbf{M}_0$ = flight Mach number

The origin of the ramjet engine is credited to M. Lorin (France) in 1913. In the United States, it has been applied operationally only to the propulsion of supersonic missiles.

23.4. The Pulsejet Engine

Figure 23.2 illustrates schematically the general arrangement of the components of a pulsejet engine. It comprises an inlet diffuser, a valve bank through which air can flow into the engine, a combustion chamber, and a tailpipe; a spark plug is located in the combustion chamber. The valves consist of several thin metal strips bearing on metal seats and are arranged so that they act as spring-loaded "shutters" for preventing gases from the combustion chamber flowing into the air-intake system.

The operating principle of the engine is substantially as follows. Assume a relative

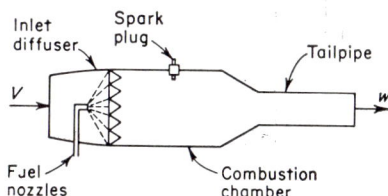

Fig. 23.2. Essential elements of a pulsejet engine. (*Ref.* 7.)

coordinate system and that the combustion chamber contains a combustible mixture of fuel and air and that the inlet valves are closed. The fuel-air mixture is ignited by the spark plug, thereby increasing the pressure and temperature of the gases in the combustion chamber. The hot gases flow out of the engine through the tailpipe with the relative velocity w, which is larger than the flight speed V. Because of their inertia, the gases in flowing out of the engine cause the pressure in the combustion chamber to fall below that of the surrounding atmosphere, and that pressure difference combined with the ram pressure acting on the valves causes the latter to open, and a new cycle commences. Once the engine has been put into operation, the spark-plug ignition system is not needed.

The pressure inside the engine varies in a cyclic manner; the frequency of the firings depends upon the dimensions of the engine. In the ideal case, the combustion is assumed to be isovolumic, but in the actual case, it departs considerably from the isovolumic and some gases do escape through the air inlet.

The thrust developed by a pulsejet engine is proportional to the average mass rate of flow of gases through the engine multiplied by the increase in their velocity.

The maximum operating altitude of the pulsejet engine is limited, but it can develop thrust at zero flight speed. The thrust at first increases with flight speed, but at some limiting subsonic speed it starts decreasing, the drag increasing faster than the thrust. The maximum flight speed of the pulsejet engine is limited to speeds below 600 mph.

The operating principle of the pulsejet engine is credited to Karavodine (France) in 1906. The modern conception is due to Paul Schmidt (Germany) in 1931.

23.5. The Turbojet Engine

Figure 23.3 illustrates schematically the arrangement of the components of a simple turbojet engine. It comprises a diffusion system, an air compressor (axial or radial), a combustion system, a turbine for driving the air compressor and auxiliaries, a tailpipe which may or may not be equipped with an afterburner, and an exhaust nozzle. Engines equipped with axial compressors are termed *axial turbojet engines*, and those with radial compressors are called *radial turbojet engines*. Depending upon the design speed for the engine, compressor design pressure ratios range from 5:1 to approximately 16:1. In the lower-pressure-ratio engines, the axial compressor is a single drum operating at the same speed as the turbine, while in the higher-pressure-ratio engines, the air compressor consists of two drums, each being driven at its most appropriate speed by different stages of a multistage turbine.

The air entering the engine is first compressed by the diffusion system, and then further compressed by the air compressor. The compressed air then flows into the combustors, wherein it is heated by burning a fuel in the air. The maximum temperature of the working fluid is limited by metallurgical considerations to a value which is safe for the dynamic stresses that must be withstood by the turbine blades. For current engines sufficient fuel is burned in the air to give a stagnation temperature for the gases entering the turbine called the *turbine inlet temperature*, of approximately $T_4 = 2160°R$. With conventional hydrocarbon fuels, the corresponding fuel-air ratio

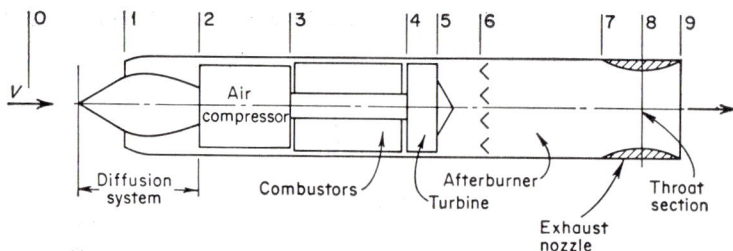

Fig. 23.3. General arrangement of components of a turbojet engine.

is approximately 0.02, so that there is considerable excess air in the combustion products. The combustion process is approximately isobaric, but the working fluid experiences a pressure decrease as it flows through the combustors. The mixture of heated air and combustion products expands in the turbine, which is directly connected to the air compressor, thereby furnishing the power required for driving the air compressor and the pertinent auxiliary apparatus. From the turbine the gases flow through the tailpipe and are finally ejected to the atmosphere after expanding in a suitably shaped exhaust nozzle.

The turbojet engine, like the ramjet engine, is a continuous-flow engine. But unlike the ramjet engine, it can develop thrust at zero flight speed, but the amount of ram pressure recovered in the diffusion system affects its performance and fuel economy. To illustrate, a 20 per cent reduction in the ram pressure increases the fuel-consumption rate per pound of thrust by approximately 10 per cent. The turbojet engine is the only thermal-jet engine which is employed operationally for propelling military and commercial aircraft. Its performance characteristics are such that it is unsurpassed for propelling aircraft in the speed range 500 to 1500 mph, approximately. Increasing the flight speed increases the ram pressure and the temperature of the air leaving the diffusion system, and at a supersonic speed of approximately $M = 3$ its characteristics tend to merge with those of the ramjet engine. The top flight speed for the turbojet engine is therefore limited to that at which a ramjet engine is more advantageous.

The ratio of the take-off thrust to the flight thrust for a turbojet engine is significantly smaller than that obtainable from a variable-pitch propeller. To augment the take-off thrust, *afterburning*, also called *tailpipe burning*, is employed. Because of the small fuel-air ratio employed in the main burners (approximately 0.02), there is always sufficient oxygen in the gases leaving the turbine for burning considerable quantities of additional fuel in the *afterburner* located between the turbine and the exhaust nozzle. In that manner the temperature of the gases entering the nozzle can be raised substantially, thereby increasing the velocity of the propulsive jet. Afterburning is very effective for augmenting thrust in flight. In an afterburning engine the temperature of the gases entering the nozzle (T_7) is approximately 3800°R. Another method for augmenting the thrust of the engine, particularly at take-off, is to reduce the compression work by injecting water-alcohol mixtures into the air compressor.

The turbojet engine is basically a gas-turbine power plant, wherein the combination of the diffuser, air compressor, combustors, and turbine constitutes a *hot-gas generator*. As in any gas-turbine power plant, the efficiencies of the individual components influence its performance characteristics, but its performance is far less sensitive to small changes in the efficiency of its components than is a gas turbine which delivers shaft power.

There is considerable flexibility in the possible arrangements for combining an axial turbojet engine and a ramjet engine.

THE CHEMICAL ROCKET ENGINE

23.6. Description of the Chemical Rocket Engine

In a chemical rocket engine an oxidizer and a fuel are reacted in an appropriate combustion chamber to produce high-temperature high-pressure gases for expansion in a suitable exhaust nozzle. Because no atmospheric air is used, the rocket engine, operating under steady-state conditions, has the following unique characteristics: (1) its thrust is independent of its flight speed; (2) its thrust is only slightly affected by the environment into which the propulsive jet is ejected; (3) it has no altitude ceiling; (4) it can function in a vacuum; (5) its thrust per unit of frontal area and its thrust per unit of engine weight are the largest obtainable from all known propulsion engines; (6) the rate at which a rocket engine performs useful work increases directly with flight speed. It was the afore-mentioned characteristics of the rocket engine that encouraged the early workers in rocket jet propulsion. They recognized that those characteristics gave rocket jet propulsion the capabilities of propelling bodies to the extremely high speeds and altitudes required for intercontinental ballistic missiles, launching artificial satellites, escaping from the earth's gravitational attraction, conducting scientific investigations of space, and making space travel a technical possibility.

Because the rocket-propelled vehicle must carry an *oxidizer* as well as a *fuel* (*the propellants*), the rate at which a rocket engine consumes propellants is several times that at which a thermal-jet engine consumes fuel, the only chemical carried in a thermal-jet-propelled vehicle. To illustrate, for a turbojet engine the *thrust specific fuel consumption* (*TSFC*), measured in pounds (fuel) per hour per pound of thrust, is of the order of 1 lb/(hr)(lb), while for a rocket engine it would be approximately 14 lb/(hr)(lb); the operating duration of a rocket engine is, however, very short, of the order of a few minutes or less.

The most important parameters for achieving high flight speeds are large values for the thrust per unit of frontal area and for the thrust per unit of engine weight. In those respects rocket jet propulsion is unsurpassed. For winged aircraft the range depends in large measure on the TSFC of the propulsion system. Because the TSFC for a rocket engine is approximately fourteen times that of an air-consuming engine, the *endurance* of a rocket-propelled conventional airplane is limited to flights of a few minutes, so that its range is quite short. To achieve a long range with rocket jet propulsion one must take advantage of its large values of thrust per unit area and per unit of engine weight and minimize the effects of its large TSFC. Consequently, a long range is achieved by utilizing the large thrust of the rocket engine for propelling the vehicle to a very high altitude and for imparting to it a very large velocity at the end of the operating period for the rocket engine (or engines), termed the *powered flight*. The velocity attained by the vehicle at the end of the powered flight is called the *burned velocity*, or the *burnout velocity*. The kinetic energy associated with the vehicle moving with the burned velocity is then used for coasting along a ballistic trajectory or glide path which gives the desired range.

23.7. Liquid-propellant Rocket Engines

A liquid-propellant rocket engine comprises the following principal components: (1) a rocket motor, (2) a pressuring system for forcing the propellants into the rocket motor against the combustion pressure, and (3) a control system. Liquid-propellant systems can be grouped into (1) *monopropellants*, and (2) *bipropellants*. A monopropellant is a liquid which does not require an auxiliary liquid (oxidizer) to cause it to release its thermochemical energy. A bipropellant system comprises a liquid oxidizer

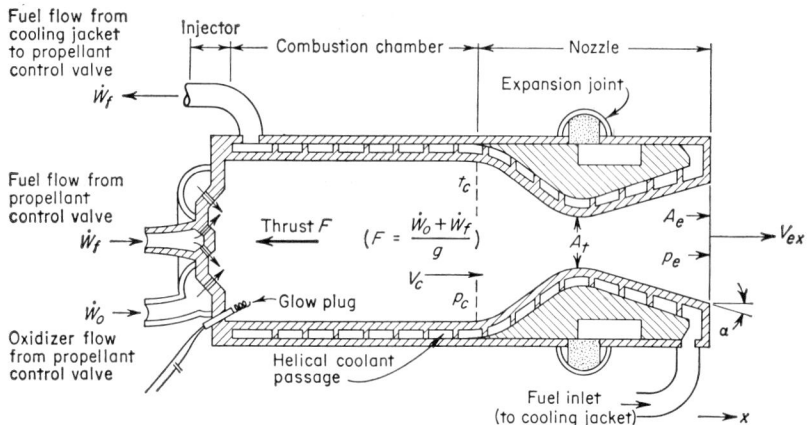

Fig. 23.4. Principal elements of a regeneratively fuel-cooled liquid-propellant rocket motor. (*Ref. 1.*)

and a liquid fuel, for example, liquid-oxygen and jet-engine fuel. If the bipropellant system requires some form of ignition system to initiate the chemical reaction, it is said to be *diergolic*, and if no ignition system is needed, it is *hypergolic*.

At this time bipropellant systems are used in all operational rocket jet-propulsion engines. Monopropellants are used mainly for generating gases for operating turbines or other devices. The discussions of liquid-propellant rocket engines will therefore be confined to those using bipropellant systems.

Liquid-propellant Rocket Motor. Figure 23.4 illustrates schematically the arrangement of the components in a liquid-propellant rocket motor. The rocket motor is the component wherein the thermochemical energy associated with the propellant system is converted into the kinetic energy associated with a gaseous propulsive jet. The rocket motor comprises an injector, a combustion chamber, a *de Laval* type of exhaust nozzle, and a cooling jacket. An ignition system is shown and is not needed if the propellants are hypergolic.

Under steady-state conditions liquid oxidizer and liquid fuel are injected into the combustion chamber at the rates $\dot{W}_o$ and $\dot{W}_f$, respectively, usually stated in pounds per second. The chemical reaction (*combustion*) of the propellants generates large volumes of hot gases at high temperature (approximately 5000 to 8000°R), depending upon the particular propellants, their *mixture ratio* W_o/W_f, and the area of the *nozzle throat* A_t. The gaseous products of combustion are ejected into the surroundings with supersonic velocity. In current engines the design point combustion pressure, also called the *chamber pressure*, ranges from approximately 150 to 850 psia, depending upon the characteristics of the propellants, the ability to cool the rocket motor, and the operating altitude range. The conventional method for cooling the rocket motor is to circulate the more appropriate of the propellants around the combustion chamber and nozzle prior to injecting it into the combustion chamber; that cooling method is called *regenerative cooling*.

Pressurizing Systems for Liquid-propellant Rocket Engines. There are three main methods for pressurizing the liquid propellants: (1) stored-gas pressurization; (2) chemical-gas pressurization; and (3) turbopump pressurization.

Figure 23.5 illustrates schematically the principal elements for a *stored-gas pressurization system*, which is inherently simple and reliable. The stored gas must be inert with respect to chemical reaction with the propellants, and it is supplied to the propellant tanks at the regulated pressure for maintaining the propellant flow rates at the desired values. Since the gas pressure in each propellant tank must exceed the combustion pressure by the sum of the pressure drops in the propellant feed line and injector, the propellant tanks become quite heavy as their dimensions are increased, as in applications utilizing high combustion pressures, long operating durations, and large thrusts. The stored-gas pressurizing system finds its application to either short-duration or small-thrust engines. It may also be applicable to the upper stages of a multistage rocket-propelled vehicle since the combustion pressure may be low (150 psia or less) and for certain ballistic missiles of relatively short range (up to approximately 75 miles) where simplicity and reliability are of utmost importance.

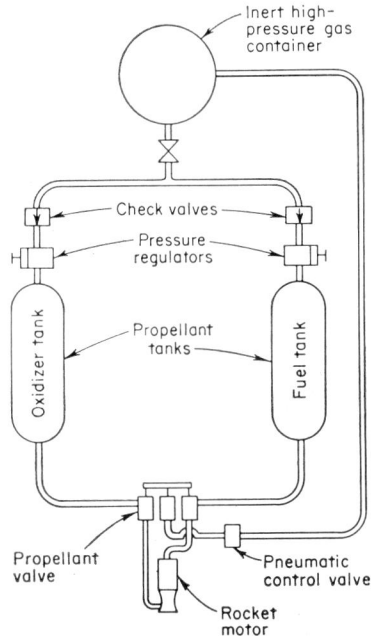

Fig. 23.5. Elements of an (inert) gas-pressurized liquid-propellant rocket-jet-propulsion system. (*Ref. 1.*)

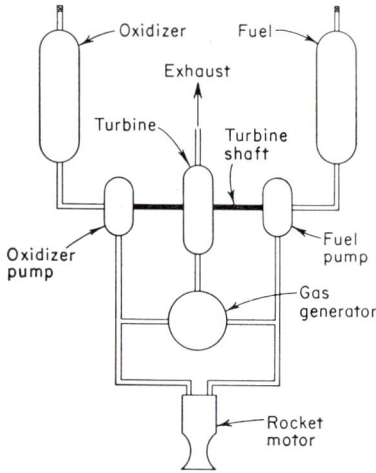

FIG. 23.6.　Elements of a turborocket pressurizing system for a liquid-propellant rocket-jet-propulsion system. (*Ref.* 1.)

A *chemical-gas pressurizing system* is one which generates the pressurizing gas as it is required. In this way the weight of the high-pressure gas-storage tank is eliminated and replaced by special gas generators of considerbaly less weight. The pressurizing gas is generated either by reacting liquid bipropellants, decomposing a monopropellant, or burning a suitable solid propellant in a gas generator. It is important that the generated gas does not react either chemically or physically with the liquid propellants, and the gas temperature must be sufficiently low to avoid overheating the materials in the tank. It may be necessary to employ two generators, one for furnishing gas to the oxidizer tank and the other for supplying gas to the fuel tank.

The weight disadvantages of both the stored-gas and chemical-gas pressurizing systems are removed by employing a *turbopump pressurizing system*, such as that illustrated schematically in Fig. 23.6. It comprises an oxidizer pump and a fuel pump driven by a turbine powered by hot gas produced in some form of gas generator. Turbopump pressurizing systems are employed where either large thrusts or long operating durations, or both, are required. Thus the rocket engines for propelling the Viking sounding rocket, intercontinental ballistic missiles, and the (German) ME-163 rocket-propelled airplane, all employ turbopump pressurizing systems. It should be pointed out that the propellants used for generating the hot gases for driving the turbine element need not be the same as those burned in the rocket motor.

Because of the great importance of low weight for the engines of long-range ballistic missiles and space vehicles, the turbopump must be light in weight. The turbines and the pumps are therefore operated at high speeds; the pump impellers are usually radial-bladed of *high-specific-speed* design. The pumps operate with large fluid velocities at their entrance section, and to suppress cavitation, the propellants must be sufficiently pressurized so that the *net positive suction head* at the inlet to each pump is large enough to prevent serious cavitation.

23.8. Solid-propellant Rocket Engines

Figure 23.7a illustrates a rocket motor burning a *cigarette-burning* solid-propellant grain, and Fig. 23.7b illustrates one using a *case-bonded internal-burning star* grain. There are other possible grain configurations. The burning directions are controlled by covering the propellant surfaces which should not burn with an inhibitor, a material which is either inert chemically or burns at a much slower rate than the propellant.

Where the propellant is cast directly into the *case* of the rocket motor, it is *bonded* to the inner wall by interposing a liner material between that wall and the propellant grain; the *liner* adheres to both the case and the grain and inhibits burning along that surface of the propellant (Fig. 23.7b). The *case-bonded* arrangement has the advantage that the propellant grain is well supported throughout its length and the case is protected from the hot combustion gases. Consequently, the metal case can be manufactured from highly heat-treated high-strength steels, thereby making them thin and light in weight.

In current solid-propellant rocket engines the exhaust nozzle operates uncooled. Its interior surface must therefore be protected from the hot combustion gases by some form of insulating material, particularly in the region of the throat section.

(a) Cigarette-burning or end-burning grain

(b) Case-bonded internal star grain

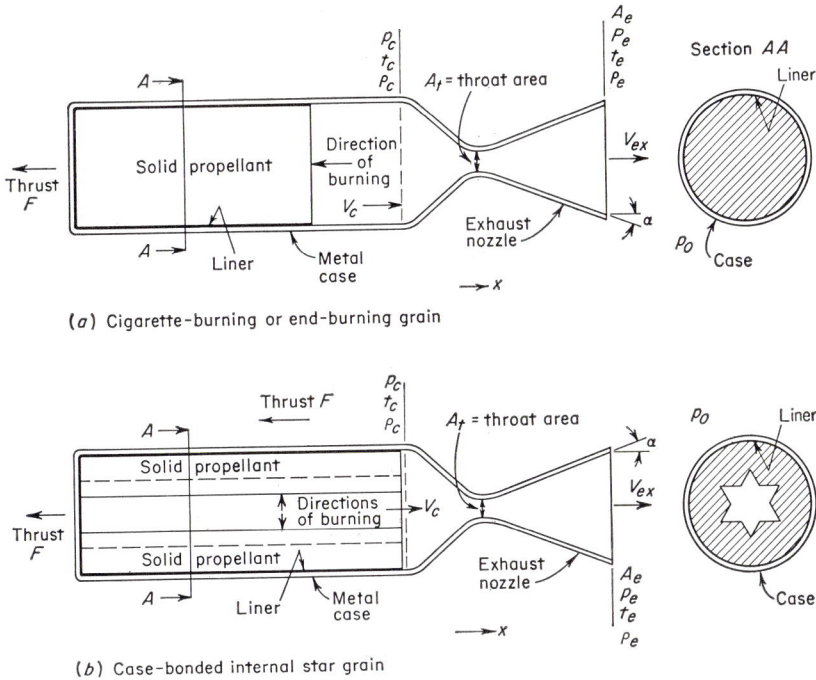

Fig. 23.7. Two solid-propellant grain configurations.

Some form of *igniter* is required for initiating the combustion of the solid propellant. It usually comprises an electrically fired *squib* for initiating the combustion, an igniter charge, and a case. The squib contains the *primary charge*, which is sensitive to the heat produced by passing an electric current through the squib. Sufficient heat is released by the primary charge to fire the main igniter charge, and the latter ignites the solid propellant.

The range and accuracy of a vehicle propelled by a solid-propellant rocket engine is governed by the attitude of the vehicle and the *burned velocity* when the thrust is cut off. Consequently, the engine must incorporate (1) means for achieving thrust termination at the correct instant and (2) thrust vector control for altering the direction of the line of action of the propulsion thrust. The means for accomplishing *thrust termination* and *thrust vector control* are not shown in Fig. 23.7.

It should be noted that although the operation of a solid-propellant rocket engine can be stopped, it cannot be restarted, as is possible for liquid-propellant engines.

Solid Propellants. These may be segregated into two main groups: (1) double-base propellants, and (2) heterogeneous, or composite, propellants. The *double-base propellants* are of several kinds, but they consist principally of gelatinized colloidal mixtures of nitrocellulose and nitroglycerine containing small additions of suitable plasticizers, ballistic modifiers, and stabilizers. Familiar double-base propellants are cordite and ballistite. Double-base propellants are used most extensively for such weapons as bazookas, barrage rockets, unguided ballistic missiles, etc. They burn smokelessly, and when stored continuously at temperatures above approximately 120°F, they tend to deteriorate. In recent years methods have been developed by the Alleghany Ballistics Laboratory for producing cast double-base-propellant grains of large size.

A *heterogeneous*, or *composite*, *propellant* is basically a physical mixture of a powdered inorganic oxidizer and an organic fuel which serves as the *binder* for the oxidizer particles. Most of the current formulations are castable, and in them the binder constitutes only

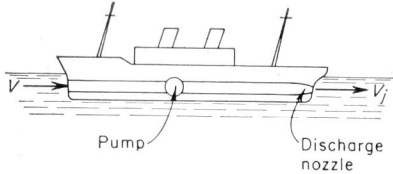

FIG. 23.8. Generalized jet-propulsion system.

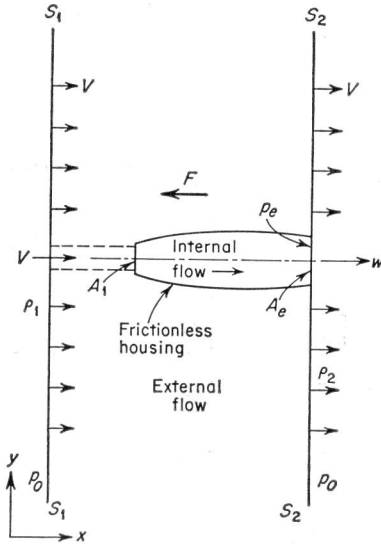

FIG. 23.9. Schematic hydraulic-jet-propulsion system.

approximately 20 per cent, by weight, of the finished propellant, the balance being solid oxidizer particles. For the propellant to have satisfactory strength properties the binder (fuel) must have a tensile strength several times that required for the propellant.

HYDRAULIC-JET PROPULSION

23.9. Ship Propulsion by Hydraulic Jet

Some of the earliest applications of the jet-propulsion principle were made to ship propulsion by the British and Swedish governments. Figure 23.8 illustrates the arrangement schematically. Water is inducted at the forward end of the ship and enters some high-pressure pumps wherein energy is imparted to it, and the water is then discharged at the rear through suitable nozzles in the form of one or more *hydraulic jets.*

EQUATIONS FOR JET-PROPULSION SYSTEMS

23.10. Basic Momentum Equations

Figure 23.9 illustrates schematically an arbitrary propulsion system immersed in a uniform flow field. Employing a *relative coordinate system*, assume one-dimensional flow and locate the propulsion system between the two planes S_1 and S_2, each of which is perpendicular to the streamlines and extends to infinity. Plane S_1 is located where the static pressure p_0 is undisturbed by the presence of the propulsion system. Plane S_2 is located where the static pressure is likewise p_0, except for the area where the high-speed fluid ejected from the propulsion system crosses S_2. Because of the reactions between the fluid flowing through the propulsion system, called the *internal flow,* and the interior surfaces in contact with the internal flow, a resultant axial force is produced. If that force acts in the direction opposite to the flow direction for the fluid, it is called a thrust, and if it acts in the same direction, it is called a drag. The resultant axial force due to the fluid flowing past the exterior surfaces of the housing, called the *external flow,* is either a thrust or a drag, depending upon whether it acts in the opposite or the same direction as the external flow. If it is assumed that the external surface of the housing surrounding the propulsion system is frictionless, then there is no external drag.

According to the momentum equation of fluid mechanics, the net external force X acting in the x direction is equal to the time rate of change in the x momentum of the fluid entering through S_1 and leaving through S_2. Thus

$$ X = \int_{S_2} \dot{M}_{x2}\, dS - \int_{S_1} \dot{M}_{x1}\, dS + \int_{S_2} (p - p_0)\, dS - \int_{S_1} (p - p_0)\, dS \qquad (23.1) $$

In the case illustrated in Fig. 23.9, $V_{x1} = V$, $V_{x2} = w$, and since the external drag is zero, the external flow does not experience a rate of change in momentum. Hence the net rate of change in x momentum crossing S_1 and S_2 is given by

$$\dot{M}_x = \rho_2 w^2 A_e - \rho_1 V^2 A_1 \tag{23.2}$$

The first pressure integral in Eq. (23.1) is equal to $(p_e - p_o)A_e$, and the second one is zero. Hence

$$X = \rho_2 w^2 A_e - \rho_1 V^2 A_1 + (p_e - p_o)A_e \tag{23.3}$$

The thrust F is the reaction force equal numerically to X but acting in the direction opposite to the fluid flow. Thus

$$F = \dot{m}_2 w - \dot{m}_1 V + (p_e - p_o)A_e \tag{23.4}$$

In Eq. (23.4) the term $\dot{m}_2 w = F_j =$ the *jet thrust*; $\dot{m}V = D_i =$ the *ram drag*; and $(p_e - p_o)A_e = F_p =$ the *pressure thrust*.

It is convenient to simplify Eq. (23.4) by eliminating the pressure thrust. Thus, let

$$F = \dot{m}_2 V_j - \dot{m}_1 V \tag{23.5}$$

in which

$$V_j = w + (p_e - p_o)\frac{A_e}{\dot{m}_2} = \textit{effective jet velocity} \tag{23.6}$$

If the gases leaving the exhaust nozzle are *underexpanded*, then $p_e > p_o$ and the effective jet velocity is larger than the *exit velocity* w. Only in the special case in which the gases are completely expanded to that of the environment p_o is $V_j = w$. The effective jet velocity is a useful criterion, since it is readily determined from measured values of F, $\dot{m}_1$, and $\dot{m}_2$, obtained under static conditions.

For *thermal jet engines*, $\dot{m}_1 = \dot{m}_a =$ the mass rate of air inducted into the engine, and $\dot{m} = \dot{m}_2 = \dot{m}_a + \dot{m}_f$ if $\dot{m}_f$ is the mass rate of fuel consumption. Let $\nu = V/V_j =$ the *effective speed ratio*, and $f = \dot{m}_f/\dot{m}_a =$ the fuel-air ratio. Then

$$F = \dot{m} V_j - \dot{m}_a V = \left(\frac{1+f}{\nu} - 1\right)\dot{m}_a V \tag{23.6a}$$

In the case of a conventional turbojet engine, $\dot{m}_f$ is not significantly different from the air bled from the air compressor for cooling the bearings and turbine disc, denoted by $\dot{m}_c$. Hence no sensible error is introduced by assuming that $\dot{m} = \dot{m}_a + \dot{m}_f - \dot{m}_c \approx \dot{m}_a$. Also no appreciable error is introduced if it is assumed that $w = V_j$. Hence, for a turbojet engine

$$F = \dot{m}_a (w - V) = \dot{m}_a V \left(\frac{1}{\nu} - 1\right) \tag{23.7}$$

Equation (23.7) is also the thrust equation for the *ideal propeller*; in that case w is the *wake velocity* of the air flowing out of the slipstream.

In the case of a *rocket motor*, since it consumes no atmospheric air, $\dot{m}_a = 0$. The mass rate of gas flow out of the exhaust nozzle $\dot{m}$ is equal to the propellant consumption rate. Hence $\dot{m} = \dot{m}_o + \dot{m}_f$, if $\dot{m}_o$ and $\dot{m}_f$ are the mass consumption rates of oxidizer and fuel, respectively. For a rocket motor

$$F = \dot{m} V_j = \dot{m} w + (p_e - p_o)A_e \tag{23.8}$$

Figure 23.8 illustrates schematically a *hydraulic-jet-propulsion* system for propelling a ship. Let V denote the forward speed of the ship, V_j the jet velocity, $\dot{m}$ the mass rate of flow of water through the propulsion system, A_e the exit area of the nozzles, and ρ the density of the water; then

$$\dot{m} = \rho A_e V_j \tag{23.9}$$

Since $p_e = p_o$ in this case, then $w = V_j$ and

$$F = \dot{m} (V_j - V) = \rho A_e V^2 \frac{1 - \nu}{\nu^2} \tag{23.10}$$

if $\nu = V/V_j = V/w$.

23.11. Power and Efficiency Relationships

In a jet-propulsion system the *propulsion element* is the exhaust nozzle and the rate at which energy is supplied to it is called the *propulsive power* and is denoted by $\mathcal{P}$. If the propulsion system propels a body in a fluid medium at the constant speed V, then the thrust F is equal to the drag D. The rate at which the propulsion system does useful work is called the *thrust power* and is denoted by $\mathcal{P}_T$. Thus

$$\mathcal{P}_T = FV = DV \tag{23.11}$$

Not all the propulsive power is converted into thrust power for maintaining the propelled body in uniform motion. A portion of that power is either dissipated within or ejected from the propulsion system. Let $\mathcal{P}_\lambda$ denote the sum of the *power losses*. In general,

$$\mathcal{P} = \mathcal{P}_T + \mathcal{P}_\lambda$$

Let it be assumed that $p_e = p_o$ and that the only energy loss is the kinetic energy associated with the propulsive jet, called the *leaving loss*, which is denoted by $\mathcal{P}_L$ and is given by

$$\mathcal{P}_L = \dot{m}\frac{(w - V)^2}{2} \tag{23.12}$$

In that special case

$$\mathcal{P} = \mathcal{P}_T + \mathcal{P}_L \tag{23.13}$$

The *ideal propulsive efficiency* is accordingly defined by

$$\eta_P = \frac{\mathcal{P}_T}{\mathcal{P}_T + \mathcal{P}_L} = \frac{\text{thrust power}}{\text{propulsive power}} \tag{23.14}$$

The ideal propulsive efficiency η_P is a useful concept since it avoids the complications introduced by accounting for extraneous losses. The actual propulsive efficiency is $\eta_p = P_T/(P_T + P_\lambda)$, with $\eta_p < \eta_P$.

For a *turbojet engine*, assuming $\dot{m} = \dot{m}_a + \dot{m}_f \approx \dot{m}_a$ and $V_j = w$,

$$\mathcal{P}_T = FV = \dot{m}_a V^2 \left(\frac{1}{\nu} - 1\right) \tag{23.15}$$

Substituting for $\mathcal{P}_L$ and $\mathcal{P}_T$ from Eqs. (23.12) and (23.15), respectively, into Eq. (23.14) gives

$$\eta_P = \frac{2\nu}{1 + \nu} \tag{23.16}$$

For *rocket-jet propulsion*,

$$\mathcal{P}_T = FV = \dot{m} V_j V \tag{23.17}$$

and

$$\eta_P = \frac{2\nu}{1 + \nu^2} \tag{23.18}$$

In the case of *hydraulic-jet propulsion* the propulsive power is the energy imparted to the water. Let η_h denote the hydraulic efficiency of the pump impeller, ω its angular velocity, and Φ its torque. Then

$$\mathcal{P} = \eta_h \Phi \omega = \mathcal{P}_T + \mathcal{P}_L \tag{23.19}$$

Since $\mathcal{P}_T = FV$ and $\mathcal{P}_L = \dot{m}(V_j - V)^2/2$, the ideal propulsive efficiency is

$$\eta_P = \frac{FV}{\Phi\omega\eta_h} = \frac{2\nu}{1 + \nu} \tag{23.20}$$

which is the same equation for a turbojet engine or an ideal propeller.

The ideal propulsive efficiency measures the effectiveness with which the propulsive power is utilized. It is apparent from Eqs. (23.16) and (23.20) that propulsion systems which have ram drag, such as the thermal-jet engines, the propeller, and hydraulic-jet propulsion, cannot attain $\eta_P = 1$, for that condition requires $\nu = 1$, in which case $F = 0$. Only the rocket-jet propulsion can operate with $\nu = 1$ and can therefore, in theory, attain $\eta_P = 1$.

The ideal propulsive efficiency η_P is mainly of academic interest; of more importance is the over-all efficiency η, which is defined by

$$\eta = \frac{\mathcal{P}_T}{E_{\text{in}}} = \eta_{\text{th}}\eta_P \tag{23.21}$$

in which

$$\eta_{\text{th}} = \frac{\mathcal{P}}{E_{\text{in}}} = \text{thermal efficiency} \tag{23.22}$$

and E_{in} is the rate at which energy is supplied to the propulsion system and constitutes the sum of the calorific value of the fuel (or propellants) and its kinetic energy. Thus, for a *thermal-jet engine*

$$E_{\text{in}} = \dot{m}_f \left(J \, \Delta H_c + \frac{V^2}{2g} \right) \tag{23.23}$$

if $J \, \Delta H_c$ is the calorific value of the fuel.

For a *rocket engine*

$$E_{\text{in}} = \dot{m} \left(J \, \Delta H_p + \frac{V^2}{2g} \right)$$

if $J \, \Delta H_p$ is the calorific value of the propellant system and $\dot{m} = \dot{m}_o + \dot{m}_f$.

Hence, for *thermal-jet engines*,

$$\eta = \frac{2\nu}{1 + \nu} \frac{\mathcal{P}}{\dot{m}_f \, (J \, \Delta H_c + V^2/2g)} \tag{23.24}$$

For *rocket engines*

$$\eta = \frac{2\nu}{1 + \nu^2} \frac{\mathcal{P}}{\dot{m}_p(J \, \Delta H_p + V^2/2g)} \tag{23.25}$$

In the case of *hydraulic-jet propulsion* a prime mover supplies the shaft power $\omega\Phi$ to the pump shaft and the propulsion power $\mathcal{P} = \eta_h\omega\Phi$. If η_{th} is the thermal efficiency of the prime mover, then

$$E_{\text{in}} = \frac{\omega\Phi}{\eta_{\text{th}}}$$

The over-all efficiency is, accordingly,

$$\eta = \frac{FV}{E_{\text{in}}} = \eta_h\eta_{\text{th}} \frac{2\nu}{1 + \nu} \tag{23.26}$$

The ratio $g\dot{m}_f/F$ is called the *thrust specific fuel consumption* (*TSFC*) and is measured in pounds of fuel per hour per pound of thrust. Hence, for thermal-jet engines,

$$TSFC = 3600 \frac{g\dot{m}_f}{F} \tag{23.27}$$

PERFORMANCE CHARACTERISTICS OF RAMJET AND TURBOJET ENGINES

This section presents the principal equations for calculating the performance characteristics of the ramjet and turbojet engines at the design point.

23.12. The Ramjet Engine

The general features of the ramjet engine were discussed in Art. 23.3. For a ramjet engine the thrust due to the internal flow (Art. 23.10) is termed the gross thrust and is denoted by F_g. If it is assumed (Fig. 23.1) that $\dot{m}_a \approx \dot{m}_a + \dot{m}_f$, then

$$F_g = \dot{m}_a \,(V_j - V_0) \tag{23.28}$$

For level unaccelerated flight, the gross thrust F_g is equal to the drag of the propelled vehicle plus the external drag of the engine body. Let D_e denote the external drag of the engine; then the net thrust F_n acting on the propelled vehicle is

$$F_n = F_g - D_e \tag{23.29}$$

It is convenient to express the gross thrust of a ramjet engine in terms of a *gross-thrust coefficient* C_{Fg}. Let A_m denote the maximum cross-section area of the engine, and $q_0 = \rho_0 V_0^2/2 = k_0 p_0 \mathbf{M}_0^2/2 = $ the *dynamic pressure* of the free-stream air; then by definition,

$$C_{Fg} = \frac{F_g}{q_0 A_m} = \frac{2A_7/A_m}{k_0 \mathbf{M}_0^2} \left(\frac{P_7}{p_0} \frac{1 + k_7 \mathbf{M}_7^2}{P_7/p_7} - 1 \right) - \frac{2A_0}{A_m} \tag{23.30}$$

For a fixed-geometry engine the Mach number $\mathbf{M}_7$ depends on the total temperature T_6, the total pressure P_6, the area ratio A_e/A_t for the exhaust nozzle, and its efficiency. For estimating purposes $k_0 = 1.4$ and $k_7 = 1.35$ for an engine burning a hydrocarbon fuel. Figure 23.10 illustrates schematically the manner in which C_{Fg} varies with flight Mach number, altitude, and fuel-air ratio for a fixed-geometry ramjet engine.

There are three distinct operating conditions which may be encountered, depending upon the heat released in the combustion chamber: (1) *critical operation*, where a normal shock is positioned at the inlet to the subsonic diffuser; (2) *supercritical operation*, when the heat release causes the back pressure at the exit from the subsonic diffuser to become large enough to expel the normal shock from the subsonic diffuser; and (3) *subcritical operation*, which occurs when the back pressure at the exit from the subsonic diffuser is too low for maintaining the normal shock at its inlet; the shock is swallowed.

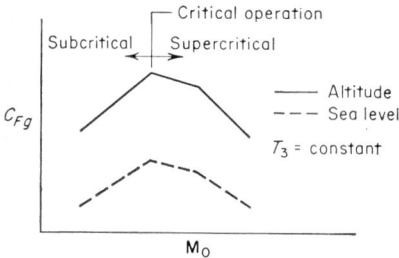

(a) Effect of altitude for a constant combustion temperature T_3

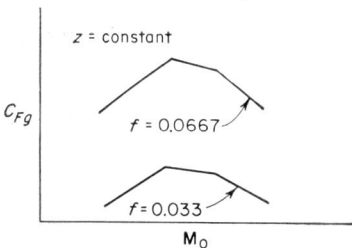

(b) Effect of fuel-air ratio of a constant altitude

Fig. 23.10. Characteristics of the gross-thrust coefficient for a fixed-geometry ramjet engine. (*Ref. 7.*)

The rate at which heat is supplied to the ramjet engine is given by

$$Q_i = \dot{W}_a \bar{c}_{pB} (T_6 - T_2) \tag{23.31}$$

if $\bar{c}_{pB}$ is the mean value of the constant-pressure specific heat for the gases.

If $T_6/t_0 = \alpha$ = the cycle temperature ratio, and k_B the mean value of the specific-heat ratio for the combustion gases, then

$$Q_i = \frac{A_0 p_0 V_0}{J} \frac{k_B}{k_B - 1} \left[\frac{\alpha}{1 + \mathbf{M}_0^2 (k_0 - 1)/2} - 1 \right] \tag{23.32}$$

By definition, the *gross-thrust specific-fuel consumption* is given by

$$F_g \text{ SFC} = 3600 \frac{g \dot{m}_f}{F_g} = \frac{7200_g}{a_0 M_0} \left(\frac{A_0}{A_m} \right) \frac{f}{C_{Fg}} = 4626 \frac{V_0}{\eta_0 \Delta H_c} \tag{23.33}$$

in which η_0 is the over-all efficiency, and ΔH_c the calorific value of the fuel in Btu per pound.

For estimating purposes the total pressure ratios for different sections of a ramjet engine operating at a flight Mach number of approximately 2.0 and $T_6 = 3600°R$ are listed below.

Part of engine	Typical values of pressure ratio ($\mathbf{M}_0 = 2.0$)
Supersonic diffuser.............	$P_1/P_0 = 0.92$
Subsonic diffuser..............	$P_2/P_1 = 0.90$
Flameholders, etc..............	$P_3/P_2 = 0.97$
Combustion chamber..........	$P_6/P_3 = 0.92$
Exhaust nozzle................	$P_7/P_6 = 0.97$

At flight Mach numbers above $\mathbf{M}_0 = 2.0$, the pressure recovery P_2/P_0 decreases rapidly.

23.13. The Turbojet Engine

The general features of the simple turbojet engine are discussed in Art. 23.5. In analyzing the operating cycle of the simple turbojet engine it is convenient to introduce the following simplifying assumptions: (1) there is no change in the mass flow rate of working fluid at any station in the engine; (2) the working fluid has the same thermodynamic properties as air; (3) the working fluid (air) is a perfect gas, and its specific heats are constant; (4) there are no pressure drops due to either friction or heat addition; (5) the working fluid (air) expands completely in flowing through the exhaust nozzle so that $p_9 = p_0$ (Fig. 23.3); and (6) the auxiliary power requirements may be neglected. Let

$$\Theta = \left(\frac{P_3}{p_0} \right)^{(k-1)/k} \qquad \Theta_d = \left(\frac{P_2}{P_0} \right)^{(k-1)/k} \qquad \Theta_c = \left(\frac{P_3}{P_2} \right)^{(k-1)/k}$$

$$\Theta_t = \left(\frac{P_4}{P_5} \right)^{(k-1)/k} \qquad \Theta_n = \left(\frac{P_7}{p_0} \right)^{(k-1)/k} = \left(\frac{P_7}{p_9} \right)^{(k-1)/k}$$

$$\alpha = \frac{T_4}{t_0} \qquad \alpha_d = \frac{T_2}{t_0} \qquad \alpha_1 = \frac{T_4}{T_2}$$

In view of the assumptions, $P_4 = P_3$, $P_7 = P_5$, $p_9 = p_0$, and

$$\Theta = \Theta_d \Theta_c = \Theta_t \Theta_n \tag{23.34}$$

Also

$$\alpha = \alpha_d \alpha_1 \tag{23.35}$$

The diffuser pressure-ratio parameter Θ_d is given by

$$\Theta_d = 1 + \eta_d \frac{k-1}{2} \mathbf{M}_0^2 \tag{23.36}$$

in which

$$\eta_d = \frac{T'_2 - t_0}{T_2 - t_0} = \text{isentropic-diffuser efficiency} \tag{23.37}$$

where $T'_2 < T_2$ is the total temperature corresponding to an isentropic diffusion from p_0 to P_2.

The heat supplied to the turbojet engine, in Btu per pound of air, is given by

$$Q_i = c_p \frac{T_4 - T_3}{\eta_B}$$

or

$$Q_i = \frac{c_p t_0 \alpha_d}{\eta_B \eta_c} \left(\frac{\alpha}{\alpha_d} - \eta_c - \Theta_c + 1 \right) \tag{23.38}$$

if η_B is the efficiency of the combustion, and η_c is the isentropic efficiency of the air compressor.

The turbojet engine, under the assumed conditions, is characterized by the fact that the work delivered by the turbine is exactly equal to that required for driving the air compressor. Thus, if Δh_t is the enthalpy drop in the turbine and Δh_c the enthalpy increase required for operating the air compressor, then

$$\eta_t (T_4 - T'_5) = \frac{T'_3 - t_0}{\eta_c} \tag{23.39}$$

if T'_3 is the isentropic-compression temperature for the air compressor and T'_5 the isentropic-expansion temperature for the turbine. The turbine pressure-ratio parameter is given by

$$\Theta_t = 1 - \frac{\Theta_c - 1}{\alpha_1 \eta \, \eta_c} \tag{23.40}$$

in which η_t and η_c are the isentropic efficiencies of the turbine and air compressor, respectively.

The pressure-ratio parameter for the exhaust nozzle Θ_n is obtained from

$$\frac{1}{\Theta_n} = \frac{\Theta_d \Theta_c}{\alpha_1 \eta \, \eta_c} (\alpha_1 \eta \, \eta_c - \Theta_c + 1) \tag{23.41}$$

The enthalpy change for the exhaust nozzle Δh_n is obtained from

$$\frac{\Delta h_n}{c_p t_0} = [\alpha \eta_c - \alpha_d (\Theta_c - 1)] \left\{ 1 - \frac{\alpha_1 \eta \, \eta_c}{\Theta_c [1 + \eta_d (\alpha_d - 1)][\alpha \eta \, \eta_c - (\Theta_c - 1)]} \right\} \frac{\eta_n}{\eta_c} \tag{23.42}$$

The *thermal efficiency* of the engine is given by

$$\eta_{\text{th}} = \frac{\Delta h_n}{Q_i} - \frac{V_0^2}{2gJQ_i} \tag{23.43}$$

The *specific thrust*, also called the *air specific impulse*, is denoted by I_a and given by

$$I_a = \frac{F}{\dot{m}_a g} = \frac{1}{g} (V_j - V_0) = \frac{1}{g} \left(\sqrt{2gJ \, \Delta h_n} - V_0 \right) \tag{23.44}$$

It should be noted that in turbojet technology the thrust due to the internal flow $F = \dot{m}_a(V_j - V)$ is called the net thrust, while the sum of the *jet thrust* (Art. 23.10) and the *pressure thrust* is called the *gross thrust*.

The *TSFC* for a turbojet-engine is given by

$$TSFC = 3600 \frac{g\dot{m}_f}{F} \tag{23.45}$$

Table **23.1**

Nondimensional group	Uncorrected form	Corrected form
Flight speed...................	$V/\sqrt{t_0}$	$V/\sqrt{\theta}$
Rotational speed..............	$N/\sqrt{T}$	$N/\sqrt{\theta}$
Air-flow rate..................	$\dot{W}_a\sqrt{T}/D^2P$	$\dot{W}\sqrt{\theta}/D^2\delta$
Thrust.......................	F/D^2P	$F/D^2\delta$
Fuel-flow rate................	$\dot{W}_f(J\,\Delta H_c)/D^2P\sqrt{T}$	$\dot{W}_f(J\,\Delta H_c)/D^2\delta\sqrt{\theta}$

$\theta = T/T_{std} = T/519 =$ corrected temperature (exact value for T_{std} is 518.699°R).
$\delta = P/p_{std} = P/14.7 =$ corrected pressure.

From considerations of dynamic and thermal similarity, the important variables entering into the performance of a given turbojet engine are the flight speed V, the total pressure of the working fluid P, the engine speed (rpm) N, the flow-passage diameter D, the total temperature T, the weight flow rate of working fluid $\dot{W}$, the thrust F, and the rate at which energy is supplied to the engine $\dot{W}_f(J\,\Delta H_c)$. By making a dimensional analysis, one obtains the parameters listed in Table 23.1.

For a given engine, the characteristic length D is a constant and may be omitted from the dimensionless groups. The performance of a given engine can be expressed by the following functional relationships:

$$\text{Corrected thrust:}\qquad \frac{F}{\delta} = f_1\left(\frac{N}{\sqrt{\theta_2}},\frac{V_0}{\sqrt{\theta_0}}, A_9\right) \qquad (23.46)$$

$$\text{Corrected air flow:}\ \frac{\dot{W}_a\sqrt{\theta_2}}{\delta_2} = f_2\left(\frac{N}{\sqrt{\theta_2}},\frac{V_0}{\sqrt{\theta_0}}, A_9\right) \qquad (23.47)$$

$$\text{Corrected fuel flow:}\ \frac{\dot{W}_f}{\delta_2\sqrt{\theta_2}} = f_3\left(\frac{N}{\sqrt{\theta_2}},\frac{V_0}{\sqrt{\theta_0}}, A_9\right) \qquad (23.48)$$

Figure 23.11 illustrates the effects of flight speed, altitude, and engine rpm upon the performance parameters of a given turbojet engine. Performance analyses indicate that for flight Mach numbers exceeding approximately 2.5, it becomes desirable to combine the turbojet engine with a ramjet engine (turboramjet).

PERFORMANCE CHARACTERISTICS OF ROCKET ENGINES

The general features of liquid-propellant rocket engines were presented in Art. 23.7, and those for solid-propellant rocket engines in Art. 23.8.

23.14. Criteria of Rocket-engine Performance

In all the discussions it is assumed that the rocket engine is operated under steady-state conditions so that the combustion pressure p_c, the combustion temperature t_c, and the velocity of the gases entering the exhaust nozzle V_c do not change during the combustion period. The thrust developed by the rocket motor (Figs. 23.4 and 23.7) is the resultant axial component of the static pressure forces acting upon its interior and exterior surfaces. The net pressure force acting on the interior surfaces depends upon the rate of propellant consumption ($\dot{m} = \dot{m}_o + \dot{m}_f$), the mixture ratio $\dot{m}_o/\dot{m}_f$, the area of the throat of the exhaust nozzle, the area ratio of the exhaust nozzle A_e/A_t, and to a less significant extent upon the static pressure of the surroundings into which the propulsive gaseous jet is discharged. In general, the internal pressure force is several times that due to the external static pressure. Because it is extremely difficult, if not impossible, to measure the afore-mentioned forces directly, the thrust F is calculated by

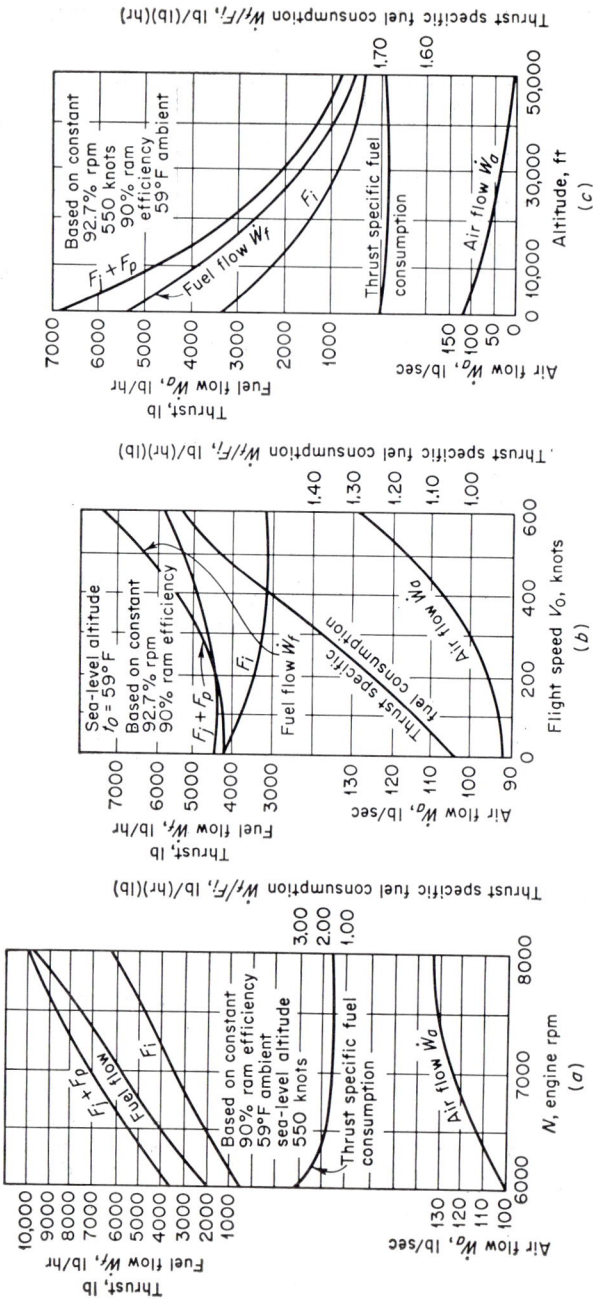

FIG. 23.11. Performance characteristics of a turbojet engine. (a) Effect of engine speed. (b) Effect of flight speed. (c) Effect of altitude. (General Electric Company. From "Marks' Mechanical Engineers' Handbook," 6th ed.)

applying the momentum theorem of fluid mechanics to the gas flowing through the rocket motor. For a rocket motor the thrust is calculated by means of Eq. (23.8).

Exit Velocity for Propulsive Jet. Refer to Figs. 23.4 and 23.7. At the entrance to the exhaust nozzle, the variables pertinent to the state of the combustion gas are p_c, t_c, ρ_c, h_c and the corresponding mean velocity of the gas is V_c. At the exit section A_e, the corresponding variables are p_e, t_e, ρ_e, h_e, and V_e. Since the expansion of the gas in the exhaust nozzle may be assumed adiabatic,

$$h_c + \frac{V_c^2}{2gJ} = h_o + \frac{V_e^2}{2gJ} = H_g = \text{const} \tag{23.49}$$

if H_g = the stagnation specific enthalpy of the combustion gas.

Hence the exhaust velocity V_e is given by†

$$V_e = \sqrt{2gJ(H_g - h_e)} \approx \sqrt{2gJ(h_c - h_e)} \tag{23.50}$$

if J = the mechanical equivalent of heat = 778 ft-lb/Btu.

If $\overline{m}$ denotes the molecular weight of the combustion gas, k the specific-heat ratio, R_u the universal gas constant, then assuming perfect gases,

$$V_e = \phi V'_e = \phi \sqrt{\frac{2gk}{k-1} R_u \frac{t_c}{\overline{m}} Z_t} \tag{23.51}$$

in which

$$Z_t = 1 - \left(\frac{p_e}{p_c}\right)^{(k-1)k} = \text{expansion factor} \tag{23.52}$$

and $\phi = V_e/V'_e$ = velocity coefficient (its value is usually between 0.92 and 1.0)
V'_e = isentropic exit velocity

Nozzle Divergence Coefficient. The thrust developed by the rocket motor is due to the component of V_e parallel to the longitudinal axis of the rocket motor, that is, the x component, which is denoted by V_{ex}. The velocities V_e and V_{ex} are related by the nozzle divergence coefficient λ, if

$$\lambda = \frac{V_{ex}}{V_e} \tag{23.53}$$

The magnitude of λ depends upon the semidivergence angle of the exhaust nozzle (ordinarily 12 to 20°) and is calculated from the relationship[23]

$$\lambda = \tfrac{1}{2} + \tfrac{1}{2} \cos \alpha \tag{23.54}$$

Hence the *thrust equation* for a rocket motor is, accordingly,

$$F = \frac{\dot{W}}{g} \lambda V_e + (p_e - p_o) A_e \tag{23.55}$$

if $\dot{W} = \dot{W}_o + \dot{W}_f$ = propellant consumption rate in pounds per second.

The propellant consumption rate $\dot{W}$ is equal to weight rate of gas flow discharged by the exhaust nozzle. In terms of the thermodynamic constants for the combustion gas,

$$\dot{W} = C_d \dot{W}' = 0.1443 \frac{A_t p_c C_d \Omega}{\sqrt{t_c/\overline{m}}} \tag{23.56}$$

in which

$$\Omega = \sqrt{k} \left(\frac{2}{k+1}\right)^{(k+1)/2(k-1)} \tag{23.57}$$

and $C_d = \dot{W}/\dot{W}'$ = discharge coefficient
$\dot{W}'$ = weight flow rate for an isentropic process

† Since V_c is quite small compared with V_e, the static values of the thermodynamic properties are employed.

Since the pressure term is difficult to measure, the thrust F is expressed in terms of the effective jet velocity V_j, as in Eq. (23.8). In a test of a rocket motor, the propellant consumption rate and the thrust are measured and the effective jet velocity V_j is calculated. The effective jet velocity is basically a property of the propellant system which is burned and is directly related to the *specific impulse*, which is discussed in this article.

Thrust Coefficient. In a firing test of a rocket motor the variables F, A_t, and p_c are readily measured. Consequently, it is convenient to express the thrust F by the relationship

$$F = C_F p_c A_t \tag{23.58}$$

The measured *thrust coefficient* C_F is accordingly given by

$$C_F = \frac{F}{p_c A_t} \tag{23.59}$$

For a given propellant system, experimental values of C_F for different values of p_c and $\mathring{W}_0/\mathring{W}_f$ are obtained from firings of small-thrust rocket motors. Such data are required for determining the throat area A_t of the exhaust nozzle for a proposed rocket motor. When experimental values of C_F are lacking, the *theoretical thrust coefficient* C'_F can be calculated by thermodynamic methods (Fig. 23.12).

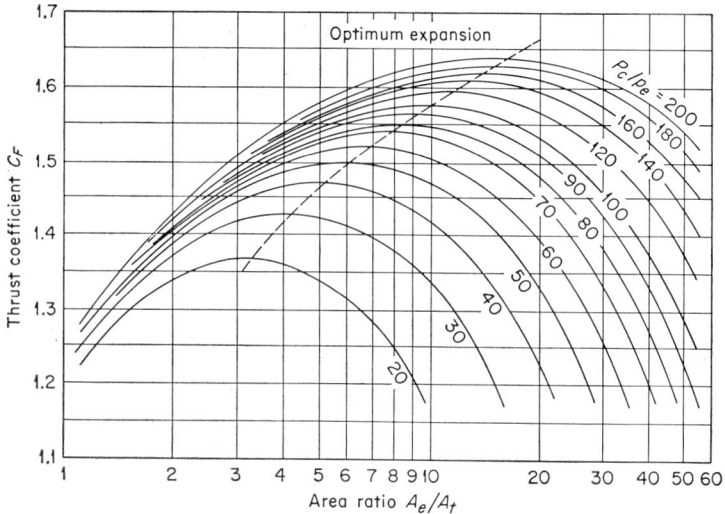

Fig. 23.12. Calculated thrust coefficient of a rocket motor as a function of area ratio for different nozzle pressure ratios (based on $k = 1.28$, $\lambda = 0.9830$, $C_d = \varphi = 1.0$). (*Ref.* 7.)

Thus

$$C'_F = \lambda C_d \phi \Omega \sqrt{\frac{2}{k-1} Z_t} + \left(\frac{p_e}{p_c} - \frac{p_0}{p_c}\right) \frac{A_e}{A_t} \tag{23.60}$$

in which λ is given by Eq. (23.54), Ω by Eq. (23.57), and Z_t by Eq. (23.52). Figure 23.12 presents C_F as a function of A_e/A_t for several constant values of p_c/p_e. The curves are based on $k = 1.28$, $\lambda = 0.9830$, and $C_d = \phi = 1$.

From Eq. (23.60) it is seen that C'_F, and consequently C_F, is independent of the molecular weight of the combustion gas and the combustion temperature. If the nozzle is designed so that the *nozzle area ratio* ($\epsilon = A_e/A_t$) is such that the gases are completely expanded, so that $p_e = p_0$, then

$$(C'_F)_{opt} = \lambda\phi C_d\Omega \sqrt{\frac{2}{k-1}Z_t} \qquad (23.61)$$

Weight Flow Coefficient. It is convenient to express the weight rate of propellant consumption $\mathring{W}$ in terms of a measured *weight flow coefficient* C_w. Thus

$$\mathring{W} = C_w p_c A_t$$

or
$$C_w = \frac{\mathring{W}}{p_c A_t} \qquad (23.62)$$

Figure 23.13 presents A_e/A_t as a function of p_c/p_e for several values of k.

Experimental values of C_w for different values of p_c and $\mathring{W}_o/\mathring{W}_f$ for a given propellant system are obtained from firings of small-thrust rocket motors. Such data are useful for determining the required propellant-consumption rate for any application of the propellant system.

The *theoretical weight flow coefficient* C_{wth}, expressed in terms of the thermodynamic constants for the combustion gas, is given, from Eqs. (23.56) and (23.62), by

$$(C_w)_{th} = 0.1443\, C_d\, \frac{\Omega}{\sqrt{t_c/\overline{m}}} \qquad (23.63)$$

Equation (23.63) is useful for estimating the value of C_w. If the flow through the nozzle occurs without any *reassociation* of the constituents of the flowing gas and with insignificant heat loss, the *discharge coefficient* C_d will be between 0.95 and 1.0. If there is reassociation phenomena, C_d may be slightly larger than unity.

Specific Impulse. By definition, the specific impulse I is given by

$$I = \frac{F}{\mathring{W}} = \frac{1}{W_p}\int_0^{\tau_b} F\, d\tau = \frac{I_T}{W_p} \qquad (23.64)$$

and
$$I_T = \int_0^{\tau_b} F\, d\tau = \text{total impulse} \qquad (23.65)$$

In a test of a solid-propellant rocket motor, the burning time $\tau_b = \int d\tau$, the total

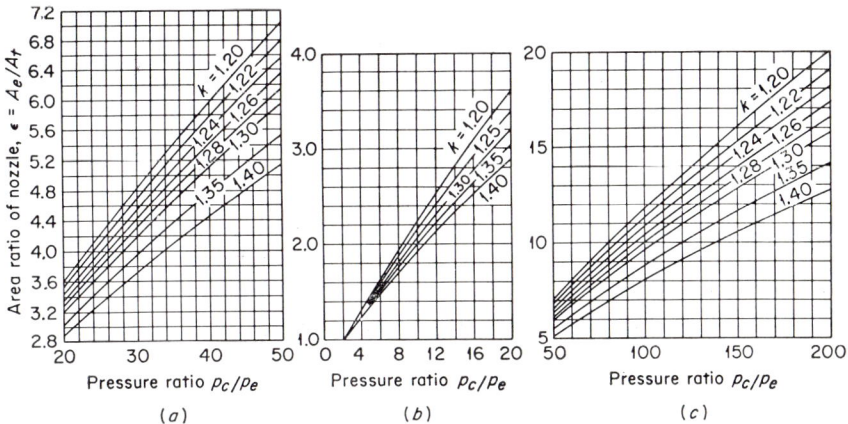

FIG. 23.13. Area ratio of the exhaust nozzle as a function of its pressure ratio for different values of the specific-heat ratio k.

Table 23.2. Calculated Specific Impulses for Different Liquid-bipropellant
Propellant Systems

$(p_c = 500$ psia; $p_e = p_0 = 14.7$ psia; isentropic one-dimensional flow;
frozen equilibrium during expansion) $\overline{m}$ = molecular weight of combustion gases;
t_c = adiabatic flame temperature; $r = \dot{W}_0/\dot{W}_f$ = mixture ratio; $k = c_p/c_v$; d = bulk density

Oxidizer	Fuel	r	t_c, °F	k	$\overline{m}$	d, g/cc	I'	$I'_d = I'd$
Bromine pentafluoride	Ammonia	6.0	6660	1.34	29	1.8	235	423
Chlorine trifluoride.....	Ammonia	3.0	4980	1.32	22	1.26	240	303
	Hydrazine	2.5	6000	1.33	23	1.46	252	368
Fluorine	Ammonia	3.0	7270	1.33	19	1.16	303	351
	Diborane	5.0	7880	1.30	21	1.07	308	330
	Hydrazine	2.0	7740	1.33	19	1.30	316	411
	Hydrogen $(I'_d)_{max}$	19.0	8350	1.34	18	0.75	336	252
	Hydrogen $(I')_{max}$	4.5	5000	1.33	8.9	0.32	373	120
	JP-4	2.9	7100	1.22	24	1.19	278	331
50% fluorine + 50% nitrogen trifluoride...	Ammonia	2.8	6540	1.32	19	1.15	292	336
Fluorine monoxide.....	Ammonia	1.9	6040	1.29	18	1.07	280	300
	Hydrazine	1.1	6380	1.28	18	1.23	288	354
	n-Octane	3.8	7340	1.33	20	1.22	301	367
Hydrogen peroxide (99.6%)	Ethyl alcohol (92.5%)	4.0	4600	1.20	23	1.24	240	298
	JP-4	6.5	4830	1.20	22	1.28	248	318
	Hydrazine	1.7	4690	1.22	19	1.24	262	325
Hydrogen peroxide (90%)	Hydrazine	1.5	4170	1.25	18	1.20	252	302
Nitrogen tetroxide	Hydrazine	1.1	4950	1.26	19	1.20	263	316
Oxygen...............	Ammonia	1.3	4940	1.23	19	0.88	263	231
	Diethylenetriamine	1.5	5550	1.24	21	1.06	266	282
	Ethyl alcohol (75%)	1.3	5150	1.22	23	0.99	246	244
	Ethyl alcohol (92.5%)	1.5	5400	1.21	23	0.98	252	247
	Ethylenediamine (88%)	1.4	6000	1.23	19	1.04	262	272
	Ethylene oxide	1.1	5750	1.24	22	0.99	261	258
	Hydrazine	0.75	5370	1.25	18	1.06	279	297
	Hydrogen $(I'_d)_{max}$	8.0	5870	1.22	16	0.43	316	136
	Hydrogen $(I')_{max}$	3.5	4500	1.26	9.0	0.26	363	95
	Isopropyl alcohol	1.7	5560	1.22	22	0.98	258	253
	JP-4 (C/H = 6.85)	2.2	5880	1.24	22	0.98	262	257
	JP-4 (C/H = 6.00)	2.3	5770	1.24	22	0.98	262	257
	Methyl alcohol	1.2	5230	1.21	22	0.95	250	247
	Methyl acetylene	2.0	6180	1.27	22	0.93	241	223
	Methyl cyclopentane	2.3	5770	1.24	22	0.98	263	258
	Nitroethane	0.65	5570	1.23	23	1.09	251	274
	Nitropropane	0.9	5620	1.23	23	1.06	256	271
	n-Octane	2.4	5790	1.23	22	0.96	265	254
	Propylene oxide	1.6	5900	1.23	23	1.00	258	258
	Turpentine	2.4	6000	1.23	22	1.04	261	271
	UDMH	1.4	5650	1.24	20	0.96	272	261
Oxygen (70%) + ozone (30%).........	JP-4	2.3	5950	1.24	22	1.04	268	279
Oxides of nitrogen ...... (70% nitrogen tetroxide, 30% nitric oxide)	Ammonia	2.1	4900	1.23	21	1.03	258	267
	Ammonia (50%) + methyl alcohol (50%)	2.1	5050	1.23	23	1.06	240	255
	Ethylene oxide	2.0	5730	1.24	24	1.14	250	275
	Methyl alcohol	2.1	5210	1.22	25	1.10	236	259
	Turpentine	3.5	5800	1.25	24	1.21	250	303
Oxygen (30%) + ozone (70%)........	JP-4	2.3	6180	1.25	21	1.08	272	294
Ozone...............	JP-4	2.4	6380	1.25	21	1.14	278	317
Red fuming nitric acid (6.5% NO₂)	n-Octane	4.5	5100	1.24	24	1.26	234	295
Red fuming nitric acid (15% NO₂)	Hydrazine	1.3	4980	1.25	20	1.26	257	324
Red fuming nitric acid (15% NO₂)	Ammonia	2.15	4220	1.24	21	1.12	236	264
	Diethylenetriamine (80%) + methylamine (20%)	3.0	5250	1.23	24	1.33	240	319

Table **23.2.** Calculated Specific Impulses for Different Liquid-bipropellant
Propellant Systems (*Continued*)

Oxidizer	Fuel	r	t_c, °F	k	$\overline{m}$	d, g/cc	I'	$I'_d = I'd$
	JP-4	4.1	5150	1.23	25	1.30	235	305
	Polyethylene	4.5	5320	1.22	25	1.40	233	326
	Turpentine	4.2	5400	1.22	26	1.36	233	316
	UDMH	3.0	5250	1.23	24	1.33	240	317
Tetranitromethane.....	Hydrazine	1.4	5250	1.27	20	1.29	258	333

NOTES: (1) UDMH = unsymmetrical dimethyl hydrazine.
   (2) To obtain values of I' and I'_d at combustion pressures other than $p_c = 500$ psia,

p_c	200	300	400	500	600	700	800	900	1000	1100	1200
Multiply by	0.89	0.94	0.98	1.00	1.02	1.03	1.05	1.06	1.07	1.09	1.10

   (3) The densities of propellants which boil below 80°F were taken as the values at the boiling
   point.
SOURCE: Values in table are based on "Theoretical Performance of Several Rocket Propellant Combinations," Rocketdyne, a Division of North American Aviation Corporation, 1959

weight of propellants consumed W_p, and the thrust F are readily measured. The *measured specific impulse* I calculated from such measurements is an average value for the burning time. In the case of a liquid-propellant rocket motor, the instantaneous-propellant-consumption rate $\dot{W}$ is readily measured.

The units for I are seconds, and the magnitude of I is independent of the value of the gravitational acceleration g. Consequently, I is sometimes defined by the following relationship:[24]

$$ I = \frac{g}{g_o} \frac{F}{\dot{W}} \tag{23.66} $$

in which g is the local acceleration due to gravity, and g_o is the standard sea-level value (32.1740 ft/sec²).

As indicated in Art. 23.14, the specific impulse I is basically a property of the propellants burned in the rocket motor, although its magnitude is influenced by the design of the rocket motor. The specific impulse and effective jet velocity are related by

$$ I = \frac{V_j}{g} \tag{23.67} $$

It is readily shown that

$$ I = \frac{C_F}{C_w} \tag{23.68} $$

For a given propellant system, liquid or solid, one can compute a theoretical value for its specific impulse, denoted by I', by applying thermochemical analysis to the combustion and expansion processes. Propellant systems can be compared in a logical manner, therefore, if one determines their calculated values of specific impulse for the same operating conditions. In the case of liquid-propellant systems, the values of I' are usually compared on the basis of $p_c = 500$ psia and $p_e = 14.7$ (Figs. 23.4 and 23.7), while for solid propellants, the customary basis is $p_c = 1000$ psia and $p_e = 14.7$. There is a tendency, however, to compare the values of I' for both liquid- and solid-propellant systems on the basis of $p_c = 1000$ psia with isentropic expansion to $p_e = 0$, that is, *vacuum expansion.*

The values of I' for a given propellant system may be computed on two bases: (1) *frozen equilibrium,* and (2) *shifting or mobile equilibrium.* In the case of frozen equilibrium, it is assumed that the mean molecular weight of the combustion gas $\overline{m}$ remains constant during the expansion process in the exhaust nozzle; i.e., the composition of the gas entering and leaving the exhaust nozzle is unaltered. In the case of mobile or shifting equilibrium, the gas composition is assumed to change during isentropic expansion in the exhaust nozzle in such a manner that its constituents are always in thermochemical equilibrium. The values of I' obtained assuming mobile equilibrium are somewhat larger than those obtained assuming frozen equilibrium.

The calculated specific impulse I' can be expressed in terms of the thermodynamic constants for the combustion gas. Thus

$$I' = \frac{V'_e}{g} = \frac{1}{g}\sqrt{\frac{2gk}{k-1}\frac{R_u}{\overline{m}}t_c\,Z_t} \qquad (23.69)$$

From Eq. (23.69) it is seen that for a given expansion ratio p_e/p_c, the value of I', and consequently I, is primarily a function of $\sqrt{t_c/\overline{m}}$, since small variations in the specific-heat ratio k have little influence upon it. Consequently, increasing t_c or reducing $\overline{m}$, or both, gives larger values for I.

For a given propellant system (fuel plus oxidizer), the combustion temperature is primarily a function of W_o/W_f; the maximum value of t_c is limited, however, by chemical-dissociation reactions. From a practical point of view, the maximum value of t_c may be limited by the available construction materials for the rocket motor and the means for cooling them.

Low values of $\overline{m}$ for the combustion gases are associated with elements in the first two rows of the periodic table, particularly hydrogen. Such propellant systems (Table 23.2) usually have small bulk densities, which require larger dimensions for the propellant containers to achieve a specified total impulse I_T. A criterion which must be considered in addition to the specific impulse is the so-called *density impulse*, denoted by I_d. By definition,

$$I_d = I \times \text{average specific gravity of propellants} \qquad (23.70)$$

Table 23.2 presents calculated values of specific impulse I' and density impulse I'_d for several liquid-bipropellant systems. It is apparent that from the point of view of use in a single-stage rocket-propelled vehicle where a large value for I_d is desirable, the systems giving the largest values for I' (fluorine-hydrogen and oxygen-hydrogen) are inferior to several other systems. Neither I' nor I'_d is a unique criterion, and each application must receive individual study. In applications where *multistage rocket* propulsion is employed (Art. 23.20), the specific impulse I is the more important criterion.

For any propellant system (liquid or solid), the maximum specific impulse is obtained when the exhaust nozzle expands the gases completely to the predominating back pressure; that is, $p_e = p_O$. The *area ratio* for an exhaust nozzle, denoted by $\epsilon = A_e/A_t$, is given by

$$\epsilon = \frac{A_e}{A_t} = \frac{[2/(k+1)]^{(k+1)/2(k-1)}}{(p_e/p_c)^{1/k}\,[2/(k-1)]\,\sqrt{Z_t}} \qquad (23.71)$$

if Z_t is given by Eq. (23.52).

Figure 23.13 presents the nozzle area ratio $\epsilon = A_e/A_t$ as a function of p_c/p_e for several values of the specific-heat ratio of the gas flowing through it.

Characteristic Velocity. This criterion is denoted by c^* and defined by the relationship

$$c^* = \frac{V_j}{C_F} = \frac{qF}{\dot{W}C_F} = \frac{p_c A_t g}{\dot{W}} \qquad (23.72)$$

The characteristic velocity c^* measures the effectiveness of the combustion of the propellants. It has the advantage that its value can be obtained without measuring the thrust developed by the rocket motor.

When no experimental data are available, an *ideal characteristic velocity* $c^{*\prime}$ can be calculated from

$$c^{*\prime} = \frac{gI'}{C'_F} = 223.0\,\frac{\sqrt{t_c/\overline{m}}}{\Omega} \qquad (23.73)$$

Equation (23.73) shows that $c^{*\prime}$ depends only upon t_c, $\overline{m}$, and k, that is, upon the propellant system and the mixture ratio W_o/W_f. The combustion pressure has only a small influence on the value of $c^{*\prime}$.

23.15. Properties and Characteristics of Liquid Propellants

The discussions will be limited to liquid-bipropellant systems. Considerable research and development have been and are being spent on synthesizing new liquid propellants and improving the older ones. Currently, there is a large number of liquid-bipropellant systems, as can be seen from Table 23.2. The selection of a propellant system for a given application must take into consideration the operating requirements that are imposed on the rocket engine. For many military applications it is specified that the engine must operate with no deterioration in performance with propellant temperatures ranging from −65 to +165°F. Such an operating requirement severely restricts the number of adequate liquid propellants. Because of the different operating requirements which may be specified, there is no short-cut method for selecting the liquid-propellant system which is the most suitable for a specific application. Each case must be studied individually, and due consideration must be given to such items as storageability, handling and transport, logistics, availability of basic materials, toxicity, cost, corrosivity, and above all, operating reliability. The importance of reliability cannot be overemphasized for space flight and long-range ballistic-missile applications.

Desirable Properties for Liquid Propellants. A few of the more important properties which should be considered in selecting a liquid-propellant system are discussed briefly below. Many of them are also applicable to solid propellants.

ENTHALPY OF COMBUSTION. The calorific value per unit weight of the propellant system (oxidizer plus fuel) should be large.

PROPELLANT (AVERAGE) DENSITY. The propellant density should be large so that a large mass of propellants can be stored in a small volume. Fuels usually have smaller densities than oxidizers so that large values for the oxidizer-fuel ratio are desirable.

VAPOR PRESSURE. A low vapor pressure at temperatures up to approximately 160°F is highly desirable. In addition to introducing storage problems, a high vapor pressure introduces cavitation problems in turbopump pressurizing systems (Art. 23.7).

FREEZING POINT. The propellant should be in the liquid state at the lowest temperature to be encountered either on the earth or in space. Propellants that freeze at temperatures above −60°F will not meet the military specifications for several applications.

IGNITIBILITY. Propellants which react rapidly after being injected into the combustion chamber are highly desirable. This is particularly the case when the propellant temperature is low.

SPECIFIC HEAT. If the liquid propellant is to be used as a *regenerative coolant* (Art. 23.7), a high specific heat is desirable. In that case a high boiling point and a large thermal conductivity are also desirable.

CORROSIVITY. The propellant should have a low chemical reactivity with materials for constructing tanks, valves, piping, rocket motors, bearings, pump parts, seals, gaskets, etc.

STORAGE HAZARDS. The hazards due to such properties as toxicity, fire and explosion, thermal- and mechanical-shock sensitivity, and the like, should be low. It is important that they be investigated systematically and thoroughly before a propellant is put into operational use. Furthermore, safe methods for handling, transporting, and storing the propellants must be developed, and also suitable clothing for protecting the operating personnel, so that they can work with the propellant with a high degree of personal safety.

23.16. Solid Propellants

It was pointed out in Art. 23.8 that solid propellants may be grouped into (1) double-base propellants and (2) heterogeneous, or composite, propellants. The discussions in this section will be limited to oxidizers and fuels for heterogeneous propellants.

Oxidizers for Heterogeneous Solid Propellants. The inorganic oxidizers that are useful for manufacturing heterogeneous solid propellants are relatively few in number. They are listed in Table 23.3.

Propellants based on perchlorate oxidizers produce exhaust gases containing hydro-

Table **23.3.** Oxidizers for Heterogeneous Propellants

Name	Chemical formula	Molecular weight	Per cent available oxygen
Ammonium nitrate..............	NH_4NO_3	80.05	20
Ammonium perchlorate.........	NH_4ClO_4	117.49	34
Potassium nitrate..............	KNO_3	101.10	39.5
Potassium perchlorate..........	$KClO_4$	138.55	46.5
Lithium perchlorate............	$LiClO_4$	106.40	60.0

chloric acid (HCl), which condenses as a fog on a moist day. The exhaust gases from propellants using $KClO_4$ are smoky since they contain condensed potassium chloride (KCl), which is a white powder. Practically all the modern castable heterogeneous propellants use ammonium perchlorate as the oxidizer. The experience with lithium perchlorate is quite limited.

Fuels for Heterogeneous Propellants. It was pointed out in Art. 23.8 that the fuel component in a heterogeneous solid propellant is the binder for the solid-oxidizer particles. A large number of organic materials have been investigated for use as fuels. In modern solid propellants the fuels are elastomeric monomers which, after thorough mixing with the oxidizer particles, are polymerized during the curing process. Some of the more important fuels (binders) are polysulfides, polyurethanes, butadiene pyridine copolymers, butadiene acrylic acid copolymers, and petrinacrylate. Of the foregoing, all have been used in the manufacture of castable solid propellants except the butadiene pyridine copolymers, which have been used for manufacturing molded heterogeneous propellants using ammonium nitrate as the oxidizer.

It is desirable that the fuel (binder) contain a small amount of oxygen in its chemical formula so that the amount of solid oxidizer to give a desired oxygen balance can be reduced. This is highly desirable where the propellant formulation also contains light metals, such as aluminum, in powdered form.

23.17. Interior Ballistics of Solid-propellant Rocket Motors

The performance criteria discussed in Art. 23.14 apply to rocket motors burning either liquid or solid propellants. The latter have made great strides during the past five years (1956 to 1961) and are competing with liquid propellants in fields in which heretofore liquid propellants were used exclusively. The attractiveness of the solid-propellant rocket engine arises basically from its greater simplicity than the liquid-propellant rocket engine, the greater ease with which it can be handled in the field, its good storage qualities, and its high degree of reliability once it has been fully developed.

The exterior ballistics of a vehicle propelled by a solid-propellant rocket engine depends upon the performance characteristics of the solid propellant, called its *interior ballistics.*

Linear Burning Rate. The combustion of a solid propellant occurs at its surface, but the combustion mechanism is incompletely understood; as a matter of fact, current knowledge of propellant combustion is too elementary to be helpful in developing improved solid propellants.[37] As the burning of the propellant proceeds, however, the burning surface recedes in the direction perpendicular to itself, and the rate at which the burning surface recedes is termed the *linear burning rate,* which is denoted by r.

Experiments show that for a given set of values for the combustion pressure p_c and the propellant temperature t_p, the linear burning rate is a characteristic property of the propellant formulation; it is independent of the size and shape of the propellant grain. The following factors influence the linear burning rate of a solid propellant: (1) the propellant formulation, (2) the method employed for manufacturing the propellant grain, (3) the physicochemical structure of the propellant, (4) the temperature of the propellant, and (5) the conditions under which the propellant is burned.

Experiments indicate that a major influence upon the linear burning rate is the rate at which heat is transferred from the hot combustion gases to the burning surface. Consequently, for a given propellant, r is a function of the combustion temperature t_c, and V_g the speed of the combustion gas parallel to the burning surface; for a cigarette-burning grain $V_g = 0$ (Fig. 23.7a). It is also found that the *propellant temperature* t_p, prior to ignition, has a significant influence upon the linear burning rate. For a material to be a satisfactory solid propellant, its linear burning must be independent of the elapsed time after the grain is ignited.

The influence of V_g on r is a secondary effect which gives rise to *erosive burning*, discussed at the end of this article. Experiments for measuring the linear burning rate are conducted with end-burning grains (Fig. 23.7a), for which $V_g = 0$. The linear burning rate is accordingly given by

$$r = F(p_c, t_p) \qquad (23.74)$$

r is usually measured in inches per second.

The form of the functional relationship given by Eq. (23.74) has to be determined experimentally. In conducting the experiments, the propellant temperature t_p is held constant and r is measured. For $t_p =$ constant, the burning-rate law, known as *Saint-Robert's law*, is given by

$$r = c \, p_c^n \qquad (23.75)$$

in which the *burning-rate coefficient* c and the *burning-rate exponent* n (also called the *pressure index*) are calculated from the experimental data.

It is customary to assume that c and n are independent of the combustion pressure. If one set of values for c and n cannot be used over the entire range of combustion pressures of interest, then different sets of values for c and n are employed for different ranges of combustion pressure. Both c and n have positive values. The pressure index n for current solid propellants has values ranging from 0.1 to 0.8, but there are some double-base formulations (Art. 23.8) for which $n \approx 0$ and may even be negative over a usable pressure range.

For convenience, it is assumed that the propellant temperature t_p has no influence upon n, so that only c is influenced by changes in t_p.

Figure 23.14 presents the linear burning rates of several heterogeneous propellants made from the same fuel (binder) and different oxidizers.

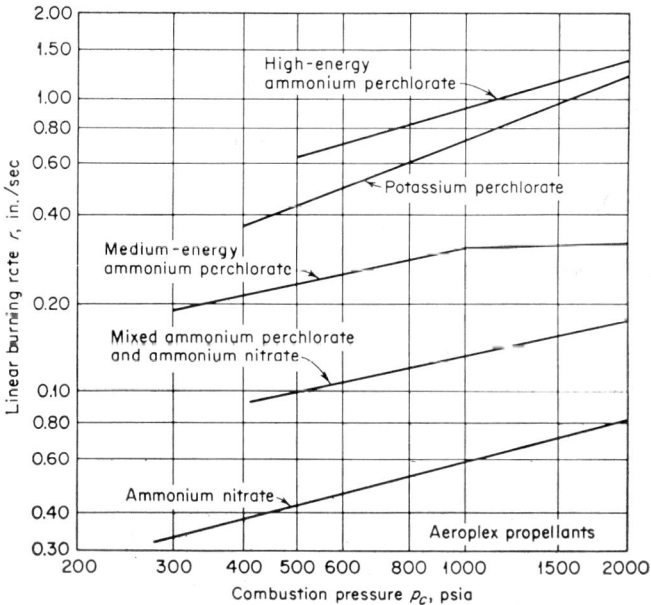

FIG. 23.14. Burning characteristics of some heterogeneous propellants using the same fuel and different oxidizers (at 60°F). (*Aerojet-General Corporation.*)

For a fixed value of the propellant temperature t_p and steady operating conditions, the weight rate of propellant consumption $\dot{W}$ is given by

$$\dot{W} = rS_c\gamma_p = c\gamma_p S_c p_c{}^n \tag{23.76}$$

if γ_p is specific weight of the solid propellant, and S_c the area of its burning surface.

Let $\mathcal{V}_c$ denote the internal volume of the rocket motor without the propellant grain, and $\mathcal{V}_p$ the volume occupied by the propellant grain at any instant τ. The *free volume* $\mathcal{V}_g$ through which the combustion gases flow is, accordingly, given by

$$\mathcal{V}_g = \mathcal{V}_c - \mathcal{V}_p \tag{23.77}$$

The *volumetric rate of propellant consumption*, denoted by $\dot{Q}_p$, is, accordingly,

$$\dot{Q}_p = \dot{\mathcal{V}}_g = rS_c \tag{23.78}$$

As the solid propellant is consumed at the rate $\dot{W}$, both the free volume $\mathcal{V}_g$ and the weight of gases contained therein increase. The difference between $\dot{W}$ and the weight rate of flow of gases into the free volume is the weight rate of flow of gas ejected through the exhaust nozzle, denoted by $\dot{W}_e$. Thus, at any instant τ,

$$\dot{W}_e = \dot{W} - \gamma_g \dot{\mathcal{V}}_g \tag{23.79}$$

Nozzle Area Ratio and Equilibrium Combustion Pressure. After the propellant is ignited and burning proceeds, the combustion pressure p_c increases until

$$\dot{W} = \dot{W}_e + \gamma_g \dot{\mathcal{V}}_g = C_w p_c A_t + \gamma_g \dot{\mathcal{V}}_g \tag{23.80}$$

if C_w is the weight flow coefficient (Art. 23.14).

When Eq. (23.80) is satisfied, the combustion pressure remains constant and its value is called the *equilibrium combustion pressure;* that condition corresponds to $dp_c/d\tau = 0$.

For a given propellant grain having a burning surface area S_c and a given rocket-motor configuration, it can be shown that the equilibrium combustion pressure depends upon the *propellant area ratio* K_n, if

$$K_n = \frac{S_c}{A_t} = \text{propellant area ratio} \tag{23.81}$$

The equilibrium combustion pressure p_c is given by

$$p_c = \left(\frac{cK_n \Delta\gamma}{C_w}\right)^{1/(1-n)} \tag{23.82}$$

In Eq. (23.82),

$$\Delta\gamma = \gamma_p - \gamma_g \tag{23.83}$$

in which γ_p is the specific weight of the solid propellant, and γ_g the specific weight of the gases contained in the free volume (see above discussion under linear burning rate).

Equation (23.83) shows that $K_n = S_c/A_t$ exerts a large influence upon the magnitude of the equilibrium combustion pressure. Since the *pressure index* n for solid propellants *is always smaller than unity*, the exponent $1/(1-n)$ in Eq. (23.82) always exceeds unity. A relatively small percentage increase in K_n, from the design value, therefore causes a much larger percentage increase in p_c from its design value. The larger the value of n, the more sensitive is the combustion pressure to small variations in the propellant burning area S_c, since the nozzle throat area A_t may be assumed to remain constant. Small values of n are usually associated with the heterogeneous propellants. The metal cases for solid-propellant rocket motors using internal-burning grains having small values of n may be designed with a smaller safety factor than those for propellants having large values of n.

The actual relationship between K_n and p_c for a given propellant is determined experimentally. In conducting the firing experiments, the propellant temperature and the burning-surface area are maintained constant, and the equilibrium combustion pressure is varied by firing different rocket motors having the same propellant burning area S_c but different nozzle throat areas A_t. The data obtained from such firings can be correlated by an equation of the form

$$K_n = bp_c{}^m \qquad (23.84)$$

It is generally assumed that the exponent m does not vary with t_p and only the coefficient b is a function of t_p.

Because K_n has a large influence upon the combustion pressure, it is important that the propellant grain be free of cracks. Such defects increase the value of K_n above its design value and can cause the combustion pressure to become damagingly high. Similar effects occur if the material for inhibiting certain surfaces of the propellant grain from burning either become separated from the grain or melt and erode faster than the propellant burning surface recedes as it burns.

Experiments show that the weight flow coefficient C_w and the combustion pressure can be related by the following empirical equation:

$$C_w = hp_c{}^q \qquad (23.85)$$

Combustion and Pressure Limits. Experiments have demonstrated that for any solid propellant there is a minimum value for p_c, called the *combustion limit*, below which stable combustion cannot be obtained. The magnitude of the combustion limit depends primarily upon the chemical composition of the solid propellant, but it also depends on the propellant temperature t_p. For double-base propellants, the combustion limit is of the order of 500 psia, whereas it may be as low as 100 psia for some heterogeneous propellants and as high as 800 psia for others. It is important, therefore, to design the solid-propellant rocket motor so that the operating combustion pressure will never be smaller than the combustion limit.

Experiments also show that if the combustion pressure is increased to higher and higher values, by systematically increasing K_n, a value of combustion pressure is finally reached where the propellant burning rate is so large that for all practical purposes the combustion process is explosive. That value of combustion pressure is called the *pressure limit*.

Effect of Propellant Temperature. It was noted in this article that the linear burning rate of a solid propellant depends upon the propellant temperature t_p. Consequently, the equilibrium combustion pressure p_c for a given value for the propellant area ratio K_n is likewise affected by the value of t_p. In general, low values of t_p tend to reduce the linear burning rate, and vice versa. The effect of t_p upon the performance of a solid propellant is referred to as its *temperature sensitivity*.

The influence of the propellant temperature upon the ballistic performance of a solid propellant is quite generally expressed in relative terms, that is, with respect to its performance at some standard value for t_p, usually 520°R. If $t_p > 520°R$, the performance deviations are positive, whereas if $t_p < 520°R$, they are negative.

Thus the *temperature-sensitivity coefficients* are generally expressed in terms of the *per cent change per degree Fahrenheit* for the variable under consideration, for a *constant value of propellant area ratio K_n*. Thus the temperature-sensitivity coefficients are:

For combustion pressure: $\Pi_{pc} = \dfrac{1}{(p_c)_{\text{std}}}\left(\dfrac{\partial p_c}{\partial t_p}\right)_{K_n}$

For thrust: $\Pi_F = \dfrac{1}{F_{\text{std}}}\left(\dfrac{\partial F}{\partial t_p}\right)_{K_n}$

For linear burning rate: $\Pi_r = \dfrac{1}{r_{\text{std}}}\left(\dfrac{\partial r}{\partial t_p}\right)_{K_n}$

in which $(p_c)_{\text{std}}$, F_{std}, and r_{std} are the values of combustion pressure, thrust, and linear burning rate, respectively, at the standard propellant temperature (usually 520°R).

The temperature-sensitivity coefficients for some heterogeneous propellants are affected by the oxidizer-fuel ratio, the particle size, and the particle-size distribution of the oxidizer powder. Experiments indicate that as a class, the heterogeneous propellants have smaller temperature-sensitivity coefficients than the double-base propellants.

The temperature sensitivity of the propellant must be considered in designing a solid-propellant rocket engine which must operate under conditions where t_p may vary widely, since it affects the minimum usable value for K_n and also the safety factor to be used in designing the case of the rocket motor. Low values for the temperature-sensitivity coefficients are especially desirable where a large value of impulse-weight ratio is important for the rocket-propelled vehicle.

The temperature sensitivity of a solid propellant to be used in a rocket engine for propelling a ballistic missile must be given careful consideration. The different burning rates obtained at different values of propellant temperature may cause the missile to follow ballistic trajectories different from the standard one, and if the errors are large, the guidance and control apparatus may be incapable of correcting the errors. The problems introduced by temperature sensitivity can be a serious disadvantage in applying a solid-propellant rocket engine to the propulsion of a ballistic missile. For many applications the problems due to temperature sensitivity can be circumvented either by employing *heating blankets* for keeping the propellant temperature close to the design temperature or by storing the solid-propellant rocket engine at the design temperature until a short time before firing it. Since the thermal conductivity of practically all solid propellants is quite small, a relatively short time exposure of the rocket engine to ambient temperatures different from the design temperature will not cause an appreciable change in t_p.

Changes in the propellant temperature, in addition to introducing the problems due to temperature sensitivity, may also produce significant alterations in the physical properties of the solid propellant. Low propellant temperatures are apt to make the propellant brittle, decrease its tensile strength, and increase the probability of cracks being formed under rough handling, vibration, or mechanical shock. Furthermore, if in addition the solid-propellant rocket motor is subjected to *temperature cycling*, alternating periods of low and high values of t_p, the possibility of cracks forming in the propellant grain and between the liner and the grain in case-bonded designs is increased. Moreover, at low values of t_p, it is more difficult to obtain satisfactory ignition of some propellant formulations.

At high values of t_p (140° to 160°F), the solid propellant may tend to soften and become so plastic that the sudden application of pressure during the ignition phase may cause deformation of the propellant grain, with a consequent abnormal increase in K_n and therefore in the combustion pressure.

Some solid propellants are subject to *cold flow*, or *slump*, when stored at temperatures only a few degrees above the standard temperature (520°R). The slump causes a change in the propellant area ratio, and hence in the linear burning rate of the propellant.

An essential part of the development effort expended on a solid-propellant rocket engine involves the experimental studies for obtaining as complete data as practicable on the effect of propellant temperature and temperature cycling upon ballistic properties, physical properties, and storage characteristics of the solid propellant. Because of the influence of t_p upon the physical characteristics of a solid propellant, the recommendations of the solid-propellant-engine manufacturer should be given serious consideration in matters pertaining to their storage and handling.

Erosive Burning. Refer to Fig. 23.7*b*. The cross-section area of the flow passage inside the propellant grain through which the combustion gases must flow in their movement toward the exhaust nozzle is termed the *port area* and is denoted by A_P. If A_C denotes the internal cross section of the casing surrounding the propellant grain and A_G the cross-section area of the propellant grain, then

$$\epsilon_P = \frac{A_C}{A_G} = \text{propellant loading ratio} \qquad (23.86)$$

To satisfy the performances required by ICBM and IRBM missile types, the propellant loading ratio should be close to 0.9.

The port area A_P is given by

$$A_P = A_C - A_G \tag{23.87}$$

The *port-to-throat area ratio*, denoted by K_P, is, accordingly

$$K_P = \frac{A_p}{A_t} = \frac{A_C - A_G}{A_t} \tag{23.88}$$

As the combustion gas flows past the burning surface of a solid-propellant grain (Fig. 23.7b), it transfers heat to the burning surface by forced convection, which tends to increase the local temperatures of the propellant, and hence its linear burning rate. Because the mass rate of gas flow increases from the fore to the aft end (nozzle end), the gas velocity increases as one proceeds from the fore to the aft end of the solid-propellant grain. As a consequence, the burning rate increases along the grain, and the grain tends to become tapered as the burning proceeds. The conditions are most severe immediately after ignition, since then the port area has its smallest value. The afore-mentioned effect of the velocity of the combustion gas upon the linear burning rate of the propellant is called *erosive burning*. The occurrence of erosive burning is usually evidenced by sharp peaks in the combustion pressure during the early-phase burning of the propellant, immediately following its ignition. At this time no completely satisfactory relationship has been developed for correlating the data on erosive burning of solid propellants.[40,49] The erosive-burning characteristics of a solid propellant is expressed in terms of the erosion ratio ϵ.

If r_e denotes the linear burning rate at a given combustion pressure and gas velocity V_g past the burning surface, and r is the burning rate at the same combustion pressure with $V_g = 0$, then

$$\epsilon = \frac{r_e}{r} = f(V_g) \tag{23.89}$$

The limited experimental data on erosive burning indicate that the erosion ratio increases with the gas velocity V_g when the latter is larger than some minimum value. No satisfactory relationship has been developed, however, for relating ϵ and V_g, nor is there a satisfactory theory for predicting the erosive-burning characteristics of a new propellant formulation.

Because of the local differences in static pressure along a grain such as an internal-burning grain (Fig. 23.7b), the static pressure decreasing from the fore to the aft end, the grain tends to become tapered as it burns, in the direction opposite to the tapering promoted by erosive burning. By proper design, assuming sufficient experimental data are available, the two tendencies to promote tapered burning can be caused practically to nullify each other. As already mentioned, as the propellant burning proceeds, the port area increases, which reduces the tendencies to erosive burning and nonuniform combustion pressures along the propellant grain.

23.18. Desired Characteristics for a Solid Propellant

As in the case of liquid propellants, there are certain characteristics which are desired for solid propellants; some of them will require considerable research and development for achieving them. The characteristics discussed for liquid propellants (Art. 23.15) that are applicable to solid propellants will not be repeated here.

SPECIFIC IMPULSE. Larger values of I than are currently being obtained are highly desirable. Modern solid-propellant formulations produce combustion gases which are compounds of the following elements: carbon (C), hydrogen (H), nitrogen (N), oxygen (O), and chlorine (Cl). For C—H—N—O—Cl systems, the maximum specific impulse obtainable is from 230 to 250 sec. The larger values of specific impulse are obtained by incorporating light metals in the propellant formulation, whether it be a double-base or a heterogeneous propellant.

PROPELLANT DENSITY. The larger the propellant density, the better. Heterogeneous propellants have densities ranging from 1.65 to 1.70 g/cc compared with approximately 0.94 g/cc for liquid propellants.

WIDE RANGE OF LINEAR BURNING RATES. With current heterogeneous propellants, linear burning rates ranging from approximately 0.1 to 2.0 in./sec are obtainable. The wider the range of burning rates for a given combustion pressure, the more flexible is the design of solid-propellant rocket engines. It is highly desirable that the linear burning rate be rather insensitive to the combustion pressure.

PHYSICAL PROPERTIES. The important physical properties to be considered in judging a solid propellant are (1) tensile strength, (2) elongation, (3) adhesion, and (4) fluidity. A large tensile strength is desired so that the deformation of the propellant grain under the operating conditions will be insignificant. A large per cent elongation is desired so that there will be no tendency for the propellant to crack when it is deformed by either pressure or temperature changes. The requirements for large values of the tensile strength and per cent elongation make it necessary currently to limit the ratio of the oxidizer to fuel (by weight) in a heterogeneous propellant.

For case-bonded rocket-motor designs, it is essential that the propellant adhere strongly to the liner bonding it to the metal case.

In the case of castable heterogeneous propellants, the slurry formed by mixing the fuel (binder) and the powdered inorganic oxidizer and light metals must have a fluidity which is adequate for obtaining good mixing and casting properties.

It is desirable that the propellant have good physical properties over the propellant temperature range and temperature cycling conditions to be encountered in the application of the rocket engine.

SMOKELESS EXHAUST. For many applications it is advantageous if the exhaust gas is smokeless.

SHOCK SENSITIVITY. The propellant should be insensitive to mechanical or thermal shock, and when burning, the deflagration process should under no circumstances cause the propellant to detonate.

SHRINKAGE DURING MANUFACTURE. The shrinkage during the curing process should be small, and the curing exotherm low; a low curing exotherm improves the safety of the manufacturing process.

PROCESS CONTROL. The propellant ingredients should be compatible with the conventional construction materials and be capable of quality control employing well-tested methods of process control. The propellant itself should also be compatible with the usual construction materials and should lend itself to process-control techniques which ensure a uniform product, especially in the case of large grains.

AGING IN STORAGE. The propellant should not deteriorate either in its performance or in its physical condition after storage periods of at least two years.

23.19. Exterior Ballistics of Rocket-propelled Vehicles

The *take-off*, or *gross*, *mass* of a rocket-propelled vehicle, denoted by M_0, is composed of the mass of its inert parts, denoted by m_i, the mass of the propellants (liquid or solid), denoted by m_p, and the mass of the *useful load, or payload*, denoted by m_u. Thus

$$M_0 = m_i + m_p + m_u \qquad (23.90)$$

In Eq. (23.90), m_p includes any auxiliary fluids required for operating the propulsion system.

The *total inert mass*, denoted by m, is given by

$$m = m_i + m_u = m_C + m_E + m_G + m_S + m_u \qquad (23.91)$$

if m_C = mass of control system

m_E = mass of propulsion system without propellants

m_G = mass of guidance equipment

m_S = mass of structure of vehicle

m_u = mass of payload

If the vehicle is propelled by a liquid-propellant rocket engine, the mass m_E includes the mass of the propellant supply tanks, gas generators and their auxiliary apparatus, valves and plumbing, and the equipment for controlling the engine. In the case where the engine is a solid-propellant engine, the mass m_E includes the mass of the casing (Fig. 23.7), the fore and aft caps, the exhaust nozzle, the restriction liner, the insulating material for protecting the fore and aft caps and the nozzle, and the thrust termination- and thrust vector-control equipment and their control apparatus.

The take-off mass M_0 is given by

$$M_0 = m + m_p \tag{23.92}$$

if, as before, m_p denotes the mass of propellants at take-off.

Assume that the rocket engine develops the thrust F for the burning time τ_b; then the *impulse-weight ratio* for the rocket engine is given by

$$\int_0^{\tau_b} \frac{F \, d\tau}{W_p + W_E}$$

If F is constant throughout the powered flight, then $\int_0^{\tau_b} F \, d\tau = I_T = F\tau_b$. A large value for the impulse-weight ratio of the rocket engine is desirable.

The impulse-weight ratio for a complete rocket-propelled vehicle is $I_T/W_0 = gI_T/M_0$ and is employed as a criterion of the design of a complete rocket-propelled vehicle. The magnitude of I_T/W_0 for a given vehicle depends upon the specific impulse of the propellants I and their mean density. If the volume available for propellants is fixed, then the density impulse I_d (Art. 23.14) becomes important, for it may be possible to obtain a larger value for I_T/W_0 from denser propellants even though they give a lower specific impulse. Each case, as stated in Art. 23.14, must be given separate study.

Mass Ratios. Certain mass ratios occur in the equations for analyzing the dynamic performance of rocket-propelled vehicles. The more important ones will be presented and discussed briefly.

PROPELLANT MASS RATIO. Let M denote the mass of the rocket-propelled vehicle at any instant τ during the *powered flight* ($\tau < \tau_b$). Assuming steady operating conditions for the rocket motor and letting $\dot{m}$ denote the mass rate of propellant consumption, then

$$M = M_0 - \dot{m}\tau = M_0 \left(1 - \frac{m_p}{M_0} \frac{\tau}{\tau_b} \right) \tag{23.93}$$

if τ_b is the duration of the powered flight.

At the instant when all the propellants are consumed, $\tau = \tau_b$ and the inert mass of the vehicle is m [Eqs. (23.91) and (23.92)]. Let

$$\Phi_p = \frac{M_0}{m} = \text{vehicle mass ratio} \tag{23.94}$$

Then

$$m_p = \left(\frac{\Phi_p - 1}{\Phi_p} \right) M_0 = yM_0 \tag{23.95}$$

By definition, the ratio

$$\zeta = \frac{m_p}{M_0} = \text{propellant mass ratio} \tag{23.96}$$

The ratios Φ_p and ζ are related by

$$\zeta = 1 - \frac{1}{\Phi_p} \tag{23.97}$$

It appears that if great care is exercised in the design of a rocket-propelled vehicle, if it is made large, it should be possible to achieve a vehicle mass ratio of $\Phi_p = 10$. For such a vehicle the take-off weight of the propellants would be 90 per cent of the take-off

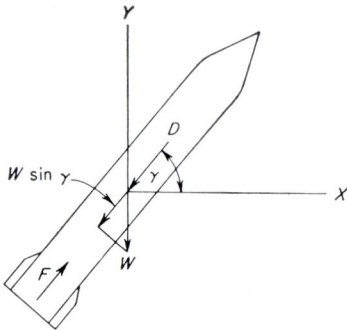

FIG. 23.15. Free-body diagram for a rocket-propelled vehicle during the powered flight.

weight of the vehicle. Because it is essential to achieve the largest possible value for Φ_p, especially for long-range ballistic-missile and launching rockets for space vehicles, great emphasis is placed on low weight for all the pertinent components of the vehicle and its propulsion engine.

The velocity attained by a rocket-propelled vehicle at the instant $\tau = \tau_b$ is called the *burnout*, or *burned velocity*, V_b. When the thrust is terminated at some time $\tau < \tau_b$, the corresponding vehicle speed is called the *cutoff velocity*, and the instantaneous mass of the vehicle at cutoff is calculated by means of Eq. (23.93). The vehicle mass ratio at cutoff is, accordingly, M_0/M.

Burnout Velocities. Figure 23.15 illustrates schematically a rocket-propelled vehicle moving along its flight path at some instant $\tau < \tau_b$. The following external forces act upon the vehicle: (1) the aerodynamic drag D, (2) the component of gravitational force due to the weight of the vehicle $W \sin \gamma = (W_0 - g\dot{m}\tau) \sin \gamma$, and (3) the thrust F. If the weight rate of propellant consumption is $\dot{W}$ and the take-off weight of the vehicle is W_0, the equation of motion for the vehicle is given by

$$F - (W_0 - \dot{W}\tau) \sin \gamma - D = (M_0 - \dot{m}\tau)\frac{dV}{d\tau} \qquad (23.98)$$

If A_m denotes the maximum cross-section area of the vehicle and ρ the density of atmosphere surrounding the vehicle, the aerodynamic drag is given by

$$D = \tfrac{1}{2}\rho C_D A_m V^2 \qquad (23.99)$$

if C_D is the drag coefficient for the vehicle and is a function of the flight Mach number and the angle of attack γ. It should be noted that ρ is a function of the altitude of the vehicle.

For a constant propellant consumption rate $\dot{m}$, the thrust is given by $F = \dot{m}V_j$ [Eq. (23.8)].

Equation (23.98) is a nonlinear, second-order differential equation with variable coefficients. It cannot be integrated directly in closed form, but requires a laborious step-by-step integration. For preliminary design, comparative purposes, optimization studies, and evaluation of different rocket engines, an exact solution of Eq. (23.98) is not essential.

From Eq. (23.99) it is seen that the drag D is proportional to A_m but the mass of the vehicle is proportional to its volume. For large vehicles, the effect of aerodynamic drag on the burnout velocity V_b is quite small, approximately 5 per cent for a missile having $W_0 = 100,000$ lb. For large vehicles, therefore, the neglect of the aerodynamic drag introduces only a small error, especially in view of the assumption that the effective jet velocity remains constant throughout the powered flight, when it actually increases somewhat with the altitude of the vehicle. For small vehicles the effect of aerodynamic drag cannot be neglected.

For comparison studies it is useful to simplify the problem and assume (1) no aerodynamic drag, (2) no gravitational force, and (3) vertical flight. The burnout velocity for this case is termed the *ideal burnout velocity*, or the *vacuum burnout velocity*, and is denoted by V_{bi}. The equation of motion, in view of the latter assumptions, becomes

$$dV = -V_j \frac{dM}{M} \qquad (23.100)$$

if M is given by Eq. (23.93).

Integration of Eq. (23.100) between the limits $V = 0$ to V_{bi}, and $M = M_0$ to $M = M_0 - m_p = m$, yields

$$V_{bi} = V_j \log_e \frac{M_0}{m} = gI \log_e \frac{M_0}{m} \qquad (23.101)$$

Equation (23.101) gives the maximum speed increment above the initial speed, which was taken to be zero, attainable by a single-stage rocket-propelled vehicle when propelled in a vacuum in the absence of gravity. For a given propellant system, the value of V_{bi} is limited by the fact that energy is expended throughout the powered flight upon such masses as the propellant tanks, structure, and the like, after they have served their usefulness, that is, after a large portion of the propellants are consumed. To reduce the disadvantage of expending energy upon nonuseful masses, the *multistage-rocket principle* was suggested more than fifty years ago. In the application of that principle the complete vehicle comprises several individual rocket-propelled vehicles, called *stages*, each of which is equipped with its own propulsion system and associated structure. The individual stages are assembled into a single vehicle at take-off. In operation, the first stage operates, and at the end of its powered flight it is jettisoned. At the same instant, the second-stage engine is put into operation, and at the end of its powered flight it is discarded. The procedure is repeated until the last stage, which is the one carrying the payload, is put into operation. Consequently, the last stage may be regarded as a single-stage rocket which has been given an initial velocity equal to the sum of the velocity increments imparted to it by each of the preceding stages. Thus if n is the number of stages and V_N the burnout velocity for the nth stage,

$$V_N = V_{b1} + V_{b2} + \cdots + V_{bn} \qquad (23.102)$$

if V_{b1}, V_{b2}, $\ldots$, V_{bn} are the burnout-velocity increments for the different stages.

It is apparent from Eq. (23.102) that by applying the staging principle, extremely large burnout velocities can be realized, that is, velocities larger than the *escape velocity* (36,700 fps at sea level).

Propellant Loading Ratio. The ratio of the weight of propellants at take-off, that is, W_p, to the weight of the rocket engine W_E is called the *propellant weight-loading density*, or the *engine weight efficiency*, and is denoted by δ_p. Thus

$$\delta_p = \frac{W_p}{W_E} = \frac{I_T/W_E}{I} \qquad (23.103)$$

The *impulse-weight ratio for the engine* I_T/W_E and the specific impulse of the propellant system I are related. A large value for δ_p has a smaller effect on V_{bi} when the ratio of the engine weight to payload is small, as in first stage, or *booster*, applications. In the case of long-range vehicles, such as an ICBM, the payload is ordinarily a small fraction of the total weight of inert parts and a large burnout velocity is desired. For such an application a large value for δ_p is essential.

23.20. Elementary Considerations of Space Travel

Currently, the only known propulsion means for achieving escape from the earth's gravitational field, establishing artificial satellites, and having the potentiality for interplanetary travel is rocket-jet propulsion.

The *escape velocity*, denoted by V_{ez}, is given by

$$V_{ez} = R \left(\frac{2g_0}{R + z} \right)^{1/2} \qquad (23.104)$$

if R = radius of the earth = 21×10^6 ft at the equator
  $g_0 = 32.174$ ft/sec^2
  z = altitude above surface of the earth

Equation (23.104) gives the velocity a body must achieve, at any altitude z, in order to overcome the earth's gravitational attraction.

The required *orbital velocity* for an *artificial satellite*, denoted by V_{so}, is given by

$$V_{so} = R \left(\frac{g_0}{R + z} \right)^{1/2}$$
(23.105)

Equation (23.105) is for a *circular orbit* and neglects the effect of the rotation of the earth.

The *satellite orbital energy*, denoted by E_{so}, is the energy per unit mass that must be expended on the satellite to bring it into its orbit; it is equal to the sum of the kinetic and potential energies per unit mass of the satellite. E_{so}, measured in foot-pounds per slug, is given by

$$E_{so} = g_0 \frac{R}{2} \frac{R + 2z}{R + z}$$
(23.106)

Equation (23.106) shows the manner in which the energy requirements per unit mass vary with the distance of the satellite from the center of the earth.

For a *fixed*, or *stationary, satellite* the dynamic requirement is that the satellite have zero relative velocity with respect to the earth.

REFERENCES

1. Zucrow, M. J.: "Aircraft and Missile Propulsion," vol. 1, Wiley, New York, 1958.
2. Zucrow, M. J., et al.: "Aerodynamics, Propulsion, Structures, and Design Practice," in vol. 2, "Principles of Guided Missile Design," Propulsion Section, pp. 149–151, Van Nostrand, Princeton, N.J., 1956.
3. Greene, S. H., and L. J. Gordon: An Effect of Carbon in an Adiabatically Expanded Gas Stream, *Jet Propulsion*, **27**:667 (June, 1957).
4. Wilde, K. A.: An Approximate Specific Impulse Equation for Condensable Gas Mixtures, *Jet Propulsion*, **27**:668 (June, 1957).
5. Glasstone, S.: "Thermodynamics for Chemists," Van Nostrand, Princeton, N.J., 1947.
6. Sutton, G. P.: "Rocket Propulsion Elements," 2d ed., Wiley, New York, 1956.
7. Zucrow, M. J.: "Aircraft and Missile Propulsion," vol. 2, chap. 10, Wiley, New York, 1958.
8. Arendale, W. F.: Fuel-binder Requirements for Composite Solid Propellants, *Ind. Eng. Chem.*, **48**:725–726 (April, 1956).
9. Wiggins, J. W.: The Use of Solid Propellant Engines for Achievement of Super Velocities, *Jet Propulsion*, **26**:1084–1087 (December, 1956).
10. Baxter, A. D.: Combustion in Rocket Motor, *J. Brit. Interplanet. Soc.*, May, 1951.
11. Crawford, B. L.: Rocket Fundamentals, *OSRD* 3992, 1944.
12. Seifert, H. S.: Twenty-five Years of Rocket Development, *Jet Propulsion*, **25**:594–603 (November, 1955).
13. Bartz, D. R.: Factors Which Influence the Suitability of Liquid Propellants as Rocket Motor Regenerative Coolants, *JPL/CIT Mem.* 20-139, Dec. 28, 1956.
14. Zucrow, M. J., and C. M. Beighley: Experimental Performance of WFNA-JP-3 Rocket Motors at Different Combustion Pressures, *J. Am. Rocket Soc.*, **22**:323–330 (November–December, 1952).
15. Bartz, D. R.: A Simple Equation for Rapid Estimation of Rocket Nozzle Convective Heat Transfer Coefficients, *Jet Propulsion*, **27**:49–51 (January, 1957).
16. Zucrow, M. J.: Liquid Propellant Rocket Power Plants, *Trans. ASME*, **69**:847–857 (1947).
17. Zucrow, M. J., and A. R. Graham: Some Considerations of Film Cooling for Rocket Motors, *Jet Propulsion*, **27**:650–656 (June, 1957).
18. Thatcher, A. G.: The Turborocket Propellant Feed System, *J. Am. Rocket Soc.*, no. 82, p. 126, September, 1950.
19. Ross, C. C.: Principles of Turbopump Design, *J. Am. Rocket Soc.*, no. 84, pp. 21–33, March, 1951.
20. Ross, C. C., and G. Barnerian: Some Aspects of High-suction Specific-speed Pump Inducers, *Trans. ASME*, **78**:1715–1721 (November, 1956).
21. Vogel, J. M.: A Quasi-morphological Approach to the Geometry of Charges for Solid Propellant Rockets, *Jet Propulsion*, **26**:102–105 (February, 1956).

22. Zucrow, M. J.: "Principles of Jet Propulsion and Gas Turbines," chap. 12, Wiley, New York, 1948.
23. Malina, F. J.: Characteristics of a Rocket Motor Unit Based on Theory of Perfect Gases, *J. Franklin Inst.*, **230**(4):433–454 (October, 1940).
24. Letter Symbols for Rocket Propulsion, *Jet Propulsion*, **25**(11):636–645 (November, 1955).
25. Tsien, H. S.: A Method for Comparing the Performance of Power Plants for Vertical Flight, *J. Am. Rocket Soc.*, **22**(4):200–203, 212 (July–August, 1952).
26. Ritchey, H. W.: Solid Propellants and the Conquest of Space, *Astronautics*, **3**(1):39–41, 75–77 (January, 1958).
27. Martinez, J. S., and G. W. Elverum: A Method of Calculating the Performance of Liquid-propellant Systems Containing the Species C, H, O, N, F, and One Other Halogen, with Tables of Required Thermochemical Properties to 6000°K, *Calif. Inst. Technol. Jet Propulsion Lab.*, Dec. 6, 1955.
28. Gordon, J. S.: Thermodynamics of High Temperature Gas Mixtures and Application to Combustion Problems, *WADC Tech. Rept.* 57-33, January, 1957.
29. Donegan, A. J., and M. Farber: Solution of Thermochemical Propellant Calculations on a High-speed Digital Computer, *Jet Propulsion*, **26**(3):164–171 (March, 1956).
30. Morgan, M. S., J. Silverman, and W. T. Webber: The Theoretical Specific Thrust of a Rocket Motor for the C-H-N-O-F System, *Jet Propulsion*, **26**(10):pt.1, 874–877 (October, 1956).
31. Penner, S. S.: "Chemistry Problems in Jet Propulsion," Pergamon, London, 1957.
32. Winternitz, P. F., and D. Horvitz: Rocket Propellant Performance and Energy of the Chemical Bond, *J. Am. Rocket Soc.*, **21**(85):51–67 (June, 1951).
33. *Jet Propulsion*, vol. 27, no. 6, June, 1957.
34. Tormey, J. F.: Liquid Rocket Propellants, *Aeronaut. Eng. Rev.*, **16**:55 (October, 1957).
35. Zucrow, M. J.: Les moteurs de fusée à propergols liquides (Liquid Propellant Rocket Motors), *Fusées et Recherche Aeronaut.*, *Bull. AERA*, vol. 1, no. 1, June, 1956.
36. Geckler, R. D., and R. E. Davis: Modern Developments in Solid Propellant Rocket Engineering, *Aeronaut. Eng. Rev.*, **16**:42 (August, 1957).
37. Geckler, R. D.: The Mechanism of Combustion of Solid Propellants, *AGARD Selected Combustion Papers*, 1954, p. 289.
38. Wimpress, R. N.: "Internal Ballistics of Solid Fuel Rockets," McGraw-Hill, New York, 1950.
39. Geckler, R. D., and D. F. Sprenger: The Correlation of Interior Ballistic Data for Solid Propellants, *J. Am. Rocket Soc.*, **24**(1):22 (January–February, 1954).
40. Green, L., Jr.: Erosive Burning of Some Composite Solid Propellants, *J. Am. Rocket Soc.*, **24**(1):9 (January–February, 1954).
41. Smith, R. P., and D. F. Sprenger: Combustion Instability in Solid Propellant Rockets, *Fourth Symposium on Combustion*, pp. 893–906, 1953.
42. Green, L., Jr.: Some Effects of Charge Configuration on Solid Propellant Combustion, *ARS Preprint* 441-57, June 10–13, 1957.
43. Stone, M. W.: A Practical Approach to Grain Design, *ARS Preprint* 445-57, June 10–13, 1957.
44. Price, E. W.: Charge Geometry and Ballistic Parameters for Solid Propellant Rocket Motors, *J. Am. Rocket Soc.*, **24**(1):16 (January–February, 1954).
45. Sutherland, G. S.: Modern Techniques in Solid Rocket Engineering, *Aero Digest*, **72**:46 (January, 1956).
46. Geckler, R. D.: Thermal Stresses in Solid Propellant Grains, *Jet Propulsion*, **26**(2):93 (February, 1956).
47. Ordhal, D. D., and M. L. Williams: Preliminary Photoelastic Design Data for Stresses in Rocket Grains, *Jet Propulsion*, **27**(6):657–662 (June, 1957).
48. Green, L., Jr.: Some Effects of Oxidizer Concentration and Particle Size on Resonance Burning of Composite Solid Propellants, *Jet Propulsion*, **28**:159–164 (March, 1958).
49. Vandenkerckhove, J. A.: Erosive Burning of a Colloidal Solid Propellant, *Jet Propulsion*, **28**(9):599–603 (September, 1958).
50. "Research and Development Technical Handbook," vol. 2, "Aviation Age," sec. D, Propulsion, 1958–1959.

Section 24

OPEN-CHANNEL FLOW

By

VEN TE CHOW, *University of Illinois, Urbana, Illinois*

OPEN-CHANNEL FLOW

24.1. Introduction

It is believed that major developments in the dynamics of open-channel flow were made largely because of man's interest in the flow of water in open channels, such as rivers and canals. This belief is evidenced by the fact that open-channel flow has been considered for a long time as an important subject in the field of civil hydraulic engineering. It is inevitable, therefore, that the subject matter in this section may appear to lean more or less toward the interest of civil engineers. However, the basic principles presented in this section are entirely universal and hence should be of equal import and value to readers of other related fields.

In this section the general treatment of the open-channel flow is based on the principles of geometry, energy, and momentum. The regimes of the flow are distinguished by the effects of viscosity and gravity. The types of the flow are classified in accordance with the variation in a flow parameter with respect to space, time, and matter (i.e., discharge). Besides the main treatment on the flow of pure liquid, the flow with air entrainment is also discussed. The problems of boundary resistance, the intersurface flow of gas and liquid, and the internal currents due to density variation are, however, excluded from this section since they are covered in other parts of this handbook (Secs. 3, 9, 17, 18, and 26).

24.2. Notation †

A flow area
b width of a rectangular channel
C (1) a coefficient
       (2) factor of flow resistance
       (3) circulation constant
       (4) characteristic
       (5) air concentration in percentage of the volume of air per unit volume of air-liquid mixture
C_r reflection coefficient
c (1) celerity
       (2) deviation from hydrostatic pressure
       (3) a coefficient of discharge
D hydraulic depth
d depth of flow normal to the channel bottom
d_0 diameter of a circular conduit
E specific energy
E_{min} minimum specific energy
$\mathbf{F}$ Froude number
F (1) a function
       (2) specific force
F_f frictional or resistance force
f shape factor of a channel section
f_c coefficient of curve resistance
G a function of $\mathbf{F}_1$ and slope S_0
g gravitational acceleration

† Any consistent system of units may be used.

H	energy head
H_a	approach velocity head
h	(1) height of a surge
	(2) piezometric head
h_a	loss in head due to acceleration
h_{cuv}	pressure head caused by streamline curvature
h_f	frictional loss in head
h_j	height of hydraulic jump
h_s	hydrostatic head
Δh	superelevation of flow in curved channels
J	$N/(N - M + 1)$
j	(1) rate of rise of flow surface
	(2) $y/y_n - 1$
K	conveyance of a channel section
K_n	conveyance for uniform flow
k	(1) coefficient of eddy loss
	(2) a variable for substitution $= 2N$
	(3) von Kármán's universal constant
L	length of channel
L_g	length of a rack on the channel bottom required for a complete withdrawal of flow
M	hydraulic exponent for critical-flow computation
M_c	hydraulic exponent M at critical depth
m	(1) half the number of intervals used in the computation of varied-flow function by series
	(2) root of an equation
	(3) $g(S_o - S_f)$
N	hydraulic exponent for uniform-flow computation
N_n	hydraulic exponent N at normal depth
n	(1) Manning's coefficient of roughness
	(2) distance normal to the curvature of streamlines
	(3) ratio of the top widths of two channels forming a transition
P	(1) wetted perimeter
	(2) total force or pressure
p	(1) number of members in a series
	(2) coefficient of a cubic equation
Q	discharge
Q_c	discharge of critical flow
Q_n	discharge of uniform flow
Q_o	overrun or a steady discharge passing through the wave front of a uniformly progressive flow
Q_0	discharge of a circular conduit flowing full at a depth equal to the diameter of the conduit and having the energy gradient equal to the slope of the conduit bottom
Q_*	supplementary discharge to a discontinuous flow
q	(1) discharge per unit width of channel
	(2) $y_2 + y_4 + \cdots + y_{2m}$, in which $y = f(x)$
	(3) factor in a cubic equation
q_*	supplementary discharge to a discontinuous flow per unit width of the channel
$\mathbf{R}$	Reynolds number
R	hydraulic radius
R_p	certain term in an infinite series
r	radius of curvature
r_c	radius of the centerline of a curved channel
r_i	radius of inner bank of a curved channel
r_o	radius of outer bank of a curved channel
r_p	a series
S	energy slope

S_f friction slope
S_0 slope of channel bottom
S_{xy} strength of a spiral flow
$\overline{S}_f$ average value of S_f
s (1) height of the side-weir sill above the channel bottom
     (2) $(y_1 + y_{2m+1} - y_2 - y_{2m})/4$, where $y = f(x)$
T (1) width of a free surface, or top width of a flow area
     (2) top width of a surge
t time
u $y/y_n{}^{N_n/N}$
V mean velocity of flow
V_b rising velocity of air bubbles
V_w velocity of a wave front
V_{xy} mean transverse velocity component normal to flow section
V' velocity of a new surge
$\overline{V}$ $V/\sqrt{2gH}$
$\overline{V}_n$ component of $\overline{V}$ normal to the shock-wave front
$\overline{V}_t$ component of $\overline{V}$ tangential to the shock-wave front
$\overline{V}_x$ x axis for $\overline{V}$
$\overline{V}_y$ y axis for $\overline{V}$
v velocity of flow passing an elementary area
v_M maximum velocity on a flow area
w unit weight of liquid
x (1) distance measured along x axis
     (2) exponent of hydraulic radius in a uniform-flow equation
     (3) length of flow profile
y (1) depth of flow
     (2) exponent of energy slope in a uniform-flow equation
y_c critical depth
y_n normal depth
y_o depth at outlet, or brink depth
y_t transitional depth in air-entrained flow
y' (1) alternate depth of y
     (2) depth of a new surge
     (3) outward normal distance above depth y_t in air-entrained flow
$\Delta y'$ drop in flow surface
$\overline{y}$ centroidal depth
Z (1) section factor for critical-flow computation
     (2) flow-surface elevation above a datum
Z_c section factor for critical-flow computation for critical depth
z (1) a variable for substitution $= \pm(1 - u^N)$ or $= \pm 1/\sqrt{u}$
     (2) distance measured along a vertical z axis
$\overline{z}$ depth of the centroid of the flow area below the free surface
α energy coefficient
α' pressure coefficient
β (1) momentum coefficient
     (2) wave angle or Mach angle of supercritical flow
     (3) a proportionality factor for determining ϵ_b
β' force coefficient
γ a coefficient for pressure head caused by streamline curvature
δ pitot-tube head in air-entrained flow
ϵ (1) a ratio equal to $v_M/V - 1$
     (2) ratio of the opening area to the total area of a rack surface
ϵ_b a mixing parameter for air-bubble transfer in air-entrained flow
θ (1) deflection angle of side boundary in supercritical flow
     (2) slope angle of channel bottom
θ_1 an integration constant
ρ density of fluid

σ a coefficient for discharge of liquid in upper region of air-entrained flow
τ_0 boundary shear on channel bed

GENERAL

24.3. Definitions

Open-channel flow, as the term implies, is the flow of a liquid with a free surface. The *free surface* is a surface of the liquid which is exposed to the pressure of a gas, usually the atmospheric pressure.

An open-channel flow is said to be *determined* if, at any section on the path of the flow, the geometry of the area of the cross section normal to the flow, hereafter called the *flow area*, and the velocity distribution in the cross section are known. In most engineering problems it is only necessary to know the *mean velocity* of flow. The mean velocity is equal to the discharge divided by the flow area. When any two of these three quantities are known, the flow is then determined at the section under consideration. Open-channel flow is generally treated as one-dimensional flow.

The flow area in an open channel is bounded by the free surface and a *wetted perimeter*. The latter is the boundary between the liquid and a solid surface forming the bed of the channel. A *hydraulic depth* D is defined as the flow area A divided by the width T of the free surface, or $D = A/T$. A *hydraulic radius* R is defined as the flow area divided by the length P of the wetted perimeter, or $R = A/P$.

It is apparent that the flow area is determined hydraulically by the discharge and mean velocity, on the one hand, and defined geometrically by the shape of the channel and the depth of flow, on the other. When the shape is fixed, the flow area becomes a function of the depth of flow. Therefore the depth of flow may be considered as a *flow parameter* that can be used to define the type of flow.

By using time, space, and discharge as the variables, a free-surface flow may be defined by

$$y = f(x,z,Q,t) \qquad (24.1)$$

in which y = depth of flow
$\quad x$ = distance measured along course of flow from an arbitrary origin
$\quad z$ = distance measured normal to depth and to course of flow from an arbitrary origin
$\quad Q$ = discharge
$\quad t$ = time measured from an arbitrary time of beginning

Unless otherwise stated, discussions in this section will be on a one-dimensional basis. Therefore the flow is defined by

$$y = f(x,Q,t) \qquad (24.2)$$

For a constant discharge,

$$y = f(x,t) \qquad (24.3)$$

24.4. Classification of Flow

By taking the depth of flow as a flow parameter, the open-channel flow may be classified on the basis of the variation of the flow parameter with respect to time, space, and discharge. For the sake of simplicity of discussion, first disregard the discharge as a variable.

By taking time as a variable, an open-channel flow is said to be *steady* if the depth of flow anywhere in the channel does not change or can be assumed constant during the time interval under consideration. The flow is *unsteady* if the depth changes with time.

By taking space as a variable, an open-channel flow is said to be *uniform* if the depth of flow is the same at every section of the channel. The flow is *varied* (or *nonuniform*) if the depth of flow changes along the path of the flow.

Varied flow may be either *rapidly varied* or *gradually varied*. The flow is rapidly varied if the depth of flow changes abruptly over a comparatively short distance; otherwise the flow is gradually varied.

The *steady uniform flow* (Arts. 3.3 and 3.4) is a fundamental type of flow which belongs to the treatment in Sec. 3. The establishment of an *unsteady uniform flow* would require that the free surface fluctuate from time to time while remaining parallel to the channel bed. Obviously, this is a rare phenomenon. The term uniform flow is therefore used hereafter to designate steady uniform flow only.

According to the above discussion, a *steady varied flow* may be either gradually varied or rapidly varied. For example, a backwater flow is a steady gradually varied flow, and a hydraulic jump is a steady rapidly varied flow. Similarly, an unsteady varied flow may be either gradually varied or rapidly varied. Consequently, there are *unsteady gradually varied flow* and *unsteady rapidly varied flow*. For example, a slow-rising flood wave is an unsteady gradually varied flow, and a surge is an unsteady rapidly varied flow.

For clarity, the classification of open-channel flow can be summarized as follows:

A. Steady flow
    1. Steady uniform flow (or uniform flow)
    2. Steady varied flow
        a. Steady gradually varied flow
        b. Steady rapidly varied flow
B. Unsteady flow
    1. Unsteady uniform flow (rare)
    2. Unsteady varied flow
        a. Unsteady gradually varied flow
        b. Unsteady rapidly varied flow

In the above discussion, the variation of the discharge is disregarded. In most problems of steady flow the discharge is constant throughout the reach under consideration, and the flow is said to be *continuous*. If the discharge along the course of flow is changed either because of addition or subtraction of flow in the channel, the flow is said to be *spatially varied*. Such flow may be found in roadside gutters, side-channel spillways, the wash-water troughs in water-treatment filters, the effluent channels around sewage-treatment tanks, and the main drainage channels and feeding channels in irrigation systems. Spatially varied flow will be treated separately in Arts. 24.27 to 24.30.

24.5. Flow Regimes

The physical condition of an open-channel flow is largely governed by viscosity and gravity. Surface tension may, occasionally, affect the flow, but its significance is negligible in most hydraulic-engineering problems.

The effect of viscosity is to create three states of flow, namely, *laminar, transitional*, and *turbulent*. It is generally recognized that the flow in a pipe changes from laminar to turbulent in the range of Reynolds number $\mathbf{R}$ between the critical value of 2000 and an indefinite upper limit which may be as high as 50,000. In defining the Reynolds number for flow in pipes, the diameter of the pipe is used as a characteristic length. In the case of open-channel flow, however, it is convenient to use the hydraulic radius as the characteristic length. An assumed corresponding range for the transition in an open-channel flow may therefore be taken as from 500 to an indefinite value as high as 12,500, since the diameter of a pipe is four times its hydraulic radius.

The effect of gravity is represented by the Froude number $\mathbf{F}$, which is equal to the ratio of the mean velocity V of flow and the celerity c of the small-gravity waves that occur in shallow water in channels as a result of any momentary change in the local depth of the water. Thus

$$\mathbf{F} = \frac{V}{c} \tag{24.4}$$

The flow is said to be *subcritical* when $V < c$ or $\mathbf{F} < 1$, *supercritical* when $V > c$ or $\mathbf{F} > 1$, and *critical* when $V = c$ or $\mathbf{F} = 1$.

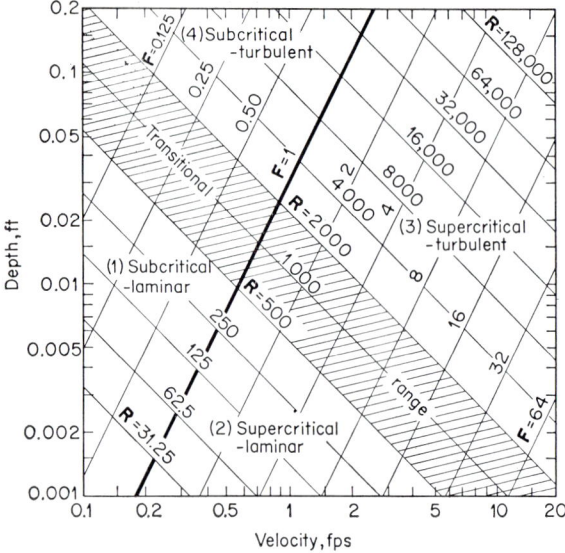

Fig. 24.1. Regimes of free-surface flow. (*After Robertson and Rouse.*[1])

The combined effect of viscosity and gravity may define four regimes of flow, namely (1) *subcritical-laminar* when $\mathbf{F} < 1$ and $\mathbf{R}$ is in the laminar range; (2) *supercritical-laminar* when $\mathbf{F} > 1$ and $\mathbf{R}$ is in the laminar range; (3) *supercritical-turbulent* when $\mathbf{F} > 1$ and $\mathbf{R}$ is in the turbulent range; and (4) *subcritical-turbulent* when $\mathbf{F} < 1$ and $\mathbf{R}$ is in the turbulent range.[1] The four regimes in a wide channel can be represented on a logarithmic plot of the velocity against the depth of flow (Fig. 24.1). The heavy line for $\mathbf{F} = 1$ and the shaded band for the laminar-turbulent transitional range intersect on the graph and divide the whole area into four general regions, each of which represents a flow regime. The subcritical-laminar and supercritical-laminar regimes are rare in channels of civil-engineering works, since the flow in such channels is mostly turbulent. However, these two regimes may be found frequently where there is very thin depth of liquid to form a so-called *sheet flow*. They may be significant in such problems as hydraulic model testing, erosion control, and gas-liquid processing in chemical plants.

24.6. Velocity-distribution Coefficients

Like the flow in a pipe, the velocity distribution in an open-channel flow is rarely uniform. As a result, the true velocity head is greater than $V^2/2g$, in which V is the mean velocity. For practical purposes, the true velocity head may be written as $\alpha V^2/2g$, with α a correction factor known as the *energy coefficient*. Thus the kinetic energy of the flow passing the whole flow area A per unit time is

$$\frac{\alpha w V^3 A}{2g} = \int_0^A \frac{wv^3}{2g}\, dA \tag{24.5}$$

in which w is the unit weight of liquid, and v is the velocity at dA. Hence

$$\alpha = \frac{\int_0^A v^3\, dA}{V^3 A} \tag{24.6}$$

The nonuniform velocity distribution also affects the computation of momentum in open-channel flow. For practical purposes, the momentum of the flow passing through a channel section per unit time may be written as $\beta w A V^2/g$, where β is a correction factor known as the *momentum coefficient*. Evidently

$$\frac{\beta w A V^2}{g} = \int_0^A \frac{w v^2}{g}\, dA \tag{24.7}$$

Hence,
$$\beta = \frac{\int_0^A v^2\, dA}{V^2 A} \tag{24.8}$$

In regular channels, the velocity distribution is close to uniform and the coefficients α and β may be assumed to be unity. In channels of complex geometry and flow condition, the values of α and β can easily be as great as 1.6 and 1.2, respectively, and can vary quite rapidly from one section to another.

If the vertical velocity in a channel is assumed logarithmically distributed, it can be shown that the relationship between the two velocity-distribution coefficients is represented by the following formulas:[2]

$$\alpha = 1 + 3\epsilon^2 - 2\epsilon^3 \tag{24.9}$$

$$\beta = 1 + \epsilon^2 \tag{24.10}$$

in which $\epsilon = v_M/V - 1$, v_M being the maximum velocity and V the mean velocity.

24.7. Pressure-distribution Coefficients

If the channel bed is horizontal and the streamlines of flow are parallel, the piezometric pressure at any point on the channel cross section is directly proportional to the depth of the point below the free surface and equal to the hydrostatic pressure corresponding to this depth. In other words, the distribution of pressure over the cross section of the channel is the same as the distribution of hydrostatic pressure. This is known as the *hydrostatic law of pressure distribution*.

When a flow has parallel streamlines, it is theoretically known as a *parallel flow*. In a parallel flow, the streamlines have neither curvature nor divergence, so that there are no acceleration components in the cross-section plane to affect the hydrostatic distribution of pressure. For practical purposes, the hydrostatic law of pressure distribution may be assumed in flow computations if the channel has a small slope (Fig. 24.2a) or the flow is gradually varied, because in such cases the curvature and divergence of streamlines are so insignificant that the effect of the acceleration components in the cross-section plane is negligible.

If the curvature of streamlines is substantial, the flow is theoretically known as *curvilinear flow*. The effect of the curvature is to produce appreciable acceleration components or centrifugal forces normal to the direction of flow. Thus the pressure distribution over a channel section will deviate from a linear hydrostatic pattern if curvilinear flow occurs in the vertical plane of the channel. Such a curvilinear flow

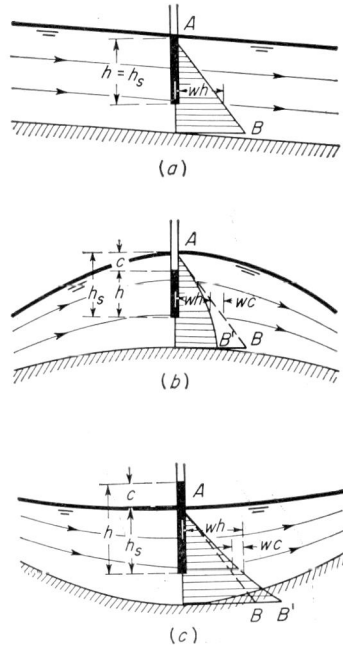

Fig. 24.2. Pressure distribution in straight and curved channels of small or horizontal slope at the section under consideration. h = piezometric head; h_s = hydrostatic head; and c = pressure-head correction for curvature. (*a*) Parallel flow. (*b*) Convex flow. (*c*) Concave flow.

may be either *convex* or *concave*, depending on whether the vertical profile of the channel is convex or concave in an upward direction (Fig. 24.2). If the hydrostatic pressure is measured by the depth of flow y, the pressure in a curvilinear flow may be written as $\alpha'y$, with α' a correction factor known as the *pressure coefficient*. Similarly, this correction applies also to flow whose divergence of streamlines is great enough to develop appreciable acceleration components normal to the flow. It can be shown that the pressure coefficient is expressed by

$$\alpha' = \frac{1}{Qy} \int_0^A hv\, dA = 1 + \frac{1}{Qy} \int_0^A cv\, dA \qquad (24.11)$$

in which Q = total discharge
$\quad\quad h$ = piezometric height measured at any point on channel section
$\quad\quad v$ = velocity at point where flow area is dA
$\quad\quad A$ = total flow area
$\quad\quad c$ = pressure deviation from an otherwise hydrostatic pressure

Evidently, c is positive for concave flow, negative for convex flow, and zero for parallel flow. Accordingly, $\alpha' > 1$ for concave flow, $\alpha' < 1$ for convex flow, and $\alpha' = 1$ for parallel flow.

In rapidly varied flow the change in depth of flow is so rapid and abrupt that the streamlines possess substantial curvature and divergence. Consequently, the hydrostatic law of pressure distribution is no longer valid.

When the slope of a channel becomes large (Fig. 24.3), the weight of the shaded liquid element of length dL is equal to $wy \cos\theta\, dL$. The pressure due to this weight is $wy \cos^2\theta$, and the head is

$$h = d \cos\theta = y \cos^2\theta \qquad (24.12)$$

with $d = y \cos\theta$ equal to the depth of flow normal to the channel bed. If the flow is curvilinear, then $h = \alpha'd \cos\theta = \alpha'y \cos^2\theta$.

The nonhydrostatic distribution of pressure of a channel section would affect the computation of total pressure or force acting on the section. Let P be the total force computed on the basis of hydrostatic pressure distribution. The force due to non-hydrostatic distribution of the pressure may be written as $\beta'P$, with β' a correction factor known as a *force coefficient*. It can be shown that

$$\beta' = \frac{1}{A\bar{z}} \int_0^A h\, dA = 1 + \frac{1}{A\bar{z}} \int_0^A c\, dA \qquad (24.13)$$

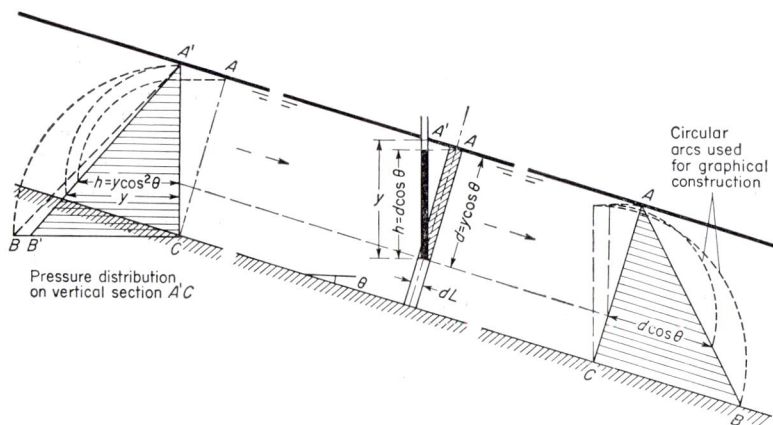

Fig. 24.3. Pressure distribution in parallel flow in channels of large slope.

in which $\bar{z}$ = depth of centroid of flow area A below free surface

h = pressure head on elementary area dA

c = pressure-head correction

Evidently, $\beta' > 1$ for concave flow, $\beta' < 1$ for convex flow, and $\beta' = 1$ for parallel flow. The coefficients α' and β' are called the *pressure-distribution coefficients*.

24.8. Energy of Flow

The energy at a section of an open-channel flow with respect to a horizontal datum may be expressed by the sum of the velocity head, the pressure head, and the potential head above the datum, or

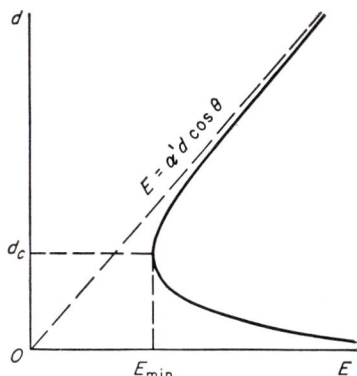

FIG. 24.4. Specific-energy curve.

$$H = \alpha \frac{V^2}{2g} + \alpha' d \cos \theta + z \qquad (24.14)$$

in which H is the total head in feet, z is the vertical distance of the section bottom above the datum, and other notation has been defined previously.

By the principle of conservation of energy, the total energy at an upstream section 1 should be equal to the total energy at a downstream section 2 plus the loss of energy h_f between the sections; or

$$\alpha_1 \frac{V_1^2}{2g} + \alpha'_1 d_1 \cos \theta_1 + z_1 = \alpha_2 \frac{V_2^2}{2g} + \alpha'_2 d_2 \cos \theta_2 + z_2 + h_f \qquad (24.15)$$

This is an *energy equation*.

With reference to a single flow section at different depths of flow, say, d_1 and d_2, the term h_f is zero. Furthermore, if the channel bottom is chosen as the datum, then $z_1 = z_2 = 0$. Thus the energy equation may be written in a general form

$$E = \alpha \frac{V^2}{2g} + \alpha' d \cos \theta \qquad (24.16)$$

This is known as the *specific energy* of the flow at the section, which is a function of the depth d or y. A plot of this equation for E against the depth is called the *specific-energy curve* (Fig. 24.4).

24.9. Momentum of Flow

For steady flow the change of momentum per unit time in the given mass of liquid in an open-channel flow is equal to the resultant of all the external forces that are acting on the mass in the direction of the momentum change, or

$$\frac{Qw}{g}(\beta_2 V_2 - \beta_1 V_1) = \tfrac{1}{2}\beta'_1 w b_1 d_1^2 \cos \theta_1 - \tfrac{1}{2}\beta'_2 w b_2 d_2^2 \cos \theta_2 + W \sin \theta - F_f \qquad (24.17)$$

This is a *momentum equation*, in which the subscripts indicate the two close flow sections enclosing the body of liquid, b_1 and b_2 are the widths of flow, W is the weight of the fluid body, θ is the average slope angle of the channel bed between the sections, F_f is the total external force due to friction and resistance on the channel bed, and other notation has been defined previously. For gradually varied or uniform flow in a uniform channel with the velocity and pressure-distribution coefficients equal to unity, it can be shown that the application of the energy or the momentum equation yields practically the same results.

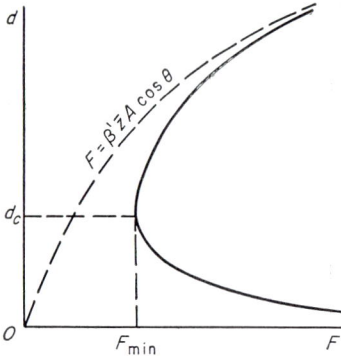

Fig. 24.5. Specific-force curve.

With reference to a particular flow section at different depths of flow, the terms $W \sin \theta$ and F_f are dropped off and the momentum equation may be written in a general form

$$F = \beta \frac{Q^2}{gA} + \beta' \bar{z} A \cos \theta \qquad (24.18)$$

in which $\bar{z}$ is the vertical distance of the centroid of the flow area A below the free surface. This is known as the *specific force* of the flow at the section. It is a function of the depth d or y. A plot of this equation for F against the depth is called the *specific-force curve* (Fig. 24.5).

24.10. Critical Flow

Critical flow may be defined in various ways. One popular definition is that the critical flow at a section for a given discharge is the flow of minimum specific energy. Thus, letting $dE/dd = 0$, the following criterion in the form of a Froude number may be obtained:

$$\mathbf{F} = \frac{V}{\sqrt{gD \cos \theta \left[\dfrac{2\alpha' + 2d(d\alpha'/dd)}{2\alpha - D(d\alpha/dd)} \right]}} = 1 \qquad (24.19)$$

By assuming constant values of α and α',

$$\mathbf{F} = \frac{V}{\sqrt{\alpha' gD (\cos \theta)/\alpha}} = 1 \qquad (24.20)$$

or

$$\alpha \frac{V^2}{2g} = \frac{\alpha' D \cos \theta}{2} \qquad (24.21)$$

Critical flow may also be defined as the flow at a minimum specific force. Thus, letting $dF/dd = 0$, the following criterion may be written:

$$\mathbf{F} = \frac{V}{\sqrt{gD \cos \theta \left[\dfrac{\beta' + \bar{z}(d\beta'/dd)}{\beta - D(d\beta/dd)} \right]}} = 1 \qquad (24.22)$$

By assuming constant values of β and β',

$$\mathbf{F} = \frac{V}{\sqrt{\beta' gD (\cos \theta)/\beta}} = 1 \qquad (24.23)$$

or

$$\beta \frac{V^2}{2g} = \frac{\beta' D \cos \theta}{2} \qquad (24.24)$$

When $\theta \approx 0$ and $\alpha = \alpha' = \beta = \beta' = 1$, Eqs. (24.21) and (24.24) become

$$\frac{V^2}{2g} = \frac{D}{2} \qquad (24.25)$$

which means that for critical flow the velocity head is equal to half the hydraulic depth. It should be noted that Eqs. (24.20), (24.21), (24.23), and (24.24) are approximate. Otherwise, $\alpha/\beta = \alpha'/\beta'$; this cannot be established by either theory or experiment. However, Jaeger[3] has proved mathematically that the exact critical state of flow is the same whether it is determined by the energy approach or by the momentum approach. This is known as the *Jaeger theorem*.

For the determination of critical flow, Eq. (24.21) [similarly for Eq. (24.24)] may be written as

$$A\sqrt{D} = Q\sqrt{\frac{\alpha}{\alpha' g \cos \theta}} \qquad (24.26)$$

The left side of this equation is apparently a function of the section geometry and hence can be expressed by a function of the depth of flow y as the flow parameter. This function may be called the *section factor for critical-flow computation* and be designated by Z. Thus

$$Z = A\sqrt{D} = f(y) \qquad (24.27)$$

When the right side of Eq. (24.26) is computed for the given Q, α, α', and θ, the value of Z is determined, and hence the corresponding depth y can be computed from the section geometry. This depth is known as *critical depth* and may be specifically designated by y_c. For the given Q through the same channel section, the flow may have different depths. Thus, from Eqs. (24.4) and (24.25), it can be shown that the flow is subcritical if $y > y_c$ and supercritical if $y < y_c$.

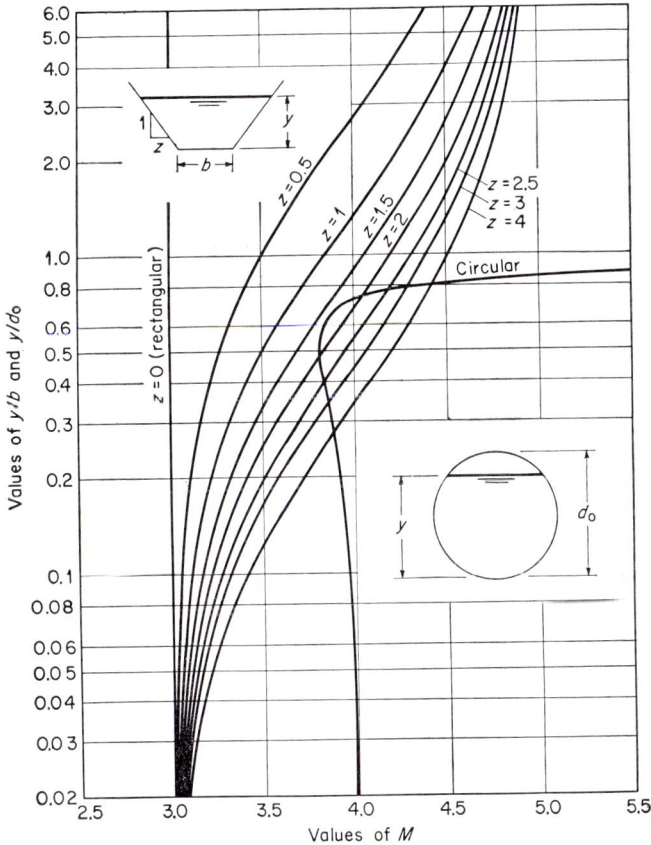

FIG. 24.6. Curves of M values.

Since the section factor Z is a function of y, it may be assumed that

$$Z^2 = Cy^M \qquad (24.28)$$

in which C is a coefficient and M is a parameter called the *hydraulic exponent for critical-flow computation*. It should be noted that M is not a constant but a variable, depending on the depth of flow and the section geometry. Except for channel sections with unusual geometrical variation or with a gradually closing top, the value of M changes only slightly in the range under general consideration. For practical purposes, therefore, M for ordinary channels may be assumed constant in the range under consideration. Sometimes, the range may be broken up into several subdivisions, with the M value in each subdivision assumed constant.

It can be shown from Eqs. (24.27) and (24.28) that

$$M = \frac{y}{A}\left(3T - \frac{A}{T}\frac{dT}{dy}\right) \qquad (24.29)$$

This equation can be used to evaluate M. For rectangular, trapezoidal, and circular channel sections, the variation of M values is shown in Fig. 24.6.

For practical purposes, the value of $\log Z$ may be plotted against $\log y$ as abscissa. The approximate value of M is equal to twice the slope of the plot.

24.11. Uniform Flow

For practical applications, the mean velocity of uniform flow is generally expressed as

$$V = CR^x S^y \qquad (24.30)$$

in which C = factor of flow resistance
R = hydraulic radius
S = energy slope
x, y = exponents

For the well-known Manning's formula, $C = 1.49/n$, in which n is the coefficient of roughness, $x = \frac{2}{3}$, and $y = \frac{1}{2}$. In Chézy's formula, C is Chézy's resistance factor, $x = \frac{1}{2}$, and $y = \frac{1}{2}$.

The discharge of uniform flow is

$$Q = CAR^x S^y = KS^y \qquad (24.31)$$

in which

$$K = CAR^x \qquad (24.32)$$

The term K is known as the *conveyance* of the channel section, which evidently depends on the channel roughness, geometry, and the depth of flow. The depth of uniform flow is known as *normal depth* and may be designated by y_n. This depth may be determined by means of Eqs. (24.31) and (24.32).

For a constant channel roughness, the conveyance is a function of y. It may be assumed that

$$K^2 = Cy^N \qquad (24.33)$$

in which C is a coefficient and N is a parameter called the *hydraulic exponent for uniform-flow computation*. Similar to M, N is not a constant but a variable, depending on the depth of flow and the section geometry. Except for unusual channel geometry, the value of N may be assumed constant in the range under consideration.

It can be shown from Eqs. (24.32) and (24.33) that

$$N = \frac{2y}{A}\left[(1 + x)T - xR\frac{dP}{dy}\right] \qquad (24.34)$$

This equation can be used to evaluate N. For rectangular, trapezoidal, and circular channels, the variation of N values is shown in Fig. 24.7.

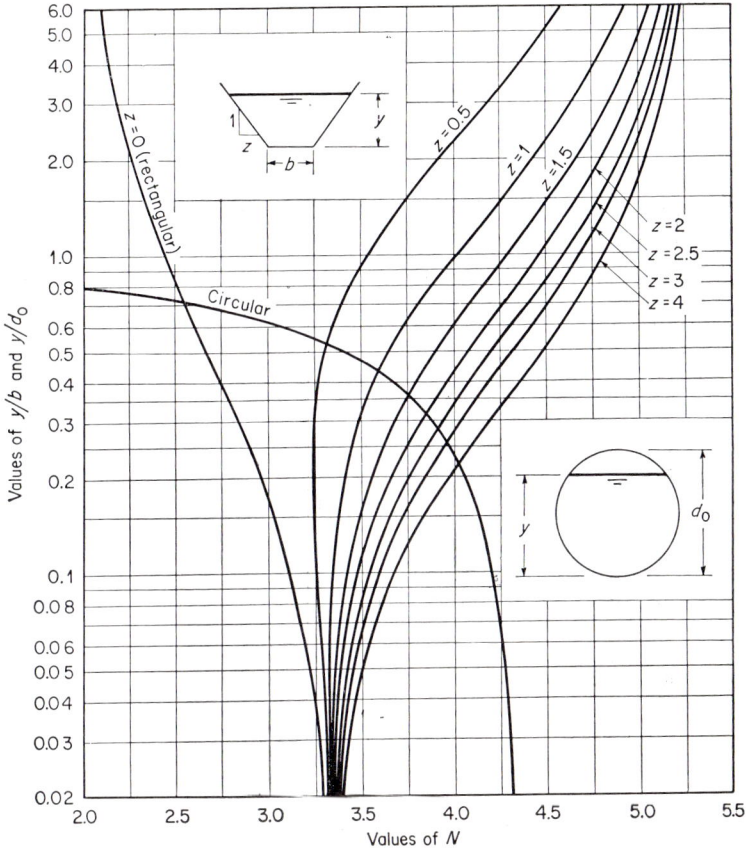

Fig. 24.7. Curves of N values.

For practical purposes, the value of log K may be plotted against log y as abscissa, resulting in an approximate straight line in the range under consideration. The average value of N is equal to twice the slope of the plot in the range.

24.12. Continuity Equations

By the law of conservation of mass, the continuity equation of unsteady continuous flow in a channel may be expressed as

$$\frac{\partial Q}{\partial x} + \frac{\partial A}{\partial t} = 0 \qquad (24.35)$$

in which Q = discharge
            A = flow area
            x = distance in direction of flow
            t = time

If y is the depth of flow and T is the width of the free surface, then $\partial A = T\,\partial y$, and Eq. (24.35) becomes

$$\frac{\partial Q}{\partial x} + T\frac{\partial y}{\partial t} = 0 \qquad (24.36)$$

At a given section, $Q = VA$. Thus Eq. (24.36) becomes

$$\frac{\partial(VA)}{\partial x} + T\frac{\partial y}{\partial t} = 0 \tag{24.37}$$

or

$$A\frac{\partial V}{\partial x} + V\frac{\partial A}{\partial x} + T\frac{\partial y}{\partial t} = 0 \tag{24.38}$$

Since the hydraulic depth $D = A/T$ and $\partial A = T\,\partial y$, Eq. (24.38) may also be written as

$$D\frac{\partial V}{\partial x} + V\frac{\partial y}{\partial x} + \frac{\partial y}{\partial t} = 0 \tag{24.39}$$

The above equations are various forms of the continuity equation of unsteady continuous flow.

For steady continuous flow, Eqs. (24.35) and (24.37) give the continuity equation as

$$Q = A_1 V_1 = A_2 V_2 = \text{const} \tag{24.40}$$

where the subscripts refer to different channel sections.

The continuity equation for discontinuous flow is given in Art. 24.27.

24.13. Dynamic Equations

By the law of conservation of energy, a general dynamic equation for gradually varied unsteady continuous flow can be derived.[4,5] The energy loss in the flow in a distance dx of the channel consists of two parts: the loss due to friction $h_f = S_f\,dx$ and the energy reduction due to acceleration $h_a = (\beta/g)(\partial V/\partial t)\,dx$. Thus the change in total head from Eq. (24.14) is

$$\partial\left(\alpha\frac{V^2}{2g} + \alpha'd\cos\theta + z\right) = -S_f\,\partial x - \frac{\beta}{g}\frac{\partial V}{\partial t}\,\partial x$$

or

$$\frac{\alpha V}{g}\frac{\partial V}{\partial x} + \frac{\alpha'\partial d\cos\theta}{\partial x} + \frac{\beta}{g}\frac{\partial V}{\partial t} + \frac{\partial z}{\partial x} + S_f = 0 \tag{24.41}$$

This is the required dynamic equation. In engineering practice, it is generally assumed that the friction slope S_f in a gradually varied flow is equivalent to the energy slope of a uniform flow in the channel at the same depth of flow. Therefore this slope can be evaluated by Eq. (24.31); that is,

$$S_f = \left(\frac{Q}{K}\right)^{1/y} \tag{24.42}$$

For channels of constant bottom slope S_0, $\partial z/\partial x = -S_0$, and hence Eq. (24.41) becomes

$$\alpha'\cos\theta\frac{\partial d}{\partial x} + \frac{\alpha V}{g}\frac{\partial V}{\partial x} + \frac{\beta}{g}\frac{\partial V}{\partial t} = S_0 - S_f \tag{24.43}$$

In practical problems, the channel slope is generally small. Thus

$$\alpha'\frac{\partial y}{\partial x} + \frac{\alpha V}{g}\frac{\partial V}{\partial x} + \frac{\beta}{g}\frac{\partial V}{\partial t} = S_0 - S_f \tag{24.44}$$

In the case of a steady flow, the above dynamic equation becomes

$$\alpha'\frac{dy}{dx} + \frac{\alpha V}{g}\frac{dV}{dx} = S_0 - S_f \tag{24.45}$$

It should be noted that in the above derivations the effect of curvature of stream-lines is ignored since the flow is assumed gradually varied. There are theoretical deri-vations, including effect due to curvature, which should be of academic significance.[6]

The dynamic equations for discontinuous flow will be given in Arts. 24.28 and 24.29.

STEADY GRADUALLY VARIED FLOW

24.14. Flow Analysis

For the analysis of steady gradually varied flow, Eq. (24.45) may be written for the slope of the flow surface as

$$\frac{dy}{dx} = \frac{S_0 - S_f}{\alpha' + \dfrac{\alpha V}{g}\dfrac{dV}{dy}} \tag{24.46}$$

A solution of this equation will give the equation of *flow profiles* in channels of small slope.

For the simplicity of discussion, it may be assumed that the channel is prismatic and $\alpha' = 1$. Since $V = Q/A$, Q is constant, and $dA/dy = T$; it can be shown that

$$\frac{\alpha V}{g}\frac{dV}{dy} = \frac{-\alpha Q^2 T}{gA^3}$$

By Eqs. (24.26) and (24.27), this can be reduced to $-Z_c{}^2/Z^2$, where Z_c is the section factor for Q at a critical state of flow and Z is the section factor for Q at the actual state of flow. By Eq. (24.42) with $y = \frac{1}{2}$, it can be shown that $S_0 = Q^2/K_n{}^2$ and $S_f = Q^2/K^2$, with K_n the conveyance for Q at a normal depth of flow and K the conveyance for Q at the actual depth of flow. Thus Eq. (24.46) becomes

$$\frac{dy}{dx} = S_0 \frac{1 - (K_n/K)^2}{1 - (Z_c/Z)^2} \tag{24.47}$$

This equation may be used to discuss and classify flow profiles.

Flow Profiles in Channels of Positive Slope. The slope of a channel is positive if it falls in the direction of flow.

When dy/dx is positive, the flow profile is a rising curve; Eq. (24.47) gives two possible cases:

(a) $\qquad\qquad 1 - \left(\dfrac{K_n}{K}\right)^2 > 0 \quad\text{and}\quad 1 - \left(\dfrac{Z_c}{Z}\right)^2 > 0$

(b) $\qquad\qquad 1 - \left(\dfrac{K_n}{K}\right)^2 < 0 \quad\text{and}\quad 1 - \left(\dfrac{Z_c}{Z}\right)^2 < 0$

In general, the values of K and Z increase or decrease continuously with the depth y. Therefore case a indicates $y > y_n$ and $y > y_c$. As $y > y_c$, the flow is subcritical. If $y > y_n > y_c$, the subcritical flow is said to occur in a *mild channel*. The mild channel is a channel in which the normal depth is greater than the critical depth, and the corre-sponding channel slope is known as *subcritical*. On the other hand, if $y > y_c > y_n$, the subcritical flow is said to occur in a *steep channel*. Similarly, case b indicates $y < y_n$ and $y < y_c$. The corresponding flow is supercritical; and it occurs in a mild channel if $y_n > y_c > y$ and in a steep channel if $y_c > y_n > y$. If $y_n = y_c$, the channel is said to have a *critical slope*, but the flow may be subcritical, critical, or supercritical, depend-ing on $y > y_c$, $y = y_c$, or $y < y_c$, respectively.

When dy/dx is negative, the flow profile is a lowering curve; Eq. (24.47) gives two possible cases:

(a) $\qquad\qquad 1 - \left(\dfrac{K_n}{K}\right)^2 > 0 \quad\text{and}\quad 1 - \left(\dfrac{Z_c}{Z}\right)^2 < 0$

(b) $\qquad\qquad 1 - \left(\dfrac{K_n}{K}\right)^2 < 0 \quad\text{and}\quad 1 - \left(\dfrac{Z_c}{Z}\right)^2 > 0$

Case a indicates that $y_c > y > y_n$ and hence the flow is supercritical in a steep channel. Case b indicates that $y_n > y > y_c$, or the flow is subcritical in a mild channel.

When $dy/dx = 0$, the flow surface is parallel to the bottom of the channel, and Eq. (24.47) gives $y = y_n$, which indicates a uniform flow. The flow is uniform critical if

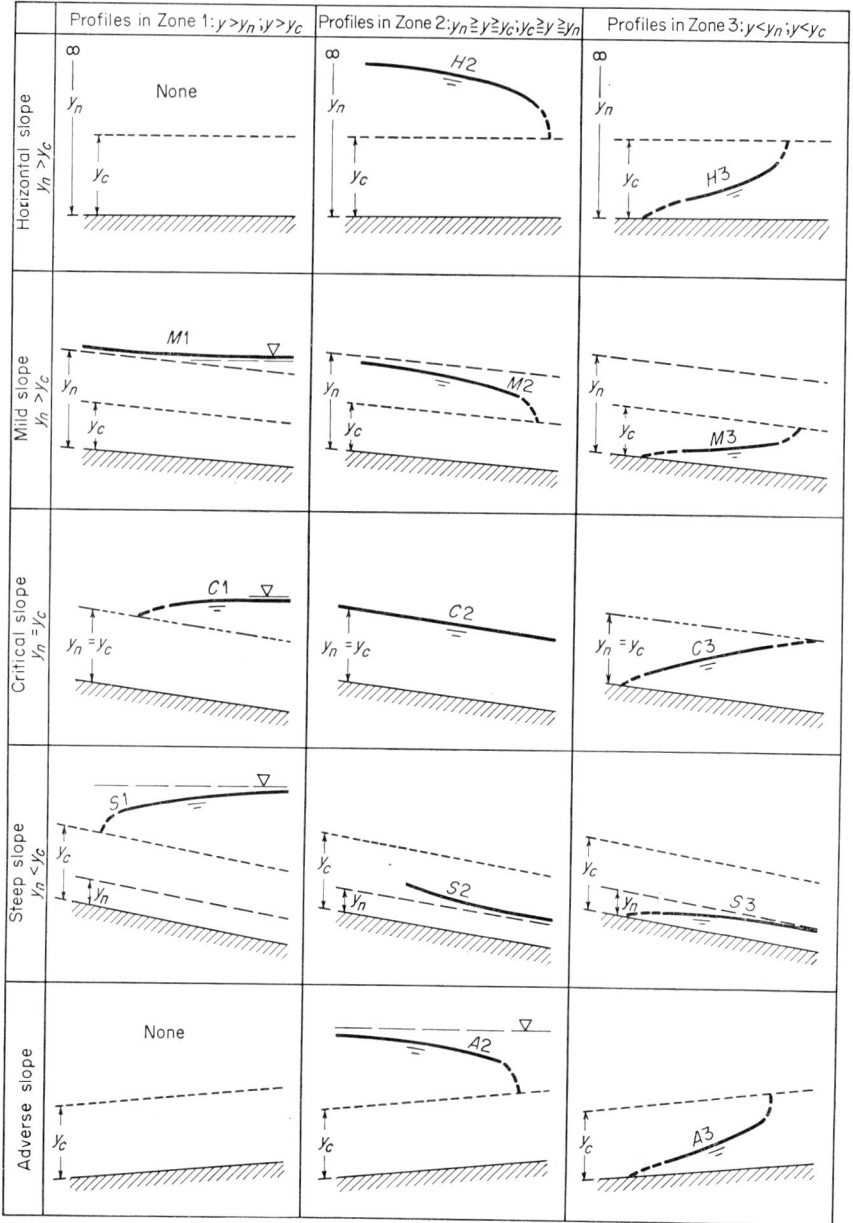

FIG. 24.8. Classification of flow profiles of gradually varied flow.

$y = y_n = y_c$, uniform subcritical if $y = y_n > y_c$, and uniform supercritical if $y_c > y_n = y$.

Flow Profiles in Channels of Adverse Slope. In a channel of adverse or negative slope, the slope of the channel rises in the direction of flow, or $S_0 < 0$. By Eq. (24.31), with $y = \frac{1}{2}$, $K_n{}^2$ must be negative. Consequently, Eq. (24.47) gives two possible cases:

(a) A subcritical flow with $y > y_c$

(b) A supercritical flow with $y < y_c$

In case a, dy/dx is negative and the flow profile is a lowering curve. In case b, dy/dx is positive and the flow profile is a rising curve. Since $K_n{}^2$ is negative and K_n is imaginary, the value of y_n cannot be realistically expressed.

Flow Profile in Horizontal Channels. In channels of horizontal slopes, $S_0 = 0$ and Eq. (24.47) cannot be directly used for discussion. By Eq. (24.31) with $y = \frac{1}{2}$, $K_n\sqrt{S_0} = Q$. Thus Eq. (24.47) for horizontal channels may be written

$$\frac{dy}{dx} = \frac{-(Q/K)^2}{1 - (Z_c/Z)^2} \tag{24.48}$$

Since $S_0 = 0$, $K_n = \infty$ and $y_n = \infty$. The above equation gives two possible cases:

(a) $y_n > y > y_c$

(b) $y_n > y_c > y$

Case a represents a subcritical flow with a lowering curve, since dy/dx is negative. Case b represents a supercritical flow with a rising curve, since dy/dx is positive.

Flow Profiles at Various Characteristic Depths. At critical depths, or $y = y_c$, Eq. (24.47) gives $dy/dx = \infty$; that is, the flow profile has a vertical slope at the critical depth. If the depth of flow is changed suddenly from a low to high stage in crossing the critical depth, a *hydraulic jump* will occur. If the depth changes from a high to low stage, then a *hydraulic drop* will occur. Near the critical depth, the streamlines of the flow usually exhibit great curvature; the flow is actually rapidly varied and cannot be accurately analyzed by Eq. (24.47).

At normal depths, or $y = y_n$, Eq. (24.47) gives $dy/dx = 0$; that is, the flow profile is parallel to the bottom of the channel; this indicates uniform flow. At large depths, or $y = \infty$, Eq. (24.47) gives $dy/dx = S_0$; that is, the flow profile is horizontal.

Classification of Flow Profiles. In a prismatic channel, the lines representing the normal depth and critical depth are parallel to the bottom of the channel and divide the profile space in the channel into three zones:

Zone 1. The space above the upper line

Zone 2. The space between the lines

Zone 3. The space below the lower line

Thus the flow profiles may be classified into 13 different types according to the channel slope and the zone in which the profile lies. These types are designated as H2, H3; M1, M2, M3; C1, C2, C3; S1, S2, S3; and A2, A3; in which the letter is descriptive of the slope: H for horizontal, M for mild (subcritical), C for critical, S for steep (supercritical), and A for adverse slope; and in which the numeral represents the zone number. Of the thirteen flow profiles, twelve are for gradually varied flow and one, C2, is for uniform flow. All profiles are represented by Eq. (24.47). Their characteristics are summarized in Table 24.1, and the shapes are shown in Figs. 24.8 and 24.9. The profiles near the critical depth and the channel bottom cannot be accurately determined by the theory of gradually varied flow; hence they are shown in dashed lines. Various flow profiles are discussed below.

M PROFILES ($S_0 < S_c$ AND $y_n > y_c$). The *M1 profile* represents the well-known backwater curve. It occurs when the downstream end of a long mild channel is submerged in a reservoir to a depth greater than the normal depth of the flow in the channel. This flow profile lies in zone 1. The upstream end of the curve is tangent to the normal-depth line, since $dy/dx = 0$ as $y = y_n$; and the downstream end is tangent to the horizontal pool surface, since $dy/dx = S_0$ as $y = \infty$. Typical examples of the M1 profile are the profile behind a dam in a natural river (Fig. 24.9a) and the profile in a canal joining two reservoirs (Fig. 24.9b).

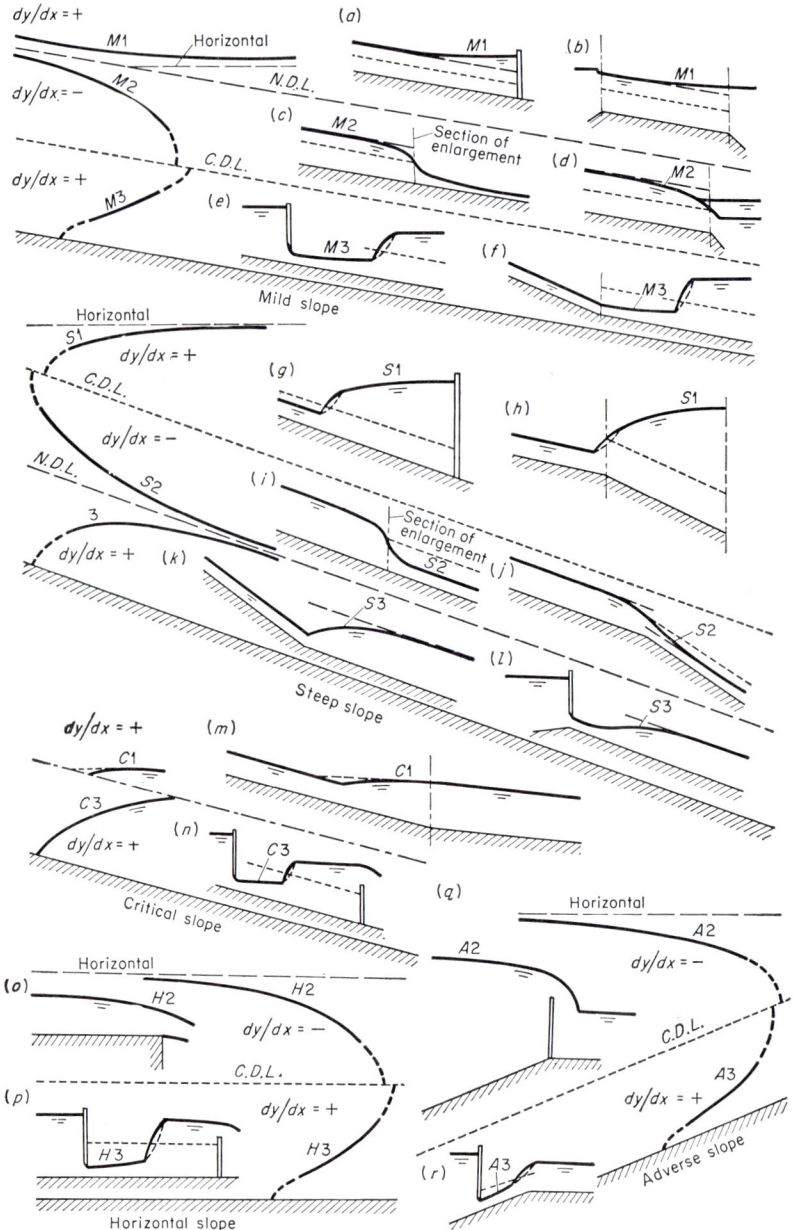

FIG. 24.9. Examples of flow profiles of gradually varied flow.

An *M2 profile* occurs when the bottom of the channel at the downstream end is submerged in a reservoir to a depth less than the normal depth. The upstream end of the flow profile is tangent to the normal-depth line, since $dy/dx = 0$ as $y = y_n$. If the amount of submergence at the downstream end is less than the critical depth, the flow

Table 24.1. Types of Flow Profiles in Prismatic Channels

Channel slope	Designation			Relation of y to y_n and y_c			General type of curve	Type of flow
	Zone 1	Zone 2	Zone 3	Zone 1	Zone 2	Zone 3		
Horizontal $S_0 = 0$	None			$y > y_n >$		y_c	None	None
		H2		$y_n > y > y_c$			Lowering	Subcritical
			H3	$y_n >$		$y_c > y$	Rising	Supercritical
Mild $0 < S_0 < S_c$	M1			$y > y_n >$		y_c	Rising	Subcritical
		M2		$y_n > y > y_c$			Lowering	Subcritical
			M3	$y_n >$		$y_c > y$	Rising	Supercritical
Critical $S_0 = S_c > 0$	C1			$y > y_c =$		y_n	Rising	Subcritical
		C2		$y_c = y = y_n$			Parallel to channel bottom	Uniform-critical
			C3	$y_c =$		$y_n > y$	Rising	Supercritical
Steep $S_0 > S_c > 0$	S1			$y > y_c >$		y_n	Rising	Subcritical
		S2		$y_c > y > y_n$			Lowering	Supercritical
			S3	$y_c >$		$y_n > y$	Rising	Supercritical
Adverse $S_0 < 0$	None			$y > (y_n)\dagger >$		y_c	None	None
		A2		$(y_n)\dagger > y > y_c$			Lowering	Subcritical
			A3	$(y_n)\dagger >$		$y_c > y$	Rising	Supercritical

† y_n in parentheses is assumed a positive value.

profile will terminate abruptly, with its end tangent to a vertical line at a depth equal to the critical depth, since $dy/dx = \infty$ for $y = y_c$. If the depth of submergence at the downstream end is greater than the critical depth, then as much of the profile will form as lies above the water surface in the reservoir. Examples are the profile at the upstream side of a sudden enlargement of a canal cross section (Fig. 24.9c) and the profile in a canal leading to a reservoir, where the pool level is shown both above and below the critical-depth line (Fig. 24.9d).

The *M3 profile* starts theoretically from the upstream channel bottom at a certain angle and terminates with a hydraulic jump at the downstream end. This type of profile occurs when a supercritical flow enters a mild channel. At the upstream end of the profile, $y = 0$; thus the velocity would be infinite. Therefore the upstream end of an M3 profile cannot exist physically. Examples of the M3 profile are the profile in a stream below a sluice (Fig. 24.9e) and the profile after the change in channel slope from steep to mild (Fig. 24.9f).

S PROFILES ($S_0 > S_c$ AND $y_n > y_c$). The *S1 profile* begins with a jump at the upstream end and becomes tangent to the horizontal pool level at the downstream end. Examples are the profiles of flow behind a dam in a steep canal emptying into a pool of high elevation (Fig. 24.9h).

The *S2 profile* is a lowering curve. It is usually very short, serving a transition between an upstream critical-flow depth and a downstream supercritical uniform flow. Examples are the profiles formed on the downstream side of an enlargement of channel section (Fig. 24.9i) and on the steep-slope side as the channel slope changes from steep to steeper (Fig. 24.9j).

The *S3 profile* is also of the transitional type, formed between a supercritical-flow depth and the normal-depth line to which the profile is tangent. Examples are the profile on the steep-slope side as the channel slope changes from steep to milder steep (Fig. 24.9k) and that below a sluice with the depth of the entering flow less than the normal depth on a steep slope (Fig. 24.9l).

C Profiles ($S_0 = S_c$ AND $y_n = y_c$). These profiles represent the transitions between M and S profiles. Assuming a wide rectangular channel, Eq. (24.47) shows that *C1* and *C3 profiles* are in general slightly curved and that the C1 profile is asymptotic to a horizontal line (Figs. 24.9m and n). If the Chézy formula is used, Eq. (24.47) will show that the two profiles are theoretically horizontal. The C2 profile represents the case of uniform critical flow.

H Profiles ($S_0 = 0$ AND $y_n = \infty$). These are the limiting cases of M profiles when the channel slope becomes horizontal. The *H2* and *H3 profiles* correspond to the M2 and M3 profiles, but no H1 profile can actually be established, since y_n is infinite. Examples of H profiles are shown in Figs. 24.9o and p.

A Profiles ($S_0 < 0$). The *A1 profile* is impossible since the value of y_n is not real. The *A2* and *A3 profiles* are similar to the H2 and H3 profiles, respectively. Examples are shown in Figs. 24.9q and r.

Control Section. A control section is a section where the depth of flow is either critical or controllable.

In the steep reach of a prismatic channel, the control section is usually at the upstream end since the flow must pass through the critical section at the upstream end and then follow either the S1 or S2 profile. When several steep reaches occur in succession, the control section is at the upstream end of the uppermost reach.

In the mild reach of a prismatic channel, the control section is usually at the downstream end since the flow must pass a determinable depth at the downstream end, such as at the brink if the reach terminates with a free overfall, or at the dam where the depth behind the dam is given.

In nonprismatic channels, the critical-flow section acting as a control section may occur at any section or sections depending on the channel geometry and the flow conditions.

Method of Singular Points. For a general analysis of flow profiles in any channels, the method of singular points applied by Massé[7,8] may be used. It can be shown that Eq. (24.47) may be written

$$\frac{dy}{dx} = S_0 \frac{1 - (Q/Q_n)^2}{1 - (Q/Q_c)^2} = \frac{F_1}{F_2} \tag{24.48}$$

Let the denominator and numerator be equal to zero, respectively:

$$F_1 = S_0 \left[1 - \left(\frac{Q}{Q_n} \right)^2 \right] = 0 \tag{24.49}$$

and

$$F_2 = 1 - \left(\frac{Q}{Q_c} \right)^2 = 0 \tag{24.50}$$

The solution of Eq. (24.49) will give $Q = Q_n$ or $y = y_n$. Hence $F_1 = 0$ represents the normal-depth line in a prismatic channel. In nonprismatic channels, uniform flow is unrealistic and $F_1 = 0$ describes a fictitious normal-flow profile known as *quasinormal profile*.

Similarly, the solution of Eq. (24.50) will give $Q = Q_c$ or $y = y_c$. Hence $F_2 = 0$ represents a *critical-flow profile*. Since Q_c is independent of the channel slope, the concept of the critical-flow profile is valid in channels of any slope.

In prismatic channels, $F_1 = 0$ and $F_2 = 0$ are two parallel lines. In nonprismatic channels, however, the two profiles are not parallel lines but may intersect at a point P. At point P, Eq. (24.48) shows $dy/dx = 0/0$, a mathematically indeterminate form. Such a point is known in mathematics as a *singular point*.

When $Q_n = Q_c$, $y_n = y_c$, which is a depth known as the *transitional depth*. The curve representing this depth at different sections in a channel is called the *transitional profile*.

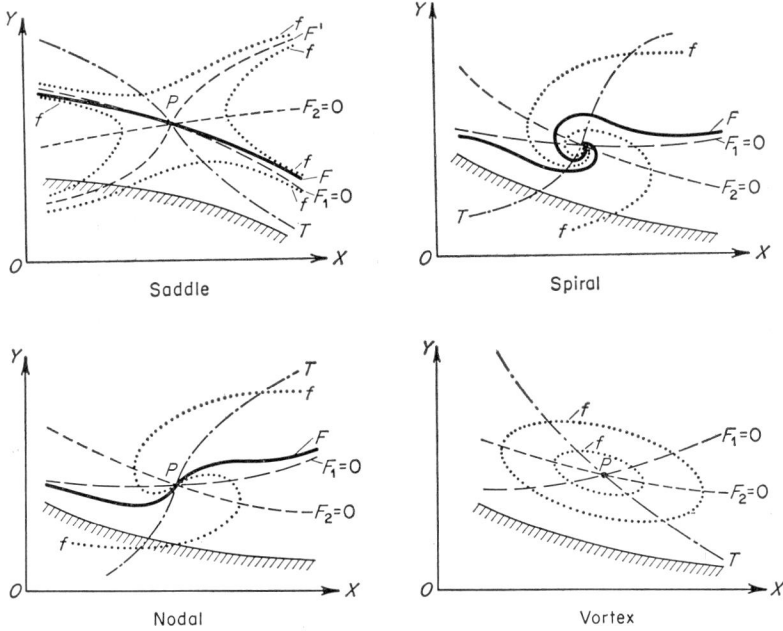

FIG. 24.10. Flow profiles around a singular point. p = singular point; F = flow profile passing through P and asymptotic to $F_1 = 0$; F' = flow profile passing through P but not asymptotic to $F_1 = 0$; f = other flow profiles; F_1 = quasi-normal flow profile; F_2 = critical-flow profile; and T = transitional profile.

A flow passing through this profile at the singular point will change its state from subcritical to supercritical or vice versa. In fact, the transitional profile must pass through the singular point, since at this point $Q_n = Q_c = Q$ or $y_n = y_c = y$. At other places where $Q_n = Q_c = Q$, Eq. (24.48) gives $dy/dx = S_0$. This means that a profile must be horizontal in crossing the transitional profile. Since the transitional profile is defined by the condition that $Q_n = Q_c$, its position is fixed by the channel characteristics, but unlike the quasi-normal and critical-flow profiles, it is independent of the change in discharge.

A general mathematical solution of the condition $dy/dx = 0/0$ will give all possible flow profiles that can be developed theoretically around the singular point.[9] The flow profiles thus developed can be classified into four types: *saddle, nodal, spiral,* and *vortex,* as shown in Fig. 24.10.

24.15. Flow-profile Computations

Three popular methods of flow-profile computation are to be discussed.

Direct-integration Method. From Eqs. (24.28) and (24.33), Eq. (24.47) may be written

$$\frac{dy}{dx} = S_0 \frac{1 - y_n^N{}_n/y^N}{1 - y_c^M{}_c/y^M} \qquad (24.51)$$

As shown in Fig. 24.11, N_n and M_c represent the hydraulic exponents N and M at the normal and critical depths, respectively. It is assumed that the logarithmic plots are practically straight lines in the range ab within which the flow profile is considered. Let $u = y/y_n{}^{N_n/N}$; the solution of Eq. (24.51) gives the following equation for the computation of flow profiles:

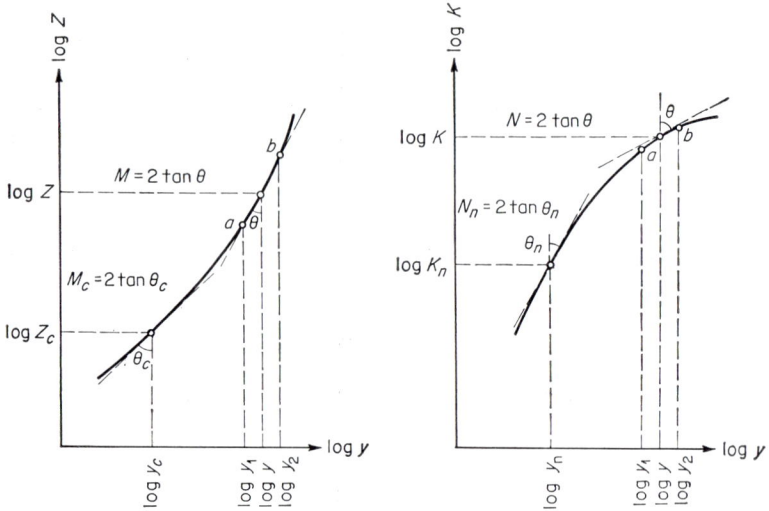

FIG. 24.11. Logarithmic plots of depth against hydraulic exponents.

$$x = \frac{y_n^{N_n/N}}{S_0} \left[u - F(u,N) + \left(\frac{y_c^{M_c/M}}{y_n^{N_n/M}} \right)^M \frac{J}{N} F(v,J) \right] + \text{const} \qquad (24.52)$$

in which $u = y/y_n^{N_n/N}$, $v = u^{N/J}$, $J = N/(N - M + 1)$, and $F(u,N)$ and $F(v,J)$ are known as *varied-flow functions*, or

$$F(u,N) = \int_0^u \frac{du}{1 - u^N} \qquad (24.53)$$

and
$$F(v,J) = \int_0^v \frac{dv}{1 - v^J} \qquad (24.54)$$

Bakhmeteff[10] suggested four methods for the evaluation of the varied-flow function:
1. For values of $u < 1$, it may be shown that

$$\int \frac{du}{1 - u^N} = u + \frac{u^{N+1}}{N + 1} + \frac{u^{2N+1}}{2N + 1} + \cdots + \frac{u^{(p-1)N+1}}{(p - 1)N + 1} + \int r_p \, du \quad (24.55a)$$

in which p is the number of members in the series $r_p = u^{pN} + u^{(p+1)N} + \cdots$, and

$$\int r_p \, du = \frac{u^{pN+1}}{pN + 1} \left(1 + \frac{pN + 1}{pN + N + 1} u^N + \cdots \right) \qquad (24.55b)$$

Obviously,
$$\int r_p \, du < \frac{u^{pN+1}}{pN + 1} \frac{1}{1 - u^N} \qquad (24.55c)$$

Equation (24.55c) can be used to determine p, or the number of the members of the series that are necessary to guarantee the required precision of the computation. The value of $F(u,N)$ is then computed by Eq. (24.55a). For reasonably small values of u, the series is rapidly convergent. The method is practicable for values of $u \leqq 0.70$.
2. For values of $u > 1$, a convergent series is obtained by making $u = 1/z^2$ and $N = k/2$. It can be shown that

$$\int \frac{du}{1 - u^N} = \frac{1}{(N - 1)u^{N-1}} + \frac{1}{(2N - 1)u^{2N-1}} + \cdots + R_p \qquad (24.56a)$$

in which

$$R_p < \frac{1}{(pN - 1)u^{pN-1}} \frac{u^N}{u^N - 1} \tag{24.56b}$$

The series shown by Eq. (24.56a) converges rapidly with the increase of the value of u. The method is practicable for $u \geqq 1.50$.

3. For $0.7 < u < 1.50$, the Poncelet formula for approximate integration may be used, namely,

$$\int_a^b y \, dx = \frac{b - a}{2m} (2q + s) \tag{24.57a}$$

in which $2m$ is the number of equal intervals into which the range ab is divided; y_1, y_2, y_3, ..., y_{2m} and y_{2m+1} are the respective values of the function $y = f(x)$, corresponding to the above intervals; $q = y_2 + y_4 + \cdots + y_{2m}$; and $s = (y_1 + y_{2m+1} - y_2 - y_{2m})/4$. The error involved in the approximation is

$$\epsilon < \frac{b - a}{2m} s \tag{24.57b}$$

The Poncelet formula determines the value

$$\Delta F(u,N) = \int_a^b \frac{du}{1 - u^N}$$

which is to be added to

$$F(a,N) = \int_0^a \frac{du}{1 - u^N}$$

to give

$$F(b,N) = \int_0^b \frac{du}{1 - u^N}$$

Starting with a certain value $F(u,N)$ previously determined by some other method, the Poncelet formula can be used to build up the subsequent consecutive values of $F(u,N)$. For each range ab, Eq. (24.57b) determines the number of intervals $2m$, into which the respective range ab should be divided in order to obtain the required precision.

4. For values of $u \geqq 1$, in the immediate vicinity of unity, the number of intervals to be used in the Poncelet formula proves to be very large. In this case, advantage can be taken of an infinite series, obtained by letting $1 - u^N = \pm z$, where the positive sign corresponds to values of $u < 1$ and the negative sign to values of $u > 1$. The infinite series thus obtained is

$$\int \frac{du}{1 - u^N} = -\left[\text{const} + \frac{1}{N} \ln z \pm \frac{N - 1}{N^2} z + \frac{(N - 1)(2N - 1)}{2N^3 \times 2!} z^2 \right.$$
$$\left. \pm \frac{(N - 1)(2N - 1)(3N - 1)}{3N^4 \times 3!} z^3 + \cdots + R_p \right] \tag{24.58a}$$

This series converges rapidly with the decrease of z, that is, as u approaches unity. The number p of series numbers required to guarantee a desired precision is determined by

$$R_p < \frac{z^p}{N} \frac{1}{1 - z} \tag{24.58b}$$

For practical applications, tables of varied-flow functions prepared by these methods are available.[2] For certain values of N, the varied-flow function is integrable. In approximate computations, for example, an average value of $N = M = J = 3$ may be used. Thus

$$F(u,3) = \tfrac{1}{6} \ln \frac{u^2 + u + 1}{(u - 1)^2} - \frac{1}{\sqrt{3}} \cot^{-1} \frac{2u + 1}{\sqrt{3}} \tag{24.59}$$

This is known as the *Bresse solution*.

In conduits with a gradually closing top, the hydraulic exponents may vary rapidly when the depth approaches the top. In other words, the plots in the range ab in Fig. 24.11 cannot be assumed as straight lines if accurate computations are desired. For circular conduits, Keifer and Chu[11] have derived a flow-profile equation which assumes variable hydraulic exponents:

$$x = \frac{d_0}{S_0}\left(X - \frac{\alpha Q^2}{d_0{}^5}\,Y\right) + \text{const} \tag{24.60}$$

in which X and Y are varied-flow functions, depending on y/d_0 and Q/Q_0. Q_0 is the discharge of the conduit flowing full at a depth equal to the diameter d_0 of the conduit and having the energy gradient equal to the bottom slope S_0. These functions can be evaluated by numerical integration. Similar flow-profile equations and varied-flow functions can also be developed for other conduits with appreciably variable hydraulic exponents.

Direct Step Method. By this method, a channel is divided into a number of short reaches of length Δx. From Eq. (24.46), using finite increments, it can be shown that

$$\Delta x = \frac{E_2 - E_1}{S_0 - S_f} = \frac{\Delta E}{S_0 - S_f} \tag{24.61}$$

in which E is the specific energy, or assuming $\alpha' = 1$ and $\alpha_1 = \alpha_2 = \alpha$,

$$E = y + \alpha\,\frac{V^2}{2g} \tag{24.62}$$

The subscripts 1 and 2 designate the channel sections at the beginning and end of the reach, respectively. In the above equations, y is the depth of flow, V is the mean velocity, α is the energy coefficient, S_0 is the bottom slope, and S_f is the friction slope. The average value of S_f is denoted by $\overline{S}_f$. When the Manning formula is used, the friction slope is expressed by

$$S_f = \frac{n^2 V^2}{2.22 R^{\frac{2}{3}}} \tag{24.63}$$

in which n is Manning's roughness coefficient, and R is the hydraulic radius.

The direct step method is essentially based on the use of Eq. (24.61), as may be illustrated by the following example.

Example 1. A trapezoidal channel having a bottom width $b = 20$ ft, side slope = 2:1, $S_0 = 0.0016$, and $n = 0.025$ carries a discharge of 400 cfs. Compute the backwater profile created by a dam which backs up the water to a depth of 5 ft immediately behind the dam. The energy coefficient $\alpha = 1.10$.

SOLUTION. The computation for the backwater profile is given in Table 24.2. The reaches are divided on the basis of various depths as shown in column 1 of the table. The computed backwater curve is plotted as shown in Fig. 24.12.

Standard Step Method. By this method, the energy at each subdivided channel section is referred to a common horizontal datum. The total heads at two end sections of a reach are

$$H_1 = Z_1 + \alpha_1\,\frac{V_1{}^2}{2g} \tag{24.64}$$

and

$$H_2 = Z_2 + \alpha_2\,\frac{V_2{}^2}{2g} \tag{24.65}$$

in which Z_1 and Z_2 are the flow-surface elevations above the datum at the two end sections. Therefore

$$H_1 = H_2 + h_f + h_e \tag{24.66}$$

in which $h_f = S_f\,\Delta x$, or the friction loss, and h_e is the eddy loss, which may be estimated as $k(\alpha_1 V_1{}^2/2g - \alpha_2 V_2{}^2/2g)$. For abrupt expansions and contractions, $k = 0.5$, ap-

Table 24.2. Computation of Flow Profile by the Direct Step Method

$Q = 400$ cfs $n = 0.025$ $S_0 = 0.0016$ $y_c = 1.10$ $\alpha = 1.10$ $y_c = 2.22$ ft $y_n = 3.36$ ft

y (1)	A (2)	R (3)	$R^{4/3}$ (4)	V (5)	$\alpha V^2/2g$ (6)	E (7)	ΔE (8)	S_f (9)	$\bar{S}_f$ (10)	$S_0 - \bar{S}_f$ (11)	Δx (12)	x (13)
5.00	150.00	3.54	5.40	2.667	0.1217	5.1217	......	0.000370				
4.80	142.08	3.43	5.17	2.819	0.1356	4.9356	0.1861	0.000433	0.000402	0.001198	155	155
4.60	134.32	3.31	4.94	2.979	0.1517	4.7517	0.1839	0.000507	0.000470	0.001130	163	318
4.40	126.72	3.19	4.70	3.156	0.1706	4.5706	0.1811	0.000598	0.000553	0.001047	173	491
4.20	119.28	3.08	4.50	3.354	0.1925	4.3925	0.1781	0.000705	0.000652	0.000948	188	679
4.00	112.00	2.96	4.25	3.572	0.2184	4.2184	0.1741	0.000850	0.000778	0.000822	212	891
3.80	104.88	2.84	4.02	3.814	0.2490	4.0490	0.1694	0.001020	0.000935	0.000665	255	1146
3.70	101.38	2.77	3.88	3.948	0.2664	3.9664	0.0826	0.001132	0.001076	0.000524	158	1304
3.60	97.92	2.71	3.78	4.085	0.2856	3.8856	0.0808	0.001244	0.001188	0.000112	196	1500
3.55	96.21	2.68	3.72	4.158	0.2958	3.8458	0.0398	0.001310	0.001277	0.000323	123	1623
3.50	94.50	2.65	3.66	4.233	0.3067	3.8067	0.0391	0.001382	0.001346	0.000254	154	1777
3.47	93.48	2.63	3.63	4.278	0.3131	3.7831	0.0236	0.001427	0.001465	0.000195	121	1898
3.44	92.45	2.61	3.59	4.326	0.3202	3.7602	0.0229	0.001471	0.001449	0.000151	152	2050
3.42	91.80	2.60	3.57	4.357	0.3246	3.7446	0.0156	0.001500	0.001486	0.000114	137	2187
3.40	91.12	2.59	3.55	4.388	0.3292	3.7292	0.0154	0.001535	0.001518	0.000082	188	2375

Table 24.3. Computation of Flow Profile by the Standard Step Method

$Q = 400$ cfs $n = 0.025$ $S_0 = 0.0016$ $\alpha = 1.10$ $h_e = 0$ $y_c = 2.22$ ft $y_n = 3.36$ ft

Station (1)	Z (2)	y (3)	A (4)	V (5)	$\alpha V^2/2g$ (6)	H (7)	R (8)	$R^{4/3}$ (9)	S_f (10)	$\bar{S}_f$ (11)	Δx (12)	h_f (13)	h_e (14)	H (15)
0 + 00	605.000	5.00	150.00	2.667	0.1217	605.122	3.54	5.40	0.000370	....	...	....	:	605.122
1 + 55	605.048	4.80	142.08	2.819	0.1356	605.184	3.43	5.17	0.000433	0.000402	155	0.062	0	605.184
3 + 18	605.109	4.60	134.32	2.979	0.1517	605.261	3.31	4.92	0.000507	0.000470	163	0.077	0	605.261
4 + 91	605.186	4.40	126.72	3.156	0.1706	605.357	3.19	4.70	0.000598	0.000553	173	0.096	0	605.357
6 + 79	605.286	4.20	119.28	3.354	0.1925	605.479	3.08	4.50	0.000705	0.000652	188	0.122	0	605.479
8 + 91	605.426	4.00	112.00	3.572	0.2184	605.644	2.96	4.25	0.000850	0.000778	212	0.165	0	605.644
11 + 46	605.633	3.80	104.88	3.814	0.2490	605.882	2.84	4.02	0.001020	0.000935	255	0.238	0	605.882
13 + 04	605.786	3.70	101.38	3.948	0.2664	606.052	2.77	3.88	0.001132	0.001076	158	0.170	0	606.052
15 + 00	605.999	3.60	97.92	4.085	0.2856	606.285	2.71	3.78	0.001244	0.001188	196	0.233	0	606.285
16 + 23	606.146	3.55	96.21	4.158	0.2958	606.442	2.68	3.72	0.001310	0.001277	123	0.157	0	606.442
17 + 77	606.343	3.50	94.50	4.233	0.3067	606.650	2.65	3.66	0.001382	0.001346	154	0.208	0	606.650
18 + 98	606.507	3.47	93.48	4.278	0.3131	606.820	2.63	3.63	0.001427	0.001405	121	0.170	0	606.820
20 + 50	606.720	3.44	92.45	4.326	0.3202	607.040	2.61	3.59	0.001471	0.001449	152	0.220	0	607.040
21 + 87	606.919	3.42	91.80	4.357	0.3246	607.244	2.60	3.57	0.001500	0.001486	137	0.204	0	607.244
23 + 75	607.201	3.40	91.12	4.388	0.3292	607.530	2.59	3.55	0.001535	0.001518	188	0.286	0	607.530

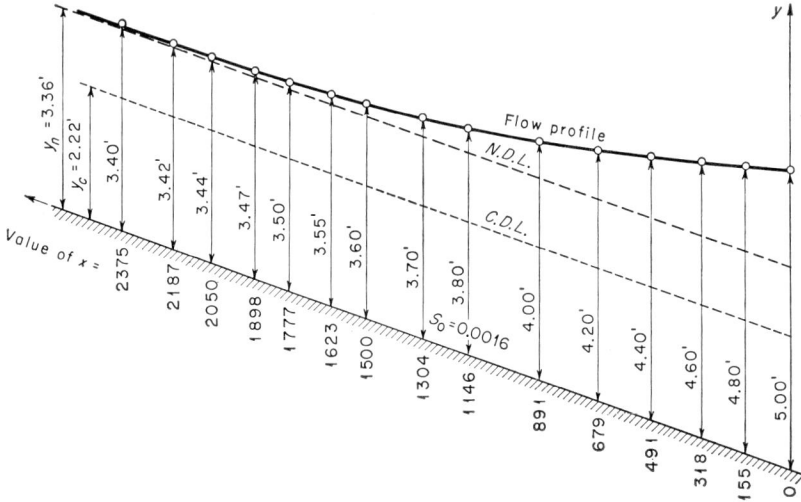

FIG. 24.12. Backwater curve computed by the direct step method.

proximately. For gradually diverging and converging reaches, k may be taken approximately as 0.2 and as from 0 to 0.1, respectively.

The use of the standard step method can be best illustrated by the following example.

Example 2. Solve Example 1 by the standard step method. The elevation at the dam site is 600 ft.

SOLUTION. Using Eqs. (24.64), (24.65), (24.66), and (24.63), the computation is given in Table 24.3. The eddy loss is assumed to be zero. The resulting backwater curve can be plotted in practically the same way as shown in Fig. 24.12.

In carrying out a step computation, a trial value of water-surface elevation for the given channel-section station is first assumed. For the example, $Z = 605.048$ is assumed for station 1 + 55 (i.e., 155 ft from the dam). The total head is then computed, or $H_1 = 605.184$ as shown in column 7. Then compute $h_f = 0.062$ and estimate $h_e = 0$. By Eq. (24.66), $H_1 = 605.122 + 0.062 + 0.00 = 605.184$ as shown in column 15. If this value disagrees appreciably with the value in column 7, a new value of Z should be assumed and the step computation repeated until a good agreement in the values is obtained.

It can be seen that the standard step method is best suited to channels where the slope of the bottom is not constant but requires trial-and-error solutions. It should be noted that in either the direct step method or the standard step method, the step computation should be carried upstream if the flow is subcritical and downstream if the flow is supercritical. Step computations carried in the wrong direction tend inevitably to make the result diverge from the correct flow profile.

24.16. Flow Problems

Delivery of a Canal. When a canal connects two reservoirs having varying levels, the discharge of the canal under various conditions of reservoir levels is called the *delivery* of the canal.[10] In the case of subcritical flow, the relationship between the upstream depth y_1 and downstream depth y_2 for a constant discharge Q can be plotted (Fig. 24.13). The resulting curve CNP is known as the *Q-constant curve*. Several auxiliary curves are also constructed, showing certain characteristic features of the Q-constant curve.

The N line is a straight line drawn from the origin of the coordinates and intersects at angles of 45° with the coordinate axes. This line represents the locus of the normal

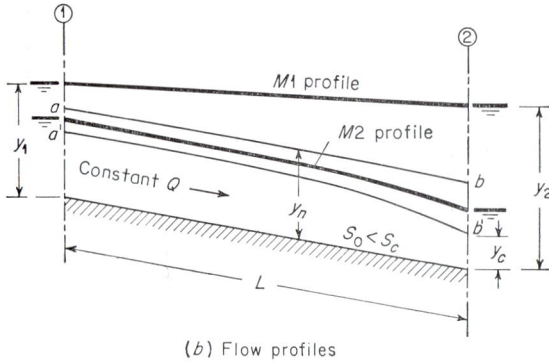

(b) Flow profiles

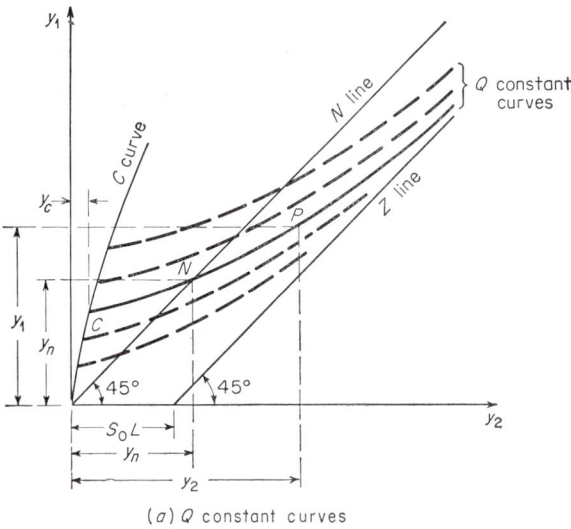

(a) Q constant curves

FIG. 24.13. Delivery in a subcritical canal.

depth for different discharges. For any point on this line, $y_1 = y_2 = y_n$. The Q-constant curve intersects this line at the point N where $y_1 = y_2 = y_n$ is the normal depth for the given Q.

The C curve is the curve on which y_2 is equal to the critical depth y_c of cross section 2 for a given discharge and on which y_1 is the corresponding depth at section 1. It is

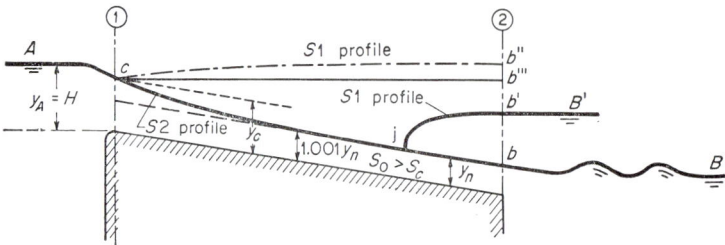

FIG. 24.14. Delivery in a supercritical canal.

Table 24.4. Classification of Flow Profiles in a Rectangular Channel of Variable Width

$$\frac{db}{dx} > 0 \begin{cases} \dfrac{d^2b}{dx^2} > 0 & \begin{cases} S_0 < S_c & \dots\dots a\text{-}1 \\ S_0 > S_c & \dots\dots a\text{-}2 \end{cases} \\[2em] \dfrac{d^2b}{dx^2} < 0 & \begin{cases} S_0 < S_c & \dots\dots b\text{-}1 \\ S_0 > S_c & \dots\dots b\text{-}2 \end{cases} \end{cases}$$

$$\frac{db}{dx} < 0 \begin{cases} \dfrac{d^2b}{dx^2} > 0 & \begin{cases} S_0 < S_c & \dots\dots c\text{-}1 \\ S_0 > S_c & \dots\dots c\text{-}2 \end{cases} \\[2em] \dfrac{d^2b}{dx^2} < 0 & \begin{cases} S_0 < S_c & \dots\dots d\text{-}1 \\ S_0 > S_c & \dots\dots d\text{-}2 \end{cases} \end{cases}$$

apparent that y_2 cannot be less than y_c of section 2 for the given Q. Hence the Q-constant curve terminates at the point C where $y_2 = y_c$.

The Z line is a straight line drawn parallel to the N line from a point on the y_2 axis at a distance S_0L from the origin 0. This line represents the condition $y_2 = y_1 + S_0L$, or the upper limit of the M1 profile. Hence the Q-constant curve approaches this line asymptotically from the left when both y_1 and y_2 become very large.

The coordinates y_1 and y_2 of any point P on the Q-constant curve for a given Q can be determined by a flow-profile computation. Generally, when points C and N and one or two other points are plotted, the Q-constant curve can be drawn in smoothly. The Q-constant curves for other discharges are constructed in the same way.

In the case of supercritical flow, the control section is at the upstream end of the canal (Fig. 24.14). Hence the discharge can be computed from the flow condition at the upstream end only, except when the downstream water level rises to such a high stage that the entrance critical section 1 is eventually submerged. When the entrance is submerged, the entrance acts like a submerged weir and the discharge will be affected by the downstream water elevation.

Nonprismatic Channels. The theory of gradually varied flow is applicable to nonprismatic channels if the change in channel geometry is not so abrupt as to produce separation of flow and large eddy losses. For the purpose of discussion, a rectangular channel of variable width b is assumed. The dynamic equation representing the slope of the flow profiles in the channel can be shown from Eq. (24.46) as

$$\frac{dy}{dx} = \frac{S_0 - S_f + (y_c^3/by^2)(db/dx)}{\alpha' - y_c^3/y^3} = \frac{F_1}{F_2} \tag{24.67}$$

By the singular-point method, Hom-ma[12] has developed the various flow profiles (Fig. 24.15) that can be classified as shown in Table 24.4.

STEADY RAPIDLY VARIED FLOW

It should be noted that most problems of rapidly varied flow are too complicated for an analytical treatment. For practical purposes the flow characteristics may be best determined by model tests. For two-dimensional irrotational flow, the problem may be analyzed by the flow-net method (Sec. 4) or Southwell's relaxation method.

24.17. Hydraulic Drop

When subcritical flow rapidly changes to supercritical flow through a critical-flow section, a *hydraulic drop* is produced.

Free Overfall. This is a special case of the hydraulic drop. It occurs where the bottom of a flat channel is discontinued (Fig. 24.16). If no energy is added from the

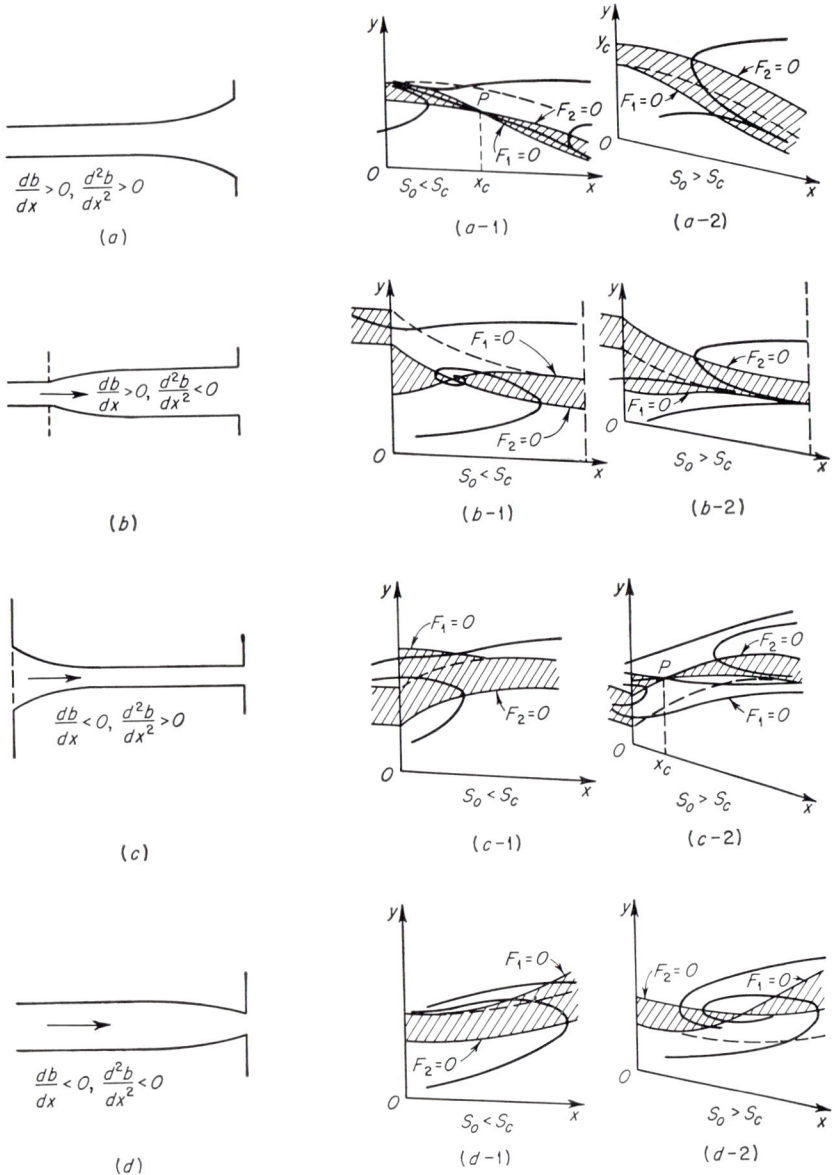

$$\frac{db}{dx} > 0, \quad \frac{d^2b}{dx^2} > 0$$

(a)

(a-1)   (a-2)

$$\frac{db}{dx} > 0, \quad \frac{d^2b}{dx^2} < 0$$

(b)

(b-1)   (b-2)

$$\frac{db}{dx} < 0, \quad \frac{d^2b}{dx^2} > 0$$

(c)

(c-1)   (c-2)

$$\frac{db}{dx} < 0, \quad \frac{d^2b}{dx^2} < 0$$

(d)

(d-1)   (d-2)

Fig. 24.15. Flow profiles in a rectangular channel of variable width.   (*After Hom-ma.*[12])

outside, the liquid surface will seek its lowest possible position corresponding to the
least possible content of energy.   As shown on the specific-energy curve, the specific
energy E at an upstream section will continue to be dissipated on the way downstream
and finally reach a minimum energy content E_{min} at the brink.   Therefore the flow at
the brink is critical.   Since the specific-energy curve and the computed critical depth y_c
are based on the theory of parallel flow, the computed critical section is actually not at

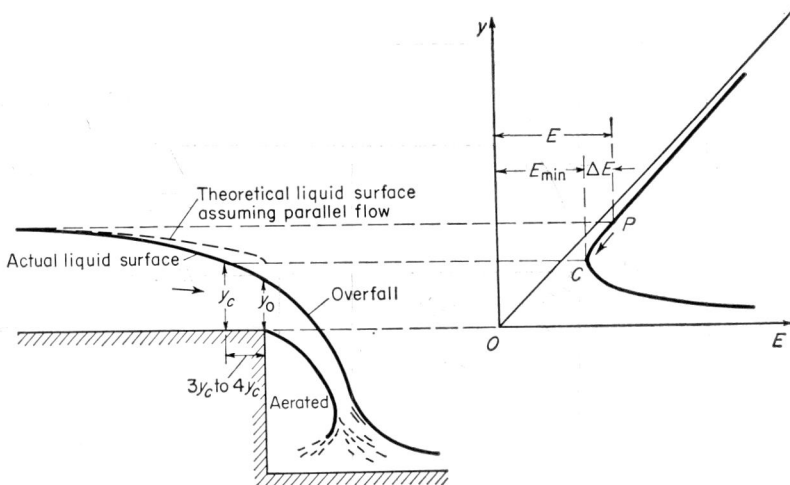

FIG. 24.16. A free overfall.

brink but at a certain distance from the brink within the channel. For rectangular channels of small slope, the computed critical depth is about 1.4 times the brink depth y_0 and it is located about $3y_c$ to $4y_c$ from the brink.

Flow over Spillways. This is an important example of hydraulic drop.

CREST SHAPE. The crest shape of a spillway is usually designed to fit the trajectory of a falling nappe over a sharp-crested weir. Extensive experiments on various falling nappes have been made in order to obtain sufficient data for spillway-shape design.[13] For practical purposes, the data thus obtained should be modified for the presence of roughness of spillway surface, maximum hydraulic efficiency, practicability, stability, and economy.

DISCHARGE. Assuming an irrotational two-dimensional flow, the flow net (Sec. 4) over a spillway is shown in Fig. 24.17a. On a section Ol normal to the streamlines, the *rotation* of the fluid at a point is

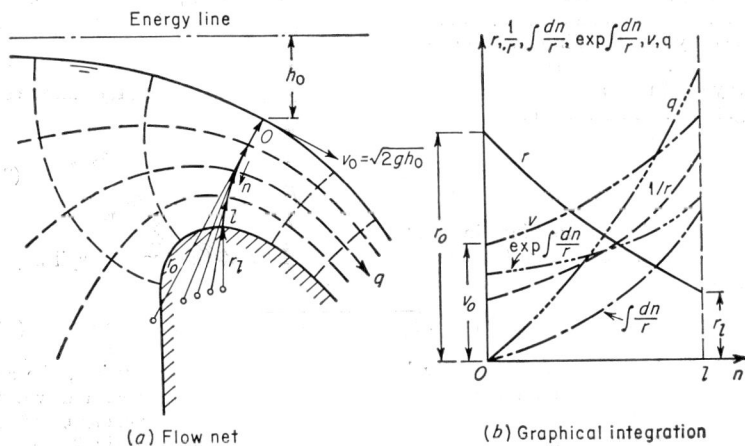

(a) Flow net   (b) Graphical integration

FIG. 24.17. Discharge over overflow spillway.

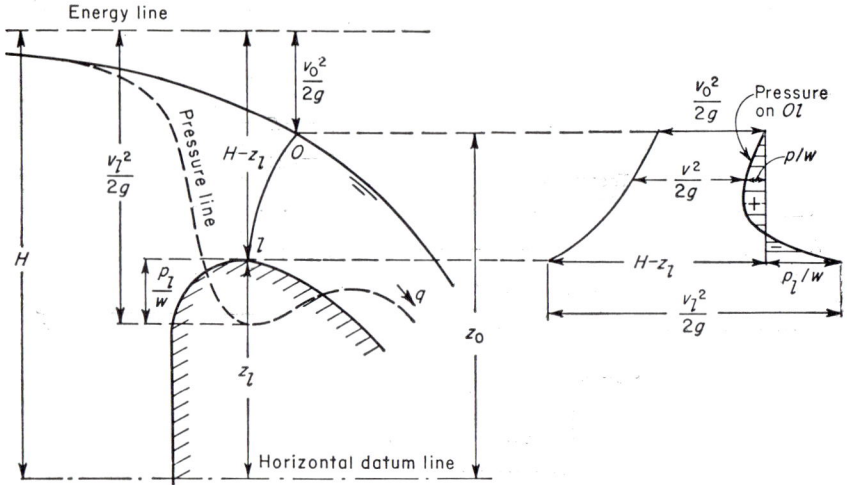

FIG. 24.18. Pressure on overflow spillway.

$$\frac{\partial v}{\partial n} = \frac{v}{r} \qquad (24.68)$$

Since, at the free surface, $n = 0$ and $v = v_0 = \sqrt{2gh_0}$, integration of the above equation gives

$$v = v_0 \exp \int_0^l \frac{dn}{r} \qquad (24.69)$$

The discharge per unit width of the spillway is therefore

$$q = v_0 \int_0^l \exp \int_0^l \frac{dn}{r} \qquad (24.70)$$

In general, r is not a continuous mathematical function of n, and hence Eq. (24.70) cannot be solved analytically. For practical purposes, however, a solution may be obtained by graphical integration as shown in Fig. 24.17b.

PRESSURE. For pressure p and unit weight w of the liquid, the head p/w on the spillway crest may also be determined approximately by a graphical procedure as shown in Fig. 24.18. The value of p/w is determined from

$$\frac{p}{w} = H - z - \frac{v^2}{2g} \qquad (24.71)$$

in which v has been determined in Fig. 24.17b.

FLOW AT THE TOE. The theoretical velocity of flow at the toe of a spillway (Fig. 24.19) is

$$V_1 = \sqrt{2g(Z + H_a - y_1)} \qquad (24.72)$$

in which H_a is the approach velocity head. Because of the energy loss, the actual velocity is always less than the theoretical value. For spillways with downstream surface slope from 1 on 0.6 to 1 on 0.8 and with average surface roughness, the actual velocity at the toe may be determined from the experience charts in Fig. 24.19.

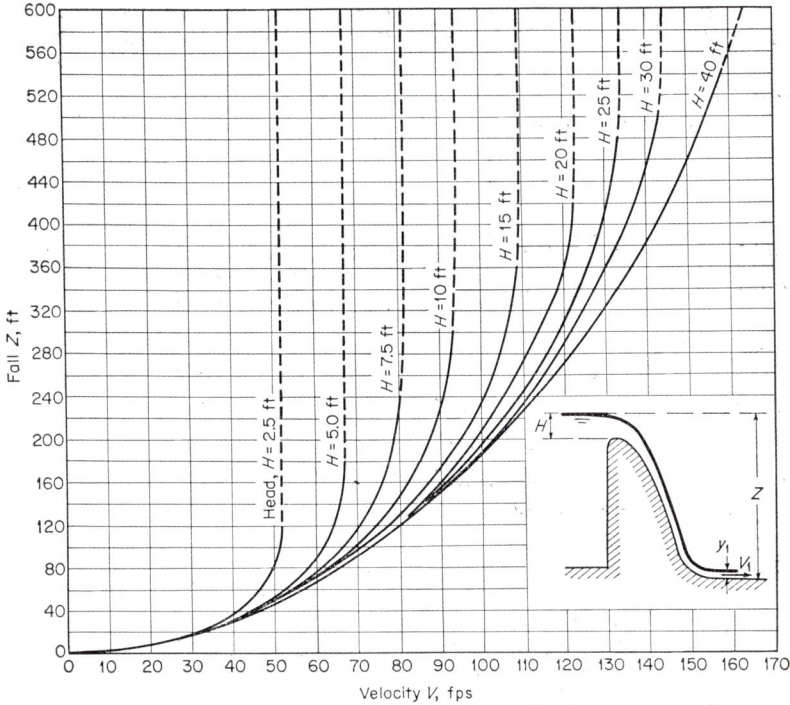

FIG. 24.19. Velocities at toe of overflow spillway.

24.18. Hydraulic Jump

When supercritical flow changes abruptly to subcritical flow, a *hydraulic jump* is produced.

Analysis. For a simple analysis of the hydraulic jump, use may be made of the specific-energy and specific-force curves (Fig. 24.20). The depths y_1 and y_2 before and

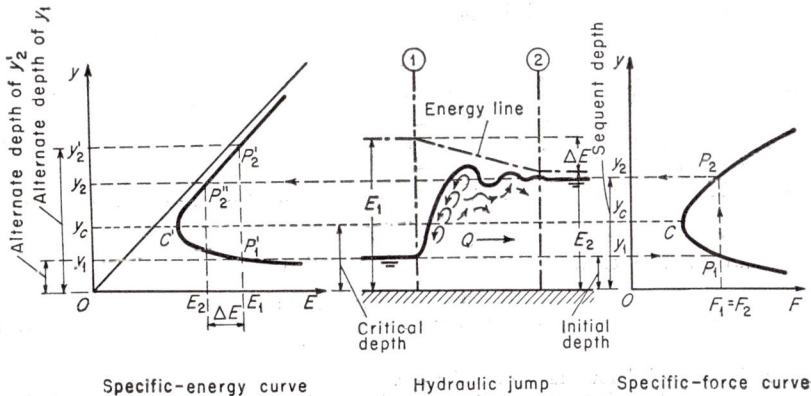

FIG. 24.20. Analysis of hydraulic jump.

$F_1 = 1$–1.7 Undular jump

$F_1 = 1.7$–2.5 Weak jump

Oscillating jet

Roller

$F_1 = 2.5$–4.5 Oscillating jump

$F_1 = 4.5$–9.0 Steady jump

$F_1 > 9.0$ Strong jump

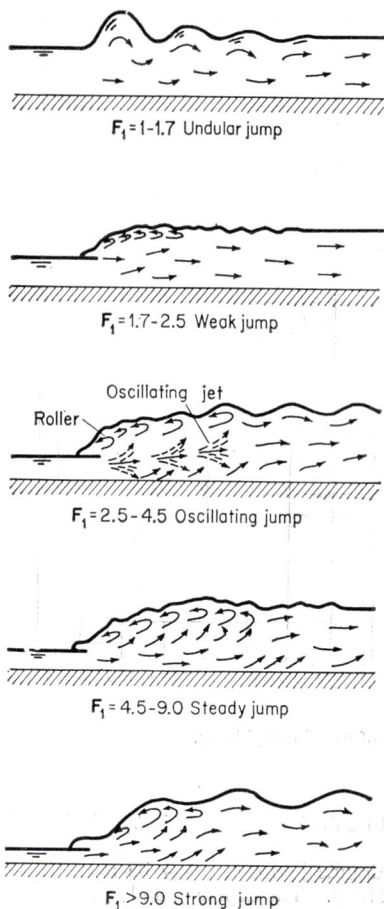

Fig. 24.21. Types of hydraulic jump.

after the jump are known as the *initial* and *sequent* depths, respectively. These depths can be determined from the specific-force curve for the same specific force, or $F_1 = F_2$ in Fig. 24.20. If no energy loss were involved in the jump, the two depths would be called the *alternate depths*, as indicated by y_1 and y'_2 for the same specific energy E_1 on the specific-energy curve. For jumps on the horizontal floor of rectangular channels, the relationship between the depth-ratio y_2/y_1 and the Froude number $F_1 = V_1/\sqrt{gy_1}$ of the initial flow can be expressed by

$$\frac{y_1}{y_2} = \frac{1}{2}(\sqrt{1 + 8F_1^2} - 1) \qquad (24.73)$$

Classification. On the basis of the Froude number F_1, the hydraulic jump may be classified into five types (Fig. 24.21):

For $F_1 = 1$, the flow is critical; no jump is formed.

For $F_1 = 1$ to 1.7, the flow surface shows undulations; an *undular jump* is formed.

For $F_1 = 1.7$ to 2.5, a series of small rollers are developed on the surface of the jump but the downstream surface remains smooth. The velocity throughout is fairly uniform, and the energy loss is low. A *weak jump* is thus formed.

For $F_1 = 2.5$ to 4.5, there exists an oscillating jet which moves from floor to surface and back again with no periodicity. Each oscillation produces a large wave or irregular period which, very commonly in canals, can travel for miles doing unlimited damage to earth banks and riprap. An *oscillating jump* is thus formed.

For $F_1 = 4.5$ to 9.0, the downstream extremity of the surface roller and the point at which the high-velocity jet tends to leave the flow occur at practically the same vertical section. The action and position of this jump are least sensitive to variation in downstream flow depth. The jump is well balanced, and the performance is at its best. A *steady jump* is thus formed.

For $F_1 = 9.0$ and larger, the high-velocity jet grabs intermittent slugs of water rolling down the front face of the jump, generating waves downstream, and a rough surface can prevail. The jump action is rough but efficient, because of high energy dissipation. A *strong jump* is thus formed.

Characteristics.

Energy Loss. From Fig. 24.20, it can be shown that

$$\Delta E = E_1 - E_2 = \frac{(y_2 - y_1)^3}{4y_1y_2} \qquad (24.74)$$

The ratio $\Delta E/E_1$ is known as the *relative loss*.

Efficiency. This is the ratio of the specific energies, respectively, after and before the jump:

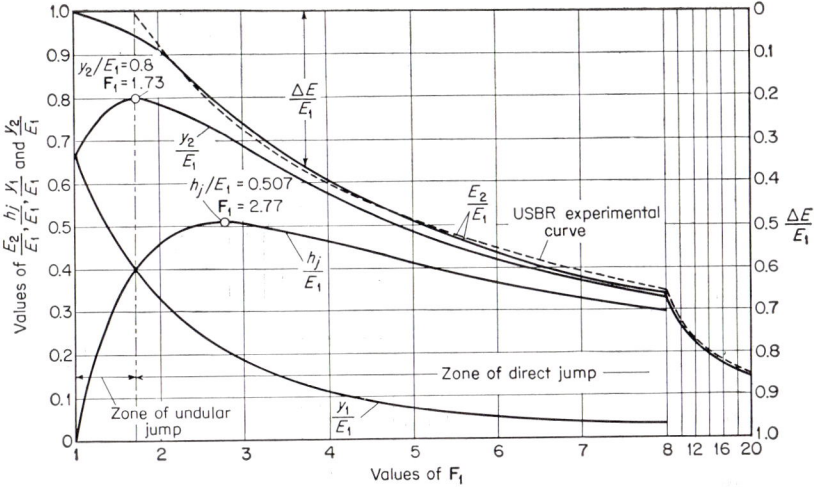

FIG. 24.22. Characteristics of hydraulic jump.

$$\frac{E_2}{E_1} = \frac{(8F_1^2 + 1)^{1.5} - 4F_1^2 + 1}{8F_1^2(2 + F_1^2)} \tag{24.75}$$

HEIGHT. The height h_j of jump is the difference between the sequent and initial depth. Dividing by E_1, it can be expressed as *relative height* and *relative depths*.

$$\frac{h_j}{E_1} = \frac{y_2}{E_1} - \frac{y_1}{E_1} \tag{24.76}$$

or

$$\frac{h_j}{E_1} = \frac{\sqrt{1 + 8F_1^2} - 3}{F_1^2 + 2} \tag{24.77}$$

The above characteristics of a jump can be expressed as dimensionless functions of F_1 and plotted as shown in Fig. 24.22. The dashed line shows the experimental curve for E_2/E_1 as obtained by the U.S. Bureau of Reclamation.[14]

LENGTH. The length of a jump may be measured from the front face of the jump to a point on the surface immediately downstream from the roller. This length cannot be determined by theory, but its ratio to the sequent depth has been found to depend on the Froude number as shown by the experimental curve for stilling basin I in Fig. 24.25.

Jump on Sloping Floor. For jumps on a sloping floor, an equation similar to Eq. (24.73) may be written

$$\frac{y_2}{y_1} = \frac{1}{2}(\sqrt{1 + 8G^2} - 1) \tag{24.78}$$

in which G is a function of F_1 and the slope S_0. By experiments, the relations among y_2/y_1, F_1, and S_0 were obtained as shown in Fig. 24.23. The length of the jump as a ratio to the sequent depth is shown also as a function of F_1 and S_0 in Fig. 24.24.

Energy Dissipation. The energy contained in the high-velocity flow below a spillway toe or a sluice gate can be dissipated by various means, among which the hydraulic jump is most commonly used.[15]

For the use of energy dissipation, various designs of stilling basins have been developed by the U.S. Bureau of Reclamation.[14] As a general reference, such designs are summarized in Fig. 24.25.

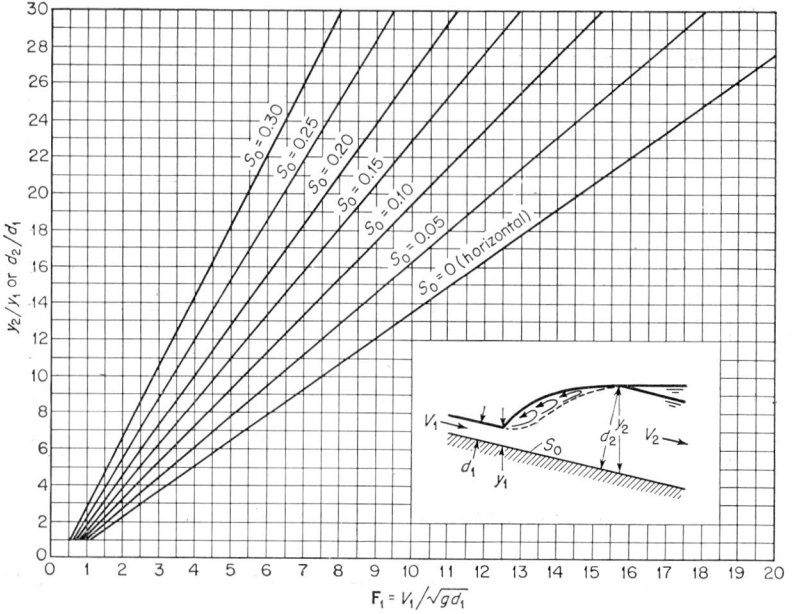

FIG. 24.23. Experimental relations between $\mathbf{F}$ and y_2/y_2 or d_2/d_1 for hydraulic jumps on sloping floor.

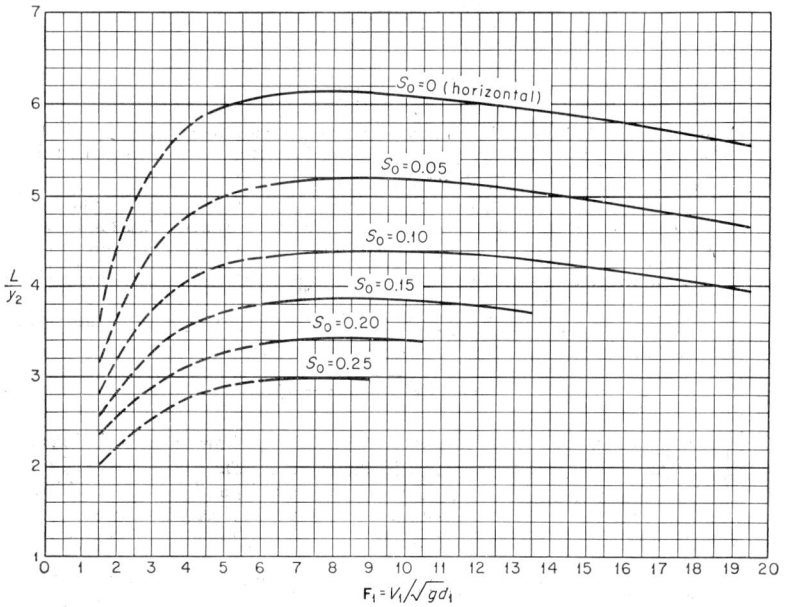

FIG. 24.24. Lengths in terms of sequent depth of hydraulic jumps on sloping floor.

24.19. Subcritical Flow in Curves

When subcritical flow occurs in curved channels, three important features of the flow are usually noted, namely, spiral flow, superelevation, and energy loss.

Spiral Flow. This refers to movement of water particles along a helical path in the general direction of the flow. The transverse velocity components of the spiral flow will create so-called *secondary flow* in the plane of the cross section normal to the direction of flow. The *strength of a spiral flow*[16] may be computed by

$$S_{xy} = \frac{V_{xy}^2}{V^2} \times 100 \tag{24.79}$$

in which V_{xy} is the mean transverse velocity component normal to the section, and V is the mean velocity of flow in the section.

Superelevation. The centrifugal force acting on the flow around a curve will produce a rise in the liquid surface at the outer bank with an accompanying lowering at the inner bank. The difference between the liquid surfaces at the outer and inner surfaces is known as *superelevation*. By the theory of a free vortex, the superelevation can be expressed as

$$\Delta h = \frac{C^2}{2g}\left(\frac{1}{r_i^2} - \frac{1}{r_o^2}\right) \tag{24.80}$$

in which r_i and r_o are the radii of the inner and outer banks, and C is a *circulation constant*. For a given discharge Q, and specific energy E at a section, C may be determined from the following equation:

$$Q = C\left(E - \frac{C^2}{2gr_o r_i}\right) \ln \frac{r_o}{r_i} \tag{24.81}$$

Energy Loss. This is usually expressed in terms of the velocity head:

$$h_f = f_c \frac{V^2}{2g} \tag{24.82}$$

in which f_c is the *coefficient of curve resistance* which can be determined experimentally.

24.20. High-velocity Flow

Supercritical flow is also known as *high-velocity flow*[17] in engineering problems where disturbances on free surface, called *shock waves*, are generally produced in a rapidly varied state of flow.

Wave Angle. When a supercritical flow changes its direction because of the deflection of the side boundary, a shock-wave front as shown in Fig. 24.26 will be produced. The *wave angle* β, also known as *Mach angle*, which the wave front, or disturbance line, makes with the initial direction of flow, can be shown as

$$\sin \beta = \frac{\sqrt{gy_1}}{V_1}\sqrt{\frac{1}{2}\left(1 + \frac{y_2}{y_1}\right)\frac{y_2}{y_1}} \tag{24.83}$$

When the shock-wave disturbance is small,

$$\sin \beta = \frac{\sqrt{gy_1}}{V_1} = \frac{1}{\mathbf{F}_1} \tag{24.84}$$

Waves Due to Boundary Deflection Neglecting Energy Dissipation. If the side boundary of the flow causes a gradual angular deflection of the stream, the shock-wave fronts thus produced will result in a gradual change of depth. The wave front is said to be positive if the deflection of boundary is toward the flow and negative if away from the flow. The positive wave front is caused by deflection of boundary toward the wave front, resulting in a rise in the liquid surface. The negative wave front, on

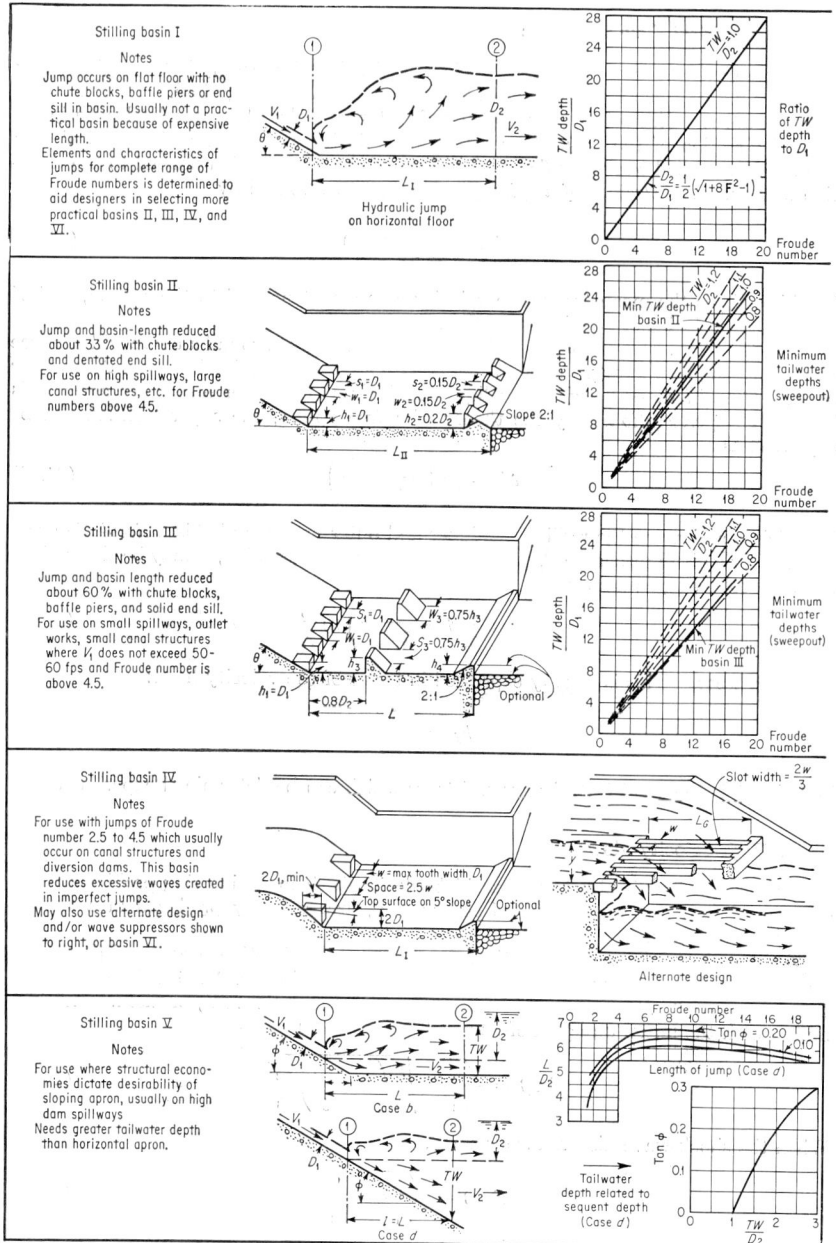

FIG. 24.25. Summary of characteristics of

Chart 1 (top left): $\frac{L}{D_2}$ vs Froude number (0 to 20). Length of jump.

Chart 2 (top middle): Loss in energy in percent / $\frac{E_L}{E_1}$ vs Froude number (0 to 20). Loss of energy in jump.

Chart 3 (top right): Jump forms.
$F_1 = 1.7–2.5$, pre jump
$F_1 = 2.5–4.5$, transition
$F_1 = 4.5–9.0$, range of good jumps
$F_1 = 9.0$–upward, effective but rough.

Chart (2nd row left): $\frac{L}{D_2}$ vs Froude number. Length of jump.

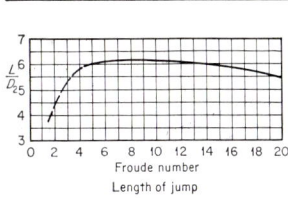

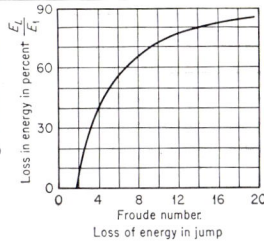

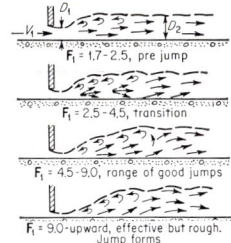

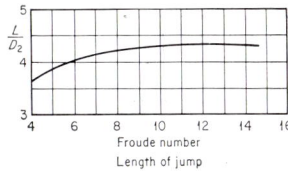

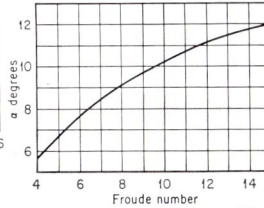

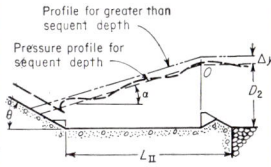

Chart (2nd row middle): a degrees vs Froude number. Water surface and pressure profiles.

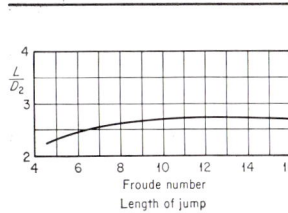

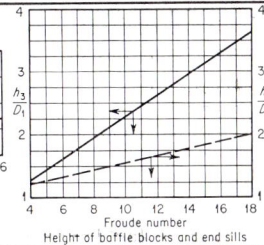

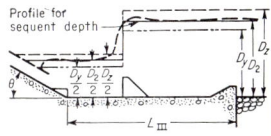

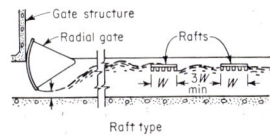

Chart (2nd row right):
Profile for greater than sequent depth
Pressure profile for sequent depth
D_2, Δy, L_{II}

Chart (3rd row left): $\frac{L}{D_2}$ vs Froude number. Length of jump.

Chart (3rd row middle): $\frac{h_3}{D_1}$, $\frac{h_4}{D_1}$ vs Froude number. Height of baffle blocks and end sills.

Chart (3rd row right):
Profile for sequent depth
$\frac{D_1}{2}$, $\frac{D_2}{2}$, $\frac{D_2}{2}$, D_2, L_{III}
Water surface and pressure profiles

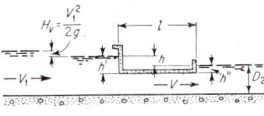

Wave suppressors (4th row):
Gate structure
Radial gate
Rafts
W $\frac{3W}{min}$ W
Raft type
$H_v = \frac{V_1^2}{2g}$, l, h, V, h'', D_2
Underpass type
Wave suppressors

Summary sheet

Notes

This sheet summarizes the main features discussed in this report, and shows some of the important charts. More charts are given in the report [14]. This sheet should be used as a reference guide only; the entire report should be read before attempting to use any of the material contained herein.

Stilling basin VI

Notes

For use on pipe or open channel outlets, sizes and discharges from table. V_1 should not exceed 30 fps. No tailwater required. Froude number usually 1.5 to 7 but not important. May substitute for basin IV. Energy loss greater than in comparable jump.

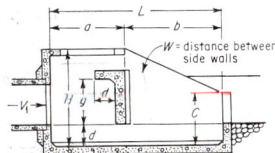

W = distance between side walls

Pipe Dia. in	Area ft2	Q	Feet and inches							
			W	H	L	a	b	c	d	g
18	1.77	21	5-6	4-3	7-4	3-3	4-1	2-4	0-11	2-1
24	3.14	38	6-9	5-3	9-0	3-11	5-1	2-10	1-2	2-6
30	4.91	59	8-0	6-3	10-8	4-7	6-1	3-4	1-4	3-0
36	7.07	85	9-3	7-3	12-4	5-3	7-1	3-10	1-7	3-6
42	9.62	115	10-6	8-0	14-0	6-0	8-0	4-5	1-9	3-11
48	12.57	151	11-9	9-0	15-8	6-9	8-11	4-11	2-0	4-5
54	15.90	191	13-0	9-9	17-4	7-4	10-0	5-5	2-2	4-11
60	19.63	236	14-3	10-9	19-0	8-0	11-0	5-11	2-5	5-4
72	28.27	339	16-6	12-3	22-0	9-3	12-9	6-11	2-9	6-2

USBR stilling basins. (*After Bradley and Peterka*.[14])

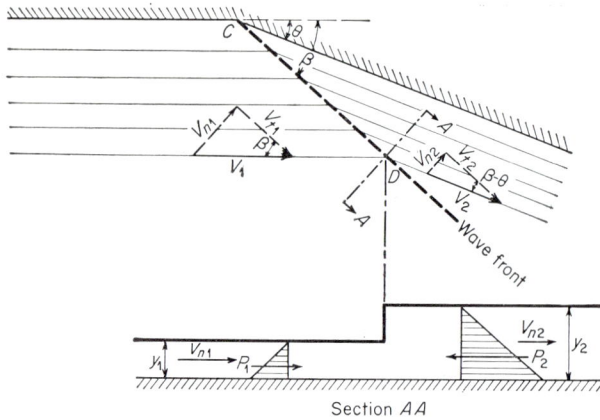

Section *AA*

Fig. 24.26. Shock wave in supercritical flow.

the other hand, is caused by deflection away from the wave front, resulting in a lowering in the liquid surface. Assuming a constant specific energy or disregarding the energy dissipation in the shock waves, von Kármán[18] was able to establish an equation which may be expressed as

$$\theta = \sqrt{3}\,\tan^{-1}\sqrt{\frac{3y}{2E - 3y}} - \tan^{-1}\frac{1}{\sqrt{3}}\sqrt{\frac{3y}{2E - 3y}} - \theta_1 \qquad (24.85)$$

or

$$\theta = \sqrt{3}\,\tan^{-1}\frac{\sqrt{3}}{\sqrt{\mathbf{F}^2 - 1}} - \tan^{-1}\frac{1}{\sqrt{\mathbf{F}^2 - 1}} - \theta_1 \qquad (24.86)$$

in which θ = deflection angle of gradually changing boundary
　　　　 y = depth of flow
　　　　 E = specific energy
　　　　 $\mathbf{F}$ = Froude number
　　　　 θ_1 = constant of integration defined by condition that for $\theta = 0$ depth y is initial depth y_1

Method of Characteristics. To facilitate the analysis of shock waves due to continuous disturbances, such as those in curved channels or in channel contractions and expansions, a graphical *method of characteristics* has been devised by Busemann[19] on the basis of the preceding theory of shock waves. From Eq. (24.85), the basic equation used in this method can be shown as

$$\frac{1}{\overline{V}}\frac{d\overline{V}}{d\theta} = \sqrt{\frac{1 - \overline{V}^2}{3\overline{V}^2 - 1}} \qquad (24.87)$$

in which θ is the deflection angle of boundary, and $\overline{V} = V/\sqrt{2gH}$, in which V = velocity at any point and H = total specific-energy head. Integration of this equation will plot on a *hodograph plane* ($\overline{V}$ versus θ plane in Fig. 24.27a) a set of epicycloids between the circles of radii $1/\sqrt{3}$ and 1 as the limiting values of $\overline{V}$. Only for supercritical flow has Eq. (24.87) any physical meaning, since the denominator is zero for $\overline{V} = 1/\sqrt{3} = 0.577$, which corresponds to critical flow, whereas the numerator is zero for $\overline{V} = 1$, which corresponds to zero depth, or no flow. Values of $\overline{V}$ between $\theta = 0$ and $\theta = 65°53'$ corresponding to $\overline{V} = 0.577$ and $\overline{V} = 1.00$, respectively, are given in Table 24.5.

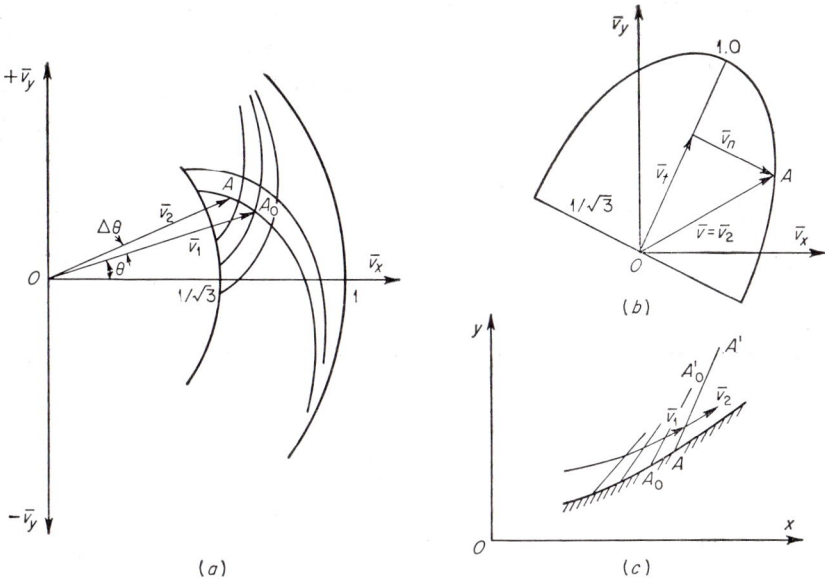

FIG. 24.27. Graphical method of characteristics.

For the determination of the direction of wave front, the following equation can be derived:

$$\frac{(\overline{V}_n)^2}{\tfrac{1}{3}} + \frac{(\overline{V}_t)^2}{1} = 1 \tag{24.88}$$

in which $\overline{V}_n$ is the component of $\overline{V}$ normal to the wave front, and $\overline{V}_t$ is the component of $\overline{V}$ tangential to the wave front. For this equation, an ellipse with major and minor axes of 1 and $1/\sqrt{3}$, respectively, may be drawn (Fig. 24.27b). The ellipse is so drawn that the velocity $\overline{V}$ is represented in direction by the radius vector OA. Therefore the direction of the major axis, or $\overline{V}_t$, obviously represents the direction of the wave front.

The procedure of the method of characteristics may be shown in Fig. 24.27 in which the shock wave due to change of boundary from A_0 to A for an angle $\Delta\theta$ is to be determined (Fig. 24.27c). The initial velocity vector is $\overline{V}_1$, and the final is $\overline{V}_2$. The initial

Table 24.5. Values of $\overline{V}$ for **Different Values of** θ **Used in the Graphical Method of Characteristics**

θ, deg	$\overline{V}$	θ, deg	$\overline{V}$	θ, deg	$\overline{V}$	θ, deg	$\overline{V}$
0	0.577	13	0.773	26	0.874	39	0.943
1	0.613	14	0.782	27	0.880	40	0.948
2	0.635	15	0.791	28	0.886	41	0.952
3	0.651	16	0.799	29	0.893	42	0.956
4	0.666	17	0.808	30	0.900	43	0.960
5	0.681	18	0.817	31	0.905	44	0.963
6	0.695	19	0.825	32	0.910	45	0.966
7	0.709	20	0.833	33	0.915	46	0.969
8	0.720	21	0.840	34	0.920	47	0.972
9	0.731	22	0.848	35	0.925	48	0.975
10	0.742	23	0.855	36	0.930	49	0.978
11	0.753	24	0.861	37	0.935	50	0.980
12	0.763	25	0.868	38	0.939	65°53′	1.000

value of vector $\overline{V}_1$ laid out along the $\overline{V}_x$ axis on the hodograph plane will be near an intersection of the vector with two epicycloids at point A_0. If the plane of flow indicates a positive wave front, one of the branches of the epicycloids leading inward is followed; in the opposite case, one of the branches going outward is followed from the origin until it intersects the radial line belonging to the angle of turn $\Delta\theta$ at point A. The radius vector to this point of intersection represents the new value $\overline{V}_2$. Its direction is represented by the vector OA in the ellipse of Fig. 24.27b. Thus the new wave front AA' in Fig. 24.27c may be drawn in parallel to the major axis of the ellipse. The depth of flow may be determined from the definition of specific energy, or $y = H - V^2/2g = H(1 - \overline{V}^2)$.

Flow in Curves. For high-velocity flow in a curved channel, cross shock waves will develop (Fig. 24.28). The shock waves are reflected back and forth across the channel, under the effect of superelevation, causing the surface profiles along the walls to have a series of maxima and minima of surface elevation, approximately at angles θ, 3θ, 5θ, ..., from the beginning of the curve. The angle θ marks half the wavelength

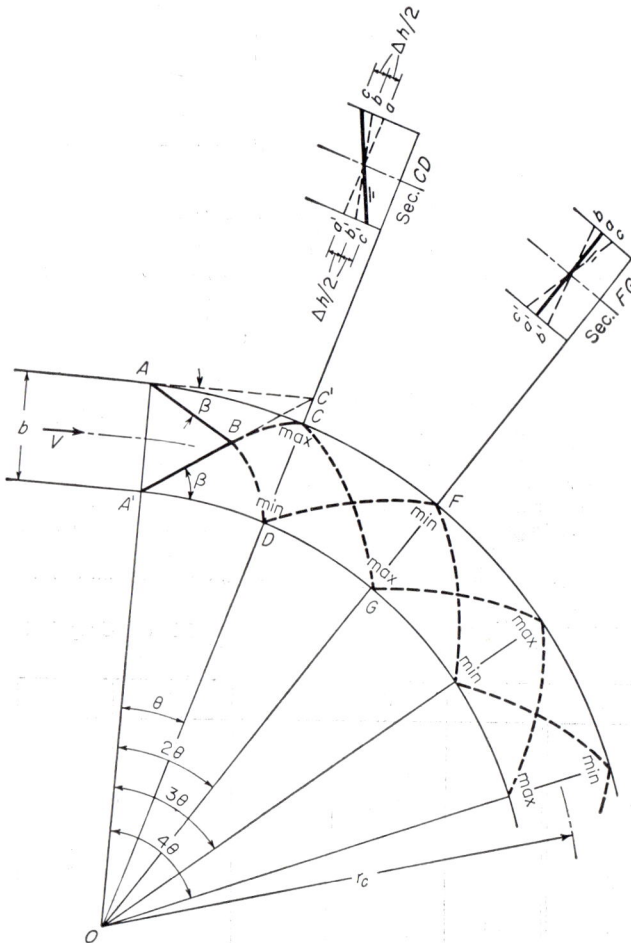

Fig. 24.28. High-velocity flow in a curved channel.

of the cross-wave-disturbance pattern. By geometry, the approximate value of θ can be shown as

$$\theta = \tan^{-1} \frac{2b}{(2r_c + b)\tan\beta} \qquad (24.89)$$

in which b is the width of the channel, r_c is the radius of the centerline of the channel, β [Eq. (24.84)] is the wave angle. The depth of flow along the walls may be determined by Eq. (24.86).

In the practical design of curved channels, the superelevation and cross-wave disturbance should be minimized. For this purpose, Knapp[17] has suggested various methods utilizing banking, multiple-curved vanes, easement curves, and diagonal sills.

Waves Due to Boundary Deflection Considering Energy Dissipation. When the shock waves have fronts of appreciable height due to the merging of successive wave fronts, the energy dissipation cannot be ignored, and thus the theory [Eq. (24.85)] and the method of characteristics become invalid. In this case, Rouse and White[20] and Ippen[17] have developed the following basic equations for the relationships among θ, β, y_1, y_2, $\mathbf{F}_1$, and $\mathbf{F}_2$:

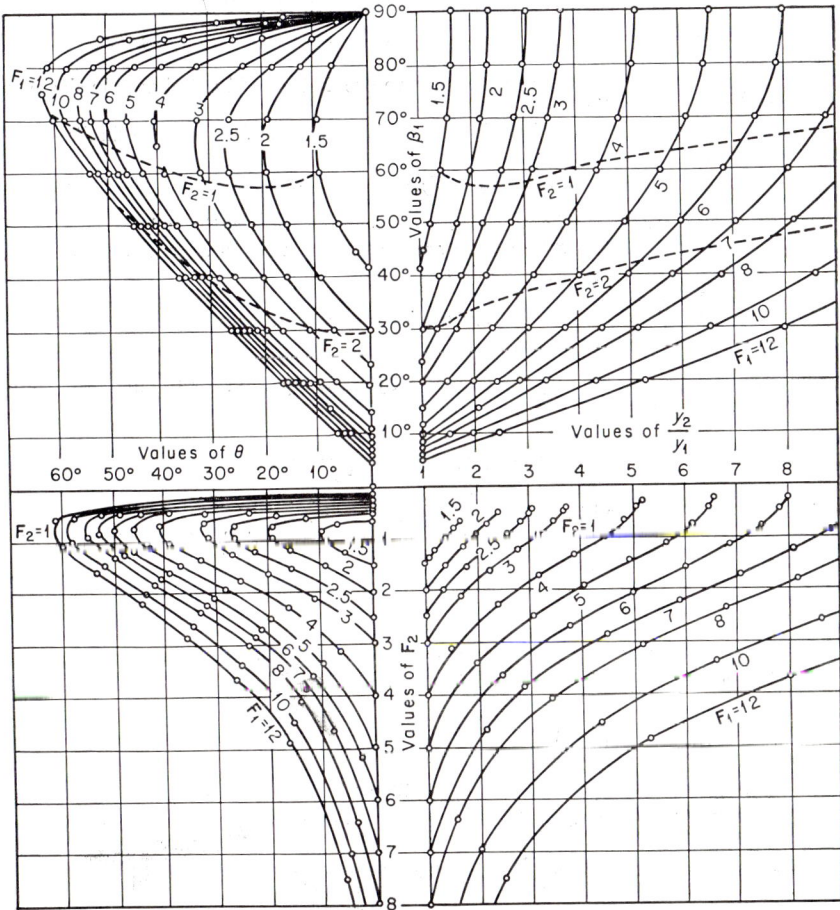

Fig. 24.29. Solution for shock waves considering energy dissipation. (*After A. Ippen.[17]*)

$$\tan \theta = \frac{(1 - y_1/y_2)\tan \beta}{1 + (y_1/y_2)\tan^2 \beta} \tag{24.90}$$

$$\frac{y_1}{y_2} = \frac{2}{\sqrt{1 + 8F_1^2 \sin^2 \beta} - 1} \tag{24.91}$$

$$\tan \theta = \frac{(\sqrt{1 + 8F_1^2 \sin^2 \beta} - 3)\tan \beta}{2\tan^2 \beta - 1 + \sqrt{1 + 8F_1^2 \sin^2 \beta}} \tag{24.92}$$

$$F_2^2 = \frac{y_1}{y_2}\left[F_1^2 - \frac{1}{2}\frac{y_1}{y_2}\left(\frac{y_2}{y_1} - 1\right)\left(\frac{y_2}{y_1} + 1\right)^2 \right] \tag{24.93}$$

A graphical solution of the above equations has been developed by Ippen[17] as shown in Fig. 24.29. For the solution of practical problems of this kind, Preiswerk[21] has adopted Busemann's shock-polar diagram[19] for use in the hydraulic analogy of supersonic flow.

UNSTEADY GRADUALLY VARIED FLOW

24.21. Gradually Varied Uniformly Progressive Flow

This type of unsteady flow has a stable wave profile that will not change in shape as it moves down a prismatic channel.

Analysis of Flow. For a uniformly progressive flow, the following continuity equation can be derived:

$$Q_0 = (V_w - V)A = V_w A - Q \tag{24.94}$$

in which Q_0 = a steady discharge called *overrun* found to pass through wave front in upstream direction of flow when upstream depth is greater than downstream depth (Fig. 24.30)

V_w = velocity of wave front

V = velocity of flow at any section where flow area and discharge are A and Q, respectively

From Eqs. (24.44) and (24.94), the following dynamic equation for the uniformly progressive flow can be written:

$$\frac{\partial y}{\partial x} = \frac{S_0 - (V_w A - Q_0)^2/K^2}{1 - Q_0^2/gA^2D} \tag{24.95}$$

This equation can be used to determine the flow profile.

For the unit width of a wide rectangular channel, use of the Chézy formula will reduce Eq. (24.95) to

$$\frac{\partial y}{\partial x} = S_0 \frac{y^3 - (V_w y - Q_0)^2/C^2 S_0}{y^3 - Q_0^2/g} \tag{24.96}$$

in which C is Chézy's resistance factor. The numerator of the fraction on the right side of this equation is a cubic expression and thus can be replaced by

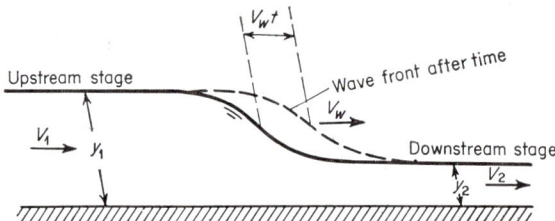

Fig. 24.30. Uniformly progressive flow.

$(y - y_1)(y - y_2)(y - y_3)$ in which y_1, y_2, and y_3 are the three roots if the expression is set equal to zero. The denominator can be replaced by $y^3 - y_c^3$, where $y_c = \sqrt[3]{Q_0^2/g}$ is called the *overrun critical depth*, or the depth corresponding to a steady discharge equal to the overrun. Therefore, Eq. (24.96) may be reduced to

$$x = \frac{1}{S_0} \int \frac{y^3 - y_c^3}{(y - y_1)(y - y_2)(y - y_3)}\, dy + \text{const} \qquad (24.97)$$

This is a mathematical solution for the flow profile of the given condition of flow.

When a flood is generated in a dry downstream channel because of the failure of a dam, Eq. (24.97) will give the wave profile of the flood as

$$x = \frac{y_n}{S_0}\left[\frac{y}{y_n} + \ln\left(1 - \frac{y}{y_n}\right)\right] \qquad (24.98)$$

in which y_n is the normal depth at the crest of the wave where the flow is assumed practically uniform. It should be noted that at the toe of the wave, the curvature of flow surface is very steep, where the flow should be considered as rapidly varied.

When the velocity of flow is very low or the velocity-head effect is negligible, Eqs. (24.94) and (24.95) give

$$Q = Q_n\sqrt{1 + \frac{j}{V_w S_0}} \qquad (24.99)$$

in which Q_n is the corresponding normal discharge, and j is the rate of rise of flow surface at a given channel section. This equation can be used to compute the discharge of a flood wave at a given station in the river, provided the velocity of flow is low.

Monoclinal Rising Wave. This is a special configuration of uniformly progressive flow which travels with a constant velocity V_w from an upstream region of uniform flow of y_1, V_1, and Q_1 to a downstream region of uniform flow of y_2, V_2, and Q_2 (Fig. 24.30). By Eq. (24.94), the wave velocity is

$$V_w = \frac{V_1 A_1 - V_2 A_2}{A_1 - A_2} = \frac{Q_1 - Q_2}{A_1 - A_2} \qquad (24.100)$$

The maximum wave velocity can be shown to be

$$\max (V_w) = \frac{1}{T}\frac{dQ}{dy} \qquad (24.101)$$

in which T is the width of the free surface. The value of dQ/dy at a given depth can be determined from a *discharge rating curve*. Equation (24.101) constitutes the well-known *Kleitz-Seddon principle*, which is generally used for the determination of flood flow in natural channels. On the basis of the Manning formula, Eq. (24.101) will give the ratio of max (V_w) to flow velocity as max $(V_w)/V = 1.67$, 1.33, and 1.44 for wide rectangular, triangular, and wide parabolic channels, respectively. On the basis of the Chézy formula, the corresponding ratios are 1.50, 1.25, and 1.33.

24.22. Flood Routing

This is a procedure to determine the configuration of a flood as it moves down a channel. In general, there are two approaches to flood routing, namely, hydrologic routing and hydraulic routing. For problems in flood-control engineering, hydrologic routing[22] is usually employed because it is based on approximate assumptions of neglecting the dynamic effects and therefore is simple and practicable. The hydraulic routing is based on hydraulic principles. For an approximate hydraulic routing, the flood flow may be assumed as a uniformly progressive flow. Strictly speaking, the dynamics of flood flow is extremely complicated, and hence the hydraulic routing is theoretically involved and unpracticable. However, one numerical method for the solution of the dynamic equations of the unsteady flood flow has been developed. This is a method of character-istics which is described as follows.

In addition to Eqs. (24.39) and (24.44), the following may be written for an unsteady flow:

$$\frac{\partial y}{\partial x} dx + \frac{\partial y}{\partial t} dt = dy \qquad (24.102)$$

$$\frac{\partial V}{\partial x} dx + \frac{\partial V}{\partial t} dt = dV \qquad (24.103)$$

Assuming $\alpha' = \alpha = \beta = 1$, the solution of Eqs. (24.39), (24.44), (24.102), and (24.103) gives

$$\frac{\partial y}{\partial x} = \frac{-D(S_0 - S_f) + \dfrac{D}{g}\dfrac{dV}{dt} - \dfrac{V}{g}\dfrac{dy}{dt} + \dfrac{1}{g}\dfrac{dy}{dt}\dfrac{dx}{dt}}{\dfrac{1}{g}\left(\dfrac{dx}{dt}\right)^2 - \dfrac{2V}{g}\dfrac{dx}{dt} + \dfrac{V^2}{g} - D} \qquad (24.104)$$

It may be assumed that a flood wave is composed of a great number of infinitesimal disturbance waves. Each disturbance wave has a discontinuous surface profile. At the point of discontinuity, $\partial y/\partial x = 0/0$, which is an indeterminate form. Thus let both the numerator and denominator of Eq. (24.104) be equal to zero, and the following equations of the characteristics can be obtained:

C_1:
$$\frac{dx}{dt} = V + c \qquad (24.105)$$

C_2:
$$\frac{dx}{dt} = V - c \qquad (24.106)$$

Along C_1:
$$V + 2c - mt = k_1 = \text{const} \qquad (24.107)$$

Along C_2:
$$V - 2c - mt = k_2 = \text{const} \qquad (24.108)$$

in which $c = \sqrt{gD}$, or celerity of the disturbance wave, and $m = g(S_0 - S_f)$. The first two equations represent two sets of curves, C_1 and C_2, called *characteristics*, which describe the characteristics of the motion of a point on the xt plane. The second two equations represent the conditions of motion of the point along the corresponding characteristics. The above equations can be solved by a graphical method of numerical integration on the xt plane (Fig. 24.31). The problem for which the method is to be applied is: When V and c at the initial instant $t = 0$ are given, find V and c at $t > 0$.

At $t = 0$, the condition may be approximated by a series of points on the x axis (Fig. 24.31a) a small distance Δx apart. At all these points V and c are known. Con-

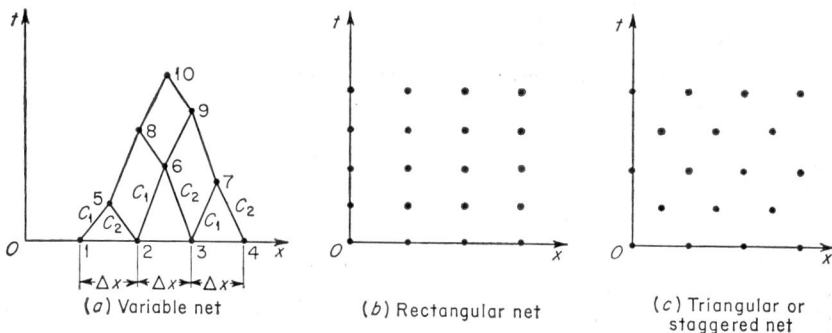

(a) Variable net   (b) Rectangular net   (c) Triangular or staggered net

Fig. 24.31. Net points used in method of characteristics.

sequently, the slopes of the characteristics C_1 and C_2 at these points are known from Eqs. (24.105) and (24.106). From the points 1, 2, 3, and 4, straight-line segments, approximating the actually curved segments, with these slopes are drawn until they intersect at points 5, 6, and 7. The values of x and t at these points of intersection are now known.

Along any particular segment issuing from the points 1, 2, 3, or 4, the constants in Eqs. (24.107) and (24.108) should satisfy the initial conditions and can therefore be determined from the values of V and c at $t = 0$. Consequently, Eqs. (24.107) and (24.108) will furnish two independent linear equations for the determination of V and c at each of the points 5, 6, and 7, since the values of t at these points are known.

Once V and c are known at points 5, 6, and 7, the slopes of the characteristics issuing from these points can be determined again from Eqs. (24.105) and (24.106). Thus the entire process of computation can be carried out similarly to produce the required information at points 8 and 9. In this way, the values of V and c at the points forming a net over a certain region of the xt plane can be approximately determined. The values of V and c at other points within the region can also be determined simply by interpolation.

In the above procedure, the net of points in the xt plane at which the solution is to be approximated is determined only gradually in the course of computation. Hence it is necessary to calculate not only the values of the unknown functions V and c, but also the values of the coordinates x, t of the net points themselves. In order to simplify the procedure, a *fixed net* in the xt plane (Fig. 24.31b and c) may be adopted for which the points may produce either fixed rectangles or triangles (staggered). Thus the procedure is required only to calculate values of V and c for the fixed values of x and t. For a comprehensive discussion of this subject, the reader should refer to the treatise on water waves by Stoker.[5]

UNSTEADY RAPIDLY VARIED FLOW

24.23. Rapidly Varied Uniformly Progressive Flow

When the front of a monoclinal rising wave has an abrupt change in curvature or a sudden change in depth, the flow in the front is rapidly varied. This effect may be produced, for example, by the sudden lift of a sluice gate in a channel (Fig. 24.32). This type of flow is known as a *surge*. The absolute wave velocity of the surge thus produced is

$$V_w = \sqrt{\frac{(A_2\bar{y}_2 - A_1\bar{y}_1)g}{A_1(1 - A_1/A_2)}} + V_1 \qquad (24.109)$$

in which A_1 and A_2 are the flow areas, and $\bar{y}_1$ and $\bar{y}_2$ are the centroidal depths of the areas before and after the wave front, respectively. The first term on the right side of the above equation represents the celerity of the wave, or

$$c = \sqrt{\frac{(A_2\bar{y}_2 - A_1\bar{y}_1)g}{A_1(1 - A_1/A_2)}} \qquad (24.110)$$

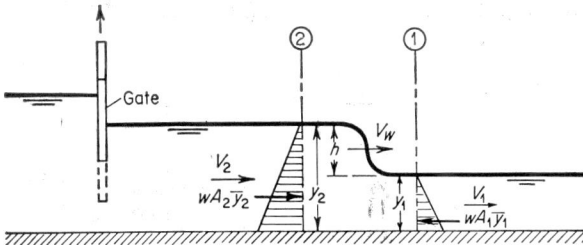

Fig. 24.32. Generation of a surge.

For rectangular channels,

$$c = \sqrt{\frac{gy_2}{2y_1}(y_1 + y_2)} \qquad (24.111)$$

Therefore Eq. (24.109) may be written

$$V_w = c + V_1 \qquad (24.112)$$

In general, there are four types of surge (Fig. 24.33): (A) positive surge moving downstream, (B) positive surge moving upstream, (C) negative surge moving downstream, and (D) negative surge moving upstream. The positive surges are *advancing* from a high to low stage of flow, whereas the negative surges are *retreating* from a low to high stage of flow. For all surges, the following may be written:

$$V_w = c \pm V_1 \qquad (24.113)$$

in which the positive sign is for surges moving downstream and the negative sign is for surges moving upstream or opposite to the direction of flow. For all types of surges, examples can be given. The flood wave front produced by the failure of a dam is of type A surge; the hydraulic bore in tidal rivers is usually of type B surge; the surge in power canals due to a sudden decrease in supply is of type C surge; and the surge in power canals due to a sudden increase in demand is of type D surge. For an extensive treatment of surges in navigation and power canals, the reader should refer to the work by Rich.[23]

24.24. Positive Surges

From Eqs. (24.100) and (24.113), the following may be written for positive surges in rectangular channels:

$$(V_1 - V_2)^2 = (y_1 - y_2)^2 \frac{(y_1 + y_2)g}{2y_1 y_2} \qquad (24.114)$$

This equation represents the relationship among the initial and final velocities and depths of the surge. By Eq. (24.111), the above equation may be reduced to

$$V_1 - V_2 = \pm \frac{h}{c} \frac{y_1 + y_2}{2y_1} g \qquad (24.115)$$

in which $h = y_2 - y_1$, or the height of surge. The positive sign applies to type B surges; the negative sign to type A surges.

When h is small compared with the depth of flow, Eq. (24.115) becomes

$$V_1 - V_2 = \pm \frac{hg}{c} \qquad (24.116)$$

Surge Due to Sudden Stoppage of Flow. If water flowing in a rectangular channel with a uniform-flow velocity V is checked instantaneously, a surge of type B will be produced. From Eq. (24.115), the height of the surge is

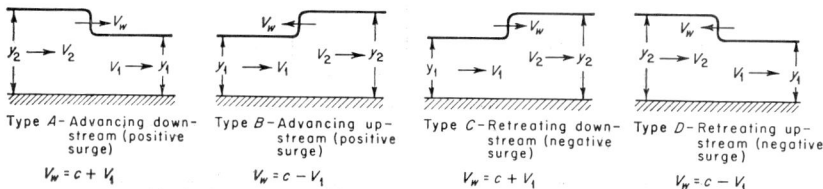

Type A - Advancing downstream (positive surge)
$V_w = c + V_1$

Type B - Advancing upstream (positive surge)
$V_w = c - V_1$

Type C - Retreating downstream (negative surge)
$V_w = c + V_1$

Type D - Retreating upstream (negative surge)
$V_w = c - V_1$

Fig. 24.33. Types of surge.

$$h = \frac{c}{g}\frac{2y_1}{y_1 + y_2} V \qquad (24.117)$$

When h is small,

$$h = \frac{c}{g} V \qquad (24.118)$$

Meeting of Two Surges. When two surges meet in opposite directions in a rectangular channel, the result is the generation of two new surges traveling in the reversed directions (Fig. 24.34). The final velocity V and depth y of flow at the section of meeting may be determined by applying Eq. (24.114) to the new surges and solving the equations simultaneously. The absolute wave velocities of the new surges can be found to be

$$V_w = \frac{V_1 y_1 - V y}{y - y_1} \qquad (24.119)$$

and

$$V'_w = \frac{V'_1 y'_1 + V y}{y - y'_1} \qquad (24.120)$$

The notation is shown in Fig. 24.34.

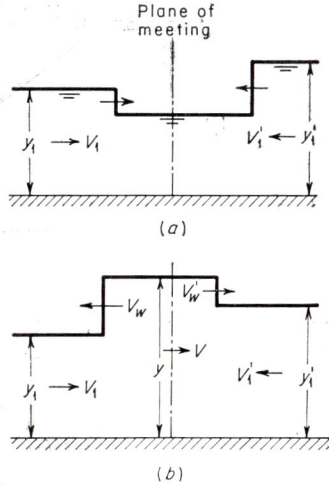

Fig. 24.34. Meeting of two surges.

Surge Crossing a Step or Friction Barrier. In surge analysis, the slope of the channel bottom and the channel friction may be simulated by a step or a friction barrier, respectively. Two new surges will be produced if a surge crosses a step or a friction barrier (Fig. 24.35). The velocities and depths of the new surges may be determined by Eq. (24.114) in a simultaneous solution with the following continuity equations:

Geometric continuity: $y_2 + F = y'_2$ (24.121)

Hydraulic continuity: $V_2 y_2 = V'_2 y'_2$ (24.122)

The wave velocities can be determined by Eq. (24.100).

24.25. Negative Surges

The negative surge may be analyzed by the principle of momentum. The velocity at any point on the wave profile can be shown to be

$$V = V_2 + 2\sqrt{gy_2} - 2\sqrt{gy} \qquad (24.123)$$

and the wave velocity

$$V_w - \sqrt{gy} \qquad V \qquad (24.124)$$

The notation is given in Fig. 24.36.

It should be noted that the negative surges do not maintain a steep wave front as the positive surges do. If the initial profile of a negative surge has a steep front, it will soon flatten out as the surge moves through the channel.

24.26. Surge through Transitions

When a surge arrives at a channel transition, it will split into two new surges, one traveling

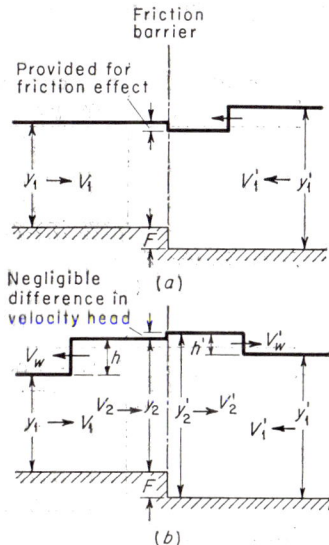

Fig. 24.35. Surge crossing a step or a friction barrier.

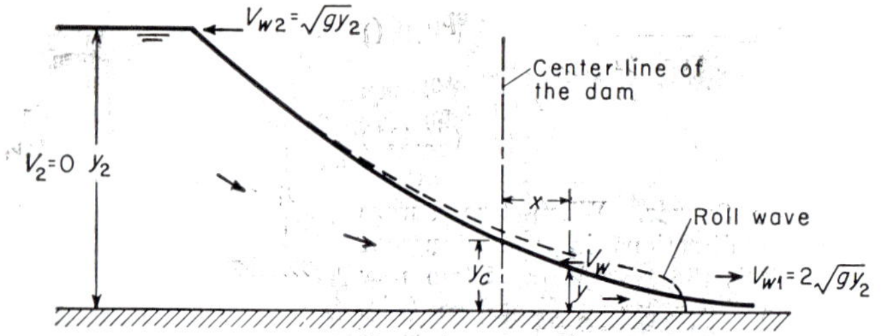

FIG. 24.36. Analysis of a negative surge.

upstream and one downstream. For surges of small height, the following simplified equations with reference to Fig. 24.37 may be written:

$$h_2 = \frac{2T_1 c_1}{T_1 c_1 + T_2 c_2} h_1 \tag{24.125}$$

and

$$h_3 = \frac{T_1 c_1 - T_2 c_2}{T_1 c_1 + T_2 c_2} h_1 \tag{24.126}$$

in which T is the top width of surge, h is the surge height, and c is the celerity. The subscript 1 refers to the initial surge arriving at the transition. Subscripts 2 and 3 refer to the new surges.

The ratio of the height of the reflected new surge to the height of the initial surge is known as the *reflection coefficient* C_r, or

$$C_r = \frac{h_3}{h_1} = \frac{c_1 - nc_2}{c_1 + nc_2} \tag{24.127}$$

in which $n = T_2/T_1$. It can be shown that $C_r = 1$ for a dead-end barrier in the channel, $C_r = 0$ for no transition, and $C_r = -1$ for an outlet to a large body of liquid. Thus $C_r > 0$ indicates a contraction, whereas $C_r < 0$ indicates an expansion.

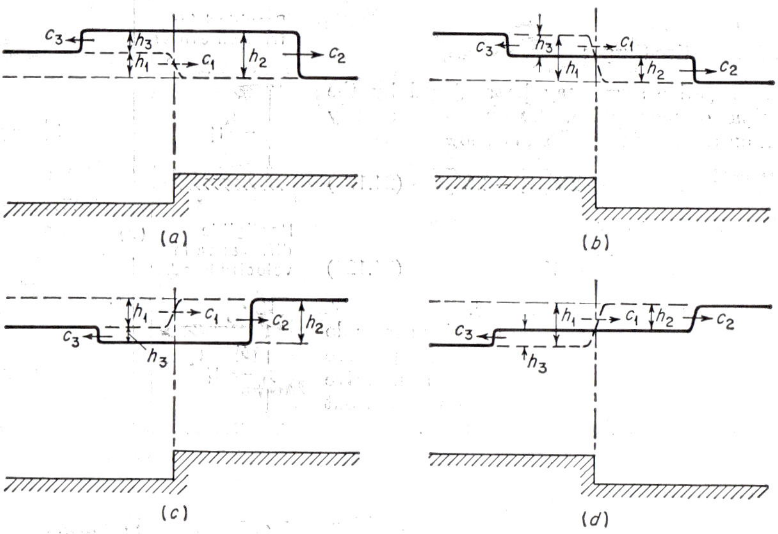

FIG. 24.37. Surge through transitions.

SPATIALLY VARIED FLOW

24.27. Continuity Equation

When a supplementary discharge at a rate of $\partial Q_*/\partial x$ is added to or taken off from an unsteady open-channel flow along the length of the channel, the continuity equation is

$$\frac{\partial Q}{\partial x} + \frac{\partial Q_*}{\partial x} + \frac{\partial A}{\partial t} = 0 \qquad (24.128)$$

When the rate $\partial Q_*/\partial x$ is constant and equal to q_* per unit length of the channel,

$$\frac{\partial Q}{\partial x} + \frac{\partial A}{\partial t} + q_* = 0 \qquad (24.129)$$

For steady spatially varied flow with a constant supplementary discharge, the continuity equation is

$$\frac{\partial Q}{\partial x} + q_* = 0 \qquad (24.130)$$

24.28. Spatially Varied Flow with an Increasing Discharge

In this type of flow, such as the flow in a lateral spillway channel, it may be found that an appreciable portion of energy loss is due to the turbulent mixing between the added discharge and the flow in the channel. For the analysis of the flow, the principle of momentum may be conveniently applied. For a constant supplementary discharge added to a prismatic channel, the following dynamic equation can be established:

$$\frac{dy}{dx} = \frac{S_0 - S_f - 2\alpha Q q_*/gA^2}{1 - Q^2/gA^2 D} \qquad (24.131)$$

The notation used in this equation has been defined previously.

For the purpose of practical design, Hinds[24] has developed a method of numerical integration by which the channel length under consideration is divided into a number of short reaches and the computation is made by steps from reach to reach. The dynamic equation used in this method may be written for the drop in flow surface in the reach as

$$\Delta y' = \frac{\alpha Q_1(V_1 + V_2)}{g(Q_1 + Q_2)}\left(\Delta V + \frac{V_2}{Q_1}\Delta Q\right) + S_f\,\Delta x \qquad (24.132)$$

in which Δx is the length of the reach, ΔV is the change in velocity, and $\Delta Q = Q_2 - Q_1 = q_*\Delta x$. The subscripts are referred to the end sections of the reach. By computing the drop in flow surface from reach to reach, using Eq. (24.132), the entire flow profile of the spatially varied flow in the channel can be determined.

24.29. Spatially Varied Flow with a Decreasing Discharge

In this type of flow, such as the flow over a side weir, the energy head in the channel is practically unaffected by the diversion of the flow from the channel. Consequently, the principle of energy can be conveniently used for the analysis of flow characteristics. For a constant supplementary discharge diverted from a prismatic channel, the following equation can be written:

$$\frac{dy}{dx} = \frac{S_0 - S_f - \alpha Q q_*/gA^2}{1 - Q^2/gA^2 D} \qquad (24.133)$$

It may be noted that this equation differs from Eq. (24.131) only in a coefficient of 2.

For the purpose of practical design, Nimmo[25] has developed a method of numerical integration similar to that developed by Hinds for flow with increasing discharge. The equation used in this method for the drop in flow surface in each reach may be written as

$$\Delta y' = \frac{\alpha Q_1 (V_1 + V_2)\, \Delta V}{g(Q_1 + Q_2)} \left(1 - \frac{\Delta Q}{2Q_1} \right) + S_f\, \Delta x \qquad (24.134)$$

This equation, similar to Eq. (24.132), may be used to compute the flow profile.

24.30. Examples

Example 3. A horizontal rectangular lateral-spillway channel has a free-overfall outlet. The inflow is uniformly distributed along the channel with a rate of q_* per unit length of the channel. Derive the equation of the flow profile, ignoring the friction loss.

SOLUTION. For the given condition, Eq. (24.131) yields

$$\frac{dx^2}{dy} - \frac{x^2}{y} = -\frac{gb^2 y^2}{q_*^2} \qquad (24.135)$$

After solving this differential equation and by determining the integration constant from the fact that at the outlet $x = L$, $y = y_o$, and the flow is critical, the equation of the flow profile may be written as

$$\left(\frac{x}{L} \right)^2 = \frac{3}{2}\frac{y}{y_o} - \frac{1}{2}\left(\frac{y}{y_o} \right)^3 \qquad (24.136)$$

Example 4. Analyze the flow in a rectangular channel of small slope with a bottom rack (Fig. 24.38).

SOLUTION. The friction loss in this problem is negligible, or $S_f = 0$. For $\alpha = 1$ and $S_0 = 0$, Eq. (24.133) gives

$$\frac{dy}{dx} = -\frac{Qy(dQ/dx)}{gb^2 y^3 - Q^2} \qquad (24.137)$$

in which b is the channel width and $dQ/dx = q_*$, which is the discharge withdrawn per unit length of the rack. Mostkow[26] found that the flow condition may be of two kinds:

1. *For vertical flow through the rack.* In this case, such as for racks composed of parallel bars, the effective head is practically equal to the specific energy E, and therefore the discharge per unit length of the rack may be expressed by

$$-\frac{dQ}{dx} = \epsilon c b \sqrt{2gE} \qquad (24.138)$$

in which ϵ is the ratio of the opening area to the total area of the rack surface, and c is the coefficient of discharge through the openings. Determining the integration constant for $x = 0$ and $y = y_1$, a solution of Eqs. (24.137) and (24.138) gives the equation of flow profile:

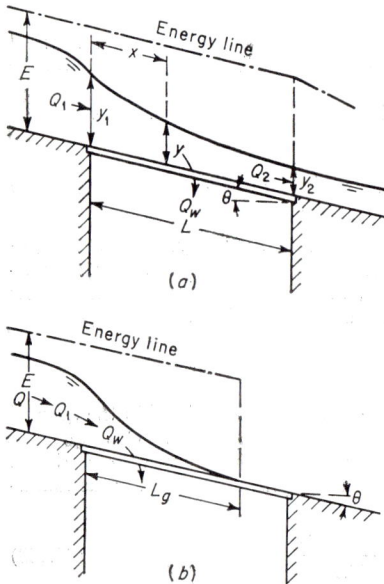

FIG. 24.38. Flow through a bottom rack.

$$x = \frac{E}{\epsilon c}\left(\frac{y_1}{E}\sqrt{1 - \frac{y_1}{E}} - \frac{y}{E}\sqrt{1 - \frac{y}{E}}\right) \tag{24.139}$$

When $y = 0$, the above equation will give the length of the rack required for a complete withdrawal of the flow, or

$$L_g = \frac{Q}{\epsilon c b \sqrt{2gE}} \tag{24.140}$$

where Q is the total discharge as shown in Fig. 24.38.

2. *For inclined flow through the rack.* In this case, such as racks composed of a perforated screen, the energy is approximately equal to the velocity head of the flow over the rack, and therefore the discharge per unit length of the rack may be expressed by

$$-\frac{dQ}{dx} = \epsilon c b \sqrt{2gy} \tag{24.141}$$

A solution of Eqs. (24.137) and (24.141) gives the equation of flow profile as

$$x = \frac{E}{\epsilon c}\left[\frac{1}{2}\cos^{-1}\sqrt{\frac{y}{E}} - \frac{3}{2}\sqrt{\frac{y}{E}\left(1 - \frac{y}{E}\right)}\right] + \text{const} \tag{24.142}$$

The integration constant may be determined from the condition that $y = y_1$ for $x = 0$. The length required for a complete withdrawal of the discharge is

$$L_g = \frac{E}{\epsilon c}\left[\frac{3}{2}\sqrt{\frac{y_1}{E}\left(1 - \frac{y_1}{E}\right)} - \frac{1}{4}\sin^{-1}\left(1 - \frac{2y_1}{E}\right) + \frac{\pi}{8}\right] \tag{24.143}$$

Example 5. Determine the flow profile along a side weir of rectangular-notch type in a prismatic horizontal rectangular channel.

SOLUTION. The discharge over any length of the weir can be computed by a weir formula, or

$$-\frac{dQ}{dx} = c\sqrt{2g}(y - s)^{1.5} \tag{24.144}$$

in which c is the discharge coefficient, and s is the height of the weir sill above the bottom of the channel. Assuming a constant specific energy, the discharge at any section of the channel is

$$Q = by\sqrt{2g(E - y)} \tag{24.145}$$

in which b is the width of the section. A solution of Eqs. (24.137), (24.144), and (24.145) gives the equation of flow profile as

$$x = \frac{b}{c}F\left(\frac{y}{E}\right) + \text{const} \tag{24.146}$$

with

$$F\left(\frac{y}{E}\right) = \frac{2E - 3s}{E - s}\sqrt{\frac{E - y}{y - s}} - 3\sin^{-1}\sqrt{\frac{E - y}{y - s}} \tag{24.147}$$

The integration constant in Eq. (24.146) may be determined from the given flow condition.

AIR-ENTRAINED FLOW

24.31. Flow Instability

Under certain conditions, such as when the slope of a channel is very steep, the free surface of a flow will become unstable, that is, wavy and ill-defined. Eventually, when a certain limiting condition is reached or the boundary layer is increased to reach the flow surface, the flow may be self-aerated or mixed with air, resulting in an *air-entrained flow*.

The instability of a free surface may be assumed to develop because of a sharp curvature of the streamlines. The pressure head caused by the centrifugal force due to the curvature may be expressed by

$$h_{cuv} = \frac{\gamma}{g} \frac{d}{dx} \left(v^2 y \frac{d^2y}{dx^2} \right) \tag{24.148}$$

in which γ is a coefficient, and v is the streamline velocity. Boussinesq[27] assumed a linear variation of the curvature with respect to the depth and found that $\gamma = \frac{1}{3}$. Adding this head to the left side of Eq. (24.45), assuming Chézy's formula for uniform flow, and letting $j = y/y_n - 1$, in which y_n is the normal depth, it can be shown that

$$\frac{d^3j}{dx^3} + \frac{\alpha y_n}{\gamma} \left(\frac{1}{y_c{}^3} - \frac{1}{y_n{}^3} \right) \frac{dj}{dx} - \frac{3g}{\gamma C^2 y_n{}^3} j = 0 \tag{24.149}$$

in which C is Chézy's resistance factor, and y_c is the critical depth. Let

$$p = \frac{\alpha y_n}{3\gamma} \left(\frac{1}{y_c{}^3} - \frac{1}{y_n{}^3} \right) \quad \text{and} \quad q = \frac{3g}{2\gamma C^2 y_n{}^3}$$

The general solution of Eq. (24.149) is

$$j = C_1 \exp (m_1 x) + C_2 \exp (m_2 x) + C_3 \exp (m_3 x) \tag{24.150}$$

in which m_1, m_2, and m_3 are the roots of the equation

$$m^3 + 3pm - 2q = 0 \tag{24.151}$$

In the case of subcritical flow, $p > 0$, $q < 0$, and $q^2 + p^3 > 0$, the equation has one real root and a pair of complex roots. Accordingly, j may have a mathematically periodic solution and a wavy free surface is possible.

In the case of supercritical flow, $p < 0$, $q > 0$. As long as the difference between y_c and y_n is small and $q^2 + p^3 > 0$, a wavy free surface is possible. If the channel slope is large and the difference between y_c and y_n is large, or $q^2 + p^3 < 0$, a wavy free surface is impossible because Eq. (24.151) is a mathematically irreducible case.

In view of the above discussion, it seems that the free surface is stable in supercritical flow if the discharge is kept constant and the Froude number is large. However, there is a limiting condition above which a supercritical flow of large Froude number may be unstable because the flow becomes unsteady. This limiting condition may be theoretically determined by the *Vedernikov*[28] *number* **V**:

$$\mathbf{V} = xf\mathbf{F} \tag{24.152}$$

in which x = exponent in Eq. (24.30)
   $\mathbf{F}$ = Froude number
   f = a shape factor of channel section defined by

$$f = 1 - R \frac{dP}{dA} \tag{24.153}$$

in which R = hydraulic radius
   P = wetted perimeter
   A = flow area

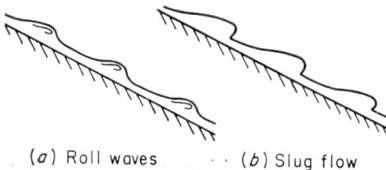

(*a*) Roll waves   (*b*) Slug flow

Fig. 24.39. Development of instability of flow.

When $\mathbf{V} < 1$, any wave in the channel will be depressed and the flow can be stable. But when $\mathbf{V} > 1$, waves will be amplified so that stable flow becomes impossible and unsteady flow prevails. According to Vedernikov's criterion, when $1 \leq$

F < 2, *roll waves* characterized by transverse ridges of high vorticity (Fig. 24.39*a*) will form. When **F** > 2, *slug flow* will form, characterized by surges of turbulent ridges with wave crests separated by highly agitated regions (Fig. 24.39*b*). When **F** > 3.5, air entrainment will generally occur. It should be noted, however, that the above theory is only approximate, since the problem of flow instability involves many uncertain factors which are yet to be determined.

24.32. Characteristics of Air-entrained Flow

When a high-velocity open-channel flow is air-entrained, the air is mixed with the liquid at a concentration increasing continuously from the bed to the free surface. The air concentration varies with a smooth transition from a finite value near the bed to a maximum value of 100 per cent at the free surface, which value is approached asymptotically (Fig. 24.40).

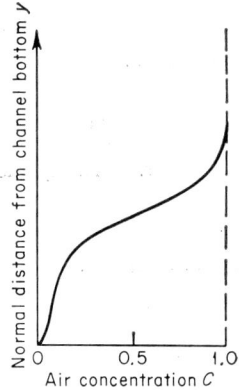

FIG. 24.40. Air concentration in air-entrained flow.

The air-entrained flow appears to consist of two distinct regions (Fig. 24.41): a lower region where air bubbles are entrained in liquid and an upper region where liquid particles are entrained in the air. Between the two regions are intermediate layers of flow, where crests of small waves separate liquid drops from air bubbles successively. Viparelli,[29] using a special pitot tube to make the measurement of a head δ across the flow section (Fig. 24.41), found that δ_{max} occurs at a transition depth y_t, which approximately separates the upper and lower regions.

In the upper region of the flow, the number of liquid drops and the liquid discharge per unit area are found to distribute in accordance with the Gaussian law of normal probability. Straub and Anderson[30] have shown theoretically that the gradient of concentration in the region is

$$\frac{dC}{dy} = \frac{2(1 - C_t)}{y\sqrt{\pi}} \exp\left[-\left(\frac{y'}{y}\right)^2\right] \qquad (24.154)$$

in which C = air concentration defined as the percentage of volume of air per unit
         volume of air-liquid mixture
       C_t = concentration at depth y_t
       y = normal distance from channel bottom
       y' = outward normal distance above depth y_t

According to Viparelli,[29] the discharge of liquid per unit area of upper region may be expressed by

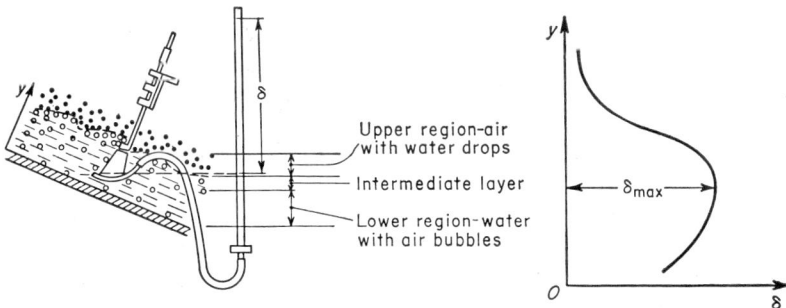

FIG. 24.41. Distribution of air and water in air-entrained flow. (*After M. Viparelli.*[29])

$$q = V \exp\left(-\frac{1}{2} \frac{y - y_t}{\sigma \delta_{\max}} \right) \tag{24.155}$$

in which V is the velocity of flow, and σ is a coefficient. For water as the liquid, experimental values of σ are between 0.0018 and 0.0025.

In the lower region of flow the distribution of the air agrees closely with an equation for turbulent mixing on the basis of an approximation for the distribution of the mixing parameter. This equation may be written as

$$\frac{dC}{dy} = \frac{-CV_b}{\epsilon_b} \tag{24.156}$$

in which C = air concentration at a normal distance y from the bed
  V_b = rising velocity of air bubbles
  ϵ_b = a mixing parameter for the air-bubble transfer

Assuming ϵ_b proportional to the mixing parameter as in momentum transfer, the following can be approximated:

$$\epsilon_b = \beta k \sqrt{\frac{\tau_0}{\rho}} \frac{y_t - y}{y_t} y \tag{24.157}$$

in which β = proportionality factor
  k = von Kármán universal constant
  $\sqrt{\tau_0/\rho}$ = shear velocity, in which τ_0 = boundary shear at the bed, and ρ = density of fluid

The law of flow in the lower region can be represented by a uniform-flow equation in the form of Eq. (24.30) or an equivalent law.[31] For example, when the transitional depth is taken as the hydraulic radius and the *mean depth* of a corresponding nonaerated flow is used in computing the flow area, the discharge of liquid can be computed by the Chézy equation involving approximately the same resistance factor as would be applied to nonaerated flow in the same channel. The mean depth of a corresponding non-aerated flow is the average depth that would exist if all the entrained air were removed up to the highest point where water is found. It therefore corresponds to the depth of a nonaerated flow of a given discharge with a velocity equal to that of the entrained flow. Mathematically, it may be defined as

$$\bar{y} = \int_0^\infty (1 - C)\, dy \tag{24.158}$$

in which y is the normal distance from the bed, and C is the concentration of air as a function of y.

REFERENCES

1. Robertson, J. M., and Hunter Rouse: On the Four Regimes of Open-Channel Flow, *Civil Eng.*, **11**(3):169–171 (1941).
2. Chow, Ven Te: "Open-channel Hydraulics," McGraw-Hill, New York, 1959.
3. Jaeger, Charles: "Engineering Fluid Mechanics," transl. from the German by P. O. Wolf, Blackie, London and Glasgow, 1956.
4. Thomas, H. A.: The Hydraulics of Flood Movements in Rivers, *Carnegie Inst. Technol. Eng. Bull.*, 1937.
5. Stoker, J. J.: Water Waves, in vol. 4, "Pure and Applied Mathematics," Interscience, New York, 1957.
6. Serre, François: Contribution à l'étude des écoulements permanents et variables dans les canaux, *La houille blanche*, no. 3, pp. 374–388, and no. 6, pp. 830–872, 1953.
7. Massé, Pierre: Ressaut et ligne d'eau dans les cours d'eau à pente variable, *Rev. gén. hydraulique*, **4**(19):7–11, (20):61–64, 1938.
8. Escoffier, Francis F.: Transition Profiles in Nonuniform Channels, *Trans. ASCE*, **123**:43–56 (1958).
9. von Kármán, T., and M. A. Biot: "Mathematical Methods in Engineering," pp. 150–158, McGraw-Hill, New York, 1940.

10. Bakhmeteff, B. A.: "Hydraulics of Open Channels," McGraw-Hill, New York, 1932.
11. Keifer, C. J., and H. H. Chu: Backwater Functions by Numerical Integration, *Trans. ASCE*, **120**:429–442 (1955).
12. Hom-ma, Masashi: "General Hydraulics," vol. 1, pp. 108–111, of "Applied Hydraulics," ed. by M. Hom-ma and T. Ishihara, Maruzen, Tokyo, 1958. (In Japanese.)
13. Studies of Crests for Overfall Dams, *Boulder Canyon Project Final Repts.*, pt. 6, *U.S. Bur. Reclamation, Hydraulic Invests. Bull.* 3, 1948.
14. Bradley, J. N., and A. F. Peterka: The Hydraulic Design of Stilling Basins, *Proc. ASCE, Papers* 1401, 1402, 1403, 1404, 1405, and 1406, **83**(HY5):1–24, 1–14, 1–22, 1–20, 1–32, and 1–17. October, 1957.
15. Elevatorski, E. A.: "Hydraulic Energy Dissipators," McGraw-Hill, New York, 1959.
16. Shukry, A.: Flow around Bends in an Open Flume, *Trans. ASCE*, **115**:751–779 (1950).
17. High-velocity Flow in Open Channels: A Symposium, *Trans. ASCE*, **116**:265–400 (1951). (This symposium consists of Mechanics of Supercritical Flow, by A. T. Ippen; Design of Channel Curves for Supercritical Flow, by R. T. Knapp; Design of Channel Transitions, by A. T. Ippen and J. H. Dawson; and Design of Channel Expansions, by Hunter Rouse, B. V. Bhoota, and En-Yun Hsu.)
18. von Kármán, T.: Eine praktische Anwendung der Analogie zwischen Uberscallströmung in Gasen und überkritischer Strömung in offenen Gerinnen, *Z. ange. Math. Mech.*, **18**:49–56 (February, 1958).
19. Busemann, A.: "Gasdynamik," vol. 4, part 1, in "Handbuch der Experimentalphysik," pp. 423–440, Akadem. Verlag G.m.b.H., Berlin, 1931.
20. Rouse, Hunter: "Fluid Mechanics for Hydraulic Engineers," McGraw-Hill, New York, 1938.
21. Preiswerk, Ernst: Anwendung gasdynamischer Methoden auf Wasserströmungen mit freier Oberfläche, *Eidgenoss. Tech. Hochschule Zürich, Mitt. Inst. Aerodynamik*, no. 7, 1938. (English transl. by S. Reiss, *NACA Tech. Mem.* 934 and 935, March, 1940).
22. Gilcrest, B. R.: Flood Routing, chap. 10, pp. 635–710, in H. Rouse (ed.), "Engineering Hydraulics," Wiley, New York, 1950.
23. Rich, G. R.: "Hydraulic Transients," McGraw-Hill, New York, 1951.
24. Hinds, Julian: Side Channel Spillways, *Trans. ASCE*, **89**:881–927 (1926).
25. Nimmo, W. H. R.: Side Spillways for Regulating Diversion Canals, *Trans. ASCE*, **92**:1561–1584 (1928).
26. Mostkow, M. A.: Sur le calcul des grilles de prise d'eau, *La houille blanche*, no. 4, pp. 570–580, September, 1957.
27. Boussinesq, J.: Essai sur la théorie des eaux courants, *Mém. presentés par divers savants à l'Acad. Sci.*, Paris, **23**:1–680 (1877); **24**(2) (1878).
28. Powell, R. W.: Vedernikov's Criterion for Ultrarapid Flow, *Trans. AGU*, **29**(6):882–886 (1948). Discussions by V. V. Vedernikov and R. W. Powell, *ibid.*, **32**(4):603–607 (1951).
29. Viparelli, M.: Fast Water Flow in Steep Channels, *Proc. Intern. Assoc. Hydraulic Research*, **2**:(D39)1–39 (1957).
30. Straub, L. G., and A. G. Anderson: Experiments on Self-aerated Flow in Open Channels, *Proc., ASCE*, **84**(HY7), pt. 1:1–35 (December, 1958).
31. Keulegan, G. H.: Laws of Turbulent Flow in Open Channels, *Natl. Bur. Standards (U.S.) Research Paper* RP1151, *J. Research Natl. Bur. Standards (U.S.)*, **21**:707–741 (1936).

Section 25

THE DIGITAL COMPUTER
FOR FLUID-FLOW CALCULATIONS

By

BERNARD A. GALLER, *University of Michigan, Ann Arbor, Michigan*
FRANK H. WESTERVELT, *University of Michigan, Ann Arbor, Michigan*

THE DIGITAL COMPUTER FOR FLUID-FLOW CALCULATIONS

25.1. Introduction

Relatively recent developments in the field of automatic digital computation have made it possible for a person to express problems for the machine in familiar mathematical and logical language. The translation of this language into machine instructions so that the desired process may be carried out is done by the machine through the use of *translator* programs. The present section serves to introduce the reader to the basic concepts of machine-computation systems, flow diagrams, and a typical translator language similar to most present translator languages. Several examples of problems common to fluid mechanics and allied fields are given to illustrate the use of the flow diagram and the translator language. It may be of interest to those readers who are not presently acquainted with these techniques of programming digital computers to know that sophomore-level students at the University of Michigan with no prior knowledge of computers have been taught to write quite difficult problems for the machine in less than six hours of instruction.

25.2. General Computation System Structure

Elements of a Computation System. The solution of problems involves a *computation system*. The system that solves the problem may consist of a common structure that is quite independent of the methods or techniques employed in the solution. The elements of a computation system are shown diagrammatically in Fig. 25.1. There are two levels within the computation system. The *control* occupies the higher level and communicates instructions, directions, and decisions directly to each of the four elements on the lower level. The control may receive information from the *storage*, or *memory*, but since control directs the other units, they may be directed to pass information into storage and thereby complete the return of information to control.

On the lower level one finds four elements:

1. *Input* consists of those devices capable of receiving data and instructions from the world external to the computation system. Input transmits this information under the direction of control to storage.

2. *Output* consists of those devices capable of transmitting data and instructions, which occur as a result of the computation system operation, to the external world. Depending upon the format required by the user, output produces results in the desired language. For example, the output may occur in the familiar decimal notation even though the computation system may operate in binary if the system converts the binary to decimal before passing the results to output. On the other hand, it may be more convenient for some purposes (e.g., discovering errors) to receive the results in some other form (e.g., octal numbers) and the output may be directed to produce this format alternatively. Most of the larger machines also

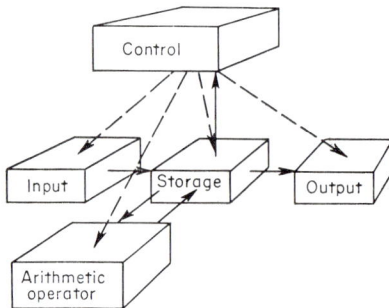

FIG. 25.1. Diagram of computation system structure. (The solid lines indicate paths followed by data words or instruction words. The dashed lines indicate the lines of control.)

allow the printing of alphabetic material as well. This facility contributes greatly to the readability of the printed output.

3. *Storage,* or *memory,* consists of all those devices that retain data and instructions in a manner that is accessible to the control and to the other units as needed. It might be noted that the storage constitutes a vital link in the structure. Every other unit communicates with storage, some units passing information both to and from storage.

Storage, as used here, includes devices that have varying speeds of accessibility. For example, the storage of information in magnetic cores may provide very high-speed access while the same information written on magnetic tapes is accessible at a much lower speed. This may be compared roughly with a memorized multiplication table for high-speed access, and a reference table of logarithms that can be used for multiplication but which has a much lower speed of access. This analogy also serves to indicate that the more voluminous materials are not usually retained in high-speed memory.

4. *Arithmetic operator* designates those devices that perform arithmetic, in a very general sense, upon both data and instructions. The arithmetic operator uses storage for the source of the material to be worked on and returns partial results and the final answers to storage. The operations to be performed are selected by control. These operations commonly include the ordinary arithmetic operations (addition, subtraction, multiplication, division) and usually a few more, such as shifting, complementing, floating-point arithmetic, rounding, logical operations such as the "and" and the "or," and many others, depending on the machine.

Human Computation System. To clarify the nature of the computation system structure and the duties required of the various elements, a familiar example may be considered: a human being, pencil and paper, desk calculator, and a reference table of logarithms. This computation system is to perform the process of raising an arbitrary real number x to an arbitrary power p. It is assumed, for simplicity, that the system has previously been instructed as to the performance of simple arithmetic and table look-up. No assumption is made that the system has any previous knowledge of the process of exponentiation that is desired.

First of all, the desired sequence of operations must be communicated to the system. In this case, the senses of sight, hearing, etc., are utilized to explain the process. This is *programming* the system. Note that nothing may be left to chance. Each possible case must be described, and the desired actions detailed in each instance. For example, suppose that the exponentiation is to occur by the following steps:

1. Given x, find the logarithm of x in the reference table. Note that the program must include suitable instructions as to the proper response if $x \leq 0$. Further, instructions must be given on the procedure to follow if x is not one of the tabulated values (i.e., interpolation).

2. Multiply the logarithm of x by the exponent p.

3. Find the antilogarithm of this product in the table (e.g., by inverse interpolation) and express the result in some desired format.

Some of the small points that must be included in our instructions have been observed. If special treatment is desired in certain cases, these must also be included. In this problem, if $p = 0.0$, the solution should be written immediately. Also, if p is an integer, some other procedure, such as a cascaded multiplication, may be used. (Cascaded multiplication is a process for generating large-integer powers p of a number without resorting to the method of multiplying the number by itself p times.) For example, x^{17} may be generated in the following way:

Step 1: $x^2 = x \cdot x$
Step 2: $x^4 = x^2 \cdot x^2$
Step 3: $x^8 = x^4 \cdot x^4$
Step 4: $x^{16} = x^8 \cdot x^8$
Step 5: $x^{17} = x^{16} \cdot x$

If these cases are to receive such treatment, however, it must be realized that the corresponding instructions must be given.

Now, if the instructed system is presented with a set of exponentiation problems, the system may proceed with the computation. The instructions that have been given to the human computation system will be largely retained in the brain, or *high-speed-access storage*. It is likely that some instructions will be retained on paper for reference. This storage has a lower speed access. Finally, the reference text contains the table of logarithms in still lower-speed-access storage. The set of problems is received on the problem paper through the input senses, and the first data set is loaded into the high-speed storage (the brain). Control (the brain) instructs the sequence of operations needed to check x to be sure that it is a value for which the solution procedure is valid. This check may be done on the desk calculator, with paper and pencil, or most likely it may be done mentally. In any case, the control directs the procedure. If x is a suitable value, control proceeds to direct the table look-up and interpolation, if needed, to obtain the logarithm of x. The human computation system could have been provided with a method for generating the logarithm of x from a truncated power-series expansion or, perhaps, a rational-function approximation. The choice of method was determined when the system was *programmed* and depended upon many factors, such as the speed, reliability, and accuracy of the possible methods.

The values of the logarithm may require interpolation, and control must recognize the cases that need such treatment. Control must also direct the interpolation process in the arithmetic operator. The multiplication by p and the inverse interpolation are also directed by control to produce the result of x to the pth power. Finally, control directs output to produce the result in whatever format was originally requested. The cycle is complete for the first data set, and the system returns to see if there are more such problems to work. Unlike the machine, it probably would not be necessary to instruct the human computation system to stop when there are no more problems. The real task is to keep the system in operation that long.

Machine Computation System. Even such a simple example as the one just presented indicates the complexity of the decision processes that are required in problem solutions. The digital computer can execute chains of instructions which are much more involved than our previous example. The problem of instructing the machine to execute these processes is the subject of Art. 25.3. The machine counterparts of the units of the human computation system are now examined.

Exactly the same types of elements are present, but the actual units are, of course, quite different. The phrase *internally stored program* has been used several times thus far and refers to the manner in which instructions are made accessible to the control. It is apparent that if a procedure is completely sequential with no possibility ever arising to transfer to instructions which are not directly in line, then a program could be stored externally and executed one instruction at a time. Nearly all calculations, even our relatively trivial exponentiation evaluations, are such that logical testing is done and the sequence of computations proceeds differently, depending upon the result of the test. In our example, the presence of negative values of x, together with certain nonintegral values of p, should cause an error halt, while other actions should proceed if these conditions do not hold. To allow the machine to *branch* (i.e., jump), even to earlier parts of the program, usually requires the instructions to be stored internally in the storage with unique locations, or *addresses*, assigned to each instruction.

The control unit is sometimes referred to as part of the *central processing unit* (CPU). This portion of the machine has the task of keeping track of which instruction is to be executed next, the decomposition of instructions into the operation, and various addresses, index registers, and so forth, that will be required to carry out the instruction, and the direction of the other units of the system in the execution of the instructions. These processes are carried out at very high speeds. Common practice now is of the order of 40,000 operations/sec with machines of 100 times that speed available in the near future.

The machine is instructed by loading the storage unit with instructions prepared, in some manner, externally and brought into the machine through the input device. The process of transmitting instructions and data from the external world into the storage commo   :curs through one or more of the following types of mechanisms:

1. Electric typewriters
2. Punched paper tape
3. Punched cards
4. Magnetic tape
5. Analogue to digital converters
6. Console switches on the machine

This list is by no means exhaustive, and great efforts are being expended currently in the area of input-output since conventional devices are extremely slow compared with the computation rate of the machine.   This area is rapidly improving, however, with current good practice now represented by the following approximate figures:

Paper tape.....................	1000 characters/sec read
Punched cards..................	2000 cards/min read
Magnetic tape.................	168,000 decimal digits/sec
High-speed printing.............	1000 lines/min

Most computers operate with less effective speeds of input-output than these.   Here the need for fast input-output is highly problem-dependent.

Storage occurs at a variety of access speeds just as in the case of the human.   It is currently the case that as the access time to obtain (or replace) a word in storage is reduced, the cost of the unit word in storage increases.   Thus the high-speed memory capacity is fairly limited.   The larger units today (1961) are of the order of 30,000 words in high-speed storage, with most units considerably smaller.   In these units the words are accessible in about 1.5 to 2 μsec from random locations.   The storage takes place in small ferromagnetic cores which are sensed electromagnetically.   Some other high-speed-storage devices include mercury delay lines and electrostatic cathode-ray tubes.   On a lower speed level one finds magnetic-drum and magnetic-tape storage. Here the decrease in access time is sometimes compensated by locating and transferring blocks of information, when needed, into the highest-speed memory available.   This is analogous to the use of reference tables in the previous example.

It is important to note at this point that the most satisfactory method of human solution of a problem is not always the best machine method.   The human computer using logarithms will usually refer to a table and interpolate, while the machine method most commonly employed in this case is the evaluation of a rational-function approximation for the logarithm.   The expansion in the series is more accurate and faster and does not require the storage of a table and is therefore well suited to a machine.

The arithmetic operator was mentioned briefly before when the elements of the computation system were discussed.   The exact nature of the arithmetic operator depends upon the machine in question.   The arithmetic operator may be a physical part of the central processing unit, which also includes the control.   There are certain advantages in the speed of processing and some saving in physical equipment possible when the combination is made.   The arithmetic operator includes one or more operating registers and, possibly, storage-buffer registers.   The operating registers are arranged to perform the desired arithmetic.   Addition and subtraction can be accomplished in a single register, sometimes referred to as the *accumulator*.   Multiplication and division require an additional register to hold the multiplier and receive the quotient; hence the term *multiplier-quotient* register is sometimes used.   These registers are also known by other names in different machines and function slightly differently as well.   Another fairly common designation refers to both registers as accumulators and differentiates between them with the terms upper accumulator and lower accumulator.   The problem of detection of over- and underflow of numbers is treated quite differently by the various machines.   Most machines provide nicely for the detection of overflow, and some even provide positions in the accumulator which will prevent the loss of information which has exceeded the normal word length.   Some machines also use the arithmetic operator during input-output as a storage buffer or loading register.   Considerable checking is also commonly carried out, and the arithmetic operator may be used to accumulate logical check sums during input and output.

25.3. Man-Machine Communication

The users of computers fall into two general groups, the professional programmers and the casual users, the latter group including research engineers, accountants, university faculty and students, and, in fact, everyone whose primary interest is the solution of a problem. The casual user does not particularly care how elegant the program of computer instructions is or how many seconds it runs on the machine, except as it is reflected in his bill. Generally, he is happy to have someone, even the computer, do most of the work for him, even to the writing of the program if it can be arranged. In particular, he does not want to spend many hours learning to communicate with the machine. It is very important for this person to have a language in which to describe to the computer his problem and its method of solution that is as close as possible to the language in which he himself expresses the problem. This language might be English, Russian, algebra, the notation of logic, or something else.

The professional programmer, on the other hand, produces programs that do the detailed clerical work that the casual user does not want to do. He writes programs to translate the English, Russian, etc., into the internal language of the computer, and therefore, while he is also "problem-oriented," his problems do not have a ready-made language available for their description. Moreover, since his programs will be used over and over a great many times, they must be as efficient as possible. He therefore takes pride in producing elegant, efficient programs, sometimes expending considerable time and energy to save three or four computer instructions in his program. Such a person needs to know a great many details about the machine and usually communicates with it by means of a very primitive code, quite different from the languages in which an engineer's problem would be stated.

The development of means of communication between the casual user and the computer is of interest. For him the philosophy has been to let the computer do more and more of the routine clerical work in instituting a program.

The users of the early machines had very little choice as to the language in which to write their programs of instructions. These early machines generally did not accept alphabetic characters, and one simply knew that if 32 was the code for "clear the accumulator and add" and if 31 was the code for "add" and 20 was the code for "store," then the way to add the numbers in storage locations 735 and 901 and put the result in 825 was to write a sequence of instructions like these:

$$32 \quad 735$$
$$31 \quad 901$$
$$20 \quad 825$$

But not only was this distasteful, it was quite certain to lead to errors, no matter how careful the author was. Since a typical program might have from several hundred to several thousand such instructions in it, the problem of remembering which locations had been used for which purposes was quite formidable, and the possibility of writing 32 753 for 32 735 created many errors that were very difficult to find.

One does not write many basic machine-language instructions before devising ways of making it easier. The first step one might take would be to write (instead of the above instructions):

$$\text{CLA} \quad X$$
$$\text{ADD} \quad Y$$
$$\text{STO} \quad Z$$

while maintaining two tables, one for operations and one for storage allocation:

CLA	32	X	735
ADD	31	Y	901
STO	20	Z	825

The early users did not do this very long, however, before they realized that this routine table maintenance and subsequent translation into machine-language instructions could be done *by the computer*. Not only would the machine be much faster at such jobs, but it would be far more accurate than a human being!

This was the beginning of automatic programming. The first efforts led to *interpretive routines*. These are programs which will accept a user's program in some sort of pseudo-language (not necessarily as close to the basic machine language as in the example above), then interpret each pseudo-instruction and execute it immediately. Thus the above example might be written:

$$735 \quad 901 \quad 825 \quad \text{ADD}$$

or, perhaps,

$$X \ Y \ Z \quad \text{ADD}$$

and executed with reference to the accompanying tables indicated above.

The disadvantage of an interpretive routine is that it usually executes the desired program rather slowly compared with the operation speed of the basic machine, since each pseudo-instruction must be analyzed for its various components, and then one needs to employ *subroutines* to carry out the computation. Even more important, if the user's program is run again at a later time, the entire interpreting must be done again. One might say that the computer did not learn anything from having seen that program before.

The latest developments have been in the direction of *assembly programs* and *compilers*. An assembly program generally does the table maintenance and translation to machine language mentioned above and perhaps a few more jobs, but the user must still write instructions that have the form of basic machine instructions. The chief advantage of an assembly program is that a machine-language version of the program is generated which need not be translated again, no matter how many times the program is run. Moreover, since the work of the assembly program is done by the time the user's program is executed, no storage need be allocated for the assembly program itself; i.e., the entire storage capacity of the computer is available to the user. This contrasts with the need for reserving about half (usually more than half in the smaller machines) of the storage capacity for an interpretive routine, which *must* be in the computer during execution.

The real advance, from the point of view of the casual user, came with the development of compilers. (In the language of a typical compiler, the above example would be written simply "$Z = X + Y$.") A compiler is a program that accepts the user's program in some pseudo-language far removed from the computer's internal language and translates it into a machine-language program. (The translations may proceed in several steps; e.g., the compiled program might be generated in the form of input to an assembly program.) The attempt has been made, with current compilers, to transfer to the computer itself the entire burden of translation to machine language and to make the user's pseudo-language as close as possible to the language with which he can best describe his problem. The basic idea is that once the human being has stated his problem and the method of solution (for example, by means of flow diagrams as described below), the computer should be able to do everything else, such as writing the computer's detailed instructions, allocating storage for various purposes, and keeping track of the tables mentioned above.

Solution of a Cubic Equation by Newton's Method. As a first example of a problem solved using the language of a compiler, consider the equation $f(x) = x^3 + x - 1 = 0$ to be solved by Newton's method. In this method one finds a good initial guess, $x = x_0$, and then improves it by successive iterations, using the formula

$$x_{i+1} = x_i - \frac{f(x_i)}{f'(x_i)} \tag{25.1}$$

until some criterion is satisfied. For instance, one might ask that successive values of x differ by very little; that is,

$$|d| = |x_i - x_{i+1}| = \left| \frac{f(x_i)}{f'(x_i)} \right| < \epsilon_1$$

and that $f(x)$ be close to zero; that is, $|f(x_i)| < \epsilon_2$.

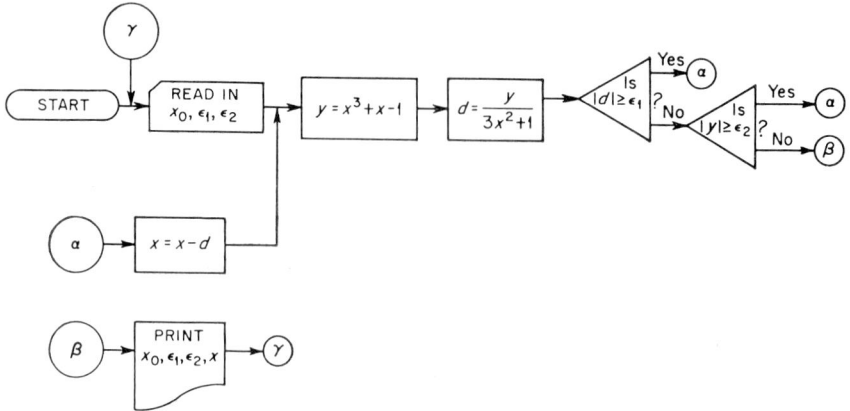

FIG. 25.2. Flow diagram for solution of a cubic equation by Newton's method.

A *flow diagram* for this example might then look like Fig. 25.2.

Several remarks about flow diagrams may help the reader understand the diagram of Fig. 25.2 more easily. The shape of the box is a clue to its role in the solution of the problem. (Although each author has his own preferences as to shapes, those used here are likely to be understood by most computer users.) A list of the shapes used here is given in Fig. 25.3. (Note that the = sign is used here in the sense, "Compute the right side of the equation and set the variable on the left equal to that value.") Then the diagram would read: Bring in the values of x_0, ϵ_1, ϵ_2 and, using $x = x_0$, compute $y = x^3 + x - 1$ and $d = y/(3x^2 + 1)$. If $|d| < \epsilon_1$, ask if $|y| < \epsilon_2$. If both conditions are satisfied, go to β, where the answer x is printed out, together with the input parameters as identifying information. The computer will then go to γ to read in new input values and start the computation again. This process will continue until no more input data are found, at which time the computer may stop or transfer to someone else's program, depending on the machine being used.

If $|d| \geq \epsilon_1$ or if $|y| \geq \epsilon_2$, the computer goes to α, in which Eq. (25.1) is applied in the

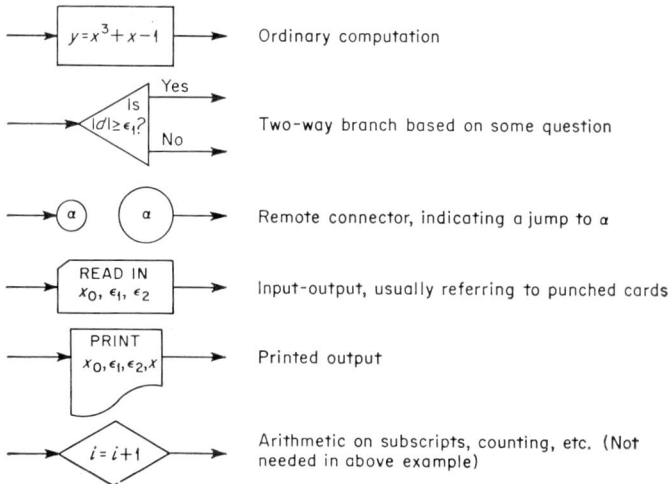

FIG. 25.3. Flow-diagram symbols.

form $x = x - d$, and then it goes again to the computation of y. This modification of x will continue until both tests are satisfied and the computer goes to β as described above. Note that no subscript is needed on x, since the current value of x is always used in the computation, and at α the *current value* is changed to a *new current value*, which is then used in the computation of y and d, and so on.

It should be emphasized that there are many other equally correct ways to draw flow diagrams for a given method of solution. But each must be complete, in the sense that every box which has an incoming arrow must have at least one outgoing arrow, and so on.

What is the status, then, of the equation $x^3 + x - 1 = 0$? The analysis of the problem and the description of the method of solution have been completed. At this point the computer ought to be able to take over and solve the problem. Unfortunately, one cannot feed the diagram directly into the machine, although this will probably be done some day. It is necessary to translate the diagram into a sequence of unambiguous *statements* that will be equivalent to the flow diagram. The following sequence of statements is written in no particular compiler language, but is close to many of the current ones (thereby avoiding some details, such as input-output format specification, etc.).

1: READ X_0, EPSILON 1, EPSILON 2
2: $Y = X^3 + X - 1$
3: $D = Y/(3X^2 + 1)$
4: GO TO 8 IF ABS$(D) \geq$ EPSILON 1
5: GO TO 8 IF ABS$(Y) \geq$ EPSILON 2
6: PRINT X_0, EPSILON 1, EPSILON 2, X
7: GO TO 1
8: $X = X - D$
9: GO TO 2

Note that statement 4, for example, asks whether $|D| \geq \epsilon_1$ or not. If the answer is "yes," the program jumps to statement 8 (which corresponds to α in the diagram); otherwise it goes on to the next statement in the sequence. The relationship of each of the above statements to the flow diagram should be clear.

After they are punched on cards (or otherwise prepared for entry to the machine), the compiler (which is a machine program itself, of course) analyzes each statement and generates a set of instructions. For example, on the IBM 704, statement 8 might be compiled as:

$$\text{CLA} \quad X$$
$$\text{SUB} \quad D$$
$$\text{STO} \quad X$$

Such statements might then serve as input to an assembly program which might change them into the octal numbers:

$$050000001732$$
$$040200001736$$
$$060100001732$$

or perhaps even into the binary numbers that serve as direct input to the computer:

$$000101000000000000000000001111011010$$
$$000100000001000000000000001111011110$$
$$000110000001000000000000001111011010$$

Such translations should obviously be done by the computer.

Most compiler languages have an additional feature not yet mentioned. The example just considered illustrates a typical phenomenon called a *loop*. This is a set of operations that is repeated many times until some criterion is satisfied. Usually, there is some variable involved in the loop which has some initial value the first time through and which has its value changed by adding (or subtracting) some amount to it each time around the loop. The criterion for ending the iteration is usually a test of some

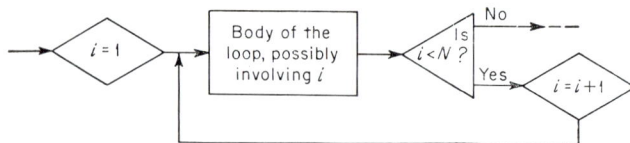

FIG. 25.4. Flow diagram for loop computation.

kind of the value of this variable. For example, a loop might involve a counting process, where an index of some kind increases by 1 on each repetition until it reaches some upper limit. Or a loop might consist of a converging iterative process, which continues until some quantity, such as the difference between successive values of the iterated variable, is small enough. A diagram of a typical loop would be something like Fig. 25.4. In such a loop, there are four major parts, the initialization of the variable, the body of the loop, the test for completion, and the modification of the variable for another time through the loop.

In the example above, the initialization was accomplished by reading in the input value of x_0. The body of the loop consisted of the computation of y and d; the testing consisted of the questions about $|d|$ and $|y|$; and the modification was accomplished by statement 8.

Since this loop structure occurs in so many problems, a special kind of statement is usually included in compiler languages so that a loop can be easily described. A common form of this statement would look like the following:

    6: 12 FOR $x = 1$, $-h$, $x < \epsilon$

This is to be interpreted as statement number 6 in some program. It indicates that all statements following statement 6 down to and including statement 12 are to be the body of the loop. The variable x is to be initialized at $x = 1$, modified by adding $-h$ on each repetition (in this case x decreases), and the body of the loop is not to be computed as soon as $x < \epsilon$. The program instead continues on to the statement following statement 12.

Using this type of statement, the first example simplifies to the following:

    1: READ X_0, EPSILON 1, EPSILON 2
    2: 4 FOR $X = X_0$, $-D$, ABS(D) < EPSILON 1 AND ABS(Y) < EPSILON 2
    3: $Y = X^3 + X - 1$
    4: $D = Y/(3X^2 + 1)$
    5: PRINT X_0, EPSILON 1, EPSILON 2, X
    6: GO TO 1

The use of this type of statement not only reduces the number of statements in a program, but enables one to write the program as he thinks of it, i.e., in terms of loops. The iteration statement just described is used freely in the examples that follow.

Solution of a Cubic Equation by the Half-interval Method As a second example, the *half-interval* method of solution of the same equation, $x^3 + x - 1 = 0$, is illustrated. In this method one specifies an interval $[a,b]$ within which a solution is expected. Using the fact that a continuous function $f(x)$ will take on the value zero for at least one x between x_1 and x_2 if $f(x_1)$ and $f(x_2)$ have opposite signs, the interval $[a,b]$ is repeatedly scanned, looking for a change in sign of $f(x)$, each time with a step size h one-half as large as the previous step size. If no change of sign is found by the time $h < \epsilon$, it is assumed that there are no solutions in $[a,b]$ (although the possibility would still exist that there are two roots less than ϵ apart).

If a change of sign is found, say, between $x_L = x^* - h$ and $x_R = x^*$, next look at $x_M = (x_L + x_R)/2$, the mid-point of the interval $[x_L, x_R]$. If $f(x_M)$ and $f(x_L)$ have the same sign, a root lies between x_M and x_R. Then set $x_L = x_M$, and look at the mid-point of the *new* interval $[x_L, x_R]$, and so on. If $f(x_M)$ and $f(x_L)$ have different signs, a root lies between x_L and x_M. Then set $x_R = x_M$, and look at the mid-point of the new

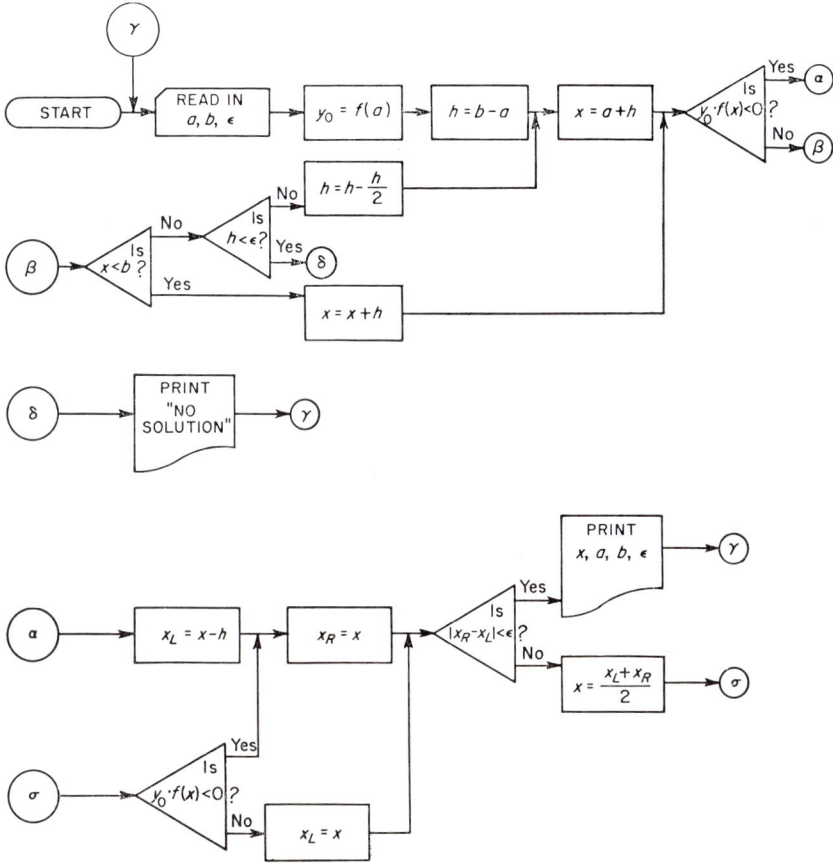

FIG. 25.5. Flow diagram for solution of a cubic equation by the half-interval method.

interval $[x_L, x_R]$, and so on, until the interval being considered is of length less than ϵ. A flow diagram is given in Fig. 25.5 for the process just described. The test for agreement of sign used here makes use of the sign of a product of two numbers, which is $+$ if the numbers have the same sign and $-$ if they have opposite signs. In order to make the method quite general, the flow diagram is written to solve the equation $f(x) = 0$ for any function continuous on the interval $[a,b]$, and the input parameters are a, b, and ϵ.

The diagram may be interpreted in the following way. After reading in the parameters a, b, and ϵ, compute $y_0 = f(a)$ to serve as the comparison standard for change of sign. Then, starting with $h = b - a$, one has a loop on x, moving from $a + h$ to b in steps of h, looking for a change of sign, as indicated by the sign of the product $y_0 \cdot f(x)$. If a change of sign is found, the program jumps to α, the beginning of the second half of the program. If no change of sign is found, h is modified to $h/2$ (by subtracting $h/2$ to conform to the addition-type modification of a loop) and compared with ϵ. It is seen then that there is a loop for h that *contains* the loop for x. If the h loop is ever finished before a jump is made to α, a comment is printed out saying "NO SOLUTION."

As an example of the computation involved, solve the equation $f(x) = x^2 - 2 = 0$ by this method, choosing the interval $[-2,2]$ in which to search for a root. Compute as follows: $y_0 = f(-2) = 2$, $f(2) = 2$ (no change of sign, therefore let $h = 2$), $f(0) = -2$ (hence there is a root between -2 and 0). This corresponds to α in the flow diagram.

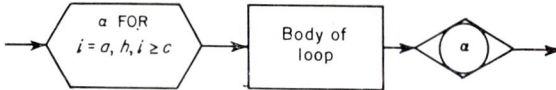

FIG. 25.6. Simplified-loop-structure diagram.

Then $x_L = -2$, $x_R = 0$, $x_M = -1$, $f(-1) = -1$; hence there is a root between -2 and -1. Set $x_R = -1$, and look at the interval $[-2, -1]$. Now $x_M = -\frac{3}{2}$, $f(-\frac{3}{2}) = \frac{1}{4}$, so the root is between $-\frac{3}{2}$ and -1, and so on.

The program, based on the flow diagram, is as follows [for $f(x) = x^2 - 2$]:

```
1: READ A, B, EPSILON
2: Y₀ = A² − 2
3: 5 FOR H = B − A, −H/2, H < EPSILON
4: 5 FOR X = A + H, H, X > B
5: GO TO 8 IF Y₀ · (X² − 2) < 0
6: PRINT "NO SOLUTION"
7: GO TO 1
8: X_L = X − H
9: X_R = X
10: GO TO 15 IF ABS(X_R − X_L) < EPSILON
11: X = (X_L + X_R)/2
12: GO TO 9 IF Y₀ · (X² − 2) < 0
13: X_L = X
14: GO TO 10
15: PRINT X, A, B, EPSILON
16: GO TO 1
```

The convention about *nested* loops such as those in statements 3, 4, and 5 is that the loop last begun is the first tested, so that for each fixed h, the entire x loop is performed. This is exactly what is needed, of course. Again it should be understood that there are many other ways to make up a flow diagram for this problem, and if the reader had not seen a loop structure here, the penalty would merely have been more statements in the program.

Multiplication of Matrices. Another convenient device often available in compiler languages is *matrix notation*. Since double, triple, and even higher-level subscripts occur naturally in the formulation of many problems, it is convenient to be able to use notation such as $X(I,J)$ for x_{ij}. Using this notation, matrix multiplication, for instance, is easily accomplished. Suppose it is desired to compute $C = A \cdot B$, in which $A = (a_{ij})$, $B = (b_{ij})$, and $C = (c_{ij})$. Then $c_{ij} = \sum_{k=1}^{n} a_{ik}b_{kj}$, in which it is assumed that A is an $m \times n$ matrix, and B is an $n \times p$ matrix.

In order to simplify the flow diagram, a new type of box based on the iteration statement is introduced (Fig. 25.6). This would be interpreted as: Perform all steps of the diagram up to α repeatedly, with $i = a$ the first time, then $i = a + h$, and so on, until $i \geq c$, just as in the corresponding iteration statement.

Then the flow diagram for matrix multiplication would look like Fig. 25.7.

The program is now immediate.

```
1: READ M, N, P, MATRIX A, MATRIX B
2: 6 FOR I = 1, 1, I > M
3: 6 FOR J = 1, 1, I > P
4: C(I,J) = 0
5: 6 FOR K = 1, 1, I > N
6: C(I,J) = C(I,J) + A(I,K) • B(K,J)
7: PRINT M, N, P, MATRIX A, MATRIX B, MATRIX C
8: GO TO 1
```

Solution of n Simultaneous Linear Equations. Consider the problem of solving a set of n simultaneous linear equations in n variables:

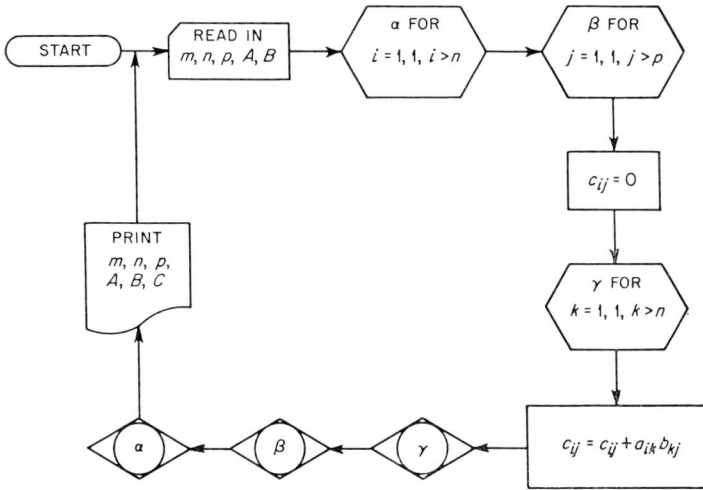

FIG. 25.7. Flow diagram for multiplication of matrices.

$$a_{11}x_1 + a_{12}x_2 + \cdots + a_{1n}x_n = a_{1,n+1}$$
$$a_{21}x_1 + a_{22}x_2 + \cdots + a_{2n}x_n = a_{2,n+1}$$
$$\cdots\cdots\cdots\cdots\cdots\cdots\cdots\cdots\cdots$$
$$a_{n1}x_1 + a_{n2}x_2 + \cdots + a_{nn}x_n = a_{n,n+1}$$

It will be convenient to consider only the $n \times (n + 1)$ matrix of coefficients $A = (a_{ij})$, $i = 1, 2, \ldots, n; j = 1, 2, \ldots, n + 1$, and to assume that there is a unique solution to the problem to avoid the difficulties that arise when the equations are dependent (or nearly dependent). One popular method of solution is the Jordan elimination method in which elements on the main diagonal of the matrix, i.e., of the form a_{kk}, are used to *clear* the other elements in their respective columns by means of appropriate multiplications and subtractions.

The procedure may be described in the following way. The first row is divided by its diagonal element a_{11}. Then, to clear a_{21} to zero, subtract a_{21} times the first row from the second row, and so on. In general, to clear a_{ik} to zero (after row k has been divided by a_{kk}), subtract a_{ik} times row k from row i ($i \neq k$). (This is the same method of addition and subtraction taught in high school algebra, but it is formalized to allow its description to the computer as a cyclic procedure.) A typical element a_{ij} is thus transformed each time by the formulas:

$$a_{kj} = \frac{a_{kj}}{a_{kk}} \tag{25.2}$$

$$a_{ij} = a_{ij} - a_{ik}a_{kj} \qquad (i \neq k) \tag{25.3}$$

in which the value of a_{kj} in Eq. (25.3) is the result of Eq. (25.2). These transformations are performed for $k = 1, 2, \ldots, n$. For each (fixed) value of k, let $i = 1, 2, \ldots, k - 1$, $k + 1, \ldots, n$, so as to operate on all rows except $i = k$. While transforming each row, cycle on j from right to left; that is, $j = n + 1, n, n - 1, \ldots, k$, and then stop at $j = k$ since for $j < k$ there is no change in the matrix. The final matrix, then, will be

$$\begin{bmatrix} 1 & 0 & 0 & \ldots & 0 & b_1 \\ 0 & 1 & 0 & \ldots & 0 & b_2 \\ 0 & 0 & 1 & \ldots & 0 & b_3 \\ & & \cdots\cdots\cdots & & \\ 0 & 0 & 0 & \ldots & 1 & b_n \end{bmatrix}$$

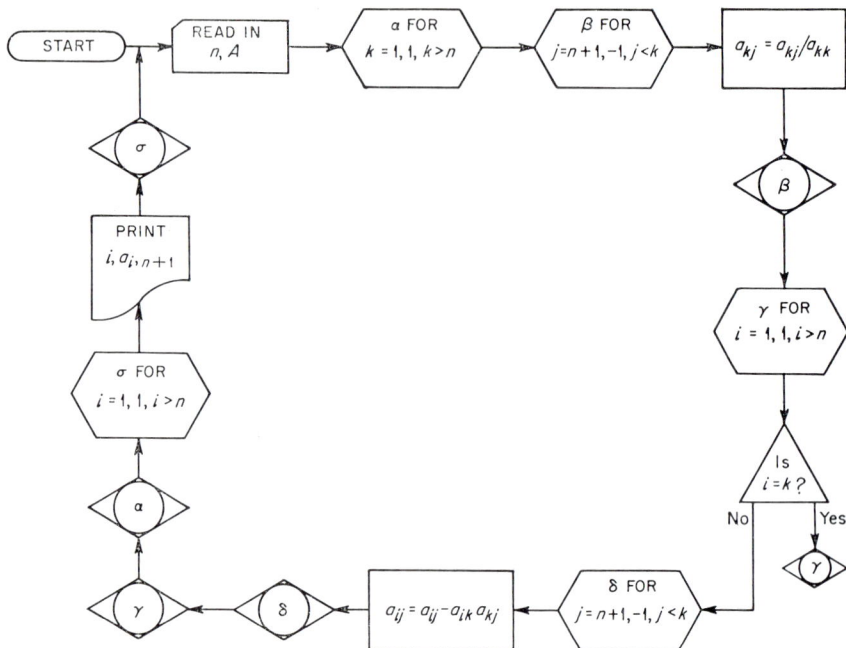

FIG. 25.8. Flow diagram for solution of n simultaneous linear equations in n variables.

and the solution to the equations is then $x_1 = b_1$, $x_2 = b_2$, . . . The flow diagram (Fig. 25.8) can be written as follows.

Again the program is immediate from the diagram.

```
 1: READ N, MATRIX A
 2: 9 FOR K = 1, 1, K > N
 3: 4 FOR J = N + 1, −1, J < K
 4: A(K,J) = A(K,J)/A(K,K)
 5: 9 FOR I = 1, 1, I > N
 6: GO TO 9 IF I = K
 7: 8 FOR J = N + 1, −1, J < K
 8: A(I,J) = A(I,J) − A(I,K) • A(K,J)
 9: CONTINUE
10: 11 FOR I = 1, 1, I > N
11: PRINT I, A(I, N + 1)
12: GO TO 1
```

It should be understood here that certain difficulties have been overlooked in this example. For instance, the effect of round-off error must be considered. Moreover, a zero might occur on a diagonal occasionally, and the division in statement 4 would be impossible. Assuming the existence of a unique solution, however, guarantees the existence of a nonzero number somewhere in the kth column below the diagonal, and by interchanging two rows, for example, a nonzero element may be obtained in the diagonal position. The program written above will solve many problems, however, without any trouble.

In almost every computer installation there is a *library* of standard, commonly used programs called *subroutines*. These are carefully prepared by the expert programmers to be efficient, fast, and accurate. The compiler languages usually allow automatic reference to these subroutines, such as cos x, and so on. The next example illustrates the use of a popular subroutine for the solution of systems of nonlinear ordinary differential equations. The subroutine may use the Runge-Kutta method, the Adams method, or some other method. The description of the method, its limitations, its requirements, and so forth, will always be set forth for the user on a specification sheet. A typical subroutine of the Runge-Kutta type is described as it would appear to the user.

Runge-Kutta Methods. The Runge-Kutta methods, which date from 1894 and are based on truncated Taylor-series approximation, are among the most popular numerical methods for the solution of ordinary differential equations, such as $y' = f(x,y)$. The advantages of these methods are accuracy, stability (i.e., small errors do not build up in such a way as to render the solution useless), the ability of the method to compute the value of y_{n+1} without any information regarding past values except the value of y_n and without the use of higher derivatives, the ease with which h can be changed at any stage, and the relatively small amount of computer storage needed for intermediate results. The disadvantages consist largely in the need for evaluating $f(x,y)$ several times for each point of the solution, thus raising the possibility of a great deal of computation if $f(x,y)$ is very complicated.

There are several methods which are called *Runge-Kutta methods*. They differ in the number of terms of the Taylor's series that are retained. Since another term in the series yields more accuracy but requires more computation time, some compromise must be made between the two. The most frequently encountered is the *fourth-order method*, which uses the first five terms (through the fourth derivative) and involves an error of the order of h^5. This is the method described here. The others differ in details.

The Runge-Knutta process is based on the use of suitably chosen points near (x_n,y_n) to produce values of $f(x,y)$ which may be used as slopes in the equation

$$y_{n+1} = y_n + hy_n' \tag{25.4}$$

The fourth-order process uses four such points, and by means of Eq. (25.4), four candidates for y_{n+1} are produced. The final choice for y_{n+1} is then obtained as a weighted average of these four points.

One first defines four numbers, with Eq. (25.4) in mind:

$$k_1 = hf(x_n,y_n)$$

$$k_2 = hf(x_n + mh, y_n + mk_1)$$

$$k_3 = hf[x_n + vh, y_n + (v - r)k_1 + rk_2]$$

$$k_4 = hf[x_n + ph, y_n + (p - s - t)k_1 + sk_2 + tk_3]$$

in which m, v, p, r, s, and t are yet to be determined. Then k_i is the increment in y obtained by using as slope *at y_n* the slope *computed at the ith nearby point*. One then determines the values of m, v, p, etc., so as to make the solution accurate as far as the fourth-order term of the Taylor's series for y_{n+1}. Then one demands that k be a weighted average of k_1, k_2, k_3, and k_4, so that $k = ak_1 + bk_2 + ck_3 + dk_4$, with $a + b + c + d = 1$. Substituting Taylor expansions for k_1, k_2, k_3, and k_4 and equating coefficients with those in the Taylor expansion of k, one obtains eight equations in the ten unknowns a, b, c, d, m, v, p, r, s, and t. There are thus two degrees of freedom in the choice of the four points to be averaged and in the choice of the weights a, b, c, and d. Typical of the choices that may be made are the following, due to Kutta and Runge, respectively:

$$\begin{cases} k_1 = hf(x_n,y_n) \\ k_2 = hf(x_n + \tfrac{1}{3}h, y_n + \tfrac{1}{3}k_1) \\ k_3 = hf(x_n + \tfrac{2}{3}h, y_n - \tfrac{1}{3}k_1 + k_2) \\ k_4 = hf(x_n + h, y_n + k_1 - k_2 + k_3) \\ k = \tfrac{1}{8}(k_1 + 3k_2 + 3k_3 + k_4) \end{cases}$$

$$\begin{cases} k_1 = hf(x_n,y_n) \\ k_2 = hf(x_n + \tfrac{1}{2}h, y_n + \tfrac{1}{2}k_1) \\ k_3 = hf(x_n + \tfrac{1}{2}h, y_n + \tfrac{1}{2}k_2) \\ k_4 = hf(x_n + h, y_n + k_3) \\ k = \tfrac{1}{6}(k_1 + 2k_2 + 2k_3 + k_4) \end{cases}$$

This process extends immediately to any number of simultaneous first-order equations as well, which makes it possible to treat higher-order ordinary differential equations, also, by transforming them to systems of simultaneous first-order equations.

In the following example it is assumed that a subroutine is available using some Runge-Kutta method, e.g., Runge's method or Kutta's method.

Solution of a System of Ordinary Differential Equations.   The system of equations to be solved is considered to be in the form of a system of first-order equations:

$$y_i' = f_i(y_1, y_2, \ldots, y_n) \qquad i = 1, 2, \ldots, n$$

For example, the system

$$\frac{d^2y}{dt^2} + t\frac{dy}{dt} + \frac{dx}{dt} + t^2 - x^2 = 0$$

$$\frac{d^3x}{dt^3} + (x^2 - t^2)\frac{dy}{dt} + 1 = 0$$

would be transformed by the user into the system

$$\begin{aligned} y' &= v \\ v' &= -tv - u - t^2 + x^2 \\ x' &= u \\ u' &= p \\ p' &= (t^2 - x^2)v - 1 \end{aligned}$$

before using the subroutine.

The part of the program that computes the derivatives (which may be called the *D program*) is to be considered as a part of the subroutine that the user must supply. The flow diagram is shown in Fig. 25.9, assuming that the solution is desired for $a < t < b$ in steps of $h = \Delta t$.

Since the subroutine may require the values of the dependent variables to be stored in sequence, i.e., as components of a vector, followed by the values of the derivatives, the system of equations to be solved is restated:

$$\begin{aligned} y_1' &= y_2 \\ y_2' &= -ty_2 - y_4 - t^2 + y_3{}^2 \\ y_3' &= y_4 \\ y_4' &= y_5 \\ y_5' &= (t^2 - y_3{}^2)y_2 - 1 \end{aligned}$$

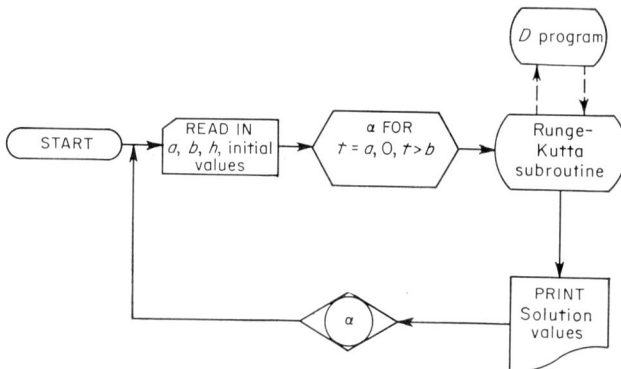

FIG. 25.9. Flow diagram for solution of a system of ordinary differential equations.

Then the program would be written as follows:

```
1: READ A, B, H, Y1, Y2, Y3, Y4, Y5
2: 4 FOR T = A, 0, T > B
3: RKSUB (5, LOC Y1, LOC T, H, 6)
4: PRINT T, Y1, Y2, Y3, Y4, Y5
5: GO TO 1
6: Y6  = Y2
7: Y7  = -T · Y2 - Y4 - T² + Y3²
8: Y8  = Y4
9: Y9  = Y5
10: Y10 = (T2 - Y3²) · Y2 - 1
11: GO TO 3
```

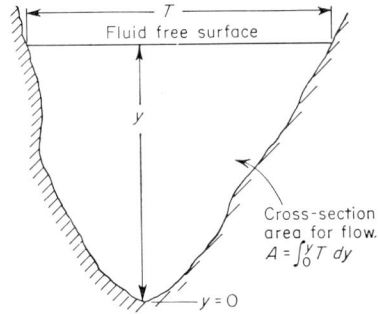

FIG. 25.10. Cross section of irregular open channel.

The D program consists of statements 6 to 11, and it should be observed that because of its role as a subroutine for the Runge-Kutta program, it has a return to statement 3, which is the entrance to the main subroutine. The D program may be as long and complicated as necessary to compute all the derivatives.

Some explanation is needed for statement 3. The name of the subroutine is RKSUB, and the quantities in the parentheses are the parameters that the subroutine needs. In this example, the first quantity indicates the number of first-order equations to be solved, in this case 5. The last number tells the Runge-Kutta subroutine the starting statement number of the D program, since the latter may be quite far away in the program.

The subroutine also needs to know where to find the block of consecutive locations within the computer in which the values of the variables and derivatives are stored. (Note that what is necessary is not the *value* of Y_1, but its *location*.) The second quantity, then, is LOC $Y1$, which means the *location* of Y_1. Similarly, the other arguments in the parentheses are LOC T and H, which are the location of T and value of H, respectively. Note that each entrance into statement 3 (other than from statement 11) produces the next solution point, which is then printed by statement 4. If only certain values are to be printed, such as every twentieth point, the test for this can be inserted, say, between statements 3 and 4, or another loop can be constructed to count to 20.

An interesting use of the iteration statement is noted, which sets the initial and final values for T but does not increment it. (The increment has the value 0.) This is used because the Runge-Kutta process itself increments T as needed, and the iteration statement is used to recognize the end of the computation.

Critical Depth in Open Channel with Irregular Cross Section. The critical depth occurs in an open channel when (Fig. 25.10)

$$\frac{TQ^2}{gA^3} - 1 = 0$$

in which Q = volume flow rate, cfs

$\quad\quad T$ = width of channel at free surface, ft

$\quad\quad g$ = acceleration due to gravity, ft/sec²

$\quad\quad A$ = channel-flow cross section, ft²

and in which both T and A are functions of the depth y, taking $y = 0$ at the point of greatest depth in the channel.

The problem may be rewritten so that one asks for the roots of

$$z = F(y) = 0 \quad\quad \text{for} \quad\quad 0 < y_{min} < y < y_{max}$$

in which $F(y) = Q^2 \cdot T(y) - g \cdot [A(y)]^3$, and it is assumed that $A(y) \neq 0$ and $g \neq 0$ for all y under consideration.

To be completely general, let it be supposed that an analytical expression is not known

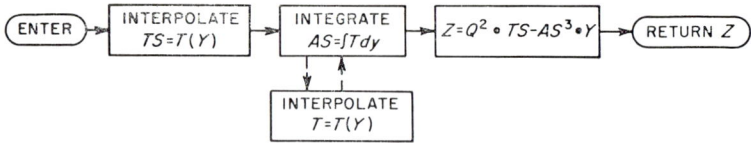

Fig. 25.11. Flow diagram for FUNCT. (Y).

to describe the channel, but that a series of measurements of the channel width T have been made for a series of depths y. It will be assumed that the measurements lie sufficiently close together to allow interpolation. The procedure will use the half-interval technique to search for the roots of $F(y)$.

T is known as a function of y through the table of measurements. So, for each trial value of y used in the half-interval method, the value for T at the surface must be found by interpolation. Also the area of the flowing channel A must be found by a numerical integration of the values of T tabulated as a function of y, from $y = 0$ to the free surface. The procedure will use two library subroutines, INTERP and SIMPSON, to perform the interpolation and integration.

The flow diagram parallels the previous half-interval method exactly, except for the evaluation of $F(x)$. Previously $F(x)$ was so simple that the complete function could be evaluated in one statement. Now a *subroutine* FUNCT is defined which is used to evaluate $F(y)$.

The flow diagram for FUNCT (Y) is shown in Fig. 25.11.

FUNCT (Y) is written as an *internal function*, that is, only the variable y is a dummy variable; all the other variables are implicit in the main program. Thus it is not necessary to give long parameter lists (which would specify the number of entries in the T versus y table, the order of interpolation to be used, the number of intervals to be used in the integration, etc.) each time FUNCT (Y) is used.

The compiler statements for the entire program may be as follows:

```
 1: READ YMAX, YMIN, EPSILON, DATA, (Y(I), T(I), I = 1, DATA), ORDER,
    NUMBER, Q, G
 2: Z0 = FUNCT (YMIN)
 3: 5 FOR H = YMAX − YMIN, −H/2, H < EPSILON
 4: 5 FOR Y = YMIN + H, H, Y > YMAX
 5: GO TO 8 IF Z0 • FUNCT (Y) < 0
 6: PRINT "NO SOLUTION USING THIS STEPSIZE"
 7: GO TO 1
 8: YL = Y − H
 9: YR = Y
10: GO TO 15 IF ABS(YR − YL) < EPSILON
11: Y = (YL + YR)/2
12: GO TO 9 IF Z0 • FUNCT (Y) < 0
13: YL = Y
14: GO TO 10
15: PRINT Y, YMIN, YMAX, EPSILON, TS, AS, Q
16: GO TO 1
17: INTERNAL FUNCTION FUNCT (Y) ENTRY
18: TS = INTERP (Y, LOC (Y(1)), 2, DATA, ORDER)
19: AS = SIMPSON (0, Y, Y1, T, NUMBER, 20, 22)
20: T = INTERP (Y1, LOC (Y(1)), 2, DATA, ORDER)
21: GO TO 19
22: Z = Q • TS − G • AS³
23: RETURN Z
24: INTERNAL FUNCTION END
```

Most of the comments will be directed to the INTERNAL FUNCTION portion of the program. As noted, before, the internal function uses only the variable Y as a dummy variable; that is, one is free to write FUNCT (W) and to expect that the value of W will be used rather than the value of Y. Otherwise, the internal function is compiled together with the main program and therefore assumes that all other variables used have the same connotation as in the main program. This will be made more clear as the INTERNAL FUNCTION is examined in detail. It is assumed that the computer library contains INTERP and SIMPSON. The arguments of INTERP are (1) Y, the value of the independent variable; (2) LOC $(Y(1))$, the location of the first independent variable table entry; (3) 2, the number of related entries at each stage, in this case, one independent and one dependent variable (a data pair); (4) DATA, the number of data (pairs) in table; (5) ORDER, the order of interpolation desired (i.e., if ORDER = 1 the interpolation made is linear, etc.). The arguments of SIMPSON are (1) 0, the lower limit of integration; (2) Y, the upper limit of integration (here Y is variable); (3) $Y1$, the name of the independent variable in the integration; (4) T, the name of the function value at $Y1$; (5) 20, the statement number entry to evaluate T; (6) 22, the statement number to which control passes after the completion of the routine SIMPSON. Statement 22 evaluates the desired value for FUNCT (Y). Statement 23 returns the calculated value. Statement 24 terminates the compilation of INTERNAL FUNCTION.

The main body of the program parallels the half-interval program exactly. The evaluation of the function of the various trial points is done through the internal function FUNCT (Y). When the final result is obtained, the statement PRINT includes the critical depth Y, the lower $(YMIN)$ and the upper $(YMAX)$ limits on the depth internal, and the stopping criterion EPSILON. Since the values of the channel free surface T and the channel flow cross-section area A that correspond to the critical depth Y have been computed earlier, these values are also included, together with the flow rate Q for which the solution is valid.

Water-hammer Problem in a Simple Conduit. In order to illustrate the use of compiler languages in the solution of fluids problems, consider the following. Suppose that a simple conduit is characterized by having constant properties throughout its length; that is to say, the diameter, modulus of elasticity, moment of inertia, etc., have the same values at every cross section. It is also assumed that the fluid properties are constant in the same way. Finally, an initial velocity and an initial pressure are assigned to the fluid. At time $t = 0$, changes are initiated in the fluid-flow velocity at one end of the conduit. Because of the elasticity of the fluid and conduit, changes in velocity and resulting pressure changes are not felt instantaneously throughout the system. Instead, a wave is propagated through the fluid which communicates the changes to the various parts of the system.

The problem may be described by a system of two simultaneous partial differential equations:

(I)
$$\frac{\partial v}{\partial t} = \frac{g}{\gamma} \cdot \frac{\partial p}{\partial x}$$

(II)
$$\frac{\partial p}{\partial t} = \frac{\gamma a^2}{g} \cdot \frac{\partial v}{\partial x}$$

in which v = velocity of flow
         p = pressure of fluid
         t = time
         g = acceleration due to gravity
         γ = specific weight of fluid
         a = propagation velocity of pressure wave in the system

These equations are applied to the simple conduit system subject to certain initial and boundary conditions. Suppose the conduit is of length L and x ranges over the values $0 \le x \le L$. Suppose further that at $x = 0$, the conduit is attached to a large source of fluid such that the pressure at $x = 0$ is constant for all time t. Finally, at $x = L$, a

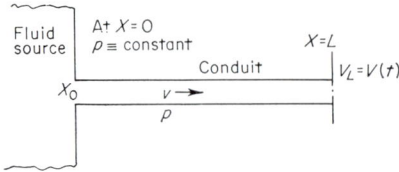

FIG. 25.12. Diagram of simple conduit for water-hammer problem. (Initial conditions: $p = p_0$, $v = v_0$ for $0 \leqslant x \leqslant L$ and $t < 0$.)

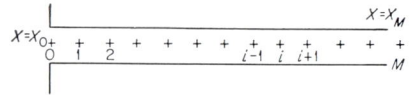

FIG. 25.13. Conduit divided into increments of length.

known variation in the fluid velocity as a function of time is imposed (Fig. 25.12).

The problem may be treated in many ways. The method introduced here is that of reducing the simultaneous partial differential equations to a system of $2 \cdot (M + 1)$ simultaneous ordinary differential equations (in which M is the number of increments along the length of the conduit). Setting $\Delta x = L/M$, the spatial derivative can be approximated by numerical difference quotients; that is, solve the following problem:

Let M = number of increments taken along the length of the conduit each of length

$$\Delta x = L/M$$

Number the end points of the intervals such that $x(0) = 0$, $x(M) = L$, and the intermediate points are sequentially numbered (Fig. 25.13) and the set of equations to be solved is:

$$\frac{dp}{dt}\bigg|_0 = 0$$

$$\frac{dv}{dt}\bigg|_{j-1} = \frac{g}{\gamma} \cdot \frac{p(j) - p(j-1)}{\Delta x}$$

$$\frac{dp}{dt}\bigg|_j = \frac{\gamma a^2}{g} \cdot \frac{v(j) - v(j-1)}{\Delta x}$$

for $j = 1, 2, 3, \ldots, M$, and finally

$$\frac{dv}{dt}\bigg|_M = \frac{d}{dt} [v(t)]_M$$

In particular, a valve-closing function may be characterized by a velocity polynomial such that the following relations are true:

(1)　　　$t < 0$　　　　　　　　　　$v_M = v_0$ (initial condition)
(2)　　　$t \geq 0$　　and　　$v_M > 0$　　$v_M = a_k t^k + a_{k-1} t^{k-1} + \cdots + a_1 t + v_0$

such that

$$\frac{dv_M}{dt} \leq 0 \quad \text{for} \quad t \geq 0$$

until the first occurrence, say, $t = t_1$ of $v_M \leq 0$, after which

$$v_M = 0 \quad \text{for} \quad t \geq t_1$$

The flow diagram is given in Fig. 25.14. The compiler statements for this problem might then be:

```
1: READ γ, g, a, L, P0, V0, M, DELTA T, TMAX, K, (A(I), I = 1,K)
2: 4 FOR I0 = 0, 1, I > M
3: Y(2 · I) = P0
4: Y(2 · I + 1) = V0
5: I1 = 8
6: 13 FOR T = 0, 0, T > TMAX
```

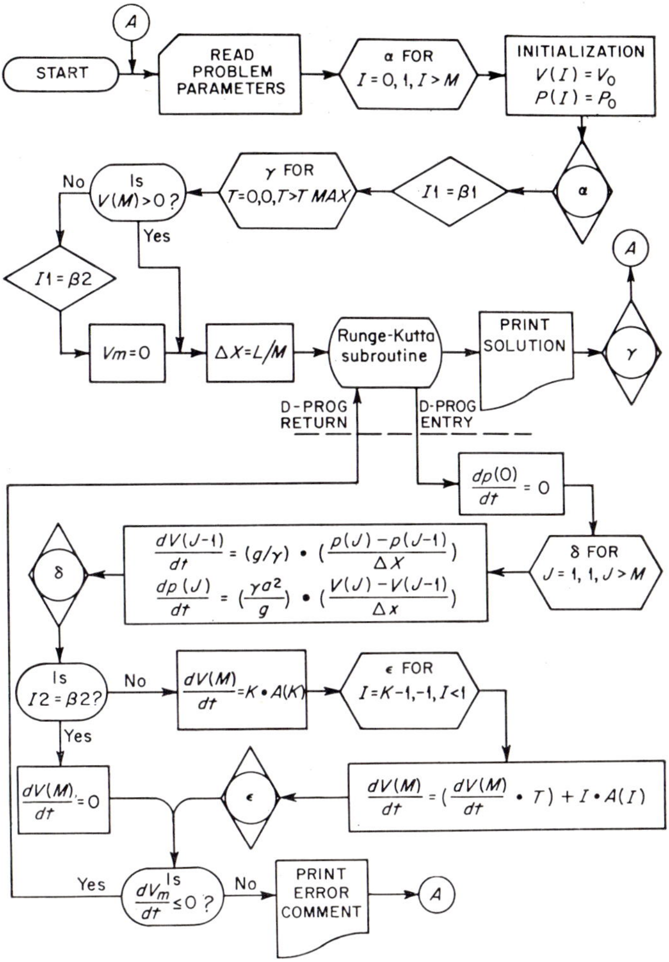

FIG. 25.14. Flow diagram for water-hammer problem in simple conduit.

7: GO TO $I1$
8: GO TO 11 IF $Y(2 \cdot M) > 0$
9: $I1 = 10$
10: $Y(2 \cdot M) = 0$
11: DELTA $X = L/M$
12: RKSUB $(2 \cdot (M + 1),$ LOC $(Y(0)),$ LOC $(T),$ DELTA $T, 15)$
13: PRINT $T, Y(0) \ldots Y(2 \cdot M + 1)$
14: GO TO 1
15: $Y(2 \cdot (M + 1)) = 0$
16: 18 FOR $J = 1, 1, J > M$
17: $Y(2 \cdot (M + J) + 1) = (g/\gamma) \cdot (Y(2 \cdot J + 1) - Y(2 \cdot J - 1))/$DELTA X
18: $Y(2 \cdot (M + J + 1)) = (\gamma a^2/g) \cdot (Y(2 \cdot J) - Y(2 - 1))/$DELTA X
19: $Y(4 \cdot M + 3) = 0$
20: GO TO 12 IF $I1 = 10$
21: $Y(4M + 3) = K \cdot A(K)$

22: 22 FOR $I = K - 1, -1, I < 1$
23: $Y(4M + 3) = Y(4M + 3) \cdot T + I \cdot A(I)$
24: GO TO 26 IF $Y(4M + 3) > 0$
25: GO TO 12
26: PRINT "RATE OF CHANGE POSITIVE, SO LONG"
27: GO TO 1

The input variables in statement 1 may be identified with those used in the problem description. The execution of the program for a variable number of cross sections using the Runge-Kutta subroutine makes desirable the substitution of the subscripted variable Y for the subscripted variables p, v, dp/dt, dv/dt. This allows the Runge-Kutta subroutine to locate all the values in storage by finding the location of the first one (see statement 12: LOC $(Y(0))$ finds the location of the first Y). The substitution occurs by associating the subscripts of the Y vector with the elements of the p, v, dp/dt, dv/dt vectors (see statements 3, 4, 17, and 18). Statements 2 to 4 initialize the values of v and p at each of the $M + 1$ cross sections. Statement 5 sets a switch to ensure that the valve function will operate only until $v_M = 0$ the first time and will become inoperable after that. Statement 6 sets up the Runge-Kutta loop and stops the solution after $T > TMAX$. Note that RKSUB increments T, so that the iteration statement has increment 0. Statement 7 uses the previously set switch; control simply passes to statement 8 (since the current value of $I1$ is 8). Statement 8 tests $v(M)$, and if $v(M) \leq 0$, then the $I1$ switch is thrown and $v(M)$ is set to 0, otherwise control bypasses these steps. Statement 11 computes DELTA X. The Runge-Knutta subroutine is supplied with a variable number of equations to solve, depending on the fineness of division specified by M.

Printing of a variable-length list is accomplished by statement 13. Statement 14 returns to READ to see if any more problems of this type are waiting to be solved. If the READ statement finds no data, control will halt the machine.

The D program is similar to that in the previous Runge-Kutta example. First, the derivative condition on p at 0 is set. Then the set of derivatives is calculated for all but the derivative of v at M. The derivative of v at M is determined by the valve function. Statement 20 returns the D program to the Runge-Kutta subroutine if v_M has been negative or zero and ensures that $v_M = 0$ henceforth. Otherwise, control goes to statements 21 to 23 to evaluate the valve-function derivative for an arbitrary Kth-degree polynomial valve function. Statement 24 is a check to ensure that the valve function of statements 21 to 24 is actually decelerating the flow (the freedom of inserting quite arbitrary valve functions makes such a check desirable). If the flow is decelerating properly, the control returns to the Runge-Kutta subroutine; if not, the error is printed out as a comment and control looks to see if there are any more problems of this type to be solved.

In general, one tries to allow the machine to call automatically for new problems, jobs, etc., and to make whatever tests, checks, and so on, are needed. This is because of the extremely high operating speeds of the machine and the resulting high cost of human interventions. If the user is uncertain of the state of the computation at any point, he should simply test the computation with IF-type statements and detail the process to be carried out in each case. The machine may then operate most effectively on the problem, minimizing the number of machine halts.

25.4. The Computer User and the Computing Center

The development of pseudo-languages, similar to the compilers discussed in the preceding pages, has greatly increased the number of casual computer users in the field of machine computation. The computer user is no longer required to master the peculiarities of each machine, its word structure, instructions, etc., in order to solve his problems. Thus the computing operation is tending to become an "open-shop" operation with more and more problems actually being written for the computer by the person with whom they originated. In effect, the person most familiar with the problem is now in the position of communicating his problem directly to the machine in a reasonably familiar language.

What should the user expect of the computing center? Obviously, the people in the computing center are no longer required to become expert in all fields in order to program the machine. Instead, the computing center should provide an up-to-date library of subroutines, an efficient system for machine operation, and expert guidance in the solution of the user's difficulties. The computing center should be able to suggest the most effective numerical and analytical methods that may be employed and should be able to render assistance in checking out and correcting programs. An important aspect of the computing center is the development of a good liaison staff to communicate between the user and the center. This will allow the user to work on his problem with a minimum of disturbance in the regular daily routine.

The user's responsibility is a thorough knowledge of his problem and the method by which he wishes to obtain the solution. He should prepare carefully flow diagrams that are complete and accurate. Then he should become familiar with the particular compiler language used by the computing center with which he will deal. These compilers will differ slightly from the examples given since the attempt here was to show the general nature of compilers rather than any particular language in detail. The basic features will be the same, however. The user will generally find a language which resembles his own mathematical notation quite closely and in which he may easily express his flow diagram.

It is interesting to observe that programs written in compiler language fare much better when new and better machines appear than do programs written in machine language. The machine-language programs are so highly machine-dependent that it is very difficult to use them on any machine except the machine for which they were originally written. Compiler languages are much less machine-dependent, and therefore the new machine may either accept the former compiler language directly or may perform a small initial translation into its own compiler language. Since progress in the field is very rapid, this problem should receive careful attention when new programs are developed.

It is hoped that the reader will expend the small effort required to equip himself with a command of the compiler language. The personnel of a computing center will always remain ready to assist in the solution of the user's problem, but they can never become as intimately acquainted with the problem as can the individual who has the problem as his primary responsibility. The compiler language gives to the user the method that he has long needed to attack his problems on the computer without losing control of the process.

REFERENCES

The computer user will find a large bibliography available to him. In general, he should acquire the compiler manual associated with the machine which he wishes to use. The references below are general and include texts on numerical methods as well as texts concerning computers.

General Information on Computers

1. Engineering Research Associates: "High-speed Computing Devices," McGraw-Hill, New York, 1950.
2. Bowden, B. V.: "Faster than Thought," Pitman, London, 1953.
3. Booth, A. D., and K. H. V. Booth: "Automatic Digital Calculators," Academic Press, New York, 1956.
4. Richards, R. K.: "Arithmetic Operations in Digital Computers," Van Nostrand, Princeton, N.J., 1955.
5. Eckert. W. J., and R. Jones: "Faster, Faster," McGraw-Hill, New York, 1956.
6. Wilkes, M. V., D. J. Wheeler, and S. Gill: "Programs for an Electronic Digital Computer," 2d ed., Addison-Wesley, Reading, Mass., 1957.
7. Berkeley, E. C.: "Computers, Their Operation and Applications," Reinhold, New York, 1956.
7a. Scott, N. R.: "Analog and Digital Computer Technology," McGraw-Hill, New York, 1960.

Digital Computer Programming

8. McCracken, D. D.: "Digital Computer Programming," Wiley, New York, 1957.
9. McCracken, D. D., H. Weiss, and T. H. Lee: "Programming Business Computers," Wiley, New York, 1959.
10. Jeenel, J.: "An Introduction to Programming for Stored-program Calculators," McGraw-Hill, New York, 1959.
11. Gotlieb, C. C., and J. N. P. Hume: "High-speed Data Processing," McGraw-Hill, New York, 1958.
12. Wrubel, M. H.: "A Primer of Programming for Digital Computers," McGraw-Hill, New York, 1959.

Numerical Analysis

13. Scarborough, J. B.: "Numerical Analysis," 4th ed., Johns Hopkins Press, Baltimore, 1958.
14. Hildebrand, F. B.: "Introduction to Numerical Analysis," McGraw-Hill, New York, 1956.
15. Householder, A. S.: "Principles of Numerical Analysis," McGraw-Hill, New York, 1953.
16. Forsythe, G. E., and P. C. Rosenbloom: "Numerical Analysis and Partial Differential Equations," Wiley, New York, 1958.

Section 26

STRATIFIED FLOW

By

DONALD R. F. HARLEMAN, *Massachusetts Institute of Technology, Cambridge, Massachusetts*

STRATIFIED FLOW

26.1. Introduction

Fluid motions in a gravitational field which are originated or influenced by variations in density within the fluid are characterized by the term stratified flow. In a strict interpretation all free-surface liquid motions are stratified flows in the sense that the lower fluid (e.g., water) is overlain by a lighter fluid which is the earth's atmosphere. In this case the difference in fluid densities is so large (1 to 800) that the density, and therefore the inertia effects, of the upper fluid can be neglected in comparison with that of the lower. Hence such problems are reduced to the analysis of a single homogeneous fluid. In conventional usage, the term stratified flow refers to motions involving fluid masses of the same state. Therefore a heavier liquid flowing beneath a lighter liquid, or a heavier gas moving under a lighter gas, will be subject to gravitational effects which depend upon the difference between the two specific weights rather than upon the absolute magnitude of the specific weight of the heavier fluid. The less dense fluid may then be regarded as if it were weightless, and the more dense as if it were subjected to a reduced gravitational acceleration $g(\rho_2 - \rho_1)/\rho_2 = \Delta\gamma/\rho_2$, wherein the ratio $\Delta\gamma/\rho_2$ represents the effective gravitational acceleration, which may vary from the limit g to zero.

Nature has been generous in providing mechanisms for bringing about changes in temperature and for providing chemical solutions and solid-particle suspensions that give rise to variations in density and therefore specific weight. Many of the familar meteorological phenomena, the motion of *cold fronts* in particular, are manifestations of stratified flow. In parallel with atmospheric phenomena, the mechanism of the vast ocean currents owes much of its complexity to the existence of stratified flows. In the realm of control and utilization of surface waters, broadly characterized by the field of hydraulic engineering, the internal motions in sediment-laden streams and the understanding and control of salinity intrusion in tidal estuaries are among the most challenging of present-day problems dealing with stratified flow.

There is little to be gained by an attempted enumeration of all the possible natural phenomena in which the mechanics of stratified flow are involved. Many investigations have been directed toward analyses of highly specialized problems, and their discussion would involve a depth of background material which is precluded by the space allotted to this topic. The emphasis is therefore placed on the fundamental mechanics of stratified flow and on the presentation of certain applications to technological problems.

For convenience of discussion, the subject matter is divided into three broad categories:

Two-layered systems. Such systems are the simplest to treat analytically, and in many cases they represent a reasonable approximation to physical problems.

Multilayered systems and continuous-density gradients. An extension toward the more complex situation in which the fluid density varies continuously.

Diffusion in stratified flow. In addition to the convective motions associated with stratified flow, a nonconvective or diffusive phenomenon may be present when the flow is turbulent.

It is not surprising that most of the research has been centered around the first of the three subdivisions. However, it is apparent that the state of knowledge in all three categories is expanding rapidly.

In the analysis of stratified flow, the fluids (whether liquid or gaseous) are considered as incompressible because of the inherently small magnitude of the velocities. The density differences are therefore due to temperature gradients and variations in solute concentrations or variations in suspended solid concentrations and are independent of the pressure intensity and the elastic properties of the fluid.

26.2. Notation

a	amplitude of interfacial wave, ft
b	amplitude of surface wave; gate opening, ft
c	concentration, ppm
C	wave celerity, fps
e	base of natural logarithms
E	coefficient of eddy diffusion, ft²/sec
f	Darcy friction factor
$\mathbf{F'}$	densimetric Froude number
g	acceleration of gravity
g'	$g\Delta\rho/\rho$
G	mean rate of energy dissipation per unit mass, ft²/sec³
h	depth of layer, ft
H	difference in elevation, ft
k	$2\pi/L$
l	mean eddy size, ft
L	wavelength, ft
L_i	intrusion length, ft
p	pressure, psf
q	discharge per unit width, ft²/sec
q_s	sediment discharge per unit width, ft²/sec
R_H	hydraulic radius, ft
$\mathbf{R}$	Reynolds number
$\mathbf{R}_i$	Richardson number
s	specific gravity
S_E	slope of energy gradient
S_0	bottom slope
t	time, sec
$\bar{u}$	average velocity in x direction
u, v, w	velocity components in x, y, z direction
V	efflux velocity
z	elevation above datum
α	τ_i/τ_0; also kinetic-energy correction factor
γ	specific weight, lb/ft³
$\Delta(\ )$	difference in ( )
ϵ	kinematic eddy viscosity, ft²/sec
η	wave elevation with respect to undisturbed level
$\boldsymbol{\theta}$	stability parameter
ν	kinematic viscosity, ft²/sec
ρ	mass density, lb-sec²/ft⁴
τ	shear stress, psf

SUBSCRIPTS

0	bottom
1	upper layer
2	lower layer
i	interface
c	critical condition

26.3. Two-layered Systems

Two-layered systems represent the simplest case of a stratified flow. In a stable flow the denser fluid always tends to occupy the lowest position, and for purposes of analysis, the interface is assumed to be a streamline separating the two fluids and coincident with

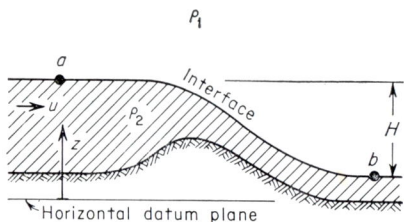

FIG. 26.1. Gravity flow in a two-layered system.

the density discontinuity. The similarity with the familar free-surface flows can be demonstrated by considering the two-layered system shown in Fig. 26.1, which might represent the downflow of cold air in a mountainous region or the spilling of salt water over a submerged barrier in an estuary. If both upper and lower fluids are assumed to be inviscid, the interface also represents a discontinuity in velocity between the moving lower layer and the stationary upper layer. For the moving lower-layer fluid, between points a and b, on the interface, the energy equation is

$$p_a + \rho_2 \frac{u_a{}^2}{2} + \rho_2 g z_a = p_b + \rho_2 \frac{u_b{}^2}{2} + \rho_2 g z_b \qquad (26.1)$$

For the static upper layer, between the same interfacial points,

$$p_a + \rho_1 g z_a = p_b + \rho_1 g z_b \qquad (26.2)$$

Since the pressures are continuous across the interface, they may be eliminated from Eq. (26.1) by this equation. If $H = z_a - z_b$ and $\Delta\rho = \rho_2 - \rho_1$, then

$$\frac{u_b{}^2 - u_a{}^2}{2} = \frac{\Delta\rho}{\rho_2} gH \qquad (26.3)$$

For the case in which the lower fluid is a liquid and the upper fluid is air, $\Delta\rho \cong \rho_2$, and Eq. (26.3) becomes identical with the free-surface equation. Therefore, as stated in the introduction, the lower-layer fluid may be considered as an analogous free-surface flow if the gravitational acceleration is reduced by the factor $\Delta\rho/\rho_2$. For convenience, the reduced gravitational acceleration is designated by a prime, $g(\Delta\rho/\rho_2) = g'$. It follows that the Froude number remains as the primary similitude parameter for the subsurface flows. In the generalized form, it is called the densimetric Froude number and may be written

$$\mathbf{F}' = \frac{u}{\sqrt{g'z}} \qquad (26.4)$$

The foregoing presentation, in emphasizing the similarity with familiar free-surface flows, represents an important simplification in analysis which is very often useful in rapidly estimating orders of magnitude for velocities or depths of stratified flows. Nevertheless, as in many fluid-mechanics problems, the effects of viscosity cannot always be ignored if more accurate answers are to be obtained. The differences between stratified and free-surface flows therefore become important. For example, in stratified flows, resistance at the fluid interface in addition to that at the fixed boundaries must be considered since discontinuities in velocity cannot exist at an interface between real fluids. In the following articles more detailed analyses of the mechanics of two-layered systems are presented.

26.4. Uniform Flow

A steady, uniform flow of a lower-layer fluid will occur along an incline when the driving gravity force per unit area (due to the density difference between the two fluids) is in equilibrium with the shear stresses exerted by the fixed boundary and the moving interfacial boundary. These flows have been referred to by various names: density currents, gravity currents, and underflows. Gravity currents due to temperature differences have been observed in the TVA system[1] where velocities of the underflow ranging from 0.15 to 0.35 fps have been measured. Numerous instances are known of the pas-

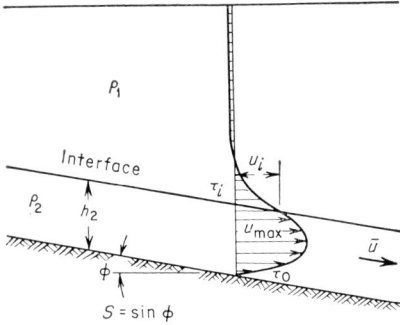

FIG. 26.2. Steady, uniform flow in lower-layer fluid.

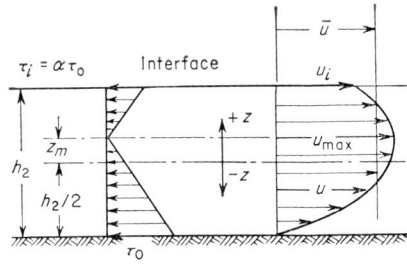

FIG. 26.3. Shear and velocity distribution in lower-layer fluid.

sage of underflows in reservoirs[2] where the density difference is due to suspended sediment.

If the depth of the upper fluid is assumed to be large compared with that of the lower fluid, the induced velocities in the upper layer may be neglected. The flow is shown schematically in Fig. 26.2. For two-dimensional flow (at a distance far enough from the origin of the current so that the velocity distribution is fully developed), the equilibrium equation is

$$\tau_0 + \tau_i = \Delta\rho\, g h_2 S \tag{26.5}$$

Under the assumption that the interface is smooth and distinct, use may be made of an analogy with flow between parallel boundaries in which the lower boundary is stationary and the upper boundary (interface) has a velocity u_i. The shear stress varies linearly from τ_0 at the bottom, to zero at the point of maximum velocity, to τ_i at the interface. By letting $\tau_i = \alpha\tau_0$, the interfacial shear stress is a constant proportion of the bottom shear and depends only on the vertical location of the maximum velocity. In the notation of the shear distribution shown in Fig. 26.3,

$$\alpha = \frac{1 - 2z_m/h_2}{1 + 2z_m/h_2} \tag{26.6}$$

After eliminating τ_i, Eq. (26.5) may be written

$$\tau_0 = \Delta\rho\, g\, \frac{h_2}{1 + \alpha}\, S \tag{26.7}$$

The shear stress τ_0 may also be expressed in terms of the friction factor f

$$\tau_0 = \frac{f}{4}\, \rho_2\, \frac{\bar{u}^2}{2} \tag{26.8}$$

By equating (26.7) and (26.8) and after solving for $\bar{u}$, the average velocity of the lower layer becomes

$$\bar{u} = \sqrt{8g'\, \frac{h_2 S}{f(1 + \alpha)}} \tag{26.9}$$

Equation (26.9) is a generalized form of the uniform-flow equation for open channels. For two-dimensional free-surface flow, $g = g'$, $\alpha = 0$, and $h_2 = R_H$; hence the Chézy equation,

$$\bar{u} = C\sqrt{R_H S} \tag{26.10}$$

is obtained as a special case of Eq. (26.9).

Laminar Flow. For the case of laminar flow, the shear-stress ratio can be found and the variation of the friction factor f with the Reynolds number can be determined analytically as shown by Ippen and Harleman.[3] The general form of the laminar velocity distribution can be expressed in terms of a single parameter J, a dimensionless number indicating a ratio of gravity and viscous forces.

$$J = \frac{(F'_2)^2}{R_2 S} \tag{26.11}$$

if
$$F'_2 = \frac{\bar{u}}{\sqrt{g'h_2}} \quad \text{and} \quad R_2 = \frac{\bar{u}h_2}{\nu}$$

In dimensionless form, the velocity distribution is

$$\frac{u}{\bar{u}} = 1 + 2\frac{z}{h_2} - \frac{1}{2J}\left[\left(\frac{z}{h_2}\right)^2 + \frac{1}{3}\frac{z}{h_2} - \frac{1}{12}\right] \tag{26.12}$$

The relation between the interface velocity u_i and u_{max} is found by differentiating the velocity distribution.

$$\frac{u_i}{u_{max}} = \frac{12J - 1}{12J^2 + 4J + \frac{1}{3}} \tag{26.13}$$

The ratio u_i/u_{max} can be shown to be a constant depending on the fluid properties if the region near the interface is treated as a problem of laminar-boundary-layer development between parallel streams. This problem has been investigated by Keulegan,[4] and for the case in which the densities and viscosities of the upper and lower fluids are approximately the same, the ratio u_i/u_{max} is equal to 0.59. Other values for a wide range of fluid properties are given by Potter.[5] From Eq. (26.13), $J = 0.14$, and the corresponding value of $\alpha = 0.64$. Equation (26.9) can be written

$$\bar{u} = 0.375 R_2^{\frac{1}{2}} (g'h_2 S)^{\frac{1}{2}} \tag{26.14}$$

The above equation for uniform laminar flow and the velocity-distribution Eq. (26.12) have been verified experimentally[3,6,7] for Reynolds numbers up to 1000, which can be regarded as the lower critical value for turbulent flow. In a study by Bata,[8] the effect of inlet length on the interfacial resistance in laminar flow is discussed. If the distance from the point of original contact of the two layers is small, it is shown that the interfacial shear depends on a parameter containing the depth-length ratio of the moving lower layer in addition to the Reynolds number of the moving fluid and the ratio of viscosities and densities of the fluids.

Turbulent Flow. In common with most turbulent-resistance problems, the uniform underflow in turbulent motion is not subject to exact analysis. In addition, experimental observations are relatively meager and because of the difficulties of field measurements are largely confined to laboratory flumes. Equation (26.9) provides a method of estimating orders of magnitude for velocities in turbulent flows. For two-dimensional flows the factor $1 + \alpha$ represents the amount by which the resistance coefficient f is increased by the presence of the interface, since $\alpha = 0$ for free-surface flows. By analogy with the corresponding free-surface flow, f may be obtained from the resistance diagram for flow in conduits (Moody diagram), using $4h_2$ as the hydraulic radius. The value of f thus obtained is to be increased by the factor $1 + \alpha$. Experimental velocity distributions by Bata and Bogich[6] in the lower-layer turbulent flow indicate that, on the average, the maximum velocity occurs at $0.7h_2$. Equation (26.6) gives a corresponding $\alpha = 0.43$ for turbulent flow. No systematic variation with Reynolds numbers $V4h_2/\nu < 10^5$ was observed. It is emphasized that Reynolds numbers for underflows tend to be smaller than for free-surface flows because of the small magnitude of the effective gravitational acceleration g'.

Any attempt to refine the analysis for turbulent flows is hindered by the fact that as the degree of turbulence increases, the interface becomes increasingly difficult to define because of mixing and resulting density gradients. The interfacial-stability problem is treated in Art. 26.7.

Sediment Transportation by Gravity Currents. Reservoir underflows are caused by sediment-laden river water entering a lake. The conditions at the so-called plunge point, where the river inflow disappears beneath the surface, are difficult to define because of the intense local mixing. The inflow becomes diluted, and the rapid reduction of velocities near the entrance is responsible for the deposition of the larger sediment particles and the formation of delta areas. Studies of gravity currents in reservoirs have shown that they consist primarily of particles in suspension less than 20 μ in diameter. The settling rate for particles of this diameter is approximately 0.001 fps. Thus turbulent fluctuations of the order of 1 per cent in a current having a mean velocity of only 0.1 fps would be sufficient to keep such particles in suspension.

Lake Mead surveys[2] have indicated the existence of underflows with a density difference as small as $\Delta\rho/\rho = 0.0005$. If the average bottom slope is taken as 5 ft/mile ($S = 0.0009$) and measurements indicate a depth of 15 ft for the moving current, the order of magnitude of the underflow velocity can be obtained from Eq. (26.9).

Example. Assume $f = 0.010$ and $\alpha = 0.43$ for turbulent flow. From Eq. (26.9)

$$\bar{u} = \sqrt{\frac{8(0.0005)(32.2)(15)(0.0009)}{0.010(1.43)}} = 0.35 \text{ fps}$$

The Reynolds number, for two-dimensional flow, is therefore

$$\frac{4Vh_2}{\nu} = 1.7 \times 10^6$$

The friction factor f for this Reynolds number is within 10 per cent of the assumed value, and a further refinement of the calculation is not warranted. The computed velocity of 0.35 fps (6 miles/day) is consistent with actual measurements in Lake Mead.

The per cent concentration of the sediment (by weight) P is related to the density difference as follows:

$$\frac{P}{100} = \frac{\Delta\rho}{\rho}\frac{1}{1 - s_f/s_s}$$

in which s_f and s_s are the specific gravities of the water and sediment, respectively. For the above conditions, $P = 0.08$ per cent and the sediment discharge per unit width is

$$q_s = \frac{0.08}{100}(0.35)15 = 0.004 \text{ cfs/ft}$$

which is equivalent to a sediment transport rate of 30 tons/(day)(foot) of width of the underflow.

A large number of channel experiments on the transportation of sediment by density currents have been carried out in the laboratory at Chatou.[9]

One meteorological counterpart of the reservoir underflows is the duststorms, which have been responsible for the transport of vast quantities of topsoil in arid regions. In the field of oceanography, Daly[10] and Kuenen[11] have proposed submarine mud flows as primary agents in the formation of certain canyons on the ocean floor.

An interesting feature of the underflows described in this section is the formation of the initial *head* of the flow. As the gravity current moves along, it displaces the lighter fluid upward. A force must be provided (to accelerate the lighter fluid initially at rest) which is larger than the gravity forces, maintaining the subsequent motion where only interfacial resistance between the upper fluid is encountered. The increased driving force for the head of the flow calls for an increase in the initial depth which is approximately twice the depth for the uniform flow. The shape of the front for liquids of small density difference was initially investigated by Ippen and Harleman[3] and later by Keulegan[12] in more detail. Some quantitative comparisons between the hydraulic experiments and observations of the head of an undercutting cold air mass were made by Berson.[13]

26.5. Nonuniform Flow

The one-dimensional equations of motion for the steady, nonuniform flow of a two-layered system have been given by Schijf and Schönfeld.[14] If the vertical accelerations in the fluids are neglected and only the mean velocities in the respective layers are considered, the equations in accordance with the notation of Fig. 26.4 are, for the upper layer,

$$\frac{dh_1}{dx} + \frac{dh_2}{dx} + \frac{u_1}{g}\frac{du_1}{dx} + S_{1E} - S_0 = 0 \tag{26.15}$$

and for the lower layer,

$$\left(1 - \frac{\Delta\rho}{\rho_2}\right)\frac{dh_1}{dx} + \frac{dh_2}{dx} + \frac{u_2}{g}\frac{du_2}{dx} + S_{2E} - S_0 = 0 \tag{26.16}$$

The continuity equations for the upper and lower layers are

$$u_1\frac{dh_1}{dx} + h_1\frac{du_1}{dx} = 0 \tag{26.17}$$

and

$$u_2\frac{dh_2}{dx} + h_2\frac{du_2}{dx} = 0 \tag{26.18}$$

S_0 is the slope of the channel bottom, and the energy gradients S_{1E} and S_{2E} are defined by

$$S_{1E} = \frac{\tau_i}{\gamma h_1} \qquad S_{2E} = \frac{\tau_0 - \tau_i}{\gamma h_2}$$

in which the shear stresses, τ_0 at the bottom and τ_i at the interface, are given by

$$\tau_i = f_i\frac{\rho}{8}|u_1 - u_2|(u_1 - u_2) \qquad \tau_0 = f_0\frac{\rho}{8}|u_2|u_2$$

In the expressions for shear and energy gradients, the densities and specific weights of the two fluids have been approximated by $\rho = (\rho_1 + \rho_2)/2$. These equations have been applied by Bata[15] for the location of interfaces in connection with the recirculation of cooling water between the intake and outlet of a thermoelectric power plant.

The equations for the two-layered, nonuniform flow may be applied to the problem of the stationary salt wedge in an estuary as a particular example of their application. When a fresh-water river discharges into a saline ocean in which the range of tide is small, there may not be sufficient energy to cause appreciable interfacial mixing, and a salt wedge overridden by the fresh water will result, as shown in Fig. 26.5. The steady-state (mean-tide level) shape and position of the wedge with respect to the ocean entrance is found by observing that the salt wedge will intrude until the fresh-water flow at the ocean entrance becomes a control section. The conditions for critical flow, after neg-

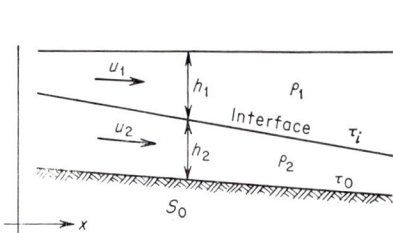

FIG. 26.4. Steady, nonuniform flow in a two-layered system.

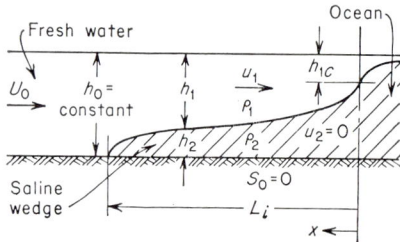

FIG. 26.5. Arrested saline wedge near the ocean entrance of a fresh-water channel.

lecting changes in the total depth h_0, are found by subtracting Eq. (26.16) from Eq. (26.15) and by substituting the continuity equations, thus:

$$(\mathbf{F'}_2)^2 + (\mathbf{F'}_1)^2 - 1 = \frac{S_{1E} - S_{2E}}{\dfrac{\Delta \rho \, d h_1}{\rho \, dx}} \qquad (26.19)$$

At the critical-flow section dh_1/dx becomes infinite and

$$(\mathbf{F'}_2)^2_c + (\mathbf{F'}_1)^2_c - 1 = 0 \qquad (26.20)$$

When both upper and lower layers are in motion there are an infinite number of solutions for Eq. (26.20). (See also Refs. 16, 17, and 18.) However, for the stationary salt wedge, the mean velocity in the lower layer is zero; hence $\mathbf{F'}_2 = 0$, and $(\mathbf{F'}_1)_c = 1$. In the region $x = 0 \rightarrow L_i$, $\tau_0 \cong 0$, and Eq. (26.19) can be written

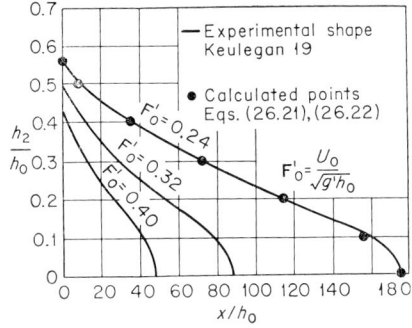

Fig. 26.6. Shape of arrested saline wedges showing effect of changing fresh-water velocity.

$$\frac{h_1}{h_0}\left[\frac{1}{5(\mathbf{F'}_0)^2}\left(\frac{h_1}{h_0}\right)^4 - \frac{1}{4(\mathbf{F'}_0)^2}\left(\frac{h_1}{h_0}\right)^3 - \frac{1}{2}\left(\frac{h_1}{h_0}\right) + 1 \right] + 3(\mathbf{F'}_0)^{2/3}\left[\frac{1}{10}(\mathbf{F'}_0)^{2/3} - \frac{1}{4} \right] = \frac{\bar{f}_i}{8}\frac{x}{h_0} \qquad (26.21)$$

If, for one condition of fresh-water flow (specified by $\mathbf{F'}_0$), the length of the wedge L_i is known, the average interfacial friction factor $\bar{f}_i$ can be computed by writing Eq. (26.21) at $x = L_i$, where $h_1 = h_0$. Hence

$$\bar{f}_i = \frac{2h_0}{L_i}\left[\frac{1}{5(\mathbf{F'}_0)^2} - 2 + 3(\mathbf{F'}_0)^{2/3} - \tfrac{6}{5}(\mathbf{F'}_0)^{4/3} \right] \qquad (26.22)$$

The shape of the saline wedge can then be computed from Eq. (26.21) as a function of x. Figure 26.6 shows the above theory compared with one of the stationary saline wedges obtained in an extensive series of experiments by Keulegan.[19] Experimental and analytical work has also been done on a number of other instances of nonuniform flow in a two-layered system. Stommel and Farmer[17,20] have investigated the effect of an abrupt change in width, and Long[21] has described the flow of superimposed layers over a barrier. In the latter case, three regimes of motion are possible: If the velocities in each layer are sufficiently small, the interface (except for a slight depression over the barrier) is disturbed only a small amount. At intermediate speeds an interfacial hydraulic jump occurs downstream from the barrier and the lower layer increases in depth in the upstream direction. At high velocities the interface swells symmetrically over the barrier.

The hydraulic jump in a two-layered system has been investigated by Tepper[22] and Yih.[23] According to an analysis based on the momentum principle, by neglecting interfacial shear, there can be only three states conjugate to a given state. If the densimetric

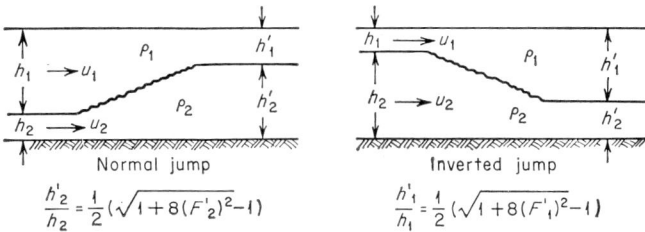

$$\frac{h'_2}{h_2} = \frac{1}{2}(\sqrt{1 + 8(F'_2)^2} - 1) \qquad\qquad \frac{h'_1}{h_1} = \frac{1}{2}(\sqrt{1 + 8(F'_1)^2} - 1)$$

Fig. 26.7. Hydraulic jumps in a two-layered system.

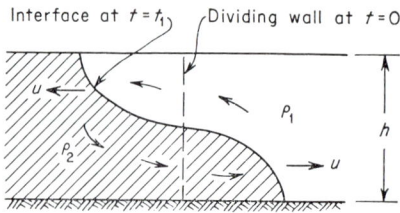

FIG. 26.8. Internal surge following removal of a dividing wall.

Froude number of either layer is predominantly large, there is only one conjugate state and the downstream conditions are uniquely determined. In the special case in which one of the layers is at rest, the jump equations are similar to the free-surface equation provided the densimetric Froude number is used. Figure 26.7 shows both normal and inverted jumps for the special case discussed above.

A few examples of unsteady, nonuniform flow in two-layered systems have been treated. The classical problem in this category is the motion following the removal of a vertical dividing wall separating liquids of different densities as shown in Fig. 26.8. In the case of a channel of uniform width (such as a lock between fresh and salt water), the initial velocity of both upper and lower interfaces is

$$u = 0.45\sqrt{g'h} \qquad (26.23)$$

For surges arising from a tideless sea and entering a rectangular channel with the water initially at rest, the numerical constant in Eq. (26.23) was found by Keulegan[24] to be 0.57.

26.6. Internal-wave Motion

In a two-layered system of fluids of different density, waves at the interface are known as internal waves. Much of the basic theory was developed before 1900 (beginning with the work of Stokes[25] in 1847) and represents the first analytical approach to problems of stratified flow.

In the most general case, two parallel streams in relative motion are considered as shown in Fig. 26.9. An oscillatory wave motion exists at both the interface and the free surface of the upper layer. The celerity or speed of propagation of the interfacial waves is given by

$$C_2 = \frac{Ru_2 + Tu_1}{R + T} \pm \left[\frac{g(\rho_2 - \rho_1)}{k(R + T)} - \frac{RT}{(R + T)^2}(u_2 - u_1)^2 \right]^{1/2} \qquad (26.24)$$

if

$$k = \frac{2\pi}{L}$$

$$R = \rho_2 \coth kh_2 \qquad T = \rho_1 \left[\coth kh_1 - \frac{b/a}{\sinh(kh_1)} \right]$$

The ratio of amplitudes of the interfacial and surface waves is

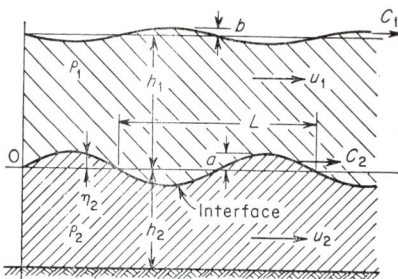

FIG. 26.9. Oscillatory wave motion in a two-layered system.

$$\frac{a}{b} = \cosh kh_1 - \frac{g \sinh kh_1}{k(u_1 - C_2)^2} \qquad (26.25)$$

In the absence of the parallel currents (that is, $u_1 = u_2 = 0$), the celerity and amplitude equations become

$$C_2{}^2 = \frac{g(\rho_2 - \rho_1)}{k(R + T)} \qquad (26.26)$$

$$\frac{a}{b} = \cosh kh_1 - \frac{g \sinh kh_1}{kC_2{}^2} \qquad (26.27)$$

The celerity equation involves the amplitude ratio, and the amplitude equation involves the celerity; hence they must be solved simultaneously. Of the various special cases that may be considered, one of the most interesting is that in which kh_2 is large (i.e., the depth of the lower layer is large compared with the wavelength). By putting coth $kh_2 = 1$, $R = \rho_2$, the celerity and amplitude equations may be approximated by

$$C_2{}^2 = \frac{g(\rho_2 - \rho_1)}{k(\rho_2 + \rho_1 \coth kh_1)} \tag{26.28}$$

$$\frac{a}{b} = -\frac{\rho_1 e^{kh_1}}{\rho_2 - \rho_1} \tag{26.29}$$

From Eq. (26.29) it can be seen that in the case of a layer of fresh water upon the salt water of the ocean, the amplitude of the interfacial waves is many times larger than that of the surface waves. Hence a wave generated at the interface would have practically no effect upon the free surface. On the other hand, the same wave generated at the free surface would produce interfacial waves of large amplitude. Ekman[26] has used this conclusion to explain the abnormal resistance of ships sailing in stratified waters. Some of the energy usually applied to overcome ordinary ship resistance is dissipated by the generation of interfacial waves.

In the open ocean, because of thermal stratification, very long internal waves are known to exist. The celerity of these waves can be obtained from Eq. (26.26) by noting that as kh becomes small, coth kh may be replaced by $1/kh$ and

$$C_2{}^2 = \frac{gh_2 h_1(\rho_2 - \rho_1)}{(h_1 + h_2)\rho_2} \tag{26.30}$$

Here it is assumed that $\rho_2 - \rho_1$ is a small quantity, that the wavelength is long compared with the total depth $h_1 + h_2$, and that the effect of the earth's rotation can be neglected. Haurwitz[27] has given a more detailed analysis, including the geostrophic effect, and has shown the occurrence of internal waves whose period closely coincides with the tidal period. The internal solitary wave consists of a single elevation of finite height traveling on the interface, as shown in Fig. 26.10. In addition, a smaller solitary wave occurs at the surface. In contrast to the oscillatory waves considered above, the solitary wave is a wave of translation, in the sense that fluid particles are displaced a finite amount in the direction of wave propagation. The wavelength of a solitary wave is theoretically infinite since the wave profile approaches the undisturbed interface asymptotically. The analysis is greatly simplified if the free surface is replaced by a rigid horizontal boundary (which in effect is to ignore the formation of the surface wave). Under this assumption, the celerity of an internal solitary wave of amplitude a is given by

$$C_0{}^2 = C_2{}^2 \left(1 + \frac{h_1 - h_2}{h_1 h_2} a\right) \tag{26.31}$$

in which C_2 is given by Eq. (26.30). The wave profile is

$$\eta = a \operatorname{sech}^2 \beta \frac{x}{h_2} \tag{26.32}$$

if

$$\beta = \left(\frac{1}{2} \frac{h_1 - h_2}{h_1} \frac{a}{h_1}\right)^{1/2}$$

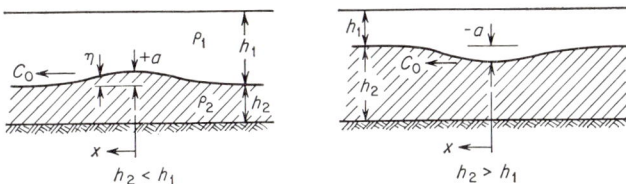

FIG. 26.10. Solitary wave in a two-layered system.

The above equations show that the relative thicknesses of the two layers have an important bearing on the formation of solitary waves. When $h_2 < h_1$, the wave is of the positive type, and when $h_2 > h_1$, the wave is inverted and the amplitude a takes a negative value. When the two layers have the same depth and the density difference is small, the existence of a solitary wave is excluded by the rigid free-surface assumption. The experimental and analytical studies of the internal solitary wave are due to Keulegan,[28,29] Long,[30] and Abdullah.[31] In general, the theoretical results have been substantiated by the laboratory experiments. A more complete analytical study of the solitary wave in two-layered systems has been given by Peters and Stoker[32] without the rigid boundary restriction on the free surface.

Additional examples and analyses of internal-wave motions in a two-layered system including the internal standing wave, or seiche, are presented by Proudman (Ref. 33, chap. 15). Internal waves are usually located in the near-surface regions of the oceans and are of considerable importance in the navigation and detection of submarines. The mixing aspect of internal-wave motion is considered in the following article.

26.7. Interfacial Mixing

Internal-wave motion must contribute appreciably to the internal mixing in stratified fluids through the mechanism of breaking of the large-amplitude interfacial waves. One approach to the question of interfacial stability is through the general celerity equation for internal waves, Eq. (26.24). Let the velocity of the lower layer be u_2, as before, and that of the upper layer be zero. In stable waves the celerity C_2 is real; however, it is readily seen that if the second term under the radical of Eq. (26.24) is greater than the first term, the celerity becomes imaginary and the waves are presumed to be breaking. By equating the terms under the radical and designating the velocity of the lower layer as u_{2c}, there results

$$\frac{u_{2c}}{\sqrt{g'h_2(L/\pi h_2)}} = [\tfrac{1}{2}(\tanh kh_2 + \tanh kh_1)]^{1/2} \qquad (26.33)$$

provided the density difference is small and the amplitude of the free-surface wave is neglected. For short wavelengths ($kh \geq 2$), the right-hand side of the above equation reduces to unity and Eq. (26.33) can be written

$$\frac{u_{2c}}{\sqrt{g'h_2(L/\pi h_2)}} = 1 \qquad (26.34)$$

Thus for a given depth of the moving lower layer, the tendency for instability increases as the wavelength L becomes shorter. Ippen and Harleman[3] have shown that in a small laboratory flume the waves at the interface of the moving lower-layer liquid in laminar motion begin to break approximately in accordance with the relation $L = \pi h_2$. Therefore it would appear from Eq. (26.34) that the interfacial instability is associated with a value of the densimetric Froude number (of the lower layer) equal to or greater than unity. The relative instability of free-surface flows, under critical conditions, is well known and tends to substantiate the above conclusions for interfacial waves.

The foregoing analysis is based on the presumption of irrotational motion. An attempt at a more sophisticated approach to interfacial-wave stability has been made by Tchen,[34] who has extended the Helmholtz stability theory to include the effects of viscosity and surface tension. Yih[35] has also discussed the stability of two-dimensional parallel flows for three-dimensional disturbances. From dimensional reasoning it is possible to obtain a stability parameter involving the effect of viscosity. It is apparent that the purely gravitational stability expressed by Eq. (26.34) must cease to be valid as the density difference, hence g', approaches zero. Since, under this condition, the left side of this equation is greater than unity for all wavelengths, the parameter defined by Keulegan[36] is

$$\theta = \frac{\nu_2 g'}{u_2{}^3} \qquad (26.35)$$

in which u_2 is the velocity of the lower layer relative to the upper layer. For a two-dimensional flow with h_2 taken as the characteristic length in the Reynolds number, the stability parameter is readily transformed into

$$\theta = \frac{1}{(F'_2)^2 R_2} \qquad (26.35a)$$

On the basis of experiments at MIT[3] and the Bureau of Standards,[36] the critical values of G are as follows:

Laminar flow (lower layer): $\theta_c = \dfrac{1}{R_2}$

Turbulent flow (lower layer): $\theta_c = 0.18$

No mixing should occur for flows with θ values greater than θ_c. The transition to turbulent flow begins at a Reynolds number of approximately 1000 in the tests cited above.

An observer of the process of interfacial mixing is impressed by the extreme stability exhibited by adjacent layers with density differences as small as a few tenths of a per cent. Even after the interfacial waves have begun to break, the amount of lower-layer fluid entrained in the upper layer is relatively small. Ultimately, this type of mixing process tends to form a new layer, with a density intermediate to that of the original layers. In this way a three-layered system is produced; consideration of the multilayered systems of stratified flow is reserved for a subsequent article. In all the foregoing it is assumed that the heavier fluid is beneath the lighter, inasmuch as the reverse case is unstable under all conditions.

26.8. Selective Withdrawal of Fluid

The ability to selectively withdraw fluid from a region in which the fluid density varies in the vertical direction is a significant advance which has been brought about by an understanding of the mechanics of stratified flow. Density differences may occur because of temperature differentials, suspended sediment, dissolved salts, or other chemicals. Consequently, a large number of technological fields are finding applications for selective withdrawal or some degree of control of stratified fluids.

Control structures are in use to provide cooler water at the condenser intakes of thermal-power plants located near sources of water which are stratified because of temperature differences. Lakes or artificial reservoirs are used as large heat exchangers for nuclear power plants, making it necessary to design intakes to withdraw the low-level cool water and to distribute the inflow of warm water near the surface. The use of thermal stratification, which exists in tropical seas, as a source of energy has raised the question of the degree of selectivity which exists at an intake in a fluid having a vertical density gradient. The reduction of reservoir sedimentation by removal, at the dam, of water containing large amounts of suspended sediment has been suggested as a means of prolonging the useful life of major structures. In the area of density variations due to dissolved salts, the control of salinity intrusion by barriers and locks separating freshwater channels from an ocean or estuary may be mentioned.

A common feature of the applications described is the fact that in all cases the fluids are miscible, essentially incompressible, and similar in viscosity and the density differences are small. Additional applications in cases of immiscible fluids of different viscosity might arise in the separation of petroleum products and in other liquid-liquid separation processes. The advent of low-cost atomic-energy sources should bring a degree of atmospheric pollution control, through selective withdrawal, within the realm of possibility.

Craya[37] has treated the withdrawal of fluid from a two-layer system with a horizontal intake located on a vertical boundary (as in the case of the upstream face of a dam). The intake is located above the initially horizontal interface (Fig. 26.11a). It is desired to determine the flow of the upper fluid necessary to raise the interface locally to the level of the intake, at which time discharge from the lower layer begins. The efflux

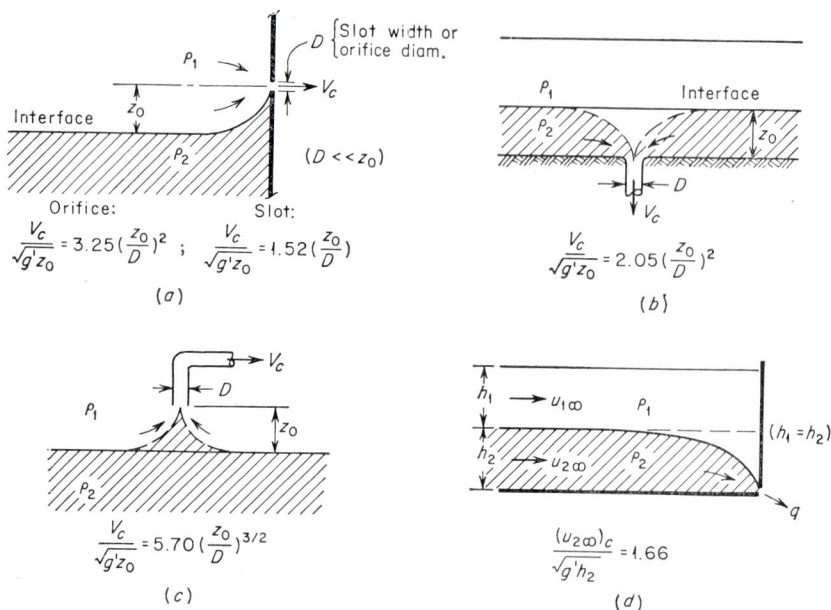

$$\frac{V_c}{\sqrt{g'z_0}} = 3.25 \left(\frac{z_0}{D}\right)^2 \quad ; \quad \frac{V_c}{\sqrt{g'z_0}} = 1.52 \left(\frac{z_0}{D}\right)$$

(a)

$$\frac{V_c}{\sqrt{g'z_0}} = 2.05 \left(\frac{z_0}{D}\right)^2$$

(b)

$$\frac{V_c}{\sqrt{g'z_0}} = 5.70 \left(\frac{z_0}{D}\right)^{3/2}$$

(c)

$$\frac{(u_{2\infty})_c}{\sqrt{g'h_2}} = 1.66$$

(d)

FIG. 26.11. Selective withdrawal of fluid for various boundary conditions in two-layered systems.

velocity at this critical condition is designated V_c. Intakes in the form of horizontal line sinks and three-dimensional point sinks are considered for the case in which the vertical extent of both the upper and lower layers is unlimited.

The critical-efflux-velocity equations for both the two- and three-dimensional conditions are shown in Fig. 26.11a. It is assumed that the size of the slit or orifice is small in comparison with the height of the opening above the original interface (z). The equations have been substantiated by the experiments of Gariel[38] for the same boundary conditions.

For the case in which the lower layer is limited in vertical extent Harleman et al.[39] have investigated, analytically and experimentally, the efflux from a vertical circular intake in the bottom boundary as shown in Fig. 26.11b. The maximum discharge (from the lower layer) without simultaneous withdrawal from the upper layer is determined. In addition to the efflux equation given in Fig. 26.11b, the effect of reentrant intake geometries is discussed in the reference cited.

In a brief exploratory study, Rouse[40] has given some experimental results for a vertical-axis circular intake pipe withdrawing the lighter of two stratified fluids from a point above the interface. Both fluids are assumed to be of unlimited extent as shown in Fig. 26.11c. The efflux equation has been reduced to a form comparable with cases a and b of the same figure.

Huber[41] has obtained an analytical solution for the steady, two-dimensional flow induced by a line sink located at the bottom corner of a rectangular channel in which two fluid strata (of equal depth) extend to infinity in the $-x$ direction (Fig. 26.11d). If the fluids are at rest, the interface will be horizontal. As the strength of the sink is increased, the lower layer will start to flow until the interface is drawn down to the sink and the upper fluid begins to take part in the flow. The shape of the interface is determined by relaxation techniques. The critical densimetric Froude number for which the upper layer is stationary is $\mathbf{F}'_2 = 1.66$. As the flow from the slit is increased, the Froude number of the upper layer increases and that of the lower layer decreases. A point is reached, however, when this trend is changed, and both discharges then increase together as the densimetric Froude numbers approach equality.

The efflux problem described above may be considered as a limiting case of a more general boundary configuration in which the vertical height of the slot is comparable with the depth of the lower layer. The boundary conditions shown in Fig. 26.12a have been investigated by Harleman, Gooch, and Ippen[42] in connection with the design of condenser water intakes for thermal-power plants. It is desired to determine, for a given gate opening b and interface elevation h_r, the limiting discharge for the colder stratum of water. In the analysis, based on the one-dimensional energy equation, it is necessary to account for both the nonuniform velocity distribution and the nonhydrostatic pressure distribution in the plane of the vertical gate. The critical Froude number for the lower-layer flow is shown as a function of h_r/b and the kinetic-energy parameter α in Fig. 26.12b. Laboratory tests have essentially verified the curves for the high values of α associated with small-scale flume tests. In

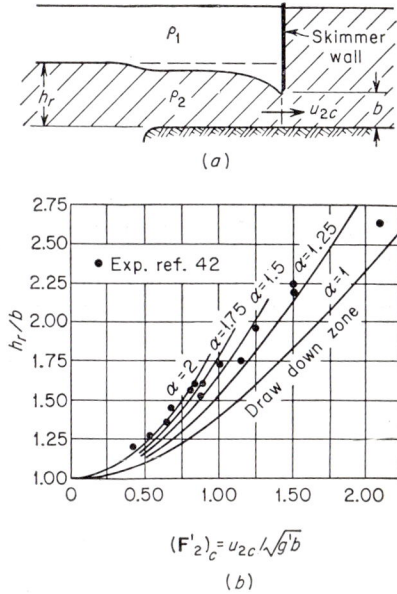

(a)

(b)

Fig. 26.12. Submerged sluice characteristics at incipient drawdown of the upper layer.

the absence of definitive field information, a value of $\alpha = 1.10$ has been assumed to be reasonable for prototype conditions of turbulent flow. Engineering applications of this type of control structure for cooling water intakes have been described by Elder,[43,44] who compares field data on water-intake temperatures obtained before and after completion of a skimmer wall. Angelin and Flagestad[45] report on a model study of a particular intake structure designed to take advantage of thermal stratification.

26.9. Multilayered Systems and Continuous-density Gradients

The state of knowledge in the case of multilayered stratified fluids and fluids with continuous-density gradients is much less well developed than in the two-layered systems. No attempt will be made to subdivide this section into the exact counterparts of the two-layer flows or to provide detailed quantitative abstracts of the various investigations.

The classical works of Love, Rayleigh, Burnside, Fjeldstad, and Wedderburn on the theory of wave motion in a heterogeneous liquid (density a function of the vertical coordinate) are presented by Lamb[25] and Proudman.[33] In the case of standing waves in a stratified body of fluid consisting of n homogeneous layers, there are $n - 1$ internal standing waves, or seiches. The wave of first order is characterized by vertical displacements in the same direction from top to bottom and a maximum amplitude at one level. The second-order wave is characterized by vertical displacements in opposite directions within an upper and lower level and by two maxima of amplitude, and so on. Observations of vertical displacements of water masses which may be due to internal waves have been made on numerous occasions[46,47] in oceanographic explorations.

The contributions of Bjerknes, Lyra, Queney, and Scorer on the problem of airflow over mountains and the combined effects of stratification and the earth's rotation are concisely summarized by Prandtl.[48] Since 1950, a renewed interest in the meteorological aspects of flows with continuous-density gradients has been apparent from the investigations of Rossby,[49] Long,[21,50,51] and Yih.[52] The latter has established the link between flows with a continuous-density variation and those with a large number of discrete layers. It has been shown that the continuous-density variation can be analyzed as the limiting case of the multilayered system. Peters and Stoker[32] have given an analysis of the problem of solitary waves in an incompressible fluid with a continuous-density variation.

One of the most interesting aspects of the motion in a fluid having a vertical density gradient is the condition necessary for the maintenance of vertical turbulence. The change of potential energy due to vertical mixing must be balanced by a change in the kinetic energy of the motion producing the mixing. If it is assumed that the kinetic energy of the turbulence remains constant, then the energy must be supplied from the mean horizontal motion u. Introducing the coefficient of eddy diffusivity for the vertical direction E_z, the time rate of increase of potential energy per unit volume is

$$gE_z \frac{\partial \rho}{\partial z}$$

if

$$E_z = -\frac{\overline{w'\rho'}}{\partial \rho / \partial z}$$

and the primed quantities are the fluctuating components of the mean quantities. The time rate at which kinetic energy is lost from the mean motion per unit volume, in terms of the coefficient of eddy viscosity ϵ_z, is

$$\rho \epsilon_z \left(\frac{\partial u}{\partial z} \right)^2$$

if

$$\epsilon_z = -\frac{\overline{\rho u'w'}}{\rho \partial u / \partial z}$$

The criterion for the maintenance of vertical turbulence is given by the ratio of the above quantities, which is known as the Richardson number:

$$\mathbf{R}_i = \frac{g \partial \rho / \partial z}{\rho (\partial u / \partial z)^2}$$

If, therefore, a motion is established such that $\mathbf{R}_i > 1$, it cannot be turbulent. Taylor,[53] Goldstein,[65] and Drazin[66] have calculated the conditions for stability for various density and velocity distributions. For the case in which the upper and lower fluids (of infinite extent and moving with uniform velocities U_1 and U_2) are separated by a layer of intermediate density, the motion is nonturbulent if $\mathbf{R}_i > \frac{1}{4}$. The presence of a solid boundary (as in the case of flow over a flat plate) leads to considerably smaller values of $\mathbf{R}_i$ for stability, as has been shown by Schlichting (Ref. 54, p. 358).

The stability considerations show that (for a body of water with an initially linear density gradient) surface cooling will promote vertical turbulence near the surface since $\partial \rho / \partial z$ is decreased. When surface waters are heated, turbulent mixing will be retarded.

If $\partial \rho / \partial z$ is very large, there will be little vertical mixing or internal friction across horizontal surfaces. In the limiting case of a surface of discontinuity of density, it is often assumed that there is neither mixing nor friction. Another remarkable property of continuously stratified flows which has been pointed out by Yih[55] is the stiffening of the streamlines of constant density against vertical displacements when the motion is laminar. Thus vertical motion is inhibited by the density variation and the presence of a gravitational field if the disturbance is weak. This phenomenon was first demonstrated by Gariel[38] in an experimental investigation of the flow produced by a thin slit (Fig. 26.11a) for a liquid with a linear density variation. The vertical thickness of the principal horizontal current created by the discharge through the slit was shown to be a function of the density gradient, discharge rate, and fluid viscosity.

For the boundary conditions shown in Fig. 26.11d, Debler[56] has reported some experiments on the discharge of a linearly stratified liquid through a horizontal slit at the bottom corner of a two-dimensional channel.   In this case the densimetric Froude number is defined as

$$\mathbf{F}'' = \frac{q}{h^2}\sqrt{\frac{h\rho_0}{g\,\Delta\rho}}$$

in which q = slit discharge
h = total depth
ρ_0 = density at channel bottom
$\Delta\rho$ = density difference between surface and bottom

The experiments show that when $\mathbf{F}''$ is less than 0.28, the flow pattern is divided into two horizontal regions: an upper, essentially stagnant region and a lower region in which the entire discharge is concentrated.   At Froude numbers greater than this critical value, the entire depth of the fluid takes part in the flow toward the outlet.   Yih[55] had previously predicted analytically a critical densimetric Froude number of $1/\pi = 0.32$ for the same boundary conditions.

26.10. Diffusion in Stratified Fluids

The mechanics of stratified flow might logically be considered in three phases, the first a study of the patterns of flow in well-defined layers, the second an investigation of the stability of the layered flow, and the third a treatment of the advanced stages of mixing well beyond the point of instability.   The first two phases have already been discussed in the foregoing articles, and it remains to consider the problem of turbulent diffusion in a stratified flow.   To place a bound on the scope of this article consistent with the foregoing articles, only incompressible fluids will be included, thus excluding the large field of free-convection heat transfer in compressible media.

The mechanism of vertical diffusion across a horizontal interface between liquids of slightly different density has been investigated experimentally by Rouse and Dodu.[57] Turbulence was generated mechanically in the upper liquid by an oscillating grid a fixed distance above the interface.   The turbulence produced in the upper stratum did not penetrate into the lower layer, but produced interfacial cusps from which streamers were lifted and diffused throughout the upper layer.   This is contrary to the formation of a buffer layer of intermediate density, as in the case of breaking interfacial waves between parallel streams.   It is concluded that the formation of the intermediate layer is a characteristic of shear-generated turbulence.

The equation expressing the turbulent mixing of incompressible fluids containing at least one property in varying amounts is known as the convective-diffusion equation. Basically, it is a conservation of mass expression, and it should not be confused with a dynamical equation of motion.   Let the concentration of the property (e.g., salinity) be denoted by c and u, v, w the mean-velocity components in the x, y, z directions.   Then

$$\frac{\partial c}{\partial t} + u\frac{\partial c}{\partial x} + v\frac{\partial c}{\partial y} + w\frac{\partial c}{\partial z} = \frac{\partial}{\partial x}\left(E_x\frac{\partial c}{\partial x}\right) + \frac{\partial}{\partial y}\left(E_y\frac{\partial c}{\partial y}\right) + \frac{\partial}{\partial z}\left(E_z\frac{\partial c}{\partial z}\right) \quad (26.36)$$

if E_x, E_y, and E_z are the coefficients of eddy diffusivity.   The equation shows that the transport of the property due to turbulent diffusion is independent of the transport due to the mean current.   Numerous solutions of simplified forms of the general Eq. (26.36) have been obtained, and one example is presented in some detail.

26.11. Unsteady, One-dimensional Diffusion

If the mean motion of the fluid is zero ($u = v = w = 0$) and the concentration gradients in the y, z directions are small compared with the gradient in the x direction, Eq. (26.36) reduces to the following:

$$\frac{\partial c}{\partial t} = \frac{\partial}{\partial x}\left(E_x\frac{\partial c}{\partial x}\right) \quad (26.37)$$

Furthermore, if the turbulence is homogeneous (E_x = const),

$$\frac{\partial c}{\partial t} = E_x \frac{\partial^2 c}{\partial x^2} \tag{26.38}$$

In this form the equation is analogous to that of one-dimensional heat conduction in a thin rod. The solution of Eq. (26.38) for a semi-infinite medium extending in the x direction with a constant concentration c_0, maintained at the boundary $x = 0$, is given by

$$\frac{c}{c_0} = 1 - \text{erf}\ \frac{x}{2\sqrt{E_x t}} \tag{26.39}$$

in which erf denotes the error function. Thus the concentration is given at any (x, t) for a particular value of E_x. Various theories of turbulent diffusion show that the coefficient of eddy diffusivity is given by

$$E_x = \text{const}\ G^{1/3} l^{4/3} \tag{26.40}$$

in which G is the mean rate of energy dissipation per unit mass of fluid, and l is a measure of the scale of the turbulence (mean eddy size). The relation has been verified experimentally by Orlob[58] and by Harleman and Ippen.[68]

In turbulent-diffusion studies in which dye or smoke particles are used as tracers, the density difference between the diffusing and surrounding fluid is measured in terms of a few parts per million and may be neglected. On the other hand, in a stratified fluid (e.g., salinity-intrusion studies) concentrations are of the order of several parts per hundred. Thus vertical density gradients exist which must result in mixing due to gravitational convective currents in addition to mixing due to turbulence. In a strict sense, the problem is no longer one-dimensional since u, w, and $\partial c/\partial z$ are not zero everywhere. A rigorous solution becomes almost hopelessly complicated if it is necessary to specify the velocity components throughout the fluid. Harleman and Jordaan[59] have shown that the mass transfer due to the gravitational convection and that due to the turbulence may nevertheless be superimposed as a one-dimensional problem if the eddy diffusivity E_x is replaced by a gross eddy coefficient $E'_x = E_x + \Delta E_x$. ΔE_x is a function of the dissipation rate G and the density difference between the diffusant and receiving fluids. This superposition is not unreasonable if it is considered that the gravitational currents result in a net circulation or eddy which is physically larger but similar from a mixing standpoint to the turbulent eddies. For low-turbulence levels (hence low rates of energy dissipation), ΔE_x may be an order of magnitude larger than E_x for a density difference as small as 1 per cent. As the turbulence level is increased, the vertical density gradients become smaller under the action of the intense turbulent mixing and ΔE_x approaches zero for the truly one-dimensional case. In practice the gross or apparent diffusion coefficient (E'_x) computed from the observed salinity distribution in an estuary may be used to predict the distribution of some other contaminant or property such as dissolved oxygen. This procedure has been shown by O'Connor[69]; however, the computed values of E'_x will be many times larger than the horizontal nonadvective flux due to turbulence which is represented by E_x. The extreme case of salinity transfer by gravitational convection, in the absence of turbulence, is shown in Fig. 26.8.

26.12. Steady-state Diffusion

Several one- and two-dimensional steady-state applications of Eq. (26.36) to the problem of salinity intrusion in tidal estuaries having various physical characteristics are summarized by Pritchard.[60] Estuaries may be classed qualitatively as (1) highly stratified, (2) moderately stratified, and (3) well mixed or vertically homogeneous. The highly stratified type of estuary is shown in Fig. 26.5. Other things being equal, an estuary tends to shift from the stratified to the vertically homogeneous type with decreasing fresh-water flow and depth and increasing tidal velocities and width. Ippen and Harleman[61,70] have shown that the one-dimensional convective-diffusion process in an estuary is quantitatively characterized by the dimensionless parameter $\bar{G}/g'V_f$, if V_f is the fresh-water velocity and $\bar{G}$ is the mean rate of energy dissipation per unit mass of

Based on theory of Morton, Taylor, and Turner[63]

c_m Concentration at axis of jet
c_0 Concentration $z = 0$
d Diameter of outlet pipe
F' Froude number,

$$F' = u_0 / \sqrt{\left(\frac{\rho_s - \rho_0}{\rho_0}\right) g d}$$

u_m Velocity at axis of jet
u_0 Velocity at $z = 0$
Z Distance from nozzle measured along axis of jet
ρ Density of jet
ρ_0 Density at $z = 0$
ρ_s Density of surrounding fluid

Velocity along axis of jet

Concentration along axis of jet

c_m/c_0 (left axis) u_m/u_0 (right axis) z/d (horizontal axis)

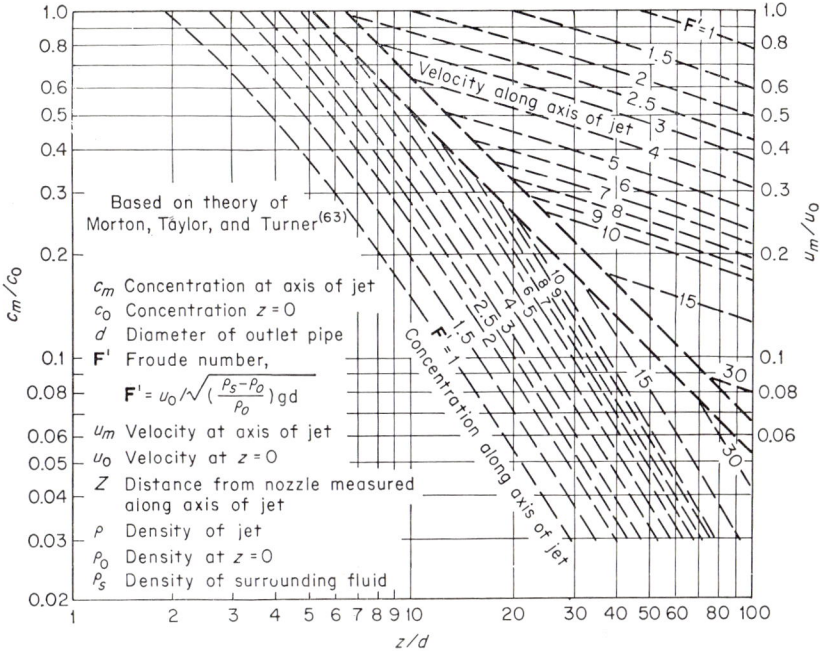

FIG. 26.13. Variation of concentration and velocity along axis of a vertical turbulent jet in a surrounding fluid of greater density. (*After Abraham.*[62])

fluid within the estuary. This latter quantity can be calculated from a knowledge of the tidal amplitudes in the estuary, since it is related to the damping of the tidal wave. The tendency toward the well-mixed class corresponds to increasing values of this dimensionless parameter.

The diffusion of jets with a density difference between the jet fluid and that of the surrounding medium is of particular interest in connection with atmospheric pollution and the disposal of wastes from ocean outfalls. The variations in the density and velocity along the axis of a turbulent jet issuing vertically upward in a surrounding fluid (of density greater than that of the jet) are shown in Fig. 26.13. The curves, due to Abraham[62] and verified experimentally by him, are based on the theory of Morton, Taylor, and Turner.[63] The role of the densimetric Froude number, using the initial value of the jet velocity, diameter, and density difference, as the primary correlating parameter, is again evident.

Because of the complexity of diffusion in stratified fluids, models have frequently been used to provide information not as yet attainable from analysis. In the case of hydraulic models employing the usual Froudian laws of similitude, it has been demonstrated by Keulegan[64] and others that the density differences in model and prototype should be equal.

REFERENCES

1. Fry, A. S., M. A. Churchill, and R. A. Elder: Significant Effects of Density Currents in TVA's Integrated Reservoir and River System, *Proc. Minn. Intern. Hydr. Conv.*, September, 1953, pp. 335–354.
2. Howard, C. S.: Density Currents in Lake Mead, *Proc. Minn. Intern. Hydr. Conv.*, September, 1953, pp. 355–368.
3. Ippen, A. T., and D. R. F. Harleman: Steady-state Characteristics of Subsurface Flow, *Natl. Bur. Standards (U.S.) Circ.* 521, pp. 79–93, 1952.

4. Keulegan, G. H.: Laminar Flow at the Interface of Two Liquids, *Natl. Bur. Standards (U.S.) Circ.* 32, p. 303, 1944.
5. Potter, O. E.: Laminar Boundary Layer at the Interface of Co-current Parallel Streams, *Quart. J. Mech. Appl. Math.*, August, 1957.
6. Bata, G. L., and K. Bogich: Some Observations on Density Currents in the Laboratory and in the Field, *Proc. Minn. Intern. Hydr. Conv.*, September, 1953, pp. 387–400.
7. Raynaud, J. P.: Étude des courants d'eau boueuse dans les retenues, *Trans. 4th Congr. on Large Dams*, New Delhi, 1951.
8. Bata, G. L.: Frictional Resistance at the Interface of Density Currents, *Intern. Assoc. Hydr. Research, 8th Congr.*, August, 1959.
9. Bonnefille, R., and J. Goddet: Étude des courants de densité en canal, *Intern. Assoc. Hydr. Research, 8th Congr.*, August, 1959.
10. Daly, R. A.: Origin of Submarine "Canyons," *J. Sci.*, ser. 5, **31**(186):401–420 (1921).
11. Kuenen, P. H.: Density Currents in Connection with the Problem of Submarine Canyons, *Geol. Mag.*, **75**(6):241–249 (June, 1938).
12. Keulegan, G. H.: An Experimental Study of the Motion of Saline Water from Locks into Fresh Water Channels, *Natl. Bur. Standards (U.S.) Rept.* 5168, March, 1957.
13. Berson, F. A.: Some Measurements on Undercutting Cold Air, *Quart. J. Roy. Meteorol. Soc.*, **84**(359):1–16 (January, 1958).
14. Schijf, J. B., and J. C. Schönfeld: Theoretical Considerations on the Motion of Salt and Fresh Water, *Proc. Minn. Intern. Hydr. Conv.*, September, 1953, pp. 321–333.
15. Bata, G. L.: Recirculation of Cooling Water in Rivers and Canals, *Proc. ASCE*, vol. 83, no. HY3, June, 1957.
16. Craya, A.: Critical Regimes of Flows with Density Stratification, *Tellus*, **3**:28–42 (February, 1951).
17. Stommel, H., and H. G. Farmer: Abrupt Changes in Width in Two Layer Open Channel Flow, *J. Marine Research*, **11**:205–214 (1952).
18. Benton, G. S.: The Occurrence of Critical Flow and Hydraulic Jumps in a Multi-layered System, *Johns Hopkins Univ., Dept. Civil Eng., Tech. Rept.* 1, February, 1953.
19. Keulegan, G. H.: Form Characteristics of Arrested Saline Wedge, *Natl. Bur. Standards (U.S.) Rept.* 5482, October, 1957.
20. Stommel, H., and H. G. Farmer: Control of Salinity in an Estuary by a Transition, *J. Marine Research*, **12**(1):13–20 (May, 1953).
21. Long, R. R.: Some Aspects of the Flow of Stratified Fluids. II. Experiments with a Two-fluid System, *Tellus*, vol. 6, no. 2, 1954.
22. Tepper, M.: The Application of the Hydraulic Analogy to Certain Atmospheric Flow Problems, *U.S. Dept. Commerce Research Paper* 35, October, 1952.
23. Yih, C. S., and C. R. Guha: Hydraulic Jump in a Fluid System of Two Layers, *Tellus*, **7**(3):358–365 (1955).
24. Keulegan, G. H.: The Motion of Saline Fronts in Still Water, *Natl. Bur. Standards (U.S.) Rept.* 5831, April, 1958.
25. Lamb, H.: "Hydrodynamics," Dover, New York, 1945.
26. Ekman, V. W.: On Dead Water, Norwegian North Polar Expedition, 1893–1896, *Sci. Results*, **5**(15):152 (1904).
27. Haurwitz, B.: Internal Waves of Tidal Character, *Trans. Am. Geophys. Union*, **31**:47 (1950).
28. Keulegan, G. H.: Characteristics of Internal Solitary Waves, *J. Research, Natl. Bur. Standards (U.S.) Research Paper* 2442, vol. 51, no. 3, September, 1953.
29. Keulegan, G. H.: An Experimental Study of Internal Solitary Waves, *Natl. Bur. Standards (U.S.) Rept.* 4415, November, 1955.
30. Long, R. R.: Solitary Waves in One- and Two-fluid Systems, *Tellus*, **8**:460 (1956).
31. Abdullah, A. J.: A Note on the Atmospheric Solitary Wave, *J. Meteor.*, **13**:381 (1956).
32. Peters, A. S., and J. J. Stoker: Solitary Waves in Liquids Having Non-constant Density, *New York Univ. Inst. Math. Sci.* IMM-NYU 259, June, 1959.
33. Proudman, J.: "Dynamical Oceanography," Methuen, London, 1953.
34. Tchen, C. M.: Approximate Theory on the Stability of Interfacial Waves between Two Streams, *J. Appl. Phys.*, **27**(12):1533–1536 (1956).
35. Yih, C. S.: Stability of Two-dimensional Parallel Flows for Three-dimensional Disturbances, *Quart. Appl. Math.*, vol. 12, no. 4, 1955.
36. Keulegan, G. H.: Interfacial Instability and Mixing in Stratified Flows, *Natl. Bur. Standards (U.S.) Research Paper* 2040, vol. 43, November, 1949.
37. Craya, A.: Theoretical Research on the Flow of Non-homogeneous Fluids, *Houille blanche*, January–February, 1949, pp. 44–55.
38. Gariel, P.: Experimental Research on the Flow on Non-homogeneous Fluids, *Houille blanche*, January–February, 1949, pp. 56–64.

39. Harleman, D. R. F., R. L. Morgan, and R. A. Purple: Selective Withdrawal from a Vertically Stratified Fluid, *Intern. Assoc. Hydr. Research, 8th Congr.*, August, 1959.
40. Rouse, H.: Seven Exploratory Studies in Hydraulics, *Proc. ASCE*, vol. 82, no. HY4, August, 1956.
41. Huber, D. G.: Irrotational Motion of Two Fluid Strata towards a Line Sink, *J. Eng. Mech. Div. ASCE*, vol. 86, no. EM4, August, 1960.
42. Harleman, D. R. F., R. S. Gooch, and A. T. Ippen: Submerged Sluice Control of Stratified Flow, *Proc. ASCE*, vol. 84, no. HY2, pt. 1, April, 1958.
43. Elder, R. A., and G. B. Dougherty: Thermal Density Underflow Diversion, Kingston Steam Plant, *Proc. ASCE*, vol. 84, no. HY2, pt. 1, April, 1958.
44. Elder, R. A.: Thermal Density Underflow Design and Experience, *Proc. 7th Hydr. Conf., State Univ. Iowa Bull.* 39, June, 1958.
45. Angelin, S., and K. Flagestad: An Investigation of Intake Arrangements for Cooling Water Supply Stratified Seawater, *Intern. Assoc. Hydr. Research, 7th Gen. Meeting*, pp. C13-1–C13-10, 1957.
46. Sverdrup, H. V., M. W. Johnson, and R. H. Fleming: "The Oceans," Prentice-Hall, Englewood Cliffs, N.J., 1942.
47. Fjeldstad, J. E.: Observations of Internal Tidal Waves, *Natl. Bur. Standards (U.S.) Circ.* 521, pp. 39–45, November, 1952.
48. Prandtl, L.: "Essentials of Fluid Dynamics," Hafner, New York, 1952.
49. Rossby, C. G.: On the Vertical and Horizontal Concentration of Momentum in Air and Ocean Currents, I, *Tellus*, vol. 3, no. 1, 1951.
50. Long, R. R.: Some Aspects of the Flow of Stratified Fluids, I, *Tellus*, vol. 5, no. 1, February, 1953.
51. Long, R. R.: A Laboratory Model Resembling the "Bishop-wave" Phenomenon, *Johns Hopkins Univ. Tech. Rept.* 3, February, 1953.
52. Yih, C. S.: On Stratified Flows in a Gravitational Field, *Tellus*, vol. 9, no. 2, 1957.
53. Taylor, G. I.: Effect of Variation in Density on the Stability of Superposed Streams of Fluid, *Proc. Roy. Soc. (London)*, **A132**:499 (1931).
54. Schlichting, H.: "Boundary Layer Theory," McGraw-Hill, New York, 1960.
55. Yih, C. S.: On the Flow of a Stratified Fluid, *3d U.S. Natl. Congr. Appl. Mech.*, 1958.
56. Debler, W. R.: Stratified Flow into a Line Sink, *Proc. ASCE*, vol. 85, no. EM3, pt. 1, July, 1959.
57. Rouse, H., and J. Dodu: Diffusion turbulente à travers une discontinuité de densité, *Houille blanche*, no. 4, August–September, 1955.
58. Orlob, G. T.: Eddy Diffusion in Homogeneous Turbulence, *Proc. ASCE*, vol. 85, no. HY9, September, 1959.
59. Harleman, D. R. F., J. M. Jordaan, and J. D. Lin: The Diffusion of Two Fluids of Different Density in a Homogeneous Turbulent Field, *MIT Hydrodynamics Lab. Tech. Rept.* 31, February, 1959.
60. Pritchard, D. W.: Estuarine Circulation Patterns, *Proc. ASCE*, vol. 81, sep. no. 717, June, 1955.
61. Ippen, A. T., and D. R. F. Harleman: Steady State Turbulent Diffusion and Gravitational Convection in an Idealized Estuary, *MIT Hydrodynamics Lab. Tech. Rept.* 38, January, 1960.
62. Abraham, G.: Diffusion in Submerged Circular Vertical Turbulent Water Jets with Density Difference between Jet and Surrounding Water, *IER Tech Rept.* 138-2, University of California, August, 1959.
63. Morton, B. R., G. Taylor, and J. S. Turner: Turbulent Gravitational Convection from Maintained and Instantaneous Sources, *Proc Roy. Soc. (London)*, ser. A, March, 1956, pp. 1–23.
64. Keulegan, G. H.: Distorted Models in Density Current Phenomena, *Natl. Bur. Standards (U.S.) Rept.* 1188, October, 1951.
65. Goldstein, S.: On the Stability of Superposed Streams of Fluids of Different Densities, *Proc. Roy. Soc. (London)*, **A132**:524 (1931).
66. Drazin, R. G.: The Stability of a Shear Layer in an Unbounded Heterogeneous Inviscid Fluid., *J. Fluid Mech.*, **4**(2):214 (June, 1958).
67. Yih, C. S.: Effect of Density Variation on Fluid Flow, *J. Geophys. Research*, **64**(12):2219 (December, 1959).
68. Harleman, D. R. F., and A. T. Ippen: The Turbulent Diffusion and Convection of Saline Water in an Idealized Estuary, *Intern. Assoc. Sci. Hydr. Publ.* 51, 1960.
69. O'Connor, D. J.: Oxygen Balance of an Estuary, *Proc. ASCE*, vol. 86, no. SA3, May, 1960.
70. Ippen, A. T., and D. R. F. Harleman: Analytical Study of Salinity Intrusion in Estuaries and Canals, Report to Tidal Hydraulics Comm., Corps of Engrs. (U.S.), Vicksburg, Miss., 1960.

Section 27

MAGNETOHYDRODYNAMICS

By

D. BERSHADER, *Stanford University, Stanford, California*
ROLF LANDSHOFF, *Lockheed Missiles and Space Division, Palo Alto, California*

MAGNETOHYDRODYNAMICS

27.1. Notation

A	cross-section area, meters^2
B	magnetic induction ("field"), webers/meter^2
c	velocity of light, 3×10^8 meters/sec
D	dielectric displacement, coulombs/meter^2
E	electric field, volts/meter
e	electronic charge, 1.60×10^{-19} coulomb
ε	internal energy per unit mass, joules/kg
F	force, newtons
G	Hartmann number, $BL(\sigma/\eta)^{1/2}$
H	magnetic-field intensity, amp-turns/meter
h	(1) Debye length, meters
	(2) perturbation on magnetic field, amp-turns/meter
I	current, amp
i	enthalpy per unit mass, joules/kg
j	current density, amp/meter^2
k	Boltzmann's constant, 1.38×10^{-23} joule/°K
k	wave propagation vector, meters^{-1}
L	(1) typical dimension of system under study, meters
	(2) self-inductance, henrys
M	Mach number, v/v_s
M$_m$	magnetic Mach number, $1/\sqrt{\Sigma} = (v/B)\sqrt{\rho\mu}$
$\mathfrak{M}$	magnetic moment, amp-meters^2
m	(1) mass (electron unless specified otherwise), 9.11×10^{-31} **kg**
	(2) mass flux, (kg)/(meters^2)(sec)
N	ratio of magnetic to dynamic pressures, $\sigma B^2 L/\rho v$
n	number density of particles, meters^{-3}
p	pressure, newtons/meter^2
P	Prandtl number, $c_p\eta/\kappa$
$\mathcal{P}$	pressure tensor, newtons/meter^2
Q	heat flow rate, (joules)/(meter^2)(sec)
q	electric charge, coulombs
R	(1) gas constant, 8.300×10^3 (joules)/(kg)(mole)(°K)
	(2) typical radial dimension, meters
R	Reynolds number, $\rho v L/\eta$
r	radial coordinate, meters
r_x	Larmor radius for species x, meters
T	temperature, °K
$\mathfrak{J}$	Maxwell stress tensor, newtons/meter^2
t	time, sec
u,v,w	components of velocity vector $\bar{v}$, meters/sec
V	electric potential, volts
v	velocity vector, meters/sec
v_A	Alfvén velocity, $B/\sqrt{\rho\mu}$, meters/sec
v_s	velocity of sound, meters/sec
W	molecular weight, kg

27–2

β	proportionality constant between magnetic induction and density in highly ionized flow, weber-meters/kg
γ	specific heat ratio
ϵ	dielectric constant, farads/meter
η	coefficient of viscosity, (kg)/(meter)(sec)
κ	coefficient of heat conduction, (joules)/(meter)(sec)($^\circ$K)
λ	(1) mean free path, meters
	(2) wavelength, meters
μ	magnetic permeability, henrys/meter
ρ	mass density, kg/meter^3
ρ_e	charge density, coulombs/meter^3
Σ	ratio of Maxwell stresses to dynamic pressure, $B^2/\rho\mu v^2$
σ	electrical conductivity, (ohm-meter)$^{-1}$ $\equiv$ mho/meter
τ	collision time (usually of electrons), sec
ν	kinematic viscosity, $= \eta/\rho$ meters^2/sec
Φ	potential energy per unit mass, joules/kg
ϕ	(1) viscous-dissipation term, sec^{-2}
	(2) magnetic flux, webers
	(3) velocity potential, meters^2/sec
Ω	(1) vorticity, sec^{-1}
	(2) constant pressure gradient in Hartmann flow
ψ	specific volume, ρ^{-1}, meters^3/kg
ω	circular frequency, radians/sec
ω_c	collision frequency, $ne^2/m\sigma$, sec^{-1}
ω_e	electron collision frequency, sec^{-1}
ω_i	ion collision frequency, sec^{-1}
ω_p	plasma frequency, $\sqrt{ne^2/\epsilon m}$, sec^{-1}
ω_s	spiral or gyration frequency of charged particle in a magnetic field, Be/m, sec^{-1}

27.2. Introduction

Magnetohydrodynamics (MHD) deals, as the name implies, with the dynamics of a fluid which interacts with a magnetic field. It has, in fact, been used to describe a variety of configurations, which include incompressible or compressible flows, liquid or gaseous state, dynamic or static configurations, particle atomic-physics analyses or continuum fluid analyses. Several alternative wordings (e.g., magnetofluidynamics, hydromagnetics, magnetogasdynamics) are also widely used.

Only fluids having nonnegligible electrical conductivity are capable of magnetic interactions. As long as the bulk of research and engineering efforts in fluid dynamics concerned fluids of vanishingly small electrical conductivity, such as air at ordinary temperatures, MHD received only limited attention. However, considerably greater interest in the dynamics of conducting fluids has arisen during the past decade in connection with attempts to harness fusion energy and as a consequence of problems in missile and spacecraft dynamics, propulsion, and communications. The discipline has, as well, been applied, more intensively than before, to a variety of astrophysical and geophysical phenomena.

The property of electrical conductivity implies that there are electric charges in motion in the fluid. In turn, it is the magnetic force between moving charged particles, or what is equivalent, the force exerted by a magnetic field (ultimately generated by the motion of charges) on a charged particle of fluid moving within the field that constitutes the magnetic part of the MHD interaction. Such forces are governed by the basic laws of electricity and magnetism as discussed below. It is the combined effect of these forces and the mechanical fluid forces that determine the ultimate dynamic behavior of the fluid and to which the term MHD implies. For order-of-magnitude orientation purposes, we note that the magnetic pressure, given by $B^2/2\mu$, corresponds to a mechanical pressure p of 1 atmos when the magnetic field B is 0.5 weber/meter^2 (5000 gauss), a value which is available with permanent magnets or electromagnets.

Conducting fluids with which one deals usually contain both neutral particles and positive and negative charges. The latter tend to be well mixed so that the fluid is neutral in the large; a gaseous fluid of this type is referred to as a plasma. Thus the uniform motion of a plasma does not in itself constitute an electric current.

Conducting fluids of common experience include mercury and electrolytes such as sea water. Also, the core of the earth contains molten metal, perhaps liquid iron (melting point = 2750°F), whose motion presumably is connected with the existence of the earth's magnetic field. The more significant early experiments in MHD were, in fact, performed with mercury as the working fluid. An example is the work of Hartmann and Lazarus,[1] dealing with channel flow under the combined influence of a mechanical pressure head and a magnetic field. Observed effects in this work and other studies, such as the wave experiments of Lundquist,[2] show comforting correspondence with the predictions of a theory based on the continuum fluid-conservation relations combined with Maxwell's equations.

A gas at ordinary temperatures is a nonconductor, but at higher temperatures thermal excitation takes place. This leads to ionization, and the free electrons thus produced render the gas conducting. Particularly highly ionized gases are present in the sun and other stars.

The description of an MHD interaction in terms of conservation equations for macroscopic physical variables, as was done for the mercury experiments mentioned above, is justified only if these variables represent good statistical averages over the component atomic behavior. This is possible if the mean free path λ is smaller than any lengths characteristic of the structure of the flow. Such may often not be the case when one deals with a plasma, but the *bulk-fluid* approach has been very useful for a large class of MHD problems and is the one primarily employed in the present section. Proper handling of the electromagnetic additions to the energy and momentum equations, however, must be consistent with basic physical features peculiar to MHD. These include:

Charge separation. Local electrostatic fields may develop due to exchange of thermal energy for electric potential energy. This leads to the so-called Debye characteristic length given by

$$h = \sqrt{\frac{\epsilon k T}{2 n e^2}}$$

Only where h is much smaller than the size of the system does one have the over-all neutrality in the large that characterizes a plasma.

Helical motions. Charged particles describe spiral paths around the magnetic lines of force. This introduces yet another length, the Larmor radius, given by

$$r_x = \frac{1}{eB} \sqrt{3 m_x k T}$$

in which the subscript x may refer either to an ion or electron. Relative magnitudes of r_x and the mean free path λ are important for the transport properties of the plasma. It is noted that when r_x and λ are larger than L, the correspondingly large helical motions interfere with the attempt at magnetic confinement of the plasma, an important consideration for fusion reactors.

Heterogeneity of plasma composition. While a small per cent of ionization produces appreciable conductivity, the behavior of slightly ionized gases is complex. This stems partly from our lack of knowledge of collision cross sections between neutrals and charged particles and also from the difference in nature between such interactions and Coulomb interactions between charged particles. The latter, being a long-range force, ensures, for example, that electron-ion collisions determine the mean free path of these particles even in the presence of large numbers of neutrals. In much of the theoretical MHD contribution to date, difficulties associated with partial ionization have been circumvented by either stipulating a high degree of ionization (say, over 50 per cent) or assuming a value for the bulk conductivity typical of a good conductor.

The characteristic lengths mentioned above are two of several characteristic quantities of importance in MHD. Those of significance for magnetoaerodynamics, for example, have been considered by Resler and Sears.[3] Landshoff[4] has tabulated many characteristic parameters so as to distinguish between those which are useful for macroscopic descriptions of MHD phenomena and those which apply to microscopic descriptions. Quite in line with conventional fluid dynamics, it turns out that similarity considerations are literally indispensable in treating and understanding MHD.

BASIC RELATIONSHIPS IN MAGNETOHYDRODYNAMICS

27.3. Fundamental Laws

Electromagnetic forces result from the interaction of electric charges. The force on any one charge q moving with a velocity v can be expressed in the form

$$\mathbf{F} = q(\mathbf{E} + \mathbf{v} \times \mathbf{B}) \tag{27.1}$$

The vectors $\mathbf{E}$ and $\mathbf{B}$ are the electric- and magnetic-field strengths at the point where the charge q is located. One can represent such fields graphically with the aid of lines of force, noting that the direction of the field is everywhere tangential to the line of force and that the intensity of the field equals the number of lines per unit area. The magnetic-field lines have no ends. Mathematically, this restriction imposed on the magnetic field is expressed by the differential equation

$$\boldsymbol{\nabla} \cdot \mathbf{B} = 0 \tag{27.2}$$

Another restriction imposed on the fields is expressed by

$$\frac{\partial \mathbf{B}}{\partial t} + \boldsymbol{\nabla} \times \mathbf{E} = 0 \tag{27.3}$$

In addition to being thus restricted, the fields are related to the past and present charge and current-density distributions ρ_e and j. By introducing a second pair of field vectors $\mathbf{D}$ and $\mathbf{H}$, the relation between the fields and the charge and current distributions is established through the differential equations

$$\boldsymbol{\nabla} \cdot \mathbf{D} = \rho_e \tag{27.4}$$

$$\boldsymbol{\nabla} \times \mathbf{H} - \frac{\partial \mathbf{D}}{\partial t} = j \tag{27.5}$$

In ordinary electrodynamics, one makes a distinction between free and bound charges and does not include the latter ones in the charge and current densities. Instead, one considers them as giving rise to an electric polarization and to a magnetization of the material. Comparing two environments (one of them possibly the vacuum) at identical values of $\mathbf{E}$ as well as $\mathbf{B}$, one finds that $\mathbf{D}$ and $\mathbf{H}$ generally differ from one material to the other. These differences are proportional to the polarization and the magnetization, which in turn are usually proportional to the fields $\mathbf{E}$ and $\mathbf{B}$ themselves, so that one has linear relations $\mathbf{D} = \epsilon \mathbf{E}$ and $\mathbf{B} = \mu \mathbf{H}$. The dielectric constant ϵ and the magnetic permeability μ depend on the material and on its physical state.

Equations (27.2) to (27.5) were formulated by Maxwell and bear his name. From the last two, one can derive the law of conservation of charge:

$$\frac{\partial \rho_e}{\partial t} + \boldsymbol{\nabla} \cdot \mathbf{j} = 0 \tag{27.6}$$

In addition to simplifying the description of materials in the electromagnetic field, the coefficients ϵ and μ also aid in keeping the units straight. In this article, use is made of the mks system of units based on the meter, the kilogram, the second, and the coulomb. All other units, such as the joule and the volt, can be expressed in terms of these four. In the mks system, the vacuum values of the dielectric constant and of the magnetic permeability are $\epsilon_0 = 8.854 \times 10^{-12}$ farad/meter and $\mu_0 = 1.257 \times 10^{-6}$ henry/meter, respectively. Their product is $1/c^2$, in which $c = 3 \times 10^8$ meters/sec is the speed of light.

In applying Maxwell's equations to MHD, considerable simplifications are possible because of the high mobility of the electrons. In a good electrical conductor a very small local excess or deficiency of electrons compared with the positive-charge carriers will be removed almost instantly by the electric field resulting from this lack of charge balance. The speed of removal is limited mainly by the inertia of the electrons. The charge equalization takes place in a time of the order $\sqrt{m\epsilon/ne^2}$, in which n, m, and e are the number density, mass, and charge of the electrons. In a metallic conductor this time is roughly 5×10^{-17} sec; in the ionosphere it is about 5×10^{-8} sec. Considering these high rates, it is not practical to calculate the electric field with the aid of Eq. (27.4) from the charge density. The electric field is related much more effectively to the current distribution through Ohm's law.

$$\mathbf{E} = -\mathbf{v} \times \mathbf{B} + \frac{1}{\sigma}\mathbf{j} \qquad (27.7)$$

This simple extension of Ohm's law includes an electric field induced by motion across a magnetic field. Later on, a more thorough discussion will extend Ohm's law still further. In applying Eq. (27.7) to MHD, $\mathbf{v}$ is the local velocity of the flow.

The so-called displacement current $\partial\mathbf{D}/\partial t$ in Eq. (27.5) is important only when currents can pile up electric charges. Because of the high rate of charge removal in a good conductor, it is usually possible to drop the term. This brings about a considerable simplification of Maxwell's equations because one can now, with the help of Ohm's law, eliminate the electric field altogether. If one, furthermore, replaces $\mathbf{H}$ by $\mathbf{B}/\mu$, one is led to the relation

$$\frac{\partial\mathbf{B}}{\partial t} = \nabla \times (\mathbf{v} \times \mathbf{B}) + \frac{1}{\sigma\mu}\nabla^2\mathbf{B} \qquad (27.8)$$

for the rate of change of a given magnetic field $\mathbf{B}$ if $\mathbf{v}$ is known. When $\mathbf{B}$ is determined by means of Eq. (27.8), the current density $\mathbf{j}$ can be found with the aid of the equation

$$\nabla \times \mathbf{B} = \mu\mathbf{j} \qquad (27.9)$$

obtained by dropping the displacement current from Eq. (27.5). From $\mathbf{B}$ and $\mathbf{j}$ together, one can further obtain $\mathbf{E}$ by means of Ohm's law.

The introduction of two pairs of field vectors served to establish the connection to the classical laws of electrodynamics in ordinary materials. In MHD, this formalism is not really used. The vector $\mathbf{D}$ completely disappears from the relevant equations, and the magnetization of materials is of no concern. One does not deal with ferromagnetic materials, and paramagnetic or diamagnetic effects due to the bound electrons in the ions are negligible compared with the effects due to conduction electrons. The permeability μ entering Eqs. (27.8) and (27.9) is thus the vacuum value. The tendency of field lines to stay temporarily out of a conducting medium, which is occasionally referred to as diamagnetism, is more conveniently regarded as a reduction of $\mathbf{B}$ associated with surface currents.

The fluid motion is governed by the theorems of conservation of mass, momentum, and energy. In ordinary hydrodynamics these theorems are formulated by treating the fluid as a continuum. The conservation equations for fluid flow need some additional terms because the fluid interacts with the electromagnetic field. The mass equation remains unchanged. In the momentum equation one has to add the density $\rho_e\mathbf{E} + \mathbf{j} \times \mathbf{B}$ of the electromagnetic force. Since the charge density ρ_e is zero, it is sufficient to retain only the part $\mathbf{j} \times \mathbf{B}$. The energy equation requires the addition of a term $(\mathbf{j} \cdot \mathbf{E})$ to account for the transfer of energy from the electromagnetic field to the fluid.

If one expresses the pressure as a tensor $\mathcal{P}$, the three conservation equations can be written very concisely as follows:

$$\frac{\partial \rho}{\partial t} + \nabla \cdot (\rho \mathbf{v}) = 0 \tag{27.10}$$

$$\rho \frac{d\mathbf{v}}{dt} = -\nabla \cdot \mathcal{P} + \mathbf{j} \times \mathbf{B} \tag{27.11}$$

$$\rho \frac{d}{dt}\left(\varepsilon + \frac{v^2}{2}\right) = -\nabla \cdot (\mathcal{P}\mathbf{v} + \mathbf{Q}) + (\mathbf{j} \cdot \mathbf{E}) \tag{27.12}$$

After indicating the x, y, and z components by the index $i = 1$, 2, and 3, the pressure tensor has the components p_{ik}. Its gradient is a vector with the components $(\nabla \cdot \mathcal{P})_i = \Sigma_k (\partial/\partial x_k) p_{ik}$, and the product $\mathcal{P}\mathbf{v}$ in the energy equation is a vector with the components $(\mathcal{P}\mathbf{v})_i = p_{ik}v_k$.

In the continuum approximation, the fluid is everywhere nearly in a state of thermal equilibrium, and the components of the pressure tensor and of the heat-flow vector $\mathbf{Q}$ are

$$p_{ij} = (p + \tfrac{2}{3}\eta \, \nabla \cdot \mathbf{v}) \, \delta_{ij} - \eta \left(\frac{\partial v_i}{\partial x_j} + \frac{\partial v_j}{\partial x_i}\right) \tag{27.13}$$

$$Q_i = -\kappa \frac{\partial T}{\partial x_i} \tag{27.14}$$

in which $\delta_{ij} = 1$, if $i = j$ and $\delta_{ij} = 0$ if $i \neq j$. The scalar pressure p, the viscosity η, the heat conductivity κ, and the internal energy ε are functions of ρ and T, which depend on the composition of the fluid and which can be found experimentally or by kinetic theory. In this form, Eq. (27.13) implicitly uses the assumption that the bulk viscosity equals zero (Stokes relation).

The equation relating p to ρ and T is known as the equation of state. A plasma can be considered as an ideal gas for which the pressure is $p = nkT$ if the particle density n includes the free electrons. By replacing particle by mass density, the familiar form $p = \rho RT/W$ is obtained. The average molecular weight is $W = \Sigma n'_s W_s / \Sigma n_s$. Only in the denominator are the free electrons included in the summation over the species s. In the numerator the prime indicates their omission from the summation. However, since the ionic weights are replaced by those of the respective neutral atoms or molecules, obtained from listed tables, the mass of the free electrons is actually included.

The gas constant R and the average molecular weight W are both proportional to the number of particles in a mole. In forming the ratio R/W, this number cancels out, and therefore it does not matter if one uses values for R and W which are related to the gram mole or to the kilogram mole. The latter choice is more convenient as well as consistent when working in the mks system. Since the listed atomic weights are dimensionless, they can be read as kilogram per kilogram mole or as gram per gram mole. The gas constant is $R = 8300$ (joules)/(kg mole)(°K). The internal energy for the ideal gas is $\varepsilon = RT/(\gamma - 1)W$, and for a monatomic gas the ratio of specific heats is $\gamma = 5/3$.

Using Ohm's law, Eq. (27.7), one can split the electrical term in the energy equation $(\mathbf{j} \cdot \mathbf{E}) = \mathbf{v} \cdot (\mathbf{j} \times \mathbf{B}) + j^2/\sigma$ into the work done by the force $\mathbf{j} \times \mathbf{B}$ and the joule heating. By a familiar manipulation of the three conservation equations, one is led to the energy equation

$$\rho \frac{d\varepsilon}{dt} + p \frac{d}{dt}\left(\frac{1}{\rho}\right) = \nabla(\kappa \, \nabla T) + \eta\phi + \frac{j^2}{\sigma} \tag{27.15}$$

with heat conduction, viscous dissipation, and joule heating on the right-hand side. Here ϕ is a positive definite quadratic form of the velocity derivatives $\partial v_i/\partial x_j$. In many problems the three dissipation terms on the right can be ignored, and entropy is then conserved along a streamline.

The formulation of Ohm's law given in Eq. (27.7) is still incomplete. Yet to be added are three effects due to:

The force $\mathbf{j} \times \mathbf{B}$

The different rate of diffusion of electrons and ions in the presence of temperature and pressure gradients

The inertia is simply accounted for by adding $\dfrac{m}{ne^2} \dfrac{\partial \mathbf{j}}{\partial t}$ to the right-hand side. This term needs to be retained only if one considers very rapid oscillations. The nature of the other two effects depends on the size of λ in relation to the radii $r_x = \sqrt{3 m_x kT / eB}$ with which particles are spiraling in the field B if they carry a charge e and are moving with thermal speed $\sqrt{3kT/m_x}$.

If a magnetic field $\mathbf{B}$ combines with an electric field $\mathbf{E}$, the center of the spiral drifts sideways in the direction of $\mathbf{E} \times \mathbf{B}$ rather than staying on a line of force. This drift is reduced roughly by a factor $[1 + (r_x/\lambda)^2]^{-1}$ because of collisions. If $\mathbf{B}$ is small, the ion drift practically vanishes compared with the electron drift, and this gives rise to the Hall current. If $\mathbf{B}$ is large, the two components drift nearly alike, which causes a mass flow but nearly cancels the Hall current. In a strong magnetic field, the effective mean free path of a charged particle in a direction perpendicular to $\mathbf{B}$ is its radius of gyration. Thus the diffusion current is also reduced significantly by a strong magnetic field. Two forms of a generalized Ohm's law are given:

For small[5] B,

$$\mathbf{E} = -\mathbf{v} \times \mathbf{B} + \frac{\mathbf{j}}{\sigma} + \frac{\mathbf{j} \times \mathbf{B} - \boldsymbol{\nabla} p_e}{n_e} \tag{27.16}$$

and for large[6] B,

$$\mathbf{E}_{\parallel} = \frac{\mathbf{j}_{\parallel}}{\sigma} \qquad \mathbf{E}_{\perp} = -\mathbf{v} \times \mathbf{B} + \frac{\mathbf{j}_{\perp} + \tfrac{3}{4}\,(n/B^2)\,\boldsymbol{\nabla}\, kT \times \mathbf{B}}{\sigma_{\perp}} \tag{27.17}$$

The symbols $\parallel$ and $\perp$ indicate the direction relative to $\mathbf{B}$, p_e stands for the partial pressure of the electron gas, and the conductivity $\sigma_{\perp}$ is approximately $\sigma/2$. The diffusion term $-\boldsymbol{\nabla} p_e/n_e$ in Eq. (27.16) is of special importance in the vicinity of a surface. To obtain a better understanding of this, one can consider a plasma in a state of equilibrium with no bulk motion, no currents and magnetic fields, and no temperature gradients. In the interior of such a plasma everything is constant; near a wall, however, electric fields arise and the electron and ion densities vary in the direction normal to the wall. Taking this to be the x direction, Eq. (27.16) simplifies to

$$E = -\frac{kT}{e} \frac{1}{n_e} \frac{dn_e}{dx}$$

After introducing a potential by $E = -dV/dx$, integration of this equation shows that the electrons obey Boltzmann's distribution law $n_e = n_0 \exp (eV/kT)$, a result well known from statistical mechanics.

If the potential is defined so that it is zero in the interior of the plasma, the ion density is, similarly, $n_i = n_0\, e^{-eV/kT}$, differing only by the sign of the exponent. From Eq. (27.4), one obtains

$$\frac{d^2V}{dx^2} = \frac{n_0 e}{\epsilon} (e^{\,eV/kT} - e^{-eV/kT})$$

Assuming the positive x direction to point into the plasma interior, the boundary condition that $V \to 0$ as $x \to \infty$ must be satisfied. Integrating away from the wall, V soon becomes small enough so that one can expand the exponentials, obtaining $d^2V/dx^2 = (2n_0 e^2/\epsilon kT)V$, with the solution $V = V_0\, e^{-x/h}$, in which $h = \sqrt{\epsilon kT/2n_0 e^2}$ is the so-called Debye length. This solution represents a sheath, which forms between the plasma interior and the wall, whose thickness is of the order h. The potential difference which is maintained by that sheath depends, among other things, on the wall material.

Langmuir and Tonks, introducing the concept of a plasma, based its definition on the ability to form such a sheath, shielding it from the walls, which implies that h should be small compared with the dimension of the container. This condition excludes only gases which have practically no ionization at all.

For some applications it is desirable to solve Eq. (27.16) for $\mathbf{j}$, and this leads to

$$\mathbf{j} = \sigma \mathbf{E}'_\| + \sigma_i\, \mathbf{E}'_\perp + \frac{\sigma_2\, \mathbf{B} \times \mathbf{E}'}{B} \tag{27.18}$$

in which

$$\mathbf{E}' = \mathbf{E} + \mathbf{v} \times \mathbf{B} + \frac{\nabla p_e}{n_e} \qquad \sigma_1 = \frac{\sigma}{1 + \alpha^2} \qquad \sigma_2 = \alpha \sigma_1 \qquad \alpha = \frac{\sigma B}{ne}$$

The parameter α is of the same order as λ/r_e, so that Eq. (27.18) does not apply in the limit of large α.

The electrical conductivity σ can be found experimentally or by kinetic theory. The latter leads to the formula $\sigma = ne^2\tau/m$, if τ is the effective collision time of an electron, i.e., the time in which collisions alone would change the velocity of an electron toward that of the surrounding ions.

A partially ionized gas can be regarded as a mixture of a completely ionized plasma and a neutral gas.[7] One can consider separate densities ρ_p, ρ_n and velocities $\mathbf{v}_p, \mathbf{v}_n$ of these two components. The density and velocity of the mixtures are $\rho = \rho_p + \rho_n$ and $\mathbf{v} = (\rho_p \mathbf{v}_p + \rho_n \mathbf{v}_n)/\rho$. Ohm's law retains the form given by Eq. (27.14) if one replaces $\mathbf{v}$ by $\mathbf{v}_p$. By writing τ_{rs} for the effective collision time of a particle of type r with all particles of type s, the effective collision time in the formula for σ can be expressed by the relation $1/\tau = 1/\tau_{ei} + 1/(\tau_{en} + \tau_{in})$. The indices e, i, and n refer to electrons, ions, and neutral atoms.

The motion of the plasma relative to the neutral component is called ambipolar diffusion. It gives rise to drag forces which dissipate some energy in the form of heat. The part of the dissipation resulting from the drag between ions and neutrals is largely not included in, and is often larger than, the joule heating.

A fluid may be bounded by a wall, by another fluid, or by a vacuum. The sheath which forms in the transition region is usually so narrow that one can ignore its presence and can consider the surface as a discontinuity.

The fields and the hydrodynamic variables on two sides of such a surface are related by jump conditions. In order to formulate these, let $\mathbf{n}$ be the unit vector normal to the surface and use the subscripts n and t to characterize vector components parallel and at right angles to $\mathbf{n}$. Denoting the increment of any quantity F across the surface in the direction $\mathbf{n}$ by ΔF, one has

$$\Delta B_n = 0 \tag{27.19}$$

$$\Delta v_n = 0 \tag{27.20}$$

$$\Delta(\mathbf{E} + \mathbf{v} \times \mathbf{B})_t = 0 \tag{27.21}$$

$$\Delta\left(p + \frac{B^2}{2\mu}\right) = 0 \tag{27.22}$$

Equations (27.19) and (27.22) imply the possibility of having a different B_t on the two sides, and this in turn requires a surface current density (amperes per meter)

$$\mathbf{j}^* = \frac{1}{\mu}\, \mathbf{n} \times \Delta \mathbf{B} \tag{27.23}$$

Similarly a different E_n requires a surface charge (coulombs per square meter)

$$\rho^*_e = \epsilon\, \Delta E_n$$

If the fluid is bounded by a vacuum, Eq. (27.20) is meaningless. Equation (27.21) requires $\mathbf{v}$ to be the fluid velocity, and p in Eq. (27.22) is of course zero on the vacuum side.

27.4. Similarity Analysis

The discussion in the previous article introduced the general equations and included remarks on associated physical phenomena. It was seen that three new variables enter the MHD flow problem, namely, $\mathbf{E}$, $\mathbf{B}$, and $\mathbf{j}$. Maxwell's equations supply the additional relations needed to yield a solution when combined with the equations of mass, momentum, and energy conservation, the equation of state and force-flux relations defining the transport parameters of σ, and κ. The complexity of the complete set of governing equations is appreciable. Therefore it is desirable to explore further the use of similarity parameters.

First, then, let us return to Eq. (27.8) and introduce nondimensional quantities based on typical values of length, velocity, and magnetic field:

$$x^* = \frac{x}{L} \qquad \mathbf{B}^* = \frac{\mathbf{B}}{B_{\text{ref}}}$$

$$y^* = \frac{y}{L} \qquad \mathbf{v}^* = \frac{\mathbf{v}}{v_0}$$

$$z^* = \frac{z}{L} \qquad t^* = \frac{t}{\tau}$$

with

$$\tau \equiv \frac{L}{v_0}$$

This gives

$$\frac{\partial \mathbf{B}^*}{\partial t^*} = \mathbf{\nabla}^* \times (\mathbf{v}^* \times \mathbf{B}^*) + \frac{1}{v_0 L \sigma \mu} \, \mathbf{\nabla}^{*2} \mathbf{B}^* \tag{27.24}$$

if $\mathbf{\nabla}^*$ represents derivatives with respect to the starred variables. For purposes of dimensional analysis, it may be assumed that nondimensional variables and derivatives are of order unity. Thus the coefficient $(v_0 L \sigma \mu)^{-1}$ determines the relative importance of the two terms on the right side of Eq. (27.24). A magnetic Reynolds number $\mathbf{R}_m$ is defined by

$$\mathbf{R}_m = v_0 L \sigma \mu \tag{27.25}$$

whose significance becomes clear when the terms in Eq. (27.24) are examined more closely. For $\mathbf{R}_m \gg 1$, the final term may be neglected, and the remaining relation is entirely equivalent to that for the vorticity of a nonviscous barotropic fluid, $\partial \Omega / \partial t = \mathbf{\nabla} \times (\mathbf{v} \times \Omega)$. This equation leads one to conclude[8] that vortex lines travel with the fluid. Similarly, the term implies that magnetic-field lines are attached to the moving fluid elements, as proposed by Alfvén. The picture of moving lines of force is convenient but must be used with care because such a motion is not observable. It may be defined, however, in terms of observable consequences by either of the following statements:

A line moving with the fluid, which is initially a line of force, will remain one.

The magnetic flux through a closed loop moving with the fluid remains unchanged.

For $\mathbf{R}_m \ll 1$, it is the second right-hand term which predominates in Eq. (27.24), giving it the character of a diffusion equation. Here the fluid and field lines seep or diffuse through each other. One may therefore consider $\mathbf{R}_m$ to be a ratio of the magnitude of transport of field lines by the fluid to relative slippage between the two. The term *magnetic Reynolds number* derives from the similarity with the usual Reynolds number

$$\mathbf{R} = \frac{L v_0}{\nu}$$

in which the kinematic viscosity has been replaced by the magnetic diffusivity $(\sigma \mu)^{-1}$. The analogy becomes stronger if one recalls that ν plays the role of a diffusivity coefficient in certain time-dependent viscous problems, e.g., Rayleigh's problem of the impulsive motion of a plate.[9] The usual relation between diffusion time τ and diffusion distance δ,

$$\delta^2 \simeq \frac{\tau}{\mu\sigma}$$

yields the result that the ratio between δ and the characteristic length $L = v_0\tau$ is related to $\mathbf{R}_m$ by

$$\frac{\delta}{L} \simeq (\mathbf{R}_m)^{-\frac{1}{2}} \tag{27.26}$$

This relation illustrates that a value of $\mathbf{R}_m$ of unity corresponds to comparable values of slip distance and transport distance during any given time τ.

Again, by use of dimensional analysis, one can show that $\mathbf{R}_m$ is a measure of motion-induced magnetic field to applied magnetic field. Whichever interpretation one chooses, it is evident that $\mathbf{R}_m$ is a measure of the nature of the field-fluid interaction rather than the magnitude of interaction. Thus, at low values of $\mathbf{R}_m$, motion across lines of force gives rise to induction drag opposing the motion, an effect which may be interpreted as a *magnetic viscosity*. At high values of $\mathbf{R}_m$, one considers the forces acting in terms of the Maxwell stresses associated with distortion of the frozen-in lines of force. These lines exhibit an elasticity, and therefore a restoring force, which, as Cowling[10] points out, may be contrasted with the damping force just mentioned for the flow with small $\mathbf{R}_m$.

By applying dimensional analysis to the momentum relation, Eq. (27.11) permits the construction of additional dimensionless ratios. The dimensions for the various terms in this equation are:
Inertial:

$$\frac{\rho v^2}{L}$$

Viscous:

$$\frac{\eta v}{L^2}$$

Magnetic:

$$\sigma v B^2 = \frac{B^2}{\mu L}$$

Ohm's-law form; Maxwell-stress form

Consider now the square root of the ratio of magnetic to viscous terms, $\mathbf{G}$.

$$\mathbf{G} = BL \left(\frac{\sigma}{\eta}\right)^{\frac{1}{2}} \tag{27.27}$$

The symbol $\mathbf{G}$ stands for Hartmann number, after the man who first considered this parameter in connection with channel-flow studies.[1] Its magnitude would indicate the relative effects of magnetic and viscous drag for, say, the flow of a viscous fluid across magnetic lines of force (low $\mathbf{R}_m$).

Next, the ratio of magnetic to dynamic pressures $\mathbf{N}$ is given by

$$\mathbf{N} = \frac{\sigma B^2 L}{\rho v} \tag{27.28}$$

$\mathbf{N}$ may also be interpreted[10] as a ratio of characteristic flow time L/v to the decay time due to deceleration caused by magnetic drag when crossing lines of force. If $\mathbf{N}$ is not small, the magnetic-drag effects may be appreciable. Figure 27.1 is a plot of $2\mathbf{N}$ for hypersonic flight conditions with assumed values of σ, B, and L, based on calculations by Resler and Sears.[3,11] It is seen that at suitable altitudes one obtains significant values of $\mathbf{N}$ over the speed range shown.

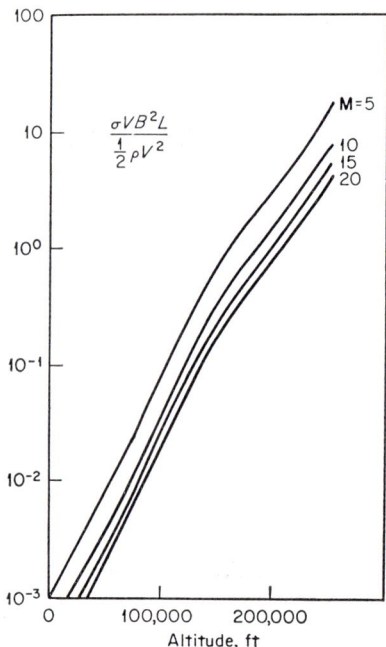

FIG. 27.1. Ratio of magnetic to mechanical force of hypersonic flight at various Mach numbers: $\sigma = 100$ mhos/meter, $B = 0.1$ webers/meter^2, and $L = 1$ meter. (Ref. 3.)

It is clear that the two ratios just discussed are directly related to the conventional Reynolds number $\mathbf{R} = \rho v L / \eta$ by

$$(\mathbf{G})^2 = \mathbf{NR} \qquad (27.29)$$

This points up the expected but nontrivial fact that viscous effects are relatively unimportant compared with inertial effects in MHD for sufficiently high Reynolds number. In low-Reynolds-number configurations, where viscous and inertial stresses are comparable, as in boundary layers, the introduction of magnetic forces would not suppress one type relative to the other.

Ratio of Maxwell stress to dynamic pressure gives

$$\Sigma \equiv \frac{B^2}{\mu \rho v^2} = (\mathbf{M}_M)^{-2} \qquad (27.30)$$

According to previous discussion, this ratio is more applicable to frozen-in flows than is Eq. (27.27). Examination of the energy relation (27.12) indicates that the above ratio also gives ratio of magnetic-energy density to kinetic energy per unit volume. The elasticity of the magnetic-force lines for which the Maxwell stress acts as a restoring force leads to the concept of MHD waves (Arts. 27.13 and 27.14). These are called Alfvén waves,[12] named after the man by whom they were introduced. $B^2/\mu\rho$ represents the square of the Alfvén-wave velocity, and so the ratio of Eq. (27.25) represents also the inverse square of what we may, by analogy, call a magnetic Mach number, $\mathbf{M}_M$.

27.5. Magnetostatic Equilibrium and Stability

The conditions for equilibrium of a perfectly conducting fluid in the presence of a magnetic field follow by setting $\mathbf{v}$, $\mathbf{E}$, and all time derivatives equal to zero in the basic equations. The resulting system of equations is

$$\nabla p = \mathbf{j} \times \mathbf{B} \qquad (27.31)$$

$$\nabla \times \mathbf{B} = \mu \mathbf{j} \qquad (27.32)$$

$$\nabla \cdot \mathbf{B} = 0 \qquad (27.33)$$

An obvious consequence of Eq. (27.31) is that p remains constant along $\mathbf{B}$ and $\mathbf{j}$ lines. One can replace $\mathbf{j}$ in the Lorentz force $\mathbf{j} \times \mathbf{B}$ with the aid of Eq. (27.32), which is then no longer needed. The resulting expression

$$\mathbf{j} \times \mathbf{B} = \mu^{-1} \left[(\mathbf{B} \cdot \nabla) \mathbf{B} - \frac{\nabla B^2}{2} \right] \qquad (27.34)$$

is generally true as long as displacement currents can be ignored. Another formulation of $\mathbf{j} \times \mathbf{B}$ as the gradient of Maxwell's stress tensor

$$(\mathbf{j} \times \mathbf{B})_i = \frac{\partial \Im_{ik}}{\partial x_k} \qquad (27.35)$$

in which

$$\mathfrak{I}_{ik} = \mu^{-1}\left(B_i B_k - \frac{B^2}{2}\delta_{ik}\right) \tag{27.36}$$

follows with the aid of Eq. (27.31).

The stresses represented by this tensor are twofold: a pressure $B^2/2\mu$ at right angles to the field and a tension $-B^2/2\mu$ along the field lines. The field lines thus tend to contract like elastic strings. When the magnetic-field lines are straight and parallel to each other, equilibrium is obtained for $p + B^2/2\mu =$ constant.

When the magnetic-field lines go in circles around the axis of a cylinder, the equilibrium condition is

$$\frac{dp}{dr} + \frac{B}{\mu r}\frac{d}{dr}(rB) = 0 \tag{27.37}$$

which requires an additional relation for its integration. For example, one can assume a cylinder of radius R carrying a current of uniform density j parallel to its axis on the inside and a vacuum on the outside of that cylinder. In cylindrical coordinates, Eq. (27.32) has the form

$$\frac{1}{r}\frac{\partial}{\partial r}(rB) = \mu j$$

so that the field is $B = \mu j r/2$ within and $B = \mu j R^2/2r$ on the outside of the cylinder. After substituting into Eq. (27.37) and using the boundary condition that $p = 0$ at $r = R$,

$$p + \frac{\mu}{4}j^2 r^2 = \frac{\mu}{4}j^2 R^2 \tag{27.38}$$

By replacing **j** by **B**, this equation shows that $p + B^2/\mu =$ constant. It is noted that the magnetic field can balance twice as large a pressure as in the first example. Intuitively, this can be understood by considering that the tension in Maxwell's stress tensor causes an inward force adding to the magnetic-pressure gradient. The particular geometry of the second example arises in the theories of the filaments in the solar atmosphere and of the static pinch.

In exploring possible equilibrium configurations one frequently assumes a simple dependence of the field or of the current density on the position in space such as the assumption of a constant current density along the axis in the above example. One's choice is limited to fields for which $\nabla \times (\mathbf{j} \times \mathbf{B}) = 0$, so that $\mathbf{j} \times \mathbf{B}$ can balance a pressure or potential gradient. In this type of discussion, one does not consider how to generate or maintain the currents which arise in a particular mathematical model, but tries to stick to plausible distributions.

It is possible to maintain symmetric configurations axially in equilibrium with both pressure and gravitational forces where the fields are confined to an interior region. Specific solutions are known for the sphere[13] and the infinite cylinder. The latter is a possible model for explaining the relatively strong magnetic fields in the spiral arms of our galaxy.

If **B** and **j** are parallel, no force is exerted. Such *force-free fields*[14-17] are in equilibrium in the absence of other forces. A case of special interest is encountered if $\nabla \times \mathbf{B} = \alpha\mathbf{B}$ with constant α. Whereas normally the decay of fields due to finite conductivity creates forces which are not balanced, this special type remains force-free. An example is the twisted field in a cylinder where the axial and tangential components of the field are proportional to the Bessel functions $J_0(\alpha r)$ and $J_1(\alpha r)$.

There exists a mathematical analogy between magnetostatic equilibrium configurations and hydrodynamic vortices in an incompressible fluid, where the magnetic field corresponds to the velocity and the current density to the vorticity. Known solutions of vortex motion can thus be transcribed and used to solve magnetostatic problems.[18] The analogy is also of possible use in discussing certain equilibrium configurations called plasmoids, which have been found experimentally.[19]

It is important to establish if an equilibrium configuration is stable or not. There

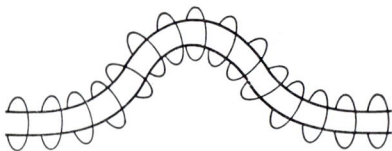

FIG. 27.2. Magnetic-field lines around a kink in a pinch discharge.

are several methods available to study this question. One can consider intuitively what happens to the static-pinch configuration, which was discussed in the last article, if the filament develops a small kink. Figure 27.2 indicates how the magnetic-field lines surrounding the filament crowd together on the concave side and spread apart on the convex side. Since the field strength is proportional to the density of the field lines, it, and therefore the magnetic pressure, increase at the bottom and decrease at the top. The resulting force tends to increase the size of the kink. The static pinch is therefore not a stable configuration and develops what is called a kink instability.

The more formal methods of stability analysis have one feature in common with the intuitive argument: one always considers small-amplitude disturbances and their consequences. One widely used technique treats the small-amplitude disturbances by linearizing the equations of motion. One carries out an analysis for the normal modes, and the equilibrium is unstable if the amplitude of any of the normal modes increases indefinitely with time. This analysis also furnishes the rate of growth of an instability.

Another method makes use of a variational principle. One defines a potential energy Φ as the sum of internal energy of the fluid

$$\mathcal{E} = \int \frac{p}{\gamma - 1}\, d\psi$$

magnetic energy

$$\Phi_m = \int \frac{B^2}{2\mu}\, d\psi$$

and, if necessary, gravitational energy

$$\Phi_g = \int \rho \theta_g\, d\psi$$

in which θ_g is the local gravitational energy, and ψ is specific volume. If an arbitrary deformation of the fluid always leads to an increased potential energy, the equilibrium is stable. To obtain the variation of the field in the space surrounding the fluid, one must take details of the external circuit into account.

As an example, consider a cylindrical conducting fluid of radius R_1 surrounded by a magnetic field (pinch geometry). The field is produced by a current I, which is assumed to flow in the surface only and which is parallel to the x axis. With this current disposition there will be no magnetic field in the interior of the fluid. The current is returned along a metal cylinder of radius R_2 surrounding the fluid cylinder. Both the fluid and the return are for simplicity considered to be perfect conductors. After it has once been produced, a steady current in such a circuit can be maintained with a zero emf. Ripples deforming the fluid surface will bring about changes of the current, and therefore of the magnetic field, but since the emf is zero, the flux remains constant. Considering a ripple where the surface of the fluid has the radius $R(x)$ which is independent of the azimuthal angle, the magnetic-field lines remain circles around the axis. The flux in that case is

$$\phi = \iint B\, dr\, dx = LI$$

in which

$$L = \frac{\mu}{2\pi} \iint \frac{dr}{r}\, dx$$

and is called the self-inductance. The magnetic-field energy is

$$\phi_m = \frac{2\pi}{\mu} \int B^2 r\, dr\, dx = \tfrac{1}{2} LI^2 = \frac{1}{2L} \phi^2$$

If one picks a deformation without change in density, the internal energy of the fluid remains constant and the question of stability hinges on how L depends on the deformation. A ripple which is given by

$$R = R_1 \frac{1 + \epsilon \sin kx}{1 + \epsilon^2/2}$$

(in which ϵ is the disturbance amplitude and k is the wave number) clearly is compatible with the condition that the fluid density should not change. For small ϵ one finds easily that the self-inductance per unit length is

$$\frac{L}{x} = \frac{\mu}{2\pi}\left(\ln \frac{R_2}{R_1} + \frac{\epsilon^2}{2}\right)$$

Introduction of the disturbance therefore decreases Φ_m, showing that the pinch configuration is unstable.

An emf in the external circuit can transfer an energy $I\delta\phi$ to the system. Stability is in that case assured if $\delta\Phi - I\delta\phi > 0$[†] for all variations. Consider again the above pinch arrangement but in series with a generator maintaining a constant current. The condition $\delta I = 0$ leads to $\delta\Phi_m - I\delta\phi = (I^2/2)\,\delta L$, and since $\delta L > 0$ as shown before, the pinch configuration connected in such a manner is again unstable.

The condition for stability of an interface between a perfectly conducting fluid with no field in its interior and a vacuum containing a magnetic field can be stated for arbitrary shapes of the interface. Using variational principles, Grad[20] has derived as a sufficient condition for stability that the center of curvature of the magnetic lines on the interface always lies toward the vacuum; sufficient for instability is a reverse curvature anywhere. The pinch configuration discussed above is clearly a special case, and its instability follows without effort from the very general theorem just stated.

An attempt to confine the fluid on the convex side of the field by introducing cusped surfaces has led to the picket-fence geometry (Fig. 27.3).

In applying the variational principle to fluids with magnetic fields in the interior, the field lines are considered to be attached to the fluid.

An important and interesting case concerns a fluid confined in the flux tubes of a curved magnetic field. The belt of charged particles discovered by van Allen in the earth magnetic field as well as the plasma one attempts to confine in the so-called mirror machine fall into the category.

Consider the effect of interchanging the fluid and the field lines between two flux tubes designated 1 and 2. The magnetic energy in a flux tube is

$$\Phi_m = \frac{1}{2\mu}\int B^2 A \, dl$$

integrated along the flux line when A is the cross-section area of the tube. The flux $\phi = BA$ is constant along a flux tube. The change in magnetic energy on interchange of these flux tubes is

$$\delta\Phi_m = \frac{1}{2\mu}(\phi_2{}^2 - \phi_1{}^2)\left(\int_1 \frac{dl}{A} - \int_2 \frac{dl}{A}\right)$$

By interchanging two tubes with the same flux, the magnetic energy remains unchanged, so that the change of the internal energy determines the stability. Since in equilibrium p is constant along a flux line, the internal energy within a flux tube having a volume $\psi = \int A \, dl$ is simply $\mathcal{E} = p\psi/(\gamma - 1)$.

When the fluid originally in tube 1 is moved into tube 2, the

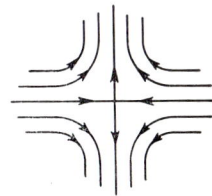

Fig. 27.3. Picket-fence geometry.

[†] Φ should not be confused with ϕ in this relation.

pressure changes from p_1 to $p_1(\psi_1/\psi_2)^\gamma$. A corresponding relation holds for p_2, and the total internal energy changes by

$$\delta \mathcal{E} = \frac{(p_2\psi_2{}^\gamma - r_1\psi_1{}^\gamma)(\psi_1{}^{1-\gamma} - \psi_2{}^{1-\gamma})}{\gamma - 1}$$

Taking $p_2 < p_1$, which means in general that tube 2 is closer to the edge than tube 1, the variation $\delta\mathcal{E}$ will be positive if also $\psi_2 < \psi_1$. Using $\phi = BA$, one obtains

$$\psi = \phi \int \frac{dl}{B}$$

so that the above inequality can be replaced by

$$\int_2 \frac{dl}{B} < \int_1 \frac{dl}{B}$$

If this inequality is satisfied for all pairs of flux tubes for which $p_2 < p_1$ and for which it is topologically possible to effect an interchange, the equilibrium is stable.

In the *stellarator*[21] the confining flux tube is bent to form a torus. The coils producing the field can be arranged so that the lines do not close after a single circuit, except for one of them called the magnetic axis. By this means it is possible to prevent interchange, and thus interchange instability.

In a pinch discharge, a superimposed axial magnetic field stabilizes some but not all modes.[22] By the addition of conducting walls, a complete stabilization can be achieved until dissipation permits the currents to penetrate to the axis.

Too large magnetic fields will make a gravitational equilibrium distribution unstable. The virial theorem[23] leads to an upper limit $\Phi_m < |\Phi_g|$ for the magnetic-field energy. Actually, no definitely stable gravitational equilibrium configurations are known. However, in some configurations the build-up rate of instabilities is so slow, they are practically stable. This is true for the cylinders which are proposed as models for galactic spiral arms.

Some interesting results appear if one enlarges the class of gravitational equilibrium configurations to include internal motions.[24] In a rotating-axis symmetric-equilibrium configuration, all points along a line of force rotate with the same angular velocity. This is known as the law of isorotation. The inclusion of internal motions has made it possible to prove the stability of all axis-symmetric solutions whose motion is $\mathbf{v} = \mathbf{B}/\sqrt{\rho\mu}$ and whose pressure is given by $p/\rho + v^2/2 + \theta_g = $ constant, if θ_g is the gravitational potential per unit mass.

MAGNETOHYDRODYNAMIC FLOWS

27.6. Magnetic Pressure

The $(\mathbf{j} \times \mathbf{B})$ term in the momentum equation is, of course, the origin of the magnetic contribution to the fluid pressure. To examine the consequence in a simple way, one may hypothesize the existence of some flow field in which $B = (0,0,B_z)$, with B_z a function of x only. Use of Eq. (27.9) yields

$$(\mathbf{j} \times \mathbf{B})_x = \left(\frac{1}{\mu}\frac{dB_z}{dx}\right)B_z = \frac{d}{dx}\left(\frac{B_z{}^2}{2\mu}\right)$$

One expects, then, that the MHD version of Bernoulli's equation should contain a magnetic-energy density term of the form $B^2/2\mu$ acting as an additional pressure component.

27.7. Poiseuille-Hartmann Flow

Now consider a case somewhat closer to a realistic flow situation: the incompressible Poiseuille channel flow of a conducting fluid in the presence of an applied magnetic field normal to the flow (Fig. 27.4). The analysis was presented by Hartmann[1] in 1937 and constitutes a pioneering effort in MHD.

Classical Poiseuille flow describes the fully developed steady channel or pipe flow of a viscous fluid under a constant-pressure gradient $-dp/dx$ in the flow direction. The coordinate x is otherwise ignorable, as implied by the term "fully developed." As Fig. 27.4 indicates, y is the channel-width coordinate, which, in turn, is the direction of the applied magnetic field $\mathbf{B}_0$ in this example; z is the channel-span coordinate, ignorable by definition in a truly two-dimensional channel flow. By assuming that the flow configuration remains two-dimensional, the continuity equation confirms that the velocity $\mathbf{v}$ continues to consist of an x component only, $\mathbf{v} = (u,0,0)$. With u a function only of y, the nonlinear convective terms in the momentum equation vanish, leaving the constant-pressure gradient, the viscous forces, and any magnetic forces to determine the dynamic behavior. By writing $dp/dx = \Gamma$,

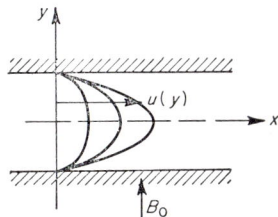

Fig. 27.4. Poiseuille-Hartmann flow. The flatter profiles correspond to larger values of Hartmann number **G**.

$$\Gamma - \eta \frac{d^2u}{dy^2} - (\mathbf{j} \times \mathbf{B})_x = 0 \tag{27.39}$$

if the subscript x means x component. To evaluate the magnetic term, it is recalled that $\mathbf{j}$ is proportional to curl $\mathbf{B}$ and therefore its divergence vanishes. One concludes that $j_y = $ constant, and this constant equals zero if it is assumed that the channel walls are insulating. Thus

$$\Gamma - \eta \frac{d^2u}{dy^2} + j_z B_0 = 0 \tag{27.40}$$

in which the constant value B_0 inserted for B_y may be justified on an approximate basis by assuming small $\mathbf{R}_m$, or more rigorously by applying div $\mathbf{B} = 0$ to the flow field in question. To integrate Eq. (27.40) to solve for the profile $u(y)$, the following procedure is required. An evaluation of j_z by use of Ohm's law gives

$$j_z = \sigma(E_z + uB_0)$$

The relation curl $\mathbf{E} = 0$ shows that the component E_z of the induced electric field is constant; it is denoted by E_{zc}. Its value is determined by the condition that the integral $\int j_z\, dy$ between the two insulating plane walls shall vanish. This is necessary because there is no net current entering or leaving the system. The solution of Eq. (27.40) is

$$u(y) = -\frac{\Gamma + \sigma E_{zc} B_0}{B_0{}^2}\left(1 - \frac{\cosh (\mathbf{G}y/L)}{\cosh \mathbf{G}}\right)$$

in which L is the channel half width, and use is made of the boundary condition that $u = 0$ at $y = \pm L$. By using the condition mentioned above for evaluating E_{zc}, one obtains the solution for $u(y)$ as

$$u(y) = -\frac{\Gamma \mathbf{G}}{\sigma B_0{}^2}\left(\frac{\cosh \mathbf{G} - \cosh (\mathbf{G}y/L)}{\sinh \mathbf{G}}\right) \tag{27.41}$$

if $\mathbf{G}$ is the Hartmann number $\sqrt{\sigma/\eta}\,B_0 L$. Figure 27.4 shows the relative shape of velocity profiles across the channel for various values of $\mathbf{G}$. Clearly, the effect of increasing $\mathbf{G}$ (i.e., increasing B_0) is to flatten the profile as a result of magnetic drag.

To obtain the induced field, use is made of Maxwell's field equation relating $\mathbf{j}$ with curl $\mathbf{B}$:

$$u\dot{j}_z = -\frac{\partial B_x}{\partial y}$$

After substituting into Ohm's law to eliminate j_z and by making use of the solution for $u(y)$, one obtains

$$B_x = B_0 \, \mathbf{R}_m \, \frac{\sinh (\mathbf{G} y/L) - y/L \sinh \mathbf{G}}{\mathbf{G} \cosh \mathbf{G} - \sinh \mathbf{G}}$$

As expected, the relative magnitudes of B_x and B_0 depend on $\mathbf{R}_m$, the magnetic Reynolds number. If one combines Eq. (27.41) with the y component momentum equation,

$$\frac{\partial p}{\partial y} = j_z B_x$$

the integral form will become

$$p(x,y) = -\frac{B_x{}^2}{2\mu} + \Gamma x + \text{const} \qquad (27.42)$$

Thus the existence of gradients of static pressure across the channel corresponding to variations in B_x is noted. This effect is a result of the action of the induced magnetic field B_x on the induced current j_z.

As mentioned in Art. 27.1, experiments on channel flow of mercury show general agreement with theoretical predictions. Results for larger channels and smaller values of B_0 showed disagreement with theory and were interpreted as due to the onset of turbulent flow. In this connection, an increase in magnetic viscosity can actually decrease the total drag by suppressing the transition to turbulence.

When a uniform magnetic field is applied in the z direction, changes of yet a different nature are introduced in the Poiseuille flow.[3] It is found, for example, that the pressure as well as the induced magnetic field h_x varies with z, thus eliminating the possibility of a strictly two-dimensional configuration.

27.8. Gas-dynamic Channel Flow

Resler and Sears[3] have made a study of MHD effects in compressible, nonviscous, steady, one-dimensional (approximately) channel or nozzle flow through a duct of slowly changing area. The conservation equations are formulated as follows:

Continuity:
$$\rho u A = \text{const}$$

Momentum:
$$\rho u \frac{du}{dx} = -\frac{dp}{dx} + \sigma \, (E - uB) \, B$$

Energy:
$$\rho u \frac{di}{dx} + \rho u \frac{du}{dx} = \sigma (E - uB) E + Q$$

Here Q represents rate of nonohmic heat addition and one assumes that $E(x)$ and $B(x)$ (note that x is the argument not the x component) have been produced by appropriate external arrangements. Calculation of the rate of change of velocity u and Mach number $\mathbf{M}$ with distance x leads to some useful information. The expressions are

$$\frac{du}{dx} = \frac{1}{\mathbf{M}^2 - 1} \left[\frac{u}{A} \frac{dA}{dx} - \frac{\sigma B^2}{p} (u - u_3)(u - u_1) - \frac{\gamma - 1}{\gamma} \frac{Q}{p} \right] \qquad (27.43)$$

in which
$$u_1 = \frac{\gamma - 1}{\gamma} \frac{E}{B} \qquad \text{and} \qquad u_3 = \frac{E}{B}$$

and

$$\frac{d\mathbf{M}}{dx} = \frac{1 + (\gamma - 1) \, \mathbf{M}^2/2}{\mathbf{M}^2 - 1} \left[\frac{\mathbf{M}}{A} \frac{dA}{dx} - \frac{\sigma B^2}{v_s p} (u - u_3)(u - u_2) \right.$$
$$\left. - \left(\frac{\gamma - 1}{\gamma} \right) \left(\frac{1 + \gamma \, \mathbf{M}^2/2}{1 + (\gamma - 1) \, \mathbf{M}^2/2} \right) \frac{Q}{v_s p} \right] \qquad (27.44)$$

in which
$$u_2 = \frac{1 + \gamma \, \mathbf{M}^2}{2 + (\gamma - 1) \, \mathbf{M}^2} u_1$$

The first and last terms on the right side of Eqs. (27.43) and (27.44) represent the familiar effects of area change and heat addition, respectively. The contributions of the MHD terms can be either positive or negative depending on the value of u relative to the characteristic velocities u_1, u_2, and u_3. The velocity u_3 is evidently that for which the effects of applied and induced electric fields cancel. Reference to the conservation equations with use of the term j^2/σ for the ohmic-energy dissipation will verify that u_1, on the other hand, is the velocity at which acceleration by the applied electric and magnetic fields equals the deceleration caused by pressure alterations due to Joule heating.

The interpretation of Eqs. (27.43) and (27.44) for a constant-area duct is made in Fig. 27.5. Consideration of the change in sign of du/dx and $d\mathbf{M}/dx$ at $\mathbf{M} = 1$ reveals that, except for two values of u, namely, u_1 and u_3, there exists a choking barrier. At u_1, it is possible to "tunnel" through the sonic speed and attain supersonic speeds in a continuous fashion, while a continuous deceleration from supersonic to subsonic flows is possible provided $u = u_3$ when $\mathbf{M} = 1$. The point $(u_1,0)$ is asymptotic for large values of x, as shown by arrows on the diagram. This is consistent with the interpretation of u_1 and with the fact that $du/dx = 0$ at $u = u_1$ for a constant-area duct. The wavy line at u_3 for $\mathbf{M} > 1$ is another asymptote corresponding to the vanishing of both du/dx and $d\mathbf{M}/dx$. That velocities approach u_3 in supersonic flow but diverge from that value in subsonic flow can be interpreted in physical terms. For this purpose the electric field $\mathbf{E}$ is replaced by imparting a velocity u_3 to the magnetic field $\mathbf{B}$ relative to the observer. Then, as Busemann has remarked, one considers ability of the magnet to "chaperone" the flow. There is an apparent aversion to such chaperoning at subsonic flows but an adjustment to the chaperoning speed in the supersonic regime. The behavior stems from the different adjustment of the physical variables to magnetic pressures in the two regimes, considered together with the effect of ohmic heating.

Some consideration has been given to configurations for possible magnetic Laval nozzles. Busemann[25] has discussed nozzles whose walls consist of specially arranged

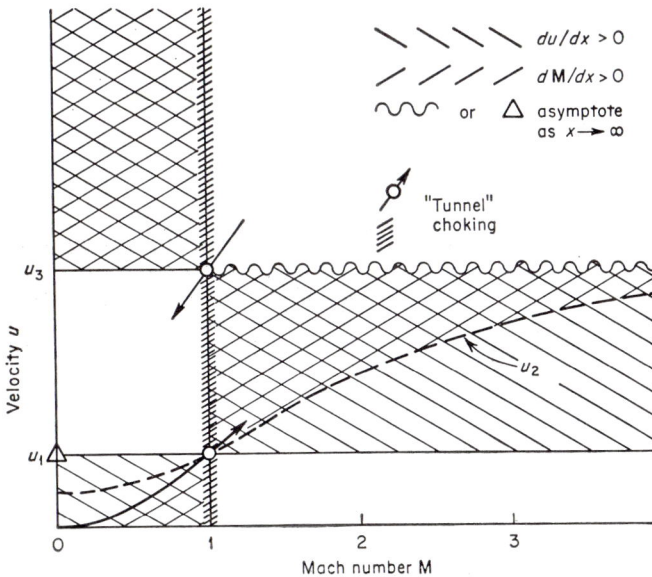

FIG. 27.5. MHD flow through a constant-area duct. *(Ref. 3.)*

sets of current-carring wires. In one type wires wound transversely to the flow in the form of a solenoid can support a Laval nozzle type of flow in that the generated fields create magnetic pressures near the wires which prevent leakage of the fluid between them. Away from the walls the pressure is relatively constant in this type of nozzle.

If several pairs of symmetrically placed longitudinal wires carrying oppositely directed currents are used for a nozzle wall, the magnetic pressure grows from zero along the centerline to a value near the wall which can exceed the stagnation pressure of the flow. The nozzle discharge capabilities are determined accordingly. As with other phases of MHD, further analysis is needed to obtain a better understanding of MHD nozzle flow.

27.9. Incompressible Boundary-layer Flows

Rossow[26] has analyzed MHD versions of the well-known Rayleigh and Blasius problems, and much of the following discussion follows his treatment. In the Rayleigh problem an infinite flat plate immersed in a stationary viscous fluid is impulsively moved in its own plane (Fig. 27.6). Consider first that an external magnetic field B_0 is fixed relative to the plate and transverse to the motion. If the plate is suddenly given a velocity u_∞ in the x direction at $t = 0$, the momentum equation reads

$$\frac{\partial u}{\partial t} + \frac{\sigma B_0{}^2}{\rho}(u - u)_\infty = \nu \frac{\partial^2 u}{\partial y^2} \tag{27.45}$$

in which the convective terms and the pressure gradient are neglected, a procedure typical of the simple Rayleigh problem. Boundary conditions for the problem are

$$u = u_\infty \quad \text{at} \quad y = 0 \quad \text{for} \quad t \geq 0$$

$$u = 0 \quad \text{for} \quad y \geq 0 \quad \text{at} \quad t = 0$$

By Laplace-transforming the velocity u according to the expression

$$\bar{u} = \int_0^\infty e^{-st} u \, dt$$

one arrives at a solution which inverts to

$$u = u_\infty \left(1 - e^{-N_t t} \operatorname{erf} \frac{y}{2\sqrt{\nu t}}\right) \tag{27.46}$$

if

$$\mathbf{N}_t = \frac{\mathbf{N} u_\infty}{L} \quad \mathbf{N} = \frac{\sigma B_0{}^2 L}{\rho u_\infty}$$

and erf is the well-known error function.

When the field vanishes, $\mathbf{N}_t$ becomes zero and Eq. (27.46) reduces to the better-known solution typical of diffusion phenomena. Velocity profiles for different values of $\mathbf{N}_t t$ are plotted in Fig. 27.7. It is clear that similarity of the profiles in terms of the diffusion variable $y/\sqrt{\nu t}$ does not exist but that the profile of u becomes less pronounced with increasing value of the magnetic parameter. This is a result of the more rapid acceleration of the free stream with the help of the magnetic field. The corresponding reduction in skin friction is shown in Fig. 27.8, if the coefficient C_f is defined in the usual way as

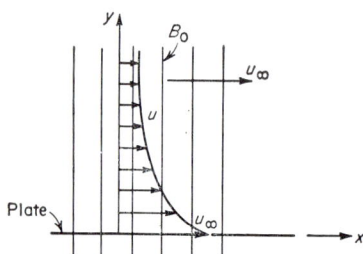

Fig. 27.6. Rayleigh problem: impulsive motion of a flat plate. (Ref. 26.)

$$C_f = \frac{\mu(\partial u/\partial y)_{\text{plate}}}{\rho u_\infty{}^2/2} = \frac{2\nu}{u_\infty \sqrt{\pi \nu t}} e^{-N_t t}$$

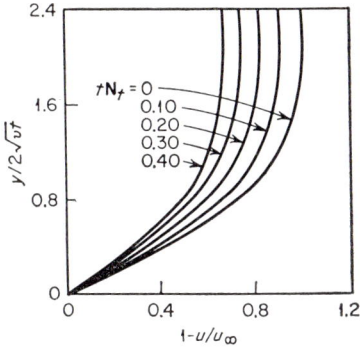

Fɪɢ. 27.7. Velocity profiles.   (*Ref. 26.*)

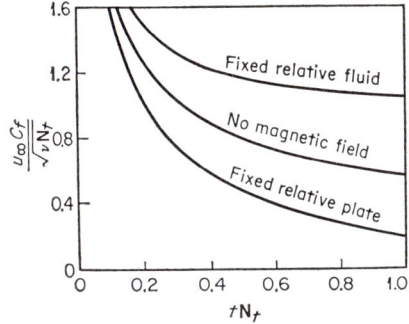

Fɪɢ. 27.8. Skin-friction results for MHD Rayleigh problem.   (*Ref. 26.*)

Reformulation of the problem with magnetic field fixed to the stationary fluid gives rise to a different physical situation. No forces develop in the free stream as before, but now magnetic-drag forces act on the layer near the plate in a direction opposite to the viscous forces. This has the effect of steepening the velocity profile and increasing the skin friction as shown in Fig. 27.8. The velocity profile for this case is

$$u = \frac{u_\infty}{2}\left[e^{-y\sqrt{N_t/\nu}}\ \text{erfc}\left(\frac{y}{2\sqrt{\nu t}} - \sqrt{N_t t}\right) + e^{+y\sqrt{N_t/\nu}}\ \text{erfc}\left(\frac{y}{2\sqrt{\nu t}} + \sqrt{N_t t}\right) \right] \quad (27.47)$$

in which the complementary error function erfc $r \equiv 1 - \text{erf } r$. The skin-friction coefficient plotted in Fig. 27.8 is given by

$$C_f = \frac{2\nu}{u_\infty}\left(\sqrt{\frac{N_t}{\nu}}\ \text{erf}\ \sqrt{N_t t} + \frac{e^{-N_t t}}{\sqrt{\pi \nu t}}\right) \quad (27.48)$$

The Blasius problem concerns the development of a boundary layer formed by a steady, incompressible flow over a semi-infinite flat plate. The momentum equation, in boundary-layer approximation and in the presence of a transverse magnetic field, is

$$u\frac{\partial u}{\partial x} + v\frac{\partial u}{\partial y} + N_t u = \nu\frac{\partial^2 u}{\partial y^2}$$

with boundary conditions

$$u = 0 \quad \text{at} \quad y = 0$$

$$\frac{\partial u}{\partial y} = 0 \quad \text{and} \quad \frac{\partial u}{\partial x} = -N_t \quad \text{at} \quad y = \infty$$

Now, continuity requires that $\partial v/\partial y = N_t$ in the free stream outside the boundary layer, but by the nature of the boundary layer,

$$\left.\frac{\overline{\partial u}}{\partial y}\right|_0^\delta = 0\left(\frac{u_\infty}{\delta}\right) \gg \left.\frac{\overline{\partial v}}{\partial y}\right|_0^\delta$$

and

$$u_\delta = u_\infty \gg v_\delta$$

if δ is the boundary-layer width.

Thus, while the magnetic field does affect the free-stream flow, there is no conflict with postulating a boundary-layer configuration except possibly if the ratio

$$\frac{\left(\dfrac{\partial v}{\partial y}\right)_{\delta}}{\partial u/\partial y\Big|_{0}^{\delta}} \gg 1$$

i.e., if $\mathbf{N} \gg 1$, where the characteristic length in this case is δ.
The transformation used by Blasius is now introduced:

$$\xi = x$$

$$\eta = y\sqrt{\frac{u_{\infty}}{\nu x}}\dagger$$

A series expansion for the stream function is taken by Rossow[26] as

$$\psi = \sqrt{u_{\infty}\nu x}[f_0 + \sqrt{\mathbf{N}_L x}f_1 + (\mathbf{N}_L x)f_2 + (\mathbf{N}_L x)^{3\!/2}f_3 + \cdots]$$

if
$$\mathbf{N}_L = \frac{\mathbf{N}}{L} = \frac{\sigma B_0{}^2}{\rho u_{\infty}}$$

and the f's are functions of η alone.

Upon further analysis one obtains a series of ordinary differential equations for the f functions, which Rossow has integrated numerically by use of the Runge-Kutta method. Velocity profiles are shown in Fig. 27.9. The decelerating effect of the magnetic field increases with fluid speed, causing a flattening of the boundary-layer profile and a decrease in skin friction:

$$\sqrt{\mathbf{R}_x}C_f = 0.664 - 1.789\mathbf{N}_L x + 0.706\mathbf{N}_L{}^2 x^2 - \cdots + \cdots \qquad (27.49)$$

Although the flow is incompressible in nature, it is instructive to examine the energy equation, which states that the convection of enthalpy is determined by the ohmic heating, heat conduction, and viscous dissipation:

$$\rho\left(u\frac{\partial i}{\partial x} + v\frac{\partial i}{\partial y}\right) = \kappa\frac{\partial^2 T}{\partial y^2} + \eta\left(\frac{\partial u}{\partial y}\right)^2 + \sigma B_0{}^2 u^2 \qquad (27.50)$$

It is well known in nonmagnetic flow that the energy and momentum equations can be combined for Prandtl-number unity ($\mathbf{P} \equiv \eta c_p/\kappa$) to give the following relation for the total energy:

$$u\frac{\partial(i + u^2/2)}{\partial x} + v\frac{\partial(i + u^2/2)}{\partial y} = \nu\frac{\partial^2(i + u^2/2)}{\partial y^2}$$

The same holds true, however, with magnetically influenced flow. This result is also compatible with the familiar conclusion that the enthalpy is a function of velocity only and that the enthalpy-velocity relation for $\mathbf{P} = 1$ is a quadratic

$$i = i_{\text{wall}} + \left(\frac{di}{du}\right)_{\text{wall}} u - \frac{u^2}{2}$$

For the insulated wall $(di/du)_{\text{wall}} = 0$, and one is left with the result that the freestream energy equation holds throughout the boundary layer. These facts are not changed by the magnetic interaction. One must conclude that the loss in kinetic energy due to magnetic "drag" is exactly balanced by the ohmic heating.

Results for the temperature distribution for an insulated wall are given in Fig. 27.10. Note that the recovery temperature is not affected. The heat transfer to a (thermally) noninsulated wall is obtained by Rossow as

$$i = \frac{\kappa(\partial T/\partial y)_{\text{wall}}}{u_{\infty}{}^2/2c_p} = \frac{\rho u_{\infty} c_p}{2\sqrt{\mathbf{R}_x}}(0.664 - 0.704\mathbf{N}_L x - \cdots + \cdots) \qquad (27.51)$$

† Blasius variable η should not be confused with viscosity coefficient.

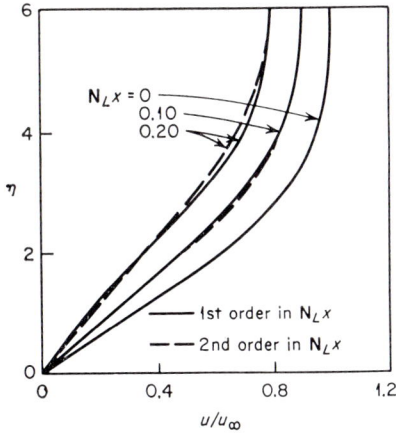

FIG. 27.9. Velocity profile for MHD Blasius problem: transverse field fixed to plate. (*Ref.* 26.)

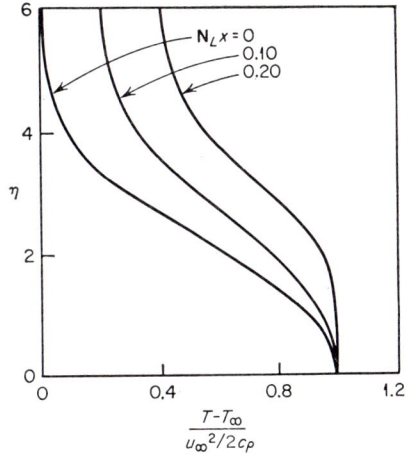

FIG. 27.10. Temperature distribution for MHD Blasius problem: transverse field fixed to plate. (*Ref.* 26.)

The quantity in parentheses reduces to the familiar value 0.664 in the limit of vanishing magnetic fields. From the earlier discussion on the Rayleigh problem, it is apparent that one would obtain different results for i in the case of field moving with the free stream and would find, as well, a dependence of recovery temperature on field strength.[26]

27.10. Couette Flow

The case of incompressible Couette flow with a magnetic field applied transversely between the bounding plates is relatively straightforward, and its solution is mathematically quite similar to that for the Poiseuille-Hartmann flow. Bleviss[27] has treated the case of compressible Couette MHD flow (Fig. 27.11). From the nature of the flow, it is stipulated that the velocities $v = w = 0$ and that x and z are ignorable coordinates in the sense that $\partial/\partial x$ and $\partial/\partial z = 0$. For simplicity, assume also that $\mathbf{E} = 0$, which, as discussed earlier, implies that the energy content of the fluid is independent of the electromagnetic interaction. The continuity equation is automatically satisfied. The x-momentum equation relates the viscous shear and the electromagnetic body force, while the y-momentum equation equates the pressure gradient in that direction with the corresponding electromagnetic force component:

$$\frac{d}{dy}\left(\eta \frac{du}{dy}\right) - \sigma B_0^2 u = 0 \qquad (27.52)$$

and

$$\frac{dp}{dy} - \sigma B_0 B_x u = 0 \qquad (27.53)$$

The form of the electromagnetic terms in the above equations stems from the following considerations:

$$\text{div } \mathbf{B} = 0 \text{ implies } \frac{dB_y}{dy} = 0 \qquad \therefore B_y = \text{const} = B_0$$

$$j_y = \left(\text{curl } \frac{\mathbf{B}}{\mu}\right)_y = 0 \qquad \therefore B_z = 0 \text{ from Ohm's law}$$

$$j_z = \sigma B_0 u$$

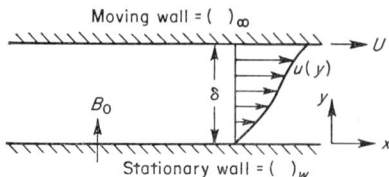

FIG. 27.11. Couette flow.   (*Ref.* 27.)

By consideration of Couette flow as a limiting case of flow between concentric cylinders in relative motion, it can be shown that $B_x = 0$ at the moving wall and increases monotonically to its maximum at the stationary wall. By utilizing this boundary condition and writing the magnetic terms in Eqs. (27.52) and (27.53) in terms of y derivatives through use of $\mathbf{j} = \text{curl} \ (\mathbf{B}/\mu)$, one may integrate to obtain

$$\eta \frac{du}{dy} + \frac{B_\varrho B_x(y)}{\mu} = \left(\eta \frac{du}{dy} \right)_\infty \tag{27.54}$$

$$p + \frac{B_x{}^2}{2\mu} = p_\infty \tag{27.55}$$

The last equation is familiar by now and illustrates again the feasibility in principle of *magnetohydrodynamic containment*, or holding the fluid off the wall by magnetic interaction. Equation (27.54), on the other hand, illustrates the form of the magnetic contribution to the off-diagonal, or shear components, of the pressure tensor. Thus it is apparent that the mechanical shear $\eta \ du/dy$ is less at the stationary wall than at the moving wall. This implies a flatter velocity profile at the stationary wall as compared with the moving wall, with some modification due to variation of η. The total drag on the stationary plate is due to skin friction plus magnetic drag, and this turns out to be the shearing stress at the moving plate.

Solution for the skin friction and drag depend on knowledge of the velocity profile. Bleviss[27] has taken the more tractable case of $p = $ constant and obtained explicit results. It turns out that the momentum equation is coupled with the energy equation,

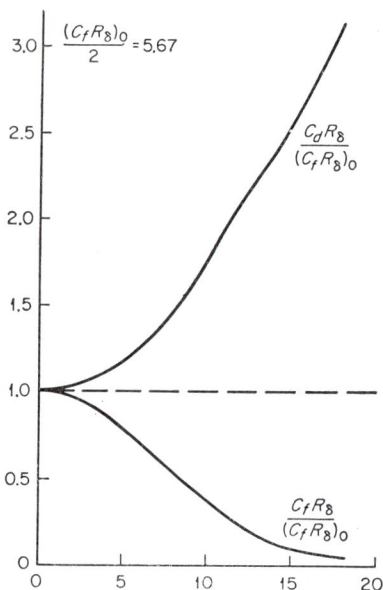

FIG. 27.12. Skin friction and total drag for MHD Couette flow with insulated wall. R_δ is a Reynolds number based on δ. (*Ref.* 27.)

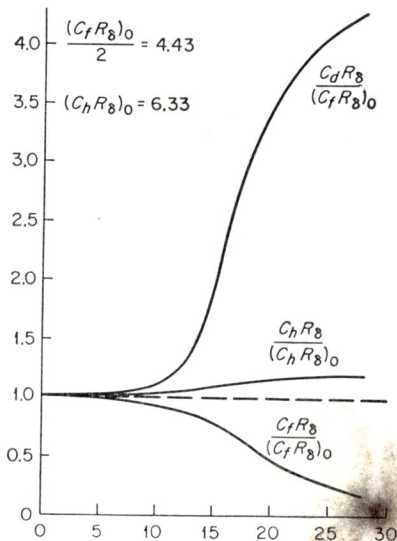

FIG. 27.13. Heat transfer, skin friction, and total drag for MHD Couette flow along heated wall. (*Ref.* 27.)

$$\frac{d}{dy}\left(\kappa\frac{dT}{dy}+u\eta\frac{du}{dy}\right)=0 \qquad (27.56)$$

through the dependence of η and σ on two thermodynamic variables (enthalpy and pressure are convenient ones). The solution procedure is straightforward, and one obtains the curves of Fig. 27.12, indicating that the decrease in skin friction is more than matched by an increase of total drag.

Other significant results include the fact that the recovery temperature at an insulated wall is unaffected by magnetic field (constant-pressure case only); in fact, the usual quadratic relation between $i(u)$ and u holds. The heat transfer from a hot wall is increased by a rather small amount (Fig. 27.13) as a result of magnetic effects. Reynolds' analogy, which says that frictional drag and heat transfer are proportional, is no longer true, for the coefficients are now related by

$$C_h = \frac{C_d}{2\mathbf{P}}\int_0^1 \frac{du^*}{\tau^*} \qquad (27.57)$$

in which

$$\tau^* \equiv \frac{(\eta\,du/dy)}{(\eta\,du/dy)_{\text{moving wall}}}$$

$$u^* \equiv \frac{u}{u_{\text{moving wall}}}.$$

The integral in Eq. (27.57) is greater than unity, with the result that the ratio of drag to heat transfer increases with application of a magnetic field.

27.11. Inviscid, Isentropic Flow of a Perfectly Conducting Fluid

The special cases specified by the above title have been treated by Mitchner[28] with the additional restriction of a transverse magnetic field. Results have been obtained for one-dimensional, nonsteady flow as well as two-dimensional steady flow. Here the magnetic field is proportional to the density, in which case the resultant pressure is a function of the density

$$\bar{p} = \text{``total'' pressure} = A\rho^\gamma + \frac{\beta^2}{2}\rho^2 \qquad (27.58)$$

The speed of propagation of small disturbances v_0 is then given by

$$v_0{}^2 = v_s{}^2 + v_A{}^2 = A\gamma\rho^{\gamma-1} + \beta^2\rho \qquad (27.59)$$

if v_A is the Alfvén speed. The formulation of one-dimensional nonsteady flow is parallel to that for the nonmagnetic case, with the exception that the usual sound speed v_s is replaced by the signal speed v_0. In particular, it is found that Riemann invariants $r_\pm$ exist which are constant along the characteristic curves C_+ and C_-.

$$u \pm \int_0^\rho \frac{v_0}{\rho}\,d\rho \equiv 2r_\pm \qquad (27.60)$$

When $B \to 0$, $v_0 \to v_s$, and the above relation reverts to the more familiar Riemann expression.

One can apply this approach to the magnetic version of the simple shock-tube problem, namely, the case of two ideal conductors separated by a diaphragm, each immersed in a uniform magnetic field of arbitrary value. The governing conservation equations of mass, momentum, and energy may be written in the usual form, provided one uses the "total" pressure $\bar{p}$ and "total" specific internal energy $\bar{\mathcal{E}}$ defined by

$$\bar{\mathcal{E}} = \mathcal{E} + \frac{B^2}{2\rho} \qquad (27.61)$$

Taken together with the requirement that B and ρ are proportional, the equations permit

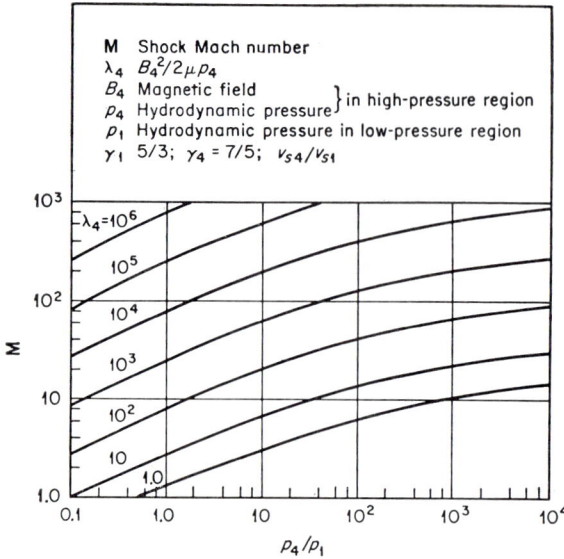

M   Shock Mach number
λ_4 $B_4^2/2\mu p_4$
B_4 Magnetic field
p_4 Hydrodynamic pressure $\Big\}$ in high-pressure region
p_1 Hydrodynamic pressure in low-pressure region
γ_1 $5/3$; $\gamma_4 = 7/5$; v_{s4}/v_{s1}

FIG. 27.14. Dependence of Mach number on hydrodynamic pressure ratio for magnetically driven shocks. (*Ref.* 28.)

a solution for pressure, density, velocity, and field strength on the high-pressure side of the shock in terms of the same quantities, and the specific-heat ratio on the low-pressure side.

Mitchner treats the special cases where the magnetic field exists only on the high-pressure side or low-pressure side of the diaphragm, respectively. The former bears correspondence to experiments with magnetically driven shocks. Figure 27.14 shows

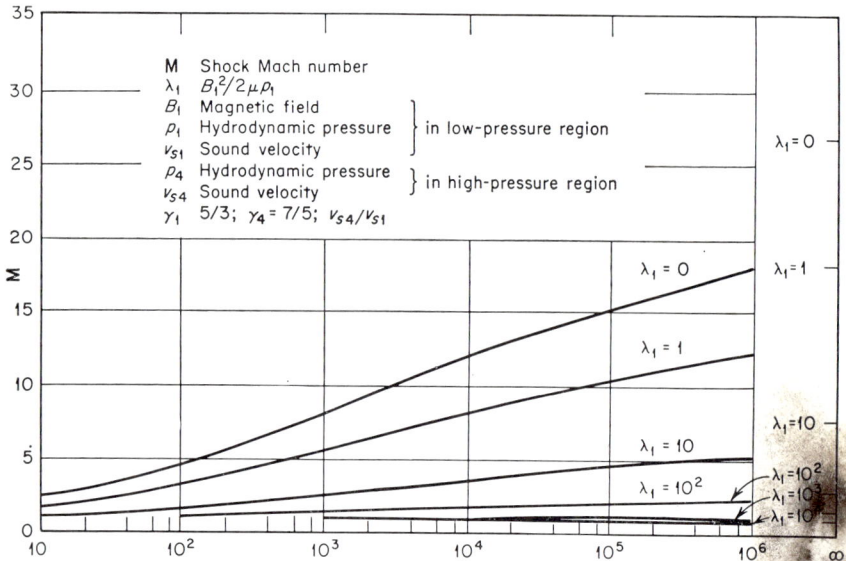

M   Shock Mach number
λ_1 $B_1^2/2\mu p_1$
B_1 Magnetic field
p_1 Hydrodynamic pressure $\Big\}$ in low-pressure region
v_{s1} Sound velocity
p_4 Hydrodynamic pressure $\Big\}$ in high-pressure region
v_{s4} Sound velocity
γ_1 $5/3$; $\gamma_4 = 7/5$; v_{s4}/v_{s1}

FIG. 27.15. Dependence of Mach number on pressure ratio for magnetohydrodynamic shocks. (*Ref.* 28.)

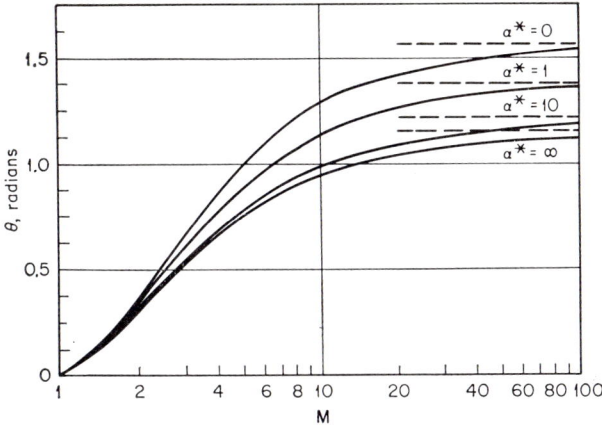

FIG. 27.16. Dependence of deflection angle on Mach number for various magnetic fields: $\alpha^* = (v_A{}^*/v_s{}^*)^2$, in which the asterisks denote critical speeds, speeds at which local signal velocity and flow velocity are equal. (*Ref.* 28.)

the obtained dependence of shock Mach number on hydrodynamic pressure ratio with initial MHD pressure ratio as a parameter. For sufficiently strong field strengths it is apparent that very strong shocks may be generated with rather modest diaphragm pressure ratios.

The second special case mentioned above is more truly an MHD configuration, for here the shock, though initially powered by a nonmagnetic driver, propagates into a magnetic field and interacts with it. Figure 27.15 is a plot equivalent to that in Fig. 27.14. Now an increase in the magnetic field downstream of the diaphragm weakens the shock and can, in fact, overcome the effect of diaphragm pressure ratios of considerable magnitude. It is apparent that the magnetic field contributes an effective pressure, but quantitatively the effect of a field B cannot be matched by substituting an increased hydrodynamic pressure $B^2/2\mu$. Its effect is, in fact, greater, as a study of the curves of Figs. 27.14 and 27.15 would show.

Two-dimensional steady MHD flow continues to show a parallelism with the hydrodynamic case in its formulation. The Bernoulli equation is found to be

$$\frac{v^2}{2} + \frac{v_s{}^2}{\gamma - 1} + v_A{}^2 = \frac{v^2{}_{max}}{2} \tag{27.62}$$

Note that when the magnetic field is sufficiently strong so that $(v_A/v_s)^2 \gg 1$, the Bernoulli equation becomes identical in form with the hydrodynamic equation for a gas with $\gamma = 2$ and with the sound speed replaced by the Alfvén speed. The same is true of the differential equation for the velocity potential.

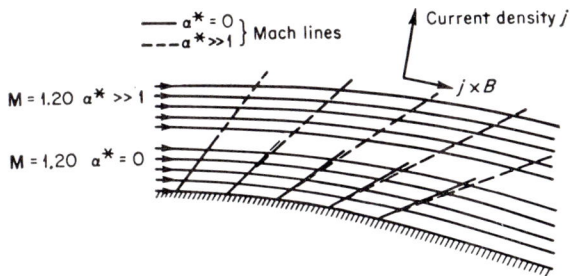

FIG. 27.17. Supersonic flow around a convex-curved conducting wall. (*Ref.* 28.)

$$(c^2 - u^2) \frac{\partial^2 \phi}{\partial x^2} - 2uv \frac{\partial^2 \phi}{\partial x \, \partial y} + (c^2 - v^2) \frac{\partial^2 \phi}{\partial y^2} = 0 \qquad (27.63)$$

The theory of characteristics which holds for nonmagnetic two-dimensional steady flow may be applied to the MHD case. Figure 27.16 illustrates the effect of magnetic field on the Prandtl-Meyer expansion of a gas with $\gamma = \frac{5}{3}$. It is seen that its effect is to increase the Mach number corresponding to a given expansion angle and, correspondingly, to decrease the maximum angle of expansion. Figure 27.17 is a comparison of hydrodynamic and MHD flow around a convex curved wall for $\gamma = \frac{5}{3}$. The magnetic field produces a more rapid expansion to a larger Mach number. This is in line with the notion of an effective $\gamma = 2$ for the magnetic influence as compared with $\frac{5}{3}$.

27.12. Linearized MHD Flows

In this article aspects of MHD-flow theory developed by the Cornell group making use of a small-perturbation procedure are discussed. Some of the work thus far is surveyed by Sears.[29] One starts by writing the velocity and magnetic field, respectively, as

$$\mathbf{V} = \mathbf{V}_0 + \mathbf{v}$$

in which $\qquad\qquad \mathbf{v} = (u,v,w) \qquad$ and $\qquad |\mathbf{v}| \ll |\mathbf{V}_0|$

$$\mathbf{B} = \mathbf{B}_0 + \mathbf{b}$$

and $\qquad\qquad \mathbf{b} = (b_x, b_y, b_z) \qquad$ and $\qquad |\mathbf{b}| \ll |\mathbf{B}_0|$

Here, $\mathbf{v}$ and $\mathbf{b}$ are, of course, the perturbations on the otherwise uniform conditions, caused, say, by the presence of a body in the flow. One adds the familiar simplifying assumption that the electrical conductivity is a scalar constant and that displacement currents may be neglected. In the work thus far, cases which have been treated include those of flow near a wavy wall and around thin airfoils, including the effects of compressibility. Particular attention has been given to the variation of magnetic Reynolds number and of angle between flow and field. Here again, the physical phenomena are best revealed by considering a few illustrative configurations.

Consider first a steady, two-dimensional, incompressible flow with $\mathbf{V}_0 = (U, 0, 0)$ with uniform magnetic field $\mathbf{B}_0 = (B_{0x}, 0, 0)$ parallel to the flow. Assume that a small two-dimensional perturbation is introduced by special boundary conditions such as a thin airfoil. Then

$$\mathbf{V} = (U + u, v, 0)$$

$$\mathbf{B} = (B_{0x} + b_x, b_y, 0)$$

Now assume that ratios of perturbation magnitudes to free-stream magnitudes are of the same order. This is a plausible assumption for fluids of high conductivity, in line with the concept for infinite conductors that the number of magnetic lines through an arbitrary area moving with the fluid is constant. If higher-order terms are neglected, the momentum equation becomes

$$U \frac{\partial V}{\partial x} = -\frac{1}{\rho} \nabla p + \frac{1}{\rho \mu} \left(B_{0x} \frac{\partial B}{\partial x} - B_{0x} \nabla B_x \right) \qquad (27.64)$$

The x component of the above vector equation is directly integrable and yields a Bernoulli equation typical of small perturbation flows:

$$p + \rho u U = \text{const} \qquad (27.65)$$

Use of Eq. (27.65) enables one to write the y component of Eq. (27.64) as

$$\Omega = \frac{B_{0x}}{\rho U} j_z \qquad (27.66)$$

in which $\qquad \Omega = \dfrac{\partial v}{\partial x} - \dfrac{\partial u}{\partial y} \qquad$ and $\qquad \mu j_z = \dfrac{\partial b_y}{\partial x} - \dfrac{\partial b_x}{\partial y}$

This, then, is a relation between fluid vorticity and density of electric current.

Other pertinent relations, namely, Maxwell's equations and Ohm's law, are also required for the analysis. These may be combined in a straightforward manner and applied to the present case to yield

$$U \frac{\partial \mathbf{B}}{\partial x} - B_{0x} \frac{\partial \mathbf{V}}{\partial x} = \frac{1}{\mu\sigma} \nabla^2 \mathbf{B} \qquad (27.67)$$

At this point assume $\sigma \to \infty$. Then Eq. (27.67) may be integrated to yield the result that $\mathbf{B}$ and $\mathbf{V}$ are proportional.

$$\mathbf{B} = \frac{B_{0x}}{U} \mathbf{V} \qquad \text{and} \qquad j_z = \frac{B_{0x}}{U} \Omega \qquad (27.68)$$

This result implies, as well, that the streamlines and magnetic lines remain parallel to each other. When the above is combined with Eq. (27.66), there results

$$\Omega = \frac{B_{0x}{}^2}{\rho\mu U^2} \Omega$$

a relation which signifies that $\Omega = 0$ as long as the magnetic Mach number

$$\mathbf{M}_m \equiv \frac{U\sqrt{\rho\mu}}{B_{0x}} = \frac{\text{flow velocity}}{\text{Alfvén wave velocity}}$$

is different from unity. Such flow is therefore irrotational with zero current density, and the known solutions for corresponding non-MHD small-perturbation flow apply. However, surface current sheets must be introduced to satisfy the boundary conditions. They result from the jump in the tangential components of $\mathbf{B}$ at the solid boundary in consequence of the solution given by Eq. (27.68). For specific configurations[30] the current sheets may be calculated by applying the conditions that the normal component of the field is continuous and that the current density within the body vanishes for insulating walls.

When these considerations are applied to a flow with large but finite conductivity, the right-hand side of Eq. (27.67) must be retained. This relation has the general form of a linearized Prandtl boundary-layer equation. By manipulating Eq. (27.67) and using Eq. (27.66), one may apply[30] a boundary-layer approach to yield a diffusion-type equation for the current density within the boundary layer:

$$\frac{\partial j_z}{\partial x} = \beta \frac{\partial^2 j_z}{\partial y^2} \qquad (27.69)$$

in which $\beta = 1/[\sigma\mu U(1 - \mathbf{M}_m{}^{-2})]$.

It is well known that if one sets x equal to a characteristic body length L, then the diffusion depth or boundary-layer thickness is of order $\sqrt{bL}$. If $\mathbf{M}_m$ is appreciably larger than unity, then this thickness is of the order $L/\sqrt{\mathbf{R}_m}$, in close analogy with ordinary viscous-boundary-layer theory. The magnetic boundary layer replaces the surface current sheet just as the viscous boundary layer replaces the vortex sheet of nonviscous flow. Further, it is clear that the magnetic-boundary-layer model applies only for large values of $\mathbf{R}_m$, say, of the order of 10^3 or more. The small-perturbation linearized approach to magnetic boundary layers must be used with caution. Sears[29] reminds us, in fact, that the approximation is not justified in many cases because the boundary conditions on B may be of the large-perturbation type, requiring use of the more complete and nonlinear equation corresponding to Eq. (27.67).

For small values of $\mathbf{R}_m$, the perturbation functions may be expanded in a power series in $\mathbf{R}_m$.

$$f = f_0 + \mathbf{R}_m f_1 + \mathbf{R}_m{}^2 f_2 + \cdots \qquad (27.70)$$

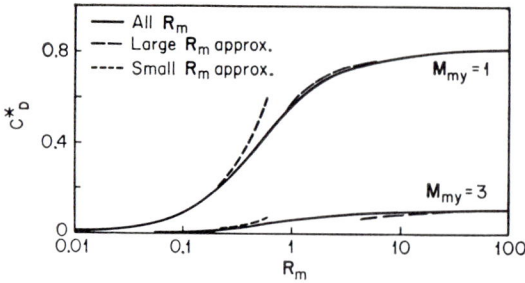

FIG. 27.18. Wavy-wall drag coefficient for magnetic Mach numbers equal to 1 and 3 plotted against magnetic Reynolds number for case of field perpendicular to flow. The second subscript on $\mathbf{M}_m$ refers to the component of magnetic field used. (*Ref.* 31.)

Since small $\mathbf{R}_m$ signifies that the ratio of induced field to applied field is small, it is not surprising to find that the first-order results of the power-series treatment correspond to ignoring any perturbation of the magnetic field in calculating the current density.

The discussion in this section so far has dealt with the case of magnetic field parallel to the flow. It is instructive to make some comparisons with the same type of flow field as before but with applied magnetic field *perpendicular to the flow*. With a similar linearized approach, subsequent analysis shows that for infinite conductivity, or $\mathbf{R}_m$, the vorticity and current density are described by a two-dimensional wave equation. On the other hand, the solution for the components of the perturbed velocity and magnetic field are described by a superposition of hyperbolic (wave) and elliptic (harmonic) functions. Thus, for example,

$$u \sim f_2(x - \mathbf{M}_m y) - g(x + \mathbf{M}_m y) + \frac{\partial \phi}{\partial x} \qquad (27.71)$$

if ϕ is a solution of Laplace's equation. The word "hyperliptic" flow has been suggested by Sears as descriptive of this flow. The wave functions represent Alfvén waves whose characteristic inclination dy/dx is M_m^{-1}. They propagate at the Alfvén velocity and are carried downstream.

For large but finite values of $\mathbf{R}_m$, the Alfvén waves alternate with an exponential factor, which, to first order in the case of flow along a wavy wall, is proportional to $\mathbf{R}_m^{-1}$; that is, the penetration depth into the fluid is proportional to the magnetic Reynolds number. Resler and McCune remark[31] that the attenuation corresponds to a diffusive rather than a dissipative mechanism. The penetration into the fluid will be larger than in the non-MHD case of wavy-wall flow where disturbances weaken appreciably in a wavelength's distance from the wall. Evidently, Alfvén waves are intimately associated

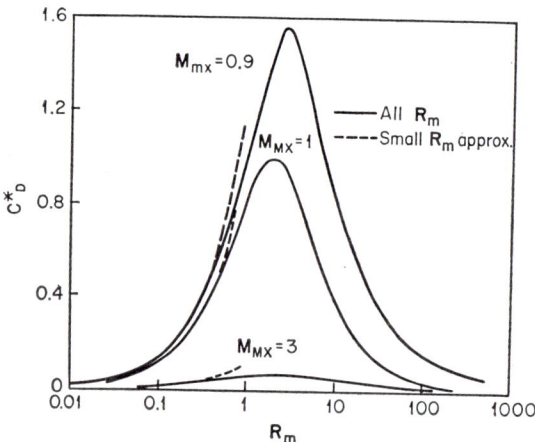

FIG. 27.19. Wavy-wall drag coefficient for various values of $\mathbf{M}_{mx}$ plotted against $\mathbf{R}_m$ for case of field parallel to flow. (*Ref.* 31.)

with the fluid-generated magnetic field since the waves are not present in flows with small R_m.

The wave behavior just discussed may be contrasted with the boundary-layer behavior found earlier in the field-parallel-to-flow case. The greater penetration into the flow in the wave configuration implies stronger MHD effects at a given value of R_m. This is justified when Figs. 27.18 and 27.19 are compared. Where wave behavior is present, the drag coefficient at $R_m = 5$ essentially corresponds to that at much higher values. This clearly is not the case with Fig. 27.19, where it appears that one has to take values of R_m well above 10^3 before the drag is sufficiently close to its asymptotic zero value.

Finally, it should be mentioned that the linearized approach has been extended to compressible flows.[32] Here one encounters the more complex spectrum of signal speeds

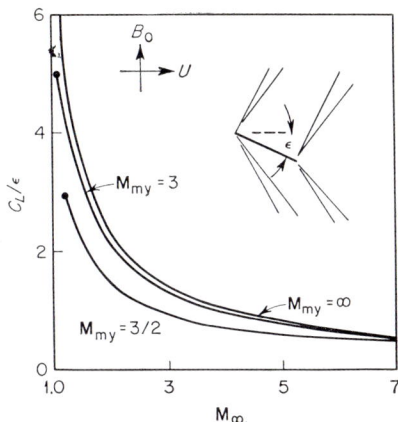

FIG. 27.20. Lift coefficient on flat plate in MHD flow. (*Ref. 31.*)

discussed elsewhere in this article. One somewhat unusual result is the existence of hyperbolic flow at subsonic speeds over a certain range of magnetic Mach number. In this regime one finds forward-facing (i.e., upstream-slanting) characteristics. Solutions for airfoil and other flows may be obtained in the compressible-flow regime which are analogous to either the Prandtl-Glauert or Ackeret theories in non-MHD compressible aerodynamics. Figure 27.20 gives results for the lift coefficient on a flat plate.

MAGNETOHYDRODYNAMIC WAVES

27.13. Small-amplitude Waves

The MHD equations are nonlinear, but for small-amplitude motion they can be linearized. In a linear theory a sum of solutions of a set of equations is again a solution. One can thus solve a general problem by expanding in terms of eigenfunctions. In an infinite medium such eigenfunctions are simple waves where the dependent variables are of the form

$$f = f_0 + f_1 e^{i(\mathbf{k} \cdot \mathbf{r} + \omega t)} \tag{27.72}$$

By substituting these expressions into the basic equations, one can separately balance zero- and first-order terms and ignore second-and higher-order terms, thus obtaining a system of linear homogeneous equations involving the f_1. The system possesses a non-zero solution if the determinant is zero. In this manner one is led to *dispersion relations* between the propagation vector $\mathbf{k}$ and the frequency ω. In ordinary hydrodynamics, this procedure leads to a theoretical description of sound waves. In MHD, one finds a larger variety of waves, depending on the relative direction of $\mathbf{k}$, the particle motion, and the fields.

In general, dispersion relations extend to complex values of $\mathbf{k}$ and ω. If one treats an initial-value problem, one Fourier-expands the space dependence of the variables. This implies that $\mathbf{k}$ is real. The frequency ω, however, may be complex, and depending on the sign of the imaginary part of ω, such a wave either decays or grows. If one treats a propagation problem, one expands the time dependence, ω remains real, and $\mathbf{k}$ may be complex. By inspecting the dispersion relation, one can distinguish between amplifying and evanescent waves.[33]

When the magnetic field has no zero-order or d-c component, the term $\mathbf{j} \times \mathbf{B}$ is of second order and is therefore omitted if one linearizes Eqs. (27.11) and (27.16). Since this is a discussion of oscillatory phenomena, one must include the inertial term (m/ne^2)

$(\partial j / \partial t)$ in Eq. (27.16). If, for simplicity, one ignores the diffusion term, this equation leads to the following linearized version of Ohm's law, $E_1 = (m/ne^2)\ (\omega_c + i\omega)j_i$, and the electrodynamic equations and the hydrodynamic equations are completely uncoupled and have independent solutions. In addition to ordinary sound waves, one obtains two types of electromagnetic waves. For the first type to be discussed, it is necessary that one retain the displacement current in Eq. (27.5). This wave has a longitudinal electric field and current and has no magnetic field. Its dispersion relation degenerates into a relation fixing ω:

$$\omega(\omega - i\omega_c) = \omega_p{}^2 \qquad (27.73)$$

if ω_p and ω_c are the plasma frequency $\sqrt{ne^2/m\epsilon}$ and the collision frequency $ne^2/m\sigma$ of the electrons. The following tabulation lists some typical values of ω_p and ω_c in metallic conductors, in the ionosphere and in shock-heated air:

	M	ω_p	ω_c
Electrons in metal........	..	1.5×10^{16}	3.0×10^{14}
F layer.................	..	2.0×10^{7}	6.0×10^{2}
Shock-heated air........	10	1.1×10^{12}	8.5×10^{12}
$p_1 = 760$ mm Hg.......	15	2.5×10^{13}	1.3×10^{13}
	20	4.1×10^{13}	2.1×10^{13}
	25	7.6×10^{13}	3.3×10^{13}
$p_1 = 10^{-2}$ mm Hg.....	10	7.5×10^{9}	1.1×10^{8}
	15	3.5×10^{10}	2.2×10^{8}
	20	9.0×10^{10}	4.5×10^{8}
	25	2.5×10^{11}	1.3×10^{9}

Note: ω in radians/second.

The roots of the dispersion equation are complex and lie above the real axis, which means that the waves are damped. Since ω does not depend on $\mathbf{k}$, the group velocity $\partial\omega/\partial k$ is zero and a disturbance made up of this type of waves does not propagate any energy.

The second type is essentially an ordinary electromagnetic wave with $\mathbf{E}$ and $\mathbf{B}$ at right angles to each other and to $\mathbf{k}$. Again retaining the displacement current, one derives the dispersion relation

$$(\omega^2 - k^2c^2)(\omega - i\omega_c) = \omega\omega_p{}^2 \qquad (27.74)$$

After noting from the above table that ω_c is usually small compared with ω_p, one has approximately

$$k^2c^2 = \omega^2 - \omega_p{}^2$$

which shows that waves with a frequency which is smaller than ω_p do not propagate.

In the presence of a d-c magnetic field $\mathbf{B}_0$, one encounters some wave modes which can be classified by the relative directions of $\mathbf{k}$, $\mathbf{B}_0$, and $\mathbf{v}$. The following discussion is valid if the frequency is small compared with the frequency of gyration eB_0/m_i of the ions in the field $\mathbf{B}_0$ and if the resistivity of the fluid can be ignored.

The general dispersion relation can be written in a form which still contains the variable $\mathbf{v}_1$ [see Eq. (27.72)].

$$\omega^2\mathbf{v}_1 - v_s{}^2(\mathbf{k} \cdot \mathbf{v}_1)\mathbf{k} = \frac{1}{\rho_0\mu} \{[(\mathbf{k} \times \mathbf{v}_1) \cdot \mathbf{B}_0](\mathbf{k} \times \mathbf{B}_0) - k^2(\mathbf{B}_0 \cdot \mathbf{v}_1)\mathbf{B}_0 + k^2B_0{}^2\mathbf{v}_1\}$$

$$(27.75)$$

The variable $v_s = \sqrt{\gamma p_0/\rho_0}$ is the speed of ordinary sound waves in fluid. From this relation one can derive the various modes and their dispersion relations. If two of the three vectors $\mathbf{k}$, $\mathbf{B}_0$, and $\mathbf{v}_1$ are parallel to each other, the triple product $(\mathbf{k} \times \mathbf{v}_1) \cdot \mathbf{B}_0$ is zero and one can distinguish three types of wave motion. Two of these are compression modes, i.e., waves for which $\mathbf{v}_1$ is parallel to $\mathbf{k}$. By inspection of Eq. (27.75) one finds that the second term on the right-hand side must be either parallel to $\mathbf{v}_1$ and $\mathbf{k}$ or else it must be at right angles to them so that the scalar product $(\mathbf{B}_0 \cdot \mathbf{v}_1)$ is zero. In the one case the wave is entirely independent of the field $\mathbf{B}_0$. Its dispersion relation is $\omega^2 = k^2 v_s{}^2$, so that the wave is traveling with the ordinary speed of sound. In the other case one is dealing with a wave traveling at right angles to the magnetic field with the dispersion relation $\omega^2 = k^2(v_s{}^2 + v_A{}^2)$. $v_A = B_0/\sqrt{\rho_0 \mu}$ is called the Alfvén velocity. There is no wave where $\mathbf{v}_1$ is parallel to $\mathbf{B}_0$ but not to $\mathbf{k}$. The third type of wave travels parallel to the field lines, with the fluid motion taking place at right angles to $\mathbf{k}$. The possibility of having such shear waves can be related to a stringlike tension of the field lines; it was predicted by Alfvén, after whom this type of waves has been named. The speed of these waves is v_A.

If there is an arbitrary angle θ between $\mathbf{k}$ and $\mathbf{B}_0$, the two vectors define a plane. There exists a pure-shear-wave mode where the fluid motion is transverse to that plane and which travels with the speed $v_A \cos \theta$. Fluid motion in the $\mathbf{k}$, $\mathbf{B}_0$ plane gives rise to two waves which are a mixture of compression and shear waves. Their speed $v = \omega/k$ is found from the dispersion relation

$$\left(\frac{\omega}{k}\right)^2 = \tfrac{1}{2}[v_A{}^2 + v_s{}^2 \pm \sqrt{(v_A{}^2 + v_s{}^2)^2 - 4 v_A{}^2 v_s{}^2 \cos^2 \theta}] \tag{27.76}$$

Figure 27.21 represents $(\omega/k)^2$ for the three modes as the radius in a polar diagram, distinguishing where $v_s > v_A$ and where $v_s < v_A$. In either case, the shear-wave speed is intermediate between the two mixed types. The three modes are often identified as the slow, intermediate, and fast wave. For $\theta = 0°$ and $\theta = 90°$, one regains the modes discussed in the previous section.

It is appropriate to warn the reader that the anisotropy of the wave motion and the multiplicity of modes in the presence of a magnetic field create considerable difficulties to the solution of a general problem. General discussions of some of these difficulties are given by Grad[34a] and by Kontorovich.[34b]

For the low-frequency waves just discussed, $v = \omega/k$ does not vary with the frequency. By turning to frequencies as high or higher than the ion-gyration frequency ω_i, it is noted first that this does not affect compression waves moving parallel to the magnetic field. When the fluid moves transverse to $\mathbf{B}_0$, there are again two basic modes. For $\mathbf{k} \parallel \mathbf{B}_0$, the basic modes are circularly polarized waves rotating around the direction of the field. The dispersion relation is

$$\left(\frac{kc}{\omega}\right)^2 = 1 - \frac{\omega_p{}^2}{\omega} \frac{1}{\omega \pm \omega_e} + \frac{m_e}{m_i} \frac{1}{\omega \mp \omega_i} \tag{27.77}$$

with alternate signs for right-hand and left-hand rotation. In the low-frequency limit, one obtains

$$\left(\frac{kc}{\omega}\right)^2 = 1 + \frac{\omega_p{}^2}{\omega_e \omega_i} = 1 + \frac{n m_i c^2}{B_0{}^2/\mu} = 1 + \left(\frac{c}{v_A}\right)^2$$

and since $v_A \ll c$, one regains the dispersion relation for Alfvén waves $(\omega/k)^2 = v_A{}^2$.

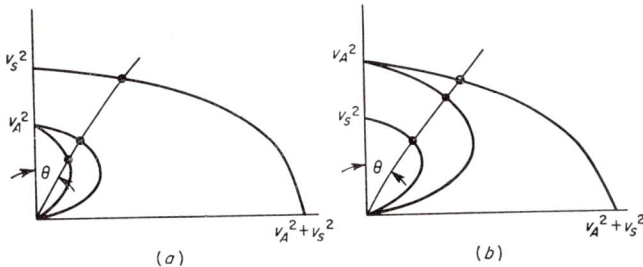

FIG. 27.21. MHD wave-velocity plots in polar form. Dependence of $(\omega/k)^2$ for three modes of wave motion on the angle θ between $\mathbf{k}$ and $\mathbf{B}_0$. (a) $v_s > v_A$. (b) $v_s < v_A$.

For $\mathbf{k} \perp \mathbf{B}_0$, an analysis, which is only valid if the material pressure is negligible compared with the magnetic pressure, leads to

$$\left(\frac{kc}{\omega}\right)^2 = 1 + \frac{\omega_p^2(\omega_p^2 + \omega_i\omega_e - \omega^2)}{(\omega^2 - \omega_e^2)(\omega^2 - \omega_i^2) + \omega_p^2(\omega_i\omega_e - \omega^2)} \tag{27.78}$$

In the low-frequency limit, one is led to the same dispersion relation as for the transverse waves. This is to be expected since the material pressure has been ignored.

In the study of radio-wave propagation in the ionosphere as influenced by the magnetic field of the earth, it is necessary to consider the general case of intermediate angles between $\mathbf{k}$ and $\mathbf{B}_0$. A discussion of the Appleton-Hartree dispersion relation which applies to this problem goes beyond the scope of this article, and the reader is referred to Mitra.[35]

27.14. Nonlinear Wave Motion; Shocks

The three modes of MHD waves which are obtained by elementary means for small-amplitude motion also appear if one does not linearize the theory. This has been demonstrated by a generalization of Riemann's method of characteristics.[36] The analysis leads to three speeds, depending on p, ρ, and B in the same manner as before. These speeds define the *characteristic motion* of certain types of disturbances.

Like ordinary hydrodynamic waves, MHD waves tend to get steeper in front and develop into shocks, i.e., surfaces across which the physical state changes discontinuously. These changes obey conservation laws, which appear as relations connecting the values of state variables on one side of the discontinuity with those on the other side. The discussion will at first be limited to the case of infinite conductivity.[37,38] To facilitate writing the shock conditions, it is convenient to introduce the notation $\Delta F = (F_{\text{ahead}} - F_{\text{behind}})$ for the difference and $\overline{F} = \frac{1}{2}(F_{\text{ahead}} + F_{\text{behind}})$ for the average of a quantity F on the two sides of the discontinuity. In addition, it simplifies the equations to replace the density ρ by the specific volume $\psi = \rho^{-1}$ and to introduce the indices n and t for the normal and the two tangential components of a vector relative to the orientation of the surface of discontinuity. If m stands for the rate of mass flow through the discontinuity, the shock conditions are:

$$m \, \Delta\psi - \Delta v_n = 0 \tag{27.79}$$

$$m \, \Delta v_n + \Delta p = -\mu^{-1}\Sigma\overline{B}_t \, \Delta B_t \tag{27.80}$$

$$\Delta\mathcal{E} + \bar{p} \, \Delta\psi = -(4\mu)^{-1} \, \Delta\psi\Sigma(\Delta B_t)^2 \tag{27.81}$$

$$m \, \Delta v_t = \mu^{-1}B_n \, \Delta B_t \tag{27.82}$$

$$0 = \Delta B_n \tag{27.83}$$

$$0 = m(\overline{\psi} \, \Delta B_t + \overline{B}_t \, \Delta\psi) - B_n \, \Delta v_t \tag{27.84}$$

The equations are so written that in the absence of a magnetic field the right-hand sides are all zero. Then the first three are the familiar Hugoniot relations, and the fourth states that the tangential components of the velocity are continuous.

By turning to the case where the field is not zero, v_n and v_t are eliminated with the aid of Eqs. (27.79) and (27.82) from Eqs. (27.80) and (27.84).

$$\left(m^2 + \frac{\Delta p}{\Delta\psi}\right)\Delta\psi + \mu^{-1}\Sigma\overline{B}_t \, \Delta B_t = 0 \tag{27.85}$$

$$(m^2\overline{\psi} - \mu^{-1}B_n^2) \, \Delta B_t + m^2\overline{B}_t \, \Delta\chi = 0 \tag{27.86}$$

A special solution of these equations is obtained if

$$m^2\overline{\psi} - \mu^{-1}B_n^2 = 0 \tag{27.87}$$

In that case $\Delta\psi$ and $\Sigma\overline{B}_t \, \Delta B_t$ are both zero. The first condition implies that there is no compression, and thus no change in entropy, across the discontinuity, making the flow pattern entirely different from the familiar shocks encountered in ordinary hydrodynamics. From the second condition it follows that ΣB_t^2, and thus the magnitude of the resultant of the two tangential components, remains unchanged. For a given **B** ahead, the possible values of **B'** behind lie on a circular cone around the unchanged B_n as indicated in Fig. 27.22.

It is possible to introduce a frame of reference where the fluid velocity is parallel to the magnetic field on each side of a shock. In such a system the magnitude of the velocity is the same on each side of the discontinuity. A shock without compression can be called a shear shock; it is in many respects an analogue of the pure shear waves encountered in the linear theory.

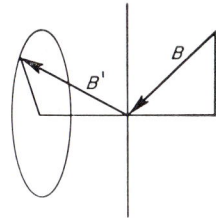

Fig. 27.22. Magnetic-field vectors on two sides of an intermediate shock.

If $m^2\overline{\psi} - \mu^{-1}B_n^2 = 0$, it is convenient to specify the coordinate system so that one of the two components $\overline{B}_t$ is zero. One can then conclude from Eq. (27.86) that this component of $\overline{B}_t$ must be zero on each side of the shock, so that it is sufficient to consider only the other component. After equating the determinant of Eqs. (27.85) and (27.86) to zero, one arrives at two values:

$$m^2 = \tfrac{1}{2}[(m_A{}^2 + m_s{}^2) \pm \sqrt{(m_A{}^2 + m_s{}^2)^2 - 4m_A{}^2m_s{}^2\cos^2\theta}] \qquad (27.88)$$

where
$$m_A{}^2 = \frac{\overline{B}^2}{\overline{\psi}\mu} \qquad m_s{}^2 = -\frac{\Delta p}{\Delta\psi}$$

and $\cos^2\theta = B_n{}^2/\overline{B}^2$. With the same substitutions one can express the corresponding relation for the shear shock in the form

$$m^2 = m_A{}^2\cos^2\theta \qquad (27.89)$$

Equations (27.88) and (27.89) have the same form as the dispersion relations which gave rise to Figs. 27.22 and 27.23. One is thus justified in referring to slow, intermediate, and fast shocks. From Eqs. (27.85) and (27.86), one can conclude that across a fast shock, B_t retains its direction and increases in magnitude, while across a slow shock, B_t may retain or reverse its direction and must decrease in magnitude. Possible shock directions are indicated in Fig. 27.23. The possibility that $B_t = 0$ behind a slow shock is noted. This type is referred to as a switch-off shock.

It is similarly possible that $B_t = 0$ ahead of a fast shock. That type is correspondingly referred to as a switch-on shock.

It is noted again that one can introduce a frame of reference where the velocity **v** on each side of the shock is parallel to the field **B**. In such a frame, all remarks made about possible directions of **B** obviously also apply to **v**.

In ordinary gas dynamics, the Hugoniot relations permit rarefaction shocks, but one can demonstrate that these are not stable. Similarly, one can exclude certain classes of MHD shocks by proving that they are not stable.[39]

Picturing a shock as a discontinuity is an idealization which is not strictly correct. In reality, there is a connecting region of finite width where transport processes establish thermal equilibrium. Ordinarily, transport properties of a gas are determined by collisions between the particles. In passing through a shock, a fluid picks up more energy than in an adiabatic compression. In an ordinary shock this energy is degraded to thermal energy, raising the entropy of the fluid. This ties in with the dissipative nature of transport processes. For an ordinary shock, the width of the transition region resulting from this dependence is a few mean free paths.

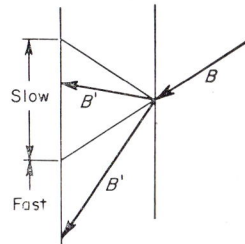

Fig. 27.23. Magnetic-field vectors on two sides of slow and fast shocks.

A similar result is obtained for an MHD shock with a transverse magnetic field in a fluid which has a large electrical conductivity, i.e., where the ratio of viscous to electrical dissipation $\sigma\mu\nu \gg 1$. In the opposite extreme, where $\sigma\mu\nu \ll 1$, the width of the transition region will be $(\sigma\mu\nu)^{-1}$ times larger. If the magnetic field is smaller than a critical value, which depends on the strength of the shock, the wide region obtained in the latter case is followed by a narrow one, across which only the hydrodynamic quantities change but the magnetic field does not.[40]

PLASMA DYNAMICS

27.15. Introduction

The continuum approach to hydrodynamics essentially ignores that the fluid is composed of many particles. Ordinarily, this is a very good approximation because the particles collide so frequently with each other that properties, such as momentum and energy, are rapidly randomized. In a plasma, however, collisions can become relatively ineffective in randomizing those properties. This does not mean that there are no collisions. As a matter of fact, a charged particle in a plasma collides simultaneously with very many other particles but each collision has only a minute effect. The result of adding very many such ineffective collisions can be split into a systematic and a random part. The systematic part leads to an orbit motion of the particle in the electric and magnetic fields resulting from the charge and current distribution in the plasma. Along an orbit, the momentum and energy of a particle change in a predictable fashion. The random part leads to a gradual drifting away from the orbital motion. The mean free path of a particle can be defined as the distance a particle travels until its momentum or energy drift becomes appreciable. In a plasma containing singly charged ions, this effective mean free path is of the order

$$\lambda = 10^8 T^2 n^{-1} \qquad (T \text{ in } {}^\circ\text{K}, \lambda \text{ and } n^{-\frac{1}{3}} \text{ in meters})$$

When λ becomes so large that the concepts pressure and temperature lose the meaning they have in continuum theory, one needs a different basis for discussing the dynamics of a plasma. An analysis of individual orbits and a statistical method are two widely used starting points for such a discussion, which will be taken up in that order. An essential assumption in both methods is the presence of a strong magnetic field.

27.16. First-order Orbit Theory[41]

In a homogeneous magnetic field electrons and ions perform a spiraling motion. The instantaneous center of the spiral, also called its guiding center, travels with a constant velocity parallel to the magnetic field. If electric or gravitational fields are present, or if the magnetic field is inhomogeneous, the guiding center will drift across the magnetic-field lines and its velocity component parallel to the field will change. The drift of the guiding center in the direction of $\mathbf{E} \times \mathbf{B}$ has been mentioned previously in the discussion of Ohm's law. A gravitational field acts similarly, but causes electrons and positive ions to drift in opposite directions so that there will be an electric-current density associated with such a drift. Drifts which produce currents also appear if the absolute value B of the magnetic field changes in a perpendicular direction to $\mathbf{B}$ or if the field lines have a curvature.

The effect of slow variations of the magnetic field is conveniently described if one introduces the so-called magnetic moment, which is defined as the product of the area encircled by the spiral, the number of gyrations per second, and the charge of the particle. Thus

$$\mathfrak{M} = \pi r_i^2 \frac{\omega_i}{2\pi} e_i = \frac{m_i v_\perp^2}{2B} \qquad (27.90)$$

or more precisely, an average of this quantity over one gyration. The magnetic moment is not exactly a constant of the motion, but rather an adiabatic invariant approaching constancy in the limit where the variations of $\mathbf{B}$ encountered by the particle during one gyration are infinitesimally small. The following discussion will make the approximation that $\mathfrak{M}$ is constant.

If a gyrating particle moves toward a region where the magnetic field increases, its transverse kinetic energy $mv_\perp^2/2$ increases in the same proportion as B. On the other hand, the total kinetic energy $mv^2/2$ in a purely magnetic field is an exact constant of the motion, and thus

$$\frac{mv_\parallel^2}{2} + \mathfrak{M}B = \frac{mv^2}{2} = \text{const} \tag{27.91}$$

The motion of the guiding center is therefore like the motion in a potential field $\mathfrak{M}B$, reflecting the particle after it reaches the *mirror point*, where the potential energy equals the total energy. If a particle is trapped between two regions where the magnetic field is strong, the integral $\oint v_\parallel dl$ taken over a complete cycle also is an adiabatic invariant.[42]

Constants of the motion and adiabatic invariants are an important tool of first-order orbit theory. Consider, for example, the quantity $P_\perp = nmv_\perp^2$, which is in some ways similar to the pressure in continuum theory. The adiabatic invariance of $\mathfrak{M}$ makes $p_\perp/\rho B$ constant as one follows the motion of the plasma. Much of the advantage of continuum theory is due to the constancy of the entropy, i.e., of p/ρ^γ, which arises because of the existence of an equation of state. By establishing the constancy of $p_\perp/\rho B$, one regains at least part of that advantage. The integral invariant, too, is very useful for calculating variations which occur in the analysis of interchange instabilities.

In a magnetic field which is everywhere parallel (say, in the z direction) but which is permitted to vary as a function of x and y, one can consider the two-dimensional flow in the xy plane.[43] Adding the different types of current densities which arise in the guiding center analysis and substituting the total into the Maxwell Eq. (27.9), one can derive an equation of motion for the plasma, which looks exactly like the momentum equation of the continuum theory, with $p_\perp$ as defined above replacing the pressure p. Since the magnetic-field lines move along with the plasma, the ratio B/ρ remains constant along the lines of flow. As the ratio $p_\perp/\rho B$ is also constant, one can eliminate B and then finds the ratio $p_\perp/\rho^2$ to be constant. This is formally equivalent with the law of conservation of entropy where $\gamma = 2$. In the two-dimensional case, therefore, one has a system of equations for the plasma which is the complete analogue to the corresponding continuum equations.

27.17. Statistical Theory

While one can gain considerable insight into some aspects of plasma dynamics by studying individual particle orbits, a more general approach can be based on statistical methods. A statistical description can be achieved by introducing the distribution functions $f_i(\mathbf{r},\mathbf{v},t)$, giving the densities of the particles in ordinary and in velocity space. The species are identified by the indices i. The integral $n_i(\mathbf{r},t) = \int f_i(\mathbf{r},\mathbf{v},t)\,d\mathbf{v}$ is the number of particles per unit volume. The distribution functions can be used to calculate mean values of various dynamical properties of the particles. The mean kinetic energy, for example, would be $m_i v_i^2/2 = n_i^{-1} \int (m_i v^2/2) f_i(\mathbf{r},\mathbf{v},t)\,d\mathbf{v}$. In a plasma, the species include electrons and at least one kind of ions.

The distribution functions obey transport equations

$$\frac{df_i}{dt} + \mathbf{v} \cdot \nabla f_i + \frac{e_i}{m_i}(\mathbf{E} + \mathbf{v} \times \mathbf{B})\nabla_v f_i = \left(\frac{df_i}{dt}\right)_{\text{coll}} \tag{27.92}$$

if $\mathbf{E}$ and $\mathbf{B}$ are macroscopic fields that satisfy Maxwell's equations. The rate of change due to collisions $(df_i/dt)_{\text{coll}}$ can be brought into manageable form by certain assumptions. The most simple and very frequently made assumption is to ignore collisions altogether and to set $(df_i/dt)_{\text{coll}}$ equal to zero. Some authors speak in this case of the Liouville equation in the space of one particle. The theory of transport phenomena is usually based on the assumption that only two particles participate in any collision. Making this assumption, Boltzmann expressed $(df_i/dt)_{\text{coll}}$ as the difference between two representative collision integrals which add and remove particles, respectively, from a given region in velocity space. The detailed form of the collision integrals in the Boltzmann equation can be found in textbooks on kinetic theory.[44]

Another assumption is that collisions produce predominantly small deflections. In that case, one can make certain expansions leading to the Fokker-Planck equation, in which the collision rate is expressed in terms of derivatives of f_i in velocity space.[45]

The collision term of both the Boltzmann and the Fokker-Planck equation is zero if the particles have a Maxwell distribution $(e^{-mv^2/2kT})$ of velocities relative to the mean velocity of the fluid. This balance arises no matter how large or small the collision rates are. If, however, the equilibrium is disturbed, the collisions tend to restore it at a rate which is proportional to the rate of the collisions. The distribution functions, therefore, remain always nearly Maxwellian if the collision rates are high. Chapman and Enskog have shown that one can in that case derive the continuum equations on which most previous considerations have been based. In this derivation one multiplies the transport equations in turn with the number 1, with the momentum $m_i v$, and with the kinetic energy $m_i v^2/2$, integrates, and sums over all i. The resulting conservation equations contain higher moments which are identified with the viscous drag and with the heat flow and which can be expressed with the aid of space derivatives of the lower moments, as in Eqs. (27.13) and (27.14), so that the system of equations is closed.

As mentioned above, collision rates in a plasma are often very small. In that case, the hydrodynamic approximation is not justified and one actually has to solve the transport equation. It is instructive to reinvestigate the theory of plasma oscillations using the Liouville equation, where collisions are considered to be absent. Introducing the velocity of the electrons as an additional variable, one finds that the method of substituting plane waves no longer leads to purely algebraic equations. Specifically, in the first-order equation expressing Ohm's law, which for $\omega_c = 0$ assumes the form $j_1 = -i(ne^2/m\omega)\mathbf{E}_1$, the coefficient on the right is multiplied by a factor

$$\frac{m}{2\pi KT} \int_{-\infty}^{\infty} \left(\frac{mv^2}{KT}\right)^l \frac{e^{-mv^2/2kT}}{1 + kv/\omega}\, dv \dagger$$

in which one has to set $l = 1$ or $l = 0$ in the discussion of longitudinal or transverse electric fields. For $k = 0$, this factor is obviously equal to 1 so that one is led to $\omega^2 = \omega_p{}^2$ as before. Formally, one can write down a dispersion relation for $k > 0$, but one finds that the denominator $1 + kv/\omega$ in the integrand introduces difficulties. For real ω, the integrand has a pole and the integral is not defined. For complex ω, this difficulty could disappear, but one can show that the formal dispersion relations have no complex roots[46] ω.

Landau,[47] replacing the substitution method by a Laplace-transform analysis, has shown that the general solution of an important class of initial-value problems can be represented as the sum of a component which dies out exceedingly fast and of an expansion in plane waves. The frequencies ω of the latter are complex roots of a dispersion relation which differs from the formal relation by shifting the path of the integration into the complex plane. The imaginary part of ω gives rise to very weak damping for large wavelengths and to strong damping when the wavelength is of the order or smaller than the Debye length h. The physical reason for the so-called Landau damping is the thermal motion of the electrons, which makes it impossible to maintain differences of the electron density between points less than a distance h apart. This mechanism is occasionally referred to as phase mixing.

An extension of this theory to waves in a plasma in a magnetic field[48] leads to solutions which do not greatly differ from the ones obtained from the simpler hydrodynamic theory. Several modes show Landau damping, but electron oscillations propagating perpendicular to the zero-order magnetic field are undamped.

In a magnetic field, charged particles are spiraling around the lines of force, and this

† In this equation only, K is used for the Boltzmann constant to distinguish it from wave number k.

restricts their motion at right angles to the field. If the radii of the spirals are small compared with L, these gyrations will cause some degree of randomness of the particle motion even in the absence of collisions. Gyrations are not as effective as collisions and, in particular, exclude any energy transfer between the components perpendicular and parallel to the magnetic field. Nevertheless, they may produce a nonthermal equilibrium where a modified continuum approach is still possible.

One such modification[49] replaces the scalar pressure by a tensor with two pressures $p_{\parallel}$ and $p_{\perp}$, parallel and perpendicular to **B**. Viscous and resistive losses being absent for no collisions, the assumption of no-heat flow in the energy equation of the continuum theory leads to constant entropy along streamlines. In the modified theory, no-heat flow leads to the constancy of $p_{\perp}/\rho B$ and of $p_{\parallel}B^2/\rho^3$ along streamlines. Such constants of motion are used mainly in investigating the stability of equilibriums by means of a variational principle.

It is not obvious why the no-heat-flow assumption should hold, and several authors have derived equations to describe properties of a plasma near equilibrium in a magnetic field.[50,51]

The structure of ordinary hydrodynamic shocks is related to the mean free path of the particles. The question arises if shocks can exist if collisions are practically absent.

A self-consistent field calculation of the dynamic pinch[52] shows that its outer surface is a sheath whose width is the geometric mean of the radii of gyration of electrons and ions in the magnetic field surrounding the discharge. Attempts have been made to look for a shock structure by a similar procedure,[53] but without a dissipative mechanism this has not been successful. Such calculations lead to oscillations in the wake of a supersonic disturbance.

If there is some dissipation, these oscillations will eventually be damped and all variables will reach their steady-state value. Details of the dissipation mechanism will affect the final state. If it is mainly due to collision processes, the excess energy will be equipartitioned between electrons and ions. Several mechanisms have been suggested which may result in a more rapid degradation than by collisions.

The oscillations mentioned before give rise to electric fields which present potential barriers to the ions. An orbit analysis shows that some ions can pass a barrier on the first approach whereas others are reflected and pass the barrier later. Such reflections have been interpreted as "collisions of ions with the electric field" and as being similar in their effect to collisions between particles.[54] This mechanism would feed the excess energy in the shock mainly to the ions. Other processes related to Landau damping feed that energy to the electrons. There is an indication that instead of being distributed by Maxwell's law, some particles may be accelerated to very high energies after the passage of a shock.

Experimentally, very fast shocks traveling at right angles to a magnetic field have thicknesses which are thinner than a mean free path calculated for the shock-heated gas.[55] So far, however, such experiments have not been of a nature where one could distinguish the consequences of the various models for dissipation of the excess energy which have just been discussed. It has been suggested that the propagation of shock waves, produced by solar disturbances, to the vicinity of the earth could perhaps explain the sudden commencement of magnetic storms.[56] This explanation requires the transition zone to have a thickness of about 10^9 cm, that is, about 10^{-2} times narrower than the mean free path calculated for collisions in the interplanetary plasma.

EXPERIMENTS AND APPLICATIONS: SOME EXAMPLES

The sophistication of MHD theory is matched by the difficulty of performing suitable experiments, either of a basic scientific nature or directed toward specific applications. Examples of some of the more interesting contributions so far are now discussed.

27.18. Studies with Liquid Conductors

Earlier, in Art. 27.7, the *Poiseuille-Hartmann* flow was discussed. Experiments were performed by Hartmann and Lazarus in which the pressure drop of mercury flowing

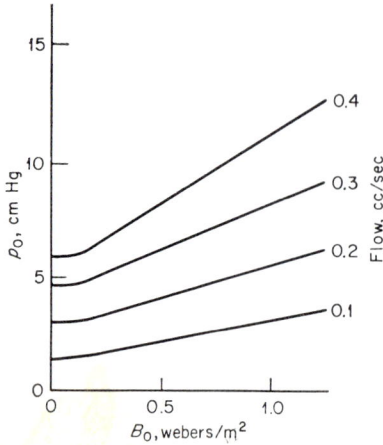

FIG. 27.24. Viscous MHD channel flow: pressure head vs. applied magnetic field with volume flow rate as parameter. (*Ref.* 1.)

through a channel was correlated with volume flow rate and applied magnetic field. Figure 27.24 gives some results; for small magnetic fields the curves are more or less horizontal, whereas at high fields they take on a positive and rather constant slope. As Cowling[10] points out, this follows directly from the expression relating average velocity $\bar{u}$ (i.e., volume flux) with pressure gradient Ω, in the flow direction, and Hartmann number G:

$$\Omega = \sigma B_0^2 \bar{u}(G \coth G - 1)^{-1} \quad (27.93)$$

The definition of G and nature of the function $\coth G$ make it clear that Ω is only feebly dependent on B_0 for small G, but is approximately proportional to B_0 for large G. Results obtained at higher pressures showed some anomalous behavior, indicating a breakdown of laminar flow. Murgatroyd,[57] by working with a still larger channel, 4 by 0.27 in. in cross section, also found indications of turbulence in the ordinary Reynolds number range 10^3 to 10^4. According to his findings, turbulence was absent when $R < 225G$. Here, then, one has the interesting result that turbulence in such flows is not a function of R alone.

Another class of experimental investigations with liquid conductors concerns *waves*

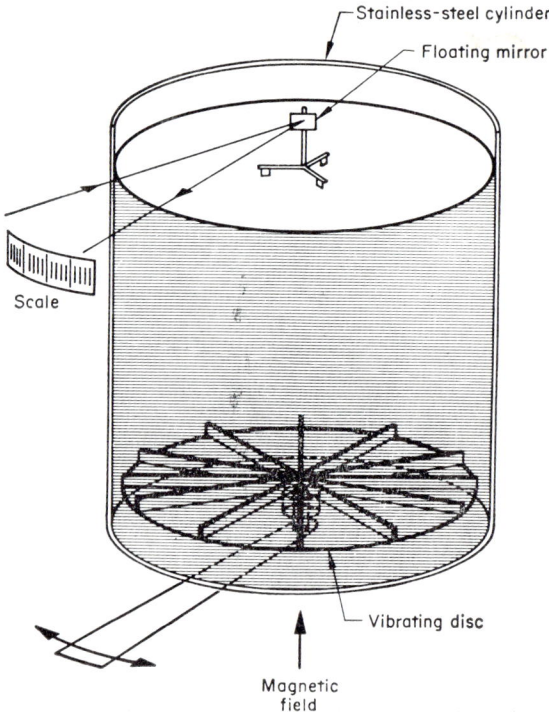

FIG. 27.25. Arrangement of the experiment on MHD waves in mercury. (*Ref.* 2.)

and *instabilities* (Arts. 27.6 to 27.14 and also Ref. 10, chap. 3). In analogy with the theory of sound waves in a viscous medium, one finds a dispersion and attenuation of MHD waves in a medium whose conductivity is less than infinite. As Lundquist[2] shows, a figure of merit for performing MHD wave experiments is $\sigma\rho^{-1/2}$. Larger values of conductivity give less effective damping, and smaller values of the density give higher wave speeds, resulting in less attenuation over a specified length of path. In the reference just mentioned, Lundquist excited waves in a cylindrical configuration of mercury by means of small-amplitude torsional vibrations of radial "spokes" on a submerged disc in the presence of a vertical magnetic field (Fig. 27.25). As

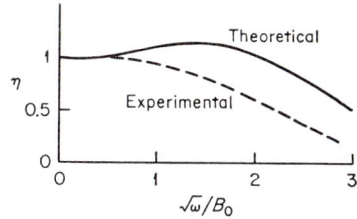

Fig. 27.26. Measurements on MHD waves in mercury. Ordinate represents ratio of surface amplitude to amplitude at bottom, ω = circular frequency, and B_0 is the applied field. (Ref. 2.)

seen in the figure, a floating mirror, set into motion by the wave behavior at the upper surface, displaces a light beam on a scale.

From the analysis, one would be led to expect standing waves, but the dissipation introduces attenuation and phase lag. Figure 27.26 gives a comparison of experimental and theoretical results. Lundquist's theoretical analysis gives the material velocity q at radial distance r and height z above bottom as

$$\frac{q(r,z)}{q(r,0)} = \sum_{\nu=1}^{\infty} \frac{2}{k_\nu r J_2(k_\nu R)} J_1(k_\nu r) \frac{\cosh \alpha_\nu(L-z)}{\cosh \alpha_\nu L} \tag{27.94}$$

in which L, R = height of surface and radius of cylindrical vessel, respectively
k_ν = roots of equation obtained by setting first-order Bessel function $J_1(k_\nu R)$ equal to zero
and

$$\alpha_\nu = \frac{i\omega k_\nu^2(\sigma\mu)^{-1} - \omega^2}{i\omega(\sigma\mu)^{-1} + v_A^2} \tag{27.95}$$

In Eq. (27.95), ω is the circular frequency, v_A is the Alfvén velocity. The peak of the theoretical curve corresponds to a resonant frequency of the system, but this could not be detected experimentally. These interesting studies were later improved somewhat by Lehnert,[58] who worked with liquid sodium. Its figure of merit $\sigma\rho^{-1/2}$ is about forty times that of mercury.

In the realm of *instability problems*, a unique experiment with liquid sodium was performed by Colgate,[59] which will be described only briefly here. The instability is of the Taylor type, which arises at the interface when a light fluid accelerates a heavy fluid. In Colgate's experiment, a thin cylindrical sheath or fountain of liquid sodium is created in a region within some field-producing coils. The field is then generated by pulse discharge of a capacitor bank into the coils and shorting the latter at the peak current. In this way, the field is maintained for a sufficient time to take several near-instantaneous photos of the sodium surface. Here the heavy fluid is sodium, and the equivalent "light fluid," which produces acceleration of the interface, is the magnetic field itself, acting through the mechanism of magnetic pressures. Minute ripples which tend to be present naturally in the sodium surface begin to grow exponentially in time, producing a mixing of the fluid and magnetic field. The observed irregularities on the sodium surface check with theory reasonably well.

27.19. Experiments with Conducting Gases

It is clear that current interest in MHD is centered largely on behavior of gases rather than liquids. Effort in the area of experiment and application is correspondingly

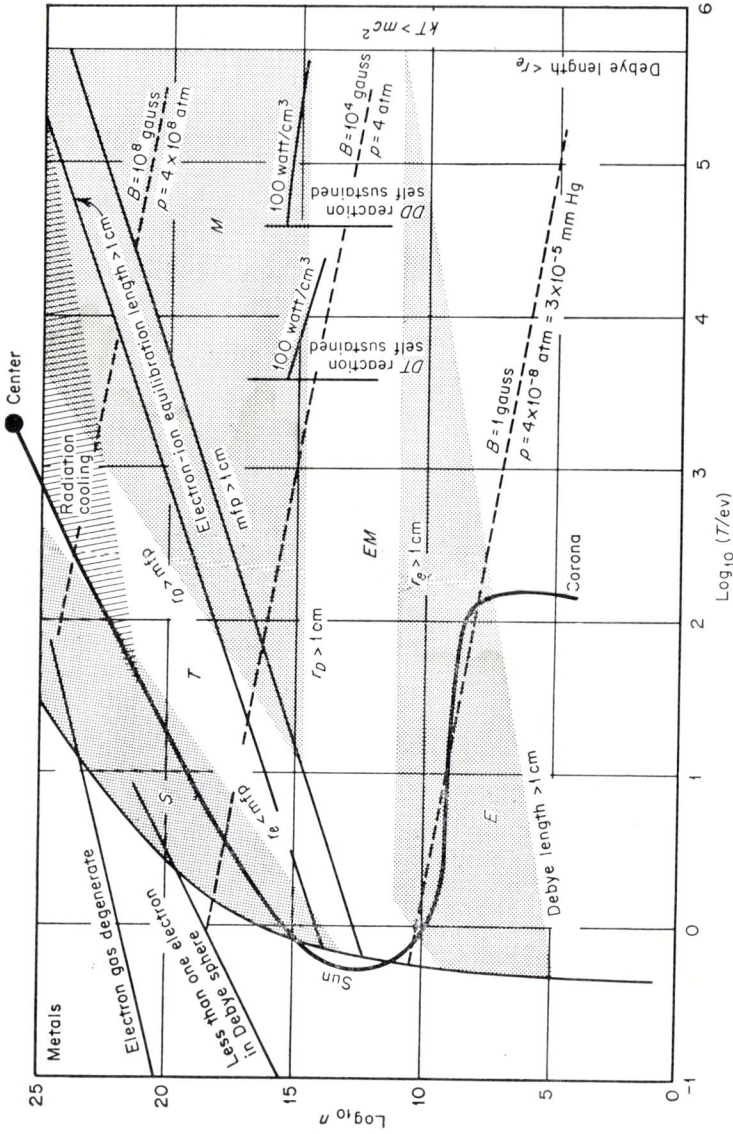

FIG. 27.27. Kantrowitz-Petschek classifications of MHD regions. Subscripts e and D represent electron and deuteron, respectively.

widespread. Fundamental studies which have been made include generation and inter-action of moving plasmas (Arts. 27.20 and 27.21) and production of MHD waves in a gas (Art. 27.22), as well as a number of studies dealing with magnetic confinement and attempts to achieve ultimate temperatures in the range 10^7 to $10^8\,°$K for thermonuclear purposes. The last-mentioned area will not be elaborated in this article. An excellent introductory survey with explicit discussions of the stellerator, scylla, the mirror machine, and other developments, along with appropriate reference lists, is given by Bishop.[60]

To assess properly a given experimental configuration or arrangement to be used for some practical purposes, it is important to compare typical magnitudes of physical variables with characteristic values. For example, what is the relation between a typical physical dimension and the mean free path, the Debye shielding distance, or the Larmor radius of one of the particles? What is the value of $\mathbf{R}_m$? And so on. Kantrowitz and Petschek[61] have prepared a composite diagram (Fig. 27.27) which serves to some extent as a framework for classification of MHD systems involving highly ionized gases. Reference to this diagram should be an aid to the fluid dynamicist in making the necessary physical analysis of an MHD system. The ordinate and abscissa are logarithmic scales of the electron density and temperature, respectively. The capital letters S, T, etc., refer to physical models of the plasma behavior which are qualitatively different in nature, according to the Kantrowitz-Petschek analysis. For region S, it turns out that the coefficients of the magnetic term and other terms in the Boltzmann equation are small compared with the collision term. Therefore the charged-particle distribution functions will be essentially Maxwellian, and the electrons and ions will pass through the gas according to classical kinetic-theory predictions. The drift velocity will be in the direction of forces exerted by applied fields. This implies that the electrical conductivity is a scalar, as indicated by the symbol S.

When the electron mean free path is larger than r_e, its Larmor radius, the magnetic term in the electron Boltzmann equation begins to play an important role. While the distribution function may approach a Maxwellian one, the drift velocity of the electrons has a component perpendicular to the electric field. This implies a tensor character for the electrical conductivity. The symbol T represents this region.

The M region is one where both the ion and electron mean free paths are larger than their Larmor radii. The respective Boltzmann equations are dominated by the magnetic-field term. Collisions, however, will still play a role in controlling the motion along the magnetic field; or if the mean free path is very large, collisions with walls take place, unless confining magnetic fields are used for "containment."

In region EM, the ion Larmor radius is larger than the size of the physical system, the magnetic term in its Boltzmann equation is no longer predominant, and the ion is largely influenced by electric forces. In the E region, the same becomes true of the electrons. Finally, when the Debye length becomes greater than the size of the apparatus, no more interactions take place and an individual particle description is more appropriate. For further discussion of Fig. 27.27, the reader is referred to Kantrowitz and Petschek.[61]

27.20. Magnetic Interaction of Shock-tube Flows

For a given gas, the equilibrium degree of ionization or electron density depends on the temperature and gas density. Knowledge of elastic-electron-collision cross sections permits calculation of the conductivity.[62] Table 27.1, prepared from data in Refs. 62 and 63, shows conducting-gas parameters correlated with conditions behind a shock of given Mach number advancing into both air and argon at an absolute pressure of 1 mm Hg and temperature of $293°$K.

The range of variables given in Table 27.1 falls quite within the range attainable by "regular" diaphragm-type shock tubes without magnetic interaction. In the case of argon and other monatomic gases, energy is not needed for dissociation and so it is possible to achieve higher temperatures with correspondingly higher degrees of ionization, for example, 31 per cent, as shown in Table 27.1. With such capabilities, shock-tube techniques have been among the most useful for studying magnetoplasmadynamics.

Table 27.1. Approximate Equilibrium Values of Conducting-gas Parameters behind Strong Shock Waves

Air:† 1 mm of Hg, 293°K

Shock Mach no.	Temperature °K	Density, NTP	Electrical conductivity, mho/cm	Electron concentration, cm^{-3}
10	3400	0.012	8×10^{-3}	3×10^{11}
12	4200	0.013	7×10^{-2}	5×10^{12}
14	5200	0.014	0.5	4×10^{13}
16	5800	0.016	1.2	1×10^{14}
18	6400	0.018	1.8	3×10^{14}

Argon:‡ 1 mm of Hg, 295°K

Shock Mach no.	Ionization, %	Electrical conductivity, mho/cm
10		
12	5	34
14	10	43
16	16	50
18	23	58
20	31	65

† Values compiled from curves in Ref. 62.
‡ Values compiled from curves in Ref. 63.

Patrick and Brogan[64] and others[63] have studied the flow of a shock-ionized gas in a transverse magnetic field. By use of pulsed techniques, fields approaching 10 webers/meter^2 (10^5 gauss) have been obtained; these behave as d-c fields during the time of transit of the ionized slug of gas. Experiment and theory agree in the one-dimensional approximation (see discussion of one-dimensional MHD flow given earlier in connection with Fig. 27.5). Both supersonic flows and subsonic flow tend toward Mach 1, so that one cannot, in general, have a continuous transition from supersonic to subsonic flow. When the interaction is sufficiently strong as measured by the parameter **N**, a supersonic flow will pass through a stationary shock located within the magnetic field; then the resultant subsonic flow will accelerate to sonic velocity around the region of exit from the field. Such standing shocks have been experimentally observed. For even stronger interactions, a reflected, upstream-moving shock occurs,[64] as required by the choked condition of the flow. The gas originally located downstream of the field is accelerated by the emerging shock to higher speeds than the gas passing through the field. Thus the latter portion of fluid must accelerate further by means of an expansion wave in order to match pressure and velocity. This wave also is observed experimentally.[63]

27.21. Magnetically Accelerated Shocks

In a somewhat different class of experiments, attention has been focused on the use of magnetic interactions to generate very strong shocks to obtain either ultrahigh velocities or temperatures. Several variations of the conventional shock tube have been used for this purpose. Among the more widely tested are the so-called T tube[65] and the conical configuration of Josephson.[66] Kolb's T tube with backstrap[67] utilizes a Lorentz force between the plasma current and the magnetic field of the backstrap current to generate stronger shocks moving down the stem (Fig. 27.28). Data with hydrogen show a considerable broadening of the Balmer lines H_β, H_γ, and H_δ due to the Stark effect associated with the higher degree of ionization (this is a perturbation of the energy level due to coulomb fields of the charged particles) when magnetic driving is

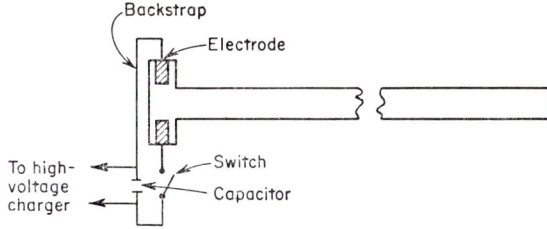

FIG. 27.28. T-type electromagnetic shock tube with a backstrap.

used as compared with the nonmagnetic case. Velocities around 10^5 meters/sec are indicated from streak camera photographs. If one assumes temperature equilibrium, conversion of kinetic to internal energy across such shocks leads to temperatures around one million degrees behind the reflected shock for an incident shock velocity of 2×10^5 meters/sec.

From a fluid-dynamic point of view, the T-tube flow has a "poor" wave diagram in that the attenuation is excessive. Contamination of the flow by evaporated wall material is also a problem. Josephson's driver is an axially symmetric arrangement in which a central electrode discharges to a ring located downstream at the walls of a conically expanding section (Fig. 27.29). The improved geometry does not contain sharp corners, and the self-pinch of the discharge is so shaped as to increase the driving force.

Some interest has centered in applying such electromagnetic shock tubes as basic gas-dynamics facilities in the very high temperature and velocity range. A disappointing feature of the T tube was the measured dependence of luminous-front velocity on the inverse square root of distance from the discharge. This is to be expected in accordance with one-dimensional blast-wave theory. However, investigators at both the Lockheed Missiles and Space Division and the Space Technology Laboratories have found that very little attenuation occurs in the coaxial type of tube even over a distance of a few feet. The reason is not clear but may be connected either with the rate at which energy is fed from the capacitor storage bank (determined, in turn, by the ringing frequency of the supply configuration) or with the evaporation of electrode material, simulating a constant-pressure driving mechanism. The prospect of having a quasi-equilibrium "slug" of test gas with an energy equivalent to, say, 10 ev (over 100,000°K) proceeding down the tube at speeds of 10^5 meters/sec (nominal Mach number well over 100, depending on the gas) is an exciting one indeed.

Gauger et al.[68] have verified the expected linear relationship between discharge current and shock velocity in the funnel-type tube: each is proportional to the square root of the energy. Ziemer[69] has employed the tube as an aerodynamic testing device in which preliminary experiments were made of the effects of a magnetic field on bow shock stand-off distance. Limitations in the use of such tubes include the low working densities (1 mm Hg or less), contamination, and secondary shocks.

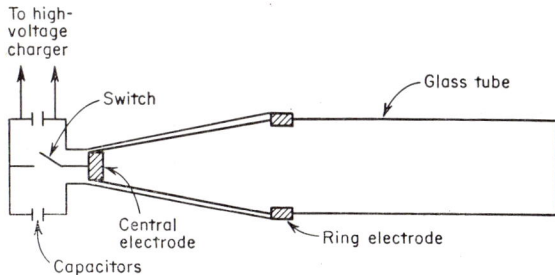

FIG. 27.29. Tapered or funnel-type electromagnetic shock tube.

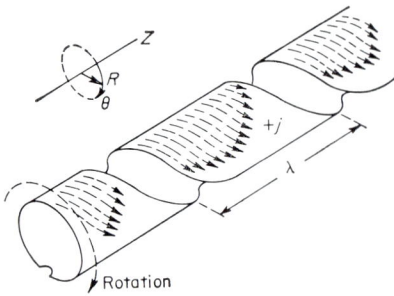

FIG. 27.30. Helical MHD waves. (*Ref.* 70.)

27.22. Hydromagnetic Plasma Waves

Alfvén's hydromagnetic waves, which Lundquist demonstrated in mercury (Art. 27.18), have now been observed experimentally by investigators at Los Alamos[70] and at Berkeley.[71] In the former work, helical oscillations (Fig. 27.30) were generated in deuterium in the pressure range 1 to 100 μ at a plasma electron temperature of 1 volt. These were found to be reproducible, permitting a mapping of the magnetic field with probes and subsequent derivation of the current-density components. The Berkeley group used a wave-guide technique in which a wave was generated at one end of a cylindrical plasma and the transmitted wave was detected at the other end about 34 in. away. The tube was filled with hydrogen at a pressure of 100 μ. Figure 27.31 gives a comparison of theoretical and experimental results for the wave velocity. Considering such difficulties as those associated with variation of ionization with radius and with pressure, the agreement is significant.

27.23. Magnetoaerodynamics

Earlier discussions of MHD flow (Arts. 27.6 to 27.12) indicated that aerodynamic applications were possible, at least in principle. Lift, drag, and heat transfer are susceptible to MHD effects, and the former two have been experimentally demonstrated (see below). It is evident, however, that these and other engineering phases of MHD are in an early stage of development. In that sense, the discussions in this section are exploratory.

Consider first the conductivity and magnetic Reynolds numbers corresponding to high-speed vehicle flight. Figure 27.32 gives experimental data of Lin[62] on the conduc-

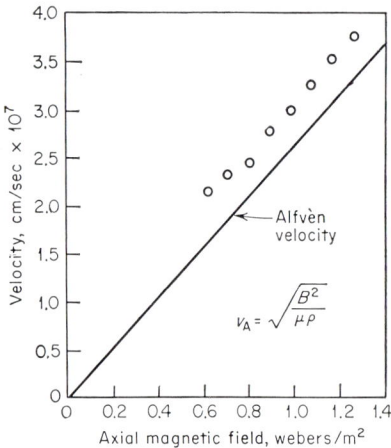

FIG. 27.31. Alfvén wave velocity vs. magnetic field. Comparison of experimental points with theoretical curve. (*Ref.* 71.)

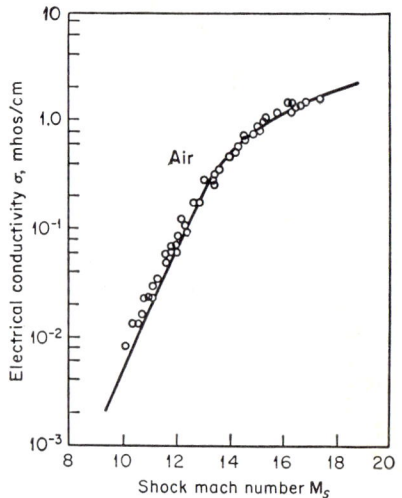

FIG. 27.32. Conductivity of shock-heated air. Pressure ahead of shock = 1 mm Hg. (*Ref.* 62.)

tivity of air after shock-heating. Calculations show more than an order of magnitude increase in σ when the air is seeded with 0.1 per cent potassium. Taking an optimistic value of 1000 mhos/meter for the conductivity and 1 meter for a characteristic length, one obtains a magnetic Reynolds number of unity corresponding to escape speed. Therefore the assumption of an infinitely conducting gas is not, in general, applicable to magnetoaerodynamics. However, appreciable interactions are still feasible if the ratio $\mathbf{N}(= \sigma B^2 L/\rho v)$ of magnetic force to dynamic force is not negligible compared with unity. It is this parameter which determines the extent of flow retardation or drag resulting from a given field-flow geometry.

Now the drag force just mentioned is antiparallel to the fluid flow as a result of the interaction of the induced current and the applied magnetic field. However, if the induced current is not parallel to the induced electric field, the resultant magnetic force has a component perpendicular to the flow. Thus the possibility of magnetoaerodynamic lift is introduced. This type of situation arises if the conductivity σ loses its scalar character in favor of a tensor behavior (T region in Fig. 27.27), corresponding to the tendency of the electrons to drift in a direction perpendicular to the magnetic and electric fields when they are allowed to make several cyclotron orbits between collisions. The terms Hall potential and Hall current are associated with this phenomenon. It is important when the magnetic field is relatively strong and the ambient density relatively low (the Hall coefficient is $\omega_s \tau$, where ω_s is the electron spiral frequency and τ the mean time between collisions). Apart from the feasibility of producing lift with the Hall phenomenon, however, the over-all role of the tensor conductivity in high-altitude magnetoaerodynamic flight has to be clarified further.[29]

An interesting analytical and experimental program dealing with magnetoaerodynamic forces has been carried out by the group at AVCO.[72] A shock-tube flow was made to pass between the wires of a loosely wound solenoid whose axis was perpendicular to flow. Analysis of the problem was made for small $\mathbf{R}_m$ and small $\mathbf{N}$ by a perturbation treatment, with arbitrary values of the Hall parameter $\omega_s \tau$. The experiments, however, included large as well as small values of $\mathbf{N}$. View camera pictures of the emitted light showed both drag (Fig. 27.33) and lift (Fig. 27.34). Measurements made from such photographs indicated a lift coefficient of 0.4 and a lift-drag ratio of unity for the experimental conditions. The results are in general agreement with the theory.

The use of MHD drag to aid in the control of missile reentry speeds for reducing

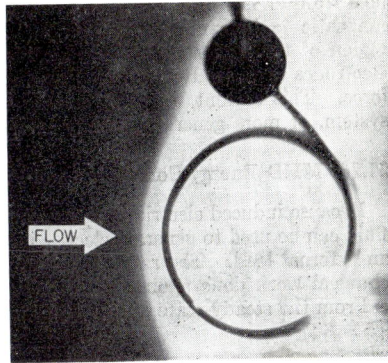

FIG. 27.33. Emitted-light photograph of end view of loosely wound solenoid in a shock-tube flow. Interaction parameter $N = 3.5$, corresponding to a strong magnetic field. This causes the solenoid to simulate a solid cylinder with much of the flow traveling around it, as the shock pattern indicates. Hall coefficient $\omega_s T = 3$. Disturbance at downstream end of coil is due to an insulation breakdown and should be ignored. (*Ref.* 72.)

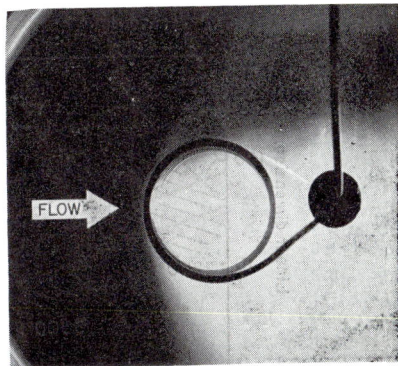

FIG. 27.34. Photograph similar to Fig. 27.33, except that $N = 1$ and $\omega_s T = 5$. The Hall effect is strong enough to produce a lift coefficient of 0.4.

heat transfer has been widely discussed. The mechanism would involve producing a magnetic field normal to the flow of ionized air formed in the shock-boundary-layer region of the typical blunt-nosed ballistic reentry body. A pair of properly placed electrodes (e.g., see Ref. 3, fig. 3) permits current to flow, resulting in the $\mathbf{j} \times \mathbf{B}$ drag force. This current, in turn, can be sent through the coils of the field-producing system, or more generally, to any external load (Art. 27.24).

27.24. MHD Energy Conversion and Propulsion

Because induced electric fields are formed in MHD flows, the motion of a conducting fluid can be used to generate electric power by insertion of electrodes and connection to an external load. The rate of enthalpy change of the gas is the resultant of the mechanical work done against the $\mathbf{j} \times \mathbf{B}$ force and the ohmic heating of the gas itself.

From the steady-state energy equation and Ohm's law, one may write

$$-\mathbf{v} \cdot (\mathbf{j} \times \mathbf{B}) - \frac{j^2}{\sigma} = -\mathbf{E} \cdot \mathbf{j} = -\rho \mathbf{v} \cdot \operatorname{grad} i \qquad (27.96)$$

or

(Rate of work done by fluid) − (rate of ohmic heating of fluid)
= (power to external system) = (rate of enthalpy loss by fluid)

Obvious parameters for an MHD generator are the magnetic-field strength and the gas conductivity (achieved by thermal ionization, with possible help from seeding techniques). Linear dimensions are evidently controlled by the magnitude of the conductivity, but depend as well on the planned loss in stagnation pressure of the gas and on the over-all power output. Heat losses in such a system would tend to decrease with increasing size; consequently, planning thus far has been for large devices. Figure 27.35 based on work by Rosa gives an estimate of the size of a 100-megawatt MHD generator as a function of gas conductivity and magnetic-field strength. Typical operating temperatures are also shown. An experimental device[73] powered by an AVCO arc tunnel has achieved a power output around 10 kw.

In the much higher temperature range (around $10^8 \,^\circ$K) the fusion process is considered a most promising technique for energy conversion. MHD techniques play an important role in the attempts made to reach such extreme temperatures, especially with respect to confinement of the gas away from the walls of containers. Again, the reader is referred to Bishop.[60]

Turning now to MHD propulsion, one's attention is focused on obtaining thrust by means of a plasma–magnetic-field interaction. The motivation for plasma propulsion stems from the need for a high-specific-impulse (ratio of thrust to propellant-mass-consumption rate) engine for use on long space flights. Plasma and ion engines should

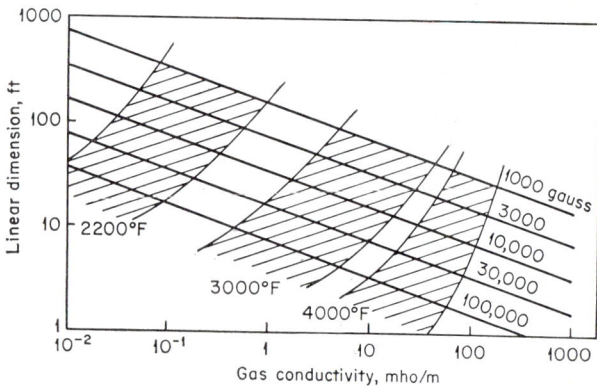

Fig. 27.35. Design parameters for a 100-megawatt MHD generator. (*Ref.* 73.)

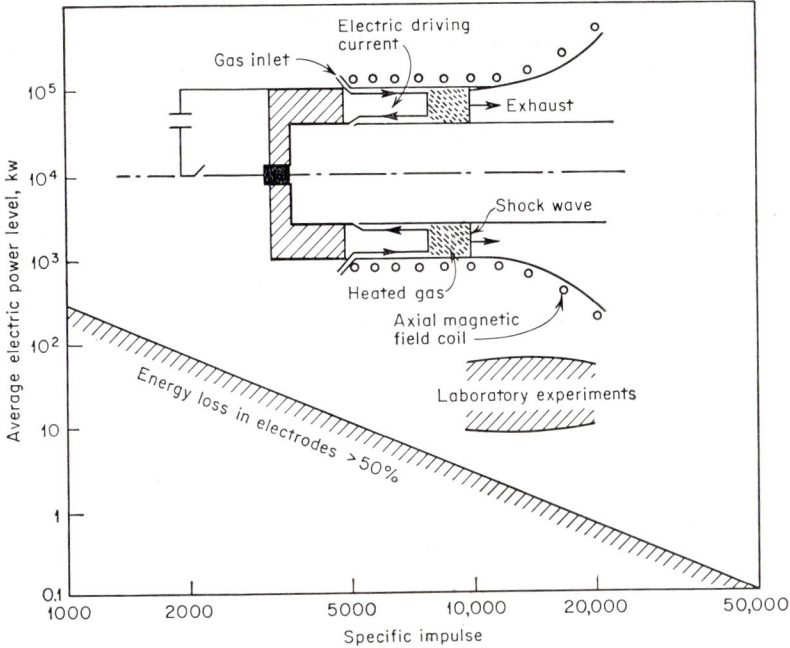

FIG. 27.36. Annular, pulsed-type MHD propulsive device. (*Ref.* 74.)

achieve a specific impulse more than an order of magnitude larger than that obtainable with high-performance chemical rockets under present development. Values of specific impulse for the latter are in the range of 300 to 400 sec.

Earlier discussion of electromagnetic shock tubes described the acceleration of a hot gas along a tube. Such configurations are, in fact, related to some proposed plasma rocket motors, a basic distinction being the need for repeated pulsing in order to provide thrust over an extended period of time. A device developed by Patrick[74] is shown in Fig. 27.36. The arrangement is an annular one in which a discharge between electrodes on the inner and outer cylinders heats propellant gas in the annulus. When this takes place, there is a strong azimuthal magnetic field due to the axial motion of currents in the electrodes. Radial currents in the gas interact with this field to produce an axial force on the gas. The function of the externally produced axial magnetic field is to interact with the radial electric field present when the switch is closed. This permits an azimuthal $\mathbf{E} \times \mathbf{B}$ drift of electrons to provide a uniform initial breakdown. Another function of the axial magnetic field in this device is to provide magnetic cushioning, or containment of the gas, in a region away from the walls, thus minimizing such wall losses.

Operation of Patrick's device as a shock tube has yielded velocities corresponding to specific impulses between 10,000 and 20,000 sec. Wall losses from the gas at temperatures from 100,000 to 400,000°K were evidently minimized by magnetic containment. Other losses which affect the efficiency are energy used for dissociation and ionization when the flow is frozen and dissipation in the electric circuitry. Tentative data reported by Rosa[73] for a chamber design to yield a specific impulse of 3500 sec are:

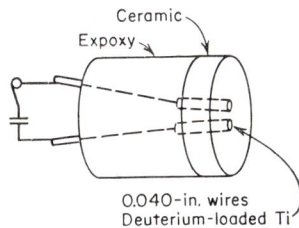

FIG. 27.37. Button-type plasma gun. (*Ref.* 76.)

Average power (assuming no valves)................	40 kw
Initial gas density.............................	2.3×10^{-9} g/cc
Tube length...................................	63 cm
Annular spacing................................	6.0 cm
Mean annular radius...........................	18 cm
Maximum current..............................	7.6×10^4 amp
Peak power....................................	10 Mw
Total energy (per pulse)........................	25 joules
Containment time..............................	18 μsec
Frozen expansion efficiency.....................	0.85
Pulsing rate (assuming no valves)................	1600 sec^{-1}

A good deal of other exploratory research related to plasma propulsion is in progress. Starr[75] reports pendulum measurements of the impulse produced by an exploding wire in a T tube backstrap configuration. Bostick[76] has developed plasma guns of different varieties. These guns, of which the button type is particularly simple in design (Fig. 27.37), have accelerated plasma consisting of metallic ions, deuterium ions, and electrons to speeds up to 10^7 in./sec. Design calculations on plasma motors employing rails lead to speeds up to 4×10^7 in./sec, with a corresponding specific impulse of 10^5 sec.

In addition to pulse-type plasma accelerators, much attention is now focused on continuous-type arc-driven plasma motors. Passage of the propellant through a high-current arc produces an appreciable amount of excitation and ionization by Joule heating. Among the more popular geometries is one shown in Fig. 27.38, which corresponds to the conical-type shock tube mentioned earlier. The discharge takes place between an axial cathode and an annular anode located somewhat downstream. Presumably, MHD aids in accelerating the gas by means of the self-pinch. Here again, however, several factors limit the efficiency of such devices. These include the frozen-flow losses due to nonrecombination upstream of the rocket exhaust and heat losses to the chamber walls. The curves in Fig. 27.38 indicate efficiency limitations on the operating regions of the arc-type plasma jet. In preliminary experiments with the AVCO arc tunnel,[77] measured efficiencies at specific impulses of 600 and 1100 sec were 65 and 50 per cent, respectively. The advantage of over-all neutrality, by the way, is an important one for plasma propulsion as compared with ion engines.

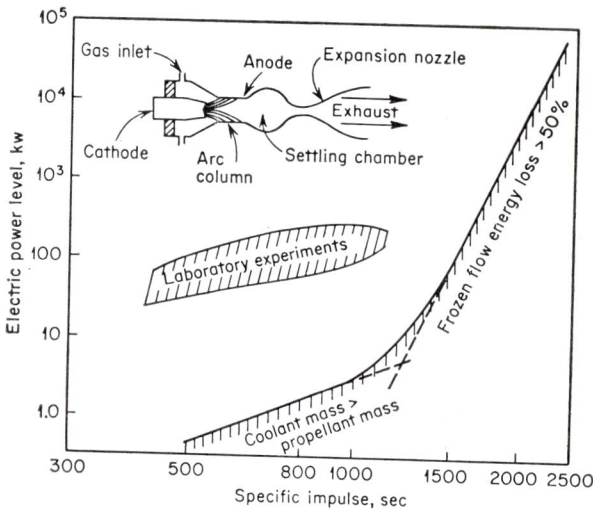

FIG. 27.38. Coaxial continuous arc-type MHD propulsive device. (Ref. 77.)

REFERENCES

1. Hartmann, J., and F. Lazarus: *Kgl. Danske Videnskab. Selskabs, Mat. = fys. Medd.*, vol. 15, nos. 6–7, 1937.
2. Lundquist, S.: *Phys. Rev.*, **76**:1805(1949).
3. Resler, E. L., Jr., and W. R. Sears: *J. Aeronaut. Sci.*, **25**:235 (April, 1958).
4. Landshoff, R. (ed.): "Magnetohydrodynamics," pp. 69ff., Stanford University Press, Stanford, Calif., 1957.
5. Schlüter, A.: *Z. Naturforsch.*, **5a**:72 (1950).
6. Rosenbluth, M. N., and A. N. Kaufman: *Phys. Rev.*, **109**:1 (1958).
7. Schlüter, A.: *Z. Naturforsch.*, **6a**:73 (1951).
8. Sommerfeld, A.: "Mechanics of Deformable Bodies," p. 130, Academic Press, New York, 1950.
9. Prandtl, L.: Division G, p. 64, in W. Durand (ed.), "Aerodynamic Theory," vol. III, Springer, Berlin, 1935.
10. Cowling, T. G.: "Magnetohydrodynamics," Interscience, New York, 1957.
11. Resler, E. L., Jr., and W. R. Sears: *J. Aeronaut. Sci.*, **26**:318 (May, 1959).
12. Alfvén, H.: *Nature*, **150**:405 (1942).
13. Prendergast, K. H.: *Astrophys. J.*, **123**:498 (1956); **128**:361 (1958).
14. Lundquist, S.: *Arkiv. Fysik.*, **2**:35 (1950).
15. Lüst, R., and A. Schlüter: *Z. Astrophys.*, **34**:263 (1954).
16. Schlüter, A.: *Z. Naturforsch.*, **12a**:855 (1957).
17. Chandrasekhar, S., and P. C. Kendall: *Astrophys. J.*, **126**:457 (1957).
18. Shafranov, V. D.: On Magnetohydrodynamical Equilibrium Configurations, *JETP*, **6**:545 (1958).
19. Bostick, W. H.: *Phys. Rev.*, **104**:292 (1956).
20. Berkovitz, J., H. Grad, and H. Rubin: Magnetohydrodynamic Stability, *Proc. 2d U.N. Intern. Conf. on Peaceful Uses of Atomic Energy*, **31**:177 (1958).
21. Spitzer, L.: *J. Phys. of Fluids*, **1**:253 (1958).
22. Rosenbluth, H. N.: *Proc. 3d Intern. Conf. on Ionized Gases*, p. 903, Venice, 1957.
23. Chandrasekhar, M. S., and E. Fermi: *Astrophys. J.*, **118**:116 (1953).
24. Chandrasekhar, S.: *Astrophys. J.*, **124**:232 (1956).
25. Busemann, A.: in D. Bershader (ed.), "Magnetodynamics of a Conducting Fluid," pp. 3ff., Stanford University Press, Stanford, Calif., 1959.
26. Rossow, V.: *NACA Rept.* 1358, 1958.
27. Bleviss, Z. O.: *J. Aeronaut. Sci.*, **25**:601 (October, 1958).
28. Mitchner, M.: in D. Bershader (ed.), "Magnetodynamics of a Conducting Fluid," pp. 61ff., Stanford University Press, Stanford, Calif., 1959.
29. Sears, W. R.: *ARS Journal*, **29**:397ff. (June, 1959).
30. Sears, W. R., and E. L. Resler, Jr.: *J. Fluid Mech.*, **5**:257ff. (February, 1959).
31. Resler, E. L., Jr., and J. E. McCune: in D. Bershader (ed.), "Magnetodynamics of a Conducting Fluid," pp. 120ff., Stanford University Press, Stanford, Calif., 1959.
32. McCune, J. E., and E. L. Resler, Jr.: Compressibility Effects in Magneto-aerodynamics, *Cornell Univ. Rept.* (sponsored by OSR and ONR), May, 1959.
33. Sturrock, P.: Kinematics of Growing Waves, *Phys. Rev.*, **112**:1488 (1958).
34a. Grad, H.: in D. Bershader (ed.), "Magnetodynamics of a Conducting Fluid," Stanford University Press, Stanford, Calif., 1959.
34b. Kontorovich, V. M.: On the Interaction between Small Disturbances and Discontinuities in Magnetohydrodynamics and on the Stability of Shock Waves, *JETP*, **35**:851 (1959).
35. Mitra, S. K.: "The Upper Atmosphere," chap. 5, sec. 2, The Asiatic Society, Calcutta, 1952.
36. Friedrichs, K. O., and H. Kranzer: Non-linear Wave Motion, *New York Univ. Rept.* NYO-6486, reissue of 1954 Los Alamos report.
37. de Hoffman, F., and E. Teller: Magnetohydrodynamic Shocks, *Phys. Rev.*, **80**:692 (1950).
38. Lüst, R.: Magnetohydrodynamische Stosswellen in einem Plasma unendlicher Leitfähigkeit, *Z. Naturforsch.*, **8a**:277 (1953).
39. Akhiezer, A. I., G. I. Linbarskii, and R. V. Polovin: The Stability of Shock Waves in Magnetohydrodynamics, *JETP*, **8**:507 (1959).
40. Marshall, W.: The Structure of Magnetohydrodynamic Shock Waves, *Proc. Roy. Soc. (London)*, **A233**:367 (1956).
41. Spitzer, L., Jr.: Physics of Fully Ionized Gases, Interscience, New York, 1956.
42. Chew, G. F., M. L. Goldberger, and F. E. Low: *Los Alamos Rept.* LA-2055, T767, 1955.
43. Longmire, C. L.: "Plasma Physics," in preparation.

44. Chapman, S., and T. G. Cowling: "The Mathematical Theory of Nonuniform Gases," Cambridge University Press, 1958.
45. Rosenbluth, M. S., W. M. MacDonald, and D. L. Judd: *Phys. Rev.*, **107**:1 (1957).
46. Berz, F.: *Proc. Phys. Soc.*, **B69**:939 (1956).
47. Landau, L.: *Phys. Z. USSR*, **10**:25 (1946).
48. Bernstein, I. R.: *Phys. Rev.*, **109**:10 (1958).
49. Chew, G. F., M. L. Goldberger, and F. E. Low: *Proc. Roy. Soc. (London)*, **A236**:112 (1956).
50. Chandrasekhar, S., A. N. Kaufman, and K. M. Watson: *Ann. Phys. New York*, **2**:435 (1957).
51. Rosenbluth, M. N., and N. Rostoker: *Phys. of Fluids*, **2**:23 (1959).
52. Rosenbluth, M.: Dynamics of a Pinched Gas, in R. Landshoff (ed.), "Magnetohydrodynamics," Stanford University Press, Stanford, Calif., 1957.
53. Davis, L., R. Lüst, and A. Schlüter: The Structure of Hydromagnetic Shock Waves, *Z. Naturforsch.*, **13a**:916 (1958).
54. Gardener, C. S., H. Goertzel, H. Grad, C. S. Morawetz, M. H. Rose, and H. Rubin: "Hydromagnetic Shock Waves in High Temperature Plasmas," *New York Univ.* NYO-2538, 1959.
55. Patrick, R. M.: Production of Very High Speed Shock Waves, *Bull. Am. Phys. Soc.*, **2**(4):283 (1959).
56. Gold, T.: Discussion on Shock Waves and Rarefied Gases, p. 103, in H. C. Van de Hulst and J. M. Burgers (eds.), "Gas Dynamics of Cosmic Clouds," North Holland Publishing Co., Amsterdam, 1955.
57. Murgatroyd, W.: *Phil. Mag.*, **44**:1348 (1955).
58. Lehnert, B.: *Phys. Rev.*, **94**:815 (1954).
59. Colgate, S.: *Univ. Calif. Rad. Lab. Rept.* 4560, September, 1955.
60. Bishop, Amasa S.: "Project Sherwood: The U.S. Program in Controlled Fusion," Addison-Wesley, Reading, Mass., 1958.
61. Kantrowitz, A. R., and H. E. Petschek: pp. 3ff., in R. Landshoff (ed.), "Magnetohydrodynamics," Stanford University Press, Stanford, Calif., 1957.
62. Lin, S. C.: Electrical Conductivity of Thermally Ionized Air Produced in a Shock Tube, *AVCO Research Lab. Research Rept.* 5, February, 1957.
63. Scheibe, M.: Ph.D. thesis, University of Maryland, Institute for Fluid Dynamics and Applied Mathematics, 1958.
64. Patrick, R. M., and T. R. Brogan: One-dimensional Flow of an Ionized Gas through a Magnetic Field, *AVCO Research Lab. Research Rept.* 13, October, 1957.
65. Fowler, R. G., et al.: *Phys. Rev.*, **82**:879 (1951).
66. Josephson, V.: *J. Appl. Phys.*, **29**:30 (January, 1958).
67. Kolb, A.: in R. Landshoff (ed.), "Magnetodynamics," Stanford University Press, Stanford, Calif., 1957.
68. Gauger, J., et al.: *Bull Am. Phys. Soc.*, ser. II, vol. 3, August, 1958.
69. Ziemer, R.: *Am. Rocket Soc. Reprint* 906-59, August, 1959.
70. Sawyer, G. A., et al.: *Phys. Fluids*, **2**:47 (January, 1959).
71. Allen, T. K., et al.: *Phys. Rev. Letters*, **2**:383 (May 1, 1959).
72. Fishman, F., et al.: in D. Bershader (ed.), "Magnetohydrodynamics of a Conducting Fluid," Stanford University Press, Stanford, Calif., 1959.
73. Rosa, R. J.: *J. Appl. Phys.* (in press), Avco-Everett Research Laboratory, Everett, Mass.
74. Patrick, R. M.: A Description of a Propulsion Device Which Employs a Magneto Field as the Driving Force, *AVCO Research Lab. Research Rept.* 28, August, 1955.
75. Starr, W. L.: A Propulsion Device Using an Exploding Wire Plasma Acceleration. *Lockheed Missile and Space Div. Reprint* 418236, Sunnyvale, Calif., December, 1958.
76. Bostick, W. H.: Plasma Motors, *4th Ann. Meeting Am. Astronaut. Soc. Preprint* 57-2, Jan. 29, 1958.
77. Brogan, T. R.: Electric Arc Gas Heaters for Re-entry Simulation and Space Propulsion, *13th ARS Annual Meeting*, New York, November, 1958.

AUTHOR INDEX

1

SUBJECT INDEX

11